Standard Catalog of UNITED STATES TOKENS 1700-1900

by Russell Rulau

To Chet, Cliff and Oliver
For inspiration
To selfless, studious contributors
For perspiration

© 1994 by Krause Publications Inc.
By special arrangement with the Civil War Token Society

All rights reserved. No portion of this publication may be reproduced or transmitted in any form or by any means, electronic or mechanical, including photocopy, recording, or any information storage and retrieval system, without permission in writing from the author, except by a reviewer who may quote brief passages in a critical article or review to be printed in a magazine or newspaper, or electronically transmitted on radio or television.

Published by

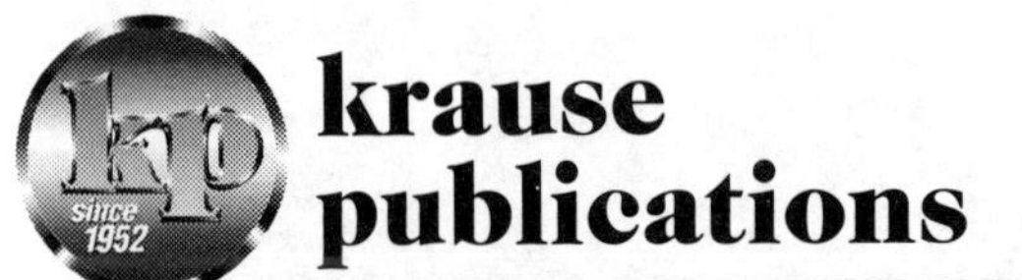

700 E. State Street • Iola, WI 54990-0001
Telephone: 715/445-2214

Library of Congress Catalog Number: 93-80096
ISBN: 0-87341-246-X

Printed in the United States of America

Introduction

A standard catalog of United States tokens, assembled on the same kind of basis that the famed "bibles" of the hobby, the *Standard Catalog of World Coins*, and the *Standard Catalog of World Paper Money*, has been a desired necessity for many years in the minds of general collectors, dealers, students, librarians and curators.

That is, the eventuality of such a volume appearing has been a foregone conclusion. Its actual physical appearance on the numismatic scene has been something else again.

Officials at Krause Publications, publishers of all this author's book products since 1980, were convinced that the need for a single-source reference for the casual user was there, as buoyant sales of my smaller books on tokens confirmed. *Hard Times Tokens*, first produced in 1980, is in its 4th edition already, and 3rd editions of *Early American Tokens*, and *U.S. Merchant Tokens 1845-1860* have already appeared, as has a 2nd edition of *U.S. Trade Tokens 1866-1889*, and a 1st edition of *Tokens of the Gay Nineties*.

Clifford Mishler and Chester L. Krause, both token enthusiasts themselves as well as being the president and chairman of KP, respectively, prevailed upon me several years ago to attempt what at one time may have seemed impossible: the writing of a massive new volume,, incorporating my five smaller era-oriented books plus a basic guide to the more common Civil War tokens, both Patriotic and Store Card.

The volume you are about to use is the result. It incorporates price changes and additional listings through early 1994, completely revising all the seven volumes making it up. It is a joint publishing venture of Krause Publications and the Civil War Token Society, not intended to replace the individual texts but rather to provide a "librarian's choice" type of reference.

My collaborators, publishers and independent contributors have spared no effort to update, revise, re-price all basic line listings and to add large numbers of new listings, new and clearer photos, and condensed type -- both easier to read and taking up less space. Result: You get more for your money per page throughout the volume. The USTT (1866-89) and Gay Nineties (1890-1900) sections have increased in size , respectively, about 60% and 150% over their last editions, for example.

The collecting of American tokens is no longer in the state of infancy that it was in the 1950's when pioneers like the Fulds and Curto were blazing trails for others to follow. My own first token article came in 1958, a piece on a few Civil War tokens ignored by others, which appeared in the California State Numismatic Association journal and won for me a bronze CSNA literary medal, my first literary award in numismatics.

Collecting U.S. tokens has become one of the most important cornerstones in numismatics, the haven for the true collector and at the same time a rather brilliant way to enjoy one's hobby and still profit from it. I have known very few token collectors who ever lost money on their collections, partially because they never looked upon the activity as an investment, but rather an enjoyment which is now springing almost magically to giant proportions.

Some types of tokens, such as counterstamps, billiard checks, territorials, Colonials, and exposition (world's fair) cards, are increasing dramatically in value. Others, tokens from saloons, bawdy houses, lumber camps or famous restaurants, are growing in demand, as are tokens with decent pictorial representations, strange or exotic denominations, etc.

In a way, it was inevitable that Russ Rulau should author the catalog. Some collectors consider me almost a father-figure to exonumia itself since I coined the term exonumist in 1960 and have spent 36 of my 55 years in numismatics writing about tokens and medals.

But, a word of caution: Token collecting, important as it is, is still only one of the cornerstones of numismatics. A truly great exonumist will often be a consummate general numismatist. Coins from ancient to modern, paper money, medallic art, orders and decorations, scrip, barter items -- even fakes and fantasies -- need to be studied and appreciated in order to better understand the role of tokens.

WHAT IS A TOKEN?

In general, a token is a metallic substitute for government coinage, or else a form of coin-shaped advertising. There are so many exceptions and supplements to this basic rule that the rule itself has little validity.

A token is whatever we choose to describe as a token, within obvious limitations. The line between token and medal is so thin and ill-defined that its very existence can be called into question.

A token does not even have to be made of metal to be described as a token. Cardboard chits for value are usually considered to be tokens rather than paper money, for example.

Various groups of purists try to narrow the meaning of the word token from time to time. Some say a token must be "worth" something to be truly a token. For example, it must be "good for" 5 cents, one tune, one shave, one ride, one cord, one bushel, one drink or one task. We have no objection to such redefinition efforts because we know they are all well-intended, as well as doomed.

English is a living language. Numismatists can influence it, but only time and wide public acceptance can constrict it.

As used in this catalog, the word token is given wide definition because the intent of the author and publisher is to make the reference "useful" to all, not to take up the cause of any ideological or semantic effort.

The items that are included are clearly listed in the introductory matter, as are those which are excluded. There are exceptions to each listing; the author and his contributors make the final choice of what is useful to the reader.

One quality a token must have, however, is set in concrete: A token must not have been issued by a government for any legal tender purpose. Such quality would make it a coin, not a token.

HOW COMPLETE IS THE COVERAGE?

The two Civil War token sections are deliberately incomplete so that a catalog could be produced which was not dominated by more than 11,000 pieces issued in the 1861-1865 period.

The three sections which cover the years 1700 through 1860 are as complete as public exposure over more than a decade and three or more editions can make them. But just as English is a living language, exonumia is a living scientific discipline; we learn more every day.

Very little from 1860 on back to Colonial times has been missed, we feel. Thousands of letters, hundreds of contributors and dozens of books have contributed to our having some degree of confidence in the pre-Civil War period.

The U.S. Trade Token era (1866-1889) and the Gay Nineties era (1890-1900) are greatly expanded over the last editions of those separate volumes, and we have been assisted by more than 100 new contributors located in every state and in several foreign countries (yes, Canadians, Latins, Europeans and Asians collect American tokens!).

In the period 1866 through 1900, we did deliberately leave out a good many tokens on the basis that their attribution to a particular site or time period was on too thin a basis. But, conversely, a number of pieces are included which may well have been misattributed, though we made every effort to be accurate.

If YOUR token is not listed, we'd like to hear from you.

If YOUR token is included and you believe your information about it is better than the catalog's, we'd like to hear from you. Drop a line to: Token Catalogs, Krause Publications, Iola, Wis. 54990.

WHAT ABOUT PRICES?

A numismatic catalog without prices may be useful, but it really satisfies no one.

A numismatic catalog with prices is necessary. Sellers will usually conclude that the printed prices are too low; buyers are generally convinced those same prices are too high. But at least a published price offers a target at which a collector's or dealer's ire can be vented.

We feel fortunate to have as contributors all of today's best professional token dealers and many veteran collectors. A good many of the quoted valuations are what has actually been paid out of pocket for a particular piece, either at auction or in private sale.

Only a small number of American tokens are worth more than $1,000, and just a handful could command more than $100,000. Yet the number of tokens which are worth more than $100 is surprisingly large, and that number is growing. Many $100-plus items of today were purchased at under $1 only 20-30 years ago.

The highest-priced tokens generally appear in the Early American and Hard Times periods, that is from 1700 through 1844. But a large number of valuable tokens are bringing high prices in the Civil War era (1861-1865), and some tokens of the Old West in the 1866-1900 period are setting auction records consistently.

The major part of tokens is moderately priced, however. One can become a dedicated and happy token collector without sacrificing home, hearth and spouse.

In general, token valuations are given in the catalog in up to four grades, those in which specimens are known. Frequently the grade headings are VG (very good), F (fine), VF (very fine) and Unc (uncirculated), but this rule is not followed universally. Many tokens are not known in uncirculated condition, so that EF (extremely fine) represents the best obtainable; in some cases grades such as Fair and G (good) are included because these are necessary to evaluate several true rarities.

The author is not now, nor ever has, engaged in the business of buying and selling tokens for profit. The prices given herein are an amalgam of the input of professionals and knowledgeable collectors, but the final judgement in each case has been the author's.

This catalog is based upon 1994-1995 market realities. In a few years some pieces included in this reference may bring much higher prices at a public auction, and other prices may be driven downward by the discovery of a hoard, or other natural market factors. The user should realize that prices given are a guide, nothing more.

There is an immutable rule in numismatics: There are no fixed prices. A fair price is always what a willing seller and willing buyer agree upon.

SEARCHING FOR TOKENS

Everyone knows someone who has put away things in odd drawers, attics, basements, sheds, farm barns and other natural "keep-it-out-of-sight" hideaways. It's a great place to start hunting.

Tokens by the hundreds and thousands have been dumped by old industrial firms, general stores, farms which once hired migrant pickers, banks, restaurants, lumber camps and all sorts of other enterprises. Dumped in some of the strangest locations!

Tokens have been unearthed from old wells, river beds, dump sites, razed building sites, cornerstones, buried lockboxes and jugs.

Today metal detectors are in the hands of many thousands of dedicated hunters who labor long hours over old plantations, battlefields, ghost towns, abandoned crossroads structures and other sites that they feel might reap benefits. The metal detector enthusiasts were not a major factor in token collecting when your author first began writing about tokens, but they are today.

A substantial number of these hunters have contacted me in recent years after seeing one of my books in their local library, and they have become an invaluable source of new information to our hobby. They hunt coins, arrowheads, tools, bullets, buttons and other metallic objects, of course, but tokens are found in every section of our nation.

Increasing one's token collection, though, depends most heavily on the traditional routes: Spending hours hunting through coin dealers' junk boxes, antique dealers' accumulations, or else buying attributed tokens from dealers or other collectors at a coin or hobby show, at public auction, or by advertising for them in the lay and the numismatic press.

Finding a pot of gold at the end of the rainbow is quite a bit more likely in token collecting than in coin collecting, but the pot may not have as much dollar value.

METHOD OF PRESENTATION

In general, the presentation of each catalog follows these general guidelines:

The name of the issuer and his location appear in bold lettering. The name of the issuer is as it appears on the token. Wherever possible, photos of both sides of the token are shown in actual size. Where enlargements are used, they are identified.

Next comes the line listing, consisting of these elements (not all these elements are used throughout):

* Catalog number (Rulau-E, HT, Miller, CWT, Rulau)

* Rarity rating (e.g. R3)

* Date. In clear, 1868, if shown on token. In parentheses, (1868), if estimated.

* Metallic composition (or other substance)

* Size (diameter) in millimeters.

* Valuation in up to four grades of preservation.

Under the line listing appears a full description of each side of the token. Lines of text are separated by a slash (/). Devices and motifs are described. If the flan is issued holed, looped or otherwise encumbered, this is stated. The edge is described as Plain, Reeded, Ornamented, Lettered etc. IMPORTANT: If the edge is not described, it may be assumed to be Plain, or else not known to the cataloger.

The descriptive material includes mintage if known; it is seldom that mintage of tokens is known. Also included are cross references to catalog numbers assigned by others in the past.

At the end of each issuer's listing of tokens may appear footnotes. These may be extensive, or cursory, depending on what historical or other background has been learned. Wherever possible, the rationale for estimating the date of appearance of each token is given. The absence of a footnote simply means that the catalogers have nothing of importance to report.

In each section of the book, states are arranged alphabetically, as are municipalities within those states, and issuers within those municipalities. Where state is believed to be known, but site is not, a grouping at the end of each state cares for this situation.

Mavericks, that is tokens which have not been localized, are cataloged alphabetically by issuer at the end of each section of the book. In such cases, we have had to estimate their date of issue based on style and other factors; in a few cases mavericks bear dates.

METALS

Aluminum .... pure aluminum, silvery##
Brass .... copper-zinc alloy, yellowish
Brass/Aluminum... brass ring around aluminum center, patented in U.S. 1899
Bronze .... copper-tin alloy, brownish
Copper ....pure copper, reddish
Cupronickel .... copper-nickel alloy*
Galvanized Iron .... zinc on iron, grayish
German Silver ....copper-nickel-zinc alloy*
Gold .... gold-copper alloy
Goldine ....Gilt brass alloy
Iron................................. pure iron, grayish, magnetic
Lead ....pure lead, dark grayish +
Nickel .... pure nickel, silvery, magnetic*
Pewter............................ copper-tin alloy, gray-white**
Pot Metal...........................lead-based alloy, dark gray
Silver .... silver-copper alloy
Steel.................................iron alloy, silvery, magnetic
Tin .... pure tin ***
Vulcanite ....hardened rubber ++
White Metal .... lead-tin alloy, grayish-white +
Zinc .... pure zinc, grayish

* It is frequently difficult to tell nickel and its principal alloys apart. New, they all resemble silver and look much alike. Pure nickel is magnetic, however, and only a small amount of impurity removes the magnetic quality. Cupronickel resists tarnish, while German silver (also called nickel-silver, argentan and other names) tarnishes much like silver. The catalog may well be in error in describing some of these nickel-alloy pieces.

** The best pewters are made of 90% tin and 10% copper, but in the 19th century antimony and bismuth partly replaced copper. In the cheapest pewters, lead replaces part of the tin. All these pewters look much alike.

*** Pure tin is seldom used in token manufacture. Old catalogs refer to "tin" pieces; what is meant is generally silvered white metal, a silver-gilt-surfaced lead-tin alloy, which is beautiful.

++ Vulcanite is, and was, expensive to use for token manufacture, but it was used in the U.S. in the 1860's to 1880's as a novelty substance for some tokens. In general, hard rubber pieces are not listed in this catalog except in the Civil War sections.

Very few trade tokens, store cards or medals were made of aluminum prior to 1890. It was too expensive for such use. But its price dropped to $1.50 a pound in 1891 and to 75 cents in 1893.

+ Lead and White Metal tokens have a unique quality; they will not "ring" when sounded with a solid metal piece. Silver, brass and nickel-alloy pieces will ring, each with a differing tone.

Warning! In some token catalogs, the term White Metal is used to describe nickel-alloy pieces, such as those made of German silver or cupronickel. This causes needless confusion, we feel.

NOTE: Certain other substances are mentioned herein, namely Leather, Cardboard, Celluloid, Bone, Ivory, Wood, Mother-of-Pearl, Bakelite, Plastic, etc. These terms are self-explanatory and should cause the reader little trouble.

ITEMS INCLUDED

Advertising Checks
Counterstamped coins
Currency tokens
Membership medals
Picker checks
Political tokens (to 1844 only)
Selected medalets (under 33mm)
Selected tags
Store cards
Tokens for value
Transportation tokens (to 1844 only)
Work checks or talleys

ITEMS EXCLUDED

Amusement tokens
Hard rubber (vulcanite) cards
Indian and post trader tokens
Shell and mirror cards
Military tokens
Telephone tokens
Transportation tokens (1845-1900)
Medals (33mm or larger)
Political campaign pieces (1845-1900)
Prison tokens

Abbreviations

abt .... about
alum .... aluminum
ANA .... American Numismatic Association
ANS .... American Numismatic Society
ATCO .... Active Token Collectors Organization
AU .... about uncirculated
AVA .... American Vecturist Association
B .... brass
B&A .... brass ring around aluminum center
BB .... Brunswick-Balke
BBC .... Brunswick-Balke-Collender
B&M .... Bowers & Merena
BM .... British Museum
Br .... brass
Brunswick die .... Number assigned the Brunswick billiard family die in "The Brunswick Token Story"
Brz .... bronze
C .... copper
Can. .... Canadian
circ. .... circulated, circulation
CN .... cupronickel
co. .... company
Co. .... County
coll. .... collection
Cop .... copper
ctmk .... countermark(ed)
ctsp .... counterstamp(ed)
CW .... Civil War
CWSC .... Civil War store card
CWT .... Civil War token
CWTS .... Civil War Token Society
dept. .... department
diff. .... different
EAT .... Early American token
EF .... extremely fine
Ek. .... Eklund
ex- .... out of (collection)
F .... fine
F.E. .... Flying Eagle
Fr .... fair
G .... good
G/B .... gilt brass
G/Br .... gilt brass
G/C .... gilt copper
G/Cop .... gilt copper
G/WM .... gilt white metal
GS .... German silver
hex. .... hexagonal
HSD .... Hoskins, Schilling & Dunn
HT .... Hard Times
HTT .... Hard Times token
inst. .... institution
irreg .... irregular
K-M .... Krause-Mishler
l. .... left
L .... lead
LL .... large letters
Md. TAMS .... Maryland Token and Medal Society
Mex. .... Mexican
mm .... millimeters
ms. .... manuscript
NBMCo. .... National Billiard Mfg. Co.
N/Br .... nickel-plated brass
no. .... number
N/Steel .... nickel-plated steel
obv. .... obverse
oct. .... octagonal
PCAC .... Presidential Coin & Antique Co.
PF .... proof
P-L .... prooflike
PL .... plain (edge)
pl. .... plated
pop. .... population
poss. .... possibly
prob. .... probably
procl. .... proclamation piece
prov. .... province
R .... rarity (rating)
R .... reeded (edge)
r. .... right
rect. .... rectangular
rev. .... reverse
R-F .... Rulau-Fuld
Rv: .... reverse
sc .... scalloped
scal .... scalloped
Scrc .... scarce
S/Br .... silvered brass
S/Brass .... silvered brass
S/Cop .... silvered copper
silv. .... silver
SL .... small letters
S.L. .... Seated Liberty
Span.-Am. .... Spanish-American
sq .... square
svd .... silvered
S/WM .... silvered white metal
TAMS .... Token and Medal Society
TOGN .... Tokens of the Gay Nineties
triang .... triangular
Unc .... uncirculated
USMT .... U.S. Merchant token
USTT .... U.S. Trade token
V .... vulcanite
VF .... very fine
VG .... very good
vulc. .... vulcanite
w/ .... with
WM .... white metal
w/o .... without
Y .... Yeoman
Yeo. .... Yeoman

Contributors To Standard Catalog U.S. Tokens

Edward Ahern
David T. Alexander
James K. Allen
Karen Allen
Active Token Collectors Organization
American Antiquarian Society
American Numismatic Association
American Numismatic Society
Amos Press
Dan Anderson
Ralph Angeletti
Anne Arundel County Historical Society
William Anton
Dr. Herman M. Aqua
Bill Aquilino
Charles D. Arceneaux
Don Bailey
Warren Baker
Richard J. Balbaton
Bank of Canada
E. B. "Ted" Banning
Autence A. Bason
Jack Baxter
Ralph W. Behringer
Bary Bender
Ronald J. Benice
Joe Bidwell
Crawford Blakeman
John Boger
Dr. Don Boller
Frederick Borgmann
Paul Bosco
Rich Bottles Jr.
Q. David Bowers
Erwin E. Brauer
Kenneth E. Bressett
Richard E. Brown
Colin R. Bruce
Lloyd Brumley
Dr. Gregory G. Brunk
R. F. Buckley
Catherine Bullowa-Moore
Bryan Burke
Ralph R. Burry
R. Lee Burton Jr.
Lester M. Burzinski
Robert Busby
John W. Byars Jr.
Dale Cade
California Exonumist Society
John W. Canfield
George Canterbury
Robert Cardiff
Carl W. A. Carlson
Thomas J. Casper
Garry Charman
John Cheramy
Chicago Historical Society
Elvira Clain-Stefanelli
C. R. Clark
Donald K. Clifford
Roger S. Cohen
Raymond Colbert
Jack Collins
Clyde D. Copper
Leon Corpuz
Bruce K. Cox
Louis Crawford
Grover C. Criswell
Robert R. Cruise
Mrs. Chipman Cunningham
Paul A. Cunningham
Denton V. Curtis
Jay P. Dalley
Allan Davisson
Walt DeLeu
Thomas Delorey
Dwight B. Demeritt
Larry Derrer
Jack R. Detwiler
William S. Dewey
Rocco A. DiGiacomo
George K. Dillingham
Dr. Richard T. Doty
Daniel Douglas
Hal V. Dunn
Marc J. Duvall
Lawrence Dziubek
Rich Eckebrecht
Lewis Egnew
James C. Ehrhardt
Robin Ellis
Lloyd L. Entenman
Emmet M. Ey
Chris Faulkner
L. B. Fauver
Harvey Fenton
Lewis K. Ferguson
Glenn H. Firestone
John J. Ford Jr.
Joseph Foster
Harry W. Fowler
William E. Fowler
Damia T. Francis
David L. Freed
Peter Fuhrman
Dr. George J. Fuld
Charlotte Gale
David M. Gale
Harvey A. Gamer
Bette J. Ganter
Jeffrey Gardiner
Thomas P. Gardner
Cora Lee Gillilland
Richard Gladdle
David Gladfelter
Jack Glass
Gary E. Glise
Milton J. Gordon
Stephen M. Gorman
George Gould
Don E. Grampp
Joseph F. Gregory
Cindy Grellman
Carling Gresham
Dick Grinolds
Larry J. Grinstead
Steven P. Guiness
Jay P. Guren
William H. Hale
James H. Hall
Kenneth L. Hallenbeck
Michael E. Hallihan
John T. Hamilton III
William E. Hamm
Dick Hanscom
Jon Harris
N. Neil Harris
Jim Hartman
Rich Hartzog
Frank L. Hattersley
Steve Hayden
Harvey L. Hebert
Randy Heldenbrand
Harold Helm
Frank Hendrickson
David E. Henkle
Robert J. Herzog
David H. Hirsch
Alfred D. Hoch
Michael J. Hodder
Fred Holabird
James H. Holtel
Wayne K. Homren
Lea Hornbeck
George Hosek
Len Hoskins
Clyde Hubbard
Su Nadin-Davis
Eric P. Newman
Arthur Newmark
Bill Noyes
Michael J. O'Brien
Larry Oller
Al Oravec
George R. Owen
John R. Palmer
Kenneth A. Palmer
James D. Partin
Randall D. Partin
Donald Partrick
Jess Peters
Norman G. Peters
Pete Peters
Mike Pfefferkorn
C. H. "Cy" Phillips
Gary A. Pipher
Kristen Pippert
Carol Plante
Gerald S. Porter
Claude Proulx
P. Frank Purvey
Ed Quagliana
Quarterman Publications Inc.
Robert M. Ramsay
Elmer E. Randall
William H. Randel
Lou Rasera
Fred L. Reed III
Ed. Reiter
Jules Reiver
Kenneth W. Rendell
Michael J. Renner
Wade Renstrom
Harley W. Rhodehamel
Howard Richoux
Travis Roberts
Tom H. Robinson
Edward Rochette
Jeff Rock
Bill Rodgers
Richard Rossa
Jerry Roughton
Bill Rouleau
Ronald Russell
Dean M. Ryder
Steven E. Saari
John M. Sallay
Robert L. Saxe
David E. Schenkman
John H. Schilling
Jerry F. Schimmel
Donald T. Schmidt
Joseph Schmidt
Jerry L. Schreckengost
Nick P. Schrier
David E. Schulz
Dr. Robert Schuman
Dr. I. N. Schuster
J. Gavin Scott
Jane Sears
Russ Sears
Dale A. Seppa
Neil Shafer
Sam Sheldon
James C. Shipley
Niles K. Shultz
Arlie R. Slabaugh
Bruce W. Smith
Smithsonian Institution
Neil Sowards
Hank Spangenberger
Peter Spooner
Stack's Inc.
Terry Stahurski
Bob Stark
Gilbert Steinberg
Louis Hudson
Indiana-Kentucky-Ohio TAMS
John D. Irwin Jr.
Albert Jakira
Edward Janis
David Jerdee
D. Wayne Johnson
Gerald E. Johnson
Kent D. Johnson
Lance Johnson
Larry Johnson
Elizabeth A. B. Jones
Richard Jones
Robert E. Julian
Donald Kagin
Charles V. Kappen
Hillel Kaslove
James H. Keller
Barbara A. Kelly
Christof Keogh
Ken Kershaw
Don Ketterling
David A. King
Ralph A. King
Charles E. Kirtley
Phil Klabel
Allan Klenman
A. J. Kooij
Bill Koponen
Paul L. Koppenhaver
Frank L. Kovacs
Edward G. Kowalczyk
Chester L. Krause
Frank W. Kroha
Kurt R. Krueger
Gary Kruesel
Larry Laevens
David W. Lane
Lynn L. Langdon
Julian Leidman
Kean Leiker
Erwin Lein
Robert D. Leonard Jr.
Ed Leventhal
Robert M. Levin
H. Joseph Levine
Donald R. Lewis
George E. Linden Jr.
Robert J. Lindesmith
Leon Lindheim
Gary Lines
Gaylor Lipscomb
Chris Loeblein
John Loperfido
Richard G. Magnuson
Albert Marecki
Robert W. Marvin
Maryland Token & Medal Society
Marshall W. Massey
William Massey
W. G. Mayer
David P. McBride
Dudley L. McClure
Richard McFerran
Donald Medcalf
Robert Merchant
Roger Merritt
Donald M. Miller
William T. Miller
Forest Mintz
Clifford Mishler
Robert G. Mitchell
Gerald Moen
Montana Historical Society
Helen E. Moore
Mormon Genealogical Library
William D. Mullins
Thomas Mulrooney
Will Mumford

Mark Andrew Steinberg
Stanley L. Steinberg
Elizabeth W. Steinle
Arthur Stetkis
Donald Stewart
JoAnn Coe Stoll
John H. Stribhei
Richard C. Striley
Harry L. Strough
Louis R. Stubler
Charles Sullivan
Harold Sundby Jr.
Ben Z. Swanson
William Swoger
Emil Szauer
Steve Tanenbaum
Don Taxay
Dr. Sol Taylor
Bob Temarantz
Clifton A. Temple
Russ Tennett
Anthony Terranova
Hank Thoele
David Thompson
Token and Medal Society
Terry Trantow
Kenneth N. Trobaugh
Dr. William E. Trout
Edmund Tylenda
Charles Urquhart
Ore H. Vacketta
Tim Vest
Igor V. Victorov-Orlov
Robert A. Vlack
Mel Wacks
Lloyd E. Wagaman
Norris Wahl
L. C. Walker
Tom Wall

Holland Wallace
William M. Wallworth
Terry E. Wantz
Sue Ward
Tom V. Warfel
Millard W. Wasczak
Douglas Watson
Thomas Wehner
Alan V. Weinberg
Randy Weir
Louis T. Wells
George C. West
Western Pa. Numismatic Society
Byron K. Weston
Bill White
Paul F. White
R. B. White
Doris Whithorn
Dennis Wierzba
Raymond J. Williams
William A. Williges
W. A. Williges (II)
John Wilson
Nancy Wilson
Wisconsin Historical Society
Stewart P. Witham
E. K. Witt
Dr. Bruce D. Wonder
Roy J. Wood
R. B. "Dick" Worthington
Dr. Alan York
Derek Young
Joseph H. Zaffern
Al Zaika
Jerry Zara
Michael Brand Zeddies
Charles Ziegler

And to those who preceded us:

Edgar H. Adams
Roland Atwood
Joseph Barnett
C. Wyllys Betts
William Leggett Bramhall
Walter Breen
P. Napoleon Breton
Charles I. Bushnell
Monica Bussell
Raymond Byrne
Pliny E. Chase
Alva Christensen
Dr. James Courteau
Virginia Culver
James J. Curto
Jack R. Detwiler
J. Doyle DeWitt
Montroville W. Dickeson
Gordon Dodrill
Frank G. Duffield
William Forrester Dunham
Thomas L. Elder
Ellis Edlow
J. Douglas Ferguson
Milton Fishgold
Sarah E. Freeman
Melvin Fuld
George R. Ganter
T. Harrison Garrett
Ralph Goldstone
Maurice M. Gould
J. Guttag
Raymond Haggenjos
Paul Hamm
John W. Haseltine
Adolfo Herrera

Dr. George Hetrich
Lee F. Hewitt
Edgar G. Heyl
Hal E. Hibler
Byron Johnson
Richard D. Kenney
Otto Kersteiner
Howard H. Kurth
Joseph N. T. Levick
Lyman Haynes Low
William T. R. Marvin
C. Mathis
Jose T. Medina
Joseph J. Mickley
Ralph A. Mitchell
Waldo C. Moore
Stuart Mosher
Benjamin Odesser
George R. Owen
Richard Picker
Fred Pridmore
Wayte Raymond
Alfred Z. Reed
Glenn A. Rome
J. William Ross
Lionel Rudduck
Alfred H. Satterlee
John W. Scott
C. P. Serrure
Ora Pumphrey Smith
Dr. Horatio Storer
Dr. Malcolm Storer
Roy H. Van Ormer
P. H. Wittlin
Isaac F. Wood
William Woodside
W. Eliot Woodward
Dr. Benjamin P. Wright
Farran Zerbe

A special word of gratitude to those Krause Publications personnel who provided direct assistance in the physical labor of assembling this volume, everything from typesetting and proofreading to photography, production and planning:

Rajean Civik
Kathryn Hines
Sue Kettleson
Carol Klopstein
Patricia Klug
Phil LaFranka
Barb Lefeber
Julie Mattson
Patsy Morrison

Jan Pence
Mary Sieber
Sandra Sparks
Rowene J. Steffen
Shelley L. Stockard
Bonnie Tetzlaff
Ethel Thulien
Paul Tofte
Sarah Werbelow

Contents

Early American Tokens

A catalog of the Merchant and Related Tokens of Colonial and Early Republican America from 1700 to 1832.

Along the waterfront in Colonial New York City, from a sketch by Tinkey. It was in such surroundings that the firms of William and John Mott - and Talbot, Allum & Lee - issued their trade tokens.

INTRODUCTION

There wasn't much private money in America in the 18th century. The British government provided scanty coinage, but the young colonies' needs were not yet sharpened. Imports of certain British and Irish pieces provided enough change to mollify tradesmen, and several colonies (Massachusetts, Virginia, Maryland) had their own semiofficial coins to help out.

This section will treat with the private tokens and merchant cards — omitting some anonymous speculations such as the Nova Eboracs, Bar cent, etc. All known tradesmen tokens of the Colonial era are included, as well as a number of private medallic issues.

Our first token was probably the Gloucester, Virginia brass shilling of 1714 issued by Rigault & Dawson, while the first private issue to achieve fairly good acceptance was the 1737 Higley copper threepence. Both issues may be found in this compilation.

The Florida proclamation "half dollars" appeared in 1760 and 1789.

In 1763 the Charles Town Social Club issued its members' medal, and in 1783 John Chalmers struck his silver coinage in Maryland.

The year 1790 witnessed the appearance of Standish Barry's threepence and the Albany Church penny. About 1793, Ricketts Circus issued its token, and in 1794-1795 Talbot, Allum & Lee issued large numbers of private copper cents.

Then 1796 and the British settlement in Kentucky and 1797 and the French settlement at Castorland and the Theatre at New York - brought forth numismatic emissions. In 1799 the New York Associate Church issued its Communion token, and the 18th century drew to a close.

These 18th century tokens are not as easy to define as later American tokens. There was no national coinage until 1793, so the need for small change was great. Even after the introduction of the U.S. copper cent and half cent, and the cent's multiples, the national coinage was slow to enter trade channels. Foreign silver and gold coinage — and many British coppers — helped fill the need.

Thus the Talbot, Allum & Lee pieces found ready acceptance as small change in New York.

The distinction between *coin* and *token* in the public mind before 1800 was blurred. The disc was *useful* — or not.

As a rule, we have omitted generalized, non-local token types from this work, such as the George Washington pieces, Bar cent, Kettle and Success counters. Some pieces are included in a special Non-Local section at the back of the catalog, and we've also included the political medalets (though the larger politicals are not cataloged here).

TYPES OF PRIVATE TOKENS INCLUDED

We have included all known currency tokens, advertising tokens, admission checks, turnpike tokens, membership medalets, campaign tokens (of less than 30mm diameter), and countermarked coins (of provable or likely early vintage).

TOKENS AFTER 1800

The first decade of the 19th century was almost devoid of token issues. In the 1806-1807 period Lancaster County, Pa., may have introduced some of its tollgate tokens for turnpikes, though some authorities feel these turnpike pieces belong to the century's second (or some later) decade. A few counterstamped coins started appearing in this decade.

About 1812-1816 Lancaster County's tollgate tokens were in full flower; the Park Theater pieces are dated 1817; Washington Market Chowder Club medalets are dated 1818, and more counterstamped pieces appeared. As can be seen, the second decade was also a time of few tokens.

The trade token as we have come to know it began developing in America in the 1820s. The Mott hardware tokens in New York, those of John Low and Horace Porter of Boston are attributed to the third decade, as are the issues of Richard Trested in New York and the North West Company in Oregon.

The year-date 1823 appears on New York tokens of C. & I. D. Wolfe, W.H. Schoonmaker and Tredwell, Kissam & Co. In 1829 Wolfe, Spies & Clark probably began its attractive token issues depicting Washington, Jackson and George IV.

In 1825 Randel (Delaware) and several New York issuers — Rathbone & Fitch, Peale's Museum and Green & Wetmore — brought out tokens. The second half of the decade witnessed Edgar in New Orleans, Low and Porter in Boston, Wright & Bale and Doremus, Suydam & Nixon in New York begin token issues.

In 1829-1831 the character of the tokens began to resemble the cent-imitation types of the coming Hard Times era. The tokens of Buchan, Farnsworth Phipps, I. Gilbert, etc., fit this pattern.

TOKEN MAKERS

British token makers — Wyon, Skidmore, Kempson, Boulton, Jacobs — are responsible for some of the late 18th century store cards, such as the Theatre at New York; Talbot, Allum & Lee; and P.P.P. Myddelton. B. Jacobs signed the New York Theatre penny, which was struck by E. Skidmore; interestingly, the one Theatre muling was apparently struck by Peter Kempson. Jacobs and Skidmore were in London, Kempson in Birmingham.

Thomas Wyon reputedly engraved, and Peter Kempson struck, the Talbot, Allum & Lee tokens, and Kempson struck the TA&L mulings in Birmingham, England. Conrad Kuchler designed the Myddelton tokens, which were struck in Birmingham by Boulton & Watt. John Walker & Co. of Birmingham is reported to have struck the North West Company tokens much later (in 1820), and the same Birmingham maker may be responsible for the 1832 products of Kirkman, Green & Wetmore and others. Bushby of London reportedly manufactured the Phoenix buttons of Oregon in the 1810-20 period.

The new U.S. Mint at Philadelphia prepared the Ricketts Circus pieces about 1793 and the Peale's Museum pieces much later, perhaps as late as 1830.

Richard Trested, an English immigrant, began in the die-sinking business at 70 William St., New York, about 1821. His signed works, such as the Castle Garden card and his own series of store cards, are rare, but it is now suspected that he may be responsible for some of the more available tokens of that era.

The New York Grand Canal opened in 1823, part of the later (1826) Erie Canal. Eighty-one miles in length and later called the Champlain Canal, it connected the Hudson River and Lake Champlain waterways from Whitehall to Waterford, N.Y. Its token provided the first instance in the United States of a single die being used for a number of different merchants' tokens — later this practice was to become commonplace and these became known in the trade as "stock dies." It is believed Thomas Kettle of Birmingham, England cut the series of cards celebrating the New York Grand Canal's opening for C. & I.D. Wolfe; Wolfe, Spies & Clark; and Tredwell, Kissam & Co.; these depicted an American eagle and the legend NEW YORK GRAND CANAL OPENED 1823.

Robert Lovett Sr., founder of a dynasty of American engravers and diesinkers, was in business as early as 1816-1822 in Philadelphia and then 1824-1825 at 249 Broadway, New York.

James Bale, Trested's apprentice, formed a partnership with Charles Cushing Wright in May, 1829, and bought out Trested's business from his widow when that worthy succumbed prematurely to complications arising from a cut finger. Though this partnership lasted only until about October, 1833, it was responsible for a number of attractive tokens — Henderson & Lossing; Joseph & L. Brewster; Farnsworth, Phipps & Co.; I. Gilbert, and others.

The metal firm of Pelletreau, Bennett & Cooke at 170 Broadway, New York, struck the Erie Canal medal in 1826. This had been designed by Charles Cushing Wright. Maltby Pelletreau was the senior partner in the firm. This firm may have struck tokens, though none has been identified.

(Earlier this firm was Clark, Pelletreau & Upson, jewelers, at 88 Broadway, in 1821-1822.)

Robert Scot, chief engraver of the U.S. Mint from 1793 to 1823, may have cut the dies for the Ricketts Circus tokens.

The useful reference, *Exonumia Symbolism & Classification* by L.B. Fauver (Menlo Park, Calif., 1982), presents die-state and die-link evidence to show that a number of early American store cards were struck by Thomas Kettle of Birmingham, England, son of the countermaker Henry Kettle.

Fauver's studies are convincing, and we are therefore echoing his conclusion that all the following store cards and politicals are Kettle products.

KETTLE STRIKES

Jackson political medalets of the 1824 campaign, DeWitt AJACK 1824-1 and 2, could not have been struck before 1827, Fauver concludes. He intimates they may also have been restruck for the 1832 reelection campaign. (The other 1824 medalets, AJACK 1824-3, 4, 5 and 6, are not Kettle pieces and are still assigned to the 1824, not the 1828 campaign.)

Horace Porter & Co., Boston (Mass 84), in brass and silvered brass.
A. W. Hardie, New York (NY 295).
W. H. Schoonmaker, New York (NY 782 to 785).
Tredwell, Kissam & Co., New York (NY 920 and 921).
C. & I. D. Wolfe, New York (NY 957).
Wolfe, Clark & Spies, New York (NY 958).
Wolfe, Spies & Clark, New York (NY 959 to 963).

THE KETTLE FIRM

Henry Kettle (firm organized late 1780's)		
KETTLE		1793-1804
HK		1798
engraver Benjamin Patrick BP		1803
Kettle & Sons (Thomas and William)		
K & S		1805-1812
Thomas Kettle	KETTLE	1812-1837
Kettle firm	H	1838-1840
do (None)		1838-1859

NOTE: The signature K & S from 1817 on belongs to another diesinking firm.

NUMBERING SYSTEMS

A special numbering system has been devised for this section so that each token entry and variety may have its own identification. Users have asked that every piece be numbered.

To keep collectors and dealers from having to renumber their collection records or business inventories, the new Rulau-E (for Early) numbers are exactly the same as previously assigned.

All other pieces are assigned numbers, where such numbers were not already in use. A few days' familiarization with the numbering system should fix it in the user's mind.

DIESINKERS AND TOKEN MAKERS ACTIVE IN THE EARLY AMERICAN TOKEN PERIOD

Engraver/Maker	Location	Dates	Marks
James Bale	New York	1833-35	BALE BALE NY
Standish Barry	Baltimore	1790	
Boulton & Watt	Birmingham	1788-1805	SOHO M.B. SOHO
Ephraim Brasher	New York	1787-92	
Bushby	London	1810-20	
John Chalmers	Annapolis, Md.	1783	
James Chinery	New York	1829-30	
W.B.D.	?	?	
Peter Getz	Lancaster, Pa.	1792-97	
John Gregory Hancock	Birmingham	1791-1806	
Benjamin Jacob	Birmingham		BN. JACOB
B. Jacobs	London	1795-1803	JACOBS B. JACOBS JACOBS F.
Charles James	London	1789-1801	C.I. JAMES ENGRAVER
Peter Kempson	Birmingham	1792-1800	P.K. P.K. FECIT
Thomas Kettle	Birmingham	1812-37	
John Kirk	London	1746-73	I. KIRK KIRK FEC.
Conrad Heinrich Kuchler	Birmingham	1790-1806	K. C.H.K.
William Little	Philadelphia	1813-19	
Robert Lovett Sr.	Philadelphia	1816-22	
	New York	1824-60's	
William Lutwyche	Birmingham	1794-1800	
Paris Mint	Paris, France	1796	
Pelletreau Bennett & Cooke	New York	1826	
Noel Alexandre Ponthon	Birmingham	1795-96	
Scovill Mfg. Co.	Waterbury, Conn.	1820-1905	
Peter Skidmore	London		
James Smither	Philadelphia	1768-1819	
Richard Trested	New York	1821-29	
United States Mint	Philadelphia	1793-1830	
John Walker & Co.	Birmingham	1820	
John S. Warner	Philadelphia	1823-68	
Charles Cushing Wright	New York	1824-47	CCW
Wright & Bale	New York	1829-33	W&B W&B NY
Peter Wyon	Birmingham	1805-14	P. WYON
Thomas Wyon (I)	Birmingham	1793-1800	

NOTE: * Birmingham and London are in England. All other cities mentioned are in U.S.

DATING THE TOKENS

A number of Early American tokens bear dates, and others can be dated by their design, style or historical association.

Still more can be dated — within a reasonable span of years - by diesinker links or by city directory evidence.

A good number of the tokens in this book are included because indirect evidence - just an educated guess — indicates they might properly belong here. Such tokens are "dated" in the catalog with a question mark framed by parentheses — (?). One must begin somewhere, and we feel that an error of inclusion is preferable to one of exclusion, since knowledgeable users of this reference will be exposed to the potential errata.

Some of America's finest numismatists have assisted in selecting tokens for inclusion, but the final decision in each case has been our own. If a mistake has been made, we accept full responsibility.

For reasons we have never fully fathomed, some old-time token collectors seem to resist "dating" the classics of the American token pantheon. Perhaps they fear stripping away the aura of mystery from these rarities. But others have done much pioneering in this direction, and now we're determined to finish the task.

Comments, criticisms and suggestions about dating may be sent to me at 700 East State St., Iola, Wis. 54990.

VALUATIONS

A panel of professional numismatists and veteran collectors has assigned valuations for the tokens in this catalog. Auction records also have been considered, especially those in 1986-1993.

Quite a few Early American tokens are difficult to price, simply because they seldom change hands.

METHOD OF PRESENTATION

The catalog number at the beginning of each line entry is the Rulau-E number of the piece. (See remarks on Numbering System).

If a date appears on the token, it is listed next on the line in the clear — e.g. 1817. If a date is given within parentheses — e.g. (1823-24) — it indicates the undated piece is attributed to such date(s) by reason of deduction or evidence.

The metallic content and diameter in millimeters are given next. Metals are rendered as they are normally understood in numismatics. White Metal is a tin-based alloy sometimes referred to in old catalogs as Tin. German Silver is a nickel-copper-zinc alloy resembling silver in its physical properties.

In the description of each piece which follows the line listing, we have tried to give full inscriptions, with the slash (/) used to separate lines of text. Other catalog listings (e.g. Wright, DeWitt, Atwood, Baker, RB • Red Book, etc.) are also given. Consult the Bibliography for explanations of catalog references.

We have used extensive footnotes to enhance the catalog entries. Such footnotes harken back to the 19th century practice of numismatic writers such as C. Wyllys Betts, Sylvester S. Crosby and Lyman H. Low, which fell into disfavor for many years. Their use has been revived at times by writers such as Robert P. King and Nathan Eglit, and we favor them.

In a few cases, extra text has been included.

The historical background of Dr. Higley, Charles Willson Peale, North West Company, Castorland, etc., is so interwoven with Early American tokens that the inclusion of the extra text seems justified.

SPECIE AND 'PIECES OF EIGHT'

The Spanish dollar, or piece of eight, was used extensively as currency in the United States before the Revolution and for long afterward. An interesting account of how pieces of eight were used as money, and cut into "bits" for fractional use, appeared in the 1964 book, *History of Southwestern Ohio, The Miami Valleys*, by Dr. W.E. Smith:

"After 1787, specie was brought to the Miami country by immigrants and soldiers. The first troops at Fort Washington (now Cincinnati) were paid in Spanish silver dollars, familiarly known as 'pieces of eight.' They were worth about four shillings.

"Specie was so scarce in Cincinnati that these Spanish dollars were cut into halves, quarters and eighths, or 'bits' for making change. These 'bits' were known locally as 'shark skins.'

"Two bits equaled a quarter, one bit half as much, and half a bit, 6-1/4 cents. In a day of severely restricted supply of money, a rabbit skin passed current at 6-1/4 cents, raccoon (skin) at 12-1/2, fox at 25, and deer at 50.

"After a time the soldiers were paid in $3 bills printed by the local government especially for soldiers, whose monthly stipend was three dollars. Because of their shape they were called 'oblongs.'

"Portuguese 'joes' (gold coins), reals and Mexican dollars were also used during the early years.

"Although church members preferred American money or negotiable bank notes for themselves, they put 'cut money' in the hat passed at church. An entry in the treasurer's book of the Hopewell Church near Morning Sun, Preble County (June, 1817) reads: 'To sale of cut money to John Brown, $3.40.'

"For the convenience of their readers, daily newspapers later published the exchange values of foreign coins. The *Liberty Hall and Cincinnati Gazette* for May 8, 1834 quoted the exchange values of the Spanish doubloon, English guinea and sovereign, and French napoleon and louis d'or (all gold coins). The first regular banks in Ohio were founded in 1808-1809 in Marietta, Chillicothe and Steubenville."

CONNECTICUT

W. MIX
East Granby, Conn.

Rulau-E	Date	Metal	Size	VG	F	VF	EF
Conn 10	(1820-40)	Copper	29mm	75.00	—	125.00	—

W. MIX in relief within rect. depression ctsp on U.S. Large cent. Examined: 1801, 1817. (Brunk 28120)

William Mix, a pewterer and maker of Britannia ware, was active in Spoonville (now East Granby) about 1820 to 1840. His normal touch (pewterer's mark) was: WM. MIX in relief within rectangular depression.

He may have been the precursor of the G.I. Mix & Co. pewter firm of Yalesville (Wallingford), Conn., circa 1860's.

N. PRATT (and) N. PRATT JR
Essex, Conn.

Rulau-E	Date	Metal	Size	VG	F	VF	EF
Conn 8	(ca 1800)	Silver	27mm	—	—	125.00	—
		N. PRATT in relief within rect. depression ctsp on Spanish-American 1785-Mo 2-reales. (H. Joseph Levine sale of June 27, 1987, lot 014)					
Conn A8	(ca 1839)	Copper	29mm	75.00	—	125.00	—
		N. PRATT JR. in prepared punch ctsp on U.S. 1809 or 1839 Half cent. 2 known. (Brunk 32700)					
Conn B8	(ca 1855)	Copper	29mm	75.00	—	125.00	—
		N. PRATT incuse, ctsp on U.S. 1817 or 1853 Large cent. 3 known. (Brunk 32690)					
Conn B8A	(ca 1855)	Copper	23mm	—	—	125.00	—
		Similar ctsp on U.S. 1809 Half cent.					
Conn B8B	(ca 1855)	Silver	18mm	—	—	125.00	—
		Similar ctsp on U.S. 1853-Arrows S.L. dime.					

Nathan Pratt (1772-1842) was a silversmith of Essex, Conn. from about 1792 on. His son, Nathan Pratt Jr. (born 1802) became active in the business about 1823.

It is possible that Conn B8, B8A and B8B were issued by Nathan Pratt after his father's death, or by another Pratt descendant unlisted in the references on silversmiths.

References to the Pratt family may be found in George M. Curtis' *Early Silver of Connecticut and its Makers* (Meriden, Conn., 1913); Stephen Ensko's *Makers of Early American Silver* (New York, 1927); Hollis French's *A List of Early American Silversmiths and their Marks* (New York, 1917), and R. M. and T. H. Kovel's *A Directory of American Silver, Pewter and Silver Plate* (New York, 1983).

Conn B8 of course belongs in *U.S. Merchant Tokens 1845-1860*, but until more can be learned about all the Pratt counterstamps, it was thought best to catalog them together.

HIGLEY COPPERS
Granby, Conn.

'The Value of Three Pence'

Rulau-E	Date	Metal	Size	G	VG	F	VF
Conn 1	1737	Copper	29mm	6000.	10,000.	—	—
		Deer standing to left, within circle. Around circle: (Hand) THE. VALVE. OF. THREE. PENCE. Rv: Three crowned hammers within circle. Around: *CONNECTICVT. 1737. Plain edge. (RB)					
Conn 2	1737	Copper	29mm	7000.	12,000.	—	—
		Obverse similar to last. Rv: Similar, but legend around circle reads: I. AM. GOOD. COPPER. 1737. Plain edge. (RB)					

'Value Me As You Please'

Rulau-E	Date	Metal	Size	G	VG	F	VF
Conn 3	1737	Copper	29mm	6000.	10,000.	—	—
		Dear standing to left, within circle. The Roman numeral III appears below the ground line. Around circle: (Hand) VALUE. ME. AS. YOU. PLEASE*. Rv: Similar to reverse of last (three crowned hammers, I. AM. GOOD. COPPER. 1737. Plain edge. (RB)					
Conn 4	1737	Copper	29mm	Ex. Rare			
		As last, but VALVE instead of VALUE. Plain edge. (RB)					

Rulau-E	Date	Metal	Size	G	VG	F	VF
Conn 5	(1737)	Copper	29mm	7000.	12,000.	—	—
		Obverse similar to last. Rv: Broad axe in center, (Hand) J. CUT. MY. WAY. THROUGH. around. Plain edge. (RB)					

Rulau-E	Date	Metal	Size	G	VG	F	VF
Conn 6	(1737)	Copper	29mm	—	—	75,000.	—
		Spoked wheel in center, (Hand) THE. WHEELE. GOES. ROUND. around. Rv: As last (Broad axe, J. CUT. MY. WAY. THROUGH.). Plain edge. Unique. (RB)					

Rulau-E	Date	Metal	Size	G	VG	F	VF
Conn 7	1739	Copper	29mm	8500.	18,000.	—	—
		Obverse similar to first 'Value Me As You Please' issue (Deer, III, etc.). Rv: As last, but 1739 instead of no date. Plain edge. (RB)					

Among the most interesting of all early American issues are the copper tokens struck circa 1737-1739 by Dr. Samuel Higley, of Granby, Connecticut. Higley, a medical doctor with a degree from Yale College, also practiced blacksmithing and made many experiments in metallurgy. In 1727 he devised a practical method of producing steel.

In 1728 Higley purchased property on a hill near Granby which furnished the site for many copper mines, the most famous being the extensive mine corridors and shafts which were worked extensively during the early and middle 18th century. In October 1773 the Connecticut General Assembly passed an act which pertained to the various subterranean caverns and external buildings of the copper mines in Simsbury and converted them for use as a public jail and workhouse.

Phelps, in his *History of the Copper Mines in Newgate Prison at Granby, Connecticut*, notes that:

"The prisoners were to be employed in mining. The crimes, by which the acts subjected offenders to confinement and labor in the prison, were burglary, horse stealing and counterfeiting the public bills or coins, or making instruments and dies therefore."

By the time Newgate Prison was abandoned in 1827, the buildings had been destroyed by fire three times. The cruel, dark, damp conditions precipitated in numerous revolts and violent incidents. Escapes were frequent.

Following his 1728 purchase, Dr. Samuel Higley operated a small but thriving mining business which extracted exceptionally rich copper. Much if not most of the metal was exported to England. Sometime around the year 1737 Higley produced a copper token. The obverse depicted a standing deer with the legend THE VALUE OF THREE-PENCE. The reverse showed three crowned hammers with the surrounding legend, CONNECTICUT, and the date 1737.

Legend tells us that drinks in the local tavern sold at the time for threepence each, and Higley was in the habit of paying his bar bill with his own coinage. There was a cry against this for the Higley copper threepence was of a diameter no larger than the contemporary British halfpennies which circulated in the area; coins which had a value of just 1/6th of that stated on the Higley coin.

Accordingly, Higley redesigned his coinage so that the obverse legend was changed to read VALUE ME AS YOU PLEASE. The pieces still bore an indication of value, the Roman numeral III below the standing deer. Two new reverses were designed, one of which pictured three hammers with the inscription I AM GOOD COPPER. The other reverse, picturing a broad axe, had the legend I CUT MY WAY THROUGH. The third obverse design, of which only a single specimen is known, depicted a wagon wheel with the legend THE WHEELE GOES ROUND.

While on a voyage to England in May 1737, on a ship loaded with copper from his own mine, Samuel Higley died. His oldest son, John, together with Rev. Timothy Woodbridge and William Cradock probably engraved and struck the issues of 1739.

Apparently the original Higley coinage was small, and circulation was effected only in Granby and its environs. Sylvestor S. Crosby relates that a goldsmith, who served his apprenticeship around 1810, said that Higley pieces were hard to find at the time and were in demand for use as an alloy for gold. The goldsmith related that his master delayed completing a string of gold beads for he was unable to find a copper Higley threepence with which to alloy the metal.

Today Higley issues of all types are exceedingly rare, and often a span of years will occur between offerings. Nearly all pieces show very extensive evidence of circulation, with most grading in the range of Good or Very Good.

R.B. in Oval (Roswell Bartholomew)

Hartford, Conn.

Rulau-E	Date	Metal	Size	VG	F	VF	EF
Conn 9	(?)	Silver	40mm	—	400.	—	600.
		R.B. in relief within toothed oval depression ctsp on U.S. 1799 or 1802 Draped Bust/Heraldic Eagle silver dollar. (Van Ormer sale 2782; Brunk 33340; Rulau-E Mav 9E)					

Rulau-E	Date	Metal	Size	VG	F	VF	EF
Conn 9A	(?)	Silver	39mm	—	250.	—	450.
		Similar ctsp on Spanish-American 8-reales. Examined: 1746, 1791, 1797, 1801, 1803.					
Conn 9B	(?)	Silver	32.5mm	—	250.	—	350.
		Similar ctsp on U.S. Bust half dollar. Examined: 1808, 1809, 1811 and 1811/10.					

Roswell Bartholomew, silversmith, was active in 1804-1830. Born 1781, he died in 1830.

ASA LAW

Hartford, Conn.

Rulau-E	Date	Metal	Size	VG	F	VF	EF
Conn 50	(ca 1800)	Copper	29mm	—	150.	—	—
		ASA/1783/LAW ctsp on U.S. 1797 Large cent. (Stanley Steinberg 1981 sale: Brunk 24010; Rulau-E Mav 28)					

Attributed to Hartford. Conn., but this has not been verified. Law was a silversmith 1783-1800. Examination of Conn 50 and Law's markings must be made to verify.

A. BRADLEY

New Haven, Conn.

Rulau-E	Date	Metal	Size	VG	F	VF	EF
Conn 11	(1820-24)	Copper	29mm	75.00	—	125.	—
		A. BRADLEY in relief within rectangular depression ctsp twice on U.S. 1800 Large cent. (Stanley Steinberg 1982 sale number 94, lot 129; Brunk 4840)					

Abner Bradley was a silversmith in New Haven. Born in 1783, he died in 1824. His hallmark could have been used by a successor firm until about 1835.

R. CUTLER

Rulau-E	Date	Metal	Size	VG	F	VF	EF
Conn 40	(1810?)	Copper	29mm	—	—	400.	—
		R. CUTLER ctsp on Connecticut 1787 cent. (Brunk 10470)					

Silversmith Richard Cutler (1736-1810) and his sons Richard Cutler Jr. (1774-1811) and William Cutler were partners in the New Haven silversmith firm of Richard Cutler & Sons 1800-1810. William Cutler was active until at least 1823.

Richard Cutler started in business about 1760, forming Cutler, Silliman, Ward & Co. about 1767. Thus he was one of America's earliest silversmiths.

C. HEQUEMBOURG JR.

Rulau-E	Date	Metal	Size	VG	F	VF	EF
Conn 12	(1804-10)	Silver	32.5mm	—	—	600.	—
		C. HEQUEMBOURG, JR in relief within rectangular depression ctsp on U.S. 1795 Flowing Hair half dollar. (Ex-Gamer, Bowers-Ruddy; Brunk 19280)					

Charles Hequembourg Jr. (born 1760, died 1851) was a silversmith in New Haven, Conn., about 1804. His teaspoon shank hallmark, which appears on the 1795 coin, is illustrated on page 295 of *The Book of Old Silver, English, American, Foreign*, by Seymour B. Wyler (1937; reprinted 1979). The hallmark is also listed in *Price Guide to Silver and their Marks* by Luckey (1978).

Hequembourg worked in New York City 1827-29 and in Buffalo, N.Y. 1835-42.

(Eagle) NEW HAVEN (Eli Whitney Blake)

Rulau-E	Date	Metal	Size	VG	F	VF	EF
Conn 26	(1822-25)	Copper	29mm	—	125.	—	175.
		(Eagle) / NEW HAVEN ctsp on U.S. 1817 Large cent.					
Conn 26E	(1822-25)	Silver	39mm	—	225.	—	350.
		Similar ctsp on France 1785 ecu. (Brunk 29500).					

This had been thought to be one of the lockplate marks of the famous American gunsmith and inventor, Eli Whitney, who began his musket manufacturing in New Haven in 1798. His first U.S. government order was for 10,000 muskets of the French 1763 Charleville pattern.

Whitney built his own arms factory with money advances from the U.S. at East Rock, two miles from New Haven — later called Whitneyville, Conn. Eli Whitney died Jan. 8, 1826 but the family business continued under his brothers-in-law P. and Eli Whitney Blake and later (1842) under his son Eli Whitney Jr.

It is believed the countermarks were applied to coins in or after 1822, as they conform to a lockplate marking of the 1822 contract — and lockplate marking US / P. & E. W. BLAKE / NEW HAVEN began about 1828. It is believed Eli Whitney Blake applied the stamps.

Whitney became one of America's foremost inventors in 1792 when he patented the cotton gin to separate cotton seeds from the fiber — work which before that time had to be done by hand. He set up a plant to make cotton gins in New Haven, but expenses of almost constant litigation in defense of his patent rights caused him to abandon the enterprise! Though he became wealthy through gun manufacture, he profited little from his cotton gin invention, which transformed the South into an agricultural power.

WATERBURY HOUSE

New Haven, Conn.

Rulau-E	Date	Metal	Size	G	VG	F	VF
Conn 27	(?)	Brass	20mm	—	—	—	1900.
		WATERBURY / 42 / CHURCH ST / N.H. / **HOUSE**. tiny WBD in field. Rv: Large 4 at center, two small dogs running left below: ornamental border.					

Rulau-E	Date	Metal	Size	G	VG	F	VF
Conn 27A	(?)	Brass	20mm	—	—	—	2500.

Obv. similar to 27. Rv: SIX at center; above is eagle with scroll above, the scroll lettered E PLURIBUS UNUM; below is a fouled anchor. Unique.

There is much controversy over dating the Waterbury House cards, though authorities from Raymond to Vlack feel they are very early. Conn 27A was unknown until 1981 when it was discovered by Charles E. Kirtley, Elizabeth City, N.C.

Joseph Barnett called this a Civil War token issue. Fuld thinks it is from the 1850-60 period.

Dating, even attributing, these pieces has caused much furor but little enlightenment. Unless proven otherwise, we accept that 'N.H.' stands for New Haven, though other meanings could be ascribed to it. We have been unable to trace the diesinker 'WBD'. Directory verification of a Waterbury House in New Haven (or elsewhere) and identification of the diesinker will be needed before certainty can be achieved. Steve Tanenbaum, White Plains, N.Y., who owns both pieces, feels they are Early American and after examining them, we agree ... for now.

W. C.
(William Cleveland)
Norwich, Conn.

Rulau-E	Date	Metal	Size	G	VG	F	VF	EF
Conn 30	(1804-25)	Copper	23mm	—	50.00	—	—	—

Large W. C in relief within toothed rect. depression ctsp on U.S. 1804 Half cent. (Kean Leiker collection)

This hallmark is given in the Ensko, Wyler and Kovel references on American silversmiths as one of those used by William Cleveland (born 1770, died 1837), who was active in silversmithy in Norwich, Conn. and other locales from 1792 to at least 1815, and probably longer.

Cleveland (or Cleaveland) was part of a family of silver craftsmen founded about 1760 by Benjamin Cleveland. The founder had, apparently, two sons who were also silversmiths, Benjamin (1767-1837, active 1790-1830); and William. There was also a younger Cleveland, Aaron, who became active about 1820 in Norwich.

William Cleveland formed several partnerships — Cleveland & Post about 1812-15 with Samuel Post, and Trott & Cleveland about 1792-94 with John Proctor Trott (1769-1852). Cleveland also is known to have moved his operations several times, to Putnam, Ohio about 1808, to Salem, Mass. about 1812, to Worthington, Mass. and to Zanesville, Ohio in 1815. The basic references on Cleveland are not clear on many points.

The attribution to Cleveland of this counterstamp is not certain, but is quite likely as the impression matches a known example. Cleveland had several hallmarks over the years.

William Cleveland's son Richard was the father of U.S. President Grover Cleveland.

ROATH
Norwich, Conn.

Rulau-E	Date	Metal	Size	VG	F	VF	EF
Conn 18	(ca 1826)	Copper	29mm	75.00	—	125.	—

ROATH in relief within rect. depression ctsp on U.S. 1816-1828 type Large cent, date worn off. (Hartzog coll.; Brunk 34520)

Roswell Walstein Roath, born in 1805, was active as a silversmith in Norwich, Conn., about 1826. Much later he moved to Denver in Colorado Territory. He still appeared in Norwich in the 1840 census.

S. AVERY
Preston, Conn.

Rulau-E	Date	Metal	Size	VG	F	VF	EF
Conn 32	(1810-30)	Copper	23mm	—	—	1200.	—

In five separate relief stamps, each within its own rectangular depression, are: S. AVERY/ WM. E. COWLES / F. CURTIS / R . T / A R. on U.S. 1793 Half cent. (B&M Patterson March, 1985 sale, lot 1717; Brunk 1445)

The S. AVERY stamp is that of silversmith Samuel Avery (1760-1836), one of four Avery brothers who were silversmiths in Preston. The others were John Avery Jr. (1755-1815), William Avery (1765-1798) and Robert Staunton Avery (1771-1846). The silversmith business had been started by their father, John Avery Sr. (1732-1794), about 1760. It flourished, apparently, until the 1830's.

None of the other stamps — apparently all silversmiths' hallmarks — has been traced. The F. CURTIS stamp could possibly indicate Francis Curtis of Woodbury, Conn., circa 1845, or Frederick Curtis of Hartford, Conn., ca 1848-50. The F. CURTIS stamp is also known on an 1821 Large cent (Brunk 10335).

William J. Cowles of Boston was a silversmith until 1761; the William E. could be a son.

The specimen illustrated realized $1210 at auction on March 26, 1985, a fantastically high price for an early silversmith hallmark on a U.S. coin.

Old stagecoach sign at the turnpike entering Winsted from New Hartford, Connecticut.

J.M.L. & W.H. SCOVILL
Waterbury, Conn.

Rulau-E	Date	Metal	Size	VG	F	EF	Unc
Conn 33	1830	White Metal	37mm	—	—	450.	—

View of factory buildings, ESTABLISHED 1802 ENLARGED 1813 / BURNT DOWN MARCH 1830 / REBUILT JULY / 1830. Rv: Nine lines of text within oak wreath. Medallic.

James Mitchell Lamson Scovill and William Henry Scovill established their brass works in 1802. The Scovill Manufacturing Company was still in business in 1980, though it sold off its brass mills several years before and became a diversified manufacturer of home products. This firm issued a number of store cards in the Hard Times era and in the 1845-1860 period, and it was a major manufacturer of Civil War tokens and later of coins for foreign governments (such as Haiti) and planchets for the U.S. Mint.

DELAWARE

J. RANDEL JR.
New Castle County, Del. and Cecil County, Md.

Rulau-E	Date	Metal	Size	VG	F	VF	EF
Del 1	1825	Copper	24mm	35.00	60.00	85.00	—

1825 within central wreath, J. RANDEL JR. / C. & D. CANAL. Rv: Blank. (Wright 870)

Rulau-E	Date	Metal	Size	VG	F	VF	EF
Del 2	(1825)	Copper	24mm	—	750.	—	—

Three concentric circles form target center, J. RANDEL JR. / C. & D. CANAL. Rv: Blank.

John Randel Jr. was the chief engineer for the 13-5/8-mile long Chesapeake and Delaware Canal from 1823 through 1825. In the fall of 1825 the company replaced him with Benjamin Wright, who completed the canal, which had begun in 1802, on Oct. 17, 1829. The canal connected the head of Chesapeake Bay with the Delaware River estuary. Randel sued the company for breach of contract, ultimately (1834) receiving $226,000 through the New Castle, Del. superior court. He used his settlement, then an enormous amount, to purchase Randalia, a large tract on Bohemia Manor near the mouth of Back Creek. He also engaged in several wild schemes, which dissipated his money. He maintained a steam sawmill on Randalia. Later he originated the elevated railway idea. The privately owned C. & D. Canal operated with locks until 1919, when the United States government bought it and converted it to its present form — a tidal, toll-free waterway 27 feet deep, capable of accommodating all but the largest vessels.

FLORIDA

JUAN ESTEVAN DE PENA
St. Augustine, Florida

Rulau-E	Date	Metal	Size	VG	F	EF
Fla 1	1760	Silver	31mm	—	—	5500.

Crude, unflattering bust of Carlos III of Spain in cuirass facing right, CARLOS . III. D. G. HISPAN . REX (AR in CARLOS are ligate; Carlos III by the grace of God King of Spain). Rv: Fully opened rose at center, with bud left and leaf right. JVAN . ESTEVAN . DE PENA . FLORIDA . around, 1760 below. Plain edge. (Herrera 56; Dickeson T.8.1; Fonrobert 1510; Ulex 275; Betts 454; Medina 63)

This is a proclamation 4-reales of Charles III of Spain, issued at Florida's capital, St. Augustine, during the viceregal period when Florida was ruled from Mexico City.

Florida was under Spanish rule from 1528 to 1763. It was ceded to Great Britain by the Treaty of Paris, Feb. 10, 1763. It was retroceded to Spain by the Treaty of Versailles, Sept. 3, 1783. West Florida was acquired piecemeal by the United States, part in 1795; part in 1810 and part in 1813. The rest of Florida was purchased by the United States from Spain, Feb. 22, 1819.

This silver proclamation coin (actually a medal which was accepted as cash) exists both cast and struck. One specimen in the ANS collection which we have examined is struck from dies, but most existing pieces are reportedly cast.

Some attempts have been made to show this was not an American piece, but both Holland and Appleton accepted it as American (see *American Journal of Numismatics*, Vol. IX, page 93.) and the scholars Herrera (1882) and Medina (1917) had no hesitation in accepting it.

Unlike the next listing, Fla 3, documents in the Archives of the Indies have not been located to authenticate it and give background details, but several can be surmised.

An official called the Alferez Real was appointed to oversee the proclamation celebrations attendant upon the succession of a new king. Among other duties, the Alferez Real frequently arranged for the striking of special silver proclamation coins which were distributed locally during the festivities. The name of this official is met with quite often on the pieces.

It is believed that Juan Estevan de Pena (there likely is a tilde above the N in Pena) was the St. Augustine Alferez Real in 1760, appointed by the governor.

One surviving specimen was in the collection of Joseph J. Mickley of Philadelphia, who had received it in the course of business as a half dollar. This was published by Montroville W. Dickeson in 1865 in *American Numismatic Manual.*

ZESPEDS
(Domingo Vicente de Zespedes)
St. Augustine, Florida

Rulau-E	Date	Metal	Size	VG	F	EF
Fla 3	1789	Silver	33mm	1500.	2000.	4000.

Crude draped bust of Carlos IV right. Around: CAROLUS IV D . G (4-dot rosette) HISPAN . REX . (Carlos IV by the grace of God king of Spain). Rv: Stylized 6-petal jasmine flower, castle for Castile above, rampant lion for Leon below. Around: LA FLORa . ORIENTAL PER ZESPEDs. PROCLAM:tur 1789. Plain edge. About 10 pieces known. (Herrera 133; Medina 148; Grove C-58; Benjamin Betts 10; Rosa 220; NASCA 1978 Clarke sale, lot 3644.

Rulau-E	Date	Metal	Size	VG	F	EF
Fla 3A	1789	Copper	33mm	—	—	6500.

As last, but struck in copper, (ANS collection; only 2 known).

This is a proclamation 4-reales of Charles IV of Spain, issued under authority of Florida Oriental (East Florida) at its capital, St. Augustine. Florida had been retroceded by Britain to Spain in 1783, and the viceregal government in Mexico split the province into two parts. East Florida, capital St. Augustine, consisted of the Florida peninsula bounded on the north by the Georgia (U.S.) frontier and on the west by the Apalachicola River.

It is this part of Florida which was purchased from Spain by the U.S. in 1819.

Florida Occidental (West Florida) extended from the Apalachicola River on the east to Lakes Maurepas and Pontchartrain and the Mississippi River on the west. It was bounded on the south by the Gulf of Mexico and on the north by the Line of 1783, which included parts of southern Mississippi, Alabama and Georgia.

The Treaty of 1795 moved West Florida's border southward to its present line, and the U.S., claiming West Florida as part of the Louisiana Purchase of 1803, seized the western part in 1810 and the rest in 1813. (Spain had retroceded Louisiana to France in 1800.)

Florida Occidental's capital under Spain was at Pensacola.

Both cast silver and struck silver examples of this piece are known. The Wayte Raymond specimen was sold by Bowers & Merena Galleries in 1987; it is in VG-F condition (obverse Fine), and that specimen is struck. Casting was the normal method in 1789.

The governor of East Florida, Vicente Manuel de Zespedes, declared that the province would proclaim the new king at St. Augustine on Dec. 12, 1789. He appointed his son, Domingo Vicente de Zespedes, to be Alferez Real, and the younger Zespedes arranged for the production of the special silver medals.

It should be mentioned that proclamation pieces were never legal tender, but they were of (approximately) silver coin weights and there is ample evidence that they circulated freely as money when so offered. Some of the Mexico City and other proclamation medals even bear their cash equivalent on them, 2R, 4R etc.

The copper specimen in the ANS cabinet is similar to the struck silver piece but has a variant bust, possibly due to reengraving the die. The copper de cloche specimen in VF in the 1990 B&M sale fetched $6500.

MAC GREGORIO
(Gregor Mac Gregor)
Amelia Island, Florida

Struck 1818

Rulau-E	Date	Metal	Size	F	VF	EF	Unc
Fla 10	1817	Bronze	33mm	1500.	2250.	4000.	5000.

Cross within circular palm wreath at center. Above: DUCE MAC GREGORIO. Below: LIBERTAS FLORIDARUM. Rv: Within open-top palm wreath at center: 29 / JUNII / 1817. Above: AMALIA. Below: VENI VIDI VICI (I came, I saw, I conquered). Plain edge. (Neuman 21614; George Leavitt 1871 sale of Clay coll., lots 437-438; Chapman 1882 sale of Bushnell coll., lot 349). There are 10 specimens known.

Rulau-E	Date	Metal	Size	F	VF	EF	Unc
Fla 10A	1817	Copper	33mm	—	—	—	—

As last. Only 2 known.

In the unsettled condition following the War of 1812, one Gregor MacGregor in 1817 with a force of freebooters captured Amelia Island off Florida and ran up his "Green Cross of Florida" flag on June 29. After making himself leader of "Republic of the Florida's" on Amelia, MacGregor founded on Admiralty court, a post office and a newspaper.

MacGregor was a revolutionary idealist but had little time or talent for practical matters. On Sept. 4, 1817, just 69 days after his invasion of Spanish East Florida territory, he boarded his ship and lay off the bar of St. Marys River for 12 days. On Sept. 15 he sailed from Florida waters.

In October he was in New Providence, Bahamas, trying to raise money and troops to return to Florida. In mid-December he sailed to Liverpool, was reported in London in Jan. 1818, and in February in Edinburgh. In October, 1818 he returned to the New World and established the "Cacique of Poyais" on the mosquito-infested coast of Honduras, and later sold both land and bonds (each quite worthless) in England for Poyais.

Researcher Carling Gresham of Florida reports that no record has been found of how or by whom the Amelia Island medals were struck, but he opines that they probably were made in England in early 1818. The workmanship is excellent, which would indicate a British provenance.

One Commodore Luis Aury succeeded MacGregor on Amelia Island, but an American force under Commodore Henley and Major Bankhead evicted him Dec. 23, 1817. Andrew Jackson's later incursion into Florida (beginning Jan. 11, 1818) had nothing to do with MacGregor or Aury on Amelia; Jackson's attack was against the Indians of West Florida.

Amelia Island was captured from the Confederacy by a Union naval force on March 3-4, 1862.

GEORGIA

B. LORD
Athens, Ga.

Rulau-E	Date	Metal	Size	VG	F	VF	EF
Ga 30	(1831-33)	Copper	29mm	—	125.	—	—

B. LORD in relief within toothed rect. depression ctsp. on U.S. 1804 Large cent. (Donald G. Partrick collection; Brunk 24900)

Rulau-E	Date	Metal	Size	VG	F	VF	EF
Ga 31	(1831-33)	Copper	23mm	—	125.	—	—

Similar ctsp on U.S. 1807 Half cent.

Benjamin Lord (born 1770, died 1843) was a silversmith of some renown, who was the principal of the firm of B.B. Lord & Co. (with Ebenezer Lord and Joel White) of Athens, Georgia, in the 1831-39 period. The mark is his hallmark, according to *A Directory of American Silver, Pewter and Silver Plate* by Ralph and Terry Kovel.

Lord began his silversmith trade in Pittsfield, N.H. in 1796. The next year he moved to Rutland, Vt., where he formed the firm of Lord & Goddard with Nicholas Goddard (1797-1807). He next appears in the directories in Athens, Ga., in the B.B. Lord & Co. silverware and jewelry manufacturing firm.

I. GILBERT
Augusta, Georgia

Rulau-E	Date	Metal	Size	VG	F	VF	EF
Ga 1	(1829-33)	Copper	28-1/2mm	1000.	1500.	2500.	—
		I. GILBERT'S SADDLERY WAREHOUSE / NO. 301 / BROAD STREET / AUGUSTA / GEO. / W&B NY. Rv: SADDLERY OF EVERY DESCRIPTION / WHOLESALE / AND / RETAIL. (Low 315)					

Rulau-E	Date	Metal	Size	VG	F	VF	EF
Ga 2	(1829-33)	Brass	28-1/2mm	1000.	1500.	2500.	—
		As Ga 1. (Low 316)					

PENFIELD
Savannah, Ga.

Rulau-E	Date	Metal	Size	VG	F	VF	EF
Ga 8	(1810-28)	Silver	32.5mm	—	—	200.	—
		PENFIELD in relief within rect. depression, ctsp on U.S. 1808 Bust half dollar. (Brunk 31610)					

Josiah Penfield was a Savannah silversmith 1810-28. Born 1785, he died in 1828. He formed Penfield & Co. with Frederick P. Marquand and Moses Eastman in 1820. (See Belden, pg. 332)

Penfield & Co. were silversmiths, jewelers, clockmakers and watchmakers.

(STEAMER) J.D.M.
(Steamer John David Morgan)
Savannah, Georgia

Ga 10

Ga 11

Rulau-E	Date	Metal	Size	G	VG	F	VF
Ga 10	(1828-36)	Copper	24mm	—	300.	—	450.
		Paddlewheel steamer in full smoke to right, initials JDM below; all within circle composed of wreath and six stars. The design is overstruck on a U.S. Half Cent of 1828. The illustrated piece is in the David Schenkman collection. 20 pieces known. (Duffield 1438; Van Ormer sale 2707; Brunk 21245)					

Rulau-E	Date	Metal	Size	VG	F	VF
Ga 11	(1828-36)	Copper	24mm	—	300.	450.
		Similar, but struck on an 1811 Half Cent. Only 2 known.				

During the 19th century a great number of U.S. and foreign coins were counterstamped in this country by merchants and individuals, for advertising and other purposes. Most were stamped with merely a set of initials, or a name.

Rarely is a coin encountered which includes some sort of design as a part of the counterstamp. The illustrated 1828 Half cent is an interesting exception: It has, in addition to the initials JDM, a paddlewheel steamboat. Even more unusual is the method of counterstamping — it was struck with a die similar in style to those used to strike coins. Thus the initials, design and surrounding circle are raised, rather than incused, on the host coin.

Frank G. Duffield, in his (1919-22) *A Trial List of Countermarked Modern Coins of the World*, listed the JDM counterstamp as number 1438.

The Duffield specimen was counterstamped on an 1828 Half cent. Kenneth Hallenbeck, in his 1967 *The Numismatist* article entitled "Counterstamped U.S. Half Cents," lists a specimen stamped on an 1811 Half cent. Others are on an 1828 Half cent and one with no date visible.

Among reference books on ships is one titled *Merchant Steam Vessels of the United States 1790-1868*. Compiled by William M. Lytle and Forrest R. Holdcamper from various government records, it lists every steam vessel registered or licensed in this country up to 1868. Only two steamers with the initials JDM are recorded in this work. One, the *Julius D. Morton*, was a sidewheel steamer of 472 tons. Built in 1848 at Monroe, Michigan, its home port was Detroit. The ship was destroyed by fire in 1863.

The other steamer listed is the *John David Morgan*, a sidewheeler of 169 tons. It was built in 1828 in New York City and operated out of Savannah, Georgia. This vessel was abandoned or dismantled in 1836.

Based on the date in the Lytle-Holdcamper list, it is logical to attribute the JDM counterstamp to the steamer *John David Morgan*, and to include it with the early merchant tokens of Savannah. The period during which this vessel operated ties in with the dates on the 1811 and 1828 coins; the other JDM steamer is from a much later period.

Why were the coins counterstamped? Since all specimens reported were stamped on Half cents, they probably had a specific use rather than advertising. Perhaps they were given to customers at the company's ticket office when fares were purchased, and collected when the vessel was boarded.

KENTUCKY

P.P.P. MYDDELTON
Kentucky

Rulau-E	Date	Metal	Size	EF	Proof
Ky 1	1796	Copper	30mm	—	5500.
		Female and two nude boys being welcomed by Liberty, BRITISH SETTLEMENT KENTUCKY 1796. Rv: Seated Britannia with British shield and downcast head, PAYABLE BY P.P.P. MYDDELTON. (RB) (4 to 6 known)			

Rulau-E	Date	Metal	Size	EF	Proof
Ky 2	1796	Silver	30mm	—	5000.
		As last. (RB) (20 known)			

Rulau-E	Date	Metal	Size	EF	Proof
Ky 4	1796				
(1806-10)	Copper	30mm		—	2000.
		Muling of Myddelton reverse with Copper Company of Upper Canada token reverse. (Struck circa 1806-1810) (RB)			

Philip Parry Price Myddelton, who owned a tract of land in Kentucky, enticed hundreds of Englishmen to emigrate and reside on his property in 1795-1796. Anticipating the need for small change, he had halfpence made by Boulton & Watt of Birmingham after designs by Conrad Kuchler. He was arrested in August, 1796, by British authorities, halting the settlement and the coinage. About 1806-1810 Boulton & Watt muled the Myddelton and Upper Canada dies to create presentation pieces, which had no connection with the Myddelton Kentucky tract.

Ponthon was diesinker for the Copper Co. of Upper Canada pieces. Ky 2 in silver proof fetched $3600 in the Nov. 1990 Schenkel sale.

H.E. THOMAS & CO.
Louisville, Ky.

Rulau-E	Date	Metal	Size	VG	F	VF	EF
Ky 33	(1832)	White Metal	28mm	—	—	—	850.

Hardware implements. H.E. THOMAS & CO. / WHOLESALE / HARDWARE STORE / MAIN / NEAR WALL ST. / LOUISVILLE / KY. Reeded edge.

The hardware implements design side is a copy of Breton 561, the T.S. Brown cards of Montreal, Quebec, which was struck in Birmingham, England, in 1832. The evidence given in Sandham to the conclusive dating of the Brown card leads to the supposition that Thomas may have had the same die struck for himself on a trial basis in white metal. The Thomas piece could be later, in the Hard Times period of course, but for now we're assigning it here. The hardware implements die used on the T.S. Brown and H.E. Thomas & Co. cards was also used on a white metal piece of Green & Wetmore of New York (Low 298, Adams N.Y. 290).

SMITH & GRANT
Louisville, Ky.

Rulau	Date	Metal	Size	VG	F	VF
Ky 30	(1827-38)	Silver	32.5mm	400.	—	600.

SMITH & GRANT in relief within ribbonlike rect. depression ctsp on U.S. Bust half dollar. Examined: 1823, 1838. (Brunk 36910)

Richard Ewing Smith (born 1800) arrived in Louisville in 1821. He and William Grant formed a silversmith and jewelry partnership about 1827, which was dissolved Nov. 10, 1831. One of the partners apparently caused the 1838 half dollar to be stamped well afterward. Smith died in 1849.

LOUISIANA

W. EDGAR JUNR.
New Orleans, La.

Rulau-E	Date	Metal	Size	VG	F	VF	EF
La 8	(1825-34)	Brass	26mm	1500.	1800.	2250.	3000.

W. EDGAR JUNR. / DEPOT / DES / HABILLEMENTS / TOUTS FAITS / RUE DE CANAL / NO. 30 / NOUVELLE / ORLEANS. RV: W. EDGAR JUNR. / CLOTHING / STORE / 30 CANAL ST. / NEW / ORLEANS. (Hartzog coll.)

The clothing store of William Edgar Jr. was located at 16 Levee Street, corner Custom House Street, in 1824. In 1825 the business moved to 30 Canal Street where it continued for several years. In 1835, Edgar & Smith's clothing store at 4 Chartres Street was probably a successor to this business. (See Sidney K. Eastwood's "New Orleans Store Cards in the Antebellum Days" in *TAMS Journal* for October, 1966.)

This token has an indifferent recent auction record. A VF specimen in B&M Nov. 1990 sale fetched $302.50, yet the *same token* in PCAC June 1991 sale realized $1700!

P. B.
New Orleans, La.

Cut segments of Spanish-American silver coins, such as quarters of 8-real or 4-real coins, occur counterstamped as follows: Script P. B. within chain circle on one side, and NOUVELLE ORLEANS around Eagle displayed on the other. The firm of James Puech and John D. Bein was active 1812 until 1834, and sold cut Spanish American silver coins to West Indian governments in that period.

The bank's own counterstamped cut segments may have been issued in and after 1816 and must have been a very large issue, though specimens surviving today are quite rare. They are listed in the section *Hard Times Tokens* as Low 82A, B and C as it has been thought by all writers from Lyman H. Low in 1899 to Ray Byrne in 1975 that these cut segments emanated in the 1832-34 period.

Puech, Bein & Co.'s lone struck store card (in copper, 25.5mm) is dated 1834 and identifies the business as "importers of hardwares, guns and pistols, cutlery and c." This store card, Low 82, appears now to have been issued to advertise the Puech, Bein firm's change from the banking to the importing business.

The long association of Puech-Bein with the Hard Times period need not be interrupted here. All the cut segments are listed along with appropriate dating remarks in the Hard Times section.

Robert Leonard and Gregory Brunk now believe that Puech Bein were not the issuers.

MARYLAND

I. CHALMERS
Annapolis, MD.

Rulau-E	Date	Metal	Size	VG	F	VF	EF
Md 1C	1783	Silver	21mm	500.	750.	1200.	—

Two birds holding long worm. Rv: Two clasped hands within wreath. Reeded edge. 1 Shilling. (RB)

Note: Excellent electros with plain edge exist!

Md 1B	1783	Silver	21mm	475.	700.	1100.	—

Similar, but shorter worm. (RB)

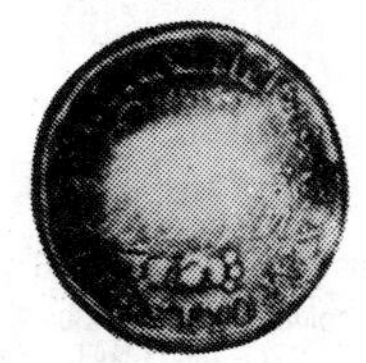
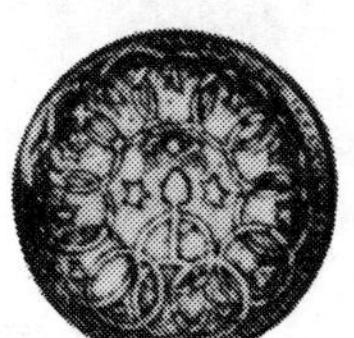

Rulau	Date	Metal	Size	VG	F	VF	EF
Md 1D	1783	Silver	21mm	Ex. Rare	—	75,000.	—

Similar obverse. Rv: Wreath of interlocked rings and stars. (RB) (Garrett lot 1313)

Rulau	Date	Metal	Size	VG	F	VF	EF
Md 1E	1783	Silver	18mm	875.	1200.	2100.	—

Star within wreath. Rv: Cross with two clasped hands. Small date. 6 Pence. (RB)

Rulau	Date	Metal	Size	VG	F	VF	EF
Md 1F	1783	Silver	18mm	700.	1200.	2100.	—
		Similar, large date. (RB)					

Rulau	Date	Metal	Size	VG	F	VF	EF
Md 1G	1783	Silver	13mm	550.	1000.	1500.	—
		Clasped hands. Rv: Wreath encircles small branch. 3 Pence. (RB)					

Goldsmith and silversmith John Chalmers struck a series of silver tokens at Annapolis in 1783. This shortage of change and the refusal of the people to use underweight cut Spanish coins, or "bits," prompted the issuance of these pieces, according to a contemporary account of a German traveler, Dr. John D. Schopf. Chalmers was born 1750, eldest son of silversmith and tavernkeeper James Chalmers of Annapolis. He took over his father's business in 1781. The silver tokens were struck at his shop at the corner of Cornhill and Fleet streets. At that time it was customary to cut a Spanish silver dollar into halves, quarters or eighths, the eighth being a "bit." Unscrupulous persons would cut five "quarters" or 10 "eighths" from a dollar, increasing their return. Schopf reported that Chalmers redeemed the fractions, exchanging his own coins for them and charging a commission for the service. His coinage was apparently extensive, the shilling occurring most frequently today.

THE TUESDAY CLUB

Annapolis, Md.

Rulau-E	Date	Metal	Size	F	VF	EF	Unc
Md 5	1746	Copper	44mm		Rare		
		Nude boy, seated, holding staff with Liberty cap atop it; to left is an altar reading: LIBERTAS / ET / NATALE / SOLUM. Around: * CAROLUS COLE ARMIGER PRAESES. Rv: Clasped hands within heart, script ANNAPOLIS left and MARYLAND right. Above: THE / TUESDAY CLUB / IN. Below: MAY. 14. 1746. Around all: * CONCORDIA RES PARVAE CRESCUNT. Plain edge. (Betts 383; Med. Ill. Geo II, 292).					

Libertas et natale solum = Liberty and native land. Concordia res parvae crescunt = By harmony small things increase.

Rulau-E	Date	Metal	Size	F	VF	EF	Unc
Md 5A	1746	WM	44mm		Rare		
		As Md 5. Plain edge.					
Md 5B	1746	Silver	44mm		Unique		
		As Md 5. Plain edge. (Lot 785 in W.W. C. Wilson sale)					

The Tuesday Club was an association of gentlemen founded in Annapolis in the 1740-45 period which existed about 40 years — or through the Revolutionary War. The club records, in possession of the Maryland Historical Society in Baltimore, are illustrated by amusing sketches and portraits of the members. In a humorous vein they give the proceedings of the club — laws, ceremonies, poetical productions, mock trials, etc.

The medal was struck in London by John Kirk to the order of Charles Cole, club president in 1746, and presented to club members to be worn on ceremonial occasions.

Scribner's Monthly for January, 1879 gives particulars of the club.

The membership medal is the first such piece issued in what is now the United States.

STANDISH BARRY

Baltimore Md.

Rulau-E	Date	Metal	Size	VG	F	VF
Md 11A	(17) 90	Silver	14mm	1400.	2200.	3600.
		Man's head left, BALTIMORE TOWN, JULY 4, 90. Rv: THREE PENCE. (RB; Zeddies coll.)				

Silversmith Standish Barry, then 27, circulated a silver token in 1790 which may depict George Washington or Barry himself. He was also a watch and clockmaker and an engraver. The tokens were an advertising venture at a time small change was scarce. The reverse die supposedly broke after only about 12 pieces were made, but more pieces are known. Edges were crudely reeded.

(BALTIMORE TOKEN)

Baltimore, Md.

Rulau-E	Date	Metal	Size	VG	F	EF	Unc
Md 7	(1830-36)	Brass	23mm	45.00	115.	200.	—
		Three-masted sailing ship right. Rv: U.S. shield surrounded by 13 stars. Thick planchet.					
Md 7A	(1830-36)	Brass	23mm	45.00	115.	200.	—
		Same as 7, counterstamped H.M.					
Md 7B	(1830-36)	Brass	23mm	45.00	115.	200.	—
		Same as 7, counterstamped A. FIELD					
Md 8	(1830-36)	Brass	23mm	45.00	115.	150.	—
		Similar to 7, but smaller stars. Thin planchet.					
Md 8A	(1830-36)	Brass	23mm	45.00	115.	200.	—
		As 8, ctsp 5					
Md 8B	(1830-36)	Brass	23mm	45.00	115.	200.	—
		As 8, ctsp J.W.					
Md 8C	(1830-36)	Brass	23mm	45.00	115.	150.	—
		As 8, ctsp S.					
Md 8D	(1830-36)	Brass	23mm	45.00	115.	200.	—
		As 8, ctsp C.S.					

Rulau-E	Date	Metal	Size	VG	F	EF
Md 8E	(1830-36)	Brass	23mm	45.00	115.	200.
		As 8, ctsp W.H.				

Rulau-E	Date	Metal	Size	VG	F	EF
Md 8F	(1830-36)	Brass	23mm	45.00	115.	200.
		As 8, ctsp J.D.				

Rulau-E	Date	Metal	Size	VG	F	VF	EF
Md 8G	(1830-36)	Brass	23mm	45.00	115.	200.	—
		As 8, ctsp P.U.					
Md 8H	(1830-36)	Brass	23mm	45.00	115.	200.	—
		As 8, ctsp B.H.					
Md 8J	(1830-36)		23mm	45.00	115.	200.	—
		As 8, ctsp 10 / ICE.					
Md 8K	(1830-36)	Brass	23mm	—	—	150.	—
		As 8, ctsp B. M. RAY					
Md 9	(1830-36)	Brass	23mm	—	200.	—	—
		Similar, but new reverse die with 13 stars in semicircle. Ctsp AHM. (Kirtley sale of April 1984, lot 126, in TAMS Journal for Feb. 1984).					

The diesinker for the Baltimore Tokens is not known, but the ship die was also used for the James Cole cards of the Hard Times period. This relationship of die work was explored by Frank Duffield, without clear conclusions, in *The Numismatist* for Dec. 1904. The counterstamps show this mute token device was adapted as a trade check by a number of firms in the area. Some day a scholar might trace the token itself.

There are three distinct reverse dies on these pieces, with differently shaped shields.

Some of the counterstampers seem to have been active as late as 1850.

J. CLARK
Baltimore, Md.

Rulau-E	Date	Metal	Size	VG	F	VF	EF
Md 20	(?)	Copper	29mm	—	150.	—	—
		J. CLARK / BALTO. ctsp on Massachusetts 1787-88 cent. (Van Ormer sale 2587; Brunk 8047)					

Of the many John, Joseph, Joshua etc. Clarks practicing the silversmith, brazier, coppersmith, pewterer and related trades in America's first six decades, none seem to have been located in Baltimore. The closest is one John J. Clark in Cambridge, Md. 1833-? and then in Portsmouth, Va. 1842-45, a silversmith.

We must conclude that another occupation than metalsmith is involved.

A. FIELD
Baltimore, Md.

Rulau-E	Date	Metal	Size	VG	F	EF
Md 100	(1850's)	Brass	23mm	—	40.00	—
		A. FIELD ctsp on worn brass planchet, possibly one of the Baltimore Ship tokens (Md 7-9) worn smooth. (Lot 439 in 1989 Gil Steinberg sale by Stack's). Some 8 to 15 specimens have been reported.				
Md 101	(1850's)	Copper	28.5mm	—	60.00	—
		Similar ctsp on 1837 Hard Times token, Low 44, HT 69. (Kirtley Dec. 1989 sale, lot 2850; Brunk 14105)				

Also see Md 7B under Baltimore Token in this reference, possibly issued by the same firm.

In the 1989 Steinberg sale, Md 100 was described as counterstamped on a James Cole worn card, Md 38.

Maryland specialist Russ Sears states he believes Md 100-101 were issued by a Baltimore oyster packer of the 1850's and 1860's. They are left in this section for ease of collector use.

MASSACHUSETTS

BALDWIN & JONES
Boston, Mass.

Rulau-E	Date	Metal	Size	VG	F	VF	EF
Mass 4	(1813-19)	Copper	29mm	—	100.	—	200.
		BALDWIN & JONES in relief in scroll-shaped depression ctsp on U.S. Large Cent. Dates examined: 1796, 1800, 1808, 1819. There are 4 pieces known. (Brunk 2065)					

Rulau-E	Date	Metal	Size	VG	F	VF	EF
Mass 5	(1819)	Copper	29mm	—	100.	—	200.
		BALDWIN & JONES in relief in rect. depression ctsp on U.S. Large cent of 1796 type, worn. (Brunk 2060)					

Jabez L. Baldwin (1777-1819) and John B. Jones (1782-1854) were partners in the silversmith's trade circa 1813-1819. After Baldwin's death in 1819, Jones continued under the same name for a time; by 1838 this was known as John B. Jones & Co., and in 1839 Jones, Ball & Low. (See token of John J. Low & Co.)

L. CARY

Rulau-E	Date	Metal	Size	VG	F	VF	EF
Mass 6	(1821-34)	Copper	29mm	—	200.	—	300.
		(Radiant sun) L. CARY (Radiant sun) in relief within scroll-shaped depression ctsp on reverse of early Large cent of 1797-1807 period. (Jules Reiver coll.; Brunk 7000)					
Mass 6A	(1821-34)	Silver	27mm	—	200.	—	300.
		Similar ctsp on Spanish-American 2-reales.					

Lewis Cary (1798-1834) worked as a silversmith about 1815 to 1834 in Boston. He used the fancy punch seen above on silver teaspoons and other objects he made and used another mark: L. CARY in relief within rectangular depression.

Collector Jules Reiver of Delaware wrote up Cary's mark in "Silversmiths' Marks Aid in Identification" in *Coin World* for March 19, 1986.

Reiver obtained a silver teaspoon showing the precise mark used on his Large cent, the punch having been applied to the shank's reverse.

The *Coin World* article reveals that some spoons from the Ineson-Bissell collection, along with matching counterstamped coins, were displayed by associate curator Donald Fennimore of the Winterthur Museum in Wilmington, Del. at the Jan. 1986 coin show of Wilmington Coin Club. So far as we know, this was the first public exhibit in America to show the relationship between silversmith marks on silverware and on coins.

S. EMERY

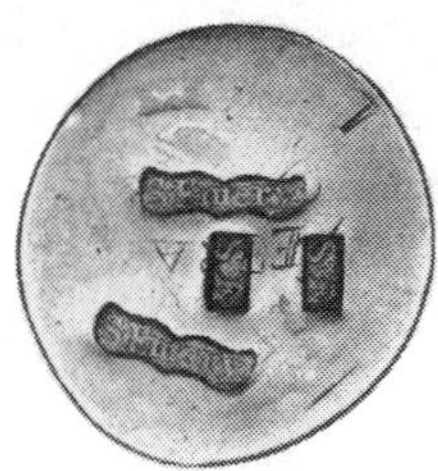

Rulau-E	Date	Metal	Size	VG	F	VF	EF
Mass 9	(1782-98)	Copper	29mm	—	250.	—	—
		S. Emery in relief within stepped rectangular depression ctsp twice on worn England George II halfpenny of 1740-54 type. S. E. in relief within rect. depression ctsp twice on the same side of the coin. (Sold 1991 by Harvey Gamer, Winnipeg, Canada; Brunk 13345)					

Before the four hallmarks were stamped, the coin had been engraved with a word, now partly obscured. It seems to read: .ET.RA.

These are the distinctive hallmarks of the silversmith Stephen Emery (1749-1801) of Boston, active in his trade at least 1782-1798. He was the father of the silversmith Thomas Knox Emery (1781-1815), active in Boston 1802-13.

Assuming the marks were applied by Stephen Emery himself and not some successor, this unpublished piece could be one of the earliest counterstamped American tokens. The marks precisely match those given in Belden (pg. 156).

R.F.
(Rufus Farnam)

Rulau-E	Date	Metal	Size	VG	F	VF	EF
Mass 13	(1817-30)	Copper	29mm	—	50.00	—	—

R.F. in relief in rect. depression ctsp on U.S. 1817-13 stars Large cent.

Rufus Farnam (1771-1833) was a silversmith located in Boston 1799-1830 and then in Hanover, N.H. until 1833. He also had operations in Norwich, Conn. ca 1810.

R.F. was a hallmark used by Farnam in Boston 1799-1830 either alone or as part of the firms of Farnam & Ward 1810-16 or Rufus & Henry Farnam 1800-07.

This mark is similar to fantasy marks created for collectors to indicate "Republique Francaise"!

FARNSWORTH, PHIPPS & CO.

Rulau-E	Date	Metal	Size	F	VF	EF	Unc
Mass 38	(1829-33)	Copper	28-1/2mm	30.00	55.00	—	300.

FARNSWORTH PHIPPS & CO. / NO 85 / KILBY STREET / BOSTON. Rv: DEALERS / IN / BRITISH FRENCH / INDIA AND / AMERICAN / DRY GOODS. Tiny W. & B. - N.Y. flanks DRY GOODS. (Wright 356; Low 314)

This token spans the Early American and Hard Time eras. Struck by Wright & Bale of New York, who were in partnership May 1829 to October 1833.

O. HOWE

Rulau-E	Date	Metal	Size	VG	F	VF	EF
Mass 15	(1792-1803)	Copper	29mm	—	25.00	—	—
Mass 17	(1803)	Copper	29mm	—	70.00	—	—

Mass 15: O + H in large divided toothed rectangular cartouche ctsp on England Halfpenny token of the "Britannia Rules the Waves" type. (Donald Partrick Coll.)

Mass 17: O.HOWE in relief in toothed rect. depression ctsp on U.S. 1803 Large Cent. (Brunk 20390; David Jerdee coll.)

Otis Howe was a silversmith born in 1788 who died in 1825. In 1816-1817 he was located in Sackets Harbor, NY. Mass 15 is probably misattributed. O + H seems to imply a partnership.

J. LORING
Boston, Mass.

Rulau-E	Date	Metal	Size	VG	F	VF	EF
Mass 40	(1820's)	Copper	29mm	—	—	400.	—

W. THOMSON in relief within rect. depression / J. Loring in script in relief within shaped-to-order depression / W. THOMSON in relief within rect. depression— in three separate stamps ctsp on U.S. 1817 Large cent. (Denton Curtis collection, Chandlers Ford, Hants., England; Brunk 24953)

The central ctsp is an exact match with the Belden reference hallmark of Joseph Loring (1743-1815), a Boston silversmith whose best work was done about 1792. Loring had apprenticed under Paul Revere II or Benjamin Burt, Belden says.

Since the cent is dated two years after Loring's death, it is probable that his silversmith son, Henry Loring, used the father's hallmark punches for several years to authenticate his own work.

The W. THOMSON punch is one of those used by New York silversmith William Thomson, active 1810-34 and possibly as long as 1845 (See Rulau-E 900-902 under New York City).

JOHN J. LOW & CO.

Rulau-E	Date	Metal	Size	VG	F	EF
Mass 48	(1828-35)	Brass	32mm			Unique
Mass 48A	(1828-35)	WM	32mm	—	—	Unique

Mass 48: JOHN J. LOW & CO. / IMPORTERS / OF / WATCHES / JEWELRY AND / MILITARY GOODS. Rv: PLATED & BRITANNIA / WARE / NO. 19 / WASHINGTON ST / BOSTON / (eleven stars). (Wright 628)

Mass 48A: As 48.

John J. Low & Co. was founded in 1828 and changed its name to Jones, Ball & Low in 1839. Later this firm became known as Shreve, Crump & Low, still in business in 1921. The only known specimen was in the W. Eliot Woodward and B.P. Wright collections, eventually passing in 1921 to the Massachusetts Historical Society. In the May, 1921, *The Numismatist*, MHS curator Malcolm Storer published the token with a photograph. It apparently has a gilt surface.

PIERCE

Rulau-E	Date	Metal	Size	F	EF	Unc
Mass 20	(1816)	Copper	29mm	75.00	125.00	—

PIERCE in relief within rect. depression ctsp on U.S. Large cent. Examined: 1797, 1802, 1816, 1817, 1818, 1827, 1831, 1848. (Hallenbeck coll.; Brunk 32050)

John Pierce (or Peirse) was a silversmith in Boston about 1810. He may have changed his name to Pierce later, and been succeeded about 1824 by O. Pierce. The reports could also be due to misspellings.

HORACE PORTER & CO.

Rulau-E	Date	Metal	Size	VG	F	EF
Mass 84	(1826-33)	S/Brass	24mm	25.00	50.00	100.
Mass 84A	(1826-33)	Copper	24mm	—	—	—

Mass 84: HORACE PORTER / & CO. / WATCHES / AND / RICH JEWELRY / WASHINGTON ST. / BOSTON. Rv: MILITARY GOODS / SILVER / PLATED / BRITANNIA / AND / FANCY / ARTICLES.

Mass 84A: As 84. (Wright 1578). This piece may not exist.

Horace Porter is listed in the Boston directories at Washington Street from 1826 through 1833. Also known in brass, not plated.

RUETER & ALLEY
RUETER & CO.

Mass 85, 85A and 86, under these titles, have proven to be post-Civil War in vintage, 1870's and 1880's. Neither name appears in any Boston directory or census record 1820-1863. The 1888 directory lists: Rueter & Co., Highland Spring Brewery, Heath corner Terrace.

L. WALKER

Rulau-E	Date	Metal	Size	VG	F	EF
Mass 21	(ca 1825)	Silver	27mm	—	125.	—

L. WALKER ctsp on reverse of Spanish-American 1756-LME-JM 2-reales. (Stanley Steinberg 1982 sale; Brunk 41560)

L. Walker was a Boston silversmith of about 1825, located in the Joys Building.

A. & G. WELLES and G. LIBBY

Rulau-E	Date	Metal	Size	VG	F	VF	EF
Mass 22	(1830)	Copper	29mm	100	—	150.	—

A & G WELLES in relief ctsp within rectangular depression, and G LIBBY 1796 ctsp incuse, all on a U.S. 1802 or 1803 Large cent. (Duffield 1585; Hallenbeck 23.505; Brunk 42540)

The A. & G. Welles stamp was a silversmith's mark applied about 1830. The G. Libby stamp is for George Libby of Warren, Maine (born 1796, died 1843). The Libby stamp is personal; 1796 was his year of birth.

Alfred and George Welles began in business about 1804 as jewelers and silversmiths. George died about 1827, but Alfred lived to 1860. They were involved in several partnerships (e.g. Welles & Gelston and Welles & Co. with Hugh Gelston).

W. WOART

Rulau-E	Date	Metal	Size	VG	F	VF	EF
Mass 90	(1790)	WM	28.7mm			2 Known	

Standing Indian as on Massachusetts cent of 1787-88. Around: W. WOART * JUS PACIS. Rv: Blank. Plain edge. (*The Colonial Newsletter* for Oct. 1985, pg. 915 and Nov. 1987, pg. 1022; William Anton Coll.; Dennis Wierzba and Steven E. Saari research)

Jus Pacis = Justice (and) Peace. The letter punches used are identical to those used to produce the Nova Costellatio coinage of 1783-85.

One William Woart appears in the 1790 census residing at Cornhill Street; he may have been a carpenter. He may have been related to the 1788-89 innkeeper John Woart at The Sign of the Dragon. William Woart married Mary Loring in 1798.

E. WOODWARD
Boston, Mass.

Rulau-E	Date	Size	VG	F	VF	EF
Mass 23	(?)	Copper	29mm	75.00	—	100.

E. WOODWARD in relief within rect. depression ctsp on U.S. 1814 Large cent. (Levine June 1985 sale, lot 1393; Brunk 44357)

This hallmark is apparently an unpublished silversmith's mark of Eli Woodward, who was active as early as 1812 in Boston (and later also in Hartford, Conn.). During the period 1847-1852 the partnership of Woodward & Grosjean were silversmiths in Boston and Hartford, using a hallmark W & G within rectangle.

H.P.C. (Hasty Pudding Club)
Cambridge, Mass.

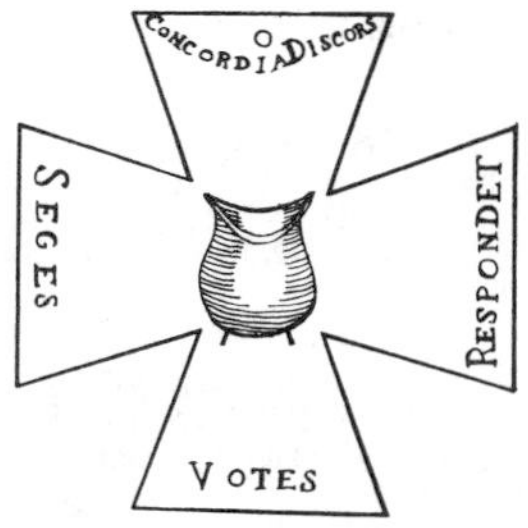

First Type
Engraved by Hand

Rulau-E	Date	Metal	Size	VG	F	VF	EF
Mass 24	1795	Silver	++			No specimen known	

++ Maltese cross-shaped planchet, 33mm. Pot with legs and handle at center. On each arm of the cross (top-left-bottom-right): CONCORDIA DISCORS / SEGES / VOTES / RESPONDET (Disagreeing in harmony, the harvest responds to the vows [of the planters]). Rv: Eye at center. On the arms: (left-top-right-bottom): HASTY / PUDDING / CLUB / 1795. Issued holed. (Sallay Type 1)

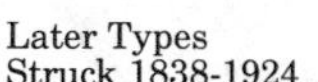

Later Types
Struck 1838-1924

Rulau-E	Date	Metal	Size	F	VF	EF	Unc
Mass 24E	1795	Silver	Oct 39mm	—	40.00	60.00	—

Hands holding spoon and bowl above a large, 3-legged pot with handle (the act of serving pudding from a pot), H.P.C. above. On a scroll below: SEGES VOTIS RESPONDENS. Rv: Sphinx left above oval wreath, CONCORDIA DISCORS. above, 1795. below. Plain edge. Issued with loop, (Storer 918; Garrett 2080; Sallay Types 2 thru 8, all similar)

Rulau-E	Date	Metal	Size	F	VF	EF	Unc
Mass 24B	1795	Copper	Oct 39mm	—	30.00	50.00	—

As last. (Storer 918)

Rulau-E	Date	Metal	Size	F	VF	EF	Unc
Mass 24C	1795	WM	Oct 39mm	—	—	—	—

As last.

The Hasty Pudding Club at Harvard University issued a number of membership medals over the years. The first medal type, engraved by hand, survives only in an old photograph in the Harvard archives; it was used in the Early American period.

Collectible medals were struck beginning in 1838 and continuing in eight die varieties for almost a century. These are found with member's names engraved within the wreath on reverse (e.g. J.M. MOORSE, 1907 as offered in the Koppenhaver Nov. 1983 sale, lot 850).

For a comprehensive examination of the hasty Pudding Club and its medals, see "The Hasty Pudding Club Medals" by John M. Sallay in *The Numismatist* for October, 1990.

PIERIAN SODALITY

Struck 1863-73

Rulau-E	Date	Metal	Size	F	VF	EF	Unc
Mass 25	1808	Silver	Oct 40mm	—	—	125.	—

PIERIAN / SODALITY. / (clasped hands) / (oval frame) / 1808. Rv: Lyre at center, surrounded by grape wreath. Closing the open-top wreath is: SIT MUSA LYRAE SOLERS. Plain edge. Issued hold. (Julian RF-11; Storer 936)

Rulau-E	Date	Metal	Size	F	VF	EF	Unc
Mass 25A	1808	Bronze	Oct 40mm				

As last. Plain edge. Issued holed. (Julian RF-11)

Though dated 1808, these medals were struck at the Philadelphia Mint for the society in 1863 and 1873, Julian reports. A name could be engraved in the oval frame on obverse. The Latin motto translates: "May there be the accustomed inspiration of music."

Pierian Sodality was a club at Harvard University.

PORCELLIAN CLUB
Cambridge, Mass.

Rulau-E	Date	Metal	Size	F	VF	EF	Unc
Mass 26	(1800-31)	Silver	**	—	100.	—	—**

** Heart-shaped flan, 35 by 43mm.
OVEY (Greek letters) / DUM VIVIMUS VIVAMUS (?) / (clasped hands) / Script FLD engraved within oval. Rv: PORCELLIAN / CLUB / INSTITUTED / 1791. Plain edge. (Storer 938)

The member whose initials are engraved was Francis Low Dutton, who received a B.A. degree in 1831.

The Porcellian group was "one of the swellest clubs in existence" according to W.D. Orcutt in "Clubs and Club Life at Harvard" (*New England Magazine*, 1892).

Harvard University, founded 1636, is the oldest institution of higher learning in the U.S. Harvard's Law School was founded in 1817 and its Divinity School in 1819. In 1823 the state of Massachusetts ceased its financial support of the university.

This medal was not used until 1800, and was the regular club medal until 1831.

Rulau-E	Date	Metal	Size	F	VF	EF	Unc
Mass 27	1831	Silver	Oct 47mm	—	75.00	—	—

Double circle rests on swords, DUM VIVIMUS VIVAMUS in circles. Flattened oval in field for engraving. Around: PORCELLIAN / CLUB / 1831. Rv: Double circle rests on swords, FIDE ET AMICITIA / P.C. K.S.T. in circles. Boar's head in field, clasped hands and casque. Above: ouey (Greek). Below: Ban d labeled 1791 1808. Plain edge. (Storer 939)

P.C. = Porcellian Club. K.S.T. — Knights of the Square Table. These two groups united in 1831. P.C. was founded 1791, K.S.T. in 1808. This medal replaced Mass 25 in 1831.

Mass 28	1809	Silver	—mm	—	—	—	—

Star of 14 rays. Within the star (engraved): FIDE ET AMICITIA / K.P.S. / 1809. Rv: Blank. Plain edge. (Storer 940)

The meaning of K.P.S. is not known, but FIDE ET AMICITIA was the Porcellian Club's motto. The specimen Storer examined was engraved: DR. JONATHAN GREELY STEVENSON (class of 1816 at Harvard), and the medal was engraved after 1835. Records show Stevenson was a member of the Knights of the Square Table.

E. G. DRAKE
Granville, Mass.

Rulau-E	Date	Metal	Size	VG	F	VF	EF
Mass 94	(1820)	Copper	29mm	100.	—	150.	—

E. G. DRAKE in relief within toothed rect. depression ctsp on U.S. 1795 or 1798 Large Cent. (Donald Partrick coll.; Brunk 12155; Rulau-E Mav 16)

Enoch Griswold Drake, born 1796, was a goldsmith. He died in 1827.

A. WATERS
Millbury, Mass.

Rulau-E	Date	Metal	Size	VG	F	VF	EF
Mass 45	1825	Copper	29mm	75.00	—	125.	—
		C.B. / A. WATERS / U S / MILLBURY/ 1825 ctsp on U.S. 1796 Large cent. (Kurt Krueger Sept. 1987 sale, lot 3537; Brunk 41980)					
Mass 46	(1825)	Copper	29mm	75.00	—	125.	—
		MILLBURY ctsp on U.S. Large cent. Examined: 1818, 1819, 1822, 1824, unknown date. 6 pieces known.(Brunk 27645)					
Mass 46A	1825	Copper	29mm	75.00	—	150.	—
		MILLBURY / 1825 ctsp on U.S. 1801 Large cent. (Brunk 27647)					
Mass 46B	1831	Copper	29mm	75.00	—	150.	—
		MILLBURY / 1831 ctsp on U.S. 1824 Large cent. (Brunk 27650)					
Mass 46C	1825	Copper	29mm	—	—	125.	—
		US / A. WATERS / MILLBURY / 1825 ctsp on U.S. 1810 Large cent.					

Asa Waters Jr. was a prominent gunsmith of Millbury, Mass. In 1818 he contracted with the U.S. Ordnance Dept. to deliver 10,000 muskets over five years at $14 each. These muskets were marked: US / A. WATERS / MILLBURY / 1828 (or another date).

In 1823 the contract was extended for 10,000 additional pieces to be delivered 1825-29. Other contracts were undertaken in 1829, 1836 (for flintlock pistols) and 1840.

The firm became A. Waters & Son about 1840, and Waters Armory about 1855. The Waters Armory made Joslyn carbines under an 1855 contract with the U.S., probably for Navy use.

Asa Waters (Sr.) was a Revolutionary War gunmaker to the Committee of Safety. He established the Sutton-Waters Armory on Singletary Creek in Sutton, Mass. about 1769 (?). His sons Elijah, the elder, and Asa Jr. (born 1769), learned the gunmaking business at their father's armory.

In 1797 Elijah and Asa Jr. built the Waters Armory in Sutton on Blackstone River below Singletary and undertook an 1808 contract for 5,000 muskets. Elijah died in 1814 and Asa Waters Jr., at 45, became sole proprietor.

The 1808 contract was undertaken by Elijah Waters, Asa Waters Jr. and Nathaniel Whitmore (Waters & Whitmore 1809-12). These muskets were marked: SUTTON/ (eagle) / U.S. / 1809 (or 1812) or some variation of that.

The armory moved from Sutton to Millbury about 1812. Some Model 1812 muskets were marked: (Eagle) / MILLBURY / 1815.

T. BRADBURY
Newburyport, Mass.

Rulau-E	Date	Metal	Size	VG	F	VF	EF
Mass 97	(1813-25)	Copper	29mm	150.	—	225.	—
		BRADBURY in relief within rect. depression ctsp on U.S. 1803 Large cent. (Brunk 4785)					
Mass 98	(1813-25)	Copper	29mm	150.	—	225.	—
		BRADBURY (as last) surrounded by four Eagles in relief within separate oval depressions, ctsp on U.S. Large cent. Examined: 1801, 1802, 1803. There are 4 pieces known. (Brunk 4787; PCAC July 1993 sale, lot 868)					

The eagles are of different sizes on two of the known pieces.

Mass 99	(1803-10)	Copper	29mm	150.	—	225.	—
		T. BRADBURY around Eagle, ctsp on U.S. 1801 Large cent. (Brunk 4790)					

Theophilus Bradbury (1763-1803) and his son Theophilus Bradbury Jr. (born 1793) were Newburyport silversmiths. The son is known to have worked at least until 1825. The counterstamps are likely the work of the son rather than the father.

Belden (see Bibliography) also records these hallmarks of the Bradburys:

(Eagle in circle) (B in rounded-corner square) (Standing Indian with bow and arrow in oval). ALL IN RELIEF.

(BRADBURY in rectangle) / (1825 in rectangle). ALL IN RELIEF.

MOULTON
Newburyport, Mass.

Rulau-E	Date	Metal	Size	VG	F	VF	EF
Mass 49	(1825-30)	Copper	29mm	70.00	—	—	100.
		MOULTON in relief within rectangular depression ctsp on U.S. Large cent. Dates examined: 1803, 1824. (Steven Guiness coll; Brunk 28670)					
Mass 49A	(1825-30)	Copper	29mm	70.00	—	—	100.
		W. MOULTON ctsp on U.S. Large cent. Examined: 1797, 1800.					
Mass 49B	(1825-30)	Copper	23mm	60.00	—	—	100.
		Similar ctsp on U.S. 1806 Half cent.					

The Moultons were a family of Newburyport silversmiths founded by William Moulton II (1664-1732) and Joseph Moulton I (1694-1756) at the end of the 17th century, which survived into the 20th century. The most likely member of the family responsible for this particular counterstamp is William Moulton IV (1772-1861), who is credited with this and other hallmarks by the Kovels' and by Louise Conway Belden (see Bibliography).

Branches of the Moulton family were silversmiths in other states as well — New Hampshire, Maine and Ohio — but all these used different hallmarks.

STORRS & COOK
Northampton, Mass. and Amherst, Mass.

Rulau-E	Date	Metal	Size	VG	F	VF	EF
Mass 50	(1827-33)	Copper	29mm	—	—	200.	—
		STORRS & COOK ctsp on U.S. Large cent. (Hallenbeck 19.781; Rulau MV333L; Brunk 38610)					

Storrs & Cook were silversmiths in both Amherst and Northhampton in the 1828-33 period. The partners were Nathan Storrs (1768-1839) and Benjamin E. Cook (1803-85). After the partnership broke up in 1833, Cook formed B.E. Cook (1833-85), which became B.E. Cook & Son in 1885, and Storrs, then 65, retired, dying just six years later.

Nathan Storrs was in partnership with Jedediah Baldwin in Baldwin & Storrs in Northampton 1792-94 and operated on his own 1794-1827.

L. POMEROY
Pittsfield, Mass.

Rulau-E	Date	Metal	Size	VG	F	VF	EF
Mass 70	1826	Copper	29mm	—	150.	—	—
		(Eagle) / L. POMEROY / 1826 / US ctsp on U.S. Draped Bust Large cent. (Brunk 32360)					
Mass 72	1842	Silver	27mm	—	150.	—	—
		L. POMEROY / C. U. S. / 1842 ctsp on Spanish-American 1819-NR-FT 2-reales. (Robert M. Ramsay coll.; Rulau HT 463; Brunk 32363)					

Lemuel Pomeroy Jr. (1778-1849) was a rifle maker active 1809-1849. The marks above were among his lockplate markings. In his lifetime he made 20,000 rifles for the U.S. government.

He made muskets under contracts awarded in 1808, 1821, 1831 and 1840. He was a grandson of Gen. Seth Pomeroy of Northampton, Mass., killed in 1777 in the Revolutionary War.

Mass 72 is clearly a Hard Times piece, but cannot be dissociated from its 1826 precursor. The coin on which 72 is stamped is one of the rarest Bogota Mint pieces of the revolutionary era.

SPRINGFIELD US M-M
(Springfield Armory)
Springfield, Mass.

Rulau-E	Date	Metal	Size	VG	F	VF	EF
Mass 80	(?)	Silver	32.5mm	—	—	—	600.
		SPRINGFIELD / US / M - M / (Eagle) ctsp on U.S. 1795 half dollar. (Ulex 457; Brunk 37755)					

This stamp was one of many used at the Springfield Armory to mark the metallic parts of guns produced for the government. The national armory opened in 1795, and its recorded markings bear dates from 1799 through at least 1870.

The only known specimen of this counterstamped piece appeared in the Ulex sale in Germany in 1908. Its present location is not known.

Rulau-E	Date	Metal	Size	VG	F	VF	EF
Mass 81	(?)	Copper	29mm	—	—	100.	—
		SPRINGFIELD ctsp on U.S. 1803 Large cent. (Brunk 37740)					
Mass 82	1807	Copper	29mm	—	—	150.	—
		SPRINGFIELD / US / 1807 ctsp on U.S. 1803 Large cent. (Brunk 33743)					
Mass 83	(?)	Silver	27mm	—	—	100.	—
		SPRINGFIELD / MASS ctsp on Spanish-American 1821 2-reales. (Brunk 37753)					
Mass 84	1832	Copper	29mm	—	—	150.	—
		SPRING / FIELD / 1832 / US ctsp on U.S. 1803 Large cent. (Brunk 37745)					
Mass 85	(?)	Copper	29mm	—	—	100.	—
		SPRINGFIELD MASS cstp on U.S. 1819 Large cent. (Brunk 37750)					

Undoubtedly more coins were counterstamped at the armory and will be reported as interest in this series increases.

J. MORSE
Westfield, Mass.

Rulau-E	Date	Meta!	Size	VG	F	VF	EF
Mass 91	(1825)	Copper	29mm	—	90.00	—	—
		J. MORSE in relief within rect. depression ctsp on U.S. Large cent. Examined: 1810, unknown date. Two specimens known. (Brunk 28540; Rulau-E Mass 35)					
Mass 92	(1825)	Silver	32.5mm	—	—	200.	—
		Similar ctsp on U.S. 1810 Bust half dollar. (B&M Sept. 1992 sale, lot 2018)					
Mass 93	(1825)	Copper	23mm	—	90.00	—	—
		Similar ctsp on U.S. 1825 Half cent.					

Jacob Morse (1751-1819) was a Westfield silversmith.

NEW HAMPSHIRE

EXETER
(J. & C. B. Barstow)
Exeter, N.H.

Rulau-E	Date	Metal	Size	VG	F	VF	EF
NH 1	(1808-12)	Copper	29mm	—	100.	—	—
		EXETER ctsp on U.S. 1798 Large cent. (Hallenbeck 5.754; Brunk 13648)					

Joshua and Charles C. Barstow used the stamp EXETER, usually in combination with other stamps (eagle; shield; J. & C. B.) to mark the lockplates on the muskets these gunsmiths manufactured for the U.S. Ordnance Department. They are known to have been in business 1808-1812, and Charles alone to 1820.

H. TOWLE
Haverhill, N.H.

Rulau-E	Date	Metal	Size	VG	F	VF	EF
Mav 50	(1835)	Copper	29mm	100.	—	200.	—
		H. TOWLE in relief within recessed rectangular depression ctsp on U.S. Large cent. Dates examined: 1802, 1807. Only 2 pieces known. (Brunk 40335; Rulau coll.)					

Henry Towle was a silversmith known to be active in 1835 and, likely, earlier and later. Born in 1788, he died in 1865.

It is possible there is a connection between H. Towle and Anthony F. Towle, founder of the Towle Mfg. Co. of Newburyport, Mass., though the official Towle Mfg. Co. history published in 1908 does not mention any silversmith predecessors to their founder.

A.F. Towle and William P. Jones founded Towle & Jones in 1857. This became A.F. Towle & Son (Edward B. Towle) in 1873, and Towle Mfg. Co. in 1882.

C. WARNER
Portsmouth, N.H.

Rulau-E	Date	Metal	Size	VG	F	VF	EF
NH 3	(1828)	Copper	29mm	—	80.00	—	125.

C. Warner ctsp on U.S. Large cent. Dates examined: 1798, 1800, 1807, 1818, 1821, 1827. (Brunk 41830; Boger coll.)

Caleb Warner (1784-1861) was a silversmith in Portsmouth circa 1824-30. He then removed to Salem, Mass., where he was engaged in the same trade in several partnerships until 1859.

One of his known markings matches that on some of the coins. The original attribution was made in 1957 by Maurice M. Gould and confirmation was made by John Boger in 1991.

Silversmiths named Cuthbert Warner were active in Baltimore, Md. ca 1785-1838 and Philadelphia, Pa. 1837-50, but their marks do not exactly match.

NEW JERSEY

JOHN STEVENS
Hoboken, N.J.

Rulau-E	Date	Metal	Size	VG	F	VF	EF
NJ 1	1829	Gilt/C	29mm	—	—	—	Unique
		PAY / THE BEARER ON / DEMAND / ONE DOLLAR / AND CHARGE THE SAME / TO / JOHN STEVENS / HOBOKEN JUNE 20 1829 / TO JOHN V. BOSKERCK / FERRY MASTER / W & B. Rv: A wreath. ONE / DOLLAR / PAYABLE IN / SPECIE / WRIGHT & BALE. Plain edge. (ANS coll.)					
NJ 1R	1829	Silver*	29mm	—	—	—	100.
		* Cast copy in silver. As the original, but cast with loop. (PCAC sale of Dec. 1986, lot 031)					

The only known specimen of the original struck token, in gilt copper, is in the ANS museum collection. The token was prepared by Wright & Bale of New York for John Stevens but was never used. The sole specimen was sold by either Mrs. Bale or Mrs. Wright after the firm broke up, to A. Ramsay McCoy, and McCoy later sold it to J. N. T. Levick. It was sold in the 1888 Levick sale and again in the 1898 Betts sale, eventually finding its way to ANS.

It is not well known. It was written up in the *American Journal of Numismatics*; (2: 109) and again by Edgar H. Adams in 1912 in *The Numismatist*.

It is the earliest known $1 denomination trade token struck in America, though the 1845 $1 token of Johnson Himrod & Co. of Erie, Pa. is the first of dollar size (38mm).

The Hoboken Ferry car check of New York City (Atwood NY 630R), a 27mm brass token, was used much later in the 19th century. There is no connection.

E. & I. BRAGAW
Newark, N.J. & Mobile, Ala.

Rulau-E	Date	Metal	Size	VG	F	VF	EF
NJ 28	(1829-33)	Copper	28mm	400.	1000.	—	3000.
		W&B NY. Rarity 7. HAT MFGS. (Low 302)					
NJ 29	(1829-33)	Brass	28mm	400.	1000.	—	3000.
		As 28. Rarity 7. (Low 303)					
NJ 30	(1829-33)	WM	28mm	400.	1000.	—	3000.
		As 28. Rarity 7. (Low 304)					

J.W. CORTELYOU
New Brunswick, N.J.

Rulau-E	Date	Metal	Size	VG	F	VF	EF
NJ 50	(1805-22)	Copper	29mm	—	—	200.	—
		J.W. CORTELYOU in relief within rect. depression ctsp on U.S. 1821 Large cent. (Brunk 9690; Rulau coll.)					

Jacques W. Cortelyou (1781-1822) was active as a silversmith from about 1805 to his untimely death from typhus at age 41. He had married Rachael Van Harlingen.

Albany, New York in 1805, corner of Church and Market streets, showing the Old Dutch Church built in 1715 and demolished in 1806. (From a lithograph after contemporary sketches.)

NEW YORK

CHURCH PENNY
(Albany Church)
Albany, N.Y.

Rulau-E	Date	Metal	Size	G	VG	F	VF
NY 1	(1790)	Copper	28mm	1100.	3000.	—	10,000.

CHURCH / PENNY within scalloped recession. Rv: Blank. (RB; Brunk 7740) (Only 7 known)

Rulau-E	Date	Metal	Size	G	VG	F	VF
NY 1A	(1790)	Copper	28mm	1100.	2700.	—	8000.

Similar, large D added above CHURCH. (RB; Brunk 7750) (Only 5 known)

The First Presbyterian Church of Albany authorized an issue of 1,000 uniface copper pennies on Jan. 4, 1790. These passed at 12 to the shilling and were used to stop contributions of worn and counterfeit coppers. The specimens known are of two types, but struck from the same die, which was later altered. They have the word CHURCH in capital letters and the word PENNY in script below, all within a circular panel of 24 scallops, and are struck on one side of the planchet only. The letter D in script appears on many of the specimens, while on others it is omitted. The significance of the D has been thought to be the initial of a town, or Latin for denarium, but, more likely, it may have stood for the Dutch Church of Albany which was close by. Since the method of exchange proved satisfactory for the Presbyterian Church, the die may have been borrowed, reengraved with a D for the Dutch Church, and used as such. One strong factor in support of this is that in both 1790 and 1793, the Dutch Reformed Church of Schenectady issued paper money for exactly the same purpose as the tokens. Though two different Dutch Churches were involved, the trend of the practice was evident. Three of these metal tokens were stolen from the Howard Kurth collection in upstate New York in 1978.

Auction records of NY1 are impressive. A VF specimen, the Jenks-Garrett piece, fetched $10,000 in Oct. 1980 (Bowers & Ruddy Galleries). A Fine piece, Roper collection, made $2530 in Dec. 1983 (Stack's Inc.). Another VF, the Oechsner specimen, realized $7700 in Sept. 1988 (Stack's Inc.).

The just-discovered VF+ Vermont specimen fetched $10,500 in Sept. 1989 (Bowers & Merena Galleries). See *Numismatic News* for Aug. 29, 1989, page 1.

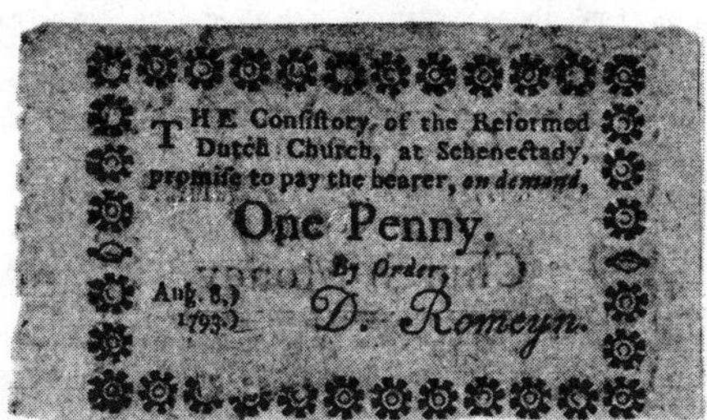

THE Consistory, of the Reformed Dutch Church, at Schenectady, promise to pay the bearer, on demand, One Penny. By Order, Aug. 8, 1793. D. Romeyn.

T. C.
(Thomas Carson)

Rulau-E	Date	Metal	Size	VG	F	VF	EF
NY 3	(1810-20)	Silver	40mm	—	350.	—	—

T. C. in relief within rect. depression ctsp twice on obverse and once on reverse of U.S. 1802 Draped Bust / Heraldic Eagle silver dollar. (Van Ormer sale 2883)

Thomas Carson was active as a silversmith in Albany 1810-50. In the 1810-18 period he was in partnership with Green Hall in the firm of Carson & Hall. A son (?), Thomas H. Carson, was a silversmith in Albany 1838-43. Thomas Carson used the TC-in-rectangle and TC-in-four-lobed cartouche depressions as markings, similar to that used on the coin.

Carson & Hall used T.C. & H-in-rectangle and CARSON & HALL-in-rectangle stamps, according to silversmith chronologies.

R. SHEPHERD
Albany, N.Y.

Rulau-E	Date	Metal	Size	VG	F	VF	EF
NY 4	(1805-13)	Silver	27mm	—	—	500.	—

R. SHEPHERD (script) in relief within rectangular depression ctsp on Spanish-American 1790 2-reales. (PCAC July 1993 sale, lot 098)

Robert Shepherd (1781-1853) and William Boyd were apprenticed to silversmith Isaac Hutton of Albany. Shepherd first advertised his own silversmith business in 1805. He may have used the hallmark shown on the coins until 1830, but he formed a partnership, Shepherd & Boyd, 1813-29. The partnership used a number of hallmarks incorporating both names, or else initials S&B, during its lifetime.

The hallmark on the 1790 coin is an exact match with that in Louise Conway Belden's work, page 379 (see Bibliography).

Among Shepherd's best known works are a flagon and pair of beakers made for the Reformed Dutch Church in Albany in 1817, and a funeral spoon for Colonel Philip P. Schuyler in 1808.

Hutton (1767-1855), under whom Shepherd apprenticed, worked 1786-1817 and for a time (1796-1814) sold military goods under the style I. & G. Hutton.

E. NEWBURY
Brooklyn, N.Y.

Rulau-E	Date	Metal	Size	VG	F	VF	EF
NY 6	(?)	Copper	29mm	75.00	—	125.	—

E. NEWBURY / BROOKLYN ctsp in relief in two separate rectangular depressions, on U.S. 1801 Large cent reverse. (Tanenbaum coll.; Brunk 29440)

Rulau-E	Date	Metal	Size	VG	F	VF	EF
NY A6	(?)	Copper	29mm	75.00	—	125.	—

E. NEWBURY in relief in rect. depression ctsp on U.S. worn Large cent. (Brunk 29430)

Ralph M. and Terry H. Kovel's *A Directory of American Silver, Pewter, and Silver Plate*, (1961), listed an Edwin C. Newbury of Brooklyn, N.Y., silversmith circa 1828. The punches used appear to be those of a manufacturing jeweler or silversmith, similar to those found on the shank of silver teaspoons or on other silver tableware.

FRANCO-AMERICANA COLONIA
Castorland, N.Y.

Rulau-E	Date	Metal	Size	VF	EF	Unc	Proof
NY 30	1796	Silver	32mm	—	—	4250.	—
		Crowned, veiled female head left, FRANCO-AMERICANA COLONIA (French-American colony) around, CASTORLAND / 1796 in exergue. Small DUV. under head. Rv: Standing female Sybele tapping maple tree, beaver below; SALVE MAGNA PARENS FRUGUM around. Thick planchet. Reeded edge. Original. (RB)					
NY 31	1796	Copper	32mm	—	—	3200.	—
		Same as last. Reeded edge.					

Rulau-E	Date	Metal	Size	VF	EF	Unc	Proof
NY 33	1796	Silver	33mm	—	—	—	200.
		Restrike on thin planchet. Reeded edge.					
NY 34	1796	Silver	33mm	—	—	—	35.00
		Later restrike. ARGENT on plain edge.					
NY 35	1796	Copper	33mm	—	—	—	130.
		Restrike on thin planchet. Reeded edge.					
NY 36	1796	Copper	33mm	—	—	—	25.00
		Later restrike. CUIVRE on plain edge.					

Rulau-E	Date	Metal	Size	VF	EF	BU	Matte Unc
NY 38	1796	Silver	33mm	—	—	25.00	25.00
		Modern restrike from newer dates. ARGENT on reeded edge.					

Rulau-E	Date	Metal	Size	VF	EF	BU	Matte Unc
NY 39	1796	Silver	33mm	—	—	22.50	22.50
		Current restrike from modern dies. Wing and ARGENT on plain edge.					
NY 40	1796	Copper	33mm	—	—	10.00	10.00
		Modern restrike from newer dies. CUIVRE on reeded edge.					
NY 50	1796	Copper	33mm	—	—	10.00	10.00
		Current restrike from modern dies. CUIVRE on plain edge.					
NY 51	1796	Bronze	33mm	—	—	10.00	10.00
		Current restrike from modern dies. Wing and BR on plain edge.					
NY 52	1796	Gold	33mm	—	—	—	—
		Current restrike from modern dies. Wing and OR on plain edge.					

In August, 1792, French settlers under Pierre Chassanis of Paris organized as the Castorland Company, settled at Castorville (at the head of navigation of the Beaver River) and also at what now is Carthage, N.Y., both in Lewis and Jefferson counties of the state. Chassanis bought the tracts from William Constable, and organized his company under agent Rudolph Tellier in 1791.

The original silver medallions, or honorariums for officers, were of the size and weight of the United States half dollar and specimens are known to have circulated as such. The reeded edge also indicates their circulation potential, as it was pointless to mill a medal's edge. They were designed by DuVivier. Restrikes off original dies, and the restrikes off replica dies have been made at the Paris Mint for nearly 200 years; they are still available today in bronze, silver and gold, with brilliant or matte finish. The author purchased some at the mint in September, 1979. The pieces are very attractive and quite collectible; their inclusion in the Red Book gives them a status few modern copies enjoy.

THE FOLLOWING ARTICLE GIVES MANY MORE DETAILS ABOUT CASTORLAND:

The office of Land Commissioners was created in 1786, and they were clothed with discretionary powers in selling the unappropriated lands of the state of New York. On June 22, 1791, Alexander Macomb of the city of New York, acting as agent of a company said to consist of himself, Daniel McCormick and Wm. Constable, all of New York, applied for the purchase of a tract of land since known as Macomb's Purchase. The whole of Macomb's contract was estimated to contain 3,670,715 acres. The proposed price was eight pence per acre.

Soon after perfecting his title to a portion of his tract, Macomb employed Wm. Constable as his agent to sell lands in Europe; and on June 6, 1792, he released, and October 3, 1792, conveyed to him tracts 4, 5 and 6, containing 551,600 acres for £50,000.

The first direct measure taken for actual settlement of the section of New York state embraced in Jefferson County was in 1792. On Aug. 31, Constable, then in Europe, executed a deed to Pierre Chassanis of Paris for 630,000 acres south of Great Lot no. 4, which now constitutes part of Jefferson and Lewis counties. Chassanis acted as "the agent for the associated purchasers of land in Montgomery County," and the lands were to be held in trust for the use of Constable and disposed of by sections of 100 acres each at the rate of eight livres tournois (equal to $1.50) per acre; in which conveyance it is declared that Chassanis should account for the proceeds of the sales to Constable, according to the terms of the agreement between them, excepting one-tenth thereof.

A deed for 625,000 acres having been made from Constable to Chassanis and delivered as an escrow to Rene Lambot, to take effect on the payment of 52,000 pounds, it was agreed that the price for this land should be one shilling per acre.

This company contemplated certain plans whose execution the stormy period of the French Revolution very probably prevented, as the agreement of Constable and Chassanis of August 30, 1792, was canceled and the tract reconveyed March 25, 1793, in consequence of the amount falling short upon survey, far beyond the expectations of all parties. On April 12, 1793, Constable conveyed 210,000 acres, by deed, for £25,000 to Chassanis, since known as the Chassanis tract, Castorland, or the French Company land.

On April 11, 1797, Chassanis appointed Rudolph Tellier, "member of the sovereign counsel of Berne," to direct and administer the properties and affairs concerning Castorland.

At a very early period a settlement was begun by Tellier and others near the High Falls, east of Black River, and several families were settled. Several extensive sales were made to Frenchmen of the better class, who had held property and titles in France before the Revolution. Among these was Henri Boutin, who purchased about 1,000 acres of Rudolph Tellier, agent of the French Company, on the east side of Black River, and in or about 1798 made an extensive clearing on the site of Carthage village, the immediate locality then and for several years afterward being known as the "Long Falls," in allusion to the succession of rapids or falls in the river.

The natural water power thus afforded attracted Boutin to the place. He and his company of men erected a few buildings for dwelling purposes, and soon thereafter Boutin set out to return to France to settle his business affairs, having determined to make Long Falls his permanent place of abode; but by accident the pioneer was drowned (probably in Black River). His company of workmen soon abandoned the improvement, and the lands passed to Vincent LeRay by purchase from James LeRay as administrator of the Boutin estate.

Soon after the advent of Boutin, Jean Baptiste Bossout came to the place. Bossout is generally known as Battise. He was a native of Troyes, France, and came to America with Baron von Steuben. Like Boutin, he was induced to come to Castorland through the agency of the French Company. After the improvement had been abandoned by the employees of Boutin, Bossout alone remained. All recollections of Jean Bossout denote that he was a worthy resident and enterprising pioneer.

The occasional travelers of this region sought to cross Black River, hence Bossout constructed a rude ferry, charging for its use a moderate toll, and also built on the east bank of the river a small public house. It has been said that he opened the first store on the village site, but this has not been proved.

To these two worthy French pioneers is due the first improvements of the lands purchased from the French Company land or Castorland.

A.S.C.
New York, N.Y.

Rulau-E	Date	Metal	Size	VG	F	VF	Unc
NY 169	1786	Lead	Square, 19 by 19mm	—	—	—	—
		A S C incused across center. Rv: NY / 1786 incused. Plain edge. (Curto coll.)					

This is a communion token, tentatively attributed to New York.

S. ASHTON

Rulau-E	Date	Metal	Size	F	VF	EF	Unc
NY 44	(?)	Brass	(?)mm	—	—	—	—
		S. ASHTON AMERICAN INN, CANAL ST. Rv: 3 D.					

There are growing indications this is an English token. John Ford believes it is English.

JOHN BARKER

Rulau-E	Date	Metal	Size	VG	F	VF	EF
NY 57	(1829-33)	Brass	19mm	500.	1000.	—	2000.
		A Washington head is right within olive wreath, AMERICAN REPOSITORY OF FINE ARTS around. Reverse: JOHN BARKER / 16 MAIDEN LANE / DEALER IN / MUSIC PRINTS / & / FANCY /STATIONARY. Only 4 pieces are known. (Baker 511; Low 338)					

Cut by Wright & Bale, which dates it to the 1829-1833 period.

Barker, stationer, is listed at 16 Maiden Lane 1829-30 in the directories.

BENEDICT

Rulau-E	Date	Metal	Size	VG	F	VF	EF
NY 60	(1820-45)	Silver	27mm	200.	—	300.	—

BENEDICT WALL ST. in relief within rectangular depression ctsp on Spanish-American 1793-LME-IJ 2-reales. (Tanenbaum coll.; Brunk 3290)

Rulau-E	Date	Metal	Size	VG	F	VF	EF
NY 61	(1827?)	Copper	29mm	75.00	—	150.	—

BENEDICT in relief within rect. depression ctsp on U.S. 1826 Large cent (struck off center) (Brunk 3270)

These hallmarks are likely those of silversmith Samuel W. Benedict (1820's to 1840's) of 5 Wall Street. See Rulau-E NY 60. In 1829-30 he was at 30 Wall St.

However, they might be hallmarks of silversmith Andrew C. Benedict (1827-40) of 28 Bowery, or even a third New York silversmith who marked Large cents 1806-35 with M. BENEDICT, Martin Benedict (1823-39). Andrew Benedict's counterstamp is listed as NY 63.

The specimen above was almost new when it was counterstamped, so it may indicate an 1826-27 date of issuance.

Benedict, S. W.	SAMUEL W. BENEDICT, Importer, Dealer and Repairer of FINE DUPLEX AND LEVER WATCHES, *No. 5 Wall-street,* Near Trinity Church, NEW-YORK. *SILVER WARE, WARRANTED STERLING SILVER.* D. BEACH, Jeweller. Always on hand a general assortment of Fine Jewelry.

A. C. BENEDICT (et al)

Rulau-E	Date	Metal	Size	VG	F	EF
NY 63	(1827-30)	Copper	29mm	—	200.	—

Four separate relief counterstamps applied to a U.S. 1820 Large cent, viz: E. T. PELL in rectangular depression; (Lion) (Sheaves ?) G in three square depressions, on line horizontally; J. W. B. in rectangular depression; A. C. BENEDICT / 28 BOWERY N.Y. in large toothed rectangular depression. (Tanenbaum coll.; Brunk 3300)

Emmett T. Pell was a New York silversmith 1824-41.

The lion-sheaves-G mark resembles the 1890-91 plate mark of Chester, England, but we believe it stands for a New York maker, possibly who emigrated from England. (It may well be Benjamin Gurnee, N.Y., 1820-34).

Joseph W. Boyd was a N.Y. silversmith circa 1820.

Andrew C. Benedict was a N.Y. silversmith at 28 Bowery, 1827-36. His firm stayed in business until 1888.

This token may have been a test piece used successively by several silversmiths to test their punches. It is tempting to believe all the hallmarks were applied at about the same time, but there could be other explanations. We assigned an 1827-30 date to the piece as this range accommodates the known overlap of the silversmiths.

M. BENEDICT

Rulau-E	Date	Metal	Size	VG	F	EF
NY 65	(1835-45)	Copper	29mm	85.00	—	125.

M. BENEDICT ctsp on U.S. Large cent. Dates examined: 1806, 1835. (Brunk 3310)

Martin Benedict was a silversmith and jeweler from 1823-1839 and possibly as late as 1845. He was part of the firm of Benedict & Squire 1825-39.

S. BOARDMAN

Rulau-E	Date	Metal	Size	VG	F	VF	EF
NY 66	(1822-27)	Copper	29mm	75.00	—	125.	—
		S. BOARDMAN in relief within rect. depression ctsp on U.S. 1807 over 6 Large cent. (Rulau-E Mav 11E; Brunk 4125)					
NY 66 E	(1822-27)	Silver	27mm	75.00	—	125.	—
		S. BOARDMAN in rect. frame ctsp on Spanish-American 1800-NG 2-reales. (H. Christensen Oct. 1987 sale, lot 840).					

Sherman Boardman was a pewterer in New York 1822-27. Then he relocated in Hartford, Conn. 1828-54.

J. BOUTIER (AND) W. ROE

Rulau-E	Date	Metal	Size	G	VG	VF
NY 68	(1817-18)	Copper	28mm	—	—	200.

J BOUTIER in relief in rect. punch / W. ROE in relief in rect. punch / Crowned WR in relief in irreg. depression — all ctsp on U.S. 1816 Large cent. (B&M 1986 von Stetten sale, lot 5065; Brunk 4520)

W. ROE and Crowned WR are both hallmarks of silversmith William Roe and J BOUTIER of silversmith John Boutier. It is not known that they were ever partners, but both were located in New York City at one time. Roe moved there from Troy, N.Y. after 1805, and Boutier died there in 1818. We conclude this coin was counterstamped 1817-18.

Boutier's widow continued the business until 1826 and so could have been responsible for the markings.

Roe was in Albany, N.Y. ca 1776, Kingston, N.Y. ca 1800, Troy ca 1805, and then New York City.

G. BOYCE

Gerardus Boyce, silversmith, was in business from about 1820. He was at 101 Spring St. 1829-1833 and at 110 Greene 1834-1841. His one reported counterstamp is on an 1831 Large cent; the mark is his hallmark.

His name is also given as Geradus, Gheradus and Jared. His counterstamped coin appears in "Hard Times Tokens."

E. BRASHER

(**NOTE:** The Ephraim Brasher doubloons and counterstamps are completely rearranged, taking into account the recent research conducted by Walter Breen, Louise Conway Belden, William Swoger, Arthur Newmark and Gregory G. Brunk.)

Rulau-E	Date	Metal	Size	VG	F	VF	EF
NY 82A	1787	Gold	30mm	—	—	625,000.	—

Sunrise over mountains at center, small BRASHER beneath. Around: + NOVA + EBORACA + COLUMBIA + EXCELSIOR. Rv: Scrawny eagle with drooping wings, U.S. shield on its breast. Above: UNUM * E * PLURIBUS. Below: + 1787 +. Brasher's hallmark, EB within an oval, is punched on the eagle's breast. Unique. Weight: 411.5 grains.

The Garrett specimen, the only known "punch on breast" variety, realized $625,000 in the 1981 Garrett IV sale by Bowers & Ruddy Galleries.

Rulau-E	Date	Metal	Size	VG	F	VF	EF
NY 82B	1787	Gold	31mm	430,000.	—	725,000.	—

Similar to NY 82A, but EB punch on eagle's wing. 8 or 9 specimens known. Weight: 407.9 grains for the Ellsworth-Garrett specimen. Ten Eyck specimen also known.

Two specimens were sold in 1979, one realizing $430,000 and the other (the Garrett specimen) $725,000. The Yale specimen was offered recently for $600,000.

A half doubloon is also known.

The Nova Eborac tokens of New York were apparently made by the maker of the Brasher pieces, according to punch linkage study by Anthony Terranova.

Rulau-E	Date	Metal	Size	VG	F	VF	EF
NY 82C	1742 (1786)	Gold	30mm	—	—	—	—

Imitation of 8-Escudos of Philip V of Spain of the Lima, Peru, Mint, with small BRASHER under water lines beneath the pillars. EB-in-oval punch is at center of the cross. Weight: 407.3 grains for the Newcomer-Garrett specimen.

'EB' OVAL PUNCH ON GOLD COINS

Rulau-E	Date	Metal	Size	VG	F	VF	EF
NY 82G	(1792)	Gold	32mm	—	—	—	1100.

EB in relief within oval depression ctsp on Portugal homeland or Portuguese Brazil 6400-reis coins (Pecas or 'Joes'), KM Brazil 134 & 149, Craig Brazil 34, Friedberg Portugal 65 and Craig Portugal 16. Dates examined: 1727-Brazil, 1735, 1747-Brazil, 1750, 1754, 1754-Brazil, 1755 (3 pieces), 1757, 1757-Brazil, 1757-R, 1760, 1763-R, 1766, 1767, 1769, 1774-Brazil, unknown date. There are 20 specimens reported, including 1757-R with additional ctsp script B in circle and 1763-R with additional stamps script B, S, IS and G. Weight 14.34 grams; average 216 grains; or .4214 to .4228 troy ounce fine gold. (Brunk 12710EE, 12710KK and 1505/12710). (Specimens labeled 'Brazil' contain either the B Bahia, R Rio or M Maranhao mintmarks — unfortunately not recorded by sources. Specimens without Brazil or R are Lisbon homeland strikings with no mintmark.)

Rulau-E	Date	Metal	Size	VG	F	VF	EF
NY 82P	(1792)	Gold	17mm	3600.	—	—	—

Similar ctsp on Portugal 1740-Lisbon half escudo, KM-218, Friedberg 71. (Stack's May 1991 sale, lot 173). The only known specimen, holed at 12 o'clock, fetched $3520 in 1991.

Rulau-E	Date	Metal	Size	VG	F	VF	EF
NY 82H	(1792)	Gold	36mm	—	—	3000.	10,000.

Similar ctsp on Spanish-American 1775-So-DA or 1787 8-escudos (doubloon). Only 2 known. Weight 27.07 grams. (Brunk 12710JJ; Stack's May 1991 sale, lot 172, which fetched $9900)

Rulau-E	Date	Metal	Size	VG	F	VF	EF
NY 82J	(1792)	Gold	25mm	—	—	—	1000.

Similar ctsp on England guinea. Dates examined: 1713, 1734, 1749 (2 pieces), 1750 (2 pieces), 1751, 1759, 1760, 1766, 1779, unknown dates. There are 13 pieces reported. KM-573, 588 or 604. Weight 8.35 grams; average 123 to 126 grains; .2461 troy oz. fine gold. (Brunk 12710HH; Kovacs coll; *Coin World* for Jan. 9, 1991, page 1)

Rulau-E	Date	Metal	Size	VG	F	VF	EF
NY 82K	(1792)	Gold	21mm	—	—	1000.	—

Similar ctsp on England half guinea. Examined: 1760, 1780. Only 2 known. KM-587 and 605. Weight 4.175 grams; .123 troy oz. fine gold. (Brunk 12710GG)

Rulau-E	Date	Metal	Size	VG	F	VF	EF
NY 82L	(1792)	Gold	16mm	—	—	1200.	—

Similar ctsp on England 1718 quarter guinea, KM-555. Unique. Weight 2.0875 grams; .0615 troy oz. fine gold. (Brunk 12710FF)

Rulau-E	Date	Metal	Size	VG	F	VF	EF
NY 82N	(1792)	Gold	24mm	—	—	1100.	—

Similar ctsp on France 1745-R louis d'or, Craig 67.20. Weight ca 8.158 grams; .2405 troy oz. fine gold. (Kagin 1983 ANA sale, lot 282; Brunk 12710II)

(For silver coins bearing an EB-in-rectangle punch, see in this reference under Ezekiel Burr of Providence, R.I.)

Ephraim Brasher (1744-1810), was one of early Republican America's best-known goldsmiths, though he never achieved the lasting fame of silversmith Paul Revere of Boston. He was once a neighbor of George Washington. He appears in New York City directories 1786-1807. He was also a silversmith and assayer and was of Dutch stock.

In 1790 his firm became E. Brasher & Company. Brasher & Alexander (with George Alexander) was a short- lived partnership 1800-Feb. 1801.

Ephraim Brasher was a brother-in-law of New York silversmith William Gilbert (1746-1818). He married Ann Gilbert in 1766. He was appointed assayer of the new U.S. Mint in 1792. He advertised at 5 Cherry Street.

It was in his duties as gold regulator for standards set by the Bank of New York beginning in 1784 that he placed his EB-in-oval punch on foreign gold coins brought to him for validation. The American State Papers records a $27 payment to John Shield, assignee of Ephraim Brasher, for assays of various coins made under contract by Brasher in 1792 for the United States Mint.

Brasher or an assignee stamped the EB punch on all foreign gold pieces brought for assay. Pieces were brought up to proper weight with a gold plug, if necessary. The punch-marked coins are usually found with edge scratches indicating they were rubbed against a test stone to check their fineness.

Louise C. Belden (in *Marks of American Silversmiths in the Ineson-Bissell Collection*, Charlottesville, Va., 1980) pictures four hallmarks definitely attributable to Ephraim Brasher.

These are: (1) EB in oval (as seen on the punchmarked pieces above); EB in oval and BRASHER in rounded rectangle; (3) E. BRASHER and N. YORK in separate rectangles; and (4) EB in rectangle.

She also admits of another, very different (5) EB in rectangle as possibly from Brasher, since spoons on which it is found are similar to those bearing marks EB-in-oval and E. BRASHER/N. YORK in rectangles. However, we list this type 5 under Ezekiel Burr.

The best account yet written about the numismatic activities of Ephraim Brasher was written by William Swoger for *Coin World* of June 1, 1992, entitled "Brasher's Gold."

Another Brasher, Amable, preferred the surname spelling Brasier. Amable Brasier was in business as a silversmith 1790-94 in New York at 79 Queen Street.Then he removed to Philadelphia 1794-1833; until 1828 he was at 12 South 3rd Street.

Amable Brasher used a hallmark A. BRASHER in rectangle while in New York, then another, A. BRASIER in rounded rectangle, in Philadelphia.

Hobbyists sometimes are led to believe the Brasher-punched foreign gold coins are worth much more than reality dictates. The authentication of a 1766 English guinea by the International Numismatic Society Authentication Bureau found in the soil in Georgia in March, 1989 prompted a front-page story in *Coin World* for Jan. 9, 1991.

The finder, treasure hunter Michael O. Smith, was quoted as saying: "... think I may be able to part with it if ... the price is right. I've been offered $40,000, but I think a major auction house is the more appropriate way to sell such a rare coin. It has been suggested that this coin could be worth in excess of $100,000."

The news article, indifferently researched and written, also quotes a Smithsonian curator as saying the 1766 guinea was "the earliest" seen. In fact, guineas dated 1713, 1734, 1749, 1750, 1751, 1759 and 1760 have been known for some time. Other earlier foreign gold coins bearing an EB punch are also known.

DAVID C. BUCHAN
New York, N.Y.

Rulau-E	Date	Metal	Size	F	VF	EF	Unc
NY 137	(1828-31)	Brass	27mm	150.	300.	—	800.
		Chair at center, MANUFACTURERS OF CURLED MAPLE & FANCY CHAIRS. Rv: DAVID C. BUCHAN / CORNER OF / NORTHMORE & / GREENWICH ST. / NEW YORK. (Wright 119; Low 224)					
NY 138	(1828-31)	Sil Br	27mm	250.	500.	—	1000.
		As 137. (Low 225)					
NY 139	(1828-31)	Brass	27mm	200.	400.	—	800.
		As 137, but NORTHMOORE instead of NORTHMORE. (Low 226)					

Rulau-E	Date	Metal	Size	F	VF	EF	Unc
NY 139A	(1828-31)	Sil Br	27mm	—	Rare	—	—
		As 139. (In ANS collection)					

David C. Buchan, chairmaker, is listed at 80 No. Moore St., corner Greenwich, 1825-1827. He then is listed at 364 Greenwich, corner No. Moore, 1828-1841. Both addresses seem to be the same site!

North Moore St. led from Chapel to the North River; it was the fourth street above Duane.

J. CHINERY

Rulau-E	Date	Metal	Size	VG	F	VF	EF
NY 141	(1829-30)	Silver	21mm	300.	—	450.	—
		J. CHINERY / DIE CUTTER / 205 WM ST. N.Y. ctsp on Spanish-American 1816 1-real. (Brunk 7680)					
NY 142	(1829-30)	Silver	16mm	300.	—	450.	—
		Similar ctsp on Spanish-American half-real coin.					
NY 144	(1829-30)	Silver	20mm	300.	—	450.	—
		J. CHINERY / DIE CUTTER/ 205 WM ST NY ctsp on obverse of Spanish-American 1772-G-P 1-real. J. CHINERY ctsp on reverse of the coin. (Robert M. Ramsay coll.)					

NY 144 is an example of a very rare variety of a Guatemala coin being stamped with the advertisement of an American merchant. Such occurrences, while infrequent, happen often enough in numismatics. Once the coin receives the merchant impress, of course, it is no longer the coin it was — though at the time in America it could continue to pass at the value of one bit, 12-1/2 cents.

James Chinery, letter and tool cutter, appears in the 1830 directory at 90 William Street. In 1834 he was at 108 Nassau Street. Chinery does not appear in the 1844 directory. A directory match with the address on the token is needed before further refinement of the issue date is possible.

W. COLLINS

Rulau-E	Date	Metal	Size	VG	F	VF	EF
NY 165	(1820's ?)	Copper	29mm	50.00	—	—	—
		W. COLLINS / W. COLLINS / W. COLLINS ctsp on worn flat copper planchet, probably a Large cent or British halfpenny. (The top and bottom lines are incused; the central is in relief in a rectangular depression similar to early jewelers' marks.) Rv: N.YORK ctsp incuse on reverse of coin. Plain edge. (Tanenbaum collection; Brunk 8920)					

Possibly related to W. & L. Collins, New York silversmiths about 1829-35. William & L. Collins, silversmiths are listed at 67 Maiden Lane in 1829-30. William Collins also kept a boarding house at 135 Cherry St. in 1830.

Etching of "The Old Brewery" at Five Points, New York City. Next door may be seen D. Brennan's grocery, liquor store and lodgings. (Counsel collection)

L. COLTON

Rulau-E	Date	Metal	Size	VG	F	VF	EF
NY 170	(1824-35)	Copper	29mm	—	—	175.	—
		L. COLTON ctsp on U.S. 1824 Large cent. (Brunk 8980)					

Levi Colton was a silversmith in New York City 1819-1835, according to Kovel.

DOREMUS, SUYDAM & NIXON

Rulau-E	Date	Metal	Size	F	VF	EF	Unc
NY 211	(1831-33)	Copper	26-1/2mm	35.00	110.	350.	—
		Inscription both sides. 209 PEARL ST., with period after NIXON. N-YORK. (Low 306)					
NY 212	(1831-33)	Brass	26-1/2mm	35.00	110.	210.	—
		Same as 211. (Low 307)					
NY 213	(1831-33)	Copper	26-1/2mm	35.00	110.	210.	—
		Similar to 211, but no period after NIXON. N. York (Low 308)					

Rulau-E	Date	Metal	Size	F	VF	EF	Unc
NY 214	(1831-33)	Brass	26-1/2mm	35.00	110.	350.	—
		Same as 213. (Low 309)					
NY 214A	(1831-33)	Brass	26-1/2mm	35.00	110.	350.	—
		Same as 214. Reeded edge. (Low 309A)					

This dry goods firm issued a number of tokens spanning the Early American and Hard Times periods. The cards listed above may have been struck for D.S. & N. by Wright & Bale. Trested's business was sold by his widow, Ann, to Wright & Bale on May 25, 1829, and W&B NY (later BALE NY and B&S NY) began to appear on tokens for D.S.&N. Some 1832-33 pieces were included as Low 310-311 under Rulau's *Hard Times Tokens*, still at the 209 Pearl Street address.

Rulau-E	Date	Metal	Size	F	VF	EF	Unc
NY 215	(1832-33)	Copper	26.5mm	35.00	110.	350.	—
		As 214, W.&B. N.Y. on obverse. Rv: LINENS SHEETINGS & DAMASKS in center. (Low 310)					
NY 215A	(1832-33)	Silv/Bs	26.5mm	35.00	110.	210.	—
		As 215.					
NY 216	(1832-33)	Brass	26.5mm	35.00	110.	350.	—
		As 215. (Low 311)					

THE DOREMUS-SUYDAM DRY GOODS FIRMS

Thomas C. Doremus and James Suydam Jr. were in business as Doremus & Suydam, dry goods store, at 171 Broadway, at least from 1821 to 1826. This became Doremus, Suydam & Co. at 171 Broadway, 1826-1828.

The firm became Doremus, Suydam & Nixon, dry goods, still at 171 Broadway, 1829-1830. The new partner was John W. Nixon. This firm was at 209 Pearl St. 1832-1833; 50 and 52 William St. 1834 until December 31, 1835. According to a note in the 1835-36 directory, the firm moved on New Year's Day, 1836, to 37 and 39 Nassau St. Its address in 1840-1841 was 39 Nassau St., corner Liberty.

The firm name became Doremus & Nixon 1844-1849, still at 39 Nassau St., corner Liberty. In the 1850's the address changed to 21 Park Place. Dated tokens at the latter address are known bearing either 1853 or 1861.

Another firm which apparently did not issue any tokens was composed of Lambert and Cornelius R. Suydam, who may have been related. L. & C. Suydam, merchants, were at 212 Pearl St. 1821-1822; 71 Maiden Lane 1826-1828; 111 Pearl St. 1829-1830.

A third firm was composed of Suydam (first name not determined) and Daniel Jackson. This firm, Suydam & Jackson, Indian contractors, issued Low 1 and varieties, a pro-Andrew Jackson political token of 1832.

Suydam & Jackson, merchants, were at 140 Pearl St., 1826-1828. They became known as Suydam, Jackson & Co. at 140 Pearl St., 1829-1830, and were located at 78 Pearl St., 1832-1835.

Henry (Hy.) Suydam and William Boyd were in business as Suydam & Boyd, dry goods, at 183 or 187 Broadway (there is a discrepancy in the 1830 directory) 1829-1830; then at 187 Pearl St., corner Cedar; 1831-1834; then at 157 Pearl St., 1834-1837. Store cards were issued from the latter two locations, spanning the Early American and Hard Times token periods.

The Doremus-Suydam firms were large issuers of store cards from 1831 to 1861 or later. Their dates of issuance are approximately:

Low 306-309A (NY 211-214A), 209 Pearl St., 1831-1833
Low 310-311 (NY 215-216), 209 Pearl St., 1832-1833 (W&B NY)
Low 242-243, 50 & 52 William St., 1834-1835 (BALE NY)
Low 244, 37 & 39 Nassau St., 1836
Low 245-245A, 37 & 39 Nassau St., 1836-1838
Low 245B-245C (NY 219-219A), 39 Nassau St., 1840-1844
(as a result, these latter should be moved from the MT to HTT books)
NY 222-223 (Doremus & Nixon), 39 Nassau St., 1844-1849
NY 224-224-224B, 21 Park Place, 1850-1853
NY 225-229, (mulings), 1853-1861

EVERDELL

Rulau-E	Date	Metal	Size	F	VF	EF	Unc
NY 217	(1835-36)	Copper	29mm	—	150.	—	250.

EVERDELL in relief within curved scroll-shaped depression ctsp on U.S. 1818 or 1831 Large cent. (Frank Kovacs coll.; Brunk 13610; Rulau-E Mav 17)

William Everdell was a diesinker at 135 William St. appearing in the 1836 directory.

A.F.

Rulau-E	Date	Metal	Size	VG	F	VF	Unc
NY 167	1824	Copper	23mm	—	—	Rare	—

A.F. in large Old English letters at center, REMEMBRANCER around, 1824 below. Rv: Open bible within rays, Hebrew letters above, palm branch below book. Plain edge. (Curto collection; Denton Curtis coll.)

This is a Communion token.

J. FISHER

Rulau-E	Date	Metal	Size	VG	F	VF	EF
NY 171	(1826-32)	Copper	29mm	75.00	125.	125.	—

J. FISHER ctsp on U.S. 1818 or 1826 Large cent. (Brunk 14255)

James Fisher was a silversmith located at 13 Collect 1821-1822 and 138 Mott St. 1825-1826. He was in business until at least 1833.

J. FOSTER
New York, N.Y. and Winchester, Va.

Rulau-E	Date	Metal	Size	VG	F	VF	EF
NY 175	(1820's)	Copper	29mm	—	175.	—	—

N. YORK / J. FOSTER, both in relief, within separate oval depressions at right angles to each other, ctsp on U.S. 1817 Large cent. (Tanenbaum coll.; Brunk 14830)

Silversmith John Foster was in business in New York, N.Y. 1809-17, then Winchester, Va. 1817-25, Woodstock, Va. 1825, and Martinsburg, Va. 1827-35. Most likely this stamp was applied while Foster worked in Virginia, using the old punches as a form of prestige — "Foster of New York."

Martinsburg has been in West Virginia since 1863.

FRANCIS PATENT SCREW
New York, N.Y.

Rulau-E	Date	Metal	Size	VG	F	VF	EF
NY 265	(1832-33)	Brass	26.5mm	500.	1000.	2000.	3000.

FRANCIS/(rosette)/PATENT SCREW/(rosette)/N. YORK. There are small letters H (?) flanking each rosette. Rv: FRANCIS/FANCY BOAT/(star)/ESTABLISHMENT/NO. 399/& 402 WATER ST./ PATENT SCREW.

Joseph Francis, boat builder, was at 402 Water St. circa 1832-1833.

FRIENDS OF LIBERTY AND TRADE

Rulau-E	Date	Metal	Size	VG	F	VF	EF
NY 176	1766	Copper	29mm	175.	350.	—	800.
		Half length bust of William Pitt left; THE. RESTOREr OF. COMMERCE 1766 around, :NO STAMPS: below. Rv: Ship at left, AMERICA diagonally to the right. Around: THANKS. TO. THE. FRIENDS. OF. LIBERTY. AND. TRADE. (RB)					
NY 177	1766	Copper (or Brass)	23mm	—	—	—	6000.
		As last, but smaller. Rare. (RB)					

The Friends of Liberty and Trade were a group of New York merchants active in the repeal of the 1765 Stamp Act. Apparently they commissioned James Smither of Philadelphia to strike these medalets in 1768 or 1769.

Smither was an engraver active in Philadelphia from 1768 to his death in 1819, though he removed to New York City late in his career. His period of greatest output was 1768-1777. A full biography of him appears in the New Netherlands 59th auction sale, lot 1969, and authorities Don Taxay and Q. David Bowers concur in the attribution. (See B&M Von Stetten-Buchenbach sale of Nov. 1986, lot 2655, where an EF halfpenny fetched $770)

GIFFIN(G)

Rulau-E	Date	Metal	Size	VG	F	VF	EF
NY 181	(1814-34)	Silver	27mm	75.00	—	125.	—

Giffin . . . in relief within rectangular depression ctsp on Spanish-American 1780-Mo-FF 2-reales. (Frank Kovacs coll.; Rulau Z32M in *USMT* 3rd ed.; Brunk 16097)

Probably a hallmark of Christopher Giffing of New York, a silversmith active 1814-1834. Giffing made fiddle-tipped silver spoons with this mark: C. Giffing in slanting relief letters within rectangular depression (see Belden pg. 191, b)

It is also possible that it is a mark of silversmith William G. Giffing Jr. of Geneva, N.Y., active 1809-1814.

ISREAL L. GREEN

Rulau-E	Date	Metal	Size	VG	F	VF	EF
NY 285	1827	Copper	29mm	75.00	—	125.	—

ISREAL L. GREEN / N. YORK / JULY 9TH / 1827 ctsp with individual letter-punches on Large cent. Examined: 1817, date worn. (Brunk 17080)

The 1817 cent also bears on reverse the stamp: STERLING. Co from a prepared punch. This latter mark also appears alone on an 1837 Hard Times token (Brunk 38200)

GREEN & WETMORE

Rulau-E	Date	Metal	Size	VG	F	VF	EF
NY 288	(1825-32)	Brass	28.5mm	35.00	90.00	—	225.

Anvil, hammer and tongs at center, DEALERS IN HARDWARE, BAR-IRON / STEEL around. Rv: GREEN /// WETMORE / CORNER OF / WASHINGTON / & / VESEY ST / NEW YORK. Plain edge. (Low 295: Wright 403)

Rulau-E	Date	Metal	Size	VG	F	VF	EF
NY 289	(1825-32)	Brass	28.5mm	35.00	100.	—	225.

Reeded edge.

Rulau-E	Date	Metal	Size	VG	F	VF	EF
NY 289A	(1825-32)	Sil Brass	28.5mm	50.00	150.	—	250.

As 288. (Low 297)

Rulau-E	Date	Metal	Size	VG	F	VF	EF
NY 290	(1832)	WM	29mm	200.	450.	—	1000.

Hardware implements. Rv: GREEN / & WETMORE / HARDWARE & / IRON MERCHANTS / CORNER OF / WASHINGTON / & VESEY ST / NEW YORK. Reeded edge. Only 2 known. (Low 298)

The hardware implements design of NY 290 is a copy of Breton 561, the T.S. Brown card of Montreal, Quebec, which was struck in Birmingham, England, in 1832. The evidence given in Sandham to the conclusive dating of the Brown card leads to the supposition that Green & Wetmore (and also H.E. Thomas & Co. of Louisville, Ky.) had the same die struck for them in white metal on a trial basis. All these cards are similar to another Canadian token, the J. Shaw & Co. piece of Quebec, Breton 565, dated by Sandham as 1837.

William Green Jr., A.R. Wetmore and D.W. Wetmore founded Green & Wetmore, hardware and iron store. This was located at 194 Greenwich 1821-1822; 179 Washington, corner Vesey, 1824-1833. The firm disappeared in the 1835 and later directories.

A.W. HARDIE

Rulau-E	Date	Metal	Size	VG	F	EF	Unc
NY 295	(1826-27)	Brass	31mm	50.00	75.00	150.	—

EXCHANGE TAYLORING ESTABLISHMENT / NAKED / AND YE / CLOTHED / ME / (8-pointed rosette). Rv: A. W. HARDIE / DRAPER & TAYLOR / EXCHANGE BUILDINGS / CORNER OF GARDEN & / WILLIAM STREET / NEW YORK. Reeded edge. (Wright 424)

Rulau-E	Date	Metal	Size	VG	F	EF	Unc
NY 295A	(1826-27)	Brass	31mm	—	—	600.	—

As 295, but Plain edge. (H.J. Levine sale of June 27, 1987)

Rulau-E	Date	Metal	Size	VG	F	EF	Unc
NY 295B	(1826-27)	Gilt/B	31mm	50.00	75.00	150.	—

As 295.

Allen W. Hardie, merchant tailor, appears at the Garden and William St. location only in the 1827 directory. This tailor moved frequently, as the following list of business addresses attests:

196 Fulton St., 1821-1825
183 Greenwich St., 1825-1826
Garden corner William, 1826-1827
173 Reed St., 1827-1828
36 Cortlandt St., 1829-1830

The tokens were struck in Birmingham, England by Thomas Kettle.

ROBERT LOVETT SR.

Philadelphia, Pa. and New York, N.Y.

This early American diesinker was active in Philadelphia 1816-1822 and in New York 1824-1860 or later. His own store card, part of the Hard Times series, appeared in 1833-1834, but he may have been responsible for several early American tokens before the HT era.

He was the father of three accomplished diesinkers — George Hampden Lovett, Robert Lovett Jr. and John D. Lovett.

This early American diesinker was active in Philadelphia 1816-1822 and in New York 1824-1860's.

Dates	Business	Residence
1816-1822	Philadelphia	
1824-1828	259 Broadway	1824-25 414 Broome St.
1829-1830	297 Broadway	1827-28 63 Church St.
1832-1835	67 Maiden Lane	1833-34 362 Hudson
1840's	183 Broadway	1840's 4 Grove St.
1848-1851	5 Dey St.	
1850's	131 Fulton St.	

F.M.
(Frederick Marquand)

New York, N.Y.

Rulau-E	Date	Metal	Size	VG	F	VF	EF
NY 300	(1829-33)	Copper	29mm	—	40.00	—	—

F M in relief within rectangular depression ctsp on U.S. 1823 Large cent. (Duffield 1592)

Frederick Marquand (1799-1882) was a New York silversmith of the 1830's. The stamp is his hallmark. (See *The Book of Old Silver* by Seymour B. Wyler, New York, 1937.)

Marquand's jewelry business was located at 166 Broadway 1829-30. He had been in Savannah, Ga. 1820-1826.

H.M.

Rulau-E	Date	Metal	Size	VG	F	VF	EF
NY 302	(1830's)	Copper	29mm	—	200.	—	—

H. M. / N. YORK / 3 / Cents (relief, in oval depression) ctsp in four separate punches on U.S. 1828 or 1831 Large cent. (Tanenbaum coll.; Brunk 17550; Rulau NY 2110 in *Merchant Tokens 1845-1860*)

These pieces could belong to the Hard Times period (1833-44) or possibly later. They are rare.

MOTTS, IMPORTERS

Rulau-E	Date	Metal	Size	VG	F	EF	Unc
NY 610	(1839?)	Copper	28mm	90.00	150.	500.	—
		Eagle displayed, U.S. shield on its breast. Around: CLOCKS, WATCHES, JEWELRY, SILVERWARE, CHRONOMETERS, / 1789. Rv: Tall ornate clock. Around: MOTT'S N.Y. IMPORTER DEALERS MANUFACTURERS / OF GOLD & SILVER WARES. Plain edge. Thick planchet. Struck from broken reverse (clock side) dies. (RB; Wright 728)					
NY 611	1789	Copper	28mm	125.	200.	700.	—
		Similar, thin planchet. Perfect dies. (RB)					
NY 611A	1789	Copper	29mm	—	1500.	—	—
		Similar. Overstruck on U.S. 1837-1839 type Large cent. (William Anton collection)					
NY 612	1789	Copper	28mm	150.	400.	1200.	—
		Similar, edge engrailed. (RB)					
NY 613	1789	Copper	28mm	285.	600.	1550.	—
		Similar, edge lettered: PAYABLE AT LIVERPOOL, LONDON OR BRISTOL.					
NY 613A	1789	Pewter	28mm	—	—	Ex.Rare	—
		Similar.					

William and John Mott were importers, dealers and manufacturers of gold and silver wares, jewelry, watches and clocks, located at 240 Water Street, then a fashionable section of New York. Their thick planchet tokens normally are struck from dies heavily broken on the clock side; they usually weigh about 170 grains. The thin planchet pieces usually are struck from unbroken dies. Perfect-die thick flan and broken-die thin flan pieces do exist.

For at least 132 years, all respected numismatic writers have considered the 1789 Mott token to be America's first true trade token, issued in or near the date it bears.

Writer Q. David Bowers (in 1988) punctured this comfortable assumption in *Rare Coin Review* with his 'Re-evaluating a Famous American Token: The Mott token gives up its secrets." In a personal conversation with your author in December, 1990, he advanced the theory it was struck in 1839 for the 50th anniversary of the founding of Mott's.

In 1986 William J. Anton of New Jersey acquired a Mott token overstruck on a United States Large cent, date not visible, bearing the reverse type used only 1837-1839. This set Bowers to reexamining the whole Mott provenance and he reread all the authors who had touched on the token in detail.

Some authorities consider the Anton overstrike a forgery!

Cornelius C. Vermeule had pointed out the similarities between the Mott eagle displayed with U.S. shield on its breast, and that of the new gold coinage eagle of 1807. Using this clue, Bowers determined that the Mott eagle almost exactly matched the eagle on the 1838 $5 and $10 gold pieces, even to the arrangment of olive branches and arrows in the bird's talons.

Charles I. Bushnell in 1859, and all major writers since (Sylvester S. Crosby, Don Taxay, Robert A. Vlack, Richard S. Yeoman among others), were lulled into accepting 1789 as the date of issue because they were unaware of Anton's overstrike and did not think of the eagle similarity.

In his 1988 article, Bowers concluded: "The Mott token was produced no earlier than 1838, and ... the eagle was copied from that on contemporary gold coins."

Though we shed a tear or two over Bowers' conclusion, it would be futile to resist the evidence and, thus, **we concur**. The Mott remains in this *EAT* work because the hobby expects to find it there, but we publish all new information — including our own considerable expansion of knowledge on the Mott family enterprises.

The Mott was thought to be struck in England in 1789, which made sense since America had no competent token engravers and minters that early. But now, we conclude that it was struck in the U.S. Its workmanship never really did seem English (compare it with the Talbot Allum & Lee tokens of 1794, for example).

In 1859 Charles I. Bushnell wrote: (in *An Historical Account of the First Three Business Tokens Issued in the City of New York*) "The firm of Mott's was well-known in its day and generation. Their store was the resort of the rich and the great, of the gay belles and beaux of the time. The learned judge who wished a pair of spectacles to aid his failing sight, the lovely maid who craved a splendid ring to deck her tapering hand, their wants supplied with heart's content from Mott's extensive stock. More than one venerable dame now living can produce, in the shape of a watch of somewhat antique style but still faithful to its early mission, her bridal gift, purchased in her days of youth and beauty from their well-furnished establishment.

"Many a venerable timepiece, solid and substantial as the maker, and bearing upon the face the name of MOTT'S, has outlived a host of modern abortions and still graces the dining rooms of some of our oldest and most respectable ... citizens, and still chronicles the days of man, and re-echoes still the steps of passing time"

Dave Bowers added that the Mott variety bearing the English lettered edge probably occurred because a Mott piece was overstruck on a lettered-edge British token of the 1790's.

The Mott firm survived well into the 19th century. The firm seems to have been known by the style "Mott's of New York" most of the time. Mott's appears in directories under these proprietors:

William & John S. Mott	1789-90	
Jeremiah Mott	1795	Goldsmith
Jordan Mott	1796-1836	Clock & watchmaker, Jeweler
J. H. & Jordan Mott Jr.	1835-36	
William & Josiah Mott	1836-42	Jewelers
William Mott Jr.	1838-39	Jewelers
Josiah C. Mott	1838-39, 1844-45, 1848-49	Jeweler

The confusing welter of directory listings above is complicated also by the fact it adopted the name Mott Brothers 1840-42 and 1848 -50. A spinoff firm (?) consisted of James S. Mott and J. Mott, clock and watchmakers, at corner Pearl & Fulton streets, 1829-35.

Hallmarks for Mott's are given in silversmith sources:

(MOTTS) (Lion right) (?) (G)
(MOTTS) (N. YORK)
MOTTS in toothed rectangle
MOTTS in rectangle
MOTTS in rectangle

William & John Mott, *merchants*, are listed in directories at 240 Water Street 1821-22. They next appear as *grocers* for 1827-28, at 739 Greenwich Street. Still listed as grocers, they appear 1829-30 at 154 15th Street, near 7th Avenue. This firm in the 1821-30 period, we believe, may have been an allied enterprise of Mott's.

A possible related firm which did not issue tokens in its own name was W.W. & R. Mott, hardware store, at 241 Pearl Street, William W. Mott was the senior partner, and the firm appears at this address 1821-1827. Then it became William W. Mott & Co., merchants at 241 Pearl Street. 1829-1830. William W. Mott died about 1832 and was succeeded in the business by his widow, Susan F. Mott.

WM. H. MOTT
New York, N.Y.

Rulau-E	Date	Metal	Size	VG	F	EF
NY 614	(1820s)	Brass	29mm	35.00	50.00	125.
		Anvil, DEALERS IN HARDWARE, CUTLERY, IRON, STEEL. Rv: WM. H. MOTT / CORNER OF / OLD SLIP & / WATER ST. / NEW YORK. (Wright 729)				

Rulau-E	Date	Metal	Size	VG	F	EF
NY 615	(1820s)	Brass	29mm	40.00	75.00	125.
		Similar, but OLD SHIP & / WATER ST. (error)				

The firm of William H. Mott, hardware, issued tokens with the address 'Corner Old Slip & Water St.' On some of the tokens the address is given in error as 'Old Ship' rather than 'Old Slip.'

The firm has not been traced at this Old Slip and Water Street corner back to the 1822 New York city directories, however.

The firm does appear in 1829-1830 as hardware merchants of 396 Hudson. His home at that time was at 442 Greenwich Street. In 1832-1833 his business address was 109 King Street.

MOTT ST. LOCKSMITHS
New York, N.Y.

Rulau-E	Date	Metal	Size	VG	F	VF	EF
NY 620	(?)	Copper	29mm	150.	—	200.	—
		LOCK SMITHS / NO. 3 / MOTT ST ctsp on U.S. 1820 Large cent. (Tanenbaum coll.; Brunk 28625)					
NY 620A	(?)	Silver	32.5mm	—	—	250.	—
		Similar ctsp on U.S. 1796 half dollar.					
NY 620B	(?)	Silver	27mm	—	—	200.	—
		Similar ctsp on Spanish-American 1798 2-reales.					

NEW YORK ASSOCIATE CHURCH
New York, N.Y.

Rulau-E	Date	Metal	Size	F	VF	EF
NY 622	1799	Lead	Oval 23x17mm	500.	750.	Rare

(All lettering in script form.) N.YORK / 1799. Rv: ASSOCIATE / CHURCH. There is a heavy raised rim on each side. Plain edge.

The words "associate church" are all in lower case letters, with the Old English "ff" standing for "ss". Robert Vlack refers to this piece as the earliest dated American Communion token. (See Thomas Warner's 1888 "Communion Tokens" in American Journal of Numismatics.)

J. P.
New York, N.Y.

Rulau-E	Date	Metal	Size	F	VF	Unc
NY 625	(1825-32)	Brass	25mm	—	150.	200.

Heraldic eagle displayed, head turned right, U.S. shield on its breast. Arc of 9 stars above. Rv: Leaves above and below * J * P *, all within circle. Continuous leaf pair border around all. Plain edge. (Lot 593 in 1989 Gil Steinberg sale by Stack's)

This token was first recorded as lot 1801 in the Oct. 1880 Woodward sale of the Ferguson Haines collection. It may have been struck by Trested, or by Wright & Bale. 3 pieces known.

THE THEATRE AT NEW YORK (Park Theater)

Rulau-E	Date	Metal	Size	F	VF	EF	Unc
NY 892	(1797)	Copper	34mm	—	—	—	4600.

View of the theater's facade, THE THEATRE AT NEW YORK above, AMERICA in exergue. JACOBS in small letters below building. Rv: MAY COMMERCE FLOURISH. Edge lettered: I PROMISE TO PAY THE BEARER ON DEMAND ONE PENNY. (RB; Wright 1130)

Rulau-E	Date	Metal	Size	F	VF	EF	Unc
NY 893	(1797)	Copper	34mm	—	—	Rare	—

Similar, plain edge.

Normal Reverse

Rulau-E	Date	Metal	Size	F	VF	EF	Unc
NY 894	(ca 1800)	Tin	34mm	—	—	—	Ex. Rare

Obverse as 892. Rv: Woman treading clothes with her bare feet in a tub. ANTIENT SCOTTISH WASHING - * HONI SOIT QUI MAL Y PENSE *. Plain edge. (Wright 1130A)

This penny token, designed by Jacobs and struck in England by Skidmore, was issued by the Park Theater in New York. The theater was constructed beginning June 1, 1795, and completed in 1798 opposite City Hall Park. The proprietors petitioned for permission to erect a portico over the sidewalk, but it was not granted. About 12 specimens of NY 892 are known, that in the Garrett collection of JHU being a proof.

The Theatre at New York/Antient (sic) Scottish Washing token is a muling made in England, utilizing the old die for the American penny. The reverse is the reverse of the Loch Leven penny. It was first published by Dr. B.P. Wright about 1900.

The Loch Leven penny was a 1797 product for Scotland, catalogued as D&H Kinross 1. The muling is not mentioned by Dalton and Hamer, however. Interestingly, the normal Loch Leven obverse (Loch Leven Castle, where Queen Mary was imprisoned in 1567), carries this signature: P.K. FECIT, indicating Peter Kempson of Birmingham made the original copper penny for Scotland.

Later there was a Park Theatre at 22nd Street and Broadway 1874 to 1882, with Henry E. Abbey as proprietor.

The New Park Theatre was erected 1883 at the northwest corner of 35th Street and Broadway. It opened Oct. 15, 1883. In 1885 this became known as Harrigan's Theatre and from 1895 until 1911 or later as Herald Square Theatre.

Rulau-E	Date	Metal	Size	F	VF	EF	Unc
NY 41	1817	Copper	19mm	15.00	20.00	35.00	—

Obverse: ADMIT in horizontal oval. Rv: 1817 in similar oval. Dentilated rims. (Wright 4)

Rulau-E	Date	Metal	Size	F	VF	EF	Unc
NY 41A	1817	Copper	19mm	15.00	25.00	40.00	—

Obverse: PAID in horizontal oval. Rv: 1817 in similar oval. Dentilated rims.

These two last admission checks to the old Park Theater in New York, opened in 1798. The theater was burned during construction in 1797, again May 25, 1820, and again in 1821. In February, 1824, a grand ball was given for the benefit of the Greeks, then in rebellion against Turkey, and $2,000 was realized. The theater was destroyed by fire Dec. 16, 1848.

The ADMIT and PAID checks were the subject of a special examination by George and Melvin Fuld in the April, 1961, *The Numismatist*. Lyman Low in the Betts sale catalog (1898) attributed their period of use to the 1820-1824 period. We feel the period of use should cover the 1817-1824 period.

Rulau-E	Date	Metal	Size	G	VG	F	VF
NY 42	1834	Silver	38mm	—	—	400.	—
		Seymour Harris / Park Theatre / No. / N-Y / August 9th / 1834 engraved in script on a U.S. 1799 silver dollar. Rv: W.R. engraved on the dollar's reverse. Unique.					

This interesting item was in the Maurice M. Gould collection. It may yet provide some clues to the Park Theatre's later existence.

PEALE'S MUSEUM

Rulau-E	Date	Metal	Size	F	VF	EF	Unc
NY 632	1825	Copper	34mm	50.00	100.	300.	700.
		Female bust left in Greek helmet and armor, PARTHENON / NEW YORK 1825. Rv: ADMIT / THE / BEARER in center. PEALE's MUSEUM & GALLERY OF THE FINE ARTS. (Wright 5: Low 269)					
NY 633	1825	White Metal	34mm	1500.	—	—	Ex. Rare
		Same as 632. (Low 270)					

Rubens Peale established his museum in 1825 in the Parthenon, at 252 Broadway opposite City Hall. The Long Room contained snakes, lizards and an Egyptian mummy. Another gallery contained paintings. Lectures and special appearances were made. In 1831 the museum was renovated and enlarged. Tickets for a whole family for one year were $10; single admissions were 25 cents. The copper ADMIT THE BEARER checks may have been used for annual subscribers. These admission checks were apparently used 1825-1841. The museum was incorporated as the New York Museum in 1841, and in 1843 was sold to P.T. Barnum.

Rubens' father, Charles Wilson Peale, opened the Philadelphia Museum in 1784; he incorporated it in 1821. This museum issued two different types of ADMIT checks, which see. Rubens' brother, Franklin Peale, became chief coiner of the U.S. Mint in 1839.

PLATT & BROTHER

Rulau-E	Date	Metal	Size	VG	F	VF	EF
NY 640	(1831-34)	Copper	29mm	75.00	—	125.00	—
		PLATT & BROTHER in relief within rectangular depression ctsp on U.S. 1831 Large cent. Another ctsp, J.B. in relief within cartouche, also appears on this piece. (Rulau Z77; Duffield 1594; Hallenbeck 16.517; Brunk 32270)					

The 'J B' has not yet been traced. If it is another silversmith, there are many possibilities. It is not unusual to find coins counterstamped by two unconnected merchants.

George W. and Nathan C. Platt were silversmiths in New York City operating under the name Platt & Brother circa 1816-1834. The counterstamp is one of four registered hallmarks of the firm.

A successor firm, Platt & Brothers, may have used the hallmark until 1851.

In 1829-30 the firm was at 140 Chatham St.

PLATT & BROTHER,
Importers of
WATCHES, JEWELRY & FINE CUTLERY,
No 12 Maiden Lane.
Constantly on hand Jewelry and Watches, Fine Cutlery, Silver Wares, and every desirable article suitable for the Trade.

D. PROSKEY

Rulau-E	Date	Metal	Size	VG	F	VF	EF
NY 641	1799 ?	Copper	29mm	—	85.00	—	—
		D. PROSKEY / * / 57 COURTLAND / ST / NEW YORK CITY ctsp on U.S. Large cent, the date of which has been reengraved to read '1799'. (Brunk 32895)					

T. PYE

Rulau-E	Date	Metal	Size	VG	F	VF	EF
NY 642	(1830)	Copper	23.5mm	—	125.	—	200.
		T. PYE / o NEW o / YORK ctsp on U.S. 1809 Half cent. (Tanenbaum coll.; Brunk 33045)					
NY 642A	(?)	Silver	26mm	—	125.	—	200.
		T (Key) PYE ctsp on U.S. 1818 Bust quarter. (Levine May 1985 sale, lot 41; Brunk 33040)					
NY 642B	(?)	Silver	32.5mm	—	125.	—	200.
		Similar ctsp on U.S. 1825 Bust half dollar.					

Thomas Pye, locksmith, was at 143 Leonard St. 1829-30. A successor, Thomas L. Pye, lockmaker, was at 285 Delancey in 1867-68.

JONATHAN RATHBONE & FRANCIS B. FITCH

Rulau-E	Date	Metal	Size	VG	F	VF	EF
NY 654	1825	Lead	Oval 49.2x25.4mm	800.	950.	—	—
		View of Castle Garden, CASTLE GARDEN above. Rv: JONATHAN RATHBONE & FRANCIS B. FITCH, PROPRIETORS, 1825. Flying eagle with scroll. Below scroll is engraved: D POMEROY 890. Only 4 to 6 specimens known.					
NY 654A	1825	S/Brass	Oval, same	800.	—	—	—
		As 654. 4 known. (John Ford coll.)					

This admittance pass was cut by Richard Trested of New York.

Castle Garden was a concert hall and scene of many receptions, including one for Marquis de Lafayette on Aug. 30, 1824. Jenny Lind appeared there in 1850. A reception for Louis Kossuth was held in 1851.

The numbers on the lead or brass pieces were stockholder or subscriber numbers. D. (aniel) Pomeroy, number 890, was a merchant located at 63 Water St. in Brooklyn. The Pomeroy specimen is in the ANS collection, New York City.

Other numbers known on the brass specimens include 347 for H. N. Benjamin (this piece, in Fine, realized $880 in the B&M Nov. 1990 sale, lot 4169); and 511 for S. R. Ryer (this piece, in VG, made $880 as lot 4170 in the same sale).

A brass specimen numbered 244 is inscribed to J.P. Whittelsey. Another brass piece is not inscribed (Levick sale, lot 352).

RATHBONE, FITCH AND POMEROY

Jonathan Rathbone is traced in the New York city directories at a number of different locations. It seems he moved constantly.

JONATHAN B. RATHBONE, MERCHANT

1821-1822	108 Broadway
1824-1825	Fort Clinton
1825-1826	50 Pearl St.
1826-1827	Castle Garden
1827-1828	29 Old Slip
1829-1830	95 Washington

Frances B. Fitch also moved around a good bit. He first appears as a teacher about 1821 and last appears as a grocer in 1830.

FRANCIS B. FITCH

1821-1822	Teacher	50 Frankfort
1826-1827		61 Canal St.
1827-1828		Whitehall
1829-1830		386 7th Ave

Daniel Pomeroy Jr. was a merchant.

DANIEL POMEROY JR., MERCHANT

1821-1826	60 Front St., Brooklyn
1826-1827	101 Water St.
1827-1830	47 Front St., Brooklyn

(Pomeroy & Rogers, 60 Front St., 1824-1826)

W.H. SCHOONMAKER

Rulau-E	Date	Metal	Size	VG	F	VF	EF
NY 782	(1829-30)	Brass	26mm	250.	500.	1000.	—
		W.H. SCHOONMAKER BROADWAY N.Y. No. 181 GUNS, PISTOLS, RIFLES & C. Rv: MILITARY GOODS SILVER PLATED BRITANNIA AND FANCY ARTICLES.					
NY 782A	(1829-30)	Sil Br	26mm	500.	750.	—	—
		Same as 782. (Wright 953)					
NY 783	(1829-30)	Ger Sil	26mm	500.	1250.	—	—
		Same as 782.					
NY 784	(1829-30)	Brass	26mm	300.	450.	—	—
		Obverse similar to 782. Rv: Bust of Andrew Jackson facing small central octagonal frame, PRESIDENT above. The reverse field is plain.					
NY 785	(1829-30)	Brass	26mm	600.	1000.	1500.	—
		Obverse as 782. Rv: George IV of England head left, GEORGE IV KING OF GREAT BRITAIN.					

The Schoonmaker cards contain mulings of the dies used for the Wolfe Spies & Clark cards (which see).

Castle Garden in the 1850's.

NY 786 (1829-30) Silver 27mm — 525. — —
H. SCHOONMAKER in relief ctsp in a rectangular depression on an 1806 quarter. (Van Ormer sale 2833; Brunk 35815)

There is no evidence of connection between the Schoonmaker tokens and the above silversmith-type impression. Yet the coincidence seems too close to ignore.

William H. Schoonmaker, military cutlery and fancy hardware, is first located in 1829 at 181 Broadway. He does not appear after 1830. Thus NY 782-785 must be assigned to the 1829-1830 period, which is consonant with the Wolfe, Spies & Clark cards.

STICKLER

Rulau-E	Date	Metal	Size	VG	F	VF	EF
NY 800	(1827-30)	Copper	29mm	—	75.00	—	125.00
		STICKLER ctsp on U.S. 1819 Large cent. (Brunk 38350)					
NY 801	(1827-30)	Copper	29mm	—	75.00	—	125.00
		Similar ctsp on U.S. 1825, 1826, 1827or 1828 Large cent.					
NY 802	(1827-30)	Copper	29mm	—	75.00	—	—
		Similar ctsp on U.S. Large cent, date worn off.					

John Stickler, silversmith, was located at 104 Broadway 1821-1822. His hallmark appears on 1819 to 1828-dated U.S. Large cents.

TALBOT, ALLUM & LEE

Rulau-E	Date	Metal	Size	VG	F	VF	Unc
NY 877	1794	Copper	29mm	45.00	—	140.	900.
		Commerce with Liberty cap on pole, standing. LIBERTY & COMMERCE. above, 1794 in exergue. Rv: Sailing ship, TALBOT ALLUM & LEE / NEW YORK / ONE CENT. Edge: PAYABLE AT THE STORE OF****. Small d's in obverse and reverse legends. (RB; Fuld 1794-4)					
NY 877A	1794	Silver	29mm	—	—	1200.	—
		Similar to 877. (Fuld 1794-4)					
NY 877B	1794	Copper	29mm	—	—	—	Rare
		Same dies as 877, but struck on a broad flan, plain edge. (Fuld 1794-4A)					
NY 878	1794	Copper	29mm	—	—	—	2 known
		Similar, large '&'. Plain edge. (Has been verified as genuine.)					
NY 878A	1794	Copper	29mm	55.00	—	170.	680.
Rulau-E	**Date**	**Metal**	**Size**	**VG**	**F**	**VF**	**Unc**
NY 879	1794	Copper	29mm	50.00	—	135.	560.
		Similar, but '&' much smaller. Edge: PAYABLE AT THE STORE OF, but differently made. (Fuld 1794-3)					
NY 879A	1794	Copper	29mm	—	—	—	Rare
		Same dies as 879, but plain edge. (Vlack 5)					
NY 880	1794	Copper	29mm	200.	—	625.	2000.
		Similar, but NEW YORK omitted from reverse, (RB: Fuld 1794-1)					

Rulau-E	Date	Metal	Size	VG	F	VF	Unc
NY 881	1795	Copper	29mm	45.00	—	140.	650.
		Obverse similar, but date change to 1795. Reverse similar, but ONE CENT omitted. Legend around periphery. Edge: WE PROMISE TO PAY THE BEARER ONE CENT. (RB; Fuld 1795-1; Wright 1088)					
NY 881A	1795	Copper	29mm	—	—	—	Unique
		As 881, but edge reads: CURRENT EVERYWHERE *****. (Fuld 1795-1A)					
NY 881B	1795	Copper	29mm	—	—	—	Unique
		As 881, but edge with twin olive leaves. (Fuld 1795-1B)					
NY 882	1795	Copper	29mm	—	—	—	Unique
		As 881, but plain edge. (Fuld 1795-1C)					

THE T.A.&L. MULINGS

Rulau-E	Date	Metal	Size	F	VF	EF	Unc
NY 883	1794	Copper	29mm	—	80.00	150.	250.
		Obverse as NY 877 (Commerce standing with Liberty cap on pole). Rv: Nude boy standing, BIRMINGHAM HALFPENNY 1793. Edge: PAYABLE IN LONDON, balance engrailed. (Fuld Mule 1; D&H Warwick 54)					
NY 883A	1794	Brass	29mm	—	—	—	Ex. Rare
		Same as 883. (Fuld Mule 1A)					

Rulau-E	Date	Metal	Size	F	VF	EF	Unc
NY 884	1794	Copper	29mm	—	50.00	80.00	250.
		Obverse as NY 877. Rv: Stork right, PROMISSORY HALFPENNY 1793. Edge: PAYABLE IN LONDON, balance engrailed. (Fuld Mule 2; D&H Hamps. 52a)					
NY 884A	1794	Brass	29mm	—	—	—	Rare
		Same dies as 884, but Brass.					
NY 885	1794	Copper	29mm	—	100.	200.	350.
		As 884, but edge reads: PAYABLE AT THE WAREHOUSE LIVERPOOL ***. (Fuld Mule 2A; D&H Hamps. 52)					
NY 885A	1794	Copper	29mm	—	—	—	Rare
		Same as 885, but Plain edge. (Fuld Mule 2B) (Donald Miller described this piece erroneously)					

Rulau-E	Date	Metal	Size	F	VF	EF	Unc
NY 887	1794	Copper	29mm	—	50.00	80.00	250.
		Obverse as NY 877. Rv: Uniformed bust left, EARL HOWE & THE GLORIOUS FIRST OF JUNE, point of hat to H of THE. Edge: PAYABLE IN LONDON, balance engrailed. (Fuld Mule 3; D&H Hamps. 25)					
NY 887A	1794	Copper	29mm	—	—	—	Rare
		Similar to NY 877. Point of hat to E of THE. Plain edge. Broken die. (Fuld Mule 4)					

Rulau-E	Date	Metal	Size	F	VF	EF	Unc
NY 886	1794	Copper	29mm	—	50.00	80.00	250.
		Obverse as NY 877. Rv: Bust left, IOHN HOWARD F.R.S. PHILANTHROPIST. Edge: X - PAYABLE IN LONDON, balance engrailed. (Fuld Mule 5; D&H Hamps. 56)					

Rulau-E	Date	Metal	Size	F	VF	EF	Unc
NY 886A	1794	Copper	29mm	—	—	—	—
		Same as 886, but counterstamped with head of John the Baptist for circulation in Malta in 1814. (Vlack collection)					

In 1814 the islands of Malta were recognized as a British dependency by the Congress of Vienna. With this turnover, a coinage of sorts was needed for the islands, but England had ceased its coinage operations in 1807.

As a result, some worn specimens of the early George III (1770 to 1775) halfpence were counterstamped with the head of John the Baptist, the patron saint of Malta. The counterstamp was easily recognized and accepted by the inhabitants as having official status, thus these pieces circulated with little or no difficulty for a short period of time.

There was also a great surplus of English tokens struck during the 1787 to 1800 period, and probably because these were no longer acceptable for trade, some were apparently counterstamped along with the halfpence. Somehow, somewhere, this specimen became one of these pieces, and thus tied Malta to England to America.

Rulau-E	Date	Metal	Size	F	VF	EF	Unc
NY 888	1795	Copper	29mm	—	—	—	400.
		Obverse as NY 881. Rv: Drum, powder horn, spears and flag, BLOFIELD CAVALRY FIFTH TROOP. Edge: Engrailed. (Fuld Mule 6; D&H Norfolk 10)					
NY 888A	1795	Copper	29mm	—	—	—	600.
		Obverse as NY 881. Rv: Cathedral, YORK 1795. Edge: FEAR GOD AND HONOUR THE KING.XX (Fuld Mule 7; D&H York 65)					
NY 888B	1795	Copper	29mm	—	—	—	Rare
		As 888A, but plain edge. (Fuld Mule 7A: D&H York 65a)					
NY 888C	1795	Copper	29mm	—	—	—	Rare
		Same dies as 888A. Edge: PAYABLE ON DEMAND. (Vlack Mule 21)					

William Talbot, William Allum and James Lee, engaged in the India trade and located at 241 Pearl Street, placed a large quantity of English-made copper cents in circulation during 1794 and 1795. These seem to have been made for T.A.&L. by Thomas Wyon, engraver, and Peter Kempson, manufacturer, in Birmingham, England. Kempson also caused to be struck, using the T.A.&L. New York cent obverse (standing Commerce with Liberty cap on pole, a bale in background, LIBERTY & COMMERCE above) a number mulings with British halfpenny token dies. Though these mules were made for English collectors of the day, they could have (and did) enter circulation to a limited degree. The mules cannot be dissociated from the American token series. George Fuld wrote up this series of cents and mules in the *Numismatic Scrapbook Magazine* for September, 1956.

The T.A.&L. firm had a brief, though flourishing, history. The company was founded in 1794, the year the cent pieces were introduced. One of the partners, James Lee, retired from the company in 1796. The firm then continued under the name Talbot & Allum until it was dissolved in 1798.

WM. THOMSON

Rulau-E	Date	Metal	Size	VG	F	VF	EF
NY 900	(1825-34)	Copper	29mm	—	75.00	—	125.00
		Script WM. THOMSON ctsp on U.S. Large cent. Examined: 1817, 1819, 1825. (Brunk 39880)					
NY 902	(1843)	Copper	29mm	—	75.00	—	125.00
		Same ctsp on U.S. 1843 Large cent.					

William Thomson, silversmith, was in business in New York circa 1810-1834. His hallmark in script appears on Large cents dated 1819 through 1843.

Thomson was at 177 Broadway and at 129 William St. in 1824-1833. His successor James Thomson may have used his hallmark.

TREDWELL, KISSAM & CO.

Rulau-E	Date	Metal	Size	VG	F	VF	Unc
NY 920	1823	Brass	26mm	25.00	40.00	100.	200.
		Eagle, NEW YORK GRAND CANAL/ OPENED/ 1823. Rv: TREDWELL / KISSAM / & CO. / HARDWARE / CUTLERY / LOOKING / GLASSES/ N.Y. (Wright 1157)					

Rulau-E	Date	Metal	Size	VG	F	VF	Unc
NY 921	(1825-26)	Brass	26mm	25.00	40.00	100.	200.
		Similar, but "228 PEARL ST." added to reverse, flanking "& CO." (Wright 1156)					
NY 921A	(1825-26)	Copper	26mm	30.00	45.00	—	100.
		As 921.					
NY 921B	(1825-26)	S/Br	26mm	32.50	47.50	100.	200.
		As 921.					

S. L. TREDWELL

Rulau-E	Date	Metal	Size	VG	F	VF	Unc
NY 919	(1833)	Copper	29mm	—	200.	—	—
		Both sides same: S.L. Tredwell, 228 PEARL ST. CHINA GLASS & EARTHENWARE.					

Seabury L. Tredwell and Joseph Kissam formed Tredwell, Kissam & Co., hardware, located at 245 Pearl Street, 1821-1825, and at 228 Pearl Street 1825-1833. They moved to 228 Pearl Street before November in 1825.

Seabury Tredwell was in business alone as S.L. Tredwell at 228 Pearl Street in 1833 and later.

NY 920 without address can be assigned to 1823, the date on the token. NY 921 to 921B at 228 Pearl St. emanated from the 1825-1826 period. NY 919 of S.L. Tredwell was issued, apparently, in 1833, so it really belongs in the Hard Times period.

RICHARD TRESTED

Rulau-E	Date	Metal	Size	VG	F	VF	EF
NY 925	(1823-24)	Copper	29mm	—	Unique	—	—

Eagle displayed, radiant Liberty cap above, scroll below. Rv: TRESTED / *68* / WILLIAM ST. / ENGRAVER & DIE SINKER / (ornament) / STAMPER / NEW YORK. Struck over a U.S. cent (die trial).

Rulau-E	Date	Metal	Size	VG	F	VF	EF
NY 924	(1823-24)	Brass	27mm	1500.	2000.	7500.	—

Obverse as 925. Rv: .R. TRESTED. / *68* / WILLIAM ST. / ENGRAVER & DIE SINKER / (ornament) / STAMPER / & PIERCER / * / * NEW - YORK *. (Bosco Apr. 1989 sale, lot 111)

NY 924A	(1823-24)	Brass	27mm	—	—	3000.	—

As 924, but small stars flank NEW YORK in place of rosettes. Obverse die changed. (Zeddies coll.)

Rulau-E	Date	Metal	Size	VG	F	VF	EF
NY 922	(1825-29)	Brass	24mm	500.	1250.	1750.	2000.
		U.S. shield within wreath, TRESTED FECIT below. Rv: TRESTED / DIE SINKER / AND STAMPER / 68 WILLM. ST. / N. YORK within wreath. (Wright 1159)					
NY 923	(1825-29)	Brass	24mm	300.	500.	600.	750.
		Obverse similar to 922. Rv: SIX / CENTS, three rosettes and two stars.					

Trested, an Englishman, is first traced as an engraver in 1821 at 70 William St. From 1823-1827 he was at 68 William Street, and occupied quarters at both 68 William Street and 76 Maiden Lane 1828-1829. He died Jan. 13, 1829. The cause of death was complications resulting from an amputated finger. On May 25, 1829, his widow Ann sold his engraving and diesinking business to Charles Cushing Wright and James Bale. Bale had been Trested's apprentice.

Trested, one of New York's earliest token-makers, cut his own and the Castle Garden cards, and may have done the earliest Doremus, Suydam & Nixon tokens. He also seems to have done token work for the Scovills in Waterbury, Conn.

NY 924A in VF realized $2600 in the Nov. 1990 B&M Schenkel sale.

WASHINGTON MARKET CHOWDER CLUB

Rulau-E	Date	Metal	Size	VG	F	VF	EF
NY 930	1818	Silver	24mm	—	—	—	4 known
		Small George Washington bust right within olive wreath, MEMBERS above, BADGE below. Rv: WASHINGTON/ MARKET / CHOWDER / CLUB / 1818. Plain edge. (Baker 338A)					
NY 931	1818	Gold	24mm	—	—	—	25,000.
		As last. The only traceable specimen was in the Johns Hopkins University collection ex-Garrett and J.N.T. Levick. (Baker 338)					
NY 931A	1818	Copper	24mm	—	—	—	—
		As last. Plain edge. (Stewart Witham coll.)					

Rulau-E	Date	Metal	Size	VG	F	VF	EF
NY 931B	1818	Bronze	24mm	—	—	—	—
		As last. (Witham coll.; Baker 338C)					
NY 931C	1818	WM	24mm	—	—	—	—
		As last. (Witham coll.; Baker 338D)					

The club may have been a fraternal group, or a marching or singing organization. Nothing is known of it.

The city erected a new market about 1771 at the foot of Dey Street at the River. This open-air marketplace became known as Washington Market in 1812.

WELLES & GELSTON

Rulau-E	Date	Metal	Size	VG	F	VF	EF
NY 933	(1840)	Copper	29mm	—	75.00	—	125.
		. . . . . D & GELSTON ctsp on U.S. 1819 Large cent. (Brunk 42530)					
NY 934	(1840)	Copper	29mm	75.00	—	125.	—
		WELLES & GELSTON ctsp on U.S. 1826 Large cent, also worn date. Only 4 known.					

It was once thought this partial inscription stood for silversmiths Gould & Gelston of Baltimore, but that firm was always known only as Gelston & Gould (circa 1816-1820). Most likely the 'D' was a misreading by Maurice M. Gould or others for 'S'.

WILLIS & BROTHERS

Rulau-E	Date	Metal	Size	G	VG	F	VF
NY 954	(1830-32)	Tin	33mm	200.	500.	1000.	—
		WILLIS & BROTHERS / 215 / PEARL ST / NEW-YORK. Rv: HARDWARE CUTLERY & EARTHENWARE around, CHINA in center.					

John R. Willis, the senior partner, and Alfred Willis and William H. Willis, were ironmongers and sold hardware and crockery at 276 Pearl St., 1829-1833.

C. & I.D. WOLFE

Rulau-E	Date	Metal	Size	VG	F	EF	Unc
NY 957	1823	Brass	26mm	15.00	22.50	50.00	—
		Eagle displayed, NEW YORK GRAND CANAL / OPENED / 1823. Rv: C. & I. D. WOLFE / 87 / MAIDEN LANE / HARDWARE / CUTLERY / MILITARY / GOODS / N.Y. (Wright 1263) Plain edge.					
NY 957A	1823	Sil Br	26mm	20.00	30.00	50.00	—
		As 957. Reeded edge.					
NY 957B	1823	Brass		—	22.50	50.00	—
		Reeded edge. As 957.					

The exact same obverse die (Eagle displayed, head turned left, U.S. shield on breast GRAND CANAL 1823) was used also on cards of C. Wolfe, Spies & Clark; and Tredwell, Kissam & Co.

C. WOLFE, CLARK & SPIES

Rulau-E	Date	Metal	Size	VG	F	VF	EF
NY 958	(1829)	Brass	26mm	500.	800.	—	1200.
		Washington head right in central oval, WASHINGTON above; C. WOLFE CLARK & SPIES / NEW YORK / HARDWARE & / MILITARY STORE around. Rv: Jackson head facing three-quarters left, JACKSON above; plain field. Reeded edge. (Baker 588; Zeddies coll.)					
NY 958A	(1829)	Copper	26mm	—	—	—	—
		Same as 958. Reeded edge. All known 958A in copper are counterfeits.					

At this late juncture, it seems unlikely we'll find out why this firm proceeded to change the ranking of its partners to C. Wolfe, Spies & Clark as in the examples which follow. Adam W. Spies became the dominant partner, however (see footnotes following WS&C below).

C. WOLFE, SPIES & CLARK

Rulau-E	Date	Metal	Size	VG	F	VF	EF
NY 962	(1829-30)	Brass	26mm	500.	800.	—	1200.
		Similar to obverse of NY 958 but name change. Rv: Central oval with Jackson military bust facing as on 958, but field now carries: CUTLERY, PLATED WARE / GUNS &C / 193 / PEARL ST. N.Y. Reeded edge. (Baker 589)					
NY 962A	(1829-30)	Sil Br	26mm	550.	900.	—	Rare
		As 962. Reeded edge. (Baker 589A)					

Rulau-E	Date	Metal	Size	VG	F	VF	EF
NY 959	(1829-30)	Brass	26mm	750.	1000.	—	1500.
		Obverse as 962. Rv: Jackson military bust facing three-quarters left in octagonal frame, PRESIDENT above; plain field. (Baker 590)					
NY 960	(1829-30)	Copper	26mm	—	—	—	—
		Same as 959. All copper pieces examined have been electrotype copies.					

Rulau-E	Date	Metal	Size	VG	F	VF	EF
NY 961	1823 (1829)	Brass	26mm	550.	1200.	—	—
		Obverse as 962. Rv: Eagle and NEW YORK CANAL GRAND CANAL / OPENED / 1823. (Wright 1261; Baker 591)					

Rulau-E	Date	Metal	Size	VG	F	VF	EF
NY 963	(1829-30)	Brass	26mm	750.	2000.	—	—
		Obverse as 962. Rv: Head left, GEORGE IV KING OF GREAT BRITAIN. (Baker 592)					

Andrew Jackson campaigned for the presidency in 1824, losing to John Quincy Adams. He won the presidency in 1828. George IV ascended the British throne in 1820.

The firm of C. & J. D. Wolfe (it reads C. & I. D. Wolfe on its tokens) traces its origins back before the war of 1812. It sold military and naval supplies, hardware and cutlery.

The 'C.' was Christopher Wolfe and the 'I. D.' was John D. Wolfe. The firm was located at 87 Maiden Lane opposite Clark & Brown's Coffee House; the business was located at the corner of Maiden Lane and Gold Street. John D. Wolfe married Miss Lorillard of the tobacco family and was reputed to be very wealthy.

C. & J. D. Wolfe appears in New York city directories at 87 Maiden Lane 1821-1828. About 1829 the firm dissolved.

Christopher Wolfe joined with Adam W. Spies and R. Smith Clark to form Wolfe, Clark & Spies in 1829, quickly changing the name to Wolfe, Spies & Clark, hardware, cutlery and military goods, at 193 Pearl Street, 1829-1833.

John D. Wolfe formed J. D. Wolfe, Bishop & Co., hardware and military goods, still located at 87 Maiden Lane, 1829-1833.

NY 957 and 957A, dated 1823, could have been in use as late as 1828. They were struck by Thomas Kettle.

NY 958 and 958A, without address, were struck by Kettle in 1829. NY 959 through 963 were struck, apparently, in the 1829-1830 period. NY 961 uses an 1823-dated die in an early example of U.S. muling, but directory evidence now shows this token could not have appeared before 1829. (See *Coin Collector's Journal* for January, 1935)

Adam W. Spies (born 1783) survived the Wolfe, Spies & Clark firm as a military merchant by many years. Entering the cutlery, gun and militaria business alone in 1823, he was part of Wolfe, Spies & Clark 1829-33. He kept the store open until his death in 1863.

After that the store remained open under Spies' name to 1877. (A related firm, Spies, Kissam & Co., was open in New York 1867-76).

WRIGHT & BALE

Rulau-E	Date	Metal	Size	F	VF	EF	Unc
NY 1001	(1829-30)	Copper	30mm	2000.	3000.	—	4000.
		Fur capped bust of Franklin left, BENJAMIN FRANKLIN around. Below: WRIGHT & BALE. Rv: WRIGHT & BALE / ENGRAVERS / AND DIE CUTTERS / 68 WILLIAM ST. NEW YORK / ..... OF EVERY DESCRIPTION / CARDS OF ADDRESS / BOOKBINDERS TOOLS. (Low 329)					
NY 1000	(1829-30)	Brass	30mm	4000.	9000.	—	12,000.
		As 1001. (Low 330)					

NY 1002	(1832-33)	Copper	19mm	150.	300.	500.	750.

Head of George Washington right within large oak wreath. Rv: WRIGHT & BALE / ENGRAVERS / & DIE / CUTTERS / 68 NASSAU STREET / PLATES & ROLLS / FOR EMBOSSING / DIES & SEALS OF / EVERY / DESCRIPTION / NEW-YORK. Thick planchet. (Wright 1275; Low 331)

NY 1003	(1832-33)	Copper	19mm	200.	300.	500.	800.

Same as 1002, but thin flan. (Low 332; Baker 594)

Rulau-E	Date	Metal	Size	F	VF	EF	Unc
NY 1003A	(1832-33)	Silv/C	19mm	—	800.	—	—

As last. Only 2 known.

HAYES & ADRIANCE
Poughkeepsie, N.Y.

Rulau-E	Date	Metal	Size	VG	F	VF	EF
NY 1015	(1816-26)	Copper	29mm	75.00	—	125.	—

HAYES & ADRIANCE in relief in rect. depression ctsp on U.S. 1803 Large cent. (Brunk 18880)

Peter P. Hayes and John Adriance were silversmiths in partnership 1816-1826.

HENDERSON & LOSSING
Poughkeepsie, N.Y.

Rulau-E	Date	Metal	Size	F	VF	EF	Unc
NY 1017	(1829-33)	Copper	15mm	300.	500.	700.	1100.

Washington head right within oak wreath. Rv: HENDERSON & LOSSING / CLOCK & WATCH / MAKERS / & DEALERS IN / WATCHES / JEWELLERY / SILVER / W&B POKEEPSIE NY. Plain edge. (Low 317)

This card was cut by Wright & Bale, whose initials W&B NY appear on the text side; a Washington head in oak wreath adorns the obverse.

Benson J. Lossing gave up the cares of business in 1835, at age 22, to study art and literature. He became a well known historian. The date of the token is hard to fix, but it likely appeared in the 1830-1833 period. Adam Henderson appears in the 1830 census, but not Lossing.

J. BARTON
Utica, N.Y.

Rulau-E	Date	Metal	Size	VG	F	VF	EF
NY 1030	(1817-32)	Copper	29mm	75.00	—	125.	—

J. BARTON in relief within toothed rect. depression ctsp on U.S. 1804 Large cent. (Brunk 2615)

Joseph Barton (1764-1832) was a silversmith, goldsmith and clockmaker in Stockbridge, Mass. 1784 to 1798 or later, according to Belden. He relocated in Utica 1817-32.

He was part of the firms of Barton & Porter 1811-17, Barton & Clark 1826, Barton & Smith 1829-31, and Barton & Butler 1831-32.

N. B. BASSETT
Schenectady, N.Y.

Rulau-E	Date	Metal	Size	VG	F	VF	EF
NY 1022	(1820's)	Silver	39mm	—	—	250.	—

N. B. BASSETT in relief within rectangular depression ctsp on Spanish-American 1807-Mo-TH 8-reales. (Brunk 2670)

Nehemiah B. Bassett was a silversmith in Albany, N.Y. 1795-1819, then in Schenectady 1820 on. He died in 1844. While in Albany he was in the partnership of Bassett and Warford with Joseph Warford 1800-05.

Normal hallmarks are BASSETT in rectangle or (Boot) BASSETT in rectangle.

L. BLOODGOOD
Utica, N.Y.

Rulau-E	Date	Metal	Size	VG	F	VF	EF
NY 1033	(1820's)	Silver	27mm	—	—	350.	—

L. Bloodgood in relief within shaped rect. depression ctsp on Spanish-American 1794 or 1800 2-reales. Rarity 9. (Kirtley Dec. 1992 fixed price list, page 1; Brunk 4080)

NY 1034	(1820's)	Copper	29mm	—	—	200.	—

Same ctsp on U.S. 1807 or 1819 Large cent.

Lynott Bloodgood began his career as a silversmith about 1805 in Albany, N.Y., but soon joined in partnership with James A. Bloodgood in Utica, N.Y. ca 1805-1810.

He was documented by George B. Cutten in the 1939 work *The Silversmiths, Watchmakers and Jewelers of the State of New York outside New York City.*

WATERVLIET ARSENAL
Watervliet, N.Y.

Rulau-E	Date	Metal	Size	VG	F	VF	EF
NY 1050	(1816-30)	Copper	29mm	—	175.	—	—

U.S. / WATERVLIET / ARSENAL / (eagle with shield on its breast) in four lines, ctsp on worn U.S. 1794 Large cent. Issued holed. (Frank Kovacs coll; Brunk 42005)

Watervliet, in Albany County on the Hudson River, is a cross-river community from Troy.

The Watervliet Arsenal's activities peaked in the 1820's and 1830's, according to Ed Green, curator of the Army Museum at the Presidio of San Francisco, Calif. By the Civil War Watervliet was making only leather items for the Army, but it was noted earlier for cannon and coastal guns. It stopped using the name 'U.S.' Watervliet Arsenal in 1872.

Curator Green dated the token above definitely to earlier than 1835. The style of eagle, he pointed out, is very similar to that impressed on 1816 muskets, and this style was changed in 1835. He said the piece probably was used as a key tag.

The museum curator said many items such as this counterstamp have surfaced in excavations, etc., and that these were used as key tags, identification discs, etc. by armory personnel.

For a discussion on counterstamped coins found on Army installations, see *Material Culture Study of Fort Bowie* by Dave Herskovicz.

A. C. OF HEBRON
(Associate Church of Hebron)
West Hebron, N.Y.

Rulau-E	Date	Metal	Size				
NY 1060	1807	Lead	sq 22x22mm	—	500.	—	—

A. - C. / H. N in two lines. Rv: 1807. Raised border. Plain edge. (Warner 54)

NY 1062	1824	Lead	oval 24mm	—	750.	—	—

A. C. / OF / HEBRON. Rv: J. I. / JULY 7. / 1824. Raised rim. Plain edge. (Warner 55)

The 'A. - C. H.N' stands for 'Associate Church Hebron'. This church was organized in 1785. The 'J.I.' on the second token is for John Irvine, pastor 1824-1831.

OHIO

P. EVENS
Cincinnati, Ohio

Rulau-E	Date	Metal	Size	VG	F	EF	Unc
Oh 12	(1829-32)	GS	24mm	200.	400.	1000.	—

Rarity 6. (Low 312)

Oh 12A	(1829-32)	Brass	24mm	140.	275.	800.	—

Rarity 7. (Low 312A)

Platt Evens is recorded as having been at these addresses:
1815-19 138 Main St.
1829-40 149 Main St.
1842-23 Main between 3rd & 4th (Evens and Farnham)
See *The Numismatist*, May 1917, page 198, for the Waldo C. Moore research on this issuer.

Issues of Evens signed BALE N.Y. on obverse are from the 1833-1835 period, listed in *Hard Times Tokens* as Low 313, 313A and 313B. An Evens token counterstamped 25 CTS in rectangular depression is also from the Hard Times period.

MUSCROFT

Rulau-E	Date	Metal	Size	VG	F	VF	EF
Oh 20	(?)	Copper	29mm	—	400.	—	—

MUSCROFT (curved)/CIN. ctsp on Connecticut 1787 cent, CON-NFC variety (Miller-43.1-Y) on obverse. Rv: Same stamp on reverse of the coin. There is also a backward N stamped separately on each side. (B&M Hoke Green 1985 sale, lot 2394; Brunk 28990)

E. WOODRUFF
Cincinnati, Ohio

Rulau-E	Date	Metal	Size	VG	F	VF	EF
Oh 50	(1824-28)	Silver	32.5mm	225.	—	350.	—

E. WOODRUFF script in relief within rectangular depression ctsp on U.S. 1805 or 1809 Bust half dollar. (Roy Van Ormer coll; Brunk 44290.)

Enos Woodruff moved from New Jersey to Cincinnati in 1813, buying into silversmith and watchmaker firm of Best & Deterly. This became Woodruff & Deterly 1817. Listed alone at 58 Main St. 1825. Woodruff & White, same address, were listed 1829-34.

The 1809 piece was discovered by Sol Kaplan of Cincinnati, then passed to Roy Van Ormer.

Canadian fur traders seized Astoria from the Americans in the War of 1812. The war provided the Hudson's Bay Company and the North West Company an opportunity to fight American traders in Oregon country. But the U.S. and British governments heard nothing of the transfer and the Treaty of Ghent in Dec. 1814 did not mention Astoria. This painting, by W. Montague Cary, depicts the Canadians in typical fur trader garb of the 19th century's second decade.

OREGON COUNTRY

NORTH WEST COMPANY
Oregon Country

Rulau-E	Date	Metal	Size	G	VG	F	VF
Ore 1	1820	Brass	28mm	—	280.	470.	—
		Laureate bust of George IV right, TOKEN / 1820. Rv: Beaver right, NORTH WEST above, COMPANY below. Plain edge. (RB) (Breton 925)					
Ore 2	1820	Copper	28mm	—	315.	530.	—

These tokens were probably struck in 1820 in Birmingham, England, by John Walker & Co. Their value is "One Made Beaver." All but one known specimen are holed, and all have been found in the region of the lower Columbia River and Umpqua River valleys in Oregon. In 1821 the North West Company merged into the Hudson's Bay Company, another British firm.

The only unholed specimen known was owned by Doug Ferguson of Canada, having been purchased in the 1952 ANA auction. A full story on the North West Company was written by Donald Stewart and appeared in the *TAMS Journal.* An extract of James J. Curto's story on the same firm follows:

The saga of the North West Company starts about 1759, at the fall of Quebec when a group of private traders — French Canadians, American frontiersmen and Scottish Highlanders — first moved into fur trade history. They were called the "Master Pedlars," the Lords of Lakes and Forests.

Always on the offensive, they banded together in 1775 to form The North West Company, to challenge and fight the great Hudson's Bay Company and its Royal Charter. Directed by men who knew every portage and rapid between the St. Lawrence and the Saskatchewan, they immediately emerged as a power great and formidable.

The leaders of the company during the early years were Isaac Todd, James McGill, Benjamin and Joseph Frobisher, Simon McFavish, Robert Grout and Peter Pond.

They were the first white men to cross the North American continent. The Mackenzie River, greatest of northern rivers owes its name to the famous leader of that North West Company expedition, Alexander Mackenzie.

Grand Portage at the head of Lake Superior was the field headquarters of the company, the great depot where trade goods from the East were unloaded to begin their final journey over rivers, lakes, portages, and through forests to their ultimate destination to be exchanged for furs. After 1800 when the international boundary placed Grand Portage in United States Territory, the headquarters was shifted to Kaministiqua, now Fort Williams, Ontario.

With approximately 2,000 employees, its own cargo and freight canoes, organized portage transport crew, lake schooners and ocean ships, it was equipped to carry goods to and from England and to the markets of the Orient. Its profits were estimated during the 15 years of its peak at 1,185,000 pounds.

In 1804, the North West Company attempted to purchase the Hudson's Bay Company outright, offering £103,000. The transaction was not completed chiefly because part of the stock was held by infants and other persons incapable of giving title or making transfer.

The ambition and boldness of the company eventually led to ruthlessness and lawlessness in inherent clashes between traders and settlements. To avoid exposure and prosecution as a result of such lawlessness, the leaders of the North West Company gradually fell apart. With disunion resulting in reduced means, loss of trade and jeopardized credit, the company opened negotiations for a merger with the Hudson's Bay Company in December, 1820. The merger was completed in 1821, ending the saga which lakes and forests will never see the likes of again.

At the time of this merger, the Hudson's Bay Company had 76 posts, the North West Company, 97.

THE BEAVER CLUB

Besides the token, the North West Company contributed another symbol, which also tied the early days of the fur trade to numismatics, its Beaver Club medal.

The Beaver Club was founded in Montreal in 1785. Originally composed of 19 members, it was formed by men of the North West Company, who qualified for membership by having spent at least one winter in the great Northwest.

The club met fortnightly in winter in brilliant and expensive style. Members wore the large gold club medals on club nights, and toasts to the fur trade and all its branches were continuously in order.

PHOENIX BUTTONS
Oregon Country

Rulau-E	Date	Metal	Size	G	VG	F	VF
Ore 5	ca 1832-33	Brass	26mm	25.00	50.00	75.00	—
		Crowned phoenix bird arising from flames at center. JE RENAIS DE MES CENDRES (I rise from my ashes) around; .NO. 27. below. Rv: Blank, with button shank.					

Rulau-E	Date	Metal	Size	G	VG	F	VF
Ore 6	ca 1832-33	Brass	25mm	25.00	50.00	75.00	—
		Similar to last, but crossed cannon under smaller phoenix, and NO. 1 beneath the cannon.					

Rulau-E	Date	Metal	Size	G	VG	F	VF
Ore 7	ca 1832-33	Brass	17mm	25.00	50.00	75.00	—
		Similar to first button described above, but smaller, and NO. 29 under phoenix bird.					

Rulau-E	Date	Metal	Size	G	VG	F
Ore 8	ca 1832-33	Brass	17mm	—	—	—
		Similar to last, but NO. 4 under phoenix.				
Ore 9	ca 1832-33	Brass	17mm	—	—	—
		Similar to last, but NO. 5 under phoenix.				
Ore 10	ca 1832-33	Brass	17mm	—	—	—
		Similar to last, but NO. 7 under phoenix.				
Ore 11	ca 1832-33	Brass	17mm	—	—	—
		Similar to last, but NO. 27 under phoenix.				
Ore 12	ca 1832-33	Brass	16mm	—	—	—
		Somewhat similar to preceding, but BALL-TYPE button; NO. 1 under phoenix.				

Cataloged above are eight tokens in four of the five or more styles of phoenix button known. They are included here, though this is not a button catalog, because of their close association with the Northwest trading activities exemplified by the North West Company tokens. All examples illustrated are from the Byron Johnson collection; in all, some 600 of these buttons of all types are known.

Phoenix buttons are buttons of brass and bronze bearing a crowned phoenix bird, a motto in French, and a numeral. They have been found in quantity in historic sites along the lower Columbia River, and less commonly throughout western North America. The buttons were not made for Napoleon, as is often claimed, but were manufactured by an English firm (probably Bushby of London) circa 1810-1820 for King Henri Christophe of Haiti.

The phoenix and the motto are taken from Christophe's coat of arms; the numbers refer to army regiments. These military uniform buttons were brought to the Northwest about 1832-1833 as trade goods by an independent trader, most likely Nathaniel Wyeth, who probably used uniform coats which he may have obtained earlier when shipping ice to the West Indies, to trade for fish for his salmon packing plant at Fort William on Sauvies Island. The buttons are found most extensively on Sauvies Island, along the Cowlitz and Clackamas rivers, at the falls at Oregon City, and at the Cascades.

They have also been found near California missions at San Juan Capistrano, San Luis Rey, Santa Barbara and Santa Ynez.

It has been ruled out that the Hudson's Bay Company or North West Company brought these buttons in. A few small ball-type buttons were originally silver-plated.

(See "Phoenix Buttons" by Emory Strong in the magazine *American Antiquity* for Jan., 1960)

PENNSYLVANIA

I.N.
(1st United Presbyterian Church)
Butler, Pa.

Rulau-E	Date	Metal	Size	VG	F	EF
Pa 3	(1819-64)	Lead	Rec 16x13mm	—	Rare	—
		I. N. within rectangular frame. Rv: Blank. Plain edge.				

I.N. = Isaiah Niblock, pastor of the First United Presbyterian Church for 45 years, 1819 to 1864. The tokens probably were made early in his pastorship.

Lancaster County

The history of the development of transportation in North America has been marked by metal tokens which have been used to pay toll or fare. The idea of using tokens for this purpose originated in Germany in the 16th century. During the Middle Ages, cities were surrounded by walls, which were closed after dark for the protection of the inhabitants of the cities.

But a means had to be found to identify citizens who, for one reason or another, could not enter the city until night time.

To identify these citizens on nocturnal business, special "gate tokens" were made, which were sold to persons who had to enter through the gates after dark. These tokens also helped pay the salary of the gatekeepers. As walls lost their military significance for protecting cities, the practice of using gate tokens continued as a sort of tax, and all who entered had to purchase tokens to gain access to the town.

Sometimes it was necessary to cross a moat, or stream, to enter the town, and appropriate "bridge toll" tokens were made for this purpose. The first such token was used to pay toll on a bridge at Regensburg in Bavaria in 1549.

With a tradition of using metal tokens for toll payment, the Germans who came to America brought this idea with them. Thus the earliest use of transportation tokens in America was in Lancaster County, Pennsylvania, where an elaborate system of toll roads was built by the "Pennsylvania Dutch" settlers of that beautiful countryside. These earliest transportation tokens used in the United States date from the 1790's.

Other turnpikes in Ohio, Kentucky and Virginia, followed suit. These early toll roads were generally called "turnpikes," because of a row of spikes which faced the traveler and were then turned when he paid his toll: "Turned spikes." Hence, "turnpike."

Frequently these roads were paved with planks, and for that reason were known as "plank roads." The planks provided a bumpy ride, but they were far better than the alternative, which was a mire of mud in the rainy season, and a cloud of dust in the dry season.

C & H TURNPIKE
Lancaster County, Pa.

Rulau-E	Date	Metal	Size	VG	F	VF	EF
Pa 526 Aa	(1806-20)	Br	Oct 27mm	—	200.	—	—
		C & H / TURNPIKE / 1 incused, relief beaded border around Rv: Blank. Plain edge. Issued holed.					
Pa 526 Ab	(1806-20)	Br	Oct 25mm	—	200.	—	—
		Similar, but plain flan. Rv: Blank. Plain edge. issued holed.					

Rulau-E	Date	Metal	Size	VG	F	VF	EF
Pa 526B	(1806-20)	Br	25mm	—	200	—	—
		As last, but 2.					
Pa 526 C	(1806-20)	Brass	24mm	—	200.	—	—
		As 526B, but issued holed.					
Pa 526D	(1806-20)	Br	C-leaf 31mm	—	200.	—	
		As 526 Ab, but numeral 3. Plain flan. Plain edge. Issued holed.					

The Clay & Hinkeltown Turnpike was a part of the Downington, Ephrata & Harrisburg Turnpike, and went into operation sometime in the 1806-1816 period. Toll gates were probably at Clay, Ephrata and Hinkeltown.

L & E TURNPIKE

Rulau-E	Date	Metal	Size	VG	F	VF	EF
526 AA	(c.1816?)	Br	Oct 26mm	—	200.	—	—
		L & E / TURNPIKE / 1 incuse on plain field. Rv: Blank. Plain edge.					

Lancaster & Ephrata Turnpike.

Tokens of the various Lancaster County toll roads were either good for payment, or else were used as zone checks to indicate how much toll (how many gates) was paid, or was due.

L. E. & M. PIKE

Rulau-E	Date	Metal	Size	VG	F	VF	EF
526 BA	(1812-45)	Br	Sq 25mm	—	250.	—	—
		L. E. & M. / 2 / PIKE incuse on plain flan. Rv: Blank. Plain edge. Corners are rounded.					
526 BB	(1812-45)	Br	Sq 23mm	—	250.	—	—
		Similar, but sharp corners. Numeral 4 instead of 2.					
526 BC	(1812-45)	Br	Sq 25x22mm	—	250.	—	—
		Similar, numeral 4, rounded corners.					

Rulau-E	Date	Metal	Size	VG	F	VF	EF
526 BD	(1812-45)	Br	Sq 26x44mm	—	250.	—	—
		Similar to 526 BC, but numeral 5 instead of 4.					
526 BE	(1812-45)	Br	Sq 44x23mm	—	250.	—	—
		L. E. & M. 5 / PIKE incuse on plain field. Rv: H incuse on plain flan. Plain edge.					
526 BE	(1812-45)	Br	Sq. size?	—	250.	—	—
		L. E. & M. PIKE 6 on plain field. Plain edge.					

Lancaster, Elizabethtown & Middletown Turnpike, 26 miles long, opened in 1812 and stopped collecting tolls in 1845. Probably the tokens were already by then out of use. The road, following Route 230 today, was used until 1920.

L. & F. TURNPIKE

Rulau-E	Date	Metal	Size	VG	F	VF	EF
526 CA	(c.1816?)	Brass	32mm	—	200.	—	—
		L. & F. TURNPIKE / G. No. 1 incuse on plain field. Rv: Blank. Plain edge.					
526 CB	(c. 1816?)	Brass	34mm	—	200.	—	—
		Similar, but issued holed.					
526 CC	(c. 1816?)	Brass	36mm	—	200.	—	—
		Similar, issued holed.					

Rulau-E	Date	Metal	Size	VG	F	VF	EF
526 CD	(c.1816?)	Brass	35mm	—	200.	—	—
		Similar, but numeral 2 instead of 1.					

Lancaster & Fruitville Turnpike. The 'G' is 'Gate.'

L. & S. TURNPIKE CO.

Rulau-E	Date	Metal	Size	VG	F	VF	EF
526 DA	(1807-20)	Br	1/2-sp 34x25mm	—	150.	—	—
		L. & S. TURNPIKE CO. / 1 incuse on plain flan. Plain edge.					
526 DB	(1807-20)	Br	Rec 39x26mm	—	150.	—	—
		Similar. Clipped corners. Numeral 4 instead of 1.					
526 DC	(1807-20)	Br	1/2-sp 35x25mm	—	150.	—	—
		Similar to 526 DB. Clipped corners.					

Lancaster & Susquehanna Turnpike was incorporated in 1794 and opened in 1807. There were four toll gates: the road went from Lancaster to Wright's Ferry (now Columbia) on the Susquehanna River. In 1918 the state of Pennsylvania took over the road.

L. & W. T. CO.

Rulau-E	Date	Metal	Size	Gate	VG	F	EF
Pa 526FA	(?)	Brass	25mm	2	—	—	200.

Lancaster & Washingtonboro Turnpike Company. This previously unlisted token and new issuer was lot 1568 in the Kirtley Greater New York sale of May, 1992. The incuse lettering is from a prepared punch.

LANC. & E. TURNPIKE

Rulau-E	Date	Metal	Size	Gate	VG	F	EF
526 EA	(c.1816?)	Brass	31mm	1	—	125.	—
526 EB	(c.1816?)	Br	Obl 34x29mm	1	—	150.	—
526 EC	(c.1816?)	Br	1/2-Sp 39x35mm	1	—	150.	—
526 ED	(c.1816?)	Br	1/2-Sp 33x29mm	1	—	150.	—
526 EE	(c. 1816?)	Br	Sq 30mm	2	—	150.	—
526 EF	(c. 1816?)	Br	1/2-Sp 40x32mm	2	—	150.	—
526 EG	(c.1816?)	Brass	30mm	2	—	150.	—
526 EH	(c.1816?)	Br	Sq 33mm	2	—	150.	—
526 EI	(c.1816?)	Br	1/2-Sp 32x28mm	3	—	150.	—

Lancaster & Elizabethtown Turnpike.

MY. MA. PIKE
Lancaster County, Pa.

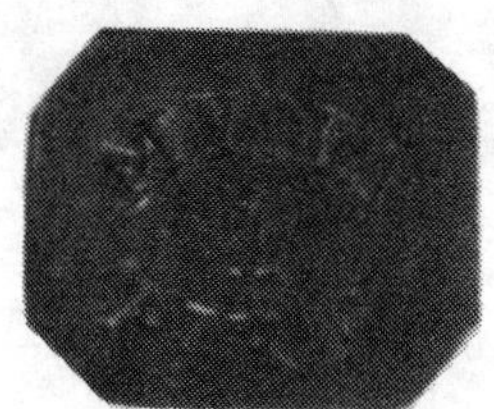

Rulau-E	Date	Metal	Size	Gate	VG	F	EF
Pa 526 HA	(1815-22)	Br	Obl 29x24mm	1	—	250.	—
Pa 526 HB	(1815-22)	Br	Obl 31x27mm	2	—	250.	—
Pa 526 HC	(1815-22)	Br	Obl 30x28mm	2	—	250.	—

Mount Joy & Marietta Pike opened in 1815 and continued in operation at least until 1822.

I. AITKEN
Philadelphia, Pa.

Rulau-E	Date	Metal	Size	VG	F	VF	EF
Pa 17	(ca 1828)	Silver	20mm	—	80.00	—	120.
		I AITKEN in relief within rectangular depression ctsp on Spanish-American 1-real, worn. (B&M 1986 Von Stetten sale, lot 454; Charles Kirtley sale 19, lot 454; Brunk 460)					
Pa 18	(ca 1828)	Copper	23mm	—	80.00	—	120.
		Similar ctsp on U.S. Half cent. Dates examined: 1826, 1828. Only 2 known.					

John Aitken (1768-1856) was a gifted artisan — goldsmith, silversmith, clockmaker, musical instrument manufacturer and copperplate engraver, who began plying his trade in Philadelphia in 1785. He appears in directories 1785-1814 but not afterward. The pieces which carry his hallmark (an exact match with that illustrated in Belden) may have been made after his retirement, or by a successor.

P. APPLE / (Eagle)

Rulau-E	Date	Metal	Size	VG	F	VF	EF
Pa 19	(1820's)	Copper	28.5mm	50.00	—	75.00	—
		P. APP(LE) / (Eagle displayed) / PHILa in relief within shaped depression ctsp on copper disc. (Bosco April 1989 sale, lot 103)					
Pa 19A	(1820's)	Copper	29mm	50.00	—	75.00.	—
		Similar ctsp on U.S. Large cent. Examined: 1810, 1818, worn date. (Brunk 1045)					

Philip Apple, one of America's best-known early coppersmiths, was in business in Philadelphia 1806-1839. It is known he also maintained a shop in West Chester, Pa. in 1826 and perhaps earlier and later.

Apple's signature appears on copper teakettles, copper mugs and other handmade products. His published signatures (both in relief within depressions) include:

P. APPLE

P. APPLE / (Eagle displayed) / PHILa

One W. Apple also signed copper products about the same early period, and coppersmith Jacob Apple was active in Philadelphia about 1852.

ASHMEAD

Rulau-E	Date	Metal	Size	VG	F	VF	EF
Pa 20	(1820?)	Copper	29mm	75.00	—	125.	—
		ASHMEAD / PHILA ctsp on U.S. 1806 Large cent. (Hallenbeck 1.761; Brunk 1240)					
Pa 21	(?)	Copper	29mm	75.00	—	125.	—
		ASHMEAD ctsp on U.S. 1818 Large cent. (Brunk 1230)					

William Ashmead was a silversmith active circa 1797-1810 or longer. Ashmead does not appear in the 1819 or 1823 directories.

The second counterstamp above, Pa 21, may possibly not be connected.

J. BEAM

Rulau-E	Date	Metal	Size	VG	F	VF	EF
Pa 23	(1818-22)	Copper	29mm	—	75.00	—	125.
		J. BEAM ctsp on U.S. 1818 Large cent. Only 3 known. (Brunk 2865)					

Jacob C. Beam was active as a silversmith circa 1818-1822 in Philadelphia.

J. BOWER
Philadelphia, Pa.?

Rulau-E	Date	Metal	Size	VG	F	VF	EF
Pa 30	(?)	Silver	27mm	75.00	—	125.	—
		J. BOWER in relief within rect. depression ctsp on Spanish-American 2-reales, date worn off (circa 1775). Also on the same side (the obverse) is J.B. in relief within oval depression ctsp twice. (Van Ormer sale 2545; Brunk 4610)					

The attribution is tentative but logical. The stamps are typical of the silversmith hallmarks of the period, and there was a Bower family of craftsmen working in Philadelphia circa 1790-1833. Known family members were Michael Bower (1790-1800) and C. Bower (1832-33); the latter used a BOWER-relief-within-rectangle punch, according to Ralph & Terry Kovel in *A Directory of American Silver, Pewter and Silver Plate.*

BROWNE & SEAL

Rulau-E	Date	Metal	Size	VG	F	VF	EF
Pa 35	(1810-11)	Copper	29mm	—	—	125.	—

BROWNE & SEAL ctsp on U.S. 1803 Large cent. (Brunk 5575)

Silversmiths Liberty Browne and William Seale Jr. formed a short-lived partnership in 1810-1811. Their marks are given in Belden, Ensko and Kovel.

R. DUNLEVY

Rulau-E	Date	Metal	Size	VG	F	VF	EF
Pa 60	(1831)	Copper	29mm	—	125.	—	—

R. DUNLEVY in relief within rect. depression ctsp twice on obverse of U.S. 1803 Large cent. (Frank Kovacs coll.; Brunk 12400)

Robert Dunlevy was a silversmith active about 1830-37. He was located at Lodge Alley in 1832-37. From 1843-46 he was part of the Dunlevy & Dowell firm (George G. Dowell), and from 1847-50 in Dunlevy & Wise (George K. Wise).

HARTFORD

Rulau-E	Date	Metal	Size	VG	F	VF	EF
Pa 65	(1830's)	Copper	29mm	100.	—	150.	—
		HARTFORD in relief within rect. depression ctsp on 1787 Fugio cent, very worn. (Levine June 1985 sale, lot 1285; Brunk 18510)					
Pa 66	(1830's)	Copper	29mm	100.	—	150.	—
		Similar ctsp on U.S. Large cent. Examined: 1819, 1838. Only 2 known.					

It seems likely this is the silversmith's hallmark of a successor of George Hartford who had been active in Philadelphia about 1794.

W. LEVIS

Rulau-E	Date	Metal	Size	VG	F	VF	EF
Pa 70	(1819)	Copper	29mm	75.00	—	—	125.
		W. LEVIS in relief within curving ribbon-shaped depression ctsp on U.S. Large cent. Dates examined: 1817, 1819. Only 3 known. (Brunk 24380; Hallenbeck 12.504)					
Pa 71	(1819)	Copper	28mm	—	125.	—	
		Similar ctsp on Spanish-American quarter-real (cuartilla), probably Mexico Mint. Apprarently unique. (Donald Partrick coll.)					

Rulau-E	Date	Metal	Size	VG	F	VF	EF
Pa 72	(1819)	Silver	27mm	75.00	—	—	150.
		Similar ctsp on Spanish-American 2-reales. Dates examined: 1773-Mo-FM, 1779, 1781-Mo, 1790, 1795, 1796, 1802. There are 7 known. (Chester Krause coll.; Duffield 1365)					
Pa 75	(1819)	Silver	32.5mm	100.	—	—	200.
		Similar ctsp on U.S. Capped Bust half dollar. Examined: 1807, 1818. Only 2 known. (Kenneth Bressett coll.; Duffield 1410)					
Pa 80	(1836-37)	Copper	29mm	75.00	—	—	125.
		W. LEVIS in relief within rectangular depression ctsp on U.S. Large cent. Dates examined: 1819, 1827, 1833, 1836. Only 6 known. (Rich Hartzog coll.)					

Rulau-E	Date	Metal	Size	VG	F	VF	EF
Pa 81	(1836-37)	Silver	19mm	75.00	—	125.	—
		Similar ctsp on U.S. Capped Bust dime. Dates examined: 1830, 1835, 1836. Only 4 known. (Van Ormer sale 2731)					

William Levis has long been a man of mystery. In 1796-97 an apparently earlier William Levis is listed as a paper maker at 6 No. 8th St.

Then William Levis, born 1785, fails to appear in the Philadelphia directories for 1816, 1819 and 1823. Despite the absence of listings in 1816-23 directories, he functioned as a silversmith and applied his ribbon-like hallmark to coins about 1819.The same man (or a son?) appears in directories in 1832-33 as a currier at 292 Filbert. We meet him next in 1836-37 at 228 No. 3rd St., where he is listed as an oil and leather merchant. (His home in 1836-37 was at 242 Filbert.) Levis died in 1842.

The Levis stamps are quite important, and research into their provenance continues.

NORTHERN LIBERTY FIRE CO. NO. 1

Rulau-E	Date	Metal	Size	F	VF	EF	Unc
Pa 85	1833	S/WM	Oval, 22 by 29mm	—	—	—	Rare
		Partially nude Miss Liberty half-length facing, 13 stars above. Rv: NORTHERN LIBERTY FIRE CO. No 1. / INSTITUTED / -*- / MAY 1, 1756. / INCORPORATED / MAR 18TH / .1833. Plain edge. (In the ANS collection)					

Membership medalet of one of the earliest firefighting companies in North America.

PHILADELPHIA MUSEUM

Rulau-E	Date	Metal	Size	VG	F	EF	Unc
Pa 398	1821	Copper	32mm	40.00	70.00	200.	—
		Bust left, CHARLES WILLSON PEALE FOUNDER 1784. Rv: ADMIT / THE / BEARER within wreath. PHILADELPHIA MUSEUM INCORPORATED 1821 around. (Wright 6; Julian UN-23)					
Pa 397	1821	Silver	32mm	—	—	—	—
		Same as 397.					
Pa 394	1821	Copper	32mm	—	—	—	—
		Similar to NY 397, but blank space within wreath on reverse. (Julian UN-22)					

Rulau-E	Date	Metal	Size	VG	F	EF	Unc
Pa 395	1821	Copper	32mm	—	—	400.	—
		As 394, but number incused inside the wreath. (Bowers & Merena Nov. 1990 sale, lot 4197)					
Pa 396	1821	Gilt Copper	32mm	—	—	—	—
		Same as 394.					

Rulau-E	Date	Metal	Size	VG	F	EF	Unc
Pa 399	1821 (1830)	Silver	32mm	—	—	700.	—
		As NY 394. 12 known. (Freeman 414; Storer 2780; Julian UN-22)					
Pa 400	1821 (1830)	Gold	32mm	—	—	Unique	—
		As NY 394. Only 1 struck. (Freeman 414a)					

Designed by Christian Gobrecht and struck at the U.S. Mint, Philadelphia, about 1830. The silver and gold medals were designed as an award for service to the Museum or for advancement of science, in memory of the late founder.

In May, 1833, silver medals were presented to Mint Director Dr. Samuel Moore, Mint Engraver William Kneass and Mint Chief Coiner Adam Eckfeldt. Also each of the five museum directors and two former directors — Dr. Robert Patterson and Joseph Parker Norris — were to receive silver medals. Each was engraved with the name of the recipient. On the John Work Garrett specimen at Johns Hopkins University in Baltimore, the engraving within the wreath reads; TO / J.P. NORRIS.

The May, 1833, authorization awarded the single gold version to Silas E. Burroughs, who helped finance the 1831-32 Titian Peale expedition to Colombia.

CHARLES WILLSON PEALE

Charles Willson Peale was perhaps the most celebrated portrait painter of his day in the U.S. Many of the men in public life of Revolutionary times were painted by him, and he painted George Washington six times — in 1772, 1778, 1781, 1783, 1786 and 1795.

He was born of English parents at Chestertown, Kent County, Maryland, on April 16, 1741. He moved to Annapolis in 1762 where he carried on trade as saddler, harnessmaker, silversmith, watchmaker and engraver. In 1767, at age 26, he received instructions in painting from Hesselius of Annapolis, and afterwards from Copley in Boston and West in England. He moved to Philadelphia in 1776, where he got caught up in patriotic fervor and became a captain of volunteers under Washington, fighting at Trenton and Germantown.

In 1784 Peale opened his museum at his residence, corner Third and Lombard streets in Philadelphia. He displayed his own large collection of paintings, and added many natural curiosities. In 1794 the Philosophical Society granted him the use of its Hall on Fifth Street below Chestnut, and the museum was transferred there in Sept. 1794. Peale became also a taxidermist and maker of dentures, including, reportedly, a set for George Washington.

By act of the Pennsylvania Legislature of March 17, 1802, Peale was authorized to occupy the east room of the lower story of the State House (now known as Independence Hall), and all the upper story. In 1809 Peale petitioned the Legislature for perpetual use of the upper part of the State House for his museum. At this time the Philadelphia Museum contained 200 stuffed animals, 1,000 specimens of birds, 4,000 specimens of insects, a mineral collection, cabinets of serpents, fishes, etc., plus over 100 portraits of statesmen and soldiers painted by Peale. There was also a skeleton of a mammoth excavated in Ulster County, N.Y.

In Feb., 1821, the museum was incorporated as The Philadelphia Museum, the incorporators being Pierce Butler, Raphael Peale, Rembrandt Peale, Coleman Sellers and Rubens Peale. Only Butler was not a Peale family member. In 1827 the museum was removed to the Philadelphia Arcade on the north side of Chestnut Street between 6th and 7th streets, where it remained until 1838. In that year it was moved to the northeast corner of 9th and Sansom streets, in a new building which cost $130,000 to erect. The company's enterprise was not successful from 1838 on, and in 1844 the museum was closed and the collections sold.

Peale died in Philadelphia on Feb. 27, 1827, aged 85 and active until the end. He had six sons and named five of them after painters — Raphael, Rembrandt, Vandyke, Titian and Rubens. His eldest daughter was named Angelica Kauffman Peale.

Rubens Peale established his own museum in New York City in 1825. (See Peale's Museum tokens under New York.)

The sixth son, Franklin Peale (named after Benjamin Franklin, whom C.W. Peale admired almost as much as he did painters), was appointed melter and refiner of the Philadelphia Mint in Jan., 1836. In 1839 he succeeded Adam Eckfeldt as chief coiner at the mint.

After the Philadelphia Museum was incorporated in 1821, admission tokens were issued with Charles Willson Peale's portrait on them. Some of the token numbers which have survived in collections include 1, 15, 18, 19, 22, 30, 41, 42, 43, 46, 48 and 53. Duffield thought there were about 50 numbered tokens distributed by management as passes to special friends, with the ADMIT THE BEARER type probably sold by annual subscription.

In the Bushnell sale one piece in silver was offered, engraved TO J.P. NORRIS. (This piece later went to Johns Hopkins University.) In the same Bushnell sale a lead trial piece was also offered.

Charles Willson Peale also opened a museum in Baltimore in 1784, and this passed into the hands of Charles Peale Polk and closed in 1796. No tokens are known from this institution.

Soon after 1796 Raphael and Rembrandt Peale opened the Baltimore Museum in the same building as the closed institution. In 1813 Rembrandt Peale erected a building on Holiday Street north of Lexington in Baltimore for a museum, which was called Peale's Museum. Many years later this building became City Hall. These institutions also had no known tokens issued.

In 1831-1832 Titian Peale led an expedition to Colombia in search of natural curiosities.

W.D. RAPP

Rulau-E	Date	Metal	Size	VG	F	VF	EF
Pa 420	(1832-35)	Copper	23mm	—	65.00	—	100.

W. D. RAPP in relief within rect. depression ctsp on early-type U.S. Half cent. Dates examined: 1804, 1807, 1809. Only 4 pieces known. (B&M Hoke Green 1985 sale, lots 2399-2400; Brunk 33530L; B & M Schenkel 1990 sale, lot 4135)

Pa 421	(1832-35)	Copper	23mm	—	55.00	—	90.00

Similar ctsp on Capped Bust-type U.S. Half cent. Dates examined: 1819, 1821, 1826, 1828, 1829, 1832. At least 6 known. (Kovacs coll.)

Pa 422	(1832-35)	Copper	29mm	—	75.00	—	110.

Similar ctsp on U.S. Large cent. Examined: 1808, 1810, 1822, 1829. Only 5 known.

Pa 423	(1832-35)	Silver	27mm	—	135.	—	—

Similar ctsp on Spanish-American 1774 2-reales. (Brunk coll.)

This is the hallmark of silversmith and watchcase maker William D. Rapp, active in Philadelphia from 1828 to about 1850. In 1837 he was located at 256 Race Street. For some reason, Rapp preferred Half cents for his advertising counterstamps.

RICKETTS' CIRCUS

Original

Restrike

Rulau-E	Date	Metal	Size	F	VF	EF	Unc
Pa 430	(1793-99)	Copper	29mm	—	—	—	Ex. Rare

Crested shield of arms within palm and olive branch. Rv: RICKETTS'S / CIRCUS at center, festoon of leaves above, oak branches below. Dentilated rims on both sides. Plain edge. (Wright 894)

Rulau-E	Date	Metal	Size	F	VF	EF	Unc
Pa 429	(1793-99)	Bronze	29mm	—	3500.	—	5000.

Similar to 430, but reeded edge. (Zeddies-Wright-Betts specimen sold Nov. 1990)

Pa 428	(1793-99)	Silver	29mm	—	—	—	Ex. Rare

Similar to 430, but reeded edge.

The arms shown on the tokens are those of Sir Cornwallis Ricketts, of The Elms, Gloucester. The arms are: Two swords on a chevron azure. Three roses, two in chief, one in base, on a field or (gold, or ermine). The crest is an arm wielding a scimitar. Palm branch on left, olive branch right.

John Bill Ricketts, a Scottish horseman, emigrated to America in 1792. He first appeared in Philadelphia, where he erected a building for a riding school for instruction of ladies and gentlemen, which opened in October 1792. Later he erected a circus for equestrian performances which was opened April, 1793.

Ricketts' Circus was attended by fashionable people of the day, and by notables — George Washington on April 22, 1793, and French ambassador Citizen Genet on June 5, 1793.

On May 12, 1795 Ricketts opened at a new amphitheater he built in Boston (box seats $1, pits 50 cents). Later he returned to Philadelphia, where he remained active until his circus was destroyed by fire Dec. 17, 1799. Afterward he attempted to retrieve his fortunes but ill luck dogged him and he returned to England.

The Ricketts' Circus tokens most likely are from the 1793-1795 days in Philadelphia. A May 15, 1793, newspaper ad tells us the box seats were $1 and the pits 50 cents, the same as he charged later in Boston. Ricketts was a skilled equestrian, and in one June, 1793, performance he sponsored a Mr. Blanchard who dropped a dog, cat and squirrel by parachute from a balloon one mile high. The animals survived! It was the first parachute test in North America, according to a Philadelphia newspaper.

In 1795 an advertisement appeared in a New York paper for Ricketts' Amphitheatre, which stood on three lots north of White Street on Broadway and was used as a circus and for panoramic and theatrical shows in New York City. By 1800, erection of buildings began on this site, such as Florence's Hotel, and the Concert Hall at 404 Broadway. (See *The Greatest Street in the World, Broadway* by Stephen Jenkins. New York, 1911, pages 155-167).

The Ricketts' tokens were a special study of the American Numismatic Society, which published researches on them in 1868 and 1878. *The Numismatist* tied all this research together in a 1912 article. They also were examined in Robert Julian's 1977 book, *Medals of the United States Mint.*

Franklin Peale, the coiner, in 1841 began a register of the dies in possession of the U.S. Mint at Philadelphia, and this included the Ricketts' Circus dies. Julian concludes that the tokens may have been made at the mint, engraver unknown, in the early 1790's. We favor 1793 as the date of mintage.

Shown above is an old print of Ricketts, mounted on his horse Cornplanter, leaping over another horse, Silva. The scroll reads: WE NEVER SHALL LOOK UPON HIS LIKE AGAIN. "Never" seems a long time, but it was undoubtedly effective advertising in 1793.

SOCIETATIS PHILALETHICAE (Truth-lovers Society)

Rulau-E	Date	Metal	Size	VG	F	VF	EF
Pa 440	1822	Silver	Oval, 43x67mm	—	—	300.	550.

The oval badge is contained in a mirror-like frame. Obverse: (all engraved incuse) JOANNES / EWEN / SOCIETATIS / PHILALETHICAE / SOCIUS / HONORARIUS / VI. APRILIS / MDCCCXXII. / O MAGNA VIS VERITATIS. (John Ewen, honorary member, Truth-lovers Society, 6 April 1822, Oh great strength of the Truth). Rv: Hallmark: WL.

The hallmark WL is for William Little III, silversmith in Philadelphia, 1813-1819 or later.

This badge is previously unpublished; it first appeared in the NASCA Providence collection sale, July 16-17, 1981.

WHARTENBY

Rulau-E	Date	Metal	Size	VG	F	VF	EF
Pa 442	(1829)	Copper	29mm	150.	—	275.	—

WHARTENBY / PHI A. in relief within two separate rectangular depressions ctsp on U.S. 1825 Large cent. (Hartzog 1982 sale; Brunk 42785; Rulau coll.)

Thomas Whartenby was a Philadelphia silversmith of note from 1811 to 1850 or later. The mark resembles his hallmark. Some of his known addresses are:

1815-16	196 So. 3rd and also 117 Cedar
1812-18	(Whartenby & Bumm)
1818-19	117 Spruce
1822-23	33 No. 3rd
1832-33	173 Pine
1836-37	Ridge Road near Buttonwood

The firm became Thomas Whartenby & Co. in 1847-52. The piece is apparently unique.

T. WILDES

Rulau-E	Date	Metal	Size	VG	F	VF	EF
Pa 445	(1829-33)	Copper	29mm	75.00	—	125.	—

T. WILDES in relief within scroll-shaped depression ctsp on U.S. Large cent. Examined: 1825, date worn off. Two specimens reported. (Brunk 43420)

Thomas Wildes was a pewterer in Philadelphia 1829-1833, then in New York City 1833-1840. His N.Y. business address was Hester at Second St. The mark was his registered "touch" (pewterer's mark).

Wildes' surviving pewter and britannia handcrafts, such as lamps and candlesticks, are uniformly scarce.

Wildes, or a successor, was responsible for some 1855-era counterstamped coins with a crowned X (see under U.S. Merchant Tokens section).

J. WINNER
Philadelphia, Pa.

Rulau-E	Date	Metal	Size	VG	F	VF	EF
Pa 450	(1818)	Copper	23mm	—	75.00	—	125.
		J. WINNER ctsp on U.S. Half cent. Examined: 1805. (Kurt Krueger coll.; Brunk 43980)					
Pa 451	(1818)	Copper	29mm	—	75.00	—	125.
		Similar ctsp on U.S. Large cent. Examined: 1807, 1817, 1836. (Donald Partrick coll.; Rulau-E Mav 60F)					
Pa 451A	(1818)	Copper	29mm	—	—	—	125.
		Similar ctsp on England Conder token of the 1790's.					

James Winner, gunsmith, during 1808-1814 was part of the Winner Nippes & Co. gunmaking firm, and then became part of Winner Nippes & Steinman. Both were Philadelphia firms.

RHODE ISLAND

J. SHAW
Newport, R.I.

Rulau-E	Date	Metal	Size	VG	F	VF	EF
RI 15	(1802-19)	Copper	29mm	—	—	—	200.

J. SHAW in relief within toothed rect. depression ctsp on obverse of U.S. 1800-03 Large cent, date worn off. Rv: Illegible relief inscription within toothed rect. depression ctsp twice on reverse of coin. (Rulau coll.; Brunk 36243)

John A. Shaw was a silversmith, jeweler and fancy goods dealer active in the 1802-1819 period in Newport, Rhode Island. He signed his works variously as I. A. SHAW and J. SHAW. (See Belden pg. 379)

E. B.
(Ezekiel Burr)
Providence, R.I.

Rulau-E	Date	Metal	Size	VG	F	VF	EF
RI 40	(1820)	Silver	27mm	—	125.	—	175.

E B in relief in rectangular punch ctsp on Spanish-American 1794-LME-IJ 2-reales. (Mayfield coll. in 1928, examined and reportedly okayed by Burdette G. Johnson, Howland Wood and Farran Zerbe; sold 1932 to Wayte Raymond for about $300; in Merkin auction of Nov. 1968, lot 521, it was offered by Don Medcalf for $3500; Brunk 12720). Also known on 1750 2-reales.

Rulau-E	Date	Metal	Size	VG	F	VF	EF
RI 41	(1820)	Silver	26mm	—	125.	—	175.

Similar ctsp on U.S. 1811 Bust quarter dollar. Weight 95 grains.

Rulau-E	Date	Metal	Size	VG	F	VF	EF
RI 41A	(1820)	Silver	32.5mm	—	200.	—	—

Similar ctsp on U.S. 1819 Bust half dollar.

Rulau-E	Date	Metal	Size	VG	F	VF	EF
RI 42	(1820)	Silver	40mm	—	300.	—	—

Similar ctsp on U.S. 1799 Bust silver dollar.

This stamp had previously been thought to be one of Ephraim Brasher of New York, accounting for the Depression-era $300 price tag and 1968 price of $3500. However, the punch matches no known punch of Brasher but does match one of those of Burr, according to Louise C. Belden and the Flint & Fales silversmith reference.

Burr (1765-1846) was a silversmith, goldsmith, tax collector and deputy sheriff, in business 1792-1820. He used EB in rectangle and EB script in oval punches on his silverware.

GEO. G. CLARK
Providence, R.I.

Rulau-E	Date	Metal	Size	VG	F	VF	EF
RI 49	(1831-34)	Silver	27mm	100.	—	150.	—

GEO. G. CLARK in relief within rect. depression ctsp on Spanish-American 1821-Zs 2-reales. (Van Ormer sale 2592)

George G. Clark practiced silversmithy in Providence 1813-37, associated with Christopher Burr (active 1800-25), Henry G. Mumford (1813), Jabez Gorham (1813-47) and William Hadwen (1816-28).

This attribution is by Q. David Bowers. The stamp probably was not impressed before the early 1830's, possibly by the Clark & Anthony firm of Hard Times tokens fame.

Counterstamps G.G. CLARK on 1803 and 1832 Large cents, and GEO. CLARK on worn Large cent, may be connected.

SOUTH CAROLINA

J. H. BAPTIS..(et al)
Charleston, S.C.

Rulau-E	Date	Metal	Size	VG	F	VF	EF
SC 3	(ca 1812)	Copper	23mm	—	100.	—	—

J. H. BAPTIS.. in relief within rect. depression ctsp on reverse of U.S. 1809 Half cent (the stamp was too large for the coin and ran off its diameter incomplete). M. BISHOP ctsp on the coin's obverse. (B&M Hoke Green 1985 sale, lot 2401; Brunk 2325)

These two stamps are probably unrelated. The hallmark-type stamp may be that of Jean Baptiste, silversmith active in Charleston circa 1807 and later.

CHARLES TOWN SOCIAL CLUB
Charleston, S.C.

Rulau-E	Date	Metal	Size	VG	F	VF	EF
SC 1	1763	Sil	Oval 33x37mm	—	—	—	Rare

Two men in 18th century gentlemen's garb shaking hands in a field, a tree at left, church and houses in right back ground. VINCTI AMICITIA above. (Legend in Latin means "Bound in Friendship"). Rv: SOCIAL CLUB / INSTITUTED / CHARLES TOWN / SOUTH CAROLINA / VI OCTOBER / MDCCLXIII. (Betts 508)

Rulau-E	Date	Metal	Size	VG	F	VF	EF
SC 2	1763	Bze	Oval 33x37mm	—	—	—	—

Same as last. Betts believed all bronze pieces were restrikes off original dies.

This little-known member's medal was struck on the Charles Town Social Club being instituted on Oct. 6, 1763. Specimens appeared in the Hollis sale (1871), the Bushnell sale, and the Chapmans' sale of the Warner collection. It was written up in the *American Journal of Numismatics*, Volumes V and XVII, and illustrated by a line drawing in Betts' 1894 catalog.

HIBERNIAN SOCIETY
Charleston, S.C.

Rulau-E	Date	Metal	Size	VG	F	VF	EF
SC 5	(1763?)	Silver	**	—	—	—	Rare

** Elliptical, ringed for suspension.

Harp of six strings formed of a winged female figure with fish's tail. Above: HIBERNIAN)I(SOCIETY. Below: CHARLESTON. SC. Rv: Harp intaglio. Both sides are engraved on a silver planchet. All devices and lettering are cut out from the flan. Plain edge. (Betts 507)

The size is not known. This is more a bangle than a medalet, apparently.

PRESBYTERIAN CHURCH
Charleston, S.C.

Rulau-E	Date	Metal	Size	VG	F	VF	EF
SC 8	1800	Silver	28mm	—	Rare	25.00	—

Chalice and paten on Communion table, THIS DO IN REMEMBRANCE OF ME above. Rv: Burning bush, NEC TAMEN CONSUMEBATUR (nevertheless it was not consumed) above. On edge: PRESBYTERIAN CHURCH OF CHARLESTON, S.C. 1800.

The tokens are hand engraved. In the Civil War (1864), Union soldiers took the church's silver tokens, thinking they were some kind of Confederate money. Only about 20 pieces have survived.

SC 10	(1830's)	WM	28mm	—	Scarce	—	—

Similar to last, but struck from dies rather than engraved. Under the table, in four lines: PRESBYTERIAN / CHURCH / OF / CHARLESTON S.C. 1800. Under the burning bush: R. LOVETT N.Y.

This latter token was cut by Robert Lovett of New York for what was evidently a greatly expanded church membership later in the century. Though this piece may be from the wrong time frame for this catalog, we thought it best to include it here. This piece may have been struck in the 1830-1850 period.

TENNESSEE

H. & I. KIRKMAN
Nashville, Tenn.

Rulau-E	Date	Metal	Size	VG	F	VF	EF
Tenn 59	(1828-32)	Copper	28mm	350.	750.	—	2000.
		Anvil and implements at center, H & I KIRKMAN above, NASHVILLE TENE. below. Rv: H & I KIRKMAN / NASHVILLE TENE / IMPORTERS OF / HARDWARE / AND CULTERY.					
Tenn 59A	(1828-32)	Brass	28mm	350.	750.	—	2000.
		As 59.					
Tenn 60	(1828-32)	Silver Copper	28mm	—	—	—	Unique
		As 59. A VF 59A realized $1700 in the Nov. 1990 Bowers and Merena sale, lot 4200.					

Both Adams and Miller (see Bibliography) misspelled this name as KIRKHAM, possibly relying on auction catalog descriptions. However, Wayte Raymond accurately pictured the token in his 1942 *The Standard Catalogue of United States Coins and Tokens.* The specimen pictured above is the John Work Garrett specimen sold by Bowers & Ruddy Galleries in 1980.

Thomas Kirkman was in business in Nashville as early as 1809. It is believed the 'H. & I.' were Hugh K. Kirkman and John Kirkman, sons of Thomas and Ellen Kirkman. The token could date from the 1828-32 period, based on its fabric; directory evidence is not possible to obtain.

The first directory for Nashville was printed in 1853. By that time Hugh Kirkman was in business for himself as an ironmaster at 41 North Summer St., and the H. & I. Kirkman hardware and cutlery firm had been succeeded by Kirkman & Ellis (John Kirkman and James Ellis), hardware & cutlery, at 34 Public Square. The K&E firm dissolved about 1858, Ellis becoming a dry goods merchant at High & Gay streets and moving to 34 Broad St. in 1860.

John Kirkman became a banker in 1858 (president, Union Bank of Tennessee, 1858-65, and vice president and later president, Third National Bank of Nashville, 1865-73 or later).

Ellen Kirkman, mother of Hugh and John, was immortalized in 1837 when the Johnson-Rayburn combine named a new 560-ton river steamer the *Ellen Kirkman.* She was built at New Albany and plied the Nashville-New Orleans route.

Kirkman Street in 1868 ran from College to Cherry, the next street south of Demonbreun.

(For a fuller account of the Kirkmans, see Russ Rulau's "Hunting an Elusive Tennessean in Salt Lake City" which appeared in *Numismatic News* for 1984.)

VERMONT

BRINSMAID'S
Burlington, Vermont

Rulau-E	Date	Metal	Size	VG	F	VF	EF
Vt 3	(1830?)	Silver	40.1mm	—	500.	—	—
		BRINSMAID'S in relief within rectangular recessed punch ctsp on U.S. 1795 silver dollar (Johnson & Jensen auction of March 28, 1982, lot 70; Brunk 5230)					

Abram Brinsmaid was born in 1770 in Great Barrington, Mass. He died in Burlington, Vt. in 1811. The silversmith's mark used on this piece, by him and his successors, is widely known among collectors of antique silverware.

The only known specimen occurs on an About Good (well worn) dollar of Bolender type 8, reverse 7, with a bold counterstamp. It was consigned to the Nathan Eglit sale conducted by Johnson & Jensen in 1982.

A successor firm, Pangborn & Brinsmaid, was active circa 1833. An earlier firm, Brinsmaid & Hildreth, used the BRINSMAID'S mark circa 1830. This is the likeliest issuer.

According to Belden, the hallmark on the token was used as late as 1843-54.

Kenneth L. Hallenbeck in "Hallmarks on U.S. Large Cents" (*TAMS Journal* for June, 1964) reported the BRINSMAID'S hallmark on a teaspoon made of coin silver, illustrating it there.

Following the BRINSMAID'S rectangular depression is a series of three small depressions, containing, respectively, B / (animal walking right) / D.

Hallenbeck cites Howard Pitcher Okie, *Old Silver and Old Sheffield Plate*, Garden City, N.Y., 1928. Beginning about 1830, the symbol 'D' was used to indicate coin silver, that is, silver .900 fine, the same as used in U.S. silver coinage.

Some of the published hallmarks of the Brinsmaid family include:

A BRINSMAID	Abraham Brin(d)smaid, 1815
B&H BRINSMAID'S	Brinsmaid & Hildreth, 1830
P&B	Pangborn & Brinsmaid, 1833
(none)	Henry Brinsmaid (Rochester, N.Y.), 1847-50

VIRGINIA

J.A.
(John Adam Jr.)
Alexandria, Va.

Rulau-E	Date	Metal	Size	VG	F	VF	EF
Va 100	(1810-23)	Copper	29mm	—	—	—	100.
		Script monogram JA in relief within square depression ctsp on U.S. 1800 Large cent. (Hallenbeck collection)					

John Adam Jr. (1780-1846) was a silversmith of Alexandria, successor of his father John Adam (1755-1798). John Jr. used this hallmark and several others: JA in rectangle; J. ADAM within irregular rectangle; I. ADAM in rectangle.

The Adam family continued as silversmiths in Alexandria until the early 20th century, the last active member being Charles Adam (1848-1925).

RIGAULT (&) DAWSON
Gloucester County, Va.

Rulau-E	Date	Metal	Size	VG	F	VF	EF
Va 1	1714	Brass	24mm	—	—	36,000	—
		Building (courthouse?) in center, GLOUCESTER COURT HOUSE VIRGINIA / XII around. Rv: Large 5-pointed star at center, RIGAULT DAWSON . ANNO DOM. 1714. Plain edge. (RB)					
Va 3	1715	Brass	24mm	—	—	Unique	—
		As last, but 1715. Plain edge.					

Two genuine specimens of the 1714 date are known, and a cast copy of the 1714 date. One genuine 1714 has a long pedigree — Mickley, Cram, Parmelee, Ten Eyck, Newcomer, Garrett, Don Kagin, Roper. Donald Kagin paid $36,000 for it in the Garrett sale, Oct. 1980, later reselling it.

The other 1714 genuine piece surfaced in March, 1981, and was first published in Nov. 1981. It had been in a family accumulation up to 200 years. It sold in a Bowers-Ruddy sale for $3,250.

The false copy was formerly in the Massachusetts Historical Society collection. It has a long pedigree — Clay, Seavey, Parmelee, Appleton, MHS, Stack's.

The 1715 piece was found with a metal detector in 1982. It has since been authenticated.

As tobacco was legal tender in Virginia at this period, the pieces may have been warehouse talleys or served some similar purpose, suggests Q. David Bowers.

Christopher Rigault (or Righault) was a large landowner on Craney Creek and Samuel Dawson was a landowner in Ware Parish, both near the Gloucester courthouse. Rigault and Dawson were apparently merchants in the courthouse area, possibly in the tobacco business.

A . S.
(Associate Synod)
Lexington, Va.

Rulau-E	Date	Metal	Size	VG	F	VF	EF
Va 5	(1781)	Lead	20mm	—	—	—	—

A . S. Rv: Blank. Plain edge.

The issuer is the Timber Ridge Associate Reformed Presbyterian Church, according to Autence A. Bason, in *TAMS Journal* for Feb. 1978.

W. PEARCE
Norfolk, Va.

Rulau-E	Date	Metal	Size	VG	F	VF	EF
Va 7	(1831-33)	Copper	29mm	75.00	—	125.	—

W. PEARCE (relief, in rect. depression) ctsp on U.S. 1822 Large cent. (Brunk 31415)

Walter Pearce was a silversmith in Norfolk from 1820 to 1833, according to Ensko (see Bibliography). He formed a partnership, Pearce and Spratley, about 1833.

RICHMOND LIGHT INFANTRY BLUES
Richmond, Va.

Rulau-E	Date	Metal	Size	F	VF	EF	Unc
Va 8	1798 (1830)	Copper	Oval 27 by 37mm	—	—	—	—

Sentry in late 18th century uniform standing, facing, his musket with fixed bayonet at "port trail arms." Around: RICHMOND LIGHT INFANTRY BLUES / * 1798 *. Rv: Blank. (Wright 893)

It is difficult to fix the issuance date of this piece, which is evidently some early form of identification or membership medalet. It is almost certainly pre-Civil War and is probably much earlier than 1860. The date '1798' refers to the founding date of the Richmond Light Infantry Blues, a militia regiment.

NON-LOCAL PIECES

(NOTE: For comprehensive coverage of George Washington tokens struck 1783-1820, some of which were cataloged in the 1st and 2nd editions of this reference as Rulau-E Non 1 to Non 22, see *Medallic Portraits of Washington* by Russell Rulau and George Fuld, Krause Publications, 1985.)

(WASHINGTON BUST)

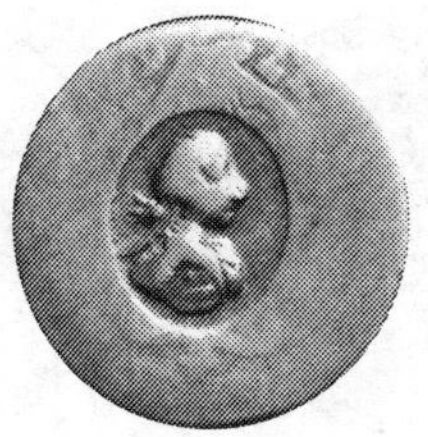

Rulau-E	Date	Metal	Size	VG	F	VF	EF
Non 100	(?)	Copper	28mm	—	500.	—	—

Military bust of Washington (?) right, in relief within 12 by 15mm oval depression, ctsp on imitation Ireland 1766 halfpenny. (Kovacs coll.; Baker 1050)

Discovered in London in 1981 by Frank Kovacs, who calls this bust Washington rather than George III because of its similarity to Crosby plate X, 17, the military jacket with epaulette and broad lapel.

There are several other Washington busts counterstamped on U.S. coins, all listed in the 1985 Rulau-Fuld revision of Baker's *Medallic Portraits of Washington*. Some of these are listed below.

Rulau-E	Date	Metal	Size	VG	F	VF	EF
Non 101	(1799)	Copper	29mm	—	—	—	Unique?
		Washington bust left (relief, within upright oval depression) ctsp on U.S. Large cent. The bust is from the hub of the Funeral medal, Baker 169 etc. (See illust. under Funeral medals in Baker. (Baker 1054)					
Non 101A	1824	Copper	29mm	300.	500.	—	1000.
		Bust of Washington left, GEORGE WASHINGTON around, in relief within 15mm circular depression, ctsp on obverse of U.S. Large cent. Rv: Bust of Lafayette right, GENERAL LA FAYETTE / 1824 around, in relief within 15mm circular depression, ctsp on reverse of the coin. Dates examined: 1816, 1817, 1818, 1820, 1822, 1823, unknown date. There are 9 pieces reported. This is Baker die 198 by Charles Cushing Wright (Raymond 35; Baker 1055; Brunk 41950)					

Dies of Non 101A also are ctsp on U.S. dimes 1820, 1821, 1822, 1823; U.S. half dollar 1824; Spanish-American 1-real, and Spanish-American 2-reales 1824. Values range from $300 VG to $3,000 EF for the larger silver.

Other similar genuine items known: Tiny Washington head right in oval depression, ctsp circa 1825 on U.S. 1820 Bust dime.

Washington military bust left in circular depression ctsp on planed-off U.S. silver dollar. Reverse side engraved script monogram ALS (?) - the so-called 'Stickney' Perkins dollar, now in possession of collector Jack Collins (Baker 1056).

Geo. Washington

Rulau-E	Date	Metal	Size	VG	F	VF	EF
Non 101P	1799	Silver	40mm	—	200.	—	—

Geo. Washington, 1799 *engraved* on obverse of U.S. 1799 Bust silver dollar. (Koppenhaver Nov. 1983 sale, lot 4)

Seemingly a Washington death remembrance.

(RADIANT EAGLE)

Rulau-E	Date	Metal	Size	VG	F	VF	EF
Non 102	(1790's)	Copper	28mm	—	—	—	2 known

Radiant, scrawny eagle in relief within upright oval depression ctsp on 1783 Nova Constellatio cent (pointed rays). (Krueger 1991 sale lot 1408).

(EAGLE ON ANCHOR)

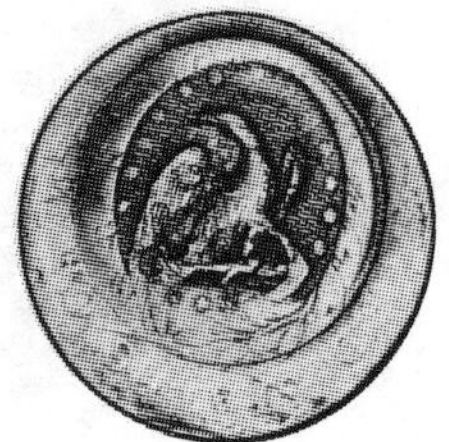

Rulau-E	Date	Metal	Size	VG	F	EF
Non 104	(1812-22)	Copper	29mm	—	Rare	—

Eagle with wings upraised perched on fouled anchor, all within starred circle, in relief, ctsp on U.S. 1802 Large cent. Rv: Eagle with folded wings perched on horizontal anchor, all within starred oval, in relief, ctsp on other side of the coin. (George Fuld report)

The devices used are those on marine buttons of the 1812-1822 period, according to Alphaeus Albert, the button authority.

ELTON'S

(Non-Local Fantasy)

Rulau-E	Date	Metal	Size	VG	F	VF	EF
Non 110	1757	Copper	36mm	—	—	—	2 Known

Trader buying skins from an Indian, within central circle. Around: THE RED MEN COME TO ELTONS DAILY. Rv: A deer (?) lying under a tree, within a central circle. Around: SKINS BOUGHT AT ELTONS, 1757. Plain edge. (Designs and lettering are *etched* on an English 1797 cartwheel penny which was first smoothed off on each side.) (Betts 397; AJN VII.90; ANS coll.)

Howland Wood in *The Numismatist* for Jan. 1913 branded the Elton card a "counterfeit." He meant a fantasy piece which did not have the benefit of a genuine precursor.

The single specimen then known appeared in the Thomas Birch & Sons sale in Philadelphia, Dec. 18, 1872, and from there went into the William S. Appleton collection, and thence to the Massachusetts Historical Society holdings in Boston.

Wood examined the MHS specimen and declared it had been acid-etched on an English 1797 penny. The piece is holed at 7 o'clock on obverse. By whom the piece was made, and why, is not known. The "when" seems easier, probably about 1870.

The ANS specimen, illustrated, is not holed. It is numbered 1913.27.1 in the ANS computerized inventory.

MEDALETS, ETC.

ELECTION MEDALETS

Rulau-E	Year	Metal	Size	F	VF	EF	Unc
Med 1	(1828)	Brass	25mm	—	35.00	—	—
		Facing military bust of Jackson, GENL. ANDREW JACKSON around. Rv: HERO / OF / NEW / ORLEANS within olive wreath. Wreath has 37 leaves and 20 berries. Reeded edge. (DeWitt AJACK 1824-1)					
Med 2	(1828)	Sil Brass	25mm	—	45.00	—	—
		As last. Reeded edge. (DeWitt AJACK 1824-1)					
Med 3	(1828)	Brass	25mm	—	35.00	—	—
		As last, but 38 leaves and 18 berries. Reeded edge. (DeWitt AJACK 1824-2)					

Rulau-E	Year	Metal	Size	F	VF	EF	Unc
Med 4	(1824)	Brass	25mm	—	50.00	—	—
		As last, but 34 leaves and 25 berries. Plain edge. (DeWitt AJACK 1824-3)					

Rulau-E	Year	Metal	Size	F	VF	EF	Unc
Med 5	(1824)	Brass	24mm	—	35.00	—	—
		Left-facing military bust of Jackson, GENL ANDREW JACKSON. Rev: THE / NATION'S / GOOD within oak and olive wreath. Plain edge. (DeWitt AJACK 1824-4)					

Rulau-E	Year	Metal	Size	F	VF	EF	Unc
Med 6	(1824)	Brass	24mm	—	50.00	—	—
		Obverse as last. Rev: THE / NATION'S / PRIDE within oak and olive wreath. Plain edge. (DeWitt AJACK 1824-5)					
Med 7	(1824)	Brass	24mm	—	100.00	—	—
		Obverse similar to last, but leaf decorations on collar and coat ornaments. Rev: Similar to last, but 5-pointed stars added above and below NATION'S. Plain edge. (DeWitt AJACK 1824-6)					

A new phenomenon, the election medalet or campaign badge, emerged in the bitter John Quincy Adams-Andrew Jackson-Henry Clay election contest. Three basic types of Jackson medalet appeared in this year, each suggested by the Congressional medal awarded to the general for his 1815 victory at New Orleans. All were struck at Waterbury, Conn., according to J. Doyle DeWitt. Since these pieces were often worn on clothing, they sometimes occur holed.

MASONIC MEDALETS

Rulau-E	Year	Metal	Size	VG	F	VF	EF
Med 11	1797	Brass	34mm	—	3800.	—	Ex. Rare

Uniformed bust of Washington left, G. WASHINGTON PRESIDENT around, 1797 below. Rv: Two pillars topped by globes; All-seeing eye, G, square and compasses, open book, three burning candles, level, plumb and gavel, trowel - all within central circle. Around: AMOR. HONOR. ET. JUSTITIA. Below: - G.W.G.G.M. -. Engrailed edge. (Baker 288B; Landmark sale 1990, lot 321). 5 pieces known.

Rulau-E	Year	Metal	Size	VG	F	VF	EF
Med 12	1797	Silver	34mm	—	—	—	45,000.

As last. Engrailed edge. (Baker 288)

Rulau-E	Year	Metal	Size	VG	F	VF	EF
Med 13	1797	Brass	34mm	—	750.	—	—

Obverse as last. Rv: Blank. 4 pieces known.

A Masonic "penny." AMOR. HONOR. ET JUSTITIA = Love, Honor and Justice. G.W.G.-G.M. = George Washington General Grand Master (of the United States). George Washington was initiated a Mason Nov. 4, 1752 into Fredericksburgh Lodge, Va. In 1788 he was chosen Master of Alexandria Lodge, Va. - later Alexandria Washington Lodge No. 22.

At a meeting Jan. 13, 1780, the Grand Lodge of Pennsylvania elected him General Grand Master of the United States. This did not meet with favor from other Grand Lodges, and the office was never established. But this action and its attendant publicity created the impression there was such a Masonic office and Washington occupied it, and this 1797 medallic token reinforced this belief. Struck in 1797, the low relief bust after Pierre Eugene du Simitiere's sketch closely resembles the 1792 Washington half dollars by Peter Getz of Lancaster, Pa. A silver specimen in the Bushnell sale passed through R. Coulton Davis of Pa. to the Garrett collection at Johns Hopkins University.

Struck by Peter Getz, Lancaster, Pa. This is the oldest Masonic medal in the U.S.

BENJAMIN FRANKLIN

Rulau-E	Year	Metal	Size	VG	F	VF	EF
Med 16	(1800-15)	Brass	37mm	—	—	—	Rare

Described by George Fuld in Franklin and Numismatics as FR.M.NL.9, this token bears a portrait of Benjamin Franklin, two olive sprigs, 17 stars, and the name BENJAMIN FRANKLIN on its obverse. The reverse depicts a group of beehives, flags, machinery, and the legend FLEISS UND ORDNUNG SEGNET DES VOLVES WOHLSTAND ("Industry and Order Bless the Welfare of the People"). Struck in brass, this very rare 37mm token was first exhibited by Thomas Elder in 1917. Originally Elder thought it was struck between 1800 and 1815.

(THE SENTIMENTAL)
London, England

Rulau-E	Date	Metal	Size	VG	F	VF	Unc
Med 18	1773	Copper	25mm	11.50	—	30.00	60.00
		Bust of William Pitt the Elder right, in wig and coat. Tiny KIRK F. under bust. Rv: LORD / CHATHAM / 1773 in three lines. Plain edge. (Betts 522)					
Med 19	1773	Silver	25mm	—	—	—	Rare
		As last. (Betts 522A)					

The copper token was given away with numbers of a magazine called *The Sentimental*, published 1773-1775. Apparently a silver version also was struck, and was given away as prizes by the owners. Betts says the copper pieces are also known silver-plated.

According to *The Numismatic Chronicle* of London for 1890 (page 54) the Pitt token was one of a series of 13 tokens given away with as many numbers of the magazine. These other tokens depict George II, Oliver Cromwell, David Garrick, Queen Charlotte and other English figures, but only Pitt (died 1778) has an American connection.

John Kirk of London (1724-1778), a pupil of James Anthony Dassier, and a maker of many coin weights of this period, cut the dies for this series of tokens. Most of his work is from the 1740-1776 period. (See "The Sentimental Magazine and its Medalets" by Sidney K. Eastwood in *Numisma* for 1939).

These medalets also occur in lead.

MOORMAN MFG. CO.
Quincy, Ill.

Rulau-E	Date	Metal	Size	F	VF	EF	Unc
		Copper-plated					
Med 33	1818	Pewter	26mm	—	—	8.00	11.00

Seated female left, with harp. NORTH AMERICAN TOKEN around, 1818 in exergue. Rv: MOORMAN MFG. CO. / QUINCY, ILLINOIS / SALUTES / THE AMERICAN / FARMER.

The obverse is an imitation of the Irish-American token dated 1781 which is associated with the American Colonial series. The piece was made in 1968 in connection with the Illinois Sesquicentennial that year. Since it bears a date and a style fitting the Early American token category and could be mistaken, it was thought best to catalog it here.

Rulau-E	Date	Metal	Size	F	VF	EF	Unc
Med 34	1968	Copper	27.1mm	—	—	8.00	11.00

Obverse as Med 33. Rv: On outline map of Illinois: MOORMAN MFG. CO. / FOUNDED 1885 / SALUTES 150 YEARS / OF ILLINOIS PROGRESS / 1818 - 1968. Plain edge. Normal flan.

Med 34 was discovered in its original card of issue, which calls it a "replica of 1818 North American token." The reverse of the card reads:

1818 NORTH AMERICAN TOKEN The North American Token circulated in the United States from 1817-1822 and was predominantly found in the newly settled territories that are now the Midwestern states.

The original design for this coin was taken from a New England cent struck in the late 1700's and has remained a popular design for subsequent American coins.

Due to a coin shortage in the United States, this piece was struck by a private mint in Ireland. These "barter" coins were used by the settlers as a token of exchange to make personal trading simpler. This token was valued at a penny.

Appropriately, its date is 1818 - commemorating the year that Illinois became a state.

1818 NORTH AMERICAN TOKEN

The North American Token circulated in the United States from 1817-1822 and was predominantly found in the newly settled territories that are now the Midwestern states.

The original design for this coin was taken from a New England cent struck in the late 1700's and has remained a popular design for subsequent American coins.

Due to a coin shortage in the United States, this piece was struck by a private mint in Ireland. These "barter" coins were used by the settlers as a token of exchange to make personal trading simpler. This token was valued at a penny.

Appropriately, its date is 1818—commemorating the year that Illinois became a state.

This is a case of "making the facts fit the circumstances." Actual North American copper and brass tokens were struck in Dublin, Ireland and occur dated only 1781, though they are believed to have been struck 1810-20. The 1781 piece was accepted in trade near the Canadian border.

CHARLES D. ARCENEAUX
Lafayette, La.

This is a series of fantasy pieces made in imitation of Colonial coins or tokens in connection with various American Numismatic Association conventions by engraver Arceneaux. He uses hand-cut dies, which break after about 200 strikes. Dies of all pieces listed below have been destroyed, Arceneaux reports.

Pine Tree Shilling, 1982

Rulau-E	Date	Metal	Size	F	VF	EF	Unc
Med 40	1982	Pewter	21mm	—	—	—	7.50

Imitation of Pine Tree shilling. Pine tree within central beaded circle, Around: MASATHVSETS / .1982. Rv: GOOD FOR / 50 C IN / TRADE / Charles D Arceneaux. Plain edge.

Rulau-E	Date	Metal	Size	F	VF	EF	Unc
Med 41	1982	Pewter	21mm	—	—	—	6.50

Obverse as last. Rv: Ancient oil lamp left, burning, on open book, 1891 below, all within central beaded circle. Around: AMERICAN . NUMISMATIC / ASSOCIATION. Plain edge.

Chalmers Shilling, 1985

Rulau-E	Date	Metal	Size	F	VF	EF	Unc
Med 45	1985	Pewter	20mm	—	—	—	9.00

Imitation of Chalmers shilling of Baltimore. Type 1. Clasped hands within circular wreath at center. Around: I. CHALMERS. BALTIMOR 1985. Rv: As reverse of last (Ancient lamp, 1891). Plain edge. Only 10 struck.

Rulau-E	Date	Metal	Size	F	VF	EF	Unc
Med 46	1985	Silver	20mm	—	—	—	Rare

As last. 4 struck. Plain edge.

Rulau-E	Date	Metal	Size	F	VF	EF	Unc
Med 47	1985	Pewter	20mm	—	—	—	5.00

Obverse as last. Rv: . Rich Hartzog / 17 1/2 C / World Exonumia. Plain edge. Only 50 struck.

Rulau-E	Date	Metal	Size	F	VF	EF	Unc
Med 48	1985	Silver	20mm	—	—	—	40.00

As last. Only 2 struck. Plain edge.

Rulau-E	Date	Metal	Size	F	VF	EF	Unc
Med 50	1985	Pewter	20mm	—	—	—	3.00

Imitation of Chalmers shilling of Baltimore. Type 2. Clasped hands, 1985 above, tiny CDA below, all within central circular wreath. Around: I. CHALMERS. BALTIMORE. Rv: As last ANA type (Ancient lamp, 1891). Plain edge. Only 40 struck.

Rulau-E	Date	Metal	Size	F	VF	EF	Unc
Med 51	1985	Silver	20mm	—	—	—	40.00

As last. Plain edge. Only 25 struck. (Rulau coll.)

Rulau-E	Date	Metal	Size	F	VF	EF	Unc
Med 53	1985	Pewter	20mm	—	—	—	3.00

Obverse as last (Type 2). Rv: As last Hartzog card (17 1/2 C). Plain edge. Only 115 struck.

Rulau-E	Date	Metal	Size	F	VF	EF	Unc
Med 54	1985	Silver	20mm	—	—	—	40.00

As last. Plain edge. Only 3 struck. (Rulau coll.)

Rulau-E	Date	Metal	Size	F	VF	EF	Unc
Med 55	1985	Gold	18mm	—	—	—	150.

As last. Overstruck on China 1/10-oz. Panda coin. Only 1 struck. (Hartzog coll.)

Pewter Blanks

Rulau-E	Date	Metal	Size	VF	EF	Unc
Med 60	ND	Pewter	19mm	—	—	—

Blank planchet on both sides. Plain edge. This is the planchet from which the 1985 strikes were made, expanding about 1mm under coining pressure.

In the 1985 Chalmers shilling series, the principal difference between the scarcer Type 1 and the Type 2 is that there is no final E in BALTIMOR in Type 1, while BALTIMORE is complete in Type 2. (See *Coin World* for Oct. 2, 1985, page 100)

There are several other die varieties, according to Rich Hartzog, with a "high" and "low" U in Exonumia.

FUGIO
(E.J. Theisen)
East Orange, N.J.

Rulau-E	Date	Metal	Size	F	VF	EF	Unc
Med 25	(1957)	Bronze	29mm	—	—	7.00	10.00
		Imitation of Fugio cent. Radiant sunface above sundial, FUGIO 1787 around, MIND YOUR / BUSINESS in two lines in exergue. Rv: THE / FOUNDERS / ISOLATIONISM / DEVELOPED U.S. / FOR IT IS A / BASIC LAW / OF LIFE. Plain edge.					
Med 26	(1957)	Gilt/Bz	29mm	—	—	8.50	12.50
		As last. Plain edge.					
Med 27	1961	Bronze	29mm	—	—	7.75	11.00
		Obverse as last (Sundial). Rv: FORTITUDE PRUDENCE DEF. BYE J (backward) T / 1961 / TEMPERANCE / JUSTICE (under bridge) / (blank space across center) / THE FOUR CARDINAL VIRTUES / DEPICTED ON FIRST COIN / OF THE UNITED STATES / COIN AUTH. BY CONGRESS / JULY 6, 1787. Plain edge.					
Med 28	1961	Bronze	29mm	—	—	7.00	10.00
		Obverse as last. Rv: As last, but DEF. E.J.T. replaces DEF. BYE. J (backward) T, which was poor die work on the earlier piece. Also, blank space across center now reads: "... THE U.S.A. OUGHT TO RELY / ON THEIR OWN VIRTUE." / (VOL. 22. PG. 339 JRNLS. C.C.). Plain edge.					

These tokens use the 1787 Fugio cent design in an attempt to recapture the Founding Fathers' neutrality and isolationism. They are included here because the date and style fit into the Early category and may cause confusion among collectors.

The first pieces were issued by Eugene J. Theisen of East Orange, N.J. in an effort to convince Congress to issue a commemorative honoring the Fugio cent of 1787 on its coming (1962) 175th anniversary. To publicize the 1957 issue, Theisen offered a $250 reward to anyone who identified the designer of the 1787 coin and the author's interpretation of the Sundial design and legends, payable until Oct. 24, 1957. There were no winners.

The author possesses much original Theisen literature of the 1957 period, advancing his peculiar view of where America should be, politically and socially. The 1961 issues expound some of these views. He theorized the Fugio cent showed America the right path.

MAVERICKS

So far as we can determine, counterstamping of coins for advertising or promotional purposes in America happened infrequently before the 1830's. The number of *attributed* counterstamps in this reference book proves that the practice did occur, though, possibly as early as the mid 1790's.

The maverick stamps admitted in this section are, we believe, early in their provenance. Some are admitted on opinion alone, based on our years of experience in examining such items.

But also we have devised several rules for admission:

(1) Prepared punches (i.e. struck from a die, not single letters punched in) appearing on *early* U.S. coins (Colonials, Large cents or Half cents dated before 1820, etc.)

(2) Relief punches (i.e. letters or designs in relief within a shaped depression), especially in cases where initials only appear. Such punches frequently emanate from metalsmiths of various kinds.

(3) U.S. — oriented punches impressed on early foreign coins. This is a tricky area, because the flood of Spanish-American silver used as host coins really began in 1834, after this book's coverage. Pre-1820 U.S. silver coins (except half dollars), on the other hand, began disappearing from circulation before 1834. (For example, in 1850 one could easily find a worn 1780 Spanish 2-reales in circulation, but seldom an 1828 American quarter).

A word on fantasies and on faked stampings: In time human greed may change this situation, but as of 1991 it was not much of a problem. The fakers are few and their products have been easy enough to spot. Best bet — consult an expert before buying, or buy from dealers you have come to trust through long association.

A. & W.

Rulau-E	Date	Metal	Size	VG	F	VF	EF
Mav 1	(?)	Copper	29mm	—	15.00	—	—
		A & W in relief in toothed rectangular depression ctsp on U.S. 1812 Large cent. (Brunk 110)					

Possibly a silversmith's hallmark. Possibility: Avery & Willis, Salisbury, N.Y., circa 1820.

W.W. AVERILL

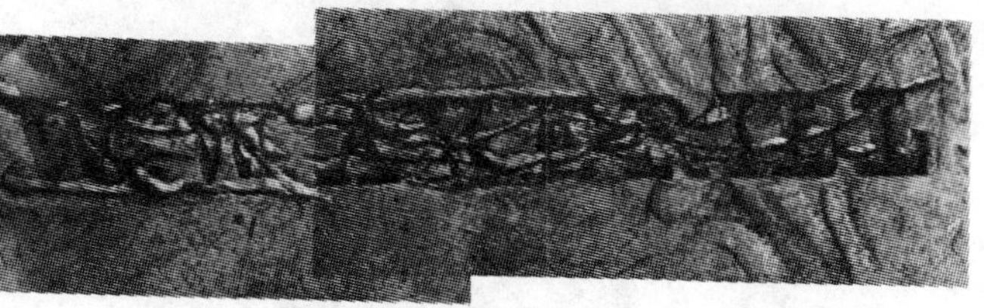

Rulau-E	Date	Metal	Size	VG	F	VF	EF
Mav 2	(?)	Silver	32.5mm	—	—	—	50.00.
		W.W. AVERILL ctsp on U.S. 1803 Half dollar. (Collection of Donald R. Lewis, Harvester, Mo.; Brunk 1400)					

The blowup photographs of the counterstamp area were made by the American Numismatic Association Certification Service (ANACS) staff in 1982.

The only known piece realized a disappointing $50 in the June, 1989 PCAC Great Eastern sale, lot 025. Maverick pieces frequently do sell cheaply.

A.B.

Rulau-E	Date	Metal	Size	VG	F	VF	EF
Mav 2B	(?)	Copper	29mm	15.00	—	25.00	—
		A . B in relief within toothed rect. depression ctsp on U.S. Large cent. Dates examined: 1795, 1800, 1803, 1804, 1818, 1828, 1830, 1833, 1838, 1843, 1849. There are 12 pieces reported. (Rulau-E Conn 9-10; Partrick coll.; Rulau coll.; Brunk 20; ANS coll.)					

Earlier we tentatively attributed this mark to silversmith A. Beach of Hartford, Conn., active circa 1823, or possibly Asa Blanchard of Lexington, Ky., who died 1838. Discovery of more specimens caused us to discard these possibilities.

The mark could be an unrecorded one of Albert Beach, New York City, active 1839-47, maker of watches, spectacles, jewelry and silverplated ware. Beach's usual mark is A. BEACH in relief in toothed rectangular punch.

The Rulau specimen carries an additional ctsp, incuse C C on obverse. Others carry a separate G W H in rectangle ctsp.

A. B. / G. W. H.

Rulau-E	Date	Metal	Size	VG	F	VF	EF
Mav 2C	(?)	Copper	29mm	10.00	—	15.00	—
		A.B. in relief in toothed rect. depression / G W H incuse in rect. cartouche, ctsp on U.S. Large cent. Dates examined: 1830, 1838. (ANS coll.)					

Also see Mav 2B.

F.B.

Rulau-E	Date	Metal	Size	VG	F	VF	EF
Mav 2D	(?)	Copper	29mm	—	25.00	—	—
		F B (possibly EB) ctsp on obverse of Kentucky pyramid token of the 1792-94 period with lettered edge. Rv: Numeral 3 ctsp on reverse of the token. (Denton V. Curtis collection, Eastleigh, Hants., England)					

There is a strong possibility this is a British stamping. This piece was found in a hoard of about 25 British 18th century tokens, including a D&H Middlesex 297, recovered from the Thames River, and sold about 1975 by a British coin dealer. It is admitted here on the possibility it, like its host coin, has an American connection.

H.B.

Rulau-E	Date	Metal	Size	VG	F	VF	EF
Mav 3	(?)	Copper	29mm		25.00		—

Large incuse H . B ctsp on U.S. 1795 Large cent, which has first been overstruck with an eagle, head turned left, device over the Liberty head. Details of the head, neckline, Phrygian cap and date are still clearly visible. The overstriking, then the incusing blow, have obscured most reverse details except the word STATES and the dentilated border near it.

Possibilities: Henry Biershing, silversmith, Hagerstown, Md., circa 1815, or Henry Brunner III, gunsmith, Salisbury, N.C. 1816-19.

Likely: Henry Bonning, Dover Castle Inn, North Adelaide, 1851.

J.P.B.

Rulau-E	Date	Metal	Size	VG	F	VF	EF
Mav 9	(?)	Silver	32.5mm	20.00	—	35.00	—

J P B monogram in relief within oval depression ctsp on U.S. 1812 Bust half dollar. (Frank Kovacs coll.)

P. B. in Heart

Rulau-E	Date	Metal	Size	VG	F	VF	EF
Mav 9G	(?)	Silver	32.5mm	60.00	—	90.00	—

P . B in relief within heart-shaped depression ctsp on U.S. 1795 Flowing Hair half dollar. (Van Ormer sale 2783; Brunk 30535)

Rulau-E	Date	Metal	Size	VG	F	VF	EF
Mav 9H	(?)	Silver	26mm	—	90.00	—	—

Similar ctsp on U.S. 1806 Bust quarter dollar.

Rulau-E	Date	Metal	Size	VG	F	VF	EF
Mav 9I	(?)	Copper	29mm	—	90.00	—	—

Similar ctsp on U.S. 1800 Large cent.

It is possible this is the stamp of Peter Barbier of Philadelphia, an 1820's silversmith.

P.J. BAKER

Rulau-E	Date	Metal	Size	VG	F	VF	EF
Mav 10	(?)	Copper	29mm	—	65.00	—	—

P.J. BAKER / A.R.M. CO. ctsp on worn 1787 New Jersey "Nova Caesarea" cent, holed. (John Cheramy coll.; Brunk 1990)

R B

Rulau-E	Date	Metal	Size	VG	F	VF	EF
Mav 10E	(ca 1780?)	Silver	24mm	—	85.00	—	—

Large R B ctsp on Massachusetts 1652-dated Oak Tree shilling which has been clipped down about 2mm and is holed. (Frank Kovacs coll., San Francisco)

The Massachusetts Oak Tree coinage was struck in the 1660-1667 period. It is possible this store card (if it is that) could have passed for a shilling late in the 18th century. The initials may also be frivolous.

W. B.

Rulau-E	Date	Metal	Size	VG	F	VF	EF
Mav 10K	(?)	Copper	29mm	—	20.00.	—	—

W.B. in relief within toothed rect. depression ctsp on U.S. 1804 Half cent. (ANS coll.)

S. BEWER

Rulau-E	Date	Metal	Size	VG	F	VF	EF
Mav 11	(?)	Copper	29mm	—	15.00	—	—

S. BEWER in relief within toothed recessed rectangle ctsp on U.S. 1818 Large cent. (Frank Kovacs coll.; Brunk 3570)

JOHN Q. BOYCE

Rulau-E	Date	Metal	Size	VG	F	VF	EF
Mav 12	(?)	Copper	28mm	—	25.00	—	—

JOHN Q BOYCE ctsp on U.S. 1783 Nova Constellatio cent. (Kagin 1978 GENA sale, lot 1623; Brunk 4690)

B BROWER & CO.

Rulau-E	Date	Metal	Size	VG	F	VF	EF
Mav 12E	(?)	Copper	34mm	—	—	50.00	—

B. BROWER & CO. in relief within rect. depression ctsp on Ireland 1805 penny, KM-148. (PCAC July 1993 sale, lot 873)

J. BURNS

Rulau-E	Date	Metal	Size	VG	F	VF	EF
Mav 13	1829	Copper	29mm	—	20.00	—	—

J: BURNS (in relief within rectangular depression) / 1829 (incuse) / (Long bar) (incuse) / DN upside down (incuse) / J: BURNS (in relief within rect. depression) — all ctsp on U.S. 1821 Large cent. (Kovacs coll.; Brunk 6060)

Possibility: John H. Burns, jeweler and silversmith, New York City, circa 1834-39.

I. C.

Rulau-E	Date	Metal	Size	VG	F	VF	EF
Mav 14	(?)	Copper	29mm	—	—	15.00	—

I . C in relief within toothed rectangular depression ctsp on U.S. 1803 Large cent. (ANS coll., ex-Wittlin 1957)

M. C.

Rulau-E	Date	Metal	Size	VG	F	VF	EF
Mav 15	(?)	Copper	29mm	—	20.00	—	—

M. C. ctsp on Connecticut AUCTORI CONNEC 1785-88 cent.

Once attributed to silversmiths Coit & Mansfield (1816-19 in Norwich, Conn.), but verification could not be achieved.

CARLETON & CO.

Rulau-E	Date	Metal	Size	VG	F	VF	EF
Mav 15B	(?)	Copper	29mm	—	25.00	—	—

CARLETON & CO. ctsp on U.S. 1803 Large cent. (Koppenhaver Nov. 1983 sale, lot 549; Brunk 6790)

H. CLARKE

Rulau-E	Date	Metal	Size	VG	F	VF	EF
Mav 15C	(?)	Copper	29mm	—	—	—	100.

H / CLARKE in relief within irregular depression ctsp on Connecticut 1787 Draped Bust cent. (Van Ormer sale 2585; Brunk 8170)

Possibly early blacksmith or metalworker. In the Nov. 1990 B&M Schenkel sale, lot 4, this piece realized $275.

COCKADE

Rulau-E	Date	Metal	Size	VG	F	VF	EF
Mav 15D	(?)	Copper	29mm	—	—	—	50.00

COCKADE in relief within rect. depression ctsp on U.S. 1807 Large cent. (ANS coll.; Brunk 8505)

M. E. COFFIN

Rulau-E	Date	Metal	Size	VG	F	VF	EF
Mav 15E	(?)	Silver	40mm	—	100.	—	—

M. E. COFFIN ctsp on both sides of U.S. 1797 Draped Bust silver dollar. (Van Ormer sale 2596; Brunk 8620)

C.D.

Rulau-E	Date	Metal	Size	VG	F	VF	EF
Mav 15T	(1820's ?)	Copper	29mm	—	—	—	25.00

C D in single letters ctsp on 1781 North American token. The 'C' could be a crude G. (Bosco April 1989 sale, lot 102)

DISPA'

Rulau-E	Date	Metal	Size	VG	F	VF	EF
Mav 15W	(?)	Copper	29mm	—	—	15.00	

DISPA' (large) in relief within serrated rectangle ctsp on apparent U.S. 1798 large cent. (Allan Davisson coll.; Cold Spring, Minn.; Brunk 11738)

EAGLE HOTEL

Rulau-E	Date	Metal	Size	VG	F	VF	EF
Mav 16B	(?)	Silver	19mm	—	150.	—	—

Eagle Hotel ctsp on U.S. 1805 Draped Bust dime. (Van Ormer sale 2629, ex-Harvey Gamer; Brunk 12790)

Eagle Hotels were in many cities. One candidate that seems promising is the Eagle Hotel of Albany, N.Y. circa 1840, in the Hard Times era. Its advertisements have similarities.

J. EDY

Rulau-E	Date	Metal	Size	VG	F	VF	EF
Mav 16C	(?)	Copper	29mm	—	25.00	—	—

J. EDY ctsp on U.S. 1822 Large cent. (Rulau coll.; Brunk 13077)

A. ESTY

Rulau-E	Date	Metal	Size	VG	F	VF	EF
Mav 16E	(?)	Silver	27mm	—	50.00	—	—

A. ESTY ctsp twice on worn Spanish-American 2-reales of Philip V. Rv: Date 1721 carved on opposite side of coin, over location where worn-off date would have been. (Rulau coll., ex-Tanenbaum; Brunk 13527)

Philip V of the House of Bourbon ruled Spain 1700-1724 and 1725-1746.

I.C.F.

Rulau-E	Date	Metal	Size	VG	F	VF	EF
Mav 17C	(?)	Copper	28mm	—	25.00	—	—

I G F in relief ctsp on Vermont 1788 cent, Ryder 27. (B&M Hoke Green sale, lot 2393)

J. F.

Rulau-E	Date	Metal	Size	VG	F	VF	EF
Mav 17E	(?)	Copper	29mm	35.00	—	45.00	—

* J * F * in relief within rect. depression ctsp on early Large cent. Dates examined: 1800, 1803, 1804, 1817, 1828, 1829, date unknown. There are 10 pieces reported. (Kovacs coll.; Brunk 21260; Rulau HT 454; Hallenbeck 10.020; Krueger 3539; Schenkel sale 4129)

R.F.
Caution: Fantasies!

Rulau-E	Date	Metal	Size	VG	F	VF	EF
Mav 18	(?)	Copper	29mm	—	20.00	—	—

RF in relief within recessed retangular depression ctsp on U.S. 1801 Large cent. (Brunk 33360)

This fantasy stamp has been applied to many U.S. coins in the 19th century. None saw circulation.

W.F.

Rulau-E	Date	Metal	Size	VG	F	VF	EF
Mav 18E	(?)	Copper	29mm	—	15.00	—	30.00

W. F. in relief within rect. depression ctsp on U.S. Large cent. Examined: 1794, 1803, 1839. (PCAC Dec. 1990 sale, lot 639; Brunk 41330)

B. L. FOWLER

Rulau-E	Date	Metal	Size	VG	F	VF	EF
Mav 18Q	(?)	Silver	40mm	—	—	—	1650.

B.L. FOWLER ctsp on U.S. 1794 Flowing hair silver dollar. (Bangs Merwin May, 1859 sale of the William Leggett Bramhall collection, lot 464)

Even in 1859 the 1794 dollar was rare. The coin graded EF, according to the auctioneers. Bramhall had been curator of the American Numismatic Society.

The present location of this specimen is not known. Collector Richard C. Striley uncovered the old sale catalog entry in 1993.

Fowler has not been traced. There was a B. Fowler Jr. of Hartford, Conn., who supervised the manufacture of underhammer guns in the 1835-38 period at Connecticut State Prison.

A. G.

Rulau-E	Date	Metal	Size	VG	F	VF	EF
Mav 18V	ND	Copper	29mm	—	—	25.00	—

A G in relief within toothed rectangular depression ctsp on U.S. 1807 Large cent (Dr. Sol Taylor coll.)

This distinctive mark does not appear in lists of marks of silversmiths, pewterers or gunsmiths.

J. G.

Rulau-E	Date	Metal	Size	VG	F	VF	EF
Mav 19	(?)	Copper	29mm	—	15.00	—	—

J . G in relief within toothed rect. depression ctsp on U.S. Large cent. Dates examined: 1798, 1817, 1829. (Kovacs coll.; Kean Leiker coll.; Brunk 21270)

This stamp does not quite match those used by several silversmiths; it may well be from another occupation entirely.

J. O. G.

Rulau-E	Date	Metal	Size	VG	F	VF	EF
Mav 19E	(?)	Copper	29mm	—	35.00	—	—

J. O. G. in relief within toothed depression ctsp on U.S. 1810 or 1820 Large cent. (Brunk 21313)

Possibly a gunsmith marking from Springfield, Mass.

G. N. GALE

Rulau-E	Date	Metal	Size	VG	F	VF	EF
Mav 19S	(?)	Silver	27mm	30.00	—	45.00	—

G. N. GALE in relief within toothed rect. depression ctsp on Spanish-American 1784-Mo-FM 2-reales. WEAVER incuse is ctsp on reverse. (Van Ormer sale 2653; Brunk 15560)

Rulau-E	Date	Metal	Size	VG	F	VF	EF
Mav 19T	(?)	Copper	29mm	30.00	—	45.00	—

Similar ctsp on 1807 or 1826 U.S. Large cent.

Supposedly Gale was a New Hampshire goldsmith, Van Ormer reported. No verification has been found.

GARDINER

Rulau-E	Date	Metal	Size	VG	F	VF	EF
Mav 20	(?)	Copper	28mm	—	50.00	—	—

GARDINER ctsp on Mott 1789 cent token of New York City. (Gould 1431; Brunk 15670)

This is the only reported ctsp on a Mott token.

GRAFF

Rulau-E	Date	Metal	Size	VG	F	VF	EF
Mav 20E	(?)	Copper	29mm	—	15.00	—	—

GRAFF in relief within serrated irregularly rectangular depression ctsp on U.S. 1817 Large cent. (Donald K. Clifford coll., St. Albans, West Va.; Brunk 16790)

J. GROVE

Rulau-E	Date	Metal	Size	VG	F	VF	EF
Mav 20F	(?)	Copper	29mm	10.00	—	20.00	

GROVE (relief, in toothed rect. depression) / J. G (relief, in toothed heart-shaped depression) ctsp in separate punches on obverse of Connecticut cent of 1785-87 type. (B&M Schenkel Nov. 1990 sale, lot 4113; Brunk 17250)

There was a J. Grove in Hagerstown, Md. who made flintlock Kentucky rifles. Kentucky rifles were made in the 1792-1814 period. (Ref: Daniel D. Hartzler, *Arms Makers Of Maryland*, York, Pa., 1977).

The coin has not been examined to determine whether its marks match known lockplate markings of J. Grove.

H. & G.

Rulau-E	Date	Metal	Size	VG	F	VF	EF
Mav 20K	(?)	Copper	29mm	—	25.00	—	—

Script H & G ctsp on U.S. 1810 or 1851 Large cent. (Koppenhaver Nov. 1983 sale, lot 565; Brunk 17520)

A. H.

Rulau-E	Date	Metal	Size	VG	F	VF	EF
Mav 21	1814	Copper	23mm	—	30.00	—	—

AH monogram / 1814 ctsp on U.S. 1809 Half cent. (Frank Kovacs coll.)

E. M. H.

Rulau-E	Date	Metal	Size	VG	F	VF	EF
Mav 21E	(?)	Silver	40mm	—	—	—	50.00

E. M. H. ctsp on Spanish-American 1804-Mo-TH 8-reales. Also *engraved* on the coin are two script monograms in neat style: RWC and FRB. (Rulau coll.)

W. S. HARTWELL

Rulau-E	Date	Metal	Size	VG	F	VF	EF
Mav 21K	(?)	Copper	29mm	—	10.00	—	15.00

W. S. HARTWELL ctsp on U.S. 1808 Large cent. (Robert M. Ramsay coll.; Brunk 18525)

C. C. HAYES / H. BROWN

Rulau-E	Date	Metal	Size	VG	F	VF	EF
Mav 22	(?)	Copper	29mm	60.00	—	90.00	—

C. C. HAYES / H. BROWN / WARRANTED in relief in three separate rect. depressions ctsp on U.S. Large cent. Examined: 1802, 1818. (Brunk 18885)

V. HOLTBY

Rulau-E	Date	Metal	Size	VG	F	VF	EF
Mav 22	(?)	Copper	29mm	—	15.00	—	—

V. HOLTBY ctsp on U.S. Large cent, date worn off. (Brunk 19925)

H. I.

Rulau-E	Date	Metal	Size	VG	F	VF	EF
Mav 23	(?)	Copper	29mm	—	20.00	—	—

Serif-type H + I in relief within rect. depression ctsp on U.S. 1810 Bust Large cent. (Kovacs coll.)

J. J.

Rulau-E	Date	Metal	Size	VG	F	VF	EF
Mav 24T	(?)	Copper	29mm	—	15.00	—	—

J. J. in relief within toothed heart-shaped depression ctsp on U.S. 1805 Large cent. (ANS coll.)

N. W. H. J.

Rulau-E	Date	Metal	Size	VG	F	VF	EF
Mav 25	1830	Copper	29mm	—	30.00	—	—

N. W. H. J. / 1830 ctsp on U.S. Large cent, date worn, possibly 1805. The entire stamp is on a single, neat punch. (Kean Leiker coll.; Brunk 29213)

A. K.

Rulau-E	Date	Metal	Size	VG	F	VF	EF
Mav 26K	(?)	Copper	29mm	—	—	—	80.00

Large serif-type A . K in relief within inverted shield-shaped depression ctsp on reverse of New Jersey 1787 Wide Shield cent. The shield depression is similar in design to the shield device on the coin, over which it is stamped. (John D. Irwin coll.)

The only known specimen was excavated in 1989 from a field in Newtown, Pa. which also yielded a 1700 Hibernia halfpenny, molded buttons, oyster shells and early pewter fragments. The A . K piece has deep green patina but was new or near-new when counterstamped.

Newton was Bucks County seat in the Revolution, and was the site of an American prison for captured British soldiers.

See "Treasures from the Plow, Profile of a Bucks County Hunter" by John D. Irwin, in *Treasure* magazine for Feb., 1990.

A. K.

Rulau-E	Date	Metal	Size	VG	F	VF	EF
Mav 28L	(?)	Copper	27.2mm	—	100.	—	—

A. K. in relief within toothed rect. depression ctsp on U.S. Large cent of Matron head type of 1816-35 (possibly 1819). Numeral 2 ctsp incuse on same side of coin. Coin has been cut down to 12-point star shape and mounted on a curved wood handle of 127.5mm length for use as some sort of marking tool. (Illustration of enlarged face of coin and of the tool are shown)

Antique collector-author John D. Irwin obtained this tool at an eastern Pennsylvania farm auction recently. The letter-punches do not match those used on Mav 26K. Irwin believes the handmade tool could have been used to mark location of stitching holes in shoe leather.

Enlargement

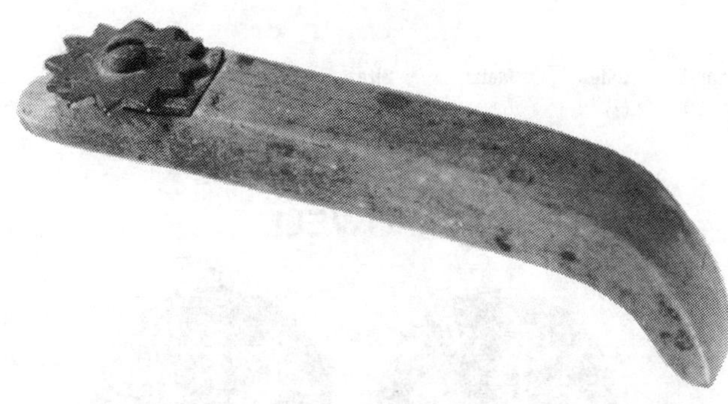

Enlargement of Mav 28L

H. K.

Rulau-E	Date	Metal	Size	VG	F	VF	EF
Mav 26M	(?)	Silver	27mm	—	25.00	—	—

H K in relief within toothed rect. depression ctsp on Spanish-American 1774 2-reales.

I K

Rulau-E	Date	Metal	Size	VG	F	VF	EF
Mav 27	(1810-19)	Copper	29mm	—	15.00	—	—

I K in toothed rectangular cartouche ctsp on England 1773 Halfpenny of George III (possibly a Machins Mil l imitation). (Steinberg Jan. 1982 mail bid sale)

Possibly Joseph Keeler, who was a silversmith in Norwalk, Conn. Born 1786, died 1824. He was active about 1810.

W. KEIM

Rulau-E	Date	Metal	Size	VG	F	VF	EF
Mav 27C	(?)	Silver	32.5mm	15.00	—	—	—

W. KEIM cstp on U.S. 1806 Bust half dollar. (Kirtley Jan. 1991 price list; Brunk 22370)

LIGHT

Rulau-E	Date	Metal	Size	VG	F	VF	EF
Mav 28K	(1800-10)	Silver	39mm	100.	—	150.	

LIGHT in relief within rect. depression ctsp on counterfeit Spanish-American 8-reales. Dates examined: 1792, 1792-Mo-FM, 1799. 3 pieces known. (B&M Schenkel sale of Nov. 1990, lot 4131; Brunk 24495)

The 1792-Mo-FM piece weighed 20.4 grams versus the statutory 27.07 grams. This counterstamp apparently was applied to lightweight contemporary counterfeits, such as those made by Glazier Wheeler, the so-called "money maker of Cohoss, N.H."

In 1744 Wheeler was arrested for making false Spanish dollars from forged dies. The o above the m in the mintmark is too close to be genuine. Wheeler escaped from prison and is known to have made more fake 8-reales in 1785 in Massachusetts.

The 1792 piece illustrated in Brunk is different from that in the B&M sale.

This stamp could be a West Indies marking.

A. B. LORD

Rulau-E	Date	Metal	Size	VG	F	VF	EF
Mav 28M	(?)	Silver	39mm	20.00	—	30.00	—

A. B LORD / PRESNT / 1815 / FEBY. 1st ctsp on Spanish-American 1821-Zs-RG 8-reales. FEBY. is stamped over JANY. (?) (*World Coin News* for May 17, 1991, pg. 46; Brunk 24900)

I. M.

Rulau-E	Date	Metal	Size	VG	F	VF	EF
Mav 29	(?)	Copper	29mm	—	—	15.00	—

I . M in relief within toothed rect. depression ctsp on U.S. 1800 Large cent. (ANS coll., ex-Wittlin 1957)

P.M.

Rulau-E	Date	Metal	Size	G	F	VF	EF
Mav 30	1821	Copper	29mm (Cent)	—	15.00	—	—

U.S. 1795 Large cent ctsp: P inside small oval depression at center. Above is ctsp P M, to right 1821, at bottom 1821. (It has been theorized that this may be an early Peale's Museum admission check of Philadelphia).

This could also be the mark of silversmith Peter Mood Sr. (1766-1821) of Charleston, S.C., or his son, Peter Mood Jr. (1796-1879).

R. METCALF

Rulau-E	Date	Metal	Size	VG	F	VF	EF
Mav 30E	1833	Silver	40mm	—	85.00	125.	—

ADAMS / 1833. ctsp on France 1732 or 1734-BB ecu. Another punch ctsp on the same side reads: R. METCALF (curved) / (Eagle) / WARRANTED (curved). (B&M 1986 Von Stetten sale, lot 5055; Brunk 260 and 27490)

Neither Adams nor Metcalf have been identified, but Metcalf undoubtedly was a maker of guns, cutlery or tools. Brunk also lists the ADAMS / 1833. stamp on a 1732 French ecu, so the issuer establishes a pattern which may be followed.

M. MILLER

Rulau-E	Date	Metal	Size	VG	F	VF	EF
Mav 31	1822	Copper	29mm	—	15.00	—	—

1822 / M. MILLER / 26 ctsp. on U.S. 1851 Large cent. (Brunk 27840)

E. MORSE

Rulau-E	Date	Metal	Size	VG	F	VF	EF
Mav 31C	(?)	Silver	24mm	—	25.00	—	—

E. MORSE ctsp on England 1825/3 shilling of George IV, KM-687. (Rulau coll.; Brunk 28519)

NICHOLS

Rulau-E	Date	Metal	Size	VG	F	VF	EF
Mav 32	(?)	Silver	40mm	—	—	—	325.

NICHOLS in relief within rect. depression ctsp on obverse of U.S. 1799 silver dollar. Rv: Large I N in relief within toothed rect. depression ctsp on reverse of the coin. (Bowers & Merena sale of Nov. 14, 1990, lot 1832)

This obviously important piece cannot be attributed because of the insufficient knowledge we have of silversmith hallmarkings. The NICHOLS stamp, itself, would seem to indicate issuance by William Stoddard Nichols of Newport, R.I., active as a silversmith 1808-1860. But the IN mark is probably of the same silversmith, and no known mark of any early I. Nichols or J. Nichols matches. One James Nichols of Charleston, S.C. would have been 50 in 1800, but his mark(s) are not recorded. Thus we must, regretfully, report this item as a maverick for now.

Rulau-E	Date	Metal	Size	VG	F	VF	EF
Mav 32E	(?)	Copper	29mm	—	—	—	100.

NICHOLS in relief within rect. depression ctsp on U.S. 1808 Large cent. (Brunk 29620)

Stamp 32E also appears on an 1863 Indian cent!

Some authorities claim the issuer was silversmith Bassett Nichols of Providence, R.I., active circa 1815.

E. L. NORFOLK (and) T. PARKER

Rulau-E	Date	Metal	Size	VG	F	VF	EF
Mav 33	(?)	Silver	27mm	—	25.00	—	—

E. L. NORFOLK / T. PARKER ctsp on U.S. 1821 Bust quarter dollar. (Partrick coll.; Brunk 29810)

J. O.

Rulau-E	Date	Metal	Size	VG	F	VF	EF
Mav 34	1820	Copper	29mm	—	25.00	—	—

J O / 1820 ctsp on U.S. Large cent, date illegible. (Kovacs coll.)

OLD STEVE

Rulau-E	Date	Metal	Size	VG	F	VF	EF
Mav 35	(?)	Silver	40mm	—	—	—	175.

OLDSTEVE incused, ctsp on U.S. 1800 Bust silver dollar reverse. (Arthur Newmark coll.; Coin Galleries sale of July 18, 1990, lot 2340; Brunk 30195)

A surname of Oldsteve is possible, but we prefer Old Steve for now.

H. OB.

Rulau-E	Date	Metal	Size	VG	F	VF	EF
Mav 35B	(?)	Copper	29mm	—	—	15.00	—

H . OB in relief within toothed rect. depression ctsp on U.S. 1797 Large cent. (ANS coll., ex-Wittlin 1957)

A P * C

Rulau-E	Date	Metal	Size	VG	F	VF	EF
Mav 35D	(?)	Silver	39mm	—	—	75.00	—

A P * C ctsp on U.S. 1795 Flowing Hair silver dollar. (Bob Stark report)

B. P.

Rulau-E	Date	Metal	Size	VG	F	VF	EF
Mav 35E	(?)	Silver	27mm	—	15.00	—	—

B. P in relief within recessed square ctsp on Spanish-American 2-reales. (Gould 415ff)

A possible silversmith's mark would be that of B. Peck, Connecticut, circa 1820.

W. P.

Rulau-E	Date	Metal	Size	VG	F	VF	EF
Mav 35G	(?)	Copper	29mm	—	15.00	—	—

W P ctsp on Voce Populi 1760 cent, Z-2A. (Kirtley Jan. 1991 price list)

M. PAWLING

Rulau-E	Date	Metal	Size	VG	F	VF	EF
Mav 35S	1830	Copper	29mm	—	15.00	—	—

M. PAWLING ctsp on reverse of U.S. 1818 Large cent. Rv: 1830 ctsp on opposite side of coin. (Brunk 31667)

F. PERKINS

Rulau-E	Date	Metal	Size	VG	F	VF	EF
Mav 35V	(?)	Copper	29mm	—	—	50.00	—

F. PERKINS ctsp on U.S 1783 Nova Constellatio cent. (PC&AC Nathan Eglit sale, June 1992, lot 029; Brunk 31667)

P. PIERCE

Rulau-E	Date	Metal	Size	VG	F	VF	EF
Mav 36	(?)	Silver	32.5mm	—	—	—	85.00

P. PIERCE ctsp on U.S. 1807 Bust-Heraldic Eagle half dollar. (Krause collection; Brunk 32097)

J. POWELL

Rulau-E	Date	Metal	Size	VG	F	VF	EF
Mav 36K	(1815-20)	Copper	27.5mm	—	—	—	175.

J POWELL in an arc ctsp on obverse of George Washington "double head" cent of supposed 1783 vintage. Rv: I.P ctsp twice on reverse of the coin. (Rulau coll., ex-Tanenbaum; Brunk 32627)

This is the only counterstamp ever reported on a Washington Double Head cent, an undated Colonial coin issued about 1815. The coin was Fine-plus when it received the incuse marks.

SCRIPT R

Rulau-E	Date	Metal	Size	VG	F	VF	EF
Mav 36R	(?)	Copper	29mm	15.00	—	25.00	—

Fancy script R ctsp on U.S. 1803 Large cent. (Brunk 33310)

Rulau-E	Date	Metal	Size	VG	F	VF	EF
Mav 36S	(?)	Silver	27mm	—	—	—	—

Similar ctsp on Spanish-American 2-reales. Dates examined: 1798, 1801. Two specimens known.

S. W. REED

Rulau-E	Date	Metal	Size	VG	F	VF	EF
Mav 37	(?)	Copper	29mm	—	25.00	—	—

S. W. REED in relief within toothed rectangular depression ctsp on U.S. 1816 Large cent. Also crude Masonic device and TOOL-MASTER ctsp on obverse. Rv: Same Reed cartouche ctsp on reverse of coin. (Brunk 33730)

There may be no connection, but an 1851 Large cent occurs ctsp: S.W. REED / 1872.

RIVERS

Rulau-E	Date	Metal	Size	VG	F	VF	EF
Mav 37C	(?)	Silver	32.5mm	100.	—	150.	—

RIVERS in relief within rect. depression ctsp twice, at right angles, on U.S. Bust half dollar. Dates examined: 1809, 1813, 1818, 1820. Four specimens known. (Brunk 34500)

Brunk (1993) called this a very early advertising mark, probably issued in the 1820's. He also noted the stamps were applied carelessly, so that first or last letters were not impressed.

S. B. RUNNELS

Rulau-E	Date	Metal	Size	VG	F	VF	EF
Mav 37T	(?)	Copper	29mm	—	25.00	—	—

S. B. RUNNELS ctsp on U.S. Fugio 1787 cent, Newman 10-T. (B&M Hoke Green sale, lot 2397; Brunk 35300)

B. S.

Rulau-E	Date	Metal	Size	VG	F	VF	EF
Mav 38	(?)	Copper	29mm	—	—	—	15.00

B * S in relief with toothed rect. depression ctsp on early U.S. Large cent of 1804-08 type. (Smithsonian Institution coll.)

C. S.

Rulau-E	Date	Metal	Size	VG	F	VF	EF
Mav 38B	(?)	Copper	29mm	—	15.00	—	—

Large crude C . S in relief within dotted rect. depression with wavy field, ctsp on reverse of U.S. Large cent of early Matron Head type, circa 1816-35. (Kovacs coll.)

H. S.

Rulau-E	Date	Metal	Size	VG	F	VF	EF
Mav 38C	(?)	Copper	29mm	—	—	20.00	—

H : S in relief within rectangular depression ctsp on U.S. 1803 Large cent. (Joseph Schmidt coll.)

I. S.

Rulau-E	Date	Metal	Size	VG	F	VF	EF
Mav 38E	(?)	Copper	29mm	—	20.00	—	—

I . S ctsp on U.S. early Large cent, circa 1803, date worn off. (Coll. of Michael Hoffman, Clinton, Mich.)

It is possible this is an unrecorded mark of silversmith John Sayre of New York, active 1796-1813. He and his brother Joel Sayre were in partnership with Thomas Richards as Sayre & Richards 1802-13. John Sayre worked in Cohoes, N.Y. after 1814.

S. & D.

Rulau-E	Date	Metal	Size	VG	F	VF	EF
Mav 37X	(?)	Silver	40mm	100.	—	150.	—

S & D in relief within toothed rect. depression ctsp on U.S. 1801 Bust silver dollar. (Brunk 35433)

Rulau-E	Date	Metal	Size	VG	F	VF	EF
Mav 37Y	(?)	Silver	32.5mm	—	60.00	—	100.

Similar ctsp on U.S. Bust half dollar. Examined: 1806, 1814. Two specimens known.

S + R

Rulau-E	Date	Metal	Size	VG	F	VF	EF
Mav 38Q	(?)	Copper	29mm	—	20.00	—	—

S + R in relief within toothed square depression ctsp on U.S. 1802 Large cent. (Rulau-E NY 660)

This token formerly was attributed to the New York silversmith firm of Sayre & Richards ca 1802-13. We have examined a number of marks used by the partners and find the S + R mark quite unlike them.

J. T. S.

Rulau-E	Date	Metal	Size	VG	F	VF	EF
Mav 39	1830	Copper	25.5mm	—	—	35.00	—

J. T. S. / 1830 stamped on planchet. Rv: Same incused (intaglio?). (Wright 527)

SCHIVELY

Rulau-E	Date	Metal	Size	VG	F	VF	EF
Mav 40	(?)	Copper	28mm	—	100.	—	—

SCHI / VELY neatly ctsp on obverse of U.S. 1787 Fugio cent, Newman type 17-S1. Rv: Same ctsp on reverse of coin. Both stamps are carefully applied in small letters at center of coin. (B&M Hoke Green 1985 sale, lot 2398; Brunk 35780)

C. SCOTT

Rulau-E	Date	Metal	Size	VG	F	VF	EF
Mav 41	(?)	Silver	32.5mm	—	45.00	—	—

C. SCOTT in large letters ctsp on U.S. 1809 Turban Head half dollar. (Rulau coll.; Brunk 35860)

Possibly Charles Scott, Pennyan, N.Y. silversmith in 1839.

G. STERRETT

Rulau-E	Date	Metal	Size	VG	F	VF	EF
Mav 41E	(?)	Silver	40mm	—	—	—	175.

G. STERRETT incused, ctsp on U.S. 1798 Bust silver dollar. (Arthur Newmark coll.; Coin Galleries sale of Nov. 1989, lot 3156; Brunk 38313)

P. STOW

Rulau-E	Date	Metal	Size	VG	F	VF	EF
Mav 42	(?)	Copper	29mm	—	20.00	—	—

P. STOW in relief within crude rectangular depression ctsp on U.S. 1801 Large cent. (Kurt Krueger coll.; Brunk 38660)

STROHECKER

Rulau-E	Date	Metal	Size	VG	F	VF	EF
Mav 44	(?)	Silver	40mm	—	—	250.	—

STROHECKER ctsp on each side of U.S. 1796 small date, large letters silver dollar. (Only known specimen reported 1983 by Harvey Gamer; Brunk 38780)

It is possible this is connected with H.F. Strohecker, importer and gun dealer of Charleston, S.C., circa 1854.

L. S. SWAN

Rulau-E	Date	Metal	Size	VG	F	VF	EF
Mav 44K	(?)	Copper	29mm	75.00	—	125.	—

L. S. SWAN in relief within rect. depression ctsp on U.S. Large cent. Examined: 1812, 1816, 1818, 1820, unknown date. Five specimens reported. (Brunk 38980)

Rulau-E	Date	Metal	Size	VG	F	VF	EF
Mav 44K	(?)	Silver	32.5mm	100.	—	150.	—

Similar ctsp on U.S. 1817 Bust half dollar.

Rulau-E	Date	Metal	Size	VG	F	VF	EF
Mav 44K	(?)	Silver	27mm	100.	—	150.	—

Similar ctsp on Spanish-American 1776 2-reales.

One report spelled this stamp as L. S. SWANN. It is, potentially, an important early U.S. issue.

T

Rulau-E	Date	Metal	Size	VG	F	VF	EF
Mav 45	(?)	Copper	29mm	—	20.00	—	—

'T' in toothed heart-shaped depression ctsp on U.S. 1822 Large cent. (Steinberg Jan. 1982 sale)

T

Rulau-E	Date	Metal	Size	VG	F	VF	EF
Mav 45C	(?)	Copper	29mm	—	25.00	—	—

'T' (serif-type, large) in relief within T-shaped depression ctsp on U.S. 1829 Large cent. (ANS coll.)

C.T. / (Unicorn)

Rulau-E	Date	Metal	Size	VG	F	VF	EF
Mav 46	(?)	Copper	23mm	—	50.00	—	75.00

(Unicorn head left) / C T (large) ctsp incuse on U.S. Half cent. Dates examined: 1800, 1804, 1805, 1809, 1828, 1829. 1855. There are 25 specimens reported. (Kurt R. Krueger, John D. Irwin, Frank Kovacs, Hartzog and Rulau collections; Van Ormer sale 2931; Brunk 6460)

Rulau-E	Date	Metal	Size	VG	F	VF	EF
Mav 46A	(?)	Silver	21mm	—	75.00	—	125.

Similar ctsp on Spanish-American 1807-Mo 1-real.

Collectors advance the theory that the issuer was a cigar brand proprietor. The unicorn head also resembles a cigar and its smoke!

C.T.

Rulau-E	Date	Metal	Size	VG	F	VF	EF
Mav 46F	(?)	Copper	29mm	—	20.00	—	—

Large C.T. in relief within toothed rectangular depression ctsp on U.S. Large cent. Dates examined: 1805, 1807, 1828, 1828-13 stars. (Hartzog coll.; Presidential Coin & Antique June 1985 sale, lot 566)

Rulau-E	Date	Metal	Size	VG	F	VF	EF
Mav 46G	(?)	Copper	23mm	—	30.00	—	—

C.T. in relief ctsp on U.S. Half cent. Dates examined: 1794, 1803, 1805, 1807, 1808, 1809, 1826, 1828, 1829. There are 19 pieces known. (Duffield 1577; Hallenbeck 3.254)

Rulau-E	Date	Metal	Size	VG	F	VF	EF
Mav 46H	(?)	Copper	21mm	—	30.00	—	—

Similar ctsp on Netherlands cent.

There is no connection between numbers 46, and 46F except the common initials and date similarities. It is certain that each is, in its own way, a logotype for some sort of mercantile operation not yet traced.

E. T.

Rulau-E	Date	Metal	Size	VG	F	VF	EF
Mav 47	(?)	Copper	29mm	—	—	25.00	—

Serif-style E. T. in relief within rectangular depression ctsp on U.S. 1803 Large cent. (Pete Peters coll.)

I.T.

Rulau-E	Date	Metal	Size	VG	F	VF	EF
Mav 48	(?)	Copper	29mm	—	—	25.00	—

Large ornate I . T in relief within serrated rect. depression ctsp on U.S. 1801 Draped Bust Large cent, which had a heavy obverse die break above RTY before counterstamping. (Kovacs coll.)

S. THOMAS

Rulau-E	Date	Metal	Size	VG	F	VF	EF
Mav 49	(?)	Copper	29mm	—	15.00	—	—

S. THOMAS ctsp on U.S. 1796 Large cent. (Brunk 39773)

W.S.T.P.R. CO.

Rulau-E	Date	Metal	Size	VG	F	VF	EF
Mav 51	(?)	Brass	Rect 36x23mm	—	—	200.	—

(All Incused): W. S. / Co. / No. 2 / T. / P. R. Rv: Blank. (Kirtley May 1992 sale, lot 1569)

P.R. = Plank road. This previously unpublished transportation token is most likely from New England or Pennsylvania.

WAGNER

Rulau-E	Date	Metal	Size	VG	F	VF	EF
Mav 52	(1820's)	Silver	19mm	—	—	125.	—
		WAGNER incused, ctsp on U.S. 1814 Bust dime. 1 Known. (Brunk 41430; Duffield 1428)					
Mav 52B	(1820's)	Silver	26mm	75.00	—	125.	—
		Similar ctsp on U.S. Bust quarter. Dates examined: 1814, 1818, 1819. 3 pieces known.					
Mav 52C	(1820's)	Silver	40mm	—	—	—	315.
		Similar ctsp on U.S. 1799 Bust silver dollar.					
Mav 52H	(1820's)	Silver	21mm	—	200.	—	300.
		Similar ctsp on Spanish-American Carlos III 1-real and 1774 1-real.					
Mav 52J	(1820's)	Silver	27mm	75.00	—	125.	—
		Similar ctsp on Spanish-American 2-reales. Dates examined: 1777, 1780, 1783. 3 pieces known.					

This early advertising counterstamp thus far has defied attribution. Also known on 1819 half dollar.

WHITCOM

Rulau-E	Date	Metal	Size	VG	F	VF	EF
Mav 54X	(?)	Silver	32.5mm	—	30.00	—	—
		WHITCOM ctsp on U.S. 1807 Bust half dollar. (Brunk 42930)					

A. WHITCOM

Rulau-E	Date	Metal	Size	VG	F	EF
Mav 55	1827	Copper	29mm	100.	—	200.
		A. WHITCOM 1827.6 in script in relief ctsp on U.S. 1806 and 1827 Large cent. (Hallenbeck 23.509; Brunk 42940)				
Mav 56	1827	Silver	32.5mm	150.	—	225.
		Similar ctsp on U.S. Bust half dollar. Dates examined: 1800, 1806, 1817, 1826. Only 4 known. (Don Ketterling coll.; Harvey Gamer coll.)				
Mav 57	1827	Silver	27mm	150.	—	225.
		Similar ctsp on Spanish-American 2-reales. Examined: 1779, 1793. Only 2 known.				

This is a commemorative advertising counterstamp. The 1827.6 refers to June, 1827.

This stamp is definitely connected with the next item, Mav 58.

The Gamer specimen was sold in 1982 for $350; it was an 1826 half dollar. The Ketterling specimen (an 1806 half dollar) was offered the same year for $300.

H. WHITCOM

Rulau-E	Date	Metal	Size	VG	F	VF	EF
Mav 58	1827	Silver	27mm	—	—	—	400.
		July 1827 / H. Whitcom (all in script) in relief within large finely-dentilated rectangular depression ctsp on Spanish-American 1779-So-DA 2-reales. The ctsp has been applied twice, at right angles to form a cross. The word 'July' is not clear; it could as easily be 'Jany' or 'June'. (Holland Wallace coll., Sausalito, Calif.)					

We have examined Mav 58 minutely. It differs from Mav 55-57 as noted above, yet these pieces are definitely linked.

Rulau-E	Date	Metal	Size	VG	F	VF	EF
Mav 58E	(?)	Copper	29mm	—	50.00	—	75.00
		H. WHITCOM ctsp on U.S. 1837 Large cent. (Brunk 42950)					
Mav 58F	(?)	Silver	32.5mm	—	—	100.	—
		Similar ctsp on U.S. 1831 Bust half dollar					

Rulau-E	Date	Metal	Size	VG	F	VF	EF
Mav 58K	1833	Silver	21mm	—	200.	—	—
		H. WHITCOM / 1833 in relief in separate rect. punches ctsp on Spanish-American Carlos IIII 1-real of 1792- 1808 type. The second '3' of the date appears to be cut over another numeral on the die. (Chester Krause coll.; Low 410: HT 469)					

WHITCOMB. ADAMS

Rulau-E	Date	Metal	Size	VG	F	VF	EF
Mav 59	(?)	Silver	27mm	50.00	—	75.00	—
		WHITCOMB. ADAMS (script) in relief within rect. depression ctsp on Spanish-American 1819 and worn-date 2-reales. (Van Ormer sale 2502)					

The worn-date piece is also ctsp 1838. Adams, Mass. has been suggested for these pieces.

O. R. WHITCOMB

Rulau-E	Date	Metal	Size	VG	F	EF
Mav 59E	(?)	Silver	27mm	—	—	45.00
		(Script) O.R. Whitcomb. engraved neatly on king's bust on Spanish-American 1800-LME-IJ 2-reales. (Rulau coll., ex-Wonder)				

HANN(A)H WINTER

Rulau-E	Date	Metal	Size	VG	F	VF
Mav 61	1778	Silver	32mm	—	—	60.00
		(Engraved on planed-off sides). Large ornate script monogram HW circled by double fret border at rim. Rv: (All script) within fret border at rim: HANNH: WINTER / DAUGHTER OF / WILLIAM & HANNH / WINTER BORN / NOVR. YE. 29 / 1778.				

Generally, engraved pieces (so-called "love tokens") are avoided in this reference. This piece is included as a classic example of the "birth token" prevalent among upper classes at this period. Though it has not been traced, this type of engraved coin would be easiest to attribute, since it contains so much precise information.

The underlying coin may have been a Spanish-American 4-reales or English half crown. The people involved could have been English rather than American.

K 1830

Rulau-E	Date	Metal	Size	VG	F	VF
Mav 65	1830	Copper	29mm	—	25.00	—
		K / 1830. 2. d. 9 ctsp on U.S. 1827 Large cent. (Stanley L. Steinberg 1983 sale)				

It has been suggested the '2. d. 9' might be an English denomination, but this seems unlikely. The 9 could be a g.

EAGLE, 18

Rulau-E	Date	Metal	Size	VG	F	EF
Mav 80	(?)	Silver	21mm	—	50.00	—
		Series of four hallmarks arranged vertically, ctsp on Spanish-American 1797-Mo-FM 1-real. On obverse: Eagle-Windmill-18-Scales. On reverse: Windmill-18-Eagle. (Kurt Krueger Sept. 7, 1983 sale, lot 153)				

The hallmarks seem to be American or European, but no trace of them can be found in the standard references on silver and pewter ware by Kovel, Wyler or others. The eagle seems distinctly American.

(PRANCING HORSE)

Rulau-E	Date	Metal	Size	VG	F	VF	EF
Mav 82	(?)	Copper	29mm	—	—	—	325

Prancing horse left in high relief ctsp on Kentucky pyramid cent token of circa 1792-94. Plain edge. (Kirtley Dec 1992 fixed price list, page 1)

(POMEGRANATES ?)

Rulau-E	Date	Metal	Size	VG	F	VF	EF
Mav 85	(?)	Copper	29mm	—	35.00	—	—

Pomegranate-like fruit ctsp three times on U.S. 1796 Draped Bust Large cent. (Frank Kovacs coll.)

It is not certain a pomegranate is shown here. The only other pomegranate appearance on a counterstamped coin in the U.S. series of which we are aware is that of Carlos C. Clark of Nashua, N.H., 1859 (Miller NH 8 in our *U.S. Merchant Tokens 1845-1860*, 3rd ed.)

The Clark pomegranate is traditional in shape, unlike those above. The stampings above are from a neat, prepared punch.

MISCELLANEOUS EARLY COUNTERSTAMPS (All on U.S. coins unless specified)

NA within rectangle (twice)	on 1803 Large cent
W. CAPEN	on 1797 Large cent (Koppenhaver Nov. 1983 sale, lot 546; Brunk 6720)

J. EGGERT	on 1807 half dollar (Hal Blackburn coll.; Brunk 13105)
D.T.	on 1808 Large cent
TROY	on 1809 Half cent (Brunk 40520; Koppenhaver Nov. 1983 sale, lot 555)
-do—	on 1848 Large cent
U S VII	on Bust-type Large cent (Koppenhaver Nov. 1983 sale, lot 562)
S.P.H. WHITE	on 1818 Large cent (Brunk 43095)
1821	on 1805 Large cent (Koppenhaver Nov. 1983 sale, lot 569)
1825 (in serrated rect. punch)	on 1788 Connecticut cent, Miller 15.1-L.1 (B&M 1990 Schenkel sale, lot 4113) ($50)

Hard Times Tokens

A complete revision and enlargement of Lyman H. Low's 1899 classic reference.

"Hard Times in 1837" (From the Library of Congress)

LOW NUMBER INDEX

This ready-finding index enables collectors who keep their holdings by Low numbers to determine its new Hard Times (HT) number.

Low No.	HT No.
1	1
1A	2
1B	3
2	4
3	5
3A	5A
4	6
4A	6A
5	7
5A	8
6	14
6A	14A
6B	14B
6C	14C
7	15
7B	15B
7C	15C
7D	15D
8	9
9	10
9B	10A
10	11
11	12
11A	12A
12	25
12A	25A
13	26
13A	26A
14	27
14A	27A
15	28
15A	28A
16	30
16A	30A
16B	30B
17	31
17B	31B
18	32
19	33
19A	33A
20	34
21	35
22	36
23	37
24	38
25	39
26	40
26A	40A
26B	40B
27	41
27A	41A
28	42
29	44
30	45
31	46
32	47
33	48
33A	48A
34	49
35	50
36	51
37	61
38	62
39	52
40	65
41	53
41A	53A
42	54
42A	54A
43	55
43A	55A
44	69
45	56
46	57
47	66
47A	66A
48	67
49	73
50	74

Low No.	HT No.
51	70
52	71
53	72
54	81
54A	82
54B	81A
55	63
56	75
57	76
58	16
59	17
60	18
61	19
62	20
62A	20A
62C	20B
63	21
64	22
64A	22A
65	23
66	24
67	68
68	64
69	58
70	59
70A	59A
71	60
71A	60A
72	175
72A	175A
73	176
73A	176A
74	428
74A	428A
75	152
76	153
77	348
78	427
79	361
80	157
81	200
82	123
82A	124
82B	125
82C	126
83	150
84	158
85	121
85A	121A
86	174
87	347
87A	347A
88	350
89	349
90	351
91	352
92	353
92A	354
93	355
94	425
95	291
96	292
97	293
98	294
99	216
100	217
101	218
102	187
102A	188
102B	188A
103	154
104	155
105	156
106	129
106A	129A
107	219
108	430
109	104
110	239

Low No.	HT No.
111	240
111A	240A
112	243
113	244
114	249
115	250
116	172
116A	172A
117	262
117A	262A
118	263
119	265
119B	266
120 vars	268
121	117
122	283
123	284
124	194
125	289
126	290
127	304
128	309
129	169
129A	169A
130	105
130A	107
130R	106
131	192-193
132	195
133	311
133B	312
134	313
135	314
136	315
137	316
138	317
139	464
140	334
141	335
142	205
143	206
144	206A
145 vars	356-358
146	359
147	360
148	204
149	413
150	202
151	272
152	412
153	305
154	306
155	204B
156	366
157	367
158	377
158A	377A
159	378
160 vars	379 vars
161	211
162	77
163	201
163A	201A
164	151-159
165	2A
166	1A
167	3A
168	13
168R	13R
169	29
169A	29A
170	43
171	70A
172	75A
172A	75B
173	139
174	347B
175	433
176	434

Low No.	HT No.
176A	434A
177	187A
178	187B
179A	267
180	205
180A	205A
181	399
182	399A
182A	389
183	77A
190	78
191	78A
192	79
193	79A
194	83
194A	83A
198	85
199	86
200	220
201	221
202	222
203	223
204	224
205	224A
206	226
206A	226A
207	227
208	227A
209	228
210	228A
210A	229
211	386
212	387
212A	388
213	390
214	391
215	392
216	393
217	394
218	395
219	396
220	235
221	335A
222	236
223	236A
224	237
225	237A
226	238
227	403
227A	404
228	405
229	405A
230	406
230A	406A
231	406B
232	407
233	241
234	182
235	182A
236	115
236A	115A
237	116
238A	245
238B	246
239	247
240	247A
241	248
242	255
243	256
244	257
245 vars	258-259
246	408
247	260
248	261
249	269
250	270
251	275
252	276
253	277

Low No.	HT No.
254	120
254A	119
254B	119A
255	278
256	279
257	282
258	282A
259	285
260	285A
261	286
262	287
262A	287A
263	288
264	122
265	163
266	164
267	165
267A	166
268	302
269	303
270	303A
271	363
272	364
272A	365
273	307
273A	307A
274	308
274A	308A
275	441
276	441A
277	441B
278	234
279	318
279A	318A
279B	319
280	320
280A	320A
281	321
282	322
282A	323
283 vars	324-325
284 vars	368-371
285	332
286	333
287	336
288	128
289	M26
290	M27
291	102
292	242
293	440
294	440A
295	273
296	273A
297	273B
298	274
300	181
301	181A
301A	181B
302	207
303	207A
304	207B
305	101
306	M3
307	M4
308	M5
309	M6
309A	M7
310	253
311	254
312	375
312A	375A
313 vars	376
314	162
315	110
316	110A
317	344
318	345
318A	346

Low No.	HT No.
319	380
320 vars	381
321	295
322	296
323	297
324	212
324A	212A
325	167
326	160 & 168
326A	161
327	170
328	171
328A	171A
329	340
330	340A
331	341
332	342
335	251
336	252
338	230
340	135
341	135A
342	136
343	137
344	118
348	210
349	210A
350 vars	231
351 vars	435
352	456
353	420
356	419
357	419A
358	418
359	418A
360	280
361	280A
362	280B
363	281
364	M17
365	339
366	M19
367 vars	M20-M22
368	M23
368A	M24
369	372
370	298
371	299
372	300
374	203
375	M9
378	132
379	133
379A	134
380	457
382	84
383	410
383A	410A
384 vars	421
385	411
386	417
386A	417A
387	215
388	215A
389	215B
392 vars	337
395 vars	327-328
396 vars	329
398	385
400 vars	140-144
403 vars	147-148
404	402
415	M1
417	271
418	416

INTRODUCTION

The series known as Hard Times tokens comprises tokens issued privately in the United States from 1833 to 1844. The pieces, mostly made of copper and the size of a United States cent of the period, can be divided into several categories:

(1) Pieces referring to the Bank of the United States and the controversy surrounding it.

(2) Those with inscriptions relating to political and satirical situations of the era.

(3) Tokens with inscriptions and designs closely resembling the regular cent coinage, but with some differences in order to evade the counterfeiting laws.

(4) Examples bearing the advertisements of private merchants - "Store cards."

(5) Die mulings: Combinations with the obverses or reverses of any of the preceding.

The Hard Times tokens with political motifs center on issues of the Andrew Jackson and Martin Van Buren Administrations (1829-1841).

Andrew Jackson, military hero of the Battle of New Orleans in 1815, defeated President John Quincy Adams' reelection bid in 1828. Jackson, not an educated man, was the subject of much ridicule. His "Roman firmness" was mentioned on tokens, as was his statement made at a Democratic banquet in April 1839: "Our federal union must be preserved," or as it was sometimes quoted, "Our federal union, it must and shall be preserved."

In 1832 Harvard College conferred upon Jackson an honorary Doctorate of laws. This LLD degree caused much amusement. As Lyman H. Low has written, "The judicious grieved, and his enemies rejoiced at the absurdity of the title; and it was not long before the honorary degree appeared upon a token which ridiculed him."

On one of the most widely circulated tokens of the era, Jackson is depicted emerging from a chest of money holding a purse in one hand and a sword in the other. This was a reference to the fear, subsequently reported in the *Albany Argus* on Oct. 1, 1842, that the liberties of the Union were threatened "by union of the purse and the sword in the same hands," a reference in this instance to the following administration of Martin Van Buren. Presidential power over the nation's money and military has been the subject for concern at intermittent intervals since that time.

In 1832 Jackson campaigned against Henry Clay. The president's stand against the Second Bank of the United States struck a popular chord and resulted in an overwhelming victory for him. In order to lessen the effectiveness of the Bank, which was chartered to continue until 1836, Jackson removed federal deposits from it and placed them in state banks. This and his July 1836 Specie Circular were among the causes of the nationwide financial panic of 1837 and the consequent depression.

In May 1836 Martin Van Buren, Jackson's vice president, was nominated for the presidency. His platform included opposition to rechartering the Bank of the United States. During his administration the main problem concerned the nation's depressed economy. Van Buren urged that an independent Treasury be established apart from the United States government and that the Treasury surplus not be distributed to the states.

His stand on this and other issues alienated many conservative Democrats and at the same time caused him to be denounced by the Whigs.

In his inaugural address Van Buren declared, "I follow in the steps of my illustrious predecessor," a reference to Jackson. Caricaturists of the time represented the newly-elected president carefully stepping in the footprints of a jackass, a sentiment which extended itself to certain tokens of the time. Seeking reelection, he was defeated overwhelmingly by William Henry Harrison in the 1840 election campaign.

Damaged by the wild issue of bank paper money in the West, and excessive speculation in the public lands, President Jackson put a stop to it - so drastically that the country plunged from inflation into disaster just weeks after Van Buren's inauguration.

On July 11, 1836 Jackson issued the Specie Circular, declaring that deposit banks and receivers of public money could accept nothing but gold or silver coin for the sale of public lands after Aug. 15. Jackson hoped this move would halt the ruinous speculation in public lands and curb the rampant inflation. The results proved destructive in practice, and in timing.

The result was to drain much of the gold westward. Consternation reigned in the East. Loans were called. In March 1837 a panic in England caused American shock waves - three great cotton firms in New Orleans went bankrupt; 128 companies in New York went under by April.

In May a run on the nation's banks started and they suspended specie (coin) payments on May 10. By that summer, 90 percent of Eastern factories had shut down. Many people starved and froze in the winter of 1837-1838.

The Panic of 1837 resulted in hoarding of coins in circulation. This period is generally referred to as the Era of Hard Times, the title of which was later adapted to include tokens of the wider 1833-1844 period.

To fill the need for small change in circulation, a wide variety of copper tokens appeared in 1837. One issue bore the legend SUBSTITUTE FOR SHIN PLASTERS, a reference to the flood of often worthless paper money issues distributed by banks, merchants, canals, turnpikes and others, which were called Shinplasters and which had backing no stronger than the financial credit of the issuer, which was sometimes nil.

Important among the minters of Hard Times tokens was the firm of J.(ames) M.(itchell) L.(amson) & W.(illiam) H.(enry) Scovill, of Waterbury, Connecticut. This firm and its successors have a rich numismatic history. In 1862 Scovill produced encased postage stamps. Later the firm supplied planchets to the United States Mint for the production of nickel alloy coins, and it made Depression scrip in 1933. The Scovill Manufacturing Company is still in business today, though it sold off its brass works in the late 1970's.

Our friend and contributor H. Joseph Levine has come into Scovill Mfg. Co. correspondence which shows conclusively that certain tokens can be dated back to 1835, as that is when Scovill struck them for the merchants involved.

These are: James Watson, Philadelphia, HT 422; Stickney & Wilson, Montgomery, Ala., and Kohn Daron & Co., Memphis, Tenn. These valuable records enable us to confirm what research had begun to indicate - that all three issuers were Hard Times era people.

In Attleboro, Massachusetts, the firm of H.M. & E.I. Richards, controlled by two cousins, Herve Manning Richards and Edmund Ira Richards, produced a wide variety of Hard Times tokens.

A succession of firms built around James Bale operated to produce Hard Times merchant cards from 1829 through 1838 or later. Charles Cushing Wright, the great early American medalist, and Bale were in partnership in New York City from May 1829 to late 1833. Bale then was in business alone 1833-1835, and Bale and F.B. Smith were in business as Bale & Smith 1835-1838. The signatures of these combinations - W & B NY, BALE, B & S NY, Etc. - are found on cards of Atwood's Railroad Hotel, Bale & Smith, J. & L. Brewster, Doremus Suydam & Nixon, P. Evens, Nathan C. Folger, Hiram Judson, and others.

In Belleville, New Jersey, John Gibbs was a senior partner of Gibbs, Gardner & Co. His business was located in a building on the same premises as Stevens, Thomas & Fuller, a company which produced dies or struck minor coins for Brazil, Liberia, Santo Domingo and various private merchants. Stevens had earlier obtained his training in Birmingham, England. The coining facility became known as the Belleville Mint.

Many different pieces associated with the Hard Times token series, including some bearing the NOT ONE CENT reverse, were made there. Similar sized copper tokens known as Bouquet Sous were made at Belleville for circulation in Canada. The floral bouquet design was used in one instance as reverse for a token issued by William Gibbs, father of John Gibbs, who proclaimed himself an "agriculturist."

Low described 183 different types of tokens from the 1833-1844 period. These tokens, mostly the size of the contemporary U.S. large cent, circulated freely at the value of one cent. A profit was shown by the issuers who paid less than face value for them.

Whig political satire note of 1837 for 6 cents depicts six Jackson "cents" and a number of other symbols associated with his presidency - donkey, hickory leaf, tall hat and spectacles, and peace pipe. It was supposedly issued by the Humbug Glory Bank. Hundreds of parody bank notes were printed with quotes from Benton and Van Buren, this one borrowing from Daniel Webster's plaint, "The gold humbug exploded."

Eugene H. Richards, a descendant of one of the founders of H.M. & E.I. Richards, informed Low that the token manufacturing firm shipped pieces by the thousands in kegs to customers at 60 to 75 cents per hundred.

A token issued by Clark & Anthony (HT 425) was struck to the number of 36,000 pieces, for which the jewelry firm paid Richards $270.

The number of well worn Hard Times tokens in existence today is abundant proof of the status which these pieces once enjoyed as a circulating medium of exchange. By 1857, when the Large cents were replaced by small Flying Eagle cents, scattered examples were still to be seen in commercial channels.

SECOND BANK OF THE UNITED STATES

Alexander Hamilton's creation, the (First) Bank of the United States, was chartered in 1792 and expired in 1812. The Second Bank was chartered in April 1816 for 20 years. The federal government had a large interest in it as a shareholder and as a director. Both these measures were opposed by the Democratic Republican Party, which dropped the "Republican" part of their title a few years later and called themselves Democrats, but were stigmatized by their opponents as "Loco-Focos" - a name given them in consequence of an occurrence at an 1835 political gathering of Democrats in New York, when their adversaries attempted to break up the meeting by extinguishing the gas lights.

Some of the company present came prepared with "Locofoco matches" and candles in their pockets and they relighted the room, and continued the meeting.

In 1834 the National Republicans began to call themselves Whigs, because they considered Jackson as a kind of tyrant whom they opposed just as Whigs of an earlier time had opposed King George III, and the new party name will be found on some of the tokens.

Jackson believed the Bank operated to benefit the rich, and that it used public funds deposited with it to benefit special interest groups. Jackson's men charged that in the election of 1828 several branches used their funds to defeat Jackson.

Nicholas Biddle, the Bank's elegant president, denied the charges and they were never proved. When Congress voted to recharter the Bank in 1832, Jackson vetoed the measure and his veto was sustained. The Bank itself became the issue in the 1832 elections, in which Jackson defeated Henry Clay. Jackson gradually pulled all the government deposits out of the Bank, placing them in certain state banks, the so-called "pet banks."

The Bank of the United States and its 29 branches, facing liquidation as a government institution with the expiration of its federal charter in March 1836, obtained a charter in Feb. 1836 from the state of Pennsylvania. After the March expiration, it continued to do business as the Bank of the United States of Pennsylvania (though its later bank notes, drafts, bills of exchange, etc., seldom made any distinction from its old, familiar name.)

During 1838 most of the nation's banks resumed the specie payments they had suspended in May 1837, and the banking system appeared to be returning to normal, when suddenly in Oct. 1839 the Hard Times returned. The Bank of the U.S. of Pennsylvania, then the nation's largest state bank, suspended operations. It had overextended itself trying to help out the Southern cotton banks, which started crashing with a roar.

The Southern banks and most Pennsylvania banks suspended specie payments again and more than 100 small banks failed. Biddle resigned, but in Feb. 1841 his bank failed outright, owing other banks over $7.5 million. Its collapse shook the country and Southern banks suspended specie payments a third time. Some 91 more banks failed in 1841.

"King Andrew the First" tramples the Constitution in this contemporary Whig satirical cartoon.

TOKEN DESIGNS

Various influences made up the political issues of that period. Many of these pieces carried utterances of the statesmen of the time on two great issues - Jackson's hostility to the Bank, and Daniel Webster's defense of the Constitution - issues which extended into the presidency of Van Buren, whose declaration in his Inaugural, "I follow in the steps of my illustrious predecessor" was seized by the caricaturists of the day, who represented him as carefully stepping in the footprints of a jackass marching solemnly along the highway, which suggested a device found on one of the types.

Even the humourous legend, "A friend to the Constitution" with the figure of a steer, on the Gibbs tokens, doubtless refers to the speeches of Webster, the great expounder of the Constitution (as opposed to the Nullification theories of John C. Calhoun), and the defender of the Bank.

Many devices allude to the firmness of character justly attributed to Jackson, which his enemies chose to call stubborness, and the "jack" was the favorite symbol of this quality. Others refer to the burden laid upon the people by the refusal to grant a new charter to the Bank; to the destruction which seemed to one party to be the inevitable consequence of the acts of the other; to the ship of state, in danger of wreck, to indicate the ruin which would follow, or sailing proudly on with prospering gales to symbolize the prosperity which the nation would enjoy if the plans of friends of a high tariff and the Bank failed or succeeded; and to the Sub-treasury system of Van Buren stigmatized as an "Executive Experiment" and "Financiering" by his opponents.

The balky mule was probably suggested in a letter from Senator Thomas Hart Benton, written Aug. 11, 1837, and printed in the *New Yorker* on Sept. 2 that year, in which, praising Jackson, he said, "His policy has balked this system, etc," referring to a movement to issue paper money. To this letter he added a toast using the same words. From this opposition to the Bank, as announced by Jackson, came also the mottoes "My policy," "Veto" and similar catchwords.

The tortoise and safe are believed to allude to the slow and insecure method of moving the government deposits from the Bank to the state banks, or to the proposed Sub-treasuries. The phoenix probably alludes to the resumption of specie payment.

Of the legends, "The Constitution as I understand it" is quoted from Jackson's second Inaugural. "Executive Experiment" is a sneer at what one party judged as the stupidity of its opponent in employing banks as "Fiscal Agents." Jackson's policy, says Benton, in the letter cited above, had "fortified the country with 80 millions of hard money," and was a plan to require all payments to be made to or by the government in specie. It was really a "sound money" policy; as we look back on it we wonder that it aroused such bitter opposition from financiers of acknowledged ability, and that the Democrat Party which claims to be the legitimate successor of "Jacksonian Democracy," should have wandered since so far from the hard money precepts of its founder.

Advocates of the "State Bank Deposit System" - seemingly advanced as a compromise between friends of the U.S. Bank and its opponents - proposed that instead of requiring all payments to and from the government to pass directly through the national Treasury or its branches called Sub-treasuries, Congress should select some of the strongest banks throughout the country as depositories or "fiscal agents." This expression will be found on some tokens.

In an 1837 message to Congress, Van Buren advocated establishment of a Sub-treasury, with enactment of a law for the exaction of specie or Treasury paper for all payments due to government, and also requiring all demands against it to be paid, inflexibly, in coin. This scheme was called "most extraordinary" by opponents, but was advocated by Benton, Calhoun, Wright and others. We find references on the tokens to these schemes.

The phrase "Substitute for shinplasters" alludes to a folly of the time, the establishment of irresponsible state and private banks over which the government had no control. These banks issued notes of nominal value, ranging from 6-1/4 cents (half bit) upward, during the dearth of currency. Even the New York Joint Stock Exchange Company put out a bill of 12-1/2 cents printed from a copper plate engraved by Charles C. Wright, which was made payable "at one day sight to J. Smith or bearer, in current Bank Bills," duly signed by its officers, and embellished with a vignette of its fine building.

The country was overwhelmed with worthless fractional notes, which for a few months in 1837 seem to have driven out all coin from circulation. This miserable currency was popularly and contemptuously called "Shinplasters," "Red Dog" (perhaps from bills with red edges put out by one Jacob Barker of New York, who, when asked to redeem his pledges replied with much indifference that as soon as he could make arrangements to do so he would publish an advertisement to this effect), "Wildcat Money," "White Dog," "Blue Pup" and many other opprobrious names varying in different localities, but all satirical.

In the summer of 1837, "John Neale of 6 John Street, near Broadway, New York," and Valentine, at 50 John Street in the same city, advertised their readiness to "supply the present scarcity of specie." The plates were neatly engraved, the printed notes were kept on sale, and all that was necessary was to add a signature or two, with the location where they should be redeemed, and pay them out as money! These burlesques on a legitimate currency were forbidden in New York by a resolution of the Legislature which took effect May 7, 1839; their value vanished in a single night, and innocent holders all over the country were obliged to pocket their losses - which were enormous.

Gresham's Law - "Bad money drives the good from circulation" - had abundant proof.

The phrase "Millions for defense, but not one cent for tribute," is carried on many pieces. Charles Cotesworth Pinckney of South Carolina, U.S. minister to France in 1796, was declined reception by the French Directory, which hoped to force the U.S. to side with France against England. War was imminent and Talleyrand secretly sent word to Pinckney that it could be averted by the payment of large bribes to certain officials. This led to the sententious remark which at once raised its author to the highest point in American public esteem.

The cry was taken up again at the outbreak of the War against the Barbary Pirates, previous to which our government, in its days of weakness, had paid an annual tribute, as did most of the European powers, to the semi-barbarous rulers of North Africa. When its strength increased, and it was realized the tribute far exceeded the cost of maintaining a navy, the young Republic threw off the Barbary yoke; acting on the patriotic spirit embodied in the maxim, the frigates *Constitution, Congress, United States, Constellation,* and others, built to oppose French arrogance, settled the tribute forever with their guns at Tripoli.

It was still a phrase to conjure with when placed on these tokens, where it served as a protection for the coppers issued during the suspension of specie payments in Van Buren's new administration, so that they might truly be said to declare their character as a nonlegal coinage. The NOT ONE CENT of the Pinckney cry is always stressed on the tokens.

THE STORE CARDS

The Store Cards supplemented newspaper advertising in many cases. Most were placed in circulation in large cities where many other forms of advertising were also available. A few pieces, such as those of Walsh's General Store in Lansingburgh, N.Y., may have represented a primary advertising medium for their issuers.

Store Cards first appeared in New York in 1794, but between 1820 and 1825 they were introduced in a more widespread manner, and they held a place of utility until about 1860. While the original intent of these pieces was probably to advertise the wares, services or persons of the tradesmen, during the stringency of a circulating medium in the Hard Times, they were for a time accepted readily as currency - not alone by the customers of the issuers, but by the general public.

During the years 1828-1841 there were an estimated 10 to 20 million private tokens struck in the United States. In the same period the U.S. Mint struck only about 29 million copper cents. Thus the tokens represented a substantial portion of the cent pieces circulating in the Jacksonian era.

New theories were advanced in 1981 to explain why there were so many merchant cards issued from about 1828 through about 1841. These theories were embodied in Thomas Schweich's penetrating analysis. "Hard Times Tokens, Relics of Jacksonian America" (see Bibliography).

These studies advance the theory that the merchant tokens were *status symbols* for the wealthy merchant class in a very inegalitarian America - much as the British tokens of the 1789-1796 period were to *that* industrialized, unequal society. Schweich's theories deserve study by serious collectors of the HTT series.

New York City's wealthy families of the HT period were concentrated in the southern tip of Manhattan, near the Battery and along Broadway. Both the token issuers and the token engravers and manufacturers were located conveniently in their midst.

SOME NON-TRADITIONAL HTT USES

Plentiful contemporary circulation evidence exists to show that the U.S. Mint Bureau and U.S. Justice Department did a great deal of public posturing about the illegality of Hard Times tokens passing as money, but that this availed little in reality.

Hard Times tokens remained in circulation in the United States as long as the government's Large cent did, though in severely decreased numbers after the 1837-1841 period. The last Large cents were struck in 1857, but they did not disappear from circulation until the 1862 Civil War change shortage.

The famous Civil War coin hoarder Aaron White had a fair number of HTT's mixed with the Large cents and Small cents he had hoarded from the change in circulation.

The tokens found at least three other uses their creators never envisioned: (1) Circulation as halfpennies in Canada. (2) Host coins for the activities of counterstampers. (3) Blanks for making tokens of South America.

Almost any copper or brass disc from 27.5 to 29.5mm found acceptance in change-short Canada before the first national cents were struck in 1858. Some Bouquet sous were specially struck for use in Canada at the Belleville Mint, but other HTT's also saw use there. Hard Times tokens and U.S. Large cents circulated side by side in Canada with both English-produced and locally-struck tokens (many American cents and tokens were later counterstamped by such Canadian firms as Devins & Bolton and Rouleau).

U.S. counterstamps do not appear on HTT's with the frequency that they do on regular Large cents, but they occur frequently enough to define patterns. Some counterstamped HTT's appear in this reference when the time of their use is proper, but more appear in our catalogs covering the 1845-1860 and 1866-1889 periods (*U.S. Merchant Tokens and U.S. Trade Tokens*), respectively.

Hard Times tokens were overstruck by an American firm for use in Colombia, South America. Some of the 1838 tokens of Manuel Maria Pla of Cartagena, 1835-40 Velez Matos pieces, 1839-40 Manuel Angulo tokens of Barranquilla and 1840's Espinosa-Olier pieces are known on HTT's. Some 1844 Jose M. Ruiz tokens of Mompos also may have been struck this way.

Other tokens of the same design of the five issuers named were coined on fresh copper blanks.

Examination of the undertypes reveals that these HTT's were used for Colombian tokens: HT 16, 1841 Webster Credit Current; HT 53, 1837-dated Bushnell restrike; HT 69, 1837 Shipwreck; HT 154, 1836 R. & W. Robinson of Attleboro, Mass.; HT 291 and HT 293, 1837 Merchants Exchange of New York. The HT 53 report has not yet been verified.

Our new 1992 catalog, *Latin American Tokens*, details the Colombian connection.

ARRANGEMENT

The store cards are arranged both on a geographic and alphabetical basis. Thus all the store cards of New York, Boston, Philadelphia, etc. may be found together.

Some rearrangement of the political cards has been effected. To make hunting for "Low numbers" easier, a special up-front Index tells the reader what each Low number is now numbered.

The new 'HT' numbers are assigned along logical lines. A complete renumbering of all Hard Times tokens was long overdue, and this was accomplished in the Third edition of our catalog, and expanded in this largest edition.

Appendices cover quasi-HTT's, satirical notes, etc.

VALUATIONS

The 1980 Garrett II sale of Hard Times tokens produced such record high prices in what had been a long-dormant facet of the hobby that most experts assumed the Garrett prices were an aberration. People simply wanted an ex-Garrett specimen in their holdings.

Garrett II proved not to have been an aberration, but rather a harbinger of things to come. In quick order came the Garrett IV, Harte, Chesterfield, NASCA HTT, Kessler-Spangenberger and Levine and other sales - plus the Hartzog and smaller groupings and - lo and behold - the Garrett II prices seem modest indeed from hindsight advantage!

Bidders found the only way they could purchase the truly rare, choice HTT's at public auction was by continuing their floor bidding beyond all their own pre-sale estimates of "top dollar." Mail bidders were mostly frozen out in the process. Far from discouraging new collectors, the constantly higher prices seemed to be spurring them to vigorous pursuit of elusive specimens.

The first three editions of this catalog arrived at a fortuitous upswing in American appreciation for the token. They benefited from - but also helped expand - that movement.

Valuations included herein reflect the actual record prices paid at auction recently for rarities, as well as dealers' retail prices on the more available items. A panel of top professional exonumists has arrived at the published valuations, and an especial debt is owed to Robert A. Vlack, H. Joseph Levine and George J. Fuld, who determined Rarity ratings for this edition.

Prices tumbled in the 1982-85 period from their 1980-81 Garrett highs, and the Third Edition recognized this moderation in values.

IMPORTANT: Uncirculated HTT's.

A special note about the Uncirculated prices in this catalog: Our Unc. prices are given for attractive, part red, no problem pieces that are unquestionably uncirculated - roughly equivalent to the MS 63 grading standard of United States coins. Many pieces sold at auction which bring low prices though described as Unc. are not choice and in some cases are not even technically "uncirculated."

Thus the Unc. prices in this catalog reflect the desire of collectors to own the finest tokens and may seem high at first glance. A special pricing panel led by our collaborator Steve Tanenbaum has extensively overhauled all Unc. prices for this new edition.

AUCTION RESULTS AFFECT PRICES:

A spate of very important sales in the 1988-1992 period once again has raised overall Hard Times token prices except in the lowest grades. These include the magnificent Steinberg, Schenkel, Middendorf, Gold Medal, Kirtley and Hartzog auction sales.

BRASS VERSUS COPPER

In this section we have removed a number of the Hard Times tokens formerly listed by Low, Vlack and others as Brass strikes of Copper pieces. Our panel of contributors is now in agreement that the best evidence of recent study through specific gravity analysis and spectro-analysis indicates that little real differences (if any) exist in the metallic composition of such pieces.

Alloying procedures in the 1830's and 1840's were indifferent. Pure copper often was copper with more than just traces of impurities present. The tokenmakers of that day were held to no standards, except the generalized standard of imitation of the legal U.S. cent.

If specimens are known which are provably Brass, and are colored much as a brass doorknob is colored, the listing has been retained. If there is genuine doubt, the listing also has been retained in this Edition.

There are certain to be differences of opinion on this subject. We recognize this, and will restore in future editions any listings which require restoration.

RARITY SCALE

R1	**Common**
R2	**Less Common**
R3	**Scarce**
R4	**Estimated 76-200 specimens survive**
R5	**Estimated 31-75 specimens survive**
R6	**Estimated 13-30 specimens survive**
R7	**Estimated 4-12 specimens survive**
R8	**Estimated 2 or 3 specimens survive**
R9	**Unique (only one known)**

DIESINKERS AND TOKEN MAKERS ACTIVE IN THE HARD TIMES TOKEN PERIOD

**** Indicates individual is known to have prepared HTT's**

John F. Bartholdt	Baltimore	1841-60	
W. H. Bridgens	New York	1840-63	
James Bale **	New York	1833-35	BALE
Bale & Smith **	New York	1835-48	B&S NY
Belleville Mint **	Belleville, NJ		
(Gibbs Gardner & Co. and Stevens Thomas & Fuller)			
Benedict & Burnham **	Waterbury, CT	1834-57	
Shubael D. Childs	Chicago	1837-1900	CHILDS
I. B. Gardiner **		1840	I.B.G.
John Gibbs **	Belleville, NJ	1833-41	
Edward Hulseman **	Attleboro, MA	1833-36	H
Edward Hulseman **	New York	1837-41	
Louisa Lander	New York	1847	LANDER
Robert Lovett Sr.	New York	1824-60's	
H.M. & E.I. Richards **	Attleboro, MA	1833-	
Scovill Mfg. Co. **	Waterbury, CT	1820-1905	
Frederick B. Smith **	New York	1835-64	
J. F. Thomas	Newark, NJ	1840's	JF THOMAS
Benjamin C. True **	Albany, NY	1832-48	* T TRUE ALB TRUE F.
Daniel True	Albany, NY	1837-77	
James Turpin	New York	1840	TURPIN
William Wagner	Pennsylvania	1844	WAGNER
John S. Warner	Philadelphia	1823-68	
Charles Cushing Wright **	New York	1824-57	CCW
Thomas Wyatt	New York	1840-60	

Nicholas Biddle signed this 1837 $10 note of the Bank of the United States, drawn on the Philadelphia main branch.

ANDREW JACKSON

Small Head

HT #	Rarity	Year	Metal	Size	VG	F	VF	EF
1	R6	(1832)	Copper	27mm	1500.	3650.	5750.	9000.
1A	R8	(1832)	Brass	—	—	7000.	11,000	14,000

Scowling Head

2	R8	(1832)	Copper	27mm	2000.	4500.	6500.	10,000

2A	R8	(1832)	White Metal	29mm	—	5000.	7000.	10,000

Aged Head

3	R7	(1832)	Copper	27mm	2000.	4500.	6500.	16,500
3A	R8	(1832)	Silver	27mm	—	—	May not exist	

This 1832 token was supposedly issued by Daniel Jackson of the firm of Suydam and Jackson, Indian contractors, Pearl St., New York. Jackson (no relation to the president) was an arch-foe of the U.S. Bank.

Die varieties of the obverse of Low 1 (see Carl Wurtzbach's article in March 1910 *The Numismatist*) are called Small Head, Aged Head and Scowling Head.

The firm of Suydam and Jackson was founded originally by Richard Suydam in 1811, at 140 Pearl Street. In 1824 Richard Suydam took in two partners, Daniel Jackson and Allen Peck, and the firm name was changed from R. Suydam to Suydam, Jackson & Peck.

One year later, in 1825, Peck was bought out and the firm became Suydam & Jackson.

In 1830 Suydam & Jackson moved from 140 Pearl Street to 78 Pearl Street, and the name was again changed, this time to Suydam, Jackson & Co. (Interestingly, another firm also occupied the space at 78 Pearl Street - Suydam & Kevan - a partnership of Richard Suydam with Alexander Kevan. This latter firm closed about 1844-45 when Suydam retired.)

Richard Suydam was another brother of the Rynier and John Suydam who founded R. & J. Suydam in 1791 at 10 Albany Pier (later 10 Coenties Slip).

HT #	Rarity	Year	Metal	Size	VG	VF	EF	Unc
4	R8	(1834)	Brass	27mm	—	17,600	25,000	—

Jackson bust right, ANDREW JACKSON / . PRESIDENT OF THE US . around. Rv: ELECTED A.D. 1828 / We (etc., the same as reverse of HT 5). Only 2 specimens are known. The Gil Steinberg specimen in VF, holed (shown above) fetched $17,600 in Stack's Sept. 1989 sale, lot 215. The other known piece is in a southwestern U.S. collection.

5	R3	(1834)	Brass	27mm	40.00	175.	600.	900.
5A	R8	(1834)	White Metal	27mm	—	—	May not exist	

HT #	Rarity	Year	Metal	Size	VG	VF	EF	Unc
6	R2	(1834)	Brass	27mm	40.00	150.	275.	800.
6A	R6	(1834)	Silvered Brass	27mm	45.00	175.	850.	1000.

Reverse reads: ELECTED A.D. 1829. Andrew Jackson actually was elected in 1828.

HT 4, 5, 6

DeWitt (see Bibliography) attributes these tokens to the political campaigns of 1834.

Remark: These Patriotic tokens are generally listed as they were by Lyman Low with the exception that they have been grouped by general design and the listing within that listing follows Low's sequence. Tokens are illustrated actual size. As many varieties are hard to attribute enlarged illustrations with helpful notes appear at the end of the section.

Dates listed within parenthesis do not appear on tokens but have been attributed as having been issued that year.

Large Shield

7	R5	1833	Brass	26mm	150.	350.	700.	1200

Period after N of N. Orleans. Reeded edge.

Small Shield

HT #	Rarity	Year	Metal	Size	VG	VF	EF	Unc
8	R6	1833	Brass	26mm	100.	350.	700.	1500.

No period after N. Comes with upset and non-upset reverse. Well struck obverses command a premium.

Running Boar

HT #	Rarity	Year	Metal	Size	VG	VF	EF	Unc
9	R1	1834	Copper	28mm	5.00	12.00	50.00	200.

HT #	Rarity	Year	Metal	Size	VG	VF	EF	Unc
10	R2	1834	Brass	28-1/2mm	25.00	125.	200.	450.
10A	R3	1834	Silvered Brass 28-1/2mm		10.00	75.00	200.	600.

NOTE: Pig's snout points to C of CREDIT. Jackson narrow shoulders.
HT 10 is on thick planchet, 10A on thin planchet.

HT #	Rarity	Year	Metal	Size	VG	VF	EF	Unc
11	R2	1834	Copper	28mm	16.50	35.00	125.	300.

NOTE: Pig's snout points between H of PERISH and C of CREDIT. Jackson wide shoulders.

Obverse 9, Reverse 11

HT #	Rarity	Year	Metal	Size	VG	VF	EF	Unc
12	R5	1834	Brass	29mm	100.	350.	400.	1000.
12A	R6	1834	Silvered Brass	29mm	—	300.	500.	1500.

Obv. Similar to 9. Rev. Number 11

HT #	Rarity	Year	Metal	Size	VG	VF	EF	Unc
13	R7	1834	Copper	28-1/2mm	2000.	4000.	5000.	—

The "victory" at New Orleans, and the "glory" due to Jackson's military successes, was a favorite theme of his friends, and the boastful way in which they rehearsed his exploits excited the unceasing and satirical jests of his opponents. (See No. 4 and notes under Nos. 25 and 30.) This was struck as a counterfoil to No. 14, as is evident from a comparison of the reverse legend on No. 14 with the obverse legend of this.

HT #	Rarity	Year	Metal	Size	F	VF	EF	Unc
13R	R1	1824	Copper-coated lead alloy	29mm	—	—	—	2.00

Modern (post-1960) replica, made of the wrong metal and carrying an erroneous date. The edge is irregular, similar to that on electrotype copies.

WHIG VICTORY

Dies by Robert Lovett

HT #	Rarity	Year	Metal	Size	VG	VF	EF	Unc
14	R5	1834	Brass, engrailed edge	25mm,	125.	300.	700.	1000.
14A	R4	1834	Brass	Plain edge	125.	350.	500.	1000.
14B	R8	1834	Silver	25mm	—	—	May not exist	
14C	R8	1834	Silver	27mm	—	—	—	7500.

(14C is struck over 1833 quarter dollar)

Obv. Rays are short and heavy.

HT #	Rarity	Year	Metal	Size	VG	VF	EF	Unc
				Edges are reeded				
15	R6	1834	Copper	27mm	500.	1300.	2500.	3500.
				Buckled dies - reeded edge				
15B	R6	1834	Copper	27mm	500.	1600.	2500.	3500.
				Buckled dies - plain edge				
15C	R6	1834	Copper	27mm	500.	1600.	2500.	3500.
				Different dies				
15D	R8	1834	White Metal	27mm	—	3000.	4000.	5500.
15E	R8	1834	Brass	27mm	—	3500.	—	—

An Unc specimen of HT 15 realized $5,300 at auction March 27, 1981. HT 15D appeared in the New Netherlands Coin Co. sale in 1953.

An F-VF specimen of HT 15E fetched $3,300 in the Dec. 1991 Gold Medal sale. Its is of a third obverse die type.

DANIEL WEBSTER

HT #	Rarity	Year	Metal	Size	VG	VF	EF	Unc
16	R1	1841	Copper	28mm	5.00	12.00	30.00	100.
Plain edge.								
16A	R9	1841	Copper	28mm	—	—	250.	—
Reeded edge.								

HT #	Rarity	Year	Metal	Size	VG	VF	EF	Unc
17	R1	1841	Copper	28mm	5.00	10.00	30.00	200.

HT #	Rarity	Year	Metal	Size	VG	VF	EF	Unc
18	R1	1841	Copper	28mm	5.00	12.00	25.00	200.

Daniel Webster was a strong advocate of the United States Bank, and his speech on the subject in May, 1832, was an important one, while that of September, 1837, in the Senate, in opposition to the Sub-Treasury Bill is regarded as "one of the most effective of all his arguments on the subjects of currency and finance." His defense of the Constitution in January, 1830, in a famous speech, won for him the title of "Defender of the Constitution," to which this token alludes. As the leader of the opponents of Jackson's policy, Webster's name appears on several of their tokens, and it is interesting to note that his first great speech in favor of the United States Bank was met by the token issued by its adversaries and the first described in this work, which declared "The Bank must perish" but "the Union must be preserved," yet the Union had no more strenuous upholder than the great supporter of the Bank.

Lightning inside wreck

HT #	Rarity	Year	Meal	Size	VG	VF	EF	Unc
19	R5	1841	Copper	28mm	75.00	150.	400.	1000.

HT #	Rarity	Year	Metal	Size	VG	VF	EF	Unc
20	R1	1841	Copper	28-1/2-29mm	5.00	12.00	30.00	110.
20A	R7	1841	Silver	29mm	—	2800.	4000.	6000.
20B	R2	1841	Copper	29mm	5.00	12.00	25.00	125.
20C	R9	1841	Copper	29mm	—	—	575.	—

Struck over South American token. (Kirtley Feb. 1991 list)

20B Rusted dies - rigging weak

HT 20

Daniel Webster was born in Salisbury N.H., 18 January, 1782. Graduating from Dartmouth in the class of 1801, he at once began the study of law in Salisbury, and in 1804 entered the office of the Hon. Christopher Gore, of Boston. He practiced a few years in New Hampshire, until elected to the House of Representatives in the National Congress by his native state. He withdrew from political life at the close of his second term and removed to Boston in 1816. Six years later he was again sent to Congress as a Representative from Massachusetts, and in 1828 was chosen Senator, and served until he became Secretary of State under Fillmore in 1850. He died at Marshfield, Mass., 24 October, 1852.

HT #	Rarity	Year	Metal	Size	VG	VF	EF	Unc
21	R2	1841	Copper	28-1/2mm	7.00	20.00	100.	250.

HT #	Rarity	Year	Metal	Size	VG	VF	EF	Unc
22	R1	1841	Copper	28-1/2mm	5.00	12.00	25.00	200.
22A	R4	1841	Gilt Copper	28-1/2mm		Not contemporary		

HT 22

About 90% of these have a slight break in the obverse die between the letters C and Y in CURRENCY, and on a few it extends to the ship, with another break through D in CREDIT, and sometimes continuing through CONSTITUTION. A third and still rarer break is visible at E in CURRENCY.

HT #	Rarity	Year	Metal	Size	VG	VF	EF	Unc
23	R4	1841	Copper	28-1/2mm	30.00	70.00	135.	250.

HT #	Rarity	Year	Metal	Size	VG	VF	EF	Unc
24	R3	(1838)	Copper	28mm	40.00	100.	350.	800.

Dies by John Gibbs

A CONTEMPORARY ACCOUNT OF THE HARD TIMES TOKENS

The *Niles' National Register* for Nov. 25, 1837, extracts several press cuttings from the *New York Journal of Commerce, The Washington Globe*, and a letter from the solicitor of the Treasury reflecting upon the copper "cents" then in circulation:

From *New York Journal of Commerce*:

Copper coin. There are great quantities of copper pieces in the market which circulate as cents, but which are not so. They are generally too light; but the worst part of their construction is the bad metal they are made of, and their consequent tendency to become foul. Worst of all, they are a vile debasement of the current coin, by which individuals very improperly make a large profit at the public expense, their spurious coins being generally sold by the bushel, at 50 to 62 1/2 cents the hundred.

They are all stamped with some device other than that of the national cent; for, to put on that would subject the operator to consequences not profitable. It is quite time for the public to refuse this trash altogether. A very discriminating spirit has been manifested in regard to *paper* change by the butchers and all those dealers who control such matters. The consequence is, that we have a comparatively sound currency, by which very little will be lost when the banks resume specie payments, and the paper change is expelled from the market.

The notes of the city of Newark are now the only notes which circulate freely in our market. All the notes of self-created loan companies, or by whatever name they may go, are, and ought to be rejected. We hope the same course will be pursued with the dirty "no cents" which are attempted to be put forth so plentifully.

From *Niles' National Register*:

The Washington "Globe" says: "Most of the coins referred to are stamped with political caricatures, and other federal devices. An emission of them hails the inauguration of *Daniel Webster* as president in 1841, while others contain inscriptions insulting to the late and present president of the United States.

"There really seems to be no bounds to the limits of federal enterprise in the manufacture of spurious substitutes for money."

(Author's comment: The comment above, made in 1837, seems to refer to the Webster Credit Current [and Currency] tokens, HT 16 to 23, since there are no political medalets hailing Webster's "election" as president. If it does, it would indicate these 1841-dated pieces were struck in 1837.)

From *Niles' National Register*, Nov. 25, 1837:

From the same paper **(The Washington Globe)** of the 23rd inst. we extract the following letter upon the subject, from the solicitor of the Treasury to N. Williams, Esq., district attorney of Maryland:

'Office of the Solicitor of the Treasury, Nov. 17, 1837,

'Sir: The secretary of the Treasury has referred to this office a communication received from Baltimore, transmitting the enclosed copper coin. It is stated to be a specimen of such as are extensively put in circulation there, and advertised in the newspapers by a commission house, which is retailing them to any one who applies for them. I have to request that you will cause inquiry to be made into the truth of these statements, and if such be the fact, institute the proper legal proceedings without delay.

'The second section of the Act of 8th May, 1792, provides that "no copper coins or pieces whatsoever, except the said cents and half cents, being those coined at the mint of the United States, shall pass current as money, or shall be paid, or offered to be paid, or received in payment, for any debt, demand, claim, matter, or thing whatsoever; and all copper coins or pieces, except the said cents and half cents, shall be paid, or offered to be paid, or received in payment, contrary to the prohibition of the aforesaid, shall be forfeited; and every person by whom any of them shall have been so paid . . . shall also forfeit the sum of ten dollars . . ."

'Very respectfully yours, H.D. Gilpin, Solicitor of the Treasury, to N. Williams, Esq., U.S. Attorney, Baltimore.'

(Author's comment: We cannot know what the enclosed token was, but it seems certain it was one of the political HTT's.)

THE CONSTITUTION

Comes with upset and non-upset reverse

HT #	Rarity	Year	Metal	Size	VG	VF	EF	Unc
25	R1	1834	Copper	28mm	5.00	15.00	70.00	200.
25A	R3	1834	Silvered Copper	28mm		Not contemporary		

The quotation, "A plain system" etc., is a sharp satire on the professed Jeffersonian Democracy of Jackson. In his speeches and public documents he was constantly upholding the doctrines of the third President, who was "the very embodiment of democracy," and to whom all titles of honor, even that of Mr., were distasteful, who dressed in the plainest style, and whose Inauguration was pre-eminently "void of pomp;" but the brilliant war record of Jackson was ever on the lips of his party followers. Somewhat egotistic in his way of expressing himself, due rather to his sense of the dignity and powers of his high office than to any great personal vanity, the satirists delighted to portray him in a dress suit, awkwardly brandishing his weapon, or in full uniform as a General, with epaulets and sword, and all the "pomp" of war, with "My glory", or some similar phrase added, as on No. 9 above, and others.

WILLIAM SEWARD

HT #	Rarity	Year	Metal	Size	VG	VF	EF	Unc
26	R4	(1834)	Brass	28mm	45.00	150.	300.	750.
26A	R6	(1834)	Silvered Brass	28mm	—	150.	350.	900.

It is difficult at this distance of time to fix the date of this and the two following tokens, or to give an entirely satisfactory explanation of the legends on Nos. 13 to 16. While the extract below from a Democratic newspaper of May, 1835, shows that the Verplanck token was a Whig issue of 1834, yet Verplanck had been elected to congress by the Democrats (1825-1833), his term having then but lately expired. But Seward and Stillwell were also the candidates of a party which called itself Whig, and were defeated by William L. Marcy in 1834, who was elected by the Democrats. This may indicate that the Seward token was struck either in 1834, when he was first a candidate, or in 1838, when he was successful. Admitting however that it was not struck until 1838, does not remove all difficulties; for since Seward and Verplanck were both rival candidates against Marcy, the legends express what were the hopes of the friends of each in 1834, yet each is called a "Whig token."

A possible explanation is found in the fact that the opponents of Jackson had at that time divided into two groups; one, called National Republicans, under the lead of Henry Clay, charged the President with overriding the Constitution, and other political crimes, while the other, under John Tyler, called "States Rights" men, opposed a high tariff, a National Bank, etc., and "agreed with the National Republicans in nothing except hostility to the President." The National Republicans began to call themselves Whigs in 1834, and the followers of Tyler soon took the name of States Rights Whigs. The two divisions had nearly come together in 1836, but did not unite in season to agree on Presidential nominations, and Van Buren was elected. Let us therefore suppose that the factions opposing Jackson, the one led by Seward and the other by Verplanck, put out both tokens in 1834, under which date they are placed: the latter faction, as a newspaper cutting of the period shows, claimed to be the special "friends of the Constitution and the laws," and called theirs the "Constitutional ticket;" apparently both factions were included under the general name of Whigs by their political adversaries who supported Jackson.

HT #	Rarity	Year	Metal	Size	VG	VF	EF	Unc
27	R5	(1834)	Brass	28mm	100.	300.	450.	900.

HT #	Rarity	Year	Metal	Size	F	VF	EF	Unc
27A	R5	(1834)	Silver plated before striking		100.	300.	900.	1700.

HT #	Rarity	Year	Metal	Size	F	VF	EF	Unc
28	R2	(1834)	Brass	28mm	75.00	125.	250.	350.
28a	R7	(1834)	Copper	28mm	—	—	May not exist	
29	R7	(1834)	Brass	28mm	1200.	3000.	3500.	6000.
29A	R7	—	Brass	28mm	1000.	2500.	3000.	5000.

NOTE: HT 29 has the reverse of number 30 below.

GULIAN VERPLANCK

HT #	Rarity	Year	Metal	Size	VG	VF	EF	Unc
30	R2	(1834)	Brass	28mm	45.00	125.	250.	400.
30A	R7	(1834)	Copper	28mm	—	—	—	Rare
NOTE: 30A was lot 259 in the Dunham sale.								
30B	R4	(1834)	Silvered Brass	28mm	40.00	125.	300.	750.

NOTE: Though HT 30 identifies its portrait as that of Gulian C. Verplanck, comparison of the portrait with that on 28, (supposedly William H. Seward) reveals that they are more or less identical.

In an article in *The Times*, May 2, 1835, headed "And all their triumphs shrink into a coin," this piece is referred to, and the extracts below, which are copied from it, give the reasons for including this and the three preceding tokens in this list, as they prove that these pieces formed a part of the circulating medium: —

A few brief years will pass away, and with them almost every trace of the existence of the Whig party. That party, however, in the pride of its power and confidence of its success, adopted the same plan for perpetuating its name that has been adopted by kings and princes. The story of their accession and their continuance in power is told by the coins and medals circulated during their reigns.***We have in our possession a coin of the grand Whig emission of 1834. On one side is an eagle, surrounded by the words "a faithful friend to our country," and on the other, an image surrounded by the words "Gulian C. Verplanck, our next Governor." It is made — most appropriately — of brass, symbolical of the modesty of the party by which it was issued. What a treasure will such a coin be to the antiquary a hundred years hence! — How will he pore over its image and superscription, and puzzle himself with most learned doubts as to its history and character! — At what epoch of the republic was it issued? What great event was it intended to commemorate, and who was the great man whose name, otherwise unrecorded — it has preserved for a hundred years? It speaks of Gulian C. Verplanck, "our next Governor." He was probably the governor-elect. The people had chosen him, but he had not yet entered upon the duties of his office. ***Why should a coin be struck off with his name and head on it? In all other countries it is the possessor and not the heir to the throne whose effigy is stamped on the coin of the realm. In looking over the almost interminable list of governors of the different States, the name of Gulian C. Verplanck can not be found. ***Most unfortunately, the coin bears no date, and for aught that appears to the contrary, it might have been issued anterior to the revolution. You cannot refer it to contemporary history, for the simple reason that you have no means of judging when it was issued. ***It is valuable because it is rare, and because from its most incomprehensible character, it will constantly call forth the discussions of antiquaries and virtuosi. It may be that in the wreck of matter of a hundred years, a few files of very old newspapers may survive. Possibly the very paper containing this article may chance to have a better fate than its brethren and furnish an addition to some collection of old and perhaps good for nothing trumpery. — Here then will be a key to unlock the mystery, and the quid nuncs of a hundred years hence will learn that in 1834, there flourished a mighty party called the great universal Whig party of the world, a party which lived and flourished on anticipation — celebrated victories which were to be won, but never were won, rejoiced over successes, which like the waters near the lips of Tantalus, were ever at hand but never reached, and struck medals in honor of governors who were never elected. ***We will mention by way of conclusion that the Verplanck Coinage of 1834 is becoming scarce. The pieces are at a premium, even now, the knowing ones among the Whigs having called in all they could possibly command.

1) William H. Seward was born in Florida, N.Y., 16 May, 1801. He was educated at Union College, and soon after attaining his twenty-first year was admitted to the Bar, where he achieved a high reputation as a criminal lawyer. Joining the Anti-Masonic party in the Morgan excitement, he was elected to the State Senate in 1830, and in 1832 made an able speech in favor of the United States Bank. Defeated as the Whig candidate for Governor in 1834, he won the position in 1838 by a majority of 10,000, and was the first representative of his party to hold that office. The remainder of his life was spent in the political arena, with the exception of the period from 1842 to 1849. In the latter year he was chosen United States Senator, and served until he became Secretary of State under President Lincoln, in 1861. He died at Auburn, 10 October, 1872.

2) Gulian Grommelin Verplanck was born in New York in 1786. He was distinguished as a scholar and writer rather than as a politician, though his first work, published anonymously, was "The State Triumvirate, a Political Tale," which was a brilliant political satire, and appeared in 1819. He was soon appointed Professor of Christian Evidences in the General Theological seminary (Protestant Episcopal), New York, but was elected to Congress in 1825 and served until 1833. Political life was however distasteful to him, and he returned to literary pursuits. He is best known by his annotated edition of Shakespeare, published in 1846, which was highly praised. Verplanck was chiefly instrumental in passing two Acts while in the State Senate of New York, that greatly increased his popularity; one was that which exempted from attachment the goods of non-resident debtors, and the other for the more permanent establishment of the State Hospital, — both of which were productive of good results. He died in March 1870.

Whatever truth there may have been in the charges of weakness and subservience to Jackson and his friends which were brought against Van Buren by his political enemies, it is now generally admitted that his financial ability was great, and as Fiske says, "The principal achievement of his administration was the divorce of Bank and State." To his successful "experiment" is due the establishment of the Subtreasury system, which finally took shape in 1846. The Independent Treasury Bill was introduced in Congress, September 2, 1837, and rejected, but was passed with some modifications in 1840, and though repealed under Tyler, at length became the established Government policy, without regard to party. Briefly the experiment was to withdraw the Government funds from State Banks,— private institutions chartered under State Laws, — and place them in the hands of United States Government officers. The result of this was to separate the Government funds from all others, and to free its Treasury from any dependence upon the banks in its fiscal operations; the collection, safekeeping, transfer and disbursement of the public money was to be performed solely by agents of the Government, — called "Fiscal Agents," — and all payments by or to the Government were made in specie. One can but wonder at the opposition these sound financial principles aroused.

The tortoise with a safe on its back on the tokens has been said to allude to the slow progress which the experiment made, and the running jackass to Van Buren's rapid growth in popularity — which is doubtful. The withdrawal of public funds from the banks, with other reasons, led to a contraction of the currency and great changes in apparent values, which under the loose methods that had previously obtained, may be said to have been the apparent causes of "Hard Times." The true causes lay further back, and are easily discernible by the student of history.

ILLUSTRIOUS PREDECESSOR

HT #	Rarity	Year	Metal	Size	VG	VF	EF	Unc
31	R3	1837	Copper	28-1/2mm	45.00	200.	450.	650.
31B	R7	1837	Thin oversize		75.00	250.	450.	750.
			planchet		—	—	—	Rare

HT #	Rarity	Year	Metal	Size	VG	VF	EF	Unc
32	R1	1837	Copper	29mm	5.00	12.00	30.00	125.

HT #	Rarity	Year	Metal	Size	VG	VF	EF	Unc
33	R1	1837	Copper	28-1/2mm	5.00	12.00	35.00	90.00
33A	R8	1837	Silver	28-1/2mm	—	—	—	7500.

Probably not a Bushnell product.

HT #	Rarity	Year	Metal	Size	VG	VF	EF	Unc
34	R1	1837	Copper	28-1/2mm	5.00	12.00	30.00	155.

LIBERTY - NOT ONE CENT

HT #	Rarity	Year	Metal	Size	VG	VF	EF	Unc
35	R2	1837	Copper	29mm	30.00	125.	300.	700.

HT #	Rarity	Year	Metal	Size	VG	VF	EF	Unc
36	R3	1837	Copper	28mm	35.00	125.	300.	800.

HT #	Rarity	Year	Metal	Size	VG	VF	EF	Unc
37	R4	1837	Copper	28mm	50.00	325.	450.	1000.

Bushnell restrike

HT #	Rarity	Year	Metal	Size	F	VF	EF	Unc
38	R7	1837	Copper	28mm	—	—	2000.	2300.
39	R7	1837	Copper	28mm	—	—	1900.	2200.

NOTE: HT 39 has the full lower serif of the 'ONE's'E.

Bushnell restrike

HT #	Rarity	Year	Metal	Size	F	VF	EF	Unc
40	R7	1837	Copper	28mm	—	—	1800.	2100.
40A	R8	1837	Silver	28mm	—	—	—	6000.
40B	R7	1837	Struck over HT 42 28mm		—	—	2000.	2500.

NOTE: Bushnell series were made in very small numbers about 20 years later than the dates they bear. See note following HT 74.

Bushnell restrike

HT #	Rarity	Year	Metal	Size	VG	VF	EF	Unc
41	R7	1837	Copper	28mm	—	—	2000.	2500.
41A	R8	1837	Silver	28mm	—	—	—	6000.

HT #	Rarity	Year	Metal	Size	VG	VF	EF	Unc
42	R1	1837	Copper	28mm	6.00	15.00	30.00	150.

Dies cut by John Gibbs

HT #	Rarity	Year	Metal	Size	VG	VF	EF	Unc
43	R8	1837	Copper	28mm	—	3000.	4000.	—

Only three pieces known.

Dies cut by James G. Moffet

44	R3	1837	Copper	28-1/2mm	20.00	100.	400.	700.

HT 45 in UNC.

HT #	Rarity	Year	Metal	Size	VG	VF	EF	Unc
45	R2	1837	Copper	28mm	12.00	40.00	90.00	275.
46	R1	1837	Copper	28mm	6.00	10.00	40.00	125.
47	R1	1837	Copper	28mm	6.00	10.00	50.00	150.
48	R1	1837	Copper	28mm	6.00	10.00	60.00	400.
48A	R4	1837	Silvered Copper	28mm	Not contemporary			
49	R1	1837	Copper	28mm	6.00	12.50	65.00	200.

HT #	Rarity	Year	Metal	Size	VG	VF	EF	Unc
50	R2	1837	Copper	28mm	6.00	12.00	25.00	150.

HT #	Rarity	Year	Metal	Size	VG	F	EF	Unc
51	R2	1837	Copper	28mm	6.00	25.00	60.00	225.
52	R1	1837	Copper	28mm	6.00	15.00	40.00	550.

Bushnell restrike

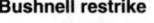

53	R7	1837	Copper	28-1/2mm	—	—	1800.	2200.
53A	R8	1837	Silver	28-1/2mm	—	—	—	6000.

Bushnell restrike

HT #	Rarity	Year	Metal	Size	VG	VF	EF	Unc
54	R7	1837	Copper	29mm	—	—	2000.	2500.
54A	R8	1837	Silver	29mm	—	—	—	6000.

Bushnell restrike

HT #	Rarity	Year	Metal	Size	VG	VF	EF	Unc
55	R7	1837	Copper	29mm	—	—	2200.	2600.
55A	R8	1837	Silver	29mm	—	—	—	6000.

HT #	Rarity	Year	Metal	Size	VG	VF	EF	Unc
56	R1	1837	Copper	28mm	6.00	10.00	35.00	175.

Reverse of HT 48.

"Shinplasters" have been referred to in the Introduction. The name was applied to bills of irresponsible banks and private parties. The device of the phoenix rising from flames seems to mean that the paper money was only fit to be burned, and that with its destruction new life would spring from its ashes. The date, November, 1837, is that of a convention held in New York on the 27th of that month, by representatives of leading banks in nineteen states to fix a date for resumption. They met again the 16th of April, 1838 and decided to resume specie payments the 10th of May following, which was successfully accomplished after a suspension of exactly one year. (See No. 65.)

HT #	Rarity	Year	Metal	Size	VG	VF	EF	Unc
57	R1	1837	Copper	28mm	6.00	10.00	40.00	130.

Reverse of HT 51.

HT #	Rarity	Year	Metal	Size	VG	VF	EF	Unc
58	R1	1841	Copper	28mm	5.00	12.00	30.00	250.

Bushnell restrike

HT #	Rarity	Year	Metal	Size	VG	VF	EF	Unc
59	R7	1841	Copper	28mm	—	—	2000.	2500.
59A	R8	1841	Silver	28mm	—	—	—	6000.

Bushnell restrike

HT #	Rarity	Year	Metal	Size	VG	VF	EF	Unc
60	R7	1841	Copper	28mm	—	—	2000.	2750.
60A	R8	1841	Silver	28mm	—	—	—	6000.

MINT DROPS

HT #	Rarity	Year	Metal	Size	VG	VF	EF	Unc
61	R2	1837	Copper	28mm	5.00	20.00	50.00	325.

HT #	Rarity	Year	Metal	Size	VG	VF	EF	Unc
62	R1	1837	Copper	28mm	6.00	10.00	40.00	350.

HT #	Rarity	Year	Metal	Size	VG	VF	EF	Unc
63	R1	1838	Copper	29mm	6.00	25.00	60.00	400.

HT #	Rarity	Year	Metal	Size	VG	VF	EF	Unc
63A	R9	1838	Copper	29mm	—	—	500.	—

HT 63 overstruck on HT 72.

HT #	Rarity	Year	Metal	Size	VG	VF	EF	Unc
64	R1	1841	Copper	28mm	6.00	10.00	25.00	150.

"Bentonian Currency" was hard money as opposed to paper. The friends of the United States Bank who favored the issue of Government paper for circulation, were constantly ridiculing their opponents by squibs in the newspapers of the day. The *Virginia Advocate*, for example, had the following in an article headed. "Who would not be a Jackson man?" — "Have you been seven times spurned by the people when you offered to serve your country, and are you in want of the wherewithal to make the pot boil? — try the hard money tack, and jingle a few Benton yellow jackets at everybody but your creditors, and it's odds if you don't rise to an embassy or a department. It is the short cut to fame, to wealth and power; and one has hardly time to put on a clean shirt . . . before he writes his name . . . on the milky way of 'glory.' . . . This Jacksonism is a crucible which like that of the astrologer, turns all baser metals to gold . . . Oh, what it is to be a Jackson man!" On the other side, Benton, in a letter written from St. Louis, in August, 1837, praised Jackson for accumulating eighty million of hard money in the country — enabling the Government to be independent, raising prices for farm products and prophesied good times, etc. He quoted Jefferson as having, in 1792, charged the Federalists with a scheme to banish gold and silver from circulation and deluge the States with paper money — which would have been accomplished in 1837 were it not that "Jackson's *policy balked this system* in the moment of its anticipated triumph," and he closed his letter by saying, "I think his successor (Van Buren) is '*made of the stuff* to sustain that policy, etc." Only a few months later, the policy of Jackson and Van Buren, or rather the heroic methods by which its supporters attempted to carry it out, regardless of the laws of business, — for the policy itself was sound — with other causes, brought the entire country to the verge of ruin. But the crash of 1837 and the Hard Times which followed were by no means solely due as the Whig leaders would have it believed — to the overthrow of their policy and the "mint drops" or hard money of Jackson and Van Buren: they were only the culmination of evils which had long been threatening disaster. The wild speculations which accompanied the rapid development of Western lands from 1820 onward, intensified by the building of railroads, as Fiske tells us; the miserable banking system of the period; the inflation of the currency by the issue of worthless bills and "shinplasters," were all potent causes. When speculation was checked, and "cheap money" abolished, prosperity returned. For this the Whigs claimed the glory, but it was due nevertheless to the "experiments" which they satirized so severely.

HT 63 - LOCO FOCO

The occurrence to which allusion appears on this token was briefly mentioned in the introductory remarks. At a meeting in Tammany Hall, on the evening of 29 October, 1835, there was a split in the party over the Congressional nominee. The friends of each had endeavored to pack the meeting; great confusion attended the efforts of the chiefs and their followers to obtain control, amid which the gas was turned off, it was alleged through the connivance of the janitor with one faction. Their opponents, however, if they did not themselves instigate the move, were equal to the occasion, and somewhat singularly, had come prepared with loco-foco matches and candles, and the room was speedily relighted. The *Morning Courier* and *New York Enquirer* dubbed the antimonopolists, who had used the matches, "Loco-focos," and the name was speedily affixed to the whole Democratic party.

MAY 10TH

HT #	Rarity	Year	Metal	Size	VG	VF	EF	Unc
65	R2	1837	Copper	28mm	5.00	15.00	70.00	300.

HT #	Rarity	Year	Metal	Size	VG	VF	EF	Unc
66	R1	1837	Copper	28mm	6.00	10.00	40.00	150.
66A	R1	1837	Copper	28mm	6.00	10.00	50.00	150.

NOTE: On 66A, both sides face the same way. On 66, each side is in inverse relation to the other.

HT #	Rarity	Year	Metal	Size	VG	VF	EF	Unc
67	R1	1837	Copper	28mm	6.00	10.00	25.00	325.

HT #	Rarity	Year	Metal	Size	VG	VF	EF	Unc
68	R1	1841	Copper	28mm	6.00	10.00	25.00	150.

I TAKE THE RESPONSIBILITY

HT #	Rarity	Year	Metal	Size	VG	F	EF	Unc
69	R1	1837	Copper	28-1/2mm	6.00	10.00	25.00	175.

HT #	Rarity	Year	Metal	Size	VG	VF	EF	Unc
70	R1	(1833)	Copper	28-29mm	6.00	10.00	30.00	80.00
70A	R3	(1833)	Copper Gilt	28-29mm	10.00	125.	200.	450.

71	R2	(1837)	Brass	28-1/2mm	10.00	60.00	80.00	300.

HT 70

Recent research has shown that this token is probably the first cent-sized political type token which achieved wide circulation, and it opened the door for a flood of similar items. The die was cut by Edward Hulseman in Attleboro, Mass. in the fall of 1833, and the tokens were struck by the button-makers, Robinson's Jones & Co. of Attleboro, who were Hulseman's employers 1833-1836.

The tokens of this and later types (HT 69, 71 and 72) refer to Jackson, who is shown with sword and purse. The next year, Jackson is seen on another Hulseman-designed token (HT 25) with sword and purse in a different stance.

The feeling which led to the adoption of the sword and purse device continued for some time after the Whigs had taken the reins of government. The *Albany Argus* for October 1, 1842 said: "The liberties of the country were alarmingly threatened under Mr. Van Buren's administration by a union of the purse with the sword in the same hands."

The dates of issue of numbers 69 and 71 are somewhat uncertain, though they are after 1833. The issue date on 72 could be as late as 1842.

72	R2	(1837-42)	Copper	28-1/2mm	6.00	18.50	100.	200.

This is an inferior copy of Low 51 (no H under safe).

HALF CENT

HT #	Rarity	Year	Metal	Size	VG	VF	EF	Unc
73	R2	1837	Copper	23mm	15.00	50.00	100.	400.

AMERICAN SILVER

HT #	Rarity	Year	Metal	Size	F	VF	EF	Unc
74	R8	1837	German Silver	26mm	—	—	30,000	35,000

Obverse has an American eagle displayed, head left, AMERICAN SILVER above. Reverse reads in three lines: TOKEN/25 CENTS/1837.

This piece was first introduced to the public by the late Charles I. Bushnell in his work (referred to in the Introduction), published in 1858. It next appeared in his collection of coins, which was dispersed by auction in 1881. Low purchased the piece for a collector and no other was known to him. Low had no hesitancy in stating that it is unique and was struck from dies made by Bushnell's order. Low held a similar unfavorable opinion of HT numbers 38, 39, 40, 41, 53, 54 and 55, but in these latter he thought a partner was admitted, and a very limited number of each was struck in copper and probably only single specimens in silver.

However, Wayte Raymond believed HT 74 was struck by Feuchtwanger, not Bushnell. It went into the F.C.C. Boyd collection.

A second specimen is now known, and possibly a third. Verified specimens are in the John Ford and Donald Partrick collections.

MARTIN VAN BUREN

HT #	Rarity	Year	Metal	Size	F	VF	EF	Unc
75	R2	(1840)	Copper	28mm	40.00	75.00	150.	400.
75A	R3	(1840)	Brass	28mm	40.00	100.	200.	500.
75B	R4	(1840)	Silvered Copper	29mm	50.00	100.	200.	700.

76	R6	(1840)	Brass	23mm	1000.	2500.	3500.	5500.

HT #	Rarity	Year	Metal	Size	F	VF	EF	Unc.
77	R5	1840	Copper	24mm	175.	400.	600.	1500.
77A	R6	1840	Brass	24mm	175.	400.	600.	1500.
77B	R9	1840	Gilt/Cop	24mm	—	—	600.	—

Numbers 77, 77A and 77B always occur holed. 77 has either a plain or diagonally reeded edge, while 77A and B have a plain edge. These pieces may not have seen currency use.

78	R4	(1836)	Brass	26mm	35.00	100.	150.	400.
78A	R7	(1836)	White Metal	26mm	300.	500.	1000.	1500.

Bust right, M. VAN BUREN and 26 stars around. (The 26th state, Michigan, was admitted Jan. 26, 1837, but its admission was certain in 1836, when the election campaign took place.) Reverse: Temple of Liberty, DEMOCRACY AND OUR COUNTRY around DeWitt MVB 1836-4.

As 77-77A above, these may not have seen currency use. They are so similar in size and fabric to the other Van Buren pieces, however, that they should not have been omitted by Low. Low must have known of them, as they are Bushnell number II.

HENRY CLAY

HT #	Rarity	Year	Metal	Size	VG	VF	EF	Unc
79	R2	(1840)	Copper	28mm	10.00	30.00	120.	350.
79A	R3	(1840)	Brass	28mm	10.00	30.00	75.00	350.
79B	R8	(1840)	Gilt/Brs	—	—	—	200.	—

Dies were cut by I.B. Gardiner, whose initials I.B.G. are under the truncation of Clay's right-facing toga-clad bust. Obverse reads: HENRY CLAY, AND THE AMERICAN SYSTEM. Reverse has UNITED / WE / STAND in three lines within laurel wreath. DeWitt HC 1840-1; Bushnell 37.

Clay was the National Democrat or Whig nominee in 1824, 1832 and 1844, and he sought the nomination in 1836, 1840 and 1848. Clay's dismal record was approached only by William Jennings Bryan, Democrat nominee in 1896, 1900 and 1908, and aspirant for the Presidency in 1904.

WILLIAM HENRY HARRISON

An entire series of holed election medalets of the 1840 campaign, all with similar designs (military bust left on obverse, log cabin on reverse), listed by Doyle DeWitt as WHH 1840-23 through 1840-27, appeared in copper, brass and other metals. All measure 29mm, the size of a U.S. large cent. Though possibly none did so, all could have circulated alongside the other tokens of the period as a cent.

AM I NOT A WOMAN

HT #	Rarity	Year	Metal	Size	VG	VF	EF	Unc
81	R1	1838	Copper	28mm	15.00	35.00	75.00	325.
81A	R3	1838	Copper	27mm	15.00	35.00	75.00	325.
81B	R8	1838	Svd/Cop	28mm	—	—	200.	—

AM I NOT A MAN

82	R8	1838	Copper	28mm	—	—	21,000	30,000

The question of slavery and its abolition had at this time found a permanent place in politics, and to a large number of people in the North such sentiments were particularly pleasing. Hence, the shrewd selection of the device of the kneeling slave, to popularize the introduction of a profitable token and to advance the cause of freedom.

The slavery question became a national issue in 1838. On August 1, 1838, local legislatures in Jamaica, Barbadoes, Grenada, St. Vincent, St. Kitts, Nevis, Montserrat and British Virgin Islands abolished Negro apprenticeship, and this boosted the morale of U.S. anti-slavery societies.

Kneeling male slave tokens, undated, with clasped hands on reverse, are earlier English pieces; relatively common. Value in VF = $30 and in Unc = $90.

Thanks to the research of Eric P. Newman, collectors may now know a good deal more about the background of HT 81 and 82. His conclusions are summarized here:

In late 1837 the American Anti-Slavery Society, located at 143 Nassau Street, New York, commissioned the firm of Gibbs Gardner & Co. of Belleville, N.J. to strike copper tokens (HT 81, the Kneeling Female piece). The tokens probably cost the AASS about 50 cents per hundred, as they contained copper then worth 39.5 cents per hundred.

Beginning May 4, 1833, the AASS published a weekly newspaper, *The Emancipator*, published by Charles W. Denison and edited by Joshua Leavitt. In its issue of Nov. 23, 1837, *The Emancipator* ran an advertisement offering the Female Slave tokens at $1 per hundred. Made of good copper and with a device on reverse similar to legal U.S. cents, they sold well.

The ad also said that it was proposed to issue Kneeling Male Slave tokens as well, and this accounts for the few pattern pieces of HT 82, which were never produced for circulation.

U.S. Mint Director Patterson moved quickly to suppress the circulation of HT 81, and it is apparent that by late December, 1837, he had succeeded in part. No further ads for the Female Slave tokens appeared in the AASS weekly or in other Journals, but since the number of pieces of HT 81 still surviving is quite large, they may well have been distributed by middlemen who paid about 62 cents per hundred for them in early 1838.

Gibbs Gardner & Co. were selected by the AASS in part because John Gibbs' Belleville Mint had also struck the 1833 Liberia cent tokens for another American anti-slavery group in Maryland.

The AASS actually distributed a British anti-slavery medal in the U.S. in 1835, selling for 25 cents each, the 1834 Emancipation Jubilee Medal.

BEEHIVE

HT #	Rarity	Year	Metal	Size	F	VF	EF	Unc
83	R4	1838	Brass	29mm	25.00	70.00	100.	250.
83A	R4	1838	Copper	29mm	25.00	40.00	75.00	250.

The date on this token clearly places it in the Hard Times era, yet it has never been published as such. In 1954 Donald M. Miller considered adding it to the HTT listing, as did R.B. White in 1973.

White brought up the possibility of this token having an English origin.

HT #	Rarity	Year	Metal	Size	F	VF	EF	Unc
A83	R7	(?)	Brass	28mm	—	—	—	—

The beehive design is quite diffeent from HT 83. The legend around reads: BY INDUSTRY WE LIVE / BY PERSEVERANCE, EXCEL.

The illustrated piece, in the collection of Denton V. Curtis, Chandlers Ford, Hampshire, England, was purchased from a Portsmouth, England coin dealer who had bought it as part of a lot of American coins, including two 1794 Large cents and an 1892-S Barber half dollar. This could indicate an American connection, but it might simply reinforce the possible English provenance of 83 and 83A.

The numeral "1000" has no discernible connection with the Hard times era of which we are aware.

COUNTERMARKS

HT #	Rarity	Year	VG	E	VF	EF
84	R8	(1837)				
		OLD HICKORY SPECIE WANTED ctsp. on a U.S. Large cent. (Hallenbeck 15.503; Brunk 30180)	—	—	200.	—
85	R8	1837				
		LIBERTY / 1837 ctsp. on U.S. 1819 Large cent. (Steinberg 1982 sale; Brunk 24480)	—	—	60.00	—
86	R8	(1834)				
		REX AND JACKASS / THE HERO OF NEW ORLEANS ctsp. on a U.S. Large cent. (DeWitt CD 1838-20; Brunk 33970)	—	—	125.	—

HT #	Rarity	Year	VG	E	VF	EF
87	R9	1837				
		From Andrew Jackson Pres- / ident of the U.S. to *engraved* on U.S. 1836 Capped bust half dollar. Andrew Jackson / Ellis / of New Haven Conn / Feb. 22d / 1837 engraved on opposite side.	—	—	200.	—

HT #	Rarity	Year	VG	F	VF	EF
88	R9	1837	—	—	100.	—

1837. / The true / currency engraved on obverse of U.S. 1805 Bust quarter. Rv: Initials I L are *engraved.* (Charles Kirtley Jan. 19, 1993 sale, lot P001)

Undoubtedly a contemporary reference to the financial panic of 1837.

ANIMAL HORN BOX

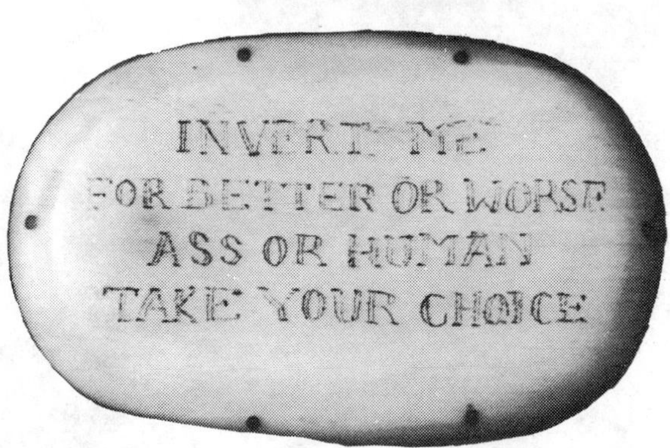

HT #	Rarity	Year	Metal	Size	F	VF	EF	Unc
90	—	(1830s)	Bone	75x45mm	—	—	200.	—

This oval box is made of animal horn bound together with brass pins. Brass hinge permits opening of box at top. Top is etched: JACKSON'S / (Reversible effigy of Andrew Jackson and jackass heads) / BEST. Bottom is etched: INVERT ME / FOR BETTER OR WORSE / ASS OR HUMAN / TAKE YOUR CHOICE. (L.B. Fauver coll. until Nov. 1987)

the Gentleman's Saloon, handsomely decor. will be thrown open as a dining room, with a fine ton. Grand Action Piano, with other instruments, for the use of the company.

Die Sinking.

B. C. TRUE respectfully tenders his thanks to his customers, for the liberal encouragement he has received from them, and solicits a continuance of their favors. He is prepared to cut Dies of any description, Rolls, Seals, Stamps, etc. in all their variety. Door-Plates of many patterns, some new and elegant ones, which he invites attention to.

N. B. Some stamps on hand, *ready cut* for *gag* mechanics, and Plates for *gag* Professors of Music, Optics, Blackleging, fancy house bullies, &c. which have on them

"Names of men so mean,
That to be despised, need but be seen."

Jan. 1, 1838.

PAPER WAREHOUSE —No. 14 Green st.,

BRICE & MONROE, offer for sale a large assortment of paper, viz: a quantity of Foolscap paper, plain and ruled; ... plain and ruled Letter; Folio Post, and Check paper ...erroyal, Medium and Demy; also 100 reams of Dor... ...m fine—50 course do; 100 reams Inveloped; 50 ...

ENLARGEMENTS

Enlargement numbers refer to HT numbers as given in text.

HT
31.

Basic design.

33.

Corner of safe opposite right part of X in EXECUTIVE; the perpendicular strap on end passes through the exact center of handle; rosettes are smaller and less leaf-like; the ground and grass are different; date small, 7 above G in agent.

34.

As figure 31 with word FINANCIERING instead of EXPERIMENT. Proportions of safe are slightly different from preceding; the straps on end pass through handle a little left of its center.

Basic design. A running mule.

32.

The jackass and ground beneath, on this and the two varieties following, are longer than on the preceding: right ear points to right part of first L in Illustrious: left ear between and beyond the letters I, which begin the two lines over the animal.

33.

The right ear points to the second L in Illustrious; the left touches top of I in In. Left foot points at P in predecessor; left hind foot nearly touches R in same word. Periods, smallest of this type.

34.

The right ear in same position as on 33; to the left similar to 32; I in In touches ear below its point. O in follow below I in Illustrious; both hind feet rest squarely on ground.

35.

37.

Not one cent is higher in wreath, which has nice berries outside, four inside.

41.

A star has been added on each side of FOR and a dash below CENT.

42.

The wreath has six berries outside, seven inside.

HT
35.

Thirteen stars, a break on the obverse die runs from the leaves on the head through the eye to the third star & then to the second.

36.

Smaller head, fifteen stars, two of them small, separated by date.

37.

Coronet inscribed UNITED within a circle of twelve stars.

38.

E PLURIBUS UNUM. Above head, chaplet of laurel leaves, plain hair cord. Thirteen stars, small 1837 lowest curl terminates right below neck, opposite the first star.

40.

Same but Beaded hair cord; lowest curl short and over 37 which is large.

41.

Motto framed. Forming a scroll.

44.

Inferior design and execution. Heavy masculine features; large lettered motto; lowest curl terminates right, above space between 7 and *.

46.

Nose sharp; point of bust above 1 in date; lowest lock horizontal (only instance) with curl terminating right; above 7; end of scroll beneath second U in UNUM.

45.

Chin & point of bust short; curl on and below neck, both terminate left, the latter above 37.

42.

Letter of the motto smaller; plain hair cord lower curl large, terminates right above 7 in date; six stars left. (others have 7)

47.

Curl on and below neck, both terminate at left; end of scroll under N in UNUM, which is double-cut at bottom.

HT

44.

The wreath has four berries outside (two opposite second E in DEFENCE), and four inside. First letters in ONE and CENT are weak occasioned by high relief of check on obv.

46.

The wreath has four berries outside (one opposite first E in DEFENCE and another, very small, on the leaf which points to c), and six inside; a small dot after TRIBUTE.

The stem of the leaf pointing to N in NOT, on sharp impressions, has the appearance of a berry, and probably was intended for such; this with the distinct one below it, would match the pair that are opposite, on the inner side of wreath, but so seldom does it appear with distinctness that we forbear to count it as a berry.

48.

The wreath has five berries inside, three outside (one opposite second E in DEFENCE).

51.

(not shown)

The wreath has six berries inside, two outside.

59.

The wreath has three berries outside and four inside; the berries are larger and letters smaller.

60.

A small six-pointed star has been added on each side of FOR and one small berry to inside of wreath.

295.

On HT 295 the second word on the scroll is spelled PLURIBUS, while on HT 297 it is spelled PIUBIBUS in error. Note that the S and N of the scroll motto are cut backwards.

38.

ONF instead of ONE, and without dash below CENT. Wreath has six berries outside, six inside.

40.

Die altered to ONE and the berries increased to seven outside and eight inside.

53.

Wreath has three berries outside, six inside.

45.

The wreath has three berries outside, six inside (in three pairs); without dash below CENT.

HT

49.

Lower curl further from 7; end of scroll under second U in UNUM.

53.

Basic design for 53, 54 and 55.

55.

Lightning added above the ship and a fire topmast and main-topmast falling forward.

69.

Letters & date larger, stars smaller and six-pointed bowsprit points to star before V.

18.

Six pointed star; letters larger; water more turbulent; lightning above; one flash ends under A in VAN; the top of the promontory is opposite the same letter; the ship is without bowsprit and has a straight deck.

19.

Six pointed star; letters larger; water more turbulent; lightning above; one flash ends under A in VAN; the top of the promontory is opposite the same letter; the ship is without bowsprit and has a straight deck.

16.

Basic design * Webster *

21.

* CREDIT 1841 CURRENCY *, straight deck, inscribed CONSTITUTION. Four stays from the bowsprit to the foremast; the top of the flag is opposite E in CREDIT; the stars are small.

20.

CURRENT instead of CURRENCY; the top of the stern on a line with the left part of the second R in the same word; a small stump of bowsprit.

20.

Better executed, a crosstree below the lower sail on the mainmast; the flag on the foremast extends only to the middle of R in WEBSTER; the stars are very small.

22.

Two stays from the bowsprit to the foremast; foretop mast-staysail set, as are eight other sails; the top of the flagstaff on the stern is opposite R in CREDIT.

23.

Leaf before and after WEBSTER, instead of a star.

ALABAMA

HUNT PYNCHON & JACKSON

Mobile, Ala.

HT	Rarity	Year	Metal	Size	VG	F	EF	Unc
98	R8	(1835)	Brass	27mm	2000.	5000.	8000.	—

HUNT, PYNCHON & JACKSON / HARDWARE AND CUTLERY. Anvil, Etc. (Miller Ala 1)

The partners were Jonathan Hunt, who appears in the 1830 and 1840 census reports; George A. Pynchon, who appears in the 1830 census, and someone named Jackson. The Jackson could be either of these men from the 1830 census: John H., Samuel or S. F. Jackson. Directory confirmation is lacking.

The card may be among the rarest of all Hard Times merchant pieces. It appeared in none of the major sales of the 1980's or 1990's, and was missing from the Dr. B. P. Wright collection.

STICKNEY & WILSON

Montgomery, Ala.

HT #	Rarity	Year	Metal	Size	VG	F	EF	Unc
99	R7	(1835)	Brass	27.5mm	500.	2000.	3000.	—

STICKNEY & WILSON / (ornament) / Alabama / (ornament) / * MONTGOMERY *. Rv: DRY GOODS GROCERIES / CLOTHING / (leaf device) / — HATS & SHOES — / * HARDWARE CROCKERY *. (Miller Ala 27; PCAC June 1991 sale, lot 23)

Henry G. Stickney and Joseph W. Wilson ordered brass tokens in 1835 from Scovill Mfg. Co., Waterbury, Conn., for their general mercantile business in Montgomery. The firm was out of business by Nov. 11, 1839.

Research by Cindy Grellman and H. Joseph Levine permits us to assign this token issue with certainty to the Hard Times era. It had previously been listed in our *U.S. Merchant Tokens 1845-1860*.

CONNECTICUT

N. PRATT (and) N. PRATT JR.

Essex, Conn.

For the counterstamp issues of silversmiths Nathan Pratt and his son Nathan Pratt Jr. see in *Early American Tokens* section, Rulau-E Conn 8 to Conn B8B.

BOLLES & CHILDS

Hartford, Conn.

HT #	Rarity	Year	Metal	Size	VG	F	VF	EF
100	R9	(1840)	Silver	26.5mm	—	—	—	400.

BOLLES & CHILDS ctsp on Spanish-American 1796-PTS-PP 2-reales, well worn. The stamp is from a die, incused. (Rulau coll.; Brunk 4197)

Bolles & Childs were silversmiths, jewelers and dry goods merchants operating in Hartford only in 1840. Their work is published by Louise Conway Belden and Ralph & Terry Kovel (see Bibliography). Several references give their hallmark incorrectly as BULLES & CHILDS.

The firm was connected with Bolles & Hastings, operating circa 1841-48 in Hartford. The various partners were Edward W. Bolles, Lucius B. Childs and Gerry Hastings.

COLLINS & CO.

HT #	Rarity	Year	Metal	Size	VG	F	VF	EF
108	R8	(1830's)	Copper	29mm	—	—	100.	—

COLLINS in relief within toothed rect. depression ctsp on U.S. Large cent. Examined: 1817, 1835. (Brunk 8870)

HT #	Rarity	Year	Metal	Size	VG	F	VF	EF
108D	R9	(1830's)	Copper	29mm	—	—	100.	—

COLLINS & CO. / HARTFORD / CAST STEEL / WARRANTED ctsp. on U.S. 1820 Large cent. (Brunk 8875)

Samuel Collins built America's first axe factory in Hartford in 1826. He had a large plant in Collinsville, Conn. (Re: Barlow, Brunk)

DAVENPORT

New Haven, Conn.

HT #	Rarity	Year	Metal	Size	VG	VF	EF	Unc
101	R3	(1835)	Copper	28mm	8.00	30.00	75.00	300.

FOBES & BARLOW

HT #	Rarity	Year	Metal	Size	VG	VF	EF	Unc
102	R2	(1835)	Copper	28mm	9.00	25.00	60.00	300.

There is a John M. Barlow in the 1840 census.

WILMOT

New Haven, Conn.

HT #	Rarity	Year	Metal	Size	VG	F	VF	EF
103	R9	(1837-46)	Copper	29mm	—	100.	—	175.

WILMOT in relief within toothed rectangular depression ctsp on U.S. 1795 or 1837 Large cent. (Rulau coll.; Brunk 43680)

Both Samuel Wilmot (1777-1846) and his son, Samuel Wilmot Jr. (1808-1846), used this hallmark in their silversmith business. This firm had been known as Wilmot & Stillman about 1800. Samuel Wilmot also worked in Georgetown, S.C. and Charleston, S.C.

A relative (?), T. T. Wilmot, was also a silversmith in New Haven about 1810.

T. K.

Norwich, Conn.

HT #	Rarity	Date	Metal	Size	VG	F	VF	EF
A103	R9	(1830's)	Copper	29mm	—	—	75.00	—

T K in relief within rect. depression ctsp on U.S. 1820 Large cent. (PCAC July 1993 sale, lot 1073)

Mark Greengold attributed this to silversmith Thomas Kinney (1796-1836) of Norwich, who in his later career moved to Cortland, N.Y. The mark matches one of those listed by Kovel (see Bibliography).

BENEDICT & BURNHAM
Waterbury, Conn.

HT #	Rarity	Year	Metal	Size	VG	VF	EF	Unc
104	R2	1837	Copper	27.5mm	12.00	50.00	75.00	300.

The store card of Benedict & Burnham of Waterbury, Conn. The firm was a creator of Hard Times tokens for other merchants. In later years, especially circa 1845-1857, the company produced a number of store cards for various merchants. In 1887 the firm supplied the U.S. government with 20,000 pounds of planchets for the striking of copper-nickel 5-cent pieces.

Aaron Benedict and Joseph Burton started manufacturing bone and ivory buttons in Waterbury in 1812. Under the name A. Benedict a reorganized firm in 1823 began making gilt buttons. Benedict & Coe succeeded in 1829, and sheet brass manufacture was added. In 1834 it became Benedict & Burnham (Aaron Benedict, Gordon W. Burnham, Bennet Bronson, Alfred Platt and others), and copper, zinc and nickel alloys were added.

On Jan. 14, 1843, the firm became Benedict & Burnham Mfg. Co. In 1895 Benedict & Burnham absorbed Holmes, Booth & Haydens Co. (organized 1853), another early token issuer of Waterbury.

J M L & W H SCOVILL
Waterbury, Conn.

HT #	Rarity	Year	Metal	Size	VG	VF	EF	Unc
105	R3	1837	Copper	28.5mm	20.00	110.	150.	325.

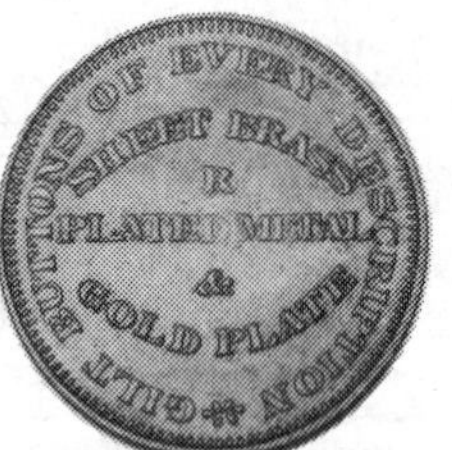

HT #	Rarity	Year	Metal	Size	VG	VF	EF	Unc
106	R2	1837	Copper	28.5mm	—	—	27.50	60.00

R on reverse 1952 Restrike.

HT #	Rarity	Year	Metal	Size	VG	VF	EF	Unc
107	R5	(1830's)	Brass	27.5mm	70.00	200.	250.	550.

Obv: J.M.L. & W.H. SCOVILL / GILT & PLATED / BUTTON / MANUFACTURER / WATERBURY . CON. in five lines. Rv: * GILT BUTTONS OF EVERY DESCRIPTION / SHEET BRASS / PLATED METAL / & / GOLD PLATE. Plain edge.

The reverse is the same as the reverse of HT 105, though the planchet is a bit smaller.

Token authority Dr. George Fuld possesses copies and photocopies of Scovill 1830-1845 correspondence which sheds much light on the firm's involvement with Hard Times tokens.

GEORGIA

I. GILBERT
Augusta, Ga.

The 1829 token issues of I. Gilbert may now be found in *Early American Tokens* section. (HT 110-110A, Low 315-316). These are valued at $1000 in VG, $2,000 in VF, $3000 in EF.

J. & D. MORRISON
Augusta, Ga.

HT #	Rarity	Year	Metal	Size	G	VG	F	VF
111	R8	(1829-33)	Copper	28mm	1300.	2000.	5000.	8000.

Like the Gilbert token above, the Morrison piece properly belongs in the Early American token category.

Only three specimens are known in private hands. In the Gold Medal sale of Dec. 1991, lot 031 was a specimen in only Fair-Abt Good condition, yet it realized $1,100.

A poor specimen (Zeddies) was offered at $850 by Kirtley in Feb., 1991.

LOUISIANA

DAQUIN BROS.
New Orleans, La.

ALL ARE 10-SIDED

HT #	Rarity	Year	Metal	Size	VG	F	VF	AU
115	R5	(1835-42)	Brass	23mm	150.	250.	700.	1200.
	No period after PAIN							
115A	R7	(1835-42)	Lead	23mm	600.	700.	1500.	2500.
	No period after PAIN							

HT #	Rarity	Year	Metal	Size	VG	F	VF	AU
116	R6	(1835-42)	Brass	23mm	150.	250.	500.	1000.

GOOD FOR on one line; period after PAIN.

HT 115 and 116 are from differing dies. The stars are smaller on 116.

Louis D'Aquin operated his bakery from 1824 at 120 Chartres Street and other locations. In 1835 it became D'Aquin Brothers at 36 New Levee Street until 1853. The partners in 1842 were F.B. D'Aquin and Adolph D'Aquin.

The firm became F. Daquin & Co. in 1853, the partners being F. Daquin, G. Montegut and L.L. Brown. Brown was sole owner 1856-61. A successor firm was in business after the Civil War.

NATHAN C. FOLGER

HT #	Rarity	Year	Metal	Size	VG	F	VF	EF
117	R7	1837	Brass	34mm	3000.	5000.	7000.	9000.

B & S = Bale & Smith.

GASQUET, PARISH & CO.

HT #	Rarity	Year	Metal	Size	VG	VF	EF	Unc
118	R6	(1835-41)	Brass	28mm	300.	750.	1000.	2000.

W.A. Gasquet & Co. operated as a dry goods store 1830-35, becoming Gasquet, Parish & Co., foreign and domestic dry goods at 47 Chartres Street in 1835.

It was located at 18 Chartres Street in 1841 and in 1842 became Gasquet & Conrey. Thus this token is clearly within the Hard Times period. (See "New Orleans Store Cards in the Ante-Bellum Days" by Sidney K. Eastwood, in *TAMS Journal* for Oct. 1966.)

HENDERSON & GAINES

HT #	Rarity	Year	Metal	Size	F	VF	EF	Unc
119	R7	(1838-42)	Brass	33mm	—	4000.	4500.	5000.
119A	R8	(1838-42)	WM	33mm	—	—	4500.	6500.

HENDERSON, WALTON & CO.

HT #	Rarity	Year	Metal	Size	VG	VF	EF	Unc
120	R7	(1835)	Brass	33mm	500.	2000.	2500.	4000.

J. HALL WALKER & WALTON

HT #	Rarity	Year	Metal	Size	VG	F	VF	EF
121	R8	1834	Brass	33mm	2000.	4000.	7500.	8500.
121A	R8	1834	Brass	33mm	2000.	5000.	7500.	8500.

JOHN A. MERLE & CO.

HT #	Rarity	Year	Metal	Size	VG	F	VF	Unc
122	R5	(1835-41)	Brass	27mm	200.	300.	550.	2000.

Reeded edge.

Four VF-EF pieces have been auctioned 1989-92, realizing respectively $550, $374, $550 and $350.

PUECH, BEIN & CO.

HT #	Rarity	Year	Metal	Size	F	VF	EF	Unc
123	R8	1834	Copper	25.5mm	—	17,000.	—	—

James Puech and John D. Bein were in business in New Orleans circa 1812 to 1834. Only 2 pieces known (Partrick, ANS).

The pedigree of HT 123 is Tilton (1880), Gould (1950), Fuld, John Ford, Ray Byrne, Levine sale, Dave Bowers. Another is in ANS collection.

PB CTSP ON SPANISH SILVER SEGMENTS
(Planters Bank)

HT #		Rarity	Year	VG	VF	EF	Unc
124	R6	(1811-17) on quarter of clipped-down 8-reales		300.	1000.	1400.	—

HT #		Rarity	Year	F	VF	EF	Unc
125	R6	(1811-17) on quarter of 8R		300.	900.	1200.	—
126	R8	(1811-17) on quarter of counterfeit 8R		300.	900.	1200.	—

Steinberg Sale 289, EF, fetched $1155 in Oct. 1989

NOTE: Imitations of these cut segments exist!

FURTHER NOTE: A "Bad" counterstamp (Brunk 1740) is also associated with this issue.

Number 124 equals 1 bit, or 12 1/2 cents, and weighs 4.9 grams. The countermarks are applied to a quarter cut segment of a 4-reales (50-cent) silver coin.

Number 125 equals 2 bits, or 25 cents, and weighs 6.7 grams. The counterstamp appears on a quarter cut segment of an 8-reales (dollar) silver coin.

The obverse counterstamp is a script PB in a chain circle of 16 links. Reverse stamp shows an eagle displayed at center, with NOUVELLE ORLEANS around.

There are 5 obverse and 3 reverse dies known.

NOTE: Robert Leonard and Gregory Brunk dispute any connection between Puech Bein and numbers 124, 125 and 126.

VALETON & CO.

BRASS, 23MM, 10-SIDED

HT #	Rarity	Year	F	VF	EF	Unc
127	R9	(1842-43)	—	9000.	—	—

WALTON & CO.

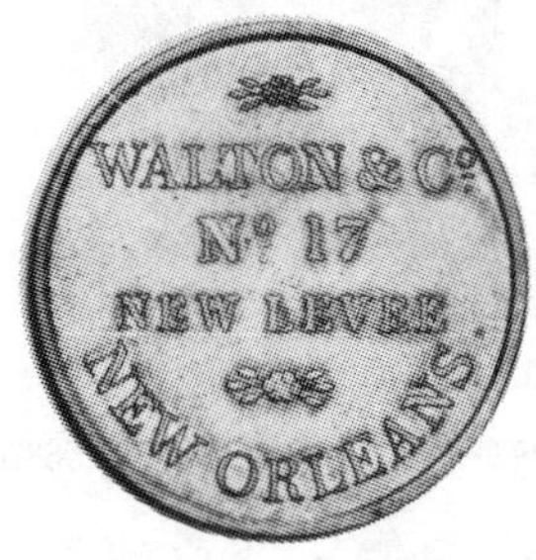

HT #	Rarity	Year	Metal	Size	VG	F	EF	Unc
128	R8	(1841-44)	Brass	33mm	250.	800.	1500.	2500.

WALTON WALKER & CO.

New Orleans, La.

HT #	Rarity	Year	Metal	Size	VG	VF	EF	Unc
129	R7	1836	Brass	34mm	2000.	7500.	8500.	10,000
129A	R8	1836	WM	34mm	—	—	8500.	10,000

MAINE

L. BAILEY

Portland, Maine

HT	Rarity	Year	Metal	Size	VG	F	VF	EF
130	R9	(1839)	Copper	29mm	—	—	125.	—
	L. BAILEY ctsp on U.S. Large cent. (Brunk 1850)							
130A	R9	(1839)	Silver	39mm	—	—	300.	—
	Similar ctsp on U.S. 1795 Bust silver dollar. (Bob Stark, University of Delaware, report)							

Lebbeus Bailey has been identified by both Dwight B. Demeritt and Frank Sellers as a Portland gunsmith. On Feb. 20, 1839, in collaboration with John B. Ripley of Claremont, N.H. and William B. Smith of Cornish, N.H., he obtained U.S. patent no. 1084 for a magazine rifle.

MARYLAND

JOHN L. CHAPMAN

Baltimore, MD.

HT #	Rarity	Year	Metal	Size	VG	F	VF	Unc
132	R5	(1834-40)	GS	17mm	150.	200.	400.	—

HT #	Rarity	Year	Metal	Size	VG	F	VF	Unc
133	R6	(1834-40)	GS	17mm	200.	270.	500.	—
	Soda, BALT							
134	R7	(1834-40)	GS	17mm	—	—	1800.	—
	Same as 133, ctsp '2' (for two sodas).							

John Lee Chapman was born at Fell's Point, Baltimore, in 1812. He began business as a druggist in 1834 at the southeast corner of Baltimore and South Streets, moving in 1841 to the opposite side of South Street. About 1846, with his brother Jonathan Chapman, he took over the glass manufacturing firm formerly conducted by his uncle George Chapman. This lasted until the outbreak of the Civil War.

Chapman was elected mayor of Baltimore in 1862, 1864 and 1866. In 1869 he was appointed naval officer of the Port of Baltimore by President Grant, and later became superintendent of the U.S. bonded warehouse there. He died Nov. 18, 1880.

HT 132 shows on obverse an eagle, and reads ONE SODA in center on reverse. The HT 133 token is similar, but there are 13 stars around the eagle, and BALT is incused below.

There are also two other tokens of Chapman (Miller Maryland 30 and 31) which probably are later than the Hard Times period.

JAMES COLE

HT #	Rarity	Year	Metal	Size	VG	VF	EF	Unc
135	R5	(1835)	Copper	23mm	100.	300.	400.	600.
135A	R5	(1835)	Brass	23mm	100.	300.	400.	600.
136	R8	(1835)	Ctsp. F.W.		—	—	200.	—
137	R8	(1835)	Ctsp. ICE		—	—	200.	—

NOTE: The ship reverse of the Cole Cards, muled with a shield in circle of 13 stars, is known as the Baltimore Token, Brass, 23mm. It may precede the Hard Times era, or possibly may be a proper addition to the general types of HT Tokens. See numbers 7 to 8D in Miller's 'A Catalogue of U.S. Store Cards or Merchants Tokens.'

From 1833 to 1845 Cole was an official of Baltimore harbor. He was born in 1802. He was harbor master 1833-39 and was state wharfinger 1839-45.

He operated a grocery on South Wolfe Street, Fell's Point, in 1835-36 while harbor master, and the tokens may be connected with this period. He was a hotelkeeper in Fell's Point 1847-49, and again a grocer on Wolfe Street 1849-51.

Selling his grocery in 1851, he tried life as a ship's captain and pilot 1851-60, then farmed in Anne Arundel County 1860-66. He opened a Baltimore restaurant at 721 So. Broadway 1866-69, then farmed and took life easy until his death in 1882.

In a late-1990 auction, VF specimens of 135 fetched $242 and $198, respectively.

H. HERRING

HT #	Rarity	Year	Metal	Size	VG	F	VF	Unc
139	R8	1834	WM	35mm	—	15,000	—	Rare
	Fair Mount							

Henry Herring opened his famed Fair Mount Hotel and Gardens in May, 1834 on the summit of Hampstead Hill. This eastern section of the city became known as Fair Mount, later the Jackson Square area. Herring was the proprietor 1834 to 1845.

HOUCK'S PANACEA

Baltimore, Md.

HT #	Rarity	Year	Metal	Size	VG	F	VF	EF
140	R7	(1836)	Silver	27mm	350.	—	500.	—

HOUCK'S / PANACEA / BALTIMORE in relief within oblong depression ctsp on U.S. Draped or Capped Bust quarter. (Dates examined: 1805, 1807, 1818, 1819). 6 pieces known. (Brunk 20140)

HT #	Rarity	Year	Metal	Size	VG	F	VF	EF
141	R4	(1836)	Silver	32.5mm	250.	—	325.	—

Similar ctsp on U.S. Draped or Capped Bust half dollar. (Dates examined: 1795, 1805, 1806, 1807, 1808, 1809, 1810, 1811, 1812, 1813, 1814, 1817, 1818, 1819, 1821, 1822, 1823, 1824, 1826, 1827, 1827/6, 1828, 1829, 1829/7, 1830, 1831, 1832, 1833, 1834, 1834-Small date — small stars, 1838 LD-SL, 1835, 1836, 1845). At least 76 specimens reported. (Van Ormer sale 2693, 2694)

HT #	Rarity	Year	Metal	Size	VG	F	VF	EF
142	R8	(1836)	Silver	39mm	1200.	—	2000.	—

Similar ctsp on early U.S. silver dollar. (Dates examined: 1795, 1800, 1834). 3 specimens reported. (Van Ormer sale 2695, 2696)

HT #	Rarity	Year	Metal	Size	VG	F	VF	EF
143	R7	(1836)	Silver	27mm	300.	—	450.	—

Similar ctsp on Spanish-American 2-reales, (Dates examined: 1741, 1775-PTS-JR, 1777-PTS-PR, 1784, 1793, 1793-LMA, 1794, 1804, date worn off). 10 specimens reported. (Ulex 304; Van Ormer 2691)

HT #	Rarity	Year	Metal	Size	VG	F	VF	EF
143A	R9	(1836)	Silver	21mm	—	—	650.	—

Similar ctsp on Spanish-American 1797-Mo 1-real. (Krause coll., ex-Vlack)

HT #	Rarity	Year	Metal	Size	VG	F	VF	EF
144	R8	(1836)	Silver	38mm	500.	—	800.	—

Similar ctsp on France 5-francs. (Dates examined: 1824-A, 1834). Only 3 pieces reported.

HT #	Rarity	Year	Metal	Size	VG	F	VF	EF
145	R9	(1836)	Silver	—	—	—	800.	—

Similar ctsp on Prussia silver thaler, date not known. (Brunk 20140FF). Apparently unique; not examined.

HT #	Rarity	Year	Metal	Size	VG	F	VF	EF
145F	R9	(1836)	Silver	39mm	—	—	800.	—

Similar ctsp on Brazil 1821 960-reis.

Interestingly, one collection, that of Stewart P. Witham, today contains 14 Houck counterstamps on Bust half dollars. In 1955 George Fuld possessed 20 such pieces of differing dates, but no records were kept. These pieces (HT 141) may be overvalued at today's price levels, but are seldom seen.

Dr. Jacob Houck was born in Frederick, Md., where he became a leading merchant. He came to Baltimore in 1828 and had a dry goods business at 121 West Baltimore St.

In 1834 Houck placed on the market his "Botanic Panacea," which sold for $1.50 a bottle. The counterstamps probably emanate from about 1836.

Houck's laboratory in 1840 was at 10 So. Charles St., then moved to 16 Hanover St., then 15 So. Liberty St., and in 1850 he was at 357 West Baltimore St. In 1851 Henry T. Houck had become proprietor, at 8 So. Eutaw St.

Houck's Panacea was "prepared solely from vegetable matter" by Jacob Houck, 16 Hanover St., and according to his full page advertisement in Matchett's *Baltimore Director*, 1842, "it may be taken with perfect safety by all ages and in all diseases." Undoubtedly this counterstamp exists on other silver coins of the Hard Times era.

In later years Jacob Houck may have permitted others to prepare his popular panacea for sale under some licensing arrangement. Recently we encountered this advertisement in the 1855 city directory of Nashville, Tenn.:

"Houck's Panacea. Dr. A. G. Goodlet, mfr. & proprietor of: Houck's Improved Panacea and Goodlet's Vegetable Lineament. 29 1/2 No. Cherry St., Nashville, Tenn.

"These remedies have popular favor in the South and North. And should be in use in every family."

Some medicine bottles of the 1850's read: "Houck's / Vegetable Panacea / Nashville Tenn." and "Houck's / Vegetable Panacea / Goodletsville, Tenn."

Bottle in Gregory Brunk collection.

Prepared Solely from Vegetable Matter, by

BALTIMORE,

Which may be taken with perfect safety by all ages and in all diseases; its cures are for the following diseases:—Dyspepsia, Loss of Appetite, Indigestion, Inflammation of the Stomach, Heart Burn, Diarrhœa, Dysentery or Flux, Piles, Fistula, Obstructed Menstruation, Ague and Fever, Bilious or Remittent Fever, Typhus Fever, Scarlet Fever, Small Pox, Erysipolous or St. Anthony's Fire, Asthma, Pleurisy, Measlés, Yellow Fever, Costiveness, Wind on the Stomach or Bowels, Cholera Morbus, Consumption, Influenza, Colds, Coughs, Inflammation of the Chest, Palsy, Gout, Rheumatism, Inflammatory Sore Throat or Quinsey, Whooping Cough, Thrush or Sore Mouth, Putrid Sore Throat, Croup, Inflammation of the Heart, Dropsy, Rickets, Diseases of the Liver, Jaundice, Difficulty of making Urine, Gleet, Hysterics, Nervous and Scrofulous Affections of the Members and Ligaments, Mercurial and Venereal Diseases, Ulcers, Sores, Affections of the Skin, and all diseases arising from Impure Blood, &c.

Price per Bottle, $1.50.

The above medicine can be obtained at

No. 16, corner of German and Hanover streets,

With proper directions for using.

☞ A liberal discount made to persons who buy to sell.

S. JACKSON

HT#	Rarity	Year	Metal	Size	VG	F	VF	EF
A145	R9	(1835)	Copper	23mm	200.	—	450.	—

S. JACKSON (curved) / BALTIMORE ctsp on U.S. 1834 Half cent. (Schenkman report; Van Ormer report; Russ Sears report; Brunk 21395)

S. Jackson was listed in the 1833 directory as a cutler and maker of surgical instruments located at the corner of Liberty and German (now Redwood) Streets. In the 1835 directory Shadrach was described as a sawyer located on Douglas Street. In the 1846-47 directory Samuel Jackson is listed as a cutler and maker of surgical instruments. The next item may or may not be connected to either.

HT	Rarity	Year	Metal	Size	VG	F	VF	EF
A145B	R9	(1835)	Copper	23mm	200.	—	450.	—

S. JACKSON ctsp on U.S. 1835 Half cent. (Brunk 21390)

Gregory Brunk believes Shadrach is the issuer; Russ Sears opts for Samuel. Samuel seems more likely to us.

DR. LEACH

HT #	Rarity	Year	Metal	Size				
146	R9	(1845-51)	Silver	32.5mm	—	300.	—	—

DR. LEACH / BALTO. ctsp on U.S. 1824 Bust half dollar. (Brunk 24065)

Dr. Leach practiced dentistry 1845-51.

RANDALL & CO.

GERMAN SILVER, 15MM

HT #	Rarity	Year	VG	F	VF	Unc
147	R6	(1840-42) Plain edge	20.00	75.00	150.	350.
147A	R5	(1840-42) Reeded edge	20.00	75.00	150.	350.

The obverse reads in five lines: MONUMENT / (flower) / RANDALL & CO / BALT / SQUARE. On reverse, Battle Monument is at center, with MINERAL WATER above and CITY HOTEL below.

HT #	Rarity	Year	Metal	Size	VG	F	VF	Unc
148	R9	(1840-42)	Lead	22mm	—	—	—	3000.

Dudley A. Randall & Co. is listed in the directories of 1840-1842 in Barnum's City Hotel. Monument Square, Baltimore. Unique. Die trial.

MASSACHUSETTS

H M & E I RICHARDS
Attleboro, Mass.

HT #	Rarity	Year	Metal	Size	VG	VF	EF	Unc
150	R2	1834	Copper	28.5mm	6.00	20.00	100.	300.

HT #	Rarity	Year	Metal	Size	VG	VF	EF	Unc
151	R2	(1834)	Copper	28.5mm	6.00	20.00	100.	250.

Herve Manning and Edmund Ira Richards formed their company in 1833. H. M. was then only 21, and E. I. just 18. Their career as Hard Times token manufacturers evidently began in 1834, utilizing the services of Edward Hulseman, the engraver at Robinson's Jones & Co. in the same city.

EDWARD HULSEMAN
Attleboro, Mass. and New York, N.Y.

Hulseman worked as a card engraver in Attleboro, Mass. from 1833 through 1836, working for Robinson's Jones & Co., the button-makers. His and their first tokens came in the fall of 1833 — HT 70 among the politicals and HT 428 (Hathaway) and 152 and 153 (Robinson's Jones) among the store cards. Hulseman also did some work for H. M. & E. I. Richards, notably the Lafayette Standing dies (HT 150, etc.), beginning in 1834.

From 1837 through 1841 he worked as an independent card engraver at 80 Nassau Street, New York City. He also executed Hard Times tokens from the New York location, notably HT 31, 32 and 81.

His 'H' signature appears under the safe on obverse of HT 69, 69A, 70, 71, 71A and 70A. The 'H' signature also appears on the Standing Lafayette type (the initial is at the right side of the ground under Lafayette's feet) used on the cards of W. P. Haskins, H. M. & E. I. Richards, Walsh's General Store and S. L. Wilkins. This Lafayette type token is said by both Low and Lindesmith to have been struck by the Richards firm, manufacturing jewelers in Attleboro, Mass., and this view now is being confirmed.

The standing figure of Marquis de Lafayette is from an engraving after Ary Scheffer's celebrated painting, and attained great popularity in the United States. Lafayette made a triumphant visit to America in 1825.

All Hulseman's tokens with the 'H' signature were cut in 1833-1834. After 1834 he stopped signing his token products. In 1838 the U.S. government started cracking down on manufacturers of cent-sized tokens, who were said to be impinging on the sovereign right of coinage.

ROBINSON'S JONES & CO.
Attleboro, Mass.

HT #	Rarity	Year	Metal	Size	VG	VF	EF	Unc
152	R2	1833	Copper	28.5mm	5.00	20.00	40.00	225.

HT #	Rarity	Year	Size	VG	VF	EF	Unc
153	R1	1833 Slanting 1 in 1833		5.00	12.00	35.00	225.
153A	R7	1833 Svd/Cop	28mm	—	300.	—	—

Robinson's Jones & Co. received the American Institute medal for their metallic buttons in the fall of 1833, and promptly issued these tokens to advertise their triumph. The dies were cut by Edward Hulseman at about the same time that he cut the dies for HT 70, the first of the "I Take The Responsibility" political tokens.

Robinson's Jones & Co. was organized in 1831 in Attleboro, Mass. and reorganized as R. & W. Robinson in 1836. Robinson's Jones employed Edward Hulseman as an in-house engraver 1833-1836, after which Hulseman removed to New York City.

This premier button-making firm is now credited with manufacturing the earliest large-circulation Hard Times tokens, such as HT 70, 25, 152, 153 and 428 (the latter the 1833 Ephraim Hathaway token.)

R. & W. ROBINSON

HT #	Rarity	Year	Metal	Size	VG	VF	EF	Unc
154	R1	1836	Copper	28.5mm	5.00	12.00	30.00	220.

A points between Y and O. Date close to buttons.

155	R1	1836	Copper	28.5mm	5.00	12.00	30.00	160.
	A points to Y. Date distant from buttons.							
155A	R6	—	Silvered Copper	28.5mm	50.00	100.	200.	400.

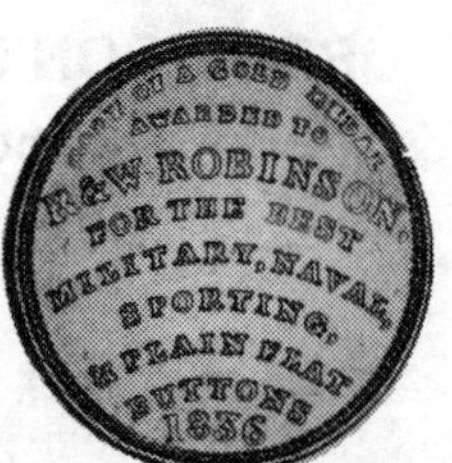

156	R3	1836	Copper	28.5mm	40.00	100.	175.	400.
	New-York							

In 1967 Robert J. Lindesmith (see Bibliography) gave rather convincing evidence that the two Robinson firms of the 1833-1836 period should have been attributed to Attleboro, Mass., rather than New York City. The NEW YORK on all obverse dies pertains to the location of the American Institute, issuer of the medal reproduced there.

Willard Robinson was one of the partners. He married a girl of the H. M. & E. I. Richards family. The R. & W. Robinson firm was reorganized from the earlier Robinson's Jones & Co. firm in 1836. In 1848 they were succeeded in turn by D. Evans & Co. (Evans was the striker of the Rhode Island series of Civil War token mulings depicting hunting scenes).

Documentary evidence shows that some of the 1836 Robinson cards were actually struck in 1839.

S.B. SCHENCK

HT #	Rarity	Year	Metal	Size	VG	VF	EF	Unc
157	R1	1834	Copper	28.5mm	5.00	20.00	40.00	100.
	W.P. Haskins							

158	R1	1834	Copper	28.5mm	5.00	20.00	40.00	150.
	This Machine							
158A	R7	(1834)	Svd/Cop	28.5mm	—	—	90.00	—

159	R2	(1834)	Copper	28.5mm	6.00	15.00	50.00	300.
	Richards							
160	R2	(1834)	Copper	28.5mm	6.00	15.00	120.	300.
	Peck & Burnham							

161	R7	(1830's)	Copper	28.5mm	—	250.	—	—
	Ctsp. GRAVES & HATCH CAST-STEEL (Brunk 16950; Krause coll., ex-Vlack)							

FARNSWORTH, PHIPPS & CO.

Boston, Mass.

HT #	Rarity	Year	Metal	Size	VG	F	EF	Unc
162	R3	(1829-33)	Copper	28.5mm	10.00	30.00	175.	280.
	W & B NY							

J. JONES

HT #	Rarity	Year	Metal	Size	VG	F	VF	EF
A162	R9	(1837)	Copper	23mm	80.00	—	125.	—
	J. JONES in relief within rect. depression ctsp on U.S. 1804 Half cent. Surrounding the J. JONES stamp are 14 counterstamps consisting of a relief S within small depression. (Charles Kirtley Oct. 1985 sale, lot 307; Brunk 22020; ex-Maurice Gould, Sol Taylor)							

HT #	Rarity	Year	Metal	Size	VG	F	VF	Unc
B162	R8	(1837)	Copper	29mm	80.00	—	125.	—
	Similar ctsp on U.S. Large cent, minus the S stamps. Dates examined: 1795, 1830, unknown. 3 pieces known.							
C162	R9	(1837)	Silver	18mm	100.	—	150.	—
	Similar ctsp on U.S. 1837 dime. Unique?							
D162	R9	(1837)	Copper	29mm	75.00	—	125.	—
	Similar ctsp on Canada token. (Brunk 22020S)							

The S-within-depression punch was a common one in the silversmith trade to indicate "sterling."

Attributed to John B. Jones, born 1782, died 1854. He began business as a silversmith in 1809. He was a member of all these firms:

Jones & Aspinwall (Zalmon Aspinwall) 1809
Jones & Pierce (John Pierce) 1810
Jones & Ward (Richard Ward) 1813-16
John Jones 1816-22
John Jones Jr. 1821-34
Baldwin & Jones (Jabez L. Baldwin) 1816-20
John B. Jones & Co. (S. S. Ball) 1838
Jones Low & Ball (John J. Low, S. S. Ball) 1839
Jones Ball & Poor (S. S. Ball, Nathaniel C. Poor) 1840-46
Jones Ball & Co. (S. S. Ball) 1850-52
Jones Shreve Brown & Co. (Benjamin Shreve, Mr. Brown) 1854

John B. Jones died in 1854. His son's last partnership was succeeded by Shreve Brown & Co. 1857-69 and then Shreve Crump & Low, 1869 to the present.

J. B. JONES

HT #	Rarity	Year	Metal	Size	VG	F	VF	EF
G162	R8	(1839)	Copper	29mm	100.	—	125.	—

J. B. JONES in relief within rect. depression ctsp on U.S. Large cent. Examined: 1818, 1819. 2 pieces known. (Brunk 22035)

The son of John B. Jones (see above), John B Jones Jr. was in business for himself 1821-34 and in various partnerships 1835-56.

WM. H. MILTON

HT #	Rarity	Year	Metal	Size	VG	F	VF	Unc
163	R1	(1830-34)	Copper	28.5mm	5.00	12.00	30.00	200.

WM. H. MILTON & CO.

HT #	Rarity	Year	Metal	Size	VG	VF	EF	Unc
164	R1	(1835-44) WAREHOUSE	Copper	28.5mm	5.00	12.00	40.00	150.
164A	R8	(1835-44)	S/Brass	28.5mm	—	—	200.	450.

HT #	Rarity	Year	Metal	Size	VG	VF	EF	Unc
165	R2	(1835-44) * WAREHOUSE*	Copper	28.5mm	7.00	15.00	60.00	175.

HT #	Rarity	Year	Metal	Size				
166	R4	(1835-44) WAREHOUSE*	Brass	28.5mm			May not exist	
166A	R8	(1835-44)	S/Brass	28.5mm	—	—	200.	450.

PECK & BURNHAM

HT #	Rarity	Year	Metal	Size	VG	VF	EF	Unc
167	R2	(1834)	Copper	28.5mm	8.00	20.00	75.00	175.
168	R2	(1834) Schenk Rev.	Copper	28.5mm	6.00	15.00	120.	300.

Peck & Burnham were located at 54 Hanover St., the address on the tokens, from 1832 through 1835. In 1836 the firm apparently dissolved, and Abel G. Peck was located at 15 Central with a dry goods firm. (Abel G. Peck & Co. were at 6 Kilby St. in 1837-1845, then at 35 and 57 Kilby St. in 1846-1847).

W. P. PHYFE

HT #	Rarity	Year	Metal	Size	VG	F	VF	EF
A168	R9	(1830's)	Silver	39mm	—	—	400.	—

W. P. PHYFE (incused) / PURE SILVER COIN (italics, in relief in rect. depression) / BOSTON (in relief in rect. depression) - ctsp in three separate stamps on Kingdom of Italy 1813 silver 5-lire. (Hartzog sale of Dec. 1, 1980, lot 1811; B&M Taylor sale of March 26-28, 1987, lot 1295; Brunk 32010)

William Phyfe was a silversmith who carried on his trade in Boston in the 1830's, and then in New York City 1840-50. From 1844-1850 he was part of the silversmith firm of Eoff & Phyfe with Garret Eoff.

ROXBURY COACHES

HT #	Rarity	Year	Metal	Size	F	VF	EF	Unc
169	R3	1837	GS	18.7mm	80.00	125.	225.	700.
169A	R8	1837	Copper	18.7mm	—	—	—	Electro

The Roxbury Coaches were those which ran through what later became Washington Street, Boston, over "the Neck," to the top of the hill in Roxbury where once stood the old church in which Apostle Eliot preached in New England's early days. The Norfolk House, a famous hostelry on the opposite side of the street, was their stopping place in John Eliot Square until the line was discontinued.

The coaches were long omnibuses carrying 16 to 20 persons inside, drawn by four horses. At first they made hourly trips from Roxbury to downtown Boston and were called "Roxbury Hourlies." The fare was 25 cents each way. Handsomely painted, their sides bore names — *Regulator*, *Conqueror* and *Aurora*, the latter with a goddess in a cloud-borne chariot on its yellow sides.

Horace King managed the business 1832-1851, later finding opposition from coaches of one Mr. Hobbs which made more frequent trips. The Roxbury Coaches succumbed to "progress" about 1856.

JOHN ELIOT SQUARE, ROXBURY, MASSACHUSETTS An Old Print Showing Two Omnibuses of the Roxbury Coaches

WILLIAM RUTTER

HT #	Rarity	Year	Metal	Size	F	VF	EF	Unc
170	R7	(1831-35)	Copper	28.5mm	200.	650.	950.	1500.

William Rutter's Red Store on Fulton St. at Cross St., mentioned on the cards, was attributed to the 1831-1835 period by Howland Wood in 1913 on sound deductive reasoning. Rutter, a man of many parts, was in business in Boston from 1813 to 1863 in a number of partnerships and alone.

1813 William Rutter, LYNN ST. (Grocer)

1816 William Rutter / Asa Hayes, 4 TOWN DOCK (Traders)

1818 William Rutter & Co. (David Manley), 17 BRAY'S WHARF

1821 William Rutter & Co. (William Manley) TOWN DOCK

1823 William Rutter, 1 TOWN DOCK (Trader)

1825 William Rutter, BIXBY & VALENTINE'S WHARF (Trader) and 1825 Rutter, Gaylord & Co. (Charles Gaylord, Mathew M. Teprell), 6 ANN ST. (Booksellers & Stationers)

1826 William Rutter, BIXBY & VALENTINE'S WHARF (Trader) but out of Gaylord & Hatch, Booksellers & Stationers and into Freeman, Rutter & Co. (John Freeman), 46 NO. MARKET ST. (Stationers) 1827 William Rutter, 152 ANN St. (Variety Store)

1829 William Rutter & Co. (Reuben Mossman & Artemas Tirrill), CROSS ST. (Paper Rags, Junk)

1830-35 William Rutter (alone), CROSS ST. (Variety Store)

1835-39 William Rutter, SNOW'S WHARF (Junk)

1839-63 William Rutter, 221 BROAD ST.

(Fulton Street, formerly under water, was platted in 1828 on new land fill. It received the name Fulton in 1831.)

H. L. WEBSTER & CO.

HT #	Rarity	Year	Metal	Size	VG	F	VF	EF
A171	R9	(1835-42)	Copper	29mm	—	—	100.	—

H L Webster & Co in relief in slanting letters within rect. depression ctsp on U.S. 1835 Large cent. (Kirtley Nov. 1991 sale, lot Q002)

In the example above, the 'L' of the stamp is blundered and appears like an 'S' tilted left.

Henry L. Webster was a silversmith operating in Boston circa 1826-42 and also in Providence, R.I. circa 1831-64. He died in 1865.

In Providence he was a partner of famed Jabez L. Gorham (Gorham & Webster 1831-37; Gorham, Webster & Price 1837-41; Jabez Gorham & Son 1841-50; Webster & Knowles 1852-64).

The H. L. Webster & Co. mark seems to have been used only in Boston. The mark matches punches shown in Louise C. Belden's *Marks of American Silversmiths* and the Kovels' silversmith reference.

JOHN ELIOT SQUARE, ROXBURY, MASSACHUSETTS. An old print showing two omnibuses of the Roxbury Coaches

ALFRED D. WILLARD

Boston, Mass.

HT #	Rarity	Year	Metal	Size	F	VF	EF	Unc
171	R1	(1835)	Copper	28.5mm	5.00	12.00	50.00	125.
171A	R9	(1835)	WM	28.5mm			Possible fake!	

EAST BOSTON COACHES

East Boston, Mass.

HT #	Rarity	Year	Metal	Size	VG	VF	EF	Unc
172	R3	1837	GS	18.7mm	100.	300.	500.	850.
172A	R8	1837	Copper	18.7mm	—	—		Electro

F. LAMSON, MERRIMACK HOUSE

Lowell, Mass.

HT #	Rarity	Year	Metal	Size	VG	F	VF	EF
173	R9	(?)	Copper	28.5mm	—	200.	—	—

F. LAMSON in relief within rect. depression ctsp eight times on obverse of S. B. Schenck 1834 Hard Times token of Attleboro, Mass. (HT 158). Rv: On reverse of token are seven stamps, all in relief within rectangular depressions, top to bottom: MERRIMACK / HOUSE / LOWELL / LOWELL / F. LAMSON. At left: NASHUA. At right: BOSTON. (B&M Patterson March, 1985 sale, lot 1716; Brunk 23760)

Neither F. Lamson nor the Merrimack House in Lowell has been traced. The presence of the names Nashua and Boston may indicate some connection (stagecoach service?). Search of Nashua directories offers no help.

There was a Merrimac House in Boston in 1863, corner Merrimac and Friend, James L. Hanson, proprietor, but it is doubtful there is any connection there.

We are tentatively assigning a Hard Times-era provenance to this piece.

R. LYMAN

Lowell, Mass.

HT #	Rarity	Date	Metal	Size	VG	F	VF	EF
173C	R9	(?)	Copper	29mm	—	75.00	—	—

R. LYMAN in rectangular cartouche ctsp on reverse of U.S. 1825 Large cent. (Brunk 25360; Rulau MV 196)

R. Lyman was a silversmith in Lowell in 1840.

S.L. WILKINS

HT #	Rarity	Year	Metal	Size	F	VF	EF	Unc
174	R1	1834	Copper	28.5mm	5.00	18.00	45.00	225.
	Lafayette H							

Samuel L. Wilkins advertised in 1832 that he had for sale a large assortment of French and American paper hangings in addition to his normal clothing and shoe stock. In 1836 he moved to number 21 Merrimack St., where he stayed six or seven years. He then retired from business and moved to Medford, Mass.

The standing figure of Lafayette, cut by Edward Hulseman, is based on Ary Scheffer's celebrated painting which attained great popularity in the United States at that time. Lafayette died in 1834.

FRANCIS L. BRIGHAM

New Bedford, Mass.

HT #	Rarity	Year	Metal	Size	F	VF	EF	Unc
175	R6	1833	Copper	28.5mm	100.	300.	500.	1250.
	Beaded borders outside circle							
175A	R9	1833	Copper	28.5mm	—	—	3000.	—
	Struck over HT Token 70)							

HT #	Rarity	Year	Metal	Size	F	VF	EF	Unc
176	R3	1833	Copper	28.5mm	40.00	100.	300.	500.
	Beads only							
176A	R5	1833	Silvered Copper			Not Contemporary		

"Cheapside" was the name given in the Hard Times period to that portion of Pleasant Street, New Bedford, which formed the east side of what was then called Market Square, fronting a large granite building used for a market, public meetings and the like. "Cheapside," parallel with Purchase Street, a block away, was bordered by the long, one-story building, shown on the token, and was a favorite resort for shoppers. Francis L. Brigham was in 1836 (according to the New Bedford directory) a dentist, having an office at 24 Purchase Street, and he was engaged in that profession when he died, 18 September, 1845, aged nearly 43. Just when he abandoned the selling of dry goods and took up dentistry, does not appear. He was remembered for some slight eccentricities.

DOW

New Bedford, Mass.

HT #	Rarity	Year	Metal	Size	VG	FF	VF	EF
A176	R8	(1836 ?)	Copper	28.5mm	—	—	100.	—

DOW ctsp on Francis L. Brigham 1833 Hard Times token. (Storer 1473; Brunk 12003)

Dow was the successor to Brigham, possibly about 1836.

N - BRIDGWATER (Perkins)

North Bridgewater, Mass.

HT #	Rarity	Year	Metal	Size	VG	F	VF	EF
177	R9	1841	Silver	40mm	—	—	—	450.

N-BRIDGWATER / 1841 ctsp on Spanish-American 1814 8-reales of Ferdinand VII. (Van Ormer sale 2556).

HT #	Rarity	Year	Metal	Size	VG	F	VF	EF
178	R9	1841	Silver	38mm	—	—	—	450.

Similar ctsp on Spain 1814-Crowned C-CJ 8-reales of Cadiz Mint, Craig 136.2. (Stanley Steinberg Nov. 1985 sale; Brunk 5175)

HT #	Rarity	Year	Metal	Size	VG	F	VF	EF
178A	R9	(1840's)	Copper	29mm	—	—	225.	—

BRIDGEWATER ctsp on U.S. 1798 Large cent. (Brunk 5170)

The stamps on these pieces are typical of the Perkins family of gunsmiths of North Bridgewater, Mass., who frequently misspelled the locale as BRIDGWATER on their punches to mark guns. The date '1841' may be an actual issue date, or may refer to the Model 1841 rifles produced for the Army Ordnance Dept.

Rufus Perkins of North Bridgewater received a contract in 1808 for 2,500 muskets to be delivered by 1813. Some of these are marked BRIDGEWATER.

James Perkins and Adam Kinsley of nearby Bridgewater had received a contract for 2,000 French Charleville-pattern muskets in 1798 and some of these were stamped BRIDGWATER / 1809.

The Model 1841 rifle (sometimes called the "Mississippi rifle" or the "Yager rifle"), a muzzle-loading .54 caliber percussion weapon, was first prepared at the Harpers Ferry (Va.) Armory in 1841, and the weapon's lockplate received stamps from a number of gunmakers who also counterstamped coins. Some of the contractors' marks were:

HARPERS FERRY / 1845 / AW/P VP (eagle head).

REMINGTON'S / HERKIMER / N.Y. / US / 1849.

ROBBINS / KENDALL & / LAWRENCE / US / WINDSOR, VT. / 1847.

ROBBINS / & / LAWRENCE / US / WINDSOR, VT. / 1850.

TRYON / US / PHILADA / PA / 1848.

E. WHITNEY / US / N. HAVEN / 1851.

George W. Tryon, Eliphalet Remington and Eli Whitney's names will conjure up many associations (Whitney was a gun inventor as well as inventor of the cotton gin, for example.)

Additional information is needed on just who was operating the North Bridgewater arms works in/after 1841.

Stanley Steinberg attributed this mark to the gun manufactory of David and John Ames of North Bridgewater (now Brockton, Mass.). John Ames had been appointed the first superintendent of Springfield Arsenal in Mass. by President George Washington.

The Rulau gunsmith listing in *U.S. Merchant Tokens 1845-1860* (2nd ed.) shows N. P. Ames at Springfield Arsenal 1839-45 but the Ames Mfg. Co. at Chicopee Falls 1835-85.

It is possible the Van Ormer and Steinberg pieces are one and the same — both are Ferdinand VII. The author has not examined them.

J. CUMMINGS

Springfield, Mass.

HT #	Rarity	Year	Metal	Size	VG	F	VF	EF
183	R8	(1840's)	Copper	28mm	—	—	75.00	—

J. CUMMINGS / SPRINGFIELD, MASS. ctsp on Canadian token. (Brunk 10270)

John Cummings was a gunsmith at 18 Kingsley Street in Hartford, Conn. 1841-43, according to authorities Gardner, Sellers and Kauffman. Just when he was at Springfield, Mass. is not known.

GIBBS TIFFANY & CO.

Sturbridge, Mass.

HT #	Rarity	Year	Metal	Size	VG	F	VF	EF
179	R7	(1835-38)	Copper	29mm	—	250.	—	—

GIBBS TIFFANY & CO. ctsp on U.S. 1826 Large cent. (Rich Hartzog coll.)

180	R8	1836	Copper	29mm	—	—	900.	—

(Eagle) / E. HUTCHINGS & CO. / AGENTS BALTO / GIBBS TIFFANY & CO. / STURBRIDGE MASS. / CAST-STEEL / 1836 ctsp on U.S. Large cent. (Brunk 20880; Russ Sears coll.)

NOTE: Hutchings was in business only 1835-1838.

JOHN J. ADAMS

Taunton, Mass.

HT #	Rarity	Year	Metal	Size	VG	F	VF	Unc
181	R1	(1835)	Copper	28.5mm	4.50	8.00	30.00	120.
181A	R6	(1835)	Brass	28.5mm	35.00	75.00	150.	600.
181B	R9	(1835)	Silver	32.5mm	—	—	2000.	—

Obverse die overstruck on one side of a U.S. 1811 half dollar. (HT 181B)

CROCKER BROS. & CO.

Taunton, Mass.

HT #	Rarity	Year	Metal	Size	VG	F	VF	EF
182	R3	(1830's)	Copper	28.5mm	20.00	50.00	75.00	175.
182A	R7	(1830's)	WM	28.5mm	—	1000.	1400.	1700.

HT 182A in VF from the Wayte Raymond coll. fetched $1430 in a Bowers & Merena 1990 sale.

Documentary evidence shows that some of the Crocker Brothers tokens were still being struck in Attleboro in 1839.

H. W. C.

Massachusetts

HT #	Rarity	Year	Metal	Size				
184	R9	(?)	Silver	32.5mm	—	—	35.00	—

H. W. C. / MASS ctsp on U.S. 1824 Bust half dollar. (Sol Taylor coll.; Brunk 17620)

A similar ctsp on U.S. 1829 Large cent was reported as Brunk 17605, without periods. It is not connected with HT 184.

Attribution to HT period is tentative.

MISSOURI

HUCKEL, BURROWS & JENNINGS

St. Louis, Mo.

HT #	Rarity	Year	Metal	Size	VG	F	VF	EF
187	R8	1836	Brass	29mm	4000.	7000.	9000.	11,000
187A	R8	1836	S/Brass	29mm	—	7000.	9000.	11,000
187B	R8	1836	WM	29mm	2000.	5500.	9000.	11,000

HT #	Rarity	Year	Metal	Size	VG	F	VF	EF
188	R8	1836	Brass	29mm	3500.	6500.	8500.	10,000
	HUCKEL erased on die.							
188A	R8	—	WM	29mm	2000.	5500.	8500.	10,000

HT 187-188A are not known in uncirculated condition.

J. MASSOT

SILVER, 38MM

HT #	Rarity	Year	VG	F	VF	EF
189	**R9**	**1840**	—	**450.**	—	—

J. MASSOT / 1840 ctsp on obverse of France 1792-D ecu (6-livres) of Louis XVI, J Craig 93.4. ST. LOUIS ctsp on reverse of the coin. (Frank Kovacs coll.; Brunk 26440)

Joseph Massot was a wholesale grocer on South Fourth Street 1840-1847. The St. Louis directories of 1840, 1842, 1845 and 1847 give differing descriptions of his address, which seems to have been unchanged — 155 So. Fourth (east side), between Cedar and Mulberry.

NEW HAMPSHIRE

HASELTON & PALMER

Dover, N.H.

HT #	Rarity	Metal	Size	Year	VG	VF	EF	Unc
192	R2	1837	Copper	28.5mm	5.00	15.00	35.00	250.
	A.C. Smith.							

A.C. SMITH

Dover, N.H.

HT #	Rarity	Year	Metal	Size	VG	VF	EF	Unc
193	R2	1837	Copper	28.5mm	5.00	15.00	35.00	250.
	Haselton Palmer							

NATHL. MARCH

Portsmouth, N.H.

HT #	Rarity	Year	Metal	size	VG	VF	EF	Unc
194	R1	1837	Copper	28.5mm	5.00	12.00	30.00	170.
	William Simes							

Nathaniel March was born in Portsmouth on June 14, 1807. He became a junior partner in the firm of Childs & March, the successor to Childs & Sparhawk. Childs left the firm soon thereafter, and business was then conducted as Nathaniel March & Co. until about 1839. After that time the business was conducted simply in his personal name, Nathaniel March. He died July 9, 1846, after which the trade was continued by Samuel A. Badger.

William Simes was born in Portsmouth on April 9, 1806. He entered business in 1828. At different times Thomas E. Call and Henry F. Gerrish were partners. His business was sold in 1860 to Moulton & Blaisdell, who continued the trade for many decades thereafter. In 1861 and 1862 William Simes was elected mayor of Portsmouth. A third nomination was subsequently declined. The token issued jointly by March and Simes is believed to have been struck by H.M. & E.I. Richards of Attleboro, Mass.

WILLIAM SIMES & CO.

HT #	Rarity	Year	Metal	Size	F	VF	EF	Unc
194	R1	1837	Copper	28.5mm	5.00	12.00	30.00	170.
	Nathl March							

E.F. SISE & CO.

Portsmouth, N.H.

HT #	Rarity	Year	Metal	Size	VG	VF	EF	Unc
195	R1	1837	Copper	28.5mm	4.00	12.00	30.00	200.

Edward F. Sise, founder of the firm of general commission and forwarding merchants which issued this card, was born in Dover, N.H. on Sept. 19, 1799, and died May 25, 1868. The firm advertised itself as importers of crockery and glassware and dealers in coal.

The "Co." was E.F. Sise and John Walker, but after Sise's withdrawal about 1854, Walker continued the business in partnership with William H. Sise and Joseph Sise. Walker retired in 1883. Joseph Sise died in 1894. This firm occupied the same premises from 1822 until at least 1895, according to Lyman H. Low.

NEW JERSEY

HOWELL WORKS GARDEN

Allaire, N.J.

HT #	Rarity	Year	Metal	Size	VG	VF	EF	Unc
200	R4	1834	Copper	22mm	45.00	150.	300.	750.
	Grapes, Signum.							

201	R3	(1835)	Copper	28mm	80.00	185.	300.	600.
	Rose, Token							

201A	R9	(1835)	Copper	29mm	—	3000.	—	Rare

Similar, ctsp on 1820 U.S. cent

The Howell Works had its origin in an establishment called the Monmouth Furnace, founded in Howell, Monmouth Co., N.J. (now Allaire), in 1814. About 1822 James P. Allaire took possession, changing the name to Howell Works, under which title they were carried on for about twenty-five years. Mr. Allaire died in 1858. A few years before his death it became the Allaire Works, famous for its marine engines, etc., the fine workmanship of which gave them a wide reputation. In this concern the well known John Roach began his career.

Just what relation the Garden had to the Works does not appear, but it was connected with them in some way, we have on good authority. From the device the tokens bear it was very likely a social resort of the workmen, under control of the company.

These tokens, as well as Howell Works "shin plasters" for various denominations, were used as currency. The paper bills were engraved by Rawdon, Wright, Hatch and Co., of New York, and were for 6 1/4, 12 1/2 cents, $1, $2, $3, $5 and $10, and possibly other denominations, payable to bearer and signed by the president of the "Howell Works Co."

J. GIBBS, MANUFACTURER
Belleville, N.J.

HT #	Rarity	Year	Metal	Size	VG	F	VF	EF
202	R5	(1841)	Copper	28mm	350.	600.	1000.	1500.

I. GIBBS USM STAGE

HT #	Rarity	Year	Metal	Size	VG	F	VF	EF
203	R8	(1835)	Brass	23mm	2000.	2500.	5000.	7500.

One Ride

The I. Gibbs USM Stage piece could have been issued as early as 1831. An advertisement in an 1831 newspaper publicized John Gibbs' Belleville to Newark (3 miles) and Belleville to New York (8 miles) stages. John Gibbs moved to New York in 1846.

Previous editions of this catalog listed the I. Gibbs piece under New York City, but we now believe that Atwood was in error in assigning it there, as the headquarters of the stage line apparently was in Belleville, New Jersey.

T. DUSEAMAN

HT #	Rarity	Year	Metal	Size	VG	VF	EF	Unc
204	R1	(1837)	Copper	28mm	10.00	32.50	75.00	400.
204A	R6	—	Gilt/C.	28mm	—	—	300.	—

T.D. SEAMAN
Belleville, N.J.

HT #	Rarity	Year	Metal	Size	VG	VF	EF	Unc
204B	R5	(1837)	Copper	28mm	185.	450.	750.	3000.

T.D. Seaman operated a hotel in Belleville around 1837 and also apparently engaged in trade as a butcher. He was probably the same as one Tobias D. Seaman who was proprietor of the Mechanics' Hotel, 188 Broad Street, Newark, N.J., from about 1845 to 1850 and, following that, in 1851 the South Ward Hotel at 398 Broadway in Newark.

It is probable that HT 204 bearing the name DUSEAMAN was in reality issued for Seaman. The workmanship is very crude and for this reason the piece was probably rejected by Seaman when he first saw it. A diecutter at the Belleville Mint simply added an extraneous U in place of the period between the D and SEAMAN, creating the *DUSEAMAN* name. After the U was added the piece was suitable for general purposes and could be sold to anyone in quantity. As such pieces sold for less than a cent but circulated at the value of one cent each, a profit was to be made.

A choice toned AU specimen of this rare card fetched $2200 in the 1989 Gil Steinberg sale.

BERGEN IRON WORKS
Lakewood, N.J.

STARS

BRASS, 21MM, PLAIN EDGE

HT #	Rarity	Year	Metal	Size	VG	VF	EF	Unc
205	R2	1840 *Store*			30.00	50.00	175.	500.
		COPPER, 21MM						
205A	R4	1840 *Store*			30.00	125.	200.	600.
205B	R6	1840 * Store*	Silvered Copper			Not contemporary		

CIRCLES

COPPER, 22MM

HT #	Rarity	Year	Metal	Size	VG	VF	EF	Unc
206	R4	1840 O Store O			30.00	80.00	200.	500.

The Bergen Iron Works was located in what is now Ocean County, New Jersey, at a place once known as Bricksburg and now called Lakewood. They were at a point where the railroad crosses Metetecunk River, about four miles from the north end of Barnegat Bay. In the 1830's the forges and furnaces of central New Jersey were engaged in treating "bog ores" — but when the abundant mines of Pennsylvania were developed the mines in New Jersey ceased operations.

The tokens were apparently issued by the company store to supply currency for their workmen and store patrons.

Bergen Iron Works apparently was associated with wildcat notes through two banks and a general store — the Ocean Bank of Bergen Iron Works and Union Bank of Tom's River. These wildcat institutions were controlled in 1851 by the Snyder family of Bergen Iron Works.

E. & I. BRAGAW

Newark, N.J. & Mobile, Ala.

HT #	Rarity	Year	Metal	Size	VG	F	VF	EF
207	R7	(1830's)	Copper	28mm	350.	600.	1500.	3000.
207A	R7	(1830's)	Brass	28mm	350.	800.	2000.	3000.
207B	R7	(1830's)	WM	28mm	350.	800.	2000.	3000.

Elias and John Bragaw were listed as "wholesale hatters" at 348 Broad "and at Mobile, Ala." until 1836. The partnership broke up in 1836, Elias continuing the business in Newark and John going into business for himself in Mobile.

The tokens, cut by Wright & Bale, would have been issued in the 1829-33 period.

NEW YORK

N. SAFFORD

Albany, N.Y.

HT #	Rarity	Year	Metal	Size	VG	VF	EF	Unc
210	R4	(1830's)	Copper	28mm	20.00	75.00	125.	350.

TEMPERANCE / N. SAFFORD / 280 / NORTH MARKET ST. / ALBANY / HOUSE. Rv: ACCOMMODATIONS FOR / MERCHANTS / AND / TRADERS / IN / GENERAL / . PRIVATE FAMILIES. (Wright 930)

HT #	Rarity	Year	Metal	Size	VG	VF	EF	Unc
210A	R7	(1830's)	WM	28mm	—	350.	625.	1000.

As 348. Plain edge.

The Temperance movement commenced in this country as early as 1808-1813 in New York and Massachusetts. The movement, originally calling only for abstinence from distilled spirits (whiskey, brandy and rum), spread rapidly under the influence of the churches. By its apogee in 1833 there were 6,000 local Temperance societies in the country.

A few Temperance advocates who were innkeepers offered "temperance house" facilities to abstaining travelers. N. Safford of Albany was such an innkeeper.

In 1840 the Washington Temperance Society, demanding total abstinence from all alcoholic beverages, was formed. In 1846 the Maine Law was passed, prohibiting the sale of intoxicants in the state of Maine. The Order of Good Templars, an international body, was formed at Utica, N.Y. in 1851. The Woman's Christian Temperance Union (WCTU), founded in Cleveland in 1874, used political methods as well as moral persuasion and health education to accomplish its aims. Prohibition was adopted in the U.S. Constitution in 1919, but it was repealed in 1933.

Safford is not in the 1830 census.

S. D. BROWER

Albany, N.Y.

HT #	Rarity	Year	Metal	Size	VG	F	VF	EF
A210	R9	1837	Copper	29mm	—	—	400.	—

S. D. BROWER / ALBANY / 1837 ctsp on U.S. 1797 Large cent. (Brunk 5315)

S. Douglas Brower was a silversmith 1837-50 in Albany. He also labored at his trade in Troy, N.Y. 1832-36 and had an outlet in New York City ca. 1834.

J. COCHRAN

Batavia, N.Y.

HT #	Rarity	Year	Metal	Size	VG	F	VF	Unc
211	R7	1844	Copper	28mm	5000.	6500.	10,000	—

James H. Cochran was a bell founder and a very ingenious mechanic, who is said to have 'made the first cent coined in the U.S.,' though what this latter phrase refers to we have not discovered. Only four specimens of his 1844 token are known, all supposedly struck over other coins.

Benjamin Franklin is said to have visited his earlier shop, in Philadelphia.

In the 1840's his workshop and residence were on Bank St., Batavia. He died at age 83 in Batavia, Genesee County, N.Y.

Only two of the four known specimens have ever been sold at public auction. The best-known piece appeared in Frossard's Dec. 1896 sale (lot 486), and then in Ben Green's July 1912 sale (lot 10006), where it was purchased by George Hetrich. It passed later to Donald M. Miller, Q. David Bowers, Rossa & Tanenbaum and to a private New York collector.

A Fine specimen appeared in Henry Chapman's Nov. 1910 sale (lot 651), where Virgil Brand purchased it. Much later it was lot 011 in the Dec. 1986 sale by H. Joseph Levine. Then it was sold for $4675 in the Oct. 1989 Steinberg sale by Stack's Inc.

PATTERSON BROS.

Buffalo, N.Y.

HT #	Rarity	Year	Metal	Size	F	VF	EF	Unc
212	R2	(1838-39)	Copper	28.5mm	15.00	35.00	65.00	250.
212A	R2	(1838-39)	Engrailed Edge		15.00	30.00	65.00	250.

John Patterson, principal, and James Patterson made up Patterson Brothers, hardware, at 170 Main Street in the 1839 directory. The business was known as John Patterson, hardware, and crockery, at 170 Main Street in the 1844 directory, and James Patterson is listed as a clerk there, John Patterson resided at 350 Washington in 1844, and James Patterson boarded at the same address, the directory reveals.

Neither Patterson appeared in the 1830 census.

Very Good specimens of 212 and 212A sell for $8.

W.A. THOMSON

Buffalo, N.Y.

HT #	Rarity	Year	Metal	Size	VG	F	EF	Unc
213	R4	(1838-39)	Copper	38mm	15.00	35.00	100.	400.

Anvil and hammer in center, NO. 9 on side of anvil. W.A. THOMSON above, WEBSTER BUILDINGS / BUFFALO below. Reeded edge. (Miller NY 25)

HT #	Rarity	Year	Metal	Size	VG	F	EF	Unc
214	R3	(1843-44)	Copper	33mm	10.00	25.00	75.00	300.

Anvil in center, W.A. THOMSON ** above, BUFFALO N.Y. below. Rv: Teakettle in center, IMPORTERS above, OF HARDWARE below. Reeded edge. (Wright 1142; Miller NY 26)

New Amsterdam village (later Buffalo) was a going concern in 1803, but was burned to the ground by the British in 1813. In 1832 Buffalo became a city; it then had 10,000 population. Its 1836 population totaled 16,000.

Thomson was a clerk 1835-38, in the latter year for Patterson Brothers hardware.

William A. Thomson is listed in the 1839 directory, in hardware at 9 Webster Block, which helps to date the larger token to the 1838-39 period.

In the 1844 directory Thomson, hardware and cutlery, is at 7 and 9 Webster Block and also at 164 Main Street. The smaller token probably emanates from Thomson's expanded operations period, as it is without address. Thomson also appears in the 1840 census, but cannot be located in the 1820 or 1830 census reports. By 1847-49 the firm was known as Thompson Brothers after the admission of Hugh Thompson.

Thomas L. Elder in "A Plea for American Token Collecting" (1915) said that the two Thomson cards were issued "between 1840 and 1845." We still do not know the source of his claim, but our foray in April, 1984 into Buffalo records at the Mormon Genealogical Library in Salt Lake City proves that Elder was very close to accurate. The assumption of the Fulds much later that these pieces emanated from the 1820's - which we repeated in the first two editions of *Early American Tokens* — is now proven inaccurate and we can confidently assign both tokens to the Hard Times period.

L. ROBINSON

Chittenango, N.Y.

HT #	Rarity	Year	Metal	Size	VG	F	VF	Unc
215	R5	(1848-58)	Copper	28mm	80.00	150.	200.	400.
	Reeded edge.							
215A	R9	(1848-58)	Copper	28mm	—	—	600.	—
	Plain edge.							
	L. ROBINSON / - OF - / * COMPOUND * / MAGNETS / MANUFACTURER. RV: * RIFLE. TRIMMINGS * / - AND - / GUNNERY / CHITTENANGO. N.Y. Reeded edge. (Wright 906)							
215B	R8	(1848-58)	WM	28mm	—	—	800.	1100.
	As 387. Plain edge.							

HT #	Rarity	Year	Metal	Size	VG	F	VF	Unc
216C	R8		Copper	26mm	—	—	600.	—
	As 215, but smaller planchet. (Krause coll.)							

The tokens of L. Robinson have been determined to be of later issuance than has been thought for many years. They are store cards of Luther Robinson, who made percussion half-stock rifles in Chittenango from 1848 through 1858.

The store cards belong in *U.S. Merchant Tokens 1845-1860*. They are rare, and will probably retain much of their price, though some of that price level was attained by association with the Hard Times period.

A variety of 215B with extra thick planchet appeared in the Dec. 1991 Gold Medal sale in EF+ and feteched $800.

J. I. TOBEY

Hudson, N.Y.

HT #	Rarity	Year	Metal	Size	VG	VF	EF	Unc
A215	R9	(1830's)	Copper	29mm	—	800.	—	—
	J. I. TOBEY / HUDSON within two rectangles, ctsp on U.S. 1794 Large cent. (Tanenbaum coll.; Brunk 40223)							

J. I. Tobey had a store from about 1827 onward on Warren Street (Main Street) and Cherry Lane, according to Columbia County Records for the 1830's. In 1827-28 Tobey was a Hudson alderman.

WALSH'S GENERAL STORE

Lansingburgh, N.Y.

HT #	Rarity	Year	Metal	Size	VG	F	VF	Unc
216	R1	1835	Copper	28.5mm	5.00	10.00	17.50	300.
	Plough							

217 218

HT #	Rarity	Year	Metal	Size	VG	VF	EF	Unc
217	R1	1835	Copper	28.5mm	5.00	15.00	40.00	350.
	Lafayette H							
218	R1	1835	Copper	28.5mm	5.00	15.00	40.00	300.
	Lansingburgh, straight							

These tokens were issued by Walsh's general store in Lansingburgh, Rensselaer County, New York. The motto SPEED THE PLOUGH, IT FEEDS ALL refers to the interest in horticulture and farming shown by the owner, Alexander Walsh, who conducted the store more than 30 years. His so-called "Plough Penny" circulated freely all over northern New York from 1835 on.

Locally Walsh's enterprise was known as Walsh's Museum due to the interesting and unusual variety of stock it contained. Walsh was very prominent; in 1825 he accompanied Governor DeWitt Clinton on the first boat in ceremonies opening the Erie Canal and received a silver medal from that event. He was an admirer of the Marquis de Lafayette, who visited the U.S. in 1825 and is depicted on two of Walsh's tokens. In 1839 Henry Clay was a guest in his Lansingburgh home. He retired from business in 1846. He died Aug. 4, 1849.

Walsh does not appear in 1820 census, but he is in 1830 census.

Imitation dies for the plough side of HT 216 were made for Thomas L. Elder. In 1909 Elder caused to be struck several uniface tokens in various metals from these dies, both in normal size and on dollar sized flans. The imitations read PLOW instead of PLOUGH.

A. HENSHAW

Newark, N.Y.

HT #	Rarity	Year	Metal	Size	VG	F	VF	EF
A218	R9	1837	Copper	29mm	—	—	225.	—

A. HENSHAW in relief within long rectangular depression ctsp on U.S. 1822 Large cent. Large 1837 in single numeral-punches incused below. (Charles Kirtley Nov. 1991 sale, lot Q041; Brunk 19257)

HT #	Rarity	Year	Metal	Size	VG	F	VF	EF
B218	R9	(1837 ?)	Silver	27mm	—	—	225.	—

Same Henshaw ctsp on Spanish-American 1789-Mo-FM 2-reales coin. Incused above is: O. BENNETT and incused below is: LYONS. (Brunk 3380)

Orra Bennett (1800-65) was a maker of percussion halfstock guns at Lyons, N.Y. from 1848 until his death 17 years later.

One Joseph Henshaw is known to have been a gunsmith and engraver in New York City 1830-36 and then in Newark, N.Y. 1836-on. (Some gunsmith references give Newark, N.J., but we believe Newark, N.Y. is correct.)

Newark and Lyons are nearby communities in Wayne County, New York, both on the New York State Barge Canal which runs from North Tonawanda to the Mohawk River east of Little Falls.

One of the two known A. HENSHAW counterstamps surfaced in 1991 and had never previously been published; the silver piece surfaced about 1975. Whether the A. Henshaw of the stamps was the Newark gunsmith is not known, but the body of circumstance is too strong to ignore. Tentative attribution.

HENRY ANDERSON

New York, N.Y.

HT #	Rarity	Year	Metal	Size	VG	VF	EF	Unc
219	R2	1837	Copper	28mm	5.00	12.00	30.00	150.

ANDERSON'S GREAT
MAMMOTH BOOT and SHOE STORE
No. 172 Chatham street.
NO STATE PRISON MONOPOLY.
Boots and shoes, all manufactured by honest mechanics. All those opposed to State Prison Monopoly—all those who feel curious to see the largest retail Boot and Shoe store in the United States—all those who wish to supply their selves with Boots and Shoes, where the nimble six pence passes for the slow shilling, will please call at 172 Chatham square, at ANDERSON'S, immediately opposite the Tradesmen's Bank, at the Mammoth Store, sign of the great shoe and boot. The proprietor is grateful for past favors and solicits the public patronage, as he flatters himself his stock is more extensive than any other retailer in the city, and his prices more moderate.

An ad from the New York Transcript for Sept. 14, 1835.

ATWOOD'S RAILROAD HOTEL

HT #	Rarity	Year	Metal	Size	VG	F	VF	EF
220	R6	(1835-8)	Copper	26.5mm	200.	250.	500.	750.
	3 Cents, Bale & Smith							
221	R7	(1835-8)	Copper	25mm	200.	300.	600.	850.
	3 Cents, Bale & Smith							

HT #	Rarity	Year	Metal	Size	VG	F	VF	Unc
222	R9	(1835-8)	Fire Gilt	20mm	—	—	—	3000.
	3 Cents, Bale & Smith							
223	R8	(1835-8)	Brass	26.5mm	—	—	1500.	2000.
	3 Cents, Bale & Smith							
223A	R9	(1835-8)	Brass	26.5mm	—	—	—	750.
	Uniface (obv.)							

HT #	Rarity	Year	Metal	Size	VG	VF	EF	Unc
224	R8	(1835-8)	WM	26.5mm	—	1000.	2000.	3000.
224A	R8	(1835-8)	Silver	26.5mm	—	—	May not exist	

J. W. B. (Joseph W. Boyd)

HT #	Rarity	Year	Metal	Size	VG	F	VF	EF
225	R8	(1834-35)	Copper	29mm	—	50.00	—	—

J. W. B. in relief within rectangle ctsp four times on obverse of U.S. 1834 Large cent. (Sol Taylor coll.)

Joseph W. Boyd was a silversmith in New York City circa 1820. He was responsible for an earlier counterstamp on an 1820 Large cent (see Rulau-E NY 63 in *Early American Tokens*, 2nd ed.) which was also counterstamped by three other N.Y. silversmiths.

We're assigning an arbitrary issue date to this piece, placing it in the Hard Times era, which seems justified.

BAILLY, WARD & CO.

HT #	Rarity	Year	Metal	Size	VG	F	VF	Unc
226	R7	(1832-43)	WM	27mm	700.	1600.	2500.	3000.
226A	R8	(1832-43)	Silver	27mm	—	—	2000.	—

BALE & SMITH

HT #	Rarity	Year	Metal	Size	VG	F	VF	Unc
227	R7 Bale & Smith, NY	(1835-8)	Copper	25mm	300.	700.	1450.	2250.
227A	R8 Bale & Smith, NY	(1835-8)	WM	25mm	—	—	2000.	3000.
228	R7 B & S, NY	(1835-8)	Copper	25mm	—	—	1800.	3500.
228A	R8 B & S, NY.	(1835-8)	WM	25mm	—	—	2500.	3500.

This firm of die sinkers and medallists was at 68 Nassau Street 1835 to 1838.

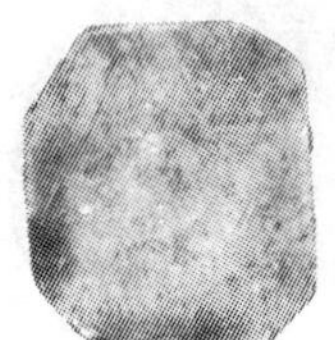

HT #	Rarity	Year	Metal	Size	VG	F	VF	Unc
229	R9 Minerva Head, Bale (Die trial)	(1833-5)	WM	19x23mm	—	—	950.	—

JOHN BARKER

HT #	Rarity	Year	Metal	Size	VG	F	VF	Unc
230	R7	(1829-33)	Brass	-mm	300.	700.	1250.	3000.

A Washington head is right within olive wreath. AMERICAN REPOSITORY OF THE FINE ARTS around. Reverse: JOHN BARKER / 16 MAIDEN LANE / DEALER IN / MUSIC PRINTS / & / FANCY / STATIONARY. Only nine pieces are known. (Baker 511; Miller 57)

Cut by Wright & Bale, which dates it to the 1829-1833 period.

BARNES & POTTER

HT #	Rarity	Year	Metal	Size	VG	F	VF	Unc
231	R8	(1835)	Copper	29mm	100.	—	150.	—
	The countermark on a U.S. cent reads: BARNES & POTTER / N. YORK / 1835. (Duffield 1392 in "A Trial List of Countermarked Modern Coins of the World"; Brunk 2430). Dates examined: 1827.							
232	R7	(1835)	Copper	29mm	—	—	250.	—
	BARNES & POTTER ctsp on U.S. Large cent.							
233	R9	(1835)	Silver	31mm	—	—	350	—
	BARNES & POTTER ctsp on U.S. 1834 half dollar. (Brunk 2420)							

The firm of Barnes & Potter appears in the 1835 directory only. They were watch case makers, at 6 Lincoln Green. The senior partner was Charles L. Barnes. The other partner may have been Samuel S. Potter, a brass founder located at 63 Willett in 1835.

G. BOYCE

HT #	Rarity	Year	Metal	Size	G	VG	F	EF
234	R9	(1832-41)	Copper	29mm	—	—	—	250.

G. BOYCE / NEW YORK ctsp on U.S. 1831 Large cent. (The countermark is in two separate stamps, NEW YORK being curved) (Brunk 4680)

Gerardus Boyce (1795-1880) was a silversmith in New York City beginning about 1814. The mark is his hallmark. (See "*The Book of Old Silver*" by Seymour B. Wyler.)

J. & L. BREWSTER
New York, N.Y & New Orleans, La.

HT #	Rarity	Year	Metal	Size	VG	VF	EF	Unc
235	R6 W & B NY	(1832-3)	Giltc	26.5mm	200.	400.	900.	1400.
235A	R7 W & B NY	(1832-3)	Brass	26.5mm	200.	500.	900.	1400.
236	R7 Bale, NY	(1833)	Giltc	26.5mm	300.	600.	900.	1400.
236A	R7 Bale, NY	(1833)	Brass	26.5mm	300.	600.	900.	1400.

Listed at 166 Water Street in New York in 1835-36. They were at 176 Water Street 1840-41. The Wright & Bale and Bale alone signatures help date these cards. Wright and Bale split before October 1833.

HT 235 and 235A are struck from different dies. Letter spacing is different.

DAVID C. BUCHAN

The token issues of chairmaker Buchan (HT 237-238A, Low 224-226) are from 1831 and may be found in our *Early American Tokens* section.

CENTRE MARKET
New York, N.Y.

HT #	Rarity	Year	Metal	Size	VG	F	VF	Unc
239	R1 Scroll Under 2nd U in Unum	1837	Copper	28mm	4.00	9.00	30.00	175.

HT #	Rarity	Year	Metal	Size	VG	F	VF	Unc
240	R1 Scroll Under N in Unum	1837	Copper	28mm	4.00	9.00	30.00	175.

HT #	Rarity	Year	Metal	Size	VG	F	VF	Unc
240A	R8	1837	Lead counterfeit?		Rare	—	—	—

CLINTON LUNCH

HT #	Rarity	Year	Metal	Size	VG	VF	EF	Unc.
A240	R6	(1835-45)	Brass	19.5mm	100.	450.	600.	1000.

Cuirassed bust left in crested Greek helmet. Rv: Eagle displayed, U.S. shield on its breast, head turned right. Seven stars in arc above, o CLINTON. LUNCH o below. (Rulau-E NY 161)

HT #	Rarity	Year	Metal	Size	VG	VF	EF	Unc.
B240	R5	(1830-45)	GS	19.5mm	100.	225.	400.	850.

As last, (Wright 197; Rulau-E NY 162)

The center of the reverse is usually weakly struck.

These tokens, long attributed to the Early American period are herewith repositioned to the Hard Times era, and will be removed from our *Early American Tokens* catalog. Though attributed to the New York by Tilton, Wright, Adams, Raymond and others, the site could never be verified through city directory evidence.

In a little-noticed paragraph in the October 1911 *The Numismatist* (pp 368-369), collector J. Coolidge Hills of Hartford, Conn. advanced the attribution to his city.

Clinton House, or Clinton Hotel, had a lower part used as a lunchroom in the 1830's and 1840's, Hills reported. The Clinton hotel continued in business until near the end of the 19th century.

We discount a Hartford connection, however, since our collaborator Steve Tannenbaum recently discovered a review in the New York City newspaper circa 1835 which described the type of food served and the prices charged for food at the Clinton Lunch. Directory evidence is still lacking, but we now believe the rare Clinton Lunch tokens — as always reported — are from New York and also can be safely attributed to the Hard Times era.

German silver tokens appear with some regularity in auction sales. In the May 1981 PCAC sale, a VF realized $425. A BU specimen was auctioned for $775 in 1988. In the 1989 Gil Steinberg sale, a BU piece, probably the finest known specimen, made $852.50. In the same Steinberg sale another piece in VF fetched $165.

Brass pieces appear less often. An AU specimen in the PCAC May 1982 sale realized $320. In the 1990 Chris Schenkel sale, an unholed EF piece fetched only $154.

COLLINS READY MADE LINEN & FANCY STORE

HT #	Rarity	Year	Metal	Size	VG	F	VF	EF
241	R7	(1834-41)	Brass	27mm	750.	1500.	2500.	4000.

William Collins was at 67 Maiden Lane 1838-39. He was at 69 Maiden Lane 1845-46. This card was cut by Robert Lovett, Sr., who used the same obverse on his own HT card.

J. H. CONNOR

HT #	Rarity	Date	Metal	Size	VG	F	VF	EF
A241	R9	(1833-38)	Silver	32.5mm	—	—	500.	—

J. H. CONNOR ctsp on U.S. 1829 Bust half dollar. (Brunk 9250).

John H. Connor was a New York silversmith 1833-38, and a partner of Garret Eoff 1833-35. Connor & Eoff were located at 6 Little Green Street.

His name is misspelled Conner in some references.

J. CRAWFORD

HT #	Rarity	Year	Metal	Size	VG	F	VF	EF
242	R8	(1837-41)	Copper	29mm	150.	—	200.	—

J. CRAWFORD in relief within rectangular depression ctsp on U.S. Large cent. Dates examined: 1807, 1827, 1833. (Hallenbeck 3.757; Brunk 9990)

John Crawford was a silversmith in New York City 1815-41. He opened a Philadelphia operation 1837-43 and may have closed his New York firm in/after 1841. Directory listings show his New York addresses:

92 John Street	1815-20
227 Grand	1832-33
99 Chrystie	1834-41

We have not yet determined his Philadelphia location(s).

Unless specimens with later-dated host coins surface, it seems reasonable to conclude that New York was the home of HT 242. (References: Ensko and Kovel silversmith chronologies; New York City directories; Kenneth Hallenbeck; Gregory Brunk)

H. CROSSMAN

HT #	Rarity	Year	Metal	Size	F	VF	EF	Unc
243	R2	1837	Copper	28.5mm	10.00	20.00	90.00	250.

Henry Crossman was a manufacturer of umbrellas at 92-1/2 Chatham St. 1830-1841, after which he was located at various other addresses. The firm became H. Crossman & Co. in 1857 while at 63 Liberty St. In 1860 it was at 94 Warren St.

HT #	Rarity	Year	Metal	Size	F	VF	EF	Unc
244	R1	1837	Copper	28.5mm	6.00	15.00	40.00	225.

W.D. CRUMBIE

HT #	Rarity	Year	Metal	Size	VG	F	VF	EF
245	R7	(1844-6)	GS	19mm	200.	250.	500.	1000.
245A	R7	(1844-6)	Blank Rev.	—	—	250.	500.	1000.

At the corner of Bowery and Houston 1844-46. This was a soda water check.

DAY NEWELL & DAY

HT #	Rarity	Year	Metal	Size	F	VF	EF	Unc
247	R6	(1834-5)	Copper	26.5mm	200.	350.	750.	900.
247A	R8	(1834-5)	Brass	26.5mm	150.	350.	900.	1200.

These locksmiths were at 589 Broadway 1834-35.

HT #	Rarity	Year	Metal	Size	F	VF	EF	Unc
248	R6	(1834-5)	GS	26.5mm	300.	600.	900.	—

T. DARBY

HT #	Rarity	Year	VG	F	VF	EF
246	R8	(1830's)	—	150.	—	200.

T. DARBY / -.- / NEW YORK ctsp on U.S. Large cent. Examined: 1816, 1831. (Brunk 10700)

Thomas Darby was a coppersmith in the 1830's. In the 1829 city directory he was listed as a brassfounder at 158 Bowery. In the 1834 listing he is a coppersmith at the rear of 160 Bowery.

J.H. DAYTON

HT #	Rarity	Year	Metal	Size	VG	VF	EF	Unc
249	R2	1837	Copper	28mm	7.00	25.00	55.00	200.

P.B. & S. DEVEAU

HT #	Rarity	Year	Metal	Size	F	VF	EF	Unc
250	R2	1837	Copper	28mm	10.00	20.00	65.00	300.
HT #	**Rarity**	**Year**			**F**	**VF**	**EF**	**Unc**
251	R7	1837 Obv. 250, Rev. 61			—	2000.	4500.	—
252	R8	1837 Obv. 250, Rev. 52			—	—	4500.	—

P.B. & S. Deveau were located at 156 Chatham Square, New York City, from 1831 to 1850, after which they moved to 74 Forsyth Street, where they stayed until 1858.

Number 251 uses a MINT DROP reverse, and 252 a NOT ONE CENT reverse.

DOREMUS, SUYDAM & NIXON

HT #	Rarity	Year	Metal	Size	F	VF	EF	Unc
253	R5	(1832-33)	Copper	26.6mm	150.	300.	750.	—
	W & B NY							
254	R5	(1832-33)	Brass	26.6mm	150.	300.	750.	—
254A	R8	Silvered Bs			—	—	250.	—
254B	R8	Gilt Brass			—	—	200.	—
255	R4	(1834-35)	Brass	26.6mm	50.00	80.00	300.	—
	50 & 52 Wm. St. Bale NY							
256	R4	(1834-35)			50.00	100.	200.	—
	Hyphen Between N-Y							
257	R4	(1836)	Copper	26.6mm	50.00	75.00	300.	—
	37 & 39 Nassau St.							
A258	R6	—	Brass	28mm	—	—	200.	—

HT #	Rarity	Year	Metal	Size	F	VF	EF	Unc
258	R4	(1836-38)	Brass	26.5mm	50.00	100.	300.	—
	B & S NY							
258A	R4	(1836-38)	Copper	26.5mm	50.00	100.	300.	—
	Reeded edge							
258B	R8	—	Gilt/B	26.5mm	—	—	—	—

HT #	Rarity	Year	Metal	Size	F	VF	EF	Unc
259	R4	(1840-44)	Gilt/B	26.5mm	45.00	75.00	150.	300.
	Nassau St.							
259A	R3	(1840-44)	Brass	26.5mm	40.00	100.	150.	300.

NOTE: HT 256 comes in two different die varieties with different letter spacing.

THE DOREMUS-SUYDAM DRY GOODS FIRMS

Thomas C. Doremus and Rynier Suydam were in business as Doremus & Suydam, dry goods store, at 171 Broadway, at least from 1821 to 1826. This became Doremus, Suydam & Co. at 171 Broadway, 1826-1828.

The firm became Doremus, Suydam & Nixon, dry goods, still at 171 Broadway, 1829-1830. The new partner was John M. Nixon. This firm was at 209 Pearl St. 1832-1833; 50 and 52 William St. 1834 until December 31, 1835. According to a note in the 1835-36 directory, the firm moved on New Year's Day, 1836, to 37 and 39 Nassau St. Its address in 1840-1841 was 39 Nassau St., corner Liberty.

The firm name became Doremus & Nixon 1844-1849, still at 39 Nassau St., corner Liberty. In the 1850's the address changed to 21 Park Place. Dated tokens at the latter address are known bearing either 1853 or 1861.

000

Another firm which apparently did not issue any tokens was composed of Lambert and Cornelius R. Suydam, who may have been related. L. & C. Suydam, merchants, were at 212 Pearl St. 1821-1822; 71 Maiden Lane 1826-1828; 111 Pearl St. 1829-1830.

000

A third firm was composed of Richard Suydam and Daniel Jackson. This firm, Suydam, Jackson & Co., Indian contractors, issued HT 1 and varieties, a pro-Andrew Jackson political token of 1832.

Suydam & Jackson, merchants, were at 140 Pearl St., 1825-1830. They became known as Suydam, Jackson & Co. and were located at 78 Pearl St., 1830-1845.

000

Henry (Hy) Suydam and William Boyd were in business as Suydam & Boyd, dry goods, at 183 or 187 Broadway (there is a discrepancy in the 1830 directory) 1829-1830; then at 187 Pearl St., corner Cedar, 1831-1834; then at 157 Pearl St., 1834-1837. Store cards were issued from the latter two locations, spanning the Early American and Hard Times token periods.

000

In addition to Suydam & Boyd, above, there was another firm, Boyd & Suydam!

Ferdinand Suydam (another brother of Rynier, John and Richard) formed the firm of F. Suydam in 1808 at 37 Front St. In 1809 William Boyd became a partner. Later in 1809 they moved to 21 South St. and became Boyd & Suydam. This lasted until 1834.

In 1834 the business became Suydam, Sage & Co., and this failed about 1851. No tokens were issued.

000

The founders of all these Suydam (Dutch) businesses were Rynier and John Suydam, who created R. & J. Suydam in 1791 at 10 Albany Pier. Albany Pier was renamed Coenties Slip before 1794.

In 1794 the firm split. John Suydam, his brother Henry Suydam and Henry J. Wyckoff formed Suydam & Wyckoff.

Rynier Suydam resurfaced in Doremus & Suydam about 1821.

Meanwhile Suydam & Wyckoff were at 11 & 13 Coenties Slip 1794-1821, and 31 South Street 1821. This firm remained there until 1835.

The Doremus-Suydam firms were large issuers of store cards from the 1820's to 1861 or later. Their dates of issuance are approximately:

Miller NY 211-214A	209 Pearl St.	1831-1833
HT 253-254	209 Pearl St.	1832-1833 (W&B NY)
HT 255-256	50 & 52 William St.	1834-1835 (BALE NY)
HT 257	37 & 39 Nassau St.	1836
HT 258-258A	37 & 39 Nassau St.	1836-1838
HT 259-259A (NY 219-219A)	39 Nassau St.	1840-1844
NY 222-223 (Doremus & Nixon)	39 Nassau St.	1844-1849
NY 224-224B	21 Park Place	1850-1853
NY 225-229 (mulings)		1853-1861

DR. L. FEUCHTWANGER

HT #	Rarity	Year	Metal	Size	F	VF	EF	Unc
260	R7	(1831-7)	GS	27mm	800.	1500.	2000.	3000.

377 Broadway

An EF specimen of HT 260, weight 104.1grains, fetched only $715 in a 1991 Bowers & Merena sale. In the same sale, an AU HT 261 realized only $660.

HT #	Rarity	Year	Metal	Size	F	VF	EF	Unc
261	R7	(1837-8)	GS	27mm	800.	1500.	2000.	3000.

2 Cortlandt St.

NOTE: A muling in lead of the two addresses has been reported.

FEUCHTWANGER'S COMPOSITION
New York, N.Y.

HT #	Rarity	Year	Metal	Size	VG	VF	EF	Unc
262	R3	1837	GS	25mm	250.	550.	700.	1200.
262A	R7	1837	WM	25mm	—	900.	1500.	2000.

HT #	Rarity	Year	Metal	Size	VG	VF	EF	Unc
263	R5	1837	GS	25mm	500.	1200.	3000.	5000.
264	R8	1837	Copper	25mm	—	—	4000.	—

HT #	Rarity	Year	Metal	Size	VG	VF	EF	Unc
265	R7	1837	GS	25mm	—	—	3500.	4500.
	3 Three Cents							
266	R8	1837	Copper	25mm	—	—	—	3500.
	Dietrial.							

NOTE: 266 is struck uniface (eagle side) over a British Conder token. 265 was struck in proof circa 1855-1860. A triple struck Proof HT 265, offered as Low 119A, realized $6600 in 1989.

HT #	Rarity	Year	Metal	Size	F	VF	EF	Unc
267	R6	1864	GS	25mm	—	—	1500.	2600.

NOTE: 265, 265A, 266 and 267 are Civil War era pieces with HT die links. They cannot be disassociated from the Feuchtwanger 3-cent pieces they imitate.

Dr. Lewis Feuchtwanger

Many Varieties

HT #	Rarity	Year	Metal	Size	VG	VF	EF	Unc
268	R1	1837	GS	18.5mm	15.00	40.00	60.00	150.

NOTE: Specimens fully struck on obverse are worth double the Unc price!

Feuchtwanger Cent Varieties

HT 268

Obv. 1. Coarse denticles. Large date close to ground above, the 3 exceptionally large, the 7 very high. Snake's tongue almost vertical. Seven tail feathers, four of them touching the ground.

Obv. 2. Similar treatment of the eagle to preceding. In date 18 low, small, closely spaced; 37 much larger, higher, also closely spaced. Eight tail feathers, five touching ground.

Obv. 3. Date closely spaced, from smaller punches as on all to follow, and in a straight line on top. The 7 frequently shows crumbling between horizontal and upright; rim breaks down at lower right. Seven tail feathers, first two and fourth (latter recut) touching ground.

Obv. 4. In date 3 low, rather distant from 7 and often joined to it at top by a line. Loop in snake's tail left of date; in all other dies loop is above 18. Snake's tongue very long, very deeply forked. Eagle's head droops. Eight tail feathers, three touching ground.

Obv. 5. Date widely and evenly spaced; slightly curved bar in ground directly above 83. Seven tail feathers, only the second barely touching ground; fourth recut at tip.

Obv. 6. Closely spaced date, bottoms in a straight line; 83 a little apart. Dash to left from upper serif of 1. Base of eagle's neck smooth. Seven tail feathers, four of them touching ground.

Rev. A. One very widely spaced. Small O's in COMPOSITION. A and P recut.

Rev. B. Stems end in marked claws. S in COMPOSITION very defective at top. Upright of F recut. N in COMPOSITION recut.

Rev. C. Star too close to final S in FEUCHTWANGER'S. Two upper berries within right branch arise from innermost leaves almost at tips.

Rev. D. O in ONE too low. Right bow plainly overlaps left one. Right ribbon almost touches both S and I.

Rev. E. IT about touch. E in ONE, T in CENT (left top) and P in COMPOSITION clearly recut N's in ONE CENT crumble.

Rev. F. ER joined at bases. Left stem, divided like a penpoint, touches M.

Rev. G. Thirteen berries, the extra one just right of bow. Berry near base of T in CENT attached to a leaf. Star too close to final N in COMPOSITION. Stems end in claws though not too distinctly. M P O spaced apart. Develops a crack through HTWANG, and another from wreath through final N to edge. N in ONE crumbles at base.

Rev. H. Thirteen berries, extra one just left of bow. E in ONE top high at top and base. Crude recutting NE CEN; crumbling develops on these letters.

Rev. I. Thirteen berries, extra one just left of bow, and looking more like an extra stem. E in CENT heavily recut. E in ONE high at base but in line with N at top.

Die combinations and rarity:
1A R4
2A R5
3B R3
3C R8
3D R7
3E R3
3G R6
4E R3
4F R8
5G R2
5H R1
6G R1
6I R1

HT #	Rarity	Year	VG	F	VF	Unc
268	R2	1837 One Cent	15.00	35.00	60.00	200.
	R3		17.00	40.00	80.00	250.
	R4		25.00	95.00	125.	300.
	R5		75.00	105.	150.	400.
	R6		100.	125.	200.	500.
	R7		—	300.	350.	600.
	R8		—	500.	900.	1500.

NOTE: Dr. Lewis Feuchtwanger in 1837 petitioned Congress to adopt his "Feuchtwanger's Composition" (German silver, a white, tarnishable copper-zinc nickel alloy) for the U.S. copper cent, reducing it to 18.5 MM. The petition, supported by Senator Thomas H. Benton, was rejected by Mint Director Patterson in 1838.

The German-born Feuchtwanger (1807) was at 377 Broadway 1831-1837; 2 Cortlandt Street 1837-1838; 7 Gold Street 1839; 320 Broadway 1840; 1-1/2 Wall Street 1842-1843; and 2 Wall Street 1843. He published a book on gems 1872, and died in 1876. At the 377 Broadway address he struck his first store card (Low 247), but in 1837, at the 2 Cortlandt St. address, he emitted the second card (HT 261) and all the One and Three Cent private patterns.

FEUCHTWANGER-MILTON CONNECTION ?

About 1984, coin dealer Jonathan K. Kern, Lexington, Kentucky, discovered a most unusual die, which he showed to the author. The steel die, for an oval-shaped medalet, bears a typical Feuchtwanger eagle to right on a snake. Under the device is the signature: I. MILTON F.

The signature indicates *James Milton fecit* (made it).

Milton was a London, England diesinker and manufacturer of tokens active in the making of 18th century British currency tokens and medals. Some of his best known products were emitted in the 1797-1800 period.

We hesitate to place a meaning on this die, but it does indicate a possible connection. The eagle-on-snake device is very Feuchtwanger-like.

W. FIELD

HT #	Rarity	Year	Metal	Size	VG	VF	EF	Unc
269	R7	(1835)	Copper	28mm	1000.	2500.	3500.	4500.
270	R7	(1835)	Copper	30mm	1000.	2500.	3000.	4500.

FIFTH WARD MUSEUM HOTEL

HT #	Rarity	Year	Metal	Size	VG	F	EF	Unc
271	R9	(1847-51)	Brass	26mm	—	—	400.	—

FIFTH WARD / (rays) / MUSEUM / (rays) / HOTEL. Rv: 2 / 6 (two shillings sixpence). Plain edge.

One specimen is in the American Numismatic Society collection. Since the hotel was located near the Hudson River piers, many of the patrons would have been British seamen or visitors.

Fifth Ward Museum Hotel was opened in 1826 at West Broadway and Franklin by Thomas Riley. A hotel and popular dining salon, it contained an Americana collection stressing Colonial history.

The hotel's intersection was a busy one in the 1830-1850 period.

An excellent history of the hotel, by Werner G. Mayer, was published in the *TAMS Journal* for June 1978 under the title "Riley's Fifth Ward Museum Hotel." An excerpt of this article appears below.

Exhibits were housed in the hotel's largest room, one flight up from the main entrance. The room was jammed with glass cases containing Riley's collection of relics, and the walls were covered with paintings of great statesmen and soldiers along with displays of their weapons and uniforms. However, the authenticity of some of the items was questionable. Featured was the Hawaiian club that was supposed to have disposed of Captain Cook, Chief Tecumseh's rifle, Andrew Jackson's pipe, and other curiosities.

Most of the exhibits were genuine, including a remnant of William Pitt's statue. Erected in 1766 by grateful American colonists who appreciated Pitt's efforts on their behalf in the English Parliament, it was later dismantled by the British (in retaliation for the 1776 destruction of King George's statue by the colonial Sons of Liberty). British soldiers cut the head and one arm off the Pitt statue, then dumped it into the Collect Pond. Some years later, Riley recovered the statue — minus the head and arm — and placed it in front of his hotel.

After Riley's death (in 1858) and the subsequent razing of the hotel, the statue was acquired by the New York Historical Society, where it remains on exhibit.

The hotel intersection was a busy one in the 1830-50 period. For many years, it was used as the site for periodic musters and contests by the New York City volunteer firemen, and in 1834 — on George Washington's birthday — a Liberty Pole was erected outside the hotel. A replica of a Liberty Pole erected by the Sons of Liberty just before the Revolutionary War, the spire was 174 feet tall and was used by the volunteer firemen in pumping contests to see which company could pump the highest stream of water. The record — 137 feet — was set in 1855 by the famous fire engine, the Mankiller.

Hand-pumping was exhausting work, and the firemen could maintain peak efficiency for only about five to ten minutes. The Liberty Pole was torn down in the year of Riley's death.

In the picture of the hotel are two sets of railroad tracks on West Broadway. City records show that the tracks were installed about 1850 and were used by the Sixth Avenue (Yount & Ward) and the Eighth Avenue (Finch, Sanderson & Co.) railroads, represented by Adams store card numbers 1005 and 250, respectively. The two railroads used a common track at the hotel, but separated uptown on Canal Street.

W. GIBBS, AGRICULTURIST

HT #	Rarity	Year	Metal	Size	VG	F	VF	EF
272	R6	(1837-40)	Copper	28.5mm	250.	300.	400.	800.

GREEN & WETMORE

The token issues of Green & Wetmore, hardware dealers of Washington & Vessey Streets, were released in the 1825-32 period and may be found cataloged in *Early American Tokens* section as Rulau-E numbers 288 through 290.

HALLOCK & BATES

HT #	Rarity	Year	Metal	Size	VG	F	VF	Unc
275	R4	(1834-7)	Brass	28mm	12.00	20.00	50.00	225.
	Reeded edge.							
276	R8	(1834-7)	Blank Rev.		—	100.	200.	500.
A276	R6	(1834-7)	Copper	28mm	—	—	70.00	—
	May not exist.							

HALLOCK, DOLSON & BATES

HT #	Rarity	Year	Metal	Size	VG	VF	EF	Unc
277	R4	(1838-40)	Brass	28mm	12.00	30.00	135.	250.

Hallock & Bates were at 234 Pearl St. 1835-37. The other partnership does not appear in the New York directories. Reeded edge.

DR. J. G. HEWETT

COPPER, 29MM

HT #	Rarity	Year	VG	F	VF	Unc
278	R4	(1837-8) Thick Planchet, 12 grams	50.00	100.	150.	500.
279	R3	(1837-8) Thin Flan, 7 grams	40.00	75.00	100.	350.

Dr. Jonas G. Hewett was at 68 Prince St. 1837-38. By 1850-51 he was at 100 Spring St.

B. HOOKS

HT #	Rarity	Year	Metal	Size	VG	F	VF	Unc
280	R7	(1833-5)	Copper	18mm	750.	2000.	3000.	4500.
	Bale							
280A	R8	(1833-5)	Silver	18mm	—	—	4000.	4500.
280B	R7	(1833-5)	S/Cop	18mm	750.	2000.	3500.	4000.

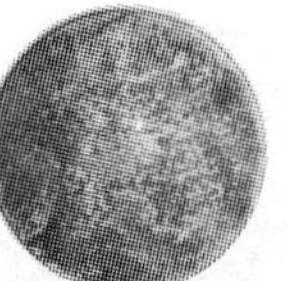

HT #	Rarity	Year	Metal	Size	VG	F	VF	Unc
281	R8	(1833-5)	Copper	18mm	—	1000.	1750.	3000.
	Ctsp. Small Dog							
281A	R9	(1833-5)			—	—	—	1200.
	Blank reverse!							

Located at 276 Broome Street, presumably. Dated on the evidence of Bale's signature. This card (280) was listed as Bushnell 76.

The obverse of the token shows a bust of Benjamin Franklin in fur cap facing left. BALE below bust, five stars at bottom. The reverse reads in five lines: B. HOOKS / 276 / BROOME / STREET / CORNER OF ALLEN ST.

The countermarked variety, HT 281, has a small dog figure counterstamped in front of the head; the reverse of this piece is blank.

IRVING, L. G. & PEASE, J.S.

New York, N.Y. & St. Louis, Mo.

HT #	Rarity	Year	Metal	Size	VG	F	VF	EF
282	R6	(1844-6)	Brass	28.5mm	500.	900.	1500.	2000.
282A	R8	(1844-6)	S/Brass	28.5mm	500.	900.	1500.	2500.

Irving was on 19th St. near Third Ave. in New York 1844-46. The store cards apparently were cut by Bale & Smith.

There are two die varieties: Legend on Irving side reads HE WHO LIVES BY THE SWEAT OF HIS BROW LIVES IN RUIN, or LIVES IN VAIN.

GEORGE A. JARVIS

New York, N.Y.

HT #	Rarity	Year	Metal	Size	VG	VF	EF	Unc
283	R2	1837	Copper	28.5mm	10.00	25.00	60.00	200.
	Stars on Rev.							

284	R1	1837	Copper	28.5mm	5.00	15.00	40.00	200.

Leaves on Rev.

WM. G. JONES

HT #	Rarity	Year	Metal	Size	VG	VF	EF	Unc.
285	R8	(1836-7)	Copper	26.5mm	160.	250.	600.	900.
285A	R6	(1836-7)	Brass	26.5mm	100.	250.	500.	750

Jones' Union Coal office was at the corner of Chambers and Washington Streets 1835-1839. The workmanship of this piece is similar to HT 257 (by Bale & Smith).

1823-24 58 WALL ST.

1835-39 COR. CHAMBERS & WASHINGTON STS.

1844-45 58 WALL ST.

1845-46 MERCHANTS EXCHANGE (6 WALL ST.)

H. LAW

HT #	Rarity	Year	Metal	Size	VG	VF	EF	Unc
286	R2	(1834-5)	Copper	28.5mm	15.00	50.00	125.	350.

Law, a baker, was at 187 Canal St. in 1834-35 only.

LEVERETT & THOMAS

HT #	Rarity	Year	Metal	Size	F	VF	EF	Unc
287	R5	(1833-5)	Copper	28.5mm	100.	150.	350.	600.
287A	R8	(1833-5)	Brass	28.5mm	150.	300.	600.	1250.

They were at 235 Pearl St. only in 1833-35.

LOVETT, SEAL ENGRAVERS

HT #	Rarity	Year	Metal	Size	VG	F	VF	EF
288	R7	(1838-9)	Brass	27mm	700.	1200.	3000.	4500.

This fine engraver was at:

1824-25 249 Broadway

1833-34 67 Maiden Lane

1850-55 5 Dey Street

His card is the same type as the Collins piece, HT 241. An AU specimen fetched $3900 in the B&M Zeddies sale, Nov. 1990, lot 4241.

S. MAYCOCK & CO.

HT #	Rarity	Year	Metal	Size	VG	VF	EF	Unc
289	R2	1837	Copper	28.5mm	10.00	30.00	75.00	225.

HT #	Rarity	Year	Metal	Size	VG	VF	EF	Unc
290	R1	1837	Copper	28.5mm	5.00	15.00	40.00	175.

MERCHANTS EXCHANGE

HT #	Rarity	Year	Metal	Size	VG	F	VF	Unc
291	R1	(1837)	Copper	28mm	6.00	15.00	20.00	200.

6 Berries in, 4 out

292	R7	(1837)	Copper	28mm	800.	1500.	4000.	5000.

5 Berries in, 3 out

The EF Oechsner specimen fetched $4675 in 1988! The EF Middendorf piece realized $2900 in 1990. The EF Gil Steinberg specimen brought a mere $1540 in 1989.

HT #	Rarity	Year	Metal	Size	VG	F	VF	Unc
293	R1	(1837)	Copper	28mm	5.00	12.00	30.00	150.

No Dash under Cent

294	R1	(1837)	Copper	28mm	5.00	8.50	30.00	125.

JAMES G. MOFFET

HT #	Rarity	Year	Metal	Size	VG	VF	EF	Unc
295	R2	(1837)	Copper	28mm	5.00	15.00	45.00	150.
	PLURIBUS. No six-petal rosettes							
295A	R8	(1837)	Overstruck on Moffett token		—	—	375.	—

296	R2	(1837)		—	—	—	—

PLUBIBUS. No rosettes.

NOTE: Confirmation of this variety will require discovery of a perfect specimen!

297	R2	(1837)	Copper	28mm	5.00	20.00	45.00	150.

Six-petal rosettes. PIUBIBUS

Moffet was at 121 Prince St. 1832-37 and it was from this address that he struck his own tokens, as well as those of Samuel Maycock and Henry Crossman.

HT 297 comes in 28mm (normal) and 30mm sizes.

J. MOORE

New York, N.Y. (?)

HT #	Rarity	Date	Metal	Size	VG	F	VF	EF
A297	R9	(1830's)	Copper	23mm	60.00	—	90.00	—
	J. MOORE in relief within rect. depression ctsp on U.S. 1825 Half cent. (Brunk 28330)							
B297	R9	(1830's)	Copper	29mm	60.00	—	90.00	—
	Similar ctsp on U.S. 1810 Large cent. (PCAC July 1993 sale, lot 995)							

Mark Greengold attributed this mark to New York City gunsmith John P. Moore (1823-88), active in mostly retail sales after 1865.

However, Gregory Brunk attributes this mark to a N.Y.C. silversmith based on the mark's appearance. Jared L. Moore (active 1825-44) or John C. Moore (active 1832-44) might qualify, but the marks do not match any published hallmarks.

N-YORK & HARLAEM RAILROAD COMPANY

GERMAN SILVER, 18MM, OCTAGONAL

HT #	Rarity	Year	VG	VF	EF	Unc
298	R6	(1835-8) B & S NY	150.	350.	500.	750.
299	R6	(1835-8) Ctsp. Rosette	200.	400.	700.	900.
300	R7	(1853-8) Ctsp. Dog	250.	500.	600.	900.
		COPPER, 18MM, OCTAGONAL				
301	R7	(1835-8) Ctsp. Leaf	750.	1000.	1500.	2500.

EDWIN PARMELE

HT #	Rarity	Year	Metal	Size	VG	VF	EF	Unc
302	R8	(1834-9)	Brass	18mm	1000.	3500.	5000.	6000.

The liquor store was at 340 Pearl St. 1834-39.

PEALE'S MUSEUM

HT #	Rarity	Year	Metal	Size	VG	VF	EF	Unc
303	R5	1825	Copper	34mm	30.00	150.	250.	700.
303A	R8	1825	WM	34mm	—	760.	2500.	3000.

Rubens Peale established his museum in 1825 in the Parthenon, at 252 Broadway opposite City Hall. The Long Room contained snakes, lizards and an Egyptian mummy. Another gallery contained paintings. Lectures and special appearances were made. In 1831 the museum was renovated and enlarged.

Tickets for a whole family for one year were $10; single admissions were 25 cents. The copper ADMIT THE BEARER checks may have been used for annual subscribers. The museum apparently closed in 1842.

Rubens' father, Charles Willson Peale, opened the Philadelphia Museum in 1784, incorporating it in 1821. This museum issued two different types of ADMIT checks, both probably pre-dating the HT period. Rubens' brother, Franklin Peale, became chief coiner of the U.S. Mint in 1839.

PHALON'S HAIR CUTTING

HT #	Rarity	Year	Metal	Size	VG	VF	EF	Unc
304	R2	1837	Copper	28.5mm	15.00	40.00	75.00	200.

Edward Phalon probably began his business as a hair dresser at 161 Chatham Street in 1834. From then until 1860 he changed location at least 11 times, one address being the 35 Bowery address on the token. In 1842 he was opposite St. Paul's at 214 Broadway, where he sold the "Amazon Toupee' for which (along with his "Wigs and Scalps") the American Institute awarded him a silver medal in 1841, and their first premium in 1842.

In 1848 he was at 61 Broadway, where his extensive advertisements touted "Chemical Hair Invigorator." At the height of his prosperity he occupied an elegant shop in the St. Nicholas Hotel, where his prices for services and cosmetics matched the brilliance of the numerous mirrors, gilded frames, marble basins, and silver-plated fixtures which adorned the salon. Here he remained until the hotel closed.

His "Night Blooming Cereus" was the best known, and last, of his successes before he retired. Low interviewed him in 1886 but Phalon could provide little information about his store card.

An 1849 advertisement for Edward Phalon's "Chemical Hair Invigorator." It indicates that Phalon opened his 197 Broadway "bathing and hair cutting rooms" in May, 1843.

ABRAHAM RIKER

HT #	Rarity	Year	Metal	Size	VG	VF	EF	Unc
305	R1	(1837)	Copper	28mm	5.00	15.00	40.00	175.
	5 Berries in, 3 out							

HT #	Rarity	Year	Metal	Size	VG	VF	EF	Unc
306	R3	(1837)	Copper	28mm	10.00	50.00	125.	300.
	6 Berries in, 2 out							

ROBERT B. RUGGLES

HT #	Rarity	Year	Metal	Size	VG	VF	EF	Unc
307	R1	(1832-35)	Copper	28.5mm	8.00	12.00	40.00	200.
	Plain edge.							
307A	R3	(1832-35) Reeded edge			8.00	15.00	100.	300.
307B	R8	(1832-35)	Brass	28.5mm	—	—	250.	—

HT #	Rarity	Year	Metal	Size	VG	VF	EF	Unc
308	R2	(1835-8)	Copper	28.5mm	8.00	15.00	60.00	250.
	Plain edge. Bale NY							
308A	R3	(1835-8) Reeded edge			8.00	15.00	90.00	250.
308B	R7	Diagonal reeding			—	100.	250.	—

R.E. RUSSELL

HT #	Rarity	Year	Metal	Size	VG	F	VF	Unc
309	R5	1837	GS	18.5mm	150.	350.	500.	1200.

SANS SOUCI

HT #	Rarity	Year	Metal	Size	VG	VF	EF	Unc
310	8	(1838-40)	Lead	18mm	300.	750.	1000.	—

Eagle with drooping wings, head turned right. Rv: SANS SOUCI across center, branch above and below. (Miller NY 769)

The 1839-40 *Longworth's American Almanac, New York Register and City Directory* lists Sans Souci under the proprietorship of Asa Hinckley at 61 Broadway. It is not listed in any other years in the New York city directories and thus may be confidently assigned to the Hard Times period. (Research by David Schenkman)

HT #	Rarity	Year	Metal	Size	VG	VF	EF	Unc
310E	R9	(?)	Lead	18mm	—	1000.	—	—

Obverse as 310. Rv: Large script monogram, possibly LB or PB.

SMITH'S CLOCK ESTABLISHMENT

HT #	Rarity	Year	Metal	Size	VG	VF	EF	Unc
311	R2	1837	Copper	28.5mm	20.00	75.00	125.	250.
	Hour Hand Right of X							
312	R8	(1837)	—	—	—	Rare		
	Clock side only							
312B	R7	—	S/Copper	28.5mm	—	—	150.	450.

HT #	Rarity	Year	Metal	Size	VG	VF	EF	Unc
313	R3	1837	Copper	28.5mm	20.00	75.00	125.	275.
	Establishment straight							

HT #	Rarity	Year	Metal	Size	VG	VF	EF	Unc
314	R1	1837	Copper	28.5mm	15.00	60.00	100.	300.
	Establishment Curved							

HT #	Rarity	Year	Metal	Size	VG	VF	EF	Unc
315	R1	1837	Copper	28.5mm	15.00	60.00	100.	175.
	Small ornaments flank 7-1/2							
316	R1	1837 Dotted Circle				Probably does not exist		

HT #	Rarity	Year	Metal	Size	VG	VF	EF	Unc
317	R2	1837	Copper	28.5mm	20.00	65.00	110.	275.
	Large Ornaments							
317A	R7	—	Gilt/C	28.5mm	—	—	250.	450.

Andrew B. Smith advertised in the *New York Examiner* in June 1837 that he was located at the corner of the Bowery and Division Street, New York, "up stairs, third story, entrance 7-1/2 Bowery." In Nov. 1838 the style of the firm was changed to A.B. Smith & Co.; in 1841 the partnership was conducted as Smith & Brothers, and they announced they had established a branch of the business at 9 North Fifth Street, Philadelphia.

SQUIRE & MERRITT

Obv. 1 - Small letters. S of STT over space between O and R of YORK. R of ROPE directly under S of SHIP, and S of MAKERS directly under S of CHANDLERS.

Obv. 2 - Small letters. S of STT directly over R of YORK. R of ROPE directly under S of SHIP, and S of MAKERS directly under S of CHANDLERS. Period under 2nd T of STT.

Obv. 3 - Large letters. O of ROPE under S of SHIP, and R of MAKERS under S of CHANDLERS. Period under 2nd T of STT.

Rev. A - Small letters. N of NAILS over I of IMPORTERS.

Rev. B - Large letters. N of NAILS over M of IMPORTERS.

OBV. 1   REV. A

HT #		Rarity	Year	F	VF	EF	Unc
			COPPER, 27MM REEDED EDGE				
		Var. 1-A - Thin planchet, beaded border, milled edge, 5 grams, 27mm					
318		R4	(1836)	75.00	150.	300.	400.
			COPPER, 27MM, PLAIN EDGE				
318A		R4	(1836)	75.00	100.	200.	550.
		"175" INCUSED					
		Very thick planchet - plain edge - 12 grams					
319		R7	(1836) Copper	Rare	—	350.	500.
		Thin planchet, milled edge - 5 grams					
320		R8	(1836) Silver	Rare	—	1000.	1500.
	320A	R3	(1836) Copper	50.00	100.	150.	400.
		"1836" INCUSED					
321		R6	(1836) Copper	100.	200.	350.	550.
		Var. 2-A - Thin planchet, beaded border, plain edge, 5 grams, 27mm					
322		R4	(1836) Copper	75.00	150.	225.	400.
		Thick planchet - 8 grams					
323		R5	(1836) Copper	85.00	175.	225.	400.
		Var. 3-B — Thin planchet, dentilated border, PLAIN EDGE, 5 grams, 27MM					
324		R4	(1836) Copper MILLED EDGE	75.00	150.	300.	400.
324A		R4	(1836) Copper	75.00	150.	225.	400.
			MILLED EDGE - "175" INCUSED				
325		R4	(1836) Copper	75.00	100.	200.	400.

HT #	Rarity	Year	Metal	Size	G	VG	VF	EF
326	R9	(ca 1834-37)	Silver	40mm	—	—	2500.	—

L.L. SQUIRE / N-YORK ctsp. on obverse of U.S. 1795 silver dollar. Rv: L.L. SQUIRE / J. MERRITT / N-YORK ctsp on reverse of the 1795 silver dollar. Low 395 may be unique. (Van Ormer sale 2850, ex-H. Chapman, Stephen Nagy, A.A. Grinnell, Ed Rice, James J. Curto, David Schenkman, Roy Van Ormer; Brunk 37830)

This firm of ship chandlers was at 175 South St., corner Roosevelt, from 1831-37. Lewis L. Squire and Jacob T. Merritt issued HT store cards circa 1836, and Squire alone issued tokens from 1840 on into the Merchant period.

J. MERRITT

HT #	Rarity	Year	Metal	Size	VG	F	VF	EF
327	R9	(1834-37)	Silver	32.5mm	—	—	350.	—

N-YORK / J. MERRITT ctsp on U.S. 1819 half dollar. The punches match Low 395. (Van Ormer 1748, ex-Schenkman 1984; Brunk 27430)

HT #	Rarity	Year	Metal	Size	VG	F	VF	EF
328	(?)	—	Copper	29mm	—	—	300.	—

J. MERRITT / N. YORK ctsp on U.S. 1829 Large cent. (Tanenbaum collection)

L.L. SQUIRE

HT #	Rarity	Year	Metal	Size	VG	F	VF	EF
329	R7	(1840)	Copper	29mm	—	100.	—	175.

L. L. SQUIRE ctsp on reverse of U.S. Large cent. (Dates examined: 1823, 1828, 1831, 1839, 1845, 1847)

HT #	Rarity	Year	Metal	Size	VG	F	VF	EF
330	R8	(1840)	Copper	23mm	—	115.	—	160.

Similar ctsp on obverse of U.S. Half cent. Dates examined: 1806, 1828. (John Cheramy coll.; Brunk 37820)

HT #	Rarity	Year	Metal	Size	VG	F	VF	EF
331	R9	(1840)	Silver	32.5mm	—	550.	—	—

Similar ctsp on obverse of U.S. 1806 Draped Bust half dollar. (Gamer-White PCAC specimen)

SILVER, 34MM

HT #	Rarity	Year	Metal	Size	VG	F	VF	EF
331A	R9	(1840)			—	—	350.	—

Similar ctsp on Spain 1821 10 reales, Craig 138.

The punch matches exactly the 'L. L. SQUIRE' punch used on HT 326, the counterstamped 1795 Silver dollar. The fact that Squire appears alone on this stamp may indicate that J. Merritt pulled out of the partnership before these pieces were issued, in or soon after 1840.

It is probable that other Squire, Merritt or Squire & Merritt counterstamps remain to be identified.

SUYDAM & BOYD

COPPER, 26.5MM

HT #	Rarity	Year	VG	F	VF	EF
332	R5	(1831-4) 187 Pearl St.	40.00	80.00	100.	200.
333	R5	(1834-7) 157 Pearl St.	40.00	80.00	125.	200.
		BRASS, 26.5MM				
333A	R5	(1834-7) 157 Pearl St.	—	—	175.	—

This firm of dry goods merchants, consisting of Hy. Suydam and William Boyd, was at 187 Pearl St. 1831-34 and then at 157 Pearl St. 1834-37. (See Doremus, Suydam and Nixon entry.)

EZRA B. SWEET

HT #	Rarity	Year	Metal	Size	F	VF	EF	Unc
334	R3	1837	Copper	27.5mm	50.00	100.	150.	275.

HT #	Rarity	Year	Metal	Size	F	VF	EF	Unc
335	R4	1837	Copper	28.5mm	60.00	125.	225.	400.

Thick Planchet

Ezra B. Sweet was in active business in New York from 1825 to 1852, changing his address 12 times. He was at 200 Canal Street from 1836 to 1839 when the tokens were issued. In addition to the business advertised on his cards, he was a bell-founder and plumber.

TISDALE & RICHMOND

HT #	Rarity	Date	Metal	Size	VG	F	VF	Unc.
A335	R9	(1833-34)	Copper	28mm	—	7500.	—	—

TISDALE & RICHMOND / KEEP / CONSTANTLY / ON HAND / SHOVELS, NAILS / HOLLOW WARE / PIG, & BAR IRON / &c. &c. &c. / No. 250 WATER ST., NEW YORK. Rv: TACK & BRAD PLATES / SHEATHING. / & BOLT. COPPER / TACKS, BRADS, / & SPARABILLS, / SUGAR KETTLES. / ROLLING MILL, / ROLLS &c. / &c. &c. / NAIL RODS, HOOP IRON & c. Plain edge. (Dr. Robert Schuman coll.)

Sparabill = Thin headless nails used to attach soles to shoes. They resembled a sparrow's bill.

Tisdale & Richmond are listed at 250 Water St. only 1833-34. They were at 210 Water St. 1834-35 and 218 Water St. 1835-36. They do not appear in the 1832 or earlier, or 1836 or later, directories.

This token, so far unique, was discovered by Charles Kirtley and researched by H. Joseph Levine in 1988. Dr. Robert Schuman first published it in *Rare Coin Review* no. 75 (1992) by Bowers & Merena Galleries.

VAN NOSTRAND & DWIGHT

HT #	Rarity	Year	Metal	Size	VG	F	VF	EF
336	R2	(1835-7)	Copper	27mm	10.00	15.00	25.00	110.

These book publishers were at 146 Nassau St. 1835-37.

C.H. WEBB, CONGRESS HALL

HT #	Rarity	Year	Metal	Size	F	VF	EF	Unc
337	R3	(1832-34)	Copper	26.5mm	25.00	40.00	125.	250.
337A	R3	(1832-34)	Brass	26.5mm	25.00	40.00	125.	200.
338	R3	(1832-34)	Copper	26.5mm	25.00	40.00	75.00	200.

Period after GENERAL

Charles H. Webb was proprietor of Congress Hall Hotel, at 142 Broadway, according to the 1833 directory. In the 1835 directory, Webb's address had changed to 438 Greenwich.

RD. WILLIAMS, UNION HALL
New York, N.Y.

HT #	Rarity	Year	Metal	Size	VG	VF	EF	Unc
339	R8	(1833-5)	Copper	19.5mm	1000.	3500.	4500.	5500.

The exact design of Richard Williams' Union Hall token reads:

Obv: UNION HALL / B (hand with heart on palm) Y / RD. WILLIAMS / CORNER / OF / HENRY & OLIVER STS.

Rev: GOOD FOR / REFRESHMENTS / AT THE BAR / BALE.

HIRAM JUDSON
Syracuse, N.Y.

COPPER, 28-1/2MM

HT #	Rarity	Year	VG	F	VF	Unc
345	R4	(1835-8) B & S NY	6.00	12.00	20.00	150.
346	R4	(1835-8) Thick Planchet	6.00	12.00	20.00	200.

NOTE: HT 345 has a Reeded edge. HT 346 has a Plain edge. HT 346 is known bearing a counterstamped numeral 1 (Rarity 9, value $950) or with counterstamped numeral 2 (value $300-$400). At this time it is not known what reason Judson had for placing these numerals on his tokens.

HT #	Rarity	Year	Metal	Size	VG	VF	EF	Unc
A346	R9	(?)	Copper	29mm	250.	400.	—	—
	H. JUDSON /Gear) ctsp on U.S. 1826 Large cent. (Tanenbaum coll.; Brunk 22235)							
C346	R9	(?)	Silver	26.5mm	250.	400.	—	—
	H. JUDSON / SYRACUSE /Gear) ctsp on Spanish-American 1775-LME 2-real coin. (Tanenbaum coll.; Brunk 22240)							
D346	R9	(?)	Silver	26mm	250.	400.	—	—
	H. JUDSON /Gear) ctsp on Spanish-American 1776-Mo 2-real coin. (Tanenbaum coll.)							

By 1851 Hiram Judson is listed as a justice and commissioner. He does not appear after 1853.

O. & P. BOUTWELL
Troy, N.Y.

HT #	Rarity	Year	Metal	Size	VG	F	VF	EF
347	R7	1835	Copper	28mm	3000.	4000.	5500.	7000.

HT #	Rarity	Year	Metal	Size	VG	F	VF	EF
347A	R9	1835	Copper	31mm	—	—	—	9000.
	Struck on U.S. Large cent							
347B	R9	1835	Silver	27mm	—	—	—	10,000
	Struck on silver 1774-PTS 2-reales							

BUCKLIN'S INTEREST TABLES

HT #	Rarity	Year	Metal	Size	G	VG	F	VF
348	R5	1834	Copper	28.5mm	125.	150.	300.	450.

HT #	Rarity	Year	Metal	Size	G	VG	F	VF
349	R5	1835	Copper	27.5mm	100.	125.	400.	1100.

2 Stars Under Head

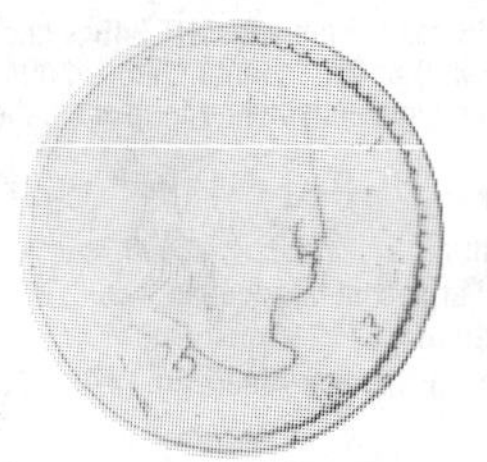

350	R7	1835	Copper	27.5mm	1500.	2000.	2500.	5000.

No Stars Under Head.

COPPER, 27-1/2MM, HEAD LEFT

351	R8	1835 No Stars on Obverse	—	—	—	8000.
352	R8	1835 Shapely Head, 28-1/2MM, 14 Stars	—	—	—	Rare

HT 352 may not exist. John Ford, Donald Miller and George Fuld have not seen one in past 35 years. Two known 352's are hand altered.

COPPER, 28-1/2MM, NO HEAD

353	R1	1835 T* under date	—	11.00	40.00	100.
354	R3	1835 Only 27 MM	—	—	30.00	100.

HT #	Rarity	Year	Metal	Size	VG	VF	EF	Unc
355	R4	1835	Copper	28.5mm	50.00	250.	850.	1100.

True Alb under date

An EF specimen realized $1,200 on March 27, 1981.

BUCKLIN'S BOOK KEEPING

West Troy, N.Y.

HT #	Rarity	Year	Metal	Size	VG	VF	EF	Unc
356	R2	(1835)	Copper	28.5mm	20.00	60.00	300.	500.

COPPER, 29-1/2MM

HT #	Rarity	Year	VG	VF	EF	Unc
357	R3	(1835) Large thin flan, 8-9 grams	20.00	60.00	150.	—

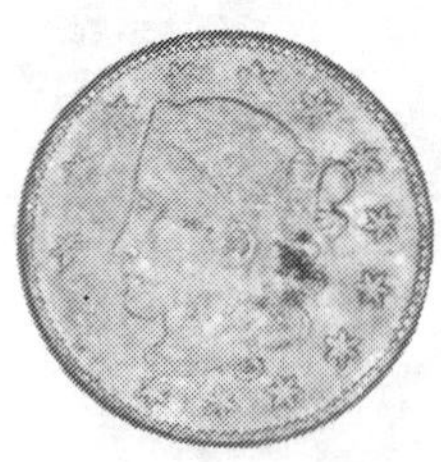

COPPER, 27MM

357A	R4	(1835) Smaller thin flan, 4-5 grams	35.00	60.00	150.	—

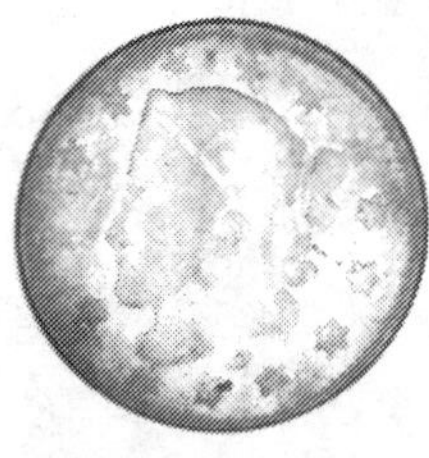

357B	R3	(1835) Thick flan, 8-9 grams	20.00	60.00	150.	—

358	R4	(1835) Different head, smaller	30.00	60.00	150.	—

Isaac B. Bucklin was a schoolteacher in Troy in 1835-37, having his residence in what was then called West Troy, now a part of the city, giving special attention to instruction in bookkeeping, and printing and selling "Interest Tables." In 1839 and later he engaged in business as a stove-dealer, at 221 River Street, still residing in West Troy. The date of his death has not been ascertained.

A specimen of HT 356 of one of its varieties has been reported counterstamped J.M. BLANCHARD. (Duffield 1613; Brunk 4003)

CARPENTER & MOSHER

Troy, N.Y.

COPPER, 28MM

HT #	Rarity	Year	G	VG	F	EF
359	R6	(1835) River St. (no number)	3000.	3500.	4000.	4500.

An EF specimen fetched $6600 in 1989.

360	R7	(1836-37) 310 River St.	2000.	3500.	4000.	6500.

All are weakly struck.

W.P. HASKINS

COPPER, 28-1/2MM

HT #	Rarity	Year	VG	VF	EF	Unc
361	R4	1834 Lafayette H	15.00	75.00	200.	400.

HT #	Rarity	Year	VG	VF	EF	Unc
362	R1	1834 Schenck	6.00	15.00	45.00	250.

William P. Haskins appears in 1830 census.

J. & C. PECK

HT #	Rarity	Year	Metal	Size	VG	F	VF	Unc
363	R1	(1835)	Copper	28.5mm	5.00	12.00	20.00	250.

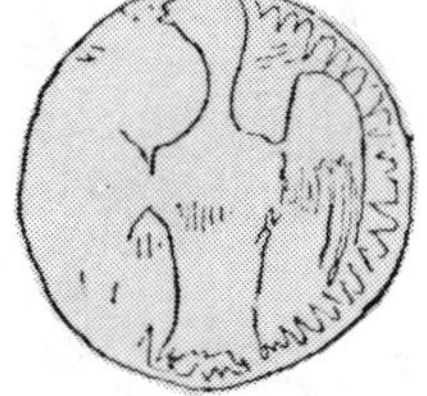

364	R6	(1835) Eagle	400.	550.	1200.	—

365	R7	(1835) Britannia seated	600.	800.	1200.	—

Types 364 and 365 are mulings of the Peck tin machine obverse with Canadian "blacksmith copper" types; 364 was numbered by Howland Wood ("The Canadian Blacksmith Coppers" in *The Numismatist* for April 1910) as 28, while 365 was not listed by Wood but was reported by Warren Baker, Montreal, Canada, to the author.

John Peck appears in 1830 census.

S. F. PHELPS

HT #	Rarity	Year	Metal	Size	VG	F	VF	EF
A365	R9	(1834-38)	Brass	29mm	—	350.	—	—

S. F. PHELPS ctsp on brass counterfeit of U.S. 1827 Large cent. (Brunk 31900)

Samuel F. Phelps was a silversmith in Troy 1834-38, according to the Kovels (see Bibliography).

N. STARBUCK & SON

Troy, N.Y.

HT #	Rarity	Year	Metal	Size	VG	F	VF	EF
366	R6	(1835)	Copper	28.5mm	150.	250.	350.	600.

No Stars Under Head

A BU piece made $3300 in the 1989 Gil Steinberg sale.

367	R8	(1835) 2 Stars Under Head	May not exist

368	R2	(1835)	Copper	28.5mm	5.00	15.00	25.00	100.

From study of HT 368 specimens, it is certain there were at least three strikings - normal, dies rotated 90 degrees, and dies rotated 180 degrees.

HT #	Rarity	Year	VG	F	VF	EF
369	R7	(1835) George II in cuirass	800.	1000.	1200.	—
370	R7	(1835) Eagle	600.	700.	900.	—

371	R5	(1835) Peck's tin machine	75.00	125.	300.	750.

Types 369, 370 and 371 are mulings of the Starbuck reverse (screw design) with Canadian "blacksmith copper" types. They were numbered by Howland Wood ("The Canadian Blacksmith Coppers" in *The Numismatist* for April 1910) respectively as 25, 27 and 29.

Nathaniel and Charles Starbuck established a plough factory in Troy in 1818. The factory was on the west side of River Street south of the old Fulton Market. In April 1821 N. & C. Starbuck admitted Ephraim Gurley to the business, which became Starbuck & Gurley and bought out the Troy Air Furnace from Gurley and his partners.

Charles Starbuck died in 1823. By 1830 the firm became known as N. Starbuck & Sons, Troy Air Furnace. It was still in business in 1845.

SIBLEY & WATSON

West Mendon, N.Y.

HT #	Rarity	Year	Metal	Size	VG	F	VF	EF
372	R8	(1832-40)	Copper	28mm	12,000.	—	—	—

Struck over U.S. Cent

The overstrike reads in 12 lines: SIBLEY & WATSON . MACHINISTs . W . MENDON . / MONROE CO. N.Y. / MANU / FACTURE, / WOOL CARD / ING MACHINES / CONDENSERS / POWER, LOOMS / BROAD & NARRO / W. JACKS / JINNEYS / & C. (An unusual feature of this overstrike is that all '&' signs are lying on their side.)

Both Hiram Sibley and Don Alonzo Watson were born in Massachusetts, departing there for New York in the 1820's, where they are traceable to various locations until both ended up in West Mendon in 1832 as business partners. The partnership was dissolved in 1840.

Sibley, the mechanic, became sheriff, and later his name was given to the engineering building at Cornell Univ. because of a bequest, apparently resulting from his involvement with the West Union and the Michigan Southern & Northern railroads.

Watson became involved in private banking after the two dissolved their partnership, but the men did have subsequent joint business ventures.

The only known specimen of this token was discovered at an Ohio token show in 1980 by Dick Grinolds of Minnesota.

OHIO

P. EVENS

Cincinnati, Ohio

HT #	Rarity	Year	Metal	Size	VG	F	VF	Unc
375	R6	(1830's)	GS	24mm	150.	300.	600.	1500.

375A	R6	(1830's)	Brass	24mm	150.	400.	600.	1500.

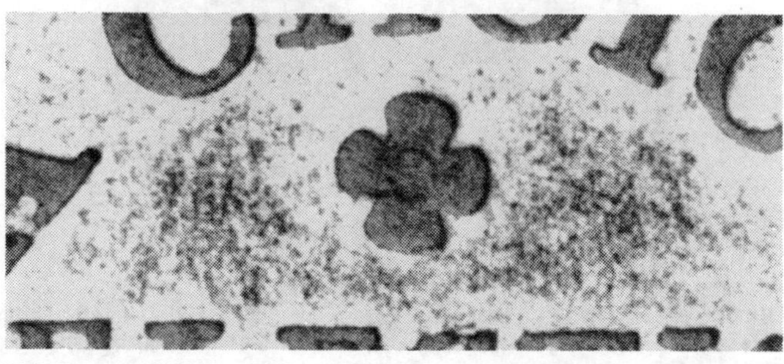

375B	R8	(1830's)	Gilt/B	24mm	—	—	900.	1500.

On 375B, the ornament above SELECTION is not a rosette, but a crosslike device. (Krause coll.)

HT #	Rarity	Year	VG	F	VF	Unc
376	R7	(1833-5) Bale NY	200.	300.	700.	1500.
		GILT COPPER, 24MM				
376A	R7	(1833-5) Bale NY	200.	300.	700.	1500.
		COPPER, 24MM				
376B	R7	(1833-5) Bale NY	200.	300.	700.	1500.
376C	R9	(1833-5) Bale NY	—	—	900.	—

As 376, but ctsp 25 CTS in relief within rect. depression, neatly placed between 149 and MAIN ST. Depression is 11mm long. (Gaylor Lipscomb coll.)

Platt Evens is recorded as having been at these addresses:
1815-19 138 Main St.
1829-40 149 Main St.
1842-43 Main between 3rd & 4th (Evens and Farnham)

See *The Numismatist*, May 1917, page 198, for the Waldo C. Moore research on this issuer.

A. LOOMIS

Cleveland, Ohio

COPPER, 28.5MM

HT #	Rarity	Year	VG	F	VF	EF
377	R7	1843 Arrows R & L	2500.	3300.	4000.	4600.
377A	R8	1843 Struck on Cent	—	—	7000.	—
378	R8	1843 Arrows Right. 28MM	10,000	—	—	—

379	R8	1843 No Rings in Beak	5000.	5800.	7500.	10,000
379A	R8	1843 Silvered Copper	—	—	8000.	10,000
379B	R8	1843 Double Struck, 20% shift	5000.	5800.	6500.	8000.

379C	R9	1843 Triple Struck on Cent	3500.	—	—	—

This overstrike has one auction record of $12,000!

380	R6	(1840's) 11 Stars Above	100.	150.	200.	600.
381	R5	(1840's) 6 Stars Above	100.	185.	250.	375.

381A	R8	(1840's) Double Struck	—	—	—	800.
381B	R8	(1840's) Fully Reeded Edge	—	—	400.	800.

381C	R9	(1840's) Struck on 1827-37 Cent	—	—	2000.	—

Anson L. Loomis was born at Sangerfield, N.Y., April 6, 1812. He died in Nov. 1863. Loomis and his wife Charlotte apparently moved to Cleveland in 1836 from St. Louis. He started business about 1837 as a grocer, expanding into the wholesale grocery and liquor business in the early 1840's.

G. & A. Loomis, grocers, were at 14 Dock St. 1837-38. Anson Loomis, grocer and ship chandler, was at 24 Dock St. in 1841. A.L. Loomis & Co., wholesale grocery and liquors, was at 34 Merwin St. in 1843-47. Loomis does not appear in directories from 1848 on.

The three rings in the eagle's beak constituted Loomis' emblem and it appears on his surviving advertisements. Loomis was an active Mason in Cleveland City Lodge 15. He was made a Master Mason Jan. 16, 1842.

The dated tokens (HT 377-379) all bear the 1843 date. The undated pieces (HT 380, 381) also bear the 34 Merwin Street address, so they could not have been emitted later than 1847; they probably appeared in the 1842-44 period.

Two unique Loomis pieces, HT 379C and 381C, were reported for the first time in 1981. HT 379C realized $12,100 in the Hartzog sale, purchased by Kurt R. Krueger. HT 381C fetched $2,300 in the Chesterfield sale, purchased for Chester L. Krause by the author.

The Loomis cards are among the most difficult to obtain of any Hard Times tokens. Of HT 377, only 10 to 12 specimens are known, while of HT 378 there are just 2 specimens known. Only 4 pieces of HT 379 are known, and 5 pieces of all HT 379 varieties (379A, B and C).

Specialists Charles Kirtley and Alan Weinberg state that all Loomis cards have partially reeded edges.

BANK OF J.G. YOUNG

Piqua, Ohio

COPPER, 29MM, PLAIN EDGE

HT #	Rarity	Year	VG	F	VF	EF
382	R9	1837 Engr. on HT Token	—	—	40.00	—

BANK / OF / J G YOUNG / PIQUA crudely hand engraved on Low 17, an 1837-dated "Illustrious Predecessor" HT token. (Ned Drees collection, Covington, Ohio)

Joseph G. Young was Piqua (Miami County) town treasurer in the 1830's and 1840's, and apparently acted as a private banker as well. He and Moses B. Corwin formed a law partnership in Nov. 1832. In 1847 Young became the founder of the newly organized Piqua Branch, State Bank of Ohio.

The item above can hardly be considered a store card, yet its existence verifies the circulation of HTT's in western Ohio at this period. Piqua is about 31 miles north of Dayton.

Listing handmade pieces is, admittedly, dangerous because unscrupulous persons could "make their own." The specimen above has been in the Drees family since the 1890's.

PENNSYLVANIA

ISAAC BARTON & CO.

Philadelphia, Pa.

HT #	Rarity	Year	Metal	Size	VG	F	VF	Unc
385	R4	(1837)	Brass	28mm	30.00	45.00	100.	350.

ISAAC BARTON & CO / NO 27 / SOUTH 2ND / STREET / (ornament) / * PHILADELPHIA *. Rv: IMPORTERS & DEALERS / WHOLESALE / (ornament) / DRY GOODS / (ornament) / & RETAIL / .IN FOREIGN & DOMESTIC. Plain edge. (Wright 60)

The reverse is similar to that on the cards of Hooper Martin & Smith (Pa 204) and Samuel & Joseph Harvey (Pa 202-203), with a change for the store's activity. Probably all three cards emanate from a single token-maker.

Isaac Barton & Co. was at 30 So. 2nd St. in 1833, then at 27 So. 2nd St., the address on the token, in 1837. In 1841-44 it was at 29 So. 2nd St.

BENDER'S EATING SALOON

BRASS

HT #	Rarity	Year	VG	VF	EF	Unc
386	R7	(1837-44) 6-1/4 Cents	200.	500.	700.	900.
387	R7	(1837-44) 12 Cents	200.	500.	700.	900.
388	R7	(1837-44) 13 Cents	200.	500.	700.	900.
389	R7	(1837-44) 19 Cents	200.	500.	700.	900.
390	R7	(1837-44) 22 Cents	200.	500.	700.	900.
391	R8	(1837-44) 25 Cents	200.	500.	700.	900.
392	R7	(1837-44) 34 Cents	200.	500.	700.	900.
393	R7	(1837-44) 35 Cents	200.	500.	700.	900.
393A	R9	(1837-44) 37-3/4 Cents	200.	500.	700.	900.
394	R7	(1837-44) 38 Cents	200.	500.	700.	900.
395	R7	(1837-44) 44 Cents	200.	500.	700.	900.
396	R8	(1837-44) 62-1/2 Cents	200.	500.	700.	900.

HT #	Rarity	Year	Metal	Size	VG	F	VF	EF
397	R9	(1837)	Copper	29mm	600.	—	900.	1250.
	BENDERS / S. E. COR. 3D & / PHILA / CHESNUT / EATING SALOON ctsp on U.S. 1802 Large cent. (Kurt Krueger Sept. 7, 1983 sale, lot 1697; Brunk 3250)							
398	R9	(1844)	Copper	29mm	—	750.	—	1250.
	BENDER'S STAR HOTEL. / CHAS. W. BENDER / PHILADA ctsp on U.S. 1838 Large cent. (Brunk 3260)							

C.W. BENDER
C. W. B(ENDER)

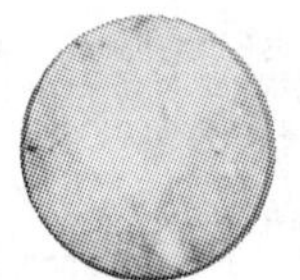

HT #	Rarity	Year	Metal	Size	VG	F	VF	Unc
399	R6	1842	GS	16mm	1500.	2000.	3600.	5800.
399A	R7	1842	Silver	14mm	2000.	2250.	4000.	6000.

Probably other denominations exist in this series. Numbers 386 to 396 likely were used in the 1837-1844 period.

Charles W. Bender does not appear in the 1833 directories. In 1836-37 he appears, with his business not stated, at 2 Chestnut Street (His residence in 1837 was at 3 Noble.)

Bender issued his tokens, HT 399 and 399A, in 1842. These contain a large star as central motif, and this can be explained when it is realized that, in 1842-48, C. W. Bender is found listed as proprietor of the Star Hotel at 71 Dock Street.

Bender is also believed to have been in business in the 1850's.

Discovery of HT 397 tends to confirm Bender as a Hard Times merchant. Other cataloguers had guessed he might be later — into the 1850's.

J.M. Saunderson & Son's Franklin House on bustling Chestnut Street, Philadelphia, in 1835. (Courtesy Yale University)

BOLIVAR

HT #	Rarity	Year	Metal	Size	VG	F	VF	EF
400	R8	(1828-48)	Silver	27mm	—	350.	—	600.
	BOLIVAR / 8TH AND CHEST STRT ctsp on Spanish-American 1784 or 1789-Mo-FM 2-reales.2 known. (Brunk 4180)							
401	R9	(1828-48)			—	400.	—	—
	BOLIVAR BOLIVAR / 8TH AND CHEST STRT ctsp on Spanish-American 178?-Mo-FF 2-reales. (Robert M. Ramsay coll.)							

HT #	Rarity	Year	Metal	Size	VG	F	VF	EF
401R	R7	(?)	Brass	27mm	900.	—	2000.	—
	BOLIVAR / 20 / 8TH AND CHEST STRT on 27mm brass disc. Uniface.							
401S	R7	(?)	Brass	27mm	900.	—	2000.	—
	Similar, but 50. (Smithsonian coll.)							

The Bolivar House was operated by William Carels at 203 Chestnut Street from 1827 to at least 1848.

HT #	Rarity	Year	Metal	Size	VG	F	VF	EF
401T	R9	(?)	Brass	23.5mm	—	—	3000.	—
	Similar to 401R, but 25. Rv: 25. Unique. (Krause coll., ex-Vlack)							

BUEHLER'S & SMITH

BRASS, 29MM, REEDED EDGE

HT #	Rarity	Year	VG	F	VF	Unc
402	R6	(1837)	75.00	100.	150.	500.
	MARTIN BUEHLER. WILLIAM BUEHLER. EDWARD SMITH + / BUEHLER'S & SMITH / 192 / MARKET / STREET / PHILADA. Rv: IMPORTERS & DEALERS / HARDWARE / CUTLERY / & / HEAVY / GOODS / IN FOREIGN & DOMESTIC. (Miller Pa 60)					
	COPPER, 29MM, REEDED EDGE					
402A	R7	(1837)	75.00	100.	150.	600.
	As 404. (Miller Pa 61; Wright 1349)					
	GILT BRASS, 29MM, REEDED EDGE					
402B	R7	(1837)	75.00	100.	150.	600.
	As 404. (Miller Pa 62)					

The 1837 directory places Buehlers and Smith, as the hardware firm was known, at 192 High (Market) St. that year. Martin Buehler & Brother had an outlet in 1848 at 195 High St., according to the 1848 directory.

CATCH CLUB

COPPER, 31MM

COPPER, 27MM

HT #	Rarity	Year	VG	F	VF	EF
403	R7	(1830's) 12-1/2 Cents	200.	300.	450.	700.
404	R7	(1830's) 12-1/2 Cents	200.	300.	400.	700.
		BRASS, 26MM				
405	R6	(1830's) 12-1/2 Cents	100.	300.	600.	900.

		SILVERED BRASS, 26MM				
405A	R7	(1830's) 12-1/2 Cents	—	—	—	900.
		BRASS, 26MM				
406	R6	(1830's) Ctsp BOOTH on Rev	100.	300.	500.	700.
		GILT COPPER, 26MM				
406A	R6	(1830's) Ctsp BOOTH on Rev	100.	300.	600.	1000.
		SILVERED BRASS, 26MM				
406B	R6	(1830's) Ctsp BOOTH on Rev	200.	300.	600.	1000.
		SILVERED BRASS, 26MM				
407	R7	(1830's) Obverse Blank	—	—	200.	350.

NOTE: No name on 407.

DICKSON, WHITE & CO.

HT #	Date	Metal	Size	VG	F	VF	Unc
485	(1837-38)	Copper	30mm	30.00	75.00	175.	350.
	A watch. DICKSON, WHITE & CO. / 129 MARKET STREET / PHILADELPHIA, Rv: IMPORTERS / OF / WATCHES / JEWELRY / PLATED WARE / FANCY GOODS & C / JOHN DICKSON / WM H. WHITE, JNO. M. HARPER. (Wright 1396; Miller Pa 122)						
486	(1837-38)	German Silver	30mm	—	—	—	500.
		As Pa 122.					
487	(1837-38)	WM	30mm	—	—	—	500.
		As 123. Plain edge. (ANS coll.)					
488	(1837-38)	Brass	30mm	—	50.00	125.	300.
		As 123. Plain edge. (ANS coll.)					

Dickson, White & Co., are listed in the directories only in 1837-1838.

S. FEATHER

COPPER, 21MM

HT #	Rarity	Year	VG	F	VF	Unc
408	R7	(1830's) 12-1/2 Cents	750.	1000.	1500.	3000.
		Obverse: S FEATHER / G / 12 -1/2 CTS. Reverse: Blank.				

This issuer is proving very elusive. He cannot be located in the Philadelphia city directories for any of these years: 1833, 1837, 1844, 1848.

GOODYEAR & SONS

HT #	Rarity	Year	Metal	Size	VG	F	VF	Unc
409	R8	(1840's)	Brass	30mm	3000.	—	6000.	10,000
	DOMESTIC HARDWARE COMMISSION MERCHANTS * / MANUFACTURERS OF PATENT PITCHFORKS * / A / GOODYEAR / & / SONS / *** / PHILADA. Rv: * GILT & ANERICAN (sic!) BUTTONS OF ALL KINDS / IVORY COMBS PLATED WARE &C * / SCOVILLS / GILT / BUTTONS. Ornate border and flourishes on each side. (Miller Pa 179; illustrated specimen in ANS collection)							

Amasa J. Goodyear made brass buttons under the name A. Goodyear & Son in New Haven, Conn. 1812-1827.

The sons, Charles and Nelson Goodyear, obtained patents for hard rubber buttons in the 1849-1851 period while in Philadelphia. These were the atecedents of today's Goodyear Rubber Co., one of the worlds's leading manufacturers of rubber products.

Goodyear Rubber Co. issued a number of tokens in New York in the 1876 period.

It is probable that HT 409, an extremely rare token, is from the 1830's or early 1840's based on its inscription and its fabrication.

SAMUEL & JOSEPH HARVEY

BRASS, 28MM, REEDED EDGE

HT #	Rarity	Year	VG	F	VF	Unc
410	R4	(1837)	20.00	25.00	75.00	300.
	SAMUEL & JOSEPH HARVEY / 195 / MARKET / STREET / * PHILADELPHIA *. Rev: .IMPORTERS & DEALERS. / HARDWARE / & / CUTLERY / IN FOREIGN & DOMESTIC (Wright 1445)					
		COPPER, 28MM, REEDED EDGE				
410A	R4	(1837)	20.00	25.00	80.00	300.

The reverse is the same as that of Hooper Martin & Smith of Philadelphia, Pa. 204. The firm appears at this address in the directories only in 1837.

The hardware firm of Samuel & Joseph Harvey must have issued its tokens in 1836-37, as they appear at 195 High (Market) Street only in the 1837 directory.

Samuel Harvey & Sons, hardware merchants, were at 62 No. Front Street 1832-33. Joseph was one son, Samuel Harvey Jr. the other. In the 1844 directory Samuel Harvey (Jr. ?) was a stonecutter at Marlboro below Bedford, while Joseph Harvey had an office at 139 High Street.

HOOPER MARTIN & SMITH

BRASS, 27MM, REEDED EDGE

HT #	Rarity	Year	VG	F	VF	EF
411	R4	(1837)	50.00	80.00	150.	300.
	HOOPER MARTIN & SMITH / 113 MARKET ST. Rv: IMPORTERS & DEALERS. / HARDWARE / & / CUTLERY / IN FOREIGN & DOMESTIC. Plain edge. (Wright 1459).					

John Hooper, merchant, is listed at 10th St. above Chestnut in the 1833 directory.

Also in the 1833 directory appeared the firm of Martin, Craven & Smith, merchants, at 113 High St., the same address on Low 385. The obvious conclusion is that the Hooper and MC&S firms merged sometime in the 1833-37 period.

John Hooper, alone, is listed as a merchant at 113 High St. in the 1844 directory.

J. MENDENHALL

HT #	Rarity	Year	Metal	Size	VG	F	VF	EF
A411	R9	(1841)	Copper	29mm	—	—	150.	—
	J. MENDENHALL in relief within rect. depression ctsp on U.S. 1845 Large cent. (B&M Taylor sale, March 1987, lot 1289; Brunk 27395)							

This piece realized $154 in the Taylor sale.

John Mendenhall was a silversmith active in Philadelphia about 1841. He apparently descended from a Pennsylvania family of silversmiths, of whom Thomas Mendenhall of Lancaster, circa 1772, was one. More research is needed on this issuer.

PHILADELPHIA CORPORATION

HT #	Rarity	Year	Metal	Size	F	VF	EF	Unc
412	R8	(1835-36) One Shilling	GS	26mm	—	—	20,000	—

HT #	Rarity	Year	Metal	Size	F	VF	EF	Unc
413	R7	(1835-36)	GS	26mm	1500.	5500.	6500.	7500.

50 Cents F.S.

The "Corporation of Philadelphia" here refers to the city government of Philadelphia. Both 412 and 413 use the same obverse. Only 2 known of HT 412.

W.D. RAPP

HT #	Rarity	Year	Metal	Size	VG	F	VF	EF
414	R7	(1832-50)	Copper	29mm	—	60.00	—	85.00

W.D. RAPP in relief within rect. depression ctsp on U.S. Large cents of various dates. Dates examined: 1808, 1810, 1822, 1828, 1829. Only 6 known. (Brunk 33530; Rulau-E Pa 422)

HT #	Rarity	Year	Metal	Size	VG	F	VF	EF
414A	R7	(1832-50)	Copper	23mm	—	50.00	—	75.00

Similar ctsp on U.S. Half cent. Dates examined: 1804, 1807, 1809, 1819, 1821, 1826, 1828, 1829, 1832. At least 9 known. (Rulau-E Pa 420 & 421)

HT #	Rarity	Year	Metal	Size	VG	F	VF	EF
414E	R9	(1832-50)	Silver	27mm	—	—	150.	—

Similar ctsp on Spanish-American 1774 2-reales. (Rulau-E Pa 423)

William D. Rapp was a Philadelphia silversmith from about 1828 until 1850. The mark is one of his standard hallmarks. There are two varieties of the mark, thick and thin letters.

Rapp's advertisement from the 1837 Philadelphia city directory.

H. REES

NOTE: The letters in the H. REES punches are distinctive — wide serif-type capitals. The same lettering is on the related stamps, H. LANDIS and PHILa.

COPPER, 29MM

HT #	Rarity	Year	VG	F	VF	EF
415	R8		—	40.00	—	70.00

H. REES straight ctsp on U.S. Large cent. Examined: 1817, 1825, 1827. (Hallenbeck 18.502; Rulau Pa-Ph 343; Brunk 33770-I)

COPPER, 23MM

HT #	Rarity	Year	VG	F	VF	EF
415A	R8		—	50.00	—	80.00

H. REES curved (upward arc) ctsp on U.S. Half cent. Dates examined: 1808, 1825, 1826. Only 3 known. (Rulau Pa-Ph 345B; Brunk 33770-II)

COPPER, 29MM

HT #	Rarity	Year	VG	F	VF	EF
415B	R5		—	35.00	—	50.00

Similar ctsp (curved) on U.S. Large cent. Examined: 1793, 1794, 1799, 1800, 1802, 1803, 1807, 1808, 1811, 1813, 1816, 1817, 1818, 1819, 1820, 1821, 1822,1825, 1826, 1827, 1828, 1829, 1830, 1831, 1833, 1836, 1837, 1838, unknown dates. At least 64 pieces reported. (Rulau Pa-Ph 344)

SILVER, 32.5MM

HT #	Rarity	Year	VG	F	VF	EF
415C	R9		—	65.00	—	100.

Similar ctsp on U.S. 1825 Bust half dollar.

SILVER, 27MM

HT #	Rarity	Year	VG	F	VF	EF
415D	R9		—	65.00	—	100.

Similar ctsp on Spanish American 1801-NG 2-reales.

SILVER, 21MM

HT #	Rarity	Year	VG	F	VF	EF
415E	R9	—	60.00	—	90.00	

Similar ctsp on Spanish-American 1795 1-real. Only 1 known. (Brunk 33770W-II)

COPPER, 29MM

HT #	Rarity	Year	VG	F	VF	EF
415G	R7		—	100.	—	150.

H. REES (curved) / PHILa (straight) ctsp on U.S. Large cent. Examined: 1818, 1823, 1830, unknown date. Only 4 known. (Hallenbeck 18.503; Rulau Pa-Ph 345; Brunk 33780)

COPPER, 29MM

HT #	Rarity	Year	VG	F	VF	EF
415J	R9		—	60.00	—	100.

H. REES (curved) / H. LANDIS (straight) ctsp on U.S. 1820 Large cent. Only 1 known. (Hartzog coll.; Rulau Pa-Ph 344A; Brunk 33770-II/23800)

COPPER, 29MM

HT #	Rarity	Year	VG	F	VF	EF
415L	R9		—	60.00	—	100.

H. REES / R. NYE ctsp on U.S. Large cent. (Brunk 33770/29985)

COPPER 29MM

HT #	Rarity	Year	VG	F	VF	EF
415N	R9		—	70.00	—	200.

H. REES (curved) / B. RAPP (relief, in toothed rect. depression) ctsp on U.S. 1798 Large cent. The Rapp stamp was applied later. Only 1 known. (Brunk 33770-II/33520)

A blacksmith advertised himself as H. Rees, Arch near Broad, in the 1837 Philadelphia directory. He was a contemporary of W. D. Rapp the silversmith (1828-50). Neither Landis nor Nye have been traced, but Nye's stamp also appears on an 1842 Large cent, so it likely was stamped later on the Rees piece.

We have withheld the Rees attribution to the Hard Times era from our catalog for some eight years, waiting to see whether any Rees stamp appeared on a post — 1838 host coin. In those years — years of intense scrutiny by hundreds of collectors into counterstamped coins — no host coin has surfaced dated later than 1838, though some 80 Rees pieces have now been identified.

Dr. Brunk reports the discovery of an 1830's patent medicine bottle labeled REES REMEDY FOR PILES, in curved format as on some of the Rees stamps. No connection has yet been made. The name Rees does not appear in our extensive computerized file of 19th century "medicines."

Rees must be one of the more prolific counterstampers of the Hard Times era, rivaling Houck's Panacea of Baltimore. While many more pieces are probably awaiting discovery, some 80 are reported already.

S & D
(Shaw & Dunlevy)

SILVER, 32.5MM

HT #	Rarity	Year	VG	F	VF	EF
416	R8	(1833)	—	—	400.	—

S & D in relief within toothed rectangular depression ctsp on U.S. 1806 or 1814 Bust half dollar. (Duffield 1442; Brunk 35433)

SILVER, 40MM

HT #	Rarity	Year	VG	F	VF	EF
416A	R9	(1833)	—	—	400.	—

Similar ctsp on U.S. 1801 Bust silver dollar.

Shaw & Dunlevy were silversmiths in Philadelphia about 1833. Edward G. Shaw had started the firm about 1825; Robert Dunlevy Jr. was admitted about 1831. In 1833 they were located at 7 Lodge Road (Alley).

A sea captain named Robert Dunlevy appears in the 1819 directory at Bird's Alley. In the 1823 volume he is located at Federal near 2nd St. This may be the father of the silversmith.

The 1833 directory lists Robert Dunlevy Jr., silversmith, at Lodge Alley. The 1837 directory places him at 7 Lodge Alley.

SMITH & BROTHERS

BRASS, 27MM, REEDED EDGE

HT #	Rarity	Year	VG	F	VF	Unc
417	R4	(1837)	30.00	50.00	75.00	350.

Anvil at center, 188 on it. MARKET above. STREET below. All within roped central circle. Outside circle: SMITH & BROTHERS / * PHILADELPHIA *. Rv: .IMPORTERS & DEALERS. / HARDWARE / AND (on saw blade) / CUTLERY / IN FOREIGN & DOMESTIC. Plain edge. (Wright 996)

SILVERED BRASS, 27MM

HT #	Rarity	Year	VG	F	VF	Unc
417A	R5	(1837)	30.00	75.00	125.	350.

Clifford and Cornelius Smith appear at 188 High (Market) 1836-44.

In 1832-33 Clifford Smith, merchant, was at 19 No. Front St. and Cornelius S. Smith, merchant, at Spruce above 12th. During 1844 Cornelius S. Smith left the partnership and became a bookseller at 3rd and Mulberry.

SNYDER & SHANKLAND

COPPER, 33MM, PLAIN EDGE

HT #	Rarity	Year	VG	F	VF	Unc
A417	R7	(1840-44)	200.	450.	900.	3000.

Standing Cupid drawing his bow right, at upper center, SNYDER & SHANKLAND above. Below: DRAPERS & TAILORS / 102 SOUTH FIFTH STREET / CORNER OF POWELL ST. / PHILADA. Rv: CONSTANTLY ON HAND / AN / ASSORTMENT / OF / FASHIONABLE CLOTH /CASSIMERES VESTINGS / &C. / WHICH WILL BE MADE / TO ORDER ON / REASONABLE TERMS. (Miller Pa 483)

BRASS, 33MM, PLAIN EDGE

HT #	Rarity	Year	VG	F	EF	Unc
B417	R7	(1840-44)	100.	300.	500.	1000.

As last. (Miller Pa 484)

WHITE METAL, 33MM, PLAIN EDGE

HT #	Rarity	Year	VG	F	EF	Unc
C417	R8	(1840-44)	—	—	2000.	3000.

As last. (Wright 1013; Miller Pa 485)

George A. Snyder and John R. Shankland were in business only 1840 to 1844. Thus these are Hard Times tokens and are removed from our *U.S. Merchant Tokens 1845-1860* volume. These attributions are due to the inquiries of H. Joseph Levine.

The Snyder & Shankland pieces have enjoyed some excellent auction records in recent years. The copper specimen in EF fetched a remarkable $3,190 in the PCAC Middendorf sale (lot 117) in Dec. 1990.

Three white metal specimens enjoyed mixed results recently. An EF in the PCAC Landmark II sale in June 1990 (lot 35) realized $1,900, yet in the 1989 Gil Steinberg sale another in EF (lot 575) fetched only $110. More recently another EF made $1,700 in the PCAC Gold Medal sale of Dec. 1991 (lot 032).

SPAYD & BELL

HT #	Rarity	Year	Metal	Size	VG	F	VF	EF
E417	R9	(1830's)	Silver	41mm	—	—	800.	—

SPAYD & BELL / PHILADA in relief in two separate rect. depressions with crenellated edges, ctsp on Spanish-American counterfeit 1790 8-reales. (Van Ormer sale 2845; Brunk 37615)

Spayd & Bell manufactured wooden planes in the 1830's, according to *American Wooden Planes and Their Marks* by Emil and Marty Pollak, pg. 269. Q. David Bowers also located a teaspoon shank with the same impression as above, indicating that the firm may also have been distributors of silverware made by others. This piece realized $120 in the Van Ormer sale, before it was attributed; as an HT piece it assumes greater significance.

SPERING, MIXSELL & INNES

HT #	Rarity	Year	Metal	Size	VG	F	VF	Unc
418	R4	(1838-40)	Brass	28mm	40.00	50.00	70.00	300.
418A	R5	(1838-40)	S/Brass	28mm	50.00	60.00	85.00	300.

This is the same address as Spering Good & Co. Directory evidence is lacking to pinpoint dates on this issuer, but there is room for deduction. In the 1837 Philadelphia directory there appear these two listings:

Spering (William), Innes (Francis) & Co., 138 Market St.

Mixsell (E.B.), Wilson & Co., 206 Market St.

Apparently the two firms merged in the 1838-1840 period. Spering, Mixsell & Co. were in business as early as 1832.

SPERING, GOOD & CO.

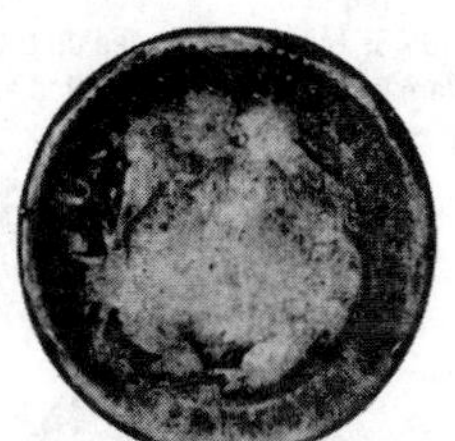

BRASS, 33MM

HT #	Rarity	Year	VG	F	VF	Unc
419	R6	(1841-43) Plain edge	70.00	110.	200.	400.
		SILVERED BRASS, 33MM				
419A	R5	(1841-43) Crudely reeded edge	—	80.00	125.	250.

Spering, Good & Co. appear in the directories from 1841 on, to at least 1848. William Spering was the senior partner. This firm evidently succeeded Spering, Mixsell & Innes about 1841. HT 419 was Wright 1026.

THIBAULT & BROS.

HT #	Rarity	Year	VG	F	VF	Unc.
420	R8	(1829-36) Ctsp on 1816 U.S. Cent (Brunk 39713)	—	—	900.	—
420A	R8	(1829-36) Ctsp on 1817 U.S. Cent	—	—	900.	—

Thibault Bros. were wholesale and retail jewelers and silversmiths on the southeast corner of Fifth and Chestnut Streets 1829-1836 only. The counterstamp reads THIBAULT & / PHILADA / BROS in relief and within oval depression, 15 by 6.5 millimeters. Duffield 1423. One reported specimen was in the Lionel Rudduck collection.

These were Francis Thibault (active at least 1780-1807), Felix Thibault (1807-1837) and Frederick Thibault (1807-1833). The firm had been Thibault & Co. from 1797, then Thibault & Brothers from 1810 on.

In 1832-33 the firm was located at 150 Chestnut St. The firm had disappeared when the 1844 Philadelphia directory was published.

JOHN THORNE

HT #	Rarity	Year	Metal	Size	VG	VF	EF	Unc
A420	R9	(1837-41)	GS	19mm	—	2500.	—	—

Eagle displayed, head right, JO THORNE (recent article in Bowers & Merena Rare Coin Review)

HT #	Rarity	Year	Metal	Size	VG	VF	EF	Unc
B420	R9	(1837-41)	GS	19mm	—	2500.	—	—

JOHN THORNE (Maverick Z95 in Rulau's U.S. Merchant Tokens 1845-1860)

C.W.

HT #	Rarity	Year	Metal	Size	VG	VF	EF	Unc
E420	R7	(ca 1842)	GS	18mm	—	500.	1000.	—

Plow right, initials C W above, eagle displayed with head turned right at top. Around all is ornate border. Rv: Blank. (Garrett 1905; Baker T-505; ex-W. W. C. Wilson sale; Krause coll.)

HT E420 had long been thought to be associated with George Washington. Steve Tanenbaum believes the piece is reposing in a more suitable venue in this volume.

WARD

HT #	Rarity	Date	Metal	Size	VG	F	VF	EF
G420	R8	(1838039)	Copper	29mm	60.00	—	90.00	—

WARD ctsp on U.S. 1816 or 1838 Large cent. (Larry Laevens coll.)

HT #	Rarity	Date	Metal	Size	VG	F	VF	EF
H420	R9	(1838-39)	Silver	39mm	—	—	150.	—

Similar ctsp on Spanish-American 1799 8-reales.

HT #	Rarity	Date	Metal	Size	VG	F	VF	EF
J420	R9	(1838-39)	Copper	29mm	—	—	150.	—

WARD / 67 MARKET ST. ctsp on U.S. 1807 Large cent.

John Ward was a silversmith located at 67 Market St. 1803 to 1839.

JAMES WATSON

BRASS, 27MM, REEDED EDGE

HT #	Rarity	Year	VG	F	VF	Unc
421	R4	(1835)	30.00	45.00	75.00	300.

Anvil at center, numeral 11 on it. * NORTH FOURTH * above, STREET below. All within beaded circle. Outside circle: JAMES WATSON / (leaf) PHILADELPHIA (leaf). Rv: * IMPORTERS & DEALERS * / HARDWARE / AND (on saw) / CUTLERY / IN FOREIGN & DOMESTIC. Plain edge. (Wright 1208)

GILT BRASS, 27MM, REEDED EDGE

HT #	Rarity	Year	VG	F	VF	Unc
421A	R5	(1835)	—	45.00	90.00	350.

As 384.

GILT BRASS, 27MM, REEDED EDGE

HT #	Rarity	Year	VG	F	VF	Unc
422	R5	(1835)	—	55.00	90.00	350.

Similar to 384, but from different die.

Scovill Mfg. Co., Waterbury, Conn., received an order for "gilt counters" from James Watson on March 2, 1835. HT 421 and 421A were struck in response to this order. HT 422 may have been struck somewhat later.

The firm was in business until 1839.

W. H. WHITE & CO.

Philadelphia, Pa.

HT #	Rarity	Year	Metal	Size	VG	FF	VF	Unc
423	R6	(1835-37)	Copper	26mm	50.00	150.	300.	750.

Watch within a circle. Around: IMPORTERS OF WATCHES, JEWELRY, & C. Rv: W. H. WHITE & CO. / 129 / MARKET ST. / PHILADA / W. H. WHITE - J. M. HARPER. (Wright 1725; Miller Pa 574)

William H. White was active as a silversmith, jeweler and importer in Philadelphia 1822-1838. William H. White succeeded H. White & Son (1818-22) in the latter year. In 1835 he admitted Benjamin H. Smith as a partner and the firm became W. H. White & Co.

In 1838 the firm became B. H. Smith & Co. (Benjamin H. Smith, William K. Smith and William H. White). The Smith firm seems to have disappeared after 1838. It cannot be traced in the 1844 directory.

W. H. White died in 1859.

This very rare early store card is now admitted as a legitimate Hard Times token and is removed from our *U.S. Merchant Tokens 1845-1860* (3rd edition).

E. GILLIAM

Pittsburgh, Pa.

HT #	Rarity	Year	Metal	Size	VG	F	VF	EF
424	R9	(1836-40)	Copper	29mm	—	—	50.00	—

E. GILLIAM ctsp on U.S. 1836 Large cent. (Brunk 16147)

According to Britten (see Bibliography), Gilliam was a clockmaker in Pittsburgh in the 1830's. This needs verification through other sources.

RHODE ISLAND

G. G. CLARK

Providence, R.I.

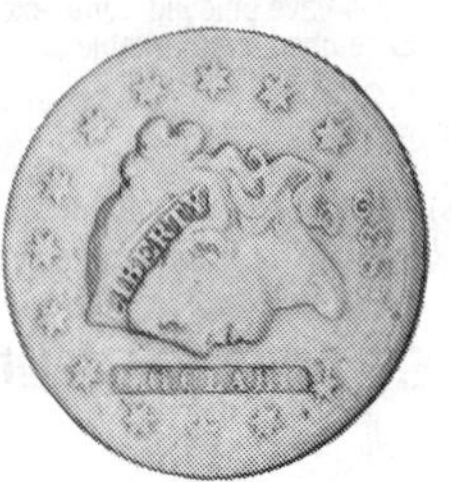

HT #	Rarity	Year	Metal	Size	VG	F	VF	EF
A424	R8	(1833-37)	Copper	29mm	175.	—	300.	—

G. G. CLARK in relief within rectangular depression ctsp on U.S. Large cent. (Rulau/ USMT Z4J; Brunk 7980) Dates examined: 1803, 1832.

George G. Clark began trade as a silversmith with Jabez Gorham 1813-18. Together with Lorenzo D. Anthony, he organized Clark & Anthony, listed in directories 1824-32 and 1836-37. Clark is listed alone 1844-68.

The stamp on the Large cents is an exact match with the teaspoon hallmark given in Louise Belden's *Marks of American Silversmiths*, page 108.

We now place these pieces squarely in the Hard Times period, standing alone from their time frame of issuance, and also as the token precursors of the Clark & Anthony HTT issues. Previously they were cataloged as mavericks in our *U.S. Merchants Tokens 1845-1860.*

For an earlier Clark counterstamp, see Rulau-E RI49) in Early American Tokens (3rd edition).

CLARK & ANTHONY

HT #	Rarity	Year	Metal	Size	VG	F	VF	Unc
425	R1	1835	Copper	28.5mm	5.00	10.00	15.00	150.

HT #	Rarity	Year	Metal	Size	VG	F	VF	EF
426	R9	(1824-33)	Copper	29mm	—	—	200.	—

Six different silversmiths' hallmarks impressed on U.S. 1803 Large cent, viz: (Donald Partrick coll.)

CLARK & ANTHONY (relief, in rect. depression)
P. MILLER (relief, in rect. depression)
F. RICHMOND (relief, in rect. depression)
E.W. MAXCY (relief, in rect. depression)
G.G. CLARK (relief, in rect. depression)
F. MILLER / PURE COIN (relief, in rect. depression)

Clark & Anthony were manufacturing jewelers in Providence, 1824-1837 or later. They issued Low. 94. (In 1790 Anthony had been located in New York City).

Pardon Miller was a Philadelphia silversmith ca. 1824-52.

Franklin Richmond was a Providence silversmith 1824-52.

E.W. Maxcy has not yet been identified.

George G. Clark was a Providence silversmith ca. 1813-1868.

The F. Miller has not been identified.

The "crossover" date of all these hallmarks seems to be about 1824-33, but the coin has been included with the HTT period because of the Clark & Anthony connection.

W.A. HANDY

HT #	Rarity	Year	Metal	Size	F	VF	EF	Unc
427	R1	1834	Copper	28.5mm	10.00	15.00	80.00	250.

EPHRAIM A. HATHAWAY

HT #	Rarity	Year	Metal	Size	F	VF	EF	Unc
428	R1	1833	Copper	28.5mm	10.00	20.00	40.00	200.
428A	R3	1833	S/Cop	28.5mm	—	25.00	40.00	250.

HT #	Rarity	Year	Metal	Size	F	VF	EF	Unc
428B	R8	1833	Copper	28.5mm	—	—	250.	—

Counterstamped with fireplace shovel on one side and spoon on other side. There are 2 pieces known.

P. MILLER
Providence, R.I.

HT #	Rarity	Year	Metal	Size	VG	F	VF	EF
429	R9	(?)	Copper	29mm	—	—	150.	—
		P. MILLER in relief within rect. depression ctsp on U.S. 1803 Large cent. (Brunk 27850)						
429A	R9	(?)	Copper	29mm	—	—	200.	—
		Similar ctsp on 1794 Talbot Allum & Lee cent.						

Pardon Miller was a Providence silversmith circa 1824-1852, according to Louise Belden. Also see HT number 426 under Clark & Anthony above.

Miller may have been an Early American rather than a Hard Times issuer, possibly in the 1824-33 period.

SOUTH CAROLINA

R.L. BAKER
Charleston, S.C.

HT #	Rarity	Year	Metal	Size	VG	F	EF	Unc
430	R6	1837	GS	19mm	900.	1500.	3600.	4500.
		An AU specimen of HT 430 fetched $3630 in the 1989 Gil Steinberg sale.						
430A	R9	1837	Copper	19mm	—	—	—	Rare

SLAVE TAGS
Charleston, S.C.

HT #	Rarity	Occupation on Badge	Fine	EF
500	R5	SERVANT 1800-1863	2000.	3200.
501	R5	PORTER 1815-1863	2000.	4000.
502	R8	CARPENTER 1812-1813	Rare	
503	R7	MECHANIC 1800-1864	3000.	12,100.
504	R8	FRUITERER 1814-1821	3500.	10,450.
505	R8	FISHER 1812	3500.	10,000.
506	R9	COOK	—	Rare
	—	B C (Bread Carter)	None now known	
	—	C C (Dog Trainer)	None now known	
510	R9	SEAMSTRESS	—	Rare

SLAVE TAGS
Charleston Neck, S.C.

HT #	Rarity	Occupation on Badge	Fine	EF
515	R8	SERVANT 1849	Ex. Rare	—
		(One piece was lot 1427 in the June 1917 Elder sale and one appeared in the Kirtley price list of Summer 1993.)		

NOTE: Dates given following occupation in the catalog above are date ranges of known specimens in public or private collections. Prices above $4000 are based on actual auction records.

Charleston was the principal slave mart in the South prior to the Civil War. Metal tags worn by slaves hired out by their owners to perform outside work for other employers are typically similar to the illustrations above (courtesy Rich Hartzog) — uniface copper tags in square; round; octagonal; irregular, or crescent shapes, the most frequently seen being square, arranged diagonally into diamond-shape.

Charleston city officials ordered slave artisans to wear badges in 1751 and extended the requirement to slave vendors of fruits and vegetables in 1783. Free blacks were also required to wear a badge at all times. These practices ended in 1790. *However, no badges dated 1751-1790 are known today!*

A Charleston ordinance of 1800 reinstituted the practice of requiring the wear of slave hire badges. Such badges had to be purchased annually for a fee ($2 for Servants, $7 for Mechanic, for example). The highest control number known on a badge is 5081, dated 1821 (in South Carolina State Museum). Badges are known in collections dated from 1800 through 1864; an 1865 has been reported but not verified.

Each badge required stamps labeled CHARLESTON (always in an upward arc scroll); date; occupation; and control number. The first three stamps are in relief within scroll-shaped or rectangular depressions, the latter incused. In some cases the word No. in relief preceeds the control number, and unnumbered badges are known. In a Bowers & Merena sale in 1990, an 1812 Servant badge bore an engraved number.

It is estimated Charleston had 15,354 slaves in 1830 and 14,673 in 1840. From 12 to 30 percent of Charleston's urban slave population may have been engaged in slavery for hire at any one time. Badge numbers apparently were issued sequentially each year.

Only about 100 slave tags are known to have survived — about 60 in museums and 40 in private hands. The Charleston Museum has 36, the ANS has 7, and a few are in the Winterthur, Smithsonian and South Carolina State museums

Until recently these pieces sold for $1000-$1200 in Fine through $2000-$3000 in EF. But the 14-piece John J. Ford collection sold by Stack's Inc. on Sept. 9, 1993 cracked this structure. The Ford pieces commanded prices (including 10% buyer fee) of $2310 (1836 Porter, VF) to $12,100 (1850 Mechanic, about VF), with a surprising $10,450 (1817 Fruiterer, EF) and $8259 (1811 Servant, EF). This sale, massively advertised and competently cataloged, probably exceeded actual resale values, though pricing on such rarities is always affected by recent public auctions.

Though slave tag reverses are blank, there are a few exceptions. The hallmark LAFAR in relief within rectangular depression appears on some badges dated 1805-1826, standing for their maker, Charleston silversmith John Joseph Lafar, active 1805-1849. One round 1802 Servant badge bears the hallmark C. PRINCE in relief; Prince has not been identified.

The 1800 badges are marked ATMAR for Ralph Atmar, Jr. working 1793-1803.

A few badges bear stamps 1862 or 1863 on reverse, with the earlier date on obverse being defaced. This was a wartime expedient.

Slave badges cover the EAT, HTT and USMT periods, but for convenience have been grouped together here under the Hard Times section.

Credit for research on the slave tags is due to Rich Hartzog, Michael Hodder, Stack's Inc. and the Charleston Museum staff.

TENNESSEE

KOHN DARON & CO.
Memphis, Tenn.

BRASS, 27MM, PLAIN EDGE

HT #	Rarity	Year	VG	F	EF	Unc
431	R7	(1835)	100.	250.	500.	800.

Large 4-petaled ornament at center, wavy rule above and below - all within beaded central circle. Around: KOHN DARON & CO above. Laurel and oak wreath below. Rv: Within open-top oak wreath: GOOD / FOR / ONE / LOAD. (Miller Tenn 28)

BRASS, 27MM, REEDED EDGE

HT #	Rarity	Year	VG	F	EF	Unc
431A	R8	(1835)	—	350.	550.	850.

As last. (Zeddies coll.; Miller Tenn 28A; PCAC June 1991 sale, lot 24)

Scovill Mfg. Co., Waterbury, Conn., correspondence dated March 30, 1835, refers to "brass medals (like J. A. Merle & Co. of New Orleans) one side Kohn Daron & Co. — other, Good For One Load."

This series of tokens is now properly positioned as Hard Times issue, thanks to research by H. Joseph Levine.

TEXAS

2 BITS TEXAS

SILVER, 27MM

HT #	Rarity	Year		VG	F	VF	EF
F432	—	1842	—	—	10.00	—	

2 / BITS / TEXAS ctsp on reverse of Mexico Republic 2-reales of 1830's, date worn off. 1842 ctsp on obverse of coin. (R. Byron White coll.)

This is a fantasy concoction made to sell to collectors. It was made by a different hand than the two concoctions listed by Dr. Gregory Brunk which read, respectively: TEXAS / 4 BITS and TEXAS / 8 BITS. Brunk opines that these and the similar LOUISIANA concoctions were made as early as 1930 to gull unsuspecting collectors.

White's 1842-dated concoction may have been produced earlier.

VERMONT

GUSTIN & BLAKE
Chelsea, Vt.

HT #	Rarity	Year	Metal	Size	G	VG	F	VF
433	R5	1835	Copper	28.5mm	100.	350.	800.	1000.

HT #	Rarity	Year			G	VG	F	VF
434	R5	1835 Retouched Rev			100.	350.	800.	1000.
434A	R7	1835 Silvered Copper			—	—	1500.	2000.

Gustin & Blake comprised Sebre Gustin, born in Chelsea, Vermont, Jan. 18, 1808 and Amos S. Blake, born in Brookfield, Vermont, Jan. 18, 1812. They were not associated long in business, Blake removing to Waterbury, Conn. to manufacture percussion caps for the government, among other things. Blake was considered wealthy when he retired.

Gustin continued the Chelsea hardware business for several years, later becoming a dentist and remaining in that practice until his death, Sept. 7, 1883. Sarah Gustin, his daughter, lived in the old family mansion before 1905 when Low interviewed her; she had in her possession the dies from which these tokens were struck.

C.C. CLARK
Windsor, Vermont

COPPER, 29MM, PLAIN EDGE

HT #	Rarity	Year	VG	F	VF	Unc
435	R9	1841 Ctsp on 1788 Mass. cent	—	—	400.	—

The countermark on a 1788 Massachusetts cent reads: C.C. CLARK 1841. (Duffield 1395; Brunk 7900)

HT #	Rarity	Year	VG	F	VF	Unc
436	R6	(1842) Ctsp on Starbuck token. (Brunk 7820)	—	250.	—	—

The countermark on Low 284 reads: CLARK.

HT #	Rarity	Year	VG	F	VF	Unc
436A	R9	(1842) Ctsp on U.S. 1828 half cent	—	—	250.	—

The counterstamp reads: CLARK.

HT #	Rarity	Year	VG	F	VF	Unc
437	R8	(1842) Ctsp on U.S. 1825 or 1842 Large cent	—	250.	—	—

The countermark reads: C.C. CLARK.

SILVER, 32MM, CORDED EDGE

437A	R9	(1842) Ctsp on Bolivia 1830 4-Sueldos	—	—	300.	—

The countermark reads: C.C. CLARK. (Robert Leonard collection; Brunk 7890)

437B	R9	(1842) Ctsp on German thaler	—	400.	—	—

(Tanenbaum coll.)

Carlos C. Clark was a maker of flintlock and percussion rifles at Windsor, Vermont from 1832 to 1846. A number of New England gunsmiths countermarked coins for use as advertising tokens, but most did this later, in the era between the Hard Times period and the Civil War, or after the Civil War.

Clark's counterstamping, probably for advertising purposes, continued long after the Hard Times period. Dated counterstamps of his are known as late as 1879, and these will appear in *U.S. Merchant Tokens 1845-1860.*

According to A. Merwin Carey, *American Firearms Makers*, (1953), Clark was a self-employed gunsmith who made flintlock and percussion rifles 1832-46. It is possible '1832' is in error in Carey and 1841 is his actual starting date in business. From 1846 to 1856 he was employed by Robbins & Lawrence, gunmakers. Then 1856-59 he again was self-employed.

In 1859 he moved from Windsor, Vt. to Nashua, N.H., and in 1863 to Manchester, N.H., but he kept a branch business in Windsor, Vt. until 1868. He was in business at least until 1879.

The date '1841' on HT 435 could possibly refer to 'Model 1841', a rifle Clark made for the U.S. government as an employee of R&L in 1849, but since Clark dated many later counterstamps with dates such as 1842, 1859, 1864 and 1879 for commemorative purposes, we believe that 1841 was the issue date.

VIRGINIA

J. A. KLEIN
Leesburg, Va.

HT #	Rarity	Year	Metal	Size	VG	F	VF	EF
439	R9	(1833-37)	Copper	29mm	—	—	1000.	—

J. A. KLEIN / LEESBURG in relief within two parallel toothed rectangular depressions ctsp on U.S. 1826 Large cent. (Brunk 23118)

John A. Klein was a silversmith in business in Leesburg during the 1833-1837 period, according to references on American silversmiths. Not much of his work is known, but a surviving silver sauce ladle bears his signature and the date 1835. Leesburg is a small town in Loudon County, Virginia.

This Hard Times discovery piece was first reported in the June 1989 issue of *TAMS Journal* (page 103) by David E. Schenkman, who cited "The Silversmiths of Loudon County, Virginia" by Robert A. Green, appearing in the July 1970 issue of *Silver-Rama.*

S.N. BOTSFORD
Norfolk, Va.

HT #	Rarity	Year	Metal	Size	VG	F	VF	Unc
440	R4	(1837)	Copper	27.5mm	20.00	35.00	125.	400.
440A	R5	(1837)	Brass	27.5mm	25.00	100.	300.	500.

Botsford also issued tokens in the Merchant Token era from Bristol, Conn. See Miller Conn 2 and 3 from the 1840's period in *U.S. Merchant Tokens 1845-1860.*

BECK'S PUBLIC BATHS
Richmond, Va.

HT #	Rarity	Year	Metal	Size	VG	F	VF	Unc
441	R3	(1832-44)	Copper	28mm	40.00	90.00	325.	500.
441A	R8	(1832-44)	WM	28mm	—	—	750.	1500.
441B	R8	(1832-44)	GS	28mm	—	—	750.	1500.

On this intriguing early token a nude female is seated, testing the bath waters. The piece was listed by Dr. Wright as number 72.

Charles Beck is recorded in the October 1832 Richmond City Deed Book as a confectioner who operated a public bath on the south side of Main Street, between 13th and 14th Streets. Local tax records reveal Beck operated the baths through the year 1844.

Most of the copper tokens found have seen a good deal of wear, indicating either their circulation as cents, or their use as admission checks for the public baths. The nude female was definitely a risque design in the second quarter of the 19th century Southland. Unc. copper tokens, and all tokens in white metal or German silver, are rare.

This token was discussed by David Schenkman in *The Numismatist* for May 1980.

UNCERTAIN LOCATION

C. AGNER

HT #	Rarity	Year	Metal	Size	VG	F	VF	EF
450	—	(?)	Silver	32.5mm	—	—	100.	—

C. AGNER (script) in relief within rect. depression ctsp on U.S. 1836 Capped Bust half dollar. (Van Ormer sale 2503; Brunk 420)

A. BRIGHAM

HT #	Rarity	Year	Metal	Size	VG	F	VF	EF
451	—	(?)	Copper	29mm	—	—	50.00	—

A. BRIGHAM in relief within rect. depression ctsp on U.S. 1837 Large cent. (Kovacs coll.; Brunk 5196)

C.L. BUTLER

HT #	Rarity	Year	Metal	Size	VG	F	VF	EF
452	—	(?)	Silver	32.5mm	—	—	100.	—

C. L. BUTLER ctsp on reverse of U.S. 1831 half dollar. (Krause coll.; Brunk 6285)

H.A. CORLISS

HT #	Rarity	Year	Metal	Size	VG	F	VF	EF
453	R8	(?)	Copper	29mm	—	—	50.00	—

H.A. CORLISS ctsp on obverse of U.S. 1832 Large cent. Same ctsp on reverse of the coin. Rarity 8. (Rulau coll.; Brunk 9620)

J. (Cannon)

SILVER

HT #	Rarity	Year	VG	F	VF	EF
A452	R9	(?)	60.00	—	100.	—
	J (Cannon right) ctsp on U.S. 1832 half dime. (Brunk 21230)					
B452	R9	(?)	60.00	—	100.	—
	Similar ctsp on U.S. 1835 dime.					
C452	R8	(?)	60.00	—	100.	—
	Similar ctsp on U.S. quarter. Dates examined. 1815, 1818, 1819.					
D452	R9	(?)	70.00	—	125.	—
	Similar ctsp on U.S. 1824 half dollar.					

The issuer's name may have been J. Cannon; he used a view of a cannon to depict it. Probably issued before 1838, by which time most of the host coins were out of circulation since they contained too much silver for the standard of 1836.

F.

HT #	Rarity	Year	Metal	Size	VG	F	F	EF
E452	—	(?)	Copper	28mm	—	—	15.00	—

Large serif-type capital F ctsp on 1841 Hard Times token, WEBSTER CREDIT CURRENT, Low 58. (Rulau coll.)

N.F.

HT #	Rarity	Year	Metal	Size	VG	F	F	EF
453	R8	(?)	Copper	29mm	—	—	25.00	—

N F (large) in relief within toothed rect. depression ctsp on U.S. 1833 Large cent. (PCAC Dec. 1990 sale, lot 641)

P. FANAN

HT #	Rarity	Year	Metal	Size	VG	F	VF	EF
455	R9	(?)	Silver	32.5mm	—	—	40.00	—

P. FANAN / TEQ ctsp on U.S. 1830 Bust half dollar. TEQ ctsp on reverse of the coin. (Frank Kovacs coll.; Brunk 13770)

G. FARRAR

HT #	Rarity	Year	VG	F	VF	Unc
456	R8	(1835) Ctsp. on 1835 Cent	—	—	85.00	—

The countermark shows G. FARRAR above a Liberty head, a rooster to left, hog running to right, and eagle on head — all on an 1835 U.S. cent. (Duffield 1399; Brunk 13835)

A.G.

HT #	Rarity	Year	Metal	Size	VG	F	F	EF
A458	R9	ND	Copper	29mm	—	—	50.00	—

Large A G (relief), in wide-toothed rectangular depression ctsp on U.S. 1807 Large cent. (Dr. Sol Taylor coll.)

This is not a mark of silversmith, pewterer or gunsmith. Pewterer Ashbil Griswold used an AG mark of totally different style.

J.B. HARDY

HT #	Rarity	Year	F	VF	EF	Unc
457	R8	1838 Ctsp. U.S. Cent	—	—	100.	—

The countermark on a U.S. 1818 Large cent reads: J.B. HARDY 1838. (Hallenbeck 8.503; Brunk 18205)

BEN T. HEALD

HT #	Rarity	Year	Metal	Size	VG	F	VF	EF
C458	R9	1837	Silver	40mm	—	600.	—	—

BEN T. HEALD, MARCH 25TH 1837 (star) ctsp. on U.S. 1799 silver dollar. (Brunk 18960; Krause coll., ex-Vlack))

An attribution to Philadelphia is uncertain. Heald is thought to have been a businessman, but the use of this large piece as a store card is doubtful. This was lot 81 in the H. Joseph Levine sale of May 30, 1981, bringing $425. It was last sold in Oct., 1993.

C.L.

HT #	Rarity	Year	Metal	Size	VG	F	VF	EF
458	—	(?)	Copper	23.5mm	—	—	25.00	—

C.L. in relief within large serrated, rectangular recessed cartouche, ctsp on U.S. 1828 Half cent. (Hallenbeck 3.003; Krause coll.)

C.P.L.

HT #	Rarity	Year	Metal	Size	VG	F	VF	EF
E458	R7	1837	Copper	29mm		—	20.00	—

C.P.L. ctsp. on obverse of an 1837-dated HT political token. (Stanley L. Steinberg 1981 sale.)

J. LYNE

HT #	Rarity	Year	Metal	Size	VG	F	VF	EF
459	R9	(?)	Copper	23mm	15.00	—	25.00	—

J. LYNE ctsp on U.S. 1828 Half cent. (Brunk 25410)

HT #	Rarity	Year	Metal	Size	VG	F	VF	EF
459A	R9	(?)	Copper	29mm	15.00	—	25.00	—

Similar ctsp on U.S. 1829 Large cent.

BRASS, 25MM, REEDED EDGE

HT #	Rarity	Year	Metal	Size	VG	F	VF	EF
459B	R9	(?)			25.00	—	40.00	—

Similar ctsp on Andrew Jackson 1828 campaign medalet, DeWitt AJACK 1824-1, Rulau-E Med 1.

BRASS, ---MM

HT #	Rarity	Year	Metal	Size	VG	F	VF	EF
459C	R9	(?)			15.00	—	25.00	—

Similar ctsp on Nuremberg, Germany New Year jeton, NEUE LHRE NEUES GLUCK / IETTON (blundered legend). (Brunk 25410EE)

With five host pieces from the late 1820's or earlier, it seems likely J. Lyne was active in the 1830's or 1840's. Tentative attribution.

I.E. NEWALL

HT #	Rarity	Year	Metal	Size	VG	F	VF	EF
A459	R9	1838	Copper	29mm	—	35.00	—	—

I. E. NEWALL / 1838 ctsp on U.S. 1838 Large cent. (PCAC Gold Medal sale, Dec. 1991; lot 535, where it fetched $28.) Tentative attribution.

The only known specimen was worn before stamping, so date 1838 may be commemorative rather than contemporary.

G. NEWCOMB

HT #	Rarity	Date	Metal	Size	VG	F	VF	EF
C459	R8	(?)	Copper	29mm	—	—	15.00	—

G. NEWCOMB ctsp three times on U.S. 1838 Large cent. (PCAC Dec. 1990 sale, lot 641; Brunk 29463)

B. O'NEILL

HT #	Rarity	Year	Metal	Size	VG	F	VF	EF
460	—	(?)	Copper	28.5mm	—	50.00	—	—

B. O'NEILL ctsp on reverse of Jackson / Donkey Hard Times token, Low 51 (1833), (Krause coll.; Brunk 30250)

M.P.

HT #	Rarity	Year	Metal	Size	VG	F	VF	EF
461	R7	(?)	GS	25mm	500.	1500.	2500.	3000.

MP monogram in relief within oval depression ctsp on reverse of an 1837 German silver 3-cent token of Dr. Lewis Feuchtwanger (HT 263). The ctsp is at top center or right center at 3 o'clock of the wreath, (B&M 1985 Kosoff sale, lot 4080; B&M Leidman sale 1986, lot 4550). About 10 pieces known. (Brunk 25505)

The stamp appears to be the hallmark of a silversmith, but the hallmark has not been published. The MP monogram is distinctive, the capital letters being sans serif and with one common leg - that being the right leg of the M and upright of the P (This is said to be "ligate").

The only MP hallmark appearing in the Kovel reference is MP (not ligate) within rectangle, belonging to New York City silversmith Matthew Petit, who is known to have been working about 1811. This is a possibility, but probably is too early to be considered. We think New York is the likeliest location, since Feuchtwanger's 3-cent pieces were made and circulated there.

One possibility:

Maltby Pelletreau, who worked 1815-40, of Erie Canal medal fame (Pelletreau, Bennett & Cooke, 1826).

C. C. PAIGE

HT #	Rarity	Year	Metal	Size	VG	F	VF	EF
461F	R9	(?)	Copper	28.5mm	—	—	35.00	—

C. C. PAIGE. ctsp on 1837 Hard Times token of the Liberty head/NOT ONE CENT type. (Rulau coll.; Brunk 30750)

PHOENIX HOUSE, B & H

HT #	Rarity	Year	Metal	Size	VG	F	VF	EF
462	R7	(1840's ?)	GS	14.4mm	—	—	400.	600.

* / PHOENIX / HOUSE / B & H / *. Rv: (Arc of 10 stars) / 5 / CENTS. Plain edge. (Rich Hartzog coll.)

This piece has every appearance of belonging in the late Hard Times era. It could be earlier.

W. POND

HT #	Rarity	Year	Metal	Size	F	VF	EF	Unc
463A	R9	1837	Copper	28mm	—	—	300.	—

W. POND (relief, in rect. depression) ctsp on1837 NOT ONE CENT Hard Times token.

S.S.B.

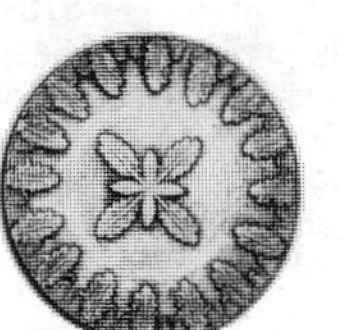

HT #	Rarity	Year	Metal	Size	VG	VF	EF	Unc
464	R6	1837	Brass	19mm	500.	1000.	1700.	3500.
464A	R9	1837 Ctsp YK			—	2400.	—	—

RUHL (?)

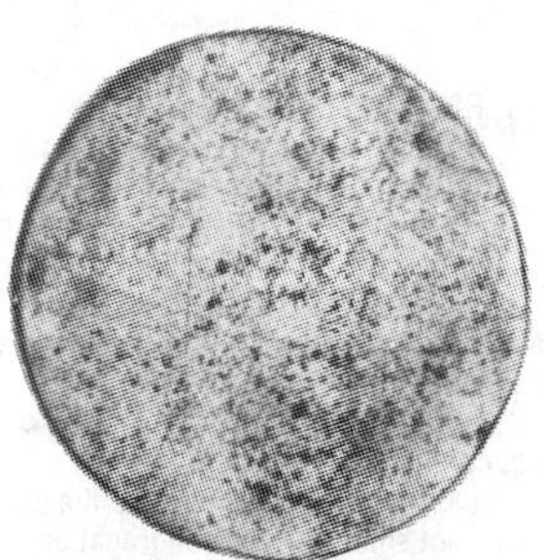

Illustration enlarged

HT #	Rarity	Year	Metal	Size	VG	F	VF	EF
A464	R9	ND	GS	18mm	—	60.00	—	—

(all incuse) NE. ... / (Eagle displayed, head turned left) / RUHL (last two letters uncertain). Plain Edge. (Dave Wilson coll.)

The upper legend might be NEW YORK. The only known specimen, first reported in Feb. 1992 is quite illegible due to erasure or wear.

In style, this piece is similar to the Wiman Coppersmith piece, Brunk 43840.

J.S.

HT #	Rarity	Year	Metal	Size	VG	F	VF	EF
C464	R9	(?)	Copper	29mm	—	35.00	—	—

J . S . incuse within oval outline, ctsp on U.S. 1816 Large cent. (Kenneth Hallenbeck coll.; HT 416)

This stamp was reported to be a hallmark of Joseph Shoemaker earlier. Comparison with known Shoemaker hallmarks makes this doubtful. Shoemaker was active as a silversmith in Philadelphia from about 1793 until his death in Sept. 1829 at age 65.

Thus it is being relocated from Pennsylvania to the uncertain locale section.

SEE DEUTERONOMY 23: 1.2!

HT #	Rarity	Year	VG	F	VF	EF
		COPPER, 23MM				
465	R8	(1834-38)	—	50.00	—	80.00

SEE DEUTERO- / NOMY 23: 1.2! ctsp on U.S. Half cent. Dates examined: 1834. (Van Ormer sae 2618; Brunk 11490)

COPPER, 29MM

HT #	Rarity	Year	VG	F	VF	EF
466	R7	(1834-38)	—	50.00	—	80.00

Similar ctsp on U.S. Large cent. Dates examined: 1831, 1833, 1843, 1851.

SILVER, 32.5MM

HT #	Rarity	Year	VG	F	VF	EF
467	R8	(1834-38)	—	60.00	—	90.00

Similar ctsp on U.S. Capped Bust half dollar. Dates examined: 1832, 1834.

SILVER 21MM

HT #	Rarity	Year	VG	F	VF	EF
467A	R9	(1834-38)	—	50.00	—	80.00

Similar ctsp on Spanish-American 1-real, date worn. (PCAC Dec. 1990 sale, lot 1164)

HT #	Rarity	Year	Metal	Size	VG	F	VF	EF
467B	R8	(1834-38)	Silver	27mm	—	60.00	—	90.00

Similar ctsp on Spanish-American 2-reales. Examined: 1778, 1794-NG. (Krueger Apr. 1991 sale, lot 1680)

The counterstamp is deep and clear and has been incused with a single punch. The Book of Deuteronomy, the fifth book of the Old Testament, sets forth the extensive laws for the Jews composed from the word of God by Moses. The passage cited is one of the Bible's less delicate — and less charitable — commandments. The standard King James version of the Bible states:

"He that is wounded in the stones, or hath his privy member cut off, shall not enter into the congregation of the Lord.

"A bastard shall not enter into the congregation of the Lord even to his tenth generation shall he not enter into the congregation of the Lord."

Just why this passage was chosen, and what viewpoint was being expressed by the counterstamper, may never be known at this distance, but we suspect shock value was a factor. The probability is that more of these counterstamped coins may be discovered and that some additional light may be shed.

The Rulau collection contains an 1831 cent with the Deuteronomy stamp, and an additional stamp in larger letters from a prepared punch: L. JEWELL. Taken alone, this might connect Jewell and the biblical passage, but the Jewell stamp alone has also been reported on cents of 1843 and 1851, proving that Mr. Jewell simply used cents for counterstamping without regard to what an earlier mutilater may have done.

The Deuteronomy citation may be connected with the religious fervor of the 1830's, which spawned among other things prohibition against alcoholic beverages — and sparked vitriolic responses from the wayward.

The oversize (32.5mm) half dollars were replaced in 1836 by smaller (31mm) half dollars containing less silver and the earlier pieces rapidly disappeared from circulation (though banks held them for many years afterward).

J.S. SIMMONS

HT #	Rarity	Year	Metal	Size	VG	F	VF	EF
468	R9	1844	Silver	25mm	—	—	45.00	—

Incused on planed-off obverse of a U.S. "no motto" quarter of about 1838-44 is: J.S. SIMMONS. / .-. / - AUG. / - 27. - / - 1844. - / * / * . 28 . * / * 72. *. Around rim is incused border of alternating dots and wavy dashes. Reeded edge. (Krause coll.)

JEREH. SMITH

HT#	Rarity	Year	Metal	Size	VG	F	VF	Unc
469	R9	1835	GS	20mm	—	500.	—	—

Five-petaled flower above date 1835, all within central circle. Around: JEREH SMITH. Rv: Large numeral 12. Only 1 piece reported.

Jereh = Jeremiah.

F. Z.

HT #	Rarity	Date	Metal	Size	VG	F	VF	EF
477	R8	(?)	Copper	23mm	—	—	65.00	—

(Cross) / F. Z. ctsp on U.S. Half cent. Examined: 1825, 1832. (PCAC July 1993 sale, lot 920; Brunk 13715)

20

HT #	Rarity	Year	Metal	Size	VG	F	VF	EF
480	R8	(?)	Copper	28mm	—	50.00	—	75.00

Numeral 20 ctsp above MINT on reverse of 1837 Hard Times token of 'Mint Drop' type, HT 61, Low 37. (PCAC Gold Medal sale, Dec. 1991, lot 005, where a part red AU specimen fetched $80). 2 specimens reported.

(Dagger)

HT #	Rarity	Year	Metal	Size	VG	F	VF	EF
516	R9	(?)	Copper	28.5mm	—	—	35.00	—

Dagger-like device ctsp on obverse (Lafayette side) of Walsh's General Store token, HT 217. (L. B. Fauver coll.)

HT #	Rarity	Year	Metal	Size	VG	F	VF	EF
517	R9	(?)	Copper	28.5mm	—	—	35.00	—

Similar ctsp on obverse (plow side) of Walsh's General Store token, HT 216. (L. B. Fauver coll.)

(Leaf)

HT #	Rarity	Year	Metal	Size	VG	F	VF	EF
515	R9	(?)	Copper	28.5mm	—	—	25.00	—

Three small leaf-shaped marks ctsp on reverse (Jackson side) of Running Boar token, HT 9. (L. B. Fauver coll.)

APPENDIX I

MISCELLANEOUS TOKENS AND MEDALS

Included in this appendix are tokens which do not belong in the body of the catalog, but which resemble genuine Hard Times pieces, or on which there is some question. The listings for Buchan, Eastern Railroad, Moss, Mullen, Peacock and Yale, and some Doremus issues, were included in the body of the catalog in the earlier editions of this book and thus have a rightful claim to continued collector exposure.

AMERICAN INSTITUTE
New York, N.Y.

GOLD, 28MM

HT #	Rarity	Year	F	VF	EF	Unc
M1	R5	(1833-60) LOVETT	—	300.	400.	600.
M2	—	FURST	—	—	500.	750.

Designed by Moritz Furst or Robert Lovett Sr., whose signatures FURST or LOVETT are in exergue on obverse, this is the award medal which served as a model for the Robinson and Robinson-Jones cards of Attleboro, Mass. The illustrated specimen, awarded in 1850, appeared in the 1981 NASCA sale of Hard Times tokens and related items. Weight is 16.63 grams.

E.R.R.
Boston, Mass.

(EASTERN RAILROAD)
BRASS, 22MM, PLAIN EDGE

HT #	Rarity	Year	VG	F	VF	EF
M9	R6	(1845-52) Check	100.	150.	200.	300.
		BRASS, 22MM, OCTAGONAL				
M10	R6	(1845-52) Up. Check	125.	200.	300.	500.
		WHITE METAL, 24MM				
M11	R8	(1845-52) Blank Rev.	—	—	—	Rare

NOTE: 377 may not exist.
Probably issued 1845-1852 period.

WM. J. MULLEN
New York, N.Y.

COPPER, 33MM

HT #	Rarity	Year	F	VF	EF	Unc
M17	R4	1835 Medallic	40.00	50.00	100.	300.

Bushnell in 1858 stated the dies for this piece were "cut by Lander in 1837." Later research has shown that Louisa Lander cut the dies in 1847 and the piece was struck by Charles Cushing Wright.

The latest of the three dates on the piece is 1835. The report by Miller of NY 616A, using the Mullen obverse portrait combined with a differing reverse date 1862 adds to the conclusion that this is not a Hard Times piece at all.

(See "The William J. Mullen Store Card" by R.J. Lindesmith, in the *Journal of the Token and Medal Society* for Dec. 1968.)

Louise Lander is unknown as a medalist except for M17. She had a solid reputation as a sculptor and left a large body of work. She had studied under Thomas Crawford. She was 21 when she executed the Mullen medal.

C.D. PEACOCK
Chicago, Il.

COPPER, 31MM, PLAIN EDGE

HT #	Rarity	Year	F	VF	EF	Unc
M19	R2	1837 Peacock Hd Rt, date inside circle	—	—	20.00	75.00
M20	R7	1837 Same, Silver	—	—	—	300.

HT #	Rarity	Year	F	VF	EF	Unc
M21	R2	1837 Head Rt, date in exergue	—	—	30.00	80.00
M22	R7	1837 Same, Silver	—	—	—	300.
		Specific gravity of M22 is 9.04.				

HT #	Rarity	Year	F	VF	EF	Unc
M23	R2	1837 Peacock Hd Lft	—	—	20.00	75.00

HT #	Rarity	Year	F	VF	EF	Unc
M24	R9	1837 Same, Silver	—	—	—	750.

NOTE: These are not Hard Times tokens, but were struck 1900-1906.

Cards M19-20 were issued by jeweler Charles Daniel Peacock with the date 1837, in the size and style of Hard Times tokens. Peacock's Jewelers (still in 1992 one of Chicago's foremost jewelry firms) was founded by Elijah Peacock (died 1889) in 1837 and C.D. Peacock, his son, died in 1903. C.D. Peacock Jr. became the firm's head on his father's death in 1903.

Numbers M19-20 were struck by Gorham Mfg. Co. in 1900 (for the Diamond Jubilee of the firm in 1897). 10,000 in copper, only 4 in silver.

Numbers M21-22 were struck by Gorham in 1902, 7,500 in copper and 4 in silver. All the Peacock tokens measure 31mm.

Number M23 was struck by Gorham with a new obverse die in 1906, in 10,000 specimens. One copy was struck in silver proof for the firm's president in 1906. Illustration of the silver piece by Joseph Schmidt. Silver piece is marked STERLING on edge and is 4mm thick!

None of the Peacock tokens are HT issues, but they cannot easily be separated from that series by collectors. C.D. Peacock had a numismatist's desire for nostalgia.

NOTES WITH DIRECT TIES TO TOKENS

CENTRE MARKET
New York, N.Y.

GOOD AT NIBLO'S GARDEN.
DUBOISE & BACON'S, 157 Broadway, ... for Music.
MIDDLETON'S, [illegible] Broadway, ... for Shoes.
MARSHALL'S, Broadway, corner of Canal street, ... for Dry Goods.
HOW'S, Broadway, corner of Howard street, ... for Bread.
GREENE'S, Broadway, corner of Howard street, ... for Books.
McCREADY'S, Broadway, corner of Grand street, ... for Drugs.
DRIGGS', Broadway, corner of Amity street, ... for Groceries.

HT #	Date	Denomination	Size	VF
N1	July 1, 1837	25 Cents	158 x 60 MM	300.

Only one specimen known.

NEW YORK JOINT STOCK EXCHANGE COMPANY

New York, N.Y.

HT #	Date	Denomination	Size	VF
N3	1837	12-1/2 Cents	158 x 75 MM	150.

HT #	Date	Denomination	Size	VF
N4	1837	25 Cents	167 x 75 MM	200.

HOWELL WORKS CO.

Allaire, N.J.

HT #	Date	Denomination	Size	VF
N5	18—	6-1/4 Cents	—	75.00
N5A	18—	12-1/2 Cents	—	75.00
N5B	18—	25 Cents	—	100.
N5C	18—	50 Cents	—	100.
N6	18—	$1	—	100.
N6A	18—	$2	—	125.
N6B	18—	Sheet of 8 notes	—	750.

BERGEN IRON WORKS
Lakewood, N.J.

HT #	Date	Denomination	Size	VF
N7	February, 1840	25 Cents	165 x 71 MM	600.
N7A	(believed to exist)	50 Cents	—	—
N7B	(believed to exist)	$1	—	—

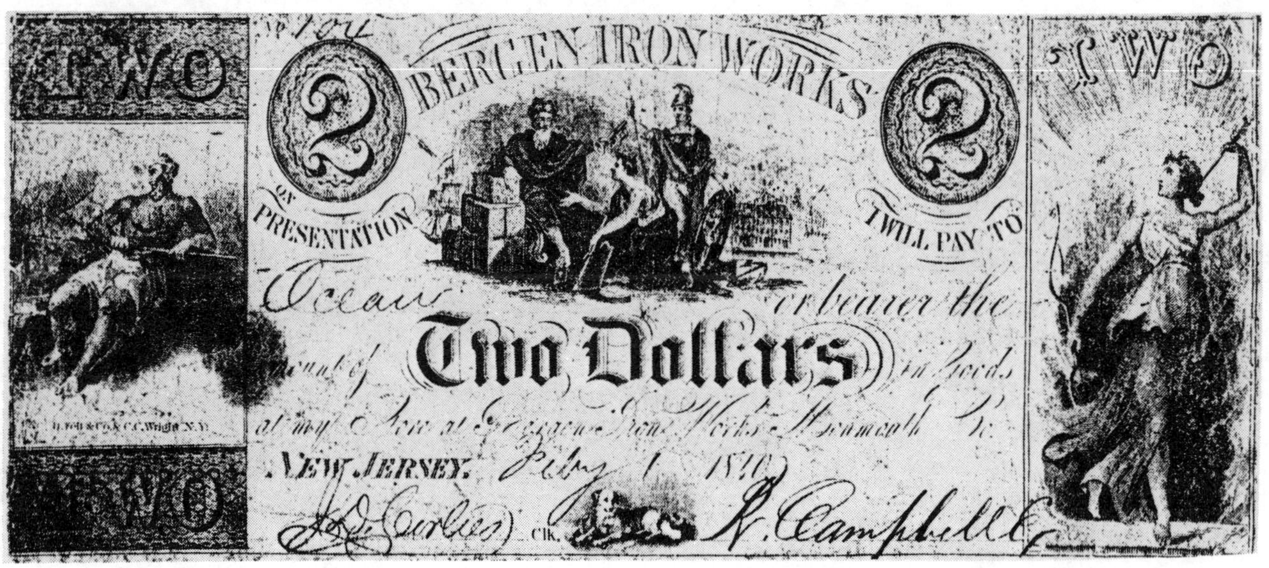

HT #	Date	Denomination	Size	VF
N7C	February, 1840	$2	171 x 71 MM	600.

HARD TIMES SATIRICAL NOTES

KITCHEN CABINET BANK

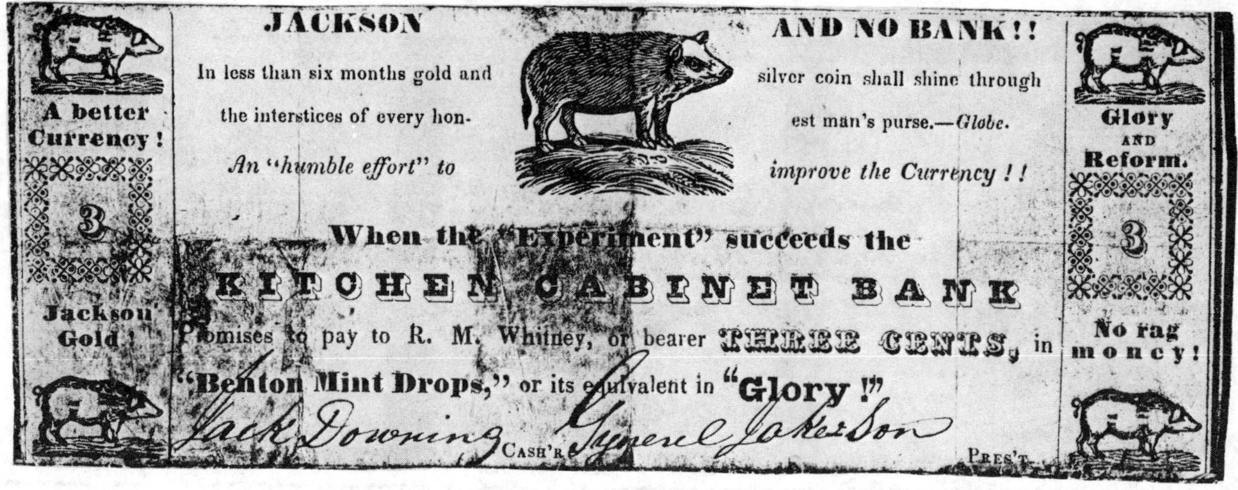

HT #	Date	Denomination	Size	VF
N9	ND	3 Cents	166 x 62 MM	1100.

SULPHUR PUMP, DROVERS' AND HOG BANKING INSTITUTION
Baltimore, Md.

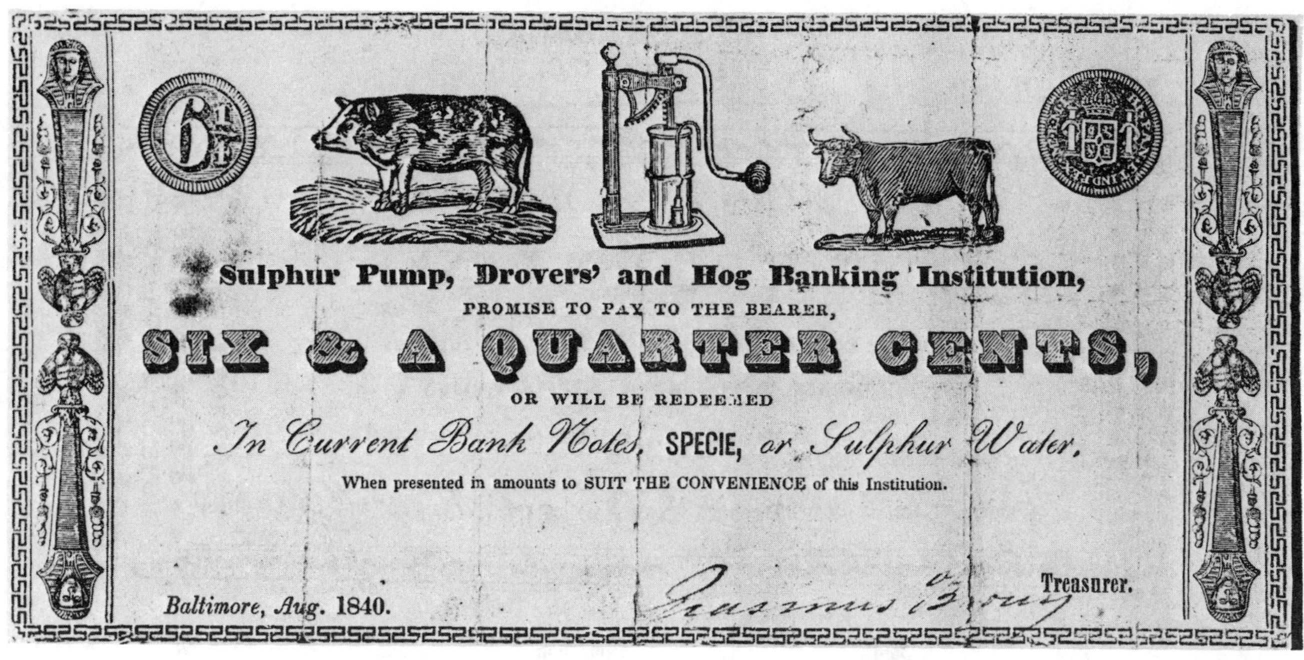

HT #	Date	Denomination	Size	VF
N10	August, 1840	61/4 Cents	176 x 82 MM	1100.

THE ELTONIAN KOMICK BANK
New York, N.Y.

HT #	Date	Denomination	Size	VF
N11	1837	6 Cents	189 x 95 MM	300.

Product of Oliver, printer, 28 Cribstone (?) St., N.Y. References on note are to Elton's Comic Almanac for 1838, and addresses 134 Division St. and 68 Chatham St. (Smithsonian Institution collection)

THE GLORY BANK
Washington, D.C.

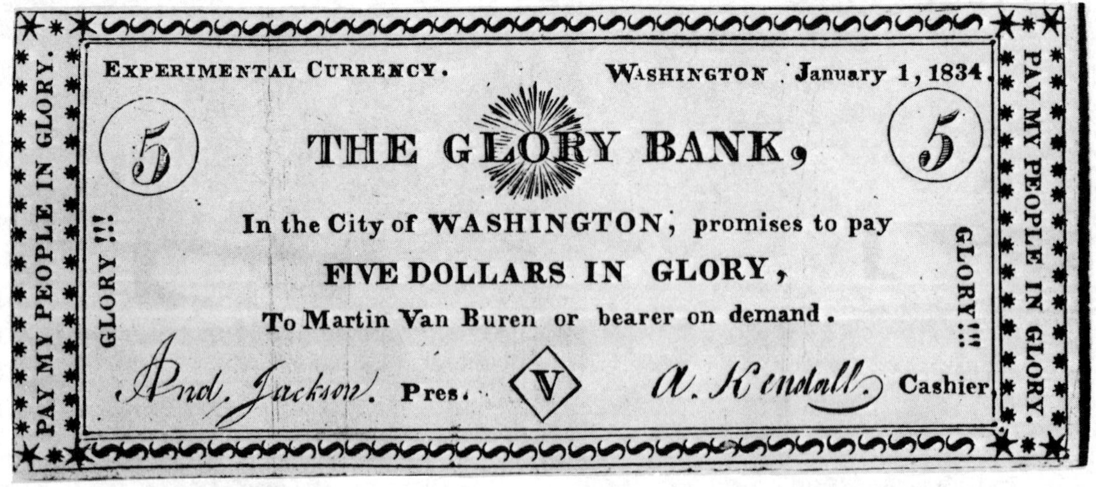

HT #	Date	Denomination	Size	VF
N13	January 1, 1834	$5	147 x 62 MM	800.

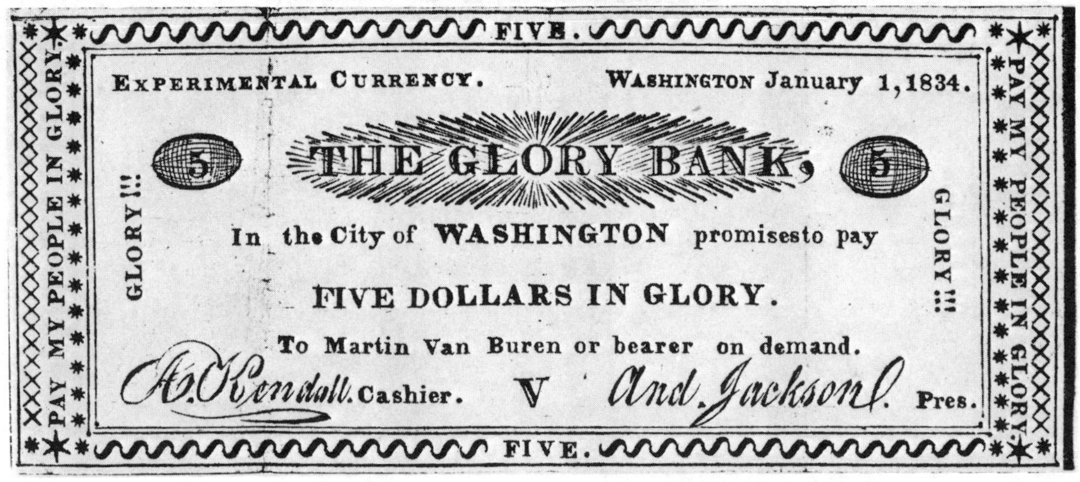

HT #	Date	Denomination	Size	VF
N14	January 1, 1834	$5	146 x 61 MM	800.

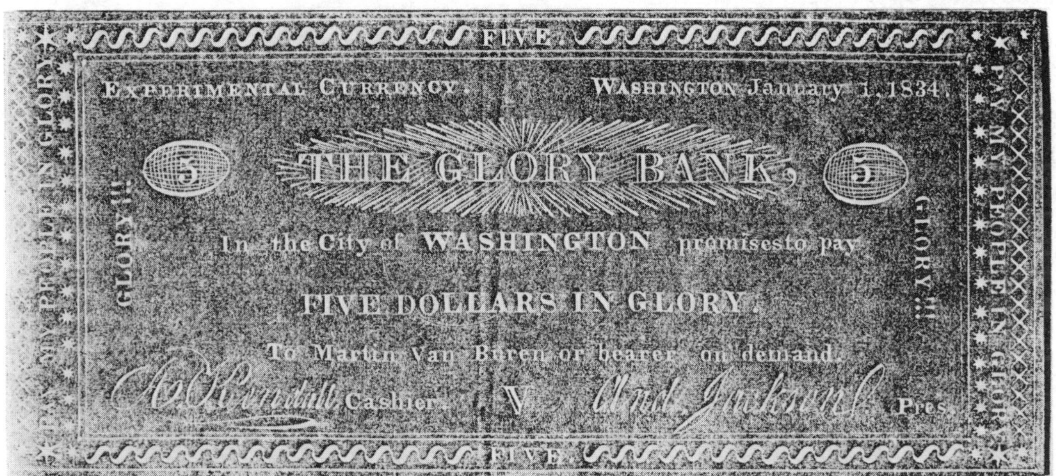

HT #	Date	Denomination	Size	VF
N15	January 1, 1834	$5	143 x 62MM	800.

FIVE No 1, FIVE

THE GLORY BANK,

In the City of Washington, promises to pay

FIVE DOLLARS IN GLORY,

to Martin Van Buren, or bearer, on demand.

Washington, January 1, 1834.

A. KENDALL, Cashier. 5 *A. JACKSON, President.*

JACKSON CURRENCY. PAY MY PEOPLE IN GLORY. V 5

PAY MY PEOPLE IN GLORY. V 5

HT #	Date	Denomination	Size	VF
N16	January 1, 1834	$5	122 x 62 MM	500.

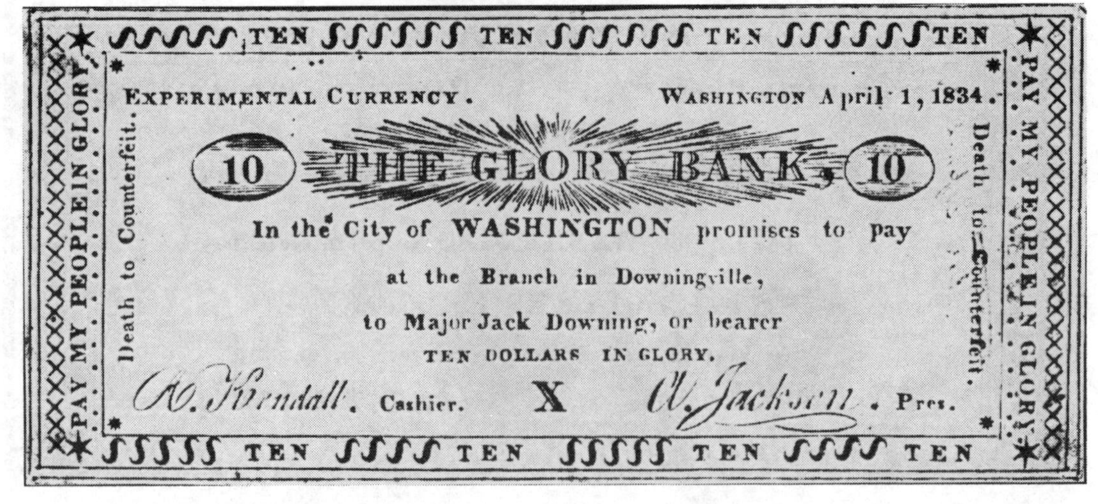

HT #	Date	Denomination	Size	VF
N16A	April 1, 1834	$10	144 x 62 MM	500.

No. A.
XX XX
Veto
PAY MY PEOPLE IN GLORY.
ARABIA.
THE GLORY BANK,
In the City of Washington, promises to pay TWENTY DOLLARS *in GLORY to Martin Van Buren, or Bearer, on demand.*
WASHINGTON, January 1, 1834.
A. JACKSON, Pres't.
A. KENDALL, Cashier.

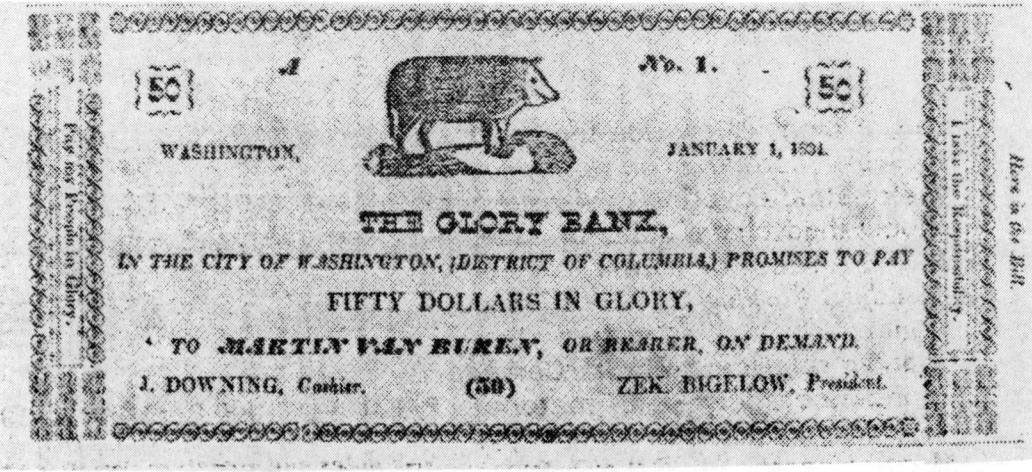

HT #	Date	Denomination	Size	VF
N16B	January 1, 1834	$20	124 x 58 MM	1100.

A No. 1.
50 50
WASHINGTON, JANUARY 1, 1834.
THE GLORY BANK,
IN THE CITY OF WASHINGTON, (DISTRICT OF COLUMBIA) PROMISES TO PAY
FIFTY DOLLARS IN GLORY,
TO MARTIN VAN BUREN, OR BEARER, ON DEMAND.
J. DOWNING, Cashier. (50) ZEK. BIGELOW, President.
Pay my People in Glory.
I take the Responsibility.
Here is the Bill.

HT #	Date	Denomination	Size	VF
N16C	January 1, 1834	$50	140 x 57 MM	200.

HUMBUG GLORY BANK

HT #	Date	Denomination	Size	VF
N17	1834	5 Cents	141 x 57 MM	1100.

HT #	Date	Denomination	Size	VF
N18	August 21, 1837	6 Cents	162 x 70 MM	1200.

Product of H.L. Winslow, New York. A surviving specimen has in ink on its blank reverse: "To Franky dear —to get a nipper with —"

8 Specimens known, on either white or yellow paper.

N18 has sales records to $1,000.

HT #	Date	Denomination	Size	VF
N18A	1834	6 Cents	159 x 70 MM	550.

As 18, but imprint line at bottom, beginning 'Entered according to Act of Congress.' is missing from the printing plate. (Bill Noyes collection)

HT #	Date	Denomination	Size	VF
N19	1834	10 Cents	142 x 58 MM	1100.

NATIONAL CURRENCY
Washington, D.C.

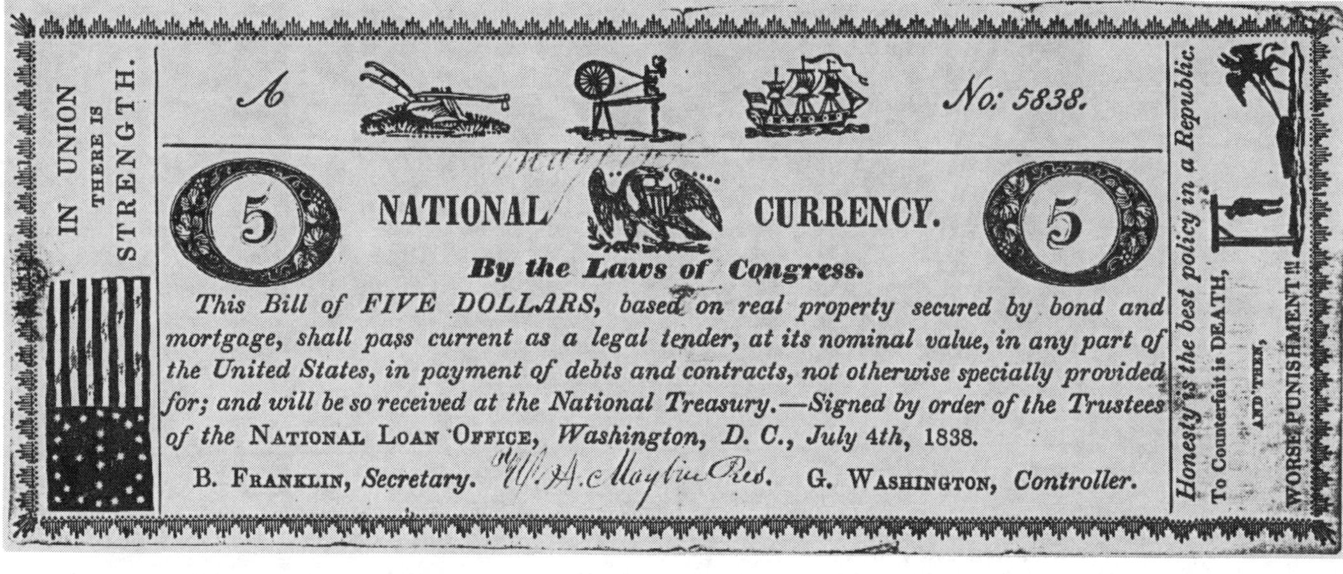

HT #	Date	Denomination	Size	VF
N20	July 4, 1838	$5	184 x 72 MM	200.

GREAT LOCOFOCO JUGGERNAUT

HT #	Date	Denomination	Size	VF
N21	ND	12-1/2 Cents	191 x 79 MM	1800.

Note N21 — Great Locofoco Juggernaut — was designed and printed in 1837 by satirist/[artist David Claypool Johnston (1798-1865). Johnston engraved banknotes and stock certificates for Tanner Kearney & Tiebout of Philadelphia 1815-19 and New England Banknote Co. of Boston circa 1835. It is known he engraved the $100 and $500 notes of Ohio Exporting & Importing Co. of Cincinnati (1816-17) and the $1, $2, $3, and $5 notes of Oriental Bank of Boston (1835).

Johnston caricatured Andrew Jackson beginning with the 1824 presidential race, and Martin Van Buren during 1837-41, but his satirical production fell off after about 1845. He taught art from about 1840 until 1861.

HT #	Date	Denomination	Size	VF
N21A	ND (1837)	12-1/2 Cents	198 x 84 MM	2000.

As N21, but imprint line added bottom center: 'Eng'd by the Locofoco Shinplaster engraving Co'. Printed on flimsy onion-skin paper similar to banknote paper of the period, and on heavy stock white paper.

HT #	Date	Denomination	Size	VF
N21B	ND (1971)	12-1/2 Cents	198 x 84 MM	65.00

Reprint by Woodbury & Co., Worcester, Mass., from original copperplate engraving in collection of American Antiquarian Society of Worcester, Mass. A total of 1,950 specimens were printed on 8-1/2 x 11 inch sheets of high quality white bond paper, unwatermarked.

SHIN PLASTER

(Illustration greatly reduced)

HT #	Date	Denomination	Size	VF
N22	May 10, 1837	50 Cents	432 x 304 MM	350.

Product of H. R. Robinson, 52 Cortlandt St., New York. This item was lot 2974 in the June 19, 1986 NASCA sale. At least three specimens known.

ROGO VILO DISHONESTO ASSOCIATO

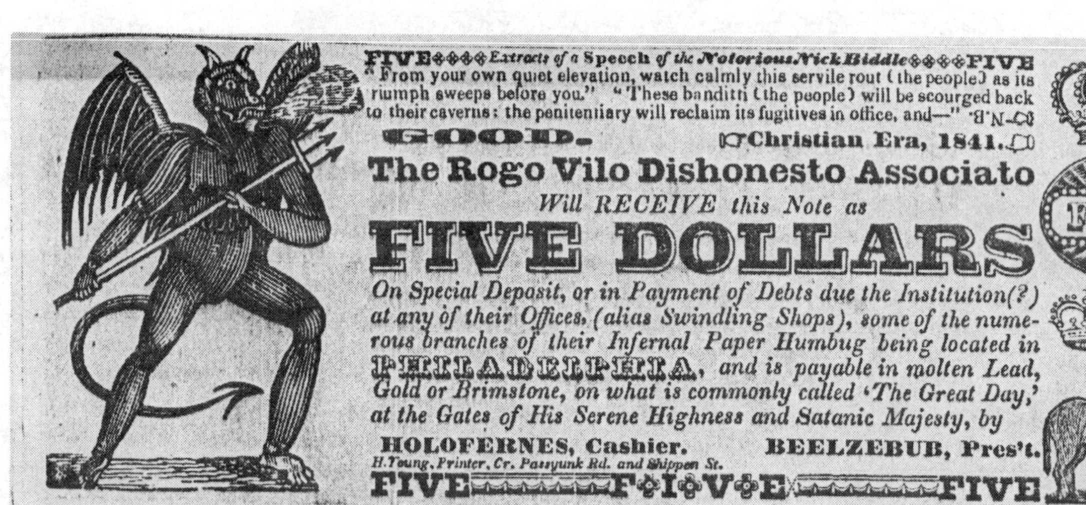

HT #	Date	Denomination	Size	VF
N23	1841	$5	165 x 62 MM	400.

Product of H. Young, Passyunk Rd. and Shippen St. Only a single specimen reported, by Robert Vlack.

HUDSON'S SPECIE CIRCULAR

Auburn, N.Y.

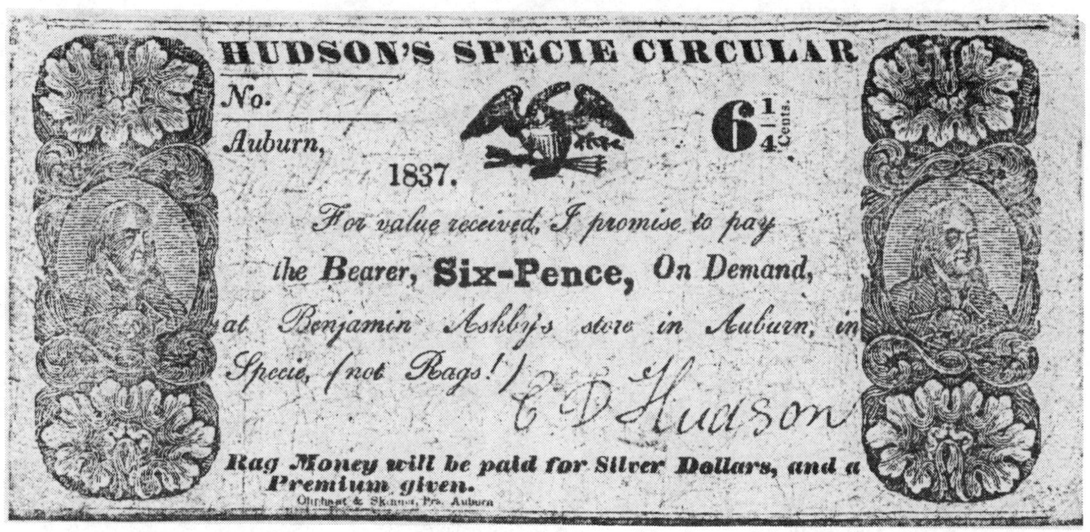

HT #	Date	Denomination	Size	VF
NA23	1837	6-1/4 Cents	147 x 66 MM	1500.

Satirical scrip for either 6-1/4 cents or 6 pence sterling, the latter a reference to English bankers holding a large share of control over Biddle's Bank of the United States. (Dr. Alan York coll.)

CORPORATION LOAN

Philadelphia, Pa. with satirical overprint on reverse

HT #	Date	Denomination	Size	VF
N24	May 20, 1837	10 Cents	145 x 58 MM	800.

Overprinted on reverse with faces and hogs to resemble Jackson and Van Buren.

HICKORY DOLLARS
Philadelphia, Pa.

HT #	Date	Denomination	Size	VF
NB24	May, 1837	$3	124 x60 MM	1100.

Andrew Jackson was known as "Old Hickory" and James K. Polk as "Young Hickory."

SUCKER INSTITUTION
Guard Wall, Pa.

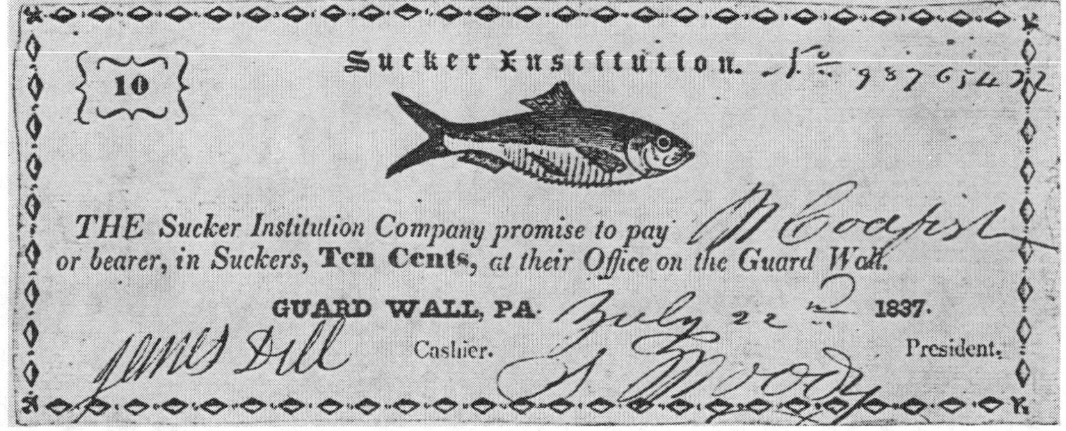

HT #	Date	Denomination	Size	VF
N25	July 22, 1837	10 Cents	145 x 56 MM	300.

Only reported specimen is in the Robert J. Lindesmith collection, Dayton Wash., ex-Stack 1956 ANA. No explanation for "Guard Wall" has been advanced.

OYSTER HOUSE

Pine Ward, Philadelphia, Pa.

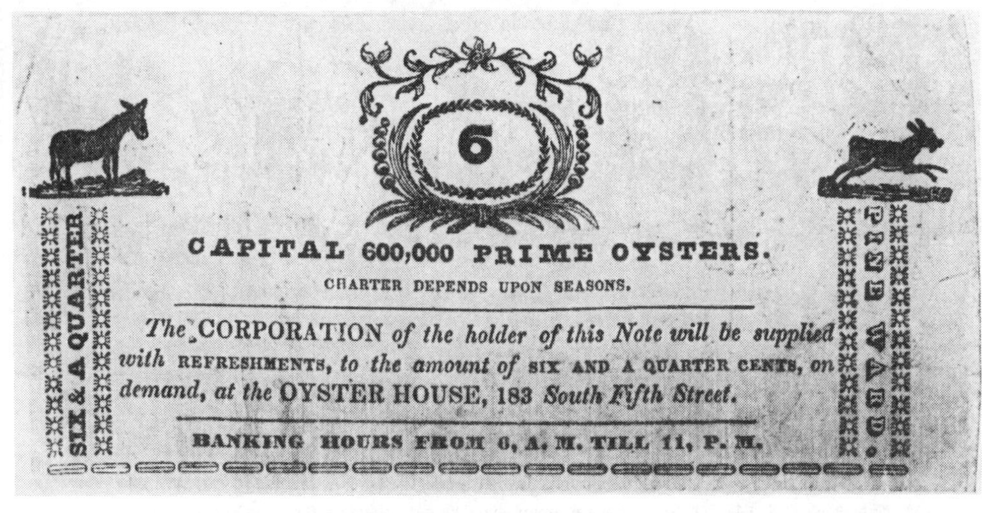

HT #	Date	Denomination	Size	VF
NA26	(ca 1837)	6-1/4 Cents	135 x 65 MM	300.

PHILADELPHIA

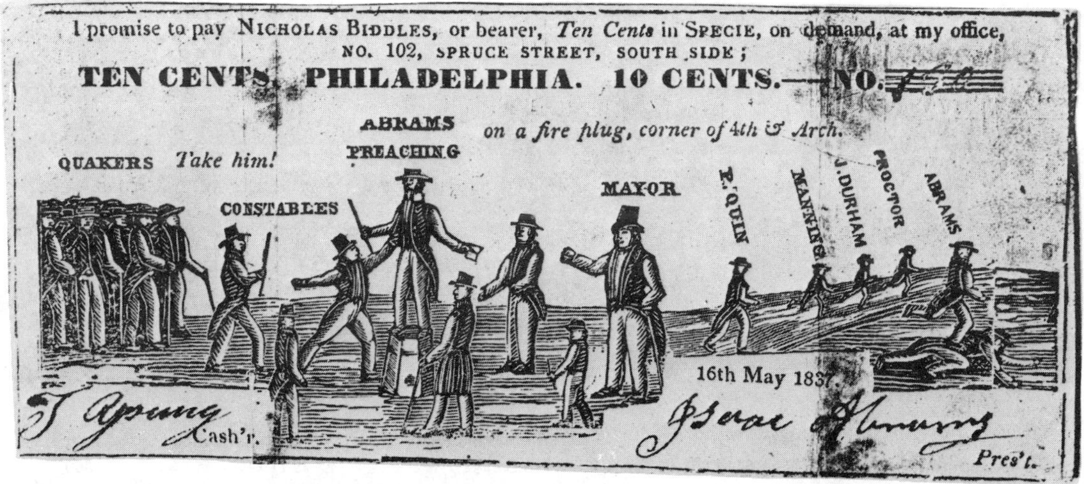

HT #	Date	Denomination	Size	VF
N26	May 16, 1837	10 Cents	146 x 63 MM	650.

NOTE: 102 Spruce Street was the back entrance to the Bank of America in Philadelphia.

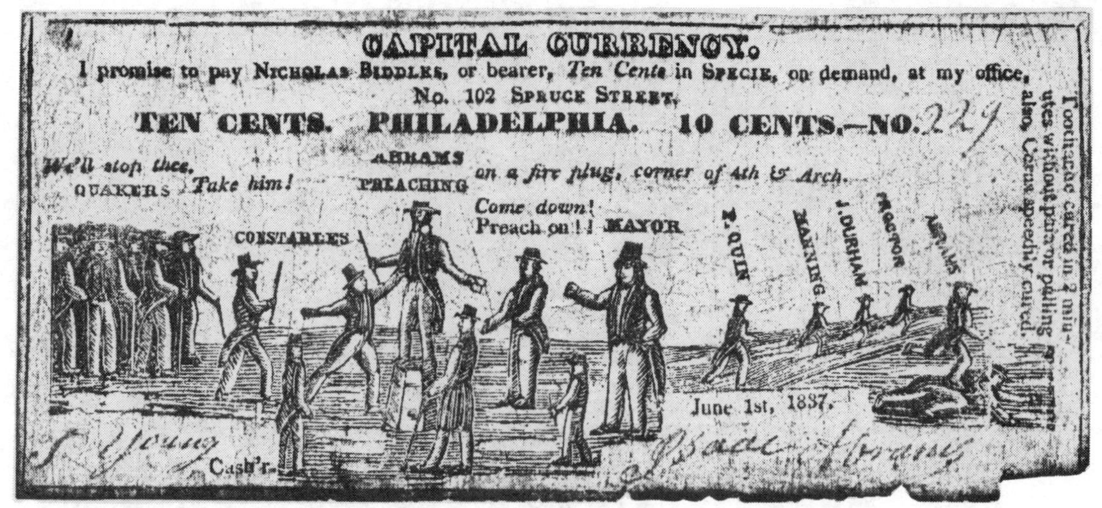

HT #	Date	Denomination	Size	VF
N26A	June 1, 1837	10 Cents	146 x 63 MM	900.

Similar to N26, but CAPITAL CURRENCY at top center, and different issue date. (Dr. Alan York coll.)

HT #	Date	Denomination	Size	VF
N26B	May 15, 1837	10 Cents	141 x 67 MM	900.

Similar to 26, but 'I promise to pay A. B. or order' in place of 'I promise to pay Nicholas Biddles, or bearer' at top left.

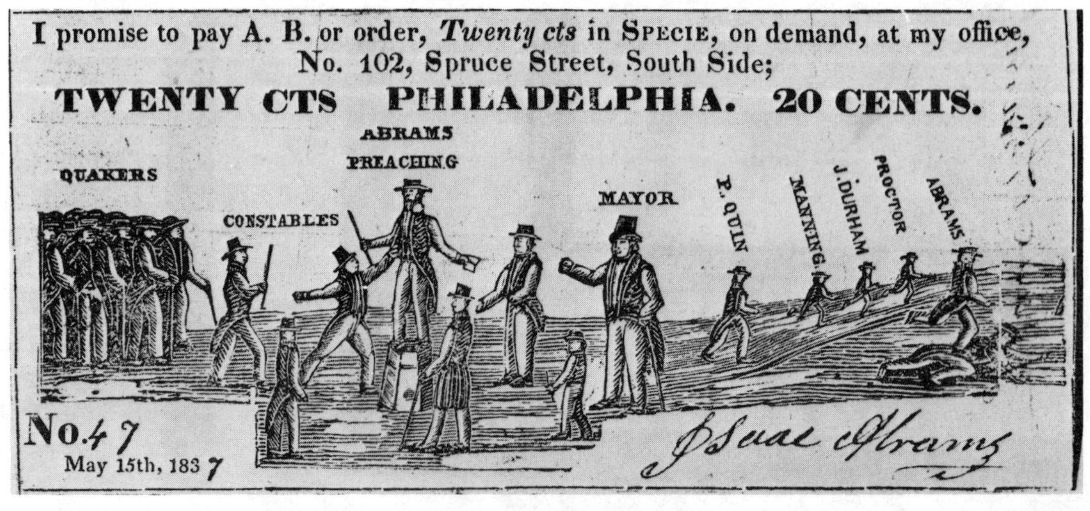

HT #	Date	Denomination	Size	VF
N27	May 15, 1837	20 Cents	146 x 63 MM	900.

DR. FAUSTUS
Philadelphia, Pa.

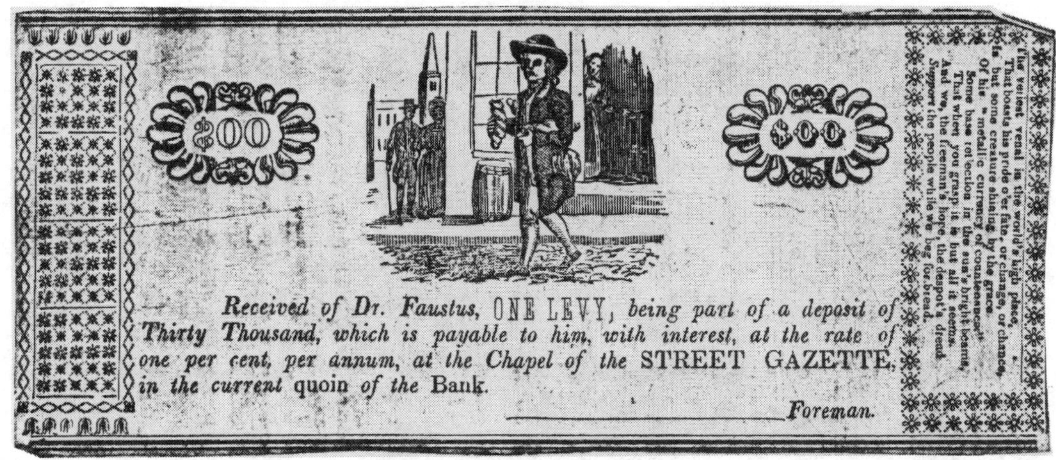

HT #	Date	Denomination	Size	VF
N28	(ca 1837)	1 Levy	140 x 59 MM	1250.

This is a Hard Times period satirical note with anti-Semitic connotations issued by an association of printers. The vignette is of a penniless Benjamin Franklin arriving in Philadelphia.

The note compares not so subtly a Jew to the devil, as those who control hard currency. The reference to "chapel" is both to the organization of printers and a Jewish place of worship, and the word "levy" as both a tax and Jewish name.

The word "quoin" refers both to a printer's typelock and is a play on the name Cohen. The unravelling of the anti-Semitic references is courtesy of Dr. Alan York, East Hampton, N.Y., who discovered this note.

JOBSTOWN, NEW JERSEY

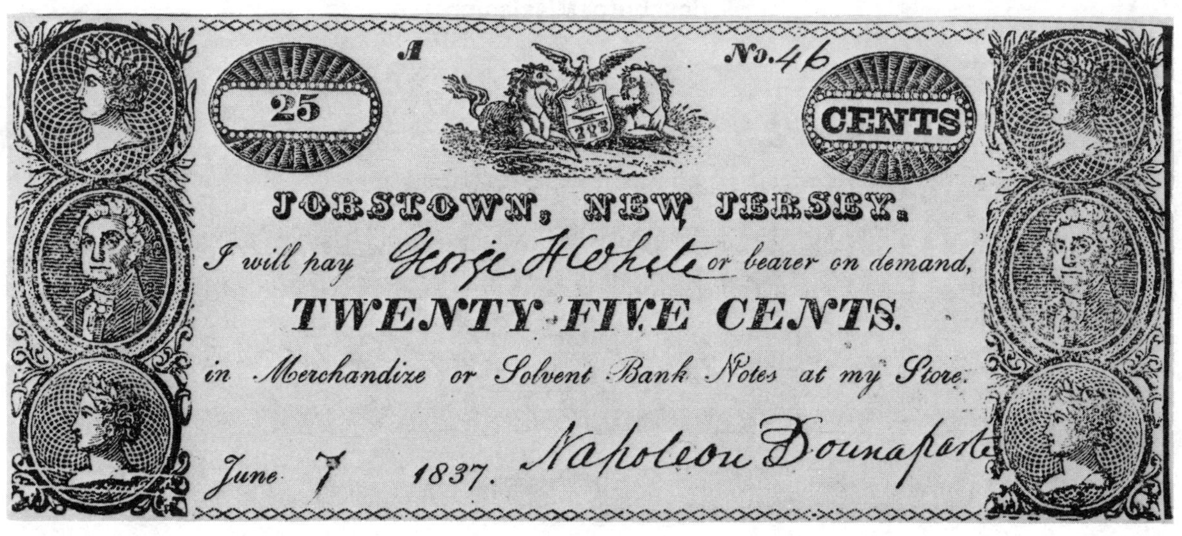

HT #	Date	Denomination	Size	VF
N29	June 7, 1837	25 Cents	159 x 66 MM	400.

HARD TIMES AND PLENTY OF MONEY
Texas

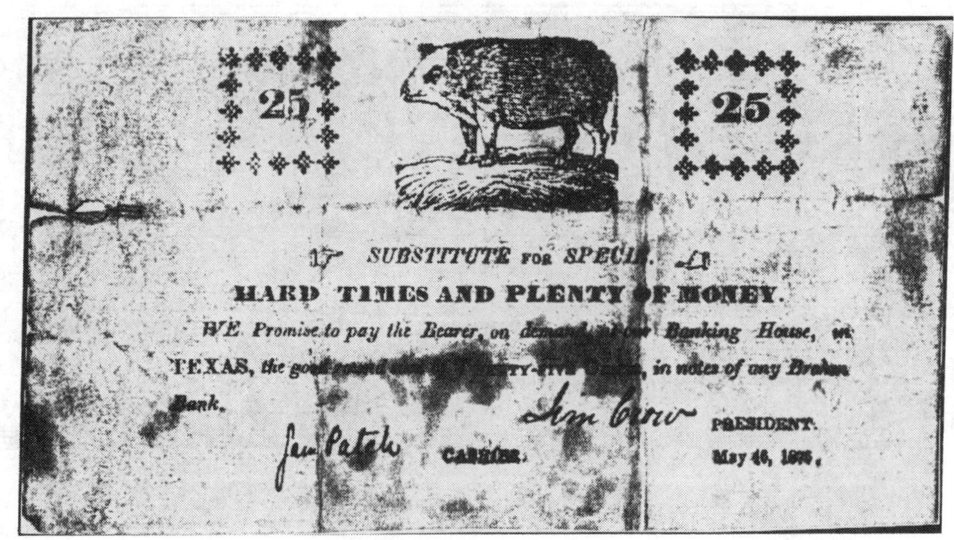

HT #	Date	Denomination	Size	VF
N30	May 16, 1876	25 Cents	125 x 69 MM	350.

Though dated 1876, this is clearly an 1837 product. In 1837 Texas was independent, not part of the United States or Mexico. It seems that the signatories, 'Jam Patch' and 'Jim Crow,' would pay off this note only in faraway Texas 39 years after issuance! All part of the satirical nature of the scrip. (Smithsonian Institution collection)

CUSTIS' BAR
Vicksburg, Mississippi

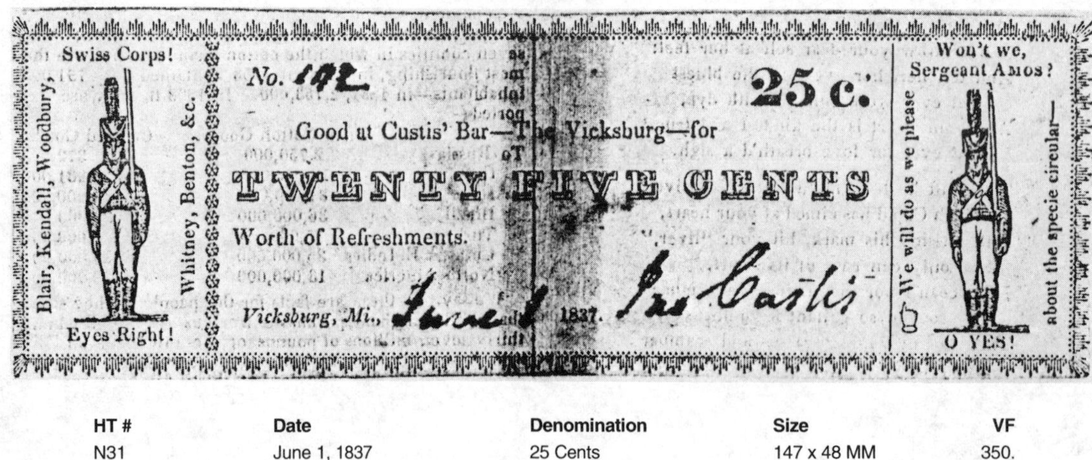

HT #	Date	Denomination	Size	VF
N31	June 1, 1837	25 Cents	147 x 48 MM	350.

KNOWN ENGRAVERS / PRINTERS OF SATIRICAL NOTES

E. W. Clay	?	?
David C. Johnston	Boston (1825-61)	NA21
Oliphant & Skinner	Auburn, NY (1837)	NA23
Oliver	New York (1837)	N11
H. R. Robinson	New York (1837)	N22
H. L. Winslow	New York (1837)	N18
H.Young	Philadelphia (1841)	N23

U.S. Merchant Tokens 1845-1860

A catalog of the unofficial coinage of America from the end of the Hard Times era to the eve of the Civil War. Includes many advertising and business promotion pieces.

INTRODUCTION

Photo courtesy Paul A. Cunningham

Phineas T. Barnum's fashionable new American Museum at the corner of Broadway and Ann Street in 1853. A Kipp & Brown horsedrawn omnibus may be seen in foreground (Kipp & Brown's Chelsea Line issued a pewter 27mm "transfer ticket" token in the 1850's — NY 411.) Barnum offered his credulous public a large menagerie, coins, objects of art, wax figures, a Swiss bearded lady, the first Siamese twins to be seen in America, and General Tom Thumb, the famous midget. This building burned in 1865.

It took the author a very long time to produce the First Edition of this reference as a separate book. For 18 years data was gathered, and we published a good many shorter catalogs which contain some of the tokens in this book. The Second Edition took three more years to complete, and the Third Edition another five years.

This section is actually a Fourth Edition.

Serious work on actually getting the *U.S. Merchant Tokens 1845-1860* manuscript in shape began at the same time we were readying our two earlier standard references, *Early American Tokens* (1700-1832) and *Hard Times Tokens* (1833-1844). *HTT* appeared in 1980 and *EAT* in 1981. We found it best to work on the three volumes simultaneously so as to capitalize upon our own research and not have to retread our footsteps over and over again.

From its first appearance in 1982 the 1845-1860 book sparked torrents of mail from interested collectors who wished to help make an eventual revision more complete. Thus, with the generous help of our contributors, we have been able to increase the catalog portion of this reference.

Now that the work is done, we understand better why some of the great writers in American token collecting never got around to publishing a catalog such as this. The labor has been enormous and the rewards difficult to prejudge — the rewards may prove illusory though we have been cheered on by many of the most active token collectors today.

* * * * * *

The first true merchant token in the United States was the 1789 copper of Messers Mott, importers of clocks, silverware and jewelry in New York. From 1789 until the end of the Hard Times period in 1844, the private currency tokens of America were mainly imitations of the Large cent or the contemporary British (and Irish) halfpennies.

Most early trade tokens were intended to — and did — serve duty as a cent. In some instances higher denomination coins were imitated, but in general the Large cent's size, metal, fabric and even design provided the physical characteristics of the tokens.

The first few years of the Merchant token period (1845-1847) witnessed a continuation of the basic cent-imitation type of token. In reality, economic Hard Times were not yet over in the West, even though the East was recovering. Pittsburgh, Chicago, St. Louis and other Western entrepots saw some distinctly Hard Times-type tokens in this period. The Illinois tokens dated 1845 almost have a rightful claim to inclusion in the Hard Times token series proper.

Token motifs and sizes — and metallic content — started changing dramatically in the 1848-1851 period. Where the earlier periods were dominated by large, heavy copper "cents" and small German silver dime (or bit) imitations, several new variations now came into vogue.

BRASS TO THE FORE

Brass replaced copper as the dominant metal, and imitations of the U.S. gold coins began to appear. Some of the imitations were of the same size as $10 gold pieces and copied the Coronet Liberty and Eagle Displayed types of the gold coins; often they were issued with reeded edges and were gilded before striking to further enhance the similarity.

They must have caused some public distress as they could easily have passed visual inspection as $10 gold coins, though they were much lighter in weight.

Counterstamped coins had been used sparingly as tokens in the Early American period and were still infrequent in the Hard Times period — that is, until 1844. But their usage widened from 1845 on, and scholars today are trying very hard to attribute more of these elusive pieces. A large number of counterstamped silver and copper coins are catalogued, but it is certain that many more pieces are awaiting identification.

The use of German silver, cupronickel, silver, white metal and various brass (copper-zinc) and bronze (copper-tin) alloys was expanded in creating tokens.

Scovill Manufacturing Co. in Waterbury, Conn. became the leading supplier of daguerreotype materials to the trade starting about 1849, and the company's brass works turned out trade tokens (mostly imitating $10 gold pieces) for its many customers. Daguerreotype galleries and the use of Scovill plates grew up all over the East, South and even the West, and the new type of attractive advertising token was not far behind.

The period 1852-1857 could be said to be, in many ways, the Golden Age of Tokens in America. Though they were not so often used as true media of exchange at this time, since the national coinage was starting to catch up with the nation's needs, the burgeoning channels of trade needed tokens for every conceivable purpose — advertising, transport, admittance, identification, politics and nostalgia, to name a few.

As the user peruses this catalog, he will find fascinating tales of magic, minstrelsy, industry, amusement, pioneering, gunsmithy and merchandising — each of which brought forth token issues. These Merchant Tokens are some of the best records posterity has of the mid-19th century's culture.

CHANGES INTRODUCED IN 1857

The year 1857 witnessed two events which were to change the shape — and the scope — of tokens in America. The United States at long last banned the further use of foreign coins as legal tender in trade, eliminated the half cent, and reduced the diameter of the cent from 29 to 19 millimeters. The Coinage Act of 1857 also changed the composition of the cent from copper to a yellowish cupronickel alloy.

The nation also underwent another business panic in 1857. It was nowhere near as severe as the Panic of 1837, but the Panic of 1857 induced the hoarding of specie and renewed the public distrust of fiat paper money.

So the period 1857-1860 absorbed all the economic and political cross-currents that were moving America toward her destiny and shaped new types of tokens to meet the challenges. Many of the tokens in this latter period are similar to earlier emissions — there are close imitations of the Large cent in this period, for example. But the merchant tokens tended to follow the legal cent and reduced-size tokens started appearing. Some even imitated the new Flying Eagle and Indian cents — notable among them issues of Alexandria, Va.; New York City, and Chicago.

Two other factors influenced token issues in these latter years of the U.S. Merchant Token period — the heated politics of slavery and secession, and the growing influence of numismatics and nostalgia on token design. Sage, Idler, Cogan, Curtis, Hill and other coin dealers issued many tokens just to sell to collectors and souvenir hunters, capitalizing on America's preoccupation with its Colonial and Revolutionary heritage.

The intense rivalry of the North and South found its reflection in many token issues of this period of gathering impatience with the political status quo.

The year 1860 was, in a good many aspects, the best single year token collectors have ever had to look back upon. The multiplicity of beautiful issues — some in proof condition — was due to the best output of a large number of talented diesinkers — the three Lovett brothers, Key, Horter, Merriam, F.B. Smith, True, H. Miller, Childs, and many others.

That same year also saw numismatic influence of another kind begin: Muling, or the illogical combination of dies to create rare varieties. This catalog has attempted to record the mules, but it claims no completeness in this area.

In December 1860, South Carolina seceded from the Union and the Civil War broke out a few months later, ushering in the largest period ever for tokens in America.

This U.S. Merchant Token section ends with the 1860 issues. In some cases, a few post-1860 issues are included where these could not logically be separated from the earlier series.

The 1858-1859 (but undated) token issues of Chicago featuring the 19mm BUSINESS CARD dies really belong in the present section, but since all are detailed in the Civil War section, they are given more careful treatment herein. These pieces have always been collected as Civil War tokens.

RESTRIKES

There is plentiful evidence to conclude that restriking of many of the 1845-1860 tokens occurred. Almost all such restriking took place, apparently, from the 1850's on to about 1875.

Activist numismatists of the day — Joseph N. T. Levick, William Leggett Bramhall, Charles I. Bushnell, William Idler, and others — are reputed to have purchased restrikes of a number of issues in the original alloy (normally brass, or occasionally copper) or in more exotic metals — silver, cupronickel, German silver, white metal, block tin, oroide, etc.

Certainly many issues exist today in modest quantity in uncirculated condition, a positive indicator that restriking for collector cabinets has taken place. By an extension of the same logic, abundant quantities of brass issues heavily worn from handling prove that the original pieces did in fact circulate at the time. (Some of the commonest New York City and Philadelphia issues — Professor Johnson, E. Lyon, Doremus & Nixon, H. B. West — can be found worn almost smooth.)

The Scovill Manufacturing Co. in Waterbury, Conn. made most of the restrikes of which we know. There is documentation to show that Levick and Bushnell and possibly others *arranged for* certain restrikes, off-metal strikes and mulings — mostly in very limited numbers for their own gratifications.

It has been asserted that the Scovill outlet in New York City actually stocked uncirculated specimens of many issues for public sale in the late 1850's and early 1860's.

The question arises: How does one tell original token from restrike? Apart from evidence of wear, we know of no certain method, given the present limited state of knowledge of die states, etc. Time, and extensive research, may yield much on this subject, though.

We submit that the restrikes make little difference to today's collectors. It has been more than a century since the last restrikes off original dies were made. Time has tended to homogenize the originals and restrikes and legitimized the restrikes' status. There simply are not enough total specimens to supply today's collector demands.

(The Robert Bashlow token restrikes of 1962, and other 1960-1963 period imitations, need not concern collectors of this 1845-1860 series. Bashlow did use original dies of certain Philadelphia makers, even managing to strike off the broken Lovett Confederate cent dies, but most of his restrikes were of Civil War and post-CW tokens and medalets. The others are just replicas made off copy dies, or cast, usually in a lead alloy with copper or gilt coating.)

In the 1870's some muling off original dies of Joseph H. Merriam was done by Merriam's successor, W. C. Brigham & Co. The mules must have been very limited in quantity, as there are no really common Merriam tokens.

The price levels in EF, Unc. and Proof-like in this catalog take into consideration the fact that restrikes of certain Scovill and other tokens exist.

OBVERSE AND REVERSE

The terms "obverse" and "reverse" in numismatics equate roughly with the "heads" and "tails" of the coin consciousness of the public.

In numismatics, though, we have had to refine the terms' meaning a great deal. Not all coins, medals and tokens have a head of someone or something on them, so the obverse side usually has to be defined as the side with the *principal device.*

Sometimes we are forced to choose which side is obverse, because the other tests do not help us. So we often use the side with the *name of the issuer* as the obverse.

With tokens there is a special problem. The "principal device" and "issuer's name" sides — as often as not — are not the same. Most of the token cataloguers of the past (Wright, Adams, Raymond, Fuld, etc.) used the issuer's name rule exclusively in descriptions.

In this catalog, we have chosen to use the "principal device" method of identifying the obverse in descriptions. It makes little sense to us to identify all the beautiful Liberty heads and other compelling devices as the reverse (tails) side, when the opposite side frequently shows little but lines of text within a wreath.

If we fly in the face of token tradition and irritate some users of this book in the process, we hope they are charitable. The practice of following tradition in token cataloguing can handle some change, and we prefer to accomplish this now.

Thus the obverse-reverse descriptions in this reference may seem unusual at first, but we have found that collectors are already comfortable with the system.

NUMBERING

Consideration was given to an entirely new "Rulau number" system whereby all the tokens in this section would be renumbered. Certainly the Adams-Miller system is now badly out of whack and needs overhaul.

However, we found we could adapt the Adams-Miller numbers (called Miller numbers herein) in most cases, and we have taken considerable liberties in certain series by adding to — or altering — the antiquated, inflexible numbering system.

Veteran collectors thus will face little difficulty, because renumbering their holders, census lists, envelopes, etc. will be minimal. Of necessity there are a good number of *unnumbered* tokens catalogued.

So that every token catalogued has a reference number we have assigned "Rulau numbers" to those pieces not fitting readily into the Adams-Miller scheme of enumeration. The Rulau numbers begin much higher than the final Miller number in each state, so there is no chance of confusion.

The Rulau numbers begin with:

New York	2000
Maryland	500
Massachusetts	500
Pennsylvania	700
All other states	100

GRADING COUNTERSTAMPED COINS

In general, the pricing of counterstamped coins appears only in one or two grades in this reference. The lower grade (whether that be VG or F) indicates a WEAK to NORMAL counterstamp. The higher grade (whether F, VF or EF) indicates a BOLD counterstamp.

The condition of the underlying coin is more or less irrelevant to the piece's price. However, a sharp EF or better coin with bold counterstamp may command higher prices than shown.

A great number of the counterstamped coins which served as merchant advertising tokens are unique. Merchants generally stamped whatever money was at hand, rather than seeking out newly-minted coins of the same date. Thus the number of exact duplicates is small.

The pricing of counterstamped coins — and their attribution — are in stages of infancy and need years of exposure and attention before they achieve the regularization that attaches to struck store cards.

Still, they are among the most exciting of the types of U.S. merchant tokens.

METALWORKER MARKS ON COINS

The appearance of a very special type of counterstamp, the hallmark of the silversmith or manufacturing jeweler, has been somewhat misunderstood by collectors. Many seem to feel that these hallmarks were impressed onto coins as "test runs" for their punches.

We disagree entirely. All silversmiths had plenty of metal to use to test their punches without resorting to pocket change. Also, the appearance of the hallmarks themselves is too neat, too orderly, too centered on each coin to be mistaken as test marks. Finally, the total number of such pieces is too great to be simply the frivolity of the silversmiths — many hallmarks are known in dozens of specimens.

We believe the silversmiths deliberately punched the coins and placed them back into circulation as one of the cheapest and most effective methods of advertising possible, in an era when such coin mutilation was not illegal and when the public rarely hesitated to accept a mutilated coin as full face value.

And our remarks on silversmiths and jewelers apply with equal force for several other metalworking craftsmen — coppersmiths, braziers, stencil cutters, pewterers, gunsmiths, tinsmiths, toolmakers (especially of knives, hatchets, etc.) and others. It is easier to trace silversmiths and gunsmiths because of the number of excellent chronologies in existence on these craftsmen, but work has begun on the marks of the other craftsmen also, and as time passes more and more of these people will be identified.

One especially desirable type of silversmith's hallmark appearing on coins is the signature from the shank of teaspoons. This type of mark will have a long reactangular depression in which letters in relief appear (such as STONE & BALL), and it is possible to add silver teaspoons with the same marks appearing on coins to one's collection. This dual-approach type of collecting is in its infancy but is growing, as token collecting and the antiques field overlap in many facets.

AMERICAN COPPERSMITHS, BRAZIERS ETC.

The practice of imprinting their names on their products was an attractive procedure of American coppersmiths; European coppersmiths followed the custom less often.

In the 18th and early 19th centuries the mark was usually incused with an intaglio die (that is, the letters are in relief within a depression), which compare favorably with those hallmarks used by silversmiths of the period. The mark usually consisted of the first initial and last name and, sometimes, the location. The recessed panel was often bordered with a design of scallops, dots, dentilations, etc. — called "toothed," "ornamented," "dentilated" or some similar phrase by numismatists.

In the 19th century coppersmiths began to use individual block letters to impress on copperware — names, locations and sometimes the year of manufacture or a patent date.

Evidence is clear that coppersmiths, brassworkers (braziers), tinsmiths, bellfounders, clockmakers, pewterers and other craftsmen working in ferrous and nonferrous base metals occasionally impressed their punches on coins also, especially on Large cents. The counterstamp of H. Wray, locksmith of Rochester, N.Y. is an example listed in this book. Later examples include the marks of Ben Parker and C. A. Strange of Bangor, Maine impressed in the 1860's.

An interesting point on the marks of clockmakers is that in most cases they are rendered in an upward arc.

HALLMARKS OF SILVERSMITHS

Silversmithy was an important fact of American life from about 1670 to 1870, but then mass-produced tableware and flatware gradually replaced the hallmarked works of individual craftsmen. Not many silversmith markings appear on pieces made in 1866 or later.

The following list of symbols and words made up the "quality marks" in general use by silversmiths, and these occur counterstamped on coins — either alone or with the mark of a craftsman. Words such as COIN, DOLLAR, STANDARD or PURE came into use about 1830 to indicate "coin silver" — that is, .900 fine, the same as U.S. silver coinage.

STERLING indicated (as it still does today) the British silver standard of .925 fine.

The words were used somewhat indiscriminately. Silver objects down to about .800 fine were still marked COIN or PURE, and the words gradually came to indicate silver all the way through, rather than silver-plated.

Hallmarked British silver table or housewares became all the rage in America, and beginning about 1847 many U.S. craftsmen added fantasy hallmarks of their own devising to their products to gull the public into believing it was purchasing imported objects. Even distributors and larger retailers would buy unmarked silver from makers and then impress their own fantasy marks!

Sometimes the fantasy marks appear in conjunction with craftsman marks, and so a few of the fantasy hallmarks can be localized.

Some American makers proudly adopted their own hallmarks, and stood behind them, even though America never had the rigid, centuries-old enforcement of standards in place in Great Britain. Some of these are mentioned below.

Quality Marks

C	Coin silver
COIN	
D	Dollar (coin silver)
DOLLAR	
PREMIUM	(used in New York City)
PURE	
PURE COIN	
PURE COIN SILVER	
PURE SILVER COIN	
S (incuse or relief)	Sterling silver
STANDARD	(used in Philadelphia)
STERLING	
10 : 15	(used in Baltimore)
11 OZ	(used in Baltimore)

American Hallmarks

(These are usually seen as three-across or three-down tiny impressions, most often in relief within small depressed cartouches but occasionally they are incused.)

(Lion passant right) (Anchor) (Gothic G)
Gorham Mfg. Co., Providence 1865-1961

(Anchor) (5 point star) (King's head right)
Green Hall, Albany 1814-18 and New York 1808-54

(Lion passant left) (S) (U.S. Shield)
Bailey & Co., Philadelphia 1848-65

(Eagle displayed) (Sheaf ?) (Harp right)
Bailey & Kitchen, Philadelphia 1833-46. Also
Peter Thomson, Boston 1825-26 and Philadelphia 1835-54

(Eagle displayed) (B) (Standing Indian)
Theophilus Bradbury & Son, Newburyport, Mass., ca 1825

(Eagle displayed in diamond-shaped depression)
Daniel Van Voorhis, New York 1786-98

A daguerreotype salon of 1853. That shown is the salon of Mathew B. Brady, who later became a famed Civil War battlefield photographer. Fashionable New York's foremost pastime starting about 1850 was the taking of daguerreotypes, and many famed salons of that day issued their own tokens — especially those connected with Scovill's in Waterbury, Conn., makers of daguerreotype supplies. Brady (who did not issue tokens) had his salon at 359 Broadway, near Barnum's American Museum.

DIESINKERS AND TOKEN MAKERS ACTIVE IN THE MERCHANT TOKEN PERIOD

C. Austin	New York	1870's	C. AUSTIN
John F. Bartholdt	Baltimore	1841-60	
Selig Baumgarten	Baltimore	1852-66	
Albert G. Bird	Philadelphia	1848	BIRD
Ira Bisbee & John Stanton	Cincinnati	1852-55	
W. H. Bridgens	New York	1840-63	
Benedict & Burnham	Waterbury, Conn.	1837-57	
Samuel H. Black	New York	1858-61	
James Adams Bolen	Springfield, Mass.	1858-74	BOLEN, J.A. BOLEN
Shubael D. Childs	Chicago	1837-1900	CHILDS
Thomas L. Clark	New York	ca 1848-55	
Emil Edler	New York	1850's	EDLER FEC.
Darwin Ellis	Mishawaka, Ind.	1860's	
Salathiel Ellis	New York	1847-65	ELLIS
A. W. Escherich	Chicago	1863	E
Z. Freund	—	1850's	Z. FREUND
G. Glaubrecht	New York	1860's	G.G., G.GL.
A. Gleason	Hillsdale, Mich.	1863	
A.J. Henning	New York	1850's	
Samuel Hiron	Birmingham, England	1846-51	S. HIRON
H. W. Hayden	—	1851-52	H.W.H.
Charles D. Horter	New York	1860-63	CDH, HORTER
J. A. Hughes	Cincinnati	1860's	
Peter H. Jacobus	Philadelphia	1858-70	PHJ
Jensch & Meyer	Chicago	1860	JENSCH & MEYER
Johnson	Cincinnati	1863	
J. M. Kershaw	St. Louis	1850's	J.M. KERSHAW
F. C. Key	Philadelphia	1849-70	KEY
William H. Key	Philadelphia	1858-92	WHK
Francis Xavier Kohler	Baltimore	1851-85	
Louisa Lander	New York	1847	
W. K. Lanphear	Cincinnati	1860's	
Ludwig Christoph Lauer	Nuremberg, Germany	1848-73	L, LAUER
E. Leichtweis	New York	1863	E.L.
Leonard	?	1840-52	LEONARD
George Hampden Lovett	New York	1848-93	GHL
John D. Lovett	New York	—	
Robert Lovett Sr.	New York	1824-60's	
Robert Lovett Jr.	N.Y. & Philadelphia	—	RL
Charles E. Maas	Philadelphia	1848-71	
B. Mead	St. Louis	1850's	
Joseph H. Merriam	Boston	1850-70	MERRIAM
Henry Miller	Louisville, Ky.	1856-63	H. MILLER
A. C. Morin	Philadelphia	1844-53	ACM
Mossin & Marr	Milwaukee	1856-75	MARR
Murdock, Stanton & Spencer	Cincinnati	1860's	
James E. Pilkington	Baltimore	1858-71	
Thomas Pope & Co.	Birmingham, England	1848-1960	POPE BIRM., T. POPE
J. Robbins	Attleboro, Mass.	—	J. ROBBINS
Louis Roloff	New York	1860's	L. ROLOFF
Scovill Mfg. Co.	Waterbury, Conn.	1820-1905	
Emil Sigel	New York	1860's	ES, E. SIGEL
Frederick B. Smith	New York	1835-64	
F. B. Smith & Hartmann	New York	1848-60	S&H, FBS&H
E. W. Strange	Taunton, Mass.	1850's	
J. W. Strange	Bangor, Maine	1850's-69	
Karl Stubenrauch	St. Louis	1850-?	
Stubenrauch & Weber	St. Louis	1850's	
Sturdivant & Maas	Philadelphia	1857	
J. F. Thomas	Newark, N.J.	1840's	JF THOMAS
Benjamin C. True	Cincinnati	1856-61	
Waller (77 Lake St.) or	Chicago	1845-46	W.
White (72 Lake St.)	Chicago	1845-46	W.
John S. Warner	Philadelphia	1823-68	
Charles Cushing Wright	New York	1824-57	CCW
Thomas Wyatt	New York	1840-60	

ALABAMA

B. FERGUSON
Huntsville, Ala.

Rulau	Date	Metal	Size	VG	F	VF	EF
Ala 100	(?)	Silver	39mm	—	—	175.	—
		(Wavy arc) / WARRANTED / HUNTSVILLE / B. FERGUSON ctsp on Peru 8-reales of 1838. (Van Ormer sale 2643, ex-Cunningham 3/1981 sale, lot 204; Brunk 14020)					

Assigned to Alabama tentatively, as Huntsville, Ala. was the only large industrial city by that name in the U.S. in the 19th century. Other possibilities, all smaller locales, include the Huntsvilles in Maryland, Tennessee, Indiana and Ohio.

MOBILE JOCKEY CLUB
Mobile, Ala.

Miller	Date	Metal	Size	F	VF	EF	Unc
Ala 2	1853	Brass	28mm	10.00	14.00	22.50	40.00
		Racehorse standing left, MOBILE JOCKEY CLUB above. *MEMBERS MEDAL * below. Rv: NOT / TRANSFERABLE / 1853.					
Ala 3	1853	Copper	28mm	10.00	14.00	22.50	45.00
		As Ala 2.					
Ala 4	1853	Silver	28mm	—	85.00	150.	275.
		As Ala 2.					
Ala 6	1853	Cupronickel	28mm	—	—	50.00	75.00
		As Ala 2. Only 15 struck. (Wright 715)					
Ala 5	1853	White Metal	28mm	—	—	50.00	75.00
		As Ala 2. Only 15 struck.					

NOTE: Ala 2 to 6 are the actual tokens of the Mobile Jockey Club. All those following are mulings made especially for collectors, in or after 1860. This series is one of the most extensively muled of the antebellum South.

Miller	Date	Metal	Size	VF	EF	Unc	P-L
Ala 7	1860	Copper	28mm	—	17.50	40.00	—
		Obverse as Ala 2. Rv: Cupid on a dolphin, 1860 in exergue.					
Ala 8	1860	Brass	28mm	—	17.50	40.00	—
		As Ala 7.					
Ala 9	1860	White Metal	28mm	—	40.00	70.00	—
		As Ala 7. Only 16 struck.					
Ala 10	1860	Silver	28mm	—	150.	275.	—
		As Ala 7.					
Ala 11	1860	Cupronickel	28mm	—	20.00	65.00	—
		As Ala 7.					
Ala 12	(1860)	Copper	28mm	—	17.50	40.00	—
		Obverse as Ala 2. Rv: Witch on broomstick, GHL beneath. WE ALL HAVE OUR HOBBIES.					
Ala 13	(1860)	Brass	28mm	—	17.50	40.00	—
		As Ala 12.					
Ala 14	(1860)	White Metal	28mm	—	15.00	40.00	—
		As Ala 12.					
Ala 15	(1860)	Silver	28mm	—	150.	275.	—
		As Ala 12.					
Ala 16	(1860)	Cupronickel	28mm	—	20.00	65.00	—
		As Ala 12.					
Ala 17	(1860)	Copper	28mm	—	—	75.00	—
		Obverse as Ala 2. Rv: Daniel Webster. Only 4 struck.					
Ala 18	(1860)	Brass	28mm	—	17.50	65.00	—
		As Ala 17.					
Ala 19	(1860)	White Metal	28mm	—	15.00	65.00	—
		As Ala 17.					
Ala 20	(1860)	Silver	28mm	—	150.	275.	—
		As Ala 17.					
Ala 21	(1860)	Cupronickel	28mm	—	20.00	65.00	—
		As Ala 17.					
Ala 22	(1860)	Copper	28mm	—	20.00	65.00	—
		Obverse as Ala 2. Rv: Edwin Forrest.					
Ala 23	(1860)	Brass	28mm	—	20.00	65.00	—
		As Ala 22.					
Ala 24	(1860)	White Metal	28mm	—	20.00	65.00	—
		As Ala 22.					
Ala 24A	1853 (1860)	White Metal	28mm	—	25.00	42.50	—
		Obverse as reverse of Ala 2 (NOT TRANSFERABLE). Rv. Same as obverse. (No name on token)					
Ala 25	1853 (1860)	Silver	28mm	—	150.	275.	—
		As Ala 24A.					
Ala 26	1853 (1860)	Cupronickel	28mm	—	20.00	65.00	—
		As Ala 24A.					
Ala 26A	1853 (1860)	Copper	28mm	—	100.	150.	—
		Obverse as reverse of Ala 2 (NOT TRANSFERABLE). Rv: George Washington bust left, small KEY below bust. PAPER PATRIAE 1732 around. Only 4 struck.					
Ala 26B	1853 (1860)	Brass	28mm	—	100.	150.	—
		As Ala 26A. Only 4 struck.					
Ala 26C	1853 (1860)	White Metal	28mm	—	40.00	50.00	—
		As Ala 26A. Only 15 struck. (Baker 636)					

The preceding mules, Ala 7 through 26C, are only a part of the series of mulings, probably made to the order of J.N.T. Levick. The Cupid, Witch, Webster, Forrest, etc. dies are also muled with the NOT TRANSFERABLE 1853 die, and with each other, to make a multiplicity of combinations — which are not listed here. Some of them are listed as Baker 633, 634, 635 and 636 because they contain Washington dies.

A Muling

D. W.
Alabama (?)

Rulau	Date	Metal	Size	VG	F	VF	EF
Ala 105	(?)	Copper	29mm	—	—	50.00	—
		D W in relief within toothed rect. depression ctsp on U.S. 1805 Large cent. (Mark Greengold coll.)					

The owner attributed this mark to D. Wallis, an Alabama gunsmith. We have been unable thus far to verify this. Mark Greengold died at age 40 in 1990.

Frank Sellers (see Bibliography) does not list a D. Wallis.

STICKNEY & WILSON
Montgomery, Ala.

These tokens, 28mm brass, Ala 27, are now removed to our Hard Times reference.

J.A. SYLVESTER & CO.
Selma, Ala.

Miller	Date	Metal	Size	VG	F	VF	Unc
Ala 28	(1850)	Brass	28mm	10.00	20.00	30.00	45.00
		Clasped hands at center; J.A. SYLVESTER / & / CO. above; SELMA / ALA. below. Rv: MERCHANT TAILORS & CLOTHIERS / FURNISHING / GOODS. / HATS. BOOTS. / SHOES. / TRUNKS / &C &C. Plain edge. (Wright 1648)					
Ala 29	1853	Copper	28mm	—	—	60.00	75.00
		Obverse as Ala 28. Rv: Reverse of NY 948 (NEW YORK CRYSTAL PALACE, 1853).					
Ala 29A	1853	Brass	28mm	—	—	60.00	75.00
		As 29.					

CALIFORNIA

RUDOLPH

Nevada City, Calif.

Rulau	Date	Metal	Size	VG	F	VF	EF
Calif 118	(1861)	Silver	18mm	50.00	—	75.00	—

RUDOLPH ctsp on U.S. Seated Liberty dime. Dates examined: 1835, 1842, 1845, 1853, 1854, 1855, 1856, 1857, 1858. There are 13 reported specimens. (Van Ormer sale 2823; Brunk 35245)

1856 1860

Rulau	Date	Metal	Size	VG	F	VF	EF
Calif 119	(1861)	Silver	25mm	60.00	—	90.00	—

Similar ctsp on U.S. Seated Liberty quarter. Dates examined: 1853-no Arrows, 1853-O, 1854, 1856, 1857, 1858, 1860, 1861. There are 13 reported specimens. (Van Ormer sale 2823, 2824, 2825)

J. F. Rudolph was a druggist in Nevada City circa 1855 to about 1861, a contemporary of Polhemus in Sacramento. He appears in the 1856 city directory. Rudolph is an unusual surname but this druggist always advertised himself just that way, by surname alone.

These pieces probably were made in 1861. The Civil War broke out in April 1861 with the bombardment of Fort Sumter, S.C.

Rudolph was located at 21 Commercial Street in Nevada City.

W. W. LIGHT

Sacramento, Calif.

Rulau	Date	Metal	Size	VG	F	VF	EF
Calif 110	(1850's)	Gold	22.5mm	6000.	—	15000.	—

W. W. LIGHT (in an arc) / DENTIST (straight), all incuse, ctsp on an 1850 Moffat $5 or an 1852 Wass Molitor $5 gold piece of San Francisco, Calif. The ctsp forms a half circle, like a letter 'D' lying on its back. (Brunk 24500)

Rulau	Date	Metal	Size	VG	F	VF	EF
Calif 111	(1850's)	Silver	25mm	350.	—	500.	—

Similar ctsp on U.S. Seated Liberty quarter. (Roy Van Ormer sale, lot 2732)

Rulau	Date	Metal	Size	VG	F	VF	EF
Calif A111	(1850's)	Copper	26mm	250.	—	350.	—

Similar ctsp on Austria 1816 1-kreuzer, KM-485, Craig-177. (This type coin was struck until 1852 with the 1816 date)

W. W. Light was a Sacramento pioneer and a dentist, contemporary with the druggist J. L. Polhemus. Light supervised production at the J. S. Ormsby & Co. private mint in 1849, after arriving from Ohio, then quickly turned to dentistry.

J.L. POLHEMUS

Sacramento, Calif.

(All Polhemus pieces have been rearranged and also renumbered to allow for new discoveries. This listing catalogs a total of 66 Polhemus counterstamps.)

1853 1856

Miller	Date	Metal	Size	VG	F	VF	EF
Calif 1	(1856-57)	Silver	18mm	100.	—	150.	—

J.L. POLHEMUS / (mortar and pestle) / DRUGGIST / 190 J. ST. COR. 7TH / SACRAMENTO CAL. in five lines ctsp on U.S. Seated Liberty dime. Examined: 1837, 1845, 1853-No arrows, 1853-Arrows, 1856. There are 5 reported specimens. (Brunk 32340; Kovacs coll.)

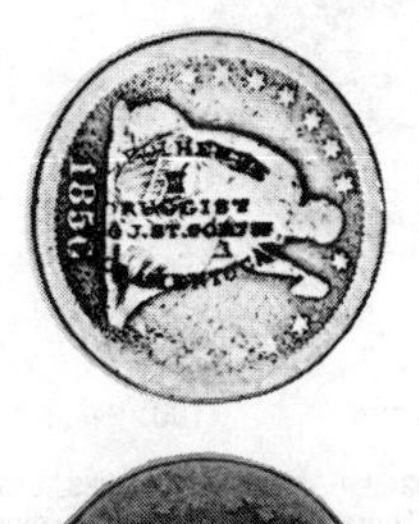

1855 1855-S

Miller	Date	Metal	Size	VG	F	VF	EF
Calif 1A		Silver	25mm	75.00	—	125.	—

Similar ctsp on U.S. Seated Liberty quarter. Examined: 1838, 1839, 1850,1853, 1854, 1855, 1855-S, 1856-S, worn dates. There are 27 reported specimens.

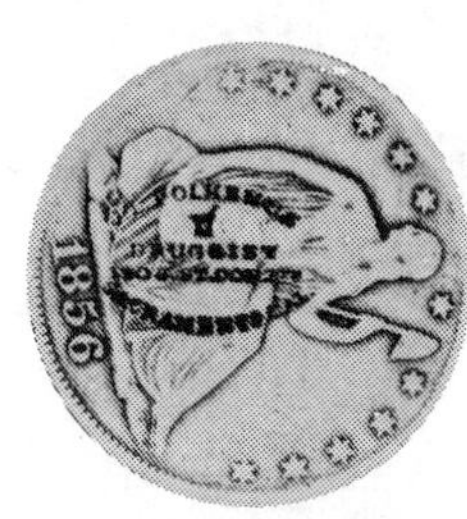

1853 1856-S

Miller	Date	Metal	Size	VG	F	VF	EF
Calif 1B		Silver	31mm	75.00	—	125.	—

Similar ctsp on U.S. Seated Liberty half dollar. Examined: 1843, 1850-O, 1853-Arrows & rays, 1854, 1855, 1856-S, worn date. There are 12 reported specimens.

Miller	Date	Metal	Size	VG	F	VF	EF
Calif 1C		Silver	38mm	300.	—	500.	—

Similar ctsp on U.S. Seated Liberty silver dollar. Examined: 1843. (Only 1 known)

Calif 1M		Gold	34mm	—	—	12000.	—

Similar ctsp on U.S. 1855 or 1857-S $20 gold piece. Only 2 known.

Calif 2	(1856-57)	Silver	21mm	125.	—	175 .	—

Similar ctsp on Spanish-American 1-real. Examined: 1776. There is 1 reported specimen.

Calif 2A		Silver	27mm	100.	—	150.	—

Similar ctsp on Spanish-American 2-reales. Examined: 1782-Ba, 1822, 1839, worn. There are 5 reported specimens.

Calif 2B		Silver	21mm	125.	—	225.	—

Similar ctsp on Chile 1844 1-real.

Calif 2C		Silver	23mm	100.	—	150.	—

Similar ctsp on Chile 1852 20-centavos.

Calif 2D		Silver	39mm	200.	—	300.	—

Similar ctsp on Chile 1-peso of 1837-49 type, KM-96. Only 1 reported.

Rulau	Date	Metal	Size	VG	F	VF	EF
Calif 2E	(1856-57)	Silver	31mm	150.	—	225.	—

Similar ctsp on Bolivia 1830 4-sueldos (or soles).

Calif 2F		Silver	39mm	200.	—	300.	—

Similar ctsp on New Granada 1838 8-reales.

Calif 2G	Silver	37mm	300.	—	450.	—

Similar ctsp on France 1830 or 1845 5-francs.

Calif 2H	Silver	36mm	150.	—	225.	—

Similar ctsp on Russia 1855 1-ruble.

Calif 2J	Silver	26mm	150.	—	225.	—

Similar ctsp on Austrian Italy 1791-M (Milan) 1-lira, Craig 52.

1819

1826

Calif 2K	Silver	24mm	100.	—	150.	—

Similar ctsp on Great Britain shilling. Examined: 1816, 1819, 1826, 1828. There are 4 reported specimens.

Calif 2L	Silver	32mm	150.	—	225.	—

Similar ctsp on East India Company 1-rupee. Examined: 1840. Only 1 specimen reported.

The earliest any of these coins could have been counterstamped is 1853, but most likely Polhemus stamped them in 1856-1857.

Dr. James L. Polhemus came to Sacramento with the gold rush in 1849, later setting up a drugstore. His first drugstore, in 1850, was on J Street opposite the famous Magnolia Saloon.

In December 1850, the pharmacy moved to 190 J Street where it remained until his death in 1866; this was at the corner of 7th Street.

Mrs. J. L. Polhemus ran the business 1867-1874.

He was a very progressive businessman and stocked many important remedies, medicines, hair colorings, etc. He was a Mason and an Odd Fellow; his date of death was Dec. 17, 1866.

An excellent writeup by John Reynolds appears in the *Journal of the Token and Medal Society* for Sept. 1964, entitled, "J.L. Polhemus Counterstamped Store Cards of Sacramento, California." Reynolds had located 23 Polhemus counterstamps in various collections, and Charles Kappen later listed these in *California Tokens* as numbers S.F. 466 thru 487.

Most of the Polhemus counterstamps known saw considerable circulation after they were stamped, and they have been extensively collected and studied for many years, unlike the great majority of counterstamped coins known today. Perhaps this extensive study makes them seem more common than they really are; prices, though, are quite firm in this series, as there are always more buyers than sellers.

It is doubtful if many more Polhemus coins remain to be found. Polhemus, along with fellow Sacramento pioneer W.W. Light, San Francisco saloonkeeper J.T. Jones, and Syracuse, N.Y. merchants Stone & Ball are the only merchants known to have counterstamped U.S. gold coins for advertising purposes. The other U.S. gold coins bearing merchant names were, presumably, personal mementos.

BERENHART, JACOBY & CO.

San Francisco, Calif.

Miller	Date	Metal	Size	VG	F	VF	Unc
Calif 3	(1851)	Brass	26mm	50.00	100.	150.	250.
		Eagle with drooping wings, shield on breast; BERENHART, JACOBY & CO. above; * ST. FRANCISCO * below. Rv: Three-masted ship left, * GENERAL MERCHANTS & IMPORTERS around. Plain edge. (Kappen S.F. 224)					
Calif 3A	(1851)	Silver	--mm	200.	—	300.	—
		BERENHART JACOBY & CO. ctsp on a Bolivia 1830 silver coin. Very Rare. (Kappen S.F. 225)					

They were in business starting 1851 at 70 and 72 Montgomery St. In 1856-57 they were at 2 Laura Place, second floor, and then they disappear from the directories.

J.T. JONES

Rulau	Date	Metal	Size	VG	F	VF	EF
Calif 100	(1851-55)	Silver	26mm	275.	—	400.	—
		CORNER MONTG. & COMMERCIAL ST. / SAN / J.T. JONES / FRAN Co. ctsp on Spain 1810-M (Madrid) 2-reales of Joseph Napoleon. The circular ctsp measures 14mm. (Kappen S.F. 1273; Brunk 22080)					

Rulau	Date	Metal	Size	VG	F	VF	EF
Calif 101		Silver	26mm	250.	—	350.	—
		Similar ctsp on Spanish-American 2-reales. Examined: 1761-LME, 1770, 1780, 1810. There are 5 specimens reported. (Gould 334; Kappen S.F. 1272; Brunk 22080; Koppenhaver Nov. 1983 sale, lot 2)					
Calif 102		Silver	26mm	275.	—	400.	—
		Similar ctsp on Bolivia 1830-J.L. 2-sueldos. (Kappen S.F. 1271)					
Calif 103		Silver	25mm	275.	—	400.	—
		Similar ctsp on U.S. Seated Liberty quarter. Examined: 1853-Arrows. Only 1 known. (Kappen S.F. 1270)					
Calif 104		Gold	Oct 42mm	—	—	15,000.	—
		Similar ctsp on Augustus Humbert 1851 $50 gold piece.					

J.T. Jones operated the Blue Wing saloon at corner of Montgomery and Commercial Streets 1851-1855. Banks, private mints, and in 1854 the U.S. Mint were in the immediate vicinity.

Gambler Charles Cora shot Marshal William Richardson after an altercation in the Blue Wing and was hanged by the Vigilantes in 1855.

In 1919 Farran Zerbe wrote that this countermark was Jones' validation for "two bit" coins passing out of his till, and not really intended as an advertising medium. The existence of Calif 103, unknown to Zerbe, makes this statement unlikely.

JOSEPH BROTHERS

Miller	Date	Metal	Size	VG	F	VF	Unc
Calif 6	(1854-60)	Copper	31mm	15.00	20.00	30.00	75.00
		JOSEPH BROTHERS / OF LIVERPOOL ENGD. / WATCH MAKERS / JEWELLERS OPTICIANS / & GENERAL IMPORTERS / 149 MONTGOMERY ST. / SAN FRANCISCO CAL. Rv: THE CHEAPEST HOUSE / IN CALIFORNIA FOR / GOOD WATCHES / DIAMONDS / JEWELLERY / SILVER WARE CUTLERY &C &C. Reeded edge. (Wright 522) (Kappen S.F. 1275)					
Calif 6A	(1854-60)	Silvered Copper	31mm	25.00	35.00	50.00	80.00
		As 6. Reeded edge. (Kappan S.F. 1276)					
Calif 6B	(1860-67)	Silvered Copper	31mm	—	50.00	125.	200.
		Similar to 6, but 607 MONTGOMERY ST in place of 149 MONTGOMERY ST. Reeded edge. (Kappen S.F. 1277)					

L.B. and J.B. Joseph were at 175 Clay St. 1851-54; then at 149 Montgomery St. 1854-60; then at 607 Montgomery St. 1860-67.

WM. KELLY

Miller	Date	Metal	Size	VG	F	VF	Unc
Calif 7	(1858-60)	Lead	31mm	—	—	—	Unique
		WM. KELLY / KELLY'S RETREAT / 186 KEARNY ST. around Liberty head to left. Rv: Eagle. (A trial piece) (Kappen S.F. 1304)					

William Kelly and Robert Olpherts owned Bob's Burton Ale House at 186 Kearny St. in 1856-57. Kelly became sole owner 1858-60, changing the name to Kelly's Retreat.

THURNAUER & ZINN

San Francisco, Calif.

Miller	Date	Metal	Size	VG	F	VF	Unc
Calif 9	(1859-61)	Brass	27.5mm	20.00	50.00	125.	200.
		Coronet Liberty head left, eight stars around, COMP. S. MARKE below. Rv: THURNAUER & ZINN / IMPORTERS / OF / BASKET TOYS / & / FANCY GOODS / SAN FRANCISCO. Plain edge. (Wright 1147; Kurth 33; R-F Sca-12)					
Calif 9A	(1859-61)	Brass	27.5mm	20.00	50.00	125.	200.
		Large C in circle. THURNAUER & ZINN / S. FRANCISCO around. Rv: Similar to Calif 9. Plain edge. (R-F Sca-11)					
Calif 9B	(1859-61)	Brass	27.5mm	20.00	50.00	125.	200.
		Obverse as obverse of 9A (Large C). Rv: As obverse of 9 (Liberty head). Plain edge. (R-F Sca-13)					
Calif 10	(1859-61)	Brass	27.5mm	20.00	50.00	125.	200.
		As Calif 9B, but TANCY for FANCY. Plain edge. (Kurth 32; R-F Sca-14)					
Calif 10A	(1859-61)	Brass	27.5mm	20.00	50.00	125.	200.
		Obverse as 9 (Liberty head). Rv: Similar to 9, but JMPORTERS for IMPORTERS. Plain edge. (R-F Sca-15)					

Miller	Date	Metal	Size	VG	F	VF	Unc
Calif 10B	(1859-61)	Brass	27.5mm	20.00	50.00	125.	200.
		As 10A, but Reeded edge. (Kurth 31; R-F Sca-15A)					
Calif 11	(1859-61)	Brass	22mm	20.00	50.00	125.	200.
		Coronet Liberty head left, 11 stars around SP. MARKE below. Rv: As reverse of Calif 10A (JMPORTERS). Plain edge. (Kurth 30A; R-F Sca-10)					

William Thurnauer and Henry Zinn were in partnership 1857-1873. In 1859-60 they were at 92 Battery St. (between Commercial and Clay Sts.). In 1861 they were at 320 & 322 Battery St.; in 1867 at the N.W. corner of Sansom (sic) and Sacramento Sts.; in 1868-69 at 403 & 405 Sansom St.; in 1870 at 516 & 518 Washington St. In 1871-72 they were at 533 Market St. and then in 1873 at 119 Battery St.

SPECIAL NOTE ON CALIFORNIA STORE CARD-GAME COUNTERS:

Inclusion of the California game counter-store cards poses special problems in this reference book. The San Francisco issues of W. Frank & Co.; Weil & Levy; and Thurnauer & Zinn, were all apparently made in Germany (by Ludwig Christoph Lauer of Nuremberg) at about the same time.

Lauer also struck the counter-store cards for Bollenhagen of New York in the 1850's, Kayser of New York in 1860, etc.

However, Thurnauer & Zinn is the only California firm which could have had its counters struck before 1861; the business started in 1857. Weil & Levy started in 1864, W. Frank in 1867. Thus the latter two firms are outside the scope of this reference. It is entirely possible that the Thurnauer & Zinn pieces were struck later also.

N. TALBOT & CO.

Shaw's Flat, Calif.

Rulau	Date	Metal	Size	VG	F	VF	EF
Calif 105	(1851)	Silver	39mm	—	900.	—	—
		N. TALBOT & CO. / SHAW'S FLAT ctsp on Mexico 1848 8-reales coin. (Duffield 1602; Brunk 39275; Hartzog coll.)					

Shaw's Flat was a gold mining boom town in Tuolumne County, on the road from Sonora to Columbia just two miles from Sonora. It was well populated in the early Fifties. In 1918 it still had an independent existence, with a distillery, saloon and general store.

CONNECTICUT

S. NORTH

Berlin, Conn.

Rulau	Date	Metal	Size	VG	F	VF	EF
Conn 110	(1830-50)	Copper	29mm	100.	—	150.	—
		S. NORTH — BERLIN, CON. / OURAM ctsp on U.S. 1820 Large cent. (Koppenhaver Nov. 1983 sale, lot 19; Brunk 29860)					
Conn 110C	(?)	Copper	29mm	100.	—	150.	—
		BERLIN CT / CAST STEEL / WARRANTED ctsp on U.S. 1837 Large cent.					

Simeon North was one of America's most successful early 19th century gunsmiths. Born in Berlin, Conn. on July 13, 1765, he started life as a farmer. In 1795 he purchased a water mill on adjoining land and started manufacturing scythes. In 1799 he started the manufacture of pistols. In April 1813, following a large order for 20,000 pistols, North built a large arms factory at Middletown, Conn. which operated in conjunction with his older Berlin shop about six miles distant. In 1828 North halted the manufacture of pistols and concentrated on making rifles.

From 1828 to 1850 Simeon North made Model 1817 and later Hall-patent breech-loading flintlock rifles and percussion carbines. The "Hall-North carbine," Model 1833, was a .58 caliber smoothbore to carry 24 balls to the pound, 45 inches in length, weighing 8 pounds 4 ounces and complete with a rod bayonet. They were the first percussion arms obtained by the Army ordnance department and they cost $20 each under the contract of June 1833.

Almost all of North's arms were stamped with logos such as: S. NORTH or US / S. NORTH / MIDLtn / CONN or some variation with a date such as 1826 or 1833 included. So far as we can determine, he did not mark weapons with the logo S. NORTH — BERLIN, CON. / OURAM, so we must assume that this marking was from one of his ancillary lines manufactured at the Berlin works, perhaps scythes or some other implements.

The North counterstamp may well be more properly included in my Hard Times Tokens reference (1833-44); research is continuing.

ROYS & WILCOX

Berlin, Conn.

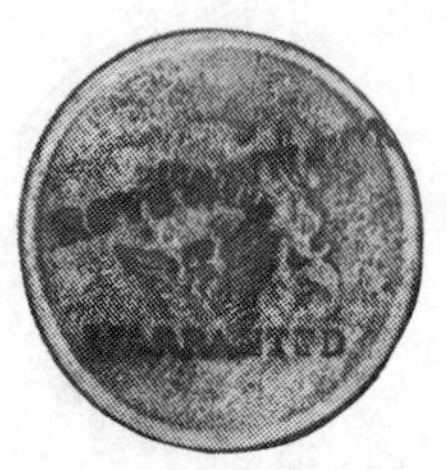

Ralau	Date	Metal	Size	VG	F	VF	EF
Conn 111	(?)	Copper	29mm	—	125.	—	175.
		ROYS & WILCOX / (Eagle) / WARRANTED ctsp on U.S. Large cent, date worn off. (Brunk 35215; Rulau Z80F)					
Conn 111C	(?)	Copper	29mm	125.	—	175.	—
		ROYS & WILCOX / CAST STEEL / BERLIN — CT ctsp on U.S. 1820 Large cent. (Brunk 35210)					

O. S. PLATT

Bridgeport, Conn.

It has been determined that Miller Conn 1 was issued after the Civil War. It appears in *U.S. Trade Tokens 1866-1889.*

I. ATKINS & CO.

Bristol, Conn.

Rulau	Date	Metal	Size	VG	F	VF	EF
Conn 112	(1844-55)	Copper	28mm	150.	—	225.	—
		I. ATKINS & CO. / BRISTOL CT. ctsp on U.S. 1837 Hard Times token. (Van Ormer sale 2519; Brunk 1295)					
Conn 112B	(1844-55)	Copper	29mm	125.	—	175.	—
		I. ATKINS & CO. ctsp on U.S. 1843 Large cent. (Brunk 1290)					
Conn 112D	(1844-55)	Copper	29mm	125.	—	175.	—
		I. ATKINS & CO. / EXTRAS ctsp on U.S. Large cent. (Brunk 1300)					

Irenus Atkins founded this company in the 1820's to manufacture clock faces. In the 1830's he was joined by his brother Rollin Atkins and by George Mitchell, doing business under several names. In 1855 the firm became Atkins Clock Mfg. Co. They also made circular saws, cotton gins, springs and machinery. (Research by Gregory Brunk)

Additional research on this and other clockmakers was done by Frank Hendrickson, King of Prussia, Pa., using the two reference works: *A Treasury of American Clocks* by Brooks Palmer, and *The American Clock* by William Distin and Robert Bishop.

ATKINS ALLEN & CO.

Rulau	Date	Metal	SizeVG	F	VF	EF	
Conn 180	(?)	Copper	29mm	—	—	—	300.
		ATKINS ALLEN & CO (curved) / BRISTOL / CONN ctsp on U.S. 1837 Large cent. (Pete Peters coll.)					

Irenus and Rollin Atkins began their clockmaking enterprise in 1826 and this became Atkins Clock Mfg. Co. in 1855. It went bankrupt in 1880.

Atkins Allen & Co. are not recorded, but this partnership could date from the Hard Times era, in the early 1840's. The only known specimen surfaced in 1993.

S.N. & H.C. BOTSFORD

Miller	Date	Metal	Size	VG	F	VF	Unc
Conn 2	(1840's)	Brass	27mm	5.00	10.00	30.00	80.00
		Eagle displayed, shield on breast, UNITED STATES OF AMERICA around. Rv: * S.N. & H.C. BOTSFORD * / OF / ALL KINDS / OF MEDICAL / ELECTRICAL / APPARATUS / BRISTOL / CONN / MANUFACTURERS. (Wright 1333)					
Conn 3	(1840's)	Brass	27mm	5.00	10.00	30.00	80.00
		Obverse as reverse of Conn 2. Rv: THADDEUS SMITH, AGENT FOR APPARATUS (etc.).					

S.N. Botsford, clock and watchmaker, also issued tokens in the Hard Times period, but from Norfolk, Va. (see Low 293-294).

BROWN & POMEROY

Bristol, Conn.

Enlarged

Rulau	Date	Metal	Size	VG	F	VF	EF
Conn 150	ND	Silver	32.5mm	—	—	225.	—
		BROWN & / POMEROY / BRISTOL / CT (all in small letters, from a prepared punch) ctsp on U.S. 1827 Capped Bust half dollar. (Gary Potter coll.; Brunk 5330)					

Jonathan C. Brown, Chauncey Pomeroy and others formed Forestville Mfg. Co. in 1835. It made clocks, at least until 1860. Brown was also a brazier.

S. COOK

Chatham, Conn.

Rulau	Date	Metal	Size	VG	F	VF	EF
Conn 170	(1850's)	Copper	29mm	60.00	—	90.00	—
		S. COOK ctsp on U.S. Large cent. Examined: 1840, 1851, 1852. (Brunk 9430)					

Henry Kauffman, in *Early American Ironware* (1966) identified S. Cook as a Chatham maker of kitchen irons, on page 50.

N. HAYWARD

Colchester, Conn.

Miller	Date	Metal	Size	VG	F	VF	Unc
Conn 4	(?)	White Metal	36mm	20.00	40.00	60.00	100.
		N. HAYWARD. Rv: Blank.					

Nathaniel Hayward appears in the 1850 census in Colchester.

CHAMBERLAIN WOODRUFF & SCRANTON (and) HOTCHKISS HALL & PLATT

Fair Haven, Conn.

Miller	Date	Metal	Size	VG	F	VF	Unc
Conn 5	(1840's)	Brass	30mm	10.00	30.00	100.	300.
		CHAMBERLAIN WOODRUFF & SCRANTON / GREAT / CASH / DRY / GOODS / ESTABLISHMENT / . FAIR HAVEN. Rv: HOTCHKISS HALL & PLATTS / SPLENDID / OF / GROCERIES / ASSORTMENT / * LONG BRICK STORE *. Plain edge. (Wright 465)					
Conn 5A	(1840's)	Brass	30mm	10.00	30.00	100.	300.
		As 5. Reeded edge. (Kovacs coll.)					
Conn 5C	(1840's)	Silvered Brass	30mm	10.00	30.00	100.	400.
		As 5. Plain edge. (Wright 161)					
Conn 5D	(1840's)	Copper	30mm	—	—	100.	400.
		As 5. Plain edge. (Slabaugh coll.)					

S. BEACH

Hartford, Conn.

Rulau	Date	Metal	Size	VG	F	VF	EF
Conn 118	(?)	Copper	29mm	—	50.00	—	100.
		KEPT AT COLTS ARMORY HARTFORD. / S. BEACH / NOV. 22 / HARTFORD. (inverted) ctsp on U.S. 1849 Large cent. (Frank Kovacs coll.; Brunk 2810)					

This was originally reported as E. Beach due to a misreading. There was a gunsmith named Albert Beach who was active in Hartford in the 1854-1880 period, who may be connected.

A. CHAPIN

Rulau	Date	Metal	Size	VG	F	VF	EF
Conn 119	(ca 1850)	Copper	29mm	60.00	—	90.00	—
		A. CHAPIN. in relief ctsp on U.S. Large cent. Examined: 1817, 1831, 1837, 1847, 1850, 1851. (Brunk 7320)					
Conn 119B	(ca 1850)	Copper	29mm	100.	—	150.	—
		A. CHAPIN. / (Eagle in circle of stars) / A. CHAPIN. ctsp on U.S. 1820 Large cent. (Brunk 7325)					

Alexander Chapin was a silversmith and buttonmaker active in Hartford circa 1846-51. He succeeded his father, Aaron, who died in 1838 (born 1753).

Though in relief, the A. CHAPIN. stamp is not contained in the usual rectangular depression so useful on teaspoon and fork shanks, etc. Originally reported by Kenneth L. Hallenbeck in the *TAMS Journal* for 1964.

COLLINS & CO.

Hartford, Conn.

Rulau	Date	Metal	Size	VG	F	VF	EF
Conn 123	(1840's ?)	Copper	29mm	125.	—	175.	—
		COLLINS & CO. / HARTFORD / CAST-STEEL / WARRANTED ctsp on obverse of U.S. 1820 Large cent. H. HORTON ctsp across reverse of the coin. (B&M Taylor sale, March 1987, lot 1272, where it realized $176; Brunk 8875).					
Conn 123C	(?)	Copper	29mm	75.00	—	100.	—
		COLLINS (in toothed rectangle) ctsp on U.S. Large cent. Examined: 1817, 1835. (Brunk 8870)					

Samuel Collins built an axe factory in Hartford in 1826, possibly the first in America. He also built a large factory in Collinsville, Conn.

ROGERS, SMITH & CO.

Hartford, Conn.

Miller	Date	Metal	Size	VG	F	VF	Unc
Conn 12	(?)	White Metal	26mm	5.00	10.00	20.00	40.00
		ROGERS, SMITH & CO. "EXTRA PLATE ON WHITE METAL." Rv: Blank.					
Conn 13	(?)	White Metal	32mm	5.00	10.00	20.00	40.00
		ROGERS, SMITH & CO. Number in center. Rv: Blank.					
Conn 13A	(?)	Copper	29mm	150.	—	250.	—
		As 13, but ctsp on U.S. 182. Large cent.					

These tokens are probably akin to those of Holmes Booth & Haydens of Waterbury, Conn., which see.

Miller	Date	Metal	Size	VG	F	VF	Unc
Conn 13D	(?)	White Metal	18mm	5.00	10.00	20.00	40.00
		ROGERS, SMITH & CO / NO / NEW-HAVEN CT (blank space in center). Rv: Blank. Plain edge. (Schenkman coll.)					

DR. BAKER

Meriden, Conn.

Rulau	Date	Metal	Size	VG	F	VF	EF
Conn 155	(?)	Silver	31mm	—	—	250.	—

CONSULT / DR. BAKER ctsp on U.S. 1856-S Seated Liberty half dollar. (Van Ormer 2522; Brunk 1930; Rulau ZE8)

Dr. Paul Baker was a dealer in patent medicines.

FRARY, BENHAM & CO.

Meriden, Conn.

Rulau	Date	Metal	Size	VG	F	VF	EF
Conn 120	(1849)	Copper	29mm	50.00	—	75.00	—

FRARY, BENHAM & CO. within curving scroll ctsp incuse on U.S. 1817 Large cent. (Frank Kovacs coll. Rulau Z15; Brunk 15010)

James A. Frary and Morris Benham were in business as makers of Britannia ware under the style Frary, Benham & Co. for only a single year, 1849, according to *Guide to American Pewter* by Carl Jacobs (New York, 1957). Frary made Britannia ware alone 1845-49. Objects made by this firm are rare to unknown, according to pewter experts.

MERIDEN BRIT'A CO.

Meriden, Conn.

Rulau	Date	Metal	Size	VG	F	VF	EF
Conn 121	(?)	Copper	26.4mm	—	75.00	—	125.

MERIDEN BRIT'A CO ctsp on worn England George II halfpenny before 1760. Same ctsp on reverse. (Hartzog coll.; Brunk 27407)

The Meriden Britannia Company manufactured and sold Britannia ware, 1852-1898. The mark on the British coin is one of its signatures. It absorbed Rogers Bros. of Hartford, Conn. in the 1860's and merged into International Silver Co. (Insilco) in 1898.

I.I. HOUGH & CO.

Middletown, Conn.

Rulau	Date	Metal	Size	G	VG	F	EF
Conn 100	(?)	Copper	29mm	—	75.00	—	125.

I.I. HOUGH & CO. / MIDDLETOWN CT ctsp on U.S. Large cent. (Hallenbeck 8.757; Brunk 20150)

Isaac Hough appears in the 1850 census under Middletown.

A. M. BOUTON

New Canaan, Conn.

Rulau	Date	Metal	Size	VG	F	VF	EF
Conn 160	(?)	Copper	23mm	—	—	125.	—

A. M. BOUTON. / WARRANTED in relief, within circular depression around rim of coin. / CAST STEEL (incuse, twice, in cross form within circular center of the relief stamp), ctsp on early U.S. Bust Half cent reverse. (Brunk 4530; Rulau Z2B).

Alexander Malachi Bouton, born 1807, died 1882. He was probably a toolmaker.

W. W. IVES

New Hartford, Conn.

Rulau	Date	Metal	Size	VG	F	VF	EF
Conn 175	(ca 1860?)	Silver	32.5mm	—	100.	—	—

W. W. IVES ctsp on obverse of U.S. 1810 Bust half dollar. Similar ctsp on reverse of coin. (Frank Kovacs coll.; Brunk 21220; Rulau-E Mav 24)

William Walter Ives, born 1816, was a farmer, according to William Swoger research.

J.E. BASSETT & CO.

New Haven, Conn.

Miller	Date	Metal	Size	VG	F	VF	Unc
Conn 14	(?)	Copper	25mm	5.00	10.00	15.00	40 .00

J.E. BASSETT & CO. / NEW HAVEN, CONN. / 236 CHAPEL ST. * HARDWARE CUTLERY & IRON. Rv: o J.E. BASSETT & CO o/ TOOL & / HARDWARE / STORE / 236 CHAPEL ST NEW-HAVEN CONN. (Wright 69)

Miller	Date	Metal	Size	VG	F	VF	Unc
Conn 15	(?)	Copper	25mm	5.00	10.00	15.00	40.00

Ice skate with curved runner front at center; scroll below; J.E. BASSETT & CO curved above. Around all is: o SKATES SOLD BY o / 236 CHAPEL ST NEW HAVEN CONN.

Miller	Date	Metal	Size	VG	F	VF	Unc
Conn 15A	(?)	Brass	25mm	5.00	10.00	20.00	50.00

As 15.

N. O.

(Nathaniel Olmsted & Son)

New Haven, Conn.

Rulau	Date	Metal	Size	VG	F	VF	EF
Conn 115	(1847)	Silver	27mm	25.00	—	50.00	—

N. O. in monogram in relief within an oval depression ctsp on Spanish-American 1809-Mo 2-reales. (Duffield 1369)

Rulau	Date	Metal	Size	VG	F	VF	EF
Conn 116	(1847)	Copper	29mm	20.00	—	40.00	—

N. OLMSTED ctsp on U.S. 1838 Large cent. (Hallenbeck 15.505; Brunk 30210)

Nathaniel Olmsted & Son were silversmiths in New Haven, active about 1840-60. The firm had been located in Farmington as early as 1808.

(See an Olmsted-related piece under J.E. Caldwell & Co., Philadelphia, Pa.)

It is possible that 115 is the mark of Nicholas Ohman of St. John, Newfoundland (See Brunk 29160).

WM. AVERY

Preston, Conn.

Rulau	Date	Metal	Size	VG	F	VF	EF
Conn 102	(?)	Silver	27mm	40.00	—	60.00	—

WM. AVERY ctsp on Spanish-American 2-reales. (Gould 79; Brunk 1440.)

Doubtful attribution.

F. HAYDEN

Waterbury, Conn.

Miller	Date	Metal	Size	VG	F	VF	EF
Conn 30	(?)	Copper	29mm	50.00	—	100.	—

F. HAYDEN WATERBURY, CONN. (retrograde) ctsp on U.S. Large cent. (Brunk 18850)

See Holmes, Booth and Haydens in the 1866-1889 section of this catalog.

THOMAS F. PAINTER

Rulau	Date	Metal	Size	VG	F	VF	Unc
Conn 103	(1845-55)	Brass	26mm	—		Ex. Rare	

Bust right at center, REV. JOHN WESLEY above. Rev: THOMAS F. PAINTER / BANJO / NF. CED. / PLAYER / .WATERBURY. Plain edge. (Schenkman collection)

The obverse is the same as Pa 191, the James Harmstead token.

This piece was discovered only in 1982 and may possibly be unique. The die work on the reverse differs considerably from the obverse, leading to the conclusion this may be a pattern using a stock die (the Wesley portrait) with some trial text for the "banjo player."

"NF. CED." = NUFF SAID. Eccentric spelling of a slang term.

SCOVILL HOUSE

Rulau	Date	Metal	Size	F	VF	EF	Unc
Conn 125	(?)	Copper	48.7mm	10.00	20.00	30.00	40.00

All within double-bordered cartouche: SCOVILL HOUSE / — BY — / BROWN. & DART. / —o— / WATERBURY. / —o— / — CONN. -. Rv: Intaglio of obverse. Plain edge. (Koppenhaver coll.)

This piece may be an I.D. plate from furniture, equipment, etc. Probably very rare.

L. S. WHITE

Rulau	Date	Metal	Size	G	VG	F	EF
Conn 140	1854	Copper	29mm	—	100.	—	150.
		L. S. WHITE PATENTED — JAN 31 1854 ctsp on U.S. 1848 Large cent. (Wright 1237; Rulau Z100; Brunk 43060)					
Conn 141	(1854)	Copper	29mm	—	85.00	—	135.
		L. S. WHITE ctsp on U.S. 1851 Large cent. (Brunk 43050)					

Leroy S. White was a breech-loading arms patentee on January 8, 1863. We could find no record of the earlier patent, which may also have been for firearms.

During the 1860's and 1870's he was also superintendent of Rogers and Brother, a silverware manufacturer.

LESLIE S. WHITE
Waterbury, Conn.

The U.S. 1887 Liberty nickel counterstamped LESLIE S. WHITE / WATERBURY, CT., is not connected with the L.S. White counterstamps above (Conn 140-141), which were issued by Leroy S. White, the inventor of firearms of Waterbury. The Leslie S. White piece appears under *U.S. Trade Tokens 1866-1889*.

D. MAXWELL & SON
West Winsted, Conn.

Rulau	Date	Metal	Size	VG	F	VF	EF
Conn 104	(?)	Copper	29mm	250.	—	350.	—

D. MAXWELL & SON / HARNESS / M'F'RS / W. WINSTED CT ctsp on U.S. 1851 Large cent. (Brunk 26520)

Rulau	Date	Metal	Size	VG	F	VF	EF
Conn 105	(?)	Silver	25mm	250.	—	350.	—

Similar ctsp on U.S. 1854 Liberty Seated quarter. (Van Ormer sale 2744)

Rulau	Date	Metal	Size	VG	F	VF	EF
Conn 105A	(?)	Silver	25mm	250	—	350.	—

Similar ctsp on U.S. 1875-S or 1876-S Liberty Seated quarter. (Ray Colbert coll.; Tanenbaum coll.)

The firm of C.G. Maxwell, harness makers, appears in the 1885 Connecticut business directory, possibly the successor.

GEORGIA

W.H. HAUSMAN
Savannah, Ga.

Miller	Date	Metal	Size	VG	F	VF	Unc
Ga 7	(1850's)	Gilt Brass	24mm	8.00	11.00	15.00	40.00

Liberty seated left, amid spinning wheel, shield, cornucopia etc., .BLUE STORE. above, SAVANNAH, GEO. below. Rv: Eagle displayed, shield on breast. W.H. HAUSMAN / CLOTHING WAREHOUSE. Reeded edge.

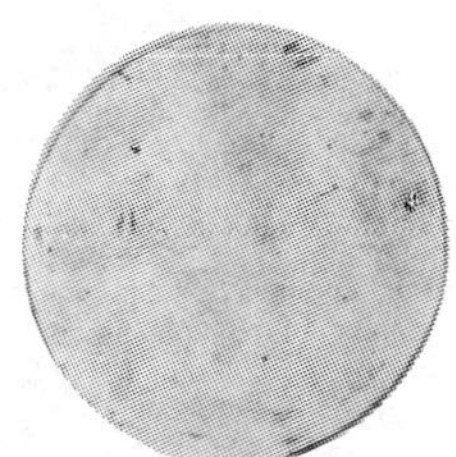

SPECIAL NOTE: The Eldorado Saloon 10-cent and Haywoods Saloon 10-cent and 25-cent tokens of Savannah, in cupronickel, 28.2mm, listed by Adams as numbers Ga 4 and Ga 5-6 respectively, have been determined to be tokens of the 1870's.

ILLINOIS

JOHN PLANE & CO.
Belvidere, Ill.

Miller	Date	Metal	Size	VG	F	EF	Unc
Ill 1	1856	Brass	28mm	5.00	9.00	18.00	40.00
		Anvil in center, date 1856 under it. JOHN PLANE & CO. BELVIDERE ILL. around. Rv: Cook stove in center, DEALERS IN HARDWARE IRON & STOVES. Plain edge. (Wright 838)					
Ill 1A	1856	Brass	28mm	—	—	75.00	Rare
		As 1, but thick planchet.					
Ill 2	1856	Copper	28mm	5.00	9.00	18.00	40.00
		As 1. Plain edge.					

The relationship between John Plane & Co. and Plane & Jennison has not yet been determined exactly, because Jennison's name cannot be located in directories. Tentative conclusion is that Plane & Jennison preceded Plane & Co. by one or several years, or that it may have been in the 1857-60 period.

Directories in the Belvidere public library indicate John Plane was in business alone from 1865 to at least 1876. The name Jennison in any combination does not appear in any 1865-1893 directory, proof that Plane and Jennison pieces must have been pre-Civil War.

PLANE & JENNISON

Belvidere, Ill.

Miller	Date	Metal	Size	VG	F	EF	Unc
III 3	(1850's)	Brass	28mm	7.00	11.00	20.00	40.00

Anvil in center, PLANE & JENNISON — BELVIDERE, ILL. Rv: Cook stove in center. DEALERS IN HARDWARE IRON & STOVES. Plain edge. (Wright 837)

GEO. WILLIAMS

Belvidere, Ill.

(See this card under N.C. Amsden, Genoa, Ill.)

BAKER & MOODY

Chicago, Ill.

Miller	Date	Metal	Size	F	VF	EF	Unc
III 4	(1853-57)	Copper	28mm	7.00	12.50	20.00	40.00
		Eagle displayed, shield on breast. BAKER & MOODY HATTERS. Rv: Hat. * 186 LAKE STREET * CHICAGO, ILL. Plain edge.					
III 5	(1853-57)	Brass	28mm	7.00	12.50	20.00	40.00
		As 4. Plain edge. (Wright 58)					
III 5A	(1853-57)	Silvered Brass	28mm	—	14.00	22.00	60.00
		As 4. Plain edge.					
III 6	(1853-57)	Brass	28mm	8.00	13.50	21.00	50.00
		As 4, but Thin planchet. Plain edge.					
III 7	(1853-57)	Brass	28mm	7.00	12.50	20.00	50.00
		As 4, Normal planchet. Reeded edge.					

Miller	Date	Metal	Size	F	VF	EF	Unc
III 7A	(1860)	Copper	28mm	—	—	200.	250.
		Obverse as reverse of III 4 (Hat). Rv: IMPORTERS / AND / JOBBERS OF / FANCY & STAPLE / DRY GOODS / 83 CEDAR ST. / NEW — YORK (Loder & Co. card of New York City). Only 5 known.					
III 7B	(1860)	Copper	28mm	—	—	200.	250.
		Obverse as reverse of III 4 (Hat). Rv: FRANCISCO & WHITMAN / (eagle) / HATTERS (Nashville, Tenn. card). Only 4 known.					
III 7C	(1860)	Brass	28mm	—	—	150.	200.
		Obverse as reverse of III 4 (Hat). Rv: SLEEPER & FENNER / UMBRELLAS / (female head left, PARASOL on coronet) / PHILADA. Only 10 to 12 known.					
III 7D	(1860)	Brass	28mm	—	—	150.	200.
		Obverse as reverse of III 4 (Hat). Rv: FRANCISCO & WIGGIN / HATTERS (Memphis, Tenn. card). Only 10 to 12 known.					

None of the mulings listed here as III 7A through 7D were known to Adams or Miller. Three of them were first recorded by Joseph Schmidt in "19th Century Illinois Exonumia" (*TAMS Journal* for Dec. 1977), while the Francisco & Whitman muling is recorded here for the first time. All the mulings were made in 1860 or later, and all have a plain edge.

The Baker and Moody partnership — Franklin Baker and Orrin C. Moody — must have been formed in the early 1850's. The 1844 directory lists O. Moody as a hatter at I.C. Stevens' store.

In 1853-54 Baker & Moody, cap and fur manufacturers, are at 186 Lake Street, the address on the tokens. In the 1859 directory they have moved to 88 Lake Street. The tokens apparently emanate from the 1853-57 period. The firm does not appear in the 1865 directory.

However, Franklin Baker in 1865 has become agent for N.W. Welch, at 20 Lake Street.

BARKER & ILLSLEY

Rulau	Date	Metal	Size	VG	F	VF	Unc
III 120	(1857-59)	Copper	20.5mm	—	10.00	—	30.00
		BUSINESS CARD die, Fuld CWT 1368. Rv: BARKER & ILLSLEY / HARDWARE / NAILS / & / STOVES / 77 STATE ST / CHICAGO. Plain edge. Rarity 3. (Fuld CWT 150B-1a; H-G 2162)					
III 120A	(1857-59)	Nickel	20.5mm	—	—	—	500.
		As last. Rarity 8. (Fuld CWT 150B-1c; H-G 2163)					

Formerly listed as a Civil War issuer, this merchant was included in the 1859 listing of the ANSP. The issuer's tokens are being deleted from CW token catalogs, according to Steve Tanenbaum.

BURBANK & SHAW

Miller	Date	Metal	Size	VG	F	VF	EF
III 8	1845	Copper	26mm	15.00	20.00	30.00	75.00
		BURBANK * SHAW. / DEALERS / IN / DRY GOODS / GROCERIES & CROCKERY. Rv: CASH PAID FOR PRODUCE. / CHICAGO / 149 / LAKE ST. / --.-- / 1845 / .W. Plain edge. Occurs with thick and thin flans.					
III 8A	1845	Silvered Copper	26mm	—	30.00	50.00	—
		As 8. Plain edge. (Wright 120)					
III 8B	1845	Silvered Copper	26mm	—	—	Rare	—
		As 8A, but thick planchet.					

Miller	Date	Metal	Size	VG	F	VF	EF
III 8C	1845	Copper	26mm	25.00	30.00	40.00	100.
		As III 8, but doubled reverse die. Doubling clear on CASH PAID FOR and CE of PRODUCE; also on 18 of 1845. Hub or ejection doubling are most likely causes, not reengraving. About 25 specimens known.					

Ill 8M	1846	Copper	26mm	5 Known

Reverse of Ill 8C (the doubled die token) is the obverse. Rv: Within an inner circle, the date 1846 is crudely executed. Above the date are two stars with a split leaf facing left between them. Below the date are two stars with a split leaf facing right between them. Plain edge.

This muling was first recorded in *The Numismatist* for Aug. 1980 by Schenkman and Levine in "Exonumia Notebook." One known specimen exhibits porous planchet. The 1846-dated side is that of Hawaii A36 in Gould and Bressett's *Hawaiian Coins, Tokens & Paper Money.*

The muling probably has no Hawaiian connection. Most likely diesinker '.W.' sold his CASH FOR PRODUCE die to another diesinker who used it to fill a customer's order. The muling may also result from whimsy, but most likely was not made for a collector since it took 134 years to be reported, and both known specimens are circulated. The known pieces are in the David Schenkman collection and the Owen & Schmidt specimen was auctioned in 1981.

The diesinker's initial .W. on these tokens has not been traced. It is possible a Mr. Waller or Mr. White of 77 or 72 Lake Street, Chicago are responsible for the tokens. One of these men might have studied under Shubael D. Childs at his infant Clark Street engraving firm during the early 1840's.

The Chicago Business Directory for 1844 fails to list either Burbank or Shaw. The 1853 directory also fails to mention the firm. Thus it may be accepted that Burbank & Shaw started business in 1844-1845 and were out of business before 1853.

Since at least 50 of the Burbank & Shaw pieces are known, we assign Rarity 5 to this piece, making it the most readily available of Illinois' rare 1845-dated merchant tokens.

Rulau	Date	Metal	Size	G	F	VF	EF
Ill 100	1846	Copper	25mm	—	100.	Rare	—

Watch face surrounded by wreath. Rv: Three ornaments above and below '1846'. (Wright 787)

An early watchmaker's check. Perhaps 15-18 known.

There is a die connection between this piece and the so-called Burbank & Shaw-Hawaiian mule listed under Chicago, Illinois in this reference.

One piece appeared in the Hetrich sale by Bowers & Ruddy, Jan. 28-30, 1982.

CHILDS & CO.

Miller	Date	Metal	Size	VG	F	EF	Unc
Ill 9	1858	Copper	25mm	—	20.00	25.00	50.00
		Chicago court house, CHICAGO. Rv: Eagle at center, CHILDS & CO. / 1858. Rarity 7. (Schmidt C78)					
Ill 9A	1858	White Metal	25mm	—	20.00	25.00	60.00
		As 9. Rarity 7. (Schmidt C78A)					
Ill 11	1860	Brass	20mm	—	15.00	20.00	50.00
		Liberty seated. Rv: CHILDS. DIE SINKER & ENGRAVER. 1860. 117 1/2 RANDOLPH ST., CHICAGO. (Schmidt N/L; Fuld Ill 150-5-14b)					

Shubael D. Childs began his engraving and diesinking business in Chicago in 1837.

Childs was located on Clark Street between Lake and Randolph in 1844. In 1860 he is listed as doing business at 117 1/2 Randolph Street. Then in 1865 there is a listing for Shubael D. Childs Jr. at 117 1/2 Randolph Street.

R. H. COUNTISS

Rulau	Date	Metal	Size	VG	F	VF	Unc
Ill 122	(1857-59)	Copper	20.5mm	—	10.00	—	30.00
		Fuld CWT die 1368. Rv: R.H. COUNTISS / GROCER / COR / OF / STATE & NORTH / & COR CLARK & / VAN BUREN / STS / CHICAGO. ILL. Plain edge. Rarity 3. (Fuld CWT 150M-2a; H-G 2202)					
Ill 122A	(1857-59)	Nickel	20.5mm	—	—	—	75.00
		As last. Rarity 9. (Fuld 150M-2c; H-G 2203)					

Ill 123	(1857-59)	Copper	20.5mm	—	10.00	—	30.00
		Fuld CW die 1368. Rv: R.H. COUNTISS / GROCER / & / TEA DEALER / CLARK ST. COR / VAN BUREN / CHICAGO. ILL. Plain edge. Rarity 3. (Fuld CWT 150M-1a; H-G 2200)					

It is probable that Ill 123 was issued earlier than Ill 122.

JAMES B. DARLING

Rulau	Date	Metal	Size	G	VG	F	EF
Ill 102	(?)	Silver	26mm	—	—	—	—
		JAMES B. DARLING / CHICAGO / ILLS. engraved on U.S. Liberty Seated quarter dollar. (Gould 16)					

F. N. DUBOIS

Rulau	Date	Metal	Size	VG	F	VF	Unc
Ill 125	(1857-59)	Copper	20.5mm	—	15.00	—	40.00
		Fuld CW die 1368. Rv: F.N. DUBOIS / SILVER WARE / BADGE & MEDAL / MANUFACTORY / P.O. BOX. 1899 / CHICAGO, ILL. Plain edge. Rarity 6. (Fuld CWT 150P-2a; H-G 2214)					

So far this issuer has not been traceable through silversmith references.

EDWARDS FINE WATCHES

This token issuer, who used CW die 1368 (BUSINESS CARD), may be a Civil War issuer. Its tokens were not mentioned in the ANSP 1859 listing. J.T. and E. M. Edwards were listed in directories 1852-1864. A patent date appears on some of their silverware, 1855.

This could also be a Merchant Era (1845-60) issuer.(Fuld CWT 150Q-1a. copper, Rarity 4).

FLAGG & MACDONALD

Rulau	Date	Metal	Size	VG	F	VF	Unc
Ill 127	(1857-59)	Copper	20.5mm	—	10.00	—	30.00
		Fuld CW die 1368. Rv: FLAGG & MACDONALD / BOOTS / & / SHOES / 181 / LAKE. ST / CHICAGO. ILL. Plain edge. Rarity 3. (Fuld CWT 150T-1a and 2a; H-G 2224-2225)					

There is a minor die variety. Flagg alone issued tokens using the BUSINESS CARD die (Fuld 1368) from 189 Lake St.; these may be Civil War issues.

FREEDMAN GOODKIND & CO.

Rulau	Date	Metal	Size	VG	F	VF	Unc
Ill 130	(1857-59)	Copper	20mm	—	8.00	—	27.50
		Fuld CW die 1368. Rv: FREEDMAN. GOODKIND & CO / DRY / GOODS / 171 / LAKE. ST / CHICAGO. ILL. Plain edge. Rarity 2. (Fuld CWT 150W-1a; H-G 2235)					
Ill 130A	(1857-59)	Nickel	20mm	—	—	—	75.00
		As last. Rarity 9. (Fuld CWT 150W-1C)					
Ill 131	(1857-59)	Copper	20.5mm	—	8.00	—	27.50
		Similar to 130, but 135 / LAKE. ST. Plain edge. Rarity 2. (Fuld CWT 150W-2a; H-G 2234)					

There are other tokens of Freedman Goodkind & Co., and of Freedman & Goodkind at 171 Lake St., but all these may be Civil War issues.

J.H.H.

Miller	Date	Metal	Size	VG	F	VF	EF
Ill 21	1858	Brass	26mm	—	Rare	—	—

Court house at center, J.H.H. — COURT HOUSE above; 1858 — CHICAGO below. Rv: Incuse J.H.H. 272. Plain edge. Rare.

Other incused numbers than 272 are known.

HAMILTON & WHITE

Miller	Date	Metal	Size	VG	F	VF	EF
Ill 12	1845	Copper	27mm	160.	185.	225.	300.

'Prairie schooner' with two horses to right at center; GOING TO / 139 above; LAKE ST. / CHICAGO ILL. below. Rv: HAMILTON & WHITE / DEALERS IN / DRY GOODS / GROCERIES / AND / PRODUCE / 1845. Plain edge. (Wright 418)

Miller	Date	Metal	Size	VG	F	VF	EF
Ill 12A	1845	Silv/C	27mm	—	—	Rare	—

As last. The silvering was done before striking. (Tilden coll.)

The rarest of all early available Illinois tokens.

Hamilton & White — Robert P. Hamilton and M.L. White — appear in the 1844 directory as a dry goods and grocery store at 13 Lake Street. The partnership, and the partners, have disappeared by the 1854 directory.

C.N. HOLDEN & CO.

Miller	Date	Metal	Size	F	VF	EF	Unc
Ill 14	(1848-52)	Brass	28mm	7.00	12.50	20.00	40.00

C.N. HOLDEN & CO. — WHOLESALE & RETAIL ONE PRICE STORE — DRY GOODS / GROCERIES / 182 / LAKE ST., CHICAGO / GOODS SOLD AT THE / LOWEST MARKET PRICE. Rv: C.N. HOLDEN & CO. — TEAS AT WHOLESALE & RETAIL — / 182 / LAKE ST., CHICAGO / ONE PRICE PEKIN TEA STORE / TEAS IN CHESTS / CADDIES & CANS / AT / N.Y. PRICES. Reeded edge. (Wright 457)

Miller	Date	Metal	Size	F	VF	EF	Unc
Ill 15	(1848-52)	Copper	28mm	7.50	14.00	22.00	40.00

As 14. Plain edge.

Miller	Date	Metal	Size	F	VF	EF	Unc
Ill 16	(1848-52)	Silvered Brass	28mm	8.00	15.00	23.50	40.00

As 14. Plain edge.

Miller	Date	Metal	Size	F	VF	EF	Unc
Ill 17	(1860)	Silvered Copper	28mm	—	—	25.00	50.00

Obverse as 14. Rv: Card of Francisco & Whitman, Nashville, Tenn. Plain edge. About 10 known.

Miller	Date	Metal	Size	F	VF	EF	Unc
Ill 17A	(1860)	Copper	28mm	8.00	15.00	25.00	50.00

As 17.

Miller	Date	Metal	Size	F	VF	EF	Unc
Ill 17 1/2	(1860)	Brass	28mm	8.00	15.00	25.00	50.00

As 17.

C.N. Holden & Co., dry goods, groceries, nails, etc., appear in the 1844 business directory at the corner of Clark and South Water Streets, near the bridge. The firm's partners were Charles N. Holden, William P. Holden and Albon H. Holden.

In the 1854 directory C.N. Holden has become an insurance agent, commissioner of deeds, land broker and stockbroker, with offices at 41 Clark Street — over Smith's Bank. The 1859 directory lists Charles N. Holden as agent for Firemans Insurance Co., northwest corner of Lake and Clark.

The tokens apparently were issued in the 1848-52 period.

The 1859 directory reveals that Albon H. Holden and Russell Green were in business as Green & Holden, lumber dealers, at 102 So. Canal Street.

J.R. JONES

Rulau	Date	Metal	Size	VG	F	VF	EF
Ill114	(?)	Gold	25mm	—	—	Rare	—

J.R. JONES. / CHICAGO. ctsp or engraved on obverse of U.S. 1823 $5 gold piece of Capped Head, large diameter variety. (ANA collection, Colorado Springs, Colo.; Brunk 22060)

This apparently unique specimen was presented by Sidney W. Smith and William J. Mertes to the American Numismatic Association Museum collection.

JUDD & CORTHELL

Rulau	Date	Metal	Size	VG	F	VF	Unc
Ill 133	(1857-59)	Copper	20.5mm	—	10.00	—	30.00

Fuld CW die 1368. Rv: JUDD & CORTHELL / BOOTS / & / SHOES / 100 / LAKE. ST / CHICAGO. ILL. Plain edge. Rarity 3. (Fuld CWT 150AH-1a; H-G 2264)

Rulau	Date	Metal	Size	VG	F	VF	Unc
Ill 133A	(1857-59)	Nickel	20.5mm	—	—	—	75.00

As last. Rarity 9. (Fuld CWT 150AH-1c; H-G 2265)

PEARSON & DANA

Miller	Date	Metal	Size	F	VF	EF	Unc
Ill 25	(1858-60)	Copper	28mm	7.00	10.00	15.00	40.00

Eagle displayed, shield on breast; PEARSON & DANA. above, * BOOTS & SHOES * below. Rv: WHOLESALE & RETAIL. / 184 / LAKE ST. / * CHICAGO * / * ILL. *. Plain edge.

Miller	Date	Metal	Size	F	VF	EF	Unc
Ill 26	(1858-60)	Brass	28mm	7.00	10.00	15.00	40.00

As 25. Plain edge. (Wright 801)

Miller	Date	Metal	Size	F	VF	EF	Unc
Ill 26A	(1858-60)	Silv/Br	28mm	—	—	—	—

As 25.

Miller	Date	Metal	Size	F	VF	EF	Unc
Ill 26B	(1858-60)	Brass	28mm	7.50	11.00	16.00	40.00

As 26, but thin planchet. Plain edge.

Miller	Date	Metal	Size	F	VF	EF	Unc
Ill 26C	(1858-60)	Brass	28mm	7.00	10.00	24.00	40.00

As 26. Reeded edge.

Pearson and Dana do not appear in the 1844 or 1854 directories.

They appear in the 1859 directory — Albert G. Pearson and William V. Dana, boots and shoes, 184 Lake Street. By the 1865 directory the firm has relocated at 166 Lake Street.

W. R. PRENTICE

Rulau	Date	Metal	Size	VG	F	VF	Unc
Ill 135	(1857-59)	Copper	20.5mm	—	10.00	—	30.00

Fuld CW die 1368. Rv: W.R. PRENTICE / FAMILY / GROCERY / 75 / CANAL. ST / CHICAGO. ILL. Plain edge. Rarity 3. (Fuld CWT 150AU-1a; H-G 2307)

J.B. SHAW

Miller	Date	Metal	Size	VG	F	VF	EF
Ill 27	(1860)	Silver	13mm	—	—	—	Unique?

Around: J.B. SHAW, CHICAGO; in center circle: BOOK / SELLER. Rv: Coronet Liberty head left (imitation of U.S. gold dollar obverse).

Only known specimen is in American Numismatic Society museum, New York.

Adams states, "Badly double struck on a silver counterfeit of a gold dollar. In the cabinet of the American Numismatic Society, probably unique."

No doubt Adams searched the ANS cabinet in preparing his book, "*United States Store Cards.*" Since no other like specimen has been reported, one must consider it unique. An unusual example of a bookseller's token.

Shaw does not appear in the 1859 or 1865 directories.

PETER STUMPS

Chicago, Ill.

Miller	Date	Metal	Size	VG	F	EF	Unc
Ill 40	(1859)	Brass	23mm	25.00	30.00	40.00	60.00

		Fireman's hat, MADE TO ORDER / CHICAGO, ILL. Rv: PETER STUMPS / BOOT / & SHOE / MAKER / 188 STATE ST. Reeded edge. (Wright 1070)					
Ill 40A	(1859)	Copper	23mm	—	—	—	Rare
		As 40. Reeded edge.					

Later pieces of this issuer, with 312 Cottage Grove Ave. address, are Civil War tokens.

Stumps does not appear in the 1844 or 1854 directories. In the 1859 directory Peter Stumps, shoemaker, is at 188 State Street. He must have gone out of business by 1865, as he does not appear in the 1865 directory.

N.C. AMSDEN
Genoa, Ill. and

GEO. WILLIAMS
Belvidere, Ill.

Miller	Date	Metal	Size	VG	F	VF	EF
Ill 44	1845	Copper	27mm	125.	150.	200.	250.
		Man striding right at center, GOING TO N.C. AMSDEN'S STORE around; GENOA / ILL. *1845* below. Rv: GEO. WILLIAMS, / DEALER / IN DRY GOODS & / GROCERIES / BELVIDERE, ILL. Plain edge. (Wright 19 and 1248)					

Miller	Date	Metal	Size	VG	F	VF	EF
Ill 44A	1845	Sil-plated Copper	27mm	—	—	—	Scarce
		As 44.					
Ill 44B	1845	Silver	27mm	—	—	—	Unique
		Same as 44, but struck over Mexican 2-reales.					

A double card. It should also be included under Belvidere, Ill. Noah C. Amsden appears in the 1850 census.

H.A. BALCH
Joliet, Ill.

Rulau	Date	Metal	Size	VG	F	VF	EF
Ill 109	(1864)	Silver	25mm	125.	—	175.	—
		H.A. BALCH / ARTIST / JOLIET ILL ctsp on U.S. Seated Liberty quarter. Examined: 1847, 1853, 1854, 1857. There are 9 reported specimens. (Gould 5; Brunk 2030)					
Ill 109A	(1864)	Silver	25mm	125.	—	175.	—
		H.A. BALCH / ARTIST ctsp on U.S. Seated Liberty quarter. Examined: 1853, 1857. There are 3 reported specimens. (Brunk 2020)					

Balch is known to have been in business 1864-66 and 1875-84. He may well have applied these counterstamps when his business opened, in 1864. However, should a post-1864 dated coin with either of these stamps surface, we shall move Balch to our section on 1866-1889 tokens.

'BUSINESS CARD' DIE
Chicago, Ill. and Other Locations

Tokens of the following issuers, all with the same obverse (revcerse) dies, have always been assumed to be Civil War pieces, and were listed as such even as early as 1863 in an article by Pliny E. Chase. However, seven of them were also in the list of merchant tokens published by the Antiquarian and Numismatic Society of Pennsylvania published in 1859 and thus cannot be legitimate Civil War issues.

However, they have been retained in the CWT category in the Fulds' *U.S. Civil War Store Cards* and all other references, since collectors have considereed them CWT's for more than a century. Most of them, except for the seven in the ANSP list, are not cataloged here, though some may have been issued before 1860. The common die is a product of S.D. Childs of Chicago and is an imitation of the then-new Flying Eagle cent reverse. All BUSINESS CARD die tokens measure 20.5 mm/

A number of the Chicago tokens are illustrated here. The issuers are:

CHICAGO
J.J. Brown
Edwards
Flagg
Freedman & Goodkind
P. Gaffney
C.E. Gerts & Co.
R. Heilbroner
W.A. Hendrie
F.A. Leavitt
Oppenheimer & Metzger
W. Treleaven
AURORA, ILL.
Gates & Trask
LYONS, IOWA
Gage Lyall & Keeler
BINGHAMTON, N.Y.
Evans & Allen
Herchman Bros.
BUFFALO, N.Y.
Reilley's Bazaar

The BUSINESS CARD die is Hetrich-Guttag 575, Fuld 1368. Many of these tokens are R2 to R4, though there are rare varieties. The nickel specimens were struck in just 2 copies each, one source states.

INDIANA

A. KLINGER
Elkhart, Ind.

Rulau	Date	Metal	Size	VG	F	VF	EF
Ind 100	(1857-59)	Copper	29mm	100.	—	150.	—
		A. KLINGER / JEWELER / ELKHART IND ctsp on U.S. Large cent. Examined: 1820, 1831, 1832, 1848, 1855, 1856. There are 7 reported specimens. (Hallenbeck 11.514)					
Ind 100C	(1857-59)	Copper	28mm	130.	—	210.	—
		Similar ctsp on 1837 Hard Times token.					

Rulau	Date	Metal	Size	VG	F	VF	EF
Ind 101	(1857-59)	Copper	28.7mm	130.	—	210.	—

Similar ctsp on Belgium 1837 5-centimes. (Kurt Krueger coll.; Brunk 23140)

Klinger was a watchmaker and jeweler listed in the 1858-59 Indiana state business directory. He does not appear in the 1860-61 edition.

In 1860 he moved his shop to Main Street in Niles, Mich.

B.H. BENHAM
Fort Wayne, Ind.

Rulau	Date	Metal	Size	VG	F	VF	EF
Ind 102	(1858-62)	Silver	27mm	—	—	300.	—

B.H. BENHAM / ARTIST / FORT WAYNE / IND. ctsp on U.S. 1825 Bust quarter. (Bowers & Ruddy Nov. 1982 sale list; Van Ormer sale 2535; Brunk 3330)

"Artist" indicates photographic artist, as daguerreotypers and ambrotypers called themselves before and just after the Civil War.

This piece fetched $160 in the 1985 Van ormer Sale. Benham was located at 106 Columbia St. 1858-62.

J. F. DAVIS
Kokomo, Ind.

Rulau	Date	Metal	Size	VG	F	VF	EF
Ind 110	(?)	Silver	39mm	—	—	155.	—

J. F. DAVIS, (Circular depression) KOKOMO, IND. in upward arc ctsp on U.S. 1803 Bust silver dollar (PCAC July 1993 sale, lot 085)

IOWA

C. CANNON
Dubuque, Iowa

Rulau	Date	Metal	Size	VG	F	VF	Unc
Iowa 101	(1856-60)	Silver	31mm	250.	—	400.	—
		C. CANNON / GROCER / NO. 41 MAIN / DUBUQUE, IOWA ctsp on U.S. Seated Liberty half dollar. Dates examined: 1854, 1858. Four pieces reported. (Brunk 6700; Rulau Ia-Du 3)					
Iowa 102	(1856-60)	Silver	27mm	250.	—	400.	—
		Similar ctsp on Spanish-American 1808 2-reales. (Van Ormer sale 2567; Rulau Ia-Du 4; Brunk 6700)					

Charles & Henry Cannon were listed as grocers in the 1857, 1860 and 1862 directories, at 41 Main St. between Fenelton Ave. and Summit on Prospect Hill. Dr. Brunk notes: "The Cannons appear to have left Dubuque at the start of the Civil War for they are not listed in later city directories."

GRAFFORT HOUSE
Dubuque, Iowa

Rulau	Date	Metal	Size	VG	F	VF	Unc
Iowa 103	(?)	Silver	26.5mm	—	—	300.	—

GRAFFORT HOUSE / DUBUQUE, IO. ctsp on U.S. 1835 Capped Bust quarter. (Van Ormer sale 2673; Brunk 16800)

CLARK HOUSE
Iowa City, Iowa

Rulau	Date	Metal	Size	VG	F	VF	EF
Iowa 105	(1858-60)	Silver	31mm	200.	—	300.	—

CLARK / HOUSE ctsp on U.S. 1856-O or 1857 S.L. half dollar. (Brunk 7860; Rulau Z4E)

Clark House was located on Jefferson Street, opposite Capital Square, shortly before the Civil War, according to the hostelry's ad in the Iowa City directory. (Attribution by Gregory Brunk)

John Hursh was proprietor. Two ctsp sizes are known.

KANSAS

R.L. FRAZER
Lawrence, Kansas

Miller	Date	Metal	Size	VG	F	VF	EF
Kan 1	(1854-60)	Silver	25mm	500.	—	800.	—
		R.L. FRAZER, JEWELER, LAWRENCE KT ctsp on U.S. 1853 Arrows & Rays quarter dollar. (Gould 80; Miller Ky 42; Brunk 15020)					
Kan 2	(1854-60)	Silver	31mm	500.	—	800.	—
		Similar ctsp on U.S. 1855 or 1858-O half dollar. (Frank Kovacs coll.)					

KT equals Kansas Territory. This term was used only from 1854 to January 1861, when Kansas became a state.

Kan 1 token was mistakenly attributed to Kentucky by Adams and Miller. These are the only legitimate merchant advertising counterstamps to mention "Territory" in this section.

KENTUCKY

S.T. SUIT
Jefferson County, Ky.

Miller	Date	Metal	Size	F	VF	EF	Unc
Ky 36	1850	Copper	29mm	8.00	11.00	20.00	35.00
		* KENTUCKY CURRENCY * / SALT RIVER / * / BOURBON / 1850. / S.T. SUIT, DISTILLER. Rv: S.T. SUIT. / FOR / MEDICINAL / USE ONLY / 1850. / * JEFFERSON CO. KY. * . Plain edge. (Wright 1073)					
Ky 37	1850	Brass	29mm	8.00	11.00	20.00	35.00
		As 36. Reeded edge. (Storer 8148; Freeman 878)					
Ky 37A	1850	Brass	29mm	8.00	11.00	20.00	35.00
		As 36. Plain edge. Pierced.					
Ky 37B	1850	Brass	29mm	8.00	11.00	20.00	35.00
		As 36. Plain edge. Unpierced.					
Ky 38	1850	Silvered Brass	29mm	—	17.50	22.50	42.50
		As 36. Reeded edge.					
Ky 39	1850	White Metal	29mm	10.00	20.00	40.00	80.00
		As 36. Plain edge.					
Ky 40	1858	Brass	28mm	50.00	—	—	—
		Obverse as 36. Rv: (All incused) BALDWIN & CO. PATENT APRIL 18, 1858.					

CLARK

Lexington, Ky.

Rulau	Date	Metal	Size	VG	F	VF	EF
Ky 130	(?)	Silver	18mm	—	—	35.00	—
		CLARK engraved on obverse of U.S. 1840 dime. JEWELLERY / LEX. KY. engraved on reverse of the coin. (PCAC July 1993 sale, lot 1166)					

BROWN, CURTISS & VANCE

Louisville, Ky.

Miller	Date	Metal	Size	VG	F	VF	Unc
Ky 1	(1845-50)	Brass	29mm	15.00	25.00	35.00	60.00
		Parrot-headed eagle with drooping wings, U.S. shield on its breast, BROWN. CURTISS & VANCE above, + LOUISVILLE KY + below. Rv: DEALERS IN DRY GOODS / 447 / MARKET ST / CORNER OF / 4TH / oXo.					
Ky 2	(1860)	Copper	29mm	15.00	25.00	40.00	65.00
		Obverse as Ky 1. Rv: Eagle, GENTLEMENS FURNISHING / ** STORE ** . (Wright 107)					

The reverse of Ky 2 is the reverse of the Taylor & Raymond card of Louisville, Ky., which see. It has also been reported that mulings exist with N. C. Folger card of New Orleans, with a Liberty head, and others.

Miller	Date	Metal	Size	VG	F	VF	Unc
Ky 3	(1860)	Copper	29mm	—	25.00	40.00	65.00
		Obverse as Ky 1. Rv: Card of C.W. Jackson of Philadelphia, coal dealers.					
Ky 4	(1845-50)	Copper	29mm	—	25.00	40.00	65.00
		Obverse as Ky 1. Rv: Blank.					

Brown, Curtiss & Vance, 447 Market St., corner of 4th, were wholesale and retail dealers in dry goods, appearing in the 1845 city directory. The partners were James D. Brown, the principal (who boarded at the Louisville House in 1845), S. W. Curtiss and John A. Vance. In 1845 Curtiss boarded at the Exchange Hotel and Vance at the Franklin Hotel, according to the directory. (Were all three bachelors who disliked sharing their off-hours with each other?)

The firm disappears by the time of the 1865 directory.

James D. Brown had been in business for himself 1836-38 as a draper and tailor on the east side of Wall St., between Main and Water. At that time his residence is listed at Hancock & Clay (with parents?). Later, 1842-43, he was in business as Brown & Ormsby, merchants, southeast corner Market and 4th.

S.D. CHOATE

Rulau	Date	Metal	Size	VG	F	VF	EF
Ky 100	(?)	Silver	18mm	—	150.	—	225.
		S.D. CHOATE / SILVERSMITH / LOUISVILLE ctsp on U.S. 1853 dime. (Schenkman collection; Brunk 7690)					
Ky 100D	(1841-51)	Silver	25mm	—	150.	—	225.
		Similar ctsp on U.S. 1853 Arrows & Rays quarter. 2 known. (Van Ormer sale 2580)					
Ky 100E	(1841-51)	Silver	27mm	—	150.	—	225.
		Similar ctsp on Spanish-American 1796 2-reales.					

Rulau	Date	Metal	Size	VG	F	VF	EF
Ky 101	(?)	Silver	18mm	—	150.	—	225.
		S.D. CHOATE / LOUISVILLE ctsp on U.S. 1838 Liberty Seated dime. (Van Ormer sale 2582, ex-Schenkman; Brunk 7685)					

Stephen D. Choate was a gold and silversmith in Louisville from 1841 to about 1852. His locations are given in *The Silversmiths of Kentucky 1785-1850* by Noble and Lucy Hiatt. These are:

1841	Jefferson (south side) betw. Brook and Floyd
1845	493 Main
1848	Fourth betw. Main and Market
Late 1848	Fifth betw. Main and Market
1851-52	99 Fourth, betw. Main and Market

(For a related item, see Pebbles under Louisville)

SANDFORD DUNCAN

Miller	Date	Metal	Size	F	VF	EF	Unc
Ky 7	(1850's)	Copper	29mm	8.00	12.50	20.00	40.00
		Eagle displayed, SANDFORD DUNCAN / 474 MAIN ST. / LOUISVILLE. Rv: IMPORTER / JOBBER OF / SILK AND FANCY / DRY GOODS / 474 MAIN ST. / LOUISVILLE. Plain edge.					
Ky 8	(1850's)	Silvered Copper	29mm	10.00	15.00	25.00	40.00
		As Ky 7.					
Ky 9	(1850's)	Brass	29mm	10.00	15.00	25.00	40.00
		As Ky 7. Reeded edge. (Wright 268)					
Ky 10	(1850's)	Brass	29mm	8.00	12.50	20.00	40.00
		As Ky 7. Plain edge.					
Ky 11	(1860)	Brass	29mm	—	—	—	75.00
		Obverse as Ky 7. Rv: Card of Richardson of Philadelphia (three umbrellas).					
Ky 11A	(1860)	WM	29mm	—	—	—	75.00
		As last.					
Ky 12	(1860)	Copper	29mm	—	—	—	75.00
		Obverse as obverse of Ky. 7. Rv: Tall hat, PUBLIC SQUARE NASHVILLE, TENN.					
Ky 12A	(1860)	Brass	29mm	—	—	—	75.00
		As Ky 12.					
Ky 13	(1860)	White Metal	29mm	—	—	—	75.00
		As Ky 12.					

An apparent predecessor, Coleman Duncan, was an associate of Snead, Anderson & Co., 7th between Main and Market, 1832-1843.

J.J.F.

Miller	Date	Metal	Size	VG	F	VF	Unc
Ky 19	(1855)	GS	13mm	—	200.	350.	—
		ST. CHARLES / (star) / J.J.F. Rv: LOUISVILLE / (star) / KY. (Wright 1635)					

John J. Felker was keeper of the St. Charles Hotel from 1848-49 to 1861.

J.J. HIRSCHBUHL

Miller	Date	Metal	Size	VG	F	VF	Unc
Ky 14	(1862-65)	GS	22mm	30.00	37.50	50.00	80.00
		(All incused) J. J. HIRSCHBUHL / -KY- / LOUISVILLE. Rv: Blank. Plain edge.					

Hirschbuhl was a jeweler located at 82 West Main 1864-65. He appears in the 1869 directory without a business address, merely residing at 91 West Broadway.

Hirschbuhl does not appear in any Louisville directories we've traced back to 1832. However, he appears in silversmith chronologies (spelled Hirshbuhl) as a partner with Jacob Dolfinger in Hirschbuhl & Dolfinger, 1859-61. Thus it seems likely the J. J. Hirschbuhl token was emitted in the 1862-65 period.

M.H. LURIA

Miller	Date	Metal	Size	VG	F	VF	EF
Ky 22	(?)	Silver	26mm	1000.	2000.	3500.	4500.
		M.H. LURIA, WATCHES & JEWELRY. An eagle. Ex. rare.					
Ky 23	(?)	Copper	26mm	800.	1500.	2500.	3000.
		Similar to Ky 22. Ex. rare.					

H. MILLER & CO.

Miller	Date	Metal	Size	F	VF	EF	Unc
Ky 24	1858	Silver	33mm	62.50	85.00	125.	300.

Shield in front of mechanic, eagle and American flags. Above: PALMAM QUI MERUIT FERAT. Below: LABORE ET HONORE / 1858. Inscribed: H. MILLER & CO. * DIE SINKERS, ENGRAVERS & BRANDCUTTERS. Rv: Shield inscribed: DIES SEALS / BRANDS &C / ENGRAVING / IN ALL / ITS BRANCHES. Inscribed: EXECUTED / BY / H. MILLER & CO. / 3RD STREET LOU'LE, K.Y. / TO COMMEMORATE THE / MECHANICS' FAIR / SEPT'R 14TH / 1858. Wreath surrounds all.

Miller	Date	Metal	Size	F	VF	EF	Unc
Ky 25	1858	Copper	33mm	20.00	30.00	40.00	60.00

As Ky 24. (Wright 704)

Miller	Date	Metal	Size	F	VF	EF	Unc
Ky 26	1858	White Metal	33mm	20.00	30.00	40.00	60.00

As Ky 24.

Henry Miller was in business as an engraver at least 1858-66.

PEBBLES

Rulau	Date	Metal	Size	VG	F	VF	EF
Ky 105	(late 1850's)	Silver	25mm	—	—	175.	—

PEBBLES / S. D. CHOATE / SILVERSMITH / LOUISVILLE ctsp on U.S. 1853 Arrows & Rays quarter. (Van Ormer sale 2581; Brunk 31475)

Pebbles, whoever he was, apparently added his own stamp to a Choate counterstamped coin (see Choate under Louisville). The Pebbles stamp, from a prepared logo, is not reported on any other coin.

H. PREISSLER

Rulau	Date	Metal	Size	VG	F	VF	Unc
Ky 120	(1850's ?)	Silver*	20mm	—	—	Rare	—

H. PREISSLER / LOUISVILLE / KENTUCKY. Rv: Two arrows crossed, surrounded by circle of 13 stars. Around: SODA / WATER. (Wright 855).

H. Miller & Co. cut the dies, Dr. Wright reported. * Alloy uncertain.

W. SCOTT

Rulau	Date	Metal	Size	VG	F	VF	EF
Ky 103	(1841-49)	Silver	31mm	100.	—	150.	—

W. SCOTT in relief in oblong serrated frame ctsp on U.S. Liberty Seated half dollar. (Gould 55; Brunk 35905)

Rulau	Date	Metal	Size	VG	F	VF	EF
Ky 103A	(1841-49)	Silver	32.5mm	—	200.	—	—

Similar ctsp on U.S. 1812 Bust half dollar.

Rulau	Date	Metal	Size	VG	F	VF	EF
Ky 103E	(1841-49)	Silver	27mm	—	—	—	150.

Similar ctsp on Spanish-American 1801 or 1820 2-reales.

Rulau	Date	Metal	Size	VG	F	VF	EF
Ky 103G	(1841-49)	Copper	28mm	—	—	100.	—

Similar ctsp on Canada token.

William D. Scott was a silversmith in Louisville circa 1841-1849.

About 1843-44 he was in partnership with John Kitts in the jewelry and silversmithing firm of Scott & Kitts, northwest corner Main and Wall. Then Scott appears to be in business alone again in 1844. He disappears with the 1852 directory.

TAYLOR & RAYMOND

Miller	Date	Metal	Size	VG	F	VF	Unc
Ky 32	(1850)	Brass	29mm	10.00	15.00	20.00	50.00

TAYLOR & RAYMOND / 481 / MAIN ST / LOUISVILLE, KY. Rv: Eagle, GENTLEMANS FURNISHING / ** STORE **.

The reverse of this card was used for a number of indiscriminate mulings.

Miller	Date	Metal	Size	VG	F	VF	EF
KY 32A	(1860)	Brass	29mm	—	—	—	350.

Obverse as reverse of 32 (GENTLEMANS FURNISHING). Rv: Resembles reverse of Mass 30 (NOT ONE CENT BUT JUST AS GOOD), but from different die. Letters and wreath neatly redesigned. (Kirtley report)

SHERMAN P. WHALEY

Louisville, Ky.

Miller	Date	Metal	Size	F	VF	EF	Unc
Ky 34	(1850's)	Brass	29mm	22.50	30.00	50.00	100. *

SHERMAN P. WHALEY. * / N.E. CORNER / OF / MARKET / AND / THIRD STS. / LOUISVILLE, KY Rv: WHOLESALE & RETAIL / CLOTHING / WAREHOUSE / (ornament). (Wright 1228)

Whaley appears in the 1850 census.

The Sherman P. Whaley business which issued the token, Ky 34, apparently operated in the 1850's. Later Whaley formed S. P. Whaley & Co. (Sherman P. Whaley, N. Q. Pope and Edward D. Fryer), auctioneers and general commission merchants, at 67 Sixth St. 1865-66. Pope dropped out in 1866. By 1869 the partners were Sherman P. Whaley and Samuel S. Jones.

LOUISIANA

J.J. ALBERT

New Orleans, La.

Miller	Date	Metal	Size	F	VF	EF	Unc
La 1	(1849-52)	Copper	24mm	900.	1500.	2000.	2500.

J.J. ALBERT / 37 / CHARTRES ST. / NEW-ORLEANS. Rv: PARIS HATS / IMPORTER / WAREHOUSE.

Miller	Date	Metal	Size	F	VF	EF	Unc
La A1	(1849-52)	Copper	24mm	900.	—	—	—

J. J. ALBERT / FRENCH HAT / STORE / 37 CHARTRES ST. / NEW-ORLEANS. Rv: IMPORTER / OF HATS / MANUFACTURED / BY Jte PINAUD / 97 RICHELIEU St. / PARIS. Plain edge. (Grellman collection)

J.J. Albert was a hatter at 89 Chartres St. 1838-1849 and then at 37 Chartres St. 1849-1853. He entered in partnership with Paul Tricou in the latter year (See La 2).

The Albert & Tricou partnership apparently dissolved in 1856, and J.J. Albert continued in business at 33 Chartres St. (corner Custom House St.) to 1861. After the Civil War Albert was a wholesaler in headwear at 60 Custom House St.

La A1 was discovered only recently and is in the possession of specialist Cindy Grellman. The only copy is pitted and corroded; it had been excavated.

ALBERT AND TRICOU

Miller	Date	Metal	Size	F	VF	EF	Unc
La 2	(1853-56)	Copper	24mm	200.	350.	500.	850.
		A high hat at center, ALBERT ET TRICOU above, CHARTRES / STREET / NEW ORLEANS in three lines below. Rv: ALBERT & TRICOU / HATTERS / CORNER ROYALE / AND / ST. LOUIS ST. / NEW ORLEANS. (Wright 10)					
La 3	(1853-56)	German Silver	24mm	300.	500.	900.	1250.
		As La 2.					

Paul Tricou was a hatter from about 1838 at several Royal St. addresses, including 213 Royal St. (corner of St. Louis St.), and the corner of Royal and Bienville Streets. From 1841 Tricou operated a second store at the corner of Custom House St. and Exchange Place.

The Albert & Tricou partnership appears in city directories 1853-56 at both the Royal and Chartres St. locations given on the token.

After the Civil War, P.P. Tricou was a dealer in gentlemen's furnishings at 5 St. Charles St., and a new firm, Henry Tricou & Co., importer of hats and caps, appears at 3 Magazine St.

N.C. FOLGER

(The Adams-Miller numbers on this issuer are so confused and incomplete in description that they are partly ignored here. Adams used numbers 10 to 24 to describe the Folger issues after 1837. The Adams-Miller numbers given here are my own adaptation; hopefully they will clear up, rather than add to, the confusion.)

Miller	Date	Metal	Size	VG	F	EF	Unc
La 10	(1853-58)	Copper	29mm	7.00	12.50	20.00	37.50
		Eagle with wings outspread at center, U.S. shield on breast. N.C. FOLGER / 17 OLD LEVEE above. COR CUSTOM HOUSE ST / NEW ORLEANS below. Four dots in rosette form at either side. (The 7 of 17 is taller than the 1; leaf in eagle's claw points between O and R of COR). Obverse rim is Plain. Rv: CLOTHING STORE / YOUTH BOYS / & / CHILDRENS / CLOTHING / TRUNKS. / BLANKETS / & / PLANTATION / GOODS / HATS & CAPS. Leaf ornaments at either side. Reeded edge.					
La 10A	(1853-58)	Copper	29mm	8.00	15.00	25.00	45.00
		As 10, but Plain edge.					
La 10B	(1853-58)	Brass	29mm	8.00	15.00	25.00	45.00
		As 10. Reeded edge.					

Miller	Date	Metal	Size	VG	F	EF	Unc
La 11	(1853-58)	Copper	29mm	8.00	15.00	25.00	45.00
		Obverse similar to 10, but from different obverse die. The 7 of 17 is level with the 1. Leaf in eagle's claw points to C of COR. Obverse rim is Beaded. Reverse as 10 (leaf ornaments). Reeded edge.					
La 11A	(1853-58)	Copper	29mm	8.00	15.00	25.00	45.00
		As 11, but Plain edge.					
La 11B	(1853-58)	Brass	29mm	7.00	12.50	19.00	40.00
		As 11. Reeded edge.					
La 12	(1853-58)	Silvered Brass	29mm	7.00	12.50	19.00	26.00
		As 11. Reeded edge.					

Miller	Date	Metal	Size	VG	F	EF	Unc
La 13	(1851-53)	Silver	29mm	—	—	150.	275.
		Obverse as La 11 (17 level; leaf points to C; Beaded rim). Rv: CLOTHING STORE / YOUTH BOYS / & / CHILDRENS / CLOTHING / CAPS / BLANKETS / & / PLANTATION / GOODS / HATS & TRUNKS. Three rosette ornaments at either side, six in all. Edge: ?					
La 14	(1851-53)	Brass	29mm	8.00	15.00	25.00	45.00
		As 13. Reeded edge.					

Miller	Date	Metal	Size	VG	F	EF	Unc
La 14A	(1851-53)	Brass	29mm	10.00	20.00	35.00	45.00
		Obverse as 10. Rev: As 14. Plain edge.					
La 14B	(1851-53)	Brass	29mm	10.00	20.00	35.00	45.00
		As 14A. Reeded edge.					
La 15	(1851-53)	Copper	29mm	8.00	15.00	25.00	45.00
		As 14A. Reeded edge. (Wright 332)					
La 15F	(1851-53)	Copper	28mm	—	—	—	45.00
		Obverse as La 11. Rv.: As La 13. Reeded edge. (Ganter coll.)					

THE MULINGS

Miller	Date	Metal	Size	VG	F	EF	Unc
La 16	(1858)	Brass	29mm	—	—	75.00	100.
		Obverse die as La 11 (17 level; leaf to C of COR, etc.) Rv: Reverse of Ky 32, the Taylor & Raymond card of Louisville. Reeded edge.					
La 17	(1858)	Copper	29mm	—	—	75.00	100.
		As 16. Reeded edge.					

Miller	Date	Metal	Size	VG	F	EF	Unc
La 18	(1858)	Brass	29mm	—	—	75.00	100.
		Obverse dies as La 10 (tall 7 in 17; leaf to point between O- R of COR, etc.). Rv: Ky 32 reverse (Taylor & Raymond. Plain edge.					
La 18A	(1860)	Brass	29mm	—	30.00	50.00	90.00
		As 18. Reeded edge.					
La 18B	(1860)	Copper	29mm	—	30.00	50.00	90.00
		As 18. Plain edge.					
La 19	(1858)	Copper	29mm	—	35.00	45.00	90.00
		Obverse die as La 10. Rv: Card of C.W. Jackson, Philadelphia, Pa 234. Edge: ?					
La 19A	(1858)	Copper	29mm	—	50.00	75.00	125.
		Obverse die as La 10. Rv: NOT ONE CENT BUT JUST AS GOOD. Plain edge. Rare.					

La 20	(1849-58)	Brass	29mm	8.00	15.00	22.50	40.00
		Similar to 10 and 11, but eagle has drooping wings. Reeded edge.					

Three different obverse dies are reported. (Also see page 58 of Schenkman's "Survey of American Trade Tokens.")

N.C. FOLGER & SON

Miller	Date	Metal	Size	VG	F	EF	Unc
La 21	(1858-61)	Brass	29mm	5.00	8.00	18.00	40.00
		A pelican feeding its young, UNION & CONFIDENCE in scroll below. N.C. FOLGER & SON. above; COR MAGAZINE & GRAVIER ST. below. Rv: Large word CLOTHING above a crescent, points downward, within a rim of 18 stars. Reeded edge. (Wright 333)					
La 22	(1858-61)	Brass	29mm	5.00	8.00	18.00	40.00
		As 21, but Plain edge.					

FOLGER & BLAKE

Miller	Date	Metal	Size	VG	F	EF	Unc
La 24	(1849-50)	Brass	29mm	9.50	18.00	30.00	50.00
		Eagle with drooping wings, shield on breast. FOLGER & BLAKE / 17 OLD LEVEE above; COR CUSTOM HOUSE ST / NEW ORLEANS below. Rv: Similar to reverse of La 13, except three sharp stars replace rosettes at either side. Reeded edge.					
La 24A	(1849-50)	Copper	29mm	9.50	18.00	30.00	50.00
		As La 24.					
La 24B	(1849-50)	Silver	29mm	—	—	150.	300.
		As La 24.					

Nathan C. Folger came to New Orleans in 1830. He had been born in Hudson, N.Y. in April 1810. He established his clothing business on arrival, occupying several locations. In 1837 he was at 33 Old Levee St. (corner of Bienvill St.) and in 1842 at 30 Old Levee St. (It is possible 33 and 30 were the same location, simply renumbered in some forgotten city street assignment.)

Hall & Blake, a competitor firm, was located at 17 Old Levee St. (corner Custom House St.) until 1849. In 1849 Nathan C. Folger and Thomas N. Blake formed a partnership, and 17 Old Levee St. became Folger & Blake's location.

The "Blake" was dropped from the firm's name in a few years, and N.C. Folger occupied the 17 Old Levee St. address until 1858. (City directories show this address was actually 17 and 19 Old Levee St.)

Charles W. Folger, Nathan's son, joined the business in 1855. Two other sons, Fred G. Folger, clerk, and Nathan C. Folger Jr., accountant, joined the business after 1858.

In 1858 the firm moved to 31 and 33 Magazine St., corner Gravier St., where it remained until the Union occupation in 1862. The Civil War seems to have ended the firm's prosperity, and it does not appear in city directories after the war.

In 1867 a Hughes & Folger Co., with N.C. Folger as a partner, was engaged in soap manufacture.

The May 1915 issue of *The Numismatist* carried Edgar H. Adams' article "The Store Cards of Nathan C. Folger of New Orleans, La." The article was illustrated by an 1855 daguerreotype of Nathan C. Folger by E. Jacobs, himself a New Orleans token issuer.

The Scovill firm in Waterbury, Conn., probably struck all the Folger tokens after the single 1837 issue by Bale & Smith of New York.

According to our rearrangement of the Folger-dominated firms' tokens, they appeared in this order:

La 9	Nathan C. Folger	1837
La 20	N.C. Folger	(1849-58)
La 24	Folger & Blake	(1849-51)
La 13-15	N.C. Folger	(1849-51)
La 10-12	N.C. Folger	(1853-58)
La 16-19	Folger Mules	(1858 or later)
La 21-22	N.C. Folger & Son	(1858-61)

CHAS. C. GAINES

Miller	Date	Metal	Size	VG	F	EF	Unc
La 25	(1847-49)	Sil-plated Brass	29mm	800.	1800.	3000.	4000.
		Padlock at center, DEALERS IN HARDWARE CUTLERY CASTINGS NAILS & C. around. Rv: CHAS. C. GAINES / 22 / MAGAZINE ST. / NEW ORLEANS. Plain edge.					
La 26	(1847-49)	Brass	29mm	700.	1600.	2700.	—
		As 25. Plain edge.					

George Fuld possesses a document showing 1,250 pieces of this token were struck by Scovill Mfg. Co. in Waterbury Conn. in the 1840's. It is a mystery where they disappeared to, as La 25-26 are very rare.

Charles C. Gaines first appears in city directories in 1849 at 26 Magazine Street. He had a second store at 40 Gravier Street. In 1855 the firm became C.C. Gaines & Co. — Charles C. Gaines. William Heyl and Freret Jordy. After 1861 the firm disappears from the directories.

D. GOWANS & CO.

Miller	Date	Metal	Size	VG	F	EF	Unc
La 28	1851	Copper	22mm	7.50	12.50	40.00	80.00
		London Crystal Palace in center, POPE BIRM. in small letters under exergue line. EXHIBITION PALACE above, LONDON / 1851 below. Rv: D. GOWANS & CO. / CONFECTIONERS / 97 / CANAL ST. / NEW ORLEANS. Plain edge. (Wright 394)					
La 29	1851	Silvered Copper	22mm	10.00	15.00	25.00	80.00
		As 28. Plain edge.					

David Gowans began his confectionery business in 1842. In 1849 it became David Gowans & Co. at 97 Canal St. In 1853 it moved to 143 Canal St., continuing to 1856. In 1853-56 the partner was Robert Morrison and the confectionery expanded into importing ales, sardines, sauces, etc. from England.

The tokens were struck by Thomas Pope of Birmingham, England, probably reflecting the firm's growing English connections. Thomas Pope & Co. was located at 56 St. Paul's Square in 1851.

Wright called the copper piece Very Rare, but it does not seem so.

G. H. HOLT

Rulau	Date	Metal	Size	VG	F	VF	EF
La 110	(?)	Silver	18mm	20.00	—	30.00	—
		G. H. HOLT ctsp on U.S. Seated Liberty dime. (Nadin-Davis sale, Nov. 20, 1982). (Brunk 19900)					
La 110B	(?)	Copper	29mm	20.00	—	30.00	—
		G.H. HOLT / J. FLATHER / J. RALL ctsp on U.S. 1853 Large cent. (Brunk report). The attribution is dubious and needs verification.					

E. JACOBS

Miller	Date	Metal	Size	F	VF	EF	Unc
La 33	(1851-59)	Copper	29mm	15.00	20.00	30.00	75.00
		Coronet Liberty head in imitation of U.S. $10 gold coin, E. JACOBS above, DAGUERREOTYPE ARTIST. below: Rv: Spread eagle as on $10 gold coin, DAGUERREO-TYPE — SALOON above, 93 CAMP ST. N.O. below. Plain edge. (Wright 497)					
La 34	(1851-59)	Brass	29mm	15.00	20.00	30.00	75.00
		As 33. Reeded edge.					
La 35	(1851-59)	Brass	29mm	15.00	20.00	30.00	75.00
		As 33. Plain edge.					
La 36	(1851-59)	Silvered Copper	29mm	—	30.00	35.00	75.00
		As 33. Plain edge.					
La 37	(1851-59)	Tin (White Metal)	29mm	—	—	—	200.
		As 33. Plain edge.					

E. Jacobs was in business 1851-1859, being succeeded in the latter year by L.S. Lipman. These tokens probably appeared in 1851, struck by Scovill.

C. LEIGHTON

Rulau	Date	Metal	Size	VG	F	VF	Unc
La 115	(1805's)	Copper	24mm	—	—	35.00	55.00
		American Institute medal design in reduced size, C. LEIGHTON / 1ST PREMIUM SHIRT MANUFACTURE around. Rv: Eagle, 10. PARK PLACE N.Y. AND 5. ROYAL ST, N.O. (Wright 594)					

Charles I. Bushnell reported that the dies for this piece were cut in Birmingham, England.

La 117	(1850's)	Brass	25mm	—	—	75.00	100.
		Spade guinea imitation. Head of George III right, GEORGIVS III DEI GRATIA around. Rv: Crowned, spade-shaped English arms at center, LEIGHTONS. PREMIUM. SHIRTS. above, NEW. ORLEANS below. (ANS collection)					

Also see Miller NY 420-424.

LORNE FROIS

Rulau	Date	Metal	Size	VG	F	VF	EF
La 119	(?)	Brass	Oct 23mm	—	—	150.	—
		MAGASIN DE NOUVEAUTES / LORNE * FROIS / 21 RUE DE CHARTRES. Rv: 21 CHARTES ST. / DRY GOODS STORE / NEW ORLEANS. Plain edge. (Mike Bowden coll., Lafayette, La.)					

The only specimen of this unpublished token was found with a metal detector in September, 1990 on a plantation near Lafayette.

L.W. LYONS & CO.

Miller	Date	Metal	Size	F	EF	Unc	P-L
La 38	(1858-60)	Brass	24mm	5.00	10.00	40.00	—
		Building in center, L.W. LYONS & CO. / CLOTHING & FURNISHING GOODS above; WHOLESALE & RETAIL / 26, 28 & 30 ST. CHARLES ST. / NEW ORLEANS. Rv: Eagle with folded wings, shield on breast. * BOY'S CLOTHING EMPORIUM * above; TRUNKS VALISES UMBRELLAS & C. below. Reeded edge. (Wright 637)					
La 38A	(1859-60)	Brass	24mm	5.00	10.00	40.00	—
		As 38. Plain edge.					
La 38B	(1859-60)	Silvered Brass	24mm	7.50	10.00	40.00	60.00
		As 38. Plain edge.					
La 39	(1859-60)	Copper	24mm	7.00	9.50	40.00	60.00
		As 38. Plain edge. Rare.					
La 40	(1859-60)	Nickel Alloy	24mm	25.00	35.00	75.00	100.
		As 38. Plain edge. Rare.					

Lewis W. Lyons was at 83 Canal St. 1855-1859 and at 26-30 St. Charles St. (corner of Common St.) 1859-68. It became Lyons & Stevens in 1868. Alfred A. Wilkins was admitted as a partner in 1861 and H.B. Stevens in 1867.

There are two distinct obverse dies; first L of L. W. LYONS points right of T of CLOTHING, or above T.

PHILLIPS CHEAP STORE

Rulau	Date	Metal	Size	VG	F	VF	EF
La 102	(1849-52)	Copper	29mm		May not exist		
		PHILLIPS / CHEAP / STORE / NAYADES ST. / N.O. ctsp on U.S. Large cent. (Reported)					
La 103	(1849-52)	Silver	38mm	200.	—	300.	—
		Similar ctsp on France 5-francs of Louis Philippe. Examined: 1831, 1833, 1844, 1848, worn date. 6 pieces reported. (Brunk 31970).					

Rulau	Date	Metal	Size	VG	F	VF	EF
La 104	(1849-52)	Silver	38mm	200.	—	300.	—
		Similar ctsp on France 1811, 1812-A, 1813-Q or 1814 5-francs of Napoleon I.					

La 104A	(1849-52)	Silver	38mm	250.	—	360.	—
		Similar ctsp on Sardinia 1844 5-lire.					

S. Phillips was in business as a dry goods and millinery merchant in New Orleans only 1849-1855. In 1849-1855 he was on Nayades Street near the Horse Station, with the Lone Star store. From 1852-1855 he advertised: "Cheap dry goods and millinery store, at auction prices."

In 1852 Nayades Street was renamed St. Charles Street, so the counterstamps had to be applied only in the 1849-1852 period.

ROBERT PITKIN

Miller	Date	Metal	Size	F	VF	EF	Unc
La 42	(1858-60)	Brass	24mm	7.50	9.50	15.00	40.00

		Four-story building in center, BOY'S CLOTHING above, SHIRTS, FINE TRUNKS, UMBRELLAS & C. below. Rv: ROBT. PITKIN / CLOTHING / AND / FURNISHING / GOODS. / 15 CAMP ST. NEW ORLEANS. below. Reeded edge. (Wright 833)					
La 42A	(1858-60)	Copper	24mm	7.50	9.50	15.00	40.00
		As 42. Edge: ?					

Robert Pitkin & Co. (partners Charles Fonda and T.B. Jackson) was at 37 Camp St. 1854-1857. In 1858 the style became Robert Pitkin at 13 and 15 Camp St., lasting until 1869. In the latter year it became Pitkin, Pierson & Co.

Scovill of Waterbury, Conn. struck the tokens issued by Pitkin.

J.B. SCHILLER

Rulau	Date	Metal	Size	VG	F	VF	EF
La 105	(1862)	Cupronickel	19mm	3000.	—	5000.	—
		J.B. SCHILLER ctsp on face of U.S. 1860 Indian head cent. Large X ctsp over ONE on reverse of cent. Plain edge. Only 8 known. (Brunk 35777)					

There are also scrip notes of this issuer, dated April 3, 1862, payable in Confederate currency, in 25 and 50-cent denominations. New Orleans was under Union siege at that time; it fell to Admiral Farragut's forces May 1, 1862. The token is thought to represent 10 cents in value.

John B. Schiller, an importer of spirits, also became the proprietor of the Sazerac Coffee House in 1859. This saloon at 16 Royal Street was in the Merchants Exchange building and became the favorite watering hole of the local business community. As an importer, Schiller was the agent for Sazerac-de-Forge et Fils of Limoges, France, and served the Sazerac brand of cognac exclusively.

Schiller invented the 'Sazerac,' or brandy cocktail, the appetizer that made New Orleans famous.

Bill Manning, in "J.B. Schiller Counterstamp" (*TAMS Journal*, Feb. 1978), advanced the theory that other denominations may exist, counterstamped V, XV or XX, but this was never substantiated by the find of any specimens.

The Schiller counterstamp was first reported in *TAMS Journal* for March 1963 by R. Lindesmith in a letter to editor Russ Rulau. It was written up by Rulau in *Coin World* in 1963 also.

It is, properly, a siege piece and thus even more important.

TATOUT BROTHERS

Miller	Date	Metal	Size	VG	F	EF	Unc
La 45	(1849)	Brass, with Plated Center	Oct, 23mm	200.	400.	1100.	—
		CHARTRES STREET. 161. / TATOUT / BROTHERS / * NEW ORLEANS *. Rv: FRENCH GERMAN AND ENGLISH FANCY GOODS * / IMPORTERS / OF. Very Rare.					

Tatout & Tessa was located at 188 Old Levee St. 1842-49. Tatout Brothers was at 161 Chartres St. 1849-58 one of the partners being Aime Tatout.

In 1858 the business became B. Tatout & Co.

An EF specimen fetched $1045. in the Bowers & Merena sale of April 1986.

THEODORE

Miller	Date	Metal	Size	VG	F	VF	EF
La 46	(1848)	Copper	Oct, 23mm	300.	500.	1200.	2000.
		NEW ORLEANS / THEODORE / 150 CHARTRES ST. Rv: NLLE ORLEANS / THEODORE / 150 RUE DE CHARTRES. Plain edge.					
La 47	(1848)	Brass	Oct, 23mm	300.	500.	1200.	2000.
		As La 46. Plain edge.					

City directories carry only one entry for G. Theodore, in 1848, a hairdresser and perfumery, at 150 Chartres St.

C. YALE JR. & CO.

New Orleans, La.

Miller	Date	Metal	Size	F	VF	EF	Unc
La 51	(1849-59)	Brass	28mm	250.	400.	550.	850.
		C. YALE JR. & CO. / NO. 27 / * MAGAZINE * / STREET / * / NEW-ORLEANS. Rv: FANCY, STAPLE. / SILK / AND / STRAW / GOODS / * C. YALE JR. & CO. * .(Low 289; Wright 1289)					
La 52	(1849-59)	Copper	28mm	250.	400.	825.	1100.
		As La 51. (Low 290)					

C. Yale Jr. & Co. was located at 27 Magazine St. 1849-61. R.H. Yale entered the business in 1853, becoming a partner in 1857. From 1859-61 John P. Fowler was also a partner.

After the Civil War the business, under sole ownership of R.H. Yale, was at 98 Common St. These cards were assigned to the Hard Times period in error; they are clearly from the Merchant Token era of 1845-60, now that their city directory provenance can be established.

A BU specimen in the Gil Steinberg collection realized $825 in Stack's Sale of October 1989.

MAINE

N.H. BRAGG & SON

Bangor, Maine

Miller Me 1, the Bragg counterstamp on an 1845 U.S. Large cent, has been relocated in my *U.S. Trade Tokens 1866-1899* reference (2nd edition). A full history of this firm shows it was known as Bragg & Basford 1854-63, Norris H. Bragg 1863-67, N.H. Bragg & Son 1867-71, N.H. Bragg & Sons 1871-1918 or later.

CHINA TEA CO.

Bangor, Maine

Rulau	Date	Metal	Size	VG	F	VF	EF
Me 100	(1858-61)	Silver	25mm	125.	—	175.	—
		China Tea Co. / BANGOR ME. ctsp on U.S. Seated Liberty quarter. Examined: 1839, 1853, 1855, 1856, 1857, 1857-O, 1858, 1861. There are 13 reported specimens. (Van Ormer sale 2578; Gould 75; Brunk 7670)					

Rulau	Date	Metal	Size	VG	F	VF	EF
Me 101	(1858-61)	Silver	32.5mm	150.	—	250.	—
		Similar ctsp on U.S. Bust half dollar. Examined: 1811. Only 1 reported. (Glen Firestone coll.)					
Me 101A		Silver	31mm	125.	—	175.	—
		Similar ctsp on U.S. Seated Liberty half dollar. Examined: 1853, 1858, date worn off. There are 4 reported specimens. (Gould 32: Miller 1A; Van Ormer sale 2579)					

Rulau	Date	Metal	Size	VG	F	VF	EF
ME 101B	(1871)	Silver	31mm	125.	—	175.	—
		Similar ctsp on U.S. 1871 Seated Liberty half dollar. (Formerly Rulau Me 100A)					

The counterstamps seem to have been applied first in the 1858-61 period. The stamp is known on coins dated from 1811 to 1871.

Bangor city directories reveal the firm was in business circa 1858-73. In or after 1874 the firm became White Tea Company.

Apparently the first proprietor (and issuer of the first counterstamps ?) was William H. Adams, at 51 West Market Square. Later, under the proprietorship of Thomas White, it relocated at 15 Central Street.

At the latter location it advertised: "We receive all our goods from Ar-Showe & Co. of Boston, Mr. Ar-Showe is a native of China, and was brought up in the tea trade in Canton...Our Japan and Oolong teas, for $1.00 per pound, cannot be excelled in the United States." They were also retailers and wholesalers of coffee, spices, tobacco and fancy groceries.

McKENNEY and J.F. McKENNEY, GUNSMITHS

Biddeford, Saco and Bath, Maine

(All counterstamps in this series have been rearranged and renumbered to permit the inclusion of new discoveries)

No locale specified

Rulau	Date	Metal	Size	VG	F	VF	EF
Me 2	(1849-50)	Copper	29mm	60.00	—	90.00	—
		McKENNEY ctsp on U.S. Large cent. Examined: 1816. Only 1 specimen reported. (Brunk 27000)					
Me 2C	(1849-50)	Copper	29mm	60.00	—	90.00	—
		MCKENNEY. / GUNSMITH ctsp on U.S. 1848 Large cent. (Brunk 27005).					
Me 2A	(1850's)	Copper	29mm	60.00	—	90.00	—
		J.F. MCKENNEY. ctsp on U.S. Large cent. Examined: 1816, 1827. Only 2 specimens reported. (Brunk 27030)					
Me 2B	(1850's)	Copper	29mm	75.00	—	125.	—
		J.F. MCKENNEY / GUNSMITH ctsp on U.S. Large cent. Examined: 1844, 1845, 1848, unknown date. There are 4 reported specimens. (Hallenbeck 13.507; Brunk 27040)					

Biddeford

Rulau	Date	Metal	Size	VG	F	VF	EF
Me 2D	(1849-50)	Copper	29mm	100.	—	150.	—
		MCKENNEY. / GUNSMITH / BIDDEFORD. (all capitals) ctsp on U.S. Large cent. Examined: 1827, 1843, 1846, 1847, 1848, 1854. There are 6 reported specimens. (Dwight Demeritt coll.; Brunk 27010)					
Me 2E		Silver	32.5mm	150.	—	250.	—
		Similar ctsp on U.S. Bust half dollar. Examined: 1810, 1833. Only 2 specimens reported. (Gould 35; Brunk 27010K)					

Rulau	Date	Metal	Size	VG	F	VF	EF
Me 2F	(1849-50)	Copper	29mm	100.	—	150.	—
		McKENNEY. / GUNSMITH. / Biddeford (lower case last word) ctsp on U.S. 1848 Large cent. Only 1 known. (Brunk N/L)					
Me 2G		Copper	29mm	150.	—	250.	—
		McKENNEY. / GUNSMITH. / BIDDEFORD. / MAINE ctsp on U.S. Large cent. Examined: 1848. Only 1 reported. (Hallenbeck 13.506)					
Me 2H		Silver	32.5mm	200.	—	300.	—
		Similar ctsp on U.S. Bust half dollar. Examined: 1810, 1833. Only 2 known. (Brunk 27020)					

Saco

Rulau	Date	Metal	Size	VG	F	VF	EF
ME 2J	(1850's)	Copper	29mm	75.00	—	125.	—
		J. F. McKENNEY. / SACO ctsp on U.S. Large cent. Examined: 1824, 1835, 1847, unknown date. There are 5 reported specimens. (Brunk 27070)					
Me 2K		Copper	29mm	100.	—	150.	—
		J. F. McKENNEY. / GUNSMITH / SACO ctsp on U.S. Large cent. Examined: 1805, 1822, 1824, 1835, 1844, 1848. There are 6 specimens reported. (Duffield 1412; Hallenbeck 13.508; Brunk 27060)					

Bath

Rulau	Date	Metal	Size	VG	F	VF	EF
Me 2P	(1850's)	Copper	29mm	150.	—	250.	—
		J. F. McKENNEY. / GUNSMITH. / BATH ctsp on U.S. Large cent. Examined: 1837, 1844. Only 2 pieces reported. (Tanenbaum coll.; Brunk 27050)					

Biddeford and Saco are adjoining cities in York County, Maine, one of the oldest counties in the nation. Bath is in Sagadahoc County. Many Biddeford businesses had Saco branches.

Gunsmith J.F. McKenney appears in directories only in 1850. His father Henry H. McKenney, was a gunsmith in Biddeford 1855-71, operating as McKenney & Bean 1867-71 (in partnership with Samuel E. Bean).

Two successor firms — Carlos H. McKenney and McKenney & Heard — were in the hardware business in Biddeford in 1918.

J.F. McKenney worked with his father in the 1850's in Biddeford, and later established his own shops in Saco and Bath. The earliest counterstamps must have been applied in the 1849-50 period. J.F. McKenney was only 20 in 1850.

Provided our analysis is correct, Rulau 2, 2C, 2D, 2E, 2F, 2G, 2H were issued by Henry H. McKenney, the father, and 2A, 2B, 2J, 2K, 2P were issues of J.F. McKenney, the son. (Research courtesy Dwight B. Demeritt)

W.R. FIELD

Brunswick, Maine

Miller	Date	Metal	Size	VG	F	VF	Unc
Me 3	(1860)	White Metal	29mm	40.00	75.00	100.	150.

W.R. FIELD * / BRUNSWICK, ME. * / 50. (The 50 is incuse). Rv: MAINE CENTRAL DINING ROOM * / 50. (The 50 is incuse). Plain edge. (Wright 316)

Me 3A	(1860)	White Metal	29mm	40.00	75.00	100.	150.

Similar, but 25 incused on each side. Plain edge. (Tanenbaum collection)

The die work appears to be that of Merriam of Boston. William R. Field appears in the 1850 census under Brunswick.

Field operated "refreshment rooms" in the Brunswick railroad station in 1861, according to *Subscriber's Business Directory,* Portland, Me., 1861.

H. BROAD

China, Maine

Rulau	Date	Metal	Size	VG	F	VF	EF
Me 111	(1853-66)	Copper	29mm	100.	—	150.	—
		CHINA ctsp on obverse of U.S. 1807 or 1849 Large cent. H. BROAD / BROAD ctsp on reverse of the coin. 2 Known. (B&M 1986 Von Stetten sale, lot 5076; Brunk 5255; Tanenbaum coll.)					
Me 111C	(1853-66)	Copper	29mm	—	—	150.	—
		BROAD ctsp on obverse of 1853 Large cent. CHINA ctsp on reverse. (PCAC July 1993 sale, lot 872)					

Hollis Broad (1812-81) was a blacksmith who moved from Orono, Maine to China Village in 1848. He sold his China home in 1866. He is buried in China Village Cemetery.

Records show he married Mary P. Shaw of China in 1835 and then in 1856 married Martha A. Shaw (sisters?). Martha Shaw Broad was born 1827 and died 1907.

C. H. DEARING

China, Maine

Rulau	Date	Metal	Size	G	VG	F	EF
Me 115	(?)	Copper	29mm	—	—	—	150.
		C. H. DEARING / BROAD / CHINA ctsp on U.S. 1849 Large cent. (Brunk 11220; Rulau Pa 715)					

MOSES HALE

Ellsworth, Maine

Rulau	Date	Metal	Size	VG	F	VF	EF
Me 103	(1853-62)	Silver	25mm	—	185.	—	250.
		AMBROTYPE / BY MOSES HALE ctsp on U.S. 1853 with Rays quarter dollar. (Gould 84; Brunk 17765)					
Me 103A	(1853-62)	Silver	27mm	—	185.	—	250.
		Similar ctsp on Spanish-American 20-reales.					

The ambrotype was a photographic process that briefly replaced the daguerreotype method in the 1850's and early 1860's. In the ambrotype process, a glass-plate negative was mounted over a black backing to display a positive image if viewed properly. Many ambrotypes depict Civil War soldiers in uniform.

Moses Hale appears in the 1850 census with a wife and five children. Attribution by Bill Rodgers, Frankfort, Ky.

W.A. HILDRETH

Gardiner, Maine

Rulau	Date	Metal	Size	VG	F	VF	EF
Me 105	1854	Silver	25mm	—	125.	—	—
		W.A. HILDRETH, PORTRAIT PAINTER / GARDINER, ME. / 1854 engraved on reverse of U.S. 1848 Seated Liberty quarter dollar. (Paul Koppenhaver Aug. 4, 1982 sale)					

DR. SHATTUCK'S WATER CURE

Waterford, Maine

Rulau	Date	Metal	Size	VG	F	VF	EF
Me 5		Copper	29mm	125.	—	175.	—
		DR. / SHATTUCK'S / WATER CURE / WATERFORD / ME. ctsp on U.S. Large cents. Examined: 1817, 1819, 1824, 1831, 1832, 1833, 1835, 1837, 1846, 1847, 1848, 1852, 1853, 1857, unknown date. There are 15 reported specimens. (Hallenbeck 19.518; Brunk 36190)					
Me 5A		Copper	28mm	100.	—	175.	—
		Similar ctsp on Canada colonial token. (Tanenbaum coll.)					

Me 6		Silver	25mm	175.	—	250.	—
		Similar ctsp on U.S. Liberty Seated quarter. Examined: 1843, 1853, 1854, 1855, 1856, 1857, 1858 unknown date. There are 13 reported specimens. (Gould 57)					

Me 6A		Silver	31mm	175.	—	250.	—
		Similar ctsp on U.S. Seated Liberty half dollar. Examined: 1853, 1855, 1857. Only 3 reported. (Gould 42)					

Dr. William P. Shattuck was a physician specializing in hydropathy, or hydrotherapy, a form of curing by cold water. In 1847 Dr. Calvin Farrar bought the old Eli Longley Inn and converted it into the Maine Hygienic Institute. Farrar sold out to Dr. Prescott, who, after a year or so, sold out to Dr. Shattuck.

Shattuck turned the Institute into a hospital for lady patients only. Shattuck could have started in the 1850's, and he appears in references dated 1874-1880. By 1894 E.M. Dudley owned the property, which again became a hotel, the Lake House. It continued as a hotel to 1941.

The buildings still stood in 1984.

A detailed account of Shattuck appears in "Taking 'The Water Cure' " by Q. David Bowers, in *Rare Coin Review* for March, 1984. Dr. Shattuck died in 1887, reportedly of gangrene.

I. MATHEWS & CO.

Winthrop, Maine

Rulau	Date	Metal	Size	VG	F	VF	EF
Me 115	(?)	Silver	31mm	150.	—	250.	—
		I. MATHEWS & CO / WINTHROP, ME ctsp on obverse of U.S. 1858 Seated Liberty half dollar. (Tanenbaum coll.; Brunk 26448)					

E. SHATTUCK
(Maine?)

Rulau	Date	Metal	Size	VG	F	VF	EF
Me 108	(?)	Copper	23mm	15.00	—	35.00	—
		E. SHATTUCK. / C. F. A. ctsp on U.S. 1828 Half cent. (Hartzog coll.; Brunk 36195)					

Tentatively assigned to Maine based on name similarity with Me 5 and 6 varieties; verification needed. There were 14 Maine families named Shattuck in the 1850 census.

There was an M.E. Shattuck, cigar manufacturer, at 409 Main St. in Worcester, Mass. in 1876.

A gunsmith named Charles S. Shattuck was active in Hatfield, Mass. 1877-1915. Shattuck is a fairly common Irish name.

Dwight B. Demeritt, a Maine specialist, doubts this is a Maine item.

MARYLAND

JAMES AULICK
Baltimore, Md.

Rulau	Date	Metal	Size	VG	F	VF	Unc
Md 500	(?)	German Silver	18mm	15.00	75.00	150.	300.
		Urn fountain. Rv: JAMES AULICK / ONE SODA. (Miller NY 48A)					
Md 500A	(?)	Copper	18mm	50.00	100.	250.	500.
		As 500. Reeded edge. (George Ganter coll.)					

This token was mistakenly attributed to New York by Miller. Aulick appears in the pre-1860 Baltimore directories.

G.W. BUCK

Miller	Date	Metal	Size	VG	F	VF	EF
Md 17	(1850-55)	Silver	16mm	25.00	50.00	100.	125.
		G.W. BUCK / NO. 28 / PRATT ST. Rv: GOOD FOR / ONE / DRINK. (Duffield 16; Schenkman B275)					

George W. Buck was proprietor of the Fulton House 1850-1867. It was on Pratt St. near Center Market Space. In 1867 his son James Buck succeeded him and the hostelry became Buck's Hotel. In city directories for 1850-55 the address was 28 West Pratt St., and then became 34 West Pratt St.

THE CHAMPAIGN FOUNTAIN

Rulau	Date	Metal	Size	VG	F	VF	EF
Md 502	(1850)	Silver	17mm	50.00	75.00	150.	250.
		Urn fountain in center, THE CHAMPAIGN FOUNTAIN around. Rv: IN VINO / VERITAS. Heavily dentilated rims. Plain edge. (Wright 1662; Van Ormer Sale 3009)					

"In Vino Veritas" is Latin for "In wine (there is) truth." Since wine is mentioned, the misspelling "champaign" seems more odd. In Old French champagne was rendered as champaigne, however.

Yet the obverse device is the urn fountain, that peculiar trademark of the ice cream, soda and mineral water parlors which recurs frequently on early 19th century tokens (e.g. R.L. Baker, Sampson's). The attribution to Baltimore is tentative.

These pieces appeared in the Groh sale in 1860, Mickley sale 1867, Betts sale 1898, Jenks sale 1921, etc. In the 1985 Van Ormer Sale, an EF specimen fetched $187.

H. H. CHASE JR.

Rulau	Date	Metal	Size	VG	F	VF	EF
Md 550	(1870)	Copper	29mm	—	125.	—	—
		H. H. CHASE, JR. ctsp on obverse of U.S. 1847 Large cent. (Robert M. Ramsay coll.; Brunk 7518)					

The counterstamp is applied in a most unusual manner. The line of text is in arc form, with each of the letters falling between the border stars of the design, and the periods and one comma on the stars themselves.

Hannibal Hamlin Chase Jr. (born 1847) moved from Massachusetts to Baltimore, according to William Swoger.

J. CLARK

Rulau	Date	Metal	Size	VG	F	VF	EF
Md 525	(?)	Copper	29mm	200.	—	300.	—
		J. CLARK, BALT. ctsp on Massachusetts cent. (Koppenhaver Aug. 1982 sale; Brunk 8047)					

H.H. COLE

Miller	Date	Metal	Size	VG	F	VF	Unc
Md 35	(1845-50)	Brass	28mm	7.50	11.00	20.00	60.00
		Eagle with drooping wings, shield on breast. H.H. COLE. / CORNER OF — BALTIMORE AND CENTRE — around; MARKET SPACE PRATT ST. in inner circle. Rv: COSTUME / HALL within wreath; IMPORTERS AND MANUFACTURER OF MEN'S YOUTH'S CLOTHING. (Duffield 29)					
Md 36	(1845-50)	German Silver	29mm	10.00	30.00	50.00	150.
		As 35. Very rare.					

Hinson H. Cole from 1827-1856 was a clothier and merchant tailor on Pratt St. An 1850 woodcut of Costume Hall shows it was a large 3-story building. Lyman H. Low noted that Scovill's struck these Cole cards.

H.A. ELLIOTT & BRO.

Miller	Date	Metal	Size	VG	F	VF	Unc
Md 46	1853	Nickel	20mm	5.00	10.00	30.00	80.00
		H.A. ELLIOTT & BRO. / 1853 / BALTO. Rv: ONE / SODA within wreath, star at top. Plain edge. (Duffield 37; Wright 290)					

In 1853 Henry A. Elliott was a druggist at the northeast corner of Lexington and Eutaw Sts. In 1855 William Elliott was admitted as a partner, the firm becoming H.A. Elliott & Bro. and the business was moved to the corner of Lexington and Pine Sts.

Duffield says this card was issued 1870-1875, but it is placed here because of its date, which is apparently the date of formation of the firm.

COL. HARDY, CRIER

Miller	Date	Metal	Size	VG	F	EF	Unc
Md 68	1858	Brass	24mm	8.00	10.00	15.00	22.50
		COL. HARDY CRIER / $10 / 1858. Rv: ALBION 11 / $20 / (fraction bar) / $7 / DUKE OF BEDFORD. (Duffield 57; Wright 179)					

John D. Hardy was an auctioneer 1853-1872 in Baltimore. Later (1873-1877) he was secretary of a city butchers' association. He died Aug. 12, 1877, aged 66.

The inscription suggests horse race betting, but nothing is known of this strange token's raison d'etre.

BENJAMIN JURY

Miller	Date	Metal	Size	VG	F	VF	Unc
Md 76	1848	German Silver	16mm	25.00	40.00	75.00	175.
		Imitation of U.S. half dime. Seated Liberty, 13 stars around, 1848 below. Rv: VAUX / HALL within central wreath, BENJAMIN JURY BALTIMORE around. Plain edge. (Wright 529; Duffield 64)					

Benjamin Jury was the proprietor of the Vauxhall in 1848-1850. The famous tavern had been founded on the east side of Light Street, between Hill and York, in 1832 or earlier. Another owner, Robert Soulsby (1839-46), also issued tokens.

A tavern still stood in Baltimore in the 1950's with the sign "Old Original Vauxhall Garden." Until about 1900 it was known as Vauxhall Garden and Hotel, the garden being a working-class family's entertainment spot, but all such Baltimore beer gardens were gradually ended — with their 19th century raison d'etre.

KEACH

Miller	Date	Metal	Size	VG	F	VF	Unc
Md 78	(1847)	German Silver	16mm	30.00	40.00	75.00	175.
		Eagle with drooping wings, shield on breast, 13 stars above, BALTIMORE below. Rv: ONE / SODA within central wreath, * KEACH * above, BALTIMORE STREET below. Plain edge. (Duffield 66; Storer 7899)					

P.R. Keach appears in the city directories only in 1847, as a mineral water manufacturer located on Wine Street. At that time Wine Street was a block-long alleylike way between Charles and Light Streets, parallel to and just south of Baltimore Street. Keach's business probably had entrances on Baltimore and Wine streets, and he dispensed his beverage on the main way; Baltimore Street.

A. KNIGHT

Rulau	Date	Metal	Size	VG	F	VF	Unc
Md 83	(1856-60)	GS	16.5mm	25.00	35.00	75.00	100.
		A. KNIGHT / 99 / BALTO. ST. / *. Rv: MINERAL / WATER within ornamental flourishes. Plain edge. (Wright 563; Duffield 71; Storer 7920)					
Md 84	(1856-60)	Copper	29mm	125.	—	175.	—
		A. KNIGHT'S / MINERAL / WATER SALOON / 99 /BALTO STREET ctsp on U.S. Large cent. Examined: 1838: Only 1 reported. (Brunk 23240)					
Md 85	(1856-60)	Silver	25mm	150.	—	225.	—
		Similar ctsp on Seated Liberty quarter. Examined: Date unknown. Only 1 reported. (Gould 37, 38; Duffield Md 72; Duffield Ctsp 1407)					

Miller	Date	Metal	Size	VG	F	VF	Unc
Md 85B	(1856-60)	Silver	27mm	125.	—	175.	—
		Similar ctsp on Spanish-American 2-reales. Examined: 1773, 1774, 1777, 1778, 1779-Mo, 1783, 1786, 1787, 1788-PTS-PN, 1789-Mo-FM, 1789, 1794, 1797, 1800, 1808, unknown date. There are 19 specimens reported. (Duffield Md 73; Gould 105; Duffield Ctsp 1363; Horatio Storer 7920a)					
Md 85E	(1856-60)	Silver	27mm	150.	—	225.	—
		Similar ctsp on Mexico 1839-G-PJ 2-reales. (Van Ormer sale 2724)					

Albert Knight of Providence, R.I. came to Baltimore in 1856, selling mineral water at 99 W. Baltimore St. until 1860. He had a mineral water business in Havana, Cuba 1860-1861, returning to Baltimore as the Civil War started. In 1863 he went to Newbern, N.C. with the Union Army Quartermaster's department to sell soda water to the soldiers, dying there suddenly.

KUNKEL'S OPERA TROUPE

SPECIAL NOTE: An unusual problem exists in cataloging this series. Most older reports on the counterstamps do not distinguish between the 2-line and the 3-line styles, and the words are precisely the same. In addition, few catalogers before 1985 recorded the mintmark and assayer's initials on Spanish-American and Mexican counterstamped pieces, so we can seldom be sure we are not counting the same reported item twice.

In the listing which follows, we catalog as certain only those 2-line or 3-line pieces we have examined, and list all other verified reports as "uncertain variety." Time and examinations will erase this artificial breakdown.

The Kunkel section has been renumbered under Md 86. The 3-line text stamp seems a bit more common than the 2-line variety.

Two-line stamp

Miller	Date	Metal	Size	VG	F	VF	EF
Md 86	(1859-61)	Silver	19mm	150.	—	200.	—
		KUNKEL'S / OPERA TROUPE in two lines ctsp on Spanish-American 1-real, date not known. (Gould 106; Brunk 23545)					

Miller	Date	Metal	Size	VG	F	VF	EF
Md 86A	(1859-61)	Silver	27mm	125.	—	175.	—
		Similar ctsp on Spanish-American 2-reales. Examined: 1778, 1779, 1785-LME-MJ, 1789, 1795. There are 5 reported specimens. (Van Ormer sale 2729)					
Md 86B		Silver	27mm	125.	—	175.	—
		Similar ctsp on Peru 2-reales, date not known. Only 1 reported specimen.					

Miller	Date	Metal	Size	VG	F	VF	EF
Md 86C		Silver	30mm	200.	—	300.	—
		Similar ctsp on Bavaria 1844 1-gulden. 1 known. (Duffield 1364)					

Three-line stamp

Rulau	Date	Metal	Size	VG	F	VF	EF
Md 86F	(1857-61)	Silver	27mm	125.	—	175.	—
		KUNKEL'S / OPERA / TROUPE in three lines ctsp on Spanish-American 2-reales. Examined: 1741-Mo-MF, 1744-Mo, 1778, 1782, 1784, 1789, 1785-LME-MJ, 1815, unknown date. There are 10 reported specimens. (Duffield 75; Van Ormer sale 2730; Brunk 23540)					
Md 86G		Silver	27mm	125.	—	175.	—
		Similar ctsp on Mexico 1833-Zs-OM 2-reales. 1 known.					

Uncertain variety

Rulau	Date	Metal	Size	VG	F	VF	EF
Md 86K	(1857-61)	Silver	26mm	150.	—	200.	—
		KUNKEL'S OPERA TROUPE in either 2-line or 3-line incuse stamp ctsp on U.S. bust quarter. Examined: 1806. Only 1 known.					
Md 86L		Silver	27mm	100.	—	150.	—
		Similar ctsp on Spanish-American 2-reales. Examined: 1736, 1741, 1755, 1774, 1779, 1780, 1783, 1785 (2 pcs), 1788 (2 pcs), 1790, 1795, 1796, 1797, 1801, 1811, unknown dates (3 pcs). There are 19 reported specimens. (Duffield 1364)					
Md 86M		Silver	27mm	100.	—	150.	—
		Similar ctsp on Mexico 1823 2-reales. Only 1 known. (Duffield 1364)					

George Kunkel was one of the early delineators of Negro minstrelsy in the United States, and during his theatrical career was connected with three historic places of amusement in Baltimore. He was born in Greencastle, Pa., in 1821, coming to Baltimore in 1855.

After 1855 he became manager of the Jenny Lind Theater in Washington, D.C., and another of the same name in Richmond, Va. In his Jenny Lind company were actors John Wilkes Booth and Joe Jefferson.

In 1859 and 1860 he was manager of the Holliday Street Theater in Baltimore, and in 1861 became manager of the old Baltimore Museum at Calvert and Baltimore Streets, founded 1814 by Rembrandt Peale, son of Charles Willson Peale of Philadelphia. His company at this time became known as Kunkel's Opera Troupe, specializing in minstrel shows with the "Mr. Bones" routines and spirited music.

In 1864 Kunkel and Thomas L. Moxley became managers of the Old Front Street Theater. He died in Baltimore Jan. 25, 1885 The counterstamped pieces could have been issued as late as 1864.

(For a discussion of minstrelsy, see under Wood's Minstrels of New York City)

W. PETERS

Miller	Date	Metal	Size	VG	F	VF	EF
Md 118	1849	Copper	29mm	125.	—	175.	—

1849 / W. PETERS / BALTO. ctsp on U.S. 1838 or 1839 Large cent. (Duffield 103; Hallenbeck 16.511; Brunk 31800; Saccone 3109)

William Peters began business as a brass founder and hardware dealer about 1840 at the corner of Pratt and Concord Sts. After 1860 he disappears from the directories.

PYFER & CO.

Miller	Date	Metal	Size	VG	F	EF	Unc
Md 125	1849	Brass	29mm	10.00	17.00	28.00	75.00

Imitation of U.S. $10 gold coin, with PYFER & CO. on Liberty's coronet. PRIZES PAID IN GOLD & SILVER around, 1849 below. Rv: PYFER & CO. on scroll above the displayed eagle, LOTTERY & EXCHANGE OFFICE. around; .BALTO. MD below. (Duffield 108; Wright 857)

Miller	Date	Metal	Size	VG	F	EF	Unc
Md 126	1849	German Silver	28mm	—	—	75.00	125.

As 125. Rare.

Philip M. and William B. Pyfer, under the style Pyfer & Co., were lottery and exchange brokers at the corner of Baltimore and Light Sts. Before 1849 Philip M. Pyfer had been a member of the lottery firm of Emory & Co., and William B. Pyfer was associated with lottery agents S. Scribner & Co.

W. RULLMANN

Miller	Date	Metal	Size	VG	F	VF	Unc
Md 130	(1856-57)	Brass	19mm	10.00	15.00	40.00	75.00

W. RULLMANN / ONE / DRINK / WASHINGTON HALL. Rv: Lyre at center within wreath of flowers; circle of 13 stars around all. (Wright 923; Duffield 113)

Weigand Rullmann was proprietor of Washington Hall in 1856-1857. Washington Hall, erected in 1836, hosted exhibitions, public meetings, balls, etc. Kernan Brothers bought it in 1867 and renamed it Baltimore Opera House.

S. SCHMIDT'S LIQUID HAIR DYE

Rulau	Date	Metal	Size	VG	F	VF	EF
Md 527	(1856)	Silver	27mm	300.	—	400.	—

S. SCHMIDT'S / LIQUID / HAIR DYE / BALTO. MD. ctsp on Spanish-American 1800-NG-M 2-reales. (Brunk 35795)

Rulau	Date	Metal	Size	VG	F	VF	EF
Md 528	(1856)	Silver	21mm	300.	—	400.	—

Similar ctsp on Spanish-American 1-real, date worn off.

Possibly this was sold by Dr. F. Schmidt, a homeopath in 1856 at 144 Lexington St.

JACOB SEEGER

Miller	Date	Metal	Size		F	VF	Unc
Md 148	(1851)	Brass	27mm		15.00	30.00	65.00

Eagle atop U.S. shield, all circled by rays and 26 stars. Rv: JACOB SEEGER / SILVER PLATER / & / MANUFACTURER / OF / FANCY ORNAMENTS / NO 21 GERMAN ST / BALTIMORE. Plain edge. (Wright 972; Duffield 127)

Miller	Date	Metal	Size		F	VF	Unc
Md 149	(1851)	Brass	27mm	(Cent)	15.00	30.00	65.00

As 148, but reeded edge. (Duffield 127)

Miller	Date	Metal	Size		F	VF	Unc
Md 150	(1851)	Copper	27mm	(Cent)	15.00	30.00	65.00

As 148. Plain edge. (Duffield 127)

Miller	Date	Metal	Size		F	VF	Unc
Md 150A	(1851)	Silvered Copper	27mm	(Cent)	20.00	35.00	75.00

As 150.

Miller	Date	Metal	Size		F	VF	Unc
Md 151	(1851)	Copper	27mm	(Cent)	15.00	30.00	60.00

As 150. Reeded edge. (Duffield 127)

Miller	Date	Metal	Size		F	VF	Unc
Md 152	(1851)	German Silver	27mm	(Cent)	—	75.00	100.

As 151. Reeded edge. (Duffield 127)

Jacob Seeger was born in Reutlingen, Wurttemberg, Germany, Oct. 26, 1809, emigrating to Baltimore in 1830. In 1832 he established his silver plating business at the corner of Baltimore and North Streets. In 1835 he moved to Fayette and Calvert Streets, and in 1841 to 21 German Street. Seeger supplied metal ornaments for the U.S. Army in the Mexican War of 1848. In 1854 he also entered the brewery business, and sold off his silver plating firm in 1865. He died Feb. 18, 1883.

Duffield felt Seeger struck his own token, though he had the dies cut elsewhere, but G. Fuld said F.X. Koehler struck it. The tokens probably appeared in 1851. The eagle side is the same as the Ross Winans piece.

Duffield's "The Merchant Cards and Tokens of Baltimore" appeared in *The Numismatist* for March 1907.

German Street, the location for Seeger's firm, had its name changed on October 24, 1918 to Redwood Street. This in honor of Lt. George Buchanan Redwood, a former newsman and the first American soldier killed in action in World War I. The antipathy towards Germany during WWI caused the street name to be considered for change.

SILVERWARE

Rulau	Date	Metal	Size	F	VF	EF
Md 532	(?)	Silver	32.5mm	—	65.00	—

SILVERWARE / BALTo / BALTo ctsp on U.S. 1825 Bust half dollar. (B&M Patterson 1895 sale, lot 1674; Brunk 36585)

SOC. DEM. T. UNION

Rulau	Date	Metal	Size	VG	F	VF	Unc
Md 530	(1850-61)	Brass	19mm	12.00	17.50	25.00	45.00

Owl standing between crossed sword and blazing torch, about which is entwined a ribbon inscribed: S. D. T. / BALTO. Rv: * SOC. DEM. * / 5 / T. UNION. Plain edge. (Wright 1014; Duffield 135; Miller Md 158)

The Socialistiche Demokratische Turnverein (Social Democrat Turners Union) was founded in Baltimore in 1850. Its headquarters were at 16 East Lombard St., then after a few years at its own home at 300 W. Pratt St. In 1852 the 10 societies comprising the Socialisticher Turnerbund (later the North American Turner League) held their first Turnfest in Baltimore, and the second was held in Baltimore in 1859. Baltimore was headquarters of the nationwide Turnerbund.

On April 21, 1861 a mob of Southern sympathizers damaged the S.D.T. building as the Turners favored the Union. The society practically went out of existence during the Civil War, and was replaced in 1867 by the Turnverein Vorwaerts (Turners Union Forward).

ROBERT SOULSBY

Miller	Date	Metal	Size	VG	F	VF	Unc
Md 159	(1845-46)	German Silver	17mm	10.00	30.00	75.00	175.
		Eagle with drooping wings, shield on breast, 13 stars around, BALTIMORE below. Rv: VOUX / HALL within central wreath, ROBERT SOULSBY above. Plain edge. (Duffield 136)					

Robert Soulsby was the proprietor of the Vauxhall from 1839 to 1846, and he either preferred the spelling "Voux Hall" or this was a diecutter's error. The Vauxhall tavern had been established in 1832 or earlier, and a successor as owner, Benjamin Jury (1848-50), issued a token for the place.

A series of small German Silver tokens was issued in Baltimore in the 1840's — Randall & Co. (1840-42), P.R. Keach (1847), Benjamin Jury (1848) and Robert Soulsby (1845-46). All are probably half dime (5-cent) value pieces.

In 1985 the obverse and reverse dies for this piece were owned by David Schenkman, Bryantown, Md.

WM. TOLAND

Miller	Date	Metal	Size	VG	F	VF	EF
Md 167	(1849-60)	Brass	--mm	—	—	200.	Rare
		No description available. Thin planchet. (Duffield 144)					

William Toland manufactured saws, trowels, etc., 1849-1864 at four different locations, the last being 85 No. Front St. In 1865 James Toland succeeded him.

ROSS WINANS
Baltimore, Md.

Rulau	Date	Metal	Size	VG	F	VF	Unc
Md 504	(1851-52)	Brass	27mm	—	—	50.00	100.
		Radiant eagle standing on a U.S. shield, beneath which is a ribbon inscribed: E PLURIBUS UNUM. Surrounding all are 26 stars. Rv: ROSS WINANS / 456 (incuse) / BALTIMORE. Reeded edge.					
Md 505	(1851-52)	Copper	27mm	—	—	50.00	100.
		As last, but numeral 8 incused. Reeded edge.					

Francis X. Koehler cut this die about 1851. Earlier he had used the identical obverse for the Jacob Seeger token of Baltimore. The tokens may have been some type of tool check or time check.

Ross Winans was born in Sussex County, N.J., Oct. 17, 1796. He came to Baltimore in 1828, becoming an engineer for the Baltimore & Ohio railroad in 1830. He helped build the Tom Thumb locomotive. In 1835 Winans and George Gillingham took over control of the B&O company shops at Mt. Clair yards. They built locomotives, engines and other machinery. In 1842 they terminated their exclusive arrangement with B&O.

In 1842 they built new shops at McHenry Alley, corner of Poppelton St., adjacent to the B&O Mt. Clair yards. They expanded in 1849 and again in 1851. Winans died April 11, 1877.

Winans also built a steam-operated cannon, Dickinson's cannon.

J. A. H.
(John A. Hancock)
Bodkin Point, Md.

Rulau	Date	Metal	Size	G	VG	F	EF
Md 508	(1853-61)	Iron	35.5mm	6.00	12.00	20.00	—
		Large initials J A H stamped incuse in center of flan. Rv: Blank, but intaglio of J A H. Plain edge.					

John Asbury Hancock, born 1837, married in 1861, died about 1878, farmed near Bodkin Point, Anne Arundel County, Maryland, beginning at age 16. His picker checks are the oldest known to the Anne Arundel County Historical Society.

The Hancock checks, reportedly used by strawberry pickers to measure work and to serve as payment talleys, are stamped on thin round sheets of a grey (galvanized?) iron. Almost all the surviving specimens, perhaps 40 or so, show rust spots. They were discovered during the AACHS drive to record data on Anne Arundel County's great tradition of produce picker tokens in 1966-68.

MARYLAND PICKER CHECKS

So that the picker checks for produce (strawberries, peas, beans, etc.) can be better understood than simply by presenting those of John A. Hancock, a few post-Civil War checks of nearby farms are catalogued here. These picker talleys were used in Anne Arundel County from just prior to the Civil War until recent years in some cases. Not pretty tokens, they were intended for utility, not for souvenir or collection purposes.

H. N. K.
(Hezron N. Kelley)
Harmans, Md.

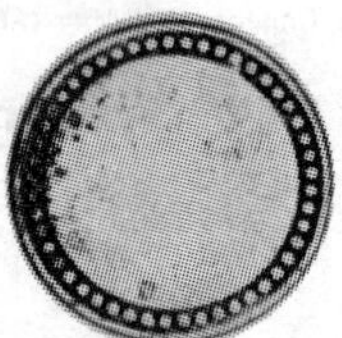

Large Numeral

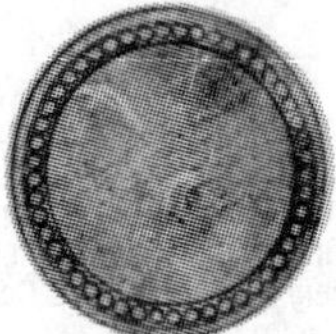

Small Numeral

Rulau	Date	Metal	Size	G	VG	F	EF
Md 510	(1874-80)	Brass	22mm	1.00	2.00	3.50	5.00
		H. N. K. / 1 incuse, surrounded by struck rim of beads within depressed rim. Rv: Blank, but similar beaded rim. Plain edge. (Varieties with large 1 and small 1)					
Md 511	(1874-80)	Brass	22mm	1.00	2.00	3.50	5.00
		Similar to last, but numeral 2 instead of 1. Plain edge. (Varieties with large 2 and small 2, and large 2 struck well off center)					

Hezron Nehemiah Kelley, born 1818, died 1880, farmed at Harmans, Anne Arundel County, Md. His picker chits were made from a stock type supplied by Baltimore makers in the 1874-1885 period.

Kelley, or his family, also used a large number of picker checks of differing design later.

L. R. S.
(Larkin R. Shipley)
Anne Arundel County, Md.

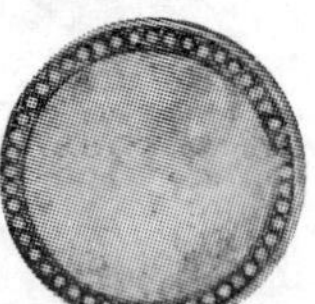

Rulau	Date	Metal	Size	G	VG	F	VF
Md 513	(1874-85)	Brass	22mm	1.00	2.00	3.50	5.00
		L. R. S. / 1 incuse, surrounded by struck rim of beads within depressed border. Rv: Blank, but similar beaded rim. Plain edge.					
Md 514	(1874-85)	Brass	22mm	1.00	2.00	3.50	5.00
		Similar to last, but numeral 2 in place of 1. Plain edge.					
Md 515	(1874-85)	Brass	22mm	1.00	2.00	3.50	5.00
		L. R. S. / 1 / P incuse within similar beaded rim. Finer letter style. Rv: Same as last. Plain edge.					

Larkin Rudolphus Shipley used these picker checks, later adding other types. His successor sons under the name I.L. Shipley Brothers, used picker checks to the 1940's.

These are from the same stock type used by H.N.K. of Harmans, Md., which see. Born in 1841, Shipley died in 1890.

J. H. R.
(John Henry Robinson)
Halethorpe, Md.

Rulau	Date	Metal	Size	G	VG	F	EF
Md 517	(1874-85)	Brass Octagonal	20mm	9.00	12.00	18.00	40.00
		J. H. R. / 1 incuse on plain field. Rv: Blank. Plain edge.					
Md 518	(1874-85)	Brass Octagonal	20mm	9.00	12.00	18.00	40.00
		Similar to last, but numeral 2 in place of 1. Plain edge.					
Md 519	(1874-85)	Brass Octagonal	24mm	9.00	12.00	18.00	40.00
		J. H. R. / 10 incuse, surrounded by struck beading within depressed circle near rim. Rv: Blank, but similar beaded rim. Plain edge.					

John Henry Robinson

Della Queen

John Henry Robinson was born a Negro slave in Anne Arundel County south of Baltimore, on Nov. 21, 1844. He was the son of Henrietta Robinson, slave cook and wetnurse in the home of Basil Smith Benson, who farmed in what now is land covered over by Baltimore-Washington International Airport. John Henry worked as a houseboy in the Benson home.

His former owner freed him in late 1864 (some accounts say 1865). The 1863 Emancipation Proclamation did not affect Maryland, which was a Union state.

After emancipation, John Henry worked first as a coachman at Carroll Manor. He married a former slave, Della Queen, who worked as a midwife and was much in demand.

After marriage John Henry Robinson turned to farming and, with money borrowed from G. Milton Benson, eldest son of his former master, purchased land on the Baltimore County side of the Patapsco River near the bridge into Lansdowne. He raised corn, vegetables and fruit, and began a cottage industry furnishing willow wood to the wicker furniture makers.

John Henry and Della raised four children, sons Ferdinand and Oscar and daughters Beulah and Ethel. All six are buried in a cemetery near Stony Run and Dorsey, John Henry Robinson lived to a ripe old age, dying Jan. 22, 1931, aged 86.

Robinson as a farmer emulated his white neighbors and hired pickers of his own. He became the first black man in Maryland to use picker checks, and possibly was the first black in the United States to issue tokens. His checks, once thought to be worth very little, have become among the most expensive such items.

Gratitude is extended to Ora Pumphrey Smith and the Anne Arundell County Historical Society for parts of the above data, and especially to Dorothy Benson Keen, author of a 1986 article in the society's journal entitled "John Henry Robinson." Mrs. Keen is the granddaughter of Robinson's original master, Basil Smith Benson. Photographs of Robinson and his wife appeared in that article.

Robinson was the first black man to use picker checks in Maryland but he was not the last. All these neighboring black families used picker checks later:

WW	William Ware, Anne Arundel County, near Ordnance Road (8 types)
UWB	Ulysses W. Brooks, Anne Arundel County, (3 types)
WD	William C. Dotson, Anne Arundel County, on Furnace Branch Road. (9 types). (Also used by his son, Daniel C. Dotson)
WD-RR	RR' stamped on WD checks for a son of William C. Dotson. (9 types)

See "Builder Uncovers Tin Box Containing Servants' Checks Used by Pumphrey" by Melvin Fuld, in *Coin World* for March 9, 1966, page 46.

MASSACHUSETTS

G. GERRY
Athol, Mass.

Rulau	Date	Metal	Size	VG	F	VF	EF
Mass 602	(1853)	Copper	29mm	50.00	—	100.	—
		G. GERRY / ATHOL MASS. ctsp on U.S. Large cent. Dates examined: 1830, 1836, 1843, 1846, 1847, 1852, 1854. At least 10 specimens known. (Brunk 16000)					
Mass 603	(1853)	Copper	29mm	25.00	—	50.00	—
		G. GERRY ctsp on U.S. Large cent. Examined: 1795, 1836, 1847. 3 known. (Brunk 15990)					

George Gerry (1816-76) founded the George Gerry & Son Textile Machinery Co. in Athol in 1853. On his death in 1876, the business passed to his son, George M. Gerry. The business remained in the Gerry family until 1981.

Its principal product was a "textile picker," which recycled old cloth by shredding it. The firm also served as a general machine shop. (Research by Dr. Gregory Brunk)

DRAPER & SANDLAND
Attleboro, Mass.

Rulau	Date	Metal	Size	VG	F	VF	Unc
Mass 600	1853	Gilt Brass	39mm	—	10.00	20.00	50.00
		DRAPER & SANDLAND, GILT BUTTON MFRS., ATTLEBORO, MASS. Rv: Calendar for year 1853. Plain edge. (Storer 37)					

WELLS W. AYER
Boston, Mass.

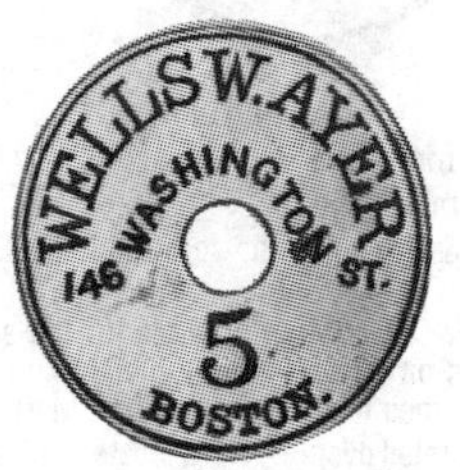

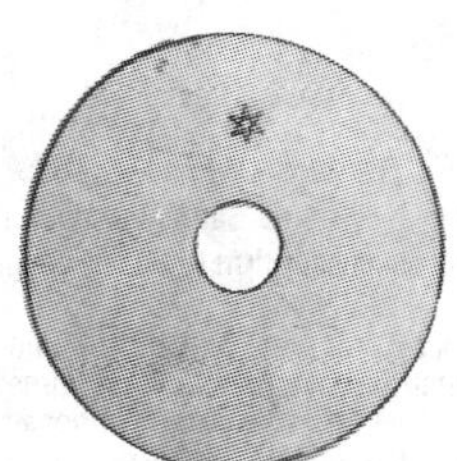

Miller	Date	Metal	Size	VG	F	VF	Unc
Mass 18	(?)	German Silver	32mm	15.00	25.00	75.00	100.00
		WELLS W. AYER / 146 WASHINGTON ST. / 5 / BOSTON. Rv: Small 6-pointed star (maker's mark?). Plain edge. Centrally holed flan. (Storer 140)					

E. B. BADGER & SONS CO.

Rulau	Date	Metal	Size	F	VF	EF	Unc
Mass 605	(1841-60)	Copper	73mm	—	50.00	75.00	100.
		Grasshopper. Below: COPPER SMITHS / BOSTON MASS. Around: ESTABLISHED 1841 / E. B. BADGER & SONS CO. / TRADE MARK. Rv: Intaglio of obverse. Plain edge. (Storer 142)					

Erastus B. Badger & Sons, established in 1841, were coppersmiths. The grasshopper was their trademark. They do not appear in the 1863 Boston directory.

BAKER, WRIGHT & HOWARD

Miller	Date	Metal	Size	VG	F	VF	Unc
Mass 19	(?)	White Metal	27mm	10.00	50.00	75.00	125.
		Numeral 87 incuse within inner circle. Around: BAKER, WRIGHT & HOWARD. / . (diamond). Rv: Numeral (25 or 87 or no number) within inner circle. Around: LADIES SALOON / 81 COURT ST. (Wright 1323; Storer 144)					

B.S. WRIGHT & CO.

Miller	Date	Metal	Size	VG	F	VF	Unc
Mass 96	(?)	White Metal	27mm	12.00	20.00	30.00	60.00
		Numeral 80 stamped into planchet. Inscribed: B.S. WRIGHT & CO. / BOSTON. Rv: Numeral (19, 42, 70, 80 or 81) stamped at center. Inscribed: LADIES' SALOON / 81 COURT ST. Plain edge. (Wright 1737)					

Miller	Date	Metal	Size	VG	F	VF	Unc
Mass 96A	(?)	White Metal	27mm	—	—	25.00	45.00
		Same, but no numeral stamped.					

This is a successor firm to Baker, Wright & Howard at the same address. See the BW&H listing.

Note that BW&H use numeral 87 and W&Co various numerals for the same purpose, whatever that purpose may be. The numerals on Boston's white metal 27mm token series suggests some sort of uniformity imposed by their token manufacturer, Merriam of Boston.

Benjamin S. Wright & Co., wholesale and retail oysters, were located at 2 Brattle Square and also 83 Court Street in Boston's 1863 directory. The 83 Court Street location had a 'ladies saloon' at 81 Court Street, the address given on the tokens. As the tokens of BW&H and W&Co state, they were apparently intended solely for use in this ladies saloon.

The 1863 directory also provides a listing for W. S. Baker, North American Oyster Co., South Market corner of Commercial, and also the foot of Clinton Street. This may be connected to BW&H.

J.J. & W. BEALS

Miller	Date	Metal	Size	F	VF	EF	Unc
Mass 20	(1850's)	Brass	28mm	5.00	10.00	15.00	45.00
		Clock face, J.J. & W. BEALS across lower portion. Rv: J.J. & W. BEALS / HAYMARKET / SQUARE / BOSTON / CLOCK ESTABLISHMENT. (Wright 68; Storer 151)					
Mass 20A		Silver	28mm	—	—	100.	250.
		(Storer 151)					
Mass 21	(1860)	Copper	28mm	—	—	50.00	100.
		Obverse as 20. Rv: N.C. FOLGER, 17 OLD LEVEE.					
Mass 22	(1860)	Brass	28mm	—	—	40.00	65.00
		Obverse as 20. Rv: GENTLEMAN'S FURNISHINGS, etc.					
Mass 23	(1860)	Copper	28mm	—	—	40.00	65.00
		As 22.					
Mass 24	(1860)	Copper	28mm	—	—	50.00	100.
		Obverse as 20. Rv: C.W. JACKSON, COAL DEALER.					
Mass 25	(1850's)	Copper	28mm	—	—	25.00	50.00
		Obverse as 20. Rv. Blank.					

Joseph J. Beals & Son, clock manufacturers, are listed in 1863 at Haymarket Square.

BOYDEN

Rulau	Date	Metal	Size	VG	F	VF	EF
Mass 609	(?)	Copper	29mm	—	75.00	—	125.
		BOSTON (incuse) / BOYDEN (relief, in rect. depression) ctsp on U.S. 1824 Large cent. (Tanenbaum collection; Brunk 6343)					

W. C. BRIGHAM & CO.

Rulau	Date	Metal	Size	VG	F	VF	Unc
Mass 607	(1850's)	WM	32mm	10.00	50.00	75.00	125.00
		Numeral 25 and 18 BRATTLE SQ. / BOSTON, MASS. in center. Around: W.C. BRIGHAM & CO'S / * DINING ROOM CHECK *. Rv: PAY AT / 50 (incuse) / THE COUNTER. Plain edge. (Storer 231)					
Mass 608	(1850's)	WM	32mm	10.00	25.00	50.00	75.00
		Obverse as last. Rv: Blank. Plain edge. (Storer 232)					
Mass 608A	(1850's)	Brass	32mm	10.00	25.00	50.00	75.00
		As last. (Storer 232)					

F.J. CHASE & CO.

Miller	Date	Metal	Size	VG	F	VF	EF
Mass 26E	(1860)	WM	27mm	10.00	50.00	75.00	125.
		Large-beaded circle at center is blank. Around: F.J. CHASE & CO / * BOSTON *. Rv: Small-beaded circle at center is blank. Around: NEW ENGLAND / DINING SALOON. Plain edge.					

The reverse of 26E is the same die as the obverse of 76, the New England Dining Saloon card, which see.

Miller	Date	Metal	Size	VG	F	VF	EF
Mass 26	(1860)	WM	27mm	—	—	50.00	100.
		Obverse as 26E. Rv: M. L. BRADFORD & CO. / CUTLERY / AND / HARDWARE (the obverse of the Bradford card of the 1865-70 period). Plain edge.					
Mass 26A	(1860)	Brass	27mm	—	—	50.00	100.
		As 26. Plain edge.					
Mass 26B	(1860)	Tin	27mm	—	—	50.00	100.
		As 26. Plain edge.					

It is possible the mulings (Mass 26 to 26B) were made in or after 1870 by Joseph H. Merriam's successors in the diesinking business.

H. COLMAN

Rulau	Date	Metal	Size	VG	F	VF	EF
Mass 502	(1847-49)	Copper	29mm	75.00	—	125.	—
		H. COLMAN / MAKER / BOSTON ctsp on U.S. 1837 Large cent. (Duffield 1396; Brunk 8960)					

Mass 502A		Copper	29mm	100.	—	175.	—
		MAKER BOSTON / H. COLMAN / BOSTON MAKER / 69 ctsp on U.S. 1837 Large cent. (Brunk 8965)					
Mass 502C		Copper	29mm	75.00	—	125.	—
		H. COLMAN / BOSTON / MAKER / BOSTON / 69 ctsp on U.S. 1837 Large cents. (Brunk 8950)					
Mass 502E		Copper	29mm	60.00	—	90.00	—
		H. COLMAN ctsp on U.S. Large cents. Examined: 1830, 1837, 1853. Only 3 reported. (Brunk 8930)					
Mass 502G		Copper	29mm	75.00	—	125.	—
		H. COLMAN / BOSTON ctsp on U.S. 1817 Large cent. (Brunk 8940)					

Henry Colman was a gunsmith operating at 11 Water St., Boston, circa 1847-49 and possibly as late as 1854. He does not appear in the 1841 or 1863 directories.

He is listed as a locksmith at 46 Devonshire Street, then at 9 Water Street, 1855-60.

CURRIER & GREELEY

Miller	Date	Metal	Size	VG	F	VF	Unc
Mass 30	(1855)	Copper	28mm	350.	450.	750.	—
		Eagle. CURRIER & GREELEY. Rv: Imitation of U.S. Large cent reverse. NOT / ONE / CENT is within the wreath; BUT JUST AS GOOD around above. Heavy die break over BUT to rim of coin; this reverse die, which is muled with many tokens, always seems to have the same die break. Plain edge.					
Mass 30A	(1855)	WM	28mm-	—	—	—	Rare
		As last. (Storer 312)					
Mass 30B	(1855)	Copper	28mm	—	—	750.	—
		As 30, but perfect dies.					
Mass 30-1/2	1855	Copper	28mm	—	20.00	30.00	—
		Imitation of U.S. Large cent. Liberty head to left; 13 stars; 1855 below. Rv: Same as reverse of Mass 30. (Bushnell 23; Kurth 83; RF Cen-1) Rarity 6. Plain edge.					

It is believed the NOT ONE CENT BUT JUST AS GOOD die was a product of the Scovill works in Waterbury, Conn., as it was extensively muled to the order of J.N.T. Levick later. There are several die varieties of Mass 30-1/2.

Mass 31	(1855)	Copper	28mm	500.	—	850.	—
		Obverse as reverse of Mass 30 (NOT ONE CENT). Rv: 3 grape leaves and bunch of grapes in central circle. Tiny incuse DUBBE on bottom of circle. Around: HEIDSIECK & FILS / * RHEIMS *. Plain edge. Excessively rare. (Storer 314)					

Mass 32	(1855)	Copper	28mm	500.	—	850.	—
		Obverse as 31. Rv: Central circle same as 31. Around: H. PIPER & CO. / * RHEIMS *. Plain edge. Excessively rare. (Storer 315)					

Mass 32F	(1855)	Copper	28mm	—	—	1000.	—
		Obverse as 31, but crudely double struck. Rv: F. KLEPPER & CO. / * / ...*... / * / BORDEAUX. Plain edge. Probably unique. (ANS coll.)					

The American Numismatic Society collection contains one of each of 31, 32 and 32F. Each merchant on these pieces is a French champagne maker. Heidsieck et Fils is still a major winery in France.

Currier and Greeley were dealers in teas and coffees.

F.W. DADMUN & CO.

Miller	Date	Metal	Size	VG	F	VF	Unc
Mass A34	(?)	White Metal	27mm	10.00	50.00	75.00	125.
		F.W. DADMUN & CO. / 15 COURT SQ. / (number in circle). Rv: MASSACHUSETTS / EATING HOUSE / (number in circle). Plain edge. (Storer 316)					

DR. DARBY

Miller	Date	Metal	Size	VG	F	VF	EF
Mass 34	(1855-60)	Silver	19mm	125.	—	175.	—
		CONSULT / DR. DARBY / BOSTON ctsp on Spanish-American 1-real coins. Examined: 1748, 1782-Mo, 1831, 1835. (Latter 2 pieces probably Mexico). There are 4 reported specimens. (Brunk 10690)					

Mass 34A		Silver	27mm	125.	—	175.	—
		Similar ctsp on Spanish-American 2-reales. Examined: 1770-LME-JM, 1772, 1775, 1776, 1778-Mo, 1780, 1785, 1789, 1790, 1793, 1794, 1798, 1799-Mo, 1807, unknown date. There are 18 reported specimens. (Gould 89)					

Mass 34B	(?)	Silver	27mm	125.	—	175.	—
		Similar ctsp on Mexico 2-reales. Examined: 1828-Mo, 1832-Mo, 1832-Zs. There are 3 specimens known. (Partrick coll.)					
Mass 34C		Silver	32mm	175.	—	250.	—
		Similar ctsp on Spanish-American 4-reales. (Gould 89)					
Mass 34E		Silver	25mm	135.	—	200.	—
		Similar ctsp on U.S. 1854-Arrows & rays Seated Liberty quarter. (H. Joseph Levine report)					

Mass 34G	(?)	Silver	27mm	250.	—	400.	—

Similar ctsp on obverse of Spanish-American 2-reales. Also on obv. of coin, ctsp: GOOD FOR / A BOTTLE / PIERCE'S / ROSETTA / HAIR TONIC. (Gould 90; Van Ormer sale 2792)

By 1870 Dr. Darby was relocated in Uniontown, D.C. He specialized in female disorders. It is possible Dr. Darby sold Pierce's Rosetta Hair Tonic, accounting for the muling in Mass. 34G.

THOMAS B. DILL

Rulau	Date	Metal	Size	VG	F	VF	EF
Mass 610	(1850's ?)	Copper	29mm	150.	—	250.	—

THOMAS B. DILL / BOSTON / (Doll) ctsp on U.S. Large cent. FOR SALE ctsp on opposite side of coin. (Brunk 11650)

An 1826 Large cent counterstamped T.B. Dill (Brunk 11645) may be connected.

GEORGE FERA

Miller	Date	Metal	Size	F	VF	EF	Unc
Mass 39	(1860)	White Metal	27mm	10.00	50.00	75.00	125.
		GEORGE FERA / * STUDIO BUILDING * / MERRIAM. Rv: PARTIES / — / SUPPLIED / MERRIAM, BOSTON / AT SHORT / — / NOTICE. Plain edge. (Wright 312)					
Mass 40	(1860)	White Metal	27mm	25.00	50.00	75.00	125.
		As 39, but ctsp numeral 20 or 82.					
Mass 41	(?)	White Metal	27mm	10.00	50.00	75.00	125.
		Apollo head right within laurel wreath, APOLLO. above, tiny MERRIAM BOSTON below bust. (Obverse of Mass 4). Rv: As obverse of Mass 39.					

There are mulings of the Fera dies which postdate the 1860 period.

George E. Fera, confectioner, is listed in the 1863 directory at 116 Tremont Street.

HESS & SPEIDEL, APOLLO GARDENS

Miller	Date	Metal	Size	VG	F	VF	Unc
Mass A4	(1859)	Brass	Oct. 30mm	—	25.00	40.00	60.00

(All incused) APOLLO GARDEN / GOOD FOR / FIVE CENTS / 576. WASHN. ST. Rv: Intaglio of obverse. Plain edge. (ANS collection)

Mass 4	(1860)	Copper	27mm	—	25.00	40.00	60.00
		Apollo head right within laurel wreath, APOLLO. above, tiny MERRIAM BOSTON below bust. Rv: APOLLO GARDENS / 576 / WASHINGTON ST. / GOOD FOR / 6 / CENTS. / * HESS & SPEIDEL *. Plain edge.					
Mass 5	(1860)	White Metal	27mm	—	10.00	15.00	40.00
		As 4. Plain edge. (Wright 445)					
Mass 6	(1860)	Gilt White Metal	27mm	—	10.00	15.00	50.00
		As 4.					
Mass 7	(1860)	White Metal	27mm	—	10.00	25.00	60.00
		As 5, cut ctsp '10'.					
Mass 8	(1860)	White Metal	27mm	—	10.00	25.00	60.00
		As 5, but ctsp '20'.					

There are at least 11 mulings of the Apollo Gardens card's obverse or reverse with portraits of Lincoln or Washington or cards of George Fera, Boston, or R. Chamberlaine, Norfolk, Va. Another muling (TURPENTINE WORKS, NEWBERN, N.C.) is dated 1862. All these mulings were made after 1860, or after the coverage of this reference book.

The Apollo Garden is listed in the 1863 Boston directory as a restaurant and billiard saloon at 576 Washington Street, under the proprietorship of Charles Hess and Leopold Speidel.

HOWARD & DAVIS

Rulau	Date	Metal	Size	VG	F	VF	EF
Mass 540	(1849-59)	Silver	27mm	150.	—	225.	—
		HOWARD & / DAVIS / BOSTON ctsp on U.S. 1819 Capped Bust quarter dollar. LY ctsp on opposite side. (Koppenhaver Aug. 1982 sale; Brunk 20260)					
Mass 541	(1849-59)	Silver	27mm	150.	—	225.	—
		HOWARD & DAVIS / BOSTON ctsp on U.S. quarters.					

Howard and Davis, manufacturers of clocks and fire engines, are listed at 34 Water St. 1848-1856 and at 43 Cornhill in 1857. The partnership broke up in 1860, when E. Howard & Co. and D.R. Davis are separately listed under "clocks" at, respectively, 17 Washington St. and 15 Washington St. They may have been clock retailers 1855-59. (Tanenbaum research)

S.F. HUDDLESTON

Rulau	Date	Metal	Size	G	VG	F	VF
Mass 504	(?)	Silver	25mm	—	100.	—	175.

S.F. HUDDLESTON / BOSTON ctsp on a Spanish 1795 2-reales of Carlos IIII. (Brunk 20540)

John S. F. Huddleston, meteorological instrument manufacturer, appears in the 1849-1863 directories, located at 96 Washington Street.

T. IRELAND

Illustration Enlarged

Rulau	Date	Metal	Size	VG	F	VF	EF
Mass 613	(1848-50)	Copper	28mm	100.00	—	150.00	—

(Small 8-spoked wheel device) / T. IRELAND in relief in two separate punches, the first circular and the second rectangular depressions, ctsp on near-new 1837 Hard Times token of March and Simes of Portsmouth, N.H., Low 124. (Brunk 21127)

The rectangular depression exactly matches the teaspoon shank hallmark photographed in Belden (pg. 245). Thomas Ireland was a silversmith in Methuen Village and in Boston, 1848-1868.

JAMESON & VALENTINE

Miller	Date	Metal	Size	VG	F	VF	Unc
Mass 45	(1857)	White Metal	27mm	10.00	60.00	100.	150.

Shield at center is stamped with numeral (18 3/4, 50 or 75). Inscribed: JAMESON & VALENTINE / SPRING LANE. Rv: Same as obverse. Plain edge. (Wright 500; Storer 493)

The firm was known as Jameson & Richardson, 1 Spring Lane, in the 1863 directory. The principal was Thomas Jameson and his partner Oliver L. Richardson.

JAMESON & VALENTINE'S
EATING & LODGING ROOMS,
REAR OF OLD SOUTH CHURCH,
Entrance, No. 1 Spring Lane, and Sewall Place, Milk St.
Ladies' Entrance, in Sewall Place. BOSTON.
Gentlemen wishing Dinners by the week, will be supplied with tickets.
☞ Board by the week on reasonable terms. ☜

Advertisement appearing in 1852 Cambridge Directory and Almanac. It had the same name at least until 1857.

KENDALL'S

Miller	Date	Metal	Size	VG	F	VF	Unc
Mass 46	(?)	White Metal	29mm	10.00	20.00	40.00	60.00

KENDALL'S on a panel. An oval. Rv: Same as obverse. Plain edge. (Wright 1482; Storer 499)

A.F. KENNARD

Rulau	Date	Metal	Size	VG	F	VF	EF
Mass 506	(?)	Copper	29mm	—	15.00	25.00	—

A.F. KENNARD cstp on U.S. 1848 or 1851 Large cent. (Brunk 22550)

Kennard was a jeweler.

In the World War I era, there was an Alexander D. Kennard, a broker in butter, cheese and eggs, who might be connected.

E. KERSHAW

Rulau	Date	Metal	Size	VG	F	VF	EF
Mass 507	(?)	Copper	29mm	—	—	125.	—
Mass 507C	(?)	Copper	29mm	—	—	125.	—

Mass 507: E. KERSHAW / PATENT / IMPROVED / BOSTON (inverted) ctsp on U.S. 1848 Large cent. (Brunk 22675; Kirtley Nov. 1991 sale, lot Q033).

Mass 507C: E. KERSHAW / BOSTON ctsp on U.S. Large cent. (Brunk 22670; John Cheramy coll.)

DR. KIMBALL

Rulau	Date	Metal	Size	VG	F	VF	EF
Mass 508	(?)	Silver	19mm	—	150.	—	225
Mass 509	(?)	Silver	27mm	150.	—	225.	—

Mass 508: DR. KIMBALL / DENTIST. / BOSTON ctsp on Spanish-American 1807 1-real. (Gould 103) (Brunk 22820)

Mass 509: Similar ctsp on Spanish-American 1793-Mo 2-reales. (There is also a larger ctsp — RIGGS — on this piece, probably frivolous). (Duffield 1362)

Rulau	Date	Metal	Size	VG	F	VF	EF
Mass 509A	(?)	Silver	32.5mm	200.	—	275.	—

Similar ctsp on U.S. 1817 half dollar. (Van Ormer 2719)

Rulau	Date	Metal	Size	VG	F	VF	EF
Mass 509B	(?)	Silver	32mm	200.	—	275.	—

Ctsp similar to 508 on Great Britain 1836 half crown. (Van Ormer sale 2718)

DR. KIRSTEAD

Rulau	Date	Metal	Size	G	VG	F	EF
Mass 511	(?)	Silver	32.5mm	—	200.	—	300.

DR. KIRSTEAD / DENTIST / BOSTON ctsp on U.S. 1817 Bust type half dollar. (Gould 36; Brunk 23095)

LEARNED & CO.

Miller	Date	Metal	Size	VG	F	VF	Unc
Mass 47	(1854-60)	White Metal	27mm	10.00	50.00	75.00	125.

Large numeral 27 stamped at center. Inscribed: LEARNED & CO. / CONGRESS ST. Rv: Same as obverse. Plain edge. (Wright 585; 523-524)

Isaac M. Learned & Co., restorator, was at 31 Congress St. 1854-1867.

MAHONY'S WHOLESALE CLOTHES

Miller	Date	Metal	Size	F	VF	EF	Unc
Mass 49	(1850's)	Brass	28mm	5.00	8.00	10.00	40.00

Eagle with shield on breast at center. .MAHONYS'. / NO. 50 ANN STT. above; BOSTON / WHOLESALE CLOTHES WAREHOUSE below. Rv: MANUFACTURERS / OF / EVERY / DESCRIPTION / OF / CLOTHING / ALSO / DEALERS IN / CLOTHS / & FURNISHING GOODS. Plain edge. (Wright 648)

E. MARSTON & CO.

Miller	Date	Metal	Size	VG	F	VF	Unc
Mass 51	(?)	White Metal	25mm	10.00	50.00	75.00	125.

E. MARSTON & CO. Rv: PAY AT THE COUNTER.

R. MARSTON & CO.

Miller	Date	Metal	Size	VG	F	VF	Unc
Mass 50	(?)	White Metal	31mm	10.00	50.00	75.00	125.

Numeral 50 within inner circle. Around R. MARSTON & CO. / * BOSTON *. Rv: Same. Plain edge. (Wright 670; Storer 539)

Donald Miller calls this token "German Silver, 25mm." Russell Marston.

Users of this catalog will note the mysterious use of numerals on many of these Boston tokens. This use needs clarification.

MECHANICAL BAKERY

Miller	Date	Metal	Size	F	VF	EF	Unc
Mass 53	(1856-58)	Brass	23mm	10.00	20.00	40.00	60.00

Sheaf of wheat, * MECHANICAL * BAKERY. Rv: ONE / LOAF. (Wright 688; Storer 561)

The Mechanical Bakery burned down in 1858.

MECHANICS SAVINGS BANK

Miller	Date	Metal	Size	VG	F	VF	Unc
Mass 54	(?)	White Metal	27mm	10.00	50.00	75.00	125.

MECHANICS SAVINGS BANK. Rv: PRESENT THIS CHECK. (Storer 562)

J.H. MERRIAM

Rulau	Date	Metal	Size	VG	F	VF	EF
Mass 513	(1854-56)	Silver	25mm	300.	—	400.	—

J.H. MERRIAM / 147-2 WASH ST / BOSTON ctsp on U.S. 1853 Seated Liberty quarter dollar. (Schenkman collection; Brunk 27410)

Joseph H. Merriam was located at 147-1/2 Washington Street only 1854-1857, when he moved to 18 Brattle Square.

JOS. H. MERRIAM

(There are a great number of mulings using the Merriam dies, all postdating the coverage of this section. Many appeared in the 1867-71 period. Only the four tokens below appear to emanate from the 1859-1860 period.)

Miller	Date	Metal	Size	F	VF	EF	Unc
Mass 55	(1859)	Copper	27mm	—	10.00	20.00	40.00

George Washington head in wreath right, WASHINGTON above. Rv: JOS. H. MERRIAM / MEDALIST / DIE SINKER / — AND — / LETTER CUTTER / ESTABLISHED 1850 / NO. 18 / BRATTLE SQUARE / BOSTON, MASS. Plain edge. (Baker 560)

Miller	Date	Metal	Size	F	VF	EF	Unc
Mass 56	(1859)	Brass	27mm	—	10.00	20.00	40.00

As 55.

Miller	Date	Metal	Size	F	VF	EF	Unc
Mass 57	(1859)	White Metal	27mm	—	10.00	20.00	40.00

As 55.

Miller	Date	Metal	Size	F	VF	EF	Unc
Mass 58	(1860)	Copper	31mm	—	—	100.	200.

Abraham Lincoln bust right, ABRAHAM LINCOLN above, BORN FEB. 12, 1809. below. Rv: JOS. H. MERRIAM / (coronet Liberty head coin within ornamentation) / DIE SINKER / 18 BRATTLE SQUARE / BOSTON / MEDALS STRUCK IN / — GOLD — / SILVER, COPPER OR TIN. Plain edge. (DeWitt AL 1860-38; Satterlee 269-271; King 576)

On his own tokens, Joseph H. Merriam describes his business as being established in 1850. He appears in Boston directories first in 1854, at 147-1/2 Washington Street. In 1857 he removed to 18 Brattle Square, the address identified with his tokens for all the succeeding years. Some of his 1863-dated Civil War tokens give 19 Brattle Square as an address, though others gave 18.

Merriam & Company (partners John C. Merriam and William N. Weeden) are at 18 Brattle Square 1865-1869. Then the firm again becomes Joseph H. Merriam 1869-70. In 1871 a successor firm, W.C. Brigham & Co., appears in the directories. The Brigham firm gave way in 1893 to William H. Pretat.

Joseph H. Merriam was the son of Joseph Merriam Jr. of Concord, Mass. He was married, but had no children. A first cousin, John M. Merriam, was an attorney in the 1903-1907 period when Albert R. Frey wrote his "The Tokens and Medals Relating to Numismatists and Coin Dealers" in *The Numismatist.* It is to John Merriam of the Boston law firm of Merriam, Hooper & Hilton that much of Frey's data was due. Joseph H. Merriam is buried in Providence, R.I.; his dates of birth and death are uncertain.

Dating Merriam's own store cards and those he struck for others is rather inexact at this point, but probably his earliest works came in 1857-1860. Only his counterstamped U.S. quarter seems earlier — from the 1854-1856 period.

Most likely Mass 55, 56, 57, 68 and 69 appeared in 1859.

Probably Mass 58 to 67, 68A, and the Apollo Gardens cards (Mass 4-8), the George Fera cards (Mass 39-40) and the New England Dining Saloon cards (Mass 76-78) appeared in 1860. Tentatively, we are accepting 1857 to 1860 as the issuance period for the Ayer, Baker-Wright-Howard, Chase, Dadmun, Jameson-Valentine, Kendalls, Learned, E. Marston, R. Marston, Mechanical Bakery, Mechanics Savings Bank, Messer, Milliken's Hotel, Tuttle, Vinton, B.S. Wright, J.S. Rogers and Hampden Brewery pieces — all of which seem to be Merriam's work. However, many of Merriam's mulings are probably from the 1870 period or later. Merriam also issued a series of 1863-dated Civil War tokens in small cent size.

Thus many of the cards included in this reference book may belong to the post-1860 period and may yet have to be included in my *U.S. Trade Tokens 1866-1889,* which includes 1861-1865 tokens that are not considered part of the Civil War token series.

W.W. MESSER

Miller	Date	Metal	Size	VG	F	VF	Unc
Mass 71	(?)	White Metal	27mm	10.00	35.00	50.00	100.

W.W. MESSER, 212 WASHINGTON ST. Rv: PARTIES SUPPLIED (etc.). Ctsp 28, 30 or another number.

Miller	Date	Metal	Size	VG	F	VF	Unc
Mass 70	(?)	White Metal	27mm	10.00	35.00	75.00	100.

Obverse as Mass 71. Rv: FAMILIES / * / SUPPLIED WITH / FRESH CREAM / & FRENCH / * / CHOCOLATE.

William W. Messer.

MILLIKEN'S HOTEL

Miller	Date	Metal	Size	VG	F	VF	Unc
Mass 75	(?)	Brass	29mm	10.00	20.00	50.00	80.00

Numeral 12 surrounded by stars at center, MILLIKEN'S HOTEL — BOSTON. Rv: Numeral 12 at center, ON THE EUROPEAN PLAN. (Storer 587)

MOUSLEY & SON

Rulau	Date	Metal	Size	VG	F	VF	EF
Mass 543	(?)	Copper	29mm	75.00	—	125.	—

MOUSLEY & SON / XX / BOSTON ctsp on U.S. 1830 Large cent. (Tanenbaum coll.; Brunk 28715)

NEW ENGLAND DINING SALOON

Miller	Date	Metal	Size	VG	F	VF	Unc
Mass 76	(1860)	White Metal	27mm	50.00	60.00	75.00	125.
		Beaded Circle at center. Around: NEW ENGLAND / DINING SALOON. Rv: Beaded oval at center encloses numeral 413 or empty oval. Around: 142 WASH. ST. BOSTON MASS. Plain edge. (Wright 1549)					
Mass 77	(?)	Brass	27mm	10.00	50.00	75.00	125.
		Obverse as Mass 76. Rv: Obverse of Mass 26 (F.J. Chase card).					
Mass 78	(?)	----	32mm	10.00	50.00	75.00	125.
		Obverse as Mass 76. Rv: Mass 55 (Merriam card).					

Diesinker Joseph H. Merriam likely muled 77 or 78 after 1860.

NOWLIN & McELWAIN

Miller	Date	Metal	Size	VG	F	EF	Unc
Mass 79	(?)	White Metal	26mm	—	200.	350.	—

Pitchers and glasses on clock face. Rv: NOWLIN & McELWAIN / JEWELERS. Plain edge. Only 2 known. (Storer 615)

This firm is not traceable in any Boston directory. The token may have been issued elsewhere, and — by its style — after the Civil War.

H. P.

Rulau	Date	Metal	Size	VG	F	VF	EF
Mass 635	(?)	Copper	29mm	—	—	35.00	—

HP (inverted) / BOSTON / HP ctsp on U.S. 1820 Large cent. Rv: HP (inverted) / CAST STEEL / HP ctsp on reverse of the coin. (Brunk 17580; PCAC July 1993 sale, lot 947)

Probably a maker of tools.

E. PERKINS

Miller	Date	Metal	Size	VG	F	VF	Unc
Mass 83	(?)	White Metal	27mm	10.00	20.00	50.00	75.00

E. PERKINS, CONGRESS STREET. Rv: E. PERKINS & CO. * CONGRESS ST. *. Cstp numeral 30, 36 or another number. (Wright 816)

Edward Perkins & Co.

S.M.B. ROUSE

Rulau	Date	Metal	Size	F	VF	EF	Unc
Mass 513	(?)	Silver	35mm	—	150.	—	250.

S.M.B. ROUSE // 1197 WASH. ST. ctsp on Prussia 1814-A Reichsthaler. (Duffield 1374; Storer 677; Brunk 35127)

Samuel M. B. Rouse was a druggist.

Z.S. SAMPSON

Miller	Date	Metal	Size	F	VF	EF	Unc
Mass 89	(1858-64)	White Metal	27mm	10.00	20.00	30.00	50.00

Large urn fountain at center, SODA inscribed on it. Around: SAMPSON'S ICE CREAM / MERRIAM BOSTON / * WATER *. Rv: GOOD FOR ONE GLASS / — OF — ICE CREAM / SODA / Z.S. SAMPSON / CORNER OF / COURT & HANOVER ST'S. / BOSTON. Plain edge. (Wright 934; Storer 697; Schenkman B49)

Z. Silsbee Sampson was listed as a physician at Court, corner of Hanover (the address on the token), in 1858. In 1860 he added the title apothecary in his advertising. He remained at this address until 1867. In 1868-69 he reappears in directories at different addresses.

The token could have been issued only 1858-1864, since Merriam cut the dies.

SPENCER RIFLE CO.

Rulau	Date	Metal	Mint	VG	F	VF	EF
Mass 550	(1862-69)	Copper	29mm	150.	—	250.	—

SPENCER. RIFLE. CO. / AMBROSE / BOSWORTH / BOSTON ctsp on U.S. 1846 Large cent. (Kurt Krueger coll.; Brunk 4490)

Spencer Repeating Rifle Co. was at Chickering's Building, Tremont Street, in 1863. They made Spencer breech-loading rifles and carbines for the Army and Navy, and Spencer breech-loading sporting rifles, in 1862-1869. (Ad in Boston 1863 directory, page 271)

H.B. STANWOOD & CO.

Miller	Date	Metal	Size	F	VF	EF	Unc
Mass 90	(?)	Brass	21.5mm	5.00	7.50	9.50	30.00

H.B. STANWOOD & CO. / IMPORTERS / 253 / WASHINGTON / STREET / * BOSTON *. Rv: * WATCHES / JEWELLERY * / DIAMONDS / * FANCY * / GOODS &C / SILVER & PLATED WARE. Reeded edge. (Wright 1040)

Storer says this token occurs with thick and thin planchets. Henry B. Stanwood (1818-1869) was a noted silversmith.

C.F. TUTTLE

Miller	Date	Metal	Size	VG	F	VF	Unc
Mass 91	(1860)	White Metal	27mm	10.00	30.00	50.00	75.00
		Head of George Washington right in wreath, WASHINGTON above. Rv: C.F. TUTTLE / NO. 130 WASHINGTON ST. / PAY AT THE / COUNTER. Plain edge. Numerals known stamped at center: 11, 13, 17, 19, 20, 23, 24, 25, 37 and no number.					

It is likely that other stamped numeral variations exist.

Miller	Date	Metal	Size	VG	F	VF	Unc
Mass 92	(1860)	Brass	27mm	—	—	75.00	100.
		As Mass 91.					

C.F. Tuttle's Restaurant was also an issuer of Civil War tokens bearing no date, but probably struck in 1863 (Fuld type Mass 115G).

Charles F. Tuttle operated a restaurant, according to the 1863 Boston directory, at 1 Water Street.

C.A. VINTON

Boston, Mass.

Miller	Date	Metal	Size	VG	F	VF	Unc
Mass 93	(?)	White Metal	27mm	10.00	50.00	75.00	125.
		C.A. VINTON / 212 WASHINGTON ST. Numeral 12 in center. Rv: Same as obverse. (Storer 776)					

The 1863 directory listed Mrs. Charles A. Vinton, confectionery, at 284 Washington Street. Storer 776.

ENOS HOOVER

Chicopee Falls, Mass. (?)

Rulau	Date	Metal	Size	VG	F	VF	EF
Mass 552	1851	Copper	29mm	75.00	—	125.	—
		ENOS HOOVER / 1851 / (Eagle with shield on breast, wings folded) ctsp on U.S. 1851 Large cent (Brunk 19990)					
Mass 552B	1850	Copper	28mm	75.00	—	125.	—
		ENOS. HOOVER. / NOV. 15 / 1850 ctsp on U.S. 1828 Large cent. (Brunk 20000)					

Attributed on the basis of the eagle, which resembles that of the Massachusetts Arms Co. at Chicopee Falls, itself a counterstamp issuer. Basis for the attribution is, admittedly, thin.

C.H. SWASEY

Dorchester, Mass.

Miller	Date	Metal	Size	VG	F	VF	EF
Mass 524	(?)	Silver	25mm	20.00	—	30.00	—
		C.H. SWASEY ctsp on U.S. 1853 with Arrows & Rays quarter dollar. (Stanley Steinberg Jan. 1982 sale; Brunk 39040)					
Mass 524A	(?)	Copper	29mm	15.00	—	25.00	—
		Similar ctsp on U.S. Large cent. Examined: 1837, 1843. (Brunk 39040 B)					

Swasey was a lumber yard proprietor, according to Steinberg. Doubtful attribution.

OLIVER H. BUSH

Fall River, Mass.

Rulau	Date	Metal	Size	VG	F	VF	EF
Mass 640	(?)	Copper	29mm	—	—	100.	—
		OLIVER' / H' BUSH / FALL' RIVER / MASS ctsp on U.S. 1825 Large cent. (Brunk 6250; PCAC July 1993 sale, lot 877)					

J.S. ROGERS & BRO.

Gloucester, Mass.

Miller	Date	Metal	Size	VG	F	VF	UNC
Mass 97	(?)	White Metal	27mm	10.00	50.00	75.00	125.
		J.S. ROGERS & BRO. GLOUCESTER, MASS. Rv: Numeral 125 stamped at center. Inscribed: PLEASE PASS THIS TO THE COUNTER. Plain edge. (Wright 911; Storer 1085)					

A scarce token, Wright reported in 1900.

WILLIAM T. CLEMENT

Greenfield, Mass.

Rulau	Date	Metal	Size	VG	F	VF	EF
Mass 620	(?)	Copper	29mm	100.	—	200.	—
		W. T. CLEMENT ctsp on Massachusetts 1788 cent. (Brunk 8310)					

William T. Clement was a gunsmith and knife maker who was in business in Greenfield, Mass. 1836-65. Later (1866-78) he was located in North Hampton, Mass.

J. RUSSELL & CO.

Greenfield, Mass.

Rulau	Date	Metal	Size	VG	F	VF	EF
Mass 660	(?)	Copper	29mm	50.00	—	85.00	—
		J. RUSSELL / 1 / CROTON ctsp on U.S. 1849 Large cent. (Brunk 35340; Miller NY 2150)					
Mass 661	1847	Copper	29mm	50.00	—	85.00	—
		1847 / J. RUSSELL / 2 / CROTON ctsp on U.S. Large cent. (Brunk 35245)					
Mass 662	(?)	Copper	29mm	50.00	—	85.00	—
		J. RUSSELL ctsp on U.S. Large cents of 1843 or 1847. 3 known. (Hallenbeck 18.757; Brunk 35335)					
Mass 663	(?)	Copper	29mm	—	—	85.00	—
		J. RUSSELL & CO. ctsp on U.S. 1818 or 1837 or 1844 or worn Large cents. 4 known. (Brunk 35350)					
Mass 664	(?)	Copper	29mm	90.00	—	150.	—
		J. RUSSELL & CO. / GREEN RIVER WORKS ctsp on U.S. 1845 Large cent. (Brunk 35355; Miller NY 2154)					
Mass 665	(?)	Copper	29mm	—	—	85.00	—
		CROTON ctsp on U.S. 1847 Large cent. (Hallenbeck 3.758; Brunk 10150)					
Mass 665B	(?)	Silver	31mm	—	—	185.00	—
		J. RUSSELL (curved) / U. S. A. / CROTON (curved) / U. S. A. (Kirtley offering 28, Dec. 1988, lot 103). Unlike Brunk 35340, the punches used to create this counterstamped piece are much smaller. First two lines and last two lines are combined on separate punches.					

John Russell (born 1797) founded Russell Cutlery Co. in 1834 in Greenfield, Mass. Originally he made chezels, butcher and carving knives stamped AMERICAN CUTLERY. In 1836 he named his Greenville factory the "Green River Works" and began stamping his products GREEN RIVER WORKS.

In 1840 Russell began shipping knives to the West and the Green River mark became a legend. From 1840 to 1860, his firm shipped 720,00 hunting knives to the West.

By 1868 Russell's firm outgrew its factory and moved to Turners Falls, Mass. In 1876 J. Russell & Co. began making pocket knives, and this helped it become one of America's best known names in knives. In 1935 it merged into the Russell Harrington Cutlery Co.

Russell's trademarks, arrow right through capital R, J. RUSSELL & CO. and RUSSELL, appear on most of its knives and other cutlery made since 1868.

The Russell counterstamps are relocated from New York to Massachusetts from earlier editions of this reference. This movement clears up the background search for the stamps' issuers, except for the appearance of CROTON in numbers Mass 660, 661, 665 and 665B. Neither a place nor any other name of Croton has surfaced in connection with the Russell Cutlery Co.

(See *Romance of Collecting Knives* by Lavona Ferguson, Fairborn, Ohio 1978)

CARLETON

Haverhill, Mass.

Rulau	Date	Metal	Size	VG	F	VF	EF
Mass 705	(1849-53)	Copper	29mm	50.00	—	85.00	—
		CARLETON in relief within rectangular depression ctsp on U.S. Large cent. Examined: 1802, 1817, 1846. (Pete Peters coll.; Brunk 6780)					

The hallmark matches published marks of silversmith James H. Carleton of Haverhill, known to be active in 1849-1853. (Belden, page 98)

A. SANBORN

Lowell, Mass.

Rulau	Date	Metal	Size	VG	F	VF	EF
Mass 621	(1849-60)	Copper	29mm	100.	—	150.	—
		A. Sanborn (script) in relief within scroll-shaped depression, ctsp on U.S. Large cent. Examined: 1802. (Brunk 35600)					

Mass 621A	(1849-60)	Copper	29mm	100.	—	150.	—

Similar ctsp on U.S. 1845 Large cent. Rv: LOWELL. in relief within rect. depression, ctsp on opposite side of the coin. (Brunk 35605)

Amos Sanborn was a manufacturer of silverware, watches, music boxes, spectacles and jewelry, listed in Lowell 1849-1865. His Hallmark appears on his counterstamped coins. The firm became A. Sanborn & Co. 1866-72, when he admitted a partner, Horace B. Bacon. Another Bacon, H.M., seems to have been the partner 1872-74. Still under the A. Sanborn & Co. name, the business was run 1874-76 by Mrs. Amos Sanborn.

(See "Merchant Advertising Countermarks of 19th Century America" in *The Numismatist* for Feb. 1989, pgs. 222-230, for an excellent overview of Sanborn and other merchant pieces.)

This Sanborn ad appeared in New England Business Directory for 1860, when his address was 25 Central, corner of Middle St.

WHITTEN'S GOLDEN SALVE
Lowell, Mass.

Rulau	Date	Metal	Size	VG	F	VF	EF
Mass 622	(1859-60)	Copper	29mm	200.	—	300.	—
		WHITTEN'S GOLDEN SALVE ctsp on U.S. 1835 or 1848 or 1856 Large cent. (Duffield 1429; Hallenbeck 23.511; Gould 8; Brunk 43280)					
Mass 623	(1859-60)	Copper	28mm	200.	—	300.	—
		Similar ctsp on Canadian token. (Rulau Z102)					

C.P. Whitten advertised his Golden Salve in the 1860 New England business directory. It supposedly healed "sores, humors, wounds and every kind of external inflammatory difficulty...on man or beast." It cost 25 cents per box.

HALE & F.
Millbury, Mass.

Rulau	Date	Metal	Size	VG	F	VF	EF
Mass 625	(?)	Copper	29mm	150.	—	250.	—
		HALE & F / MILLBURY / MASS ctsp on worn-smooth U.S. Large cent. (Dragon) / MILLBURY / MASS ctsp on opposite side of coin. (Frank Kovacs coll.)					

The "dragon" could be a "griffin" or another mythical monster, facing right. The "F" following HALE & could be another letter or symbol; it is indistinct.

May be connected wih Hale & Warrant, Brunk, 17740.

LAMSON GOODNOW & CO.
Shelburne Falls, Mass.

Rulau	Date	Metal	Size	VG	F	VF	EF
Mass 525	(1849-56)	Copper	29mm	150.	—	250.	—
		LAMSON, GOODNOW & CO / S. FALLS WORKS ctsp on U.S. 1846 or 1851 Large cent. (Tanenbaum coll.; Brunk 23755)					

Lamson, Goodnow & Co. were listed in the 1849 New England Mercantile Union directory as cutlery manufacturers in Shelburne Falls, Mass. They are undoubtedly connected with the gunsmith firm of Lamson, Goodnow & Yale in Windsor, Vt. 1857-64. The 1860 edition of the N.E. Mercantile Union directory lists the Shelburne Falls firm under a new title, Lamson & Goodnow.

HAMILTON & CHAPIN
Springfield, Mass.

Rulau	Date	Metal	Size	G	F	VF	EF
Mass 526	1851	White Metal	31mm	—	30.00	125.	250.
		Building at center, THE CRYSTAL PALACE above, WORLD'S SHOW / IN / LONDON / 1851 below. Rv: HAMILTON & CHAPIN / IMPORTERS OF / CHINA / GLASS CROCKERY / AND / SOLAR LAMPS / SPRINGFIELD, MASS.					

Not listed in Miller, Storer or Sabo. H. Joseph Levine Sale, Dec. 14, 1981. This is struck by Richard Paine of Springfield.

HAMPTON BREWERY

Miller	Date	Metal	Size	VG	F	VF	Unc
Mass 125-1/2(?)		White Metal	--mm	50.00	75.00	125.	200.
		Sheaf of wheat, HAMPTON BREWERY / SPRINGFIELD, MASS. Rv: Blank. Plain edge. (Storer 1665)					

R. PAINE

Rulau	Date	Metal	Size	VG	F	VF	EF
Mass 521	(1846-48)	Copper	29mm	—	175.	—	250.
		BY R. PAINE / SPRINGFIELD ctsp on Massachusetts 1787 cent. (Duffield 1415; Brunk 30780)					
Mass 522	(1846-48)	Silver	19mm	—	100.	—	150.
		Similar ctsp on Spanish-American 1804 1-real. 2 known. (Gould 114)					
Mass 523	(1846-48)	Silver	27mm	125.	—	175.	—
		BY R. PAINE / SPRINGFIELD / M. CROSIER / B/ B / BH / BH ctsp in a complex manner on a Spanish-American 1782 2-reales. The BY R. PAINE / SPRINGFIELD and M. CROSIER stamps are from prepared logos, each BH from a silversmith-type punch, and each B from single-letter punches, all probably applied at different times. (Van Ormer sale 2777)					
Mass 680	(?)	Copper	29mm	—	75.00	—	125.
		R. PAINE ctsp on U.S. Large cent. (Brunk 30770).					
Mass 681	(?)	Silver	27mm	—	100.	—	150.
		Similar ctsp on U.S. quarter.					
Mass 682	(?)	Silver	27mm	—	100.	—	150.
		Similar ctsp on Spanish-American 1782 2-reales.					
Mass 684	(?)	Copper	29mm	—	—	200.	—
		PAINE / SPRINGFIELD / (Horse's head) ctsp on U.S. Large cent. (Brunk 30765)					

Richard Paine (born about 1806) was employed by the Ames Mfg. Co. from about 1842 as an inspector of naval contracts. This ended about 1845 when Ames Mfg. Co. refused to use Maynard primers in the Jenks carbines, and Paine entered the engraving business. The Springfield city directory for 1845 lists Paine as a stamp cutter, diesinker and inspector of arms. In Dec. 1846 he received a naval contract to inspect Jenks carbines made by Remington & Sons at Ilion, N.Y., residing in Springfield but traveling to Ilion as needed for his work. He resigned the Navy duties in 1848 due to the press of other business.

He last appeared in the 1857-58 directory. A total of 9 counterstamped coins is now known for Paine, but more may be discovered. It is thought the 'BY R. PAINE' stamp was his marking for his duties as a naval inspector, which would date it to the 1845-48 period.

(Research courtesy A. W. Lindbert, Gregory G. Brunk and ANS Museum staff)

PIONEER BASE BALL CLUB

Rulau	Date	Metal	Size	F	VF	EF	Unc
Mass 528	1858	White Metal	32mm	—	350.	500.	650.
		Batter awaiting baseball, small J.A. BOLEN under the ground. PIONEER BASE BALL CLUB around, 13 stars below. Rv: ORGANIZED APRIL 30. 1858. / PLAY / GROUND / ON / HAMPDEN / PARK / SPRINGFIELD, / (crossed bats and three balls) / MASS. Plain edge. (Wright 831) (Only 125 struck)					
Mass 529	1858	Copper	32mm	—	400.	600.	750.
		As last. (Only 75 struck)					

James A. Bolen, the Springfield diesinker, issued a lengthy series of his own cards 1862-1869.

Cataloguer E.L. Johnson of Springfield, Mass., in his 1882 listing of Bolen products, said the dies for this piece were cut in 1861 for Charles E. Vinton, that only 75 copper and 125 white metal pieces were struck, and that Vinton was given the dies.

Originally (in 1857) there were 40 members in the Pioneer Base Ball Club. They played their first game in 1857 but were not organized until the next year when Hampden Park was opened. Daniel J. Marsh in 1908 said he ordered Vinton to have the medals struck, and there were also a few made in silver, plus one or two in gold. The dies' location was not known to Marsh; they had disappeared from Vinton's estate and may still exist.

M. SMITH

Rulau	Date	Metal	Size	VG	F	VF	EF
Mass 575	1857	Copper	29mm	75.00	—	125.	—

1857 / M. SMITH / PATENT / CAST-STEEL / MASS / M. SMITH ctsp on U.S. 1846 Large cent. (Tanenbaum coll.; Brunk 37215)

There was a gunsmith of Springfield, Mass. active in 1869 who advertised himself as "M. Smith." More research is needed on this piece.

SPRINGFIELD, MASS.

Rulau	Date	Metal	Size	VG	F	VF	EF
Mass 560	(?)	Silver	27mm	50.00	—	75.00	—

Springfield Mass. (on scrolls) ctsp on Spanish-American 1821-Mo 2-reales. (Kurt Krueger Sept. 1983 sale; Brunk 37753)

Gregory Brunk believes this piece is associated with the Springfield National Armory.

TILLY, HAYNES & CO.

Springfield, Mass.

Miller	Date	Metal	Size	F	VF	EF	Unc
Mass 129	1851	Copper	27mm	50.00	125.	250.	400.

Building at center. Above: THIS BUILDING FOR THE INTERNATIONAL / EXHIBITION. In exergue: LONDON / 1851. Rv: TILLY, HAYNES & CO. / GREAT / EXHIBITION OF / CLOTHING AND RICH / FURNISHING GOODS. / NO 18, 20, 22, 24, 26 MAIN ST / OAK HILL ESTABLISHMENT / SPRINGFIELD / MASS. Plain edge.

Miller	Date	Metal	Size	F	VF	EF	Unc
Mass 130	1851	White Metal	27mm	35.00	75.00	150.	—

As Mass 129. Plain edge. (Wright 1148)

A. HUNTLEY

Taunton, Mass.

Miller	Date	Metal	Size	VG	F	VF	EF
Mass 135	(?)	Lead	23mm	—	—	—	V. Rare

Head on obverse. (Storer 1720)

J.W. STRANGE

Taunton, Mass.

Miller	Date	Metal	Size	VG	F	VF	Unc
Mass 136	(1859-71)	—	23mm	10.00	25.00	100.	200.

J. W. STRANGE, STEEL LETTER CUTTER. Eagle.

Miller	Date	Metal	Size	VG	F	VF	Unc
Mass 136E	(?)	?	34mm	5.00	10.00	15.00	30.00

J. W. STRANGE / LETTER CUTTER / TAUNTON. Rv: ? & W. R. R. Plain edge. (Steinberg sale list 87, lot 131)

Tag for a railway company made by Jirah W. Strange.

N. CODY

Webster, Mass.

Rulau	Date	Metal	Size	VG	F	VF	EF
Mass 695	(1847-52)	Copper	29mm	50.00	—	75.00	—

N. CODY in relief within toothed rect. depression ctsp on U.S. Large cent. Examined: 1803, 1816, 1827, 1851, 1847. 5 pieces known. (Brunk 8560; PCAC July 1993 sale, lot 889)

Nathan Cody (1784-1852) was a machinist and blacksmith in Webster. The counterstamps must have been applied circa 1847-52. Research by William Swoger (see Bibliography).

Buffalo Billy Cody was a second cousin of his, according to Brunk.

M. TIDD

Woburn, Mass.

Rulau	Date	Metal	Size	VG	F	VF	EF
Mass 563	(1847-50)	Copper	29mm	60.00	—	100.	—

M. TIDD ctsp on U.S. Large cents. Dates examined: 1807, 1840, 1845. Unknown date. 5 pieces known. (Brunk 40080)

Rulau	Date	Metal	Size	VG	F	VF	EF
Mass 565	(?)	Copper	29mm	60.00	—	100.	—

M. TIDD / WOBURN ctsp on U.S. Large cents. Dates examined: 1803, 1831, 1837, 1835, 1838. 5 pieces known. (Brunk 40090)

Rulau	Date	Metal	Size	VG	F	VF	EF
Mass 567	(?)	Copper	29mm	—	100.	—	—

J. D. R. / M. TIDD / WOBURN / & D. L. ctsp on U.S. 1835 Large cent. (Kovacs coll.)

Rulau	Date	Metal	Size	VG	F	VF	EF
Mass 570	(?)	Copper	29mm	75.00	—	125.	—

M. TIDD / WOBURN / MASS. ctsp on U.S. Large cents. Dates examined: 1822, 1823, 1828, 1835, 1846. 5 pieces known. (Brunk 40100)

Marshall Tidd was a maker of pistols and rifles, 1846-68. He had shops in Woburn and North Woburn. A commemorative ctsp occurs on Canada Large cent!

H. W. COOLIDGE

Massachusetts ?

Rulau	Date	Metal	Size	VG	F	VF	EF
Mass 700	(?)	Copper	29mm	—	50.00	—	—

H. W. COOLIDGE in relief within rect. depression ctsp on U.S. 1838 Large cent. (Hartzog coll.; Brunk 9460; Rulau Z4).

Henry Ware Coolidge was born in 1838.

MICHIGAN

A.J. SUTHERLAND

Ann Arbor, Mich.

Rulau	Date	Metal	Size	VG	F	VF	EF
Mich 100	(1860)	Copper	28.5mm	—	200.	—	300.

A.J. SUTHERLAND / ANN ARBOR ctsp on U.S. 1841 Hard Times token (Webster Credit Currency), Low 64. (Van Ormer sale 2869; Brunk 38925)

Rulau	Date	Metal	Size	VG	F	VF	EF
Mich 100A	(1860)	Copper	29mm	—	200.	—	300.

Similar ctsp on U.S. Large Cent.

Andrew J. Sutherland was a gunsmith, active 1860-80.

J. M. BIERD

Carrollton, Mich.

Rulau	Date	Metal	Size	VG	F	VF	EF
Mich 105	(?)	Copper	33.4mm	—	75.00	—	—

J. M. BIERD. / CARROLLTON. / MICH. ctsp on England 1831 penny of William IV, KM-707. (Paul Cunningham coll.)

The stamp was carefully applied with individual letter punches.

O.S. CLARK

Cheboygan, Mich.

Rulau	Date	Metal	Size	VG	F	VF	EF
Mich 101	(?)	Copper	34mm	—	—	250.	—
		O.S. CLARK . BLACKSMITH / ** / CHEBOYGAN. MICH. ctsp on Ireland penny of 1822-23, date worn. (Van Ormer sale 2593; Brunk 8095)					

J. DIMMICK

Detroit, Mich.

Miller	Date	Metal	Size	F	VF	EF	Unc
Mich 2	(1850's)	Copper	28mm	4.00	6.50	15.00	40.00
		Eagle displayed, U.S. shield on breast. CRYSTAL PALACE above; 114 JEFF. AVENUE. DETROIT MICH below. Rv: J. DIMMICK / WHOLESALE DEALER / IN / GOLD JEWELRY. / CLOCKS. WATCHES / TOYS. LACES. GUNS. / PISTOLS. YANKEE / NOTIONS PLATED / WARE &C &C. Plain edge. (Wright 259)					
Mich 3	(1850's)	Brass	28mm	4.00	6.50	15.00	40.00
		As 2. Reeded edge.					
Mich 3C	(1850's)	Silv/B	28mm	—	—	—	100.
		As 2. Plain edge. (Ganter coll.)					

DANIEL BALL & CO.

Grand Rapids, Mich.

Miller	Date	Metal	Size	F	VF	EF	Unc
Mich 7	(1850's)	Brass	28mm	5.50	7.00	11.00	30.00
		Safe at center, which opens to right (!). * DOMESTIC & FOREIGN EXCHANGE OFFICE. around. Rv: Eagle displayed, shield on breast, * DANIEL BALL & CO. * / GRAND RAPIDS MICH.					

Miller	Date	Metal	Size	F	VF	EF	Unc
Mich 8	(1850's)	Brass	28mm	5.50	7.00	11.00	30.00
		Similar to 7, but safe opens to left. Eagle's wing points between D--A of DANIEL. (Wright 53)					
Mich 9	(1850's)	Brass	28mm	5.50	7.00	11.00	30.00
		Similar to 8, but eagle's wing points before D of DANIEL.					

FOSTER, MARTIN & CO.

Miller	Date	Metal	Size	F	VF	EF	Unc
Mich 12	(1850's)	Brass	28mm	6.50	8.00	12.50	30.00
		Anvil in center, FOSTER, MARTIN & CO. / HARDWARE, STOVES, IRON, & C. / MONROE ST., / GRAND RAPIDS, MICH. Rv: Stove in center, MANUFACTURERS OF / COPPER, TIN, & SHEET IRON-WARE. (Wright 335)					

This firm was succeeded by Foster & Parry, which see.

FOSTER & PARRY

Grand Rapids, Mich.

Miller	Date	Metal	Size	F	VF	EF	Unc
Mich 10	(Late 1850's)	Brass	28mm	4.00	6.00	10.00	30.00
		Cooking stove in center, . FOSTER & PARRY above, GRAND RAPIDS MICH. below. Rv: Padlock in center, nine stars and WHOLESALE & RETAIL forming inner circle around. Outer circle reads: DEALERS IN STOVES / * IRON & HARDWARE *. Plain edge.					
Mich 11	(Late 1850's)	Copper	28mm	4.00	6.00	10.00	30.00
		As 10.					
Mich 11T	(?)	Brass	28mm	—	—	25.00	50.00
		As 10, but 141 WATER ST. above padlock. (Slabaugh coll.)					

There are minor die varieties of Mich 10 and 11. The brass card received wide distribution and is often encountered worn. It must have circulated as a cent until about 1858.

A successor company, FOSTER & METCALF, issued Civil War tokens with a similar cook stove motif dated 1861, which circulated through 1863.

A probable successor company, FOSTER, STEVENS & CO. INC., was still in the hardware business in Grand Rapids in 1918.

W.D. Foster in 1880-81 dealt in safes, tools, pumps, saws.

MISSISSIPPI

BENJN. F. FOTTERALL
Vicksburg, Miss.

Miller	Date	Metal	Size	F	VF	EF	Unc
Miss 3	(1850's)	Copper	29mm	7.50	10.00	25.00	50.00
		Eagle with chain links in its mouth behind U.S. shield, a rising sun over landscape below. BENJN. F. FOTTERALL. above, * VICKSBURG. * below. Rv: SILK. FANCY / AND / STAPLE GOODS. / OF / ALL KINDS. Plain edge.					
Miss 3A	(1850's)	Copper	29mm	7.50	10.00	25.00	50.00
		As 3. Reeded edge.					
Miss 4	(1850's)	Brass	29mm	7.50	10.00	25.00	80.00
		As Miss 3. Reeded edge. (Wright 337)					
Miss 4A	(1850's)	Silvered Brass	29mm	7.50	10.00	25.00	50.00
		As 3.					
Miss 4B	(1850's)	Brass	29mm	—	—	—	80.00
		As 4, but Plain edge. (Smithsonian Institution coll.)					
Miss 5	(1860)	Brass	29mm	—	—	—	100.
		Obverse as 3. Three umbrellas, etc. (Richardson card of Philadelphia). Rare muling.					
Miss 6	(1860)	Copper	29mm	—	—	—	100.
		Obverse as 3. Rv: Eagle on mortar, etc. (Haviland Stevenson & Co. of Charleston, S.C.) Muling.					
Miss 7	(1860)	Brass	29mm	—	—	—	100.
		Obverse as 3. Rv: WATCHES, CLOCKS, etc. Rare muling.					
Miss 8	(1860)	Brass	29mm	—	—	—	100.
		Obverse as 3. Rv: Locomotive headlight (Olcott card of Rochester, N.Y.). Rare muling.					
Miss 9	(1860)	White Metal	29mm	—	—	—	100.
		As Miss 8.					
Miss 10	(1860)	Copper	29mm	—	—	—	100.
		Obverse as 3. Rv: HAVILAND STEVENSON & CO., etc. (Charleston, S.C. card). Only 2 or 3 struck.					
Miss 11	(1860)	Lead	29mm				150.
		Different eagle. Pattern (Zeddies coll.)					
Miss 12	(1860)	Copper	29mm				150.
		Obverse as Miss 3. Rv: Olcott card of Rochester, N.Y. Muling. (Zeddies coll.)					

There is some doubt about Miss 10. This could be a mis-description for Miss 6.
Benjamin F. Fotterall appears in the 1850 census.

MISSOURI

M.A. ABRAHAMS
Independence, Mo.

Miller	Date	Metal	Size	VG	F	VF	Unc
Mo 40	(1840's?)	Brass	28mm	—	400.	700.	—
		George Washington head right, *** M.A. ABRAHAMS around, numeral 10 below. Rv: THE PEOPLES OUTFITTING STORE / INDEPENDENCE / MO. / *. Reeded edge. (Wright 2A; Baker 507)					

M.A. Abrahams' outfitting depots for the Western wagon trains were at Independence and Weston. See the note under this issuer under Weston, Mo.

M. A. Abrahams appears in the census list for 1850 in Independence, Mo., though the name is given in the census incorrectly as A. M. Abrahams. (Census lists in these days were frequently in error). He does not appear in the census lists of either 1840 or 1860 anywhere in Missouri.

According to the 1850 census, Abrahams, then 39, was a merchant who had been born in Pennsylvania. His wife Phebe, then apparently 38 (the record is unclear), was born in England. The couple had five children, aged 4 to 14, four of whom were born in Pennsylvania and one in New York. Abrahams did not own any real estate in 1850; the family resided in Blue Township, Jackson County, Mo. It is possible the 'M.' in his name was Moses.

More than a dozen county histories, cemetery records and genealogies were checked, but M. A. Abrahams appears in none of them, according to Bruce W. Smith, Fort Wayne, Ind., who conducted the research over several years. Smith concludes that Abrahams must have been disliked and may well have retired early and gone elsewhere after making a fortune in the outfitting business. In the 1840's and 1850's it was common for merchants to set up trailhead outfitting depots, charge outlandish prices, and then retire.

Smith reconstructs Abrahams' early life this way: Born 1811 in Pennsylvania and lived there, probably in Philadelphia, until after 1840. In 1840 he and his children may have been living with a 60-year-old relative, Moses Abrahams, at the time of the 1840 census. His fifth child was born in New York in 1846, so he went to Missouri in the 1846-1850 period.

Smith, who has done extensive research on the Abrahams tokens of Weston and Independence, estimates that 5 to 8 Independence and 50 to 75 Weston pieces exist.

S. LOWE
Independence, Mo.

Rulau	Date	Metal	Size	VG	F	VF	EF
Mo 110	(1857-61)	Silver	33mm	—	—	235.	—
		S. LOWE INDP. MO. ctsp on Denmark 1834 rigsdaler of Frederick VI. (Joseph Lepczyk sale of Feb. 1982, lot 44; Brunk 25145)					

Schuyler Lowe, born 1834 in Kentucky, migrated to Jackson County, Mo., 1853. In 1857 he became partner in the drug firm of Lowe & McMurry. He sold out in 1858 and in spring, 1860 established his own drugstore. He had been in insurance 1858-60.

He enlisted in the Missouri State Guards in June 1861, entering the Confederate Army as a captain in Feb. 1862. He fought at Wilson's Creek, Lexington, Pea Ridge, Second Corinth, Siege of Vicksburg, and was captured Feb. 1864. He was released June 1, 1865 and returned to Independence. He was a realtor 1865-68, farmer 1868-73, livestock dealer 1873-77, stock agent for Missouri Pacific Railway at Kansas City 1877-81.

The counterstamp may be personal. If a store card, it may emanate from the 1857-61 period. The rigsdaler is of his birth year, 1834. He died 1881.

I. B. B.
(Isaac B. Burbbayge)
St. Louis, Mo.

Rulau	Date	Metal	Size	VG	F	VF	EF
Mo 100	(1853-59)	Silver	15.5mm	—	150.	—	225.
		I. B. B. / ST. LOUIS / MO. ctsp on U.S. Bust half dimes. Dates examined: 1836, 1836/5, 1839, 1852. (Brunk 20960)					
Mo 100A	(1853-59)	Silver	15.5mm	—	150.	—	225.
		Similar ctsp on U.S. Seated Liberty half dime. Examined: 1839, 1841-O, 1852.					

Rulau	Date	Metal	Size	VG	F	VF	EF
Mo 101	(1853-59)	Silver	18mm	—	150.	—	225.
		Similar ctsp on U.S. dimes. Dates examined: 1828, 1834, 1838. There are 6 specimens known.					
Mo 102	(1853-59)	Silver	25mm	—	150.	—	225.
		Similar ctsp on U.S. Seated Liberty quarters. Dates examined: 1853.					
Mo 102B	(1853-59)	Silver	31mm	—	150.	—	225.
		Similar ctsp on U.S. Seated Liberty half dollars. Dates examined: 1852, 1853. (Duffield 1437)					

Rulau	Date	Metal	Size	VG	F	VF	EF
Mo 102D	(1853-59)	Silver	27mm	—	185.	—	300.
		Similar ctsp on Spanish-American 2-reales. Dates examined: 1803, 1807-LME-JP.					

Burbbayge is listed in St. Louis directories from 1840 to 1859. He was an "intelligencer" (private procurer and detective) and general agent. He sold slaves and a wide variety of goods, including maps of western rivers.

His business addresses: 1839-40 — 160 No. Main. 1842 — 1 Laurel. 1845 — N.W. corner Locust & 2nd. 1855 — 32 Vine. 1857-59 — 14 Vine. In 1860 his successor is recorded as Juste E. H. Fontaine.

Burbbayge is a French name. It is misspelled in contemporary records as BURBAYAGE, BURBAYGE or BURBBAGGE, but BURBBAYGE is correct, according to Eric P. Newman, St. Louis, who researched this token issuer.

In the 1840-41 directory, Isaac Burbbayge and one Keller were partners in Burbbayge & Keller, tinners and copper manufacturers at 169 No. Main St. The counterstamps are found on coins dated 1803 to 1853. Probable dates of issue of the counterstamps are 1853-1859.

DR. BOHANNAN
St. Louis, Mo.

Miller	Date	Metal	Size	VG	F	VF	EF
Mo 4	(?)	White Metal	25mm	—	—	—	Unique
		DR. BOHANNAN MEDICAL OFFICE, 63 PINE ST. Rv: Inscription in 11 lines.					

M.B. COX & CO.

Miller	Date	Metal	Size	VG	F	VF	Unc
Mo 6	(?)	Copper	25mm	25.00	50.00	75.00	100.
		M.B. COX & CO., WHOLESALE DEALERS IN HATS & CAPS, etc., as shown. Eagle in field. (Wright 1381)					
Mo 6A	(?)	German Silver	25mm	100.	125.	—	—
		As 6.					

E. MEAD

Rulau	Date	Metal	Size	VG	F	VF	EF
Mo 115	1846	Silver	27mm	100.	—	150.	—
		E. MEAD (block letters) / Jany 17 (script) / 1846 (script) ctsp on Spanish-American 1799-Mo-FM 2-reales. (Kurt Krueger coll.; Brunk 27230)					
Mo 115A	1846	Silver	25mm	100.	—	150.	—
		Similar ctsp on U.S. 1854 S.L. quarter.					

Edmund Mead was a silversmith active circa 1846-1850. The firm was a successor to E. Adriance, about 1820, and Mead & Adriance, circa 1835.

FITZGIBBON DAGUERREOTYPE GALLERY

Miller	Date	Metal	Size	VG	F	VF	Unc
Mo 21	1850	Copper	29mm	30.00	40.00	50.00	75.00
		Eagle displayed, U.S. shield on breast FITZGIBBON DAGUERREOTYPE / * GALLERY . * . (Obverse of NY 263). Rv: OVER D. NICHOLSONS GROCERY STORE / NO 1 /4TH STREET / ST LOUIS / MO / .1850. Plain edge. (Wright 325)					
Mo 21B	1850	Silvered Copper	29mm	30.00	40.00	50.00	75.00
		As 21.					
Mo 21A	1850	Copper	29mm	—	—	—	—
		As 21. Reeded edge.					
Mo 22	1850	Brass	29mm	30.00	40.00	50.00	75.00
		As 21. Reeded edge.					

John H. Fitzgibbon took daguerreotype instruction in 1841 in Lynchburg, Va., and in 1846 moved to St. Louis. He opened a daguerreotype studio on Fourth Street between Market and Chestnut, and by 1850 the England-born Irishman was the best-known daguerreotyper in the city. He had a spacious gallery above Nicholson's Grocery, and it was filled with more than 1,000 photos of visitors to his studio.

A disciple of Louis Daguerre, whom he admired greatly, Fitzgibbon called the daguerreotype an "enchanter's wand" which can "command the sun to stand still." The photography process had only been invented in 1839, just two years before Fitzgibbon studied it. In 1854 Fitzgibbon assembled a traveling gallery for a professional picture-taking tour of southwest Missouri, northwest Arkansas and the Indian Nations. During this tour he photographed the mysterious fiddler known as the Arkansas Traveler. By 1858 his St. Louis gallery covered 13 rooms and included the largest collection of Indian photographs in the country.

Apparently because of the Civil War, Fitzgibbon sold his St. Louis gallery in 1861 and moved to Vicksburg, Miss. After undergoing the winter siege of 1863, he tried to escape through Union lines, was captured and spent the rest of the war as a prisoner. He moved to New York after the war to stay with his eldest daughter, who had married the famous black-face minstrel and stage actor Dan Bryant.

In 1866 he returned to St. Louis and opened a new photo gallery. He married photographer Maria Louisa Dennis in 1869, and she managed his studio. By the late 1870's Fitzgibbon became a writer (pen name Gibbon Fitz), editor and publisher of *The St. Louis Practical Photographer* in 1877. He died in August 1882.

It is believed the Fitzgibbon pieces of New York City dated 1853 (NY 263 and 264) may have been made by Fitzgibbon of St. Louis for a commercial booth he had at the New York Crystal Palace that year. (Fitzgibbon research by Bruce W. Smith and Mike Pfefferkorn)

E. JACCARD & CO.

Miller	Date	Metal	Size	VG	F	VF	Unc
Mo 8	(1860)	Brass	27mm	—	—	45.00	85.00
		(Empty oval) / E. JACCARD & CO / ST. LOUIS, / MO. Rv: U.S. Shield with blank oval at its center. Plain edge. (Wright 495)					
Mo 9	(1860)	Copper	27mm	—	—	45.00	85.00
		As 8. Plain edge.					
Mo 10	(1860)	White Metal	27mm	—	—	45.00	85.00
		As 8. Plain edge.					
Mo 11	(1860)	Silver	27mm	—	—	100.	300.
		As 8. Plain edge.					

E. (Eugene) Jaccard & Co. were manufacturing jewelers from 1837 on. By 1865 the firm was known as Mermod & Jaccard until at least 1884, and then as Mermod, Jaccard & King Jewelry Co.

E. LONG

Miller	Date	Metal	Size	F	VF	EF	Unc
Mo 12	(1850's)	Brass	29mm	30.00	35.00	45.00	60.00
		Imitation of U.S. $10 gold piece. Liberty's coronet is inscribed E. LONG. S.E. CORNER 4TH & MARKET ST, / ST. LOUIS, MO. Rv: Around the eagle: E. LONG'S — DAGUERRIAN GALLERY. Reeded edge. (Wright 617)					
Mo 12A	(1850's)	Copper	29mm	—	—	60.00	—
		As last. Reeded edge. (Zeddies coll.)					
Mo 13	(1850's)	Copper	29mm	30.00	40.00	50.00	75.00
		Obverse as obverse of 12. Rv: Reverse of Mich 10, FOSTER & PARRY, padlock, etc.					
Mo 14	(1850's)	White Metal	29mm	50.00	75.00	100.	200.
		As 13.					
Mo 15	(1850's)	Brass	29mm	30.00	35.00	45.00	60.00
		As 13. Plain edge.					
Mo 16	(1850's)	Brass	29mm	30.00	35.00	45.00	60.00
		As 13. Reeded edge.					

H.H. LONG

Miller	Date	Metal	Size	F	VF	EF	Unc
Mo 17	(1850's)	Brass	29mm	30.00	40.00	50.00	75.00

Coronet Liberty head left; H.H. LONG / S.E. CORNER 3D & MARKET ST. / ST. LOUIS, MO. Rv: Spread eagle; H.H. LONG'S / DAGUERRE-OTYPE GALLERY. Reeded edge. Normal planchet. (Wright 618)

Miller	Date	Metal	Size	F	VF	EF	Unc
Mo 18	(1850's)	Brass	29mm	30.00	40.00	50.00	75.00

As 17, but Plain edge. Very thick planchet.

Miller	Date	Metal	Size	F	VF	EF	Unc
Mo 19	(1850's)	White Metal	29mm	50.00	75.00	100.	200.

As 17. Thick planchet.

It is likely these were struck in the 1850-1851 period.

S. MANOVILL

Miller	Date	Metal	Size	VG	F	VF	EF
Mo 20	1855	White Metal	26mm	75.00	100.	200.	400.

Clasped hands within wreath, ST. LOUIS HARMONIE GESELL-SCHAFT. Rv: Large C enclosing 25, with GUT FUR on curve of C. Around: S. MANOVILL — 1855.

Wright about 1900 noted that this card was unknown to the Levick, Tilton, Mason and Betts collections. Extremely rare.

"Harmonie Gesellschaft" in German means "Harmony (singing) Society." The words "Gut Fur" equal "Good For."

NICHOLSON'S

Miller	Date	Metal	Size	VG	F	VF	Unc
Mo 23	(1850's)	German Silver	15mm	60.00	70.00	100.	150.

An eagle. NICHOLSON'S HALF DIME TOKEN.

Miller	Date	Metal	Size	VG	F	VF	Unc
Mo 24	(1850's)	German Silver	15mm	60.00	70.00	100.	150.

A pair of scales. GOOD AT NICHOLSONS *. Rv: a wreath encloses HALF / DIME. Inscribed: STATE OF MISSOURI. (Wright 758)

Miller	Date	Metal	Size	VG	F	VF	Unc
Mo 25	(1850's)	White Metal	15mm	—	—	125.	200.

Scales mounted on an upright. Around: RETAILERS TOKEN / ST. / * LOUIS *. Rv: 20 GOOD / FOR . ONE / DOLLAR / AT / NICHOL-SON'S.

Miller	Date	Metal	Size	VG	F	VF	Unc
Mo 25A	(1850's)	Lead	16mm	—	—	200.	—

As last. Pattern. (Bowers & Merena Saccone 1989 sale, lot 3281)

D. Nicholson's grocery store was located at Number 1 Fourth Street in St. Louis in 1850, and was apparently one of the most thriving such enterprises in the city at that time. Its half dime tokens are very scarce. Dr. Wright called Mo 24 scarce even in 1899.

David Nicholson was born in County Perth, Scotland, Dec. 9, 1814. He died in St. Louis Nov. 26, 1880. A grocer's clerk in Glasgow, he emigrated to Canada, coming to St. Louis in 1838. In 1843 he became the junior partner in Strachan & Nicholson, grocers. In 1870 Nicholson (also a carpenter) erected a new grocery at Sixth Street between Chestnut and Market. This developed ultimately into one of the largest wholesale grocery houses in the West.

He became a wealthy builder, constructing Temple Building and Nicholson Place. He was an unswerving Union sympathizer from 1861 to 1865, whereas his friend Fitzgibbon the daguerreotyper was a Southern sympathizer who went to Vicksburg in 1861.

J.J. OUTLEY

Rulau	Date	Metal	Size	VG	F	VF	EF
Mo 117	(1858)	Silver	25mm	—	150.	—	225.

J.J. OUTLEY / ARTIST ctsp on U.S. Seated Liberty quarter dollar. (Gould 91; Brunk 30420)

Rulau	Date	Metal	Size	VG	F	VF	EF
Mo 117C	(1858)	Silver	31mm	—	150.	—	225.

Similar ctsp on U.S. Seated Liberty half dollar. Dates examined: 1856, 1858-O. (Schenkman & Krueger collections; Van Ormer sale 2776)

The term "artist" refers to a photographic artist, as the early daguerreotypers frequently called themselves. Attribution by Bill Rodgers, Frankfort, Ky.

John J. Outley is listed in St. Louis directories 1852 to the early 1890's.

PENNEY

Rulau	Date	Metal	Size	VG	F	VF	EF
Mo 118	(?)	Silver	19mm	—	200.	—	—

PENNEY / ST. LOUIS ctsp on U.S. early Bust type dime. (Brunk 31610)

H. PROUHET

Miller	Date	Metal	Size	VG	F	VF	Unc
Mo 27	(?)	Copper	31mm	20.00	40.00	150.	300.

H PROUHET / NO 9 / NORTH 4TH STREET / ST. LOUIS MO. Rv: Blank. Known specimens are holed. (Wright 853)

Miller	Date	Metal	Size	VG	F	VF	Unc
Mo 27A	(?)	Copper	31mm	50.00	85.00	110.	—

As Mo 27, but stamped '148' on reverse. (Miller 27)

ST. LOUIS POST OFFICE

Miller	Date	Metal	Size	VG	F	VF	Unc
Mo 29	(1850's	White Metal	25mm	—	—	500.	—

An eagle perched on a shield draped with flags. ST. LOUIS POST OFFICE above. Rv: Blank for engraving of a name. Known specimens are holed. (Wright 1059)

Miller	Date	Metal	Size	VG	F	VF	Unc
Mo 29A	(1850's)	White Metal	25mm	—	—	500.	—

As 29; engraved on reverse: EDWILL & BERRY. (Miller 29)

Miller	Date	Metal	Size	VG	F	VF	Unc
Mo 32	(1850's)	White Metal	24mm	—	—	500.	—
		Similar to 29, engraved on reverse: LEPERE & RICHARDS. J.M. KERSHAW at bottom of rev.					

Miller	Date	Metal	Size	VG	F	VF	Unc
Mo 32A	(1850's)	WM	24mm	—	—	500.	—
		As 32, but engraved on reverse: W. H. BARKSDALE. (Elmer Randall coll.)					
Mo 30	(1850's)	Copper	28mm	—	—	500.	—
		An eagle with wings for flight, above a shield. ST. LOUIS / POST OFFICE above. Rv: Blank for engraving of a name.					
Mo 30A	(1850's)	Copper	28mm	—	—	500.	—
		As 30, engraved on reverse: STATE SAVINGS ASS. (Miller 30)					
Mo 31	(1850's)	Copper	28mm	—	—	500.	—
		As 30, engraved on reverse: CLAFIN, ALLEN & CO.					

Miller	Date	Metal	Size	VG	F	VF	Unc
Mo 33	(1850's)	Copper	28mm	—	—	500.	—
		As 30, engraved on reverse: HUME & CO. STUBENRAUCH & WEBER at bottom of rev.					
Mo 33A	(1850's)	Copper	28mm	—	—	500.	—
		As 30, engraved on reverse; PRATT — FOX.					

Miller	Date	Metal	Size	VG	F	VF	Unc
Mo 34	(1850's)	Copper	28mm	—	—	500.	—
		As 30, engraved on reverse: SCOTT & BROS.					
Mo 35	(1850's)	Copper	28mm	—	—	500.	—
		As 30, engraved on reverse: W. & H.V.					
Mo 35A	(1850's)	Copper	28mm	—	—	500.	—
		As 30, engraved on reverse: VIRTUE YORSTON & CO. (Hans Schulman sale of Jan. 1957, lot 3374)					
Mo 35B	(1850's)	Copper	28mm	—	—	500.	—
		As 30, engraved on reverse: Carr & Kennell. (Gil Steinberg 1989 sale, lot 462)					
Mo 35C	(1850's)	Copper	28mm	—	—	500.	—
		As 30, engraved on reverse: Appleton Noyes & Co. (Gil Steinberg 1989 sale, lot 461)					

The St. Louis Post Office checks were likely boxholder identification discs or served some similar function. Probably each engraved specimen is unique, and undoubtedly there are others which have survived.

19th century W.E. Woodward auction catalogs also list these engraved varieties: HUBBARD & PAYNE, type of Mo 29 in copper; uninscribed, type of Mo 32 in WM; FRANK LAPERE, type of Mo 33 in copper; C.C. THOMPSON, type of Mo 33 in copper. Also E. F. WILLIAMSON on copper-plated WM. These catalogs were issued April 1850, April 1856 and April 1890, indicating the P.O. tokens were first used in the 1840's.

J. & W. VAN DEVENTER

St. Louis, Mo.

Miller	Date	Metal	Size	VG	F	VF	Unc
Mo 37	(1844-45)	Silver	28mm	200.	250.	500.	750.
		Eagle with drooping wings, shield on breast. J & W VAN-DEVENTER / 162 MAIN ST above, ST. LOUIS below. Rv: WHOLESALE / AND / RETAIL / CLOTHING / EMPORIUM / NO 162 MAIN ST / CORNER / WASHINGTON AV. Thick planchet. Plain edge.					
Mo 38	(1844-45)	Silver	28mm	200.	250.	500.	750.
		As 37. Thin planchet. Plain edge.					

Miller	Date	Metal	Size	VG	F	VF	Unc
Mo 39	(1844-45)	Brass	28mm	20.00	30.00	50.00	100.
		As 37. Plain edge. (Wright 1699)					
Mo 39A	(1844-45)	Brass	28mm	20.00	30.00	50.00	100.
		As 39. Reeded edge.					

M.A. ABRAHAMS

Weston, Mo.

Miller	Date	Metal	Size	VG	F	VF	Unc
Mo 41	(1840's)	Brass	28mm	25.00	50.00	85.00	400.
		George Washington head right, *** M.A. ABRAHAMS *** around, numeral 10 below. Rv: THE PEOPLES OUTFITTING STORE / WESTON / MO. * . Reeded edge. (Wright 2; Baker 506)					

This store card recalls a long vanished period of the history of this country, when the western border of Missouri was the frontier of the United States, and beyond was an almost unsettled and untracked wilderness. An outfitting store in those days was nothing less than an establishment which outfitted emigrants and traders for their long wagon journeys to California, Oregon, and New Mexico at about the time when the great California, Oregon, and Santa Fe overland trails teemed with prairie schooners (some of 7,000 pounds capacity) drawn by numerous yokes of oxen.

The contents of an outfitting store such as that kept by Abrahams was an amazing sight, for on hand there was everything an overlander was likely to need from an oxen yoke to a side of bacon.

M.A. Abrahams also had a store of the same character at Independence, the head of the Santa Fe trail, the chief frontier town in the 1830's and 1840's and up to the time that the initial point moved a little further westward to Westport, now Kansas City.

Weston was some distance up the Missouri River. These cards are now quite scarce, and are principally valued because of the portrait of Washington which they bear. The portrait is by no means a flattering one of the Father of His Country.

Recent auction records in higher grades include: 1988 AU $302 and $330; 1991 AU $400; 1992 Unc. $450.

NEW HAMPSHIRE

D.H. HILLIARD
Cornish, N.H.

Rulau	Date	Metal	Size	VG	F	VF	EF
NH 100	(1843-50)	Copper	29mm	100.	—	150.	—
		D.H. HILLIARD / CORNISH / N.H. ctsp on U.S. 1820 Large cent. Rv: G HW / CORNISH / N.H. in three separate punches ctsp on coin's reverse. (Brunk 19650)					
NH 100A		Copper	29mm	100.	—	150.	—
		D.H. HILLIARD ctsp on U.S. 1834 Large cent. (Brunk 19645)					

David Hall Hilliard is listed as a gunsmith in Cornish, New Hampshire 1842-1877. In 1850 he appears in the Cornish census records.

Until his death in 1877, he made underhammer guns. His sons Charles and George E. carried on the business 1877-1879 as Hilliard Rifle Works.

G.W. HOWE
Keene, N.H.

Miller	Date	Metal	Size	G	VG	F	EF
NH 7	(?)	Copper	29mm	—	50.00	—	75.00
		G.W. HOWE / KEENE / N.H. ctsp on U.S. 1822 Large cent. (Duffield 1406; Brunk 20350)					

C.C. CLARK
Nashua, N.H. & Manchester, N.H.

Miller	Date	Metal	Size	VG	F	VF	EF
NH 8	1859	Silver	25mm	150.	—	250.	—
		C.C. CLARK / NASHUA, N.H. / (two pomegranates) / 1859 ctsp in four lines on U.S. 1806 Quarter dollar. (Davis McKinney collection, 1975; Van Ormer sale 2591; Brunk 7930)					
NH 8A	1879	Silver	40mm	200.	—	350.	—
		C.C. CLARK / 1842-1879 ctsp on U.S. 1799 Silver dollar. (Kurt Krueger sale, Oct. 10, 1978). Issued in Manchester. (Brunk 7910)					
NH 8B	1879	Silver	40mm	200.	—	350.	—
		C.C. CLARK / 1842 / 1864 / 1879 (small 3-stemmed flower) ctsp on U.S. 1802 Silver dollar. (Presidential Coin & Antique sale, June 14, 1973). Issued in Manchester. (Brunk 7920)					

Carlos C. Clark was a self-employed maker of flintlock and percussion rifles at Windsor, Vermont from 1832 to 1846. He also made percussion pistols. (There is some doubt whether '1832' is accurate; he may have started business later, about 1841.)

From 1846 to 1856 Clark was employed in the same city by Robbins & Lawrence, makers of percussion rifles. Samuel E. Robbins, N. Kendall and Richard S. Lawrence founded this firm in 1844 as Robbins, Kendall & Lawrence. Kendall withdrew in 1846. Robbins & Lawrence received a U.S. government contract on Jan. 5, 1848 for 'Model 1841' percussion rifles. In 1849 they received additional contracts for rifles and carbines. The R&L firm was dissolved in 1857.

Clark in 1856-59 was self-employed again, making telescopic sights for rifles in Windsor. In 1859 he moved to Nashua, N.H., keeping his Windsor operation. Then in 1863 he relocated at Manchester, N.H., and he closed the Windsor operation in 1868. From 1868-75 at Manchester he made percussion hunting rifles. It is believed he retired in 1879.

Clark was among the first New England gunmakers to place his gunsmith punches on circulating coins as an advertising medium. Many others imitated him later. Clark placed dates on a number of his counterstamps, probably for commemorative purposes. In the Hard Times era he produced four known counterstamped pieces, one dated 1841 and the other three undated. (See HT 435 varieties)

The 1859 counterstamp above probably celebrates his relocation at Nashua. Both 1879 pieces were issued at Manchester and they seemingly honor his retirement. They also seem to indicate his business was founded in 1842 and that he may have moved to Nashua in 1864 rather than 1863.

(Reference: *American Firearms Makers* by A. Merwyn Carey, New York, 1953. *American Gun Makers* by Arcadi Gluckman and L.D. Satterlee, Harrisburg, Pa., 1953. Personal correspondence from Robert D. Leonard Jr., Westfield, N.Y.)

C. C. CLARK,
GUNSMITH.
All kinds of Fire Arms repaired at short notice.
25 Stark Block, Manchester, N.H.

Advertisement appearing in the 1868 New Hampshire Business Directory.

A. DUTTON
Nashua, N.H.

NH 130	(1850-68)	Copper	28.5mm	—	35.00	—	—
		A. DUTTON / NASHUA, N.H. engraved in script on U.S. 1834 S. Wilkins Hard Times store card. (John Cheramy coll.; Brunk 12585)					

A. P. Dutton, a tailor, had a gentlemen's clothing store in Nashua in 1867-68, according to directory evidence. The A. Dutton of the token may have been a predecessor, but probably was the same man.

N.P. McKEAN

Rulau	Date	Metal	Size	VG	F	VF	EF
NH 102	(?)	Silver	40mm	300.	—	425.	—
		N.P. McKEAN / NASHUA / N.H. ctsp on U.S. 1795 Silver dollar. (Tanenbaum coll.; Brunk 26970)					

J. SIDNEY MILLER

Rulau	Date	Metal	Size	VG	F	VF	EF
NH 104	(1858)	Cupronickel	19mm	200.	—	300.	—
		J. SIDNEY MILLER / ARTIST, / NASHUA, N.H. / MILLER ctsp on U.S. 1857 Flying Eagle cent. (Brunk 27770)					
NH 104C	(1858)	Copper	29mm	175.	—	250.	—
		J. SIDNEY MILLER. / ARTIST. ctsp on U.S. 1845 Large cent. (Frank Kovacs coll.; Brunk 27760)					
NH 104D	(1858)	Silver	15.5mm	175.	—	250.	—
		Similar ctsp on U.S. 1853 half dime.					

James Sidney Miller was an early daguerreotyper and ambrotype photographer of Nashua. According to the 1853 city directory, James and his brother, Sydney Miller, also a photographer, lived with their father on East Pearl Street. In 1862 Miller was in Newport News, Va., according to his recently discovered Civil War dog tag.

The term "artist" was almost universally adopted by the earliest daguerreotypers to describe their profession. It is found frequently on counterstamped coins.

N.W. ROBY
Nashua, N.H.

Miller	Date	Metal	Size	VG	F	VF	Unc
NH 2	(?)	Brass	27mm	—	Possibly Unique		
		N.W. ROBY, ENGINEER FOR ROGERS & SON, NASHUA, N.H. Rv: Eagle.					

Noah W. Roby was still living in Nashua in 1887, at 15 Merrimack Street, apparently no longer in business at that time. Rogers & Son cannot be traced in 1887 in Nashua. (See *Bayley's Nashua Pocket Manual & Business Directory* for 1887-88)

DR. G.G. WILKINS
Pittsfield, N.H.

SPECIAL NOTE: Dr. George G. Wilkins was the most prolific counterstamper of coins in the United States. He probably stamped up to 100,000 coins. These were mostly Large cents and Small cents in the 1857-60 period, but his activities extended at least until 1863 and probably even 1876. He seems to have stamped everything that crossed his path, although we know of no silver dollars or gold coins. The premier cataloger of Wilkins tokens, Q. David Bowers, revealed that some 480 pieces are now known in collections. The listing which follows accounts for about 400 of these.

Bowers reported two different styles of counterstamp, large letters, with very little space between the N and S of WILKINS (these stamped 1857-63, with most done 1857-60); and small letters, with full space between the N and S of WILKINS (these stamped in and after 1863). The large letters variety of the curved arc reading DR. G. G. WILKINS is far more available; only 25 small letters pieces were recorded by Bowers. We have attempted in the listing which follows to follow the Bowers arrangement of these pieces.

Gregory Brunk estimates that as many as 100,000 coins were stamped in a 20-year span, 1857-1876.

TYPE I — Large letters in semicircular arc (Little space between N and S)
TYPE II — Small letters in one-third circular arc (Full space between N and S)

TYPE I STAMPS

Rulau	Date	Metal	Size	VG	F	VF	EF
NH 106	(1857-60)	Copper	29mm	10.00	—	25.00	—
		DR. G.G. WILKINS in an upward arc ctsp on U.S. Large cent. Dates examined: 1800, 1812, 1816, 1817, 1818, 1820, 1824, 1825, 1828, 1829, 1830, 1831, 1832, 1833, 1834, 1835, 1836, 1837, 1838, 1839, 1841, 1842, 1843, 1844, 1845, 1846, 1847, 1848, 1849, 1850, 1851, 1852, 1853, 1854, 1855, 1856, 1857. There are 180 reported specimens. (Duffield 1427; Hallenbeck 23.525; Brunk 43490). The dates 1837-1856 are most often encountered.					

Rulau	Date	Metal	Size	VG	F	VF	EF
NH 107		CN	19mm	10.00	—	20.00	—
		Similar ctsp on U.S. Flying Eagle cent. Dates examined: 1857, 1858. There are 44 reported specimens. (Gould 4)					

Rulau	Date	Metal	Size	VG	F	VF	EF
NH 107A		CN	19mm	10.00	—	20.00	—
		Similar ctsp on U.S. Indian cent. Dates examined: 1859, 1860, 1861, 1862, 1863. There are 97 specimens reported. (Gould 4). The 1859 is the most common.					

Rulau	Date	Metal	Size	VG	F	VF	EF
NH 108		Silver	14mm	50.00	—	75.00	—
		Similar ctsp on U.S. silver 3-cent piece. Examined: 1853. Only 1 known. (Gould 73)					
NH 109		Silver	15.5mm	25.00	—	50.00	—
		Similar ctsp on U.S. half dime. Examined: 1840, 1842, 1853, 1855, 1857. There are 8 specimens reported.					
NH 110		Silver	18mm	30.00	—	50.00	—
		Similar ctsp on U.S. dime. Examined: 1842, 1853, 1853-Arrows, 1857. There are 6 specimens reported. (Kurt Krueger report)					
NH 110A		Silver	25mm	50.00	—	75.00	—
		Similar ctsp on U.S. quarter, date worn. Only 1 known.					
NH 110B		Silver	27mm	50.00	—	75.00	—
		Similar ctsp on Spanish-American 2-reales. Examined: 1776-LME. Only 1 known.					
NH 111		Copper	28.5mm	50.00	—	75.00	—
		Similar ctsp on U.S. Hard Times token. Examined: 1834 Perish Credit, 1835 John J. Adams. Only 2 reported.					
NH 111A		Copper	28mm	50.00	—	75.00	—
		Similar ctsp on New Brunswick 1864 cent.					
NH 111B		Copper	28mm	50.00	—	75.00	—
		Similar ctsp on Canada token. Examined: 1813 Breton 994, 1843 Breton 910, 1844 Breton 527. 3 pieces reported.					
NH 111C		Silver	18mm	50.00	—	75.00	—
		Similar ctsp on Canada 10-cents dated 1858.					

Rulau	Date	Metal	Size	VG	F	VF	Unc
NH 111M		Copper	27mm	50.00	—	75.00	—
		Similar ctsp on England halfpenny.					
NH 111N		Silver	15mm	50.00	—	—	75.00
		Similar ctsp on England 1838 3-pence.					
NH 111P		Silver	19mm	50.00	—	75.00	—
		Similar ctsp on England 1838 6-pence.					
NH 111Q		Copper	26mm	50.00	—	—	75.00
		Similar ctsp on Austria 1816 kreuzer.					
NH 111R		Copper	25mm	50.00	—	—	75.00
		Similar ctsp on East India Company 1804 pice, KM-205.					
NH 111S		Brass	31mm	50.00	—	75.00	—
		Similar ctsp on Sumatra 1804 4-keping, Craig 27a.					
NH 111T		Copper	25mm	50.00	—	75.00	—
		Similar ctsp on France 5-centimes, date worn.					
NH 111U		Copper	28mm	50.00	—	75.00	—
		Similar ctsp on French Colonies Chas. X 10-centimes.					

TYPE II STAMPS

Rulau	Date	Metal	Size	VG	F	VF	EF
HN 112	(1863-)	Copper	29mm	50.00	—	75.00	—
		DR. G. G. WILKINS in an upward arc ctsp on U.S. Large cent. Dates examined: 1816, 1825, 1835, 1836, 1846, 1848, 1852, 1853. There are 9 reported specimens. (Q. David Bowers report; Brunk 43490)					
NH 113		CN	19mm	50.00	—	75.00	—
		Similar ctsp on U.S. Flying Eagle cent. Examined: 1857, 1858. Only 3 specimens known.					
HN 113A		CN	19mm	50.00	—	75.00	—
		Similar ctsp on U.S. Indian cent. Examined: 1860. There are 3 reported specimens.					
NH 113B		Bronze	19mm	50.00	—	75.00	—
		Similar ctsp on U.S. Indian cent. examined: 1864, 1865, 1873. Only 3 pieces known.					
NH 113C		Copper	19mm	50.00	—	—	75.00
		Similar ctsp on U.S. Civil War token. Examined: 1863, Undated. Only 2 reported.					
NH113D		Brass	25mm	50.00	—	75.00	—
		Similar ctsp on Malacca keping dated AH 1247 (AD 1831-32). (KM-8.1)					

WITH CITY NAME

Rulau	Date	Metal	Size	VG	F	VF	EF
NH 114	(?)	Copper	29mm	125.	—	200.	—
		DR. G. G. WILKINS (curved) / PITTSFIELD, N.H. ctsp on U.S. Large cent. Dates examined: 1828, 1833, 1848, 1851, 1854, 1855. Only 6 known. (Brunk 43510; Smithsonian coll.)					
NH 114A		CN	19mm	125.	—	200.	—
		Similar ctsp on U.S. 1857 or 1858 Flying Eagle cent.					
NH 114B		Bronze	19mm	125.	—	200.	—
		Similar ctsp on U.S. 1865 Indian cent.					
NH 114C		Copper	28mm	125.	—	200.	—
		Similar ctsp on Canada 1859 Large cent.					
NH 114D		Silver	27mm	125.	—	200.	—
		Similar ctsp on Spanish-American 1776-LME 2-reales.					

WITH DATE 1876

Rulau	Date	Metal	Size	VG	F	VF	EF
NH 115	1876	Copper	29mm	100.	—	150.	—
		DR. G. G. WILKINS in upward arc ctsp on obverse of U.S. Large cent. 1876 in different punch style ctsp on reverse of the coin. Dates examined: 1817, 1836, 1839, 1843, 1844, 1845, 1853, 1854. (All dates specified except 1817 and 1844 are in ANS collection). There are 8 specimens reported. (Brunk 43500)					

George G. Wilkins was born in 1820 and died in 1879. He does not appear in the Pittsfield census for 1850 but was there in 1860 and 1870. He seems to have arrived in Pittsfield in the mid-1850's, and begun counterstamping coins in either 1857 or 1858.

It is doubtful Wilkins had a doctor's degree, but he styled himself "Doctor" and practiced dentistry. Licenses for dentistry were not required at that time. Wilkins remained a bachelor throughout his life.

In 1866 Wilkins bought a lot north of the Congregational church on Main Street, and here he built a 2-story frame store (nicknamed "Fort Wilkins"). To his dentistry practice he now added the sale of furs and pelts, liquor, and pets (dogs); he practiced hairdressing, and kept a saloon and eating house. In 1871 he added patent medicines to his wares and, still later, guns and ammunition.

Wilkins was intensely disliked by the citizens of Pittsfield. Court records show he was convicted twice in 1873 of selling liquor without a license. In 1874 he was charged with conspiracy to commit arson but was not indicted. A local newspaper accused him of slander in 1874. In 1876 Wilkins sought treatment for alcoholism.

He died on Nov. 8, 1879 of dropsy.

(For a complete overview of Dr. Wilkins, see Q. David Bowers' *The Strange Career of Dr. Wilkins.* Wolfeboro, N.H., 1987).

NEW JERSEY

PINE & PATRICK

Beverly, N.J.

Rulau	Date	Metal	Size	VG	F	VF	EF
NJ 120	(?)	Copper	29mm	—	—	45.00	—
		PINE & PATRICK / BEVERLY, N.J. in relief within rect. depression ctsp on U.S. 1845 Large cent. (H. Joseph Levine May 1985 sale, lot 36; Brunk 32145)					

S.A. WHITNEY

Glassboro, N.J.

Miller	Date	Metal	Size	VG	F	VF	Unc
NJ 16	1852	Brass	27mm	5.00	10.00	14.00	40.00
		Fancy glass demijohn with handles at center, S.A. WHITNEY, GLASSBORO. N.J. around, ornament below. Rv: DUE BEARER IN M'DZE AT COUNTER OF MY STORE. / ONE CENT / S.A. WHITNEY / 1852. Plain edge. (Wright 1239)					
NJ 17	1852	Silver	27mm	—	—	—	300.00
		As 16. Plain edge.					

This firm also issued cent-denomination tokens dated 1869 (Adams NJ 18 to 22A)

BARNETT'S FOUNDRY & MACHINE WORKS

Newark, N.J.

Miller	Date	Metal	Size	F	VF	EF	Unc
NJ 27	(1859)	Cast Iron	35.4mm	—	100.	200.	400.
		BARNETT'S / MALLEABLE / AND GRAY IRON / FOUNDRY'S / & / MACHINE WORKS / NEWARK, N.J. Rv: NEWARK MANUF'R'S DEPOT / HARDWARE / & / MACHINERY / 50 & 52 / McWHORTER ST. / NEWARK, N.J. Plain edge. (Wright 1326; Saccone 3290)					

Oscar Barnett first advertised in 1859. In 1846 John Barnett had become a plater of metal, and the family business turned to malleable iron in 1854. The token could be later, in the 1870's.

J.O. HARGER & CO.

Miller	Date	Metal	Size	VG	F	VF	Unc
NJ 30-1/2	(?)	White Metal	23mm	25.00	50.00	75.00	100.
		J.O. HARGER & CO. / THE / LEADING / JEWELERS / 579 / BROAD ST. / NEWARK, N.J. Rv: Watch at center. Around 'KEEPERS OF CITY TIME'.					

MECHANICS HOTEL

Rulau	Date	Metal	Size	VG	F	VF	Unc
NJ 100	(1855)	Silver?	18mm	—	—	—	Rare
		MECHANICS HOTEL / T.R. Rv: Blank.					

William and Sarah Starrs sold the Mechanics Hotel to Tobias D. Seaman in 1845, and he in turn sold it to D.S. Hetzel and P.A. Sisco in 1850. After 1855 the hotel does not appear in the directories. Seaman is best known as the issuer of Hard Times tokens (Low 148, 148A and 155) about 1837. Just who "T.R." was has not been discovered.

R.H. D'ANGELO

Rulau	Date	Metal	Size	VG	F	VF	EF
NJ 110	(1854-55)	Silver	27mm	—	—	500.	—
		R. D'ANGELO / WARM & COLD —BATHS / 238 BROAD ST. / NEWARK N.J. ctsp on reverse of Spanish-American 2-reales worn nearly smooth. Rev: SOL. ctsp four times on obverse of coin. (Van Ormer sale 2606; Brunk 10660)					
NJ 112	(?)	Silver	21mm	—	—	500.	—
		R. H. D'ANGELO / WARM & COLD —BATHS / 238 BROAD ST. / NEWARK, N.J. ctsp on Mexico 1838 1-real. (Van Ormer sale 2608)					
NJ 113	(?)	Silver	27mm	—	—	500.	—
		Similar ctsp on Spanish-American 2-reales pieces. Dates examined: 1770, 1780. (Van Ormer sale 2609, 2610)					
NJ 114	(?)	Silver	27mm	—	—	500.	—
		Similar ctsp on Mexico 1828-Zs 2-reales. (Van Ormer sale 2611)					

D'Angelo is listed as a barber in the 1854-55 Newark directory, at 238 Broad St.

R. HEINISCH

Rulau	Date	Metal	Size	VG	F	VF	EF
NJ 125	(1859-60)	CN	19mm	—	—	125.	—
		R. HEINISCH (curved) / -.- / NEWARK, N.J. ctsp on U.S. Flying Eagle cent of 1857-58 type. (John Boger coll.; Brunk 19055)					

Rochus Heinisch was a manufacturer of scissors, knives, razors and cutlery, located at 114 Market Street in Newark in 1859-1860. His factory apparently was in New York City at the corner of Nassau and Fulton Streets. The stamp was his logo placed on his products.

ZEH & HAHNEMANN CO.

Newark, N.J.

Rulau	Date	Metal	Size	F	VF	EF	Unc
NJ 116	(1850's)	Copper	29mm	—	—	—	175.
		Seated figure, PRESSES AND PRESS TOOLS. At lower right: (tiny) Z. FREUND. Rv: ZEH / & / HAHNEMANN / CO. / NEWARK, / N.J. within wreath. (Van Ormer sale 2929)					
NJ 116A	(1850's)	WM	29mm	—	—	—	300.
		As last, struck on a blank white metal planchet. Only 1 known.					
NJ 116B	(1850's)	Copper	30.3mm	—	—	—	300.
		As 116, but struck on a blank copper planchet. Plain edge. (Smithsonian coll.)					

The only reported specimen of NJ 116, which surfaced in 1985, is overstruck on an 1850 U.S. Large cent. It escaped cataloging until the Bowers & Merena sale of the Van Ormer collection in Sept. 1985.

The only known specimen of NJ 116A appeared in the Kirtley sale of Aug. 5-15, 1989 as lot 256, in choice AU condition.

One source indicates this firm may not have been founded until 1904. Not verified.

SMITH'S HOTEL

New Brunswick, N.J.

Rulau	Date	Metal	Size	VG	F	VF	EF
NJ 102	(?)	Silver	27mm	200.	—	400.	—
		SMITH'S HOTEL / NEW BRUNSWICK. N. J. ctsp on Spanish-American 1779 2-reales. There are 2 specimens reported. (Gould 121; Brunk 36895)					
NJ 102A	(?)	Silver	27mm	200.	—	400.	—
		Similar ctsp on Mexico 1828-Go-MI 2-reales.					
NJ 102B	(?)	Silver	21mm	200.	—	300.	—
		Similar ctsp on Spanish-American 1-real. Examined: 1774, 1828.					
NJ 102C	(?)	Copper	-mm	—	—	200.	—
		Similar ctsp on France copper coin.					

A printed advertisement of Smith's Hotel located by Dr. Gregory Brunk reveals that it was "long known as the Bull's Head" and was located at 222 Burnet Street, corner of Hiram Street, in New Brunswick.

GUARANTEE DEVELOPMENT CO.

North Beach Haven, N.J.

Miller	Date	Metal	Size	VG	F	VF	EF
NJ 31	1722 (1914)	Nickel	27mm	—	35.00	65.00	100.
		GUARANTEE DEVELOPMENT CO. / NORTH / BEACH / HAVEN, / NEW JERSEY (ornamental cross). Rv: Imitation of Spanish homeland 2-reales coin of 1722, with quartered Castile and Leon arms at center and legend around: HISPANIARUM + REX + 1722 +.					

This token was reported by Edgar Adams and others, including Wayte Raymond, as an overstrike on a silver Spanish 2-reales of 1722. In his 1962 reference, *A Catalogue of U.S. Store Cards or Merchants Tokens,* Donald M. Miller clarified that the piece was struck from new dies, cut by S.D. Childs of Chicago.

It has now been proven that this token, long thought to be an early piece, was actually struck in 1914. It is quite scarce.

It has also been reported in WM-plated steel.

BALL BROTHERS

South Orange, N.J.

Rulau	Date	Metal	Size	VG	F	VF	EF
NJ 104	(?)	Copper	23.5mm	—	100.	—	150.
		BALL / BROTHERS / GROCERS / SOUTH ORANGE / NEW JERSEY ctsp on U.S. 1853 Half cent. (Brunk 2110)					

S. KENNEDY

Trenton, N.J., and

SLATER WALTON & CO.

Philadelphia, Pa.

Miller	Date	Metal	Size	VG	F	VF	Unc
NJ 32	(?)	White Metal	22mm	—	—	175.	275.
		Eagle on shield, S. KENNEDY / TRENTON, N.J. Rv: Shield. SLATER WALTON & CO. 24 / CHER RY ST. / PHILA DA. Reportedly only 8 struck.					

J.H. PARKER

Trenton, N.J.

Rulau	Date	Metal	Size	VG	F	VF	EF
NJ 109	(?)	Copper	29mm	—	60.00	—	—
		J.H. PARKER / TRENTON ctsp on U.S. 1839 Large cent. Similar ctsp on reverse of coin. (Frank Kovacs coll.; Brunk 31000)					

G. PINE

Trenton, N.J.

Miller	Date	Metal	Size	VG	F	VF	Unc
NJ 33	(?)	Silvered Copper	24mm	50.00	150.	300.	—
		G. PINE. 23 W. STATE ST. TRENTON. N.J. / GOLD / & / SILVER / PLATER. Rv: Imitation of U.S. quarter dollar (eagle, etc.) Electrotype lead, silvered. (Saccone 3293)					

BODINE BROS.

Williamstown, N.J.

Miller	Date	Metal	Size	F	VF	EF	Unc
NJ 10	1856	Brass	27mm	25.00	60.00	80.00	125.
		BODINE BROS. 1856. ONE CENT DUE BEARER IN MDZE AT COUNTER OF OUR STORE. Rv: Intaglio of obverse; struck as a shell.					

Joel Bodine purchased a glasshouse in Williamstown in 1839, with partners Gabriel Iszard and William Coffin Jr. Bodine became sole owner in 1842, but admitted three sons (Job F., William H. and Joel A.) in 1846. It then became Joel Bodine & Sons. The business was known as Bodine Brothers 1855-1866 and then became Bodine, Thomas & Co.

Bodine Brothers also issued an 1863-dated Civil War token, Fuld NJ 925A-1b, in brass.

NEW YORK

J. DICKSON

Albany, N.Y.

Rulau	Date	Metal	Size	G	VG	F	EF
NY 2000	(?)	Copper	29mm	—	—	90.00	—
		J. DICKSON / ALBANY ctsp on U.S. 1827 Large cent. (Stanley L. Steinberg collection; Brunk 11630)					

Jeweler?

HASCY

Rulau	Date	Metal	Size	VG	F	VF	EF
NY 2002	(ca 1849)	Copper	29mm	60.00	—	90.00	—
		HASCY ctsp on a U.S. 1840 or 1845 Large cent, the name in relief within a depressed rectangle. (Brunk 18610)					

Alexander R. Hascy was a silversmith 1831-1850. The mark is either his hallmark or that of Nelson Hascy.

KNIGHT'S

Rulau	Date	Metal	Size	VG	F	VF	EF
NY 2003	(1855)	Copper	29mm	100.	—	150.	—
		KNIGHT'S / 15 BEAVER ST. / ALBANY ctsp on U.S. Large cent. Dates examined: 1826, 1831. (Tanenbaum coll.; Brunk 23210)					

NY 2004	(1855)	Silver	25mm	125.	—	175.	—

Similar ctsp on U.S. Liberty Seated quarter. (Tanenbaum report)

Mrs. Knight was proprietor of a variety store in the 1855 directory.

MEADE BROTHERS

Miller	Date	Metal	Size	F	VF	EF	Unc
NY 530	(1850's)	Brass	28mm	20.00	30.00	40.00	60.00

Eagle displayed, shield on breast. DAGUERRIAN GALLERIES. above; EXCHANGE ALBY below. Rv: AMERICAN DAGUERREOTYPE / MEADE BROTHERS / 233 / BROADWAY / NEW YORK / * GALLERIES *. (Wright 687)

NY 530A	(1850's)	Brass	28mm	20.00	30.00	40.00	60.00

Obverse as 530. Rv: MEADE & BROTHER / IMPORTERS / OF / * DAGUERREOTYPE GOODS *. (Wright 686)

W. J. SCOTT

Albany, N.Y.

Rulau	Date	Metal	Size	VG	F	VF	EF
NY 2004	(1848)	Copper	29mm	60.00	—	90.00	—
		W.J. SCOTT ctsp on U.S. Large cent. Dates examined: 1817, 1818, 1830, 1834, 1837, date worn. There are 6 specimens reported. (Brunk 35930)					
NY 2004C	(1848)	Copper	29mm	60.00	—	90.00	—
		W. J. SCOTT / ALBANY ctsp on U.S. 1831 Large cent. Apparently unique. (Brunk 35935)					

W. J. Scott was a gunsmith, in partnership with R.H. Scott from 1848 to his death about 1870. The firm W.J. & R.H. Scott is listed in the directories 1848-70, R. H. Scott alone 1870-74.

In 1859 the firm advertised that they sold military goods at 9 Beaver St. In 1862 they moved to 60 State St. and expanded their line to include baseball, firefighting, theatrical goods, fishing tackle, buttons. They repaired guns and swords and made stencils, stamps and door plates.

The 1862 ad said they did business at "the sign of the big gun and pistol."

H. G. FOWLER

Auburn, N.Y.

Rulau	Date	Metal	Size	VG	F	VF	EF
NY 5	(?)	Copper	--mm	—	—	175.	—

NY 5 was listed by Adams, Raymond and others under Auburn, N.Y. Wright, whose listings included full descriptions, did not mention it. Brunk also chose not to catalog it. Does any collector possess NY 5?

It has been determined that this issue is not connected with D. C. Fowler of Syracuse, N.Y.

EVANS & ALLEN

Binghamton, N.Y.

This issuer used Civil War die 1368 (BUSINESS CARD) on its copper 20.5mm tokens. Evans & Allen appear in Binghamton directories circa 1850. It is possible these pieces should be included in this reference and deleted from Civil War token catalogs. Research is continuing.

CLARK

Boonville, N.Y.

Rulau	Date	Metal	Size	VG	F	VF	EF
NY 2005	(?)	Copper	29mm	—	—	60.00	—

BOONVILLE. N.Y. ctsp on obverse of U.S. 1848 Large cent. .CLARK ctsp on reverse of coin. (Hartzog collection; Brunk 7840)

CROWN STEAM LAUNDRY

Brooklyn, N.Y.

Miller	Date	Metal	Size	F	VF	EF	Unc
NY 13	(?)	Brass	--mm	—	150.	—	250.

CROWN STEAM LAUNDRY, 474 MYRTLE AVE., BROOKLYN. Rv: Blank.

E. DAY

Rulau	Date	Metal	Size	VG	F	VF	EF
NY 2500	(?)	Silver	27mm	75.00	—	125.	—
		E DAY / BROOKLYN ctsp on Mexico 1825-M-JM 2-reales. (Frank Kovacs coll.)					
NY 2501	(?)	Copper	29mm	60.00	—	90.00	—
		Similar ctsp on U.S. 1846 Large cent. (Brunk 11115)					
NY 2502	(?)	Copper	29mm	—	—	90.00	—
		E. DAY ctsp on U.S. 1817 Large cent. (Brunk 11110)					

LUCIEN KNAPP

Miller	Date	Metal	Size	F	VF	EF	Unc
NY 14	(?)	Cupronickel	24.5mm	—	—	—	Rare

FOR ALDERMAN / LUCIEN KNAPP / 3d WARD. Rv: Blank.

M. LEASK

Brooklyn, N.Y.

Miller	Date	Metal	Size	VG	F	VF	Unc
NY 15	(?)	White Metal	31mm	10.00	30.00	50.00	100.

M LEASK, 6 SANDS ST, BROOKLYN, N.Y. / LACES / EMBROIDERIES / RIBBONS / FLOWERS & C / LADIES' / & CHILDRENS' / UNDER / GARMENTS / OF EVERY / DESCRIPTION. Rv: MANUFACTURERS OF / MOURNING / & / ILLUSION / GOODS / DRESS CAPS, / HEAD DRESSES / & c / ". (Wright 586A)

NASSAU WATER WORKS

Rulau	Date	Metal	Size	VG	F	EF	Unc
NY 2006	1859	Bronze	34mm	—	—	30.00	50.00
		Neptune seated left, NASSAU WATER WORKS above, COMMCD. JULY / 1856 in exergue. Rv: Building in center, WATER INTRODUCED IN THE CITY OF BROOKLYN / DECEMBER 1858 above, CELEBRATED APRIL / 1859 in exergue. (Wright 744)					
NY 2007	1859	Silver	34mm	—	—	100.	200.
		As 2006.					
NY 2008	1859	White Metal	34mm	—	—	30.00	50.00
		As 2006.					

J.M. TAYLOR

Rulau	Date	Metal	Size	G	VG	F	VF
NY 2010	(1854)	Silver	25mm	—	40.00	—	60.00
		J.M. TAYLOR / BROKER / BROOKLYN, L.I. ctsp on U.S. Liberty Seated 1853 with Arrows quarter dollar. 17 pieces known. (Gould 66; Van Ormer sale 2876; Brunk 39470)					
NY 2010A	(?)	Silver	26mm	—	40.00	—	60.00
		Similar ctsp on U.S. Bust quarters. Dates examined: 1818, 1819, 1834.					
NY 2012	(?)	Silver	31mm	—	60.00	—	90.00
		Similar ctsp on U.S. Liberty Seated 1853 with Arrows half dollar.					
NY 2012A	(?)	Silver	31mm	—	60.00	—	90.00
		Same as 2012, but additional ctsp SCHEICK. on obverse.					

Rulau	Date	Metal	Size	G	VG	F	VF
NY 2011	(1854)	Silver	27mm	—	40.00	—	60.00
		Similar ctsp on Spanish-American 2-reales. Examined: 1755-Mo, 1770, 1777, 1780, 1799, 1801, 1802, 1822, Unknown date. There are 10 reported specimens. (Gould 126)					

WASHINGTON HOUSE

Rulau	Date	Metal	Size	VGF	VF	EF	
NY 2710	(1860's)	Silver	32.5mm	—	175.	—	—
		Washington House (upper & lower case letters) ctsp very lightly four times on U.S. 1832 Bust half dollar. (B&M Patterson 1985 sale, lot 1718; Brunk 41955; Rulau Z97M)					

Washington House, located at 195 York St., near the Brooklyn Navy Yard, also issued scrip notes in 10 and 15-cent denominations portraying George Washington. The notes, in crisp Unc. (unsigned) are worth $450 each, according to specialist Dr. Alan York.

YOUNG & PALMER

Brooklyn, N.Y.

Rulau	Date	Metal	Size	G	VG	F	EF
NY 2015	(?)	Copper	28mm	—	125.	—	175.
		YOUNG & PALMER / BROOKLYN ctsp on Canada 1813 Trade & Navigation halfpenny token, Breton 965. (Brunk 44700)					

F. CUTLER

Buffalo, N.Y.

Miller	Date	Metal	Size	VG	F	VF	Unc
NY 19	(?)	Copper	30mm	—	—	—	V.Rare
		F. CUTLER. WEBSTER BUILDING, BUFFALO.					

LABORERS UNION

Miller	Date	Metal	Size	VG	F	VF	EF
NY 21	(?)	Copper	31mm	—	—	75.00	125.
		LABORERS UNION / -*- / ... / * BUFFALO, N.Y. * Rv: Blank. Rare.					

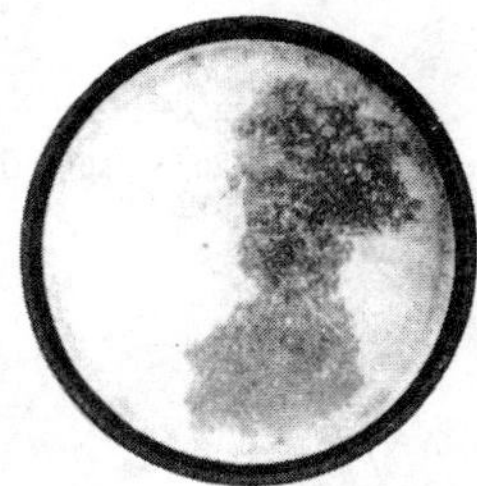

Miller	Date	Metal	Size	VG	F	VF	Unc
NY 21C	(?)	WM	31mm	—	—	75.00	125.
		Similar to last, but No 1 at center of obverse. Rare. (Saccone sale 3296)					
NY 21A	(?)	WM	31mm	—	—	75.00	125.
		As last, but No 2 at center. Counterstamped below is: 1844. Rv.: Blank.					

NY 21C, cataloged here for the first time, was offered in the Bowers & Merena sale of the Saccone collection, Nov. 6-8, 1989.

Buffalo was a hotbed of the labor movement in the 1850's. The term Laborers Union (vs. the current Labor Union) was used at that time.

STEPHENSON'S JEWELRY STORE

Buffalo, N.Y.

Miller	Date	Metal	Size	VG	F	VF	Unc
NY 24	(1840's)	Brass	23mm	—	5.00	8.00	25.00
		Buffalo running right, 200 / MAIN STREET above. Around all: STEPHENSON'S JEWELRY STORE / * N.Y. *. Rv: IMPORTERS & DEALERS / IN FINE / WATCHES / JEWELRY / AND / SILVERWARE.					
NY 24A	(1840's)	Copper	23mm	—	6.50	9.50	25.00
		As 24. (Wright 1048)					

Thomas Stephenson was in business as a silversmith and jeweler 1835-1848 in Buffalo.

E.J. CHAPIN

Clyde, N.Y.

Rulau	Date	Metal	Size	G	VG	F	VF
NY 2018	(?)	Copper	29mm	—	120.	—	180.
		E.J. CHAPIN / CLYDE, N.Y. / DEALER / WATCHES, CLOCKS / & JEWELRY ctsp on U.S. Large cent. (Hallenbeck 3.517; Brunk 7350)					
NY 2018A	(?)	Copper	29mm	—	120.	—	180.
		E.J. CHAPIN / DEALER / IN / WATCHES / CLOCKS & / JEWELRY / CLYDE, N.Y. ctsp on U.S. Large cents. (Brunk 7360)					
NY 2019	(?)	Copper	29mm	—	120.	—	180.
		E.J. CHAPIN / CLYDE, N.Y. ctsp on U.S. Large cents. (Brunk 7340)					
NY 2019D	(?)	Silver	25mm	—	120.	—	180.
		E.J. CHAPIN ctsp on U.S. Seated Liberty quarters. Dates examined: 1853, 1854. (Brunk 7330)					

H.A. JARVIS

Courtland, N.Y.

Rulau	Date	Metal	Size	VG	F	VF	EF
NY 2020	(?)	Silver	27mm	—	50.00	—	100.
		H.A. JARVIS / COURTLAND NY ctsp on Spanish-American 1796 2-reales. (Brunk 21580)					

W.P. DEWITT

Elmira, N.Y.

Rulau	Date	Metal	Size	VG	F	VF	EF
NY 2022	(1857)	Silver	18mm	—	50.00	—	75.00
		W.P. DEWITT / ELMIRA ctsp on U.S. dime. Examined: 1840, 1841, 1843, 1853, unknown date. 7 pieces known. (Schenkman collection; Brunk 11560)					

NY 2024	(?)	Silver	18mm	—	60.00	—	90.00

Similar ctsp on U.S. Bust dime. Examined: 1832. (Van Ormer sale 2619)

NY 2026	(?)	Copper	29mm	—	50.00	—	75.00

Similar ctsp on U.S. Large cent. Examined: 1803, 1845, 1850, 1853, 1854, worn date. 7 pieces known.

NY 2025	(?)	Copper	28mm	—	50.00	—	75.00

Similar ctsp on Canadian tokens. 2 known.

NY 2025B	(?)	Silver	27mm	—	75.00	—	100.

Similar ctsp on Spanish-American 1777 2-reales.

NY 2025E	(1857)	Silver	31mm	—	100.	—	150.

Similar ctsp on U.S. Seated Liberty 1853 half dollar.

NY 2025F	(?)	Silver	25mm	—	100.	—	150.

Similar ctsp on U.S. 1853 or 1854 S.L. quarter. (Van Ormer sale 2620)

NY 2023	(1857)	Copper	29mm	60.00	—	90.00	—

W. P. DEWITT ctsp on U.S. Large cent. Examined: 1836, 1837. Only 2 known. (Brunk 11555)

William P. DeWitt was a gunsmith listed in the 1853 and 1857 *Elmira City Directories* at 418 Water Street, opposite Chemung Canal Bank. He continues to appear until the 1892 edition. The counterstamping probably dates from about 1857.

Recent research shows he was in business 1848-1891.

A. T. HAVILAND

Rulau	Date	Metal	Size	VG	F	VF	EF
NY 2560	(?)	Copper	29mm	—	—	50.00	—

A. T. HAVILAND ctsp on U.S. 1818 Large cent. (Brunk 18750)

Addison Townsend Haviland was a machinist in Elmira, N.Y. Born 1829, he died in 1891. Tentative attribution.

POTTER & BASSETT
Elmira, N.Y.

Rulau	Date	Metal	Size	VG	F	VF	EF
NY 2510	(?)	Silver	27mm	—	—	125.	—

POTTER & / ELMIRA NY / BASSETT ctsp on Spanish-American 1795 2-reales of Carlos IIII. (Joseph Schmidt report; Brunk 32565)

O.C. SHALER
Gilboa, N.Y.

Rulau	Date	Metal	Size	VG	F	VF	EF
NY 2028	(1850's)	Copper	29mm	30.00	—	75.00	—

O.C. SHALER / GILBOA, N.Y. ctsp on U.S. 1856 Large cent. (Steve Tanenbaum collection; Brunk 36130)

The *Bradstreet Directory* for 1866 lists a G.C. Shaler in Gilboa, engaged in the stove and tinware business — possibly a successor.

J. MARCH
Hoosick, N.Y.

Rulau	Date	Metal	Size	VG	F	VF	EF
N 2512	(?)	Copper	29mm	—	—	60.00	—

J. MARCH / HOOSICK crudely ctsp on U.S. Large cent, ca 1816. (Brunk 26003)

This piece fetched $88 in the B&M Taylor sale in 1987 (lot 1288).

JAMES, CLARK & CO.
Hudson, N.Y.

Miller	Date	Metal	Size	F	VF	EF	Unc
NY 30	(1853)	Brass	28mm	5.00	8.00	16.00	40.00

Corner view of building within central circle, JAMES, CLARK & CO. above, five stars below. Rv: CLOTHING MANUFACTURERS / COR. / WARREN / & / FOURTH ST. / HUDSON / -.- / * N.Y. *. Reeded Edge. (Wright 192)

NY 31	(1853)	Brass	28mm	5.00	8.00	16.00	40.00

As 30, but error CLOTING on reverse. Plain edge.

NY 32	(1860)	Brass	28mm	—	—	—	75.00

Obverse as 30. Rv: Sidewheeler sailing right, DRY GOODS & UPHOLSTERY above, * FOR SHIPS & STEAMBOATS * below. Plain edge. (Muling of James, Clark with Doremus & Nixon, N.Y., card)

NY 33	1853 (1860)	Copper	28mm	—	—	—	75.00

Obverse as 30. Rv: Crystal Palace in center, NEW YORK CRYSTAL PALACE above, 1853 / ********* below. Plain edge. (Muling of James, Clark with H.B. West, N.Y., card)

NY 33A	1853 (1860)	Brass	28mm	—	—	—	75.00

As 33. Plain edge.

NY 160	(1860)	White Metal	28mm	—	—	—	100.

Obverse as 30. Rv: IMPORTERS / AND / JOBBERS OF / FANCY & STAPLE / DRY GOODS / 130 BROADWAY / NEW-YORK. Plain edge. (Muling of James, Clark with Loder & Co., N.Y., card)

Though Adams and Miller listed NY 160 under James, Clark & Co. in New York City, we can find no justification for this. The piece is simply another indiscriminate Scovill muling of genuine store card dies made for some collector's order. There is no evidence James, Clark & Co. were themselves in business as importers in New York. The James, Clark mulings were made in or after 1860, in all probability. Only NY 30 and 31 were genuine store cards.

R. MARTIN
Hudson (N.Y. ?)

Rulau	Date	Metal	Size	VG	F	VF	EF
NY 2160	(?)	Silver	32.5mm	200.	—	250.	—

R. MARTIN / HUDSON ctsp on U.S. Bust half dollars. Dates examined 1812, 1830. (Brunk 26160)

J. BURRITT & SON
Ithaca, N.Y.

Rulau	Date	Metal	Size	VG	F	VF	EF
NY 2165	(1840's)	Silver	32.5mm	—	300.	—	450.

J. BURRITT / & SON / ITHACA ctsp on U.S. 1809 Bust half dollar. (Brunk 6120)

Rulau	Date	Metal	Size	VG	F	VF	EF
NY 2166	(1840's)	Copper	28.5mm	—	300.	—	450.

Similar ctsp on 1837 Hard Times token. (Bosco Apr. 1989 sale, lot 017)

Rulau	Date	Metal	Size	VG	F	VF	EF
NY 2167	(1840's)	Silver	32.5mm	—	300.	—	450.

J. BURRITT / & SON ctsp on U.S. 1834 half dollar. (Brunk 6110)

Joseph Burritt was a silversmith who came to Ithaca from Connecticut in 1816. His son, Joseph C. Burritt, joined the firm in 1838. The business became Burritt, Clark & Co. about 1864 and was then at 34 Oswego Street.

It is possible these pieces belong in the Hard Times era.

NIAGARA CUTLERY CO.
Lockport, N.Y.

Rulau	Date	Metal	Size	VG	F	VF	EF
NY 2029	(?)	Silver	38mm	—	400.	—	—

NIAGARA CUTLERY CO. / LOCKPORT, N.Y. ctsp on reverse of Bolivia 1836-PTS-LM 8-sueldos. Rv: J. F. C. ctsp on obverse of the same coin. (Brunk 29605)

On the only known specimen, reported by Dr. George Fuld, the 'NIA' of NIAGARA is so weak that it is difficult to see. The NIAGARA CUTLERY CO. / LOCKPORT, N.Y. stamp is professional and was applied to the coin in a single impression; the J. F. C. initials may be individual letter punches and are probably frivolous and not connected with the Niagara counterstamp.

G.L. SWIFT
Marathon, N.Y.

Rulau	Date	Metal	Size	VG	F	VF	EF
NY 2030	(1847-57)	Copper	29mm	—	125.	—	175.

G.L. SWIFT / DRUGGIST / MARATHON, N.Y. ctsp on U.S. 1847 Large cent. (Hallenbeck 19.784; Brunk 39135)

JOSIAH BAKEWELL & CO.
Middletown, N.Y.

Miller	Date	Metal	Size	VG	F	VF	EF
NY 39	(?)	Brass	27mm	—	—	125.	—

Similar to NY 39A, but BAKEWELL & CO. in place of W.B. SEARS & CO. Thick flan.

Miller	Date	Metal	Size	VG	F	VF	EF
NY 39E	(1857)	Copper	29mm	—	—	200.	—

JOSIAH BAKEWELL / 104 ELM ST (curved) / * ctsp on U.S. 1840 Large cent. (John Boger coll.; Brunk 2015)

In the 1857 directory, Josiah Bakewell is listed as a saw manufacturer on North St., in partnership with Elisha P. Wheeler and Edward M. Madden (Wheeler, Madden & Bakewell).

The WM&B initials on the Bakewell token, Miller NY 39, and on the W.B. Sears & Co. token, NY 39A, are thus explained. The relationship between Sears and Bakewell has yet to be uncovered.

Josiah Bakewell resided in Wallkill, N.Y., a small place next to Middletown. The 1860 census reveals he was born in England, was married, and had two children.

W.B. SEARS & CO.

Miller	Date	Metal	Size	VG	F	VF	EF
NY 39A	(1857)	Brass	27mm	—	—	125.	—

W M & B in cross form around a small shield at center, W.B. SEARS & CO. above; MIDDLETOWN N.Y. below. Rv: Blank. Beveled edge.

WM & B = Wheeler, Madden and Bakewell. See NY 39.

W. SMITH
Middletown, N.Y.

Rulau	Date	Metal	Size	VG	F	VF	EF
NY 2032	(?)	Copper	29mm	60.00	—	100.	—

W. SMITH / MIDDLETOWN / N.Y. ctsp on obverse of U.S. 1844 Large cent. MIDDLETOWN / N.Y. ctsp on reverse of the coin. (Tanenbaum coll.; Brunk 37310)

Since the counterstamp begins with a very prominent period; it is quite possible Smith had another initial which didn't fit onto the coin. The .W. SMITH punch is separate from and much larger than the MIDDLETOWN / N.Y. punch. The latter appears more professional; MIDDLETOWN is presented in an upward arc.

J. H. ADAMS
New York, N.Y.

Rulau	Date	Metal	Size	VG	F	VF	EF
NY 2033	(?)	Copper	29mm	—	125.	—	—

J.H. ADAMS / 30 NASSAU ST. / NEW YORK ctsp on U.S. 1851 Large cent. (Tanenbaum coll.; Brunk 327)

Joseph H. Adams sold hardware and other items in his Nassau St. store in the 1850's.

HERR ALEXANDER

Miller	Date	Metal	Size	F	VF	EF	Unc
NY 42	1847	Gilt brass	30mm	30.00	75.00	100.	150.
		Bearded bust in toga right, tiny C.C.W. beneath truncation of the bust, small ornament at bottom. HERR ALEXANDER around. Rv: PRESENTED / TO / HERR ALEXANDER / AS A TESTIMONY / OF ESTEEM FROM / HIS FRIENDS / IN / NEW YORK. / 1847. Plain edge. (Wright 1304; Kuethe MT-007)					
NY 42A	1847	Gilt Brass	30mm	30.00	75.00	100.	150.
		As 42. Thin planchet. Plain edge.					
NY 42B	1847	Copper	30mm	—	—	100.	225.
		As 42. Plain edge.					

The dies were cut by Charles Cushing Wright.

This medallic token is often considered the earliest magician's token of America, though more properly it is a commemorative medalet. It is one of the most desirable of all New York tokens of the pre-Civil War era.

Herr Alexander's real name was Alexander Heimberger.

BENZIGER BROTHERS

Miller	Date	Metal	Size	VG	F	VF	Unc
NY 60	(?)	Gilt Lead	28mm	8.00	15.00	40.00	75.00
		* NEW YORK & CINCINNATI * BOOKS / VESTMENTS AND / CHURCH / ORNAMENTS * /. Rv: RELIGIOUS MEDALS / OF / GOLD SILVER / AND OTHER METAL / MEDALS / FOR / SOCIETIES / -0- / MADE TO ORDER. Plain edge. (Wright 78)					

BERJEW'S DINING SALOON

Rulau	Date	Metal	Size	VG	F	VF	EF
NY 2034	(1854-58)	Silver	27mm	200.	—	300.	—
		BERJEW'S / DINING SALOON / 53 FULTON ST. N.Y. ctsp on Spanish-American 2-reales obverse. H. NELSON is ctsp on reverse. (Brunk 3450)					

Rulau	Date	Metal	Size	VG	F	VF	EF
NY 2035	(1854-58)	Silver	34mm	250.	—	400.	—
		Similar ctsp on Spanish-American 1808-So-FI (Chile) silver 4-reales. (Tanenbaum collection)					

Charles F. Berjew is listed as an eatinghouse in the 1859 directory at 743-1/2 8th Ave. He does not appear in the 1853 or 1861 directories.

J. CONGER BERRY

Rulau	Date	Metal	Size	VG	F	VF	EF
NY 2036	(ca. 1851-52)	Copper	29mm	—	—	200.	—
		J CONGER BERRY / 33 / ATTORNY ST. N.Y. ctsp on U.S. 1851 Large cent. (Tanenbaum coll.; Brunk 3490)					

This is a very ornate counterstamp. All lettering is in relief within recessed designs. J CONGER BERRY and ATTORNY ST. are within a serrated (toothed) depression shaped in semicircular fashion so that the depression's center is normal. The numeral 33 is in a small rectangular field recessed at the center of the semicircle's center.

The token was obtained in a Rich Hartzog sale of Feb., 1979.

John Conger Berry sold tools at 33 Attorney (not Attorny) Street at least 1844-1853. He appears in the 1844-53 directories. His residence in 1849 was at 428 Grand. He was at 55 Columbia St. in the 1859 directory.

S.H. BLACK

Miller	Date	Metal	Size	VG	F	VF	Unc
NY 61	1858	Copper over Lead	29mm	7.50	11.00	16.00	40.00
		Imitation of U.S. Large cent. Liberty head left, LIBERTY on coronet. S.H. BLACK, ELECTROTYPER around, * 1858 * below. Rv: Within the olive wreath: 390-1/2 / BROADWAY / N.Y. Around: MEDALS, CARDS & C. TO ORDER. Plain edge.					
NY 62	1858	Silver over Lead	29mm	—	—	Ex. Rare	
		As NY 61. Plain edge.					

Miller	Date	Metal	Size	VG	F	VF	Unc
NY 63	1859	Copper over Lead	29mm	7.50	10.00	15.00	40.00
		Similar to 61, but S.H. BLACK, ELECTROTYPER & GILDER around, 1859 below. Rv: Similar to 61, but 410 / B'WAY, / N.Y. in center. (Wright 82)					

Miller	Date	Metal	Size	VG	F	VF	Unc
NY 64	1859	Copper over Lead	29mm	7.50	11.00	16.00	40.00
		Obverse as NY 63. Rv: Similar, but 43 / LISPENARD / ST. / N.Y. at center of wreath. Plain edge.					

FRIEND & BLACK

Miller	Date	Metal	Size	VG	F	VF	Unc
NY 65	1860	Copper over Lead	29mm	7.50	10.00	15.00	40.00

Similar to 61, but FRIEND & BLACK, ELECTROTYPERS around, .1860. below. rv: Similar, but 25 / HOWARD / ST. / N.Y. at center of wreath. Plain edge.

SAMUEL H. BLACK

Miller	Date	Metal	Size	VG	F	VF	Unc
NY 67	1860	Copper over Lead	29mm	7.50	10.00	15.00	40.00

Imitation of U.S. Large cent, LIBERTY on coronet of Liberty head. 13 stars around, 1860 below. (Date is small). Rv: NO / CENT / — within olive wreath at center, SAMUEL H. BLACK. ELECTROTYPE around. Plain edge.

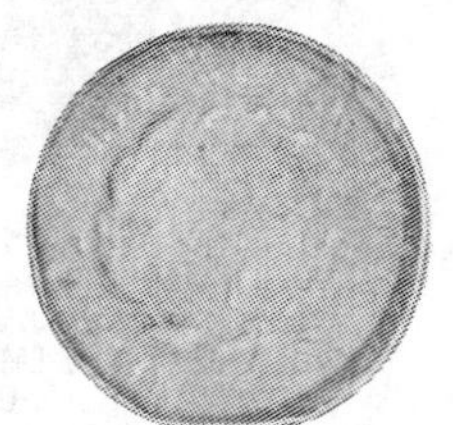

Miller	Date	Metal	Size	VG	F	VF	Unc
NY 67A	1860	Copper over Lead		7.50	11.00	16.00	40.00

Imitation of U.S. Large cent, LIBERTY on coronet of Liberty Head. SAMUEL H. BLACK, ELECTROTYPER around, 1860. (large) below. Rv: As reverse of 68 (142 ELM ST.) Plain edge.

Miller	Date	Metal	Size	VG	F	VF	Unc
NY 68	1861	Copper over Lead	29mm	20.00	30.00	40.00	100.

Obverse as NY 67A, but date 1861. Rv: Similar to 65, but 142 / ELM / ST. / N.Y. at center of wreath.

Samuel H. Black was a popular electrotyper in the years preceding the Civil War. His unusual store cards, close imitations of the Large cents of the government which ceased issuance in 1857, seemed almost an attempt to keep the series alive as he issued them with dates each year 1858 through 1861.

Black's "cents" were made of lead, over which copper had been fused electrolytically — a practical demonstration of his business advertisement, "electrotyper and gilder, medals, cards, etc. to order."

His cards provide an exact, year by year recitation of his constant address changes (no less than five addresses are given on the tokens), and of his brief Friend & Black partnership in 1860.

His business disappears from the New York directories after 1861, so he may have gone off to war, or the war may have caused him to abandon his business for another.

THEODOR BOLLENHAGEN & CO.

Miller	Date	Metal	Size	F	VF	EF	Unc
NY 69	(1850's)	Brass	34mm	5.00	15.00	20.00	50.00

Game counter imitation of $20 gold piece. Coronet Liberty head left, THEODOR BOLLENHAGEN & COMP. above, 49 M LANE below. Rv: Radiant sun above city hall. In exergue: CITY HALL / NEW YORK. Reeded edge. (Kurth 63, RF Sny-5)

Miller	Date	Metal	Size	VG	F	VF	Unc
NY 70	(1850's)	Brass	27.5mm	5.00	6.50	10.00	30.00

Similar to NY 69, but $10 gold size. Plain edge. (Kurth 59, RF Sny-3)

Miller	Date	Metal	Size	VG	F	VF	Unc
NY 70A	(1850's)	Brass	27.5mm	5.00	6.50	10.00	30.00

As NY 70, but Reeded edge. (Kurth 59, RF Sny-3A)

Miller	Date	Metal	Size	VG	F	VF	Unc
NY 70E	(1850's)	Brass	27.5mm	5.00	6.50	20.00	45.00

Obverse as NY 70. Rv: SPIEL / MARKE in oak wreath. Plain edge. (Kurth 60, RF Sny-4)

Miller	Date	Metal	Size	VG	F	VF	Unc
NY 71	(1850's)	Brass	22mm	5.00	6.50	10.00	20.00

Similar to NY 69, but $5 gold size. Plain edge. (Kurth 54, RF Sny-2)

Miller	Date	Metal	Size	VG	F	VF	Unc
Y 71E	(1850's)	Brass	22mm	5.00	6.50	10.00	30.00

Obverse similar to NY 71, but 49 MAIDEN LANE beneath Liberty head instead of 49 M. LANE. The Liberty head is smaller than on NY 71.

Miller	Date	Metal	Size	VG	F	VF	Unc
NY 72	(1850's)	Brass	19mm	5.00	6.50	10.00	20.00

Similar to NY 69, but $2½ gold size. Plain edge. (Kurth 46, RF Sny-1)

Miller	Date	Metal	Size	VG	F	VF	Unc
NY 72A	(1850's)	Brass	19mm	5.00	6.50	10.00	20.00

As NY 72, but Reeded edge. (Kurth 46, RF Sny-1A)

Bollenhagen was a toy and fancy goods dealer who imported his gaming counters from Germany. Lyman H. Low said Bollenhagen packed counters in the boxes in which his playing cards were sold. Bollenhagen is also believed to have been responsible for the general Liberty Head/Eagle spiel marken in this country, according to Low and also Bushnell, and for the generalized City Hall New York counters (Rf Cit-1 through Cit-11). See Rulau and Fuld's *American Game Counters*, Iola, Wis., 1972.

BONDY BROTHERS & CO.

Miller	Date	Metal	Size	VG	F	VF	Unc
NY 73	(?)	Brass	--mm	175.	—	300.	—

BONDY BROTHERS & CO., BELT MANUFACTURERS. Eagle at center. Rv: Blank.

Miller	Date	Metal	Size	VG	F	VF	Unc
NY 73A	(?)	Copper	--mm	—	—	Ex. Rare	

As 73.

Miller	Date	Metal	Size	VG	F	VF	Unc
NY 74	(?)	Copper	29mm	125.	—	250.	—

BONDY BROTHERS & CO. BELT MANUFS, NEW YORK ctsp around the obverse of a U.S. Large cent of 1851.

Z. BOSTWICK

Rulau	Date	Metal	Size	VG	F	VF	EF
NY 2180	(1846-48)	Copper	29mm	—	—	65.00	—

Z. BOSTWICK (script) in relief within rect. depression ctsp on U.S. 1843 Large cent. (Duffield 1431; Brunk 4480)

Zalmon Bostwick was a silversmith active about 1846-1852. He does not appear in the 1845 directory. In the 1848 directory Zalmon Bostwick (late Thompson), silverware manufacturer, was located at 128 William St.

BOWEN & McNAMEE

Miller	Date	Metal	Size	VG	F	VF	Unc
NY 75	(1844-45)	Brass	29mm	3.00	5.00	10.00	40.00

Eagle with drooping wings at center, shield on breast. BOWEN & McNAMEE above, NEW YORK below. Rv: IMPORTERS AND DEALERS / (ornament) / SILK GOODS / 16 / WILLIAM ST / (ornament) / (ornament) IN (ornament). (Wright 88)

Miller	Date	Metal	Size	VG	F	VF	Unc
NY 76	(1844-45)	Copper	29mm	3.00	5.00	10.00	40.00

As 75. (On 75 and 76, all letters are serif type)

NY 77 (1846-50) Brass 29mm 3.00 5.00 10.00 50.00
Obverse similar to 75, but from differing dies. All lettering on 77 and 78 is in sans serif type. Rv: IMPORTERS AND DEALERS IN / 16 / WILLIAM ST. / COR-BEAVER / N.Y. / SILK-GOODS.

NY 78 (1846-50) Copper 29mm 3.00 5.00 10.00 40.00
As 77.

Henry C. Bowen and Theodore McNamee were importers of and dealers in silk goods at 16 William Street 1843-1848, according to contemporary directories. They advertised in 1844 that they dealt in Italian, French and India silk goods.

JAS. S. BRADLEY

NOTE: All Bradley listings have been renumbered due to the discovery of new specimens. Bradley was a prolific and imaginative user of coins for advertising counterstamps. There is much dispute about pricing these pieces — some dealers pricing lower and some much higher.

Rulau	Date	Metal	Size	VG	F	VF	EF
NY 79	(?)	Silver	27mm	125.	—	175.	—
		JAS. S. BRADLEY, N.Y. ctsp on Spanish-American 2-reales. (Duffield 1355; Gould 85; Brunk 4890)					
NY 79B	(?)	Silver	27mm	125.	—	175.	—
		JAS. S. BRADLEY, N.Y. / FINE PICTURES / FINE PICTURES ctsp on Spanish-American 2-reales. Date examined: 1780. (Brunk 4910)					
NY 79D	(?)	Silver	27mm	135.	—	200.	—
		JAS. S. BRADLEY, N.Y. / FINE PICTURES / CHEAPEST IN THE CITY ctsp on Mexico 1826-Zs 2-reales. (Brunk 4900)					

Rulau	Date	Metal	Size	VG	F	VF	EF
NY 79F	(?)	Silver	27mm	100.	—	150.	—
		JAS. S. BRADLEY / GILDER & FRAME / MAKER / 154 WM. ST. N.Y. ctsp on Spanish-American 2-reales. Dates examined: 1753, 1767, 1776, 1779, 1780, 1781, 1783-Mo-F, 1785-LME-MI, 1787-Mo, 1789, 1791, 1793, 1796, 1799, 1808, 1815-Mo, 1818, 1819, and with dates worn off. At least 20 specimens reported. (Gould 323; Van Ormer sale 2553; Brunk 4920)					
NY 79G	(?)	Silver	27mm	—	—	175.	—
		Similar ctsp on Mexico 1834 2-reales.					
NY 79J	(?)	Silver	40mm	—	250.	—	350.
		Similar ctsp on Spanish-American 1776 8-reales.					
NY 79L	(?)	Silver	27mm	165.	—	250.	—
		JAS. S. BRADLEY / GILDER & FRAME / MAKER / 154 WM. ST. N.Y. / CHEAPEST IN THE CITY ctsp on U.S. 1806 quarter. (Gould 74; Brunk 4930)					
NY 79N	(?)	Silver	21mm	165.	—	250.	—
		Similar ctsp on Spanish-American 1-real.					
NY 79P	(?)	Silver	27mm	125.	—	200.	—
		Similar ctsp on Spanish-American 2-reales. Dates examined: 1759, 1781, 1789, 1796 and with dates worn off. About 8 specimens reported.					
NY 79S	(?)	Silver	27mm	125.	—	225.	—
		JAS. S. BRADLEY / FINE PICTURES / CHEAPEST IN THE CITY / GILDER & FRAME / MAKER & MIRRORS / 154 WM. ST. N.Y. ctsp on Spanish-American 1780 2-reales. (Brunk 60; Gould 323)					

Rulau	Date	Metal	Size	VG	F	VF	EF
NY 79T	(?)	Silver	27mm	125.	—	200.	—
		FINE PICTURES / CHEAPEST IN THE CITY / JAS. S. BRADLEY / GILDER & FRAME / MAKER / 154 WM. ST. N.Y. / & MIRRORS ctsp on Spanish-American 1780 2-reales. (Van Ormer sale 2552)					

Rulau	Date	Metal	Size	VG	F	VF	EF
NY 79U	(?)	Silver	27mm	—	—	300.	—
		CHEAPEST IN THE CITY / JAS. S. BRADLEY / GILDER & FRAME / MAKERS / 154 WM. ST. N.Y. ctsp on obverse of Spanish-American 1781 or 1807-LME-JP 2-reales. Rv: J. M. TAYLOR / BROKER / CHATHAM ST. / COR. JAMES N.Y. ctsp on reverse of coin. (Van Ormer sale 2551)					
NY 79V	(?)	Silver	27mm	—	—	225.	—
		FINE PICTURES / JAS. S. BRADLEY / GILDER & FRAME'MAKER / 154 WM ST N.Y. / FINE PICTURES ctsp on Spanish-American 1784 2-reales. (PCAC Dec. 1990 sale, lot 119; Brunk 4870X)					
NY 79Y	(?)	Silver	27mm	—	—	400.	—
		JAS. S. BRADLEY / GILDER & FRAME / MAKER / 158 WM ST N.Y. ctsp on Spanish-American 2-reales. (Brunk 4925)					

The rare version of these counterstamps, 79Y, occurs with a different address, 158 instead of 154, William Street.

J.M. BRADSTREET & SONS

Rulau	Date	Metal	Size	F	VF	EF	Unc
NY 80	1862	Silver	34mm	—	—	—	700.
		J.M. BRADSTREET & SONS. MERCANTILE AGENCY. Rv: BRADSTREET, HOFFMAN & CO. COLLECTORS OF CLAIMS. JULY 4 1862.					
NY 81	1862	Copper	34mm	—	150.	250.	350.
		As 80. Plain edge. (Wright 134)					
NY 81A	1862	WM	34mm	—	150.	250.	350.
		As 80. Plain edge. (Tanenbaum coll.)					
NY 82	1862	Brass	34mm	—	150.	250.	350.
		As 80. Plain edge. (Wright 133)					

Rulau	Date	Metal	Size	F	VF	EF	Unc
NY 82A	(1860-62)	White Metal	34mm	—	100.	250.	350.
		Church building at center, OLD MIDDLE DUTCH CHURCH above, NASSAU ST. N.Y. below. Rv: As NY 80. Plain edge. (One specimen is known in copper)					
NY 82B	(1860-62)	Copper	34mm	—	150.	250.	350.
		As 82A. Plain edge.					
NY 82C	(1860-62)	Brass	34mm	—	150.	250.	350.
		As 82A. Plain edge.					
NY 82J	(1860-62)	Silver	34mm	—	—	150.	—
		Obverse as 82A (Old Middle Dutch Church). Rv: A / RIDING SCHOOL / FOR / BRITISH / DRAGOONS. Plain edge.					
NY 82K	(1860-62)	Copper	34mm	—	250.	350.	500.
		Lincoln portrait. Rv: As NY 80 reverse.					

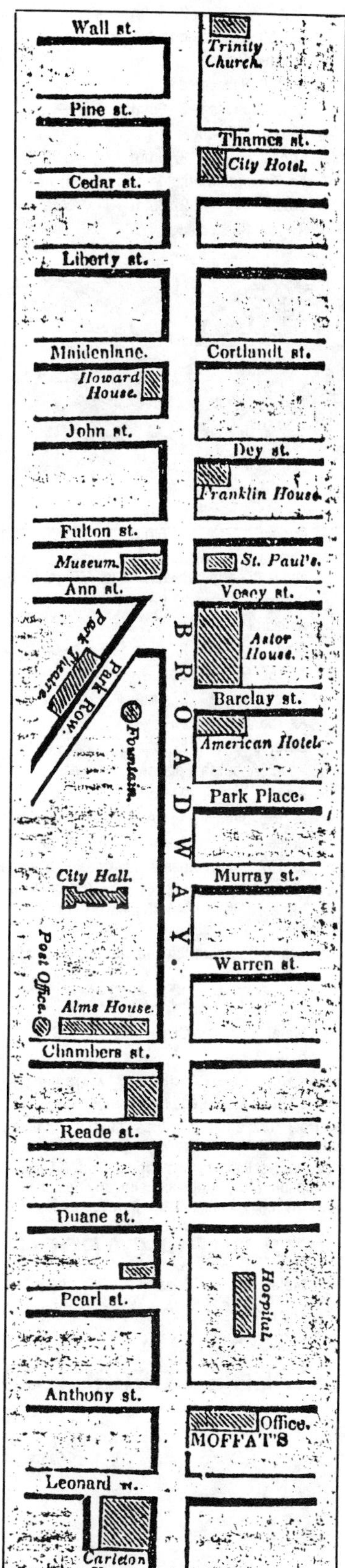

NEW YORK, 1849.

This excellent sketch map from an 1849 directory shows Broadway and a number of its hotels and other buildings in the vicinity of City Hall. Note Astor House, American Hotel, Carleton House, Howard House, City Hotel, Park Theater, etc.

BROADWAY VARIETIES

Rulau	Date	Metal	Size	VG	F	VF	EF
NY 2038	(?)	Silver	27mm	—	125.	—	175.

ADMIT TO / BROADWAY / VARIETIES ctsp on Spanish-American 2-reales. Dates examined: 1773-Mo, 1775, 1776, 1782, 1789, 1792-Mo-FM, 1809, 1817-NG-M; unknown date. There are 9 specimens known. (Brunk 5270; Van Ormer sale 2557)

See the *TAMS Journal* for April 1973, page 73.

Counterstamps on NG (Nueva Guatemala) coins of Ferdinand VII are very unusual in the American series.

BUCKINGHAM PALACE

Miller	Date	Metal	Size	VG	F	VF	Unc
NY 140	(?)	Brass	--mm	10.00	15.00	20.00	50.00

BUCKINGHAM PALACE ADMISSION TICKET.

E.E. BULKLEY

Rulau	Date	Metal	Size	VG	F	VF	EF
NY 2041	(1848-50)	Copper	23.5mm	—	—	100.	—

E. BULKLEY / N.Y. ctsp on obverse of U.S. Half cent of 1853. Rv: E. E. BULKLEY ctsp on coin's reverse. (Tanenbaum collection; Brunk 5740)

In the obverse stamp, the striker did not allow room for the upper punch to fit completely, so that the first 'E.' does not show. He rectified this on reverse, but did not utilize the separate 'N.Y.' stamp there. It appeared in the Jess Peters ANA sale of 1980.

The issuer has not been determined. There are two possible issuers who appear in the 1844, 1848 and 1849 city directories:

Edwin Bulkley, Paper, 240 Pearl St. 1844-45; 110 John St. 1847-49.

Erastus Bulkley, Furniture, 56 Beekman St. 1844-49.

There was an E. Bulkley in the 7th Ward in the 1850 census, but no connection has been made.

ELEANOR RUGG BYRNE

Miller	Date	Metal	Size	F	VF	EF	Unc
NY 141	1859	Copper	31mm	—	30.00	40.00	60.00
		Portrait bust of Byrne right, hair tied in a bun at back. ELEANOR RUGG BYRNE around. Rv: (seven stars) / BYRNEORE / (star) / GOLD / 1859 / (five stars). Plain edge. (Wright 130) (only 72 pieces struck)					
NY 141A	1859	Copper	31mm	—	40.00	60.00	100.
		As 141, but Reeded edge. (only 3 pieces struck)					
NY 142	1859	Brass	31mm	—	30.00	40.00	60.00
		As 141. Reeded edge.					
NY 143	1859	Tin (White Metal)	31mm	—	30.00	40.00	60.00
		As 141.					
NY 143A	1859	Gold	31mm	—	1000.	—	—
		As 141. (The only known specimen was Lot 2039 in Stack's 1955 Clifford Smith sale)					

The 1859 tokens were struck to commemorate the invention of a composition metal by Byrne, used in the manufacture of jewelry.

One or both the dies of these pieces broke during striking, accounting for their scarcity. A Bangs, Merwin & Co. auction of Sept. 12-14, 1860, referred to the series as medalets. The obverse is well executed, the reverse less so.

CARDEN & CO.

Rulau	Date	Metal	Size	VG	F	VF	EF
NY 2515	(1850's)	Silver	33mm	—	—	100.	—

CARDEN & CO. / 293 B'WAY ctsp on England 1817 half crown. (B&M Taylor sale, March 1987, lot 1268; Brunk 6761)

CARRINGTON & CO.

Miller	Date	Metal	Size	F	VF	EF	Unc
NY 144	(1850's)	Silver	32mm	—	—	150.	250.
		Man on horseback at center. Above: THE HAVANA EXPRESS / THE FIRST EXPRESSMAN. Below: CARRINGTON & CO. / 78 / BROADWAY. Rv: * GENERAL PURCHASING AGENCY, * / CARRINGTON / & CO / NEW YORK. / PURCHASE GOODS / TO ORDER IN / LARGE OR SMALL / QUANTITIES / ESTABLISHED, 1851.					
NY 145	(1850's)	Copper	32mm	5.00	10.00	15.00	40.00
		As 144. Reeded edge. (Wright 142)					
NY 146	(1850's)	Brass	32mm	—	10.00	15.00	40.00
		As 144.					
NY 147	(1850's)	White Metal	32mm	5.00	10.00	15.00	40.00
		As 144.					
NY 147A	(1850's)	Silvered WM	32mm	—	—	—	40.00
		As 144.					

D. CHANDLER

Rulau	Date	Metal	Size	VG	F	VF	EF
NY 2042	(1847-48)	Copper	26mm	—	75.00	—	125.

D. CHANDLER / NEW-YORK ctsp on obverse of U.S. 1819 Large cent. Similar ctsp on reverse of coin. Similar ctsp on edge of coin, which has been hammered flat and overall size of coin reduced to 26mm from 29mm. (Tanenbaum coll.; Brunk 7290)

This counterstamped coin used as an advertising check must be accorded honors for inventiveness on the part of its producer!

David Chandler, carpenter, 246 5th Ave.

CHANEY

Rulau	Date	Metal	Size	VG	F	VF	EF
NY 2190	(?)	Silver	21mm	—	—	150.	—

CHANEY DIE CUTTER N.Y. ctsp on Spanish-American 1-real. (Brunk 7305)

CHESEBROUGH STEARNS & CO.

Miller	Date	Metal	Size	F	VF	EF	Unc
NY 150	(1850's)	Copper	27.6mm	7.50	11.00	15.00	40.00
		Eagle with drooping wings, U.S. shield on its breast. IMPORTERS & JOBBERS OF / SILK GOODS around. Rv: .CHESEBROUGH STEARNS & CO. / (ornament) / (ornament) 37 (ornament) / NASSAU / (ornament) ST (ornament) / (ornament) / NEW-YORK. Reeded edge.					
NY 150A	(1850's)	Copper	27.6mm	—	—	—	—
		As last. Plain edge.					
NY 151	(1850's)	Brass	27.6mm	5.00	11.00	15.00	40.00
		As 150. Reeded edge. (Wright 165)					
NY 152	(1850's)	Silvered Brass	27.6mm	5.00	8.00	15.00	40.00
		As 150. Reeded edge.					
NY 152A	(1850's)	Silvered Brass	27.6mm	—	—	—	—
		As last. Plain edge.					
NY 153	(1850's)	Copper	27.6mm	5.00	11.00	16.00	40.00
		As 150, but no ornaments or dashes on reverse. Reeded edge.					
NY 154	(1850's)	Brass	27.6mm	5.00	11.00	16.00	40.00
		As 153. Reeded edge.					

Miller	Date	Metal	Size	F	VF	EF	Unc
NY 155	(1850's)	Copper	27.6mm	5.00	11.00	16.00	40.00
		As 150, with ornaments and dashes. DR SELLECK has been added above the eagle. Reeded edge. (Wright 973)					
NY 155A	(1850's)	Copper	27.6mm	—	—	—	—
		As last. Plain edge.					
NY 156	(1850's)	Brass	27.6mm	5.00	8.00	15.00	40.00
		As 155. Reeded edge.					
NY 156A	(1850's)	Silvered Brass	27.6mm	5.00	8.00	15.00	40.00
		As 155. Reeded edge.					
NY 156B	(1850's)	Silvered Brass	27.6mm	—	—	—	—
		As 156A, but thin planchet. Plain edge.					
NY 157	(1850's)	Brass	27.6mm	5.00	8.00	15.00	40.00
		As 150, but spelling NASSAW instead of NASSAU. Reeded edge.					
NY 158	(1850's)	Brass	27.6mm	5.00	8.00	15.00	40.00
		As 157, but ornaments are larger. Reeded edge.					

NOTE: NY 150-154 could have been issued as early as 1847. The firm appears in the 1848 and 1849 directories at 37 Nassau St. In 1844-45 Ellsworth Chesebrough, merchant, was at 122 Pearl.

The partners were Ellsworth Chesebrough and Thomas G. Stearns.

T.L. CLARK

Miller	Date	Metal	Size	VG	F	VF	Unc
NY 159	(?)	Brass	22mm	—	70.00	150.	250.

T.L. CLARK, 247 GRAND ST., MANUFACTURERS BRASS CHECKS, CARDS, & C. (Betts sale number 48)

Thomas L. Clark of New York, a maker of brass checks, cut his own cards and those of R.F. Thomas, according to the contemporary writings of Bushnell.

Clark also cut the dies for Gosling, Upsons Capital, Swift & Fargo, Museum Hotel, Smithsonian House, A.D. Thompson, Moss' Hotel and similarly-designed pieces. Clark thus is responsible for the famous mulings (Smithsonian-Thompson, Moss-Thompson, etc.)

COLUMBIA GARDEN

Miller	Date	Metal	Size	VG	F	VF	Unc
NY 164	(?)	Lead	12mm	—	—	—	Rare

Star. Rv: Eagle.

COOPER'S COFFEE ROOM

Rulau	Date	Metal	Size	VG	F	VF	EF
NY 2044	(1856)	Silver	21mm	250.	—	400.	—
		COOPER'S / COFFEE ROOM / 103 NASSAU ST ctsp on Spanish-American 1808 Carlos III silver 1-real. (Tanenbaum collection and another, Van Ormer sale 2600; Brunk 9480)					
NY 2044A	(1856)	Silver	21mm	250.	—	400.	—
		Similar ctsp on Spanish-American 1803-Mo or 1808 1-real.					

(See T.H.M. under Mavericks for related item). James G. Cooper sold coffee and soda in 1856.

NY 2044B	(1856)	Silver	27mm	250.	—	400.	—
		Similar ctsp on Spanish-American 1803 2-reales.					

J. COOKE

Rulau	Date	Metal	Size	VG	F	VF	Unc
NY 2517	(?)	WM	28mm	—	—	125.	—
		J. COOKE / 331 BWAY ctsp in small letters on blank white metal planchet of uncertain alloy. Rv: Large fancy 1 / 3. Plain edge. (Paul Bosco April 1989 sale, lot 148)					

This previously unreported token seems to be another of the class of pre-Civil War hotel and dining room pieces denominated in English money. 1 / 3 = One shilling three-pence.

J. & I. COX

Rulau	Date	Metal	Size	G	VG	F	EF
NY 2046	(1844-48)	Copper	29mm	—	100.	—	150.
		J. & I. COX / NEW YORK in two stamps ctsp on U.S. Large cent. (Brunk 9825)					

John and James Cox were silversmiths about 1817-1853. The mark is their hallmark.

The same firm, J. & I. Cox, sold furnishings at 15 Maiden Lane in 1847-1849. In 1844-45 the furnishings and imported silverware store had been at both 15 Maiden Lane and 349 Broadway.

John Cox, jeweler, was located at 256 Bowery 1847-48.

CULVERS PATENT

NY 2580	(?)	Silver	18mm	—	—	300.	—
		CULVERS / PATENT ctsp on U.S. 1853 Arrows & Rays S.L. dime (Brunk 10250; Rulau Z4G)					

Culver & Co.'s patent hot air furnace, 52 Cliff St., New York.

JOHN K. CURTIS

Miller	Date	Metal	Size	F	VF	EF	Unc
NY 179	1859	Silver	31mm	—	—	100.	225.
		Old man in Colonial garb seated at a table, examining a coin with a magnifying glass. Around: A REAL ANTIQUE, BUT ALAS! IT IS INDECYPHERABLE. Below: THE ANTIQUARY / 1859. Rv: AUTOGRAPHS, PORTRAITS, CURIOSITIES & ANTIQUES / *** / JOHN K. CURTIS, / JEWELER / AND / NUMISMATIST, / 83 / BLEECKER ST. / N.Y. Reeded edge.					
NY 180	1859	Copper	31mm	10.00	15.00	20.00	40.00
		As 179. Reeded edge. (Wright 218)					
NY 181	1859	Brass	31mm	10.00	15.00	20.00	40.00
		As 179. Reeded edge.					
NY 182	1859	White Metal	31mm	10.00	15.00	20.00	40.00
		As 179. Reeded edge.					

NY 175	1860	Silver	31mm	—	—	100.	225.
		Bust right, JOHANNES ALLAN. ANTIQUARIUS SCOTUS. above, NATUS FEB. 26, 1777. below. In tiny letters under truncation of bust is: G.H.L. Rv: Braided circle at center, Within circle: ***** / JOHN K. CURTIS / WATCH-MAKER / & MANUFACTURING / JEWELER / 83 / BLEECKER ST. & / 882 BROADWAY / NEW YORK. / 1860. Reeded edge.					
NY 176	1860	Copper	31mm	10.00	15.00	20.00	40.00
		As 175. Reeded edge.					
NY 177	1860	Brass	31mm	10.00	15.00	20.00	40.00
		As 175. Reeded edge.					
NY 178	1860	White Metal	31mm	10.00	15.00	20.00	45.00
		As 175. Reeded edge.					

NY 183	1859 (1860)	Silver	31mm	—	—	80.00	125.
		Obverse as obverse of NY 175 (Johannes Allan). Rv: As obverse of NY 179 (The Antiquary). Reeded edge.					
NY 184	1859 (1860)	Copper	31mm	10.00	15.00	20.00	40.00
		As 183. Reeded edge.					
NY 185	1859 (1860)	Brass	31mm	10.00	15.00	20.00	40.00
		As 183. Reeded edge.					
NY 186	1859 (1860)	White Metal	31mm	10.00	15.00	20.00	40.00
		As 183. Reeded edge.					

NY 187	1859 (1861)	White Metal	31mm	—	10.00	15.00	30.00
		Obverse as obverse of NY 179 (The Antiquary). Rv: Six-masted sidewheeler moving left in crowded harbor; crowd on pier at lower right waving to ship. This is the *Great Eastern*, which entered New York harbor in 1860. Reeded edge.					
NY 188	1859 (1861)	Brass	31mm	—	10.00	15.00	30.00
		As 187. Reeded edge.					
NY 189	1859 (1861)	Copper	31mm	—	10.00	15.00	30.00
		As 187. Reeded edge.					

NY 171	1861	Silver	32mm	—	—	—	250.
		Military bust of Washington left. Around: GEORGE WASHINGTON, THE CINCINNATUS OF AMERICA. Below: B. 1732 D. 1799. Rv: Similar to reverse of NY 175, but three stars replace '1860' inside the circle. Outside the circle has been added: "SAVE MY COUNTRY HEAVEN" / 1861. Reeded edge. (Baker 529)					

NY 172	1861	Copper	32mm	—	15.00	25.00	45.00
		As 171. Reeded edge. (Baker 529)					
NY 173	1861	Brass	32mm	—	15.00	25.00	45.00
		As 171. Reeded edge.					
NY 174	1861	White Metal	32mm	—	15.00	25.00	45.00
		As 171. Reeded edge.					

All the John K. Curtis store cards were cut by George Hampden Lovett of New York, whose initials appear under the Johannes Allan bust on several pieces. We believe NY 179-182 (The Antiquary) was Curtis' first token, followed by NY 175-178 (Johannes Allan), and then followed by the Allan-Antiquary and Antiquary-Great Eastern mulings. Last to be issued were the NY 171-174 George Washington pieces, we believe.

The mulings could have been issued later than 1861 by Lovett, but there is no evidence of this.

Efforts to establish why Curtis used the Johannes Allan motif at the time of issue have proved fruitless, although a search of the numismatic literature of the 1860's was made. The piece is of excellent workmanship. John Allan was a New York City antiquary who had immigrated from Scotland. Allan died in 1863.

The ship *Great Eastern* was a steamship equipped with sails and screw paddle. It had a length of 692 feet, a breadth of 83 feet and a depth of 58 feet. Rated at 25,000 tons burden, with four decks and 6,500 square yards of canvas. Its draught was twenty feet of water, thirty feet when loaded. Engines were of 300 horsepower. It was said to accommodate 10,000 troops.

Other tokens of this ship may be found under *GREAT EASTERN*, New York, N.Y.

DAWSON WARREN & HYDE'S

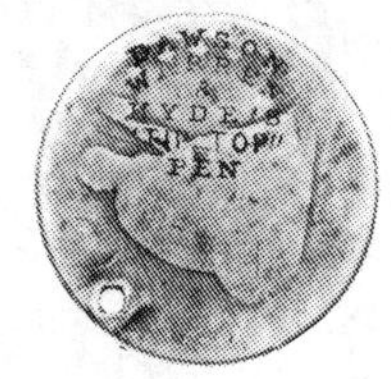
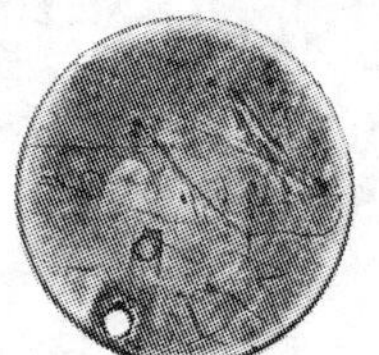

Rulau	Date	Metal	Size	VG	F	VF	EF
NY 2045	(1854-62)	Silver	25mm	150.	—	250.	—
		DAWSON / WARREN / & / HYDE'S / "TIP-TOP" / PEN ctsp on worn U.S. Seated Liberty quarter. (Tanenbaum coll.; Brunk 11080)					
NY 2045A	(1854-62)	Silver	18mm	150.	—	250.	—
		Similar ctsp on U.S. 1853 dime.					

The 1859 city directory listed DW&H as a Gold Pen business at 4 Maiden Lane. The 1860 directory lists the business as "jewelry."

DIETZ & CO.

Rulau	Date	Metal	Size	VG	F	VF	EF
NY2046A	(1859-62)	Copper	29mm	—	—	250.	—
		DIETZ & CO / PATENT / APPLIED / FOR / MANUFACTURERS ctsp on U.S. 1826 Large cent. (Tanenbaum coll.; Brunk 11635)					

Dietz and Co. (James M. and Michael A. Dietz) appear from 1859 through the Civil War at 132 William St. as manufacturers, importers and dealers in all articles pertaining to the lamp trade. The New York office was a branch of the London, England main office, opened in 1840.

J. SMITH DODGE

Miller	Date	Metal	Size	F	VF	EF	Unc
NY 209	(1850's)	Brass	26mm	50.00	100.	150.	200.
		Eagle displayed, shield on breast. TEETH THREE DOLLARS EACH / PLATE EXTRA. Rv: J. SMITH DODGE / DENTIST / 407 FOURTH ST., / NEW YORK. (Wright 256)					

Earlier, 1848-49, dentist Dodge was located at 13 Bond Street. In 1844-45 he had been at 47 Bond Street, where he advertised himself "late Dodge and Parmele."

DOREMUS & NIXON

Miller	Date	Metal	Size	F	VF	EF	Unc
NY 222	(1844-49)	Copper	28mm	5.00	8.00	12.00	60.00
		IMPORTERS & JOBBERS OF DRY GOODS / DOREMUS / & / NIXON / 39 / NASSAU ST / COR / LIBERTY / OPP THE P.O. Rv: DRY GOODS FOR. / * / HOTELS / STEAM BOATS / & SHIPS. Plain edge.					
NY 223	(1844-49)	Brass	28mm	5.00	8.00	12.00	60.00
		As 222. Plain edge.					

NY 224	(1850-53)	Copper	28mm	6.00	9.00	15.00	50.00
		Three-masted sailing ship right, . DOREMUS & NIXON. / 21 PARK PLACE N-YORK. Rv: Three-masted steamboat right, . DRY GOODS & UPHOLSTERY . / FOR SHIPS & STEAMERS.					
NY 224B	(1850-53)	Brass	28mm	5.00	8.00	12.00	40.00
		As 224. Reeded edge. (Wright 262)					
NY 224C	(1850-53)	Brass	28mm	5.00	8.00	12.00	40.00
		As last. Plain edge.					
NY 224D	(1850-53)	S/Brass	28mm	5.00	8.00	12.00	40.00
		As last. Plain edge.					
NY 224A	1860	Copper	28mm	50.00	100.	150.	250.
		Obverse as reverse of 224. Rv: Abraham Lincoln. (King 583)					
NY 225	1860	Brass	28mm	50.00	100.	150.	250.
		As 224A. (King 583)					
NY 226	1860	Silvered Brass	28mm	50.00	100.	150.	250.
		As 224A.					
NY 226B	1860	White Metal	28mm	50.00	100.	150.	250.
		As 224A.					
NY 227	1853 (1860)	Copper	28mm	—	—	75.00	100.
		Obverse as reverse of NY 224. Rv: Building, NEW YORK CRYSTAL PALACE / 1853 / (nine stars). (This is the reverse of H.B. West, NY 948)					
NY 228	1861	Brass	28mm	—	—	75.00	100.
		Obverse as reverse of NY 224. Rv: Eagle, UNITED STATES / WAR OF 1861. (This is the obverse of a Civil War dog tag)					
NY 229	(1861)	Copper	--mm	—	—	75.00	100.
		Obverse as reverse of NY 224. Rv: WAR OF 1812.					

NY 224A-229 are mulings which do not bear the token issuer's name. The three-masted steamer die is unique to Doremus & Nixon, however. All these tokens were struck at Scovill Mfg. Co., Waterbury, Conn.

Doremus, Suydam & Nixon (later Doremus & Nixon), and an apparent predecessor firm, Suydam & Boyd, issued tokens over many years — from the early 1820's to the late 1850's or later. Thus their token issues span the Early, Hard Times and Merchant periods.

DS&N and D&N's known addresses were:

1820's-1833	209 PEARL ST.
1835-36	50 & 52 WILLIAM ST.
1836-37	37 & 39 NASSAU ST.
1844-46	39 NASSAU ST.
1850's	21 PARK PLACE

PHILIP A. DOUGHERTY

Miller	Date	Metal	Size	VG	F	VF	Unc
NY 210	1859	Cop. over Lead	19mm	10.00	15.00	30.00	85.00
		Imitation of Indian head cent. Indian head left at center, PHILIP A. DOUGHERTY above, 1859 below. Rv: GOOD / FOR / 6 / CTS. within wreath. Plain edge.					

Philip A. Dougherty's establishment was at the southwest corner of South and Maiden Lane. His token has always been elusive, and was called Rare as long ago as 1885.

It is believed that Samuel H. Black prepared this token.

DRUIDICAL EXHIBITION

Miller	Date	Metal	Size	VG	F	VF	Unc
NY 230	(?)	Brass	29mm	5.00	10.00	15.00	50.00
		Eagle, UNITED STATES OF AMERICA. Rv: ADMIT THE BARER (sic) / TO THE / DRUIDICAL / * EXHIBITION *. Plain edge. (Wright 7)					
NY 230A	(?)	Brass	29mm	—	—	—	60.00
		As last. Reeded edge.					

Miller	Date	Metal	Size	VG	F	VF	Unc
NY 230C	(?)	Brass	29mm	5.00	10.00	15.00	50.00
		Similar, but reverse spelling corrected to BEARER in top line. Plain edge. (Krause coll.)					

A secret Druidical order was founded in London, England in 1781. A New York City lodge of this order may have been responsible for these tokens, researcher Robert J. Lindesmith opines.

Druidism was the religious faith of the Celts of Gaul and the British Isles, flourishing from the 2nd century B.C. to the 2nd century A.D., surviving in some parts of the British Isles outside Roman rule until Christianity supplanted it in the 4th and 5th centuries A.D. There was an Archdruid as supreme authority, and the Druids functioned as priests, teachers, judges and civil administrators.

There were three classes of Druids — prophets, bards and priests. Prophetesses and sorceresses assisted the male Druids. Druids were versed in astrology, magic and the mysterious powers of plants and animals. They held the oak and the mistletoe in reverence, and used stone monuments called domens as altars and temples. The religion disappeared with the advent of Christianity, surviving only in myth and lore.

EBLING'S COLUMBIAN GARDEN

Miller	Date	Metal	Size	VG	F	VF	EF
NY 165	(?)	Silver	27mm	—	175.	—	250.
		EBLING'S / COLUMBIAN / GARDEN in three lines ctsp on Spanish-American 2-reales. Dates examined: 1789-Mo, 1793, 1800. Only 3 known. (Gould 93; Brunk 13010)					

Miller	Date	Metal	Size	VG	F	VF	EF
NY 165A	(?)	Silver	27mm	—	165.	—	250.
		EBLING'S / COLUMBIAN / GARDEN / 200 / BOWERY in six lines ctsp on Spanish-American 2-reales. Dates examined: 1734, 1754, 1775, 1784, 1789, 1793-Mo, 1798, 1800, dates worn off. There are 10 specimens known. (Duffield 1357; Van Ormer sale 2632, 2633; Brunk 13020)					

Joseph E. Ebling is listed as a confectioner at 200 and 200-1/2 Bowery in 1848-1850's. In 1839 his address was 73 Houston St.

David Schenkman once possessed a variety of the second type above, with three additional punches on each side: V (walking figure) D.

EVENING NEWS

Miller	Date	Metal	Size	VG	F	VF	Unc
NY 232	(?)	Lead	23mm	25.00	40.00	75.00	—
		EVENING * NEWS, numeral 20. Rv: Wreath encloses numeral 20. Plain edge. Very rare.					

FARMERS' AND MECHANICS' LIFE INSURANCE CO.

Miller	Date	Metal	Size	F	VF	EF	Unc
NY 234	1860	Silver	32mm	—	—	75.00	150.
		Bust facing left, FARMERS' AND MECHANICS' LIFE INSURANCE CO. / NEW YORK / 1860. Rv: ONE HUNDRED THOUSAND DOLLARS DEPOSITED / * / WITH THE / ** / NEW YORK STATE INSURANCE DEPARTMENT / -.- / 'I AM INSURED'. (Wright 305)					
NY 235	1860	Brass	32mm	—	—	25.00	60.00
		As 234.					
NY 236	1860	Copper	32mm	—	—	25.00	60.00
		As 234.					
NY 237	1860	White Metal	32mm	—	15.00	25.00	60.00
		As 234.					

FINCK'S HOTEL

Miller	Date	Metal	Size	VG	F	VF	Unc
NY A251	(?)	Silver	20mm	—	—	—	Unique
		As next. Only 1 piece struck.					
NY 251	(1850's)	Brass	20mm	—	15.00	35.00	50.00
		FINCK'S / * 6 (on tablet) * / HOTEL. Rv: Blank. Plain edge.					
NY 252	(1850's)	Brass	20mm	—	15.00	35.00	50.00
		As 251, but 9 on tablet. Plain edge.					
NY 253	(1850's)	Copper	20mm	—	15.00	35.00	75.00
		As 252.					
NY 254	(1850's)	Brass	20mm	—	15.00	35.00	50.00
		As 251, but 12. Plain edge. (Wright 321)					
NY 255	(1850's)	Brass	20mm	—	15.00	35.00	50.00
		As 251, but 15.					
NY 256	(1850's)	Silver	20mm	—	—	60.00	200.
		As 255.					
NY 257	(1850's)	Brass	20mm	—	15.00	35.00	50.00
		As 251, but 18.					
NY 258	(1850's)	Brass	20mm	—	15.00	35.00	50.00
		As 251, but 21.					
NY 258A	(1850's)	Silver	24mm	—	—	—	250.
		As 258.					
NY 259	(1850's)	Brass	20mm	—	15.00	35.00	50.00
		As 251, but 24.					
NY 259B	(1850's)	Silver	20mm	—	—	—	250.
		As 259. (24)					
NY 259A	(1850's)	Brass	20mm	—	15.00	35.00	50.00
		As 251, but 27.					
NY 260	(1850's)	Silver	20mm	—	—	60.00	200.
		As 259A.					
NY 261	(1850's)	Brass	20mm	—	15.00	35.00	50.00
		As 251, but 30.					
NY 262	(1850's)	Copper	20mm	—	15.00	35.00	75.00
		As 261.					

Finck's Hotel was located on West Street near Fulton and was favorably known among market men in the 1850's.

John F. and Henry Finck, liquors, were listed at 86 Vesey Street 1847-48.

FITZGIBBON DAGUERREOTYPE GALLERY

Miller	Date	Metal	Size	F	VF	EF	Unc
NY 263	1853	Brass	28mm	30.00	40.00	50.00	75.00
		Spread eagle with arrows, * FITZGIBBON DAGUERREOTYPE GALLERY. Rv: Crystal Palace, NEW YORK CRYSTAL PALACE / 1853.					
NY 264	1853	Copper	28mm	30.00	40.00	50.00	75.00
		As 263.					

It may well be that these are merely mulings and should be listed under Fitzgibbon in St. Louis, Mo. However, they show up frequently in circulated grades and may have been passed out at the Fitzgibbon booth at the Crystal Palace exhibition.

FRENCH'S HOTEL

Miller	Date	Metal	Size	VG	F	VF	Unc
NY 275	(1845-49)	German Silver	32mm	75.00	100.	150.	—
		FRENCH'S / * 37 * / HOTEL. Rv: Blank. (Wright 346)					

Richard French kept his hotel at City Hall Square, corner Frankfort. He appears in the 1849 directory.

In the 1845 directory he had two hotels, at 94 Chatham and 4 Catharine Slip. In the 1848 directory only the 94 Chatham Street hotel is listed.

E.P. FURLONG

Miller	Date	Metal	Size	VG	F	VF	Unc
NY 276	(?)	Brass	24mm	3.00	5.00	10.00	35.00
		St. Patrick banishing the snakes from Ireland, SAINT / PATRICK. Rv: SAINT — PATRICK'S — * SALVE * — PRICE / 25 CENTS / E.P. FURLONG / 92 / FULTON ST. N.Y. (Wright 353; Storer 7807)					
NY 276A	(?)	White Metal	24mm	—	—	—	75.00
		As 276. Plain edge.					

W.G.
(William Gale)

Enlarged

Rulau	Date	Metal	Size	VG	F	VF	EF
NY 2048	(1844-50)	Copper	29mm	40.00	—	60.00	—
		W.G. in relief within rectangular depression ctsp on U.S. 1801 or 1819 Large cent. (Hallenbeck 23.006; Brunk 41335)					
NY 2048A	(?)	Silver	18.5mm	—	—	75.00	—
		Similar ctsp on U.S. 1835 Bust dime. (Krueger 3557)					
NY 2048E	(1857)	Copper	29mm	—	—	90.00	—
		WM. GALE & SON ctsp on U.S. 1856 Large cent. (Brunk 15565)					

William Gale (born 1799) was a silversmith involved in several partnerships 1823-62. In 1850 he admitted his son, William Gale Jr., born 1825, and William Gale & Son lasted 1850-70.

Gale's silverware outlet was located at 116 Fulton circa 1844-49.

GIROUD, INVENTOR

Miller	Date	Metal	Size	VG	F	VF	Unc
NY 279	(?)	German Silver	18mm	—	—	75.00	—
		GIROUD INVENTOR. PATENT MECHANICAL LAMPS. Rv: Blank.					

W. C. E. GOBELL

Rulau	Date	Metal	Size	VG	F	VF	EF
NY 2521	(?)	Copper	29mm	—	—	70.00	—
		W.C.E. GOBELL (curved) / N.Y. ctsp on U.S. 1851 Large cent. (Rulau coll., ex-Gary Meyer; Brunk 16360)					

It is believed this piece was issued before the Civil War.

GOSLING'S RESTAURANT

Miller	Date	Metal	Size	VG	F	VF	Unc
NY 286	(1847-48)	Brass	28mm	20.00	30.00	50.00	80.00
		GOSLING'S / RESTAURANT. Rv: 306 / BROADWAY. (Wright 390)					

Leonard Gosling, restaurant, 64 Nassau Street, is listed 1847-48.

D.H. GOULD

Miller	Date	Metal	Size	F	VF	EF	Unc
NY 287	(1848-51)	Brass	28mm	5.00	10.00	12.00	45.00
		Imitation of U.S. $10 gold piece, D.H. GOULD on coronet. BOARDING & LODGING above, *** NO 10 **** below. Rv: GOULD'S SALOON above eagle, 10 FULTON ST N.Y. below. (Wright 393)					
NY 287A	(1848-51)	Silvered Brass	28mm	5.00	8.00	12.00	45.00
		As 287.					

David H. Gould appears in the 1845, 1848 and 1849 directories as the proprietor of a "refectory" at 10 Fulton Street. Thus NY 287-287A could have been issued as early as 1848, when the token type was introduced by Scovill Mfg. Co. in Waterbury, Mass.

GREAT EASTERN

Rulau	Date	Metal	Size	F	VF	EF	Unc
NY 2050	1859	White Metal	31mm	—	15.00	20.00	40.00
		Ship at center, to right, GREAT EASTERN above, 1859 below. Rv: DESIGNED BY I.K. BRUNEL / LENGTH 692 FEET / DEPTH / 58 FEET. / TONNAGE / 23.000 / BREADTH 83 FEET. / BUILT BY SCOTT RUSSELL. (Tiny MERRIAM above word SCOTT. Plain edge. (Schenkman C15)					

Rulau	Date	Metal	Size	F	VF	EF	Unc
NY 2051	1859	Copper	31mm	—	15.00	20.00	45.00
		Obverse as last. Rv: DESIGNED BY I.K. BRUNEL / LENGTH 692 FEET / BREADTH / 83 FEET / DEPTH / 58 FEET / 23.000 TONS / BUILT BY SCOTT RUSSELL. Plain edge. (Schenkman C16)					
NY 2052	1859	WM	31mm	—	15.00	20.00	40.00
		As last. Plain edge. (Schenkman C16)					

Dies for three above cut by Joseph H. Merriam of Boston, Mass.

Rulau	Date	Metal	Size	F	VF	EF	Unc
NY 2054	1860	WM	32mm	—	15.00	20.00	40.00
		Six-masted sidewheeler steamship '*Great Eastern*' entering New York harbor as crowd on pier waves and smaller ships scurry about. Rv: PURCHASED ON BOARD THE GREAT EASTERN / TONNAGE / 24,000 / HORSE POWER / 2,600 / LENGTH 692 FT. / BREADTH / 83 FT. / DEPTH 60 FT. / 1860. Reeded edge. (Obverse is the reverse of NY 187, a John K. Curtis muling by George H. Lovett)					

NY 2054A 1860 Copper 31mm — — 20.00 40.00

As 2054. Reeded edge.

NY 2054B 1860 Brass 31mm — — 20.00 40.00

As 2054. Reeded edge.

NY 2053 1860 WM 31mm — — 20.00 40.00

Obverse as 2054 (Lovett's arrival scene). Rv: Within palm wreath: THE STEAMSHIP / GREAT EASTERN / ARRIVED / AT / NEW YORK / JUNE 28. 1860 / FIRST TRIP / FROM / ENGLAND TO AMERICA. Reeded edge.

NY 2053A 1860 Copper 31mm — 15.00 20.00 40.00

As 2053. Reeded edge.

NY 2053B 1860 Brass 31mm — 15.00 20.00 40.00

As 2053. Reeded edge.

NY 2055 (1860) WM 42mm — 15.00 20.00 35.00

'*Great Eastern.*' Inscription: THE GREAT EASTERN STEAMSHIP / SCREW PADDLE & SAIL / LENGTH 692 FEET / BREADTH 83 FEET / DEPTH 58 FEET. Rv: 25000 TONS BURTHEN / 4 DECKS / SPREADS 6500 SQ. YDS. / OF CANVAS / DRAUGHT OF WATER / 20 FEET & / WHEN LADEN 30 FT / 3000 HORSE POWER / WILL ACCOMMODATE 10,000 TROOPS. (Wright 1113)

NY 2053-2054 were cut by George Hampden Lovett of New York.

There were also tokens issued for the *Great Eastern* by Labayen y Hermano, ship chandlers of Matanzas, Cuba in 1858 (Fonrobert 7744), and for a visit to the *Great Eastern* in Dublin, Ireland in 1886. Both pieces are rare; both are in white metal, the first 32.3mm and the latter 32.8mm. There are also several British medals for the ship. (See William Christensen's *"The Medals of the Great Iron Ship"* (1983).

GREEN & BROAD

	Date	Metal	Size	VG	F	VF	EF
NY 2198	(1841-45)	Copper	29mm	—	—	125.	—

GREEN & BROAD / NEW YORK ctsp on U.S 1839 Large cent. (Koppenhaver Aug. 1982 sale; Brunk 17020)

Abraham H. Green and John H. Broad were locksmiths at Avenue C corner Third in 1842, then at Fourth corner C in 1844-45. Broad alone was a locksmith at 531 Fourth in 1846.

HASTINGS HOTEL

New York, N.Y. ?

NY 2200 (1840's) Brass 27mm — — — —

Eagle with arrows and palm branch in its talons, head turned left, surrounded by border of 16 stars. Rv: G.S. TWIGG / 3 D = / .HASTINGS HOTEL. Plain edge.

NY 2201 (1840's) Brass 29mm — — — —

As last, but eagle and stars are redrawn and sharper in execution. Rv: L.J. DURKEE / 3 D . / .HASTINGS HOTEL. Plain edge.

Both pieces above are in the American Numismatic Society collection under American tokens, so we tentatively assign them to New York City. The eagle is certainly American in style, yet we harbor a doubt that these are, actually, U.S. tokens. So far as we know, neither has ever before been published. Note the odd number (16) of stars.

HAVENS, HATTER

Miller	Date	Metal	Size	F	VF	EF	Unc
NY 302	(?)	White Metal	25.5mm	5.00	8.00	12.00	40.00

HAVENS HATTER / 202 / BROADWAY / N.Y. / ONE PRICE / AND / NO DEVIATION / COPYRIGHT / SECURED. Rv: A HAT BOUGHT / FOR / 10 CTS LESS / THAN THE REGULAR / PRICE MARKED BY / PRESENTING / THIS ONE CHECK. (Wright 438)

R. HEASLEY & CO.

Rulau	Date	Metal	Size	VG	F	VF	EF
NY 2202	(1847)	Copper	29mm	75.00	—	125.	—

R. HEASLEY & CO. (curved) / NEW YORK ctsp on U.S. 1843 Large cent. 2 pieces known. (Tanenbaum coll.; Brunk 18990)

Robert Heasley first appears in the directories in 1842 as a locksmith at 81 Perry. By 1844-45 he has a partner; the directory lists Heasley & Kedey, locksmiths, 267 Beeker. Simultaneously, Heasley is also listed as a sexton and undertaker.

The 1847 directory entry is the only one matching the token: R. Heasley & Co., lockmakers, 81 Perry. From 1848 to the onset of the Civil War, Heasley was in business alone, at various addresses. (Tanenbaum research)

A. J. HENNING

Rulau	Date	Metal	Size	VG	F	VF	Unc
NY 2525	(1860's)	Copper	25mm	10.00	15.00	35.00	75.00

A. J. HENNING DIE SINKER / & / * ENGRAVER *. Rv: Within open wreath: 37 / FULTON ST / N.Y. Plain edge. (Michael B. Zeddies coll.)

In 1859 Henning cut the dies for the 69mm bronze medal honoring Washington Irving (1783-1859), the novelist, according to Leonard Forrer in his *Biographical Dictionary of Medalists.*

This token is considered a Civil War token.

E. HILL

NOTE: All tokens NY 305 through NY 340 contain reeded edges!

Miller	Date	Metal	Size	F	VF	EF	Unc
NY 305	1860	Silver	29mm	—	—	150.	250.

Washington bust facing left, in an arched frame of a single line; small KEY beneath the bust. Around: PATRIAE PATER 1732. Rv: E. HILL, / DEALER IN / COINS, MEDALS, / MINERALS, / AUTOGRAPHS / ENGRAVINGS, / OLD CURIOSITIES &C / NO. 6 / BLEECKER ST. N. YORK / 1860. (Baker 542)

Miller	Date	Metal	Size	F	VF	EF	Unc
NY 306	1860	Brass	29mm	5.00	10.00	15.00	40.00

As NY 305.

Miller	Date	Metal	Size	F	VF	EF	Unc
NY 307	1860	Copper	29mm	5.00	10.00	15.00	40.00
		As 305. (Baker 542)					
NY 308	1860	White Metal	29mm	5.00	10.00	15.00	40.00
		As 305. (Baker 542)					

Miller	Date	Metal	Size	F	VF	EF	Unc
NY 309	1860	Silver	29mm	—	—	150.	225.
		Bust of Webster in toga right, DANIEL WEBSTER around. Rv: As NY 305.					
NY 310	1860	Brass	29mm	5.00	10.00	15.00	40.00
		As 309.					
NY 311	1860	Copper	29mm	5.00	10.00	15.00	40.00
		As 309.					
NY 312	1860	White Metal	29mm	5.00	10.00	15.00	42.50
		As 309. (Wright 454)					
NY 313	1860	Silver	29mm	—	—	150.	225.
		Bust of Edwin Forrest. Rv: As NY 305.					
NY 314	1860	Brass	29mm	5.00	10.00	15.00	40.00
		As 313.					
NY 315	1860	Copper	29mm	5.00	10.00	15.00	40.00
		As 313.					
NY 316	1860	White Metal	29mm	5.00	10.00	15.00	40.00
		As 313.					

Miller	Date	Metal	Size	F	VF	EF	Unc
NY 317	1860	Silver	29mm	—	—	150.	225.
		Jolly man's bust facing, holding cigar and exhaling smoke. NO PLEASURE CAN EXCEED above, THE SMOKING OF THE WEED below. Rv: As NY 305.					
NY 318	1860	Brass	29mm	5.00	10.00	15.00	40.00
		As 317.					
NY 319	1860	Copper	29mm	5.00	10.00	15.00	40.00
		As 317.					
NY 320	1860	White Metal	29mm	—	—	15.00	40.00
		As 317.					
NY 321	1860	Silver	29mm	—	—	150.	225.
		Cupid. Rv: As NY 305.					
NY 322	1860	Brass	29mm	—	—	15.00	40.00
		As 321.					
NY 323	1860	Copper	29mm	5.00	10.00	15.00	40.00
		As 321.					
NY 324	1860	White Metal	29mm	5.00	10.00	15.00	40.00
		As 321.					
NY 325	1860	Silver	29mm	50.00	100.	150.	225.
		Obverse as reverse of NY 305 (Hill). Rv: F.C. KEY & SONS / DIE SINKERS & / MEDALISTS . 320 / * ARCH ST. * / PHILADELPHIA.					
NY 326	1860	Brass	29mm	—	—	25.00	60.00
		As 325.					
NY 327	1860	Copper	29mm	—	—	25.00	60.00
		As 325.					
NY 328	1860	White Metal	29mm	—	—	25.00	60.00
		As 325.					
NY 329	1860	Silver	29mm	—	—	150.	225.
		Obverse as reverse of NY 305 (E. Hill). Rv: K E Y in large letters.					
NY 330	1860	Brass	29mm	—	—	25.00	40.00
		As 329.					
NY 331	1860	Copper	29mm	—	—	25.00	40.00
		As 329.					
NY 332	1860	White Metal	29mm	—	—	25.00	42.50
		As 329.					

Miller	Date	Metal	Size	F	VF	EF	Unc
NY 333	1860	Silver	29mm	—	—	150.	225.
		Obverse as reverse of NY 305 (E. Hill). Rv: WOODGATE& CO. . IMPORTERS / OF / BRANDIES / WINES, 83 GINS &C / WATER STREET, / NEW-YORK / 1860.					
NY 334	1860	Brass	29mm	—	—	17.50	40.00
		As 333.					
NY 335	1860	Copper	29mm	—	—	17.50	40.00
		As 333.					
NY 336	1860	White Metal	29mm	—	—	17.50	40.00
		As 333.					
NY 337	1860	Silver	29mm	—	—	150.	225.
		VIRTUE, LIBERTY & INDEPENDENCE. Rv: As NY 305 (E. Hill store card).					
NY 338	1860	Brass	29mm	—	—	17.50	40.00
		As 337.					
NY 339	1860	Copper	29mm	—	—	17.50	40.00
		As 337.					
NY 340	1860	White Metal	29mm	—	—	17.50	40.00
		As 337.					

J.M. HILL

Rulau	Date	Metal	Size	VG	F	VF	EF
NY 2058	(1847-49)	Copper	29mm	150.	—	250.	—
		J. M. HILL / NEW YORK ctsp on U.S. 1819 Large cent. (Tanenbaum coll.; Brunk 19600)					

Joseph M. Hill was a locksmith at 6 Third Avenue who appears in the 1849 city directory. In the 1848 directory Hill, Hardware, was at 385 Bowery.

R. HOE & CO.

Rulau	Date	Metal	Size	VG	F	VF	EF
NY 2290	(?)	Copper	29mm	—	50.00	—	75.00
		R. HOE & CO. / 3 ctsp on U.S. 1839 Large cent. Similar ctsp on reverse of coin. (Frank Kovacs coll.; Brunk 19795)					
NY 2291	(?)	Copper	29mm	—	75.00	—	125.
		HOE & Co NEW YORK (curved) ctsp on U.S. Large cent.					
NY 2291B	(?)	Copper	29mm	—	75.00	—	125.
		HOE & Co. / NEW YORK ctsp on U.S. Large cent. Examined: 1835, date worn. (Brunk 19800)					
NY 2291E	(?)	Copper	29mm	—	40.00	—	60.00
		R. HOE & Co. ctsp on U.S. Large cent. Examined: 1827, 1829, 1835, 1839, date unknown. There are 6 specimens known. (Brunk 19790)					
NY 2291F	(?)	CN	19mm	—	40.00	—	60.00
		Similar ctsp on U.S. 1860 Indian cent.					
NY 2291G	(?)	Copper	26mm	—	50.00	—	75.00
		Similar ctsp on Austria 1816 Kreuzer.					

The '3' on NY 2290 probably does not indicate the 3-cent denomination. We have examined a few counterstamps which do seem to suggest such a designation, however.

R. Hoe & Co. were manufacturers of printing presses and saws; they began operations about 1805. Saws were probably the main product of this Manhattan firm when the counterstamps were applied.

By 1840 they operated plants at 29-31 Gold St. and the corner of Broome and Sherriff.

The 1918 directory finds Hoe, still making printing presses and machinery, located in Manhattan.

R. Hoe & Co. was located in Scarsdale, N.Y. in 1982, a manufacturer of industrial saw blades. It is still in business.

C. HORN

Rulau	Date	Metal	Size	VG	F	VF	EF
NY 2204	(1863-64)	CN	19mm	200.	—	300.	—
		C. HORN / GROCER / 304 W. 16 ST. / N.Y. ctsp on U.S. Indian cent. Dates examined: 1860, 1862. (Van Ormer sale 2690)					
NY 2204A	(1863-64)	Copper	29mm	200.	—	300.	—
		Similar ctsp on U.S. 1855 Large cent. (Brunk 20070)					
NY 2204D	(1863-64)	Copper	29mm	100.	—	175.	—
		C. HORN / GROCER / 304 W. 16 ST. / NEW YORK / (wing) (star) (wing) / FINE TEAS / COFFEES & SPICES in seven lines ctsp on U.S. 1853 Large cent. (Brunk 20075; Tanenbaum coll.)					

According to directory evidence, Horn was in business as a grocer at 304 West 16th Street, New York, in 1863 and 1864. Thus these should be considered as Civil War tokens by collectors of that series.

CHARLES D. HORTER

Miller	Date	Metal	Size	F	VF	EF	Unc
NY 356	1860	Silver	26mm	—	—	200.	350.
		Obverse as obverse of NY 651 (the building occupied by both Horter and Rahm). Rv: CHARLES D. HORTER / 178 WILLIAM ST., / NEW YORK / DIE SINKER / AND / ENGRAVER / * / MEDALS / SEALS, STAMPS & LETTER CUTTER.					
NY 357	1860	Copper	26mm	15.00	50.00	80.00	150.
		As 356. (Wright 461)					
NY 358	1860	White Metal	26mm	15.00	50.00	80.00	150.
		As 356.					

See NY 651-653. Louis Rahm, a coppersmith, occupied the first floor and Charles D. Horter, a diesinker, occupied the second floor of the newly erected building at 178 William Street in 1860. Horter became one of the most prolific producers of Civil War tokens soon afterward.

The obverse of NY 356 (Horter) and 651 (Rahm) are the same. Both men were of German extraction.

C. C. HOUGHTON

Rulau	Date	Metal	Size	VG	F	VF	EF
NY 2205	(?)	Copper	29mm	—	75.00	—	—
		C C HOUGHTON / 153 / CLINTON / ST / N Y ctsp on U.S. 1851 Large cent. (Frank Kovacs coll.; Brunk 20160)					

HOUGHTON MERRELL & CO.

Miller	Date	Metal	Size	VG	F	VF	Unc
NY 359	(1847-48)	Brass	28mm	10.00	15.00	25.00	50.00
		Three open umbrellas at center, UMBRELLAS AND PARASOLS, around. Rv: HOUGHTON MERRELL & CO / 48 / CEDAR / ST. / (Ornament) / * N.Y. *. Plain edge. (Wright 469)					

The obverse die is the same as that used on W.H. Richardson tokens of Philadelphia.

In 1847-48 this firm was at 48 Cedar. In 1848-49 these umbrella makers were located at 63 William Street. Ed. L. Houghton, umbrellas, appeared at 48 Cedar in 1844-45.

HUDNUT'S MINERAL

Miller	Date	Metal	Size	VG	F	VF	Unc
NY 360	(?)	Cupronickel	--mm	Scarce	—	75.00	—
		HUDNUTS MINERAL. Rv: Blank.					

HUTCHINGS

Rulau	Date	Metal	Size	VG	F	VF	EF
NY 2060	(?)	Silver	27mm	—	150.	—	250.
		HUTCHINGS / 395 B'WAY / N.Y. ctsp on Spanish-American 1807 2-reales. (Gould 99; Brunk 20870)					

J.E.

Miller	Date	Metal	Size	VG	F	VF	Unc
NY 406	(?)	Brass	20mm	10.00	20.00	70.00	125.
		Eagle displayed, five stars above. Rv: J.E. within ornamental scroll work. (Wright 503)					
NY 405	(?)	Copper	20mm	10.00	20.00	70.00	125.
		As 406.					

J.P.

Miller	Date	Metal	Size	VG	F	VF	Unc
NY 407	(?)	Copper	25mm	10.00	20.00	70.00	125.
		Eagle. Rv: J.P. (Wright 1478)					

JAQUITH

Rulau	Date	Metal	Size	VG	F	VF	EF
NY 2210	(1848-56)	Copper	29mm	125.	—	175.	—
		JAQUITH / 98 B. WAY ctsp on U.S. 1832 Large cent. (Gould Nov. 1957 listing; Hallenbeck 10.502; Rulau NY-NY 120 in *USTT 1866-1889;* Brunk 21560)					
NY 2210A	(?)	Copper	28mm	125.00	—	175.00	—
		Similar ctsp on Hard Times token. (Brunk 21550)					

Nathan Jaquith was a daguerreotyper located at 98 Broadway 1848-1856. In 1857 he moved to 167 Broadway.

J. N. R. JAQUITH

New York, N.Y. ?

Rulau	Date	Metal	Size	VG	F	VF	EF
NY 2211	(?)	Copper	29mm	35.00	—	60.00	—
		J.N.R. JAQUITH ctsp on U.S. 1851 Large cent. (Frank Kovacs coll.; Brunk 21575)					

MILES E. JENKINS

Rulau	Date	Metal	Size	VG	F	VF	EF
NY 2215	(?)	Silver	31mm	100.	—	175.	—
		MILES E. JENKINS / NEW — YORK ctsp three times on obverse of U.S. Seated Liberty half dollar, date worn off. (Donald R. Lewis coll.; Brunk 21615)					

The owner of the illustrated specimen, Donald R. Lewis, Harvester, Mo., has obtained an ANA certificate of authenticity for the piece, number E-9182-Z. Only a small number of the counterstamped U.S. coins have thus far obtained such opinions of genuineness though we feel certain more will be obtained as time passes and these pieces increase in value. However, this type of authentication was for the coin, not the stamp!

JENNINGS, WHEELER & CO.

Miller	Date	Metal	Size	F	VF	EF	Unc
NY 378	(?)	Brass	29mm	7.50	10.00	12.50	40.00
		43 CHAMBERS ST / JENNINGS / WHEELER / & CO. / NEW-YORK. The lettering is small. Rv: WHOLESALE / CLOTHING / WAREHOUSE. Reeded edge. (Wright 507)					
NY 379	(?)	Brass	29mm	7.50	10.00	12.50	40.00
		As 378. Plain edge.					

Miller	Date	Metal	Size	F	VF	EF	Unc
NY 380	(?)	Brass	29mm	7.50	10.00	15.00	40.00
		Obverse similar to 378, but lettering is much larger and two stars now flank NEW YORK. Rv: As 378. Plain edge.					
NY 380A	(?)	Brass	29mm	7.50	10.00	15.00	40.00
		As 380. Reeded edge.					

Miller	Date	Metal	Size	F	VF	EF	Unc
NY 381	(?)	Brass	29mm	12.50	17.50	25.00	50.00
		Clasped hands and JUSTICE & FRATERNITY / THE / CONSTITUTION / MUST BE MAINTAINED within inner circle. Around outside: CLOTHING / ** WAREHOUSE **. Rv: As obverse of 380. Very rare.					
NY 382	(?)	Copper	29mm	7.50	10.00	12.50	40.00
		As 381.					
NY 383	(?)	Brass	29mm	7.50	10.00	12.50	40.00
		As 381. Reeded edge.					
NY 384	(?)	Brass	29mm	7.50	10.00	12.50	40.00
		As 381. Plain edge.					
NY 385	(?)	Silvered Brass	29mm	10.00	12.50	15.00	40.00
		As 381. Reeded edge.					
NY 385A	(?)	Brass	29mm	12.50	17.50	25.00	40.00
		Similar to 381, but address is 47 & 49 CHAMBERS ST.					
NY 385B	(?)	Brass	27mm	7.50	10.00	15.00	40.00
		Exactly as NY 381, but size reduced to 27mm. Plain edge.					
NY 386	(1860)	Copper	29mm	5.00	10.00	15.00	40.00
		Map of North America. Rv: As obverse of NY 381, but address has changed again, to: 45-47 CHAMBERS ST. Plain edge.					
NY 387	(1860)	Copper	29mm	5.00	10.00	15.00	40.00
		As 386. Reeded edge.					
NY 388	(1860)	Brass	29mm	5.00	10.00	15.00	40.00
		As 386. Plain edge.					
NY 388A	(1860)	Brass	29mm	—	—	—	40.00
		As last. Reeded edge.					
NY 389	(1860)	Brass	29mm	—	—	100.	200.
		Obverse as reverse of 386. Rv: Bust of Abraham Lincoln. (DeWitt AL 1860-41(B).) (King 581)					
NY 389A	1860	Copper	29mm	—	—	100.	200.
		As 389. Plain edge. (King 581)					
NY 390	(1860)	Brass	29mm	25.00	50.00	75.00	100.
		Obverse as reverse of 386. Rv: Bust of Louis Kossuth.					
NY 391	(1860)	Copper	29mm	25.00	50.00	75.00	100.
		As NY 390.					
NY 392	(1860)	Brass	29mm	25.00	55.00	75.00	100.
		Obverse as reverse of NY 386. Rv: New York Crystal Palace.					
NY 393	(1860)	Brass	29mm	35.00	60.00	85.00	110.
		Obverse as reverse of 386. Rv: N.C. FOLGER & SON, NEW ORLEANS card.					
NY 394	(1860)	Brass	29mm	17.50	35.00	75.00	100.
		Map of North America. Rv: Ship to right (card of Doremus, Suydam & Nixon of New York). No issuer's name on token.					
NY 394A	(1860)	Copper	29mm	—	—	75.00	100.
		As last.					
NY 395	(1860)	Brass	29mm	—	—	75.00	100.
		Map of North America. Rv: New York Crystal Palace. (No issuer's name on token.)					
NY 395A	(1860)	Copper	29mm	—	—	75.00	100.
		As last.					

The indiscriminate mulings of Jennings Wheeler dies with other Scovill Mfg. Co.-produced token dies probably occurred on the orders of collector J.N.T. Levick.

PROFESSOR JOHNSON

Miller	Date	Metal	Size	F	VF	EF	Unc
NY 396	(1850's)	Copper	28mm	5.00	7.00	9.00	30.00
		Imitation of U.S. $10 gold piece; LIBERTY on coronet. Around in two lines: PROFESSOR JOHNSON'S SOAP & STARCH POLISH. / 317. BOWERY N.Y. Rv: Above eagle: FOUNTAIN BLACKING / UNITED STATES; below: BRUSH & FRENCH BLUEING. Plain edge.					
NY 397	(1850's)	Brass	28mm	5.00	7.00	9.00	30.00
		As 396. Plain edge. (Wright 517)					
NY 397A	(1850's)	Brass	28mm	5.00	7.00	9.00	30.00
		As 396. Reeded edge.					
NY 398	(1850's)	German Silver	28mm	—	—	50.00	100.
		As 396. Reeded edge.					

Miller	Date	Metal	Size	F	VF	EF	Unc
NY 399	(1860)	Brass	28mm	5.00	8.00	12.00	75.00
		Obverse as reverse (eagle side) of 396. Rv: Eagle, THERE IS NO DIFFICULTY TO HIM THAT WILLETH. Reeded edge. (No issuer's name on token).					

Miller	Date	Metal	Size	F	VF	EF	Unc
NY 400	1852	Brass	23mm	5.00	8.00	10.00	30.00
		Similar to 396, but date added. Token is in reduced size.					
NY 400A	1852	Copper	23mm	—	—	—	30.00
		As 400. Reeded edge.					

NY 401	1852	Brass	23mm	5.00	8.00	10.00	35.00

Bust of Louis Kossuth three-quarters right. Around: PROFESSOR JOHNSON 317 BOWERY .1852. Rv: Eagle displayed, UNITED STATES above, STARCH POLISH below. Reeded edge.

NY 402	(1850's)	Brass	22mm	5.00	8.00	11.00	30.00
		Liberty head left, PROF. JOHNSON CHEMICAL BLUEING. Rv: Same as obverse.					
NY 402A	(1850's)	Brass	22mm	—	—	—	—
		Similar to 402, but one side has different letter spacing, etc.					

All Prof. Johnson cards were struck by Scovill Mfg. Co., Waterbury, Conn. We have not examined NY 402 and 402A to discern the differences Miller mentions.

Lajos (Louis) Kossuth, the Hungarian rebel leader of 1848-49, made his visit to America in 1852 and was lionized by the New Yorkers and others. His portrait appeared on game counters of the period (the reverse of NY 399 is from such a counter). NY 401 uses Kossuth's portrait to help sell Prof. Johnson's home products.

'Professor' William Johnson was a wholesale perfumer and the inventor of Walnut Oil shaving soap, Sunflower soap, Jenny Lind hair gloss, Benzoin and Honey soap, Starch polish, Mirfiam balsam, Brown Windsor soap, New York Omnibus soap, etc. Fountain blacking, French blueing and Chemical blueing were also his products.

Earlier, in 1848-49, he had been located at 55 Frankfort Street.

H. & M. KAYSER & CO.

Miller	Date	Metal	Size	F	VF	EF	Unc
NY 409A	(1860)	Brass	22mm	700.	1200.	1500.	1700.
		Eagle with drooping wings, U.S. shield on its breast. Around: NO NORTH NO SOUTH ONE FLAG ONE UNION. 6-pointed star below. Rv: H. & M. KAYSER & CO. / IMPORTERS / OF / FANCY GOODS / NEW-YORK. Plain edge.(RF Sny-10; Kurth 53B; Fuld NY 630AMa-1a)					

NY 409	(1860)	Brass	22mm	—	—	1800.	—
		Eagle perched on rock in sea devouring a snake. NO NORTH NO SOUTH / ONE FLAG ONE UNION. Rv: As last. Plain edge. (RF Sny-11; Kurth 53C)					
NY 409C	(1860)	Copper	22mm	700.	1200.	1500.	1700.
		As 409. Plain edge. (RF Sny-11A; Kurth 53C)					
NY 410	(1860)	Lead	22mm	—	—	—	1300.
		As 409. Plain edge. (RF Sny-11B; Kurth 53C)					

The sentiments expressed on these $5 gold size game counter-store cards were popular in 1860 and early 1861, as the Union threatened to break up following Abraham Lincoln's election.

KNICKERBOCKER DAGUERN GALY (Knickerbocker Daguerrian Gallery)

Rulau	Date	Metal	Size	VG	F	VF	EF
NY 2062	(1850's)	Copper	29mm	—	200.	—	400.
		KNICKERBOCKER / DAGUERn / GALy COR B-WAY / & PINE St NY ctsp on U.S. 1840 Large cent. (Tanenbaum Coll.; Brunk 23200)					

LADIES RESTAURANT

Miller	Date	Metal	Size	VG	F	VF	Unc
NY 414	(?)	Brass	28mm	50.00	100.	125.	150.
		LADIES RESTAURANT. 280 8TH AVE. Rv/1.					
NY 415	(?)	Brass	28mm	50.00	100.	125.	150.
		As 414, but 3/ on reverse.					
NY 415B	(?)	Brass	28mm	50.00	100.	125.	150.
		LADIES RESTAURANT / -AND- / ICE CREAM / SALOON / -280- / -8TH. AVENUE-. Rv: 3/6- on plain field. Plain edge.					
NY 415A	—	Brass	28mm	50.00	100.	125.	150.
		As 414, but 5/6 on reverse.					

M. LEASK

Miller	Date	Metal	Size	VG	F	VF	Unc
NY 418	(?)	White Metal	33mm	12.50	30.00	50.00	100.
		*M. LEASK * / REAL LACE & / IMITATION SETTS / X / REVIERE / + & + / CRAPE GOODS / IN / EVERY VARIETY. / 93 PRINCE ST. NEAR BROADWAY, NEW YORK. Rv: MANUFACTURER OF / MOURNING / & / ILLUSION / GOODS, / DRESS CAPS, / HEAD DRESSES / &C. (Wright 586)					

This issuer also has a token under Brooklyn, N.Y. (Adams NY 15)

F. LEHR

Miller	Date	Metal	Size	F	VF	EF	Unc
NY 419	1860	Brass	18mm	100.	150.	200.	350.
		Abraham Lincoln head right; A. LINCOLN, R. CAND'T FOR PRESIDENT — 1860. Rv: F. LEHR'S NEEDLE THREADERS / * N.Y. * above an eagle. Below: 50 CHATHAM ST. Reeded edge. (Wright 593 DeWitt AL 1860-75)					
NY 419A	1860	Copper	18mm	100.	150.	200.	350.
		As 419. Reeded edge. (King 635)					

C. LEIGHTON

Miller	Date	Metal	Size	F	VF	EF	Unc
NY 420	(1850's)	Brass	24mm	5.00	8.00	15.00	50.00
		Turbaned Liberty head. Rv: Seated Liberty (facsimile of American Institue award medal). C. LEIGHTON / 1st PREMIUM SHIRT MANUFACTURER.					

Miller	Date	Metal	Size	F	VF	EF	Unc
NY 421	(1850's)	Copper	24mm	8.00	12.00	30.00	50.00
		Obverse as reverse of NY 420 (Seated Liberty). Rv: Eagle. 10 PARK PLACE N.Y. AND 5 ROYAL ST. N.O. Legend begins and ends near tips of wings. Thick planchet. (Wright 590)					
NY 422	(1850's)	Brass	24mm	5.00	8.00	15.00	50.00
		As 421.					
NY 423	(1850's)	White Metal	24mm	5.00	8.00	15.00	55.00
		As 421.					
NY 424	(1850's)	Brass	24mm	5.00	15.00	20.00	60.00
		As 421, but on reverse eagle's wings are more spread. The legend begins and ends near the top of each wing.					

Charles Leighton, linen manufacturer, appears in the 1848 and 1849 directories at 10 Park Place.

J.N.T. LEVICK

Miller	Date	Metal	Size	F	VF	EF	Unc
NY 426	1860	Silver	28mm	—	100.	150.	250.
		A wreath encloses two pipes crossed, over a tobacco box inscribed REGALIAS. Just above the inscription is a small crown. Above the pipes in a half-circle is: LEVICK 904 BROADWAY / NEW YORK. In exergue: 1860. Rv: Bust facing of a jolly old man smoking a cigar. NO PLEASURE CAN EXCEED / THE SMOKING OF THE WEED. (The reverse design is known familiarly as "The Smoker.")					
NY 427	1860	Copper	28mm	—	—	30.00	40.00
		As 426.					
NY 428	1860	Brass	28mm	—	—	30.00	40.00
		As 426.					
NY 429	1860	White Metal	28mm	—	—	30.00	40.00
		As 426. Plain edge. (Wright 600)					
NY 430	1860	Copper	29mm	—	20.00	30.00	50.00
		Obverse as NY 426. Rv: Washington bust facing left, in an arched frame of a single line; small KEY beneath the bust. Around: PATRIAE PATER 1732.					
NY 431	1860	Brass	28mm	—	20.00	30.00	50.00
		As 430.					
NY 432	1860	White Metal	28mm	—	—	30.00	50.00
		As 430.					
NY 433	1860	Copper	28mm	—	—	30.00	40.00
		Obverse as NY 426. Rv: Bust of Webster in toga right, DANIEL WEBSTER around.					
NY 434	1860	Brass	28mm	—	—	30.00	40.00
		As 433.					
NY 435	1860	White Metal	29mm	—	—	30.00	40.00
		As 433.					
NY 436	1860	Copper	29mm	—	—	15.00	40.00
		Obverse as NY 426. Rv: Bust of Edwin Forrest.					
NY 437	1860	Brass	29mm	—	—	15.00	40.00
		As 436.					
NY 438	1860	White Metal	29mm	—	—	15.00	40.00
		As 436.					
NY 439	1860	Copper	29mm	—	—	15.00	40.00
		Obverse as NY 426. Rv: Cupid on a spouting dolphin, ornate frame around rim. (This is the obverse of NY 486, the George Hampden Lovett store card.)					
NY 440	1860	Brass	29mm	—	—	15.00	40.00
		As 439.					
NY 441	1860	White Metal	29mm	—	—	15.00	40.00
		As 439.					
NY 442	1860	Copper	29mm	—	—	30.00	40.00
		Obverse as NY 426. Rv: F.C. KEY & SON card of Philadelphia.					
NY 443	1860	Brass	29mm	—	—	20.00	40.00
		As 442.					
NY 444	1860	White Metal	29mm	—	—	20.00	40.00
		As 442.					
NY 445	1860	Copper	29mm	—	—	20.00	40.00
		Obverse as NY 426. Rv: KEY in large letters.					
NY 446	1860	Brass	29mm	—	—	30.00	40.00
		As 445.					
NY 447	1860	White Metal	29mm	—	—	20.00	40.00
		As 445. (For NY numbers 448 to 451, see under Woodgate & Co., New York, Miller numbers NY 993 to 995.)					
NY 452	1860	Copper	29mm	—	—	15.00	40.00
		Obverse as NY 426. Rv: VIRTUE, LIBERTY & INDEPENDENCE.					
NY 453	1860	Brass	29mm	—	—	15.00	40.00
		As 452.					
NY 454	1860	White Metal	29mm	—	—	15.00	40.00
		As 452.					
NY 455	1860	Copper	29mm	—	—	15.00	40.00
		Obverse as NY 426. Rv: Store card of E. Hill, 1860.					
NY 456	1860	Brass	29mm	—	—	15.00	40.00
		As 455.					
NY 457	1860	White Metal	29mm	—	—	15.00	40.00
		As 455.					

Miller	Date	Metal	Size	F	VF	EF	Unc
NY 458	1860	Copper	28mm	—	—	15.00	40.00
		Obverse as NY 426. Rv: REPREStd BY J.N.T. LEVICK.					
NY 459	1860	Brass	28mm	—	—	15.00	40.00
		As 458.					
NY 460	1860	White Metal	28mm	—	—	15.00	40.00
		As 458. Reeded edge.					
NY 460A	1860	Silver	28mm	—	—	150.	250.
		As 458. Reeded edge. (Ganter coll.)					
NY 461	(1860)	Copper	28mm	—	—	15.00	40.00
		Muling without name Levick on the token. Obverse: "The Smoker," as reverse of NY 426. Reverse: Bust of Edwin Forrest.					
NY 462	(1860)	Brass	28mm	—	—	15.00	40.00
		As 461.					
NY 463	(1860)	White Metal	28mm	—	—	15.00	40.00
		As 461.					

J. E. LIND

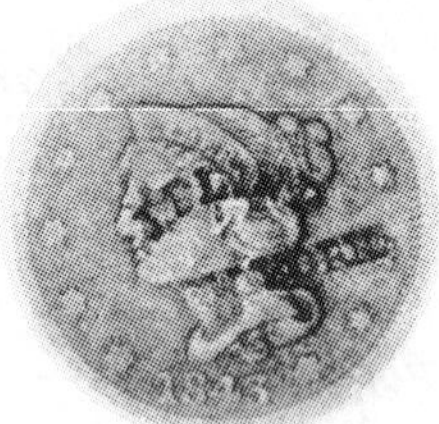

Rulau	Date	Metal	Size	VG	F	VF	EF
NY 2570	(?)	Copper	29mm	—	—	50.00	—
		J. E. LIND (curved) / NEW YORK ctsp on U.S. 1843 Large cent. (Kirtley Nov. 1991 sale, lot Q048; Brunk 24535)					

LODER & CO.

Miller	Date	Metal	Size	F	VF	EF	Unc
NY 465	(1850's)	Copper	28mm	5.00	8.00	12.00	40.00
		Spread eagle with shield on breast, LODER & CO / 83 CEDAR ST above, NEW-YORK below. Rv: IMPORTERS / AND / JOBBERS OF / FANCY & STAPLE / DRY GOODS / 83 CEDAR ST. / NEW-YORK. Plain edge.					
NY 465A	(1850's)	Copper	28mm	—	—	—	40.00
		As last. Reeded edge.					
NY 466	(1850's)	Brass	28mm	5.00	8.00	12.00	40.00
		As 465.					
NY 467	(1850's)	Silvered Brass	28mm	5.00	8.00	12.00	40.00
		As 465.					
NY 468	(1860)	Silver	28mm	—	—	150.	250.
		Obverse as 465. Rv: Map of North America.					
NY 469	(1860)	Silver	28mm	—	—	150.	250.
		Obverse as 465. Rv: DR. SELLECK (etc.)					
NY 470	(1860)	Copper	28mm	—	—	25.00	50.00
		As 469.					
NY 471	(1860)	Silver	28mm	—	—	150.	250.
		Obverse as 465. Rv: DOREMUS & NIXON card.					

NY 472 (1860) White Metal 28mm — — 75.00 100.
As 471.

NY 473 (1860) Brass 28mm — — 75.00 100.
Obverse as 465. Rv: Vessel reverse of Doremus & Nixon card, NY 224.

NY 474A (1860) Copper 28mm 5.00 8.00 12.00 40.00
Obverse as 465. Rv: Similar to 465, but address: 130 BROADWAY.

NY 474 (1860) Copper 28mm 10.00 15.00 25.00 40.00
Obverse as NY 474A. Rv: Similar to 474A, but address 83 CEDAR ST.

NY 475 (1860) Brass 28mm 10.00 15.00 25.00 40.00
As 474. Reeded edge.

NY 475A (1860) Brass 28mm 10.00 20.00 25.00 40.00
Obverse as NY 474A. Rv: Similar to 465, but address: 130 BROADWAY. Reeded edge.

NY 476 (1860) Silvered Brass 28mm 10.00 15.00 25.00 40.00
As 475A.

NY 477 (1860) Brass 28mm 17.50 50.00 75.00 100.
Obverse as last. Rv: Card of Doremus & Nixon.

NY 478 (1860) Copper 28mm 25.00 50.00 75.00 100.
Obverse as last. Rv: IMPORTERS & JOBBERS &C.

NY 478A (1860) Brass 28mm 10.00 15.00 25.00 40.00
As 478.

NY 478B (1860) Silvered Brass 28mm 10.00 15.00 25.00 40.00
As 478. Plain edge.

Lewis B. Loder & Co., dry goods, were at 83 Cedar Street in the 1849 directory.

GEORGE H. LOVETT

Miller	Date	Metal	Size	F	VF	EF	Unc
NY 486	(1858)	Silver	31mm	—	—	150.	250.

Cupid on a spouting dolphin, an ornate border around the rim. Rv: MEDALS STRUCK IN GOLD, SILVER, BRONZE &C / (flying bird) / GEO. H. LOVETT. / MEDAL / DIE-SINKER, / 131 / FULTON STREET, / NEW YORK. / (13 six-pointed stars). Reeded edge.

NY 487 (1858) Brass 31mm 10.00 15.00 30.00 50.00
As 486. Reeded edge.

NY 488 (1858) White Metal 31mm 12.50 17.50 35.00 50.00
As 486. Reeded edge.

NY 488A (1858) Copper 31mm 10.00 15.00 30.00 50.00
As 486. Reeded edge.

NY 489 (1860) Copper 31mm 10.00 15.00 30.00 50.00
"The Antiquary." Rv: As 486.

NY 490 (1860) Brass 31mm 10.00 15.00 30.00 50.00
As 489.

NY 491 (1860) White Metal 31mm 12.50 17.50 35.00 50.00
As 489.

NY 491A 1860 White Metal 28mm — 10.00 20.00 35.00
Witch on broomstick, G.H.L. below. Around: WE ALL HAVE OUR HOBBIES. Rv: DEDICATED / TO / COIN / AND / MEDAL / COLLECTORS within a wreath, 1860 in exergue.

NY 491B 1860 Brass 28mm — 10.00 20.00 35.00
As 491A. (Wright 374)

NY 491C 1860 Copper 28mm — — 20.00 35.00
As 491A. Plain edge. (Ganter coll.)

NY 492 (1858) Silver 31mm — — 150. 250.
John Bull and Brother Jonathan exchanging lightning bolts across the sea. At left: HOW ARE YOU JONATHAN. At right: PURTY WELL OLD FELLER / HOW'S YERSELF. Rv: As reverse of NY 486. Rare.

NY 492A (1858) White Metal 31mm — 10.00 20.00 35.00
As 492.

NY 492B (1858) Brass — — — — 80.00
As last. Plain edge.

NY 493 (1858) Copper 31mm — — 35.00 75.00
As 492. Scarce.

NY493A 1858 Copper 31mm 10.00 15.00 20.00 40.00
Obverse as NY 492 (John Bull and Brother Jonathan). Rv: ATLANTIC TELEGRAPH / SUCCESSFULLY / LAID / 5TH OF / AUGUST, / 1858. Plain edge.

NY 494 1858 Brass 31mm 20.00 25.00 35.00 55.00
As 493A.

NY 495 1858 White Metal 31mm 20.00 25.00 35.00 55.00
As 493A.

NY 492A 1858 White Metal — 20.00 25.00 35.00 55.00
Obverse as 486. Rv: As obverse of 492. Muling.

NY 495B 1858 S/WM 31mm — — 35.00 60.00
Boy riding dog, left, BOY AND DOG. above. Tiny W. H. BRIDGENS NEW. YORK. under exergue line. Rv: As reverse of 493A (ATLANTIC TELEGRAPH). Plain edge.

An interesting point about the Lovett tokens celebrating the 1858 laying of the Atlantic cable is that the event never was successful! The 1858 cable laying took place, but the cable soon failed. The cable was finally laid successfully by the British liner *Great Eastern* in 1866.

Miller	Date	Metal	Size	F	VF	EF	Unc
NY 495F	(1858)	Copper	32mm	—	—	—	45.00

As 495B (BOY AND DOG). Rv: Fasces in rays. UNITED WE STAND * / * DIVIDED WE FALL. Plain edge. (Wright 98)

NY 495J (1860) Brass 28mm — — — 75.00
Obverse as reverse of NY 433 (Daniel Webster). Rv: As 491A (Dedicated to Coin and Medal Collectors). Plain edge. Only 4 struck. (Levick 1865 sale, lot 260; Levine-Magriel sale 1988, lot 1181)

NY 495K (1860) Brass 28mm — — — 75.00
Obverse as 495J (Webster). Rv: As obverse of 491A (Witch, We All Have Our Hobbies). Plain edge. Only 4 struck. (Levick 1865 sale, lot 262; Levine-Magriel 1988 sale, lot 1182)

NY 495L	(1860)	WM	29mm	—	—	—	40.00
		Obverse as 495J (Webster). Rv: As reverse of NY 439 (Cupid on Dolphin). Plain edge. Only 16 struck. (Levick 1865 sale 266; Levine-Magriel 1988 sale, lot 1183)					
NY 495N	(1860)	WM	29mm	—	—	—	40.00
		Obverse as reverse of NY 436 (Edwin Forrest). Rv: As 495K (Witch). Plain edge. (Levine-Magriel 1988 sale, lot 1184)					

George Hampden Lovett was at 5 Dey Street with his father, Robert Lovett Sr., 1848-1849, according to city directories.

J.D. LOVETT

Miller	Date	Metal	Size	F	VF	EF	Unc
NY 496	(?)	Silver	25mm	—	—	150.	250.
		Seal press. J.D. LOVETT * ENGRAVER * / 1 COURTLAND ST. / N.Y. Rv: WEDDING & VISITING CARDS / SEALS / DIES / JEWELRY, / &C / ENGRAVED / ***. Reeded edge.					
NY 497	(?)	Copper	25mm	10.00	15.00	20.00	40.00
		As 496. Reeded edge.					
NY 498	(?)	Brass	25mm	10.00	15.00	20.00	40.00
		As 496. Reeded edge. (Wright 627)					
NY 499 K	(?)	White Metal	25mm	10.00	15.00	20.00	40.00
		As 496. Reeded edge.					

NY 500	1860	Silver	25mm	—	—	150.	250.
		All within oval on a plain field: Congress Hall at Saratoga, NEW CONGRESS HALL above, 1860 below. Rv: As reverse of 496. Reeded edge.					
NY 501	1860	Copper	25mm	10.00	15.00	20.00	40.00
		As 500. Reeded edge.					
NY 502	1860	Brass	25mm	10.00	15.00	20.00	40.00
		As 500. Reeded edge.					
NY 503	1860	Brass	25mm	10.00	15.00	20.00	40.00
		Obverse as obverse of NY 496 (seal press). Rv: As obverse of NY 500 (New Congress Hall). A muling. Reeded edge.					

John D. Lovett was at 1 Cortlandt Street as early as 1848-49.

R. LOVETT

Miller	Date	Metal	Size	F	VF	EF	Unc
NY 504	(1856)	Silver	29mm	—	—	150.	250.
		Bust of Benjamin Franklin left, B. FRANKLIN above. Below, on a scroll: ERIPUIT COELO FULMEN SCEPTRUMQUE TYRRANIS. Rv: R. LOVETT / STONE / SEAL ENGRAVER / & / MEDALIST / NEW YORK.					
NY 505	(1856)	Copper	29mm	15.00	22.50	30.00	50.00
		As 504. Plain edge.					
NY 506	(1856)	Brass	29mm	15.00	22.50	30.00	50.00
		As 504. (Wright 624)					

Robert Lovett Jr. was one of three sons of Robert Lovett Sr. who became engravers. Later (1858-1860) he issued store cards from Philadelphia (see PA 330 to 356A) and still later he designed a good many Civil War tokens and the famous Confederate cent.

H.M. LUDLUM

Rulau	Date	Metal	Size	G	VG	F	EF
NY 2066	(1847-49)	Copper	29mm	—	100.	—	175.
		H. M. LUDLUM / N.Y. in tapered rectangular cartouche, ctsp on U.S. 1817 Large cent. (Tanenbaum collection; Brunk 25250)					

Henry M. Ludlum Jr. was a silversmith located at 251 Spring Street in 1848-49. In 1847-48 he had been at 500 Broome Street.

R. LUNDY

Rulau	Date	Metal	Size	VG	F	VF	Unc
NY 2064	(?)	Silver	27mm	150.	—	250.	—
		R. LUNDY / IRON, AWNING / FRAMEMAKER / 172 CHAMBERS ST in four lines ctsp on Spanish-American 1774-Mo-IR 2-reales. (Gould 107; Brunk 25280)					

E. LYON

Miller	Date	Metal	Size	F	VF	EF	Unc
NY 507	(1850's)	Brass	28mm	5.00	8.00	10.00	40.00
		Liberty head left. E. LYON on coronet. * E. LYON * above, 424. BROADWAY. NEW YORK. below. Rv: Eagle displayed, U.S. shield on breast, MAGNETIC POWDER & PILLS FOR INSECTS & RATS.					

NY 508	(1850's)	Brass	28mm	5.00	8.00	10.00	40.00
		Obverse similar to 507, but six stars over head in place of * E. LYON *. Rv: As 507. Reeded edge. (Wright 636)					
NY 508A	(1850's)	Brass	28mm	—	—	—	40.00
		As last. Plain edge.					
NY 509	(1850's)	Brass	28mm	5.00	8.00	10.00	40.00
		As 508, but five smaller stars replace six large stars. Reeded edge.					

NY 510	(1850's)	Brass	22mm	5.00	8.00	10.00	40.00
		Similar to 508 but seven stars. Token reduced in size.					
NY 510A	(1850's)	Copper	22mm	5.00	8.00	10.00	40.00
		As last.					

NY 511	(1850's)	Brass	23mm	5.00	8.00	10.00	40.00
		Male bust (Lyon's?) right, E. LYON above, 424 BROADWAY NEW-YORK. below. Rv: Liberty seated amid spinning wheel, ploy, shield etc. MAGNETIC POWDER & PILLS above, . FOR INSECTS & RATS. below. Reeded edge.					

All the Lyon pieces apparently were struck by Scovill Mfg. Co., Waterbury, Conn. The peculiar configuration of Seated Liberty on NY 511 also appears on the Hausman card of Savannah, Ga.

Emanuel Lyon is listed as a "chemist and inventor" and maker of rat poisons in the 1849 directory, located at 420 Broadway. His advertisement in that directory claims other distinctions, including Magnetic Powders for destroying bedbugs, cockroaches, fleas, flies, etc.

His advertisement is valuable in another respect; it lists the 1848-49 proprietors of several hotels:

D. D. Howard — Irving House
Coleman & Stetson — Astor House
S. Thayer Cozzens (late) — American Hotel
Preston H. Hodges — Carlton House

H.M.

Rulau	Date	Metal	Size	VG	F	VF	EF
NY 2110	(?)	Copper	29mm	100.	—	175.	—
		H.M. / N. YORK / 3 / CENTS ctsp on U.S. 1828 or 1831 Large cent. (The word CENTS is in relief in script within a recessed rectangle, while other lettering is incuse.) (Brunk 17550)					

This is an unusual piece, early in appearance. It may well be earlier than the Merchant period and belong in the Hard Times token period.

MALCOLM & GAUL

Miller	Date	Metal	Size	F	VF	EF	Unc
NY 515	(1850's)	Copper	29mm	5.00	10.00	15.00	40.00
		Eagle displayed, shield on its breast. MALCOLM & GAUL / 62 LIBERTY ST. above, NEW-YORK below. Rv: IMPORTERS / AND / JOBBERS OF / BRITISH FRENCH / AND / AMERICAN / DRY GOODS. Plain edge.					
NY 516	(1850's)	Brass	29mm	5.00	10.00	15.00	40.00
		As 515. Reeded edge. (Wright 651)					
NY 517	(1850's)	Silvered Brass	29mm	5.00	10.00	15.00	40.00
		As 515.					

Malcolm & Gaul, dry goods, 62 Liberty St., appear in the 1849 directory.

MACKRELL & RICHARDSON

Rulau	Date	Metal	Size	VG	F	VF	EF
NY 2112	(1844-59)	Copper	29mm	150.	—	225.	—
		MACKRELL & / RICHARDSON / NEW YORK ctsp on U.S. Large cent. Examined: 1835, 1839, worn date of 1814-30 type, unk. date. 4 pieces known. (Hallenbeck 13.500; Rulau USTT NY-NY 170; Tanenbaum coll.; Brunk 25587)					

William H. Mackrell and Lemuel S. Richardson were listed as locksmiths 1839-46 at 228 Houston and 1847-59 at 292 Houston. The 1848 directory, in addition to the locksmith listing, says "manufacturer of cast bolts, shutter hinges, locks etc."

J.G. MERRITT

Miller	Date	Metal	Size	F	VF	EF	Unc
NY 535	(1850's)	Brass	28mm	5.00	7.50	12.50	30.00
		*NO 12 BOWERY * / J. G. MERRITT / * NEW YORK *. Rv: * MENS & BOYS * / CLOTHING / * EMPORIUM *. (Wright 695)					
NY 535A	(1850's)	Silver	28mm	—	—	125.	250.
		As 535.					

The addresses for Joseph G. Merritt, clothier, given in city directories are:
1840-41 — 396 Water St.
1847-49 — 18 Catharine Slip
1850's — 12 Bowery

MERRITT & LANGLEY

Miller	Date	Metal	Size	VG	F	VF	Unc
NY 536	(?)	German silver	31.5mm	15.00	30.00	45.00	60.00
		MERRITT & LANGLEY'S DEY ST. HOUSE *. Rv: DEY ST. DINING SALOON / *. No counterstamp. Plain edge.					
NY 536AA	(?)	German silver	31.5mm	—	—	45.00	—
		As 536, but ctsp /6 (six pence) on reverse. (ANS coll.)					
NY 536AB	(?)	German silver	31.5mm	—	—	45.00	—
		As 536, but ctsp /9 on reverse. (ANS coll.)					
NY 536A	(?)	German silver	31.5mm	15.00	30.00	45.00	60.00
		As 536, but ctsp 1/-on reverse.					
NY 539	(?)	German silver	31.5mm	15.00	30.00	45.00	60.00
		As 536, but ctsp 1/3 on each side.					
NY 539A	(?)	German silver	31.5mm	—	—	45.00	—
		As 536, but ctsp 1/6 on reverse. (ANS coll.)					
NY 538	(?)	German silver	31.5mm	15.00	30.00	45.00	60.00
		As 536, but ctsp 2/-on each side.					
NY 537	(?)	German silver	31.5mm	15.00	30.00	45.00	60.00
		As 536, but ctsp 2/3 on each side.					
NY 537A	(?)	German silver	31.5mm	—	—	60.00	—
		As 536, but ctsp 2/9 on reverse. (ANS coll.)					
NY 537B	(?)	German silver	31.5mm	—	—	45.00	—
		As 536, but ctsp 3/ on reverse. (ANS coll.)					
NY 540	(?)	German silver	31.5mm	15.00	30.00	45.00	60.00
		As 536, but ctsp 3/3 on each side.					
NY 541	(?)	German silver	31.5mm	15.00	30.00	45.00	60.00
		As 536, but ctsp 3/6 on each side.					
NY 542	(?)	German silver	31.5mm	15.00	30.00	45.00	60.00
		As 536, but ctsp 3/9 on each side.					
NY 543	(?)	German silver	31.5mm	15.00	30.00	45.00	60.00
		As 536, but ctsp 4/- on each side.					
NY 544	(?)	German silver	31.5mm	15.00	30.00	45.00	60.00
		Similar to 536, but 54 & 56 / DEY ST. / NEW YORK in three lines added to center of obverse. Rv: As 536, with space for a counterstamp. Plain edge. (Wright 696)					
NY 545	(?)	German silver	31.5mm	15.00	30.00	45.00	60.00
		As 544, ctsp -/6 on reverse.					
NY 546	(?)	German silver	31.5mm	15.00	30.00	45.00	60.00
		As 544, ctsp -/9. Plain edge. (The counterstamp stands for nine English pence. A numeral to left of the slash indicates shillings.)					
NY 547	(?)	German silver	31.5mm	15.00	30.00	75.00	100.
		As 544, ctsp 1/- (one shilling). Plain edge.					
NY 548	(?)	German silver	31.5mm	15.00	30.00	45.00	60.00
		As 544, ctsp 1/3.					
NY 549	(?)	German silver	31.5mm	15.00	30.00	45.00	60.00
		As 544, ctsp 1/6.					
NY 550	(?)	German silver	31.5mm	15.00	30.00	45.00	60.00
		As 544, ctsp 1/9.					
NY 551	(?)	German silver	31.5mm	15.00	30.00	45.00	60.00
		As 544, ctsp 2/-.					
NY 552	(?)	German silver	31.5mm	15.00	30.00	45.00	60.00
		As 544, ctsp 2/3.					
NY 553	(?)	German silver	31.5mm	15.00	30.00	45.00	60.00
		As 544, ctsp 2/9.					

NY 554	(?)	German silver	31.5mm	15.00	30.00	45.00	60.00
		As 544, ctsp 3/-. Plain edge.					
NY 555	(?)	German silver	31.5mm	15.00	30.00	45.00	60.00
		As 544, ctsp 3/3.					
NY 556	(?)	German silver	31.5mm	15.00	30.00	45.00	60.00
		As 544, ctsp 3/6.					
NY 557	(?)	German silver	31.5mm	15.00	30.00	45.00	60.00
		As 544, ctsp 4/-. Plain edge.					

MESCHUTT'S METROPOLITAN COFFEE ROOM

Miller	Date	Metal	Size	VG	F	VF	EF
NY 558	(1855)	Copper	29mm	—	125.	—	175.
		MESCHUTT'S / METROPOLITAN / COFFEE ROOM / 433. BD.WAY in four lines ctsp on U.S. Large cents. Dates examined: 1798-1803 type, 1802, 1821, 1822, 1828, 1829, 1831, 1836, 1846, dates worn off. There are 14 specimens reported. (Duffield 1413; Hallenbeck 13.511; Brunk 27460)					

NY 559	(1855)	Copper	28mm	—	150.	—	225.
		Similar ctsp on Ireland halfpennies. Dates examined: 1803, 1805. (Duffield 1367; Wright 697)					

NY 559C	(1855)	Silver	27mm	—	150.	—	250.
		Similar ctsp on Spanish-American 2-reales. Dates examined: 1777, 1780, 1782, 1785-LME, 1797, dates worn off. 8 pieces known. (Gould 108; Duffield 1366)					

Miller	Date	Metal	Size	VG	F	VF	Unc
NY 560	(1855)	White Metal	--mm	—	75.00	—	—
		Similar ctsp on thick white metal planchet, which is also counterstamped '9'. Rv: Blank. Plain edge.					
NY 561	(1855)	White Metal	--mm	—	75.00	—	—
		Similar ctsp on thick white metal planchet, which is also ctsp '0' with diagonal line. Rv: 1/-. Plain edge.					
NY 562	(1855)	Lead	--mm	—	75.00	—	—
		Similar ctsp on lead planchet, which is also ctsp '3'.					
NY 562A	(1855)	Lead	--mm	—	75.00	—	—
		Similar ctsp 1/9. Plain edge.					

Frederick Meschutt is listed in the 1864 New York State Business Directory as proprietor of an eating house at 599 Broadway. Apparently he moved his establishment after issuing the tokens above.

METAIRE JOCKEY CLUB

Rulau	Date	Metal	SizeVG		F	VF	Unc
NY A562	1851	Silver	28mm	—	—	300.	500.
		Horse standing right. Around: METAIRE JOCKEY CLUB / MEMBER'S MEDAL. Rv: NOT / TRANSFERABLE, / 1851. Plain edge. (Arlie Slabaugh report)					

METROPOLITAN CAVE

Miller	Date	Metal	Size	F	VF	EF	Unc
NY 563	(?)	Brass	28mm	40.00	75.00	100.	—
		METROPOLITAN / CAVE / COR. BROADWAY & WHITE ST. Rv: 1/. (There are varieties of this and the following cards).					
NY 564	(?)	Brass	28mm	40.00	75.00	100.	—
		As 563, but 2/.					
NY 565	(?)	Brass	28mm	40.00	75.00	100.	—
		As 563, but 3/. (Wright 699)					
NY 566	(?)	Brass	28mm	40.00	75.00	100.	—
		As 563, but 3/6.					
NY 567	(?)	Brass	28mm	40.00	75.00	100.	—
		As 563, but 5/.					
NY 568	(?)	Brass	28mm	40.00	75.00	100.	—
		As 563, but 8/6.					
NY 569	(?)	Brass	28mm	40.00	75.00	100.	—
		As 563, but 9/6.					
NY 570	(?)	Brass	28mm	40.00	75.00	100.	—
		As 563, but 11/.					
NY 571	(?)	Brass	28mm	40.00	75.00	100.	—
		As 563, but 11/6.					

METROPOLITAN INSURANCE COMPANY

Miller	Date	Metal	Size	F	VF	EF	Unc
NY 572	1852	Silver	29mm	—	—	100.	250.
		Three-masted sailing ship right, METROPOLITAN above, INSURANCE COMPANY below. Rv: MARINE & FIRE / CAPITAL / $300,000 / WITH A LARGE / SURPLUS, / 108 BROADWAY / NEW-YORK, / 1852. Plain edge.					
NY 573	1852	Copper	29mm	5.00	7.00	9.00	35.00
		As 572. Plain edge. (Wright 700)					
NY 573A	1852	Copper	29mm	5.00	7.00	9.00	35.00
		As 573, but Thick planchet.					
NY 574	1852	Brass	29mm	7.50	9.50	11.00	35.00
		As 572. Plain edge.					
NY 574A		Silvered Brass	29mm	7.50	9.50	11.00	35.00
		As 572. Plain edge.					
NY 574B	1852	WM	—				2 Known
		As 572. Plain edge. Extremely thick planchet. (Tanenbaum coll.; Levine 1988 sale)					

All struck by Scovill Mfg. Co., Waterbury, Conn. There are similar tokens of this issuer (Adams NY 575-580) which are dated 1865 or 1866, all outside the scope of this section.

LEOPOLD DE MEYER

Miller	Date	Metal	Size	VG	F	VF	Unc
NY 581	(?)	Brass	28mm	35.00	75.00	—	Rare
		Bust left within wreath. Rv: LEOPOLD / DE MEYER'S / CONCERT. (Wright 1391)					

L. MILLER'S HAIR INVIGORATOR

Miller	Date	Metal	Size	VG	F	VF	EF
NY 582	(1848-51)	Silver	21mm	—	125.	—	175.
		L. MILLER'S / HAIR / INVIGORATOR ctsp on Spanish-American 1-real. (Brunk 27790)					

NY 582A (1848-51) Silver 27mm — 125. — 175.
Similar ctsp on Spanish-American 2-reales. Dates examined: 1810. (Gould 111)

NY 582B (1848-51) Silver 21mm — 125. — 175.
USE / L. MILLER'S / HAIR / INVIGORATOR ctsp on Spanish-American 1-real. Dates examined: 1807. (Brunk 27800)

NY 582C (1848-51) Silver 27mm — 125. — 175.
Similar ctsp on Spanish-American 2-reales. Date examined: 1784, date worn.

NY 582F (1848-51) Silver 21mm — 125. — 175.
USE / L. MILLER'S / HAIR / INVIGORATOR / 295 BOWERY / ctsp on Spanish-American 1-real. Date examined: 1781-Mo-FF, date worn off. (Gould 110; Brunk 27810)

NY 582G (1848-51) Silver 27mm — 150. — 200.
Similar ctsp on Spanish-American 2-reales. Date examined: 1773. (Gould 110)

NY 582J (1848-51) Silver 27mm — 125. — 175.
USE / L. MILLER'S / HAIR / INVIGORATOR / N.Y. ctsp on Spanish-American 2-reales. Dates examined: 1772, 1773, 1788, 1805, 1821. (Duffield 1368; Brunk 27830)

NY 582K (1854) Silver 25mm — — 175. —
Similar ctsp on U.S. 1853 S.L. quarter.

NY 582P (1863) Silver 25mm 200. — 300. —
USE / L MILLER'S (curved) / HAIR / INVIGORATOR (curved) / N.Y. (the identical stamp to Civil War token Fuld 630-AZ-1a) ctsp on U.S. 1853-A&R Seated Liberty quarter. (Tanenbaum coll.; Brunk N/L)

NY 582Q (1863) Silver 27mm 200. — 300. —
Similar ctsp on Spanish-American 1772 2-reales. (Tanenbaum coll.)

NY 582S (?) Silver 21mm — 75.00 — —
295 BOWE (RY) / N.Y. ctsp on Spanish-American 1-real. (Kirtley Dec. 1990 list; Brunk 4627).

Lewis Miller, barber extraordinaire, was located at 295 Bowery in 1848-1849, and probably later.

During the Civil War, he used a punch as on NY 582P with curved lines on blank planchets made of copper or of cupronickel, which he then passed as Civil War cents (Fuld 630AZ-1a and 1d). He also issued struck CWT's about 1863 and copper planchets with incused inscriptions. From these Civil War tokens we know he advertised his hair invigorator at 25 cents and his hair dye at 50 cents.

J. L. MILLER

Rulau	Date	Metal	Size	VG	F	VF	EF
NY 2067	(?)	Copper	29mm	—	75.00	—	125.00

J. L. MILLER / TIVOLI / NY ctsp on reverse of U.S. 1817 (?) Large cent. (Hartzog coll.; Brunk 27750)

It is possible this is a New York City piece for a place called the "Tivoli," or a card of Tivoli, N.Y. The letters are uneven, so individual letterpunches could have been used.

MODEL ARTIST'S

Miller	Date	Metal	Size	G	VG	F	EF
NY 583	(?)	Silver	27mm	200.	—	300.	—

ADMIT TO THE MODEL ARTIST'S / 127 GRAND ST. / NEAR B'WAY ctsp on Spanish-American 1778, 1782, 1793 or 1797 2-reales. 5 pieces known. (Gould 339; Brunk 28140)

Miller	Date	Metal	Size	G	VG	F	EF
NY 584	(?)	Silver	27mm	200.	—	300.	—

Similar ctsp on U.S. 1807 Bust type quarter dollar. (Gould 90)

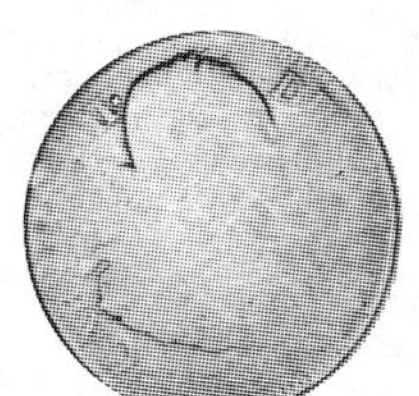

Miller	Date	Metal	Size	G	VG	F	EF
NY 583A	(?)	Silver	27mm	200.	—	275.	—

ADMIT / TO THE / MODEL ARTIST'S / 127 GRAND ST. / NEAR B-WAY ctsp on reverse of Spanish-American 1797-NG-M and 1820 silver 2-reales. (Tanenbaum collection)

This was an early "nude review," according to John J. Ford.

W. B. MOFFATT

Rulau	Date	Metal	Size	VG	F	VF	EF
NY 2580	(1855)	Copper	29mm	60.00	—	90.00	—

W. B. MOFFATT ctsp on U.S. Large cent. Examined: 1816. (Brunk 28155)

Rulau	Date	Metal	Size	VG	F	VF	EF
NY 2581	(1855)	Silver	25mm	60.00	—	90.00	—

Similar ctsp on U.S. 1854 Seated Liberty quarter.

Rulau	Date	Metal	Size	VG	F	VF	EF
NY 2582	(?)	Silver	21mm	60.00	—	90.00	—

MOFFATT ctsp on Spanish-American 1-real. (Brunk 28145)

Rulau	Date	Metal	Size	VG	F	VF	EF
NY 2583	(?)	Silver	27mm	60.00	—	90.00	—

Similar ctsp on Spanish-American 2-reales. Examined: 1747, 1830, 1843. 3 pieces known.

Rulau	Date	Metal	Size	VG	F	VF	EF
NY 2585	(?)	Silver	27mm	75.00	—	125.	—

W. B. MOFFATT / (Arrow through) W. B. M. ctsp on Spanish-American 2-reales. Only 1 reported. (Brunk 28160)

According to William Swoger, these are the counterstamps of physician William B. Moffatt, who was located at 336 Broadway in the 1840's and 1850's. In the city directory for 1849 he advertised his Life Pills and Phoenix Bitters.

He wrote: "The LIFE PILLS owe their title to the fact that they prolong and save life in thousands of instances every year, if not every month, week and day."

He added: "The PHOENIX BITTERS are so named because they possess the power of reviving the smothered embers of vitality throughout the physical constitution of man, as the phoenix is said to be re-vitalized in the smouldering ashes of its own dissolution by fire."

Great copy writing for quack remedies! His lengthy advertisement promised relief for virtually every ailment known to man or woman, even to travelers to California "in the absence of physicians and friends."

MORSONIC AMULET

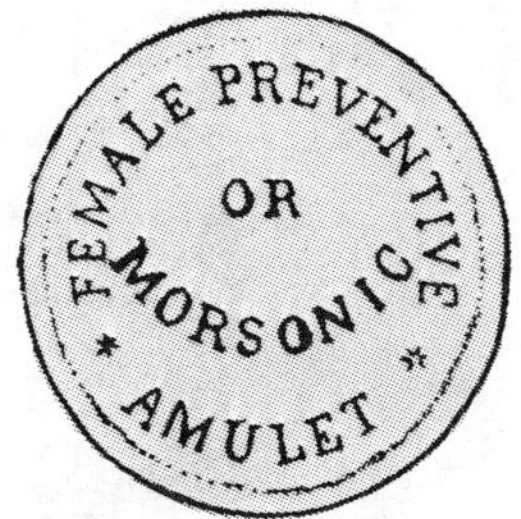

Miller	Date	Metal	Size	VG	F	VF	Unc
NY 238	(?)	Brass	34mm	—	—	750.	—

Coronet Liberty head left in central beaded circle; 15 stars in border. Rv: FEMALE PREVENTIVE / OR / MORSONIC / * AMULET *.

NY 239	(?)	White Metal	34mm	—	500.	750.	—
		As 238. (Wright 311)					
NY 239C	(?)	Silver	27mm	—	—	850.	—
		As 238, but struck over Prussia silver coin too small for the dies.					

NY 514	(?)	Copper	34mm	—	500.	750.	—
		Eagle displayed, U.S. shield on its breast, surrounded by circle of 18 stars. Rv: Around rim: MALE MORSONIC AMULET FOR MARRIED PEOPLE. (Wright 652)					

All types are rare. Electrotypes of both designs are known!

Walter Breen was of the opinion that the "Morsonic" amulet was a paean for "more sons" in an era when sons were valued more highly than daughters. The term "female preventive" tends to bear out his theory.

It would be of extreme interest to learn just what claims their makers advanced for these amulets.

Steve Tanenbaum believes all the amulets were made as electrotypes originally. All are of great rarity.

A. MORTON

Rulau	Date	Metal	Size	VG	F	VF	EF
NY 2530	1857	Copper	29mm	75.00	—	125.	—
		A / MORTON / NEW-YORK / 1857 in single letterpunch with small letters ctsp on U.S. 1843 or 1854 Large cent. (Charles Kirtley sale of Aug. 22, 1987, lot 123; Brunk 28570)					
NY 2531	1857	Silver	15.5mm	75.00	—	125.	—
		Similar ctsp on U.S. half dime. Examined: 1832, 1857.					

In 1856 Morton advertised that he manufactured gold pens and cases at 25 Maiden Lane.

MOSS' HOTEL

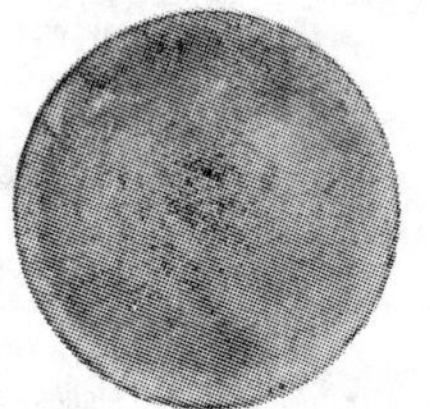

Miller	Date	Metal	Size	F	VF	EF	Unc
NY 587	(1852-54)	Copper	27mm	8.00	10.00	15.00	30.00
		MOSS' / HOTEL / COR. BOWERY & BAYARD. Rv: Blank. Plain edge.					
NY 588	(?)	Brass	27mm	8.00	10.00	15.00	30.00
		As 587. Plain edge.					
NY 589	(?)	Brass	27mm	20.00	30.00	40.00	60.00
		As 587 obverse. Rv: 6 d. (Stands for sixpence.) Plain edge.					
NY 589A	(?)	Brass	27mm	20.00	30.00	40.00	60.00
		As 589, but reverse is: 9 d. Plain edge.					
NY 590	(?)	Brass	27mm	20.00	30.00	40.00	60.00
		As 589, but reverse is: 1/-. (Stands for one shilling). Plain edge.					
NY 592	(?)	Brass	27mm	20.00	30.00	40.00	60.00
		As 589, but reverse is: 1/3. Plain edge.					
NY 593	(?)	Brass	27mm	20.00	30.00	40.00	60.00
		As 589, but reverse is: 1/6. Plain edge.					
NY 594	(?)	Brass	27mm	20.00	30.00	40.00	60.00
		As 589, but reverse is: 1/9. Plain edge.					
NY 595	(?)	Brass	27mm	20.00	30.00	40.00	60.00
		As 589, but reverse is: 2/-. Plain edge.					
NY 596	(?)	Brass	27mm	20.00	30.00	40.00	60.00
		As 589, but reverse is: 2/3. Plain edge.					
NY 597	(?)	Brass	27mm	20.00	30.00	40.00	60.00
		As 589, but reverse is: 2/6. Plain edge.					
NY 598	(?)	Brass	27mm	20.00	30.00	40.00	60.00
		As 589, but reverse is 2/9. Plain edge.					

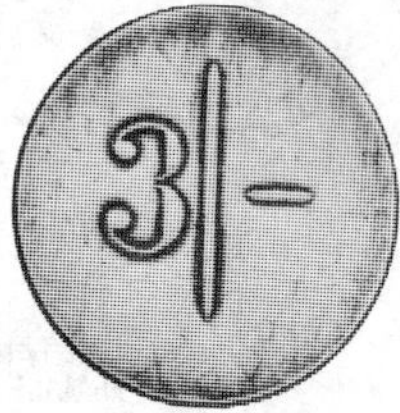

NY 599	(1852-54)	Brass	27mm	20.00	30.00	40.00	60.00
		As 589, but reverse is: 3/-. Plain edge.					
NY 599A	(?)	Brass	27mm	20.00	30.00	40.00	60.00
		3/-. Rv: 3/. (Both sides as reverse of 599; no name on token.)					
NY 600	(1852-54)	Brass	27mm	20.00	30.00	40.00	60.00
		As 589, but reverse is: 3/3. Plain edge.					
NY 601	(?)	Brass	27mm	20.00	30.00	40.00	60.00
		As 589, but reverse is: 3/6. Plain edge.					
NY 601A	(?)	Brass	27mm	20.00	30.00	40.00	60.00
		3/6. Rv: 3/6. (Both sides as reverse of 601; no name on token.)					
NY 602	(?)	Brass	27mm	20.00	30.00	40.00	60.00
		As 589, but reverse is: 3/9. Plain edge. (Wright 727)					
NY 603	(?)	Brass	27mm	20.00	30.00	60.00	80.00
		As 589, but reverse is: 4/-. Plain edge.					
NY 604	(?)	Copper	27mm	22.50	35.00	45.00	65.00
		Obverse as 589, Rv: Obverse of NY 861 (SWEENY'S HOTEL). Plain edge.					
NY 605	(?)	Brass	27mm	22.50	35.00	45.00	65.00
		Moss-Sweeny mule, same as NY 604. Plain edge.					
NY 606	(?)	Copper	27mm	22.50	35.00	45.00	65.00
		Obverse as 589. Rv: Obverse of NY 823 (SMITHSONIAN HOUSE, 606 BROADWAY). Plain edge.					
NY 607	(?)	Brass	27mm	22.50	35.00	45.00	65.00
		Moss-Smithsonian mule, same as NY 606. Plain edge.					
NY 608	(?)	Copper	27mm	22.50	35.00	45.00	65.00
		Obverse as 589. Rv: Obverse of NY 899 (A.D. THOMPSON). Plain edge.					
NY 609	(?)	Brass	27mm	22.50	35.00	45.00	65.00
		Moss-Thompson mule, same as NY 608. Plain edge.					

The cards of Moss' Hotel, Smithsonian House, Sweeny's Hotel and A.D. Thompson are die-linked by mulings. All but Sweeny's Hotel have their denominations indicated in pence and shillings, indicating possibly that they were hostelries catering to British Empire seamen.

The Moss cards were struck by Thomas L. Clark of New York, which see.

Daniel Moss was first listed in 1853-54 directory as a dining Saloon at 15 Bowery Street.

WM. J. MULLEN

Miller	Date	Metal	Size	F	VF	EF	Unc
NY 616	(1847)	Copper	33mm	40.00	50.00	100.	300.
		Male bust to left, WM. J. MULLEN GOLD DIAL MANUFACTURER above, ESTABLISHED 1828 N-YORK. Rv: Laboratory and five youths at work; three figures in air, one winged. Inscription: MEDALS AWARDED AS THE FIRST SUCCESSFUL MAKER OF GOLD WATCH DIALS IN AMERICA; A SILVER MEDAL BY THE FRANKLIN INSTITUTE in 1832; A GOLD MEDAL BY THE AMERICAN INSTITUTE, 1834; A MEDAL AWARDED BY THE MECHANICS INSTITUTE, N.Y., 1835. Plain edge. (Low 365; Wright 735).					
NY 616A	(1847)	Silver	33mm	—	—	—	500.
		As last.					

Louisa Lander cut the dies, and Charles Cushing Wright struck the medallic tokens in 1847. For many years the 1835 date, and Bushnell's mistaken statement that the dies "were cut by Lander in 1837," led this piece to be considered as Hard Times era issue. It is now correctly positioned.

Louisa Lander was 21 in 1847. A student of Thomas Crawford, she became a sculptress of note, but was a medalist only once, with this beautiful token.

WILLIAM P. MULLEN

Miller	Date	Metal	Size	F	VF	EF	Unc
NY 616A	1862	Copper	33mm	25.00	50.00	75.00	100.
		Same bust left as on NY 616, sprig underneath. WILLIAM P. MULLEN PRISON AGENT / I WAS IN PRISON AND YE CAME UNTO ME. Rv: COMMISSIONED / IN 1854 / BY THE GOVERNOR OF / PENNA. TO VISIT / THE PRISONS OF THE STATE TO / &C. 1862.					

JIM MYERS

Miller	Date	Metal	Size	VG	F	VF	Unc
NY 617	(Late 1840's)	Brass	29mm	75.00	125.	—	—
		Eagle with drooping wings, U.S. shield on breast. .JIM MYER'S. above, GREAT AMERICAN CIRCUS below. Rv: Three uninscribed circles, the central one beaded. Reeded edge. (Wright 740; Batty 4471b)					

NATIONAL JOCKEY CLUB

Miller	Date	Metal	Size	VG	F	VF	EF
NY 618	(?)	Brass	25mm	—	—	60.00	80.00
		Jockey on horse to right, ground beneath. Rv: NATIONAL / JOCKEY / CLUB / NEW-YORK. Rare. Reeded edge.					

N. YORK

Rulau	Date	Metal	Size	VG	F	VF	EF
NY 2700	(?)	Copper	29mm	60.00	—	90.00	—
		N. YORK in script ctsp on U.S. 1800, 1805, 1806 or 1832 Large cent. (Duffield 1385; Brunk 44660; Rulau Z118)					
NY 2701	(?)	Copper	29mm	60.00	—	90.00	—
		N. YORK in script ctsp on obverse of U.S. 1802 Large cent; eagle and sheaf of wheat ctsp on reverse of the coin. (Duffield 1386; Hallenbeck 25.750)					
NY 2702	(?)	Copper	29mm	100.	—	150.	—
		Similar ctsp on various Colonial and state coppers. Examined: New Jersey cent; Connecticut 1787 and 1788 cent; counterfeit England 1733 halfpenny. 4 known.					
NY 2703	(?)	Copper	29mm	100.	—	150.	—
		Similar ctsp on Vermont cent. Examined: 1787, 1788. 2 known.					

This stamp is in script and difficult to read. It probably was impressed in the Hard Times period or earlier.

Gregory Brunk now attributes this N. YORK mark as the hallmark of New York City silversmith John Burger, active 1784-1808. (See Belden 84-86)

Burger was a "regulator" of foreign gold coins.

NEW YORK S. D. & CO.

Miller	Date	Metal	Size	VG	F	VF	Unc
NY 624	(?)	Silver	Square, 22mm	—	—	50.00	Rare
		NEW YORK S. D. & CO.					

N. C. N. & H. MFG. CO.

Rulau	Date	Metal	Size	VG	F	VF	EF
NY 2227	(1859)	CN	19mm	—	30.00	—	—
		NCN & H. MFG. CO. N-Y ctsp on reverse of U.S. 1859 Indian cent. Rv: H. GETTY'S / PATENT / JULY 6, 1858 ctsp on obverse of the coin. (Van Ormer sale 2658; Brunk 16013)					

PRESCOTT'S SODA WATER

Miller	Date	Metal	Size	VG	F	VF	EF
NY 645	(1847-50)	German silver	17mm	15.00	25.00	50.00	100.
		Eagle with drooping wings, 20 FOR A DOLLAR above. Rv: .PRESCOTT'S. / 11 / WALL ST. / N.Y. / SODA WATER. in five lines. Plain edge. (Wright 844; H-G 5955)					
NY 645A	(1847-50)	GS	17mm	15.00	25.00	50.00	100.
		As last. Reeded edge.					

Though his token advertised his soda water, Henry W. Prescott was primarily a wine merchant, located at 11 Wall Street circa 1847-50. He appears as such in the 1848 and 1849 directories.

This piece was called a Civil War token erroneously by Hetrich-Guttag. It had been listed in the 1858 Numismatic and Antiquarian Society of Philadelphia booklet.

100 STREET

Miller	Date	Metal	Size	VG	F	VF	Unc
NY 625	(1850's)	Copper	28mm	50.00	75.00	100.	—
		(Three ornaments) / 100 STREET / (three ornaments) Rv: Same, but period after STREET.					

Dr. Horatio Storer reported this was an admission ticket to a Maison de Joie in New York.

QUINBY

Rulau	Date	Metal	Size	VG	F	VF	EF
NY 2068	(1856)	Silver	29mm	200.	—	300.	—
		QUINBY / 385 BROADWAY ctsp on Peru 1828-LMA-JM 2-reales. (Tanenbaum coll.; Brunk 33115)					
NY 2069	(?)	Silver	27mm	200.	—	300.	—
		QUINBY / 385 BROADWAY ctsp on Spanish-American 2-reales. (Gould 118)					
NY 2069A	(1856)	Silver	25mm	200.	—	300.	—
		Similar ctsp on U.S. 1854 S.L. quarter.					

Charles Josiah Quinby was a daguerreotyper at 385 Broadway 1856-60. He moved to Charleston, S.C. in 1860, returning to New York after the Civil War.

LOUIS RAHM

Miller	Date	Metal	Size	VG	F	VF	Unc
NY 651	(1858)	Silver	26mm	—	—	150.	300.
		Very old building occupied by Horter and Rahm; sign HORTER at top: RAHM over main entrance; HORTER / DIE / SINKER over upstairs entrance. ERECTED 1630 above; 178 / WILLIAM ST. N.Y. below. Rv: LOUIS RAHM / 176 WILLIAM ST. / N.Y. / COPPERSMITH / ALL KINDS / OF COPPER & / BRASSWORK. Plain edge.					
NY 652	(1858)	Copper	26mm	10.00	15.00	25.00	75.00
		As 651. Plain edge. (Wright 866)					
NY 653	(1858)	White Metal	26mm	—	—	50.00	100
		As 651. Plain edge.					

REES & CO.

New York ?

Miller	Date	Metal	Size	VG	F	VF	Unc
NY 2135	(?)	Silver	31mm	75.00	—	150.	—
		REES & CO / 385 BROADWAY ctsp on U.S. 1853 Arrows & Rays S.L. half dollar. (Partrick coll.; Brunk 33755)					

Note that the address is identical to Quinby, NY 2068, above!

STEPHEN RICHARDSON

Miller	Date	Metal	Size	VG	F	VF	Unc
NY 656	(1850's)	Brass	23mm	5.00	7.50	12.50	30.00
		Male bust left, STEPHEN RICHARDSON / MANUFR OF above; * JEWELRY * below. Tiny letters under bust: EDLER FEC. Rv: Eagle with drooping wings, shield on breast, OFFICE NO. 177 BROADWAY above * NEW - YORK.*. Reeded edge. (Wright 889)					
NY 656A	(1850's)	Silvered Brass	23mm	5.00	10.00	15.00	30.00
		As 656.					
NY 656B	(1850's)	Copper	23mm	5.00	10.00	15.00	30.00
		As 656.					

The dies were cut by someone named Edler, who signed these tokens EDLER FEC. Adams was in error in assigning these tokens to W. Idler the coin dealer as diesinker.

WM. H. RICHARDSON

Miller	Date	Metal	Size	F	VF	EF	Unc
NY 657	(?)	Brass	24mm	5.00	7.00	9.00	35.00
		Obverse same as obverse of Pa 421 (UMBRELLAS VERY SUPERIOR etc.). Rv: WM. H. RICHARDSON / 229 / BROADWAY / UP STAIRS / NEW YORK. Plain edge. (Wright 888)					
NY 657A	(?)	Brass	24mm	5.00	7.00	9.00	35.00
		As 657. Reeded edge.					
NY 658	(?)	Brass	24mm	5.00	7.00	9.00	35.00
		Similar to 657, but 418 MARKET ST., PHILADA. added on reverse.					

J.L. & D.J. RIKER

Miller	Date	Metal	Size	F	VF	EF	Unc
NY 661	1852	Brass	23mm	5.00	8.00	10.00	40.00
		Liberty head left, NEW YORK on coronet. Eight stars above, J.L. & D.J. 1852 RIKER below. Rv: MANUFACTURERS / — OF — / KNIFE / SCISSORS / * — AND — * / SCYTHE / SHARPENERS. Reeded edge. (Wright 892)					
NY 661A	1852	Brass	23mm	—	—	—	—
		As last. Plain edge.					
NY 662	1852	Brass	23mm	5.00	8.00	10.00	40.00
		Imitation of U.S. $5 gold piece. Obverse as 661. Rv: Eagle displayed.					

John L. Riker and Daniel J. Riker were manufacturers of sharpeners and other instruments located at 152 Delancy 1848-1849 and probably later.

RISLEY & MCCOLLUM'S HIPPODROME

Miller	Date	Metal	Size	VG	F	VF	Unc
NY 663	(?)	Brass	33mm	15.00	35.00	100.	175.
		Man standing, riding two horses to right. RISLEY & MC COLLUM'S / HIPPODROME. Rv: Ostrich drawing a chariot left at top, elephant with castle on its back to left below. Across center, TROISIEME (French for "third"). (Wright 897)					
NY 664	(?)	Copper	33mm	15.00	35.00	100.	175.
		As 663.					
NY 665	(?)	Silvered Brass	33mm	15.00	35.00	100.	175.
		As 663.					

This token has been reported with a DIEUXIEME reverse; very rare.

ROBBINS, ROYCE & HARD

Miller	Date	Metal	Size	F	VF	EF	Unc
NY 666	(1859)	Silver	19mm	—	—	100.	250.
		Nude bust of George Washington left. REPRESENTED BY WM. LEGGETT BRAMHALL. Rv: ROBBINS ROYCE & HARD / WHOLESALE / DEALERS IN / DRY GOODS / 70 READE ST. / NEW YORK. Only 7 struck. (Baker 568)					
NY 667	(1859)	Copper	19mm	—	—	25.00	45.00
		As 666. Only 52 struck.					
NY 668	(1859)	Brass	19mm	—	—	25.00	45.00
		As 666. Plain edge. Only 52 struck.					
NY 669	(1859)	Cupronickel	19mm	—	25.00	35.00	55.00
		As 666. Just 25 struck.					
NY 670	(1859)	WM	19mm	—	—	25.00	45.00
		As 666. Only 15 struck.					

Miller	Date	Metal	Size	F	VF	EF	Unc
NY 686	(1860)	Silver	19mm	—	—	250.	500.
		Profile bust of Abraham Lincoln right, surrounded by dotted circle. * ABRAHAM LINCOLN * / NATUS FEB. 12, 1809. Rv: As reverse of NY 667. Only 20 struck.					
NY 687	(1860)	Copper	19mm	—	—	75.00	150.
		As 686. Only 35 struck.					
NY 688	(1860)	Brass	19mm	—	—	75.00	150.
		As 686. Only 35 struck.					
NY 689	(1860)	Cupronickel	19mm	—	—	75.00	150.
		As 686. Only 250 struck.					
NY 690	(1860)	White Metal	19mm	—	—	75.00	150.
		As 686. Only 15 struck.					
NY 696	(1860)	Silver	19mm	—	—	175.	300.
		Oval shield bears on a scroll: WIDEAWAKES; above and below it a rose and leaves. ABRAHAM LINCOLN HONEST ABE OF THE WEST. Rv: As reverse of NY 666. Only21 struck.					
NY 697	(1860)	Copper	19mm	—	—	50.00	100.
		As 696. Only 35 struck.					
NY 698	(1860)	Brass	19mm	—	—	50.00	100.
		As 696. Only 35 struck.					
NY 699	(1860)	Cupronickel	19mm	—	—	50.00	100.
		As 696. Only 35 struck.					
NY 700	(1860)	White Metal	19mm	—	—	30.00	60.00
		As 696. Only 1500 struck.					

Miller	Date	Metal	Size	F	VF	EF	Unc
NY 691	(1860)	Silver	19mm	—	—	175.	300.
		Obverse: Lincoln obverse as on NY 686. Rv: As obverse of NY 711 (70 READE & 112 DUANE). Only 3 struck.					
NY 692	(1860)	Copper	19mm	—	—	75.00	150.
		As 691. Only 15 struck.					
NY 693	(1860)	Brass	19mm	—	—	75.00	150.
		As 691. Only 15 struck.					
NY 694	(1860)	Cupronickel	19mm	—	—	75.00	150.
		As 691. Only 15 struck.					

NY 695	(1860)	White Metal	19mm	—	—	75.00	150
		As 691. Only 15 struck.					
NY 701	(1860)	Silver	19mm	—	—	250.	400.
		Obverse as obverse of NY 696 (Shield, WIDEAWAKES). Rv: As obverse of NY 711 (70 READE & 112 DUANE). Only 3 struck.					
NY 702	(1860)	Copper	19mm	—	—	50.00	100.
		As 701. Only 15 struck.					
NY 703	(1860)	Brass	19mm	—	—	50.00	100.
		As 701. Only 15 struck.					
NY 704	(1860)	Cupronickel	19mm	—	—	50.00	100.
		As 701. Only 15 struck.					
NY 705	(1860)	White Metal	19mm	—	—	50.00	100.
		As 701. Only 15 struck.					

NY 711	(1860)	Silver	19mm	—	—	200.	400.
		ROBBINS ROYCE & HARD / JOBBERS / OF / STAPLE / & FANCY / DRY GOODS / 70 READE & 112 DUANE STS. / NEW YORK. Rv: As reverse of NY 667. Only 3 struck.					
NY 712	(1860)	Copper	19mm	—	—	35.00	75.00
		As 711. Only 15 struck. Also in Bronze.					
NY 713	(1860)	Brass	19mm	—	—	35.00	75.00
		As 711. Only 15 struck.					
NY 714	(1860)	Cupronickel	19mm	—	—	55.00	100.
		As 711. Only 15 struck. (Wright 899)					
NY 715	(1860)	White Metal	19mm	—	—	35.00	75.00
		As 711. Only 15 struck. Thick & thin planchets.					

NY 671	(1860)	Silver	19mm	—	—	100.	250.
		Obverse as obverse of NY 666 (Washington). Rv: As reverse of NY 711 (JOBBERS OF STAPLE & FANCY DRY GOODS). 20 struck. (Baker 569)					
NY 672	(1860)	Copper	19mm	—	—	15.00	40.00
		As 671. 35 struck.					
NY 673	(1860)	Brass	19mm	—	—	15.00	40.00
		As 671. 35 struck.					
NY 674	(1860)	WM	19mm	—	—	15.00	40.00
		As 671. 15 struck.					
NY 675	(1860)	CN	19mm	—	—	15.00	40.00
		As 671. Several hundred struck.					
NY 676	THE HANNIBAL OF AMERICA.						
	R Bust of Lincoln.						
		Silver.	7 struck.	—	—	—	275.
NY 677	Same.	Copper	35 struck	—	—	—	50.00
NY 677	Same.	Brass	?5 struck	—	—	—	50.00
NY 677	Same.	Tin	35 struck	—	—	—	50.00
NY 677	Same.	CN	250 struck	—	—	—	40.00

ROBBINS, ROYCE & HARD MEDALLIC CARDS

REV., A nude bust of Washington, profile, facing to the left; Legend: "Represented by Wm. Leggett Bramhall."

OBV., WIDEAWAKES

	Silver	3 struck
Same	Copper	15 struck
Same	Brass	15 struck
Same	Copper-nickel	15 struck
Same	White metal	15 struck

OBV., A profile bust of Abraham Lincoln, in citizen's dress, facing to the right, and surrounded by a dotted circle; Legend: "*Abraham Lincoln.* Natus Feb. 12, 1809."

	Silver	3 struck
Same	Copper	15 struck
Same	Brass	15 struck
Same	Copper-nickel	15 struck
Same	White metal	15 struck

During the winter of 1858-59, on the order of William Leggett Bramhall, NY 666-670 were executed by George H. Lovett. The cupronickel variety was struck on planchets which were procured at the U.S. Mint at Philadelphia by Lovett. Bramhall was under the impression that this was possibly the first token issued of the size of the cupronickel cent struck in that metal.

As the reverse of this card did not suit his purpose, he next issued NY 671 to 675. While the Adams listing would indicate that it was a muling of the two reverses, the listing of the numbers struck definitely shows that it was just an error listing.

The Adams listing of 676 to 680, is not really a store card, though listed here as such. This Lincoln political medalet (DeWitt AL 1860-73 King 70) was engraved and struck by George H. Lovett shortly after May 1860, on the orders of Bramhall. The Lincoln likeness was taken from a photograph given Bramhall by a friend, George B. Lincoln of Brooklyn. Of this medalet there were 7 struck in silver, 15 each in copper, brass, and white metal; and 250 in copper-nickel. Size 19mm. Bramhall considered this to be the first political medalet struck in CN of uniform size with the nickel cent.

As the reverse die of the above was injured, it was altered by the substitution of an oval shield bearing on a scroll WIDEAWAKES — above and below it, a rose and leaves. This was done in order to supply the demand for a quantity of these medalets, and to eliminate the term "The Hannibal of America" which was severely criticized by some. This political medalet (De Witt AL 1860-74; King 71) is found in the above list under Adams numbers 681 to 685 and again under numbers 706 to 710. Of this piece there were 21 struck in silver; 35 each in copper, brass, and copper-nickel; and about 1,500 in white metal.

During the fall of 1860, he was persuaded by some of his friends to issue a limited number of "mules" in the different metals. The number of these mules was limited to 3 of each insilver and 15 of each of the other four metals used. Of the three sets of silver, he retained one and believed the other two sets were in the possession of Robert Hewitt and Joseph N.T. Levick of New York. The metallic cards are worth $275 in Unc. silver and $50 each in Unc. in other metals.

Adams, NY 716 to 720 is the same as 666 to 670. Adams, NY 721 to 725 is the same as 671 to 675.

ROOT & CO.

Miller	Date	Metal	Size	F	VF	EF	Unc
NY 731	(1850's)	Copper	28mm	10.00	20.00	27.50	60.00
		Eagle displayed, shield on breast, ROOT & CO. above, N.Y. / DAGUERRIAN GALLERY 363 BROADWAY. below. Rv: Within wreath: FIRST / PREMIUM / AWARDED TO / ROOT & CO. / FOR BEST / DAGUERREOTYPES. Plain edge.					
NY 732	(1850's)	Brass	28mm	7.50	17.50	22.50	40.00
		As 731. Reeded edge. (Wright 914)					
NY 732A	(1850's)	Silv/Br	28mm	—	—	25.00	40.00
		As last. Reeded edge.					
NY 733	(ca 1860)	Copper	28mm	—	—	—	40.00
		Obverse as reverse of 731. Rv: Eagle, THERE IS NO DIFFICULTY TO HIM THAT WILLETH. (No issuer's name on token)					
NY 734	(ca 1860)	Brass	28mm	—	—	—	40.00
		As 733.					

The reverse of NY 733 is the reverse of a game counter depicting Louis Kossuth, made by Scovill Mfg. Co., Waterbury, Conn. in 1852. The muling is probably one of the Levick-inspired series.

S. ROOT

Miller	Date	Metal	Size	VG	F	VF	EF
NY 2145	(1854-58)	Silver	27mm	—	300.	—	—
		S. ROOT / 363 BROADWAY / N.Y. ctsp on Spanish-American 1806-LME 2-reales. (Koppenhaver Aug. 1982 sale; Brunk 35025)					

Samuel Root, daguerreotypist, was in business with his brother Marcus Aurelius (M.A.) Root at 363 Broadway until 1852, when M.A. moved to Philadelphia. Samuel was at 363 Broadway in 1853; he disappears with the 1859 directory.

ROYAL PREVENTIVE

Miller	Date	Metal	Size	VG	F	VF	Unc
NY 742	(?)	Bronzed Copper	25.5mm	—	350.	—	600.
		Eagle surrounded by circle of stars. Rv: ROYAL / PREVENTIVE. (Wright 920)					
NY 743	(?)	Brass	25.5mm	—	350.	—	600.
		As 742.					
NY 744	(?)	White Metal	25.5mm	—	350.	—	600.
NY 744A	(?)	Bronzed/WM	25.5mm	—	350.	—	600.
		As 742.					

RUSHTON, CLARK & CO.

Rulau	Date	Metal	Size	VG	F	VF	EF
NY 2140	(1848-58)	WM	18mm				200.
		RUSHTON, CLARK / DRUGGISTS / N.Y. / & CO. Beaded border. Rv: Blank. Plain edge. (Tanenbaum coll.)					

William L. Rushton was in business at 10 Astor House and also on Broadway at least as early as 1830. In 1840-1842 he was in partnership with William H. Aspinwall. He styled himself Rushton & Co. 1843-1848. Rushton, Clark & Co. (with George Clark) is listed 1848-1853. By 1859 Frederick V. Rushton was running the business.

Throughout this entire time frame (since 1830), Rushton maintained a location at 10 Astor House and one or more locations on Broadway. Rushton, Clark & Co. 1848-53 was at 165 Broadway and 273 Broadway.

Discovery of a totally unpublished early store card happens less frequently since the Rulau series of token catalogs began in 1980, but this fits that exception. Steve Tanenbaum acquired this piece about 1975; it is unique at the moment.

RUSSELL & ERWIN

Rulau	Date	Metal	Size	VG	F	VF	EF
NY 2590	(1840-60)	Copper	29mm	—	—	100.	—
		RUSSELL & ERWIN ctsp on U.S. 1838 Large cent, which also bears the ctsp of J. H. ROOT of Bristol, Conn., Brunk 35020. (William Swoger report; Brunk 35327)					

Isaac D. Russell and C. B. Erwin were hardware dealers at 92 John Street in mid-1840's. Erwin withdrew by 1850, but the business continued under the same name into the 1850's.

SACHEM OYSTER SALOON

Miller	Date	Metal	Size	VG	F	VF	EF
NY 748	(?)	Silver	25mm	250.	—	400.	—
		SACHEM / OYSTER SALOON / 273 BOWERY ctsp on Spanish-American 1783 or 1804 or 1818 2-reales. Only 4 pieces known. (Gould 119; Brunk 35535)					

Reportedly the Tammany Hall political movement began in the Sachem Oyster Saloon. The political movement was an outgrowth of the democratic social organization, the Society of the Sons of St. Tammany, organized in the 1780's in New York City.

A.B. SAGE & CO.

Miller	Date	Metal	Size	F	VF	EF	Unc
NY 749	1860	Silver	32mm	—	—	150.	250.
		View of building. CITY HALL, WALL ST. N.Y. Rv: A.B. SAGE & CO. / DEALERS IN / COINS / MEDALS & TOKENS / BOOKS, STATIONARY / ENGRAVINGS & PAINTINGS / AUTOGRAPHS / & / CURIOSITIES / CIRCULATING LIBRARY / 24 DIVISION ST. / NEW YORK / 1860.					
NY 750	1860	Copper	32mm	—	—	15.00	40.00
		As 749.					
NY 751	1860	Brass	32mm	—	—	15.00	40.00
		As 749. Plain edge.					
NY 752	1860	White Metal	32mm	—	—	15.00	40.00
		As 749. Plain edge.					
NY 753	1860	Silver	32mm	—	—	150.	250.
		View of house. SIR HENRY CLINTON'S HOUSE / NO. 1 / BROADWAY, / N.Y. Rv: As 749. Plain edge.					
NY 754	1860	Copper	32mm	—	—	15.00	40.00
		As 753. Plain edge.					
NY 755	1860	Brass	32mm	—	—	15.00	40.00
		As 753. (Wright 931)					
NY 756	1860	White Metal	32mm	—	—	25.00	60.00
		As 753. Reeded edge.					

Miller	Date	Metal	Size	F	VF	EF	Unc
NY 757	1860	Silver	21mm	—	—	100.	250.
		Washington bust left in Roman mantle, PATER PATRIAE around. Rv: A.B. SAGE & CO'S CIRCULATING LIBRARY 24 DIVISION ST. N.Y. TERMS 1 YEAR $2.00 — 6 MONTHS 1.00 — 3 MONTHS .50 1860, in ten lines, the first three and last one being curved.					
NY 758	1860	Copper	21mm	—	—	15.50	40.00
		As 757. Plain edge. (Baker 571)					
NY 759	1860	Brass	21mm	—	—	15.50	40.00
		As 757. (Baker 571)					
NY 760	1860	White Metal	21mm	—	—	15.50	40.00
		As 757. (Baker 571)					
NY 760A	1860	Cupronickel	21mm	—	—	30.00	60.00
		As 757. (Fuld collection)					

Miller	Date	Metal	Size	F	VF	EF	Unc
NY 761	1859	Silver	21mm	—	—	100.	250.
		Obverse as NY 757 (Washington bust in Roman mantle). Rv: GOOD FOR ONE CHANCE / IN / RAFFLE / FOR / NUMISMATIC / BOOKS / AT / A.B. SAGE & CO. / N.Y. / NOV. 1859 in ten lines, the first and last being curved. (Baker 572)					
NY 762	1859	Copper	21mm	—	—	15.50	40.00
		As 761. Plain edge. (Baker 572)					
NY 762A	1859	Copper		—	—	—	50.00
		As 762, but thick flan. (2.5mm thick).					
NY 763	1859	Brass	21mm	—	—	25.00	60.00
		As 761.					
NY 764	1859	White Metal	21mm	—	—	25.00	60.00
		As 761.					

Miller	Date	Metal	Size	F	VF	EF	Unc
NY 765	1860	Brass	21mm	—	—	20.00	40.00
		Obverse as reverse of NY 761 (RAFFLE. NOV. 1859). Rv: As reverse of NY 757 (CIRCULATING LIBRARY 1860).					
NY 765A	1860	Copper	21mm	—	—	—	40.00
		As 765. Plain edge. (Ganter coll.)					

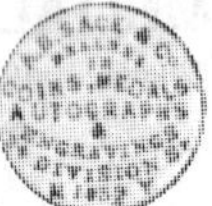

Miller	Date	Metal	Size	F	VF	EF	Unc
NY 766	1859	Copper	16mm	—	—	30.00	60.00
		Bust in Roman mantle right, in a half wreath of palm branches, GEORGE WASHINGTON around. Rv: A.B. SAGE & CO. DEALERS IN COINS, MEDALS, AUTOGRAPHS & ENGRAVINGS 24 DIVISION ST. N. 1859 Y. in nine irregular lines. (Fuld collection)					
NY 767	1859	Brass	16mm	—	—	20.00	45.00
		As 766.					
NY 768	1859	White Metal	16mm	—	—	20.00	45.00
		As 766. (Baker 570)					

Aug. B. Sage also issued several series of tokens utilizing some of the dies of his store card series.

The Sage non-store card tokens fall into four basic series: (1) Aug. B. Sage's Historical Tokens; (2) Aug. B. Sage's Numismatic Gallery; (3) Aug. B. Sage's Odds & Ends; (4) Masonic medalets. There are also mulings of a number of the Historical Token dies with each other which do not proclaim themselves members of any of the enumerated series. Several examples of this interesting group of Sage tokens are illustrated herewith. These pieces in Toned Unc. (copper or brass) are worth from $30 to $40 each on the collector market.

There are in all 9 Numismatic Gallery designs, 3 Odds and Ends, 1 Masonic medalet, and 14 Historical tokens.

The set of 14 Historical tokens was sold for $4 by Augustus B. Sage in 1859. Originals were all in copper, plain edge. Later copper with reeded edges, in both thick and thin planchets, were issued. Later also brass, white metal and silver tokens appeared. All were muled with each other, and there are more than 100 varieties known.

Historical Tokens No. 7

Historical Tokens No. 11

Numismatic Gallery No. 6

Odds & Ends No. 2

Odds & Ends No. 3

EDWARD SCHMIDT

Miller	Date	Metal	Size	F	VF	EF	Unc
NY 780	(?)	Brass	30mm	—	20.00	40.00	60.00
		EDWARD SCHMIDT. RESTAURANT, 194 FULTON ST., N.Y. Numeral 1 stamped at center. Rv: Eagle.					
NY 779	(?)	Brass	30mm	—	20.00	40.00	60.00
		As 780, but numeral 2.					
NY 781	(?)	Brass	30mm	—	20.00	40.00	60.00
		As 780, but numeral 50.					

SCOVILLS DAGUERREOTYPE MATERIALS

Miller	Date	Metal	Size	F	VF	EF	Unc
NY 805	(1850)	Gilt Brass	29mm	20.00	30.00	40.00	75.00
		Imitation of U.S. $10 gold piece, with SCOVILLS on Liberty's coronet. Five stars above: NEW YORK 101 WILLIAM ST below. Rv: Displayed eagle at center; SCOVILLS above; DAGUERREOTYPE MATERIALS below. Reeded edge.					

The Scovill firm of Waterbury, Conn. had its own outlet 1846-50 at 101 William St., New York. At this time the manufacture of daguerreotype plates became an important part of their business.

SCOVILL MANUFACTURING COMPANY

Miller	Date	Metal	Size	F	VF	EF	Unc
NY 802	(1855)	Copper	29mm	20.00	30.00	40.00	75.00
		Liberty head with SCOVILLS on coronet. SCOVILL MANUFACTURING CO., — DAGUERREOTYPE GOODS / MANUFACTURERS / OF / ROLL BRASS / GERMAN-SILVER / PLATED METAL / GILT BUTTONS BRASS BUTTONS & / PLATED WARE / &C &C &C. Rv: Eagle displayed, shield on breast. DAGUERREOTYPE / MATERIALS. above; 57 / MAIDEN. LANE. N.Y. below. Plain edge.					
NY 802A	(1855)	Copper	29mm	20.00	30.00	40.00	75.00
		As last. Reeded edge.					
NY 803	(1855)	Brass	29mm	20.00	30.00	40.00	75.00
		As 802. Reeded edge. (Wright 966)					
NY 803A	(1855)	Brass	29mm	20.00	30.00	40.00	75.00
		As last. Plain edge.					
NY 803B	(1855)	Silvered Brass	29mm	15.00	20.00	27.50	40.00
		As 802. Plain edge.					

SEA ISLAND SHIRTS

Miller	Date	Metal	Size	VG	F	VF	Unc
NY 806	(?)	Brass	23mm	20.00	35.00	50.00	100. *
		FURNISHING GOODS * / SEA / ISLAND / & / WASHINGTON / SHIRTS / & / COLLARS. / *** NEW-YORK. ***. Rv: ******** / (ornament) 57 (ornament) / LIBERTY / STREET. / -.- / ******. Plain edge. Thin flan.					

SEITZ BROS.

Miller	Date	Metal	Size	VG	F	VF	Unc
NY 807	(?)	Brass	23mm	—	—	75.00	—
		SEITZ BROS. ONE BIER. Rv: Female head. Plain edge.					

W. C. SINCLAIR

Rulau	Date	Metal	Size	VG	F	VF	EF
NY 2150	1847	Silver	27mm	60.00	—	90.00	—
		W. C. SINCLAIR / 1847 ctsp on Spanish-American 1816 2-reales. (Brunk 36655)					
NY 2150A	1847	Copper	29mm	60.00	—	90.00	—
		Similar ctsp on U.S. Large cent. (Hallenbeck 19.506; Rulau Z86)					
NY 2151	(?)	Copper	29mm	60.00	—	90.00	—
		W. C. SINCLAIR ctsp on U.S. Large cent. Examined: 1847, unknown date. Only 2 known. (Brunk 36650)					
NY 2152	(?)	Copper	29mm	60.00	—	100.	—
		W. C. SINCLAIR / N. Y. ctsp on U.S. 1819 Large cent. (Brunk 36660)					

F.B. SMITH & HARTMANN

Miller	Date	Metal	Size	F	VF	EF	Unc
NY 817	1860	Copper	29mm	20.00	30.00	40.00	65.00
		Indian head left, UNITED STATES OF AMERICA around, 1860 below. Rv: F.B. SMITH & HARTMANN / MEDAL / & GENERAL / DIE SINKERS. / & / 122 FULTON ST / COR. NASSAU / * NEW YORK *. Reeded edge.					
NY 818	1860	Brass	29mm	20.00	30.00	40.00	65.00
		As 817. Reeded edge. (Wright 1000)					
NY 819	1860	White Metal	29mm	20.00	30.00	40.00	65.00
		As 817. Reeded edge.					

Miller	Date	Metal	Size	F	VF	EF	Unc
NY 820	1860	Brass	29mm	—	—	50.00	80.00
		Obverse as 817 (Indian head, 1860). Rv: Race horse left. Around: FLORA TEMPLE / QUEEN OF THE TROTTING TURF. Tiny S & H under ground.					
NY 820A	1860	WM	29mm	—	—	50.00	80.00
		As 820.					

Miller	Date	Metal	Size	F	VF	EF	Unc
NY 820C	1860	Brass	29mm	20.00	30.00	40.00	75.00
		Obverse as NY 817 (Indian head, tiny S & H under truncation). Rv: Racehorse standing left, GEORGE M. PATCHEN above, THE GREAT TROTTING STALLION below. Tiny S & H under ground beneath horse. Reeded edge. Thick flan. (Spangenberger collection)					
NY 820D	1860	White Metal	29mm	20.00	30.00	40.00	75.00
		As 820A. Reeded edge. Thick flan.					
NY 820E	(1860)	Copper	29mm	—	—	60.00	100.
		Obverse as reverse of NY 820A (Dan Patchen). Rv: Horse standing, FLORA TEMPLE above, QUEEN OF THE TROTTING TURF below (reverse of NY 820). Reeded edge. Thick flan. (Wright 1571). A muling.					
NY 820F	(1860)	WM	29mm	—	—	—	100.
		As 820E.					

F.B. Smith & Hartmann were the successors to the successful diesinking and engraving business of Bale & Smith (James Bale and F.B. Smith). Smith & Hartmann came into being in 1848. According to Richard D. Kenney ("Early American Medalists and Die-Sinkers," New York, 1954), they were in turn succeeded by Smith & Horst.

Kenney says this Smith-Hartmann to Smith-Horst change took place in 1857 which is in error, as the date of 1860 on the Smith-Hartmann store cards attests. Also, in Leonard Forrer's "Biographical Dictionary of Medalists," Smith & Hartmann are credited with being in business in 1860. Smith signed political tokens in 1864. Herman Hartmann died in 1865.

It is interesting to realize that the Smith & Hartmann combine continued a lengthy business of diesinkers under a number of different owners dating back to 1821. Viz:

Richard Trested 1821-1829
Charles Cushing Wright & James Bale 1829-1833
James Bale 1833/1835
James Bale & F.B. Smith 1835-1848
F.B. Smith & Herman Hartmann 1848-1865
Smith & Horst 1865-on

History of the famous horse George M. Patchen is in the book THE AMERICAN TROTTER by John Hervey (Chicago, 1946).

Father of George M. Patchen, 2:23 -1/2 was Cassius M. Clay, 18.

Mother's pedigree was never cleared up but supposed to have been by Headem, a thoroughbred son of Imperial Trustee. Her foal (1849) proved to be a brown colt without white that at maturity stood over 16 hands high, was of great strength and power but somewhat lacking in quality, and is known in history as George M. Patchen, 2:23 -1/2, the first trotting stallion to reach 2:25 (in 1860).

After four times lowering the world's record for his sex, he left it at 2:23 -1/2, while in one of his many races with Flora Temple, 2:19 3/4, then the Queen of the Turf. He was beaten by a head in 2:21.

George M. Patchen lived to be 15. That he did not found a tribe of his own has been made the subject of criticism, in reality unjust. G.M. Patchen was a truly great performer.

Both George M. Patchen and Flora Temple are depicted on Smith & Hartmann tokens.

JAS. S. SMITH & CO.

Miller	Date	Metal	Size	VG	F	VF	Unc
NY 813	(1853-61)	Cop. Decagonal	24mm	5.00	8.00	15.00	45.00
		Military hat at center, JAS. S. SMITH & CO. / MILITARY GOODS. Rv: MANUFACTORY & SALES ROOM / 15 DUTCH ST. / N. YORK. ('15 DUTCH ST. / N. YORK' in a circle).					
NY 814	(1853-61)	Brass Decagonal	24mm	5.00	8.00	15.00	45.00
		As 813. (Wright 1002)					
NY 815	(1853-61)	Silvered Copper Decagonal	24mm	5.00	8.00	15.00	45.00
		As 813.					
NY 816	(1853-61)	Brass Decagonal	24mm	10.00	15.00	25.00	60.00
		As 813, but 'NO. 15 / DUTCH ST. / N. YORK' in three horizontal lines.					

James S. Smith, military goods, was listed in the 1848 and 1849 directories at 139 Fulton Street.

He first appeared at 15 Dutch St. in 1853. The style was changed to James S. Smith (no '& Co.') 1862-64.

SMITHSONIAN HOUSE

Miller	Date	Metal	Size	VG	VF	EF	Unc
NY 823	(1859-61)	Copper	26mm	5.00	10.00	15.00	40.00
		SMITHSONIAN / 606 / BROADWAY / HOUSE. Rv: Blank. (Wright 1008) The lettering is crude.					
NY 823B	(1859-61)	Brass	26mm	—	20.00	30.00	—
		As last.					
NY 823A	(?)	Copper	26mm	10.00	20.00	30.00	60.00
		Obverse similar. Rv: Large 2/6 (two shillings sixpence).					
NY 824	(?)	Brass	26mm	10.00	20.00	30.00	60.00
		As 823A.					

NY 825	(?)	Brass	26mm	10.00	20.00	30.00	60.00
		Obverse as 823. Rv: Large 3/.					
NY 825B	(1859-61)	Brass	26mm	15.00	25.00	40.00	60.00
		Obverse as 823. Rv: Large 4/6.					
NY 826	(?)	Brass	26mm	15.00	25.00	40.00	60.00
		Obverse as 823. Rv: Large 10/6.					
NY 826F	(?)	Copper	26mm	—	—	20.00	40.00
		Obverse as 823. Rv: As obverse of Thompson card, NY 899.					

LEWIS L. SQUIRE & SONS

Miller	Date	Metal	Size	F	VF	EF	Unc
NY 832	(?)	Silver	29mm	—	—	150.	250.
		LEWIS L. SQUIRE & SONS / SHIP CHANDLERS / AND / ROPE MAKERS. / 283 / FRONT ST. / ** NEW YORK **. Rv: DEALERS / IN / ANCHORS / OILS / PAINTS / BLOCKS &C. / OAKUM SPIKES NAVAL STORES / IMPORTERS OF CHAIN CABLES. Plain edge.					
NY 833	(?)	Copper	29mm	5.00	10.00	15.00	40.00
		As 832. Thick planchet. Plain edge.					
NY 834	(?)	Copper	29mm	5.00	10.00	15.00	50.00
		As 832. Thin planchet. Plain edge. (Wright 1035)					
NY 835	(?)	Brass	29mm	5.00	10.00	20.00	50.00
		As 832.					
NY 836	(?)	White Metal	29mm	5.00	10.00	45.00	75.00
		As 832. Very thick planchet.					
NY 837	(?)	Lead	29mm	—	—	—	150.
		Obverse as 832. Rv: VIRTUE LIBERTY & INDEPENDENCE.					

Lewis L. Squire & Sons were successors of Squire & Merritt, ship chandlers of the Hard Times period. In 1844-54 they are listed at 283 Front St.

L.L. Squire & Jacob T. Merritt — 175 South St., corner Roosevelt -	1831-1837
L.L. Squire -	1840-1841
L.L. Squire & Sons -	1844-1854 (283 Front St.)

JOS. STINER & CO.

Miller	Date	Metal	Size	VG	F	VF	Unc
NY 839	(1850's)	Brass	22mm	10.00	15.00	20.00	40.00
		JOS. STINER & CO. / IMPORTERS / TEAS & COFFEES / RETAILERS / NEW YORK. Rv: ESTABLISHED / 1/4 / (six-pointed star) / 1840. Plain edge.					

NY 839A	(1850's)	Brass	22mm	10.00	15.00	20.00	40.00
		As 839, but a letter has been ctsp inside the star. Examined: O, P, Q, R, T, U, W, Y.					
NY 840	(1850's)	Brass	--mm	12.00	16.00	20.00	40.00
		Similar to 839, but 1/2 and six-pointed star in reverse field. Plain edge.					
Miller	**Date**	**Metal**	**Size**	**VG**	**F**	**VF**	**EF**
NY 840A	(1850's)	Brass	--mm	12.00	16.00	20.00	40.00
		As 840, but a letter has been ctsp inside the star. Examined: O, P, S, T, U, W, Y.					
NY 840E	(1850's)	Brass	--mm	20.00	30.00	40.00	60.00
		Similar to 830, but 3/4 and six-pointed star in reverse field. Plain edge.					
NY 840F	(1850's)	Brass	--mm	20.00	30.00	40.00	60.00
		As 840E, but 'S' ctsp within star.					
NY 840H	(1850's)	Brass	--mm	20.00	30.00	40.00	60.00
		Similar to 839, but large numeral 1 and six-pointed star in reverse field. Plain edge.					
NY 840J	(1850's)	Brass	--mm	20.00	30.00	40.00	60.00
		As 840H, but 'U' or 'W' ctsp within star.					

It is not known what purpose was served by the countersunk (actually in relief within star-shaped depression) letters, but it is probable that more exist which have not been reported. The date 1840 is the founding date for the firm, which also issued tokens in 1876 (Adams numbers 838 and 838A) under the name Stiner Tea Company.

The 1/4, 1/2 and 3/4 probably pertain to fractions of a pound of coffee or tea.

Joseph Stiner & Co. do not appear in either the 1841, 1849 or 1854 New York city directories. Yet their tokens clearly state "established 1840." Perhaps they were established elsewhere, or under a different name.

Joseph Stiner & Co. appears in the 1861 directory. By 1875 Joseph Stiner & Co. has 23 Manhattan locations.

Also in 1875 Jacob Steiner & Co. had 18 Manhattan locations; a partner, Moses H. Moses, operated 1875-76 in Brooklyn under the style J. Stiner & Co. at 785 Columbia. Other Brooklyn locations in 1872 were Myrtle Ave. corner Prince and 255 Grand. One Philip Stiner had 18 Manhattan locations in 1875.

The Stiners were either an early conglomerate or chain store operation. The ctsp letters could be for store locations, or tea brands, or something else entirely.

STEWART BROS.

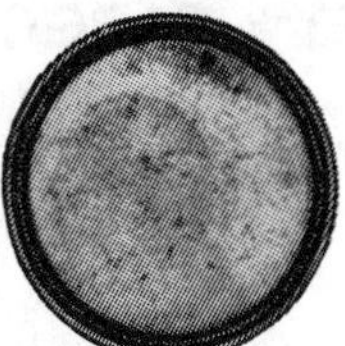

Rulau	Date	Metal	Size	VG	F	VF	EF
NY 2240	(1850's)	Brass	23mm	—	—	35.00	—
		STEWART BROS. / SHIRT / MAKERS. / 257 G'NWICH ST. N.Y. Rv: Blank. Plain edge. (Schenkman coll.)					

SWEENY'S HOTEL

Miller	Date	Metal	Size	VG	F	VF	Unc
NY 850	(1852-59)	German Silver	30mm	10.00	22.50	27.50	50.00
		SWEENY'S HOTEL / (diagonal line, the shilling sign) / CORNER OF / CHATHAM & DUANE STS. NEW YORK. Rv: D. SWEENY & SON / (diagonal line).					

NY 851	(?)	German Silver	30mm	10.00	22.50	27.50	50.00
		As 850, but 1/ replaces diagonal line on each side. (Means 'one shilling')					
NY 852	(?)	German Silver	30mm	10.00	22.50	27.50	50.00
		As 851, but 1/3.					
NY 853	(?)	German Silver	30mm	10.00	22.50	27.50	50.00
		As 851, but 2/.					
NY 854	(?)	German Silver	30mm	10.00	22.50	27.50	50.00
		As 851, but 2/6. (Wright 1646)					
NY 855A	(1852-59)	German Silver	30mm	10.00	22.50	27.50	50.00
		As 851, but 3/.					

NY 856	(1859-63)	German Silver	30mm	10.00	22.50	27.50	50.00
		SWEENY'S / — 64 — / CHATHAM ST. / — N.Y. — / HOTEL. Rv: SWEENY'S / DINING / (empty space) / SALOON / 64 CHATHAM ST. N.Y. (Wright 1081)					
NY 857	(?)	German Silver	30mm	8.00	15.00	25.00	50.00
		As 856, but numeral 13 in field.					
NY 858	(?)	German Silver	30mm	15.00	22.50	27.50	50.00
		As 856, but 50.					
NY 859	(?)	German Silver	30mm	15.00	22.50	27.50	50.00
		As 856, but 87.					
NY 860	(?)	German Silver	30mm	15.00	22.50	27.50	50.00
		As 856, but 94.					
		Also known with ctsps 1/, 1/3, 2/ and 20/.					

NY 861	(?)	Copper	25mm	10.00	17.50	22.50	40.00
		SWEENY'S / HOTEL. Rv: Blank.					
NY 862	(?)	Brass	26.5mm	10.00	17.50	22.50	40.00
		Obverse as 856. Rv: Numeral 15 in blank field.					
NY 863	(?)	Copper	30mm	12.50	20.00	25.00	50.00
		Obverse as 856. Rv: SMITHSONIAN / 606 / BROADWAY / HOUSE.					
NY 864	(?)	Brass	20mm	—	—	15.00	40.00
		As 863.					
NY 865	(1853-59)	Brass	30mm	—	—	15.00	40.00
		Obverse as 856. Rv: A. D. THOMPSON / DINING / SALOON / 25 PINE ST.					
NY 865F	(?)	Copper	30mm	—	—	15.00	40.00
		SWEENY'S (curved) / HOTEL (straight). Rv: Blank. Plain edge.					

Daniel Sweeny kept his "refectory" at 66 Chatham Street (next door to the hotel and dining saloon?) in 1847-1853, according to city directories.

He opened his hotel at 64 Chatham in 1859-63, moving it to 68 Chatham 1864-78.

SWIFT & FARGO AMERICAN HOTEL

Miller	Date	Metal	Size	VG	F	VF	Unc
NY 867	(1850's)	Brass	27mm	5.00	10.00	20.00	40.00
		SWIFT & FARGO AMERICAN HOTEL, 135 FULTON ST. Rv: Diagonal line.					
NY 868	(?)	Brass	27mm	12.50	20.00	27.50	65.00
		As 867. Rv: 6d.					
NY 870	(?)	Brass	27mm	12.50	20.00	27.50	65.00
		As 868, but 1/6.					

NY 869	(?)	Brass	27mm	12.50	20.00	27.50	65.00
		As 868, but 2/.					
NY 871	(?)	Brass	27mm	12.50	20.00	27.50	65.00
		As 868, but 2/6.					
NY 872	(?)	Brass	27mm	12.50	20.00	27.50	65.00
		As 868, but 5/.					
NY 873	(?)	Brass	27mm	12.50	20.00	27.50	65.00
		As 868, but 5/6.					
NY 874	(?)	Brass	27mm	12.50	20.00	27.50	65.00
		As 868, but 7/.					
NY 875	(?)	Brass	27mm	12.50	20.00	50.00	70.00
		As 868, but 9/6.					
NY 876	(1850's)	Brass	27mm	20.00	27.50	50.00	70.00
		As NY 868, but 13/ on reverse. (Thirteen shillings was a most unusual denomination in the first half of the 19th century.)					

Before 1849 there was an American Hotel at Broadway and Barclay, whose proprietor was S. Thayer Cozzens. He died about 1849.

Swift & Fargo were not his successors. Their American Hotel was at 135 Fulton Street. Edward W. Fargo, hotel, corner 3rd Avenue and East 24th Street, was listed in 1848-49. He may have been one of the partners. The probable date of issue of NY 867-876 was in the early 1850's.

T.P.D.

Miller	Date	Metal	Size	VG	F	VF	Unc
NY 913A	(?)	Brass	16mm	10.00	15.00	30.00	50.00
		Eagle within circle of 13 stars. Rv: T.P.D. / 5C. (Wright 1154)					
NY 914	(?)	Brass	16mm	10.00	15.00	30.00	50.00
		As last, but 25.					
NY 913	(?)	Brass	28mm	10.00	15.00	30.00	50.00
		Similar, but 50. Reeded edge.					
NY 913P	(?)	Brass	28mm	10.00	15.00	40.00	60.00
		Similar to 913, but T.P.D. (periods added).					

G. TAYLOR & SON

Miller	Date	Metal	Size	VG	F	EF	Unc
NY 890	(1844-45)	Brass	29mm	5.00	8.00	15.00	50.00
		Odd-looking eagle with drooping wings, shield on breast. G. TAYLOR & SON / NO 45 CEDAR ST. above; NEW YORK. below. Rv: IMPORTERS / AND / AGENTS FOR / SCOVILLS GILT / WILLISTONS / LASTING / HORN BONE AND / ALL OTHER KINDS / OF / BUTTONS. Reeded edge. (Wright 1093; Bushnell 69)					

Gad Taylor, 158 Pearl St., was the New York commission agent for J.M.L. & W.H. Scovill of Waterbury, Conn., the great button and token makers, as early as 1828. He was near bankruptcy and bailed out by Scovill 1833-34, then took bankruptcy in the Panic of 1837, losing his agency to Russell, Mattison & Co. Taylor was hired as a salesman by Russell, Mattison.

In late 1843 Gad Taylor and his son had their own outlet for Scovill buttons at 45 Cedar St. Robert J. Lindesmith (in "Dating the Store Card of G. Taylor & Son," in TAMS Journal for Jan. 1968) opined that NY 890 commemorated the reopening of Gad Taylor's business. The style, however, appears a bit later.

Here is a rundown on Gad Taylor's known locations:

Gad Taylor	91 Maiden Lane	1836-38
Gad Taylor	43 Cedar St.	1838-41
Gad Taylor	45 Cedar St.	1841-43
Russell, Mattison & Taylor	45 Cedar St.	1843-44
Gad Taylor & Son	45 Cedar St.	1844-49
Taylors & Richards	45 Cedar St.	1849-52
Taylors, Richards & Co.	45 Cedar St.	1852-54
Taylor, Richard & Owens	45 Cedar St.	1854-56
Taylor, Richard & Owens	36 Vesey St.	1856-59

TAYLORS & RICHARDS

Miller	Date	Metal	Size	VG	F	EF	Unc
NY 891	(1849-50)	Brass	29mm	5.00	8.00	15.00	40.00
		Eagle displayed, shield on breast. TAYLORS & RICHARDS / NO. 45 CEDAR ST. above; NEW-YORK. below. Rv: Same reverse as NY 890. Reeded edge. (Wright 1096)					

Gad Taylor and his son (the Taylors') apparently took on a partner (Richards) at the 45 Cedar St. address in 1849 (see G. Taylor & Son).

J.M. TAYLOR

Miller	Date	Metal	Size	VG	F	VF	EF
NY 889	(1850's)	Silver	27.5mm	—	40.00	—	60.00
		J.M. TAYLOR / BROKER / CHATHAM ST. / COR. JAMES N.Y. ctsp on U.S. Draped Bust quarters. Dates examined: 1803, 1805. (Brunk 39480)					

NY 889A	(1850's)	Silver	27mm	—	40.00	—	60.00
		Similar ctsp on U.S. Capped Bust quarters. (Dates examined: 1815, 1818, 1820)					
NY 889B	(1850's)	Silver	25mm	—	40.00	—	60.00
		Similar ctsp on U.S. Capped Bust quarters of reduced size. (Dates examined: 1837)					

Miller	Date	Metal	Size	VG	F	VF	Unc
NY 889C	(1858)	Silver	25mm	—	35.00	—	50.00
		Similar ctsp on U.S. Seated Liberty quarters. Dates examined: 1852, 1853-Arrows, 1854-Arrows, 1854, 1856, 1857. At least 58 specimens are known, including 46 pieces dated 1853! (Duffield 1422; Gould 93)					

Miller	Date	Metal	Size	VG	F	VF	Unc
NY 889D	(1850's)	Silver	31mm	—	60.00	—	90.00
		Similar ctsp on U.S. Seated Liberty half dollars. Dates examined: 1853-Arrows, 1854-Arrows, 1856). There are 8 known specimens.					
NY 889E	(1850's)	Silver	31mm	—	60.00	—	90.00
		As 889D, with added ctsp: SCHLICK. on 1853-Arrows half.					
NY 889F	(1850's)	Silver	21mm	—	60.00	—	80.00
		Similar ctsp on Spanish-American 1-real coin, 1796 and date not known.					

Miller	Date	Metal	Size	VG	F	VF	Unc
NY 889G	(1850's)	Silver	27mm	40.00	—	60.00	—
		Similar ctsp on Spanish-American 2 reales. Dates examined: 1752, 1771, 1773, 1779, 1781-Mo, 1786-Mo, 1796-Mo, 1801, 1803-LME-JP, 1804, 1819, 1821, 1822, date worn. At least 20 specimens known. (Gould 126)					

J.M. Taylor was a broker who issued advertising countermarks during the 1850's for his offices in New York (above) and in Brooklyn (which see).

Besides the counterstamped coins, Taylor overprinted broken bank notes in the 1850's with this stamp: J.M. TAYLOR / BROKER / 169 / CHATHAM SQUARE / N.Y.

His address in 1854 was 169 Chatham Street.

R.F. THOMAS

Miller	Date	Metal	Size	VG	F	VF	Unc
NY 898	(1849-50)	Brass	28mm	5.00	10.00	20.00	55.00
		R.F. THOMAS — MANUFACTURING JEWELER / REAR / 247 / GRAND ST. / N.Y. / 3RD FLOOR. Rv: R.F. THOMAS / JEWELER / 247 GRAND ST., N.Y. (Wright 1139)					

This jeweler was at 276 Bowery 1848-49. The token, with address 247 Grand St., 2nd floor, probably was issued 1849-50 when directories show he was there. He was at 257 Grand 1851 and disappears 1853.

The dies were cut by Thomas L. Clark, New York City, according to Bushnell who wrote from the advantage of contemporary examination.

A.D. THOMPSON

Miller	Date	Metal	Size	VG	F	VF	Unc
NY 899	(1850-58)	Copper	27mm	—	—	15.00	40.00
		A.D. THOMPSON / DINING / SALOON / 25 PINE ST. Rv: Blank. Plain edge. (Wright 1142)					
NY 900	(?)	Brass	27mm	15.00	25.00	35.00	50.00
		As 899.					
NY 901	(?)	Copper	27mm	15.00	40.00	60.00	80.00
		Obverse as 899. Rv: 1/6.					
NY 902	(?)	Brass	27mm	20.00	40.00	60.00	80.00
		As 901.					
NY 903	(?)	Copper	27mm	20.00	40.00	60.00	80.00
		As 901, but 2/.					
NY 904	(?)	Brass	27mm	20.00	40.00	60.00	80.00
		As 903.					
NY 905	(?)	Copper	27mm	20.00	40.00	60.00	80.00
		As 910, but 2/6.					
NY 906	(?)	Brass	27mm	20.00	40.00	60.00	80.00
		As 905.					

For mulings of the Thompson cards with Moss' Hotel, Smithsonian House or Sweeny's Hotel, see under these issuers.

Austen D. Thompson kept his "coffee rooms" at 13 Pine 1843-46, then 23 Pine St., 1847-49. This is one door from the tokens' "dining saloon" at 25 Pine St. His coffee room-restaurant is listed at 25 Pine 1850-53; then 20 Pine in 1859. The tokens were first cataloged 1859.

With this listing, we can safely assign all the tokens of Thompson, Smithsonian House, Sweeny's Hotel and Moss' Hotel to the 1850-59 period. These issuers' tokens are all muled with each other by their common maker, who was Thomas L. Clark of New York.

S.H. THOMPSON

Miller	Date	Metal	Size	VG	F	VF	Unc
NY 911	(?)	Brass	25mm	30.00	50.00	75.00	100.
		S.H. THOMPSON, Rv: Blank.					
NY 912	(?)	Brass	25mm	30.00	50.00	75.00	100.
		Obverse as 911. Rv: 2/6.					

EDWARD TODD & CO.

Rulau	Date	Metal	Size	VG	F	VF	EF
NY 2160	(1870's)	Silver	18mm	—	125.	—	175.
		EDWARD TODD / — & CO — / NEW YORK / 5 ctsp on smoothed-off reverse of U.S. 1840 Seated Liberty dime. (Van Ormer sale 2888; Brunk 40245)					

This firm manufactured silverware in New York 1869-1927.

C.C. TRACY

Rulau	Date	Metal	Size	VG	F	VF	EF
NY 2072	(1848-49)	Silver	27mm	200.	—	300.	—
		C.C. TRACY / SAW FILER / 458 HUDSON ST. / NEW YORK ctsp on Spanish-American 2-reales. (Dates examined: 1790-LME-IJ, 1805) (Brunk 40380).					

NY 2073	(1848-49)	Silver	27mm	200.	—	300.	—

C.C. TRACY / SAW FILER / NEW YORK ctsp on Spanish-American 2-reales. (Dates examined: 1780). (Gould 127; Van Ormer Sale 2889; Brunk 40375)

Caleb C. Tracy the saw filer kept his business at 458 Hudson St. circa 1848-51. In 1847-48 he was at 91 Hammersley; he was first listed in 1844.

U.S. HOTEL

Rulau	Date	Metal	Size	VG	F	VF	Unc
NY 2076	(1850's)	Brass	33mm	30.00	50.00	75.00	125.

U.S. HOTEL / NEW-YORK. (Lot 1864 in the 1863 Bangs Merwin & Co. sale of the Haines collection)

UPSONS CAPITOL

Miller	Date	Metal	Size	F	VF	EF	Unc
NY 928	(?)	Brass	27mm	100.	150.	175.	225.
		UPSONS CAPITOL, 349 BROADWAY, COR. LEONARD. Rv: 6d.					
NY 929	(?)	Brass	27mm	100.	150.	175.	225.
		As 928, but 3/.					
NY 930	(?)	Brass	27mm	100.	150.	175.	225.
		As 928, but 4/6.					
NY 931	(?)	Brass	27mm	100.	150.	175.	225.
		As 928, but 7/6.					
NY 931A	(?)	Brass	27mm	100.	150.	175.	225.
		As 928, but 16/.					

Dies cut by Thomas L. Clark.

VALENTINE & BUTLER

Rulau	Date	Metal	Size	VG	F	VF	EF
NY 2600	1855	Silver	25mm	—	—	150.	—

VALENTINE / -&- / BUTLER / — N.Y. — / PATENT / OCT 30 / 1855 ctsp on U.S. 1845-O S.L. quarter. (Brunk 41045)

Valentine & Butler manufactured rotary locks, safes etc. from the 1850's to 1880's in New York. The partners were Alfred A. Valentine (born 1819) and William H. Butler. In the 1850's they were at 92 Maiden Lane, then at 78 & 80 Walker in the late 1860's. By 1880 their address was 291 Broadway. Valentine retired in 1880's but Butler carried on under his own name.

ISAAC STEVENS VANDERBILT

Miller	Date	Metal	Size	VG	F	VF	Unc
NY 932	1859	Cop. over Lead	19mm	20.00	25.00	40.00	100.

Imitation U.S. Flying Eagle cent. ISAAC STEVENS VANDERBILT above flying eagle, 1859 below. Rv: Within the cent-type wreath is: HAPPY / NEW YEAR. Plain edge. (Wright 1184)

Dr. Wright called this piece Rare in 1901. It may be a product of electrotyper Samuel H. Black, as the Philip A. Dougherty 1859 piece apparently is.

D. VENTEN

Miller	Date	Metal	Size	F	VF	EF	Unc
NY 934	1860	Brass	18.5mm	100.	250.	350.	500.

Bust of Abraham Lincoln, 1860. Rv: D. VENTEN'S NEEDLE THREADERS, 178 DUANE ST. Only 3 struck. (King 636)

WALTON

Rulau	Date	Metal	Size	VG	F	VF	EF
NY 2077	(1858-62)	Copper	29mm	—	75.00	—	125.
		WALTON (curved) / 67 WARREN ST. / N.Y. ctsp on U.S. 1844 Large cent. (Tanenbaum coll.; Brunk 41664)					
NY 2078	(?)	Silver	32.5mm	—	125.	—	175.
		WALTON & CO / NEW YORK ctsp on U.S. 1836 bust half dollar. (Brunk 41665)					

Isaac M. Walton, hardware, appears in the 1859-1862 directories at 67 Warren St. He is listed at 68 Pearl St. in 1864. He does not appear in the 1853 directory.

JAMES T. WARE

New York, N.Y.

Miller	Date	Metal	Size	F	VF	EF	Unc
NY 935	(1850's)	Brass	28.5mm	25.00	50.00	75.00	150.

Man standing with tall hat, driving a one-horse dray to right. Rv: JAMES T. WARE / 25 / CENTS. Plain edge. Thick planchet. (Wright 1202)

NY 935A	(1850's)	Brass	28.5mm	—	—	—	Unique

As 935, but '3' punched over '2' to revalue token to 35 cents. (Tanenbaum coll.)

The tall hat was the badge of trade of the driver. In a ceremonial sense, it still is in places where horse carriages exist, such as New York's Central Park.

URIAH WELCH

New York, N.Y. & Richfield Spa, N.Y.

Miller	Date	Metal	Size	F	VF	EF	Unc
NY 945	(?)	Copper	33mm	5.00	15.00	40.00	70.00
		Cock on one leg to left, ST. NICHOLAS, NEW YORK above, URIAH WELCH, PROPRIETER, below. Rv: Griffin head left, within oak wreath. NEW AMERICAN RICHFIELD SPA, N.Y. above, URIAH WELCH, PROP or. below. (Wright 1222)					
NY 945A	(?)	White Metal	33mm	5.00	15.00	40.00	80.00
		As 945.					

HERMANN WENDT

New York, N.Y.

Rulau	Date	Metal	Size	VG	F	VF	EF
NY 2165	(1841-60)	Copper	28mm	100.	—	150.	—

HERMANN WENDT / HERMANN WENDT (each line in upper arc) stamped so that the result is circular, ctsp on 1841 Hard Times token, HT 58 (Low 69). Both sides stamped. (Tanenbaum coll.)

Hermann Wendt (spelled Herman in some years' directories) appears in New York City directories from 1840 to 1860 or later. He was a maker of cutlery, and the stamp would be his signature marking as applied to knives, tableware, tools etc. His listings follows:

1840	31 Gold St.	Cutler
1842-1853	29 Gold St.	Cutler
1859	52 Beekman St.	Manufacturer
1860	52 Beekman St.	Cutler

H.B. WEST'S TRAINED DOGS

Miller	Date	Metal	Size	F	VF	EF	Unc
NY 948	1853	Copper	29mm	3.00	5.00	10.00	40.00
		Man in small carriage pulled by two dogs to right. H.B. WEST'S above, TRAY & TROY. / FAMOUS TRAINED DOGS below. Rv: View of Crystal Palace at center. NEW YORK CRYSTAL PALACE around, 1853. / ********* below. Plain edge.					
NY 948A	1853	Copper	29mm	3.00	5.00	10.00	40.00
		As 948. Reeded edge.					
NY 949	1853	Brass	29mm	3.00	5.00	10.00	40.00
		As 948. Reeded edge. (Wright 1224)					
NY 949A	1853	Silvered Brass	29mm	3.00	5.00	12.00	42.50
		As 948. Plain edge.					
NY 949B	1853	Silvered Brass	29mm	—	—	—	42.50
		As last. reeded edge.					
NY 950	(1860)	Brass	29mm	—	—	30.00	75.00
		Obverse as NY 948. Rv: Obverse of Brown, Curtis & Vance card of Louisville, Ky.					
NY 951	(1860)	Brass	29mm	—	—	100.	200.
		Obverse as NY 948. Rv: "The Rail Splitter of the West." (DeWitt AL-1860(E).) Very rare. (King 586)					
NY 951A	(1860)	Cupro-Nickel	29mm	—	—	100.	200.
		As 951. Plain edge. (King 586)					
NY 951B	(1860)	Cupro-Nickel	29mm	—	—	100.	200.
		As 951. Plain edge. (King 586)					
NY 951F	1860	Copper	28mm	—	—	125.	225.
		Obverse as 948. Rv: Beardless Lincoln bust right, ELLIS on truncation. Around: HON. ABRAHAM LINCOLN / 1860. Plain edge. (King 584)					
NY 951G	(1860)	—	29mm	—	—	—	Unique
		Obverse as NY 948. Rv: As reverse of Sleeper & Fenner card (Eagle). Only 1 known. (Tanenbaum coll.)					
NY 951 H	(1860)	—	29mm	—	—	—	Unique
		Obverse as NY 948. Rv: As reverse of Doremus & Nixon card (Steamship, NY 224). Only 1 piece struck. (Woodward sale of June 29, 1886, lot 850; Tanenbaum coll.)					
NY 952	(1860)	Brass	29mm	—	—	30.00	75.00
		Obverse as NY 948. Rv: Obverse of N.C. Folger card of New Orleans, La.					

A. WISE

Miller	Date	Metal	Size	F	VF	EF	Unc
NY 955	(1850's)	Copper	26mm	5.00	7.50	10.00	25.00

COMPETITION DEFIED WITHOUT ANY EXCEPTION / IN FANCY / AND STAPLE / DRY GOODS / BY THE / UNION STORE / OF / A. WISE / (ornament). Rv: ONE DOLLAR WILL BE PAID FOR 99 OF THESE TOKENS / BY THE / UNION STORE / NO 185 6th AVENUE / NEW YORK. Reeded edge. (Wright 1255)

WOOD'S MINSTRELS

New York, N.Y.

Rulau	Date	Metal	Size	VG	F	VF	EF
NY 2079	(1853-55)	Silver	27mm	—	200.	—	300

GEO. CHRISTY / AND / WOODS / MINSTRELS / 444 B.WAY / N. YORK / (dancing figure at each side) ctsp on Spanish-American 2-reales. (Dates examined: 1774-Mo, 1778, 1787-LME-MI), 1803, Carlos IV date worn. (Gould 88; Brunk 7720)

Rulau	Date	Metal	Size	VG	F	VF	EF
NY 2080	(1853-55)	Silver	27mm	—	200.	—	300.
		Similar ctsp on Mexico 2-reales. (Dates examined: 1826. 1846) (Van Ormer sale 2583, ex-Agnar Wahlberg 1979)					
NY 964A	(1855-57)	Silver	27.5mm	—	200.	—	300.
		ADMIT / TO / WOOD'S / MINSTRELS / 444 BDWAY / N.Y. ctsp on U.S. 1796 or 1806 Draped Bust quarter. (Gould 74; Brunk 44140;Duffield 1382)					

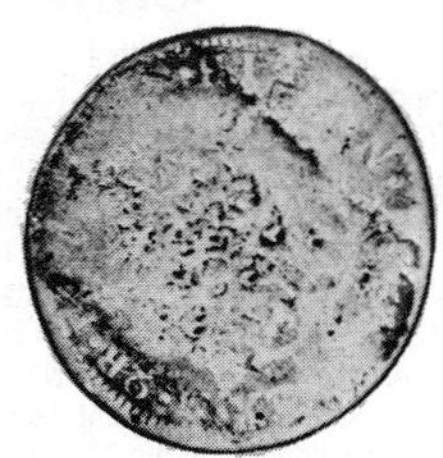

Rulau	Date	Metal	Size	VG	F	VF	EF
NY 964B	(1855-57)	Silver	27mm	—	130.	—	200.
		Similar ctsp on Spanish-American 2-reales. (Dates examined: 1774, 1775, 1776-PTS-PR, 1778, 1782, 1785, 1788, 1789, 1790, 1793, 1794, 1806, 1815.) There are 14 reported specimens.					

Rulau	Date	Metal	Size	VG	F	VF	EF
NY 964C	(1855-57)	Silver	32mm	—	200.	—	300.
		Similar ctsp on Spanish-American 4-reales. (Dates examined: 1813, date worn). (Gould 314; Kirtley Nov. 1991 sale, lot Q008)					
NY 964D	(1855-57)	Silver	27mm	—	—	—	300.
		ADMIT / TO / WOOD'S / MINSTRELS / 444 Bd WAY / N Y ctsp on Mexico 1827-Zs-AO 2-reales, type KM-374.12. The A of AO on this coin is not an inverted V but a properly cut A, thus an unreported coinage variety. (Brunk 44140X; Rulau coll., ex-Ray Lefman)					

NY 964G	(1857)	Silver	21mm	—	130.	—	200.

Similar ctsp on Spanish-American 1-real coin. (Dates not known)

Miller	Date	Metal	Size	F	VF	EF	Unc
NY 964	1857	Silver	25mm	7.00	14.00	20.00	50.00

Five-story building in center, ADMIT TO WOOD'S MINSTRELS / TEMPLE OF MINSTRELSY above; ERECTED / 1857 / 561 & 563 BDWAY N.Y. below. Rv: WARRANTED PURE SILVER / WOOD'S / MINSTRELS / PERFORM EVERY / EVENING / GIVING A SELECT / AND / VARIED / ENTERTAINMENT / * INTRINSIC VALUE 25 CTS. *. Plain edge. (Wright 8)

NY 965	1857	Copper	25mm	—	—	—	Rare

As 964. Plain edge.

Wood's Minstrels built their permanent home at 561-563 Broadway in 1857, after having performed at 444 Broadway for several years. The silver token commemorating the 1857 opening which served as an admission piece is very unusual among pre-Civil War tokens — its statement "Warranted pure silver, Intrinsic value 25 cts." sets it apart.

The silver token (NY 964) is not scarce, so it must have been struck and circulated in large numbers.

The new Wood's Minstrels building opened on October 15, 1857 and was known as "Wood's new marble building." It was located on the site of the old Lyceum of Natural History. The minstrel theater closed in 1859 and this building was taken over by the Merchants and Manufacturers Bank.

The original Wood's Minstrel Hall had been located at 446 and 448 Broadway. This burned in 1854.

In 1862 the Jewish synagogue located at 514 Broadway was remodeled for use by Wood's Minstrels.

Christy Minstrels

Edwin P. Christy (1815-1862) founded the Christy Minstrels about 1842. This became the most important of the early minstrel companies. The Christy Minstrels first performed in Buffalo, N.Y. in 1842, moving to New York City in 1846 and performing there successfully for nearly a decade. Their location was the American Opera House, 472 Broadway. Edwin Christy retired in 1854 but the troupe continued on without him. An offshoot became known in 1853 as George Christy and Wood's Minstrels and later simply as Wood's Minstrels. The troupe's progress is documented on its counterstamped and struck tokens.

The father of the American minstrel show — blackfaced performers whose material caricatured the singing and dancing of Negro slaves — was Thomas Dartmouth Rice (1808-1860), who introduced the song and dance *Jim Crow* in Louisville, Ky. in 1828. Rice's blackface specialty was adapted in the 1840's to the minstrel show, with a whitefaced interlocutor and blackfaced "end men" such as Mr. Tambo and Mr. Bones, though the adaptation was by others than Rice — principally Daniel Emmett and Edwin Christy.

Daniel Decatur Emmett (1815-1904) organized his Virginia Minstrels in 1843 in New York City. This troupe continued until 1858 as one of the two most important minstrel groups, the other being the Christy (later H. Wood's) Minstrels. In 1858 Emmett joined Dan Bryant's minstrel troupe and in 1859 wrote his famous song *Dixie* as a "walk around" (minstrel show concluding number) — in time to have it adopted as the unofficial anthem of the Confederacy. Emmett was played by Bing Crosby in the memorable Hollywood film *Dixie* which produced one of the most stirring musical events in film history — the concluding "walk around" in which Dixie produced Rebel yells and high emotion. Emmett retired in 1888 but in 1895 toured with A.G. Field's minstrel troupe at age 80.

Stephen Foster wrote songs for the Christy Minstrels. Other important early minstrel troupes were those of Campbell, Haverly, George Kunkel, Daniel Bryant and the Buckley Brothers.

The *New York Herald* in August 1853 lists in the entertainment section, an advertisement which reads as follows:

"Wood's Minstrels and Ethiopian Delineators, 444 Broadway above Howard Street. Open every evening, H. Wood, manager and proprietor. The entertainment of Wood's Minstrels embraces all elements of Ethiopian Minstrelsy, the company being composed of the oldest and most experienced performers. They are the originators of their own peculiar style consisting of Overtures, Quick Steps, Choruses, Quartettes, Glees, Duets, Songs, Ballads, Extravaganzas, Burlesque, Lectures, Thrilling Tragedy, and Eccentric Comedy, comprising together a melange of the most talented and pleasing soirees, all their pieces composed expressly for them and which they defy the world to equal. Doors open at 6-1/2 o'clock, to commence at 8 o'clock. Tickets 25 cents."

In 1853 all the minstrel shows, museums and other amusement establishments were located on Broadway above the 100's. Generally speaking, in this period the places of entertainment were located in the 400's, 500's and 600's on Broadway. Lower Broadway, below Liberty Street, consisted mainly of express agents, steamship companies, dry good stores and real estate agencies. No evidence of places of entertainment, other than the Castle Garden were found on this part of Broadway.

Minstrel shows contemporary to Wood's, for which no store cards exist were: Christy's Minstrels, located in the American Opera House at 472 Broadway, and Buckley's Minstrels, located in the Chinese Hall at 539 Broadway, the Buckley Brothers proprietors.

Other places of entertainment for which storecards exist, and which are contemporary to Wood's Minstrels, were Barnum's American Museum; the Crystal Palace, which was an international exhibition hall modeled after the Crystal Palace in England and the Castle Garden, which was the Metropolitan Opera House of its day.

Minstrels in New York City

Wood's Marble Hall was at 561-563 Broadway (west side, near Prince Street), and was famous for minstrels. Actor George Holland joined Wood & Christy Minstrels on Oct. 15, 1857. The hall was torn down in July 1877.

Wood's Minstrel Hall, 514 Broadway (near Spring Street), opened in July 1862. It became Wood's Theatre in 1866, then Harrigan and Hart's Theatre 1876-1881. It was torn down in 1881.

Minstrels on Broadway at the same time included:

Christy

Dan Bryant

Kelly & Leon (1866-70, Broadway near 8th in Blitz' Hall)

Campbell

Wood

Pell & Trowbridge

Morris Brothers

J.H. Haverly's Mastodon Minstrels from 1883 on were at Broadway and 28th.

Apollo Hall, 412 Broadway, was a political gathering place for anti-Tammany Hall people. In May 1844, Congo Minstrels (later Negro Minstrels) played there.

San Francisco Minstrels in 1874 moved to Broadway and 28th, until 1883.

Buckley's Hall, 585 Broadway, opened with Buckley's Minstrels on Aug. 25, 1856. It had 12 name changes to May 8, 1865, when it became San Francisco Minstrels, remaining to 1870. In 1875-81 it was Tony Pastor's Metropolitan (with Lillian Russell, Irwin Sisters, etc.).

METROPOLITAN HALL (Tripler's Hall; Winter Garden)

Tripler's Hall, also known as Metropolitan Hall, opened in 1850 at 677 Broadway, near Bond Street. Its opening performance occurred Sept. 27, 1850, when HENRIETTA SONTAG gave a concert.

JENNY LIND, the Swedish Nightingale, sang there in October 1850.

Novelist WASHINGTON IRVING and WILLIAM CULLEN BRYANT gave a memorial program there for novelist James Fenimore Cooper, who had died in September 1851. The program was staged Feb. 28, 1852.

Metropolitan Hall and the adjoining LaFarge House were destroyed by fire Jan. 8, 1854.

The theater was rebuilt in September 1854 under the name New York Theatre and Metropolitan Opera House. Then in 1855 it became known as Laura Keene's Varieties. In 1856 it became Burton's Theatre. In 1859 it became Winter Garden (and Conservatory of the Arts).

The building was totally destroyed by fire March 23, 1867.

WM. P. WOODCOCK

Miller	Date	Metal	Size	F	VF	EF	Unc
NY 966	(1858-60)	Copper	31mm	10.00	20.00	45.00	80.00

A woodcock in a mountain valley setting. Tiny G.H.L. in exergue. Rv: BUTCHER in Old English type at center, within laurel wreath. At open top of the wreath are a crossed cleaver, sharpening steel and butcher knife. Around: WM. P. WOODCOCK / NO. 2 / TOMPKINS MARKET, N.Y. Reeded edge.

NY 967	(1858-60)	Brass	31mm	—	—	45.00	80.00

As 966. Reeded edge.

NY 968	(1858-60)	White Metal	31mm	—	20.00	45.00	80.00

As 966. Reeded edge. (Wright 1272)

Dies were cut by George Hampden Lovett. This token rates as one of the most beautiful ever conceived for a butcher.

William P. Woodcock the butcher was at 2 Tompkins Market at least 1848-1858.

Apparently the Woodcocks were well established in the New York butcher trade in the 1848-49 period, because, in addition to William P., two other Woodcocks appear in directories:

Jonas G. Woodcock, butcher, 32 Fulton Market

Thomas H. Woodcock, butcher, 32 Fulton Market

WOODGATE & CO.

	All 1860 — 28mm	EF	Unc
NY 969	WOODGATE & CO., / IMPORTERS / OF / BRANDIES, / WINES, 83 GINS & C / WATER STREET / NEW YORK / 1860. Rv. REPREStd. BY J. N. T. LEVICK, Copper. Reeded edge. (Wright 1273; Baker 593A1)	15.00	40.00
NY 969A	Same. Silver	150.	250.
NY 970	Same. Brass	15.00	40.00
NY 971	Same. White metal.	15.00	40.00

NY 972	Same. Rv. Bust of Washington. PATRIAE PATER. 1732. Copper. Reeded edge. (Baker 593A)	15.00	50.00
NY 972A	Same. Silver. 5 struck	150.	250.
NY 973	Same. Brass.	15.00	50.00
NY 974	Same. White metal.	20.00	70.00
NY 975	Same. R Bust of Webster. Copper.	15.00	40.00
NY 976	Same. Brass.	15.00	40.00
NY 977	Same. White metal.	15.00	40.00
NY 978	Same. R Bust of Forrest. Copper.	15.00	40.00
NY 979	Same. Brass.	15.00	40.00
NY 980	Same. White metal.	15.00	40.00

NY 981	Same. Bust of a man smoking a cigar. "NO PLEASURE CAN EXCEED," &c. Copper.	10.00	50.00
NY 983	Same. White metal.	10.00	50.00
NY 984	Same. R Cupid. Copper.	10.00	50.00
NY 985	Same. Brass.	10.00	50.00
NY 986	Same. White metal.	10.00	50.00
NY 987	Same. R "F. C. KEY & SONS, 123 ARCH ST. PHILADA." Copper.	20.00	50.00
NY 988	Same. Brass.	20.00	50.00
NY 989	Same. White metal.	20.00	50.00
NY 990	Same. Rv. large letters "KEY," 329 Arch St., Phila. Copper.	20.00	50.00
NY 991	Same. Brass.	20.00	50.00
NY 992	Same. White metal.	20.00	50.00
NY 993	Same. Rv. Two crossed pipes above cigar box. "LEVICK, 904 BROADWAY, NEW YORK. 1860." Copper.	10.00	40.00
NY 994	Same. Brass	10.00	40.00
NY 995	Same. White metal.	10.00	40.00
NY 996	Same. Rv. "VIRTUE, LIBERTY & INDEPENDENCE." Silver.	150.	250.
NY 997	Same. Copper.	10.00	40.00
NY 998	Same. Brass.	10.00	40.00
NY 999	Same. White metal.	10.00	40.00

WYMAN (THE) WIZARD

New York, N.Y.

Miller	Date	Metal	Size	VG	F	VF	EF
NY 1004A	(1854)	Copper	29mm	225.	—	325.	—
		WYMAN / WIZARD / & / VENTRILOQUIST ctsp on a U.S. Large cent. 3 Known. (ex-Fuld; Brunk 44525)					

NY 1004	(1854)	Silver	27mm	225.	—	325.	—
		Similar ctsp on Spanish-American silver 1782 or 1787-NG 2-reales. 3 known. (Gould 129).					

His name was John Wyman. This is also reported on a 1-real coin.

J.L. SMITH

Norwich, N.Y.

Rulau	Date	Metal	Size	VG	F	VF	—
NY 2083	(?)	Silver	18mm	100.	—	150.	—
		J.L. SMITH / NORWICH, N.Y. ctsp on reverse of U.S. 1842 dime. (Brunk 37160)					

L. COON

Oswego and Ithaca, N.Y.

Rulau	Date	Metal	Size	VG	F	VF	EF
NY 2650	1850's)	Copper	28mm	—	—	75.00	—
		L. COON (italics) / WARRANTED (italics) / CAST - STEEL / PATENT ctsp on Canada 1825 "To Faciliate Trade" halfpenny token. (Brunk 9465; John Boger coll.)					

Levi Coon began his gunsmith business in Oswego about 1821. In 1850 he formed L. Coon & Sons with his sons Levi Coon Jr. and David Coon, removing to nearby Ithaca, N.Y. Levi Coon was born in 1792.

In the book *New York State Gunmakers* by Holman J. Swinney (1951), the author notes that he inspected a gun of the Ithaca firm marked L. COON. The counterstamp could date from the Hard Times period but more likely is from the 1850's.

David Coon, who ran the business until 1858, patented a burglar alarm in May, 1857 (patent no. 17,406), but the firm and its founder had made flintlock, percussion and revolving rifles.

M.L. MARSHALL

Oswego, N.Y.

Miller	Date	Metal	Size	VG	F	VF	Unc
NY 1007	1860	Silver	29mm	—	—	80.00	225.
		Man fishing from bank, tree in background, date 1860 below, all within central circle. Around: M. L. MARSHALL'S VARIETY STORE / OSWEGO N.Y. Rv: DEALER / IN / BERLIN WOOLS. / EMBROIDERY GOODS. / FISHING TACKLE / & FANCY GOODS / GENERALLY. Plain edge.					
NY 1008	1860	Copper	29mm	5.00	12.00	17.50	45.00
		As 1007.					
NY 1009	1860	Brass	29mm	5.00	12.50	17.50	45.00
		As 1007.					
NY 1010	1860	White Metal	29mm	5.00	15.00	20.00	45.00
		As 1007. Plain edge.					
NY 1010A	(?)	Silver	38mm	—	100.	—	150.
		M. L. MARSHALL ctsp on U.S. 1856 Seated Liberty silver dollar. (Duffield 1411; Brunk 26105). Only 25 reportedly struck.					
NY 1010B	(?)	Silver	26mm	—	100.	—	150.
		Similar ctsp on U.S. 1806 Bust quarter.					

Marshall also issued later, Civil War-era tokens dated 1862 and 1863. A token very similar to NY 1007 but with two trees on far bank and date 1862 (Adams NY 1011-1012, Wright 668, HG 6330, Fuld 695A) measures 29mm. The 1863 piece, 20mm, showing a fish and indentifying Marshall as a dealer in "rare coin," is very common and popular and enjoyed wide circulation as a cent during the war.

Marshall was still in business as a dealer in guns, fishing tackle and sporting goods, in 1876.

Morgan L. Marshall was born in Vernon, N.Y. in 1822. He died May 6, 1883. Nicknamed "Blunt," he was a famed fisherman.

C. D. BLAKE

Plattsburgh, N.Y.

Rulau	Date	Metal	Size	VG	F	VF	EF
NY 2280	(?)	Copper	29mm	—	75.00	—	125.

C. D. BLAKE PLATTSBURGH N.Y. ctsp on U.S. early Large cent, date worn off. (Brunk 3955)

SAWPIT, N.Y.

Port Chester, N.Y.

Rulau	Date	Metal	Size	VG	F	VF	EF
NY 2148	(?)	Copper	29mm	25.00	—	50.00	—

SAWPIT N-Y ctsp on U.S. 18.1 Large cent. (Possibly 1831) (Brunk 35715)

Sawpit was the name of a community in Westchester County, New York, now known as Port Chester. During the 1824-25 visit of Marquis de Lafayette to America. Sawpit was one of his stops, and is mentioned in the chronicle of his travels.

The Postal Guide for 1877 gives the town name as Port Chester. The name was changed in the 1830's. (Research courtesy James K. Allen, Franklin, N.C., who grew up in Rye and adjoining Port Chester)

FRANK M. BRUNK

Rensselaer, N.Y.

Miller	Date	Metal	Size	F	VF	EF	Unc
NY 1023	(?)	Brass	28mm	—	—	—	500.

FRANK M. BRUNK. 5C. Rv: Blank.

Supposedly only 7 pieces exist, the dies being destroyed by fire.

URIAH WELCH

Richfield Spa, N.Y.

See NY 945 under New York City for tokens of the New American in Richfield Spa.

D. R. BARTON

Rochester, N.Y.

Rulau	Date	Metal	Size	VG	F	VF	EF
NY 2149	(?)	Copper	29mm	75.00	—	125.	—

D. R. BARTON / ROCHESTER within beaded rect. cartouche ctsp incuse on U.S. Large cent. Very worn cent, and some wear on ctsp. (Tanenbaum coll.; Brunk 2595)

D.R. Barton's edge tool factory was founded 1835. In 1875 it was bought by Mack & Co.

ETTENHEIMERS

Rulau	Date	Metal	Size	F	VF	EF	Unc
NY 1017A	(1840's?)	Brass	26mm	—	1000.	—	—

ETTENHEIMERS / WATCH & / JEWELRY / STORE. / 53 / BUFFALO ST. / o ROCHESTER, N.Y. o. Heavy beaded border on obverse. Rv: Blank but number 26 incused. Plain edge. (William Carr report, Medina, N.Y.)

So far as we know, the illustration and description above are the first time this rarity among American tokens has ever been fully cataloged. The Carr piece, holed at 3 o'clock, was sold by private treaty in the late 1980's. None of the early token catalogers ever saw the piece.

J. FLINT

Rulau	Date	Metal	Size	VG	F	VF	EF
NY 2153	(?)	Silver	31mm	—	125.	—	—

J. FLINT / ROCHESTER / J. FLINT / ROCHESTER ctsp on U.S. 1859-S Seated Liberty half dollar. (Tanenbaum coll.; Brunk 14467)

LOUIS HOF

Rulau	Date	Metal	Size	VG	F	VF	EF
NY 2085	(1851-61)	Silver	29mm	150.	—	250.	—

LOUIS HOF / BREWER / 138 BROWN ST. / ROCHESTER ctsp (trebled) on each side of France 1793-W 30-sols. The trebling makes the legends difficult to read. (Tanenbaum collection; Brunk 19820)

Louis Hof appears in the Rochester directories in 1849-50 at Ames St. He appears at 138 Brown St. 1851-52, then Brown St. without number 1853-56, then 140 Brown St. 1857-58, then Brown St. without number 1859, and again at 138 Brown St. in 1861.

In 1863-64 he was at 168 Brown St., then at Brown St. without number 1864-65, and again at 168 Brown St. 1868-70. His brewery is last listed in 1895.

From these directory listings, it is logical to conclude the counterstamp was applied in the 1851-61 period. The directories were issued about every two years at this time, so there is that much error factor built in.

OLCOTT & BROTHER

Miller	Date	Metal	Size	VG	F	EF	Unc
NY 1018	(1845-55)	Brass	27mm	5.00	10.00	20.00	40.00

Two kinds of railroad headlamp in center. OLCOTT BROTHER / LOCOMOTIVE / & above; R. R. LAMP / MANUFACTURERS / ROCHESTER N.Y. Rv: MANUFACTURERS / OF / LOCOMOTIVE / CONDUCTORS / SIGNAL / & OTHER R.R. / LAMPS. Reeded edge. (Wright 783)

Miller	Date	Metal	Size	VG	F	EF	Unc
NY 1019	(1845-55)	Brass	28mm	5.00	10.00	20.00	40.00
		Large railroad headlamp in plain field. Rv: OLCOTT & BROTHER / MANFTRS OF / LOCOMOTIVE / HEAD LIGHTS / ROCHESTER. N-Y. Reeded edge.					
NY 1019A	(1845-55)	Brass	28mm	—	—	—	40.00
		As last. Plain edge.					
NY 1021	(1845-55)	Silvered Brass	-28mm	10.00	15.00	20.00	40.00
		As 1019. Reeded edge. (Wright 784)					
NY 1019A	(1845-55)	Copper	28mm	10.00	15.00	20.00	40.00
		As 1019.					
NY 1019B	(1845-55)	Silvered Copper	28mm	10.00	15.00	20.00	40.00
		As 1019.					
NY 1021A	(1845-55)	Brass	28mm	15.00	20.00	35.00	55.00
		As 1019, but there are no rays within the lamp. Rare.					
NY 1020	(1845-55)	Tin (White Metal)	28mm	—	—	75.00	100.
		Obverse as obverse of 1019 (large headlamp). Rv: Reverse of Sleeper & Fenner card of Philadelphia (eagle, MOST EXTENSIVE IN THE UNITED STATES).					

Olcott & Brother, manufacturers of railroad lamps, advertised in the *American Railroad Journal* in 1855. In 1861 Milton Olcott made locomotive lamps at a factory on Mill St. In 1863 Kelly & Co. succeeded Olcott, and Kelly was still in business in 1912.

P. H. ROCHESTERS BANKING OFFICE

Rulau	Date	Metal	Size	VG	F	VF	EF
NY 2285	(?)	Silver	27mm	—	125.	—	175.
		P. H. / ROCHESTERS BANKING OFFICE / ROCHESTER, N.Y. ctsp on Spanish-American 2-reales. (Brunk 34735)					

FREDERICK STARR

Miller	Date	Metal	Size	F	VF	EF	Unc
NY 1022	1851	Brass	22mm	5.00	8.00	15.00	35.00
		Piano at center, * MUSICAL INSTRUMENTS * / MUSIC / ROOMS above; SHEET / MUSIC / & MERCHANDISE below. Rv: Within a floreate wreath is: PREMIUM / PIANOS / NO 45 47 49 51 / MAIN ST / ROCHESTER. Around outside is: FREDERICK STARR / STATE FAIR 1851. (Wright 1043)					
NY 1022A	1851	Silvered Brass	22mm	6.00	9.00	15.00	35.00
		As 1022.					

Frederick Starr (1799-1869) operated a piano factory with 100 employees in a 4-story building on Main St. The building had been partly destroyed by fire in 1849. In 1862 Starr retired and his foreman, DeWitt Gibbons, continued the business until his death in 1894. The firm was still active — "Rochester's Old Reliable Music House" — at 172 East Main St., in 1912.

G. G. TOWNSEND

Rulau	Date	Metal	Size	VG	F	VF	EF
NY 2287	(?)	Copper	34mm	—	75.00	—	125.
		G. G. TOWNSEND / ROCHESTER N.Y. ctsp on reverse of England 1831 copper penny of William IV. (B&M Patterson 1985 sale, lot 1709; Brunk 40363)					

H. WRAY
Rochester, N.Y.

Rulau	Date	Metal	Size	VG	F	VF	EF
NY 2288	(1840's)	Copper	29mm	—	100.	—	150.
		H WRAY / ROCHESTER ctsp on reverse of U.S. 1832 Large cent. (L. B. Fauver coll.; Brunk 44427)					
NY 2289	(1840's)	Copper	29mm	—	100.	—	150.
		H WRAY ctsp on U.S. 1838 Large cent. (Brunk 44425)					

Henry Wray was a well-known lockmaker of Poughkeepsie and Rochester, N.Y. 1844-1870's, who usually signed his brass products HWRAY or HWRAY / POKEEPSIE.

It is not known at this time how the Poughkeepsie and Rochester locations square, but the attribution seems too clear to be ignored. (Reference: *American Copper & Brass* by Henry J. Kauffman, New York, 1968).

Wray advertised in 1845.

G. H. REMINGTON
Rome, N.Y.

Rulau	Date	Metal	Size	G	VG	F	EF
NY 2087	(?)	Copper	29mm	—	75.00	—	125.
		G. H. REMINGTON / ROME / N.Y. ctsp on U.S. Large cent. (Gould 1418; Brunk 33910)					

WILLIAM R. BROWN
Saratoga, N.Y.

Rulau	Date	Metal	Size	F	VF	EF	Unc
NY 1024	(1850's)	Brass	29mm	5.00	8.00	10.00	45.00
		Imitation of Liberty Head $10 gold piece, W. R. BROWN on Liberty's headband, nine stars above, WILLIAM R. BROWN below. Rv: Legend around eagle is: CONGRESS HALL SARATOGA SPRINGS. Reeded edge. (Wright 104)					
NY 1025	(1850's)	Copper	20mm	—	—	20.00	40.00
		CONGRESS HALL. Long serratures around legend. Rv: Blank.					

BENEDICT & BARNEY
Syracuse, N.Y.

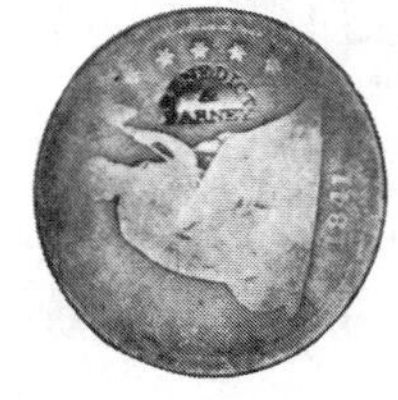

Rulau	Date	Metal	Size	VG	F	VF	EF
NY 2292	(1852-53)	Silver	25mm	—	125.	—	175.
		BENEDICT / & / BARNEY ctsp on U.S. 1841-O Seated Liberty quarter. (Van Ormer sale 2534; Brunk 3290)					

Benedict & Barney, manufacturers of gold pens, were listed at 1 East Genesee St. in Syracuse in the 1853 edition of *Syracuse Business Directory*. Principals of the firm were George and James Barney and A. Benedict.

P. DICKINSON
Syracuse, N.Y.

Rulau	Date	Metal	Size	VG	F	VF	EF
NY 2293	(1837-50)	Copper	29mm	75.00	—	—	—
		P. DICKINSON in relief within serrated rectangular depression, ctsp on U.S. 1802 (?) Large cent. (Kovacs coll.; Brunk 11625)					

On the only known specimen, the hallmark is struck unevenly and partially doubled, but there is little question it matches Louise Belden's pg. 135 photo of this teaspoon shank stamp. The host cent is worn almost smooth.

Pliny Dickinson was a silversmith on his own 1837-43, and then as a partner with John Hannum in Dickinson & Hannum 1844-51. From 1851-60 Dickinson advertised himself as an insurance agent.

This cent could have been stamped any time from 1837 to 1850. The discovery of additional specimens may yield clues.

FOWLER, DRUGGIST

Rulau	Date	Metal	Size	VG	F	VF	EF
NY 2091	(?)	Copper	29mm	150.	—	250.	—
		FOWLER DRUGGIST / GENESEE ST. / SYRACUSE, N.Y. / (figure of Liberty) ctsp on U.S. Large cent. (Duffield 1400; Hallenbeck 6.750; Brunk 14890)					

D.C. Fowler was a partner in the drug firm of Fowler & Whitnall, listed in 1866. In the 1868 directory he is listed as a physician. (Brunk research)

ALEX. HENDERSON

Rulau	Date	Metal	Size	VG	F	VF	EF
NY 2295	(?)	Silver	37.3mm	—	—	275.	—
		ALEX. HENDERSON VET'Y SURGEON. / SYRACUSE / N.Y. ctsp on France 1816-A 5-franc coin of Louis XVIII. (Kurt Krueger coll.; Brunk 19185)					

Alexander Henderson first appeared in the Syracuse directory as a veterinary surgeon. In the 1855 directory he also was listed as a farrier. His veterinary surgeon listings continued to 1880, when his son Matthew became his business partner. (Brunk research)

D. LEFEVER

Rulau	Date	Metal	Size	VG	F	VF	EF
N 2540	(1850's)	Copper	29mm	100.	—	150.	—
		D. LEFEVER ctsp on U.S. 1830 or 1842 Large cent. Rarity 8. (Rulau collection; HT 459; Brunk 24205)					

The mark is one used by a famous gun works to stamp its early products.

Daniel M. Lefever founded his firearms company in the 1850's, making fine grade Damascus barrel shotguns. It was operated under the name Daniel M. Lefever 1850's-1876; Nichols & Lefever (with John A. Nichols) 1876-78; Lefever Arms Co. 1878-1902; and D. M. Lefever Sons & Co. 1902-15. The company was purchased by Ithaca Gun Co. in 1915; Ithaca is still in business making shotguns.

C. S. BALL

Rulau	Date	Metal	Size	VG	F	VF	EF
NY 2298	(1850)	Copper	29mm	—	75.00	—	125.
		C. S. BALL in relief within rect. depression ctsp on U.S. Large cents. (Dates examined: 1829, 1837, 1838). The illustrated specimen, probably 1838, is in the Rich Hartzog collection. (Brunk 2130)					
NY 2299	(1850)	Copper	28mm	—	75.00	—	125.
		Similar ctsp on various Canadian trade tokens. Four specimens reported. (Brunk report)					

This was the hallmark used on teaspoon shanks by Calvin S. Ball Jr., silversmith, who about 1852-1853 became part of the firm of Stone & Ball (which see).

Calvin S. Ball Sr., his father, born 1798, was active as a silversmith in Pompey, N.Y. circa 1825.

This is a major discovery in the Stone & Ball counterstamp series.

STONE & BALL

(SPECIAL NOTE: There are three major types of Stone & Ball counterstamps. Type I carries this *incused* stamp: STONE & BALL / SYRACUSE / N.Y. Type II carries this *incused* stamp: STONE & BALL. Type III carries this *relief* stamp within rectangular indent: STONE & BALL.

Of the three types, Type II is the most common, Type I is less often encountered, and Type III is quite rare. In all three editions of this reference book, we have attempted to catalog all three types accurately, but unfortunately earlier writers did not always distinguish between the types, especially between Types II and III.)

TYPE I STAMP

Rulau	Date	Metal	Size	VG	F	VF	EF
NY 1027A	(1853-54)	Copper	29mm	75.00	—	125.	—
		STONE & BALL / SYRACUSE / N.Y. ctsp on U.S. Large cent. Dates examined: 1831, 1838, 1841. There are 3 specimens reported. (Brunk 38540)					
NY 1027B		Silver	18mm	75.00	—	125.	—
		Similar ctsp on U.S. Seated Liberty dime. Examined: 1854, 1855. There are 3 pieces known.					

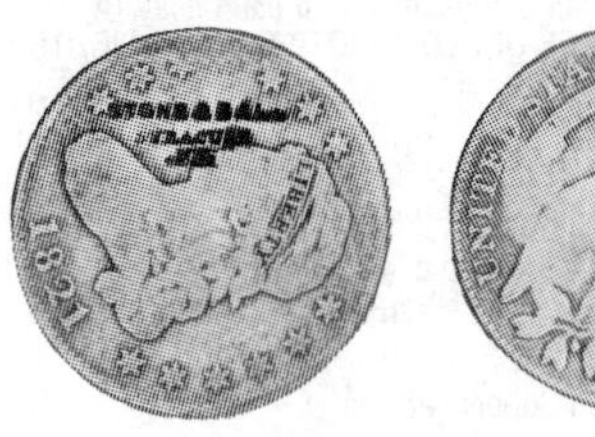

Rulau	Date	Metal	Size	VG	F	VF	EF
NY 1027C		Silver	27mm	75.00	—	125.	—
		Similar ctsp on U.S. Bust quarter. Examined: 1821, 1824, 1825. There are 4 pieces known. (Gould 65)					

Rulau	Date	Metal	Size	VG	F	VF	EF
NY 1027D		Silver	25mm	50.00	—	75.00	—
		Similar ctsp on U.S. Seated Liberty quarter. Examined: 1853--Arrows, 1854, 1855. There are 21 specimens reported.					

Rulau	Date	Metal	Size	VG	F	VF	EF
NY 1027E		Silver	31mm	75.00	—	125.	—
		Similar ctsp on U.S. Seated Liberty half dollar. Examined: 1853-No arrows, 1853-Arrows, 1854-Arrows. Only 3 known.					
NY 1027W		Copper	29mm	200.	—	300.	—
		Similar ctsp on Connecticut 1787 cent. Only 1 specimen reported.					
NY 1027F		Silver	21mm	75.00	—	125.	—
		Similar ctsp on Spanish-American 1-real coin. Examined: 1782, 1821. Only 2 known.					

Rulau	Date	Metal	Size	VG	F	VF	EF
NY 1027G		Silver	27mm	75.00	—	125.	—
		Similar ctsp on Spanish-American 2-reales. Dates examined: 1777, 1781, 1782, 1800, 1813-LME-JP, 1816. There are 6 specimens reported.					
NY 1027H		Copper	29mm	100.	—	150.	—
		Similar ctsp on Great Britain halfpenny token; type not known. Only 1 known.					

TYPE II STAMP

Rulau	Date	Metal	Size	VG	F	VF	EF
NY 1027J	(1853-54)	Copper	29mm	—	60.00	—	90.00
		Incuse ctsp STONE & BALL on U.S. Large cents. (Dates examined: 1802, 1831, 1838, 1841, 1843, 1845, 1848, 1852, 1853) There are 10 known. (Brunk 38530)					

Rulau	Date	Metal	Size	VG	F	VF	EF
NY 1027K	(1853-54)	Silver	15.5mm	—	60.00	—	90.00
		Similar ctsp on U.S. 1839 half dime.					

Rulau	Date	Metal	Size	VG	F	VF	EF
NY 1027L	(1853-54)	Silver	18mm	—	50.00	—	75.00
		Similar ctsp on U.S. Seated Liberty dimes. (Dates examined: 1827, 1842, 1853, 1854)					
NY 1027M	(1853-54)	Silver	27mm	—	60.00	—	80.00
		Similar ctsp on U.S. Bust quarters. (Dates examined: 1821, 1825)					
NY 1027N	(1853-54)	Silver	25mm	—	40.00	—	60.00
		Similar ctsp on U.S. Seated Liberty quarters. (Dates examined: 1836, 1839, 1853, 1854). There are 10 known.					
NY 1027P	(1853-54)	Silver	31mm	—	50.00	—	90.00
		Similar ctsp on U.S. Seated Liberty half dollars. (Dates examined: 1853, 1854). There are 4 known.					

Rulau	Date	Metal	Size	VG	F	VF	EF
NY 1027Q	(1853-54)	Gold	22mm	3000.	—	4500.	—
		Similar ctsp on U.S. $5 gold piece. (Dates examined: 1854)					

Rulau	Date	Metal	Size	VG	F	VF	EF
NY 1027R	(1853-54)	Silver	21mm	—	50.00	—	90.00
		Similar ctsp on Spanish-American 1-real coins. (Dates examined: 1821-Mo)					

Rulau	Date	Metal	Size	VG	F	VF	EF
NY 1027S	(1853-54)	Silver	27mm	—	50.00	—	90.00
		Similar ctsp on Spanish-American 2-reales. (Dates examined: 1757, 1777, 1784, 1785). There are 5 pieces known.					

TYPE III STAMP

Rulau	Date	Metal	Size	VG	F	VF	EF
NY 1027V	(1853-54)	Copper	29mm	100.	—	150.	—
		Relief ctsp STONE & BALL in one line within rect. depression on U.S. Large cents. (Dates examined: 1841, 1845, 1853) (Brunk 38535)					

Rulau	Date	Metal	Size	VG	F	VF	EF
NY 1027Y	(1853-54)	Copper	25mm	—	100.	—	150.
		Similar ctsp on Ireland 1822 halfpenny. (Rulau coll.)					
NY 1027X	(1853-54)	Silver	19mm	200.	—	300.	—
		Similar ctsp on U.S. 1827 Bust dime. (Van Ormer sale 2861)					
NY 1027Z	(1853-54)	Silver	27mm	200.	—	300.	—
		Similar ctsp on U.S. Bust quarters. (Date examined: 1825). (Al D. Hoch coll.)					
NY 2300	(?)	Silver	25mm	—	200.	—	300.
		R. ROWE; STONE AND BALL / SYRACUSE N Y ctsp incuse on U.S. 1853 Seated Liberty quarter. (Kurt Krueger Sept. 1983 sale, lot 159)					

Stone & Ball was a leading jewelry and silversmith firm from March 1853 until February 1869, succeeding an earlier firm, B.R. Norton & Hotchkiss. The partners were Seymour H. Stone and Calvin S. Ball. Ball continued the business under his own name until October 1903, then sold out to Stetson & Crouse.

The young partners conceived the idea of perpetuating their new firm's name by stamping it on every 25-cent piece that they handled. The coins were then placed in the till and used for change. Other silver denominations, and copper cents, also received the counterstamp. Foreign coins, especially Spanish-American silvers and British Isles coppers, were then still in active circulation.

The practice, starting in March 1853, was dropped by early 1855. Undoubtedly other specimens than those reported here must exist.

(See "Stone & Ball Counterstamp on Lima Mint 1813 2 Reales Coin" in *TAMS Journal* for Oct. 1962; also article on Stone & Ball in *Numismatic Scrapbook Magazine* for 1961, page 1689.)

A. C. YATES
Syracuse, N.Y.

Miller	Date	Metal	Size	F	VF	EF	Unc
NY 1028	(1850's)	Brass	29mm	5.00	8.00	12.00	40.00
		Fat man standing, facing, holding poster which says: A. C. YATES / CLOTHING / STORE / SYRACUSE / N.Y. Around is: SIGN OF THE OLD MAN WITH SPECS. Rv: Eagle displayed, shield on breast. CLOTHING EMPORIUM above, 13 & 15 NORTH SALINA ST below. Reeded edge.					
NY 1028A		Brass	29mm	5.00	8.00	12.00	40.00
		As last. Plain edge.					
NY 1029	(1850's)	Copper	29mm	5.00	8.00	12.00	40.00
		As 1028. Plain edge. (Wright 1291)					
NY 1030	(1860)	Brass	29mm	—	—	100.	200.
		Obverse as 1028. Rv: Lincoln splitting rails, THE RAIL SPLITTER OF THE WEST. (DeWitt AL 1860-41F)					
NY 1031	1853 (1860)	Copper	29mm	—	—	50.00	85.00
		Obverse as 1028. Rv: Building, NEW YORK CRYSTAL PALACE / 1853.					
NY 1032	1853 (1860)	Brass	29mm	—	—	50.00	85.00
		As 1031.					
NY 1033	(1860)	Copper	29mm	—	—	50.00	85.00
		Obverse as 1028. Rv: Three-masted steam sidewheeler, DRY GOODS & UPHOLSTERY / * FOR SHIPS & STEAMERS * (Doremus & Nixon reverse, NY 225).					
NY 1034	(1860)	Brass	29mm	—	—	50.00	85.00
		As 1033.					
NY 1034A	1860	WM	28mm	—	—	100.	200.
		Obverse as 1028. Rv: Abraham Lincoln bust by ELLIS, 1860 below bust. Plain edge. (King 585)					
NY 1034B	1860	Copper	28mm	—	—	100.	200.
		As 1034A. Plain edge.					
NY 1034C	1860	CN	28mm	—	—	100.	200.
		As 1034A. Plain edge. (King 585)					

B. BABCOCK JR.

Troy, N.Y.

Rulau	Date	Metal	Size	VG	F	VF	EF
NY 2315	(1844-45)	Copper	29mm	125.	—	175.	—
		B. BABCOCK JR. / TROY, N.Y. ctsp on U.S. Large cents. (Dates examined: 1816, 1818) (Brunk 1680)					

Benjamin Babcock Jr. was a tin and coppersmith at 286 River St. listed in the 1844-45 Troy city directory. He continued to be listed personally at various addresses through the 1894 directory, but not in the section under metal workers. (Brunk research)

A. D. CUSHING

Rulau	Date	Metal	Size	VG	F	VF	EF
NY 2610	(?)	Copper	29mm	—	—	75.00	—
		PATENT / A. D. CUSHING / TROY ctsp on U.S. 1822 Large cent. (Brunk 10460; PCAC July 1993 sale, lot 897)					

A. GARDNER

Rulau	Date	Metal	Size	VG	F	VF	EF
NY 2620	(?)	Copper	29mm	—	—	—	—
		A. GARDNER / TROY ctsp on 1787 Fugio cent reverse. (Kirtley Nov. 1991 sale, lot Q037; Brunk 15680).					

A. GARDNER is known counterstamped on an 1858-S Seated Liberty half dollar. Probably not connected.

E. L. PERCY

Troy, N.Y.

Miller	Date	Metal	Size	F	VF	EF	Unc
NY 1051	(1850's)	Brass	29mm	5.00	9.00	10.00	35.00
		Eagle displayed, U.S. shield on breast, TRUNKS & TRAVELLING BAGS above, * MANSION HOUSE BLOCK NO. 2. TROY. N.Y. * below. Rv: E.L. PERCY. / TRUNKS & / TRAVELING BAGS / WHOLESALE & RETAIL / HOOP SKIRTS / HOSIERY / GLOVES &C / MANSION HOUSE BLOCK. Plain edge. (Wright 815)					

Scovill Mfg. Co.'s diecutters must have had an interesting day, spelling TRAVELLING (two L's) on the eagle side, and TRAVELING (one L) on the other.

S.W. CHUBBUCK

Utica, N.Y.

Miller	Date	Metal	Size	F	VF	EF	Unc
NY 1055	(?)	Copper	32mm	35.00	45.00	75.00	125.
		S. W. CHUBBUCK / MANUFACTURER / OF / AND DEALER IN / TELEGRAPH CHEMICAL (both on scrolls) / & PHILOSOPHICAL / APPARATUS. / UTICA, N.Y. Rv: MORSE TELEGRAPH ALPHABET and 10 more lines, the fourth and fifth lines being straight.					
NY 1056	(?)	Silvered Copper	32mm	35.00	45.00	75.00	125.
		As 1055.					
NY 1057	(?)	Silver	32mm	—	—	225.	400.
		As 1055.					
NY 1058	(?)	Brass	32mm	35.00	45.00	75.00	125.
		As 1055. (Wright 168)					
NY 1059	(?)	White Metal	32mm	—	50.00	60.00	125.
		As 1055.					

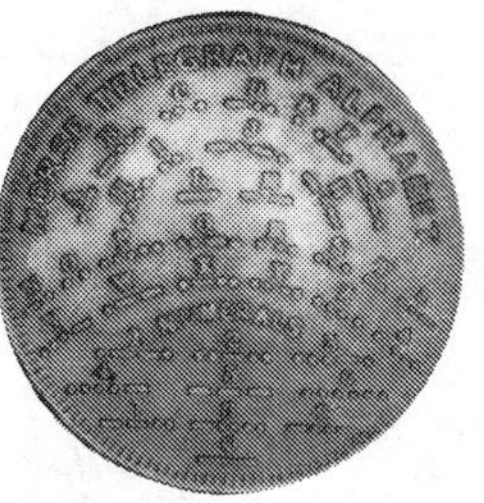

Miller	Date	Metal	Size	F	VF	EF	Unc
NY 1060	(?)	Silver	32mm	—	—	225.	400.
		As 1055, but 4th and 5th lines curved on reverse.					
NY 1061	(?)	Copper	32mm	30.00	50.00	60.00	125.
		As 1060.					
NY 1062	(?)	Brass	32mm	30.00	50.00	60.00	125.
		As 1060.					
NY 1063	(?)	White Metal	32mm	30.00	50.00	60.00	125.
		As 1060.					

Samuel W. Chubbuck was apparently a man of talented parts. His tokens reveal him to be a manufacturer of telegraph, chemical and philosophical apparatus. His 1863 scrip note reveals no occupation.

Chubbuck was born in 1799 and died in 1875. He was a silversmith in both Utica and Morrisville, N.Y., eventually (1847-1849) forming the Utica silver firm of Storrs & Chubbuck with Henry S. Storrs.

DICKINSON & CO.

Rulau	Date	Metal	Size	VG	F	VF	EF
NY 2100	(?)	Copper	29mm	25.00	—	50.00	—
		DICKINSON & CO ctsp on U.S. 1818 Large cent. (Tanenbaum coll.; Brunk 11620)					

This company is reputed to be a forerunner to Dickinson & Comstock, an issuer of Civil War tokens. (Fuld NY 905A)

T.L. KINGSLEY & SON

Utica, N.Y.

Miller	Date	Metal	Size	F	VF	EF	Unc
NY 1064	(1858-60)	Brass	25mm	5.00	8.00	10.00	30.00
		T. L. KINGSLEY & SON / GREAT / WARDROBE / CLOTHING / 112 GENESEE ST. UTICA N.Y. Rv: BRANCHES AT / 109 / GENESEE ST. / AUBURN / 63 / DOMINICK ST., ROME. Reeded edge. (Wright 555)					
NY 1064A	(1858-60)	Brass	25mm	5.00	8.00	10.00	30.00
		As last. Plain edge.					

Civil War patriotic tokens (Fuld 258/446) were struck over Miller NY 1064. The overstrikes indicate the dies were used later to create rare varieties, probably for collectors.

DRYSDALE

Valley Stream, N.Y.

Rulau	Date	Metal	Size	VG	F	VF	EF
NY 2320	(?)	Copper	29mm	—	75.00	—	125.
		DRYSDALE (curved) / V.S. N Y ctsp on U.S. 1839 Large cent. (Frank Kovacs coll.; Brunk 12295)					

PHISTER, MAKER

Vernon, N.Y.

Rulau	Date	Metal	Size	VG	F	VF	EF
NY 2321	(?)	Copper	29mm	—	75.00	—	125.
		PHISTER / MAKER / VERNON, N.Y. ctsp on U.S. 1826 Large cent. (Tanenbaum coll.; Brunk 31998)					

PHISTE is known ctsp on 1864 U.S. 2-cent piece (Brunk 31997). There may be no connection.

H.A. GRISWOLD
Whitehall, N.Y.

Rulau	Date	Metal	Size	VG	F	VF	EF
NY 2630	(1850's)	Silver	31mm	—	—	90.00	—
		H.A. GRISWOLD ctsp on U.S. 1840 Liberty Seated half dollar. (Bowers & Ruddy 1982 sales list; Brunk 17240; Rulau Mich 110)					
NY 2631	(1850's)	Silver	38mm	—	—	225.	—
		Similar ctsp on U.S. 1840 Liberty Seated silver dollar. (Van Ormer sale 2631)					
NY 2632	(1850's)	Silver	26.5mm	—	—	90.00	—
		Similar ctsp on U.S. 1819 Capped Bust quarter. (Van Ormer sale 2678)					
NY 2633		Copper	29mm	—	—	75.00	—
		Similar ctsp on U.S. 1819 Large cent.					
NY 2634		Copper	28mm	—	—	75.00	—
		Similar ctsp on Hard Times token. (Rulau Mich 112B)					

Griswold was a jeweler and silversmith in Whitehall during the 1850's, according to Kovel (see Bibliography)

C.A.M. SMITH
Windsor, N.Y.

Miller	Date	Metal	Size	VG	F	EF	Unc
NY 1068	(1855)	Copper	28mm	7.50	12.50	25.00	45.00
		Imitation of U.S. cent reverse. ONE / CENT within wreath, C. A. M. SMITH WINDSOR, N.Y. around. Rv: GENERAL / DEALER / IN / DRY GOODS / GROCERIES / * &C. C. * (Wright 997)					

NORTH CAROLINA

J. MARTINE
Fayetteville, N.C.

Rulau	Date	Metal	Size	VG	F	VF	EF
NC 100	(?)	Silver	19mm	300.	—	450.	—
		J. MARTINE / FA'/t N.C. in relief within a rectangle, ctsp on U.S. 1820 Bust type dime. (Dom Mulrooney coll.; Brunk 26170)					
NC 101	(?)	Silver	32.5mm	400.	—	600.	—
		Similar ctsp on U.S. Bust half dollar. Examined: 1828, 1829.					

James Martine was a coppersmith who began business in Cumberland County in 1826. Fayetteville is the county seat. This stamp could be earlier than 1845.

Martine later became a pewterer in Fayetteville circa 1826-1836. He also sold medicines with S.J. Hinsdale, according to *The Story of Fayetteville* by James Oates.

James Martine was a director of Fayetteville Bank in 1849. If the stamps are from his coppersmith and pewterer trade, they would belong in the Hard Times period.

D.J. GILBERT
Wilmington, N.C.

Miller	Date	Metal	Size	VG	F	VF	Unc
NC 1	(Late 1850's)	Brass	31mm	100.	300.	500.	900.
		Similar to 1A.					
NC 1A	(Late 1850's)	German silver	31mm	100.	300.	500.	900.
		HARNETT. / BILLIARD / * SALOON * / MARKET ST. / WILMINGTON N.C. Rv: D.J. GILBERT'S / CHECK / GOOD FOR / 25.					

The Gilbert pieces were struck before 1859, as may be attested by the inclusion of one of them in the Philadelphia Numismatic Society catalog of store cards, printed about 1859. Number 1A was Bushnell 1882 sale lot 1052.

D.J. Gilbert, a merchant, aged 31, appeared in the 1850 census for New Hanover County, N.C. Gilbert did not appear in the 1840 or 1860 census records. Thus he apparently entered business in the 1840's and lasted until the 1850's. All work on the token is in relief, but the numeral 25 is incused. (Research on census records by Aubrey T. Haddock; see "Exonumia Notebook" on page 3325 of the Dec. 1981 *The Numismatist).*

OHIO

H. E. SHALLENBERGER
Amanda, Ohio

Rulau	Date	Metal	Size	VG	F	VF	EF
Ohio 110	(1850 ?)	Silver	20mm	—	—	350.	—
		AMANDA. / O. / H. E. SHALLENBERGER. ctsp on worn-smooth silver coin, probably Spanish-American 1-real. Holed, for wear. (Rulau coll.; Brunk 36135)					

R. BROOKS
Berlin, (Ohio?)

Rulau	Date	Metal	Size	VG	F	VF	EF
Ohio 200	(?)	Copper	29mm	—	—	35.00	—
		R Brooks / BERLIN O ctsp on U.S. 1845 Large cent. The two incuse stamps are from completely different letter-punches. (Pete Peters coll.)					

M.A. COHN
Cincinnati, Ohio

Miller	Date	Metal	Size	VG	F	VF	EF
Ohio 190	(1860's)	Brass	--mm	100.	250.	750.	1000.
		M.A. COHN, 68 W. --TH ST. Rv: Blank. (Miller Mo 5)					

Matthew Cohn was a Civil War coffee house proprietor.

DODD, HATTER

Miller	Date	Metal	Size	F	VF	EF	Unc
Ohio 7	(ca 1850)	Brass	28mm	7.50	10.00	15.00	40.00
		Imitation of U.S. $10 gold piece, DODD on coronet. Six stars above, CINCINNATI 144 MAIN ST below. Rv: Around eagle: DODD HATTER CINCINNATI. Reeded edge.					

DODD & CO., HATTERS

Miller	Date	Metal	Size	F	VF	EF	Unc
Ohio 8	(ca 1851)	Brass	28mm	7.50	10.00	15.00	40.00
		Similar to obverse of 7, but seven stars above head. Rv: Around eagle: DODD & CO HATTERS CINCINNATI. Reeded edge. (Wright 255)					
Ohio 9	(ca 1851)	Copper	28mm	10.00	12.50	17.50	40.00
		As 8. Plained edge.					
Ohio 10	(ca 1851)	Silvered Brass	28mm	10.00	15.00	20.00	50.00
		As 8. Plain edge.					
Ohio 10B	(1860)	Brass	28mm	7.50	10.00	25.00	50.00
		Obverse as 8. Rv: High silk hat at center, FRANCISCO & CO. above, * HATTERS * below. (Obverse of Adams Tenn 12). Plain edge.					
Ohio 10C	(1860)	Copper	28mm	—	—	50.00	75.00
		As Ohio 10B.					

Dr. Benjamin P. Wright in 1898 reported as number 254 a variety of Ohio 8 with 'DOOD' instead of 'DODD' on the headband of Liberty's coronet. This variety has not been traced, but may exist.

William Dodd was a hat manufacturer early in the 19th century, the first really large hatter in the city to produce hats which excelled in quality over imported (from New York, etc.) hats. His company seems always to have been located at 144 Main St., then a fashionable section, and his advertisements appeared in the Forties and Fifties.

Associated with William Dodd were George S. Dodd, Edward S. Dodd, John Roberts and George W. Pickard, and up to 40 hands were employed in season. The firm lasted until about 1868.

W.B. CHAPMAN
A.M. STEVENS
W.J.M. GORDON
T.B. HARRIS

(All cards are similar, but different druggist name appears on obverse to indicate issuer.)

Miller	Date	Metal	Size	VG	F	VF	Unc
Ohio 70	(1857)	German Silver	19mm	20.00	35.00	60.00	100.
		At center a soda fountain; in a curve above W.B. CHAPMAN, below 6TH AND VINE. All within a circle. Inscription around: ONE GLASS OF SODA OR BLUE LICK WATER *. Rv: W.B. CHAPMAN / A.M. STEVENS / W.J.M. GORDON / T.B. HARRIS. Plain edge. (Wright 162; Miller Pa 88)					
Ohio 71	(1857)	German Silver	19mm	20.00	35.00	60.00	—
		As 70. Reeded edge. (Miller Pa 88A)					

Miller	Date	Metal	Size	VG	F	VF	Unc
Ohio 72	(1857)	German Silver	19mm	15.00	30.00	40.00	70.00
		As 88, inscribed W.J.M. GORDON / WESTERNROW / & EIGHTH. Rv: As Ohio 70. (Wright 388; Miller Pa 181)					

Miller	Date	Metal	Size	VG	F	VF	Unc
Ohio 73	(1857)	German Silver	19mm	20.00	30.00	50.00	70.00
		As 88, inscribed T.B. HARRIS / S.E. COR. OF / 4TH & MAIN. Rv: Ohio 70. Plain edge. (Wright 429; Miller Pa 193)					
Ohio 74	(1857)	German Silver	19mm	20.00	30.00	50.00	70.00
		As 73. Reeded edge. (Miller Pa 194)					

Miller	Date	Metal	Size	VG	F	VF	Unc
Ohio 75	(1857)	German Silver	19mm	20.00	35.00	60.00	75.00
		As 70, but urn on pedestal at center. Inscribed around A.M. STEVENS / 4TH & RACE. (Wright 1050; Storer 8145; Miller Pa 490)					
Ohio 75A	(1857)	GS	19mm	—	—	—	Rare
		As last, but blank reverse.					

All four soda-dispensing druggists collaborated to issue these similar soda water checks. All are scarce, especially in the highest grades of preservation.

William B. Chapman opened his drug store about 1840. In 1842 he was at S.W. corner of Court and Vine Streets, moving in 1849 to 6th and Vine, the address on the tokens. It occupied the corner (first floor) of the Ohio Mechanics Institute, with entrances on both streets. Chapman was active in OMI — corresponding secretary in 1851 and then serving on the committee for OMI's 17th exhibition in 1859. In 1860 the business was taken over by a son, William C. Chapman, and the senior Chapman is listed as a physician in 1862.

Thomas B. Harris began his soda fountain in 1846. In 1856 he was located at 4th and Main, the address on tokens. He was there in the 1857 directory also. Then in 1861 he has become a physician, abandoning the druggist practice.

William J.M. Gordon started business in 1848 as Gordon & Israel at N.E. corner Westernrow and 8th. The address remained the same, but the business name was W.J.M. Gordon 1849-50; Gordon & Co. 1850-51; W.J.M. Gordon again 1855; Gordon & Brothers 1858.

Ashbel M. Stevens was apparently in business 1849-56, but only appears at the address on the token (4th and Race) in 1857. In 1858 this became A.M. Stevens & Co. when a partner, William Snyder, was admitted. In 1859 the drug store moved to a different address and admitted a relative, Ashur M. Stevens.

Thus 1857 must be the date of issue of this joint token venture; it is the only year all company names and addresses are "right."

Blue Lick Water was a mineral water obtained from Blue Lick springs on Kentucky's Licking River some 30 miles south of Cincinnati. It was a diuretic and purgative which was widely recommended for many ailments.

J. DRAPER (AND) PEPIN

Miller	Date	Metal	Size	VG	F	VF	EF
Ohio 195	(?)	Copper	29mm	—	—	165.	—
		J. DRAPER / PEPIN in relief within two separate rect. depressions ctsp several times on U.S. 1816 or 1832 Large cent. (B&M Taylor sale, March 1987, lot 1278; Brunk 12197; Rulau Z10G)					

Joseph Draper became Cincinnati's first silversmith in 1832, working until 1856. He also sold watches and jewelry.

Pepin has not been traced.

F. ECKSTEIN, JR.

Miller	Date	Metal	Size	VG	F	VF	Unc
Ohio 10-1/2	(1856)	Copper	19mm	15.00	25.00	40.00	75.00
		An eagle. F. ECKSTEIN JR. / COR. FOURTH AND MAIN STS. Rv: An urn fountain. ONE GLASS / SODA. (Wright 280)					

This firm is a predecessor (1846-56) to Suire, Eckstein (which see). In 1857, Suire Eckstein is listed at the northeast corner of 4th and Main. No listing appears that year for Frederick Eckstein Jr.

S.C. ERWIN

Miller	Date	Metal	Size	F	VF	EF	Unc
Ohio 11	(ca 1858)	Brass	22mm	5.00	7.50	10.00	30.00
		Eagle displayed, shield on breast, S.C. ERWIN. HATTER: / 149. MAIN ST. CINA. Rv: High silk hat within oak wreath. Plain edge. (Wright 295)					
Ohio 11A	(ca 1858)	Brass	22mm	5.00	7.50	10.00	30.00
		As 11. Reeded edge.					

Samuel C. Erwin advertised extensively in local periodicals in the Fifties as a hat manufacturer. In 1860 he left the hat business for a time, going into insurance with W. Byron Carter, at Trust Building, 3 West 3rd St. He later returned to the hat business, until the 1880's.

EVENS' SEWING MACHINES

Miller	Date	Metal	Size	VG	F	VF	Unc
Ohio 15	(1861)	Brass	22mm	—	—	75.00	150.
		EVENS' / ALL KINDS OF / SEWING / MACHINES / REPAIRED / 64 W. 4TH ST. Rv: Beaded circle at center. Within circle: JOHN STANTON / STAMP / & BRAND / CUTTER / CINCINNATI. Plain edge.					

Platt Evens Jr. was the son of the tailor Platt Evens who issued tokens in the Hard Times period (Low numbers 312 to 313B).

Evens was a manufacturer of seal presses and a seal engraver, at least in the 1852-1864 period. His principal place of business was at 187 Walnut St. 1852-1858, then 207 Walnut St. in 1864. A separate office at 64 West 4th St. advertised that it repaired sewing machines in 1861.

Waldo C. Moore in June 1917 in *The Numismatist* ("P Evens, Engraver"), attributed the Evens token to 1858. It is also known in tin-plated brass; same prices.

E. & D. KINSEY

Miller	Date	Metal	Size	F	VF	EF	Unc
Ohio 19	1851	Copper	22mm	35.00	50.00	75.00	100.

Exhibition hall in London, EXHIBITION PALACE above, LONDON / 1851 in exergue. Rv: E. & D. KINSEY / SILVER / WARE / MANUFACTURERS / 5TH ST. / CINCINNATI. Plain edge.

Miller	Date	Metal	Size	F	VF	EF	Unc
Ohio 19A	1851	Silvered Copper	22mm	37.50	55.00	75.00	100.

As 19. Plain edge. (Wright 556)

The obverse, cut by Thomas Pope & Co. of Birmingham, England, was also used on the store cards of D. Gowans & Co. of New Orleans and Tilly, Haynes & Co. of Springfield, Mass. The London Crystal Palace served as the model for the New York Crystal Palace of 1853, itself the subject of a number of store cards (e.g. H.B. West of New York City).

Edward and David Kinsey emigrated to Cincinnati from northern Wales, starting their silverware manufactory by 1837. In 1837 their business was known as "E. Kinsey, manufacturer of silver plate and spoons" at the corner of 3rd and Walnut. The partnership was dissolved in 1862, though each Kinsey stayed in business separately — Edward at East South Broadway, 3rd door below Fourth, and David at 24 West 5th Street.

For an excellent overview of the 19th century token issues of Cincinnati, see "The Early Tokens of the Queen City, Cincinnati, Ohio" by Russ Rulau in the April and June 1974 issues of *TAMS Journal*.

L.O. LOEWE

Miller	Date	Metal	Size	VG	F	VF	Unc
Ohio 192	1860	White Metal	19mm	35.00	50.00	75.00	150.

Lion's head in center, L.C. LOEWE / 1860. Rv: Large letter 'C' encloses numeral '3' at center, circle of 13 stars around. Rare. (Wright 616; Miller NY 20)

SUIRE, ECKSTEIN & CO.

Miller	Date	Metal	Size	VG	F	VF	Unc
Ohio 30-1/2	(1857)	German silver	16mm	—	25.00	40.00	55.00

Large numeral 5 within circle at center, SUIRE, ECKSTEIN & CO * around. Rv: Large numeral 5 within circle at center, DRUGGISTS / COR. 4TH &. VINE STS.

This piece has also been located by Adams and Miller under Pa 503, definitely in error.

Suire, Eckstein & Co., wholesale druggists, were at 4th and Main in 1857, consisting of Francis E. Suire, Frederick Eckstein and Andrew B. Merriam. Eckstein left in 1865 and it became Suire & Co.

WINDER
Cincinnati, Ohio

Rulau	Date	Metal	Size	VG	F	VF	EF
Oh 130	(?)	Silver	27mm	—	—	175.	—

WINDER / COR. W. ROW / & COURT / CIN. O. ctsp in rather small incuse letters on Spanish-American 1803-LME-IJ 2-reales. (Saccone sale, lot 3115; Brunk 43855)

This piece surfaced only in November, 1989. It was unknown to Brunk, Van Ormer, Rulau and all earlier catalogers.

FELCH & RICHES
Columbus, Ohio

Rulau	Date	Metal	Size	VG	F	VF	EF
Ohio 150	(ca 1856-57)	Copper	29mm	—	60.00	—	90.00

FELCH & RICHES (curved) / HIGH ST. / SEALS & C. (curved) ctsp on U.S. 1838 Large cent. (Brunk 13940)

Felch & Riches were steel, copper, wood and seal engravers located at High Street in Columbus, four doors north of the American Hotel, according to the 1857 edition of *Williams Ohio State Register*. They may also have been responsible for countermarking coins for their clients. Their advertising indicated they also engraved "cards and door plates."

TANNER
Dayton, Ohio

Rulau	Date	Metal	Size	VG	F	VF	EF
Ohio 156	(?)	Copper	29mm	—	50.00	—	100.

TANNER / DAYTON. O ctsp on U.S. 1853 Large cent. (John Cheramy coll.; Brunk 39320)

L. ELDRED
Lodi, Ohio

Rulau	Date	Metal	Size	VG	F	VF	EF
Ohio 160	(?)	Copper	29mm	—	—	125.	—

L. ELDRED / LODI / MEDINA ctsp on U.S. Large cent. (Hallenbeck 5.508; Rulau NY - Md 4)

J. McHANNON
Oxford, Ohio

Rulau	Date	Metal	Size	VG	F	VF	EF
Ohio 165	(?)	Copper	29mm	—	100.	—	200.

J. McHANNON / OXFORD. O. ctsp on U.S. 1838 Large cent. (Brunk 26867)

G.W. COLLINS
Urbana, Ohio

Rulau	Date	Metal	Size	VG	F	VF	EF
Ohio 180	(1857-60)	Silver	25mm	—	150.	—	225.

G.W. COLLINS / URBANA, O. ctsp on U.S. Seated Liberty quarter. Dates examined: 1853, 1854. (Van Ormer sale 2599; Brunk 8900)

G.W. Collins advertised his "Ambrotype & Photograph Gallery" at Weaver's Block, east side of Public Square in Urbana. He was also a wholesaler of daguerreotype, ambrotype and photographic goods in the 1857-59 period.

The address in 1858 was 154 Scioto St.

OREGON TERRITORY

UNION MINE
Oregon Territory

CAUTION: FANTASIES!

Rulau	Date	Metal	Size	VG	F	VF	EF
Ore 100	(1970 ?)	Silver	32.5mm	—	—	2.50	—

UNION MINE / 5 Dol. / OREG. / TERR crudely ctsp with single-letter punches on planed-off reverse of genuine U.S. 1839 Bust half dollar. (An accompanying ANACS certificate attests to authenticity of the host coin, not the stamping)

Rulau	Date	Metal	Size	VG	F	VF	EF
Ore 101	(1986 ?)	Silver	38mm	—	—	5.00	—

Similar stamp, but ctsp on U.S. Seated Liberty silver dollar, date not reported.

Ore 102	(1980 ?)	Copper	27mm	—	—	—	2.50

UNION / MINE / 10 Doll. crudely ctsp on planed-off reverse of a copper replica of Oregon 1849 $10 gold piece, KM 101.

Your author and Dr. Brunk agree that these pieces were made by the same forger who emitted the Texas fantasies. The same letterpunches for I, T and E were used.

In addition to the three pieces described above, some 35 to 50 Union Mine pieces are in the hands of dealers or collectors in Idaho, Oregon, Missouri, Minnesota and other states. Reported are $50 stamped on U.S. $20 gold piece; $20 on U.S. $5 gold piece; $10 on an unidentified coin; $1 on U.S. silver quarter.

These pieces may have first surfaced in Texas about 1958. They surfaced in Boise, Idaho and Portland, Oregon about 1970. They were offered at a show in Long Beach, Calif. in February 1986.

A 1988 letter from a coin dealer in response to articles appearing in the coin press stated the mine tokens were "fantasy concoctions that did not exist more than (a few) years ago." He added:

"I personally examined (some) pieces in the possession of an Oregon coin dealer a year and a half ago at Long Beach. They are beyond 'questionable.' They should fool no one but the most uninitiated."

These pieces are concoctions, hence they are worth only a bit more than their bullion content, as the planing and stamping would have ruined the host coins' numismatic value. We have assigned such values above in the belief these pieces are fantasies. That they are listed here at all is well justified, however; collectors have come to rely on editions of *U.S. Merchant Tokens 1845-1860* for reliable information on dating, pricing and background.

STORY OF THE UNION MINE

Union Mine supposedly was 27 miles up the south fork of the Clearwater River (called Couscouska or Koos Kooska River in 1850-70) from its confluence with the Snake River. This area is now in the state of Idaho in the vicinity of the Nez Perce Indian Reservation. Its site would be somewhere between Craigmont (formerly Vollmer) in Lewis County and Ferdinand in Idaho County. It is supposed to have opened in 1851 and shut down in the winter of 1863.

The coins allegedly were planed off and stamped by Joshawa Hickley in the 1856-60 period, raising their face value in all cases, for trade in raw gold and highbred horses with Nez Perce and Flathead Indians. Hickley was said to be step-uncle of Cyrus Heddin, well-known historian of Josephine and Douglas counties, Oregon. (In early life Heddin had been a blacksmith involved in the 1849 California gold rush.)

Union Mine Outpost (closed spring, 1865) supposedly redeemed these pieces for full value in bank notes or specie. It was a log structure on the Clearwater.

For background reading, see: "Are Union Mine Tokens Authentic?" in *Numismatic News* for Dec. 20, 1988, by Dudley L. McClure; another McClure article on the same subject in *Numismatic News* for June 10, 1986; and a Union Mine article by Bill Bogynska in *Coins* magazine for July 1987.

PENNSYLVANIA

SPECIAL NOTE: Extensive revisions to the dating of store cards under Philadelphia have been made in this section. The footnotes under many Philadelphia token issuers have also been enlarged, revised or added. This new research is due primarily to the efforts of H. Joseph Levine of Presidential Coin & Antique Co. Other recent Pennsylvania research is due in part to the contributions of Steve Tanenbaum, Gregory G. Brunk, William Swoger and others.

KNECHT
Easton, Pa.

Rulau	Date	Metal	Size	VG	F	VF	EF
Pa 700	(1860's)	Silver	21mm	200.	—	300.	—

AMBROTYPE / BY KNECHT ctsp on Spanish-American 1789-Mo 1-real. (Gould 104; Brunk 23185)

Pa 700A	(1860's)	Silver	27mm	200.	—	300.	—

Similar ctsp on Spanish-American 2-reales. (Date examined: 1779)

Reuben Knecht was a well-known wet-plate photographer in Easton. He was also a mathematician. He appears in directories in the 1860's and 1870's.

JOHNSON HIMROD & CO.
Erie, Pa

Miller	Date	Metal	Size	G	VG	F	EF
Pa 3	1845	White Metal	38mm	100.	350.	1000.	2000.

Large numeral 100 at center, — JOHNSON HIMROD & CO. — ERIE around. Rv: DUE / THE BEARER / ONE DOLLAR / IN MERCHANDISE OR / CASTINGS / AT OUR USUAL / RETAIL PRICES / 1845. Plain edge. (Wright 515)

This piece is probably the earliest dollar-sized $1 trade token issued in the United States. It is very rare. The firm was a foundry.

J. B. S.

Pa 3C	(1845 ?)	WM	38mm	—	—	—	2000.

J. B. S. within rectangle ctsp on obverse of Miller Pa 3. (ANS collection)

Possibly this is a successor firm to Johnson Himrod & Co.

G. LOOMIS & CO.
Erie, Pa.

Rulau	Date	Metal	Size	VG	F	VF	Unc
Pa 704	(1847-48)	Silver	43mm	200.	—	300.	—

G. LOOMIS & CO. in relief within rectangular depression; G. LOOMIS in relief within rectangular depression; ERIE incuse — all three counterstamps on France 1784 silver ecu. (Brunk 24840)

Guy Loomis (1794-1874) came to Erie about 1837, entering the jewelry business the same year. He manufactured silver spoons and the relief and incuse stamps are his hallmarks. In 1853-54 he was located at 4 Brown's Block; then 1854-55 on East 6th St. near Holland; 1859-early 1870's on State St. near 5th.

He styled his business G. Loomis & Co. beginning 1847.

Loomis, once a captain in the military forces, died Sept. 23, 1874. Ragnar Cederlund and Robert P. King reported this counterstamp in *The Numismatist* for June 1933.

Loomis' firm was still listed in the 1890's.

JOSHUA YOUS
Greencastle, Pa.

Rulau	Date	Metal	Size	VG	F	VF	EF
Pa 703	(1859-60)	Copper	29mm	—	50.00	—	75.00
		J. YOUS ctsp on U.S. Large cent. Dates examined: 1808, 1812, 1819, 1820, 1831, 1837, 1839, 1843, 1845, 1848, 1852, date worn off. (Partrick coll.; Van Ormer sale 2928; Brunk 44820)					
Pa 703A	(1859-60)	Copper	29mm	—	60.00	—	90.00
		JOSHUA / YOUS ctsp on U.S. Large cent. (Donald Partrick coll.; Brunk 44825)					
Pa 703B	(1859-60)	Copper	29mm	—	100.	—	150.
		J. YOUS / RIDGLEY ctsp on U.S. 1808 Large cent. (Partrick coll.)					
Pa 703E	(1859-60)	CN	19mm	—	50.00	—	75.00
		J. YOUS. ctsp on U.S. 1857 Flying Eagle or 1859 or 1860 Indian cent. (Partrick coll.)					

The attribution to Joshua Yous of Greencastle, Pa. is by Roy Van Ormer; it is confirmed by gunsmith sources.

Joshua Yous made percussion fullstock and patch box rifles in Greencastle 1854-61. The same curved stamp was applied to his guns. He was born 1827 and died 1905.

WM. GRUMBINE

Hanover, Pa.

Rulau	Date	Metal	Size	VG	F	VF	EF
Pa 701	(?)	Silver	27mm	400.	—	600.	—
		WM GRUMBINE / COACH / MAKER / HANOVER, PA ctsp on Spanish-American 1772 or 1796 2-reales. (Van Ormer sale 2679; Brunk 17330)					
Pa 701A	(?)	Copper	29mm	400.	—	600.	—
		Similar ctsp on U.S. Large cent.					

Grumbine (1824-88) was one of about 25 coachmakers in Hanover employing 2,000 people.

G.W. WELSH

Hanover, Pa.

Rulau	Date	Metal	Size	VG	F	VF	EF
Pa 702	(?)	Silver	27mm	400.	—	650.	—
		G. W. WELSH / COACH MAKER / HANOVER PA ctsp on Spanish-American 1776-LME (Peru) or 1800 2-reales. There are 3 pieces reported. (Van Ormer sale 2905; Brunk 42580)					

The 1800 piece, with the stronger counterstamp, made a startling $660 in the Van Ormer sale in Sept. 1985.

BUEHLER & HOWARD

Lewistown, Pa.

Rulau	Date	Metal	Size	VG	F	VF	EF
Pa 760	(?)	Silver	38mm	—	100.	—	150.
		BUEHLER / & HOWARD / LEWISTOWN / WM. MANN ctsp on obverse of France 1831 5-francs of Charles X. Rv: WM MANN / LEWISTOWN / LEWISTOWN ctsp on reverse of the coin. (Van Ormer collection sale, lot 2559; Brunk 5705)					

Postal guides for the 1870's list Lewistowns in Maryland, New Jersey and Ohio, all tiny places. They also list Lewistowns as county seats in Illinois and Pennsylvania. The city in Pa. (on the Juniata River) is today an important place, in Mifflin County.

We discount the three tiny places as the site for this stamp. The Ill. city had 2,500 people in 1918, the Pa. city had 10,750 the same year.

We're guessing Pa. for this piece, subject to directory evidence. Probably issued in the 1845-57 period. French silver ecus (dollars) were fairly popular in that period along the Ohio, Missouri and Mississippi rivers but once demonetized in 1857 quickly disappeared from circulation. (Spanish-American pieces, however, stayed on in circulation for a time after 1857, contemporary accounts show, especially in the Southwest and West.)

M. L.

Milton, Pa.

Rulau	Date	Metal	Size	VG	F	VF	EF
Pa 820	(?)	Silver	27mm	200.	—	—	—
		M. L. / MILTON, PA ctsp on Spanish-American 1788 2-reales. (Herman Aqua coll.)					

MT. HOLLY PAPER CO.

Mount Holly Springs, Pa.

Miller	Date	Metal	Size	F	VF	EF	Unc
Pa 4	1860	Silver	20.5mm	—	—	250.	500.
		Uniformed Washington bust left, F. K. on truncation of bust. Around: MT. HOLLY PAPER CO. MT. HOLLY SPRINGS PA. (The PA. is upside down). Rv: 1860 within open-top olive wreath.					
Pa 5	1860	Brass	20.5mm	—	—	—	300.
		As Pa 4. Unique.					
Pa 6	1860	Tin (White Metal)	20.5mm	—	—	100.	200.
		As Pa 4.					
Pa 7	1860	Copper	20.5mm	—	—	100.	200.
		As Pa 4. (Wright 732)					

These pieces, by F. Key of Philadelphia, are rare. Supposedly only a total of 20 specimens was struck in all metals. Edward Cogan, in his March 25-26, 1862 sale catalog, said the brass piece was struck in only one specimen. Both dies apparently broke. The reverse type is the same as that used by Cogan on his own store cards, Pa 90-90G.

There were four owners of the Mount Holly Paper Co. One of them, Sylvester Magargee, lived in Philadelphia. Edward Cogan, ever the entrepreneur, may have had the 20 pieces struck as samples to sell the idea of tokens to Magargee, but the latter rejected them. This scenario was envisioned by Elizabeth Steinle, South Charleston, W. Va. collector.

Mt. Holly Paper Co. built its plant on Mountain Creek in 1856. The original owners were the Given brothers, Mullins, Kempton and Sylvester Magargee. The firm made fine letter and general writing paper, and patented "Commercial Safety Paper," designed to eliminate alterations on checks and documents. It is still in business, now known as Eaton-Dikeman Co., and still uses the original building.

Confederate troops captured the plant briefly in 1863 on their way to the Battle of Gettysburg, and some CSA documents have turned up on paper bearing the firm's imprint, which evidently was taken by the invading army.

(See "Trolley to Holly" by Elizabeth W. Steinle in *TAMS Journal* for Dec. 1978)

NOTE: Mrs. Steinle notes that the two dies of Pa 4-7 broke at different times. She says the obverse (Washington) die broke during the striking of the Mt. Holly tokens. The '1860' side die broke later, she says, using as evidence the fact that she possesses a Cogan store card using the 1860 die that shows a die crack not on the Mt. Holly brass piece.

ALDRIDGE & EARP

Philadelphia, Pa.

Miller	Date	Metal	Size	VG	F	VF	Unc
Pa 8	(1847-48)	Brass	28mm	5.00	10.00	20.00	60.00
		Ornamental comb at center, LOOKING GLASSES, COMBS / . & FANCY GOODS. Rv: ALDRIDGE & EARP / 164 / MARKET / ST / * PHILADA *					
Pa 8A	(1847-48)	Copper	28mm	5.00	10.00	20.00	60.00
		As 8.					
Pa 8B	(1847-48)	Silvered Brass	28mm	5.00	10.00	20.00	60.00
		As 8. (Wright 11)					

Aldridge & Earp, fancy goods, were at 164 High Street (Market Street) in the 1848 directory, their first listing. The firm consisted of Samuel H. Aldridge and G. Bakewell Earp.

In the 1849 directory they had moved to 191 Market St.

In 1857 many Philadelphia streets were renumbered and the new numbers reflected in the 1858 directories.

A. D. ANGUE

Miller	Date	Metal	Size	F	VF	EF	Unc
Pa 19	(1847-48)	Brass	29mm	7.50	10.00	15.00	60.00
		Man with two umbrellas standing to right. ALWAYS PROVIDE FOR A RAINY DAY around. Rv: Inscription in four lines.					
Pa 19A	(1847-48)	Silvered Brass	29mm	7.50	10.00	15.00	60.00
		As 19.					
Pa 20	(1847-48)	Brass	29mm	7.50	10.00	15.00	60.00
		Obverse as 19. Rv: Inscription in three lines.					
Pa 21	(1847-48)	Brass	29mm	7.50	10.00	15.00	60.00
		Obverse similar to Pa 19, but man is carrying four canes instead of two umbrellas. Rv: A. D. ANGUE CHEAP UMBRELLA & PARASOL / MANUFACTORY / 35 / NORTH / 3RD / STREET / PHILADA. Reeded edge.					
Pa 21A	(1847-48)	Brass	29mm	10.00	15.00	20.00	60.00
		Obverse similar to last, but man has only two canes. Rv: As Pa 19. (Wright 21)					

Albert D. Angue, umbrella manufacturer, is listed at 35 North 3rd Street in the 1848 directory. In the 1849 directory he was in the wine and liquor trade.

H. ARENSFELD

Rulau	Date	Metal	Size	VG	F	VF	EF
Pa 711	(1850's)	Copper	29mm	—	175.	250.	—
		H. ARENSFELD / LOCKSMITH / PHILA. ctsp on worn U.S. Large cent or 1851 cent. (H. Christensen Oct. 1987 sale, lot 836; Brunk 1055)					
Pa 712	(?)	Copper	29mm	150.	—	225.	—
		H. ARENSFELD / LOCKSMITH ctsp on U.S. 1820 Large cent. (Brunk 1050)					

Henry Arensfeld appears as a locksmith at 19 Norris Alley in the 1849 directory.

BAILEY & CO.

Rulau	Date	Metal	Size	G	VG	F	EF
Pa 708	(1850)	Copper	29mm	—	75.	—	125.
		BAILEY & CO. ctsp on U.S. Large cent. (Hallenbeck 2.523; Brunk 1770)					
Pa 709	(1850)	Copper	29mm	—	120.	—	180.
		BAILEY & CO. / 136 CHESTNUT ST. / PHILA. ctsp on U.S. Large cent. (Hallenbeck 2.524; Brunk 1780)					

The 1860-era tokens by Bailey & Co., jewelers, bear the address 819 Chestnut St. Bailey & Kitchen, jewelers and silversmiths, were at 136 Chestnut 1843-48.

Bailey & Co. (Joseph T. Bailey) were first listed at 136 Chestnut in 1846, remaining there until 1857 when the street address was renumbered as 428.

Miller	Date	Metal	Size	F	VF	EF	Unc
Pa 28	(1858-60)	Gilt Brass	30mm	20.00	25.00	35.00	65.00
		Three hallmarks across center: British lion in oval, S in circle and U.S. shield in oval. JANY. 1ST. 1855 / BAILEY & CO. / BRITISH / STERLING above; SILVER / WARE / 819 CHESTNUT ST. / PHILADELPHIA below. Rv: WATCHES / DIAMONDS / PEARLS / SILVER & PLATED / WARES. Plain edge. (Wright 66)					
Pa 29	(1860)	Gilt Brass	30mm	20.00	25.00	35.00	65.00
		As 28. Reeded edge.					
Pa 30	(1860)	Silvered Brass	30mm	20.00	25.00	35.00	50.00
		As 28. Plain edge.					
Pa 31	(1860)	Silvered Brass	30mm	20.00	25.00	35.00	50.00
		As 28. Reeded edge.					
Pa 32	(1860)	Brass	30mm	20.00	25.00	35.00	50.00
		As 28. Reeded edge.					
Pa 33	(1860)	Silver	30mm	35.00	50.00	75.00	200.
		As 28. Reeded edge.					
Pa 33AA	(1860)	Silver	30mm	35.00	50.00	75.00	200.
		As 33. Plain edge.					
Pa 33A	(1860)	?	30mm	—	25.00	35.00	100.
		Liberty head. Rv: As obverse of Pa 28.					

This firm also issued encased postage stamps in 1862. Bailey & Co. moved to 819 Chestnut (from 428 Chestnut) in 1858.

J. C. BAILEY

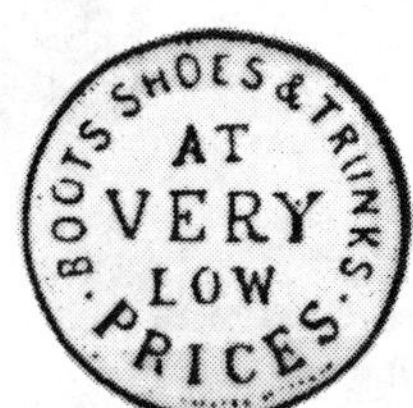

Miller	Date	Metal	Size	F	VF	EF	Unc
Pa 34	(1860's)	Brass	28mm	8.00	12.00	20.00	75.00
		* J. C. BAILEY * / 1109 SPRING GARDEN ST. Rv: BOOTS SHOES & TRUNKS / AT / VERY / LOW / PRICES. (Wright 1320)					

Dr. Wright called this piece rare about 1900. He added that this token is often confused with the Civil War store card of J. C. Bailey City Hotel, which was issued in Jersey City, N.J.

John C. Bailey was listed at 4th below Thompson 1856-57 and then 1232 Cadwalader in 1858. The tokens must have been made in or after 1861.

BARNUM HOTEL

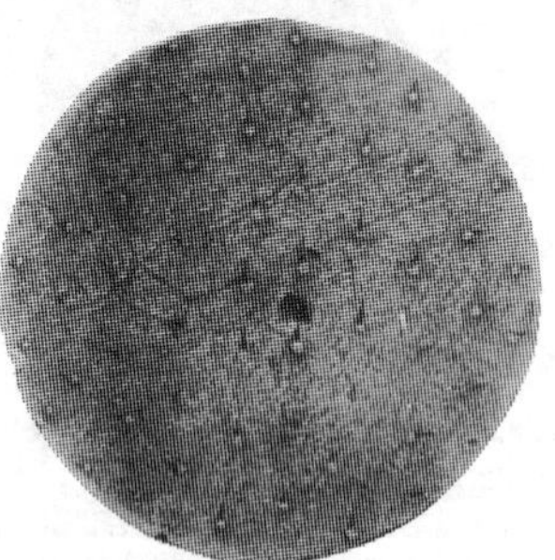

Rulau	Date	Metal	Size	VG	F	VF	Unc
Pa 730	(?)	Copper	38mm	—	—	—	65.00
		Within cartouche at center: BARNUM HOTEL. / EUROPEAN PLAN. / N. E. COR. 7TH. & SANSOM STS / PHILADA. / JOSEPH HAMLIN. Rv: Blank, but covered by pattern of dots. Plain edge. (ANS collection)					

We have been unable to find a directory listing.

A. BARRON

Miller	Date	Metal	Size	VG	F	VF	Unc
Pa 36A	(1855-57)	Brass	--mm	85.00	125.	200.	400.
		A. BARRON, 2D ST. EXCHANGE SALOON. PHILA. All incused. Very rare.					
Pa 36C	(1855-57)	Silver	21mm	200.	—	300.	—
		A. BARRON / 2D ST. / EXCHANGE / SALOON / 262 N. 2D ST. / A. B. WILLOW / PHILA ctsp on Spanish-American 1-real. (John Ford coll.; Brunk 2539)					

Archibald Barron is listed 1855-57 at 262 No. 2nd. This was renumbered as 432 No. 2nd in 1858.

C. M. BERRY

Rulau	Date	Metal	Size	VG	F	VF	EF
Pa 35	(1857)	Copper	29mm	100.	—	150.	—
		C. M. BERRY / N.W.C. 5TH & / PHILA. / CHESNUT / SALOON ctsp on U.S. Large cents. Examined: 1853, unknown date. Only 2 known. (Hallenbeck 2.510; Brunk 3480)					
Pa 35AA	(1857)	Copper	28.5mm	—	—	150.	—
		Similar ctsp on 28.5mm blank copper planchet. (Saccone 1989 sale, lot 3089)					
Pa 35A	(1857)	Silver	21mm	100.	—	150.	—
		Similar ctsp on Spanish-American 1-real coin.					

Rulau	Date	Metal	Size	VG	F	VF	EF
Pa 36	(1857)	Silver	27mm	90.00	—	150.	—
		Similar ctsp on Spanish-American 2-reales. Dates examined: 1771, 1773, 1777-Mo, 1779, 1781-Mo-FF, 1787, 1787-PTS-PR, 1789-Mo-FF, 1789-Mo-FM, 1790, 1791, 1792, 1795, 1796, 1799, 1805-Mo-TH, 1812. There are at least 22 pieces reported. (Gould 80; Van Ormer sale 2536 and 2537; Saccone sale 3085 thru 3088)					
Pa 36A	(1857)	Silver	27mm	90.00	—	150.	—
		Similar ctsp on Mexico 2-reales. Examined: 1826					

Rulau	Date	Metal	Size	VG	F	VF	EF
Pa 36M	(1857)	Silver	27mm	250.	—	400.	—
		Similar ctsp on reverse of Spanish-American 1773 2-reales. Rv: Knight's Mineral Water Saloon of Baltimore ctsp on opposite side of the coin, the obverse. (Brunk 7605/23240). Rare muling.					

Caspar M. Berry first appears in the 1848 directory as an agent at 555 South 2nd Street. The saloon, listed 1857-60, was on the corner of 5th and Chestnut Streets (spelled CHESNUT on these and other early Phila. counterstamps).

Berry appears in the 1850 census, where his residence address is given as 438 Moyamens.

S. J. BESTOR

Miller	Date	Metal	Size	VG	F	VF	EF
Pa 50	(1858)	Silver	34mm	—	—	—	800.
		Equestrian figure of Washington right, tree at left, small PHJ on ground. THE FATHER OF OUR COUNTRY BORN, FEB. 22, 1732. DIED, DEC. 14, 1799. Rv: Seated female figure points to clock face, TIME IS MONEY above. S. J. BESTOR, IMPORTER OF WATCHES & JEWLERY * PHILADELPHIA, PA. *. Reeded edge. (Baker 514)					
Pa 51	(1858)	Copper	34mm	—	—	200.	400.
		As Pa 50.					
Pa 52	(1858)	Silvered Copper	34mm	—	—	—	400.
		As Pa 50. (Wright 75)					
Pa 53	(1858)	Brass	34mm	—	—	20.00	40.00
		Obverse as Pa 50. Rv: A calendar. (No firm name on token). Reeded edge.					

Peter H. Jacobus of Philadelphia, a diesinker, cut these token dies in 1858. The portraiture, according to Baker, is fictitious and not based on an actual portrait.

BRIDESBURG BARREL MANUFG. CO.

Miller	Date	Metal	Size	VG	F	VF	Unc
Pa 54	(1850-58)	Brass	32mm	—	—	200.	400.
		Barrel at center, 6-pointed star at bottom. Around: BRIDESBURG BARREL MANUFG CO. Rv: Blank. Very rare. (Rulau-E Pa 54)					
Pa 54A	(1850-58)	Brass	32mm	—	—	200.	400
		As 54, but numeral 1 stamped on back.					
Pa 55	(1850-58)	Brass	32mm	—	—	200.	400.
		As 54, but numeral 2 stamped on back.					
Pa 56	(1850-58)	Brass	32mm	—	—	200.	400.
		As 54, but numeral 5 stamped on back.					
Pa 57	(1850-58)	Brass	32mm	—	—	200.	400.
		As 54, but numeral 10 stamped on back.					
Pa 58	(1850-58)	Brass	32mm	—	—	200.	400.
		As 54, but numeral 50 stamped on back.					

Miller	Date	Metal	Size	F	VF	EF	Unc
Pa 58A	(1850-58)	Brass	32mm	—	—	800.	1500.
		Barrel. Around: BRIDESBURG BARREL MANUFG CO. / *. Rv: 100 (incused). Plain edge. (Ex-Sol Kaplan coll.; Kirtley July 1992 sale, lot AD85; Ganter coll.)					

Pa 58A is a previously unlisted denomination. The 1858 catalog of the Numismatic Society of Philadelphia listed this token with denominations 1, 5, 10 and 50. In 1986 a 20 was sold in the B&M Liedman sale for $770.

Directory evidence linking this token issue to Philadelphia is lacking.

BROWNING BROTHERS

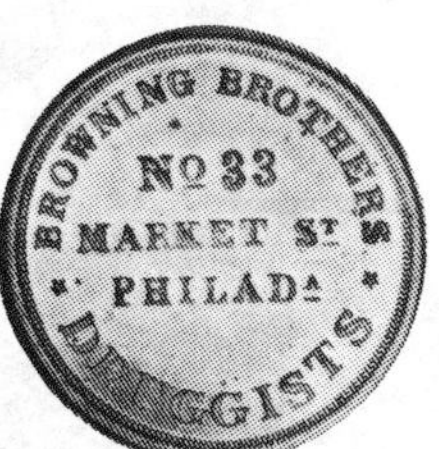

Miller	Date	Metal	Size	F	VF	EF	Unc
Pa 59	(1848-51)	Brass	30mm	7.50	15.00	30.00	60.00
		Eagle with drooping wings, shield on its breast. MANUFACTURERS above, * OF DRUGS & DYE STUFFS * below. Rv: BROWNING BROTHERS / NO 33 / MARKET ST / PHILADA / * DRUGGISTS *. Plain edge. (Wright 106)					
Pa 59A	(1848-51)	Copper	30mm	7.50	15.00	40.00	75.00
		As 59. Plain edge.					

Charles, Maurice and D. G. Browning are listed 1838-1851.

S. O. BUNTING

Rulau	Date	Metal	Size	VG	F	VF	EF
Pa 732	(?)	Silver	17mm	—	175.	—	—
		S. O. BUNTING / PHIL ctsp on silver coin worn too smooth for identification. (Joseph Schmidt coll.; Brunk 5853)					

There is no listing for an S.O. Bunting. A Samuel C. Bunting, merchant, is listed 1816-1843.

BUSH'S ALLEGHENY HOTEL

Rulau	Date	Metal	Size	VG	F	VF	EF
Pa 734	(1855-57)	Silver	25mm	—	150.	—	225.
		BUSH'S / ALLEGHENY / HOTEL / PHILA (top and bottom lines curved) ctsp on U.S. 1853 Arrows & Rays S.L. quarter. (Van Ormer sale 2563; Brunk 6230)					

The only known specimen fetched $121 in the 1985 Van Ormer sale.

Charles Bush is listed 1855-57 at 280 Market; this was renumbered 814 Market 1858-59. In 1860 Allegheny House had a new owner, James Ott.

J. E. CALDWELL & CO.

Rulau	Date	Metal	Size	VG	F	VF	EF
Pa 735	(1851-60)	Copper	29mm	100.	—	150.	—
		Seven separate punches applied to obverse of U.S. 1851 Large cent. The first is indisputably a merchant stamp, a silversmith's hallmark, viz: J. E. CALDWELL / — & CO. — / PHILADA. The others are: BOSTON / BOSTON / DURAND / DURAND / DURAND / N O & SON. (Hartzog coll.; Brunk 6570)					

James E. Caldwell & Co. were manufacturing silversmiths in Philadelphia from 1848 to at least 1979. They were at 902 Chestnut St. in the 1850's.

The 'N O & SON' mark is probably Nathan Olmsted & Son, contemporary (1847) silversmiths in Farmington and New Haven, Conn., also counterstamp issuers (see under Farmington, Conn.).

There were several contemporary Durands who were also silversmiths — in New York and in Newark, N.J.

CARELS' RESTAURANT

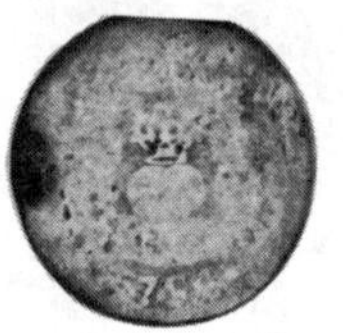

Rulau	Date	Metal	Size	VG	F	VF	EF
Pa 711	(1848)	Silver	19mm	—	125.	—	175.
		CARELS' / N.E. C. 8TH & / PHILA / CHESTNUT / RESTAURANT ctsp in five lines on Spanish-American 1754 1-real. (Van Ormer sale 2568, ex-Schenkman; Brunk 6760)					

William Carels appears in the 1850 census.

In the 1828, 1844 and 1848 directories William Carels Jr. is listed as proprietor of the Bolivar House at 201 and 203 Chestnut Street.

(See Bolivar House under Philadelphia in the Hard Times Token section. Carels began buiness in 1828.)

A. CHEW

Miller	Date	Metal	Size	VG	F	VF	Unc
Pa 88 1/2	(?)	Brass	22mm	—	75.00	200.	400.
		A. CHEW, 1882 CTN. AV. 5. Rv: Small eagle with shield.					

G. CLARK

Rulau	Date	Metal	Size	F	VF	EF	AU
Pa 713	(1857)	Copper	23.5mm	—	40.00	100.	150.
		G. CLARK / PHILA. ctsp on U.S. 1855 Half cent. There are 10 specimens reported, all on near-new 1855 Half cent coins. (Brunk 7970)					

George Clark was a blacksmith at 1118 Wistar St., listed 1857-1875. He must have used fresh Half cents before placing them in circulation.

EDWARD COGAN

Miller	Date	Metal	Size	F	VF	EF	Unc
Pa 89	1859	Copper	32mm	—	10.00	20.00	45.00
		Bust of Washington right, tiny LOVETT on truncation of bust. GEORGE WASHINGTON around. Rv: EDWARD COGAN DEALER IN BOOKS, COINS, MEDALS AND ENGRAVINGS. 1859 PHILADELPHIA in seven lines. Reeded edge. (Baker 527)					
Pa 89A	1859	White Metal	32mm	—	10.00	20.00	45.00
		As 89. Reeded edge. (Baker 527)					
Pa 89B	1859	Silver	32mm	—	85.00	135.	225.
		As 89. Reeded edge. (Baker 527) Only 18 struck.					

Miller	Date	Metal	Size	F	VF	EF	Unc
Pa 90	1860	Copper	21mm	8.00	15.00	20.00	40.00
		EDWARD COGAN / COIN / DEALER / 48 N. TENTH ST., / PHILADELPHIA. Rv: 1860 within open-end wreath. Reeded edge.					
Pa 90A	1860	Copper	21mm	8.00	15.00	20.00	40.00
		As 90. Plain edge.					

Miller	Date	Metal	Size	F	VF	EF	Unc
Pa 90B	1860	Brass	21mm	8.00	15.00	20.00	40.00
		As 90. Reeded edge.					
Pa 90C	1860	Brass	21mm	8.00	15.00	20.00	40.00
		As 90. Plain edge.					
Pa 90D	1860	S/WM	21mm	8.00	15.00	20.00	40.00
		As 90. Reeded edge.					
Pa 90E	1860	S/WM	21mm	8.00	15.00	20.00	40.00
		As 90. Plain edge.					
Pa 90F	1860	Silver	21mm	—	100.	150.	250.
		As 90. Reeded edge. (Steinle coll.; Wright 201)					
Pa 90G	1860	Silver	21mm	—	100.	150.	250.
		As 90. Plain edge. (Steinle coll.)					
Pa 91	1860	WM	20mm	—	—	20.00	45.00
		Obverse as obverse of Pa 229 (Washington right). Rv: As reverse of Pa 90 (1860 in wreath). Plain edge. (Adams Pa 91 and 96)					
Pa 92	1860	Copper	29mm	—	—	20.00	45.00
		As Pa 91. Plain edge. (Baker 208P)					
Pa 92A	1860	Copper	20mm	—	—	20.00	45.00
		As Pa 92, but on thick flan. Plain edge.					
Pa 93	1860	Brass	20mm	—	—	20.00	45.00
		As Pa 91. Plain edge. (Baker 208M)					
Pa 94	1860	Brass	20mm	—	—	20.00	45.00
		As Pa 91. Reeded edge.					
Pa 95	1860	WM	20mm	—	—	20.00	45.00
		As Pa 91. Reeded edge.					
Pa 95A	1860	Svd WM	20mm	—	—	25.00	50.00
		As Pa 91. (Baker 208Q)					
Pa 97	1860	CN	20mm	—	—	25.00	50.00
		As Pa 91. Plain edge.					
Pa 98	1860	CN	20mm	—	—	25.00	50.00
		As Pa 91. Reeded edge.					
Pa 98A	1860	Silver	20mm	—	—	150.	250.
		As Pa 91. (Baker 208N)					

Pa 91-98A occurred when the diesinker took William Idler's small Washington head die and muled it with Edward Cogan's 1860-in-wreath die, without the knowledge of either Idler or Cogan. This information was recorded by Joseph N. T. Levick in his May 29, 1865 catalog, according to numismatist Elizabeth W. Steinle, a Cogan specialist. Levick called these pieces "patterns of the diesinker."

Pa 99	(1860)	White Metal	21mm	—	—	25.00	60.00
		THE HIGHEST PREMIUM (etc.). Rv: As obverse of Pa 90.					
Pa 100	(1860)	Brass	21mm	—	—	25.00	50.00
		As Pa 99.					
Pa 101	(1860)	Copper	21mm	—	—	25.00	50.00
		As Pa 99.					
Pa 102	(1860)	Cupronickel	21mm	—	—	25.00	60.00
		As Pa 99.					

Some renumbering has been necessary in the Cogan series, since the report of four verified new varieties of type Pa 90, all of which are included in the collection of Elizabeth Steinle, South Charleston, W. Va.

WILLIAM CONOWAY

Miller	Date	Metal	Size	VG	F	VF	Unc
Pa 102A	(?)	Brass	24mm	200.	—	—	—
		Eye DEFY. Rv: Blank. Ex. Rare.					

CONRAD & ROBERTS

Miller	Date	Metal	Size	VG	F	VF	Unc
Pa 102-1/2	(1843-44)	Brass	25mm	—	—	Scarce	—
		132 NTH 3RD ST., PHILA. Rv: Blank. Plain edge. Very thin flan.					

Harry Conrad and George H. Roberts were listed 1843-44 at 132 No. 3rd Street as hardware merchants. They were then at 123 No. 3rd 1845-51.

N. CUSTER

Rulau	Date	Metal	Size	VG	F	VF	EF
Pa 825	(?)	Copper	29mm	75.00	—	—	—
		N. CUSTER Philada ctsp on obverse of U.S. 1837 Large cent. Rv: Philadelphia ctsp on opposite side of coin. (Herman Aqua coll.)					

C. H. D. & CO.

Pa 714	(?)	Silver	31mm	—	50.00	—	75.00
		C. H. D. & CO. / (propeller shaped ornament) / PHILA. ctsp on U.S. 1836 lettered edge half dollar. (B&M Patterson 1985 sale, lot 1668; Brunk 6425)					

DEALY

Rulau	Date	Metal	Size	VG	F	VF	EF
Pa 715	(?)	Copper	23mm	75.00	—	125.	—
		DEALY / PHILADA. ctsp on U.S. 1808 Half cent. (H. Joseph Levine sale of May 1985, lot 44; Brunk 11180)					
Pa 715A	(?)	Copper	28mm	75.00	—	125.	—
		Similar ctsp on U.S. 1820 Large cent.					

James Dealy operated a shoe "findings" and tool store in Philadelphia 1837-1860, according to directory evidence.

HENRY DISSTON

Miller	Date	Metal	Size	G	VG	F	EF
Pa 124	(1844)	Silver	27mm	—	175.	—	250.
		HENRY DISSTON / (eagle) / PHILA. ctsp on Spanish-American 2-Reales. (Brunk 11745)					

Henry Disston, saw maker, rear of 99 Mulberry, in the 1844 city directory. He had been at 21 Broad St. in 1840-42. Disston used this die to stamp brass discs mounted on his tools to identify their maker.

The firm was still in business in 1976 as a supplier of saws and tools.

GEO. DOLL & CO.

Miller	Date	Metal	Size	F	VF	EF	Unc
Pa 126	(1858)	Brass	22mm	7.00	15.00	25.00	40.00
		George Washington bust facing, GENERAL WASHINGTON above. Rv: GEO. DOLL & CO. / IMPORTERS OF / FANCY GOODS &C / NO. 14, NORTH 6TH ST., PHILADELPHIA. Plain edge. (Wright 258; RF Spe-1; Kurth 50; Baker 531)					
Pa 126A	(1858)	Brass	22mm	—	—	—	100.
		As 126, but blank reverse.					

George Doll & Co. were at 10 1/2 No. 6th St. 1851-57. This was renumbered 14 No. 6th St. in 1858.

WM. A. DROWN

Miller	Date	Metal	Size	F	VF	EF	Unc
Pa 127	(1844)	Brass	--mm	35.00	60.00	75.00	100.
		WM. A. DROWN. 86 MARKET ST. UMBRELLAS AND PARASOLS. Plain edge.					
Pa 128	(1844)	Brass	--mm	35.00	60.00	75.00	100.
		As 127. Reeded edge.					

Drown was at 86 Market 1837-57. This was renumbered 246 Market in 1857-58.

W.A. DROWN & CO.

Miller	Date	Metal	Size	F	VF	EF	Unc
Pa 129	1857	Copper	29mm	5.00	10.00	15.00	40.00
		W. A. DROWN & CO. / 246 / MARKET ST. / PHILADELPHIA. Rv: UMBRELLAS * & PARASOLS / 1857 / WM: A. DROWN / WM: H. PEARSON / WM: A. DROWN. JR: / 246 / MARKET STREET / * PHILADA: *.					
Pa 130	1857	Brass	29mm	5.00	10.00	15.00	40.00
		As 129.					
Pa 131	1857	White Metal	29mm	5.00	10.00	15.00	40.00
		As 129.					
Pa 132	1857	Cupronickel	29mm	5.00	10.00	15.00	40.00
		As 129.					

Pa 133	1857	Copper	29mm	5.00	15.00	20.00	40.00
		Obverse as 129. Rv: W. A. DROWN & CO: / (small umbrella) / * 1857 * / MANUFACTURERS / OF / UMBRELLAS / & / PARASOLS.					
Pa 134	1857	Brass	29mm	5.00	15.00	20.00	40.00
		As 133.					
Pa 135	1857	White Metal	29mm	5.00	10.00	15.00	40.00
		As 133. (Wright 266)					
Pa 136	1857	Cupronickel	29mm	5.00	10.00	15.00	40.00
		As 133.					

Pa 137	1857	Copper	29mm	10.00	15.00	20.00	40.00
		Obverse as reverse of 133. Rv: As reverse of 129.					
Pa 138	1857	White Metal	29mm	12.50	17.50	22.50	40.00
		As 137.					
Pa 139	1857	Brass	29mm	10.00	15.00	20.00	40.00
		As 137.					
Pa 140	1857	Cupronickel	29mm	12.50	17.50	22.50	40.00
		As 137.					
Pa 141	1857	Copper	29mm	—	—	20.00	50.00
		Obverse as reverse of 129 (names of partners). Rv: Blank.					

C. EVANS

Rulau	Date	Metal	Size	VG	F	VF	EF
Pa 739	(1860's)	Silver	27mm	75.00	—	125.	—
		C. EVANS / PHILAD'A ctsp on Spanish-American 1800-LME-IJ 2-reales. (ANS collection; Brunk 13535)					

Charles Evans & Son in 1869 issued a catalog of their iron and brass ware & machinery.

W. P. FAIRBANKS

Rulau	Date	Metal	Size	VG	F	VF	EF
Pa 800	(1867)	Silver	18mm	—	—	75.00	—
		(Steam engine left) / W. P. FAIRBANKS ctsp on U.S. 1838-O dime. (Koppenhaver Aug. 1982 sale; Van Ormer 2640; Brunk 13735; Rulau Z13)					

William Park Fairbanks was a piano maker and tuner after the Civil War, says William Swoger.

FIREMAN'S MEDAL

Rulau	Date	Metal	Size	F	VF	EF	Unc
Pa 780	1860	Copper	31mm	—	—	50.00	—

Firefighter standing, head turned right. Tiny R L below. Around: WHEN DUTY CALLS WE GO / * UNITED WE STAND — DIVIDED WE FALL *. Rv: Within laurel wreath: FIREMANS / MEDAL. / 1860 / (firefighter's hat). Plain edge.

Struck by Robert Lovette Jr. of Philadelphia. This medalet is known in brass, silver and other metals.

R. FLANAGAN

Miller	Date	Metal	Size	G	VG	F	VF
Pa 165	(1847-48)	Silver	27mm	—	175.	—	250.

R. FLANAGAN'S / PUNCH / (punchbowl and ladle) / 112. N. 6TH ST ctsp on Spanish-American Pillar-type 2-reales. (Gould 95; Brunk 14390)

Pa 165A	(?)	Silver	27mm	—	165.	—	250.

Similar ctsp on Spanish-American Bust-type 2-reales. Dates examined: 1772, 1779, 1784-Mo-FF, 1787, 1789-Mo-FM, 1793 LME-IJ, 1797, 1806, 1807, 1809-Mo-TH. About 13 pieces known.

Miller	Date	Metal	Size	G	VG	F	EF
Pa 165B	(?)	Silver	27mm	—	175.	—	250.

Similar ctsp on Mexico 2-reales. Dates examined: 1838. (Van Ormer sale 2646)

Pa 165C	(?)	Silver	26.5mm	—	175.	—	275.

Similar ctsp on U.S. Draped Bust quarter. Dates examined: 1807. (Van Ormer sale 2647)

Pa 165D	(?)	Brass	29mm	—	200.	—	300.

R. FLANAGAN / NO 112 N 6TH ST in relief within circular ring depression ctsp on 1848 campaign token of Zachary Taylor, DeWitt ZT 1848-17. (Brunk 14395)

Pa 165E	(?)	Brass	29mm	—	200.	—	300.

Similar ctsp on 1848 campaign token of Lewis Cass, DeWitt LC 1848-5. (Brunk report)

Robert Flanagan in 1837 advertised that he operated the Lyons Hotel at 112 North 6th Street in Philadelphia. This is the address on all the known counterstamps. Lyons Hotel had a drinking establishment called Vulcan Hall, with which "R. Flanagan's punch" may have been associated.

Flanagan is listed at 112 No. 6th 1835-57; this was renumbered as 156 No. 6th in 1858.

Two of the counterstamps are on 1848 campaign tokens, while the rest (perhaps 15 pieces) are on Spanish-American, Mexican or U.S. 2-bit or 25-cent pieces. The foreign coins legally circulated in this country until 1857.

Dating the counterstamps to the 1847-48 period would seem logical from the assembled evidence thus far.

HENRY B. FUSSELL

Miller	Date	Metal	Size	VG	F	VF	Unc
Pa 171	(1847-50)	Brass	25mm	3.50	5.50	20.00	60.00

Two opened parasols. MANUFACTURER / OF / SUNSHADES / &C / * CHEAP FOR CASH *. Rv: HENRY B. FUSSELL / NO. 2 / N FOURTH ST. / N.W. CORNER / OF / MARKET ST. / * PHILADELPHIA *. Plain edge. (Wright 354)

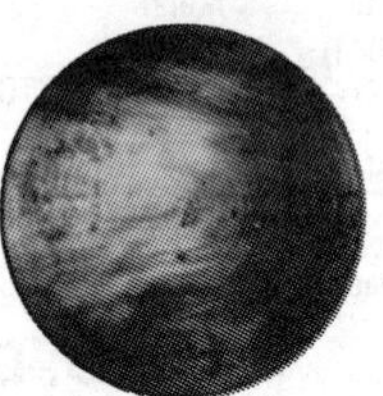

Pa 171A	(1847-50)	Mother-of-Pearl	26mm	—	—	75.00	100.

(All incuse). H. B. FUSSELL / — NO. 2 — / NTH. 4TH. ST. / PHILA. Rv: Blank. Plain edge. (Tanenbaum collection; another ex-Fuld, Mosher)

Pa 171A may not be a token but an umbrella cap, button or something similar. Fussell is listed 1847-52.

H.M.G.

Rulau	Date	Metal	Size	VG	F	VF	Unc
Pa 717	(?)	Copper	29mm	—	35.00	—	60.00

H M G / PHILA ctsp on U.S. Large cents. (Dates examined: 1827, 1833, 1837, 1838, 1852). There are 11 reported specimens. (Brunk 17560).

JAMES HARMSTEAD

Miller	Date	Metal	Size	F	VF	EF	Unc
Pa 191	(1846-48)	Brass	26mm	7.50	9.00	15.00	40.00
		Bust of Wesley right, REV. JOHN WESLEY above. Rv: * JAMES HARMSTEAD * / -*- / NO 40 / NORTH / -*- / FOURTH ST / PHILAD. / -*- / BOOK SELLER. Reeded edge. (Wright 426)					
Pa 191A	(1846-48)	Silvered Brass	26mm	7.50	15.00	20.00	40.00
		As 191.					
Pa 192	(1846-48)	Copper	26mm	7.50	9.00	10.50	40.00
		As 191.					
Pa 192A	(1846-48)	White Metal	26mm	—	—	30.00	75.00
		As 191. Thick flan.					

James Harmstead started in business 1835-36 as stationers at 4th and Noble. An 1838 ad noted he offered "the standard and authorized publications of the Methodist Episcopal Church."

SAML. HART & CO.

Miller	Date	Metal	Size	F	VF	EF	Unc
Pa 195	(1858-59)	Silvered Copper	25mm	7.00	9.00	16.00	40.00
		Shield of arms (with the four playing card suits divided by crossed diagonal bars), griffin's head as crest. SAML. HART & CO'S CLUB HOUSE CARDS. around. Rv: 307 BROADWAY N.Y. 416 SO. THIRTEENTH ST PHILA. / SAML. HART & CO'S / CARD / COUNTER. Reeded edge. (Adams NY 299; Rulau Sny-8B; Kurth 80)					
Pa 195A	(1858-59)	Copper	25mm	7.00	9.00	16.00	35.00
		As 195. Reeded edge. (Adams NY not listed; Rulau Sny-8C; Kurth 80)					
Pa 196	(1858-59)	Brass	25mm	7.00	9.00	11.00	30.00
		As 195. Plain edge. (Adams NY 298; Rulau Sny-8; Kurth 80)					
Pa 196A	(1858-59)	Brass	25mm	7.00	9.00	11.00	30.00
		As 195. Reeded edge. (Adams NY not listed; Rulau Sny-8A; Kurth 80)					

Miller	Date	Metal	Size	F	VF	EF	Unc
Pa 197A	(1854-57)	Copper	29mm	8.00	12.00	20.00	45.00
		Queen of Diamonds card in center. SAML HART & CO 256 SO. 30TH ST / .PHILA. .Rv: Jack of Clubs card in center. SAML HART & CO. NO 1 BARCLAY ST / .NEW YORK. Reeded edge. (Adams NY 296; Rulau Sny 7; Kurth 79; Wright 431)					
Pa 197B	(1854-57)	White Metal	29mm	12.00	16.00	30.00	50.00
		As 197A. (Adams NY 297; Rulau Sny-7A; Kurth 79)					

The Hart & Co. piece listed by Adams and Miller as NY 300 is in fact a Canadian gaming counter which has no connection with Samuel Hart & Co. (See numbers Can-11 and Can-11A in "American Game Counters" by Russ Rulau and George Fuld; 1972)

Samuel Hart began in business in 1844 in Philadelphia as a stationer. The firm name became Samuel Hart & Co. in or before 1849, when it was listed as an importer of fine stationery and a manufacturer of blank and playing cards. In 1851 the firm began manufacturing steel pens, and in 1853 travelling bottles in leather cases and fancy mother-of-pearl articles. But Hart was always best known for playing cards. Hart's cousin Isaac Levy was his agent for distribution.

Samuel Hart & Co. and another playing card manufacturer, Lawrence & Cohen (1832-1871), merged in 1871 to form New York Consolidated Card Co., which lasted until merging into another firm in 1931. Lewis I. Cohen of New York, Samuel Hart's uncle, had founded the firm which became Lawrence & Cohen in July 1832. As an indication of how important Hart was to playing cards, cards of the NYCCC carried the name SAMUEL HART on their Ace of Spades for many years.

For a full treatment of the Hart & Co. tokens, see Edgar Heyl's "The Samuel Hart & Co. Tokens" in *TAMS Journal* for Feb. 1970.

JULES HAUEL & CO.

Rulau	Date	Metal	Size	VG	F	VF	EF
Pa 742	(1854)	Silver	25mm	—	175.	—	250.
		JULES HAUEL & CO. / PHILADELPHIA. ctsp on both sides of U.S. 1853 Arrows & Rays S. L. quarter. (Brunk coll. and Van Ormer sale 2687; Brunk 18730)					

Jules Hauel was an importer and perfumer at 46 So. 3rd St., Philadelphia, 1840-47. Then 1848-52 at 120 Chestnut. Jules Hauel & Co. were at 170 Chestnut 1853-57 in a "spacious new building." This was renumbered as 704 Chestnut in 1858.

"Bears Grease" was one of Hauel's popular products about 1850.

HOOPES & TOWNSEND

Rulau	Date	Metal	Size	VG	F	VF	EF
Pa 205.5	(?)	Copper	22mm	20.00	50.00	125.	200.
		HOOPES & TOWNSEND / * PHILADA. * around empty center. RV: Blank. Plain edge. Rare. (Miller Pa 205 1/2).					
Pa 205.5A	(?)	Copper	22mm	20.00	50.00	150.	250.
		Same as last, but eagle displayed with U.S. shield on its breast, arrows and branches in its talons, ctsp in center of obverse. Rv: Large O.K. ctsp in center of reverse. Apparently unique. (Kirtley sale list 32, 1989, lot 35)					

Barton Hoopes, Edward Hoopes and S.S. Townsend were first listed at Buttonwood Street below Broad 1853-1860. They were a "bolt, nut and washer works."

WILLIAM IDLER

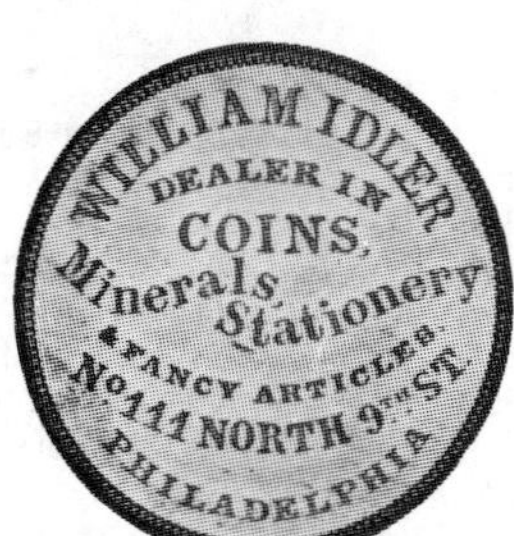

Miller	Date	Metal	Size	F	VF	EF	Unc
Pa 210	(1859)	Silver	33mm	—	100.	175.	400.
		Imitation of obverse of Washington half dollar of 1792. (The numeral '1' in 1792 is actually a capital 'J'.) Rv: WILLIAM IDLER / DEALER IN / COINS, / MINERALS STATIONERY / & FANCY ARTICLES. / NO. 111 NORTH 9TH ST. / PHILADELPHIA.					
Pa 211	(?)	Copper	33mm	—	35.00	60.00	175.
		As Pa 210.					
Pa 212	(?)	Brass	33mm	—	35.00	60.00	175.
		As Pa 210. Plain edge.					
Pa 212A	(?)	White Metal	33mm	—	35.00	60.00	175.
		As Pa 210. Plain edge.					

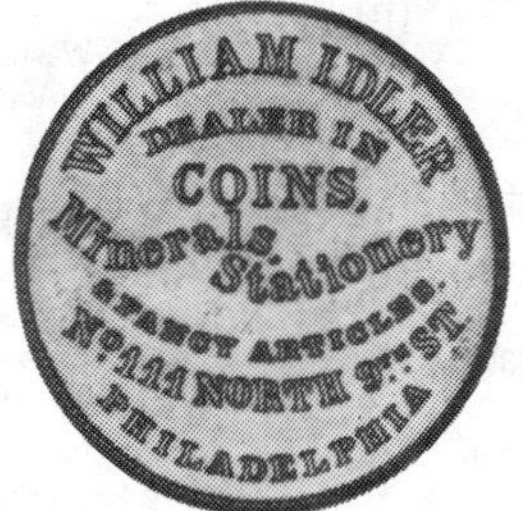

Pa 213	(1859)	Silver	33mm	—	100.	175.	375.
		Imitation of reverse of Washington half dollar of 1792. Rv: As reverse of Pa 210.					
Pa 214	(?)	Copper	33mm	—	35.00	60.00	125.
		As Pa 213. (Wright 484)					
Pa 215	(?)	Brass	33mm	—	35.00	60.00	100.
		As Pa 213. Plain edge.					
Pa 215A	(?)	White Metal	33mm	—	35.00	60.00	150.
		As Pa 213.					

Pa. 210-215A are increasing dramatically in price. As an example, 215A in prooflike Unc. fetched $2 in the Feb. 1935 Charles Fisher auction, and $165. in Sept. 1989 Kurt Krueger sale.

Pa 215B	(1860)	Silver	20mm	40.00	100.	150.	250.
		Imitation of Baltimore penny. Rv: Similar to reverse of 210. (Baker 544)					
Pa 217	(?)	Copper	20mm	—	—	30.00	60.00
		As 215B.					
Pa 218	(?)	Cupronickel	20mm	—	—	30.00	60.00
		As 215B.					
Pa 219	(?)	Brass	20mm	—	—	30.00	60.00
		As 215B.					
Pa 220	(?)	Bronze	20mm	—	—	30.00	60.00
		As 215B.					
Pa 211	(?)	Silvered White Metal	20mm	—	—	30.00	60.00
		As 215B.					
Pa 222	(?)	Nickel	20mm	—	—	50.00	75.00
		As 215b.					

Pa 223	(1860)	Copper	20mm	—	—	30.00	60.00
		Obverse of Baltimore penny copy. Rv: CONTINENTAL PAPER MONEY (etc.).					
Pa 224	(?)	Copper	20mm	—	—	30.00	60.00
		As 223. Reeded edge.					
Pa 225	(?)	Cupronickel	20mm	—	—	30.00	60.00
		As 223. Reeded edge.					
Pa 226	(?)	Cupronickel	20mm	—	—	30.00	60.00
		As 223. Plain edge.					
Pa 227	(?)	Brass	20mm	—	—	30.00	60.00
		As 223. Plain edge.					
Pa 228	(?)	Brass	20mm	—	—	30.00	60.00
		As 223. Reeded edge.					
Pa 228A	(?)	White Metal	20mm	—	—	30.00	60.00
		As 223.					

Pa 229	(1860)	Brass	33mm	—	10.00	20.00	45.00
		Bust of Washington right, tiny LOVETT under the truncation. GEORGE WASHINGTON around. Rv: As reverse of Pa 210. (Baker 545)					
Pa 229A	(?)	Silver	33mm	—	75.00	100.	225.
		As Pa 229. (Baker 545)					
Pa 230	(?)	White Metal	33mm	—	10.00	20.00	45.00
		As Pa 229. (Baker 545)					
Pa 230A	(?)	Copper	33mm	—	10.00	20.00	45.00
		As Pa 229. (Baker 545)					
Pa 230B	(?)	Nickel	33mm	—	10.00	20.00	45.00
		As Pa 229. (Baker 545)					

Pa 230D	(1860)	Copper	20mm	—	10.00	25.00	50.00
		W. IDLER / DEALER IN / COINS, / MINERALS. / ANTIQUES &C. / 111 N. 9TH ST. / PHILADA:. Rv: CONTINENTAL / PAPER / MONEY, / AUTOGRAPHS, / ENGRAVINGS / &C. / BOUGHT & SOLD / W. IDLER. 111 N. 9TH ST. Plain edge.					
Pa 230E	(1860)	Copper	20mm	—	—	—	50.00
		As last. Reeded edge. (Ganter coll.)					
Pa 230F		Brass	20mm	—	15.00	25.00	50.00
		As last.					

William Idler first appears in directories at 111 No. 9th in 1859, permitting the dating of his store cards.

E. IVINS

Miller	Date	Metal	Size	F	VF	EF	Unc
Pa 231	(1861?)	Copper	25mm	65.00	125.	175.	225.
		Washington bust in Roman mantle right, tiny R L on truncation of bust (for Robert Lovett Jr.). Around: GEN. GEORGE WASHINGTON. FIRST PRES. U. S. 1789. Rv: U.S. shield surrounded by circle of 25 stars. Inscribed: E. IVINS, MANUFAC//TURER OF METALLIC TRIMMINGS, FIFTH & COLUMBIA AV. PHILADELPHIA. Plain edge. (Baker 546)					
Pa 231A	(?)	Cupronickel	25mm	75.00	150.	200.	250.
		As 231. (Wright 493; Baker 546)					
Pa 232	(?)	Brass	25mm	50.00	100.	150.	200.
		As 231. (Baker 546)					
Pa 233	(?)	White Metal	25mm	95.00	150.	200.	250.
		As 231. (Baker 546)					
Pa 233A	(?)	Silver	25mm	—	—	200.	350.
		As 231. (Baker 546)					

Some collectors now consider the Ivins cards to be Civil War tokens.

C.W. JACKSON

Miller	Date	Metal	Size	VG	F	VF	Unc
Pa 234	(1851)	Copper	28mm	7.00	10.00	15.00	50.00
		C. W. JACKSON / BROAD / & LOMBARD STS / *COAL DEALER*. Rv: SEE DIRECTORY. IN CASE OF REMOVAL. / GOOD / FOR 5. C.S. / IN A TON / OF COAL. Plain edge. (Wright 496)					
Pa 235	(1851)	Brass	28mm	7.00	10.00	15.00	50.00
		As 234. Plain edge.					
Pa 235A	(1851)	Gilt Copper	28mm	17.50	22.50	37.50	60.00
		As 234. Plain edge.					
Pa 235B	(?)	Cupronickel	28mm	20.00	25.00	30.00	75.00
		As 234. Plain edge.					
Pa 236	(?)	Brass	28mm	20.00	25.00	30.00	50.00
		As 234, but 6 on reverse in place of 5. Plain edge.					
Pa 237	(?)	Brass	28mm	20.00	25.00	30.00	50.00
		As 234, but 25 on reverse in place of 5. Plain edge.					
Pa 237A	(1855)	Copper	29mm	—	—	15.00	45.00
		Obverse as 234. Rv: Wreath, NOT ONE CENT BUT JUST AS GOOD. Plain edge.					

Charles W. Jackson appears in the 1850 census. He was located at Broad & Lombard streets 1851-1856.

JOHNSON & CONAWAY

Rulau	Date	Metal	Size	VG	F	VF	Unc
Pa 720	(1847-52)	Lead	24mm	—	65.00	200.	—
		Spread eagle with U.S. shield on breast, head turned right. Around: * JOHNSON & CONAWAY *. Below: PHILA. Rv: MANUFACTURERS / OF / SAWS / SQUARES & &C / * 24 CHERRY ST *. Plain edge. Thick flan.					
Pa A720	(1847-52)	Copper	27mm	—	100.	—	150.
		JOHNSON & CONAWAY in arc ctsp along upper rim of reverse of Austria 1816-A 1-kreuzer. PHILa ctsp twice (vertically on either side of shield of arms) on obverse of the coin. (Robert A. Vlack coll., acquired in 1987; it later appeared in the PCAC sale number 45, as lot 83; Brunk 21783)					
Pa B720	(1847-52)	Copper	29mm	—	100.		150.
		JOHNSON & CONAWAY / PHILADA ctsp on U.S. 1832 Large cent. (Brunk 21785)					

The value of collecting counterstamped coins to numismatic research is well illustrated by such pieces as A720 above. Nowhere in the vast literature about coin circulation in America have we located any mention of the circulation of Austrian coppers alongside other foreign coins in the United States. Those coppers which circulated most freely until forbidden by law in 1857 were British, Irish, Canadian and, to a lesser extent, French, Spanish, East Indian, Belgian.

The Austrian 1-kreuzer copper coin dated 1816, a large (27mm), thick piece, is occasionally found counterstamped by American merchants and private persons, however.

This interesting coin (Krause-Mishler 485; Craig 177) was struck from 1816 through 1852 using the same date, 1816. It was struck bearing one of six mintmarks: A (Vienna), B (Kremnitz), E (Carlsburg), G (Graz), O (Oravicza) or S (Schmollnitz).

Mintage statistics mostly were not kept, but the coin was made in the hundreds of millions of specimens, as the output alone of the Kremnitz (Kremnica, Czechoslovakia) Mint (B mark) aggregated 54,516,000 pieces over that 37-year span.

The counterstamped 1-kreuzer pieces that we have seen are mostly one of a kind, i.e. one piece from one merchant. This seems to indicate that the kreuzer was not a factor in actual circulation, but was sometimes spent by immigrants from Bohemia or Hungary who were reduced by need to parting with souvenirs taken along from the "old country." Shopkeepers in the 1850's and earlier seem to have accepted almost any copper that had roughly the size of the large cent, as a cent. (Colonial American coins and tokens, Hard Times tokens, British Conder tokens and many other non-official, unredeemable pieces circulated quite freely as cents.)

* * *

Charles Johnson and George Conaway were first listed in the directories in 1847. The 1853 directory lists William Conaway as "successor and late partner of the firm of Johnson & Conaway."

JONES EXCHANGE HOTEL

(**NOTE:** The numbering in this series has been changed from the second edition to permit the inclusion of additional listings.)

Miller	Date	Metal	Size	VG	F	VF	EF
NY 238	(1849-50)	Brass	27mm	125.	175.	300.	500.
		(All incused) JONES / (Eagle) / 6. Rv: EXCHANGE / 6 / HOTEL. All on blank brass planchet.					
NY 238A		Copper	29mm	200.	—	300.	—
		Same as 238, but ctsp on U.S. Large cent. (Brunk 21925)					
NY 238B		Brass	27mm	125.	175.	300.	500.
		As NY 238, but 12 1/2. Brass planchet.					
NY 238C		Brass	27mm	125.	175.	300.	500.
		As NY 238, but 25. (Wright 520)					
NY 238D		Brass	27mm	125.	175.	300.	500.
		As 238, but NY.					
NY 238J	—	Brass	26.6mm	—	—	500.	—
		(All incused): JONES / (ornament) 12 (ornament) / 1/2. Rv: EXCHANGE / 12-1/2 / HOTEL. Plain edge. Rare. (PCAC July 1993 sale, lot 077)					
NY 239	(?)	Silver	21mm	175.	—	275.	—
		JONES / EXCHANGE / HOTEL / 77 DOCK ST. ctsp on Spanish-American 1-real coin. (Brunk 21930)					
NY 239A	(?)	Silver	27mm	175.	—	250.	—
		Similar ctsp on Spanish-American 2-reales. Dates examined: 1796, 1807, date worn. There are 3 known specimens. (Gould 100)					
NY 239B	(?)	Silver	--mm	200.	—	300.	—
		Similar ctsp on unspecified Russian silver coin. Unique.					
NY 239C		Silver	--mm	200.	—	300.	—
		Similar ctsp on unspecified silver coin of Prussia. Unique.					

Miller	Date	Metal	Size	VG	F	VF	EF
NY 239F	(1849-50)	Silver	27mm	150.	—	225.	—
		JONES / EXCHANGE / HOTEL / 77 DOCK ST. / PHILA ctsp on Spanish-American 2-reales. Dates examined: 1776, 1779, 1785, 1787, 1794, 1796, 1807, date worn. There are 9 reported specimens. (Brunk 21940; Van Ormer sale 2708)					

Miller	Date	Metal	Size	VG	F	VF	EF
NY 239G		Silver	21mm	175.	—	250.	250.
		Similar ctsp on Spanish-American 1808 1-real. Only 1 known. (Van Ormer sale 2710; Brunk 21935)					

Miller	Date	Metal	Size	VG	F	VF	EF
NY 239H		Silver	27mm	175.	—	275.	—
		JONES' / EXCHANGE HOTEL / 77 DOCK ST. / PHILADa. ctsp on Spanish-American 2-reales. Dates examined: 1821, date worn. 2 pieces known. (Van Ormer sale 2709; Brunk 21950)					

There are minor varieties in the punches used by Jones. Previous catalogers did not differentiate, nor will we.

Richard B. Jones' Exchange Hotel at 77 Dock Street, a four-story structure, advertised in March 1850 that it had recently undergone thorough alteration and that it served meals at any hour, day or evening, and dinners noon to 4 p.m.

Rooms were 25 or 37 1/2 cents per night in 1850, which probably accounts for the denominations on NY 238 to 238D, and helps explain why Jones used so many Spanish-American 2-reales (2-bit) counterstamps in his business.

He catered to railroad and steamboat passengers, his ad points out. (Research courtesy Gregory G. Brunk)

Jones appears in the directories 1848-1858.

F.C. KEY & SONS

Miller	Date	Metal	Size	F	VF	EF	Unc
Pa 259A	(ca 1857)	Copper	29mm	—	—	25.00	45.00
		Wildey, Rv: F.C. KEY & SONS / DIE SINKERS & MEDALISTS / 123 / * ARCH ST. * / * / PHILADELPHIA.					
Pa 259	(ca 1857)	WM	29mm	—	—	25.00	45.00
		As 259A. (Miller Pa. 259)					
Pa 260	1876	Brass	29mm	—	—	25.00	50.00
		Continental soldier. Rv: As 259A. Plain edge. (Pa. 260)					
Pa 261	(1876)	WM	29mm	—	—	25.00	50.00
		As 260. (Miller Pa. 261)					
Pa 261A	(1876)	WM	29mm	—	—	25.00	50.00
		Libertas Americana medal imitation. Rv: as 259A. Plain edge. (Wright 548; Miller Pa. 261A)					

Pa 262	(1858)	WM	29mm	—	10.00	25.00	45.00
		George Washington head left, tiny KEY under truncation of neck. PATRIAE left, PATER left. Rv: As 259A. (Baker 548)					

Pa 262A	(1858)	WM	29mm	—	10.00	25.00	45.00
		Edwin Forrest bust right in toga, within laurel wreath. Rv: As 259A. Plain edge. (Miller Pa. 262A)					

Pa 262B	(1858)	WM	29mm	—	10.00	20.00	45.00
		Obverse as 262. Rv: Edwin Forrest bust right. EDWIN FORREST around. Plain edge. (Miller Pa. 262B)					
Pa 263B	(1858)	WM	29mm	—	—	25.00	45.00
		Obverse as 262 (Washington head left). Rv: Daniel Webster. (Miller Pa. 263B)					
Pa 263A	(1858)	Copper	29mm	—	—	40.00	70.00
		As last, but ctsp 'M'. Plain edge. (Miller Pa. 263A)					

Pa 263M	(1857)	Silver	29mm	—	—	175.	275.
		Washington head left within frame, tiny KEY under truncation. PATRIAE PATER 1732 around. Rv: F.C. KEY & SONS / DIE-SINKERS & MEDALISTS / 123 / ARCH ST / PHILADA, all within circle of stars. Unpublished in Adams or Miller. Plain edge. (Baker 549) Also known in copper, brass & wm, 15.00 in EF, 45.00 in Unc					

Frederick C. Key and Sons was located at 123 Arch St. from about 1850-58. This location was renumbered as 329 Arch St. in 1857-58.

LINGG

Rulau	Date	Metal	Size	F	VF	Unc
Pa 719	1860's		31mm	—	Unique	—
		Equestrian figure in uniform left, on an emmence, head facing, a city and American army in background (central device of Baker 50). There is no legend. Rv: (All lettering incused) LINGG / 37 (in circle) / 1602 MARKET Plain edge. (H. Joseph Levine sale of May 14, 1983, lot 53; Baker S-551)				

This item offered in the 1983 Levine sale was the first ever for publication of this piece, this merchant and this Washington effigy without inscription. Probably the work of Robert Lovett Jr. of Philadelphia.

The "Lingg" may be connected with the later Linggs who produced centennial cards in the 1870's.

He is not listed through 1860.

WILLIAM W. LONG

Miller	Date	Metal	Size	F	VF	EF	Unc
Pa 327	(1854-57)	Copper	29mm	12.50	15.00	20.00	40.00
		Keystone, square, compass and all-seeing eye in center. * WILLIAM W. LONG * / NOS. 376, 378 & 380 SO 3RD ST. PHILDA. Rv: Bee, tree trunks, two eyes, ant, arranged across center to spell 'BRILLIANT'. Above: PISTOL & RIFLE GALLERIES / BAGATELLE & SHUFFLE / BOARDS / LIQUORS, OYSTERS / SEGARS, &C. Below: REFECTORY & / MUSEUM / HOTEL / BILLIARDS & BOWLING. (Wright 619)					
Pa 328	(1854-57)	Silver	29mm	—	—	75.00	200.
		As 327.					
Pa 329	(1854-57)	Brass	29mm	—	—	40.00	80.00
		As 327.					
Pa 329A	(1854-57)	White Metal	29mm	—	—	40.00	100.
		As 327. Very thick planchet.					

The obverse contains Masonic emblems. The reverse carries an unusual pictogram, which must have caused lively conversation in Long's multi-activity enterprise.

Long appears in the directories at 376-380 So. 3rd St. 1854-57. This was renumbered as 754 So. 3rd St. in 1857.

R. LOVETT JR.

Miller	Date	Metal	Size	F	VF	Unc	P-L
Pa 330	(?)	White Metal	32mm	17.50	20.00	40.00	—
		Statue, STEPHEN GIRARD around. Rv: R. LOVETT, JR: DIE SINKER, PHILADELPHIA, PA. / DIES FOR / AGRICULTURAL (on scroll) / (plow) / SOCIETIES (on scroll) / COLLEGES &C. / MEDALS STRUCK IN / — GOLD, — / SILVER AND BRONZE / (branch). Plain edge.					
Pa 331	(?)	White Metal	32mm	17.50	20.00	40.00	—
		As 330. Reeded edge.					
Pa 332	(?)	Brass	32mm	17.50	20.00	40.00	—
		As 330. Plain edge. (Wright 625)					
Pa 333	(?)	Brass	32mm	17.50	20.00	40.00	—
		As 330. Reeded edge.					
Pa 334	(?)	Copper	32mm	17.50	20.00	40.00	—
		As 330. Plain edge.					
Pa 335	(?)	Copper	32mm	17.50	20.00	40.00	—
		As 330. Reeded edge.					
Pa 336	(?)	Cupronickel	32mm	20.00	22.50	40.00	—
		As 330. Thick planchet.					
Pa 336A	(?)	Cupronickel	32mm	20.00	22.50	40.00	—
		As 330. Thin planchet.					

Miller	Date	Metal	Size	F	VF	EF	Unc
Pa 337	(?)	Brass	32mm	—	40.00	50.00	—
		George Washington on horseback. Rv: As reverse of 330. Plain edge.					
Pa 339	(?)	Brass	32mm	—	40.00	50.00	—
		As 337. Reeded edge.					
Pa 340	(?)	White Metal	32mm	—	40.00	50.00	—
		As 337. Reeded edge.					
Pa 341	(?)	White Metal	32mm	—	40.00	50.00	—
		As 337. Plain edge.					
Pa 342	(?)	Copper	32mm	—	40.00	50.00	—
		As 337. Reeded edge.					
Pa 343	(?)	Cupronickel	32mm	—	40.00	50.00	—
		As 337. Reeded edge.					
Pa 343A	(?)	Silver	32mm	—	100.	350.	—
		As 337. Reeded edge. Rarity 8. (Baker 556)					

Miller	Date	Metal	Size	F	VF	Unc	P-L
Pa 344M	(?)	White Metal	31mm	—	10.00	20.00	—
		Naval battle between USS Constitution and HMS Guerriere. Rv: FREE TRADE AND SAILORS RIGHTS / CONSTITUTION / AND / GUERRIERE / 1812 / (laurel wreath with anchor for bow) / * LOVETT'S SERIES NO. 3. PHILADA.					
Pa 344N	(?)	Copper	31mm	15.00	17.50	40.00	45.00
		As 344. Reeded edge.					
Pa 344	(?)	WM	31mm	15.00	17.50	40.00	45.00
		Obverse as 344M. Rv: As reverse of 330.					
Pa 344A	(?)	Copper	31mm	15.00	17.50	40.00	45.00
		As Pa 344.					

Miller	Date	Metal	Size	F	VF	EF	Unc
Pa 344E	1860	Brass	30mm	11.00	15.00	20.00	30.00
		Fireman standing right, WHEN DUTY CALLS WE GO above, UNITED WE STAND DIVIDED WE FALL below. Rv: Date 1860 at center, wreath around. A fireman's hat appears where bow of wreath normally appears. Reeded edge.					

Miller	Date	Metal	Size	F	VF	EF	Unc
Pa 348	(1859)	German Silver	15mm	10.00	15.00	25.00	50.00
		St. George slaying the dragon. (Probably an imitation of the Benedetto Pistrucci rendering of the same scene on British gold sovereigns, which it greatly resembles). Rv: R. LOVETT, JR. / DIE / SINKER / (facing head of Franklin) / PHILADELPHIA. Plain edge.					
Pa 349	(1859)	Copper	15mm	10.00	15.00	25.00	50.00
		As 348. Plain edge.					
Pa 350	(1859)	Brass	15mm	10.00	15.00	25.00	50.00
		As 348. Plain edge.					
Pa 350A	(1859)	German Silver	15mm	—	—	—	50.00
		As 348. Reeded edge. (Ganter coll.)					

Miller	Date	Metal	Size	F	VF	EF	Unc
Pa 351	(1859)	German Silver	15mm	10.00	15.00	45.00	50.00
		Obverse as 348 (St. George). Rv: * / DIE / SINKER within laurel wreath. Around: R. LOVETT, JR. / PHILADELPHIA. Plain edge.					

Miller	Date	Metal	Size	F	VF	EF	Unc
Pa 352	(1859)	German Silver	15mm	10.00	15.00	45.00	50.00
		Obverse as 348 (St. George). Rv: Similar to reverse of 348, except that spread-winged eagle replaces head of Franklin. Plain edge.					

Miller	Date	Metal	Size	F	VF	EF	Unc
Pa 353	1860	Copper	19mm	20.00	30.00	40.00	75.00
		Liberty head wearing Phrygian cap left (design of Confederate cent obverse). Around: R. LOVETT, JR. ENGRAVER & DIE SINKER.; below: 1860. Rv: Within wreath at center: 200 / SO. / FIFTH ST. Above: METALLIC BUSINESS CARDS; below: PHILADELPHIA. Plain edge.					
Pa 354	1860	Brass	19mm	20.00	30.00	40.00	75.00
		As 353. Plain edge.					
Pa 355	1860	Cupronickel	19mm	25.00	35.00	45.00	85.00
		As 353. Plain edge.					
Pa 356	1860	Nickel	19mm	20.00	30.00	40.00	75.00
		As 353. Plain edge.					
Pa 356A	1860	White Metal	19mm	20.00	30.00	40.00	75.00
		As 353. Plain edge.					

Robert Lovett Jr.'s Philadelphia addresses are given in the directories as:
142 Chestnut 1839
11 So. 6th 1840-45
32 So. 5th 1846-48
28 So. 5th 1849-57
Renumbered 200 So. 5th 1858

ROBERT LOVETT JR.

Miller	Date	Metal	Size	F	VF	EF	Unc
Pa 346	1858	Bronze	36mm	15.00	40.00	60.00	100.
		Minerva seated left, coining press below dividing 18 -- 58. GOLD & SILVER MEDALS FOR COLLEGES, FAIRS &C. Rv: ROBERT LOVETT JR. / SEAL ENGRAVER / & DIE SINKER / PHILADELPHIA. (Wright 626)					
Pa 347	1858	White Metal	36mm	20.00	40.00	60.00	100.
		As 346.					

MORGAN & ORR

Miller	Date	Metal	Size	VG	F	VF	Unc
Pa 367	1855	Copper	35mm	35.00	75.00	100.	225.
		MADE BY MORGAN & ORR, PHILA. / FOR THE / REPUBLIC / OF / PERU / 1855. Rv: HECHO POR EL GOBIERNO PERUANA / EN / PHILA / DELPHIA / ANO / 1855. Reeded edge. (Wright 722)					

Joshua Morgan and Arthur Orr were manufacturers of coining presses at 461 Callowhill from 1849. This was renumbered as 1219 Callowhill in 1858. One of their presses, used to strike Trade dollars, is on exhibit in the ANA building in Colorado Springs.

Miller	Date	Metal	Size	VG	F	VF	Unc
Pa 367A	1855	Brass	35mm	35.00	75.00	125.	250.
		As 367.					
Pa 368	1855	White Metal	35mm	50.00	75.00	100.	250.
		As 367.					
Pa 369	1855	Cupronickel	35mm	50.00	75.00	100.	250.
		As 367.					

H. MULLIGAN

Miller	Date	Metal	Size	VG	F	VF	Unc
Pa 370	(1858-60)	Brass	33mm	7.00	10.00	30.00	75.00
		Eagle displayed, shield on breast, EVERY ARTICLE SOLD / IS WARRANTED above. Around all: * THE LARGEST ASSORTMENT & LOWEST PRICES IN THE U.S. Rv: H. MULLIGAN, / IMPORTER / OF / WATCHES / MANUFACTURER OF / JEWELRY AND A SILVERWARE / 444 / N. 2ND ST. / PHILADELPHIA. (Wright 736) Plain edge.					
Pa 370A	(1858-60)	Brass	33mm	7.00	10.00	30.00	75.00
		As 370. Reeded edge.					

There are also Civil War store cards of this issuer.

Mulligan appears at Cortland Place in 1852. Then at 272 No. 2nd in 1853-57; renumbered as 444 No. 2nd in 1858-60. In 1860 he claimed to have "the largest wholesale and retail stock of watches in the U.S."

Miller	Date	Metal	Size	VG	F	VF	Unc
Pa 370S	(1858)	Silver	27mm	250.	—	400.	—
		H. MULLIGAN / 444 N. 2d ST / PHILA. ctsp on Spanish-American 1774 2-reales. (Van Ormer sale 2767; Brunk 28825)					

Probably pre-dates Mulligan's struck store cards. The counterstamp is made from one of Mulligan's regular hallmarks used in his silversmith and jewelry trade — he started business about 1840. This piece realized $230 in the Van Ormer sale.

C.H. NEEDLES

Miller	Date	Metal	Size	VG	F	VF	Unc
Pa 378	(1855-60)	German Silver	19mm	8.00	12.00	20.00	40.00
		A wine goblet at center, * C.H. NEEDLES * / 12 & RACE STS. Rv: GOOD FOR ONE / GLASS / OF / SODA / * WATER *. Plain edge. (Fuld NC-19d)					
Pa 379	(1855-60)	White Metal	19mm	8.00	12.00	20.00	40.00
		As 378. Plain edge. (Wright 750; Fuld NC-19e)					

Caleb H. Needles appears in 1842 directories as a druggist at S.W. 12th and Sassafras, remaining there until 1884, one year before his death. Sassafras St. was renamed Race St. in 1855. Thus the token must have been issued 1855 or later.

Caleb headed a family of druggists: Edward, Tristram and William H. Needles. A fourth son, Caleb H. Needles Jr., associated with Edward in the 1880's to form the brokerage firm of Needles & Brother.

J. NOCK

Miller	Date	Metal	Size	VG	F	VF	Unc
Pa 720	(1853-54)	Copper	29mm	200.	—	250.	—
		J. NOCKS PATENT / (eagle) / PHILAD ctsp on U.S. 1852 Large cent. Rv: J. NOCK / PHILADA ctsp on reverse of the coin. (ANS collection; Brunk 29750)					

Joseph Nock was a Philadelphia gunsmith. He is later listed in 1866 in Washington, D.C., according to *American Gunsmiths* by Frank M. Sellers (1983).

Earlier, 1839, he was a locksmith at 157 No. 3rd. Then 1840-45 there is no listing. He is again listed as a locksmith at various Phila. locations 1846-54.

PARTRIDGE & RICHARDSON

Miller	Date	Metal	Size	VG	F	VF	Unc
Pa 382	(1858-60)	Brass	22mm	7.50	10.00	16.00	40.00
		Horsewoman to right; * TO THE BEE-HIVE * above; 17 NORTH 8TH ST. PHILADA below. Rv: Beehive within wreath at center; * PARTRIDGE & RICHARDSON * / DRESS TRIMMINGS. Reeded edge. (Wright 804)					

Artemus Partridge and Mr. Richardson are listed at 13 1/2 No. 8th 1853-57. This was renumbered as 17 No. 8th in 1858-60.

PHILA and (Eagles) (Samuel Hildeburn)

Rulau	Date	Metal	Size	VG	F	VF	EF
Pa 755	(?)	Silver	32.5mm	125.	—	200.	—
		PHILA in relief within toothed rect. depression surrounded by four punches depicting eagles in relief, ctsp on U.S. 1822 or 1824 half dollar. (Van Ormer sale 2781; Brunk 31910)					
PA 755B	(?)	Copper	23mm	125.	—	200.	—
		Similar ctsp on U.S. Half cent. Examined: 1832, 1835, worn date. 4 pieces known.					

Roy Van Ormer attributes this group of marks to the Hildeburn family of silversmiths, active 1810-50. We have now been able to verify the attribution. The eagles are exact matches to known Hildeburn works.

Samuel Hildeburn (1810-37) founded the family business, known as Hildeburn & Watson (1829-33) and Hildeburn & Brothers (1849-50). Dictionaries of silversmith hallmarks do not give this PHILA-and-eagles mark without the Hildeburn name, but we have accepted the fact that all such directories are, of necessity, incomplete.

PENNYPACKER & SIBLEY

Miller	Date	Metal	Size	VG	F	VF	Unc
Pa 390A	(?)	Brass	23mm	10.00	20.00	50.00	75.00
		PENNYPACKER / & / SIBLEY. Rv: Blank. Plain edge. (Wright 813)					
Pa 391	(?)	Copper	23mm	10.00	20.00	50.00	75.00
		As Pa 390A.					
Pa 390	(?)	Brass	23mm	10.00	20.00	50.00	75.00
		Obverse as 390A. Rv: Numeral 25.					
Pa 390B	(?)	Brass	23mm	10.00	20.00	50.00	75.00
		Obverse as 390A. Rv: Numeral 1.					

These pieces may be post 1860; verification needed. We can find no listing through 1860.

W. RICHARDSON & CO.

Miller	Date	Metal	Size	F	VF	EF	Unc
Pa 416	(1844)	Brass	28mm	6.00	8.00	10.50	27.50

Open umbrella. UMBRELLAS / * MARKET ST. * / NO 106 / PARASOLS. Rv: W. RICHARDSON & CO. / MANUFACTURERS / NO / 106 / MARKET ST / PHILADA. (Wright 886)

First listing at 106 Market 1843-57.

W. H. RICHARDSON

Miller	Date	Metal	Size	F	VF	EF	Unc
Pa 417	(1853)	Brass	28mm	7.50	9.50	12.50	35.00
		Three open umbrellas, UMBRELLAS AND PARASOLS around, —o— below. Rv: W. H. RICHARDSON / —o— / NO 5 / SOUTH 4TH / * ST * / —o— / PHILADA. Reeded edge.					
Pa 418	(?)	Brass	28mm	7.50	9.50	12.50	35.00
		As 417. Plain edge.					
Pa 419	(?)	Copper	28mm	7.50	9.50	12.50	35.00
		As 417. Plain edge.					
Pa 420	(?)	Silvered Brass	28mm	9.50	11.50	14.50	35.00
		As 417. Plain edge. (Wright 885)					

Miller	Date	Metal	Size	F	VF	EF	Unc
Pa 423	(1845)	Brass	28mm	4.00	6.00	9.50	35.00
		Three open umbrellas in center, UMBRELLAS AND PARASOLS. Rv: W. H. RICHARDSON / 104 / MARKET / ST. / * PHILADA *. Ornaments on both sides. Plain edge. (Wright 885A)					
Pa 424	(1845)	Brass	28mm	5.00	6.00	9.50	35.00
		As 423. Reeded edge.					
Pa 424A	(1845)	Silvered Brass	28mm	7.00	9.50	11.50	35.00
		As 423.					
Pa 425	(1845)	Copper	28mm	5.00	7.50	12.00	35.00
		As 423.					

Miller	Date	Metal	Size	F	VF	EF	Unc
Pa 426	(1846-50)	Brass	28mm	4.00	7.50	9.50	35.00
		Similar to 423, but no ornaments on either side. Reeded edge.					
Pa 427	(1846-50)	Brass	28mm	4.00	7.00	12.00	35.00
		As 426. Plain edge.					

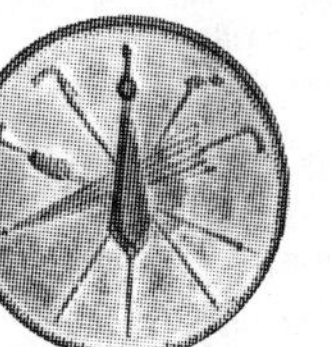

Miller	Date	Metal	Size	F	VF	EF	Unc
Pa 422	(1859)	Brass	24mm	5.00	7.00	12.00	35.00
		Umbrellas and canes, crossed. Rv: W. H. RICHARDSON / 807 / MARKET ST. / * PHILADA *.					

WM. H. RICHARDSON

Miller	Date	Metal	Size	F	VF	EF	Unc
Pa 421	(1858)	Brass	24mm	5.00	7.00	12.00	35.00
		UMBRELLAS / VERY / SUPERIOR / EXPRESSLY / FOR / RETAILERS / PARASOLS. Rv: WM. H. RICHARDSON / 418 / MARKET ST. / * PHILADELPHIA *. Reeded edge. (Wright 887)					
Pa 421A	(1858)	Brass	24mm	5.00	7.00	12.00	35.00
		As 421. Plain edge.					

Miller	Date	Metal	Size	F	VF	EF	Unc
Pa 421B	(1858)	Brass	24mm	5.00	7.00	12.00	35.00
		Umbrellas. Rv: Similar to reverse of 421, but address added: 229 BROADWAY, N.Y.					

William H. Richardson was at 5 So. 4th St. 1853-57. He had been at 104 Market St. 1845-50. 106 Market was renumbered as 418 Market in the 1858 directory.

M. A. ROOT

Miller	Date	Metal	Size	F	VF	EF	Unc
Pa 431	(1850's)	Brass	29mm	8.50	11.00	25.00	45.00
		Eagle displayed, UNITED STATES OF AMERICA. M. A. ROOT, 140 CHESTNUT ST. (Same as Obv. of 433). Reeded edge.					
Pa 432	(1850's)	Copper	29mm	8.50	11.00	25.00	45.00
		As 431. Reeded edge.					
Pa 433	(1850's)	Brass	29mm	8.50	11.00	25.00	40.00
		M. A. ROOT'S DAGUERRIAN / GALLERY / 140 / CHESTNUT / ST. / PHILADA. Rv: Wreath encloses: FIRST / PREMIUM / AWARDED TO / ROOT & CO. / FOR BEST / DAGUERREOTYPES. Reeded edge. (Wright 915)					
Pa 434	(1850's)	Brass	29mm	8.50	11.00	25.00	40.00
		As 433. Plain edge.					
Pa 435	(1850's)	Silvered Brass	29mm	10.00	12.50	25.00	40.00
		As 433.					
Pa 436	(1850's)	Copper	29mm	8.50	11.00	25.00	45.00
		As 433.					
Pa 437	(1857)	Brass	29mm	12.50	16.00	25.00	40.00
		Similar to 433, but address is: 144 CHESTNUT ST.					

Marcus Aurelius Root is first listed as a teacher of writing in the 1845 directory. His first listing as a daguerreotypist appears in the 1847 directory, where M. A. Root is described as "teacher of writing and photographist."

He remained listed at 140 Chestnut Street through 1856. He must have moved to 144 Chestnut in 1857, before the Philadelphia renumbering began.

See the Root & Co. store cards listed under New York City.

SHARPLESS BROTHERS

Miller	Date	Metal	Size	F	VF	EF	Unc
Pa 469	(1857)	Brass	28mm	5.00	7.00	10.00	35.00
		Beehive at center, SHARPLESS BROTHERS above; LATE / TOWNSEND SHARPLESS / & SONS. Rv: DRY GOODS / WHOLESALE & RETAIL / AT THEIR / NEW STORE / N.W. COR. OF 8TH & CHESTNUT. Plain edge. (Wright 944; Rulau USTT Pa-Ph 365; Bushnell 6)					

Miller	Date	Metal	Size	F	VF	EF	Unc
Pa 470	(1857)	GS	28mm	—	—	50.00	75.00
		As 469. (Bushnell 6)					
Pa 471	(1857)	Gilt/Br	28mm	—	—	10.00	35.00
		As 469.					
Pa 472	(1857)	Silv/Br	28mm	—	—	10.00	35.00
		As 469.					
Pa 473	(1857)	WM	28mm	—	—	50.00	75.00
		As 469.					
Pa 474	(1857)	Silver	28mm	—	—	150.	300.
		As 469. Rare.					

In 1858 Charles I. Bushnell, the well-known token collector, listed the brass and German silver versions of the Sharpless card in his listing of political and tradesmen pieces. He said the dies were cut by Maas & Sturdivant of Philadelphia.

Sturdivant & Maas, engravers, commenced business in 1857. This was made up of H. M. Sturdivant, seal engraver, and William Maas, printer. The firm broke up in 1858, establishing the date of issue of these tokens quite precisely.

The New York Historical Society publishes a valuable work, *Dictionary of Artists in America* by George C. Groce and David H. Wallace. The 3rd printing of this book (1966) gives details on engravers and diesinkers, among other artisans, and proved helpful in this case. (Research by Robert Lindesmith)

In the 1872 Philadelphia directory, Sharpless & Son, dry goods importers and jobbers, were located at the same location, corner 8th and Chestnut. By 1918 there were Sharpless & Sharpless listed as "men's furnishings;" Sharpless Brothers listed as hardware dealers; and P.E. Sharpless & Co., wholesale butter and egg merchants with branches in other cities.

SLEEPER & FENNER

Miller	Date	Metal	Size	F	VF	EF	Unc
Pa 475	(?)	Brass	28mm	10.00	12.50	15.00	40.00
		Umbrella and parasol. SLEEPER & FENNER.					

Miller	Date	Metal	Size	F	VF	EF	Unc
Pa 476	(1850's)	Brass	28mm	8.00	10.50	13.00	40.00
		Imitation of U.S. $10 gold piece, with PARASOL on coronet of Liberty, SLEEPER. UMBRELLAS. & FENNER around, PHILADA below. Rv: Around eagle is: MOST EXTENSIVE IN THE UNITED STATES ***. Reeded edge. (Wright 991)					
Pa 477	(1850's)	Copper	28mm	8.00	10.50	13.00	40.00
		As 476. Plain edge.					
Pa 477A	(1850's)	Copper	28mm	9.00	11.50	14.00	40.00
		As 476. Reeded edge.					
Pa 478	(1850's)	Silvered Brass	28mm	10.00	12.50	15.00	40.00
		As 476.					

Israel and William Sleeper were located at 126 Market Street in Philadelphia. They are the "Sleeper" of Sleeper & Fenner. R. Fenner was the other partner. Sleeper & Fenner were first listed 1846.

JAMES R. SMITH

Miller	Date	Metal	Size	VG	F	VF	Unc
Pa 480	(1846-52)	Brass	29mm	25.00	30.00	33.00	50.00
		Obverse as obverse of Pa 481 (Eagle with drooping wings, FOREIGN & DOMESTIC DRY GOODS). Rv: JAMES R. SMITH / -*- / — 107 — / MARKET / — ST — / (ornament) / PHILADA. Plain edge. (Wright 1001)					
Pa 480A	(1846-52)	Brass	29mm	25.00	30.00	33.00	50.00
		As 480. Reeded edge.					

SMITH, MURPHY & CO.

Miller	Date	Metal	Size	F	VF	EF	Unc
Pa 481	(1845-57)	Brass	29mm	20.00	23.00	30.00	60.00
		Eagle with drooping wings, shield on breast. FOREIGN & DOMESTIC above, . DRY GOODS . below. Rv: SMITH MURPHY & CO. / 97 / MARKET / ST. / PHILADA. Plain edge. (Wright 1004)					
Pa 481A	(1850's)	Silvered Brass	29mm	20.00	23.00	30.00	60.00
		As 481. Plain edge.					
Pa 482	(1850's)	Brass	29mm	20.00	23.00	30.00	60.00
		James Harris. Rv: SMITH, MURPHY CO.					
Pa 482A	(1850's)	Silvered Brass	29mm	—	—	30.00	60.00
		As last. (Zeddies coll.)					

This location was renumbered as 237 Market in 1858.

ROBERT STEEL

Miller	Date	Metal	Size	VG	F	VF	Unc
Pa 489	(?)	German Silver	--mm	20.00	75.00	150.	300.
		ROBERT STEEL, 815 CHESTNUT ST. Numeral '30'.					

Robert Steel, a hatter, was at the southeast corner of 3rd and Willow in the 1844 directory.

STODDART'S FAMILY DRY GOODS STORES

Rulau	Date	Metal	Size	VG	F	EF	Unc
Pa 722	(1855-56)	Silver	25mm	400.	—	600.	—
		STODDART'S / FAMILY DRY GOODS / STORES / 278. 280 & 282 / NTH 2ND ST. / PHILA. ctsp on Spanish-American 2-reales. Examined: 1756, 1791, 1826-Mo, date worn. Only 5 known. (Gould 122; Brunk 38490)					

Curwen Stoddart is listed in the 1844 directory with stores at 280 North 2nd Street and also 335 Market Street. This became Stoddart & Brother, dry goods, in 1855.

G. STOKES

Miller	Date	Metal	Size	F	VF	EF	Unc
Pa 500	(1858-59)	WM	22mm	—	—	150.	200.
		G. STOKES. / FINE / CLOTHING / 607 / CHESTNUT ST. PHILA. Rv: Cutaway cross-section of the Atlantic cable. Grooved edge. Planchet is 6mm thick. (Wright 1063; Rulau Pa-Ph 380)					
Pa 500A	(1858-59)	Copper	22mm	—	—	150.	200.
		As 500. Grooved edge. Planchet 6mm thick. Rarity 8. (Rulau Pa-Ph 381)					

Granville Stokes purchased a portion of the first Atlantic cable, cut off quarter inches in thickness and had a suitable die made for striking one side, the other side showing the arrangement of the wires. The first cable was laid, unsuccessfully, in 1858 (tokens celebrated this event even though the cable did not work long; these were issued by George H. Lovett of New York). The successful cable was laid by the British liner *Great Eastern*, in 1866.

These tokens were originally thought to have been issued after the second cable laying between Ireland and Newfoundland. Recent research by Bryan Burke, San Bernardino, Calif., shows they must have been issued in the 1858-59 period — thus their inclusion here in U.S. Merchant Tokens 1845-1860 and their removal from U.S. Trade Tokens 1866-1889.

Directory evidence shows Stokes did business in Philadelphia from 1843 to 1865. His business addresses were:

262 High (now Market) St.	1843 to 1856
209 Chestnut St.	1857
607 Chestnut St.	1858-62
609 Chestnut St.	1862 to 1865

Stokes later issued an 1862-dated Civil War token. The 31mm brass token is Fuld Pa 750-T1b (Miller 498) and carries the address 609 Chestnut St.

STOLTZ'S SEGAR STORE

Miller	Date	Metal	Size	VG	F	VF	EF
Pa 501	(1849-60)	Silver	27mm	200.	—	300.	—
		A. K. STOLTZ'S / SEGAR STORE / PHILADA ctsp on Spanish-American 2-reales (Dates examined: 1778, 1779, 1782, 1789) 4 specimens known. (Gould 123; Van Ormer Sale 2857; Brunk 38520)					
Pa 501A	(1870's)	Silver	25mm	250.	—	400.	—
		Similar ctsp on Canada quarter dollar. (Dates examined: 1872-H) (Brunk coll.)					

Adam R. Stoltz, tobacconist, was at Noble above New Market in 1849. Then at 307 No. 3rd 1854-60.

A. B. TAYLOR

Miller	Date	Metal	Size	F	VF	EF	Unc
Pa 504	1860	German silver	20mm	12.50	16.00	35.00	50.00
		A. B. TAYLOR / SODA WATER / 1860 / PHILADA. / WALNUT & NORTH ST. Rv: THE BEST PREPARATIONS / TAYLOR'S / ORILOTE / AND / DENTICRETE / FOR THE TEETH					
Pa 504A	1860	Copper	20mm	—	—	—	75.00
		As 504. Plain edge. (Ganter coll.)					
Pa 504C	1861	German silver	20mm	175.	200.	250.	300.
		As 504, but '1861' instead of '1860'. Plain edge (Fuld 750 U-1c)					
Pa 505	1860	German silver	20mm	12.50	16.00	35.00	50.00
		Obverse as 504. Rv: A FULL ASSORTMENT OF / DRUGS, / MEDICINES / PERFUMERY / AND / FANCY ARTICLES / ALWAYS ON HAND. Plain edge. (Wright 1092)					
Pa 505A	1860	Silver	20mm	—	—	—	400.
		As 505. Plain edge. (Ganter coll.)					
Pa 505B	1860	Silver	20mm	—	—	—	400.
		As 505A, but thick (1.98mm) planchet. Plain edge. (Ganter coll.)					
Pa 506	1860	Copper	20mm	50.00	65.00	80.00	100.
		Obverse as 504. Rv: Eagle. Plain edge. (Fuld NC-23a) Rarity 8.					
Pa 506A	1860	Brass	20mm	50.00	65.00	80.00	100.
		As 506. Plain edge. (Full NC-23b) Rarity 8.					
Pa 506B	1860	Silver	20mm	—	—	—	Unique
		As 506. Plain edge. (Fuld NC-23c)					

Miller	Date	Metal	Size	F	VF	EF	Unc
Pa 507	(1860)	Cupronickel	20mm	12.50	16.00	35.00	50.00
		COR. OF WALNUT & NINTH STS. / A. B. TAYLOR / DRUGGIST / & / APOTHECARY / PHILADA. Rv: As reverse of 504.					
Pa 507A	(1860)	Pure Nickel	20mm	15.00	22.50	35.00	50.00
		As 507. Magnetic.					
Pa 507B	(1860)	Silver	20mm	—	—	—	400.
		As 507. Plain edge. (Ganter coll.)					
Pa 508	(1860)	Copper	20mm	12.50	16.00	35.00	50.00
		As 507.					

Miller	Date	Metal	Size	F	VF	EF	Unc
Pa 509	(1860)	Cupronickel	20mm	12.50	16.00	35.00	50.00
		Obverse as 507. Rv: As reverse of 505.					
Pa 510	(1860)	Copper	20mm	12.50	16.00	35.00	50.00
		As 509.					
Pa 511	(1860)	German silver	20mm	—	—	35.00	50.00
		As 509.					
Pa 511A	(1860)	White Metal	20mm	—	—	35.00	50.00
		As 509.					
Pa 511B	(1860)	Silver	20mm	50.00	100.	150.	300.
		As 509.					
Pa 512	(1862-66)	Copper	20mm	12.50	15.00	35.00	50.00
		TAYLOR / APOTHECARY / 1015 / CHESTNUT ST / PHILADA. Rv: As reverse of 509. Plain edge. (Fuld NC-24a)					
Pa 511C	(1860)	Silver	20mm	—	—	—	400.
		Obverse as 507. Rv: Benjamin Franklin bust left. Unique?					
Pa 511E	1860	WM	20mm	—	—	—	350.
		Obverse as 504. Rv: As 511C (Franklin). Plain edge. (Ganter coll.)					

Alfred B. Taylor was a druggist at 11th and Walnut 1848-55; then at S.E. corner 9th and Walnut 1856-60; then 834 Walnut in 1860. There is no listing for 1861. From 1862-66 he was at 1015 Chestnut St.

J. K. THOMAS, KOSSUTH EXCHANGE

Miller	Date	Metal	Size	VG	F	VF	EF
Pa 518	(1850's)	Brass	25mm	—	150.	—	225.
		KOSSUTH EXCHANGE / J / THOMAS / K / . PHILADA. Rv: Blank. All lettering incused. Plain edge. (Wright 567)					

Miller	Date	Metal	Size	VG	F	VF	EF
Pa 518A	(1850's)	Silver	21mm	300.	—	450.	—
		KOSSUTH EXCHANGE / J / THOMAS / K / . PHILADA. ctsp on Spanish-American 1-real. (Dates examined: 1778, 1782) 3 pieces known. (Brunk 23440)					

Pa 518B	(1850's)	Silver	21mm	300.	—	450.	—
		Similar ctsp on Mexico 1-real, date worn off.					

Pa 518C	(1850's)	Silver	27mm	300.	—	450.	—
		Similar ctsp on Spanish-American 2-reales. (Dates examined: 1747, 1778, date worn). There are 3 pieces reported.					

James K. Thomas, "papier mache," is in the directories at 27 No. 7th St. 1852-57. He then is listed at 1339 N.W. Washington 1858, and 1339 Mt. Vernon in 1859.

James K. Thomas, "open house," is at 625 Arch St. in 1860.

G. L. WATT

Rulau	Date	Metal	Size	VG	F	VF	EF
Pa 760	(?)	Copper	29mm	100.	—	150.	—
		G.L. WATT / PHILADa. ctsp on U.S. 1842 or 1843 Large cent. (Brunk 42260)					
Pa 761	(?)	Copper	28mm	100.	—	150.	—
		Similar ctsp on Hard Times token.					

WINE STORE

Miller	Date	Metal	Size	VG	F	VF	Unc
Pa 584	(1846-48)	Brass	27mm	50.00	100.	300.	450.
		Bunch of grapes. (In retrograde) WINE STORE, 96 NORTH 3RD ST.; NEAR RACE. Rv: Blank.					

Elias Simpson & Jacob Dessau are listed at 96 No. 3rd St. in the 1846 directory, under the style Simpson & Dessau. Simpson & Dessau, "liquors and wines," appear at 96 No. 3rd and also 200 No. 5th in 1848. They moved to 141 No. 3rd in 1849.

(Crowned 'X')
(Thomas Wildes)

Rulau	Date	Metal	Size	VG	F	VF	EF
Pa 723	(1855)	Copper	25mm	—	85.00	—	135.
		Ornate crown over large X ctsp on obverse of U.S. Half cent. Rv: (8-notched cogwheel) / PHILAD / (oval on its flat side) in three lines ctsp on reverse of the coin. Dates examined: 1835. There are 2 specimens known. (Bowers & Merena June 1985 sale, lot 2404; George Fuld report in 1981; Brunk 44545)					
Pa 723A	(1855)	Copper	25mm	—	85.00	—	135.
		Ornate crown over large X ctsp on obverse of U.S. Half cent. Dates examined: 1833, 1835. There are 5 pieces known, three 1833 and two 1835. (Kurt Krueger Sept. 1983 sale, lot 1267; *The Numismatist* for July 1922; Brunk 44540)					
Pa 723B	(1855)	Copper	29mm	—	100.	—	150.
		Similar ctsp to 723A (Crown over X) on U.S. Large cent. Dates examined: 1855. There are 3 specimens known. (Rulau coll.)					
Pa 723C		Copper	21mm	75.00	—	125.	—
		Similar ctsp on 1840 Hard Times token of Bergen Iron Works, HT 205. Only 1 known.					
Pa 723D		Copper	29mm	75.00	—	125.	—
		Similar ctsp on Great Britain halfpenny, date not known. Only 1 reported.					

Several references on pewter ware reveal that Thomas Wildes worked in Philadelphia as a pewterer 1829-1833. He then removed to New York, where he continued as a pewterer 1833-1840. The sources do not reveal what he did, or where, from 1841 on.

The sources are: *Guide to American Pewter* by Carl Jacobs (New York, 1957) and *American Pewter* byJ.B. Kerfoot (New York, 1942), and photo no. 331 in the latter reference.

Both a large 'X' and a large crowned 'X' as seen on these pieces were pewterers' marks for superior quality goods. An identical crowned X to those on the coins was matched by Dr. Brunk against the photograph of a pewter lamp stamped also with Wildes' name. Since some of the coins were also marked PHILAD, Dr. Brunk made the assumption that the stamping was done in or before 1833.

However there are pieces dated 1835, 1840 and 1855, which effectively denies the assumption. We believe there are several possibilities:

(1) Wildes was the creator of the stamped coins, in or soon after 1855 (both 1855 cents known were near perfect before being counterstamped). He may possibly have moved back to Philadelphia.

(2) A relative such as a son might be responsible for the scenario in (1) above.

(3) Another pewterer, or possibly several working at different times, may be the creator. (Most known Half cents were also in excellent condition when stamped).

Wildes created pairs of lamps and pairs of candlesticks which are considered quite scarce. He worked in Britannia metal as well as pewter.

These enigmatic coins were first published by Commodore W.C. Eaton, USN, writing in *The Numismatist* for 1922. They remained a total puzzle until Dr. Brunk uncovered much of the data above in 1987, though they received attention from many writers (Fuld, Krueger, Bowers, Merena, Rulau and others) over the years. We all owe Dr. Brunk thanks for getting us started toward solving this puzzle.

The counterstamp is well done and has little resemblance to the normal merchant impression of this period. The crown is in relief within an oval depression, and the large X is also punched in from a prepared die of ornate form. Indeed, both crown and X may have been a single punch.

The stamp more nearly resembles a West Indies official countermark. However, no West Indian site claims it and the presence of the backstamp PHILAD (first reported 1981) indicated an American connection.

Wildes counterstamped other coins with a differing mark. This was T. WILDES in relief within a scroll-shaped depression, known on Large cents dated 1825 and with worn-off date. These are included in the *Early American Tokens* section.

A. C. YATES & CO.
and
YATES & CO.

Miller	Date	Metal	Size	F	VF	EF	Unc
Pa 587	(1850's)	Brass	28mm	4.00	6.00	10.00	30.00
		Eagle. Rv: A. C. YATES & CO., 6TH & CHESTNUTS STS.					

Pa 588	(1850's)	Brass	27mm	4.00	6.00	10.00	30.00
		Fancily attired gentleman standing, leaning against a column, * THE LEADING AND POPULAR CLOTHING HOUSE OF PHILADA. Rv: * LEDGER BUILDING, COR. 6TH & CHESTNUTS STS. Plain edge. (Wright 1292)					
Pa 588A	(1850's)	Silv/Bs	27mm	8.50	10.00	13.00	35.00
		As 588. Plain edge.					
Pa 588B		WM	27mm	—	—	—	60.00
		As last. Plain edge.					
Pa 588 1/2	(1876)	White Metal	24mm	10.00	12.00	15.00	35.00
		Happy and sad faces united. Over happy face is: I ALWAYS BUY THESE. Over sad face: I WILL IN FUTURE. Rv: YATES & CO. / POPULAR / CLOTHIERS / LEDGER BUILDING / 6TH & / CHESTNUT STS. (Wright 1290)					

Abraham C. Yates appears in the 1850 census.

DR. WM. YOUNG
Philadelphia, Pa.

Rulau	Date	Metal	Size	VG	F	VF	EF
Pa 730	(1841-55)	Silver	27mm	—	300.	—	450.
		DR WM YOUNG / NO 152 SPRUCE ST / PHILA ctsp on U.S. Bust quarter. Dates examined: 1802, 1805. (Van Ormer sale 2927; Brunk 44810)					
Pa 731	(1841-55)	Silver	27mm	—	300.	—	450.
		Similar ctsp on Spanish-American 1801 or date worn 2-reales. (Brunk report)					

Dr. William Young had offices at 152 Spruce St. from 1841 to 1857, according to Philadelphia directories. Earlier, in 1838, he had been at 33 S. 4th St., running an "infirmary for diseases of the skin." In 1849 he styled himself an "oculist," and in 1859 he admitted his son, William Young Jr.

M. P. MORSE
Pittsburgh, Pa.

Miller	Date	Metal	Size	VG	F	VF	Unc
Pa 590	(1845-47)	Copper	27mm	3.00	5.00	7.00	75.00

Ancient oil lamp burning, resting on two books on a table; * SIC ITUR AD ASTRA * above; M. P. MORSE. Rv: MORSE'S LITERARY DEPOT / NO. 85 / FOURTH ST. / PITTSBURGH / PA. / *. Plain edge. (Wright 725)

M. P. Morse appears only twice in the Pittsburgh directories. In the 1847 directory his literary depot is listed at 4th St. between Wood and Market; in the 1850 volume he is listed at 76 Fourth St. Since the address on the token is 85 Fourth St., we must assume that is the same location as the 1847 listing.

This in turn would date the token to the 1845-47 period, though an issue date anywhere in the 1845-49 period cannot be ruled out. A search was made of all these Pittsburgh directories: 1837, 1839, 1841, 1844, 1852, 1856-57, 1857 and 1858-59, without success.

M. P. Morse appears in the 1850 census under Pittsburgh. He was 28 years old in 1850; his place of birth is listed as Massachusetts, and occupation "literary depot." (All Morse research courtesy Jim Hartman, Beaver, Pa.)

H. MUNSON

Miller	Date	Metal	Size	VG	F	VF	EF
Pa 735	(1847)	Copper	29mm	—	75.00	—	125.
		H. MUNSON ctsp on U.S. 1842 Large cent.					
Pa 736	(1847)	Silver	15.5mm	—	75.00	—	125.
		Similar ctsp on U.S. 1834 Half dime. (Brunk 28890)					

H. Munson was a gunsmith and letter cutter located at 2nd and Liberty, according to Stanley L. Steinberg. Frank Sellers' *American Gunsmiths* (page 219) confirms that he was active in Pittsburgh in 1847. No first name is given, merely the initial H.

W. STEVENSON
Pittsburgh, Pa.

Miller	Date	Metal	Size	VG	F	VF	Unc
Pa 591	(?)	Brass	32mm	100.	150.	350.	600.
		W. STEVENSON, WATCHMAKER & JEWELER. Rev: Blank.					
Pa 592	(?)	Copper	32mm	100.	150.	350.	600.
		As 591.					

William Stevenson appears in the 1850 census.

L. L. BEVAN
Pottsville, Pa.

Rulau	Date	Metal	Size	VG	F	VF	EF
Pa 724	(?)	Silver	32mm	250.	—	400.	—
		L. L. BEVAN / EATING SALOON / POTTSVILLE, PA. ctsp on Spanish-American 4-reales. (Gould 81)					
Pa 724D	(?)	Silver	38mm	—	—	500.	—
		Similar ctsp on U.S. 1847 Seated Liberty silver dollar. (Herman Aqua coll.)					
Pa 725	(?)	Silver	27mm	200.	—	300.	—
		Similar ctsp on Spanish-American 1784 2-reales. (Brunk 3555)					

L. P. KNERR
Reading, Pa.

Rulau	Date	Metal	Size	VG	F	VF	EF
Pa 810	(1850)	Copper	29mm	—	35.00	—	75.00
		L. P. KNERR ctsp on U.S. Large cent. Examined: 1796, 1803, 1819, 1836, 1840, 1842, 1843, 1847, 1848, 1849, date worn. At least 13 known. (Brunk 23190)					
Pa 811	(1850)	Silver	27mm	—	—	100.	—
		Similar ctsp on Spanish-American 1793 2-reales.					

Levi P. Knerr (born 1820) was a machinist in Reading circa 1850. He and his wife Mary appear in the 1850 census.

H. O. SCHOENER
Reading, Pa.

Rulau	Date	Metal	Size	VG	F	EF	Unc
Pa 726	1850	Copper	29mm	300.	—	400.	—
		H. O. SCHOENER / READING / 1850 ctsp on U.S. 1793 Large cent, Flowing hair variety.(Brunk 35813)					

Henry O. Schoener appears in the 1860 census. He was a gunsmith active in Reading 1850-1863. In 1855-56 his address was 4th Street near Washington.

J. V. GEIGER
Towanda, Pa.

Rulau	Date	Metal	Size	VG	F	VF	EF
Pa 745	(1861)	Silver	39mm	200.	—	300.	—
		J. V. GEIGER / TOWANDA, PA. ctsp on Spanish-American 1800 8-reales. (Van Ormer sale 2657; Brunk 15920)					
Pa 745A	(1861)	Copper	29mm	60.00	—	90.00	—
		J.V. GEIGER ctsp on U.S. Large cent. (Brunk 15915)					

J.V. Geiger began his gunsmith business in Towanda in 1861. His specialties were flintlock and percussion fullstock rifles. He is last listed in 1890.

C. M. MAXWELL
Wilkes-Barre, Pa.

Rulau	Date	Metal	Size	BG	F	VF	EF
Pa 815	(?)	Copper	28mm	100.	—	—	—
		C. M. MAXWELL / AGENT. / WILKES BARRE ctsp on England 1806 half penny, KM-662. (Herman Aqua coll.)					

RHODE ISLAND

S. PORTER
Newport, R.I.

Miller	Date	Metal	Size	VG	F	VF	Unc
RI 1	(?)	Brass	29mm	15.00	30.00	75.00	125.

S. PORTER / 32 / HIGH ST / NEWPORT. Rv: MERCHANT TAILOR / HATTER / HOSIER / AND / GENERAL OUTFITTER. (Wright 842)

J. E. HUDSON
Providence, R.I.

Rulau	Date	Metal	Size	G	VG	F	EF
RI 100	(?)	Silver	25mm	—	125.	—	200.

J. E. HUDSON / PROV. R I ctsp on U.S. 1854 Seated Liberty quarter dollar. (Gould 85; Brunk 20550)

James Ellery Hudson was born in Natick in 1850. Early in his career he was a printer. Later he became very active in state politics. On his death in 1931, he left 67 descendants. His biography is given in *Rhode Island: Three Centuries of Democracy* by Charles W. Carroll (1932). (Research by Gregory Brunk)

GORHAM MFG. CO.

Rulau	Date	Metal	Size	VG	F	VF	EF
RI 110	(1865)	CN	19mm	100.	—	150.	—

C / 3 1/2 PINTS / (Lion passant right) (Anchor) (Gothic G) each in relief in separate square depression / STERLING / 1801 ctsp on shaved obverse of U.S. 1860-64 type Indian cent. (Rulau coll., ex-Tanenbaum; Brunk 32187)

Rulau	Date	Metal	Size	VG	F	VF	EF
RI 111	(1866-)	CN	22mm	50.00	—	90.00	—

GORHAM. MFG. CO. / PATENT 1861 ctsp on U.S. 1866 Shield nickel. (Brunk 16610; Rulau RI-Pr 11)

Rulau	Date	Metal	Size	VG	F	VF	EF
RI 112	(1853-65)	Silver	25mm	50.00	—	100.	—

GORHAM CO. / (Anchor) in relief / 0605 SILVER ctsp on U.S. 1853-S Seated Liberty quarter. (Brunk 16600; Rulau RI-Pr 12)

Rulau	Date	Metal	Size	VG	F	VF	EF
RI 112A	(?)	Copper	29mm	60.00	—	90.00	—

GORHAM & CO / PROVIDENCE RI ctsp on U.S. 1829 Large cent. (Brunk 16605)

Rulau	Date	Metal	Size	VG	F	VF	EF
RI 114	(?)	Silver	40mm	—	100.	—	150.

G — - O / GO WITH GORHAM / GO GORHAM (in relief) ctsp on Spanish-American 1813-PTS-PJ 8 reales, K-M 84. (Dave Jones coll., Louisville, Ky.)

Rulau	Date	Metal	Size	VG	F	VF	EF
RI 113	(1865)	Silver	25mm	60.00	—	90.00	—

GORHAM . MFG / (Lion passant right) (Anchor) (Gothic G) — all marks incused — ctsp on U.S. 1858 S.L. quarter. (Dirk Mayberry coll.; Brunk 16607)

The numbers 1801 on 110 and 0605 on 112 seem to be control numbers, not stamped from prepared punches as the other stamped elements.

The registered hallmark of the Gorham firm since about 1847 has been: Lion-Anchor-G, all in a line, either in relief or incused.

The issues gradually being discovered seem to overlap the 1845-60 and 1866-89 eras and run through the Civil War period as well. Dating of the counterstamped pieces may be aided by the following formula, which has been newly revised to coincide with the patient detective work published by Louise Belden (see Bibliography).

JABEZ GORHAM	(worked under George G. Clark)	1813-24
GORHAM & BEEBE	(Jabez Gorham, Stanton Beebe)	1825-31
GORHAM & WEBSTER	(Jabez Gorham, Henry L. Webster)	1831-37
GORHAM WEBSTER & PRICE	(Jabez Gorham, Henry L. Webster, — Price)	1837-41
J. GORHAM & SON	(Jabez & John Gorham)	1841-50
GORHAM & CO.	(John Gorham, Lewis Dexter, Gorham Thurber)	1852-65
GORHAM MFG. CO.	(John Gorham, J.F. P. Lawton, Gorham Thurber)	1865-1961

In addition, there may have been a few other short-lived partnerships or company names:

GORHAM & THURBER	(John Gorham, Gorham Thurber)	1850-51
GORHAM SILVER (CO.)	(Jabez Gorham)	1831
GORHAM & SON	(Jabez & John Gorham)	1841

Jabez Gorham, born in 1792, established the great Gorham silverware empire. At age 21 he became associated with the silversmith firm of George G. Clark, 1813-24. Clark in the Hard Times period became well known to collectors through the Clark & Anthony copper tokens of Providence.

Gorham began his own business in 1825 as Gorham & Beebe, and meanwhile was in partnership with William Hadwen of Nantucket Island 1816-28. In the 1890's, Gorham Mfg. Co. became well known in numismatics as its own private mint in New York City which struck silver Bryan money, Cuban revolutionary pesos and many fine medals.

* * *

Number RI 110 above needs some explanation. Every marking on this remarkable little piece has meaning:

C = Coin, a purity mark for coin (90%) silver.
3 1/2 PINTS = Capacity of a Gorham bowl, ewer or urn of silver.
Lion-Anchor-G = Hallmark of Gorham.
STERLING = Purity mark for sterling (92.5%) silver.
1801 = A control number, we believe. Uncertain function.

S. SMITH

Miller	Date	Metal	Size	VG	F	VF	Unc
RI 6	(?)	White Metal	28mm	20.00	50.00	100.	150.

S. SMITH / 20 / PROV. R.I. Rv: MERCHANTS / NO. / 20 / SALOON.

Miller	Date	Metal	Size	VG	F	VF	Unc
RI 7	(?)	White Metal As 6, but '21'.	28mm	20.00	50.00	100.	150.
RI 8	(?)	White Metal As 6, but '24'.	28mm	20.00	50.00	100.	150.
RI 9	(?)	White Metal As 6, but '30'.	28mm	20.00	50.00	100.	150.
RI 10	(?)	White Metal As 6, but '37'.	28mm	20.00	50.00	100.	150.
RI 11	(?)	White Metal As 6, but '40'.	28mm	20.00	50.00	100.	150.
RI 12	(?)	White Metal As 6, but '43'.	28mm	20.00	50.00	100.	150.
RI 12A	(?)	WM As RI 6, but '47'.	24mm	20.00	50.00	100.	150.
RI 13	(?)	White Metal As 6, but '75'.	28mm	20.00	50.00	100.	150.
RI 13A	(?)	White Metal As 6, but '81'.	28mm	20.00	50.00	100.	150.
RI 14	(?)	White Metal As 6, but '93'.	28mm	20.00	50.00	100.	150.
RI 15	(?)	White Metal As 6, but '95'.	28mm	20.00	50.00	100.	150.
RI 16	(?)	White Metal As 6, but '100'.	28mm	20.00	50.00	100.	150.
RI 17	(?)	Brass Similar to RI 6, but '18'.	24mm	20.00	50.00	100.	150.
RI 17D	(?)	Brass As 17, but '30'.	24mm	20.00	50.00	100.	150.
RI 17A	(?)	Brass As 17, but '40'.	24mm	20.00	50.00	100.	150.
RI 17B	(?)	Brass As 17, but '56'.	24mm	20.00	50.00	100.	150.
RI 17C	(?)	Brass As 17, but '62'.	24mm	20.00	50.00	100.	150.

Miller	Date	Metal	Size	VG	F	VF	Unc
RI 18	(?)	Brass As 17, but '68'.	24mm	20.00	50.00	100.	150.
RI 18A	(?)	Brass As 17, but '90'. (Wright 1006)	24mm	20.00	50.00	100.	150.

Dies by Merriam of Boston. Also reported: '25' and '50'.

PROVIDENCE INSTITUTION FOR SAVINGS

Providence, R.I.

Miller	Date	Metal	Size	VG	F	VF	Unc
RI 21	(1859?)	White Metal	27mm	5.00	15.00	40.00	75.00

PROVIDENCE INSTITUTION / * FOR SAVINGS *. Rv: PRESENT THIS / CHECK / AT THE COUNTER / WHEN THE NUMBER / IS CALLED. Plain edge. (Wright 852)

The dies for this piece were cut by Merriam of Boston. Incused on each side of the token, at center, is a numeral. The illustrated specimen is numbered 72. Dr. Wright's hand-drawn illustration in 1898 showed no number at center, so unnumbered specimens may also exist.

SOUTH CAROLINA

BERNARD S. BARUC

Charleston, S.C.

Miller	Date	Metal	Size	F	VF	EF	Unc
SC 2	(1854-56)	Copper	22mm	200.	300.	—	—

Palmetto tree at center, BERNARD S. BARUC / IMPORTER OF FANCY / GOODS & TOYS above; * 208 KING STREET * / CHARLESTON S.C. below. Rv: Eagle with olive branch and three arrows in talons. IN UNITATE FORTITUDO above. SPIEL MUNZE below. Plain edge. (Kurth 36, RF Ssc-1)

Miller	Date	Metal	Size	F	VF	EF	Unc
SC 2A	(1854-56)	Brass	22mm	200.	300.	—	—

As SC 2. Plain edge. (Kurth 36; RF Ssc-1A)

Bernard Baruch, adviser to President Franklin D. Roosevelt, was a grandson of the issuer of this game counter-store card. Only about 7 pieces each of 2 and 2A are believed to exist.

Bernard S. Baruc first appears in the 1855 directory at 208 King Street, and he appears again in the 1856 directory. He is not listed 1857-1858 but reappears in 1859 as a "clerk" with no address given. He disappears from the directories for good in 1860.

HAVILAND STEVENSON & CO.

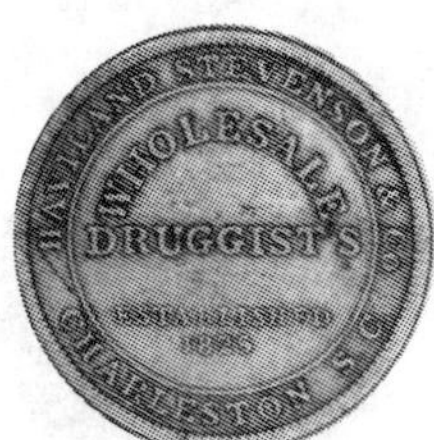

Miller	Date	Metal	Size	VG	F	VF	Unc
SC 3	1825 (1850)	Copper	28mm	20.00	35.00	50.00	80.00
		Eagle with upraised wings alighting on a mortar and pestle, a ribbon in its beak reading: ESTABLISHED A.D. 1825. Rv: HAVILAND STEVENSON & CO. / WHOLESALE / DRUGGISTS / ESTABLISHED / 1825 / CHARLESTON, S.C. (Wright 439)					
SC 3A	1825 (1860)	Copper	28mm	25.00	40.00	60.00	80.00
		Obverse as SC 3 (eagle on mortar & pestle). Rv: Lincoln chopping wood, RAIL SPLITTER OF THE WEST. (DeWitt AL 1860-41K; King 588)					
SC 4	1825 (1860)	Brass	28mm	20.00	35.00	50.00	70.00
		As 3A. Reeded edge. (King 588)					
SC 4A	1825 (1860)	Silvered Brass	28mm	22.50	37.50	50.00	70.00
		As 3A. (King 588)					

The mulings with the 1860 Rail Splitter dies by Ellis were made indiscriminately for collectors. It is unlikely Haviland Stevenson & Co. favored Lincoln! No issuer name appears upon 3A, 4 or 4A.

W. Stevenson, W. Haviland, 1850 census.

W.W. WILBUR

Miller	Date	Metal	Size	F	VF	EF	Unc
SC 5	1846	Brass	29mm	6.00	10.00	15.00	60.00
		Auctioneer standing left, raising his hammer. Inscription around: W. W. WILBUR AUCTION & COMMISSION MERCHANT / CHARLESTON SO CA /.1846 Rv: Palmetto tree at center. MERCHANTS & MANUFACTURERS AGENT * / COLLECTION BROKER. NOTARY PUBLIC &C. (No period after CA on obverse.)					
SC 5A	1846	Copper	29mm	6.00	10.00	15.00	60.00
		As 5.					
SC 6	1846	German silver	29mm	75.00	—	Very Rare	
		Similar to 5, but period after CA.					
SC 7	1846	Copper	29mm	6.00	10.00	15.00	60.00
		As 6.					
SC 8	1846	Brass	29mm	6.00	10.00	15.00	60.00
		As 6.					
SC 7A	1846	Copper	29mm	6.00	10.00	15.00	60.00
		As 6, but smaller palmetto tree.					
SC 8A	1846	Brass	29mm	6.00	10.00	15.00	60.00
		As 7A (smaller tree).					

Miller	Date	Metal	Size	F	VF	EF	Unc
SC 9	1846	Brass	29mm	11.00	14.00	19.00	60.00
		Similar to 6, but GOING AT ONLY A PENNY added under auctioner. Period after CA. (Wright 1243)					
SC 10	1846	Copper	29mm	11.00	14.00	19.00	60.00
		As 9.					
SC 10A	1846	Cupronickel	29mm	—	—	—	Rare
		As 9.					
SC 11	1846	German silver	29mm	—	—	Very	Rare
		As 9.					
SC 12	1846	Copper	29mm	6.00	10.00	15.00	60.00
		Similar to 9, but no period after CA on obverse.					
SC 13	1846	Brass	29mm	6.00	10.00	15.00	60.00
		As 12.					

In 1846, and until the outbreak of the Civil War, Charleston was one of the principal slave marts in America. Its auction houses thrived on the sale of Negroes and other property.

TENNESSEE

C.C. CLEVES
Memphis, Tenn.

Miller	Date	Metal	Size	F	VF	EF	Unc
Tenn 8	(1852-56)	Brass	26mm	28.00	50.00	75.00	125.
		Wreath encloses book, inkwell and pens. Rv: C. C. CLEVES / BOOKSELLER / AND / STATIONER / NO. 12 FRONT ROW / MEMPHIS / TENNESSEE. (Wright 195)					

Miller	Date	Metal	Size	F	VF	EF	Unc
Tenn 8A	(1852-56)	Brass	26mm	—	—	100.	—
		As 8, but name spelled C.C. CLEAVES. (Kurt Krueger Sept. 1989 sale, lot 1508)					

C. C. Cleves, bookseller and stationer, was at 12 Front Row, corner Monroe Street, in Memphis in the 1853 directory for Nashville, the first-ever directory published in the state of Tennessee.

By 1857 the firm had become Cleves & Guion and was located at 241 Main Street. It has not been traced after that.

FRANCISCO & CO.

Miller	Date	Metal	Size	F	VF	EF	Unc
Tenn 11	(1850's)	Copper	28.5mm	10.00	15.00	20.00	40.00
		Man's tall beaver hat in center, FRANCISCO & CO. above, * HATTERS * below. Rv: Eagle displayed, U.S. shield on its breast. Above: 348 MAIN ST. Below: MEMPHIS, TENN. Plain edge.					
Tenn 12	(1850's)	Brass	28.5mm	10.00	15.00	20.00	40.00
		As 11. Reeded edge. (Wright 339)					
Tenn 13	(1850's)	Silvered Brass	28.5mm	—	—	30.00	45.00
		As 11.					
Tenn 14	(1850's)	Brass	28.5mm	10.00	15.00	20.00	40.00
		Obverse as 11 (Hat). Rv: Similar to 11, but 289 MAIN ST.					
Tenn 15	(1852)	Brass	28.5mm	35.00	50.00	75.00	100.
		Obverse as 11. Rv: Bust of Louis Kossuth.					
Tenn 16	(1852)	White Metal	28.5mm	37.50	52.50	77.50	110.
		As Tenn 15.					
Tenn 17	(1860)	Copper	28.5mm	20.00	30.00	45.00	75.00
		Obverse as 11. Rv: DODD, CINCINNATI card.					
Tenn 18	(1860)	Brass	28.5mm	20.00	30.00	45.00	75.00
		As Tenn 17.					
Tenn 19	(1860)	Copper	28.5mm	20.00	30.00	45.00	75.00
		Obverse as reverse of Tenn 14 (Eagle, 289 MAIN ST.). Rv: Padlock. (No name on token.)					
Tenn 19A	(1860)	Brass	28.5mm	—	—	45.00	75.00
		As 19. Plain edge. (Michael Zeddies coll.)					

See the Francisco footnotes under Nashville, Tenn.

FRANCISCO & WIGGIN

Miller	Date	Metal	Size	F	VF	EF	Unc
Tenn 20	(1850's)	Copper	29mm	15.00	20.00	30.00	60.00
		Spread eagle, FRANCISCO & WIGGIN, MEMPHIS. Rv: PEABODY HOTEL / * 307 MAIN ST. Plain edge.					
Tenn 22	(1850's)	Copper	29mm	15.00	20.00	30.00	60.00
		As 20. Reeded edge.					
Tenn 23	(1850's)	Brass	29mm	15.00	20.00	30.00	60.00
		As 20. Plain edge. (Wright 340)					
Tenn 24	(1850's)	White Metal	29mm	30.00	40.00	75.00	100.
		As 20. Plain edge.					
Tenn 25	(1850's)	White Metal	29mm	30.00	40.00	75.00	100.
		As 20. Thick planchet. Plain edge.					

See the Francisco footnotes under Nashville, Tenn.

E. KECK VARIETY STABLE

Rulau	Date	Metal	Size	VG	F	VF	EF
Tenn 100	(1856-58)	Silver	31mm	500.	—	750.	—
		VARIETY STABLE / 360 & 362 / COR. MAIN & CAYOSO / E. KECK PROP. / MEMPHIS TENN. ctsp on U.S. 1854 or 1856 Seated Liberty half dollar. (Schenkman collection; Van Ormer sale 2897; Brunk 41105)					

Elias Keck was a partner in Fletcher & Keck at Main & Cayoso Streets 1859-60. Earlier, 1856-57, he ran the stage agent's office at the Commercial Hotel in Memphis.

S. McD. & CO.

Miller	Date	Metal	Size	VG	F	VF	Unc
Tenn 42A	(1850's)	Brass	28mm	—	20.00	40.00	80.00
		S. Mc. D. / & CO. Rv. / 10/CENTS.					
Tenn 42	(1850's)	Brass	28mm	—	20.00	40.00	80.00
		S. Mc. D. / & CO. Rv. / 25 CENTS.					

Miller	Date	Metal	Size	VG	F	VF	Unc
Tenn 42B	(1850's)	Copper	29mm	—	—	150.	—
		Similar design overstruck on U.S. Large cent of various years, including 1838.					

These drayage checks appeared in lots 1642, 1822 and 1828 of the 1863 Bangs Merwin & Co. sale of the Benjamin Haines collection.

MEMPHIS JOCKEY CLUB

Miller	Date	Metal	Size	VG	F	VF	Unc
Tenn 31	1858	Gilt Brass Oval	62 by 51mm	50.00	100.	—	Rare
		Jockey on horse in front of clubhouse, MEMPHIS JOCKEY CLUB. 1858 above, QUI MERUIT PALMAM FERAT below. Rv: Blank. Plain edge. The flan is slotted at bottom. All letters and design are incuse.					

The Latin legend means: "Let he who bears the palm, merit it." Very rare.

The Fulds (in their "Token Collectors Page") felt this piece might be a jockey's award piece, rather than a membership medal. If so, this piece might not belong in this catalog; Adams intended to include only jockey club membership medalets.

M.H. MILLER & CO.

Miller	Date	Metal	Size	F	VF	EF	Unc
Tenn 33	(1850's)	Brass	27.5mm	25.00	40.00	50.00	60.00
		Hat at center. M. H. MILLER & CO. / HATTERS above; 257 / MAIN STR. / * MEMPHIS TEN. * below. Rv: Eagle. COMPOSITIONS *** SPIEL-MARKE ***. Reeded edge. (Wright 703; Kurth 33B; R-F Ste-2)					
Tenn 34	(1850's)	Silver	27.5mm	—	—	—	V. Rare
		As 33. Reeded edge. (R-F Ste-2A)					
Tenn 34A	(1850's)	Silvered Brass	27.5mm	30.00	50.00	60.00	75.00
		As 33. Reeded edge. (R-F Ste-2B)					

Miller	Date	Metal	Size	F	VF	EF	Unc
Tenn 32	(1850's)	Brass	27.5mm	25.00	40.00	50.00	60.00
		Obverse as 33. Rv: Coronet Liberty head left, LIBERTY on coronet. Eight stars above, COMP. S. MARKE below. Reeded edge. (Kurth 33A; R-F Ste-1)					
Tenn 32A	(1850's)	Copper	27.5mm	—	—	50.00	60.00
		As 32. (Zeddies coll.)					

WESTERN FOUNDRY

Miller	Date	Metal	Size	VG	F	VF	Unc
Tenn 46	(1856-57)	Brass	22mm	—	—	—	Rare
		WESTERN FOUNDRY / MEMPHIS TENNESSEE around blank central space. Large numeral 25 incused at center. Rv: Blank. Dentilated rim on both sides. Plain edge. Rarity 9. (Fuld 600G-1bc; Wright 1226; Rulau Tn-Me 60)					
Tenn 46A	(1856-57)	Brass	22mm	—	—	—	Rare
		Variety of Tenn 46 described by Donald Miller as "Large 25." (Rulau Tn-Me 60A)					

Curtis & Knapp's Western Foundry appears in the 1857 directory, located at Poplar near the Mississippi River. It does not appear in the 1859, 1860, 1865, 1866, 1868 or 1869 directories.

BEN. F. WYANT
Memphis, Tenn.

Rulau	Date	Metal	Size	VG	F	VF	EF
Tenn 102	(1859-60)	Silver	31mm	300.	—	400.	—
		BEN. F. WYANT / MAY FLOWER / SALOON / NO 137 MAIN ST. / MEMPHIS-TENN. in five lines ctsp on U.S. Seated Liberty half dollar. Dates examined: 1854, 1855-O, 1857-O, 1858-O. Only 4 reported. (Schenkman coll.; Rulau Tn-Me 74; Van Ormer sale 2923, 2924; Brunk 26543)					

Benjamin F. Wyant is listed at the 137 Main Street address in the 1859 and 1860 Memphis city directories. It is likely he was at the same address in 1858.

FRANCISCO & WHITMAN
Nashville, Tenn.

Miller	Date	Metal	Size	F	VF	EF	Unc
Tenn 53	(1852-54)	Brass	29mm	12.50	17.50	22.50	40.00
		Tall hat, * PUBLIC SQUARE * above, NASHVILLE TENN. below. Rv: Eagle with U.S. shield on breast, displayed. FRANCISCO & WHITMAN above, HATTERS below. Reeded edge.					
Tenn 53A	(1852-53)	Brass	29mm	12.50	17.50	22.50	40.00
		As Tenn 53. Plain edge.					
Tenn 54	(1852-53)	Silvered Brass	29mm	15.00	20.00	25.00	45.00
		As Tenn 53.					

Tenn 55	(1852-53)	Copper	29mm	15.00	20.00	25.00	45.00
		As Tenn 53. Plain edge. (Wright 341)					
Tenn 56	(1860)	Brass	29mm	12.50	17.50	22.50	55.00
		Obverse as reverse of Tenn 53. Rv: Hat, FRANCISCO & CO. / * HATTERS * (Obverse of Tenn 11)					
Tenn 57	1860	White Metal	29mm	50.00	100.	150.	200.
		Obverse as reverse of Tenn 53. Rv: Abraham Lincoln. (DeWitt AL 1860-41) (King 582)					
Tenn 57A	1860	Copper	29mm	50.00	100.	150.	200.
		As Tenn 57. (King 582)					

Francisco & Whitman were wholesale and retail dealers in hats, caps and furs, located at 23 Public Square, appearing in the first-ever Nashville city directory which was published in 1853.

By the time the second directory was issued in 1855, the business (now referred to as a "hat store") was under the proprietorship of A. J. Francisco and this business (still at the 23 Public Square address) is listed through 1860.

No directories were published during the Civil War, the next appearing in late 1865. By then A. J. Francisco was located at 55 North College and, in the 1868 directory, at 47 Public Square, North side.

We are unable to trace Francisco & Company and Francisco & Wiggins in Memphis thus far, but assume these businesses were contemporary with and related to the Francisco operations in Nashville — the tokens are of the same style and made by the same firm, Scovill Mfg. Co. in Waterbury, Conn.

The Francisco pieces were muled in or after 1860 by Scovill's without the knowledge or permission of Francisco. This is made obvious by the existence of Tenn 57 and 57A — no true Southerner of 1860 would have permitted Abraham Lincoln's likeness on his tokens!

No dates can be assigned with certainty to the Memphis pieces of Francisco & Co. and Francisco & Wiggin. The 1853 Nashville directory was the first ever published in the state of Tennessee (as the directory itself informs us) and it included some listings for Memphis, Knoxville etc., plus scattered listings in Kentucky, Georgia, Alabama, etc. Some Memphis listings also appear in the 1855 and 1857 Nashville directories.

Our reconstruction for the Francisco-related businesses below is tentative, but reasonably certain for Nashville between 1852 and 1869. No tokens are known bearing the A. J. Francisco name.

MEMPHIS

Francisco & Wiggin (hoteliers ?)
Peabody Hotel
307 Main St. 1850's
Francisco & Company (hatters)
348 Main St. 1850's
289 Main St. 1850's

NASHVILLE

Francisco & Whitman (hatters)
23 Public Square 1852-54
A. J. Francisco (hatters)
23 Public Square 1854-60
55 No. College 1865-67
47 Public Square 1868-69

TEXAS

C. GRAVES
Dallas, Texas

Rulau	Date	Metal	Size	VG	F	VF	EF
Tex 100	(?)	Silver	31mm	—	—	100.	—
		GUNSMITH ctsp on obverse of U.S. 1854-O half dollar. C. GRAVES / DALLAS / * * * ctsp on reverse of the coin. (Brunk 16960)					

This gunsmith is not listed in Frank Sellers' massive directory, *American Gunsmiths* (Highland Park, N.J., 1983).

The letter punches appear to have been applied individually on a very worn half dollar. This piece could be post-Civil War in provenance if genuine; there is always the possibility it is a fantasy creation.

TEXAS FANTASY CONCOCTIONS

(NOTE: The items listed below, were they genuine, would have emanated from the Republic of Texas period, 1836-1845, or somewhat later, up to 1857 when foreign coin circulation in the United States was halted by law. None of the items are genuine; they were made to bilk collectors in recent years, by taking genuine host coins and adding "sexy" fantasy counterstamps.)

Warning: Fantasy Concoctions!

Rulau	Date	Metal	Size	VG	F	VF	EF
Tex X1	1842	Silver	27mm	—	—	7.50	—
		2 / BITS / TEXAS ctsp on reverse of Mexico Republic 2-reales of 1830's, date worn off. 1842 ctsp on obverse of coin. (Byron White report)					

This is stamped from the same punches used on the Union Mine fantasies of Oregon!

Tex X2	Undated	Silver	32.5mm	5.00	—	7.50	—
		TEXAS / 4 BITS in relief within two separate rect. depressions ctsp on U.S. 1795 half dollar. (Brunk 39660)					

Tex X3	Undated	Silver	39mm	6.00	—	8.00	—
		TEXAS / 8 BITS in relief within two separate rect. depressions, ctsp on Spanish-American 8-reales. Dates examined: 1778, 1797. (Brunk 39670)					

Prices given above represent underlying bullion value plus a small amount for curiosity value. The underlying host coins, unfortunately, are now mutilated and have lost their numismatic value.

Types X2 and X3 apparently were done by the same hand, in the 1950's. This person also made the Louisiana fantasies, which read LOUISIANA / 4 BITS and LOUISIANA / 8 BITS, respectively, counterstamped on silver coins of France and Italy.

VERMONT

J. S. ROBINSON
Barre, Vt.

Rulau	Date	Metal	Size	VG	F	VF	EF
Vt 102	(1866)	Copper	29mm	—	100.	—	150.

J.S ROBINSON. / BARRE. VT. ctsp on U.S. 1847 Large cent. (Tanenbaum coll.; Brunk 34700)

J.S. Robinson's sash and blind factory was opened 1866, and moved to a larger site in 1872.

Rulau	Date	Metal	Size	VG	F	VF	EF
Vt 102C	1869	Copper	33mm	—	100.	—	150.

J. S. ROBINSON / 1869 S.H. & T. / BARRE, VT. ctsp on Canada 1850 penny bank token. (Brunk 34705)

F. MARSH
Ludlow, Vt.

Rulau	Date	Metal	Size	VG	F	VF	EF
Vt 103	(?)	Copper	29mm	—	100.	—	150.

LUDLOW, VT. / F. MARSH. ctsp on U.S. 1824 Large cent. (Rulau collection; Brunk 26075)

J. DEMERITT
Montpelier, Vt.

Rulau	Date	Metal	Size	VG	F	VF	EF
Vt 104	(1866)	Copper	29mm	—	125.	—	175.

J. DEMERITT / MONTPELIER / VERMONT ctsp in tiny letters on U.S. 1847 Large cent. (Tanenbaum coll.; Brunk 11350)

John Demeritt appears in the 1850 census. He was born in Madbury, N.H. in 1809 and died in Montpelier, Vt. in 1896. He is first located in the Montpelier directories in 1829 as a cutler. He went West in 1849, probably for the gold rush, and was back in Montpelier as a gunsmith in 1855.

He served as an armorer at the Springfield Armory in Massachusetts in the 1860's.

Following the Civil War, he returned to Montpelier and had a cutlery and gunsmith business there until his death. He appears in Montpelier directories 1866-1896.

The tiny letter-punch used to create this advertising piece also appears on metal parts of his guns. It must have been applied to the coin in either the 1855-60 or post-1866 period, most likely about 1866. (Research courtesy Dwight B. Demeritt and gleanings from gunsmith references cited in the bibliography)

ROBBINS, KENDALL & LAWRENCE
Windsor, Vt.

Rulau	Date	Metal	Size	VG	F	VF	EF
Vt 101	(1844-46)	Copper	28mm	—	250.	—	300.

ROBBINS, / KENDALL & / LAWRENCE / U.S. ctsp on Nova Scotia 1812 halfpenny token or Canada 1823 token. 2 known. (Bowers & Ruddy Nov. 1982 sale list; Brunk 34550)

The above counterstamp could have been applied only in the period specified, as Kendall was associated only in this time frame. See the next entry for Robbins & Lawrence Co.

The partners were Samuel E. Robbins, Nicanor Kendall and Richard S. Lawrence.

ROBBINS & LAWRENCE CO.
Windsor, Vermont

Rulau	Date	Metal	Size	VG	F	VF	EF
Vt 100	(1846-56)	Silver	18mm	—	300.	—	400.

ROBBINS & / LAWRENCE CO / WINDSOR. VT ctsp on U.S. 1838 Seated Liberty dime. (Van Ormer sale 2815; Brunk 34560)

For further discussion of this issue, see under Carlos C. Clark of Nashua, N.H.

Robbins & Lawrence was formed in the 1830's as Kendall and Lawrence; they manufactured a type of revolving pistols known as pepperboxes. In 1844 Samuel E. Robbins joined the business, and its name was changed to Robbins, Kendall & Lawrence. Kendall left the company in 1846, at which time the name became Robbins & Lawrence.

Robbins was a promoter and financier, and under his direction the company expanded. In 1846 it accepted a government contract to make Model 1841 rifles for the War Department. Two years later it was awarded two more contracts, one for the manufacture of the well known Sharps carbines, and the other for more Model 1841 rifles. These contracts were completed in 1853, and the next year the company obtained a contract with the British government for a quarter of a million firearms, a huge order for the time. In preparing to do the work the company developed the turret lathe, which is to this day an important machine.

The British cancelled the contract, however, just as production was starting, and shortly thereafter (in 1856) the company went bankrupt. Lawrence became a principal in the Sharps Rifle Company, which remained in business until 1881, and manufactured many rifles and carbines during the Civil War. It is not known what happened to Robbins after the company declared bankruptcy.

The counterstamp was made with the same logotype punch used to mark the company's lockplates on the Model 1841 rifles.

This piece fetched $300 in the Van Ormer sale.

DODGE
Woodstock, Vermont

Rulau	Date	Metal	Size	G	VG	F	EF
Vt 106	1850	Copper	29mm	—	25.00	—	50.00

DODGE / 1850 ctsp on U.S. 1830 Large cent. (Brunk 11810)

Grover Dodge was a general gunsmith in Woodstock, Vermont before the Civil War. (Attribution by Stanley L. Steinberg, Malden, Mass.)

The Sellers gunsmith reference gives known dates of Dodge's activities as 1840-1843.

A.W. WHITNEY
Woodstock, Vt.

Rulau	Date	Metal	Size	VG	F	VF	EF
VT 109	(1850's)	Copper	25mm	100.	—	150.	—

A.W. WHITNEY. / WOODSTOCK VT ctsp on Netherlands East Indies 1823-S (Surabaya) 1/2-stuiver, KM-285, Craig 66. (Van Ormer sale 2912; Brunk 43220)

Aaron W. Whitney was a manufacturer of tools in Woodstock. He is probably the predecessor of P.A. Whitney, whose counterstamped coins dated 1862-69 may be found under Whitney & Woodbury in *U.S. Trade Tokens 1866-1889* section. The illustrated piece was hammered down at $77 in the 1985 Van Ormer sale.

VIRGINIA

MANSION HOUSE
Alexandria, Va.

Rulau	Date	Metal	Size	F	VF	EF	Unc
Va 100	(1857-60)	Copper	29mm	125.	—	175.	—

MANSION HOUSE / ALEXa ctsp on U.S. Large cent. (Dates examined: 1817, 1849, 1851, 1857) (Schenkman 1040AB; Brunk 25930)

Va 100C	1857	Silver	31mm	175.	—	250.	—

MANSION / HOUSE / 1857 ctsp on U.S. Seated Liberty half dollar. (Dates examined: 1855, 1855-O) (Brunk 25920)

Va 100E	(1858-60)	CN	19mm	100.	—	150.	—

MANSION / HOUSE / ALEXa ctsp on U.S. 1858 Flying Eagle cent. (Brunk 25935)

Va 101	(1878-80)	Brass	24mm	—	25.00	30.00	—

GOOD FOR / 5 ¢ / MANSION HOUSE. Rv: Blank. Plain edge. (Schenkman 1040AA5)

James Green opened the Mansion House Hotel in 1849. He died in 1880, and in 1881 the hotel's name was changed to Braddock House. In 1871 the Mansion House was called the "best hotel in Alexandria" by the *Commercial Travelers Guide Book*; rooms were $3 per night.

MARSHALL HOUSE
Alexandria, Va.

Rulau	Date	Metal	Size	VG	F	EF	Unc
Va 103	1859	Copper	19mm	5.00	15.00	20.00	40.00

Liberty capped female head left, 13 stars around. Rv: MARSHALL / 1859 / HOUSE. (The 9 of 1859 is usually weakly struck.) (Wright 667; Schenkman 1040 AC)

Colonel Ellsworth, the 'Martyr,' and Private Brownell, the 'Avenger,' are pictured on this Civil War ferrotype.

The Marshall House in Alexandria, a Washington, D.C. suburb, became famous in 1861. Col. Ephraham E. Ellsworth, 24, commander of Ellsworth's Zouaves, garrisoned Alexandria. The Marshall House owner, a hot-blooded Southern sympathizer named Jackson, flew the Stars and Bars over his hotel. When Ellsworth warned him to lower the rebel banner, Jackson refused.

Col. Ellsworth and Pvt. Brownell then entered the hotel and pulled the Confederate flag down. As they descended the stairs, Jackson shot and killed Ellsworth and Brownell returned the fire, killing Jackson. Brownell was awarded the Medal of Honor for his part, the first honoree in the Civil War.

CHARLES J. RAINE
Lynchburg, Va.

Miller	Date	Metal	Size	VG	F	VF	Unc
Va 5	1860	Brass	28mm	9.00	17.00	25.00	80.00

Eagle with drooping wings, olive branches and four arrows in its talons, 13 stars around in inner circle. FASHIONABLE CLOTHING around, 1860 below. Rv: CHARLES J. RAINE / 139 / MAIN ST. / LYNCHBURG, VA. Plain edge. (Wright 867; Schenkman 3180 AGa)

Va 5A	1860	Copper	29mm	—	—	—	200.

As 5, but struck on extra thick planchet. (Schenkman 3180 AGb)

WRIGHT
Lynchburg, Va.

Rulau	Date	Metal	Size	VG	F	VF	EF
Va 110	(1849-56)	Silver	32mm	—	150.00	—	—

WRIGHT ctsp on Spanish-American Carlos III (?) 4-reales coin, date worn off. (Charles Kirtley 1987 sale)

Va 111	—	Silver	27mm	60.00	—	90.00	—

Similar ctsp on Spanish-American 2-reales. (Brunk 44433)

Va 113	(?)	Copper	29mm	60.00	—	90.00	—

J. WRIGHT ctsp on U.S. Large cent. Examined: 1820, 1833, 1835. (Brunk 44445)

Va 114	(?)	Copper	28mm	60.00	—	90.00	—

Similar ctsp on Canada token.

Va 115	(?)	Copper	33mm	—	—	90.00	—

Similar ctsp on England penny.

James R. Wright was a silversmith in Lexington, Virginia, active in the 1849-1856 period. Before that he had been making silverware in Lynchburg, Virginia about 1846.

His signature Wright appears on teaspoon shanks.

A counterstamp WRIGHT exists on a U.S. 1851 Large cent. We have not seen it to compare with Va 110.

R. C. BARCLEY
Norfolk, Va.

Miller	Date	Metal	Size	VG	F	VF	Unc
Va 6	(1851)	Copper	29mm	8.50	12.50	20.00	75.00

Open book at center. FINE CUTLERY STATIONARY / BOOKS / & / STATIONARY /.& PAPERHANGINGS. Rv: R. C. BARCLEY BOOKSELLER & BINDER / (ornament) / MAIN ST / NORFOLK / VA. / * * *. (Wright 61; Schenkman 3680 Ga) (Often found with one or two letters ctsp on the book.)

Miller	Date	Metal	Size	VG	F	EF	Unc
Va 7	(1851)	Brass	29mm	10.00	20.00	35.00	150.

As 6. (Schenkman 3680 Gb)

In 1851 Barcley was at 11 East Main Street, at the head of Mark Square.

R. CHAMBERLAINE

Miller	Date	Metal	Size	VF	EF	Unc	Proof
Va 10	(1860)	Tin	27mm	—	—	300.	500.

Washington head right within olive wreath, tiny M below bow. WASHINGTON above. Rv: Star within wreath at center. Around: R. CHAMBERLAINE, NORFOLK. (Baker 525; Schenkman 3680X)

The M equals Joseph H. Merriam of Boston.

Richard Chamberlaine appears in the 1850 census.

Miller	Date	Metal	Size	VF	EF	Unc	Proof
Va 10A	(1862)	WM	28mm	—	—	300.	500.

Washington bust in uniform left, tiny BOLEN under bust. Around: THE FATHER OF OUR COUNTRY. Rv: As reverse of Va 10. (Baker 526; Schenkman 3680 Ya)

Va 10B	(1862)	Copper	28mm	—	—	375.	—

Same as last. Possibly unique. (Baker 526; Schenkman 3680 Yb)

Richard Chamberlaine went into business about 1860, at 93 East Main Street. He was a merchant and oyster packer. All his tokens were struck by Merriam of Boston; the mulings were made in the 1870's.

JORDAN COUGH CANDY
Norfolk, Va.

Miller	Date	Metal	Size	VG	F	EF	Unc
Va 13 1/2	(1850's)	Silver	27mm	150.	—	250.	—

JORDAN — COUGH CANDY / NORFOLK, VA. ctsp on 1775 Spanish-American 2-reales. (Schenkman 3680AT; Brunk 22135)

C. Jordan & Son had a thriving business in Norfolk beginning with the firm's founding in 1837. Jordan sold his "Jordan's Vegetable Cough Candy" in the East as a remedy for colds and pulmonary complaints and this is the item advertised on the counterstamp.

According to his 1867 advertisement in the Norfolk city directory, Jordan's candy factory was located at 52 So. Church St. and his retail store at 77 East Main St. He sold a wide variety of fruits, nuts, tobacco, canned goods, toys, glassware and notions in addition to his own candies and confections.

CITY OF PETERSBURG

Petersburg, Va.

Miller	Date	Metal	Size	G	VG	F	Unc
Va 14	(?)	Brass	27mm	—	100.	250.	500.
		Dog standing right on strip of ground, circle of 13 stars around. Rv: CITY / OF / PETERSBURG within circle of 13 stars. (Schenkman 3960D)					

The purpose for which this piece was intended is not known.

One appeared in the J. N. T. Levick sale of 1884, when even then it was considered rare. The token's provenance assigns it to the pre-Civil War era, but its attribution has defied all attempts.

JAMES E. WOLFF

Petersburg, Va.

Miller	Date	Metal	Size	F	VF	EF	Unc
Va 18	(1850's)	Copper	26mm	5.00	10.00	15.00	40.00
		Tall hat above NO. 17 / SYCAMORE ST. Around all: JAMES E. WOLFF / .PETERSBURG, VA. Rv: Wolf running left; WHOLESALE & RETAIL / DEALER IN above; HATS, / CAPS, FURS &C. below. Plain edge. (Wright 1264; Schenkman 2960ANa)					
Va 19	(1850's)	Copper	26mm	5.00	10.00	15.00	40.00
		As 18. Reeded edge.					
Va 20	(1850's)	Brass	26mm	7.50	10.00	18.00	40.00
		As 18. Plain edge. Normal planchet.					
Va 20A	(1850's)	Brass	26mm	—	—	—	—
		As 18. Plain edge. Thick planchet.					

Miller	Date	Metal	Size	F	VF	EF	Unc
Va 22	(1850's)	German silver	26mm	10.00	15.00	30.00	60.00
		As 18. Plain edge.					
Va 23	(1850's)	German silver	26mm	—	—	30.00	60.00
		As 18. Reeded edge. (Schenkman 3960ANh) (Va 21, cupronickel, does not exist)					
Va 24	(1850's)	White Metal	26mm	—	—	30.00	60.00
		As 18. Plain edge.					
Va 25	(1850's)	White Metal	26mm	—	—	30.00	60.00
		As 18. Reeded edge.					

A number of Wolff mulings exist, all from the post-1860 period. They are included in my 1866-1889 reference.

W. C. T.

Portsmouth, Va.

Rulau	Date	Metal	Size	VG	F	VF	EF
Va 130	(1853?)	Copper	29mm	—	35.00	—	50.00
		W C T / PORTSMOUTH, VA ctsp on U.S. Large cent. Dates examined: 1817, 1818, 1826, 1827, 1838, 1841, 1844, 1848, 1850, 1852, date worn. There are 12 specimens reported. (Koppenhaver Nov. 1983 sale, lot 16; Levine June 1985 sale, lot 1369; Brunk 41320)					

WISCONSIN

WM. HART

Mayville, Wis.

Rulau	Date	Metal	Size	VG	F	VF	EF
Wis 100	(?)	Silver	25mm	175.	—	225.	—
		WM. HART / JEWELER / MAYVILLE. / WIS. ctsp on U.S. Seated Liberty quarter dollar. Dates examined: 1853, 1854, 1857. There are 4 known. (Van Ormer sale 2680 & 2681; Brunk 18480)					
Wis 101	(?)	Copper	29mm	125.	—	175.	—
		WM. HART / MAYVILLE. / WIS. ctsp on U.S. 1850 Large cent. (Brunk 18490; Van Ormer 2683)					
Wis 102	(?)	Silver	27mm	150.	—	200.	—
		Similar ctsp on Spanish-American 1779 2-reales.					

W. H. BYRON & CO.

Milwaukee, Wis.

Miller	Date	Metal	Size	VG	F	VF	Unc
Wis 1	(1850's)	Brass	28mm	25.00	30.00	50.00	75.00
		Imitation of U.S. $10 gold piece, with BYRON & Co on Liberty's coronet. Seven stars above, MILWAUKEE 153 WATER ST below. Rv: Eagle at center, W. H. BYRON & Co. above, IRON & HARDWARE below. Reeded edge. (Wright 126)					
Wis 1A	(1850's)	Brass	28mm	—	—	50.00	75.00
		As last. Plain edge.					

William H. Byron resided in Milwaukee during the U.S. 1850 census.

I. A. HOPKINS

Miller	Date	Metal	Size	VG	F	VF	Unc
Wis 2	1850	Brass	28mm	6.00	7.50	10.00	30.00
		Eagle displayed shield on breast. HOPKINS / 1850 above, WESTERN — PUBLISHING — HOUSE. Rv: + I. A. HOPKINS + / 146 / — * — / U.S. BLOCK / — * — / MILWAUKEE / BOOKSELLER & PUBLISHER. Plain edge.					
Wis 3	1850	Copper	28mm	6.00	7.50	10.00	30.00
		As 2. Plain edge. (Wright 459)					

Miller	Date	Metal	Size	VG	F	VF	Unc
Wis 4	(1850's)	Brass	28mm	8.00	10.00	15.00	32.50
		Eagle displayed, shield on breast. HOPKINS WESTERN PUBLISHING .HOUSE. around. Rv: Same as reverse of Wis 2. Plain edge.					
Wis 5	(1850's)	Copper	28mm	8.00	10.00	15.00	32.50
		As 4. Plain edge.					
Wis 6	(1850's)	Silvered Brass	28mm	9.00	11.00	17.00	35.00
		As 4. Plain edge.					

J. McD. SMITH
Milwaukee, Wis.

Miller	Date	Metal	Size	VG	F	VF	Unc
Wis 9	(?)	Copper	28mm	75.00	—	—	Rare

J. McD. SMITH COR OF MAIN & DETROIT STS. Ex. Rare.

No information available on this piece. Smith appears in the 1850 census.

A. B. VAN COTT
Racine, Wis.

Miller	Date	Metal	Size	VG	F	VF	Unc
Wis 10	(1850's)	Brass	28.5mm	5.00	10.00	15.00	40.00

Pocket watch with chain in center, WATCHES. CLOCKS. JEWELRY. * & FANCY GOODS *. Rv: Eagle displayed, U.S. shield on breast, A. B. VAN COTT above, RACINE — WISCONSIN below. Thick planchet. Plain edge.

Miller	Date	Metal	Size	VG	F	EF	Unc
Wis 11	(1850's)	Brass	28mm	5.00	10.00	15.00	40.00
		As 10, but thin planchet. Plain edge.					
Wis 12	(1850's)	Copper	28mm	5.00	10.00	15.00	40.00
		As 10. Plain edge. (Wright 1182)					
Wis 13	(1850's)	Brass	28mm	5.00	10.00	15.00	40.00
		Obverse as obverse of 10 (pocket watch). Rv: Eagle displayed, shield on breast, in center. A. B. VAN COTT. RACIM (error) above, WISCONSIN below. Plain edge.					
Wis 14	(1850's)	Copper	28mm	5.00	10.00	15.00	40.00
		As 13. Plain edge.					

Though Wis 13 and 14 contain the error RACIM instead of RACINE, they seem much more plentiful than the correct versions, Wis 10, 11 and 12. They also are found with the most wear, indicating lengthy use in circulation. All Wis 13 and 14 error pieces apparently are struck on thin planchets.

Miller	Date	Metal	Size	VG	F	EF	Unc
Wis 15	(1860)	Copper	28mm	—	—	70.00	125.

Obverse as obverse of 10 (pocket watch). Rv: MOST EXTENSIVE IN THE UNITED STATES *** around an eagle with outspread wings, U.S. shield on its breast. (Reverse is the reverse of Pa 476, Sleeper & Fenner Umbrella and Parasol firm in Philadelphia).

Albert B. Van Cott appears in the 1850 census.

S B C
Racine, Wis.

Rulau	Date	Metal	Size	VG	F	VF	EF
Wis 114	(?)	Brass	28mm	—	25.00	—	—

S B C ctsp on Van Cott Racine token (Miller Wis 10).

NON-LOCAL

VOTE THE LAND FREE

Rulau	Date	Metal	Size	VG	F	VF	EF
Y1	(1848)	Copper	29mm	—	65.00	—	95.00

VOTE THE LAND / FREE ctsp on U.S. Large cents of various dates. (Dates reported: 1812, 1816, 1817, 1818, 1819, 1827, 1829, 1833, 1835, 1836, 1837, 1838, 1840, 1841, 1842, 1843, 1844, 1845, 1846, 1847, 1848.) There are 49 pieces reported. (DeWitt MVB 1848-3; Duffield 1387; Brunk 41255)

Rulau	Date	Metal	Size	VG	F	VF	EF
Y2	(1848)	Silver	27mm	100.	—	150.	—
		Same ctsp on Spanish-American 2-reales of various types. (Reported: 1811-Mo; 1819; PTS mint with date worn off) Only 3 known. (DeWitt MVB 1848-4 and 1848-5)					
Y2A	(1848)	Silver	25mm	100.	—	150.	—
		Similar ctsp on U.S. 1843 S.L. quarter.					

Foreign silver coins flooded the country beginning in 1834 as regular U.S. silver coins were snapped up by speculators and hoarders as bullion, and thus the legalization of foreign coins by the Act of 1793 permitted a torrent of Spanish-American, British and other coins.

The Free Soil Party of Martin Van Buren in 1848 counterstamped copper U.S. cents and also silver quarters and their foreign equivalents as campaign advertisements. Though large numbers of coins were counterstamped, especially coppers, the surviving specimens are scarce today.

Free Soilers were strong in New York, Ohio and Massachusetts.

These pieces were not simply campaign medalets; they were also a circulating medium and thus included in this catalog, though campaign medalets themselves are excluded from this section.

DO YOUR DUTY

Rulau	Date	Metal	Size	VG	F	VF	Unc
Y4	1846	Brass	18mm	25.00	100.	150.	250.

Beehive at center, DO YOUR DUTY around, .1846. below. Clasped hands at center, UNION IS above, .STRENGTH. below. Plain edge.

Little is known about this piece, which is scarce, yet available from time to time. Some have associated it with the Mormon movement because of the beehive, a Mormon symbol, but this is possibly in error as the Mormons are not proven to have had any metallic remembrances this early.

Still, a 1984 volume, "*Currency of Utah*," assigns this to Salt Lake City, Utah.

CONTRAHENDO ET SOLVENDO

Rulau	Date	Metal	Size	VG	F	VF	Unc
Y3	1857	Brass	27mm	—	—	40.00	80.00

CONTRAHENDO ET SOLVENDO / PUN. / GO. / SEM. PAR. Rv: SUSPENDER BUTTONS / TWO / CENTS / 1837 1857. Plain edge. Flan pierced with two "buttonholes."

Rulau	Date	Metal	Size	VG	F	VF	Unc
Y3C	1857	Brass	19mm	5.00	12.50	25.00	40.00

CONTRAHENDO ET SOLVENDO / o2o (very large 2) / S. P. Rv: SUSPENDER BUTTONS / 1837 / o o / 1857. Plain edge. (Wright 1077; Rulau Z81)

Rulau	Date	Metal	Size	VG	F	VF	Unc
Y3E	1863	Brass	19mm	—	—	—	80.00

Obverse as Y3C. Rv: THURSDAY / 1863. Plain edge. (Rulau MV 61)

Y3C was previously listed as Z81 in the Maverick section of the 1st edition of this reference. Y3E was previously listed as MV 61 in my reference, U.S. Trade Tokens 1866-1889. Both pieces have been reassigned here, along with the new report on Y3, to keep this obviously connected set together.

The three pieces were apparently struck by the Thomas Kettle firm in Birmingham, England.

An intriguing explanation for these pieces has been worked out by my friend and fellow researcher, L. B. (Ben) Fauver of California, under the title of "The Emancipation Token," in the Summer 1983 issue of *Copperhead Courier*. This explanation would ascribe a political motive to all three pieces, with the dates 1837 and 1857 referring to the financial panics in those years, and the date 1863 to the Emancipation Proclamation. Fauver opines that the initials S.P. stand for Slave Power, a pro-Southern catchphrase of the 1850's, and that "suspender buttons" either means an embarrassment (if your suspenders fail) or a strength (since the buttons hold up your pants).

We can accept some of Fauver's reasoning. He says that "Thursday 1863" refers to the Emancipation Proclamation, since Jan. 1, 1863, the date of the decree, fell on a Thursday, and that Thursday is Jupiter's (or Thor's) day, indicating a clap of thunder falling on the Southern doctrine of Slave Power. The reasoning, we believe, is too thin, though we do not necessarily reject all of it.

It is difficult, 133 years afterward, to understand all the colloquialisms, catchwords and allusions of 1857, but let us examine the physical evidence. One side of each of the three pieces carries Latin phrases; for this reason we suspect that Kettle used ONLY LATIN on that side, and that the abbreviations PUN. GO. SEM. PAR. are all Latin, and not English. The Sem. Par. is quite likely Semper Paratus — Always Ready — the same as the U.S. Coast Guard motto. We haven't thought of an appropriate meaning in Latin for PUN. GO., but perhaps a user of this book can.

"Contrahendo et Solvendo" refers to togetherness and solvency (financial?). We think the S.P. on the latter two pieces may well be simply Semper Paratus again, since that's the Latin side. The small O's on the latter two pieces are, we believe, indicators of the places a button-hole punchout would have occurred if the holes had been punched as on Y3.

Now, the phrase "suspender buttons." We think the tokens themselves ARE imitations of suspender buttons, thus the holes or places for them!

Admittedly, everything here is guesswork, and our conclusions are weakened by the fact that they really lead nowhere. The pieces seem connected in philosophy (though not in fabric) with the 1857 Aaron White "hoarder" counters and their SUS PENDENS and other Latin phrases satirizing paper money, such as "Never keep a paper dollar in your pocket til tomorrow."

Readers should examine Fauver's excellent book, *Exonumia Symbolism & Classification* (Menlo Park, Calif., 1983) for an insight into many token mysteries.

* * *

As if all the above were not enough, read on:

Rulau	Date	Metal	Size	F	VF	EF	Unc
Y3G	1864	Copper	19mm	—	—	—	—
		Obverse as Y3C. Rv: Palm tree at center. YNGENIO ECUADOR above, 1864 below. Plain edge. (Pesant 82; Eklund note 2090)					

The reverse of Y3G is a Cuban hacienda token issue for Ecuador Sugar Estate in what is now called Matanzas Province.

Latin America token researcher David Henkle of Chicago came up with more puzzling data. The reverse of Y3G (Palm tree, 1864) is also muled with no less than 6 different patriotic Civil War token dies, each of which is a Rarity 9; (He identified these dies as Fuld CWT 1145 (Lincoln, 1864), 1241 (O.K.), 1244 (Shield, FREEDOM), 1275 (NO COMPROMISE), and old Fuld no. 125.

Henkle and his sources, including Roberto Pesant among others, say these ECUADOR/CWT mulings were done in the United States.

In our own research in Latin America tokens, we came across the fact that the Y3C obverse die has been claimed for all these countries: Cuba, Brazil, Ecuador and Mexico — all on the flimsiest deduction.

For example, a collector identified S.P. as equaling Sao Paulo, Brazil. He was responding to the listing of the token in the maverick identification section of the *TAMS Journal*.

A 19th century dealer thought Yngenio Ecuador must have been in the Republic of Ecuador.

NONE COINED

Non-Local

Rulau	Date	Metal	Size	VG	F	EF	Unc
Y35	(?)	Copper	29mm	—	32.50	—	
		NONE COINED / IN / 1815 ctsp on shaved reverse of U.S. 1841 Large cent.					

EAGLES ON HALF CENTS

Rulau	Date	Metal	Size	VG	F	EF	Unc
Y5	(?)	Copper	25mm	—	75.00	—	125.
		Eagle with folded wings, shield on breast, all incuse, ctsp on U.S. 1828 Half cent. (Brunk 45100)					
Y6	(?)	Copper	25mm	—	35.00	—	—
		Eagle with wings extended and letter A, all incuse, on obverse; letter H incuse, on reverse — all ctsp on U.S. 1828 Half cent. (Duffield 1578)					

NOTE: Many eagle stamps may have come from the stamping tools used by cutlery makers, gunsmiths, toolmakers, etc. and may yet be attributed to makers or locales.

EAGLES ON LARGE CENTS

Rulau	Date	Metal	Size	VG	F	EF	Unc
Y7	(?)	Copper	29mm	—	25.00	—	—
		Eagle with wings folded, head turned left, grasping three arrows and an olive branch, all incuse — ctsp on U.S. 1802 Cent.					
Y8	(?)	Copper	29mm	—	25.00	—	—
		Heraldic eagle with shield on breast, incuse, ctsp on U.S. 1794 Cent. (Duffield 1582)					
Y9	(?)	Copper	29mm	—	25.00	—	—
		Eagle on arrows and olive branch ctsp on U.S. Large cent. (Hallenbeck 28.032)					
Y10	(?)	Copper	29mm	—	25.00	—	—
		Large eagle, incuse, ctsp on U.S. Large cent. (Hallenbeck 28.009)					

Rulau	Date	Metal	Size	VG	F	VF	Unc
Y11	(?)	Copper	29mm	—	25.00	—	—
		Eagle over 18 in octagon, ctsp on U.S. Large cent. (Hallenbeck 28.008)					
Y12	(?)	Copper	29mm	—	25.00	—	—
		Small eagle on arrows, ctsp on U.S. Large cent. (Hallenbeck 28.031)					

Rulau	Date	Metal	Size	VG	F	VF	Unc
Y12A	(?)	Copper	29mm	—	25.00	—	—
		Similar ctsp on U.S. 183. Large cent.					
Y13	(?)	Copper	29mm	—	25.00	—	—
		Eagle ctsp on U.S. Large cent. (Duffield 1458; Hallenbeck 28.007)					

Rulau	Date	Metal	Size	VG	F	VF	Unc
Y14	(?)	Copper	29mm	—	25.00	—	—
		Spread eagle with shield on breast ctsp on both sides of U.S. 1832 Large cent.					

Rulau	Date	Metal	Size	VG	F	VF	Unc
Y15	(?)	CN	26.3mm	—	50.00	—	—
		Spread eagle ctsp in gold collar on 26.3mm cupronickel planchet. (Tom Wall collection)					

Y16 (?) Copper 29mm — 30.00 — —
Eagle with drooping wings and shield on its breast, head turned right, ctsp on U.S. 1828 Large cent. There are no talons, arrows or branches under eagle. (Krause coll.)

Y17 (?) Copper 29mm — 40.00 — —
Large T above eagle on globe ctsp on U.S. 1822 Large cent. (Steinberg 1982 sale)

Rulau	Date	Metal	Size	VG	F	EF	Unc
Y18	(?)	Copper	29mm	—	25.00	—	—

Eagle to left ctsp on reverse of U.S. 1822 Large cent. (Cheramy coll.)

Y19 (?) Copper 29mm — 30.00 — —
Squat eagle, head turned left, ctsp on various U.S. Large cents. Dates examined: 1846, 1851. (Brunk 45120B)

Y20 (?) Copper 29mm — 30.00 — —
Eagle with U.S. shield on breast, head turned left, ctsp on U.S. 1807 Large cent.

Y21 (?) Copper 29mm — 35.00 — —
Eagle with outspread wings atop scroll ctsp on obverse of U.S. 1830 Large cent. Three flying geese ctsp on reverse of the coin.

Y22 (?) Copper 29mm — 25.00 — —
Eagle (NO DESCRIPTION AVAILABLE) ctsp on U.S. 1846 Large cent.

Y23 (?) Copper 29mm — — 25.00 —
Eagle with shield on breast, head turned left, ctsp on U.S. 1805 Large cent.

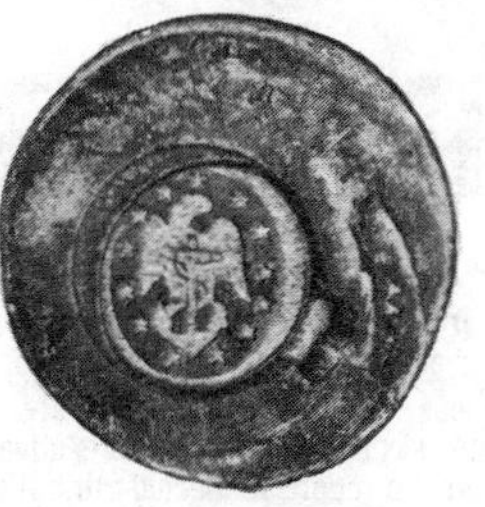

Y24 (?) Copper 29mm — — 35.00 —
Eagle on an anchor, surrounded by 13 stars, all in relief within upright oval depression ctsp on U.S. Large cent circa 1800. (Van Ormer sale 1669)

This logotype may have been from a button-stamping die intended for Rhode Island.

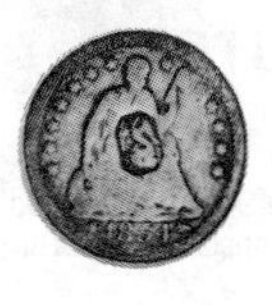
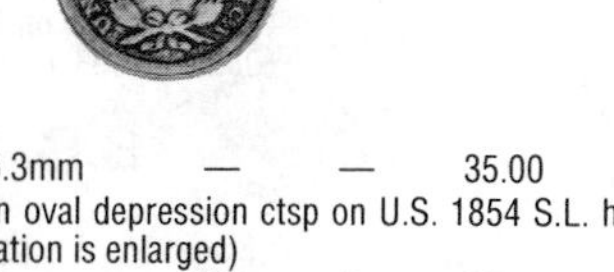

Y24A (?) Silver 15.3mm — — 35.00 —
Eagle in relief within oval depression ctsp on U.S. 1854 S.L. half dime. (Upper illustration is enlarged)

Rulau	Date	Metal	Size	VG	F	VF	EF
Y25	(?)	Silver	27mm	—	—	35.00	—

American eagle punch ctsp twice on Spanish-American 1789-Mo 2-reales. (Christensen Oct. 1987 sale, lot 916)

MISCELLANEOUS COUNTERSTAMPS ON LARGE CENTS

Rulau	Date	Metal	Size	VG	F	VF	EF
Y30	(?)	Copper	29mm	—	20.00	—	—

Incuse 3-leaf clover, chicken and acorn ctsp on U.S. 1850 Large cent. (Krause coll.)

Y31 (?) Copper 29mm — 20.00 — —
Dog standing right, ctsp on U.S. 1854 Large cent. (Hartzog coll.; Brunk 45050)

The same dog stamp as on Y31 occurs on a Hard Times token of E.F. Sise.

Rulau	Date	Metal	Size	VG	F	VF	EF
Y35	(?)	Silver	27mm	—	—	35.00	—
		Two running dogs (greyhounds?) facing in opposite directions, ctsp on Spanish-American 1802 2-reales. (Kovacs coll.)					

MAVERICKS

Included in this section are store cards, counterstamped coins and miscellany which: (1) Have a reasonable expectation of proving to be from the 1845-1860 period; (2) Possess characteristics of a mercantile issuance; (3) Were examined by the author or his consultants.

In general, unattributed tokens are worth less — sometimes much less — than pieces firmly slotted in geographical, occupational and calendar niches. Thus it is advantageous to all collectors and dealers to attribute Mavericks. To report suspected attributions, readers may write: Russ Rulau, Krause Publications, Iola, WI 54990.

Some of the Maverick issuers in this section have avoided attribution far too long already — their provenance was unknown to Dr. Wright in 1898, Frank Duffield in 1919 and every exonumist since — despite continuous exposure within the hobby. In such category are the maddeningly elusive "O. & G.," "Corey's Ointment," and other pieces.

But, not to despair! Recently we pinned down the elusive "Shoo Fly" counterstamp to the Shoo-Fly Mfg. Co. of Philadelphia from 1855 on (a chemical spray to keep insects off barn and pasture animals). The "Glynn Gunsmith" and "Whitten's Golden Salve" pieces also are now solved! So is P.E. Ballou! The Maverick listing will shrink as research bears fruit — and swell as other research discovers more Mavericks!

L. ALDEN

Rulau	Date	Metal	Size	VG	F	VF	EF
ZE1	(?)	Copper	29mm	—	20.00	—	—
		L. ALDEN ctsp on U.S. Large cent. Dates examined: 1802, 1803, date worn off. (Duffield 1586; Hallenbeck 1.501; Brunk 550)					
ZE1A	(?)	Silver	27mm	—	25.00	—	—
		Similar ctsp on Spanish-American 1799 2-reales.					

G. AUTEN

Rulau	Date	Metal	Size	VG	F	VF	EF
ZE2	(?)	Copper	29mm	—	20.00	—	—
		G. AUTEN ctsp on U.S. Large cent. Dates examined: 1830, 1832, (Duffield 1593; Hallenbeck 1.758; Brunk 1390)					

B.B. & CO.

Rulau	Date	Metal	Size	VG	F	VF	EF
ZE3	(?)	Copper	29mm	—	30.00	—	—
		B.B. & CO ctsp on U.S. Large cent. Dates examined: 1837, 1846, 1847, 1848. (Van Ormer sale 2530; Robert Ramsay coll; Brunk 1530)					

D.B. (Dan Black)

Rulau	Date	Metal	Size	VG	F	VF	EF
ZE4	(?)	Nickel alloy	28mm	—	—	Rare	—
		DB monogram incused on a blank nickel-alloy planchet. The DB monogram has been enameled blue. Plain edge. (Don Mulrooney coll.)					

An old envelope in which this piece was housed proclaimed it to be a Dan Black tavern token of circa 1838. It also bore a number, C-392, which has not been deciphered, and was marked scarce.

M.B. CO.

Rulau	Date	Metal	Size	VG	F	VF	EF
ZE5	(?)	Copper	29mm	—	—	5.00	—
		M. B. Co ctsp on obverse of U.S. 1848 Large cent. Same ctsp on reverse of the coin. (Frank Kovacs coll., Brunk 25473)					

T.B.

Rulau	Date	Metal	Size	VG	F	VF	EF
ZE6	(?)	Copper	27mm	—	—	10.00	—
		(All incused) T / (eagle with folded wings, head left. U.S. shield on its breast) / B. Rv: Blank. Plain edge. (John Cheramy coll.)					

Possibly a gunmaker's piece, not yet attributed.

S.O. BAILF

Rulau	Date	Metal	Size	VG	F	VF	EF
ZE7	1859	Copper	29mm	—	20.00	—	—
		1859 / 1 / S.O. BAILF / 1859 ctsp on U.S. 183. Large cent (date partially illegible). The final letter of the surname could be F, E, P or R, and there may be one or more final letters missing. (The actual name might be intended for BAILEY) (Frank Kovacs coll.; Brunk 1875)					

A.B. BAILEY (and) L.P. SUMMERS

Rulau	Date	Metal	Size	VG	F	VF	EF
ZF1	(?)	Copper	29mm	15.00	—	20.00	—
		A.B. BAILEY / L. P. SUMMERS ctsp on U.S. 1843 Large cent. (Kovacs coll.; Brunk 1800 / 38880)					

L. BALLOU

Rulau	Date	Metal	Size	VG	F	VF	EF
ZG1	(?)	Silver	27mm	—	—	37.50	—
		L BALLOU ctsp on U.S. 1835 Capped Bust quarter. (Kirtley July 1992 sale, lot N113)					
ZH1	(?)	Silver	32.5mm	—	—	50.00	—
		Similar ctsp on U.S. 1823 Bust half dollar. (Brunk 2210)					

BARR & LONG

Rulau	Date	Metal	Size	VG	F	VF	EF
ZJ1	(?)	Silver	17mm	125.	—	175.	—
		BARR & LONG ctsp on Spanish-American Carlos III half real ca. 1772-90. (Brunk 2515)					
ZK1	(?)	Silver	25mm	125.	—	175.	—
		BARR & LONG / DEALERS IN / WATCHES CLOCKS &C ctsp on U.S. 1855 Seated Liberty quarter. (Brunk 2520; PCAC July 1993 sale, lot 080)					

BEAN & CO.

Rulau	Date	Metal	Size	VG	F	VF	EF
Z1	(?)	Silver	18mm	—	—	75.00	—
		BEAN & CO. / HOUSEFURNISHING GOODS ctsp on U.S. 1854 dime. (Duffield 1393; Brunk 2890)					

B. B. BEAN

Rulau	Date	Metal	Size	VG	F	VF	EF
ZM1	(?)	Copper	29mm	—	—	30.00	—

B. B. BEAN / (Arm & Hammer) (Anvil) ctsp on U.S. 1853 Large cent. (PCAC July 1993 sale, lot 858)

WM. R. BLISS

Rulau	Date	Metal	Size	VG	F	VF	EF
Z1M	(?)	Copper	29mm	—	—	10.00	—

WM. R. BLISS in arc ctsp on U.S. 1828 Large cent. (Kovacs coll.; Brunk 4035)

SIG. BLITZ, MAGICIAN

Rulau	Date	Metal	Size	VG	F	VF	EF
Z2	(?)	Copper	29mm	—	—		500.

SIG. BLITZ / MAGICIAN ctsp on Connecticut 1787 cent. (Brunk Coll., ex-Kuethe; Brunk 4040)

This magician piece was not mentioned in the Kuethe monograph on magic tokens in *TAMS Journal* for 1976, page 52, though the piece came from the Kuethe collection.

W. H. BOYD

Rulau	Date	Metal	Size	VG	F	VF	EF
Z2F	(?)	Silver	39mm	—	—	30.00	—

W.H. BOYD ctsp twice on Mexico 8-reales, date worn off. Same ctsp once on reverse of the coin. (Charles Ziegler coll.; Brunk 4718)

E. BRAINARD

Rulau	Date	Metal	Size	VG	F	VF	EF
Z2G	(?)	Copper	29mm	—	—	20.00	—

E. BRAINARD ctsp on U.S. 1801 Large cent. Same ctsp on reverse of the coin. (Stanley Steinberg 1982 sale; Brunk 5010)

Rulau	Date	Metal	Size	VG	F	VF	EF
Z2H	(?)	Copper	29mm	—	—	20.00	—

Similar ctsp on U.S. 1851 Large cent. (Kovacs coll.)

J. BRAMBLE

Rulau	Date	Metal	Size	VG	F	VF	EF
Z2I	(1854)	Copper	23mm	—	—	50.00	75.00

J. BRAMBLE (curved) / (six-pointed star) ctsp on U.S. Half cent. Dates examined: 1851 (12 pieces), 1853 (3 pieces), 1854 (7 pieces), worn, (1 piece). (Van Ormer sale 2555; Rulau coll.; Brunk 5020)

Bramble apparently used new, or near-new Half cents for his counterstamping activity, which indicates that this was done in 1854. An 1854-dated specimen in the Rulau collection was in AU or Unc condition when it received the impression.

Both B's in the upward-curving arc BRAMBLE are broken at the top, so that the B's somewhat resemble H's closed at the bottom. This may be symptomatic of the B letter-punch used to create the marking punch; specimens examined have strong, deep counterstamps applied with seemingly equalized pressure.

Bramble may have been a prolific issuer, indicating some mercantile purpose for his stamped Half cents.

BRASS IVORY IRON

Rulau	Date	Metal	Size	VG	F	VF	EF
Z2J	(?)	Copper	23mm	—	—	30.00	—

BRASS / IVORY / IRON / 20 ctsp on U.S. Half cent with date worn off. (Steven Guiness coll.; Brunk 5070)

J. L. T. BROWN

Rulau	Date	Metal	Size	VG	F	VF	EF
Z2K	1856	Copper	28mm	—	—	75.00	—

J. L. T. BROWN / 1856 ctsp on Liberia 1833 cent token, KM-Tn l. Rv: J. L. T. BROWN / J. LOGAN / 56 (large) ctsp on reverse of the token. (Kovacs coll.)

M. L. BULLARD

Rulau	Date	Metal	Size	VG	F	VF	EF
Z2L	(?)	Copper	28mm	—	—	—	—

M. L. BULLARD ctsp twice on Russia 1814 2-kopeks, KM-118. (Kirtley Nov. 1990 sale, lot A640; Brunk 5777)

W. BURKE

Rulau	Date	Metal	Size	VG	F	VF	EF
Z2M	1859	Copper	29mm	20.00	—	40.00	—

1859 / W. BURKE / 1855 1855 ctsp on U.S. Large cent. (Hallenbeck 2.783; Brunk 5977)

J. M. BUSHEY

Rulau	Date	Metal	Size	VG	F	VF	EF
Z2N	(1853-58)	Copper	29mm	—	—	35.00	—

J. M. BUSHEY ctsp on U.S. 1853 Large cent. (Pete Peters coll.)

In the only reported specimen, the Bushey stamp has been overstamped by a Devins & Bolton (Montreal) counterstamp circa 1858.

J. C.

Rulau	Date	Metal	Size	VG	F	VF	EF
Z2R	(?)	Copper	23.5mm	30.00	—	60.00	—

J C in relief within leaf-shaped depression ctsp on U.S. 1835 Half cent. (Rulau coll.)

It was speculated that this countermark was associated with silversmith John Coddington (1690-1743) of Newport R.I., but no confirmation has been found. The Coddington hallmark reads IC within leaf, whereas this reads JC within leaf. This could be an unpublished Coddington family successor mark.

S. E. CAMPBELL & CO.

Rulau	Date	Metal	Size	VG	F	VF	EF
Z2N	(?)	Copper	29mm	—	75.00	—	125.

S.E. CAMPBELL & CO. / No- 1 / WARRANTED / CAST STEEL ctsp on U.S. 1848 Large cent. (Kurt Krueger coll.; Brunk 6673)

E. L. CARE

Rulau	Date	Metal	Size	VG	F	VF	EF
Z2S	(?)	Silver	32.5mm	—	35.00	—	—

E. L. CARE (curved) / B. C. O. (straight) in a single punch ctsp on U.S. 1826 bust half dollar. (Charles Kirtley sale, 1987; Brunk 6763)

C. CAST STEEL

Rulau	Date	Metal	Size	VG	F	VF	EF
Z2L	(?)	Copper	29mm	—	25.00	—	—

C in relief within square depression, four times, and CAST STEEL incuse, twice, ctsp on worn smooth U.S. Large cent. Rv: C in relief within square depression, once; Y in relief within square depression, once, and CAST STEEL in arc, incuse, ctsp on reverse of the coin. (Kean Leiker coll.; Brunk 7065)

S. C. CAST STEEL

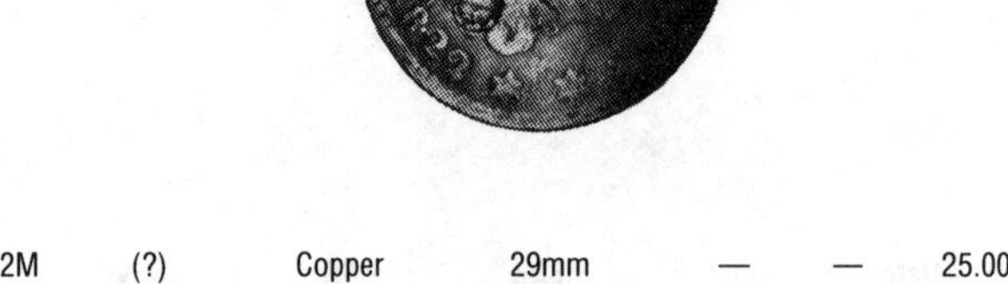

Rulau	Date	Metal	Size	VG	F	VF	EF
Z2M	(?)	Copper	29mm	—	—	25.00	—

S C / CAST STEE(L) / S C ctsp on U.S. 1822 Large cent. (Brunk 7065)

"Cast Steel" was a common product guarantee in the 19th century, as were also "Warranted," "Sterling" and similiar phrases. Some authorities contend the "Cast Steel" pieces, emanating from many different stamps, were more pocket pieces than advertising countermarks. We reserve judgment on this matter, preferring to wait for more samples and more data.

CELEBRATED CUTLERY

Rulau	Date	Metal	Size	VG	F	VF	EF
Z2T	(?)	Copper	29mm	—	—	40.00	—

CELEBRATED / CUTLERY ctsp on U.S. 1839 Large cent. (B&M Taylor sale, March 1987, lot 1269; Brunk 7157)

CHAT. G C
(Chatauqua Gold Cure)

Rulau	Date	Metal	Size	VG	F	VF	EF
Z3	(?)	Silver Shield shaped	22 by 30mm	—	—	V.Rare	

(All engraved) Hypodermic syringe at center. CHAT G C / NO around; THANK YOU below. Rv: Blank. (Wright 163)

Possibly some sort of identification disc, with space for a number. The Wright specimen has not been located.

DR. J. CHEEVER

Rulau	Date	Metal	Size	VG	F	VF	EF
Z4C	(?)	Copper	29mm	—	—	65.00	—

DR. J. CHEEVER ctsp on U.S. 1821 Large cent. (Brunk 7555)

CITY HOTEL

Rulau	Date	Metal	Size	VG	F	VF	EF
Z4B	(?)	Silver	15mm	—	—	50.00	—

CITY HOTEL ctsp on U.S. 18, half dime. (Brunk 7805)

J. P. CLARKE

Rulau	Date	Metal	Size	VG	F	VF	EF
Z4K	(?)	Silver	31mm	—	—	30.00	—

PATENT / J. P. CLARKE ctsp on U.S. 1854 Seated Liberty half dollar. (Van Ormer sale 2588) (Brunk 8055)

A. B. COLE

Rulau	Date	Metal	Size	VG	F	VF	EF
Z7	1855	Copper	--mm	—	—	40.00	—

A.B. COLE (straight) / 1855 (in arc) ctsp on French Colonies coin. (Donald Patrick coll.)

Rulau	Date	Metal	Size	VG	F	VF	EF
Z7A	1853	Copper	29mm	—	—	40.00	—

A.B. COLE / 1853 ctsp on U.S. 1847 Large cent. (Brunk 8775)

COREY'S OINTMENT

Rulau	Date	Metal	Size	VG	F	VF	EF
Z5	(?)	Silver	26mm	—	100.	—	150.

TRY / COREY'S / OINTMENT ctsp on U.S. Liberty Seated quarter dollar. Dates examined: 1853, 1856, 1857, 1858, 1861. There are 9 pieces known. (Duffield 1397; Gould 15; Brunk 9560)

Rulau	Date	Metal	Size	VG	F	VF	EF
Z6	(?)	Silver	31mm	—	100.	—	150.

Similar ctsp on U.S. 1854 or 1855 half dollar. 4 pieces known.

Rulau	Date	Metal	Size	VG	F	VF	EF
Z6A	(?)	Silver	18mm	—	100.	—	150.

Similar ctsp on U.S. Seated Liberty dime.

A. CORWIN

Rulau	Date	Metal	Size	VG	F	VF	EF
Z9	(?)	Copper	23mm	—	—	20.00	—

A. CORWIN in relief within rect. depression ctsp on U.S. 1826 Half cent. (Partrick coll.; Brunk 9715)

F. COULTON & CO.

Rulau	Date	Metal	Size	VG	F	VF	EF
Z10	(?)	Copper	29mm	30.00	—	—	—

F. COULTON / & CO. ctsp on U.S. 1838 Large cent. (Brunk 9780)

This piece surfaced early in 1982 in a Stanley L. Steinberg sale, where it was described as a possible firm of New Orleans ship chandlers.

Search of the pre-Civil War New Orleans directories reveals that no firm of that name was listed in New Orleans.

GEO. COWING

Rulau	Date	Metal	Size	VG	F	VF	EF
Z9	(1850's)	Copper	29mm	—	—	40.00	—

GEO. COWING / MAKER ctsp on U.S. 1845 Large cent. (Brunk 9817)

P.H. CURRAN

Rulau	Date	Metal	Size	VG	F	VF	EF
Z4J	(?)	Copper	29mm	—	—	25.00	—

P. H. CURRAN engraved backward on holed, very worn U.S. 1853 Large cent. To be used as a seal or stamp. (Kirtley sale list 33, 1989)

CUTTING'S

Rulau	Date	Metal	Size	VG	F	VF	EF
Z10B	1854	Silver	25mm	75.00	—	125.	—
		CUTTING'S / PAT. JULY 4 & 11 / 1854 ctsp on U.S. 1857 Seated Liberty quarter. (Van Ormer sale 2604; Brunk 10485)					
Z10C	1854	Copper	29mm	50.00	—	90.00	—
		Similar ctsp on U.S. Large cent. (Hallenbeck 3.778)					

R. H. DEWEY

Rulau	Date	Metal	Size	VG	F	VF	EF
Z10D	(?)	Silver	25mm	—	—	200.	—

AMBROTYPE / BY R. H. DEWEY ctsp on U.S. 1854 Seated Liberty quarter. (Van Ormer sale 2506; Brunk 11540)

E. DONNELLY

Rulau	Date	Metal	Size	VG	F	VF	EF
Z10F	1853	Copper	29mm	—	40.00	—	—

E. DONNELLY / 1853 ctsp on U.S. 1827 Large cent. (Kurt R. Krueger collection; Brunk 11885)

W.P.E.

Rulau	Date	Metal	Size	VG	F	VF	EF
Z11	(1850's)	Tin	22mm	—	—	—	Rare

Eagle with shield on breast. Rv: W.P.E. within wreath. (Lot 1879 in the 1863 Bangs Merwin & Co. sale of the Haines collection)

JOHN ELLIS

Rulau	Date	Metal	Size	VG	F	VF	EF
Z11A	(?)	CN	19mm	—	—	50.00	—

JOHN ELLIS / COPPER AND / GENERAL ENGRAVER *engraved* on shaved reverse of U.S. 1861 Indian cent. (PCAC July 1993 sale, lot 120)

EMPIRE HOUSE

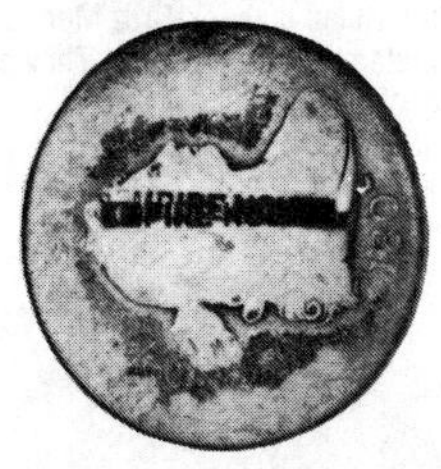

Rulau	Date	Metal	Size	VG	F	VF	EF
Z11C	(?)	Silver	26mm	—	—	125.	—

EMPIRE HOUSE ctsp on U.S. 1807 Draped Bust quarter. (Van Ormer sale 2637, ex—Koppenhaver sale 2/1980, lot 133; Brunk 13390)

Hotels with this name were located in many places.

E. P. EVERETT

Rulau	Date	Metal	Size	VG	F	VF	EF
Z11E	(?)	Copper	29mm	20.00	—	30.00	—

E. P. EVERETT in an arc ctsp on U.S. Large cent. Dates examined: 1827, 1836, 1837, 1842, 1843, 1845, 1846, 1847, 1849, 1850, 1852, 1853, 1855. There are 17 specimens reported. (Hallenbeck 5.753; Brunk 13630)

G.F.

Rulau	Date	Metal	Size	VG	F	VF	EF
Z12	(?)	Copper	23mm	—	—	18.50	—

Large G.F. ctsp on U.S. 1854 Half cent. (Mishler coll.)

Probably counterstamped before the Civil War. There were few surviving half cents after the Civil War period; they had been withdrawn from circulation in 1857 and had never been popular in trade channels before that.

R. F.

Rulau	Date	Metal	Size	VG	F	VF	EF
Z13	1845	Silver	39mm	—	—	—	100.

18 45 / R. F. ctsp on U.S. 1800 Bust silver dollar.

G. A. FATE

Rulau	Date	Metal	Size	VG	F	VF	EF
Z13C	(?)	Silver	32.5mm	—	—	200.	—

G. A. FATE in upward arc ctsp on U.S. 1834 Bust half dollar. (Brunk 13850; Rulau coll., ex-Ortiz Murias)

Both letters A in the counterstamp lack a crossbar. They may have been inverted V's used in preparing the die for this punch.

R. W. FERNALD

Rulau	Date	Metal	Size	VG	F	VF	EF
Z14	(?)	Silver	32.5mm	20.00	—	30.00	—
		R. W. FERNALD ctsp on U.S. 1833 or 1835 Bust type half dollar. 3 known. (Schenkman collection; Brunk 14050)					
Z14A	(?)	CN	22mm	—	—	20.00	—
		Similar ctsp on U.S. 1866 Shield nickel.					
Z14B	(?)	Silver	25mm	—	—	25.00	—
		Similar ctsp on U.S. 1858 Seated Liberty quarter. 2 known.					

FRENCH & SON

Rulau	Date	Metal	Size	VG	F	VF	EF
Z16	(?)	Silver	31mm	—	60.00	—	90.00

FRENCH & SON ctsp on U.S. Liberty seated, New Orleans Mint half dollar. Rv: Same ctsp. Dates examined: 1840, 1855, 1857. 4 pieces known. (Gould 22; Brunk 15090)

G & B

Rulau	Date	Metal	Size	VG	F	VF	EF
Z18	(?)	Copper	29mm	—	40.00	—	75.00

G & B / 3 C-ctsp on U.S. 1851 Large cent. 2 known. (Spangenberger collection; Brunk 15365)

The unusual 3-cent indication on this counterstamp sets it apart from most of its fellows of this early period. However, the piece may eventually prove to be post-Civil War in provenance.

G.G.G. & G.G.G.G.
(Goodwin's Grand Grease Juice)

Rulau	Date	Metal	Size	VG	F	VF	EF
Z20	(?)	Copper	29mm	—	100.	—	—
		USE / GOODWIN'S / GRAND / GREASE JUICE / FOR THE HAIR / G.G.G. ctsp on U.S. 1835 or 1840 Large cent. 3 pieces known. (Robert Sagers collection)					
Z21	(?)	Copper	29mm	15.00	—	25.00	—
		USE / G.G.G. / & / G.G.G.G. ctsp on U.S. Large cent. Dates examined: 1803, 1810, 1812, 1814, 1817, 1823, 1823/2, 1824, 1826, 1828, 1829, 1832, 1837, 1838, 1840, 1841, 1843, 1844, 1845, 1846, 1847, 1848, 1850, 1851, 1852, 1853, 1854, 1855, 1856, 1857, date worn. There are 55 reported specimens. (Duffield 1426; Hallenbeck 7.001; S-O 3080; Van Ormer sale 2663; Brunk 15390)					

Rulau	Date	Metal	Size	VG	F	VF	EF
Z21A	(?)	Silver	18mm	25.00	—	35.00	—
		Similar ctsp on U.S. Seated Liberty dime. Examined: 1842. Only 1 known.					
Z21C		Silver	25mm	30.00	—	50.00	—
		Similar ctsp on U.S. Seated Liberty quarter. Examined: 1853-Arrows, 1854. There are 4 specimens reported.					
Z22		Silver	32.5mm	125.	—	175.	—
		Similar ctsp on U.S. Bust half dollar, date worn. Only1 known. (Gould 81)					

Rulau	Date	Metal	Size	VG	F	VF	EF
Z22A		Silver	31mm	115.	—	165.	—
		Similar ctsp on U.S. Seated Liberty half dollar. Examined: 1854. Only2 known. (Van Ormer sale 2664)					
Z23		Copper	28mm	75.00	—	125.	—
		Similar ctsp on Hard Times token.					
Z23A	(?)	Copper	29mm	—	—	100.	—
		Similar ctsp on American 1789 colonial copper.					

Rulau	Date	Metal	Size	VG	F	VF	EF
Z24	(?)	Copper	29mm	15.00	—	25.00	—
		USE / G.G.G. ctsp on U.S. Large cent. Dates examined: 1798, 1803, 1812, 1817, 1819, 1832, 1834, 1835, 1837, 1838, 1842, 1843, 1846, 1847, 1848, 1850, 1851, 1852, 1853, 1854, 1855, date worn. There are 38 specimens reported. (Brunk 15380)					
Z25		Silver	14mm	60.00	—	90.00	—
		Similar ctsp on U.S. silver 3-cent piece. Examined: 1851, 1852, 1853. There are 3 pieces known.					
Z26		Silver	19mm	60.00	—	90.00	—
		Similar ctsp on U.S. Bust dime. Examined: 1822, 1832, 1835, 1836. Only 4 known.					

Rulau	Date	Metal	Size	VG	F	VF	EF
Z26A		Silver	18mm	25.00	—	35.00	—
		Similar ctsp on U.S. Seated Liberty dime. Examined: 1837, 1841, 1842, 1843, 1850, 1853-Arrows, 1854, 1855, 1856. There are 28 pieces reported. (Gould 23; Van Ormer sale 2660 & 2662)					
Z27		Silver	16mm	35.00	—	45.00	—
		Similar ctsp on U.S. Bust half dime. Examined: 1832, 1835, 1836, 1837. Only 4 known.					

Rulau	Date	Metal	Size	VG	F	VF	EF
Z28		Silver	15.5mm	25.00	—	35.00	—

Similar ctsp on U.S. Seated liberty half dime. Dates examined: 1838, 1839, 1843, 1848, 1849, 1853, 1854, 1856, worn date. There are 9 known pieces. (Gould 23; Van Ormer sale 2661)

Rulau	Date	Metal	Size	VG	F	VF	EF
Z29		Silver	25mm	30.00	—	50.00	—

Similar ctsp on U.S. Seated Liberty quarter. Examined: 1853, 1854, 1855. There are 6 known pieces. (Gould 23)

Rulau	Date	Metal	Size	VG	F	VF	EF
Z30		Copper	28mm	30.00	—	50.00	—

Similar ctsp on New Brunswick 1843 halfpenny token.

Rulau	Date	Metal	Size	VG	F	VF	EF
Z31		Copper	28mm	30.00	—	50.00	—

Similar ctsp on Canada 1814 Halifax token. (Van Ormer sale 2659)

Rulau	Date	Metal	Size	VG	F	VF	EF
Z31A		Copper	--mm	30.00	—	50.00	—

Similar ctsp on miscellaneous Canada tokens. There are 2 pieces reported.

For well over a century numismatists have pondered the enigmatic, ephemeral and maddening initials G.G.G. & G.G.G.G. About 30 years ago the gifted Boston numismatist Maurice M. Gould (half in jest, we believe) advanced the explanation that it stood for Goddard's Goose Grease and Goddard's Great Goose Grease. Unfortunately no one could find a patent medicine or other product from "Goddard" and so we collectors accepted the Gould *riposte* as the best we could get. (A few others said it was a gonorrhea remedy.)

Then in 1985, collector Robert Sagers discovered Z20 above, a Large cent with a rather complete legend and 'G.G.G.' intact! Dr. Brunk was able to squeeze it into his new counterstamp reference and now we have something more to work with.

However, we are not done. How does "juice" square with the fourth G? Where was Goodwin's Grand Grease Juice produced? And when?

The latest-dated coin on which the G.G.G.'s appear is 1857.

-0—0—0-

Some suggested possibilities:

"Get going great guns."

GASKILL & COPPER

Rulau	Date	Metal	Size	VG	F	VF	EF
Z32	(?)	Copper	29mm	—	15.00	—	—

GASKILL & COPPER ctsp on U.S. 1837 Large cent. (Robert M. Ramsay coll.; Brunk 15757)

GIFFIN

Rulau	Date	Metal	Size	VG	F	VF	EF
Z32M	(?)	Silver	27mm	—	—	150.	—

Giffin . . . in relief within rectangular depression ctsp on Spanish-American 1780-Mo 2-reales. (Frank Kovacs coll.; Brunk 16097)

It could very well be one of the registered marks of Christopher Giffing of New York City, a silversmith active 1814-1834. Giffing made fiddle-tipped silver spoons with this mark: C. Giffing in slanting relief letters within rectangular depression. (See Belden pg. 191,b)

GOLD PILE SALVE

Rulau	Date	Metal	Size	VG	F	VF	EF
ZA32	(?)	Copper	29mm			300.	—

USE / GOLD PILE / SALVE / WARRANTED / TO / CURE / J.H.D. ctsp on U.S. Large cent. Dates examined: 1843, 1851. (Levine Dec. 1989 sale, lot 129; Brunk 16420)

A. GOVE

Rulau	Date	Metal	Size	VG	F	VF	EF
Z33	(?)	Copper	29mm	—	—	30.00	—

.A. GOVE in relief within toothed rectangular depression ctsp on U.S. 1816 Large cent. (PCAC July 1993 sale, lot 939; Brunk 16750)

Rulau	Date	Metal	Size	VG	F	VF	EF
Z33B	(?)	Copper	29mm	—	—	30.00	—

A. GOVE ctsp on U.S. 1820 Large cent. (Brunk 16745)

W. GREAVES & SONS

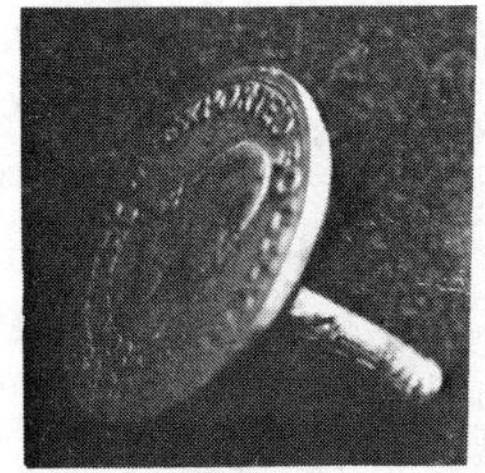

Rulau	Date	Metal	Size	VG	F	VF	EF
Z35	(?)	Brass	25mm	—	—	Poss. Unique	

Washington head right; around; EXPORTED SOLELY BY; W. GREAVES & SONS. SHEAF . . WORKS. Rv: Blank. (Baker 538)

The only traceable specimen was in the Johns Hopkins University collections, according to George Fuld. This item is actually a bolt from a saw blade, as the photo shows. Ex-New York sale, 1983.

GREBLE (AND) H.S. TARR

Rulau	Date	Metal	Size	VG	F	VF	EF
Z35V	(?)	Silver	39mm	—	—	60.00	—

GREBLE / H.S. TARR ctsp on Spanish-American 1798-Mo-FM 8-reales. (Robert M. Ramsay coll. Lancaster, Pa; Brunk 39325)

(Balance Scales) H

Rulau	Date	Metal	Size	VG	F	VF	Unc
Z35W	(1850's)	GS	16mm	—	225.	—	—

Balance scales within circle of stars. Rv: 5 C in circle of stars. H ctsp above 5 C. (Kirtley Feb. 1991 price list)

This unpublished store card surfaced only in 1991. It resembles the Nicholson cards of St. Louis.

CH.

Rulau	Date	Metal	Size	VG	F	VF	EF
Z37	(1855-60)	Copper	25mm	50.00	—	80.00	—

CH. / 4 CTS . ctsp on U.S. Half cent. Examined: 1833, 1855. There are 8 known pieces, 7 dated 1855. (Brunk 6410)

I. H.

Rulau	Date	Metal	Size	VG	F	VF	EF
Z36	(?)	Copper	29mm	—	20.00	—	—

I. H. in relief within heart-shaped serrated depression ctsp on reverse of U.S. 1819 Large cent. (Krueger coll.)

J.R.H.

Rulau	Date	Metal	Size	VG	F	VF	EF
Z36C	(?)	Copper	29mm	—	—	20.00	—

J.R.H. in relief in recessed toothed cartouche ctsp on U.S. 1805 Large cent. (Stanley Steinberg 1982 sale)

Steinberg speculated this could be for J.R. Hutchins, a Williamsport, Pa., gunsmith. Doubtful.

M. HAAS

Rulau	Date	Metal	Size	VG	F	VF	EF
Z38	(1860)	Copper	29mm	—	35.00	—	—

LINCOLN / & / HAMLIN ctsp on obverse of U.S. 1850 Large cent. Rv: M. HAAS ctsp on reverse of the coin. (Kurt Krueger Sept. 7, 1983 sale, lot 2179b; Brunk 17635 and 24510)

Abraham Lincoln and Hannibal Hamlin were the Republican candidates in 1860. Haas, we presume, was an admirer.

O. HALL

Rulau	Date	Metal	Size	VG	F	VF	EF
Z38C	(?)	Copper	29mm	—	20.00	—	—

O. Hall / 3 / 8 in three separate punches ctsp on U.S. 1819 Large cent. (Kirtley Nov. 1990 sale, lot A662)

THANNBERGER'S

Rulau	Date	Metal	Size	VG	F	VF	EF
Z39	(?)	Brass	20mm	—	—	200.	—

Coronet Liberty head left, LIBERTY on headband, 13 stars around. Rv: 5 / CENTS within oak wreath at center, THANNBERGER'S above. Plain edge. (ANS coll.)

C. HANNUM

Z40	(?)	Copper	29mm	15.00	—	25.00	—

C. HANNUM ctsp on U.S. large cent. Dates examined; 1798, 1817, 1822, 1826. (Brunk 18110)

C. W. HANNUM

Z40E	(?)	Copper	29mm	15.00	—	25.00	—

C. W. HANNUM ctsp on U.S. Large cent. Examined: 1807, 1818. (Hallenbeck 8.502; Brunk 18120)

HARDT'S EATING ROOMS

Rulau	Date	Metal	Size	VG	F	VF	EF
Z40M	(?)	Brass	23.2mm	—	—	—	Rare

(All incused- HARDT'S EATING / 12 1/2 / .ROOMS. Rv: Blank. Incised, dentilated rim on each side. Plain edge. (Hartzog coll.)

This style appears to be pre-Civil War.

JOSIAH HAYDEN & CO.

Rulau	Date	Metal	Size	VG	F	VF	EF
Z41	(?)	Copper	29mm	—	25.00	—	50.00

JOSIAH / HAYDEN / & CO. ctsp on U.S. Large cent (Hallenbeck 8.510; Brunk 18860)

H. HEASELDEN

Rulau	Date	Metal	Size	VG	F	VF	EF
Z43	(?)	Copper	29mm	15.00	—	25.00	—

H. HEASELDEN ctsp on U.S. Large cent. Examined: 1818, 1833, 1841. 4 pieces known. (Brunk 18980)

HEDDEN

Z44	(?)	Silver	27mm	—	—	30.00	—

HEDDEN ctsp on Spanish-American 1812 2-reales. (Kirtley March 1989 sale, lot 020; Brunk 19035)

JB. HEPP

Z45C	(?)	Copper	29mm	—	—	35.00	—

Jb. HEPP ctsp on U.S. 1852 Large cent. (Rulau coll., Ex-Gary Meyer; Brunk 19265)

The abbreviation Jb. probably signifies the Christian name Joab.

P. HESS

Rulau	Date	Metal	Size	VG	F	VF	EF
Z45	(?)	Silver	32.5mm	—	50.00	—	100.

P. HESS ctsp on U.S. 1795 half dollar. (Duffield 1403; Brunk 19350)

I. HILL

Z46	(?)	Copper	28.5mm	—	—	40.00	—

I. HILL ctsp on obverse of 1837 Hard Times token (Liberty / NOT ONE CENT, Low 34). Same ctsp on reverse of token.

Z46A	(?)	Copper	29mm	—	—	40.00	—

Similar ctsp on U.S. 1837 Large cent. (Brunk 19570)

B. C. HOFF

Z46B	(1859?)	Copper	29mm	12.50	—	25.00	—

B.C. HOFF ctsp on U.S. Large cent. Dates examined: 1823, 1846, 1851. (Brunk 19830)

Z46BA	(1859?)	Copper	28mm	—	27.50	—	—

Similar ctsp on U.S. Hard Times token. (Brunk report)

Z46BC	(1859?)	Copper	--mm	—	—	20.00	—

Similar ctsp on Canadian token, otherwise not identified.

Z46C	(1859?)	Silver	15.5mm	20.00	—	35.00	—

Similar ctsp on U.S. 1835 Capped Bust half dime.

Z46D	(1859?)	Silver	25mm	—	23.00	—	32.00

Similar ctsp on U.S. Seated Liberty quarter. Dates examined: 1852, 1853-Arrows & Rays, 1854, 1856, 1857, 1858. At least 18 pieces known. (Van Ormer sale 2613)

Rulau	Date	Metal	Size	VG	F	VF	EF
Z46DA	(1859?)	Silver	31mm	—	37.50	—	55.00

Similar ctsp on U.S. 1854 or 1858 Seated Liberty half dollar. (Brunk report)

Whatever his business, B. C. Hoff was a prolific advertiser by way of counterstamped coins. Physical evidence of the coins themselves seems to point toward a just-prior to Civil War issuance; 30 pieces reported with this stamp.

Recently a U.S. Morgan silver dollar of 1880 with this ctsp has been discovered, worth $85.

HOGLE

Rulau	Date	Metal	Size	VG	F	VF	EF
Z46E	(?)	Silver	32.5mm	—	35.00	—	—

HOGLE ctsp on U.S. 1814 over 3 Bust half dollar. (Rulau coll.; Brunk 19840)

J. HOLT

Rulau	Date	Metal	Size	VG	F	VF	EF
Z46H	(?)	Copper	29mm	—	—	25.00	—

J. HOLT ctsp twice on U.S. 1798 Large cent. (Kovacs coll.; Brunk 19910)

C. HOLMES

Rulau	Date	Metal	Size	VG	F	VF	EF
Z46G	(?)	Silver	17.9mm	25.00	—	—	—

C. HOLMES ctsp on reverse of U.S. 1839 Seated Liberty dime. C. ctsp on obverse of the coin. (Rulau coll.; Brunk 19865)

E. L. HOWARD

Z46J	(?)	Copper	29mm	—	30.00	—	—

E.L. HOWARD ctsp on obverse of U.S. 1819 or 1837 Large cent. Similar ctsp on reverse of the coin. (Rulau coll.; Brunk 20275)

E. HOWE JR.

Rulau	Date	Metal	Size	VG	F	VF	EF
Z46K	(1850's)	Copper	29mm	—	—	60.00	—

E. HOWE, JR. PAT. / No. / SEPT 10. 1846. ctsp twice on obverse of U.S. 1851 Large cent. Also ctsp once on reverse of coin. (Brunk 20330)

J. HOWE

Rulau	Date	Metal	Size	VG	F	VF	EF
Z46L	(?)	Silver	27mm	—	—	35.00	—

J. HOWE ctsp on each side of U.S. 1825/3 Bust quarter. (Pete Peters coll.)

JOHN HULTON

Rulau	Date	Metal	Size	VG	F	VF	EF
Z46M	(?)	Silver	39mm	90.00	—	—	—

JOHN. HULTON ctsp on U.S. 1800 Draped Bust silver dollar, About Good condition. (Van Ormer sale 2689)

The specimen cataloged was accompanied by an envelope on which was written: "This dollar was brought to father by John Hulton who had carried it for a pocket piece for years. He finally had to give it up for grain which he bought of father. It was the last dollar he had in the world."

D. ISHAM

Rulau	Date	Metal	Size	VG	F	VF	EF
Z46N	(?)	Silver	31mm	—	—	35.00	—

D. ISHAM ctsp on reverse of U.S. 1837 Half dollar. (Stanley Steinberg collection; Brunk 21190)

Rulau	Date	Metal	Size	VG	F	VF	EF
Z46P	(?)	Silver	26mm	—	—	35.00	—

Similar ctsp on England 1827 Shilling.

J. K. J.

Rulau	Date	Metal	Size	VG	F	VF	Unc
Z47	(1840-60)	Brass	18mm	20.00	30.00	40.00	60.00

Eagle with drooping wings, U.S. shield on breast. Rv: J.K.J./TEN/ CENTS. Plain edge. (Wright 1472)

N. JACKMA

Rulau	Date	Metal	Size	VG	F	VF	EF
Z48	(?)	Copper	29mm	—	25.00	—	—

N. JACKMA ctsp twice on obverse of U.S. 1844 Large cent. Coin has large round hole near top, possibly for use as a tag. (Rulau coll.; Brunk 21253)

L. JEWELL

Rulau	Date	Metal	Size	VG	F	VF	EF
Z48M	(1850's)	Copper	29mm	—	30.00	—	—

L. JEWELL ctsp on U.S. Large cent. Dates examined: 1843, 1851. (Brunk 21690)

Rulau	Date	Metal	Size	VG	F	VF	EF
Z48N	(1850s)	Copper	29mm	—	90.00	—	—

SEE DEUTERO- / NOMY 23: 1.2: / L. JEWELL ctsp on U.S. 1831 Large cent obverse. Rv: L. JEWELL ctsp on reverse of the coin. (Rulau coll.)

L. Jewell has not been traced, but it has been determined that he was not connected with the biblical passage on Z48N. The L. JEWELL stamp is larger and from different styles of letter punches than the Deuteronomy, which it has been deduced was applied during the Hard Times period, in the late 1830's.

The Deuteronomy counterstamped pieces are listed in my *Hard Times Tokens* (third edition). The story goes:

The Book of Deuteronomy, the fifth book of the Old Testament, sets forth the extensive laws for the Jews composed from the word of God by Moses. The passage cited is one of the Bible's less delicate — and less charitable — commandments. The standard King James version of the Bible states:

"He that is wounded in the stones, or hath his privy member cut off, shall not enter into the congregation of the Lord.

"A bastard shall not enter into the congregation of the Lord even to his tenth generation shall he not enter into the congregation of the Lord."

Q. David Bowers opined that the Deuteronomy reference may have been a slur of a Hard Time-era politician.

Just why this passage was chosen, and what viewpoint was being expressed by the counterstamper, may never be known at this distance, but we suspect shock value was a factor. The Deuteronomy stamp has been reported on half cents of 1834, large cents of 1831 and 1833, and half dollars of 1832 and 1834. We have concluded that the Deuteronomy stamp was applied sometime between 1834 and 1838, reinforced by the fact that the overweight silver half dollars were replaced by smaller versions in 1836.

G. A. JEWETT

Rulau	Date	Metal	Size	VG	F	VF	Unc
Z49	(?)	Copper	29mm	15.00	—	25.00	—

G.A. JEWETT ctsp on U.S. Large cent. Examined: 1842, 1850, 1851. (Brunk 21720)

D. A. JONES

Rulau	Date	Metal	Size	VG	F	VF	EF
Z51	1846	Copper	28.5mm	30.00	—	40.00	—

D. A. JONES / 1846 ctsp on Schenk-Haskins 1834 Hard Times token (Low 80). (Stanley Steinberg 1982 sale)

Rulau	Date	Metal	Size	VG	F	VF	EF
Z51A	(?)	Copper	29mm	20.00	—	30.00	—

D. A. JONES ctsp on U.S. Large cent. Examined: 1819, 1835, 1842. (Brunk 21970)

H. JONES

Rulau	Date	Metal	Size	VG	F	VF	EF
Z52	1854	Silver	40mm	—	100.	—	150.

H. JONES/ 1854 / B / PATENT ctsp on U.S. 1795 silver dollar. (Gould 4; Van Ormer sale 2712; Brunk 22000)

R. JON (ES)

Rulau	Date	Metal	Size	VG	F	VF	EF
Z53	1849	Copper	29mm	20.00	—	40.00	—

R. JON ctsp on obverse of U.S. 1817 Large cent. 1849 ctsp on reverse of the coin. (Stanley Steinberg 1982 sale)

S. K. & CO.

Rulau	Date	Metal	Size	VG	F	VF	EF
Z53C	(?)	Copper	29mm	—	20.00	—	—

S. K & CO ctsp twice on U.S. 1827 Large cent. (Brunk 35448)

E. KELLOGG

Rulau	Date	Metal	Size	VG	F	VF	EF
Z53F	(?)	Copper	29mm	—	20.00	—	35.00

E. KELLOGG (curved) ctsp on U.S. Large cent. Examined: 1846, 1852, 1853, worn date. 4 pieces reported. (Brunk 22440)

Rulau	Date	Metal	Size	VG	F	VF	EF
Z53G	(?)	Silver	27mm	—	—	50.00	—

Similar ctsp on U.S. 1825 Bust quarter.

Rulau	Date	Metal	Size	VG	F	VF	EF
Z53H	(?)	Copper	29mm	—	—	—	40.00

E. KELLOGG (straight) ctsp on U.S. 1852 Large cent. (Brunk 22445)

Rulau	Date	Metal	Size	VG	F	VF	EF
Z53J	(?)	Silver	27mm	—	—	—	60.00

Similar ctsp on Spanish-American 1788-Mo-FM 2-reales, KM-88.2. (William Wallworth coll.)

J. E. KEYES

Rulau	Date	Metal	Size	VG	F	VF	Unc
Z53P	1859	White Metal	25mm	—	—	Rare	—

Imitation of U.S. Liberty Seated quarter dollar obverse, with date 1859 in exergue. Rv: J. E. / KEYES / (ornament) at center, within oak wreath. Plain edge.

This unusual piece was first reported in *Coin Collector's Journal* for December, 1939, page 127.

J. M. KING & CO.

Rulau	Date	Metal	Size	VG	F	VF	EF
Z53Q	(1840's)	Copper	29mm	—	—	50.00	—

J. M. KING & CO. ctsp on U.S. 1846 Large cent. (Brunk 22935)

A merchant of this name is known to have sold stamps and dies in 1838, but his location is not known. (See Romaine, 1960, page 176a)

L. S. L.

Rulau	Date	Metal	Size	VG	F	VF	Unc
Z54	1855	Lead	16mm	—	—	—	65.00

L. S. L. (in script). Rv: U. P. C. / TOKENS / 1855. (Wright 631)

W.W.L.

Rulau	Date	Metal	Size	VG	F	VF	EF
Z140	(?)	Brass	35mm			25.00	

(All incused): PAY AT THE BAR / 6 1/4 / WWL monogram. Rv: Blank. (Half bit)

Rulau	Date	Metal	Size	VG	F	VF	EF
Z140A		Brass	35mm			25.00	

As last, but 12 1/2. (One bit). (Kirtley sale list 32, 1989, lot 9)

Rulau	Date	Metal	Size	VG	F	VF	EF
Z140B		Brass	35mm			25.00	

As last, but 18 3/4. (1 1/2 bits)

Rulau	Date	Metal	Size	VG	F	VF	EF
Z140C		Brass	35mm			25.00	
		As last, but 31 1/4. (2 1/2 bits)					
Z140D		Brass	--mm			25.00	
		At last, but 44. (3.52 bits!)					
Z140E	(?)	Brass	--mm			25.00	
		As last, but 50. (4 bits)					
Z140K	(?)	Copper	23mm	20.00	—	30.00	—
		Monogram WWL (same as on the brass tokens above) ctsp on U.S. Half cent. Examined: 1825, 1826, 1828, 1829, 1851. There are 43 pieces known. (Brunk 41390)					
Z140L		Copper	29mm	25.00	—	40.00	—
		Similar ctsp on U.S. Large cent. Examined: 1851. Only 1 known.					

A set of 7 brass tokens (two 50's and one each of the other denominations), housed in a 2-piece brass box marked CHINA, was offered for sale in 1989 by Charles Kirtley, Elizabeth, N.C., for $175.

A likely issuer is William W. Long of Philadelphia, who would have used gaming counters in the 1850's.

T. LEWIS

Rulau	Date	Metal	Size	VG	F	VF	EF
Z54M	(?)	Copper	29mm	—	—	25.00	—
		T. LEWIS. in large serif letters ctsp on U.S. 1846 Large cent. (Rulau collection)					
Z54MA	(?)	Silver	27mm	—	—	30.00	—
		Similar ctsp on U.S. 1820 quarter. (Brunk 24420)					

OLIVER P. LIPPINCOTT

Rulau	Date	Metal	Size	VG	F	VF	EF
Z54N	(?)	Copper	29mm	—	—	50.00	—

OLIVER P. LIPPINCOTT'S ctsp in circular fashion around rim of U.S. 1846 Large cent. POCKET / PIECE ctsp on reverse of the coin. (Brunk 24600)

This piece appeared as lot 575 in Joseph Lepczyk's auction of June 3, 1982.

E. W. LOOMIS

Rulau	Date	Metal	Size	VG	F	VF	EF
Z54P	(?)	Copper	28.5mm	20.00	—	35.00	—

E. W. LOOMIS ctsp on. Hard Times store card. Examined: Wm. H. Milton, Boston, Low 266, and N.Y. Merchants Exchange.

Rulau	Date	Metal	Size	VG	F	VF	EF
Z54Q	(?)	Copper	29mm	20.00	—	35.00	—

Similar ctsp on U.S. Large cent. (Brunk 24830; Duffield 1431; Hallenbeck 12.750). Dates examined: 1800, 1814, 1816, 1817, 1819, 1822, 1834, 1840, 1846, 1847, 1848, 1849, 1850, 1851, 1853, 1854. There are 19 pieces reported.

M. W. & H.

Rulau	Date	Metal	Size	VG	F	VF	EF
Z54R	(?)	Copper	23mm	—	—	30.00	—

(Running lion) / (Girl's head) / M W & H all in relief, ctsp within 3-section oblong depression on U.S. 1851 Half cent. (Duffield 1580; Brunk 25530)

Rulau	Date	Metal	Size	VG	F	VF	EF
Z54S	(?)	Copper	29mm	20.00	—	30.00	—

Similar ctsp on U.S. Large cent. Examined: 1846, 1851.

An unidentified pseudo hallmark.

S. M.

Rulau	Date	Metal	Size	VG	F	VF	EF
Z54AS	(?)	Copper	23mm	25.00	—	35.00	—

S . M ctsp on U.S. 1833 or 1835 Half cent. 6 pieces known. (Rulau coll.; Brunk 35457)

T. H. M.

Rulau	Date	Metal	Size	VG	F	VF	EF
Z54T	(?)	Silver	39mm	—	—	300.	—

T. H. M. in relief within depression ctsp three times on Spanish-American 1803 8-reales. Also another ctsp on same side (the obverse): COOPER'S / COFFEE ROOM / 103 NASSAU ST. (Van Ormer sale 2601)

We believe the T. H. M. hallmark is an unlisted one of silversmith Thomas Henry Marshall, a gifted itinerant craftsman who worked in Albany, N.Y. 1832-36; Troy, N.Y. circa 1836, and Rochester, N.Y. 1838-52. The only hallmark of his recorded in literature on silversmiths is T. H. MARSHALL in relief within rectangular depression.

However, he worked a long time and could have used additional marks (many craftsmen did). It would be difficult to decide where to assign this piece geographically, even if it could be shown to be his.

Cooper's Coffee Room (which see under New York City) may have *overstamped* this piece circa 1855 — it would have made little difference to the issuer or the public that other initials were on the coin.

MANNING McKEOWN & CO.

Rulau	Date	Metal	Size	F	VF	EF	Unc
Z56	(?)	Nickel	26mm	10.00	15.00	30.00	45.00

MANNING McKEOWN & CO. / ONE GLASS / SODA. Rv: Blank. (Wright 1537)

E. C. MARSH

Rulau	Date	Metal	Size	VG	F	VF	EF
Z58	(?)	Copper	29mm	—	25.00	—	40.00

E. C. MARSH ctsp on U.S. Large cent. Dates examined: 1803, 1817, 1821, 1837, 1838, 1840, 1846, 1848, 1850, 1851, 1852, 1853, 1855. There are 15 pieces known. (Brunk 26070)

McAVOY & CO.

Rulau	Date	Metal	Size	VG	F	VF	EF
Z59	(?)	Copper	29mm	—	—	60.00	—

Mc AVOY & CO (in arc) / CAST — STEEL ctsp on U.S. 1843 Large cent. (Brunk 26610)

T. McDONALD

Rulau	Date	Metal	Size	VG	F	VF	EF
Z59C	(?)	Copper	29mm	—	35.00	—	—

T. McDONALD ctsp on each side of U.S. 1843 or 1844 Large cent. (Rulau coll.; Brunk 26762)

C. McFARLAN

Rulau	Date	Metal	Size	VG	F	VF	EF
Z59D	(?)	Copper	29mm	15.00	—	20.00	—

C. McFARLAN in small letters ctsp on U.S. Large cent. Examined: 1802, 1853. (Kovacs coll.; Brunk 26810)

Rulau	Date	Metal	Size	VG	F	VF	EF
Z59E	(?)	CN	19mm	—	—	20.00	—

Similar ctsp on U.S. 1859 Indian cent.

D. MC KAY

Rulau	Date	Metal	Size	VG	F	VF	EF
Z59F	(?)	Copper	29mm	—	—	20.00	—

D. McKAY ctsp on U.S. 1798 or 1846 Large cent.

Rulau	Date	Metal	Size	VG	F	VF	EF
Z59G	(?)	CN	19mm	—	—	20.00	—

Similar ctsp on U.S. 1864 or 1865 Indian cent.

Rulau	Date	Metal	Size	VG	F	VF	EF
Z59H	(?)	CN	22mm	—	—	20.00	—

Similar ctsp on U.S. 1886 Shield nickel. (Brunk 26940)

MEXICAN DIME HOTEL

Rulau	Date	Metal	Size	G	VG	F	EF
Z61	(?)	Silver	27mm	—	50.00	—	80.00

MEXICAN DIME HOTEL ctsp on Spanish-American 2-reales. (Gould 109; Brunk 27515)

MILLINGTON & HUTCHINS

Rulau	Date	Metal	Size	VG	F	VF	EF
Z61B	(?)	Silver	27mm	—	100.	—	—

MILLINGTON & / HUTCHINS ctsp on U.S. 1818 Capped Bust quarter. (Van Ormer sale 2759; Brunk 27920)

MIND YOUR BUSINESS

Rulau	Date	Metal	Size	VG	F	VF	EF
Z61C	(?)	Copper	29mm	—	—	30.00	—

MIND YOUR BUSINESS / M W H ctsp on U.S. 1848 Large cent. WE ARE ONE ctsp on reverse. (Koppenhaver Nov. 1983 sale, lot 30; Brunk 27985)

J. L. MOORE

Rulau	Date	Metal	Size	VG	F	VF	EF
Z62	(?)	Silver	26mm	—	55.00	—	75.00

J. L. MOORE / PATENT ctsp on U.S. 1831 quarter dollar. (Krause coll.; Brunk 28355)

MORGAN & IRWIN

Rulau	Date	Metal	Size	VG	F	VF	EF
Z62A	1857	Silver	19mm	60.00	—	90.00	—
		MORGAN / & / IRWIN / 1857 ctsp on U.S. 1829 Capped Bust dime.					
Z62B	1857	Silver	18mm	60.00	—	90.00	—
		Similar ctsp on U.S. 1854 or 1857 Seated Liberty dime. (Van Ormer sale 2765; Brunk 28400)					

MOSCOW VAY

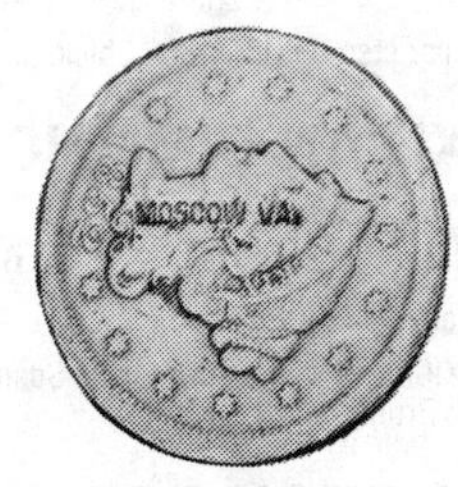

Rulau	Date	Metal	Size	VG	F	VF	EF
Z62BA	(1863)	Copper	29mm	15.00	—	25.00	—
		MOSCOW VAY ctsp on U.S. 1852 Large cent. (Hartzog coll.; Brunk 41140)					
Z62BB	(1863)	CN	19mm	15.00	—	25.00	—
		Similar ctsp on U.S. 1863 Indian cent.					

P. MUNDIN

Rulau	Date	Metal	Size	VG	F	VF	EF
ZA62	(?)	Copper	29mm	—	—	30.00	—

P. MUNDIN in relief within toothed, wavy depression ctsp on U.S. Coronet-type Large cent, date worn off. (Kean Leiker coll.; Brunk 28853)

MYERS

Rulau	Date	Metal	Size	VG	F	VF	EF
ZB62	(ca 1846-50)	Copper	29mm	20.00	—	35.00	—

MYERS in large, neat bold letters ctsp on U.S. Large cent. Dates examined: 1803, 1846, 1851. 4 specimens reported. (Brunk 29080)

The Rulau specimen is incused on a near-new 1846 cent from a prepared punch. The specimen was acquired in 1988 from a veteran collector, through Numisco Inc. of Chicago.

S. MYERS

Rulau	Date	Metal	Size	VG	F	VF	EF
Z62C	(?)	Silver	27mm	100.	—	150.	—

GOOD / 25 CTS. / S. MYERS ctsp on Spanish-American Carolus IIII Mo-mint 2-reales. (Brunk 29120)

Rulau	Date	Metal	Size	VG	F	VF	EF
Z62D	(?)	Silver	27mm	100.	—	150.	—

Similar ctsp on Prussia base silver (.521 fine) 1797 4-groschen of Friedrich Wilhelm, Craig 84. (Van Ormer 2768)

NEW ENGLAND HOUSE

Rulau	Date	Metal	Size	VG	F	EF	Unc
Z63	(?)	Silver	39mm	—	50.00	100.	—

NEW ENGLAND HOUSE ctsp twice on counterfeit 1818 Spanish-American 8-reales coin. (Gould 300; Brunk 29490)

N.Y. BAKERY

Rulau	Date	Metal	Size	VG	F	EF	Unc
Z65	(?)	Silver	32mm	175.	—	300.	—

N.Y. BAKERY ctsp on 1808 or 1829 Bust Half dollar. (Brunk 2010) Probably a Hard Times-era issue.

C. H. NILES

Rulau	Date	Metal	Size	VG	F	VF	EF
Z65E	(?)	Copper	28.5mm	—	20.00	—	—

C. H. NILES ctsp on Henry Anderson, New York, 1837 Hard Times token, Low 107. (Brunk 29710)

O. & G.

Rulau	Date	Metal	Size	G	VG	F	EF
Z67	(?)	Copper	23mm	—	35.00	55.00	80.00
		* / O & G / ** (in circle of dots) ctsp on U.S. 1835 half cent. There are 40 known. (Duffield 1579; Brunk 29995)					
Z68	(?)	Copper	29mm	—	35.00	—	80.00
		Similar ctsp on plain copper flan of 29mm (U.S. Large cent size). (Duffield 1579)					
Z68A	(?)	Copper	23mm	—	50.00	—	80.00
		Similar ctsp on U.S. Half cent other than 1835. Examined: 1825, 1828, 1832, 1833, 1834, 1837. There are 10 known. (Van Ormer 2773)					
Z68B	(?)	Copper	29mm	—	50.00	—	80.00
		Similar ctsp on U.S. 1837 or worn date Large cent.					

The illustrated specimen is the Al Oravec collection piece. The half cent was EF before overstriking.

The bulk of these pieces were new or near-new 1835 Half cents before counterstamping. No satisfactory explanation for O & G has ever been advanced.

The opinion that they were transport pieces for an "Ohio & Georgia" railroad is pure conjecture.

I. OCKULY

Rulau	Date	Metal	Size				
Z69	(?)	Silver	32.5mm	—	—	45.00	—
		I. OCKULY ctsp on U.S. 1832 Bust half dollar. (Kean Leiker collection; Brunk 30060)					

P. F. PACK

Rulau	Date	Metal	Size	VG	F	VF	EF
Z70	(?)	Silver	18mm	—	—	30.00	—
		P. F. PACK ctsp on U.S. 1838 dime. (Dom Mulrooney coll.; Brunk 30605)					

PAGE'S PATENT

Rulau	Date	Metal	Size	VG	F	VF	EF
Z73	(1845-50)	Copper	28.5mm	40.00	—	60.00	—
		PAGE'S PATENT ctsp on 1834 Hard Times token of W. A. Handy of Providence, R.I., Low 78, Plain edge. (Brunk 30660)					
Z73A	(1845-50)	Copper	29mm	40.00	—	60.00	—
		Similar ctsp on U.S. 1812 Large cent.					

PINKS, ROBINSON & RICE

Rulau	Date	Metal	Size	VG	F	VF	EF
Z74	(?)	Copper	29mm	75.00	—	—	—
		PINKS, ROBINSON & RICE ctsp on U.S. 1800 Large cent. (Koppenhaver Aug. 1982 sale; Brunk 32170)					

F. PITSLEY

Rulau	Date	Metal	Size	VG	F	VF	Unc
Z75	(?)	German Silver Shield shaped	25.5 by 29mm	—	—	—	Rare
		F. PITSLEY / RUL. Rv: Blank.					

According to Dr. Wright in 1899, this is an unfinished die trial for some type of card. Like Wright's Chatauqua Gold Cure piece (which see above), it is shield-shaped.

PURE COIN (SILVER)

Rulau	Date	Metal	Size	VG	F	VF	EF
Z75F	(?)	Copper	29mm	20.00	—	35.00	—
		PURE COIN ctsp on U.S. Large cent. Examined: 1802, 1803, 1819, 1828, 1854. (Brunk 32980)					
Z75H	(?)	Silver	38mm	—	—	80.00	—
		PURE SILVER COIN ctsp on Napoleonic Italy 1813-B 5-lire. (Brunk 32990)					
Z75J	(?)	CN	19mm	—	—	40.00	—
		PURE in relief within 15mm oval depression, ctsp on U.S. 1858 Flying Eagle cent. (Brunk 32975; Rulau coll., ex-Gamer: Van Ormer sale 2764)					

These are silversmiths' markings, PURE or PURE COIN indicating "pure silver" — though objects fabricated of "pure" did contain some alloy. The "pure" designation meant 9/10th fine, or .900 fine, the same as U.S. coinage. The term came into silversmith use in 1830 and told the customer that the object was not merely silver plated but was silver all the way through.

Silversmith markings indicating .900 fineness in America included letter C, letter D, DOLLAR, PREMIUM, RARE, PURE COIN, PURE SILVER COIN, PURE COIN SILVER and STANDARD.

The term STERLING, in use about 1860, indicated .925 fine, which it still does.

O. P. Q. & CO.

Rulau	Date	Metal	Size				
Z75Q	(?)	Copper	23mm	—	30.00	—	—
		O. P. Q. & CO. in relief within rect. depression ctsp on U.S. 1806 Half cent. (Van Ormer sale 2741; Brunk 29997)					

The punch appears like that of a silversmith's hallmark, but has not been traced. There is a possibility this is connected with the Quintard silversmith family of New York (1731-1843) but no connection has been made.

R. A. M.
(Royal Arch Masons)

Rulau	Date	Metal	Size				
Z76	(?)	Copper	29mm	—	—	25.00	—
		Triangle divided across center with line. In chief: 265; in base: R. A. M. — all ctsp on U.S. 1840 Large cent.					
Z76A	(?)	Copper	29mm	—	—	25.00	—
		Similar ctsp on U.S. 1841 Large cent.					

Masonic chapters numbered 265 were located in several states.

G. H. R.

Rulau	Date	Metal	Size	VG	F	EF	Unc
Z79	(?)	Copper	23.5mm	15.00	—	25.00	—
		G. H. R. ctsp on U.S. 1826 Half cent.					

G. L. RAIFSNIDER

Rulau	Date	Metal	Size				
Z80	(?)	Copper	29mm	—	—	30.00	—
		G. L. RAIFSNIDER in arc ctsp on U.S. 1847 Large cent. (Kovacs coll.; Brunk 33410)					

J. RICE

Rulau	Date	Metal	Size				
Z80A	(?)	Copper	28mm	—	—	20.00	—
		J. RICE ctsp three times on U.S. Hard Times token, 1834, of Troy, New York (Haskins, Low 79). (Kirtley March 1989 sale, lot 024; Brunk 34065)					

LE. RIGGS. M.D.

Rulau	Date	Metal	Size	VG	F	VF	EF
Z80B	(?)	Silver	33mm	—	—	—	200.
		LE. RIGGS. M.D. in upward arc ctsp on U.S. 1812 Bust half dollar. (Brunk 34370; Rulau coll., ex-Ortiz Murias)					

T. L. RIVES

Rulau	Date	Metal	Size	VG	F	VF	Unc
Z80C	(1850's)	GS	15mm	—	125.	—	—
		Mortar and pestle, T. L. RIVES above, 4TH & MARKET ST. below. Rv: GOOD FOR / HALF / DIME. (Bowers & Ruddy sale, Oct. 30, 1982, lot 2896)					

This token was thought to be St. Louis, Mo. and more recently thought to be Philadelphia. It could be either, or another city. It needs directory research.

A. A. ROBBINS

Rulau	Date	Metal	Size				
Z80D	(?)	Copper	29mm	—	15.00	—	—
		A.A. ROBBINS ctsp on U.S. 1831 Large cent. (Brunk 34565)					

J. RORER & SONS

Rulau	Date	Metal	Size				
Z80E	(?)	Copper	29mm	—	—	25.00	—
		J. RORER / & SONS ctsp on U.S. 1817 Large cent. (Frank Kovacs coll.; Brunk 35035)					

S P L

Rulau	Date	Metal	Size	VG	F	VF	EF
Z80M	1851	Copper	23mm	—	60.00	—	90.00

SPL monogram ctsp on U.S. 1851 Half cent. There are 23 pieces reported. (Brunk 35485)

Frank Kovacs says a dozen specimens were found in southern California in 1970, all on nearly Unc. 1851 Half cents. The Kovacs coll. has three specimens. No evidence exists that SPL means Southern Pacific Lines.

F. A. ScH.

Rulau	Date	Metal	Size	VG	F	VF	EF
Z82	(?)	Copper	29mm	—	10.00	—	—

F. A. ScH / (three linked rings) in relief within rect. depression ctsp on U.S. 1843 Large cent. (Partrick coll.)

J. SEAYRES

Rulau	Date	Metal	Size	VG	F	VF	EF
Z82C	(?)	Copper	29mm	—	20.00	—	—

J. SEAYRES in relief within rect. depression ctsp on U.S. 1802 Large cent. (Donald G. Partrick coll.; Brunk 35987)

J. SEETIN

Rulau	Date	Metal	Size	VG	F	VF	EF
Z83	(?)	Copper	30mm	—	—	300.	—

CURRENCY / J (Eagle) S / J SEETIN ctsp on New Jersey colonial cent. Rv: GOOD FOR / 25 / CENTS ctsp on reverse of the coin. (Kovacs coll.; Brunk 36020)

SHIFFLER HOUSE

Rulau	Date	Metal	Size	VG	F	VF	EF
Z84	(?)	Copper	23mm	—	50.00	—	—

SHIFFLER / HOUSE ctsp on U.S. 1833 Half cent. (Van Ormer sale 2786; Brunk 36430)

SLACK SELLERS & GRAYSON

Rulau	Date	Metal	Size	VG	F	VF	EF
Z87	(?)	Copper	29mm	—	60.00	—	—

SLACK SELLERS / & GRAYSON (all in arc) ctsp twice on obverse of U.S. 1819 Large cent. (Brunk 36710)

One authority believes Slack, Sellers and Grayson were coal merchants.

C. C. SMITH & CO.

Rulau	Date	Metal	Size	VG	F	VF	EF
Z88	1854	Copper	29mm	30.00	—	50.00	—

C.C. SMITH & CO. / 1854 ctsp on U.S. 1837 Large cent. (Duffield 1421; Hallenbeck 19.509; Brunk 36970)

There has also been reported an 1853 Seated Liberty quarter stamped C.C. SMITH which may not be connected. (Brunk 36960)

SMITH ROGERS & CO.

Rulau	Date	Metal	Size	VG	F	VF	EF
Z89	(?)	Copper	29mm	—	50.00	—	—

SMITH ROGERS & CO. ctsp on U.S. 1828 Large cent. (Brunk 36915)

This is not connected with Rogers, Smith & Co. of Hartford, Conn., the famous silverplaters who started 1856, moved to Meriden, Conn. 1884 and merged into Meriden Britannia Co. 1902.

G. H. SNOW

Rulau	Date	Metal	Size	G	VG	F	EF
Z90	(?)	Copper	29mm	—	15.00	—	25.00

G. H. SNOW ctsp on U.S. 1847 Large cent. (Duffield 1608; Brunk 37460)

J. F. SQUIER

Rulau	Date	Metal	Size	VG	F	VF	EF
Z90C	(?)	Copper	29mm	10.00	—	15.00	—

J. F. SQUIER ctsp on U.S. 1848 Large cent. (Kovacs coll.; Brunk 37810)

J. STAPLETON

Rulau	Date	Metal	Size	VG	F	VF	EF
Z91	1858	Copper	29mm	—	25.00	—	—

1858 (engraved) / J. STAPLETON ctsp on U.S. 1793 Large cent. (Frank Kovacs coll.; Brunk 37990)

T. M. STEWARD

Rulau	Date	Metal	Size	VG	F	VF	EF
Z91M	1857	Silver	31mm	—	—	60.00	—

T. M. STEWARD. / 1857 ctsp on U.S. 1853 Arrows & Rays Seated Liberty half dollar. (Frank Kovacs coll.; Brunk 38275)

T. STUART

Rulau	Date	Metal	Size	VG	F	VF	EF
Z92	(1850's)	German Silver	--mm	—	—	—	Rare

T. STUART. (Three varieties of this otherwise unknown card constituted lot 1752 in the 1863 Bangs Merwin & Co. sale of the Benjamin Haines collection.)

H. T.

Rulau	Date	Metal	Size	VG	F	VF	EF
Z93	(?)	Silver	27mm	—	—	35.00	—

H. T. in relief within toothed rectangular depression ctsp on Spanish-American 1789-Mo-FF 2-reales. (Pete Peters coll.)

WILLIAM T.

Rulau	Date	Metal	Size	VG	F	EF	Unc
Z94	(?)	Copper	29mm	15.00	—	30.00	—

WILLIAM T. ctsp on U.S. 1803 Large cent. (Brunk 43570)

JOHN THORNE

Rulau	Date	Metal	Size	VG	F	VF	EF
Z95	(1850's)	GS	17mm	—	—	200.	—

* JOHN. THORNE * / **/ ******* / (eagle displayed, head right). Rv: Blank. Plain edge. (ANS collection)

A. V.

Rulau	Date	Metal	Size	VG	F	VF	EF
Z95M	(?)	Copper	23.5mm	15.00	—	30.00	—

A. V. in relief in recessed, serrated cartouche ctsp on U.S. 1834 Half cent. 8 pieces known. (Krause collection; Brunk 100)

D. G. VAIL

Rulau	Date	Metal	Size	VG	F	VF	EF
Z96	(?)	Copper	29mm	20.00	—	30.00	—

Incuse counterstamp D. G. VAIL on U.S. Large cent of the 1816-39 type (date worn off; Brunk 41020).

H. VANGORDER

Rulau	Date	Metal	Size	VG	F	VF	EF
Z97	(1850's)	Copper	29mm	—	—	27.50	—

H. VANGORDER ctsp on U.S. Large cents of various dates. (Dates examined: 1839, 1846, 1849, 1850). 4 pieces reported. (Brunk 41085)

W. & P.

Rulau	Date	Metal	Size	VG	F	VF	EF
Z97C	1852	Copper	28mm	—	35.00	—	—

W & P / 1852 ctsp on 1837 Hard Times token, Low 31. (John Cheramy coll.; Brunk 41353)

T. W.

Rulau	Date	Metal	Size	VG	F	VF	EF
Z97F	(?)	Copper	23mm	—	25.00	—	—
Z97G	(?)	Copper	23mm	—	25.00	—	—

Z97F: T. W. ctsp in large serif letters on U.S. 1826 Half cent. (Rulau coll.; Brunk 39215)

Z97G: As last, but ctsp on both sides, on U.S. 1853 Half cent. (Tom Wall coll.)

G. WB. 44

Rulau	Date	Metal	Size	VG	F	VF	EF
Z97E	(?)	Copper	29mm	—	—	20.00	—

G. WB (ligate) / 44 ctsp on U.S. 1813 Large cent. (Kovacs coll.)

The WB ligate monogram is quite distinctive, probably the issuer's mark.

WELLER

Rular	Date	Metal	Size	VG	F	VF	EF
Z79N	(?)	Copper	29mm	—	—	20.00	—

. WELLER in relief within toothed rect. depression ctsp on U.S. 1840 Large cent.

The initial before Weller is illegible.

E. L. WEMPLE

Rulau	Date	Metal	Size	VG	F	VF	EF
Z97Q	(?)	Copper	29mm	—	20.00	—	—

E. L. WEMPLE ctsp on U.S. 1821 Large cent. (Duffield 1589; Hallenbeck 23.507; Brunk 42590)

WENDEL & BRO.

Rulau	Date	Metal	Size	VG	F	VF	EF
Z98	(1859)	Silver	19mm	50.00	—	75.00	—

WENDEL & BRO. ctsp on U.S. 1835 dime. (Schenkman coll.; Brunk 42620)

Rulau	Date	Metal	Size	VG	F	VF	EF
Z98A	(?)	Silver	25mm	50.00	—	75.00	—

Similar ctsp on U.S. 1853 or 1854 Seated Liberty quarter. (Dom Mulrooney coll. & Kurt Krueger coll.)

Rulau	Date	Metal	Size	VG	F	VF	EF
Z98B	(?)	Silver	24mm	—	—	75.00	—

Similar ctsp on Canada 1858 20-cent piece.

DAN WHITE

Rulau	Date	Metal	Size	VG	F	VF	EF
Z98K	(?)	Copper	29mm	—	—	40.00	—

DAN WHITE (Blacksmith's anvil) ctsp in circular fashion around head on U.S. 1850 Large cent. (PCAC July 1993 sale, lot 1103)

H. M. WHITBECK'S CIRCUS

Rulau	Date	Metal	Size	VG	F	VF	EF
Z99	(ca 1853)	Silver	18mm	200.	—	300.	—

H. M. WHITBECK's (curved) / CIRCUS ctsp on U.S. 1840 dime. (Brunk 42920)

Rulau	Date	Metal	Size	VG	F	VF	EF
Z99A	(ca 1853)	Silver	27mm	200.	—	300.	—

Similar ctsp on Spanish-American 2-reales. Dates examined: 1722, 1772, 1777, 1779, 1788, 1796, 1800-Mo, 1815-Mo, worn date. There are 9 pieces known. (Brunk 42920X; Rulau USTT MV 390; Van Ormer 2910)

Rulau	Date	Metal	Size	VG	F	VF	EF
Z99B	(ca 1853)	Silver	27mm	200.	—	300.	—

Similar ctsp on Mexico 1828-Zs 2-reales. (Van Ormer sale 2911)

The Whitbeck Circus and "Original One-Horse Show" operated around the year 1853, according to research by Dr. Brunk. The circus' winter quarters or other semi-permanent site has not been identified.

In the 1985 Van Ormer sale, a strong stamp on 1800-Mo 2-reales fetched $209, while a weaker stamp on the Mexico 1828 piece made $93.50.

D. WIGG

Rulau	Date	Metal	Size	VG	F	VF	EF
Z103	(?)	Copper	29mm	30.00	—	50.00	—

D. WIGG / (horseshoe) ctsp twice on U.S. Large cent. Examined: 1837, date worn. 1849 Large cent. (Hallenbeck 23.512)

Rulau	Date	Metal	Size	VG	F	VF	EF
Z103A	(?)	Silver	25mm	30.00	—	50.00	—

Similar ctsp on U.S. 1854 quarter. (Brunk 43315)

Rulau	Date	Metal	Size	VG	F	VF	EF
Z103F	(?)	Copper	29mm	30.00	—	50.00	—

D. WIGG ctsp on U.S. Large cent. Examined: 1819, 1849. (Brunk 43315)

Wigg may have been a blacksmith.

J. WILSON

Rulau	Date	Metal	Size	VG	F	VF	EF
Z103F	1856	Copper	29mm	—	—	25.00	—

J. WILSON / LONDON / 1856 ctsp on U.S. 1829 Large cent. (Levine June 1985 sale, lot 1385; Brunk 43745)

The best possibilities are Pennsylvania, Indiana and Michigan, but there were also Londons in Missouri and Nebraska at this time. The workmanship seems American, so we are ruling out the Londons in England and Ontario.

T. H. WITHERBY

Rulau	Date	Metal	Size	VG	F	VF	EF
Z104	1838	Copper	29mm	—	40.00	—	60.00

Incuse counterstamp T. H. WITHERBY / CAST-STEEL / WARRANTED applied twice to a U.S. 1838 Large cent. (Hallenbeck 23.540; Brunk 44070)

A. F. WOOD

Rulau	Date	Metal	Size	VG	F	VF	EF
Z107	(?)	Silver	31.6mm	—	35.00	—	55.00

A.F. WOOD in small incuse letters ctsp on Spain (homeland) 1818-S-CJ 4-reales. (Rich Hartzog coll.; Brunk 44170)

J. D. WYNN

Rulau	Date	Metal	Size	VG	F	VF	EF
Z110	(?)	Copper	29mm	—	20.00	—	—

J. D. WYNN ctsp on obverse of U.S. 1825 (?) Large cent. Rev: Same ctsp on reverse of coin. (Rulau coll.; Brunk 44537)

C. H. YEATON

Rulau	Date	Metal	Size	VG	F	VF	EF
Z115	(?)	Copper	29mm	—	20.00	—	—

C. H. YEATON ctsp on U.S. 1846 Large cent. (Brunk 44590)

YORK

Rulau	Date	Metal	Size	VG	F	VF	EF
Z117	(?)	Copper	29mm	—	—	25.00	—

YORK in relief within rectangular depression ctsp on U.S. Large cent of the 1820's or 1830's, date worn off and on 1795 cent. (Brunk 44630)

Rulau	Date	Metal	Size	VG	F	VF	EF
Z117A	(?)	Copper	23mm	—	—	25.00	—

Similar ctsp on U.S. 1857 half cent. There are 7 known.

YOUNG THE MAGICIAN

Rulau	Date	Metal	Size	VG	F	VF	EF
Z120	(1854)	Silver	27mm	200.	—	300.	—

YOUNG / THE / MAGICIAN ctsp on Spanish-American 1774 or 1809 2-reales. (Brunk 44690)

Rulau	Date	Metal	Size	VG	F	VF	EF
Z121	(1854)	Silver	31.5mm	200.	—	300.	—

Similar ctsp on U.S. 1842 Half dollar. (Gould 45; Brunk 44690K)

Rulau	Date	Metal	Size	VG	F	VF	EF
Z121A	(1854)	Silver	18mm	200.	—	300.	—

Similar ctsp on U.S. 1841 dime.

Rulau	Date	Metal	Size	VG	F	VF	EF
Z121B	(1854)	Silver	27mm	200.	—	300.	—

Similar ctsp on U.S. 1815 Bust quarter.

(King's Head, Lion Passant, Anchor)

Rulau	Date	Metal	Size	VG	F	VF	EF
Z150	(ca 1847)	Copper	29mm	—	—	35.00	—

Three hallmarks impressed on obverse of U.S. 1847 Large cent: King's head right within oval depression / Lion passant left within octagonal depression / Anchor within octagonal depression.

The king's head was used only 1806-1837 in England. The lion passant is correct for London. The anchor is without meaning in this combination, and there is no date-letter (for example 'u' for 1835-36 or Gothic 'A' for 1837). So the mark may well be an American silversmith's (or merchant's, since unmarked silverware could be purchased from makers) fantasy mark, attempting to gull the contemporary buyer into thinking he was getting hallmarked English silver — all the rage about 1847.

(Screaming Eagle's Head)

Rulau	Date	Metal	Size	VG	F	VF	EF
Z153	(?)	Silver	25mm	—	—	25.00	—

Screaming eagle's head left, in relief, within oval depression, ctsp twice on U.S. 1877 Seated Liberty quarter. (Charles Kirtley report)

Possibly a metalsmith's hallmark.

(Plant) ?

Rulau	Date	Metal	Size	VG	F	VF	EF
Z170	(?)	Silver	32.5mm			18.00	

Plant with two leaves (?) ctsp on U.S. 1812 Bust half dollar. (Jack Baxter coll., Texas)

1

Rulau	Date	Metal	Size	VG	F	VF	EF
Z180	(?)	Copper	29mm			20.00	

Large serif-type numeral 1 ctsp on U.S. 1803 Large cent. (Rulau coll., ex-Gamer)

MISCELLANEOUS COUNTERSTAMPS

J. BANCROFT	(Duffield 1352)	on Spanish-American 1786 2-reales
W. & J. BARNES/429 6 AVE	(Duffield 1353)	on Mexico 1842 centavo
BEWARE OF PICKPOCKETS	(Duffield 1383)	on U.S. 1834 Half dollar
S. LOOMIS	(Duffield 1410)	on U.S. 1796 quarter or U.S. 1845 half dime
D. MUNSON	(Hallenbeck 13.757)	on U.S. Large cent
do	(Duffield 1414)	on U.S. half dime or U.S. 1834 dime
S. YOUNG	(Duffield 1430)	on U.S. 1796 Half dollar
E.M.	(Duffield 1432)	on U.S. 1795 Silver dollar
F.L. R. monogram	(Duffield 1433)	on U.S. 1845 quarter
M.L. / DOLLAR	(Duffield 1439)	on U.S. 1814 Half dollar
RIR in relief on each side	(Duffield 1441)	on U.S. 1816 quarter
G.W.C. (twice)		on 1835 Half cent
ALEX SOWL		on 1806 Bust quarter dollar
S.W.I.		on England 1743 halfpenny
S in relief within square depression, 4 incuse dots below the square (Sterling quality mark)		on 1807 Bust half dollar

G.G.S. (script)	on 1818 Large cent (Kovacs coll.)

A. LAUER	on 1851 Large cent
J&H	on U.S. 1826 Large cent (Rulau coll.)
P. MOREY (both sides)	on U.S. 1840 Large cent (Rulau coll.)
J.A.J.B. within oval frame (twice)	on U.S. 1805 Large cent (Rulau coll.)

Civil War Store Cards and Patriotic Civil War Tokens 1861-1865

Consultants on Pricing
Members, Civil War Token Society

* STEVE TANENBAUM *
* CINDY GRELLMAN *
* STEVE HAYDEN *

NOTE: "Uncirculated" in this section equates to MS 63-64 in the U.S. coin numerical grading system!

The American Civil War and Its Token Coinage

Only in two periods of American history has the need for a private token coinage been absolute, that is because the reigning authority proved unable to provide a circulating metallic medium of exchange sufficient to the needs of commerce.

These two periods were the Colonial/Early Republican era, and the period of the War Between the States. In the first instance, the colonial masters in Great Britain failed to provide their subjects in America with adequate means of making payments and providing small change, and this period began to end with the opening of the United States Mint in 1792.

In the second instance something quite unplanned happened: People began hoarding hard currency, even one-cent pieces, in 1862 and within a year there was no one willing to pay out coin of the realm. Though the Mint remained in operation and all sorts of paper substitutes for small change appeared, from paper scrip and cardboard chits to postage stamps (both loose and encased), the needs of commerce simply demanded something better, something familiar and durable.

Voila! The red copper private cent to replace the yellowish cupronickel Flying Eagle cents (1857-58) and Indian Head cents (1859-61).

During the post-Mint opening period, say from 1793 through 1832, private tokens appeared which passed current, but they were a supplement to an insufficient coinage. In the Hard Times period (1837-44) all silver and gold specie disappeared into private hoards, and even government cents and half cents became more difficult to find. But neither the Early American nor Hard Times periods witnessed the extreme hoarding accompanying the earlier stages of the Civil War.

Civil War tokens were of two basic types, the so-called "patriotic" tokens which contained no sponsor's name who would redeem them for cash, and the "store cards" which did name a redeemer. (The redeemer was often ephemeral when it came time to pay up, but most merchant issuers in fact did redeem their creations.)

The great cataloger of Civil War tokens, Dr. George Hetrich, wrote the first of the definitive works on this series in 1924, and a portion of his introductory remarks, now 70 years old, are nearly as valid today as when written. So we quote:

"The small coins, known to collectors as tokens, issued during the Civil War, have been neglected in the past, and have not received the attention of the collectors which they deserve.

"They represent a very important period of the history of our country, and should receive more attention from the American collectors for this reason, if for no other. It seems that the main reason for this neglect has been due to the lack of an adequate list of the different varieties printed in a convenient form, and the compilers trust this want the present volume will fill.

"A little attention given these coins will repay the collector. An interest in these pieces is soon aroused and easily maintained, and it will not be very long before one discovers that the addition of a new variety to his collection will be attended with as much satisfaction as the acquisition of a new variety of the more pretentious series of United States coins.

"Early in 1862 all metallic currency was gradually withdrawn from circulation. Citizens, anticipating the possible increase in value of all metals, commenced hoarding gold, silver and even copper to such an extent that in a short time there were no metallic coins of any denomination in circulation. Tradesmen were thus forced to issue a medium that would supply the place of small coins, and the first of these coins issued on account of the lack of the proper Government currency made their appearance in Cincinnati in the fall of 1862.

"In the spring of 1863 New York followed this example. The first to be made in New York was the Lindenmueller currency, of which a million pieces were struck. William H. Bridgens, the die-cutter, then issued the Knickerbocker currency, which consisted of numerous varieties, and were struck in large quantities."

Hetrich continued: "The issue of similar pieces became general throughout the Eastern and Middle Western states, until it was estimated that not less than 25,000,000 of these private tokens were in general circulation, which must have included between seven and eight thousand varieties.

"These little coins filled the wants of the tradespeople, and were accepted as a means of exchange for the value, which usually was one cent. They undoubtedly were a source of great relief and convenience; but their irresponsible character soon attracted the attention of the federal authorities.

"It is said that the Third Avenue Railroad of New York requested (Gustavus) Lindenmueller to redeem a large number of his tokens, which they had accepted in the course of business, but this he laughingly refused to do. The railroad had no redress, and it is not improbable that incidents of this character forced the Government to put a stop to their issue.

"This was done by the passage of an act of Congress in 1864, forbidding private individuals to issue any form of money."

Our hobby has learned a lot since Dr. Hetrich's day. The great majority of Civil War tokens bear the date 1863, and a good number bear the 1862 or 1864 dates. Hardly any bear an 1865 date.

But Chicago, not Cincinnati, seems to have given birth to the Civil War token idea. A few 1861-dated tokens were struck there, and undated specimens bearing the words BUSINESS CARD on reverse were struck in 1860-1862 following a motif originally used as early as 1858. The BUSINESS CARD dies generally imitate the wreath reverse of the Flying Eagle cent, replacing ONE / CENT with BUSINESS / CARD.

Collecting Civil War Tokens

The collecting of these substitute cents began almost as soon as they started appearing. Pliny E. Chase listed Civil War tokens known to him in 1863, in the *Journal of the American Philosophical Society*.

One of the largest collections of CWT's ever assembled, the Groh collection, served as the basis for the 1882-1883 catalog which appeared serially in Coin Collector's Journal. The Groh holdings are part of the American Numismatic Society's cabinet in New York City.

Edgar H. Adams undertook the first illustrated listing of CW store cards in 1916-1917 in *Coin and Medal Bulletin*. The bulletin was discontinued after the March, 1917 issue but Adams made his notes on the incomplete catalog available to Dr. Hetrich and Julius Guttag of the Guttag Brothers coin firm.

The Hetrich-Guttag tome, "Civil War Tokens and Tradesmen's Store Cards" was published in Birdsboro, Pennsylvania in 1924 and it long served as THE definitive work on the subject. H&G listed 6,000-plus tokens, and over the years it was reprinted twice.

During World War II Joseph Barnett and the Stack Brothers of New York published data on additional CWT's in the years 1943-1944. Barnett's conclusions were often erroneous, but they served to reinvigorate interest in the series when they were published in *The Numismatist* in those years. Stack's used their Numismatic Review as a venue.

Your author acquired his first Civil War token, an 1863-dated Indian Head/OUR ARMY copper, in the summer of 1939 while residing on a turkey ranch in what is now El Cajon, California. I had no clear idea then what it was, but it had been taken in trade as a cent during the 1930's by the Hansen Grain and Feed Mill in El Cajon by my grandaunt's late husband. My grandaunt Rose Hansen sold the feed mill, but I obtained from her all the "odd" coins her husband had put aside the many years he ran the business.

These were mostly old U.S. coins like an 1822 half dollar, 1865 2-cent piece, a number of Indian Head cents, and a rather large number of Philippine centavos and 5-centavo pieces (many seamen brought these to ranches in the area). I learned the term Civil War token only in 1940, from a sale catalog of the old Tatham Stamp & Coin Co. of Springfield, Mass. which advertised in comic books.

It took a long time to learn more about CWT'S. The first numismatic article I ever had published was in 1958. It listed some Civil War tokens which others had either overlooked or ignored.

Melvin and George Fuld of Baltimore, father and son, published in 1960 a small black booklet called "Patriotic Civil War Tokens" which, for the first time, brought CWT's to the average collector. The Fulds applied a scientific approach to the whole subject of die examination, and followed up their breakthrough volume with an even more ambitious project, "U.S. Civil War Store Cards". Both these books and their revisions were published under the aegis of the Whitman Numismatic division of Western Publishing Co., Racine, Wisconsin.

A special mention is in order for the 1960 "Black Book" of Patriotic Civil War Tokens by the Fulds. It retailed in 1960 by Western Publishing Co. for just $1. This 77-page book bearing 22 full-page plates was crammed with useful information and must qualify as one of the greatest numismatic book bargains of all time! It brought CWT's to every collector; even a child could find $1 at that time. The debt the hobby owes to the Fulds and to Western Publishing can never be repaid.

The revisions eventually were taken over in the 1970's by the Civil War Token Society, aided in no small measure by the photographic and cataloging efforts of Douglas Watson and Krause Publications of Iola, Wisconsin. The CWTS itself was founded in 1967 as a not-so-indirect result of the boom in Civil War token collecting ushered in by that little power-pill catalog.

The current standard Fuld works on Patriotic and Store Card tokens are listed in the Bibliography, and we commend those collectors who want full coverage on all the 11,000-plus varieties of this series to consult these books. In the present volume we offer coverage only of the commonest variety of each merchant's card (some "commonest" being ultra-rare!) and the commonest variety of each Patriotic die combination (again, many being very rare).

Copper is the most commonly encountered material used in both Patriotic and Store Card tokens, but Brass is also encountered with a degree of frequency. Other metals were used, such as Lead, but only infrequently.

Collectors of the Civil war era and shortly thereafter had special exotic off-metal varieties struck for themselves, in: Silver, pure Nickel, German Silver, Cupronickel, White Metal, and even Gold. Other pieces were Gold or Silver or Zinc-plated. Some genuine circulation pieces exist made of Vulcanite (hardened rubber), Zinc and Iron, but they are seldom met with.

CWT's exist struck over silver dimes and cupronickel cents, and a few genuine CWT's were actually counterstamped on U.S. coins.

Designing Civil War Tokens

It is interesting to note that the widespread use of Civil War tokens, most of which were of pure copper and measured 19 to 20 millimeters in diameter, actually led the United States government to imitate certain of the best features of the tokens in the legal tender coinage.

The thick off-yellow 19mm cupronickel cents in use 1857-1864 were a distinct improvement over the bulky 29mm copper Large cents in use 1793-1857. But their coloration was always unsettling, especially to the huge numbers of European immigrants arriving in those days and accustomed to red copper pennies, pfennigs, centimes and other similar small change.

Though it's doubtful any U.S. Mint official would ever acknowledge that the despised private "copperheads" influenced the decision, the fact is that the Indian cent was made of red bronze beginning in 1864, and a red bronze 23mm 2-cent piece was introduced the same year. (A good number of the larger Civil War copper "cents" happened to measure 23mm!)

The 1864 bronze cents were also made thinner than their cuni predecessors, the weight dropping from 4.67 grams to 3.11 grams. Coincidence? Hardly.

The Flying Eagle cents of 1857-58 and Indian Head cents of 1859-64 were struck in an alloy of 880 parts copper and 120 parts nickel. It was an alloy that no other civilized nation was using at the time for the hundredth of their monetary unit.

The bronze adopted in 1864 for the Indian Head cent and the Shield two-cent piece was 950 parts copper to 50 parts tin and zinc, an alloy that stood the test of time through 1942 and again 1947-1961 in the cent (the unneeded 2-cent piece was last struck for circulation in 1872).

George Fuld pointed out in his 1960 catalog of Patriotic tokens that merchants could make a tidy profit on the circulation of Civil War tokens, as the small-size pieces contained only 23/100ths of a cent's worth of copper.

The diesinkers who prepared Civil War tokens kept several thoughts in mind when selecting designs: (1) Patriotism was rampant in the North after the outbreak of war in April, 1861; (2) Many designs could be prepared to imitate government coinage without actually committing the crime of counterfeiting; (3) Works of medallic art were not required, merely clear motifs and legible inscriptions.

The "heads" side of Patriotic CWT's quite often depicted a Miss Liberty in her Phrygian cap reminiscent of America's early coinage, or else an Indian head with headband similar to the government cent design of 1859.

Other heads depicted were of popular heros: Washington, Lincoln, McClellan, Grant, Andrew Jackson, Franklin, Stephen Douglas.

Flying eagles were used, U.S. shields, cannon, horsemen, U.S. flags, Monitor (the ironclad warship which defeated the Merrimac in 1862), and many more mundane subjects such as a beehive, steer, crowing cock, clasped hands, coiled snake, saddle, thistle, mortar and pestle, etc.

Within the wreath which appeared on so many CW tokens were words. Some of the favorites were: OUR / ARMY, OUR / NAVY, ARMY / & / NAVY, UNION / FOR / EVER, OUR / CARD, BUSINESS / CARD, and the favorite of them all: NOT / ONE / CENT. (The latter being a replay of the popular Hard Times token evasion of governmental interference.)

Another Hard Times carryover was the motto MILLIONS FOR DEFENCE, NOT ONE CENT FOR TRIBUTE. It was used sparingly, though.

Perhaps the most famous motto to appear on CW tokens was:

IF ANYBODY ATTEMPTS TO TEAR IT DOWN / SHOOT HIM ON THE SPOT. This motto's history is interesting; the story was touched upon in an earlier part of this reference, U.S. Merchant Tokens 1845-1860, under Mansion House, Alexandria, Virginia:

Following the election of Abraham Lincoln, the state of South Carolina seceded from the Union on December 20, 1860. On Jan. 9, 1861, the ship *Star of the West* was fired upon by a battery at Charleston. Six other states seceded in January and, on Feb. 4, 1861, representatives of the seven seceding states met at Montgomery, Alabama to form the Confederate States of America.

The Confederates demanded the surrender of Fort Sumter in Charleston harbor April 10, and when the garrison under Major Robert Anderson refused, the fort was bombarded April 12-13 and war, though never declared, broke out.

Feelings on both sides were intense at first. Southerners were convinced they could fight more gallantly and win, and Northerners expected a quick defeat of the rebellious South, which eventually numbered 11 states with 5,000,000 white citizens and very little manufacturing capacity.

A rabid Southern sympathizer named Jackson owned the Mansion House in Alexandria, a suburb of Washington, D.C. He ran up the Stars and Bars, the Confederate flag, above his hotel. Alexandria was garrisoned by Ellsworth's Zouaves, a militia unit raised and commanded by a young (24) and handsome Colonel Ephraham E. Ellsworth. Ellsworth warned Jackson to lower the flag, and Jackson refused.

Col. Ellsworth and Private Brownell entered the hotel and took the Stars and Bars down. As they descended the stairs, Jackson shot and killed Ellsworth. Brownell in turn killed Jackson, earning from the press the title "The Avenger" and from his government the first Medal of Honor awarded in the Civil War.

A number of dies (408 through 416) carry the "Shoot Him On The Spot" motto encircling the word DIX at center, and these usually appear combined with a U.S. flag die proclaiming THE FLAG OF OUR UNION (dies 203-212 and 214-215). On one famous error variety (die 414) SPOT is misspelled as SPOOT.

Legend has it that Dix stood for the South as well as being the French word for Ten. *Dixie*, a minstrel show "walk-around" tune written in 1859 by Charles Decatur Emmett, was adopted as soon as it was written by the South as its regional anthem, even before war and secession were thought of as realities. The name "Dixieland" of the Rebel anthem became synonymous with the Confederacy.

While almost all Civil War tokens represented one cent, there are some which bear other numerals and it is clear that cents are meant since some say specifically "10 / CENTS" or "25 CENTS" etc. Such numerals include 5, 10, 15, 20, 25, 30, 35, 50, 100 and 500 and encompass dies numbered 453, 456A, 464, 465, 465A, 480A, 494, 496, 497, and 1391 through 1405.

Diesinkers of Civil War Tokens

Some Civil War diesinkers signed their works. CDH stands for Charles D. Horter of New York, for example, and signatures such as L. ROLOFF, E.L. (Leichtweis), BRIDGENS, KEY, R.L. (Lovett), JDL (another Lovett) appear prominently.

Other diesinkers can be deduced by die combinations with known works, but 130 years after the War ended we still do not know who prepared many of these pieces.

We append a listing of known engravers and their signatures, but caution that it is incomplete and can be very confusing!

The listing is of diesinkers known to be working in the 1861-1865 time period, but this does not necessarily indicate that they prepared Civil War tokens!

Selig Baumgarten, Baltimore, 1852-66
W. H. Bridgens, New York, 1840-63, BRIDGENS
James A. Bolen, Springfield, Mass., 1858-74, BOLEN, J. A. BOLEN
Shubael D. Childs, Chicago, 1837-1900, CHILDS
Charles H. Cox, Indianapolis, 1860-81
C. W. Dury, Cincinnati, 1864-82
Darwin Ellis, Mishawaka, Ind., 1860's
A. W. Escherich, Chicago, 1861-63, E
Peter Frentz, New Albany, Ind., 1856-68
Louis Germani, Cincinnati, 1859-62
G. Glaubrecht, New York, 1860's, G.G., G.GL.
A. Gleason, Hillsdale, Mich., 1863
Peter Hartlaub, Cincinnati, 1864-76
Henry Darius Higgins, Mishawaka, Ind., 1846-96
Charles D. Horter, New York, 1860-63, CDH, HORTER
J. A. Hughes, Cincinnati, 1860's-74
Peter H. Jacobus, Philadelphia, 1858-70, PHJ
H. & W. Johnson, Cincinnati, 1863
F. C. Key, Philadelphia, 1849-70, KEY
William H. Key, Philadelphia, 1858-92, WHK
Francis X. Kohler, Baltimore, 1851-85
William K. Lanphear, Cincinnati, 1860-67
E. Leichtweis, New York, 1863, E.L.
M. Lindermann, Cincinnati, 1863-64
George H. Lovett, New York, 1848-93, GHL
John D. Lovett, New York, dates uncertain, JDL
Robert Lovett Jr., Philadelphia, dates uncertain, RL
Lutz, Cincinnati, 1863, LUTZ
J. D. MacKenzie, Cincinnati, 1860-99
Joseph H. Merriam, Boston, 1850-70, MERRIAM
Henry Miller, Louisville, 1856-63, H. MILLER
Mossin & Marr, Milwaukee, 1856-75, MARR
James Murdock Jr., Cincinnati, 1861-95
Murdock & Spencer, Cincinnati, 1865-69
Eugene M. Rexford, Indianapolis, 1863-67
Louis Roloff, New York, 1860's, L. ROLOFF
Scovill Mfg. Co., Waterbury, Conn., 1820-1905
Emil Sigel, New York, 1860's, ES, E. SIGEL
Frederick B. Smith, New York, 1835-64 and later
William W. Spencer, Cincinnati, 1860-1909
John Stanton, Cincinnati, 1853-97
Benjamin C. True, Cincinnati, 1856-61
B. Waldkirch, Evansville, Ind., 1858-63
John S. Warner, Philadelphia, 1823-68

REVERSE DIE PHOTOS

1000 1001 1002 1003 1004
1005 1006 1007 1008 1009
1010 1011 1012 1013 1014
1015 1016 1017 1018 1019
1020 1021 1022 1023 1024
1025 1026 1027 1028 1029
1030 1031 1032 1033 1034

REVERSE DIE PHOTOS

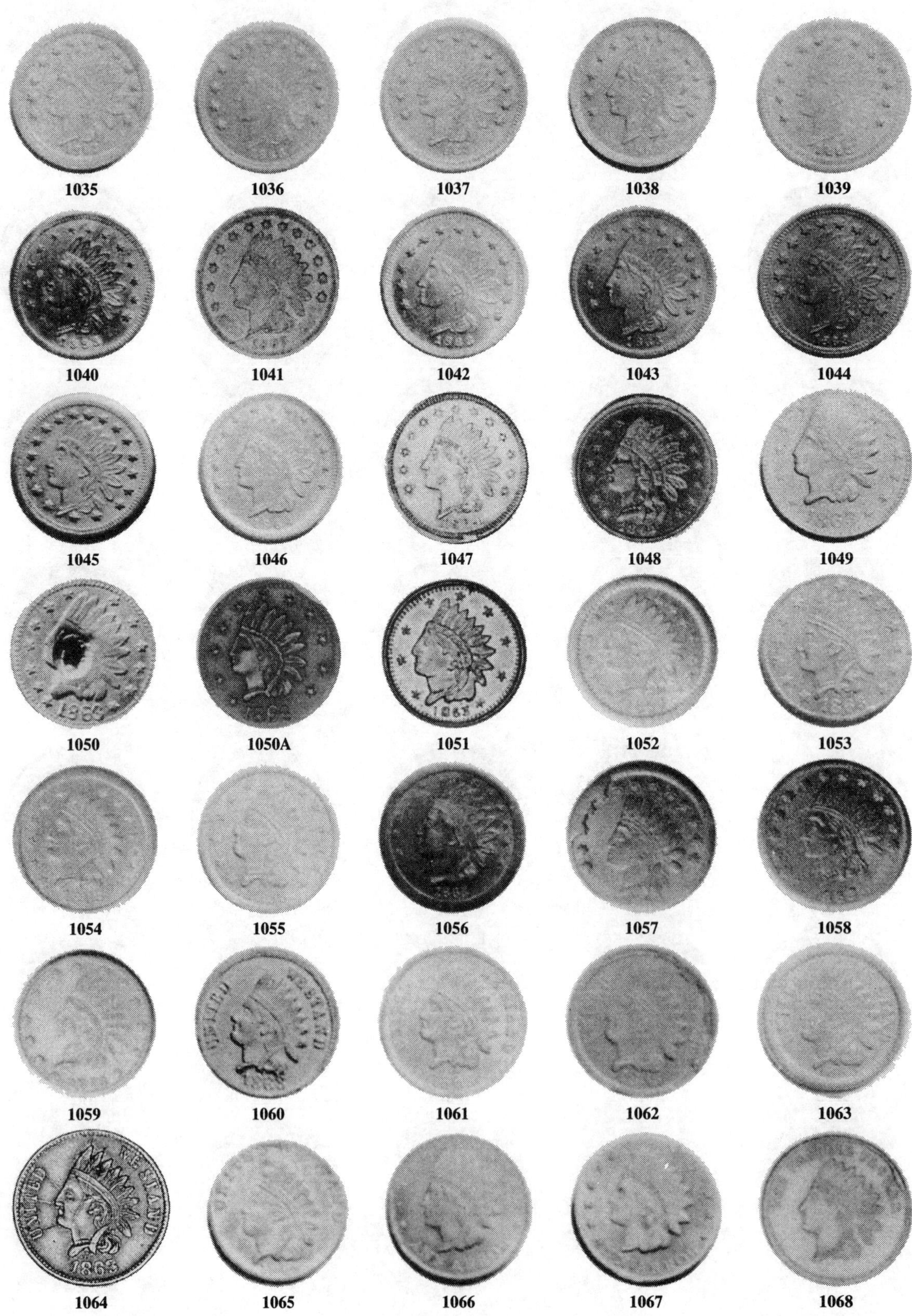

1035 1036 1037 1038 1039

1040 1041 1042 1043 1044

1045 1046 1047 1048 1049

1050 1050A 1051 1052 1053

1054 1055 1056 1057 1058

1059 1060 1061 1062 1063

1064 1065 1066 1067 1068

REVERSE DIE PHOTOS

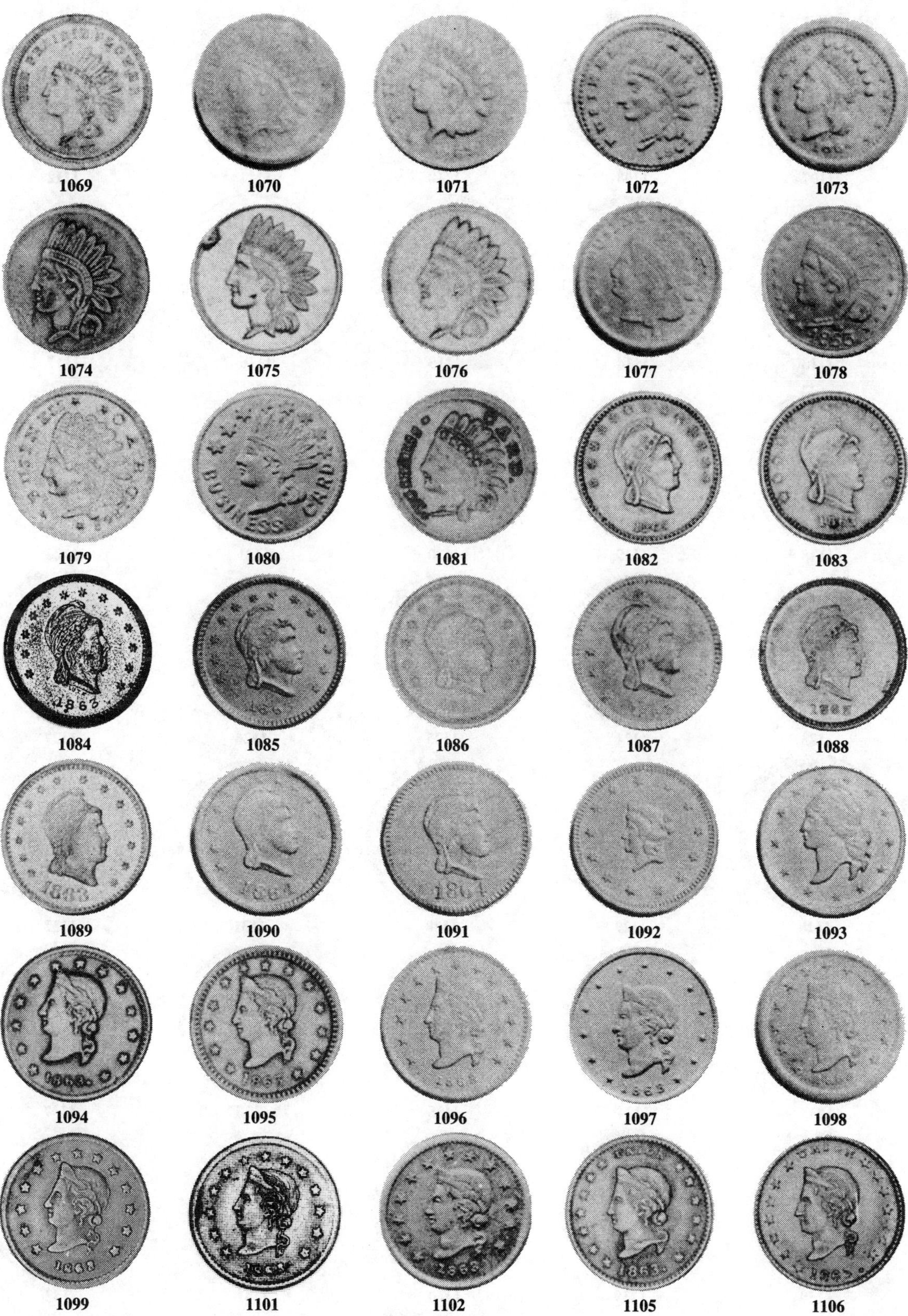

REVERSE DIE PHOTOS

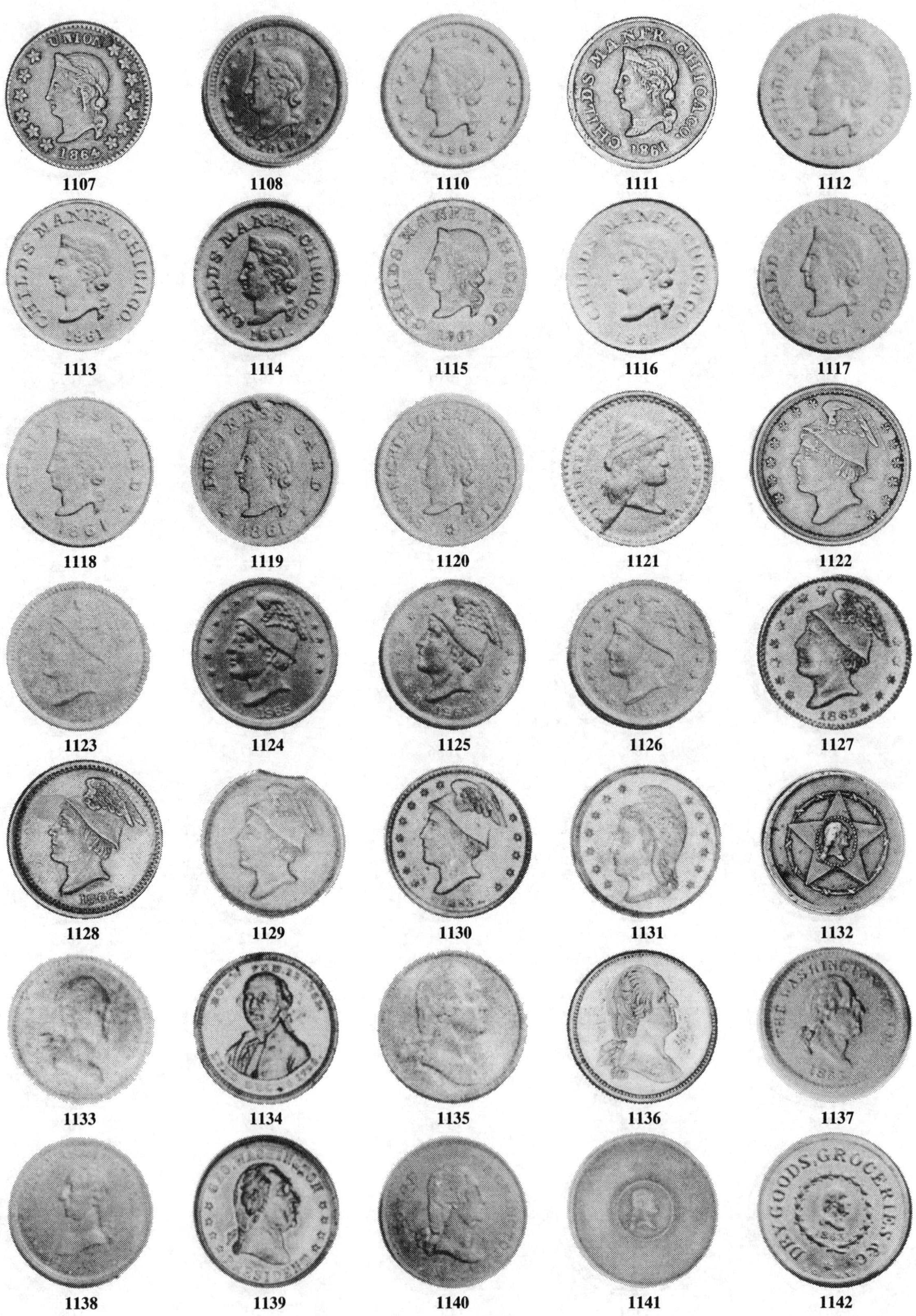

REVERSE DIE PHOTOS

1143 1144 1145 1146 1147

1148 1149 1150 1150A 1151

1152 1153 1154 1155 1156

1157 1158 1159 1160 1161

1162 1163 1164 1165 1166

1167 1168 1169 1170 1171

1172 1173 1174 1175 1176

REVERSE DIE PHOTOS

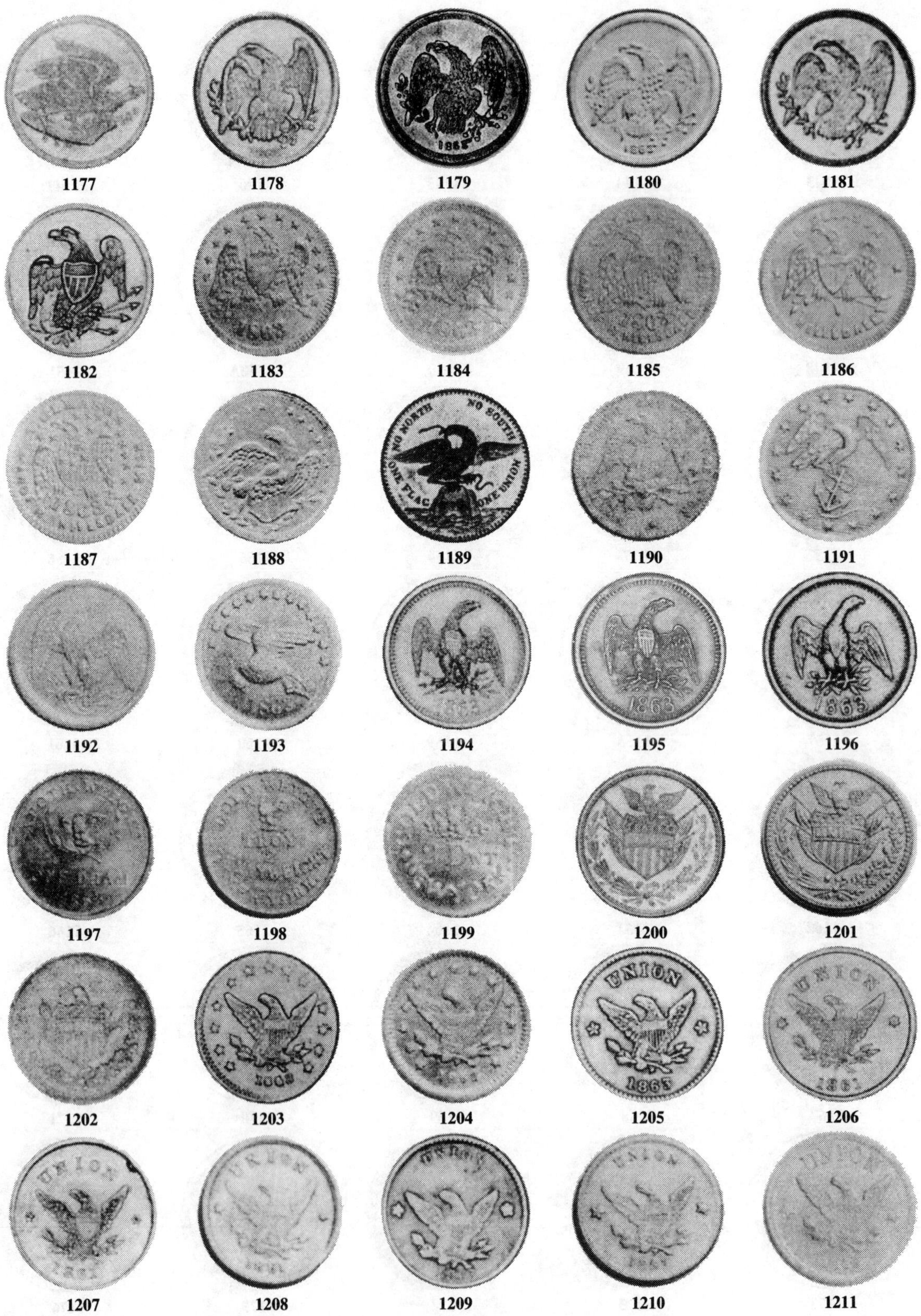

1177 1178 1179 1180 1181

1182 1183 1184 1185 1186

1187 1188 1189 1190 1191

1192 1193 1194 1195 1196

1197 1198 1199 1200 1201

1202 1203 1204 1205 1206

1207 1208 1209 1210 1211

REVERSE DIE PHOTOS

REVERSE DIE PHOTOS

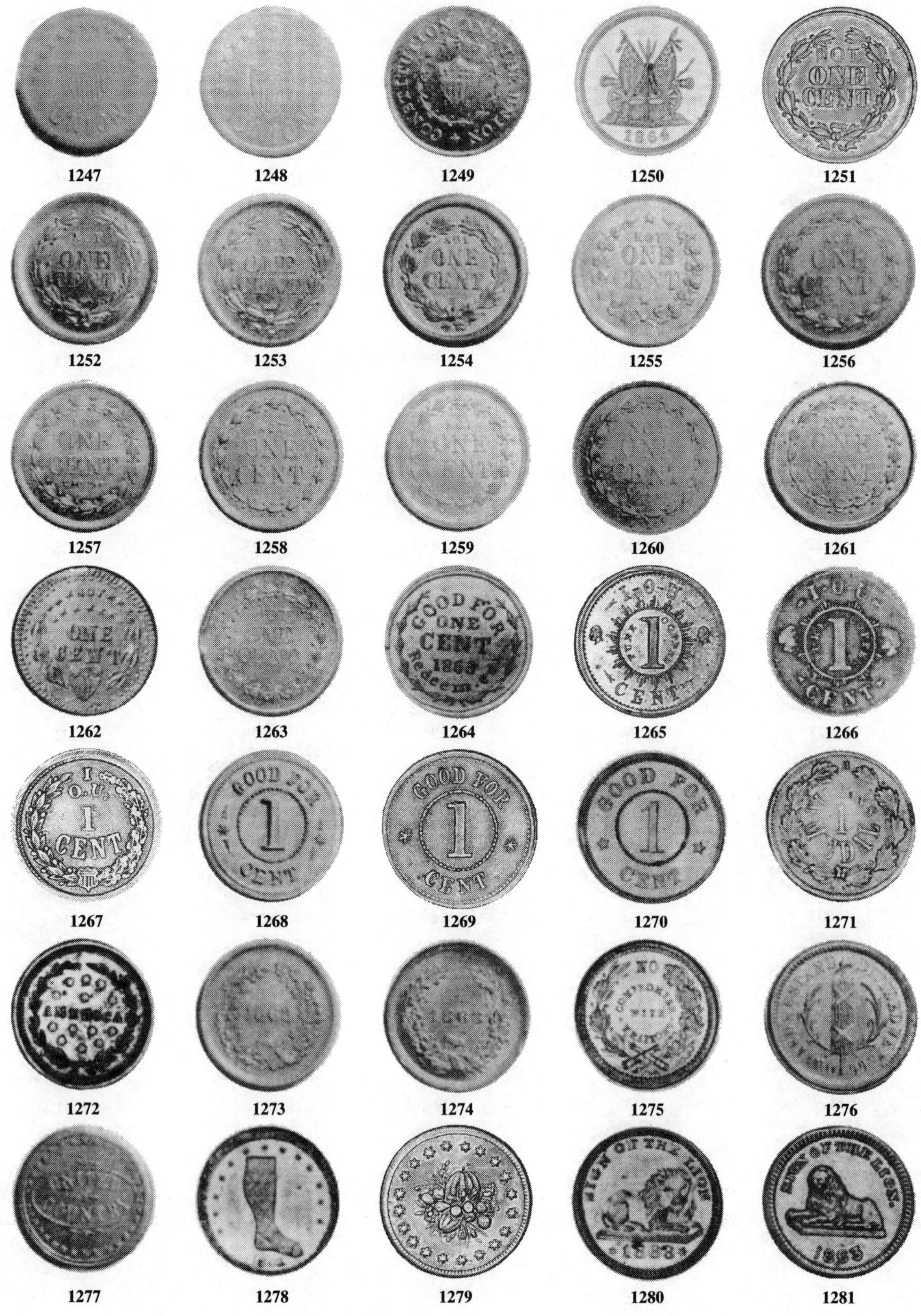

1247 1248 1249 1250 1251

1252 1253 1254 1255 1256

1257 1258 1259 1260 1261

1262 1263 1264 1265 1266

1267 1268 1269 1270 1271

1272 1273 1274 1275 1276

1277 1278 1279 1280 1281

REVERSE DIE PHOTOS

1282 1283 1284 1285 1286
1287 1288 1289 1290 1291
1292 1293 1294 1295 1296
1297 1298 1299 1300 1301
1302 1303 1304 1305 1306
1307 1308 1309 1310 1311
1312 1313 1314 1315 1316

REVERSE DIE PHOTOS

1317 1318 1319 1320 1321
1322 1323 1324 1325 1326
1327 1328 1329 1330 1331
1332 1333 1334 1335 1336
1337 1338 1339 1340 1341
1342 1343 1344 1345 1346
1347 1348 1349 1350 1351

REVERSE DIE PHOTOS

1352 1353 1354 1355 1356

1357 1358 1359 1360 1361

1362 1363 1364 1365 1366

1367 1368 1369 1370 1371

1372 1373 1374 1375 1376

1377 1378 1379 1380 1381

1382 1383 1384 1385 1386

REVERSE DIE PHOTOS

1387 1388 1389 1390 1391

1392 1393 1394 1395 1396

1397 1397A 1398 1399 1400

1401 1401A 1402 1403 1404

1404A 1405 1406 1407 1408

1409 1410 1411 1412 1413

1414 1415 1416 1417 1417A

REVERSE DIE PHOTOS

1418 1419 1420 1421 1422

1423 1424 1425 1426 1427

ALABAMA

Huntsville

WHITE & SWANN

CWT	Rarity	Reverse Die	Metal	Edge	VG	VF	EF	Unc
425A-1a	R8	1047	C	R	400	800	1,000	1,200

WHITE & SWANN / --- / HUNTSVILLE / *+* / - ALA. -

CONNECTICUT

Bridgeport

E. W. ATWOOD

CWT	Rarity	Reverse Die	Metal	Edge	VG	VF	EF	Unc
35A-1a	R3	1002	C	PL	4	6	8	15

E. W. ATWOOD / (ornament) / DEALER / -IN- / BOOKS / NEWSPAPERS / &C / (wreath)

A. W. WALLACE

CWT	Rarity	Reverse Die	Metal	Edge	VG	VF	EF	Unc
35B-1a	R3	1201	C	PL	4	6	8	15

A. W. WALLACE'S / (ornament) / VARIETY / BAKERY / -.- / . BRIDGEPORT. CT.

Norwich

WELLER'S NEWS DEPOT

CWT	Rarity	Reverse Die	Metal	Edge	VG	VF	EF	Unc
345A-1a	R3	1266	C	PL	8	15	20	45

WELLER'S / NEWS / DEPOT / * NORWICH *

Waterbury

NEW YORK STORE

CWT	Rarity	Reverse Die	Metal	Edge	VG	VF	EF	Unc
560A-1a	R4	—	C	PL	8	12	20	40

NEW YORK STORE / (ornament) / WATERBURY / CONN. / (ornament) / * SOUTH MAIN ST. * Rv: REDEEMABLE / (ornament) / IN SUMS OF / - 5 CTS. - / OR MORE / (ornament) / * IN POSTAGE CURRENCY *

Willimantic

DR. O. G. KEITTERIDGE

CWT	Rarity	Reverse Die	Metal	Edge	VG	VF	EF	Unc
600A-1a	R9	1147	C	PL		—	RARE	—

Dr. O. G. Keitteridge / Willimantic. / C. T. / 1864 / * / Main St.

ARCH SALOON

CWT	Rarity	Reverse Die	Metal	Edge	VG	VF	EF	Unc
600B-1b	R9	1147	BR	PL		—	RARE	—

Arch Saloon / (ornament) / No 10 / O. Rudd / (ornament)

ILLINOIS

Alton

WALTER & SMITH

CWT	Rarity	Reverse Die	Metal	Edge	VG	VF	EF	Unc
10A-1b	R8	—	BR	PL		—	RARE	—

WALTER & SMITH / ALTON / ILLS. / GOOD FOR / 10 / * CENTS *. Rv: Within beaded circle: JOHN STANTON / + / STAMP / BRAND / CUTTER / * / CINCINNATI.

Aurora

IRA H. FITCH

CWT	Rarity	Reverse Die	Metal	Edge	VG	VF	EF	Unc
25A-1a	R3	1207	C	PL	4	12	20	35

IRA H. FITCH / DEALER IN / LEATHER. / HARNESS / &C. / BROADWAY. AURORA. ILL.

GATES & TRASK

CWT	Rarity	Reverse Die	Metal	Edge	VG	VF	EF	Unc
25B-1a	R4	1368	C	PL	4	8	10	25

GATES & TRASK / DEALERS / IN / WATCHES / JEWELRY / & / SILVERWARE / AURORA. ILL.

Belvidere

GEORGE B. AMES

CWT	Rarity	Reverse	Metal	Edge	VG	VF	EF	Unc
45A-1b	R2	—	BR	PL	4	8	10	20

GEORGE B. AMES / DEALER IN / DRUGS, / BOOKS, &C. / * BELVIDERE, ILL. * Rv: (13 stars in arc) / GEORGE B. AMES / (mortar & pestle) / 1863

Bloomingdale

C. P. SEDGWICK & CO.

CWT	Rarity	Reverse Die	Metal	Edge	VG	VF	EF	Unc
65A-6a	R5	1275	C	PL	4	12	15	35

C. P. SEDGWICK & CO. / VARIETY / GOODS, / BLOOMINGDALE / ILL.

Cairo

R. C. CULLEY

CWT	Rarity	Reverse Die	Metal	Edge	VG	VF	EF	Unc
95A-1b	R8	Blank	BR	PL		—	RARE	—

-.- / R. C. CULLEY. / WATCHMAKER / & / JEWELER / (ornament) / CAIRO, ILLS.

D. FORD

CWT	Rarity	Reverse Die	Metal	Edge	VG	VF	EF	Unc
95B-1a	R6	1122	C	PL	5	10	20	40

-o- / D. FORD. / WATCHMAKER / AND / JEWELER / * CAIRO * / ILLS.

Chemung

WM. MOORE

CWT	Rarity	Reverse Die	Metal	Edge	VG	VF	EF	Unc
140A-2a	R6	1105	C	PL		—	SCARCE	—

WM. MOORE / DEALER / IN / DRY GOODS. / GROCERIES. / DRUGS / &C. / CHEMUNG. ILL.

B. A. WADE & CO.

CWT	Rarity	Reverse Die	Metal	Edge	VG	VF	EF	Unc
140B-2a	R5	1357	C	PL	20	90	120	175

B. A. WADE & CO. / DEALERS / IN / DRY GOODS / GROCERIES / &C&C. / *** / CHEMUNG, ILL.

Chicago

BAIERLE'S SALOON

CWT	Rarity	Reverse Die	Metal	Edge	VG	VF	EF	Unc
150A-1b	R9	—	BR	PL		—	RARE	—

BAIERLE'S / *** / SALOON / -*- / CHICAGO. Rv: GOOD FOR ONE / (beer mug in wreath)

NOTE: This token measures only 14mm.

G. BAUERNSCHMIDT

CWT	Rarity	Reverse Die	Metal	Edge	VG	VF	EF	Unc
150C-1b	R9	1296	BR	PL		—	RARE	—

GOOD FOR / 4 / CENTS / G. BAUERNSCHMIDT

NOTE: This token measures 18mm. It is known bearing ctsps 1, AB, IB and FP.

A B

CWT	Rarity	Reverse Die	Metal	Edge	VG	VF	EF	Unc
150D-1b	R9	1296	BR	PL		—	RARE	—

GOOD FOR / 1 / CENTS / AB

NOTE: The 1 is stamped over a 4 and AB is incused with a Q in the background. Measures 18mm.

F B

CWT	Rarity	Reverse Die	Metal	Edge	VG	VF	EF	Unc
150E-1b	R9	1296	BR	PL		—	RARE	—

GOOD FOR / 1 / CENTS / FB

NOTE: The 1 is stamped over a 4. Measures 18mm.

I. B.

CWT	Rarity	Reverse Die	Metal	Edge	VG	VF	EF	Unc
150F-1a	R9	1296	BR	PL		—	RARE	—

GOOD FOR / CENT. / I. B.

NOTE: I. B. incuse. Measures 18mm.

IRA BROWN

CWT	Rarity	Reverse Die	Metal	Edge	VG	VF	EF	Unc
150G-1a	R5	1096	C	PL	4	12	15	30

IRA BROWN / BOOK DEALER / - 61 - / WEST KINZIE / - ST. - / CHICAGO

J. J. BROWN'S GROCERY

CWT	Rarity	Reverse Die	Metal	Edge	VG	VF	EF	Unc
150H-1a	R4	1368	C	PL	4	15	25	45

J. J. BROWN'S / GROCERY / 171 / WEST / HARRISON. ST / CHICAGO. ILL

A. CANDLER

CWT	Rarity	Reverse Die	Metal	Edge	VG	VF	EF	Unc
150I-4a	R3	1356	C	PL	4	10	15	35

WATCHES CLOCKS & JEWELRY / (ornament) / A. CANDLER / 393 / STATE ST / (ornament) / CHICAGO

CHILDS

CWT	Rarity	Reverse Die	Metal	Edge	VG	VF	EF	Unc
150J-5a	R2	1206	C	PL	4	8	10	20

CHILDS. DIE SINKER & ENGRAVER (ornament) around / 117 1/2 / (line) / RANDOLPH / ST. / (line) / CHICAGO

CHILDS' MANUFACTURER

CWT	Rarity	Reverse Die	Metal	Edge	VG	VF	EF	Unc
150K-4a	R2	1203	C	PL	4	8	10	25

CHILDS' / MANUFACTURER / (ornament) OF (ornament) / ADVERTISING / COIN / CHICAGO, ILL.

DODD'S ELGIN DAIRY

CWT	Rarity	Reverse Die	Metal	Edge	VG	VF	EF	Unc
150N-2a	R4	1111	C	PL	4	8	10	32

DODD'S ELGIN DAIRY / - PURE - / - MILK - / 57 / WEST / MADISON / (ornament) ST. (ornament)

NOTE: This piece comes with a heavy reverse die break.

D. DRYER & CO.

CWT	Rarity	Reverse Die	Metal	Edge	VG	VF	EF	Unc
150O-1a	R6	1080	C	PL		—	RARE	—

D, DRYER & CO. / GROCERIES / PROVISIONS / 359 CANAL St.

EDWARDS FINE WATCHES & JEWELRY

CWT	Rarity	Reverse Die	Metal	Edge	VG	VF	EF	Unc
150Q-1a	R4	1368	C	PL	5	15	20	35

EDWARDS / FINE / WATCHES / & / JEWELRY / 101 / CLARK. ST / CHICAGO ILL

A. W. ESCHERICH

CWT	Rarity	Reverse Die	Metal	Edge	VG	VF	EF	Unc
150R-1a	R4	1080	C	PL	5	10	20	80

A. W. ESCHERICH.404 ST, CLARK ST, around. CHICAGO / ILLINOIS. / 1861 / * / in center.

FLAGGS

CWT	Rarity	Reverse Die	Metal	Edge	VG	VF	EF	Unc
150S-1a	R3	1368	C	PL	4	8	10	20

FLAGGS.CHEAP.STORE / BOOTS / & / SHOES / 189 / LAKE. ST / CHICAGO

JAMES FOSTER JR. & CO.

CWT	Rarity	Reverse Die	Metal	Edge	VG	VF	EF	Unc
150U-2a	R9	1047	C	R		—	RARE	—

JAMES FOSTER JR. & CO. OPTICIANS * around. 48 CLARK ST. / CHICAGO / ILL. center.

FREEDMAN & GOODKIND

CWT	Rarity	Reverse Die	Metal	Edge	VG	VF	EF	Unc
150V-2a	R3	1118	C	PL	4	8	10	20

FREEDMAN & GOODKIND / DRY / (line) GOODS (curved line) / & / MILLINERY / 171 / LAKE ST. / CHICAGO

FREEDMAN & GOODKIND & CO.

CWT	Rarity	Reverse Die	Metal	Edge	VG	VF	EF	Unc
150W-1a	R2	1368	C	PL	4	8	10	20

FREEDMAN.GOODKIND & Co. / DRY / GOODS / 171 / LAKE. ST / CHICAGO.ILL

P. GAFFNEY

CWT	Rarity	Reverse Die	Metal	Edge	VG	VF	EF	Unc
150X-1a	R3	1368	C	PL	4	8	10	20

P. GAFFNEY / GROCER / & / TEA / DEALER / 150 / N. HALSTED. ST / CHICAGO

F. GALL

CWT	Rarity	Reverse Die	Metal	Edge	VG	VF	EF	Unc
150Y-1a	R2	1286	C	PL	4	8	15	30

NEW YORK / (ornament) / MEAT (ornament) / (ornament) MARKET / (ornament) / F. GALL / CHICAGO / -*- / N. 92 MILWAUKEE AVE.

G. E. GERTS & CO.

CWT	Rarity	Reverse Die	Metal	Edge	VG	VF	EF	Unc
150Z-1a	R3	1368	C	PL	4	8	10	20

G. E. GERTS & CO / BRUSH / FACTORY / & STORE / 204 / RANDOLPH. ST / CHICAGO

HAAS & POWELL

CWT	Rarity	Reverse Die	Metal	Edge	VG	VF	EF	Unc
150AA-1a	R4	1111	C	PL	4	8	15	30

HAAS & POWELL / (ornament) / BUTCHERS / (ornament) / NORTH MARKET

WM. HARLEV

CWT	Rarity	Reverse Die	Metal	Edge	VG	VF	EF	Unc
150AB-1a	R2	—	C	PL	4	8	10	40

Wm. HARLEV, / TRUNKS / -& / VALISES on a banner / 94 / MIL'. AVE./ CHICAGO.
Rv: With trunk in center, Wm. HARLEV, / ONE PRICE above. CLOTHING / 94 MILWAUKEE AVE. below.

HARLEV & JOHNSON

CWT	Rarity	Reverse Die	Metal	Edge	VG	VF	EF	Unc
150AC-1a	R2	—	C	PL	4	8	10	40

HARLEV & JOHNSON / TRUNKS / & / VALISES on a banner / 94 / MIL' AVE. / CHICAGO

R. HEILBRONER

CWT	Rarity	Reverse Die	Metal	Edge	VG	VF	EF	Unc
150AD-1a	R2	1368	C	PL	4	8	10	20

R. HEILBRONER / FANCY / DRY / GOODS / 217 / S. CLARK. ST / CHICAGO. ILL

W. A. HENDRIE

CWT	Rarity	Reverse Die	Metal	Edge	VG	VF	EF	Unc
150AE-1a	R4	1368	C	PL	4	20	30	50

W. A. HENDRIE / WATCHES. / CLOCKS / & / JEWELRY / 35 CLARK. ST / CHICAGO. ILL

W. HILD

CWT	Rarity	Reverse Die	Metal	Edge	VG	VF	EF	Unc
150AF-1b	R9	1296	BR	PL		—	RARE	—

GOOD FOR / 5 / CENTS / W. HILD

NOTE: The 5 is stamped over a 4 and W. HILD incuse. Measures 18mm.

S. A. INGRAM

CWT	Rarity	Reverse Die	Metal	Edge	VG	VF	EF	Unc
150AG-1a	R9	1007	C	PL		—	RARE	—

S. A. INGRAM, / * WATCHES * / (ornament) / AND / (ornament) / CLOCKS / CHICAGO. ILL.

O. KENDALL'S SONS & CO.

CWT	Rarity	Reverse Die	Metal	Edge	VG	VF	EF	Unc
150AI-2a	R6	1098	C	PL	20	90	120	225

* O. KENDALL'S SONS & CO * / BREAD / GOOD FOR / ONE / LOAF

F. A. LEAVITT

CWT	Rarity	Reverse Die	Metal	Edge	VG	VF	EF	Unc
150AJ-1a	R3	1368	C	PL	4	8	10	20

F. A. LEAVITT / FAMILY / (ornament) / GROCERY / 355 STATE. ST / CHICAGO. ILL

MARSH & MINER

CWT	Rarity	Reverse Die	Metal	Edge	VG	VF	EF	Unc
150AK-2a	R4	1030	C	PL	4	10	15	30

MARSH & MINER / MILITARY / CLOTHIERS / 33 & 35 / LAKE. ST. / CHICAGO

A. MEYER

CWT	Rarity	Reverse Die	Metal	Edge	VG	VF	EF	Unc
150AL-1a	R6	1080	C	PL	10	35	55	100

A, MEYER. S. CLARK, ST 377. around. In center RAG, STOR / CHICAGO / ILL.

C. E. MEYER

CWT	Rarity	Reverse Die	Metal	Edge	VG	VF	EF	Unc
150AM-1b	R7	—	BR	PL		—	RARE	—

C. E. MEYER / 196 RANDOLPH ST. Beer mug in center. Rv: (ornament) / GOOD FOR / - * - / ONE GLASS / (ornament) / BEER

G. R. MEYER

CWT	Rarity	Reverse Die	Metal	Edge	VG	VF	EF	Unc
150AN-1a	R9	—	C	PL		—	RARE	—

GOOD FOR / 5 Cts / G. E. MEYER Rv: House, flagpole and flying flag surrounded by trees.

J. U. MUNGERS

CWT	Rarity	Reverse Die	Metal	Edge	VG	VF	EF	Unc
150AO-1a	R5	1080	C	PL	10	50	75	125

BOARDING HOUSE 33. CANAL ST. around. J. U. MUNGERS (in script) / SALOON / * / in center.

P. H. ODENWALD

CWT	Rarity	Reverse Die	Metal	Edge	VG	VF	EF	Unc
150AP-1b	R9	1296	BR	PL		—	RARE	—

* GOOD FOR * / 4 / CENTS / PH. / ODENWALD

NOTE: Measures 18mm.

OPPENHEIMER & METZGER

CWT	Rarity	Reverse Die	Metal	Edge	VG	VF	EF	Unc
150AQ-1a	R3	1368	C	PL	4	8	10	20

OPPENHEIMER & METZGER / JEWELRY / & / WATCH / MATERIALS / 104 / LAKE. ST / CHICAGO / ILL

WM. OSTENDORF

CWT	Rarity	Reverse Die	Metal	Edge	VG	VF	EF	Unc
150AR-1b	R8	—	BR	PL		—	RARE	—

Wm. OSTENDORF / 210 / RANDOLPH / STREET / CHICAGO Rv: (ornament) / GOOD FOR / - * - / ONE GLASS / (ornament) / BEER

PASSAGE CERTIFICATES

CWT	Rarity	Reverse Die	Metal	Edge	VG	VF	EF	Unc
150AS-1a	R5	—	C	PL	4	10	15	45

* PASSAGE CERTIFICATES * / FROM / LIVERPOOL / - TO - / CHICAGO / NO. 6. Rv: BANK DRAFTS / FOR / 1L AND / UPWARDS / (ornament) ON THE (ornament) / ROYAL BANK OF / IRELAND / 1861

W. G. PECK

CWT	Rarity	Reverse Die	Metal	Edge	VG	VF	EF	Unc
150AT-8a	R3	1356	C	PL	4	10	15	30

W. G. PECK / (ornament) / GROCER / 192 STATE ST. / (ornament) / CHICAGO

F. W. R.

CWT	Rarity	Reverse Die	Metal	Edge	VG	VF	EF	Unc
150AV-1b	R8	1296	BR	PL		—	RARE	—

GOOD FOR / 4 / CENTS / F. W. R.

NOTE: F. W. R. incuse. Measures 18mm.

L S R

CWT	Rarity	Reverse Die	Metal	Edge	VG	VF	EF	Unc
150AW-1b	R8	1296	BR	PL		—	RARE	—

GOOD FOR / 5 / CENT. / L S R

NOTE: 5 and L S R incuse. Measures 18mm.

H. REGENSBURG

CWT	Rarity	Reverse Die	Metal	Edge	VG	VF	EF	Unc
150AX-1a	R3	1080	C	PL	5	10	15	40

H. REGENSBURG / GROCERY / & / BAKERY. / NO. 30 / N. WELLS. St. / CHICAGO.

WM. REINHARDT

CWT	Rarity	Reverse Die	Metal	Edge	VG	VF	EF	Unc
150AY-1a	R2	1286	C	PL	4	8	15	30

GREAT WEST MARKET / FRESH & SALT MEAT, / WM. REINHARDT / 153 / RANDOLPH / W. / CHICAGO

NOTE: Obverse has heavy die break.

F. E. RIGBY

CWT	Rarity	Reverse Die	Metal	Edge	VG	VF	EF	Unc
150AZ-3a	R2	1208	C	PL	4	8	10	20

WALL PAPERS / 81 / RANDOLPH ST. / CHICAGO / F. E. RIGBY.

J S

CWT	Rarity	Reverse Die	Metal	Edge	VG	VF	EF	Unc
150BA-1b	R8	1352A	BR	PL		—	RARE	—

GOOD FOR / 4 / CENTS / J S

NOTE: J S incuse. Measures 18mm.

J. F. SIEHLER

CWT	Rarity	Reverse Die	Metal	Edge	VG	VF	EF	Unc
150BB-3a	R4	1354	C	PL	10	20	30	75

DEUTSCHES GAST & BOARDING HAUS around. J. F. SIEHLER / LARABEE / ST. / NEAR / CLYBOURNE AVE. / CHICAGO in center. Rv: Name reads BIER on shield.

C & S STEIN

CWT	Rarity	Reverse Die	Metal	Edge	VG	VF	EF	Unc
150BC-2a	R3	1116	C	PL	4	8	10	25

C & S. STEIN. / (curved line) / DRY GOODS / (curved line) / STORE. / 177 / LAKE ST. / * CHICAGO. ILL. *

P. STUMPS

CWT	Rarity	Reverse Die	Metal	Edge	VG	VF	EF	Unc
150BD-1a	R8	—	C	PL		—	RARE	—

* P. STUMPS * / M'F'R / & DEALER IN / FIREMENS HATS / AND BELTS / * 312 * / COTTAGE GROVE AVE. Rv: Fireman's hat in center. MADE TO ORDER on fireman's belt around. CHICAGO, ILL below cap.

W. TRELEAVEN

CWT	Rarity	Reverse Die	Metal	Edge	VG	VF	EF	Unc
150BE-1a	R5	1368	C	PL	5	15	20	45

W. TRELEAVEN / GOLD. PEN / MAKER / & / JEWELER / 150 LAKE. ST / UP. STAIRS / CHICAGO. ILL

S. WILSON'S

CWT	Rarity	Reverse Die	Metal	Edge	VG	VF	EF	Unc
150BF-1A	R8	1205	C	C		—	RARE	—

S. WILSON'S / . * . / BILLIARD / SALOON / BAR / CHECK

NOTE: George and Melvin Fuld listed the supplementary index as Chicago, but described it under "Special Non-Local," as did Barnett (SNL-4a).

C. WINSAUER

CWT	Rarity	Reverse Die	Metal	Edge	VG	VF	EF	Unc
150BG-1a	R4	1345	C	PL	15	30	75	125

C. WINSAUER / Crossed swords and guns in center. GUNSMITH / N. 111 S. WELLS / CHICAGO. below.

De Kalb

I. L. ELLWOOD

CWT	Rarity	Reverse Die	Metal	Edge	VG	VF	EF	Unc
200A-1a	R5	1137	C	PL	10	25	40	110

I. L. ELLWOOD / (line) / HARDWARE. / (ornament) / TIN. STOVES / (line) / DE KALB ILL.

Dixon

ED WEIBEZAHN

CWT	Rarity	Reverse Die	Metal	Edge	VG	VF	EF	Unc
210A-1a	R7	1105	C	PL		—	SCARCE	—

ED. WEIBEZAHN / DEALER / IN / GROCERIES / & DRY / GOODS / DIXON. ILL.

Durand

H. L. MOSLEY

CWT	Rarity	Reverse Die	Metal	Edge	VG	VF	EF	Unc
225A-1a	R3	—	C	PL	5	10	15	25

H. L. MOSLEY / (ornament) / DURAND / (ornament) ****** ILLS. ****** Rv: * (ornament) GROCERIES (ornament) * / (ornament) / HARDWARE, / ** - ** / GROCKERY, / (ornament) / * (ornament) NOTIONS (ornament) *

NOTE: Spelling error in word "CROCKERY".

Elgin

M. MCNEIL

CWT	Rarity	Reverse Die	Metal	Edge	VG	VF	EF	Unc
270A-1a	R5	1209	C	PL	30	85	110	160

M. Mc. NEIL / DEALER / IN / DRY GOODS / GROCERIES / BOOTS & / SHOES / ELGIN. ILL.

El Paso

P. H. TOMPKINS

CWT	Rarity	Reverse Die	Metal	Edge	VG	VF	EF	Unc
275A-1a	R7	1108	C	PL	30	110	125	200

P. H. TOMPKINS / DEALER / IN / DRY GOODS. / GROCERIES / &C. / EL PASO. ILL.

Fairview

C. VANDORN

CWT	Rarity	Reverse Die	Metal	Edge	VG	VF	EF	Unc
300A-1a	R8	—	C	PL	20	70	90	125

C. VANDORN / LARGEST & / CHEAPEST / STORE / FAIRVIEW. ILL. Rv: I. O. U. - * - CENTS - * - around 5 in center.

Freeport

D. S. BOGAR

CWT	Rarity	Reverse Die	Metal	Edge	VG	VF	EF	Unc
320A-1a	R8	1095	C	PL	10	45	85	150

D. S. BOGAR / FARMERS STORE / DRY / GOODS & / GROCERIES / FREEPORT / ILLS.

D. S. BREWSTER

CWT	Rarity	Reverse Die	Metal	Edge	VG	VF	EF	Unc
320B-1a	R4	1209	C	PL	5	15	25	60

D. S. BREWSTER / DEALER / IN / BUTTER / - * - / EGGS & C. / FREEPORT. ILL.

J. D. DIFFENBAUGH

CWT	Rarity	Reverse Die	Metal	Edge	VG	VF	EF	Unc
320C-1a	R3	1095	C	PL	5	10	15	45

J. D. DIFFENBAUGH / CONFECTIONER / AND / DEALE IN / FRUIT / FREEPORT / ILL.

NOTE: Error in spelling DEALER.

W. P. EMMERT

CWT	Rarity	Reverse Die	Metal	Edge	VG	VF	EF	Unc
320D-2a	R8	1357	C	PL	20	80	115	200

W. P. EMMERT. / HARDWARE / STOVES, IRON / & / TIN WARE / FREEPORT. ILLS.

HELENA HERTRICH

CWT	Rarity	Reverse Die	Metal	Edge	VG	VF	EF	Unc
320E-1a	R6	1196	C	PL	10	25	50	100

FREEPORT BREWERY / BY / HELENA / HERTRICH. / ADAMS / ST. / FREEPORT. ILL.

Lacon

ELLSWORTH & HALSEY

CWT	Rarity	Reverse Die	Metal	Edge	VG	VF	EF	Unc
472A-1a	R8	1046	C	R		—	SCARCE	—

ELLSWORTH & HALSEY / GENERAL / MERCHANDISE / & / GOODS / FOR / LADIES / WEAR / LACON, ILL'S

La Salle

ADAMS & HATCH

CWT	Rarity	Reverse Die	Metal	Edge	VG	VF	EF	Unc
495A-1a	R4	1105	C	PL	5	15	20	60

ADAMS & HATCH / DRY / GOODS. / CARPETS. / BOOTS & / SHOES / LA SALLE. ILL.

Lena

W. A. BOLLINGER

CWT	Rarity	Reverse Die	Metal	Edge	VG	VF	EF	Unc
500A-1a	R5	1357	C	PL	4	12	20	60

W. A. BOLLINGER / DEALER / IN / HARDWARE / IRON & STEEL / LENA. ILLINOIS. Lock in lower field.

M. WEAVER

CWT	Rarity	Reverse Die	Metal	Edge	VG	VF	EF	Unc
500B-1a	R2	1106	C	PL	4	10	12	40

M. WEAVER / DEALER IN / DRY GOODS / -***- / & GROCERIES / LENA. ILL.

Lodi

C. H. TAYLOR

CWT	Rarity	Reverse Die	Metal	Edge	VG	VF	EF	Unc
520A-1a	R9	1107	C	PL		—	RARE	—

C. H. TAYLOR / STOVES / FINE / (line) / TABLE & / (line) / (line) / POCKET / (line) / CUTLERY / LODI, ILL.

Marengo

H. G. SKINNER

CWT	Rarity	Reverse Die	Metal	Edge	VG	VF	EF	Unc
540A-1a	R4	1357	C	PL	8	25	35	65

H. G. SKINNER / ACT. / DEALER IN / GROCERIES / & PROVISIONS / MARENGO / ILL.

Mendota

A. ERLENBORN

CWT	Rarity	Reverse Die	Metal	Edge	VG	VF	EF	Unc
560A-1a	R5	1205	C	PL	5	20	30	55

A. ERLENBORN / DEALER / IN / GROCERIES &C. / MAIN STREET / MENDOTA. / - * - / ILLS.

Naperville

ROBERT NAPER

CWT	Rarity	Reverse Die	Metal	Edge	VG	VF	EF	Unc
615A-1a	R7	1046	C	R	20	90	140	250

ROBERT NAPER / - / DRY / GOODS / (ornament) / GROCERIES / &C. / NAPERVILLE. ILLS.

Ottawa

A. & H. AISCHULER

CWT	Rarity	Reverse Die	Metal	Edge	VG	VF	EF	Unc
660A-2a	R3	1338	C	PL	8	20	35	90

A & H. AISCHULER / * OTTAWA * / Large rossette in center.

Palatine

DEAN & SLADE

CWT	Rarity	Reverse Die	Metal	Edge	VG	VF	EF	Unc
680A-1a	R4	1195	C	PL	5	25	35	85

DEAN & SLADE / DRY GOODS / HARDWARE / &C. / PALATINE. ILL.

Paris

COLLINS BRO'S

CWT	Rarity	Reverse Die	Metal	Edge	VG	VF	EF	Unc
690A-1a	R5	1036	C	PL	10	40	55	85

COLLINS BRO'S / - * - / DRUGGISTS / - * - / PARIS, ILLS

A. C. CONNELY'S

CWT	Rarity	Reverse Die	Metal	Edge	VG	VF	EF	Unc
690B-1a	R4	1026	C	PL	10	20	30	50

A. C. CONNELY'S / DRY / GOODS / STORE / PARIS, ILL.

JAMES MILLER

CWT	Rarity	Reverse Die	Metal	Edge	VG	VF	EF	Unc
690C-2a	R5	1029	C	PL	10	35	45	65

JAMES MILLER / DRY / GOODS / STORE / PARIS. ILL.

PENOYER & LARKIN

CWT	Rarity	Reverse Die	Metal	Edge	VG	VF	EF	Unc
690D-1a	R6	1028	C	PL	10	30	40	65

PENOYER & LARKIN / GROCERS / & PROVISION / DEALERS / PARIS, ILL.

SISK & WHALEN

CWT	Rarity	Reverse Die	Metal	Edge	VG	VF	EF	Unc
690E-1a	R6	1026	C	PL		—	RARE	—

SISK & WHALEN / RESTAURANT / E. SIDE PUB. SQ. / PARIS, ILLS.

Peru

LININGER & BRO.

CWT	Rarity	Reverse Die	Metal	Edge	VG	VF	EF	Unc
695A-1a	R4	1357	C	PL	5	15	20	50

LININGER & BRO. / DEALERS / IN / DRY GOODS, / * NOTIONS, * / BOOTS & SHOES / PERU, ILL.

Pontiac

DEHNER & MAPLES

CWT	Rarity	Reverse Die	Metal	Edge	VG	VF	EF	Unc
700A-1a	R5	1105	C	PL	10	30	45	100

DEHNER & MAPLES / DRY * / * GOODS / GROCERIES / CROCKERY / * &C. * / PONTIAC, ILL.

Rockford

A. J. DAVIS

CWT	Rarity	Reverse Die	Metal	Edge	VG	VF	EF	Unc
755A-2a	R3	1105	C	PL	5	15	20	45

A. J. DAVIS / *** / GROCER / (ornament) / ROCKFORD. ILLS.

HOLMES & NORTON

CWT	Rarity	Reverse Die	Metal	Edge	VG	VF	EF	Unc
755B-1a	R4	1209	C	PL	10	20	35	60

HOLMES & NORTHON / mortar & pestle / DRUGGISTS / ROCKFORD / ILL.

HOPE & CLOW

CWT	Rarity	Reverse Die	Metal	Edge	VG	VF	EF	Unc
755C-1a	R3	1094	C	PL	5	10	20	40

HOPE & CLOW / STOVES / HARDWARE / IRON & C. / padlock / ROCKFORD. ILL.

WILLIAM KNAPP

CWT	Rarity	Reverse Die	Metal	Edge	VG	VF	EF	Unc
755D-1a	R3	1107	C	PL	5	10	15	60

WILLIAM KNAPP / ARTESIAN / - * - / WELL / - * - / DRILLER / ROCKFORD. ILL.

Rockton

V. A. LAKE

CWT	Rarity	Reverse Die	Metal	Edge	VG	VF	EF	Unc
762A-1a	R8	1018	C	R		—	SCARCE	—

* V. A. LAKE * / GRAIN / DEALER / ROCKTON, ILL.

Sandwich

M. B. CASTLE

CWT	Rarity	Reverse Die	Metal	Edge	VG	VF	EF	Unc
775A-1a	R5	—	C	PL	4	10	12	35

SANDWICH / BANK / M. B. CASTLE / SANDWICH / - * - / ILLINOIS Rv: DEPOSIT / EXCHANGE / (ornament) & (ornament) / LOAN / *** OFFICE ***

NOTE: The M is apparently recut over a W, so it is uncertain whether this is the correct spelling, or whether the 775B (W. B. Castle) is the correct spelling. H-R1162.

W. B. CASTLE

CWT	Rarity	Reverse Die	Metal	Edge	VG	VF	EF	Unc
775B-1a	R2	1316	C	PL	4	12	15	35

W. B. CASTLE / DRUGGIST / SANDWICH / ILLS.

A. G. GREENMAN

CWT	Rarity	Reverse Die	Metal	Edge	VG	VF	EF	Unc
775C-1a	R4	1316	C	PL	10	20	35	75

A. G. GREENMAN / mortar & pestle / DRUGGIST / SANDWICH / * ILL. *

Springfield

J. C. YAGER

CWT	Rarity	Reverse Die	Metal	Edge	VG	VF	EF	Unc
795A-2a	R2	1274	C	PL	5	10	15	35

J. C. YAGER, / (ornament) / TRUNK / MAKER / * / SPRINGFIELD ILL

Sycamore

LOTT & WARNER

CWT	Rarity	Reverse Die	Metal	Edge	VG	VF	EF	Unc
825A-2a	R5	1117	C	PL	30	100	125	175

LOTT & WARNER / - * - / DRY GOODS / (ornament) / GROCERIES / & C. / SYCAMORE. ILLS.

Waukegan

KINGSLEY & WHIPPLE

CWT	Rarity	Reverse Die	Metal	Edge	VG	VF	EF	Unc
890A-1a	R8	1105	C	PL	30	100	125	200

KINGSLEY / & / WHIPPLE / GROCERIES & / PROVISIONS / - * - / WAUKEGAN / ILL.

J. L. LOVEDAY & CO.

CWT	Rarity	Reverse Die	Metal	Edge	VG	VF	EF	Unc
890B-1b	R4	1408	BR	PL	6	8	10	20

J. L. LOVEDAY & CO. / - DRY GOODS - / + + / AND / + + / GROCERIES / * WAUKEGAN ILL. *

D. P. MILLEN

CWT	Rarity	Reverse Die	Metal	Edge	VG	VF	EF	Unc
890C-2a	R8	1107	C	PL	20	75	100	160

D. P. MILLEN / DEALER / IN / BOOTS / & SHOES / WAUKEGAN / LAKE CO. / ILL.

Woodstock

M. D. STEVERS

CWT	Rarity	Reverse Die	Metal	Edge	VG	VF	EF	Unc
920A-1a	R7	1195	C	PL		—	RARE	—

M. D. STEVERS / (ornament) / GRAIN / DEALER / (ornament) / WOODSTOCK. ILL.

INDIANA

Albany

ALLEGRE & WROUGHTON

CWT	Rarity	Reverse Die	Metal	Edge	VG	VF	EF	Unc
5A-1a	R5	1122	C	PL	10	30	40	80

ALLEGRE & WROUGHTON / DEALERS / IN / DRY GOODS / & / GROCERIES / ALBANY. IND.

Alexandria

WOLFE & SHERMAN

CWT	Rarity	Reverse Die	Metal	Edge	VG	VF	EF	Unc
10A-1a	R4	1037	C	R	10	30	40	70

WOLFE & SHERMAN / STAPLE & FANCY / DRY / GOODS / ALEXANDRIA, IND.

Anderson

J. P. BARNES

CWT	Rarity	Reverse Die	Metal	Edge	VG	VF	EF	Unc
20A-1a	R4	1299	C	PL	5	15	25	40

J. P. BARNES / DEALER / IN / STOVES / - & - / TIN WARE / ANDERSON. IND.

T. & N. C. MCCULLOUGH

CWT	Rarity	Reverse Die	Metal	Edge	VG	VF	EF	Unc
20B-1a	R5	1326	C	PL	5	15	25	40

T. & N. C. McCULLOUGH / DEALERS / IN / HARDWARE / ANDERSON /* IND *

Avilla

BAUM WALTER & CO.

CWT	Rarity	Reverse Die	Metal	Edge	VG	VF	EF	Unc
70A-1a	R6	1037	C	R	10	60	80	125

BAUM WALTER & CO. / DEALERS IN / DRY / - GOODS - / GROCERIES / & C. / AVILLA, IND.

Bethel

THOMPSON & WILEY

CWT	Rarity	Reverse Die	Metal	Edge	VG	VF	EF	Unc
100A-2a	R4	1180	C	PL	10	20	40	75

THOMPSON & WILEY / DEALERS / IN / DRY GOODS / AND / GROCERIES / - * - / BETHEL, IND.

Bowling Green

O. H. P. ASH

CWT	Rarity	Reverse Die	Metal	Edge	VG	VF	EF	Unc
120A-3a	R5	1042	C	R	6	15	20	40

O. H. P. ASH'S / CHEAP / CASH / STORE / BOWLING / GREEN, IND.

ASH & BLACK

CWT	Rarity	Reverse Die	Metal	Edge	VG	VF	EF	Unc
120B-1a	R3	1030	C	PL	6	15	20	40

ASH & BLACK / CASH / STORE / BOWLING GREEN

Brazil

CONNELY'S NEW YORK STORE

CWT	Rarity	Reverse Die	Metal	Edge	VG	VF	EF	Unc
130A-2a	R4	1022	C	PL	6	20	25	50

CONNELY'S / NEW / YORK / STORE / BRAZIL, IND.

Brooklyn

COX & LANDERS

CWT	Rarity	Reverse Die	Metal	Edge	VG	VF	EF	Unc
135A-1a	R8	1046	C	R		—	SCARCE	—

COX & LANDERS / DRY / GOODS / CLOTHING / BOOTS / & / SHOES / * BROOKLYN. IND. *

Brookville

H. LINCK

CWT	Rarity	Reverse Die	Metal	Edge	VG	VF	EF	Unc
140A-1a	R6	1019	C	PL	8	25	35	55

H. LINCK / DRY / - GOODS - / GROCERIES / & / HARDWARE / BROOKVILLE, IND.

Brownsburg

G. W. NASH

CWT	Rarity	Reverse Die	Metal	Edge	VG	VF	EF	Unc
145A-1a	R7	1311	C	R	30	100	125	175

G. W. NASH / DRUGS / MEDICINES / WINES / * LIQUORS * / NOTIONS / & C. / BROWNSBURG, IND.

Brownstown

S. S. EARLY & CO.

CWT	Rarity	Reverse Die	Metal	Edge	VG	VF	EF	Unc
150A-1a	R6	1088	C	PL	15	30	50	85

S. S. EARLY & CO. / DEALERS / IN / DRY GOODS & / GROCERIES / BROWNSTOWN, / IND.

Butler

J. LUTES

CWT	Rarity	Reverse Die	Metal	Edge	VG	VF	EF	Unc
155A-1a	R5	1122	C	PL	8	20	30	55

J. LUTES / DEALER IN / DRY GOODS / AND / GROCERIES / BUTLER, / IND.

Cadiz

C. BOND

CWT	Rarity	Reverse Die	Metal	Edge	VG	VF	EF	Unc
160A-1a	R4	1037	C	R	8	20	25	45

C. BOND above. Crossed square and compass in center. DRUGGIST / CADIZ, IND. below.

HIATT & SHOWALTER

CWT	Rarity	Reverse Die	Metal	Edge	VG	VF	EF	Unc
160B-1a	R7	1037	C	PL	10	30	45	85

HIATT & SHOWALTER / DRY / GOODS / GROCERIES / - & C - / CADIZ, IND.

Centerville

GENTRY'S GROCERS

CWT	Rarity	Reverse Die	Metal	Edge	VG	VF	EF	Unc
165A-1a	R8	1046	C	R		—	RARE	—

GENTRY'S / GROCERIES / * (ornament) * / CENTERVILLE / - IND. -

Columbia City

GAFFNEY & MCDONNELL

CWT	Rarity	Reverse Die	Metal	Edge	VG	VF	EF	Unc
175A-1a	R7	1226	C	PL	10	25	35	60

GAFFNEY & McDONNELL / GROCERIES / LIQUORS / CIGARS / & C. / COLUMBIA CITY / IND.

HARLEY & LINVILL

CWT	Rarity	Reverse Die	Metal	Edge	VG	VF	EF	Unc
175B-1a	R4	1088	C	PL	5	15	20	55

HARLEY & LINVILL / HARDWARE, / STOVES / & / TIN WARE, / COLUMBIA CITY / IND.

W. W. KEPNER & SON

CWT	Rarity	Reverse Die	Metal	Edge	VG	VF	EF	Unc
175C-1a	R6	1088	C	PL	8	20	30	50

W. W. KEPNER & SON / DRY GOODS / & / GROCERIES, / COLUMBIA CITY / * IND. *

DR. C. KINDERMANN

CWT	Rarity	Reverse Die	Metal	Edge	VG	VF	EF	Unc
175D-2a	R3	1373	C	R	5	20	25	35

DR. C. KINDERMANN / DRUGGIST / - & - / BOOK / SELLER / COLUMBIA CITY, IND.

S. S. LAVEY

CWT	Rarity	Reverse Die	Metal	Edge	VG	VF	EF	Unc
175E-1a	R7	—	C	R	20	90	110	150

S. S. LAVEY / WATCHMAKER / - & - / JEWELER / COLUMBIA CITY, IND. Rv: DEALER / IN / CLOCKS / WATCHES / - & - / JEWELRY

JOHN C. WASHBURN

CWT	Rarity	Reverse Die	Metal	Edge	VG	VF	EF	Unc
175F-1a	R6	1169	C	PL	8	20	25	45

JOHN C. WASHBURN / DRY GOODS / & / GROCERIES / COLUMBIA CITY / * IND. *

Como

JACOB GROYEN

CWT	Rarity	Reverse Die	Metal	Edge	VG	VF	EF	Unc
185A-1a	R4	1176	C	PL	10	30	40	75

JACOB GROYEN / . - . / GROCER / (ornament) / MAIN ST / . - . / COMO, IND.

Corunna

SAM'L BECK

CWT	Rarity	Reverse Die	Metal	Edge	VG	VF	EF	Unc
190A-1a	R5	1127	C	PL	8	25	35	75

SAM'L. BECK / DEALER / IN / BUTTER, EGGS / HIDES, AND / PELTS, / CORUNNA, / IND.

IRA W. BOWEN

CWT	Rarity	Reverse Die	Metal	Edge	VG	VF	EF	Unc
190B-3a	R6	1181	C	PL	8	20	25	50

IRA W. BOWEN, / DEALER / IN / DRUGS, / MEDICINES, / GROCERIES / & / HARDWARE, / *CORUNNA, IND. *

JOHN CHILDS

CWT	Rarity	Reverse Die	Metal	Edge	VG	VF	EF	Unc
190C-1a	R5	1089	C	PL	8	15	20	40

JOHN CHILDS / DEALER / IN / DRY GOODS, / GROCERIES, / * - & C. - * / CORUNNA, / * IND. *

J. L. & G. F. ROWE

CWT	Rarity	Reverse Die	Metal	Edge	VG	VF	EF	Unc
190D-1a	R5	1088	C	PL	8	15	20	40

J. L. & G. F. ROWE / DEALERS / IN / DRY GOODS / GROCERIES & C. / CORUNNA / * IND. *

Danville

R. K. CARTER

CWT	Rarity	Reverse Die	Metal	Edge	VG	VF	EF	Unc
230A-1a	R8	1046	C	R	30	90	125	175

R. K. CARTER / DRY / * GOODS * / GROCERIES / BOOTS / & / - SHOES - / DANVILLE, IND.

CRADDICK & HOMAN

CWT	Rarity	Reverse Die	Metal	Edge	VG	VF	EF	Unc
230B-1a	R6	1046	C	R	8	20	30	70

CRADDICK & HOMAN / DEALERS / IN / * BOOKS * / STATIONERY / TOBACCO / & / CIGARS / * DANVILLE, IND. *

S. A. RUSSELL

CWT	Rarity	Reverse Die	Metal	Edge	VG	VF	EF	Unc
230C-1a	R8	1046	C	R	30	100	135	200

S. A. RUSSELL / ***** / MERCHANT / . - . - . / DANVILLE / IND.

Dublin

A. JENKS

CWT	Rarity	Reverse Die	Metal	Edge	VG	VF	EF	Unc
250A-1a	R7	1037	C	R	—	RARE		—

A. JENKS / DEALER IN / DRY GOODS / - & - / * GROCERIES * / DUBLIN, IND.

Elkhart

WM. BROOKS

CWT	Rarity	Reverse Die	Metal	Edge	VG	VF	EF	Unc
260A-3a	R5	1206	C	PL	8	15	20	40

WM. BROOKS / * HARDWARE * / AND / STOVES / BATTLE CREEK / & / ELKHART.

NOTE: Inside border shows beading all around. This card is a joint token of Battle Creek, MI, and Elkhart, IN, and was mistakenly listed by Hetrich and Guttag under Battle Creek, IN, which does not exist.

J. DAVENPORT & SON

CWT	Rarity	Reverse Die	Metal	Edge	VG	VF	EF	Unc
260B-1a	R8	1003	C	PL	—	SCARCE		—

J. DAVENPORT & SON. / DEALERS / * IN * / DRY GOODS / (ornament) / IND / ELKHART.

C. T. GREENE & CO.

CWT	Rarity	Reverse Die	Metal	Edge	VG	VF	EF	Unc
260C-1a	R8	1003	C	PL	30	90	110	175

C. T. GREENE. & CO. / GROCERS / (ornament) / PROVISION / (ornament) / DEALERS / ELKHART IND.

JOHN GUIPE

CWT	Rarity	Reverse Die	Metal	Edge	VG	VF	EF	Unc
260D-1a	R5	1114	C	PL	10	20	30	60

JOHN GUIPE above. Shoe and boot in center. * DEALER * / - * - / ELKHART, IND. below.

Evansville

BITTROLFF & GEISSLER

CWT	Rarity	Reverse Die	Metal	Edge	VG	VF	EF	Unc
280A-1a	R9	Blank	C	PL	—	RARE		—

BITTROLFF & GEISSLER. / JEWELERS / EVANSVILLE / IND . Small eagle below.

P. L. GEISSLER

CWT	Rarity	Reverse Die	Metal	Edge	VG	VF	EF	Unc
280B-1bo	R9	—	BR	PL	—	RARE		—

P. L. GEISSLER / WATCH MAKER / 4 (cstp) / EVANSVILLE, IND. Rv: Blank struck over McClellan token.

Fortville

J. H. THOMAS

CWT	Rarity	Reverse Die	Metal	Edge	VG	VF	EF	Unc
285A-1a	R4	1088	C	PL	5	10	15	40

J. H. THOMAS / DEALER / IN / DRY GOODS / GROCERIES & C / FORTVILLE, / IND.

Fort Wayne

C. ANDERSON

CWT	Rarity	Reverse Die	Metal	Edge	VG	VF	EF	Unc
290A-1a	R4	1228	C	PL	5	15	20	35

C. ANDERSON / DEALER / IN / GROCERIES / & / PROVISIONS / FT. WAYNE, IND.

NOTE: This piece comes with a badly broken reverse die.

ANDERSON & EVANS

CWT	Rarity	Reverse Die	Metal	Edge	VG	VF	EF	Unc
290B-1a	R5	1226	C	PL	5	15	20	40

ANDERSON & EVANS / - * - / GROCERS / Ft. WAYNE / IND.

T. K. BRACKENRIDGE

CWT	Rarity	Reverse Die	Metal	Edge	VG	VF	EF	Unc
290C-2a	R4	1226	C	PL	8	12	15	40

PHOENIX GROCERY / T. K. BRACKENRIDGE / GROCERIES / & / PROVISIONS / Ft. WAYNE / * IND. *

A. D. BRANDIFF & CO.

CWT	Rarity	Reverse Die	Metal	Edge	VG	VF	EF	Unc
290D-1a	R6	1299	C	PL	8	15	25	45

A. D. BRANDIFF & Co. / HARDWARE / & / STOVES / Ft. WAYNE /* IND. *

W. H. BROOKS, JR.

CWT	Rarity	Reverse Die	Metal	Edge	VG	VF	EF	Unc
290E-4a	R6	1229	C	PL	5	10	12	35

W. H. BROOKS Jr. / WHOLESALE / DEALER IN / WALL & / WINDOW PAPER, / FT WAYNE, / IND.

I. LAUFERTY

CWT	Rarity	Reverse Die	Metal	Edge	VG	VF	EF	Unc
290F-1a	R5	1337	C	PL	8	20	25	45

I. LAUFERTY / - 91 - / COLUMBIA / - ST - / Ft. WAYNE, / IND.

P. PIERR

CWT	Rarity	Reverse Die	Metal	Edge	VG	VF	EF	Unc
290G-1a	R6	1088	C	PL	8	15	20	40

P. PIERR / DRY GOODS / - & - / GROCERIES / FT. WAYNE, / IND.

C. SCHOERPF & CO.

CWT	Rarity	Reverse Die	Metal	Edge	VG	VF	EF	Unc
290H-1a	R3	1316	C	PL	10	20	30	45

C. SCHOERPF & Co. / WHOLESALE / (ornament) / DRUGGISTS / Ft. WAYNE / IND.

Franklin

HULSMAN & ALEXANDER

CWT	Rarity	Reverse Die	Metal	Edge	VG	VF	EF	Unc
295A-1a	R5	1046	C	R	20	40	55	90

HULSMAN & ALEXANDER / SALOON / - SALE - / & / LIVERY / STABLE / FRANKLIN, IND.

Fremont

G. W. FOLLETT

CWT	Rarity	Reverse Die	Metal	Edge	VG	VF	EF	Unc
305A-1a	R5	1037	C	R	20	40	55	90

* G. W. FOLLETT * / DRY / GOODS / GROCERIES / (ornament) / BOOTS & SHOES / - & - / HARDWARE / FREMONT, IND.

Galveston

R. S. MCKEEN & CO.

CWT	Rarity	Reverse Die	Metal	Edge	VG	VF	EF	Unc
320A-1b	R9	—	BR	R	—	RARE		—

* R. S. McKEEN & CO * / * / 40 / * . * / DRAYAGE / * / GALVESTON Rv: ', MURDOCK & SPENCER ', / 139 / W' FIFTH / STREET / CINCINNATI

NOTE: Same as Obv. Ohio 165DZ.

Goshen

W. A. BEANE

CWT	Rarity	Reverse Die	Metal	Edge	VG	VF	EF	Unc
350A-1a	R7	1111	C	PL	20	70	80	125

DEMOCRAT JOB PRINTING OFFICE * around border. - * - / W. A. BEANE / - * - / GOSHEN / IND. / - in center.

HASCALL, ALDERMAN & BROWN

CWT	Rarity	Reverse Die	Metal	Edge	VG	VF	EF	Unc
350B-1a	R5	1111	C	PL	8	20	25	50

HASCALL, ALDERMAN & BROWN around border. DRY (ornament) / (ornament) / GOODS / (line) / GROCERIES / & C. / GOSHEN / * IND. * in center.

J. L. KINDIG

CWT	Rarity	Reverse Die	Metal	Edge	VG	VF	EF	Unc
350C-2a	R5	1046	C	R	8	15	20	45

J. L. KINDIG / DRY / * GOODS * / --- / MERCHANT / GOSHEN, IND.

WM. H. LASH & CO.

CWT	Rarity	Reverse Die	Metal	Edge	VG	VF	EF	Unc
350D-1a	R6	1111	C	PL	10	25	40	70

* WM. H. LASH & CO. * / DRY / GOODS, / ** / GROCERIES /* & C. * / GOSHEN, IND.

JOSEPH LAUFERTY

CWT	Rarity	Reverse Die	Metal	Edge	VG	VF	EF	Unc
350E-2b	R5	1339	BR	PL	10	25	40	70

JOSEPH LAUFERTY / * (flower) * / CLOTHIER / - * - / CHEAPSIDE / BL'K / GOSHEN, IND.

LAWRENCE & NOBLE

CWT	Rarity	Reverse Die	Metal	Edge	VG	VF	EF	Unc
350F-1a	R4	1114	C	PL	8	25	30	45

LAWRENCE & NOBLE / STOVES / & / HARDWARE / (padlock) / GOSHEN. IND.

C. G. MARCH

CWT	Rarity	Reverse Die	Metal	Edge	VG	VF	EF	Unc
350G-1a	R5	1111	C	PL	10	30	40	70

* C. G. MARCH * / WHOLESALE / (line) / GROCER & / (line) / DRUGGIST / (line) / IMPR. OF / - * - / LIQUORS & CIGARS / GOSHEN. IND.

Granville

C. CROOKS & CO.

CWT	Rarity	Reverse Die	Metal	Edge	VG	VF	EF	Unc
355A-1a	R5	1037	C	R	15	40	60	90

C. CROOKS & CO. / DRY / - GOODS - / HARDWARE / * BOOTS * / & / SHOES / GRANVILLE, IND.

Greenfield

CARR RYON & CO.

CWT	Rarity	Reverse Die	Metal	Edge	VG	VF	EF	Unc
360A-1a	R6	1046	C	R	15	70	85	135

CARR RYON & CO. / - * - / DRY / GOODS / - * - / GREENFIELD, IND.

Greensboro

BALDWIN & SWEET

CWT	Rarity	Reverse Die	Metal	Edge	VG	VF	EF	Unc
365A-1a	R8	1387	C	PL		—	SCARCE	—

* BALDWIN & SWEET * / DEALERS / * / ALL KINDS / OF / GROCERIES / GREENSBORO IND

Hagerstown

E. & L. SMALL

CWT	Rarity	Reverse Die	Metal	Edge	VG	VF	EF	Unc
370A-1a	R6	1007	C	PL	15	35	45	70

E. & L. SMALL / DEALER / IN / DRY GOODS / BOOTS / & / SHOES / HAGERSTOWN. IND.

Hartford City

JAS. LYON

CWT	Rarity	Reverse Die	Metal	Edge	VG	VF	EF	Unc
395A-1a	R7	1037	C	R	15	35	45	80

* JAS. LYON * / DRY / GOODS / GROCERIES / BOOTS / & SHOES / HARTFORD CITY, IND.

Huntington

WM. BICKEL

CWT	Rarity	Reverse Die	Metal	Edge	VG	VF	EF	Unc
430A-1a	R8	1226	C	PL	10	30	50	125

Wm. BICKEL / DEALER / IN / BOOKS, TOYS / AND / NOTIONS, / HUNTINGTON / IND.

BIPPUS & MORGAN

CWT	Rarity	Reverse Die	Metal	Edge	VG	VF	EF	Unc
430B-1a	R5	1301	C	PL	8	20	30	125

BIPPUS & MORGAN / DEALERS / IN / HARDWARE / HUNTINGTON / IND.

SAM BUCHANAN

CWT	Rarity	Reverse Die	Metal	Edge	VG	VF	EF	Unc
430C-1a	R6	1169	C	PL	20	40	60	125

SAM BUCHANAN / DEALER / IN / AGRICULTURAL / (ornament) / IMPLEMENTS / HUNTINGTON / IND.

JESSE DAVIES

CWT	Rarity	Reverse Die	Metal	Edge	VG	VF	EF	Unc
430D-2a	R4	1316	C	PL	10	20	30	125

** JESSE DAVIES ** / DEALER / IN / DRUGS / - AND - / MEDICINES HUNTINGTON / IND.

J. W. GRIFFITH

CWT	Rarity	Reverse Die	Metal	Edge	VG	VF	EF	Unc
430E-1a	R8	1316	C	PL	40	80	90	150

** J. W. GRIFFITH ** / DEALER / IN / DRUGS / AND / MEDICINES / HUNTINGTON / IND

J. H. INSWORTH & CO.

CWT	Rarity	Reverse Die	Metal	Edge	VG	VF	EF	Unc
430F-1a	R5	1169	C	PL	10	20	30	125

J. H. INSWORTH & CO. / DEALERS / IN / DRY GOODS / (ornament) / GROCERIES / HUNTINGTON / IND.

J. S. REAM

CWT	Rarity	Reverse Die	Metal	Edge	VG	VF	EF	Unc
430G-1a	R9	1171	C	PL	20	75	100	200

J. S. REAM, / DEALER / IN / GROCERIES / AND / PROVISIONS, / HUNTINGTON / IND.

SCHAFER & BRO.

CWT	Rarity	Reverse Die	Metal	Edge	VG	VF	EF	Unc
430H-1a	R8	1316	C	PL		—	SCARCE	—

SCHAFER & BRO. / DRUGGISTS / - & - / APOTHECARIES, / HUNTINGTON, / IND.

Indianapolis

ALVORD, CALDWELL & ALVORD

CWT	Rarity	Reverse Die	Metal	Edge	VG	VF	EF	Unc
460A-1a	R5	1037	C	R	7	15	25	45

ALVORD, CALDWELL & ALVORD. / WHOLESALE / GROCERS / 68 / E. WASH. ST. / INDIANAPOLIS

BOSTON STORE

CWT	Rarity	Reverse Die	Metal	Edge	VG	VF	EF	Unc
460B-1a	R4	1037	C	R	7	15	20	35

BOSTON STORE / DRY / GOODS / 10 / E. WASH. ST. / * INDIANAPOLIS *

C. E. GEISENDORF & CO.

CWT	Rarity	Reverse Die	Metal	Edge	VG	VF	EF	Unc
460C-1a	R5	—	C	PL	7	20	30	50

C. E. GEISENDORF & CO. / WOOL / DEALERS / - & - / MAN'FRS. Rv: HOOSIER WOOLEN / * / FACTORY / - * - / INDIANAPOLIS, IND.

G. W. GEISENDORFF & CO.

CWT	Rarity	Reverse Die	Metal	Edge	VG	VF	EF	Unc
460D-1a	R3	—	C	PL	7	15	20	45

G. W. GEISENDORFF & CO. / WOOL / DEALERS / - & - / MAN'FRS. Rv: HOOSIER WOOLEN / * / FACTORY / - * - / INDIANAPOLIS, IND.

M. H. GOOD

CWT	Rarity	Reverse Die	Metal	Edge	VG	VF	EF	Unc
460E-2a	R6	1037	C	R	7	20	25	50

M. H. GOOD / WHOLESALE / & / RETAIL / DRY / GOODS / INDIANAPOLIS

J. B. GROUT

CWT	Rarity	Reverse Die	Metal	Edge	VG	VF	EF	Unc
460F-2a	R4	1037	C	R	7	10	25	50

CITY / SHOE / STORE / J. B. GROUT / 3 & 5 / W. WASH. ST. / INDIANAPOLIS

J. C. HERETH

CWT	Rarity	Reverse Die	Metal	Edge	VG	VF	EF	Unc
460G-1a	R3	1037	C	R	7	20	25	40

J. C. HERETH / SADDLER / 89 / E. WASH. ST / INDIANAPOLIS

C. L. HOLMES

CWT	Rarity	Reverse Die	Metal	Edge	VG	VF	EF	Unc
460H-1a	R5	1037	C	R	7	15	20	50

CITY / GROCERY / - * - / C. L. HOLMES / INDIANAPOLIS

J. B. JOHNSON

CWT	Rarity	Reverse Die	Metal	Edge	VG	VF	EF	Unc
460I-1a	R3	1037	C	R	7	20	30	45

J. B. JOHNSON / GROCER / - & - / PRODUCE / DEALER / INDIANAPOLIS

CHARLES KUHN

CWT	Rarity	Reverse Die	Metal	Edge	VG	VF	EF	Unc
460J-1a	R4	1037	C	R	7	15	20	45

CHARLES KUHN / BUTCHER / 107 MICH. ST. / INDIANAPOLIS

J. F. LENOUR

CWT	Rarity	Reverse Die	Metal	Edge	VG	VF	EF	Unc
460K-2a	R6	1311	C	R	15	45	60	110

J. F. LENOUR / DRUGGIST / No 5 / BATES / HOUSE / INDIANAPOLIS

JOSEPH MCCREERY

CWT	Rarity	Reverse Die	Metal	Edge	VG	VF	EF	Unc
460L-1a	R3	—	C	PL	7	15	20	40

JOSEPH McCREERY / No. 85 / EAST / WASHINGTON ST. / IND'PLS. / - * - / * - IND. - *

MORITZ, BRO. & CO.

CWT	Rarity	Reverse Die	Metal	Edge	VG	VF	EF	Unc
460M-1a	R5	1037	C	R	7	20	30	60

MORITZ, BRO. & CO. / CLOTHIERS / CLOTHS / CASSIMERES / & / VESTINGS / INDIANAPOLIS

R. R. PARKER

CWT	Rarity	Reverse Die	Metal	Edge	VG	VF	EF	Unc
460N-1a	R5	—	C	PL	10	25	45	60

R. R. PARKER / SELLS / LADIES / AND GENTS / FURNISHING / GOODS / 30 W. / WASHINGTON, ST. / INDIANAPOLIS IND. Rv: Half length figure in center shows shirt labeled PARKER / SHIRTS / WILL FIT. Above figure, R. R. PARKER, and below, INDIANAPOLIS, IND.

POMEROY, FRY & CO.

CWT	Rarity	Reverse Die	Metal	Edge	VG	VF	EF	Unc
460O-1a	R6	1037	C	R	10	25	35	50

POMEROY, FRY & CO. / - * - / IRON / * (ornament) * / MERCHANTS / INDIANAPOLIS

ROLL & SMITH

CWT	Rarity	Reverse Die	Metal	Edge	VG	VF	EF	Unc
460P-1a	R4	1037	C	R	5	15	20	40

ROLL & SMITH / CARPETS / & / WALL PAPER / 16 ILL. ST. / INDIANAPOLIS

ROOS & SCHMALZRIED

CWT	Rarity	Reverse Die	Metal	Edge	VG	VF	EF	Unc
460Q-1a	R4	1037	C	R	7	15	20	45

ROOS & SCHMALZRIED / BUTCHERS / (ornament in center) / * / INDIANAPOLIS

J. F. SENOUR

CWT	Rarity	Reverse Die	Metal	Edge	VG	VF	EF	Unc
460R-3a	R5	1311	C	R	15	45	60	110

J. F. SENOUR / DRUGGIST / No 5 / BATES / HOUSE / INDIANAPOLIS

SMITH & TAYLOR

CWT	Rarity	Reverse Die	Metal	Edge	VG	VF	EF	Unc
460S-1a	R5	1084	C	PL	7	15	20	45

SMITH & TAYLOR / NO. / 20 / TOY STORE / NO. 20. / WASHINGTON ST. INDIANAPOLIS

M. SPENCER

CWT	Rarity	Reverse Die	Metal	Edge	VG	VF	EF	Unc
460T-1a	R6	1037	C	R	7	20	25	50

M. SPENCER / GROCER / 202 / E. WASH. ST. / INDIANAPOLIS

MRS. A. THOMSON & SON

CWT	Rarity	Reverse Die	Metal	Edge	VG	VF	EF	Unc
460U-1a	R7	1037	C	R	15	40	55	80

MRS. A. THOMSON & SON / STATIONERS / No 7 / PENN / ST. / INDIANAPOLIS

TYLER'S BEE HIVE

CWT	Rarity	Reverse Die	Metal	Edge	VG	VF	EF	Unc
460V-1a	R6	1351	C	PL	15	25	40	60

TYLER'S / BEE HIVE / DRY GOODS / 2 WEST / WASHINGTON. ST. / -- * -- / INDIANAPOLIS

VOEGTLE & METZGER

CWT	Rarity	Reverse Die	Metal	Edge	VG	VF	EF	Unc
460W-1a	R6	—	C	PL	7	20	30	50

VOEGTLE & METZGER, / No. 83 / EAST / WASHINGTON / STREET. / IND'PLS. / * IND. *

WEAVER & MAGUIRE

CWT	Rarity	Reverse Die	Metal	Edge	VG	VF	EF	Unc
460X-1a	R6	1037	C	R	7	20	40	55

WEAVER & MAGUIRE / GROCERS / -- / COR. / ILLS. ST. & IND / AVE. / INDIANAPOLIS

J. B. WILSON

CWT	Rarity	Reverse Die	Metal	Edge	VG	VF	EF	Unc
460Y-1a	R4	1037	C	R	7	15	20	55

J. B. WILSON / IN / HARDWARE / - & - / CUTLERY / INDIANAPOLIS

A. D. WOOD

CWT	Rarity	Reverse Die	Metal	Edge	VG	VF	EF	Unc
460Z-1a	R7	1037	C	R	10	35	45	70

A. D. WOOD / HARDWARE / MERCHANT / INDIANAPOLIS . Small square and compass in center.

Jamestown

G. W. WAYLAND

CWT	Rarity	Reverse Die	Metal	Edge	VG	VF	EF	Unc
470A-1a	R9	1046	C	R	—		RARE	—

G. W. WAYLAND / GOODS / - DRUGS - / MEDICINES / NOTIONS / & C. / JAMESTOWN, IND.

Jonesboro

ROBT. COODER

CWT	Rarity	Reverse Die	Metal	Edge	VG	VF	EF	Unc
495A-1a	R6	1046	C	R	—		SCARCE	—

ROBT. COODER / DRY / GOODS / - & - / GROCERIES / JONESBORO, IND.

Kendallville

BEYER, MEYER & BRO.

CWT	Rarity	Reverse Die	Metal	Edge	VG	VF	EF	Unc
500A-1a	R9	1316	C	PL	—		SCARCE	—

BEYER, MEYER & BRO. / WHOLESALE / & / RETAIL / DRUGGIST / KENDALLVILLE / IND.

BOSWORTH & WHITFORD

CWT	Rarity	Reverse Die	Metal	Edge	VG	VF	EF	Unc
500B-1a	R8	1091	C	PL	15	35	55	90

BOSWORTH & WHITFORD / DEALERS / IN / GROCERIES / - & - / PROVISIONS / KENDALLVILLE / IND.

M. M. BOWEN

CWT	Rarity	Reverse Die	Metal	Edge	VG	VF	EF	Unc
500C-1a	R8	1127	C	PL	10	40	50	70

M. M. BOWEN / DEALER IN / GROCERIES / PROVISIONS / & CEGARS / * / KENDALLVILLE, IND.

W. & J. R. BUNYAN

CWT	Rarity	Reverse Die	Metal	Edge	VG	VF	EF	Unc
500D-2a	R7	1226	C	PL	10	30	40	70

W. & J. R. BUNYAN / DEALERS IN / DRUGS / MEDICINES / PAINTS, OILS / & C. / * KENDALLVILLE, IND. *

J. F. CORLE

CWT	Rarity	Reverse Die	Metal	Edge	VG	VF	EF	Unc
500E-2a	R5	1181	C	PL	8	25	35	55

- J. F. CORLE - / DEALER IN / * / DRY GOODS & / GROCERIES / - * - / KENDALLVILLE, IND.

S. C. EVANS & CO.

CWT	Rarity	Reverse Die	Metal	Edge	VG	VF	EF	Unc
500F-2a	R6	1089	C	PL	8	20	25	55

S. C. EVANS & CO. / DEALERS / IN / DRY GOODS, / GROCERIES & C. KENDALLVILLE, / - * - / * IND. *

G. C. GLATTE

CWT	Rarity	Reverse Die	Metal	Edge	VG	VF	EF	Unc
500G-2a	R5	1181	C	PL	8	15	20	45

G. C. GLATTE / DEALER / IN / GROCERIES / PROVISIONS / & C. / KENDALLVILLE. IND.

J. H. GOTSCH

CWT	Rarity	Reverse Die	Metal	Edge	VG	VF	EF	Unc
500H-1a	R9	1321	C	PL	20	90	110	175

J. H. GOTSCH / DEALER / IN / CLOCKS, / WATCHES, / & / JEWELRY, KENDALLVILLE, IND.

E. GRADEN

CWT	Rarity	Reverse Die	Metal	Edge	VG	VF	EF	Unc
500I-1a	R3	1127	C	PL	8	15	20	45

E. GRADEN / (ornament) LIVERY & (ornament) / * / SALE / STABLE KENDALLVILLE, IND.

JACOBS & CO.

CWT	Rarity	Reverse Die	Metal	Edge	VG	VF	EF	Unc
500J-1a	R8	1083	C	PL	15	60	80	120

JACOBS & CO. / DEALERS / IN / DRY GOODS / & CLOTHING / - & - / KENDALLVILLE, IND.

JONES & MOSHER'S

CWT	Rarity	Reverse Die	Metal	Edge	VG	VF	EF	Unc
500K-1a	R7	1229	C	PL	15	50	65	100

JONES & MOSHER'S / BAKERY / & / PROVISION / STORE, / KENDALLVILLE, / * IND. * / —

J. J. JOYCE

CWT	Rarity	Reverse Die	Metal	Edge	VG	VF	EF	Unc
500L-1a	R5	1335	C	PL	—		SCARCE	—

J. J. JOYCE / DEALER / IN / GROCERIES / - * - / PROVISIONS / KENDALLVILLE / IND.

J. LANTS

CWT	Rarity	Reverse Die	Metal	Edge	VG	VF	EF	Unc
500M-1a	R5	1318	C	PL	15	40	60	80

*** J. LANTS *** / DEALER / - IN - / BOOTS & / SHOES, / KENDALLVILLE, / * IND. *

S. J. M. LOOMIS

CWT	Rarity	Reverse Die	Metal	Edge	VG	VF	EF	Unc
500N-2a	R6	1089	C	PL	10	15	25	50

S. J. M. LOOMIS / DEALER / IN / DRY GOODS / AND / GROCERIES / KENDALLVILLE / * IND. *

F. W. MESING

CWT	Rarity	Reverse Die	Metal	Edge	VG	VF	EF	Unc
500O-1a	R4	1335	C	PL	20	45	60	100

F. W. MESING / DEALER / IN / GROCERIES / & / LIQUORS / KENDALLVILLE / IND

MILLER & CROW

CWT	Rarity	Reverse Die	Metal	Edge	VG	VF	EF	Unc
500P-1a	R4	1350	C	PL	10	20	40	60

* MILLER & CROW * / DEALERS / IN / GROCERIES / (ornament) & (ornament) / PROVISIONS / KENDALLVILLE / IND.

G. S. ROWELL & SON

CWT	Rarity	Reverse Die	Metal	Edge	VG	VF	EF	Unc
500Q-1a	R5	1091	C	PL	10	15	20	50

G. S. ROWELL & SON / * / PRODUCE / DEALERS / - * - / KENDALLVILLE, IND.

STEER & BOWEN

CWT	Rarity	Reverse Die	Metal	Edge	VG	VF	EF	Unc
500R-1a	R6	1326	C	PL	15	20	30	55

STEER & BOWEN / DEALERS / IN / HARDWARE / KENDALLVILLE / * IND. *

JOSEPH THEW

CWT	Rarity	Reverse Die	Metal	Edge	VG	VF	EF	Unc
500S-1a	R8	1318	C	PL	30	70	90	165

JOSEPH THEW / MANUFR. / & / DEALER IN / BOOTS / & / SHOES, / KENDALLVILLE, IND.

W. S. THOMAS

CWT	Rarity	Reverse Die	Metal	Edge	VG	VF	EF	Unc
500T-2a	R7	1181	C	PL	10	15	25	55

W. S. THOMAS / DEALER / IN / DRY GOODS / & / GROCERIES / KENDALLVILLE, IND.

D. S. WELCH

CWT	Rarity	Reverse Die	Metal	Edge	VG	VF	EF	Unc
500U-4a	R5	1226	C	PL	10	15	25	55

D. S. WELCH / - * - / DRY GOODS / AND / GROCERIES, / KENDALLVILLE, / * IND. *

Kokomo

J. V. CULLEN

CWT	Rarity	Reverse Die	Metal	Edge	VG	VF	EF	Unc
510A-1a	R6	1122	C	PL	20	50	80	100

J. V. CULLEN / DEALER / IN / GROCERIES / KOKOMO, / (ornament) / * IND. *

HASKETT & CO.

CWT	Rarity	Reverse Die	Metal	Edge	VG	VF	EF	Unc
510B-1a	R5	—	C	PL	20	45	70	100

HASKETT & CO / NEXT / DOOR TO / JAY & DOLLMAN, / KOKOMO, / IND. Rv: GO TO THE / *** / PRAIRIE / STORE / FOR / DRY GOODS

I. N. PATTISON

CWT	Rarity	Reverse Die	Metal	Edge	VG	VF	EF	Unc
510C-1a	R7	1316	C	PL	20	65	90	125

I. N. PATTISON / DRUGGIST / KOKOMO / IND . Mortar and pestle in center.

La Porte

L. ELIEL

CWT	Rarity	Reverse Die	Metal	Edge	VG	VF	EF	Unc
530A-1a	R6	1114	C	PL	8	20	30	55

L. ELIEL / o * o / CLOTHIER / NO 1. / TEECARDEN BL'K / o * o / LA PORTE. IND.

J. FALLER & SON

CWT	Rarity	Reverse Die	Metal	Edge	VG	VF	EF	Unc
530B-1a	R6	1003	C	PL	15	30	40	80

J. FALLER & SON / WATCHMAKERS. / (ornament) / < AND > / (ornament) / JEWELERS / LA PORTE, IND.

JAS. LEWIS & CO.

CWT	Rarity	Reverse Die	Metal	Edge	VG	VF	EF	Unc
530C-2a	R3	1114	C	PL	8	15	20	45

JAS. LEWIS & CO. above beehive in center. * LA PORTE. IND. *, below.

J. M. NEUBURGER

CWT	Rarity	Reverse	Metal	Edge	VG	VF	EF	Unc
530D-1a	R6	1357	C	PL	10	30	45	80

J. M. NEUBURGER / CLOTHIER / BALL'S / CORNER / . * . / LA PORTE, IND.

NEUBURGER & HAMBURGER

CWT	Rarity	Reverse Die	Metal	Edge	VG	VF	EF	Unc
530E-1a	R7	1119	C	PL	15	60	80	100

NEUBURGER & HAMBURGER / < * > / CLOTHIERS / NO. 1 / UNION BL'K / LA PORTE / * IND. *

W. W. WALLACE

CWT	Rarity	Reverse Die	Metal	Edge	VG	VF	EF	Unc
530F-1a	R5	1115	C	PL	10	20	35	60

W. W. WALLACE. / WHOLESALE / - & - / RETAIL / GROCER / * LA PORTE, IND. *

L. D. WEBBER

CWT	Rarity	Reverse Die	Metal	Edge	VG	VF	EF	Unc
530G-2a	R3	1118	C	PL	8	25	30	70

L. D. WEBBER. / (ornament) / STOVES / - & - / HARDWARE / (ornament) / LAPORTE. IND.

Ligonier

O. ARNOLD

CWT	Rarity	Reverse Die	Metal	Edge	VG	VF	EF	Unc
550A-1a	R3	1316	C	PL	8	20	25	50

O. ARNOLD / * / DRUGGIST / AND / GROCER, / LIGONIER, / IND.

BARNEY BRO.

CWT	Rarity	Reverse Die	Metal	Edge	VG	VF	EF	Unc
550B-3a	R5	1224	C	PL	8	15	20	40

BARNEY BRO. / x / - * - / GENERAL / DRY GOODS / LIGONIER, / IND.

J. C. BEST

CWT	Rarity	Reverse Die	Metal	Edge	VG	VF	EF	Unc
550C-1a	R6	1299	C	PL	8	15	20	50

J. C. BEST / HARDWARE / STOVES / TIN WARE / & C. / LIGONIER, IND.

J. DECKER

CWT	Rarity	Reverse Die	Metal	Edge	VG	VF	EF	Unc
550D-1a	R4	1084	C	PL	8	15	20	50

J. DECKER / GROCERIES / AND / PROVISIONS / LIGONIER, / * / * IND. *

S. MIER & CO.

CWT	Rarity	Reverse Die	Metal	Edge	VG	VF	EF	Unc
550E-1a	R4	1083	C	PL	8	12	15	40

*** S. MIER & CO. *** / DRY GOODS / CLOTHING & / PRODUCE / DEALERS, / LIGONIER, / * IND. *

GEO. C. NILL

CWT	Rarity	Reverse Die	Metal	Edge	VG	VF	EF	Unc
550F-2a	R5	1310	C	PL	8	15	20	45

GEO. C. NILL / DRUGS / GROCERIES / STATIONERY & C / LIGONIER, / IND.

J. PEARCE

CWT	Rarity	Reverse Die	Metal	Edge	VG	VF	EF	Unc
550G-1a	R5	1169	C	PL	10	40	50	85

J. PEARCE, / DRUGS, / GROCERIES / & NOTIONS, / LIGONIER / IND.

NOTE: Another variety of this piece exists, that indicates the state name as Michigan, which is a die error.

E. REEVE

CWT	Rarity	Reverse Die	Metal	Edge	VG	VF	EF	Unc
550H-1a	R4	1088	C	PL	8	15	20	50

E. REEVE / GROCERIES, / CROCKERY, / GLASSWARE / & C. / LIGONIER, / IND.

STRAUS BROTHERS

CWT	Rarity	Reverse Die	Metal	Edge	VG	VF	EF	Unc
550I-1a	R4	1084	C	PL	8	12	15	35

STRAUS BROTHERS / GENERAL / DRY GOODS / CLOTHING & / PRODUCE / DEALERS / LIGONIER, IND.

C. G. VAIL

CWT	Rarity	Reverse Die	Metal	Edge	VG	VF	EF	Unc
550J-1a	R7	1088	C	PL	15	50	70	100

C. G. VAIL / (ornament) / DRY GOODS / GROCERIES / * - & C. - * / * LIGONIER, * / IND.

J. C. ZIMMERMAN

CWT	Rarity	Reverse Die	Metal	Edge	VG	VF	EF	Unc
550K-2a	R5	1224	C	PL	8	15	20	50

J. C. ZIMMERMAN / x / - * - / DRY GOODS / CLOTHING & C. / LIGONIER, / * IND. *

Lisbon

C. D. BAUGHMAN & BRO.

CWT	Rarity	Reverse Die	Metal	Edge	VG	VF	EF	Unc
560A-1a	R6	1318	C	PL	20	75	100	125

C. D. BAUGHMAN & BRO. / DEALERS / IN / DRY GOODS / - AND - / GROCERIES / LISBON, / IND.

Logansport

BOOTH & STURGES

CWT	Rarity	Reverse Die	Metal	Edge	VG	VF	EF	Unc
570A-1a	R6	1318	C	PL	8	25	30	60

* BOOTH & STURGES * / DEALERS / IN / BOOTS / AND / SHOES, / LOGANSPORT, / * IND. *

H. C. EVERSOLE

CWT	Rarity	Reverse Die	Metal	Edge	VG	VF	EF	Unc
570B-1b	R9	—	BR	PL		—	RARE	—

H. C. EVERSOLE / BROADWAY / LOGANSPORT, IND. Rv: DEALER / IN / CLOCKS / WATCHES / - & - / JEWELRY

NOTE: Same as Rev. Ind. 175E-1.

M. H. GRIDLEY

CWT	Rarity	Reverse Die	Metal	Edge	VG	VF	EF	Unc
570C-1a	R6	1326	C	PL	8	25	45	75

M. H. GRIDLEY above eagle in glory in center. LOGANSPORT, / * IND. * / (ornament) below.

A. KENDALL

CWT	Rarity	Reverse Die	Metal	Edge	VG	VF	EF	Unc
570D-1a	R7	1171	C	PL	10	25	35	65

A. KENDALL / DEALER / IN / GROCERIES / & / FLOUR / (ornament) / LOGANSPORT. IND

KING & REED

CWT	Rarity	Reverse Die	Metal	Edge	VG	VF	EF	Unc
570E-1a	R5	1304	C	PL	10	30	40	75

KING & REED / DEALERS / IN / STOVES / & / TIN WARE / (ornament) / * LOGANSPORT. IND. *

KRUG & REED

CWT	Rarity	Reverse Die	Metal	Edge	VG	VF	EF	Unc
570F-1a	R8	1304	C	PL	20	50	75	125

* KRUG & REED * / DEALERS / IN / STOVES / - & - / TIN WARE, / LOGANSPORT, / IND.

NOTE: The spelling KRUG is probably an error intended to read KING.

MCDONALD & CO.

CWT	Rarity	Reverse Die	Metal	Edge	VG	VF	EF	Unc
570G-1a	R7	1122	C	PL	15	35	45	90

** MCDONALD & CO. ** / DEALERS / IN / DRY GOODS / - AND - / CARPETS, / LOGANSPORT, / * IND. *

A. J. MURDOCK

CWT	Rarity	Reverse Die	Metal	Edge	VG	VF	EF	Unc
570H-1a	R9	1171	C	PL	20	50	75	150

A. J. MURDOCK / DEALER / IN / DRY GOODS / & / GROCERIES, / LOGANSPORT, IND.

Lynn

ELLIOTT & HINSHAW

CWT	Rarity	Reverse Die	Metal	Edge	VG	VF	EF	Unc
580A-1a1	R7	1046	C	PL	20	50	75	110

ELLIOTT & HINSHAW / DRY GOODS / - & - / GROCERIES / LYNN, IND.

J. A. HINSHAW

CWT	Rarity	Reverse Die	Metal	Edge	VG	VF	EF	Unc
580B-3a	R6	1042	C	R	20	50	75	110

J. A. HINSHAW / DRY / GOODS / - & - / GROCERIES / LYNN, IND.

Mechanicsburg

ELLIOTT & SWAIN

CWT	Rarity	Reverse Die	Metal	Edge	VG	VF	EF	Unc
600A-1a	R9	1124	C	PL		—	SCARCE	—

ELLIOTT & SWAIN / DRY GOODS, / GROCERIES / * / HARDWARE & C / MECHANICSBURG / (ornament) / INDIANA.

EZRA SWAIN

CWT	Rarity	Reverse Die	Metal	Edge	VG	VF	EF	Unc
600B-1a	R6	1124	C	PL	20	50	75	110

** EZERA SWAIN ** / DRY GOODS / GROCERIES / HARDWARE & C / MECHANICSBURG / (oranment) / INDIANA.

Middlebury

C. STUTZ

CWT	Rarity	Reverse Die	Metal	Edge	VG	VF	EF	Unc
615A-1a	R5	1037	C	R	15	30	75	95

C. STUTZ / DRY / * GOODS * / CLOTHING / (ornament) / BOOTS & SHOES / MIDDLEBURY, IND.

Middletown

W. W. COTTERAL, P. M.

CWT	Rarity	Reverse Die	Metal	Edge	VG	VF	EF	Unc
620A-2a	R5	1046	C	R	10	20	30	65

W. W. COTTERAL, P. M. above large square and compass in center. MIDDLETOWN, IND. below.

Mishawaka

H. D. HIGGINS

CWT	Rarity	Reverse Die	Metal	Edge	VG	VF	EF	Unc
630A-5a	R3	1328	C	PL	5	8	10	30

H. D. HIGGINS. / JEWELER / (ornament) / OPTICIAN / & / MF'R OF / BAROMETERS / MISHAWAKA

B. HOLCOMB

CWT	Rarity	Reverse Die	Metal	Edge	VG	VF	EF	Unc
630B-1a	R4	1049	C	PL	5	10	12	35

B. HOLCOMB / (line) / DEALER / (line) / IN / GROCERIES / (ornament) / STONEWARE / OIL & C. / MISHAWAKA.

S. H. JUDKINS

CWT	Rarity	Reverse Die	Metal	Edge	VG	VF	EF	Unc
630C-1a	R5	1114	C	PL	10	20	30	45

S. H. JUDKINS / (ornament) / GROCERIES / (ornament) / PROVISIONS / (ornament) / MISHAWAKA, IND.

Mooresville

W. H. P. WOODWARD

CWT	Rarity	Reverse Die	Metal	Edge	VG	VF	EF	Unc
640A-1a	R6	1046	C	R	10	35	45	90

W. H. P. WOODWARD / DRY / GOODS / & C. / MOORESVILLE, IND.

New Castle

M. L. POWELL

CWT	Rarity	Reverse Die	Metal	Edge	VG	VF	EF	Unc
690A-3a	R6	1299	C	PL	10	40	60	90

M. L. POWELL, / - / DEALER IN / * / STOVES / & / TIN WARE. / NEW CASTLE, IND.

New Paris

A. M. DAVIS

CWT	Rarity	Reverse Die	Metal	Edge	VG	VF	EF	Unc
710A-1a	R9	1003	C	PL		—	SCARCE	—

A. M. DAVIS. / DRY / GOODS / --- / GROCERIES / CROCKERY / * DRUGS * / & C. / NEW PARIS. IND.

North Vernon

JOHN WENTZEL

CWT	Rarity	Reverse Die	Metal	Edge	VG	VF	EF	Unc
715A-1a	R5	1299	C	PL	10	35	45	75

JOHN WENTZEL / DEALER / IN / STOVES / & / TIN WARE, / NORTH VERNON, IND.

Oldenburg

J. HOLKER

CWT	Rarity	Reverse Die	Metal	Edge	VG	VF	EF	Unc
730A-1b	R9	1391	BR	R		—	RARE	—

J. HOLKER / GOOD FOR / 1 - DRINK / AT THE / BAR / OLDENBURG, IND.

Peru

J. KREUTZER

CWT	Rarity	Reverse Die	Metal	Edge	VG	VF	EF	Unc
740A-1a	R5	1346	C	PL	8	30	40	70

* J. KREUTZER * / DEALER / IN / GLASS / QJEENSWARE / & / GROCERIES, / * PERU, IND. *

NOTE: The spelling of QUEENSWARE.

J. S. QUEEBY

CWT	Rarity	Reverse Die	Metal	Edge	VG	VF	EF	Unc
740B-6a	R2	1384	C	PL	4	8	10	20

* J. S. QUEEBY, * / DEALER / IN / DRY GOODS / & / NOTIONS, / PERU, IND.

SAINE & MILLER

CWT	Rarity	Reverse Die	Metal	Edge	VG	VF	EF	Unc
740C-1a	R6	1318	C	PL	10	30	50	80

SAINE & MILLER / GROCERIES / * / NOTIONS / BOOTS & SHOES / - * - / PERU, IND.

Pierceton

MURRAY & BRO.

CWT	Rarity	Reverse Die	Metal	Edge	VG	VF	EF	Unc
760A-1a	R6	1088	C	PL	10	25	35	60

MURRAY & BRO / DRY GOODS / - & - / GROCERIES, / PIERCETON, / * IND. *

REED & SPAYDE

CWT	Rarity	Reverse Die	Metal	Edge	VG	VF	EF	Unc
760B-1a	R5	1183	C	PL	10	45	65	150

REED & SPAYDE / DEALERS IN / DRY GOODS / & / GROCERIES / PEIRCE-TON...IND.

NOTE: Error in spelling PIERCETON.

Plainfield

JOHNSON & OURSLER

CWT	Rarity	Reverse Die	Metal	Edge	VG	VF	EF	Unc
770A-1a	R8	1037	C	R	15	40	60	90

DRY GOODS / & / CLOTHING / JOHNSON & OURSLER / PLAINFIELD, IND.

M. OSBORN

CWT	Rarity	Reverse Die	Metal	Edge	VG	VF	EF	Unc
770B-2a	R7	—	C	R	15	40	60	90

M. OSBORN / GROCERIES / NOTIONS / TOYS / & / FANCY ARTICLES / PLAIN-FIELD, IND. Rv: QUEENSWARE / WILLOW / & / WOODEN / WARE / AT / M. OS-BORN'S

I. M. SHIDLERS

CWT	Rarity	Reverse Die	Metal	Edge	VG	VF	EF	Unc
770C-1a	R6	—	C	PL	15	40	60	90

DRY GOODS / & / CLOTHING / AT / I. M. SHIDLERS / (ornament) / POST OFFICE / BUILDING / PLAINFIELD, IND. Rv: ISAAC M. SHIDLER / DEALER / IN above hat and cap in center. BOOTS & SHOES / AND / NOTIONS below.

TANSEY & BALLARD

CWT	Rarity	Reverse Die	Metal	Edge	VG	VF	EF	Unc
770D-5a	R5	1312	C	R	15	40	60	90

TANSEY & BALLARD / DEALERS / IN / DRUGS / & / MEDICINES / PLAINFIELD, IND.

Plymouth

J. M. DALE

CWT	Rarity	Reverse Die	Metal	Edge	VG	VF	EF	Unc
780A-1a	R7	1342	C	PL	15	30	45	85

J. M. DALE / DRY GOODS / GROCERIES, / CROCKERY, / BOOTS, SHOES & C / PLYMOUTH/ * IND. *

H. B. DICKSON & CO.

CWT	Rarity	Reverse Die	Metal	Edge	VG	VF	EF	Unc
780B-1a	R4	1229	C	PL	8	15	20	40

H. B. DICKSON & CO. / HARDWARE, / STOVES / AND / TIN WARE / PLYMOUTH, / IND.

H. HUMRICHOUSER

CWT	Rarity	Reverse Die	Metal	Edge	VG	VF	EF	Unc
780C-1a	R5	1222	C	PL	8	20	30	50

H. HUMRICHOUSER / GRAIN / & / PRODUCE / DEALER, / PLYMOUTH, / IND.

Richmond

C. C. BUHL

CWT	Rarity	Reverse Die	Metal	Edge	VG	VF	EF	Unc
800A-2a	R5	1299	C	PL	8	20	30	60

C. C. BUHL / DEALER / IN / STOVES AND / TIN WARE, / 51 / MAIN ST. / RICH-MOND, IND.

G. P. EMSWILER & CO.

CWT	Rarity	Reverse Die	Metal	Edge	VG	VF	EF	Unc
800B-3a	R7	1042	C	R	8	25	35	60

G. P. EMSWILER & CO. / FANCY GOODS / & / TOYS / 49 MAIN, ST. / RICHMOND, IND.

E. F. HIRST

CWT	Rarity	Reverse Die	Metal	Edge	VG	VF	EF	Unc
800C-1a	R7	1008	C	PL	8	25	35	60

E. F. HIRST / WATCH - / - MAKER / & / JEWELER / 38 MAIN ST / RICHMOND IND.

Rochester

D. S. GOULD

CWT	Rarity	Reverse Die	Metal	Edge	VG	VF	EF	Unc
810A-1a	R6	1046	C	R	10	40	60	80

* D. S. GOULD * / DRY GOODS / - & - / GROCERIES / OPP. / COURTHOUSE / SQR. / ROCHESTER, IND.

Seymour

J. F. JOHNSON

CWT	Rarity	Reverse Die	Metal	Edge	VG	VF	EF	Unc
830A-2a	R7	1223	C	PL	20	60	80	150

* J. F. JOHNSON * / NEWS / DEALER, / SEYMOUR, / IND.

South Bend

W. W. BEMENT

CWT	Rarity	Reverse Die	Metal	Edge	VG	VF	EF	Unc
860A-1a	R9	—	C	PL		—	RARE	—

W. W. BEMENT / EDGE / TOOL / (ornament) / MANF'R / SOUTH BEND. IND. Rv: H. D. HIGGINS / (ornament) / JEWELER / (ornament) / OPTICIAN / (ornament) / MISHAWAKA, IND.

BLOWNEY & JOHNSON

CWT	Rarity	Reverse Die	Metal	Edge	VG	VF	EF	Unc
860B-1a	R8	1161	C	PL	30	60	90	175

BLOWNEY & JOHNSON / MFR'S / COMPOSITION / ROOFING / (ornament) / SOUTH BEND IND.

S. M. CHORD

CWT	Rarity	Reverse Die	Metal	Edge	VG	VF	EF	Unc
860C-1a	R3	1233A	C	PL	5	10	12	30

* + S. M. CHORD + * / DEALER IN / DRY GOODS / GROCERIES / CROCKERY / CARPETS & C. / + SOUTH BEND IND. +

HAMMONDS

CWT	Rarity	Reverse Die	Metal	Edge	VG	VF	EF	Unc
860D-1a	R5	1106	C	PL	10	30	45	100

HAMMONDS / . * . / SHOE / STORE / . * . / SOUTH BEND, IND.

J. C. KNOBLOCK

CWT	Rarity	Reverse Die	Metal	Edge	VG	VF	EF	Unc
860E-1a	R4	1099	C	PL	8	12	15	40

J. C. KNOBLOCK / AGT. / BAKER / - & - / CROCKER / (ornament) / SOUTH BEND. IND.

A. M. PURDY

CWT	Rarity	Reverse Die	Metal	Edge	VG	VF	EF	Unc
860F-1a	R4	1110	C	PL	8	20	25	60

A. M. PURDY / NURSERYMAN / & / FRUIT / * / GROWER / ***** / SOUTH BEND, IND

GEORGE WYMAN

CWT	Rarity	Reverse Die	Metal	Edge	VG	VF	EF	Unc
860G-5a	R6	1205	C	PL	8	20	30	55

GEORGE WYMAN / FANCY / DRY GOODS / SOUTH BEND / IND.

Sullivan

PRICE BROTHERS

CWT	Rarity	Reverse Die	Metal	Edge	VG	VF	EF	Unc
870A-2a	R6	1042	C	R	15	45	60	100

PRICE BROTHERS / DRY / GOODS / CLOTHING / BOOTS & SHOES / & C. / SULLIVAN, IND.

Swan

D. H. HAINES & BRO.

CWT	Rarity	Reverse Die	Metal	Edge	VG	VF	EF	Unc
880A-1a	R6	1223	C	PL	15	50	70	100

D. H. HAINES & BRO. / DEALERS / IN / DRY GOODS / GROCERIES / & C / SWAN. IND.

Terre Haute

FRANK HEINIG & BRO.

CWT	Rarity	Reverse Die	Metal	Edge	VG	VF	EF	Unc
890A-1a	R8	—	C	PL	—	SCARCE		—

FRANK HEINIG & BRO. above large eagle in center. * TERRE HAUTE, IND. * below. Rv: UNION STEAM BAKERY / GOOD / FOR ONE / FIVE / CENT / * LOAF OF BREAD *

NOTE: This piece may possibly be post-Civil War vintage.

Valparaiso

BARTHOLOMEW & MCCLELLAND

CWT	Rarity	Reverse Die	Metal	Edge	VG	VF	EF	Unc
915A-2a	R5	1238	C	PL	10	25	35	75

BARTHOLOMEW & McCLELLAND. * around edge. DRY GOODS / BOOTS & SHOES / * & C. * / IND. / VALPARISO.

NOTE: Spelling of VALPARAISO.

Vincennes

CHAS. F. RAKER

CWT	Rarity	Reverse Die	Metal	Edge	VG	VF	EF	Unc
930A-1b	R9	1394	BR	R	—	RARE		—

CHAS. F. RAKER / DEALER / IN / DRY GOODS / - & - / GROCERIES / VINCENNES, IND.

Wabash

GORDON & THURSTON

CWT	Rarity	Reverse Die	Metal	Edge	VG	VF	EF	Unc
940A-1a	R6	—	C	PL	15	50	70	100

GORDON & THURSTON / DEALERS / IN / DRUGS, / BOOKS / & / JEWELRY, / WABASH, IND. Rv: DRUGS & MEDICINES above. Mortar and pestle in a circle of 13 stars in center. . 1863 . below.

Warsaw

D. CARLILE

CWT	Rarity	Reverse Die	Metal	Edge	VG	VF	EF	Unc
950A-4b	R8	1400	BR	PL	15	80	100	150

D. CARLILE / DEALER / IN / OYSTERS / CONFCTIONERY / CIGARS / & C. / WARSAW, IND.

NOTE: Incorrect spelling of CONFECTIONERY.

JOHN LANE

CWT	Rarity	Reverse Die	Metal	Edge	VG	VF	EF	Unc
950B-1a	R9	Blank	C	PL	—	RARE		—

- * - / JOHN LANE / WATCH MAKER / - & - / JEWELER, / WARSAW, / IND.

D. R. POTTENGER & CO.

CWT	Rarity	Reverse Die	Metal	Edge	VG	VF	EF	Unc
950C-1a	R7	1316	C	PL	15	25	70	110

D. R. POTTENGER & CO. / DRUGGISTS, above small mortar and pestle in center. WARSAW, IND. below.

Wheeling

J. G. WILLIAMS & CO.

CWT	Rarity	Reverse Die	Metal	Edge	VG	VF	EF	Unc
970A-1a	R9	1046	C	R	—	SCARCE		—

* J. G. WILLIAMS & CO. * / DRY / GOODS / * / HARDWARE / BOOTS / & / SHOES / WHEELING, IND.

Wolf Creek

G. HAINES

CWT	Rarity	Reverse Die	Metal	Edge	VG	VF	EF	Unc
995A-1a	R6	1046	C	R	10	20	30	50

WOLF / CREEK / PIKE / (ornament) / * G. HAINES *

IOWA

Cedar Rapids

NEW YORK STORE

CWT	Rarity	Reverse Die	Metal	Edge	VG	VF	EF	Unc
150A-1a	R6	—	C	PL	75	150	225	325

YOU CAN BUY / *** / GOODS CHEAP / AT THE / NEW YORK / STORE / CEDAR RAPIDS, IOWA. Rv: REYNOLDS & CO above female head to left in center. NEW YORK STORE below.

Lansing

WM. FLEMMING & BRO.

CWT	Rarity	Reverse Die	Metal	Edge	VG	VF	EF	Unc
560A-1a	R7	1037	C	R	75	150	225	275

WM. FLEMMING & BRO. / LUMBER / (ornament) / LATH / - & - / SHINGLES / LANSING, IOWA

Lyons

GAGE, LYALL & KEELER

CWT	Rarity	Reverse Die	Metal	Edge	VG	VF	EF	Unc
570A-1a	R6	1368	C	PL	75	150	225	325

GAGE, LYALL & KEELER. / GROCERS / MAIN. ST / LYONS / IOWA.

Waterloo

H. & G. GOODHUE

CWT	Rarity	Reverse Die	Metal	Edge	VG	VF	EF	Unc
930A-1a	R9	1046	C	R	—	SCARCE		—

H. & G. GOODHUE / LATH SHINGLES / - & - / LUMBER / SASH, / BLIND / & DOOR / FACTORY / WATERLOO, IOWA

KANSAS

Leavenworth

A. COHEN

CWT	Rarity	Reverse Die	Metal	Edge	VG	VF	EF	Unc
550A-1a	R7	1085	C	PL	500	1,250	1,500	2,000

A. COHEN / CLOTHING, / AND GENTS / FURNISHING GOODS / 21 DELAWARE ST / LEAVENWORTH / KANSAS

KENTUCKY

Covington

ARBEITER HALLE

CWT	Rarity	Reverse Die	Metal	Edge	VG	VF	EF	Unc
150A-4a	R2	1042	C	R	10	30	40	80

ARBEITER / - * - / HALLE / PIKE / ST. / COVINGTON, KY.

COV. & CIN. FERRY CO.

CWT	Rarity	Reverse Die	Metal	Edge	VG	VF	EF	Unc
150B-1a	R7	1042	C	R		—	SCARCE	—

COV. & CIN. / - * - / FERRY / COMPANY

J. DOLMAN

CWT	Rarity	Reverse Die	Metal	Edge	VG	VF	EF	Unc
150C-1a	R4	1278	C	PL	10	30	40	80

* J. DOLMAN * / STOCKING / (ornament) / MANUFACTURER / * COV. KY. *

V. C. ENGERT

CWT	Rarity	Reverse Die	Metal	Edge	VG	VF	EF	Unc
150D-2a	R5	1026	C	PL	10	50	70	100

V. C. ENGERT / GERMANIA / SALOON / 6' ST. / COVINGTON, KY.

Henderson

W. S. JOHNSON & BRO.

CWT	Rarity	Reverse Die	Metal	Edge	VG	VF	EF	Unc
370A-1a	R9	—	C	PL		—	RARE	—

W. S. JOHNSON & BRO, / (ornament) / DRUGGISTS / (ornament) / HENDERSON / KY. Rv: * SODA CHECK * above 1 (in circular design) in center. GLASS below.

Lexington

J. L. KEININGHAM

CWT	Rarity	Reverse Die	Metal	Edge	VG	VF	EF	Unc
480A-1a	R8	1047	C	R		—	RARE	—

J. L. KEININGHAM / GROCER / LEXINGTON / - KY. -

JOHN W. LEE

CWT	Rarity	Reverse Die	Metal	Edge	VG	VF	EF	Unc
480B-3a	R7	—	C	R		—	SCARCE	—

JOHN W. LEE / BAKER / CONFECTIONER / 10 MAIN ST. / LEXINGTON, KY . Rv: ONE / HALF / PINT / OF / MILK

Louisville

H. MILLER & CO.

CWT	Rarity	Reverse Die	Metal	Edge	VG	VF	EF	Unc
510A-1b	R7	—	BR	PL		—	SCARCE	—

MADE BY H. MILLER & CO. / 1 / PINT / LOUISVILLE . Rv: - A. - / WEBER / (ornament)

H. PREISSLER

CWT	Rarity	Reverse Die	Metal	Edge	VG	VF	EF	Unc
510B-1a	R5	—	C	PL		—	SCARCE	—

H. PREISSLER / LOUISVILLE / KENTUCKY . Rv: 2 crossed arrows on a snake.

Newport

J. BUTCHER'S

CWT	Rarity	Reverse Die	Metal	Edge	VG	VF	EF	Unc
640A-2a	R6	1030	C	PL	15	60	90	125

J. BUTCHER'S / DRY / GOODS / STORE / NEWPORT, KY.

NEWPORT & COVINGTON BRIDGE COMPANY

CWT	Rarity	Reverse Die	Metal	Edge	VG	VF	EF	Unc
640B-3a	R7	1042	C	R		—	RARE	—

N'PT & COV / three stars (rose) three stars / BRIDGE / three stars (rose) three stars / COMPANY

MAINE

Bangor

R. S. TORREY

CWT	Rarity	Reverse Die	Metal	Edge	VG	VF	EF	Unc
100A-2a	R4	1200	C	PL	20	40	50	75

* R. S. TORREY, * / INVENTOR / OF THE / MAINE STATE / BEEHIVE / (ornament) / 1864 / BANGOR, ME.

MARYLAND

Baltimore

MOUNT VERNON CLUB

CWT	Rarity	Reverse Die	Metal	Edge	VG	VF	EF	Unc
60A-1b	R7	1001	BR	PL	100	250	325	450

* MOUNT VERNON * / 5 / CLUB

SHAKESPERE CLUB

CWT	Rarity	Reverse Die	Metal	Edge	VG	VF	EF	Unc
60B-1b	R6	1001	BR	PL	100	250	325	450

SHAKESPERE CLUB / 5 / BALTO.

Hagerstown

G. R. BOWMAN

CWT	Rarity	Reverse Die	Metal	Edge	VG	VF	EF	Unc
560A-1b	R8	—	BR	PL		—	RARE	—

G. R. BOWMAN / CONFECTIONER / 1862 / HAGERSTOWN, Md.

Snow Hill

*** See Charleston, WV (CWT #100B-1a)

MASSACHUSETTS

Boston

COMER'S COMMERCIAL COLLEGE

CWT	Rarity	Reverse Die	Metal	Edge	VG	VF	EF	Unc
115A-1e	R7	—	V	PL		—	SCARCE	—

COMER'S / (ornament) / COMMERCIAL / (ornament) / COLLEGE, / (ornament) / BOSTON. Rv: * COLLEGE * / 1 / BANK

DUNN & CO'S

CWT	Rarity	Reverse Die	Metal	Edge	VG	VF	EF	Unc
115B-2a	R5	1414	C	PL	8	15	20	45

* DUNN & COs * above. 1864 within wreath of 24 leaves in center. OYSTER HOUSE below.

EXCELSIOR CLUB

CWT	Rarity	Reverse Die	Metal	Edge	VG	VF	EF	Unc
115C-1e	R9	1284	V	PL		—	RARE	—

EXCELSIOR / 22 / ELM / ST. / CLUB.

MERRIAM & CO.

CWT	Rarity	Reverse Die	Metal	Edge	VG	VF	EF	Unc
115D-1e	R8	1284	V	PL		—	RARE	—

* MERRIAM & CO. * / 19 / BRATTLE / SQR. / BOSTON

JOS. H. MERRIAM

CWT	Rarity	Reverse Die	Metal	Edge	VG	VF	EF	Unc
115E-1a	R5	1284	C	PL	15	60	75	100

JOS. H. MERRIAM / MEDALIST, / DIE SINKER / - AND - / LETTER CUTTER / ESTABLISHED 1850 / No. 18 / BRATTLE SQUARE. BOSTON.

PULMONALES

CWT	Rarity	Reverse Die	Metal	Edge	VG	VF	EF	Unc
115EA-1a	R5	1371	C	PL		—	RARE	—

** PULMONALES ** / * / (ornament) FOR (ornament) / * / COUGHS / (ornament) AND (ornament) / COLDS

SAM'S INN

CWT	Rarity	Reverse Die	Metal	Edge	VG	VF	EF	Unc
115F-1e	R9	1284	V	PL		—	RARE	—

* SAM'S * / 10 / INN

C. F. TUTTLE

CWT	Rarity	Reverse Die	Metal	Edge	VG	VF	EF	Unc
115G-1a	R6	—	C	PL	20	70	90	125

* C. F. TUTTLE'S * above. Steer's head in center. RESTAURANT below. Rv: * 130 WASHINGTON ST. BOSTON * / GOOD FOR / 5 / CENTS IN / REFRESHMENTS

Fall River

E. P. FRANCIS

CWT	Rarity	Reverse Die	Metal	Edge	VG	VF	EF	Unc
260A-1a	R5	—	C	PL	5	10	12	50

E. P. FRANCIS with thirteen stars around border. CITY / HOTEL / - . - / FALL RIVER / MASS / 1854 in center. Rv: BILLIARD ROOM & RESTAURANT around border. No. / 27 = 31 / PLEASANT / STREET in center.

Harvard

A. & C. F. WRIGHT

CWT	Rarity	Reverse Die	Metal	Edge	VG	VF	EF	Unc
320A-1a	R5	1120	C	PL	10	40	60	100

BAY STATE / HORSE POWER / SEND FOR / CIRCULAR / A & C. F. WRIGHT / HARVARD. / MASS.

Nantucket

U. S. SANITARY COMMISSION

CWT	Rarity	Reverse Die	Metal	Edge	VG	VF	EF	Unc
530A-1a	R5	1138	C	PL	8	20	35	95

GOD LOVETH A CHEERFUL GIVER / GREAT FAIR / IN AID OF THE / U. S. / SANITARY / COMMISSION, / NANTUCKET, / MASS. / AUGUST, 1864.

Worcester

CHARLES LANG

CWT	Rarity	Reverse Die	Metal	Edge	VG	VF	EF	Unc
970A-1a	R4	—	C	PL	8	35	50	75

* CHARLES LANG * above head to left in center. * 1863 * below. Rv: DIE SINKER / & / GEN'L / ENGRAVER / *** / WORCESTER, MS.

MICHIGAN

Addison

SMITH BROTHERS

CWT	Rarity	Reverse Die	Metal	Edge	VG	VF	EF	Unc
3A-1a	R4	—	C	PL	10	25	30	40

* SMITH BROTHERS, * / sheaf of wheat / ADDISON, MICH . Rv: DEALERS IN / (ornament) / DRY GOODS / GROCERIES / & HARDWARE / -- / --1863-- .

Adrian

BLACKMAN & DIBBLE

CWT	Rarity	Reverse Die	Metal	Edge	VG	VF	EF	Unc
5A-1a	R4	1183	C	PL	5	15	20	35

BLACKMAN & DIBBLE / ******* / DRUGGISTS / (ornament) / * / ADRIAN....MICH. *

BUCK & FARRAR

CWT	Rarity	Reverse Die	Metal	Edge	VG	VF	EF	Unc
5B-2a	R4	1099	C	PL	6	15	20	35

BUCK & FARRAR / DEALERS / IN / HARDWARE, / STOVES, / & TIN, / ADRIAN, MICH.

J. A. CASTLE

CWT	Rarity	Reverse Die	Metal	Edge	VG	VF	EF	Unc
5C-3a	R3	1098	C	PL	5	10	12	35

J. A. CASTLE / GROCER / MAUMEE / ST. / ADRIAN.MICH.

REMMINGTON & BENNETT

CWT	Rarity	Reverse Die	Metal	Edge	VG	VF	EF	Unc
5D-3a	R5	1105	C	PL	5	12	15	40

REMMINGTON & BENNETT / DRUGGISTS / (ornament) / & / GROCERS. / MAUMEE ST. / ADRIAN

S. SAMMONS

CWT	Rarity	Reverse Die	Metal	Edge	VG	VF	EF	Unc
5E-1a	R6	1098	C	PL	5	20	25	40

S. SAMMONS / INN / KEEPER / MANSION / (ornament) / HOUSE / (ornament) / * MAUMEE St. ADRIAN *

WM. S. WILCOX

CWT	Rarity	Reverse Die	Metal	Edge	VG	VF	EF	Unc
5F-2a	R4	1097	C	PL	5	8	10	35

WM. S. WILCOX / (line) / DEALER / (line) / IN / HARDWARE / (ornament) / ADRIAN.MICH.

Albion

IRA MAYHEW

CWT	Rarity	Reverse Die	Metal	Edge	VG	VF	EF	Unc
25A-1a	R3	—	C	PL	4	6	8	15

ALBION COMMERCIAL COLLEGE. / IRA MAYHEW, / (ornament) PRES'T, (ornament) / ALBION, / * MICH. * Rv: MAYHEW'S PRACTICAL BOOK-KEEPING - 1863- around. THE / CHEAPEST / AND THE / BEST in center.

COMSTOCK & BRO.

CWT	Rarity	Reverse Die	Metal	Edge	VG	VF	EF	Unc
25B-2a	R5	1203	C	PL	8	15	20	40

COMSTOCK & BRO. / Mortar and pestle / DRUGGISTS, / ALBION, / MICH.

Almont

D. W. RICHARDSON

CWT	Rarity	Reverse Die	Metal	Edge	VG	VF	EF	Unc
35A-2a	R4	1099	C	PL	10	25	30	50

D. W. RICHARDSON / - * - / DRUGS / AND / BOOKS / - * - / ALMONT, MICH.

Ann Arbor

PHILIP BACH

CWT	Rarity	Reverse Die	Metal	Edge	VG	VF	EF	Unc
40A-1a	R3	1015	C	PL	5	8	10	20

PHILIP BACH / -- / DRY / * GOODS * / -- / 1863.

DEAN & CO.

CWT	Rarity	Reverse Die	Metal	Edge	VG	VF	EF	Unc
40B-1a	R3	1015	C	PL	5	8	10	20

DEAN & CO. / HOUSE / FURNISHING / * GOODS. * / 1863.

C. H. MILLEN

CWT	Rarity	Reverse Die	Metal	Edge	VG	VF	EF	Unc
40C-1a	R4	1095	C	PL	4	10	15	25

C. H. MILLEN / DEALER / IN / DRY GOODS / & GROCERIES / ANN ARBOR / MICH.

STEBBINS & WILSON

CWT	Rarity	Reverse Die	Metal	Edge	VG	VF	EF	Unc
40D-1a	R2	1314	C	PL	5	8	10	20

* STEBBINS & WILSON * / DRY GOODS / AND / GROCERIES / BUSINESS CARD

NOTE: D in DRY is close to T in STEBBINS.

WM. WAGNER

CWT	Rarity	Reverse Die	Metal	Edge	VG	VF	EF	Unc
40E-2a	R3	1095	C	PL	5	12	15	25

WM. WAGNER / . * . / MERCHANT / TAILOR. / DEALER IN / CLOTHING / ANN ARBOR, MICH.

Atlas

F. J. & J. PALMER'S WOOLEN FACTORY

CWT	Rarity	Reverse Die	Metal	Edge	VG	VF	EF	Unc
45A-2a	R3	1031	C	PL	10	30	40	60

F. J. & J. PALMER'S / WOOLEN / FACTORY / ATLAS, / GENESEE, CO. MICH.

Battle Creek

V. P. COLLIER

CWT	Rarity	Reverse Die	Metal	Edge	VG	VF	EF	Unc
60A-2a	R7	1187	C	PL		—	SCARCE	—

V. P. COLLIER / * GENERAL * / (ornament) / * HARDWARE * / No. 40 / BATTLE CREEK MICH

J. B. LEONARD

CWT	Rarity	Reverse Die	Metal	Edge	VG	VF	EF	Unc
60B-1a	R7	1186	C	PL		—	SCARCE	—

J. B. LEONARD / BOOT / - & - / SHOE / MAKER, / BATTLE CREEK, MIC

J. STUART & SON

CWT	Rarity	Reverse Die	Metal	Edge	VG	VF	EF	Unc
60C-1a	R5	1098	C	PL		—	SCARCE	—

J. STUART & SON / STOVES / (ornament) / HARDWARE / IRON & / NAILS / BATTLE CREEK.

Bay City

BINDER & CO.

CWT	Rarity	Reverse Die	Metal	Edge	VG	VF	EF	Unc
65A-1a	R4	1095	C	PL	10	20	25	40

BINDER & CO. / DEALERS / IN / DRY GOODS / GROCERIES / HARDWARE / & C. / BAY CITY, MICH.

Brighton

ROSWELL BARNES

CWT	Rarity	Reverse Die	Metal	Edge	VG	VF	EF	Unc
85A-1a	R6	1037	C	R	20	50	70	150

ROSWELL BARNES / MAKER & DEALER / - IN - / BOOTS & SHOES / BRIGHTON, MICH.

WM. R. COBB

CWT	Rarity	Reverse Die	Metal	Edge	VG	VF	EF	Unc
85B-1a	R5	1039	C	R	25	60	80	160

WM. R. COBB / DRY / GOODS / - & - / GROCERIES / (ornament) / BRIGHTON, MICH.

W. H. NAYLOR

CWT	Rarity	Reverse Die	Metal	Edge	VG	VF	EF	Unc
85C-1a	R5	1039	C	R	20	60	70	120

W. H. NAYLOR / DEALER IN / HARDWARE / - & - / CUTLERY. / BRIGHTON, MICH.

Buchanan

WEAVER & FOX

CWT	Rarity	Reverse Die	Metal	Edge	VG	VF	EF	Unc
90A-2a	R3	1110	C	PL	10	25	30	50

WEAVER & FOX / STOVES / TIN. / HARDWARE / & C / BUCHANAN / MICH.

Cassopolis

BOYD & BRADLEY

CWT	Rarity	Reverse Die	Metal	Edge	VG	VF	EF	Unc
135A-1a	R9	1003	C	PL		—	RARE	—

BOYD & BRADLEY. / WHOLESALE / + & + / RETAIL * / (ornament) / GROCERIES / MICH / CASSAPOLIS.

Charlotte

C. CUMMINGS

CWT	Rarity	Reverse Die	Metal	Edge	VG	VF	EF	Unc
160A-1a	R6	1168	C	PL	10	25	35	65

C. CUMMINGS / DRY GOODS / GROCERIES, / BOOTS SHOES & C. / CHARLOTTE / MICH

HIGBY & BROTHER

CWT	Rarity	Reverse Die	Metal	Edge	VG	VF	EF	Unc
160B-1a	R3	1225	C	PL	10	25	35	55

HIGBY & BROTHER / GENERAL / MERCHANTS / CHARLOTTE, / * MICH. *

J. MIKESELL & BRO.

CWT	Rarity	Reverse Die	Metal	Edge	VG	VF	EF	Unc
160C-1a	R5	1225	C	PL	10	25	30	45

J. MIKESELL & BRO. / DEALERS / IN / GROCERIES, / AND / PROVISIONS. / CHARLOTTE, MICH.

C. J. PIPER

CWT	Rarity	Reverse Die	Metal	Edge	VG	VF	EF	Unc
160D-1a	R5	1317	C	PL	15	40	50	90

C. J. PIPER / (ornament) / GROCERIES, / BOOTS, SHOES & C. / CHARLOTTE, / MICH.

Chelsea

CONGDON BROTHERS

CWT	Rarity	Reverse Die	Metal	Edge	VG	VF	EF	Unc
175A-2a	R6	1186	C	PL		—	SCARCE	—

CONGDON BROTHERS / DRY / GOODS / GROCERIS / - & - / HARDWARE / CHELSEA...MICH.

NOTE: Incorrect spelling of GROCERIES.

Clarkston

M. H. CLARK

CWT	Rarity	Reverse Die	Metal	Edge	VG	VF	EF	Unc
180A-1a	R5	1042	C	R	5	10	12	30

M. H. CLARK / DRY / GOODS / HARDWARE / BOOTS / & / SHOES / CLARKSTON, MICH.

R. & J. T. PETER

CWT	Rarity	Reverse Die	Metal	Edge	VG	VF	EF	Unc
180B-2a	R5	1042	C	R	10	25	30	65

R & J. T. PETER / * / (ornament) / DRUGGISTS / CLARKSTON

Coldwater

N. T. WATERMAN

CWT	Rarity	Reverse Die	Metal	Edge	VG	VF	EF	Unc
185A-1a	R8	1111	C	PL		—	RARE	—

N. T. WATERMAN / (ornament) / BOOKS / & / JEWELERY / (ornament) / COLDWATER.MICH.

Constantine

E. H. SHELDON

CWT	Rarity	Reverse Die	Metal	Edge	VG	VF	EF	Unc
190A-1a	R2	—	C	PL	4	10	12	20

BUY YOUR HARDWARE / (ornament) / OF / E. H. SHELDON / (ornament) / CONSTANTINE / -- MICH -- Rv: E. H. SHELDON. ***** 1863 ***** around shield with ribbon in center.

Corunna

H. A. CRANE

CWT	Rarity	Reverse Die	Metal	Edge	VG	VF	EF	Unc
200A-1a	R5	1094	C	PL	5	10	15	40

H. A. CRANE / (ornament) / STOVES / & / HARDWARE. / *** / CORUNNA, MICH.

G. W. GOODELL

CWT	Rarity	Reverse Die	Metal	Edge	VG	VF	EF	Unc
200B-1a	R4	1094	C	PL	5	15	20	40

G. W. GOODELL / (curved line) / DRUGS, / (curved line) / MEDICINES / (line) / & C. / (line) / CORUNNA, MICH.

Detroit

W. J. ADDERLEY

CWT	Rarity	Reverse Die	Metal	Edge	VG	VF	EF	Unc
225A-3a	R3	1069	C	R	4	8	10	25

* W. J. ADDERLEY * / GROCER / 157 / GRATOIT / ST. / DETROIT

AMERICAN COFFEE MILLS

CWT	Rarity	Reverse Die	Metal	Edge	VG	VF	EF	Unc
225B-3a	R6	1042	C	R	10	25	35	60

AMERICAN / COFFEE / MILLS / 25 JEFF. AVE / DETROIT

T. H. ARMSTROMG

CWT	Rarity	Reverse Die	Metal	Edge	VG	VF	EF	Unc
225C-2a	R5	1042	C	R	8	15	20	45

T. H. ARMSTRONG / DEALER / IN / HATS / CAPS AND FURS / DETROIT

BLINDBURY'S HOTEL

CWT	Rarity	Reverse Die	Metal	Edge	VG	VF	EF	Unc
225D-1a	R2	1018	C	R	4	8	10	20

BLINDBURY'S / HOTEL / ANTISDEL / & / HILLS / DETROIT, MICH.

G. BAMLET

CWT	Rarity	Reverse Die	Metal	Edge	VG	VF	EF	Unc
225E-1a	R6	1039	C	R	8	20	25	35

G. BAMLET / GROCER / & / PRODUCE / DEALER / 17 GR. RIV. ST / DETROIT

L. W. BARIE

CWT	Rarity	Reverse Die	Metal	Edge	VG	VF	EF	Unc
225F-1a	R5	1019	C	R	4	10	12	35

L. W. BARIE / BAKER / 114 / FORT / ST / DETROIT

GEO. BEARD & SON

CWT	Rarity	Reverse Die	Metal	Edge	VG	VF	EF	Unc
225G-1a	R5	1025	C	R	8	20	25	40

GEO. BEARD & SON / OYSTER / FRUIT / FISH & GAME / DEPOT / DETROIT

H. W. BEESON

CWT	Rarity	Reverse Die	Metal	Edge	VG	VF	EF	Unc
225H-1a	R4	1025	C	R	4	10	12	40

H. W. BEESON / GROCERIES / & / SHIP / - STORES - / 22 WOODWARD AVE / DETROIT

FR. BEHR

CWT	Rarity	Reverse Die	Metal	Edge	VG	VF	EF	Unc
225I-1a	R9	—	C	PL	—	RARE	—	

FR. BEHR / Bear standing up holding a mug in right paw. Rv: EIN GLAS BIER / wreath with ten pin and ball.

FRED'K. C. BLOME

CWT	Rarity	Reverse Die	Metal	Edge	VG	VF	EF	Unc
225J-1a	R4	1042	C	R	8	12	15	30

FRED'K C. BLOME / DRY / GOODS / 61 WOOD. AVE / DETROIT

BROEG & GERBER

CWT	Rarity	Reverse Die	Metal	Edge	VG	VF	EF	Unc
225K-1a	R3	1025	C	R	8	20	25	40

BROEG & GERBER / BUTCHERS / 35 / MICH. / AVE. / DETROIT

F. A. BURKHART

CWT	Rarity	Reverse Die	Metal	Edge	VG	VF	EF	Unc
225L-2a	R7	1039	C	R	4	12	15	30

F. A. BURKHART / BUTCHER / COR. / HASTING - / - & GRATOIT / STS. / DETROIT

CHARLES BUSCH

CWT	Rarity	Reverse Die	Metal	Edge	VG	VF	EF	Unc
225M-1a	R3	1018	C	R	4	10	12	30

CHARLES BUSCH / HARDWARE / STOVES - / & / - GRATES / 201. JEFF. AVE. / DETROIT

CAMPBELL & CALNON

CWT	Rarity	Reverse Die	Metal	Edge	VG	VF	EF	Unc
225MA-3a	R6	1042	C	R	10	25	35	50

CAMPBELL & CALNON / GROCERS / MICH. / GRAND AVE. / DETROIT.

CAMPBELL. LINN & CO.

CWT	Rarity	Reverse Die	Metal	Edge	VG	VF	EF	Unc
225N-1a	R2	—	C	PL	4	6	8	15

CAMPBELL. LINN & CO. / Thistle in center / .BUSINESS CARD. Rv: SCOTCH STORE / DRY GOODS / AND / MILLINERY / * DETROIT MICH *

H. A. CHRISTIANSEN

CWT	Rarity	Reverse Die	Metal	Edge	VG	VF	EF	Unc
225O-1a	R3	1018	C	R	4	10	12	25

H. A. CHRISTIANSEN / GROCERIES / & / PROVISIONS / - . - / 259 JEFF. AVE / DETROIT

G. & W. CLARK

CWT	Rarity	Reverse Die	Metal	Edge	VG	VF	EF	Unc
225P-2a	R5	1039	C	R	8	20	30	50

G & W. CLARK / BUTCHERS / COR. / LARNED & 1'ST / DETROIT

S. COHEN

CWT	Rarity	Reverse Die	Metal	Edge	VG	VF	EF	Unc
225Q-1a	R5	1027	C	R	8	25	35	55

S. COHEN / CLOTHING / DEALER / - . - / 155 JEFF. AVE / DETROIT

A. W. COPLAND

CWT	Rarity	Reverse Die	Metal	Edge	VG	VF	EF	Unc
225R-1a	R6	1039	C	R	8	20	25	55

A. W. COPLAND'S / STEAM / BAKERY / 20 MONROE, AVE. / DETROIT

C. L. CROSBY

CWT	Rarity	Reverse Die	Metal	Edge	VG	VF	EF	Unc
225S-2a	R6	1042	C	R	8	20	25	55

C. L. ROSBY / FRUIT / - & - / PRODUCE / DEALER / DETROIT

GEO. E. CURTIS

CWT	Rarity	Reverse Die	Metal	Edge	VG	VF	EF	Unc
225T-1a	R4	1027	C	R	4	12	15	30

GEO. E. CURTIS / LEATHER / & / FINDINGS / - * - / 215 JEFF. AVE. / DETROIT

GODFREY DEAN & CO.

CWT	Rarity	Reverse Die	Metal	Edge	VG	VF	EF	Unc
225U-1a	R3	1037	C	R	4	10	12	25

GODFREY DEAN & CO / PAINTERS / & / PICTURE FRAME / MAKERS / DETROIT

DETROIT CITY FLOUR MILLS

CWT	Rarity	Reverse Die	Metal	Edge	VG	VF	EF	Unc
225V-3a	R4	1039	C	R	8	12	15	30

DETROIT / CITY / FLOUR / MILLS / COR. / LARNED & 2' STS.

D. DICKSON

CWT	Rarity	Reverse Die	Metal	Edge	VG	VF	EF	Unc
225W-2a	R5	1040	C	R	15	40	60	90

D. DICKSON / GROCER / & / PROVISION / DEALER / 1' & LARNED, STS / DETROIT

E. A. DRURY

CWT	Rarity	Reverse Die	Metal	Edge	VG	VF	EF	Unc
225X-1a	R4	1025	C	R	8	12	15	40

E. A. DRURY / GROCER / 150 / WOODWARD / AVENUE / DETROIT

FRANCIS ECCARD

CWT	Rarity	Reverse Die	Metal	Edge	VG	VF	EF	Unc
225Y-1a	R3	1024	C	R	4	10	12	30

FRANCIS ECCARD / TOBACCONIST / (ornament) / DETROIT

WM. EISENLORD

CWT	Rarity	Reverse Die	Metal	Edge	VG	VF	EF	Unc
225Z-3a	R6	1042	C	R	8	20	25	50

PENINSULAR / HOTEL / DETROIT / (ornament) / * Wm. EISENLORD *

FARMERS CLOTHING STORE

CWT	Rarity	Reverse Die	Metal	Edge	VG	VF	EF	Unc
225AA-1a	R6	1042	C	R	30	75	90	150

FARMERS / CLOTHING / STORE / 251 & 253 / GRATOIT, ST. / DETROIT

C. FITZSIMONS & CO.

CWT	Rarity	Reverse Die	Metal	Edge	VG	VF	EF	Unc
225AB-1a	R5	1039	C	R	8	15	20	45

C. FITZSIMONS & CO. / GROCER / 7 & 9 / WOODWARD / AVE / DETROIT

L. S. FREEMAN

CWT	Rarity	Reverse Die	Metal	Edge	VG	VF	EF	Unc
225AC-2a	R6	1025	C	R	8	20	25	45

L. S. FREEMAN / NEWS / DEALER / OPPOSITE / BIDDLE / HOUSE / DETROIT, MICH.

FRISBIE'S CARD

CWT	Rarity	Reverse Die	Metal	Edge	VG	VF	EF	Unc
225AD-1b	R2	—	BR	PL	4	6	8	15

FRISBIE'S CARD / - . - within center of wreath. Rv: 53 WOODWARD & 167 JEFFERSON AV'S / WHOLESALE / & RETAIL / (ornament) / * DRY GOODS * / * DETROIT MICH *

F. GEIS & BRO'S

CWT	Rarity	Reverse Die	Metal	Edge	VG	VF	EF	Unc
225AE-1a	R5	1037	C	R	4	10	12	30

F. GEIS & BRO'S / FIRE & - / - WATER - / - PROOF / ROOFING / COR. / CONG & BRUSH / STS. / DETROIT

F. GEISS & BRO'S

CWT	Rarity	Reverse Die	Metal	Edge	VG	VF	EF	Unc
225AF-6a	R4	1042	C	R	4	8	10	20

F. GEISS & BRO'S / FIRE & - / - WATER - / - PROOF / ROOFING / COR. / CONG & BRUSH / STS. / DETROIT

F. GIES & BRO'S.

CWT	Rarity	Reverse Die	Metal	Edge	VG	VF	EF	Unc
225AG-1a	R7	1037	C	R	4	8	10	20

F. GIES & BRO'S / FIRE & - / - WATER - / - PROOF / ROOFING / COR. / CONG & BRUSH / STS. / DETROIT

C. B. GOODRICH

CWT	Rarity	Reverse Die	Metal	Edge	VG	VF	EF	Unc
225AH-3a	R6	1042	C	R	15	50	70	100

C. B. GOODRICH / DEALER IN / BOOTS & SHOES / OPP. / PERKINS / HOTEL / DETROIT

F. HAMMAN

CWT	Rarity	Reverse Die	Metal	Edge	VG	VF	EF	Unc
225AI-2a	R5	1042	C	PL	8	20	25	50

F. HAMMAN & CO / LIQUOR / STORE / COR. / MACOMB AVE / & GR. RIV. ST. / DETROIT

HANNA & CO.

CWT	Rarity	Reverse Die	Metal	Edge	VG	VF	EF	Unc
225AJ-3a	R7	1042	C	R	8	25	35	60

HANNA & CO. / - WHOLESALE - / TOBACCONISTS / 112 / WOODWARD / AVE. / DETROIT

HEINMANN'S

CWT	Rarity	Reverse Die	Metal	Edge	VG	VF	EF	Unc
225AJa-1a	R5	1025	C	R	8	20	25	65

BUY / CLOTHING / AT / HEINMAN'S / UNDER THE / RUSSELL / HOUSE / & / SAVE 25 PER. CT.

HERINTONS

CWT	Rarity	Reverse Die	Metal	Edge	VG	VF	EF	Unc
225AK - 1a	R4	1106	C	PL	5	15	20	45

HERINTONS / DOUBLE THREAD / $15 / SEWING / MACHINE / DETROIT, MICH.

HIGBY & STEARNS

CWT	Rarity	Reverse Die	Metal	Edge	VG	VF	EF	Unc
225AL-1a	R4	1025	C	R	5	15	20	40

HIGBY & STEARNS / ** (flower) ** / DRUGGISTS / * (flower) * / DETROIT

HILTERSCHEID BRO'S

CWT	Rarity	Reverse Die	Metal	Edge	VG	VF	EF	Unc
225AM-1a	R5	1039	C	R	5	15	20	35

HILTERSCHEID BRO'S. / MEAT / MARKET / COR. FORT. & / RUSSELL, ST / DETROIT

JACOB HOCHSTADT

CWT	Rarity	Reverse Die	Metal	Edge	VG	VF	EF	Unc
225AN-2a	R6	1042	C	R	8	25	30	55

JACOB HOCHSTADT / BUTCHER / COR. / 2ND. & / MICH. AVE. / DETROIT

C. J. HOLTHOFER

CWT	Rarity	Reverse Die	Metal	Edge	VG	VF	EF	Unc
225AO-1a	R5	1024	C	R	8	15	20	40

C. J. HOLTHOFER / DEALER IN / DRY / GOODS / DETROIT

WM. B. HOWE

CWT	Rarity	Reverse Die	Metal	Edge	VG	VF	EF	Unc
225AP-1a	R5	1027	C	R	10	20	30	50

Wm. B. HOWE / BOOK / SELLER / 192 JEFF. AVE / DETROIT

EDWARD KANTER

CWT	Rarity	Reverse Die	Metal	Edge	VG	VF	EF	Unc
225AQ-2a	R7	1042	C	R	10	40	60	80

EDWARD KANTER / GROCERIES / PRODUCE / & / SHIP / CHANDLERY / DETROIT

P. N. KNEELAND

CWT	Rarity	Reverse Die	Metal	Edge	VG	VF	EF	Unc
225AR-3a	R6	1042	C	R	8	25	35	55

P. N. KNEELAND / DEALER / IN / -- STOEVS -- / & / TIN WARE / COR. GRAND RIVER / & GRISWOLD ST / DETROIT

NOTE: STOVES is spelled STOEVS on this token.

LAPHAM & THAYER

CWT	Rarity	Reverse Die	Metal	Edge	VG	VF	EF	Unc
225AS-1a	R5	1040	C	R	10	30	50	70

LAPHAM & THAYER / NEW / - & - / SECOND HAND / FURNITURE / 14 / MCIH. AVE / DETROIT

NOTE: MICHIGAN AVE. is spelled MCIH. on this token.

LEWIS & MOSES

CWT	Rarity	Reverse Die	Metal	Edge	VG	VF	EF	Unc
225AT-3a	R3	1025	C	R	8	15	20	40

LEWIS & MOSES / DEALERS / IN / CROCKERY / & / GLASSWARE / 221 JEFF. AVE / DETROIT

C. LOTZ

CWT	Rarity	Reverse Die	Metal	Edge	VG	VF	EF	Unc
225AU-3a	R7	1042	C	R	20	80	100	150

C. LOTZ / GROCER / COR. / HASTINGS / & / CATHERINE, STS. / DETROIT

MARTIN BRO'S

CWT	Rarity	Reverse Die	Metal	Edge	VG	VF	EF	Unc
225AV-1a	R7	1042	C	R	20	50	90	150

MARTIN BRO'S / CHEAP / BOOTS / - & - / SHOE / STORE / 154 WOODWARD AVE.

M. MARX

CWT	Rarity	Reverse Die	Metal	Edge	VG	VF	EF	Unc
225AW-2a	R7	1039	C	R	10	40	60	90

M. MARX / GROCER / & / LIQUOR / DEALER / 94 GRATOIT, ST. / DETROIT

MATHER & SHEFFERLY

CWT	Rarity	Reverse Die	Metal	Edge	VG	VF	EF	Unc
225AX-1a	R3	1025	C	R	4	12	15	30

MATHER & SHEFFERLY / CROCKERY / STORE / 138 & 140 / WOODWARD / AVE. / DETROIT

MESSMORE & LUCKING

CWT	Rarity	Reverse Die	Metal	Edge	VG	VF	EF	Unc
225AY-2a	R6	1042	C	R	5	15	20	40

MESSMORE & LUCKING / BUTCHERS / 209 / WOODWARD / AVE. / DETROIT

ROBT. MILLAR

CWT	Rarity	Reverse Die	Metal	Edge	VG	VF	EF	Unc
225AZ-2a	R6	1042	C	R	8	10	15	35

ROBT. MILLAR / GROCER / & / LIQUOR / DEALER / 200 WOODWARD AVE. / DETROIT

GEO. MOE

CWT	Rarity	Reverse Die	Metal	Edge	VG	VF	EF	Unc
225BA-3a	R4	1042	C	R	8	25	35	55

GEO. MOE / GROCER / - & - / LIQUOR / DEALER / DETROIT

GEO. H. PARKER

CWT	Rarity	Reverse Die	Metal	Edge	VG	VF	EF	Unc
225BB-2a	R7	1040	C	R	20	40	60	100

GEO. H. PARKER / DEALER IN / HIDES / LEATHER / & / WOOL / COR. STATE & / FARMER STS / DETROIT

PERKINS HOTEL

CWT	Rarity	Reverse Die	Metal	Edge	VG	VF	EF	Unc
225BC-1a	R7	1042	C	R	15	45	65	100

PERKINS / HOTEL / COR. GR. RIVER / MIDDLE / STS / DETROIT

W. PERKINS, JR.

CWT	Rarity	Reverse Die	Metal	Edge	VG	VF	EF	Unc
225BD-4a	R6	1042	C	R	15	25	40	65

W. PERKINS, JR / GROCER / - & - / PROVISION / DEALER / DETROIT

G. C. POND

CWT	Rarity	Reverse Die	Metal	Edge	VG	VF	EF	Unc
225BE-6a	R5	1042	C	R	10	25	35	55

G. C. POND / GROCER / & / PROVISION / DEALER / DETROIT

F. PROUTY

CWT	Rarity	Reverse Die	Metal	Edge	VG	VF	EF	Unc
225BF-1a	R7	1040	C	R	15	25	35	65

F. PROUTY / GROCER / & / PROVISION / DEALER / GR RIVER ST / DETROIT

RANDAL'S PHOTOGRAPHIC GALLERY

CWT	Rarity	Reverse Die	Metal	Edge	VG	VF	EF	Unc
225BG-2a	R7	1040	C	R	25	65	90	125

RANDAL'S PHOTOGRAPHIC GALLERY / FISHERS / BLOCK / DETROIT

RAYMOND'S PHOTOGRAPHIC GALLERY

CWT	Rarity	Reverse Die	Metal	Edge	VG	VF	EF	Unc
225BH-2a	R5	1042	C	R	25	75	100	150

RAYMOND'S / PHOTOGRAPHIC / GALLERY / 205 / JEFF. AVE / DETROIT

JOSEPH RIGGS

CWT	Rarity	Reverse Die	Metal	Edge	VG	VF	EF	Unc
225BI-2a	R5	1042	C	R	5	15	20	55

JOSEPH RIGGS / GROCERIES / PROVISIONS / & / FLOUR / DETROIT

J. A. RODIER

CWT	Rarity	Reverse Die	Metal	Edge	VG	VF	EF	Unc
225BJ-3a	R6	1042	C	R	15	30	40	65

J. A. RODIER / BOOT / & / SHOE / DEALER / DETROIT

ALONZO ROLFE

CWT	Rarity	Reverse Die	Metal	Edge	VG	VF	EF	Unc
225BK-2a	R5	1042	C	R	8	15	25	45

ALONZO ROLFE / PRODUCE / FRUIT / & / COMMISSION / MERCHANT / DETROIT

DR. L. C. ROSE

CWT	Rarity	Reverse Die	Metal	Edge	VG	VF	EF	Unc
225BL-3a	R5	1042	C	R		—	SCARCE	—

DR. L. C. ROSE / TREATS ALL / - CHRONIC / FEMALE / & VENEREAL / - DISEASES / DETROIT

M. ROSENBERGER

CWT	Rarity	Reverse Die	Metal	Edge	VG	VF	EF	Unc
225BM-3a	R5	1042	C	R	15	25	50	85

M. ROSENBERGER / DEALER IN / READY MADE / CLOTHING / 140 GR. RIV. ST / DETROIT

J. SCHMIDT

CWT	Rarity	Reverse Die	Metal	Edge	VG	VF	EF	Unc
225BN-1a	R3	1025	C	R	4	8	10	30

J. SCHMIDT / GROCER / COR. MICH. AVE / & / BATES, STS. / DETROIT

JOHN SCHRODER & CO.

CWT	Rarity	Reverse Die	Metal	Edge	VG	VF	EF	Unc
225BO-4a	R4	1042	C	R	4	8	10	25

JOHN SCHRODER & CO. / CLOTHING / HATS / & / CAPS / BOOTS & SHOES

H. A. SEALY

CWT	Rarity	Reverse Die	Metal	Edge	VG	VF	EF	Unc
225BP-2a	R6	1040	C	R	8	15	20	40

H. A. SEALY / BUTCHER / -- 65 -- / GR. RIVER ST. / DETROIT

CHEAP JOHN SEELEY

CWT	Rarity	Reverse Die	Metal	Edge	VG	VF	EF	Unc
225BQ-2a	R6	1039	C	R	5	15	20	50

CHEAP / - JOHN - / SEELEY / DETROIT

J. B. SHAGNON

CWT	Rarity	Reverse Die	Metal	Edge	VG	VF	EF	Unc
225BR-2a	R7	1042	C	R	20	50	75	130

J. B. SHAGNON / GROCER / & / PROVISION / DEALER / DETROIT

E. B. SMITH

CWT	Rarity	Reverse Die	Metal	Edge	VG	VF	EF	Unc
225BS-2a	R6	1042	C	R	8	25	30	50

E. B. SMITH / BOOK SELLER / & / STATIONER / - 116 - / WOODWARD / AVE / DETROIT

SETH SMITH & SON

CWT	Rarity	Reverse Die	Metal	Edge	VG	VF	EF	Unc
225BT-1a	R9	—	C	PL		—	RARE	—

SETH SMITH & SON / BARREL / & / TEA BOXES / DETROIT MICH Rv: GENERAL DEALER / IN / FAMILY / GROCERY / FLOUR & FEED / GLASSWARE / ETC ETC / 390 / GRAND RIVER AVE

WM. B. SMITH

CWT	Rarity	Reverse Die	Metal	Edge	VG	VF	EF	Unc
225BU-1a	R5	1040	C	R	5	15	20	45

WM. B. SMITH / BUTCHER / 129 & 131 / WOODBRIDGE / ST / DETROIT

YANKEE SMITH'S SALOON

CWT	Rarity	Reverse Die	Metal	Edge	VG	VF	EF	Unc
225BV-1a	R4	1025	C	R	8	15	25	45

YANKEE / SMITH'S / SALOON / NO. 1 MICH. AVE / DETROIT

GEO. SNOOKS FISH DEPOT

CWT	Rarity	Reverse Die	Metal	Edge	VG	VF	EF	Unc
225BW-2a	R5	1042	C	R	8	25	35	50

GEO. SNOOKS / FISH / DEPOT / COR. / 1' & LARNED STS / DETROIT

WM. SNOW

CWT	Rarity	Reverse Die	Metal	Edge	VG	VF	EF	Unc
225BX-1a	R4	1039	C	R	6	12	15	30

Wm. SNOW / WIRE - / - CLOTH / HARDWARE / - & - / CUTLERY / DETROIT

J. D. & C. B. STANDISH'S PORK & WOOL

CWT	Rarity	Reverse Die	Metal	Edge	VG	VF	EF	Unc
225BY-1a	R2	—	C	PL	4	8	10	15

* J. D. & C. B. STANDISH'S * / PORK / - & - / WOOL / DEALERS, / DETROIT / * CARD. * Rv: Shield with 13 stars within a large circle of 24 stars.

L. J. STAPLES

CWT	Rarity	Reverse Die	Metal	Edge	VG	VF	EF	Unc
225BZ-4a	R5	1042	C	R	8	15	25	45

L. J. STAPLES / WHOLESALE / GROCER / & / CONFECTIONER / WOODWARD / 185 DETROIT. AVE

GOFF STENTON

CWT	Rarity	Reverse Die	Metal	Edge	VG	VF	EF	Unc
225CA-1a	R5	1039	C	R	8	15	25	45

GOFF STENTON / MEAT. / MARKET / COR. / RIVARD & JEFF / AVE. / DETROIT

MRS. A. STRINGER

CWT	Rarity	Reverse Die	Metal	Edge	VG	VF	EF	Unc
225CB-1a	R7	1039	C	R	10	30	40	70

MRS. A. STRINGER / DRY / GOODS / MILLINERY / & / DRESS MAKING / MICH. AVE / DETROIT

G. W. SUTHERLAND

CWT	Rarity	Reverse Die	Metal	Edge	VG	VF	EF	Unc
225CC-1a	R6	1024	C	R	8	15	20	45

G. W. SUTHERLAND / GROCER / MARKET / SQUARE / DETROIT

I. & C. TAYLOR

CWT	Rarity	Reverse Die	Metal	Edge	VG	VF	EF	Unc
225CD-2a	R6	1042	C	R	15	30	50	80

I. & C. TAYLOR / GROCERS / - & - / PROVISION / DEALERS / DETROIT

THE TEA STORE

CWT	Rarity	Reverse Die	Metal	Edge	VG	VF	EF	Unc
225CE-1a	R7	1039	C	R	10	35	45	70

THE / TEA / STORE / - 146 - / WOODWARD / AVE / DETROIT

W. E. TUNIS

CWT	Rarity	Reverse Die	Metal	Edge	VG	VF	EF	Unc
225CF-1a	R6	1040	C	R	15	30	45	80

W. E. TUNIS / GENERAL / NEWS / - / DEALER, / DETROIT / CLIFTON, C. W. / & MILWAUKEE

TURNER HUBBELL & CO.

CWT	Rarity	Reverse Die	Metal	Edge	VG	VF	EF	Unc
225CG-3a	R5	1042	C	R	10	25	35	70

TURNER HUBBELL & CO / WHOLESALE / BOOT & SHOE / MANUFACTURERS / 195 JEFF. AVE / DETROIT

C. C. TYLER & CO.

CWT	Rarity	Reverse Die	Metal	Edge	VG	VF	EF	Unc
225CH-1a	R6	—	C	PL	20	50	75	125

C. C. TYLER & CO. / WILL PAY / ONE / CENT / IN GOODS Rv: DETROIT, / BOOTS / & / SHOES / MICHIGAN

R. G. TYLER & CO.

CWT	Rarity	Reverse Die	Metal	Edge	VG	VF	EF	Unc
225CI-1a	R3	1367	C	PL	4	6	8	15

* R. G. TYLER * / WHOLESALE / GROCER / DETROIT MICH.

VENN & WREFORD

CWT	Rarity	Reverse Die	Metal	Edge	VG	VF	EF	Unc
225CJ-1a	R5	1037	C	R	8	15	20	45

VENN & WREFORD / BUTCHERS / 271 / JEFF. / AVE. / DETROIT

HENRY WEBER

CWT	Rarity	Reverse Die	Metal	Edge	VG	VF	EF	Unc
225CK-4a	R5	1042	C	R	8	15	20	40

HENRY WEBER / FURNITURE / DEALER / 129 / WOODWARD, A. / DETROIT

B. WEBSTER

CWT	Rarity	Reverse Die	Metal	Edge	VG	VF	EF	Unc
225CL-2a	R7	1042	C	R	10	30	40	75

B. WEBSTER / WHOLESALE - / - & RETAIL / FISH / DEALER / DETROIT

W. W. WHITLARK

CWT	Rarity	Reverse Die	Metal	Edge	VG	VF	EF	Unc
225CM-3a	R6	1042	C	R	10	20	30	75

W. W. WHITLARK / WITH / GROVER - / & BAKER / S. M. CO. / FISHERS BLOCK / DETROIT

WILKINS & MARTINS

CWT	Rarity	Reverse Die	Metal	Edge	VG	VF	EF	Unc
225CN-3a	R3	1042	C	R	5	15	20	40

WILKINS & MARTINS / CELEBRATED / INK / - & - / BLACKING / DEPOT / DETROIT

J. W. WINCKLER

CWT	Rarity	Reverse Die	Metal	Edge	VG	VF	EF	Unc
225CO-2a	R6	1039	C	R	8	15	20	45

J. W. WINCKLER / BAKER / 81 LARNED / ST. / DETROIT

F. M. WING

CWT	Rarity	Reverse Die	Metal	Edge	VG	VF	EF	Unc
225CP-3a	R6	1042	C	R	8	20	30	50

F. M. WING / GROCER / & / COMMISSION / 83 CONG. ST. / DETROIT

G. WINTER

CWT	Rarity	Reverse Die	Metal	Edge	VG	VF	EF	Unc
225CQ-2a	R7	1042	C	R	20	40	60	80

G. WINTER / HATTER / 250 / BIDDLE / HOUSE / DETROIT

A. WITGEN

CWT	Rarity	Reverse Die	Metal	Edge	VG	VF	EF	Unc
225CR-2a	R4	1039	C	PL	5	15	20	45

A. WITGEN / GROCERIES / - & - / MEAT / MARKET / DETROIT

HENRY WOLFF

CWT	Rarity	Reverse Die	Metal	Edge	VG	VF	EF	Unc
225CS-1a	R2	1018	C	R	4	8	10	25

HENRY WOLFF / TRUNK / MANUFACTORY / 211 / JEFF. AVE. / DETROIT, MICH.

Dowagiac

A. N. ALWARD

CWT	Rarity	Reverse Die	Metal	Edge	VG	VF	EF	Unc
250A-1a	R8	1094	C	PL		—	SCARCE	—

A. N. ALWARD / BOOKS, / STATIONERY / & WALL / PAPERS / DOWAGIAC. MICH.

ANDREWS & COOPER

CWT	Rarity	Reverse Die	Metal	Edge	VG	VF	EF	Unc
250B-2a	R8	1106	C	PL	20	40	60	125

ANDREWS & COOPER / FAMILY / GROCERIES / & / PROVISIONS / FRONT / ST. / DOWAGIAC. MICH.

A. M. DICKSON & CO.

CWT	Rarity	Reverse Die	Metal	Edge	VG	VF	EF	Unc
250C-1a	R7	1099	C	PL	20	50	80	125

A. M. DICKSON & CO. / DRY / GOODS. / CLOTHING / BOOTS / & SHOES / DOWAGIAC, MICH.

D. LARZELERE & CO.

CWT	Rarity	Reverse Die	Metal	Edge	VG	VF	EF	Unc
250D-1a	R6	1094	C	PL	20	50	80	175

D. LARZELERE & Co. / DRY (line) / (line) GOODS &, / (line) / GROCERIES / - & - / CLOTHING (line) / DOWAGIAC, MICH.

D. POND

CWT	Rarity	Reverse Die	Metal	Edge	VG	VF	EF	Unc
250E-2a	R8	1105	C	PL		—	RARE	—

D. POND / GROCER. / - AND - / CONFECTIONER / DOWAGIAC, MICH.

G. A. WHEELOCK

CWT	Rarity	Reverse Die	Metal	Edge	VG	VF	EF	Unc
250F-2a	R8	1205	C	PL		—	RARE	—

G. A. WHEELOCK / DEALER / IN / GROCERIES / & PROVISIONS / DOWAGIAC / MICH.

East Saginaw

CHARLES W. BERNACKI

CWT	Rarity	Reverse Die	Metal	Edge	VG	VF	EF	Unc
280A-2a	R8	1101	C	PL		—	SCARCE	—

CHARLES W. BERNACKI / DRUGGIST / mortar and pestle / EAST / SAGINAW / MICH.

N. W. CLARK & CO.

CWT	Rarity	Reverse Die	Metal	Edge	VG	VF	EF	Unc
280B-2a	R7	1042	C	R	8	15	25	45

N. W. CLARK & CO / MERCHANTS / * (ornament) * / COMMERCIAL / BLOCK / EAST SAGINAW, MICH.

S. T. LEGGETT

CWT	Rarity	Reverse Die	Metal	Edge	VG	VF	EF	Unc
280C-1a	R6	1211	C	PL		—	SCARCE	—

S. T. LEGGETT / PRACTICAL / WATCHMAKER / - & - / JEWELER / EAST / SAGINAW / MICH.

JOHN MCKAY

CWT	Rarity	Reverse Die	Metal	Edge	VG	VF	EF	Unc
280D-2a	R8	1042	C	R	10	15	25	70

JOHN MC KAY / OYSTER / FRUIT / & / FISH / DEPOT / EAST SAGINAW

A. SCHMITZ

CWT	Rarity	Reverse Die	Metal	Edge	VG	VF	EF	Unc
280E-1a	R5	—	C	PL	15	25	40	80

A. SCHMITZ / picture of plow / EAST / SAGINAW / MICH. Rv: DEALER / IN / IRON. / (ornament) NAILS. / (ornament) / STOVES. / CROCKERY / & / PAINTS.

TOWN BRANCH STORE

CWT	Rarity	Reverse Die	Metal	Edge	VG	VF	EF	Unc
280F-1a	R8	1047	C	R		—	SCARCE	—

TOWN BRANCH / + / STORE REDEEMABLE / IN / GOODS

NOTE: No concrete evidence has been found of the existance of this store having been located in the Saginaw area, attributed here by Barnett.

CHARLES TURNER

CWT	Rarity	Reverse Die	Metal	Edge	VG	VF	EF	Unc
280G-1a	R9	1101	C	PL		—	SCARCE	—

CHARLES TURNER / DEALER / IN / FURS / & SKINS. / EAST SAGINAW / MICH.

Eaton Rapids

A. C. DUTTON, M. D.

CWT	Rarity	Reverse Die	Metal	Edge	VG	VF	EF	Unc
300A-1a	R5	1310	C	PL	15	50	60	110

A. C. DUTTON M. D / BOOKS. / STATIONERY / - * - / GROCERIES & C. / EATON RAPIDS / MICH.

H. M. FROST

CWT	Rarity	Reverse Die	Metal	Edge	VG	VF	EF	Unc
300B-1a	R5	1310	C	PL	15	30	40	85

H. M. FROST / - * - / DRUGGIST / - AND - / GROCER / EATON RAPIDS / MICH.

FROST & DANIELS

CWT	Rarity	Reverse Die	Metal	Edge	VG	VF	EF	Unc
300C-1a	R4	1225	C	PL	10	20	35	55

FROST & DANIELS / DRY GOODS, / - / - * - / GROCERIES, / BOOTS, SHOES & C. / EATON RAPIDS / - / MICH.

P. LEONARD

CWT	Rarity	Reverse Die	Metal	Edge	VG	VF	EF	Unc
300D-1a	R6	1168	C	PL	15	30	45	85

P. LEONARD / DRY GOODS / - * - / GROCERIES / BOOTS SHOES & C / EATON RAPIDS, / MICH.

A. MESTER & CO.

CWT	Rarity	Reverse Die	Metal	Edge	VG	VF	EF	Unc
300E-1a	R5	1340	C	PL		—	SCARCE	—

A. MESTER & CO. / MARBLE / WORKS, / EATON RAPIDS, / * MICH. *

WM. F. STIRLING

CWT	Rarity	Reverse Die	Metal	Edge	VG	VF	EF	Unc
300F-1a	R3	—	C	PL	8	15	20	40

Wm. F. STIRLING / DRY GOODS / (ornament) / UNION BLOCK, / EATON RAPIDS, / MICH. Rv: THE CELEBRATED / (ornament) / TEA / (ornament) / ESTABLISHMENT.

Flint

GILES BISHOP

CWT	Rarity	Reverse Die	Metal	Edge	VG	VF	EF	Unc
320A-1b	R2	—	BRZ	PL	8	15	20	35

* GILES BISHOP * / . GROCERIES . / * / AND / * / LIQUORS / BUSINESS CARD Rv: * DRUGGIST * / mortar and pestle / * FLINT, MICH. *

CLARK'S DRUGS

CWT	Rarity	Reverse Die	Metal	Edge	VG	VF	EF	Unc
320B-1a	R5	1101	C	PL	15	30	50	80

* CLARK'S * / *** / DRUG'S, / MEDICINES, / GROCERIES. / & C. / FLINT, MICH

Grand Haven

H. BROUWER & BRO.

CWT	Rarity	Reverse Die	Metal	Edge	VG	VF	EF	Unc
360A-1a	R6	1094	C	PL	10	25	35	80

H. BROUWER / & BRO. / DRY GOODS, / GROCERIES, / BOOTS & / SHOES. / GRAND HAVEN, MICH.

GEO. E. HUBBARD

CWT	Rarity	Reverse Die	Metal	Edge	VG	VF	EF	Unc
360B-1a	R5	1226	C	PL	10	20	25	50

GEO. E. HUBBARD / DEALER / IN / STOVES / AND / HARDWARE / GRAND HAVEN / MICH.

G. V. SCHELVEN

CWT	Rarity	Reverse Die	Metal	Edge	VG	VF	EF	Unc
360C-1a	R7	1108	C	PL		—	SCARCE	—

G. V. SCHELVEN / (line) . (line) / DEALER / (line) IN / GROCERIES / AND (line) / CANDIES / (line) . (line) / GRAND HAVEN MICH

Grand Rapids

GEO. P. BARNARD

CWT	Rarity	Reverse Die	Metal	Edge	VG	VF	EF	Unc
370A-1a	R5	1101	C	PL	10	35	45	85

GEO. P. BARNARD / (line) / BOOK / (line) / SELLER / (line) & / STATIONER / GRAND / RAPIDS / MICH.

COURLANDER & PRESSGOOD

CWT	Rarity	Reverse Die	Metal	Edge	VG	VF	EF	Unc
370B-1a	R7	1337	C	PL	10	40	60	90

RUSIAN CLOTHING / STORE, / COURLANDER / & PRESSGOOD, / GRAND RAPIDS, / MICH.

NOTE: Spelling error in RUSSIAN.

FOSTER & METCALF

CWT	Rarity	Reverse Die	Metal	Edge	VG	VF	EF	Unc
370C-1b	R4	—	BR	PL	4	8	10	20

FOSTER & METCALF / cook stove / GRAND RAPIDS, MICH. Rv: 1861 / (line) / WORKERS IN / COPPER, TIN, BRASS, / AND / HEAVY SHEET IRON, / - . - / PLUMBING, / GAS FITTING / ETC. ETC. ETC. / (ornament)

GOODRICH & GAY

CWT	Rarity	Reverse Die	Metal	Edge	VG	VF	EF	Unc
370D-1b	R2	1305	BR	PL	4	8	10	15

GOODRICH & GAY / DEALERS / IN / HARDWARE / IRON, STEEL, / NAILS & GLASS. / * GRAND RAPIDS, MICH *

KRUGER & BOOTH

CWT	Rarity	Reverse Die	Metal	Edge	VG	VF	EF	Unc
370E-1a	R6	1101	C	PL	10	30	45	85

* KRUEGER & BOOTH * / DEALERS IN / SADDLES / ***** / HARNESS / TRUNKS / GRAND RAPIDS / MICH.

C. KUSTERER

CWT	Rarity	Reverse Die	Metal	Edge	VG	VF	EF	Unc
370F-1a	R3	—	C	PL	25	50	70	110

C. KUSTERER / horse and wagon / GRAND RAPIDS / *** MICH *** Rv: CITY BREWERY / MANF'R / OF LAGER BEER / (line) / STOCK (line) / (line) & CREAM / (line) (ornament) ALE (ornament).

L. A. MERRILL

CWT	Rarity	Reverse Die	Metal	Edge	VG	VF	EF	Unc
370G-1a	R6	1101	C	PL	35	100	150	200

L. A. MERRILL / ********* / PHOTOGRAPHIC / *** / ARTIST / GRAND RAPIDS / MICH.

J. W. PEIRCE

CWT	Rarity	Reverse Die	Metal	Edge	VG	VF	EF	Unc
370H-1b	R2	1358	BRZ	PL	4	6	8	15

J. W. PEIRCE / DRY GOODS / AND / GROCERIES / . GRAND RAPIDS MICH .

E. W. POWERS

CWT	Rarity	Reverse Die	Metal	Edge	VG	VF	EF	Unc
370I-1a	R6	1101	C	PL	10	35	55	90

E. K. POWERS / ******* / CONFECTIONER / & DEALER IN / SODA WATER / GRAND RAPIDS / MICH.

L. H. RANDALL

CWT	Rarity	Reverse Die	Metal	Edge	VG	VF	EF	Unc
370J-1a	R3	—	C	PL	4	8	10	20

L. H. RANDALL. / WHOLESALE / & / RETAIL / GROCER / GRAND RAPIDS. MICH.

A. ROBERTS & SON

CWT	Rarity	Reverse Die	Metal	Edge	VG	VF	EF	Unc
370K-1b	R4	1362	BR	PL	5	10	12	25

A. ROBERTS & SON / DRY GOODS / GROCERIES / CROCKERY / & C / . GRAND RAPIDS .

TOMPKINS PHOTOGRAPH AND AMBROTYPE GALLERY

CWT	Rarity	Reverse Die	Metal	Edge	VG	VF	EF	Unc
370L-1a	R6	1105	C	PL		—	SCARCE	—

TOMPKINS / PHOTOGRAPH / AND / AMBROTYPE / GALLERY. / GRAND / RAPIDS / MICH

Hastings

D. C. HAWLEY

CWT	Rarity	Reverse Die	Metal	Edge	VG	VF	EF	Unc
440A-1a	R6	1101	C	PL	10	25	35	80

D. C. HAWLEY / ... / GROCERIES / & / PROVISIONS / HASTINGS. / MICH.

Hillsdale

J. O. AMES

CWT	Rarity	Reverse Die	Metal	Edge	VG	VF	EF	Unc
450A-2b	R8	1187	BR	PL		—	RARE	—

J. O. AMES / (ornament) / (ornament) BOOKS (ornament) / - & - / STATIONERY. / HILSDAL MICH.

NOTE: Spelling of HILLSDALE.

O. S. BETTS

CWT	Rarity	Reverse Die	Metal	Edge	VG	VF	EF	Unc
450B-1a	R6	1183	C	PL	8	20	30	70

O. S. BETTS / DEALER IN / WATCHES JEWELRY / - & - / SILVERWARE / HILLSDALE ..... MICH.

CARD, PEARCE & CO.

CWT	Rarity	Reverse Die	Metal	Edge	VG	VF	EF	Unc
450C-3a	R8	1186	C	PL	20	60	85	140

CARD, PEARCE & Co. / ENGINES, / *** / * AND * / *** / AGRICULTURAL / IMPLEMENTS / HILLSDALE ..... MICH.

FARNAM'S

CWT	Rarity	Reverse Die	Metal	Edge	VG	VF	EF	Unc
450D-1a	R8	1185	C	PL		—	RARE	—

FARNMAN'S / (ornament) / (line) / BRONCHIAL / (line) / (ornament) / TABLETS

FRENCH & PARSONS

CWT	Rarity	Reverse Die	Metal	Edge	VG	VF	EF	Unc
450E-1a	R7	1111	C	PL		—	SCARCE	—

FRENCH & PARSONS / (ornament) / DRUGGISTS / & / GROCERS / (ornament) / HILLSDALE, MICH.

J. GOTTLIEB

CWT	Rarity	Reverse Die	Metal	Edge	VG	VF	EF	Unc
450F-3b	R8	1187	BR	PL		—	SCARCE	—

J. GOTTLIEB / (ornament) / (line) / CLOTHIER / (line) / (ornament) / HILLSDALE, MICH.

A. GLEASON

CWT	Rarity	Reverse Die	Metal	Edge	VG	VF	EF	Unc
450G-1a	R4	1183	C	PL	4	8	10	35

A. GLEASON / DIE SINKER / (ornament) & (ornament) / ENGRAVER / HILLSDALE_MICH.

E. C. KEATING

CWT	Rarity	Reverse Die	Metal	Edge	VG	VF	EF	Unc
450H-3a	R7	1186	C	PL	20	40	65	100

E. C. KEATING / (ornament) / GROCER / AND / PRODUCE DEALER / HILLSDALE .... MICH.

D. H. LORD & CO.

CWT	Rarity	Reverse Die	Metal	Edge	VG	VF	EF	Unc
450I-2a	R7	1186	C	PL	20	60	75	150

D. H. LORD & Co. / DEALERS IN / (ornament) / BOOTS / (ornament) / SHOES & C. / HILLSDALE, MICH.

C. T. MITCHELL & CO.

CWT	Rarity	Reverse Die	Metal	Edge	VG	VF	EF	Unc
450J-1a	R6	1185	C	PL	20	60	75	150

C. T. MITCHELL & Co. / HARDWARE / (ornament) / DEALERS. / HILLSDALE, MICH.

C. E. MOTT & CO.

CWT	Rarity	Reverse Die	Metal	Edge	VG	VF	EF	Unc
450K-1a	R4	1111	C	PL	8	20	30	45

C. E. MOTT & CO. / DRY / GOODS / CARPETING / (ornament) & C. (ornament) / HILLSDALE, MICH

MOTT & BRO.

CWT	Rarity	Reverse Die	Metal	Edge	VG	VF	EF	Unc
450L-3a	R4	1117	C	PL	10	30	35	50

MOTT & BRO / (line - ornament - line) / DRUGGISTS / (curved line) / AND / GROCERS / HILLSDALE. MICH.

SAMM & KUHLKE

CWT	Rarity	Reverse Die	Metal	Edge	VG	VF	EF	Unc
450M-2a	R5	1186	C	PL	10	45	60	125

SAMM & KUHLKE / (ornament) / GROCERS / (ornament) / HILLSDALE ... M

UNION PLANNING & STAVE MILLS

CWT	Rarity	Reverse Die	Metal	Edge	VG	VF	EF	Unc
450N-2a	R7	1186	C	PL	25	75	130	150

UNION PLANING & STAVE MILLS, / R. ROWE / (ornament) / HILLSDALE / MICH.

GEO. W. UNDERWOOD

CWT	Rarity	Reverse Die	Metal	Edge	VG	VF	EF	Unc
450O-2a	R5	1117	C	PL	10	25	35	50

GEO. W. UNDERWOOD / (ornament) / DRUGGIST / - & - / GROCER / (ornament) / HILLSDALE, MICH.

Hudson

BAKER & BROWN

CWT	Rarity	Reverse Die	Metal	Edge	VG	VF	EF	Unc
480A-2a	R6	1186	C	PL	—	SCARCE	—	

* BAKER & BROWN * / DRY / GOODS / - AND - / GROCERIES / (ornament) / HUDSON ... MICH.

A. H. BOWEN

CWT	Rarity	Reverse Die	Metal	Edge	VG	VF	EF	Unc
480B-1a	R7	1183	C	PL	—	SCARCE	—	

* A. H. BOWEN * / (ornament) / BAKER / - & - / GROCER / HUDSON ... MICH

GILLETT & NILES

CWT	Rarity	Reverse Die	Metal	Edge	VG	VF	EF	Unc
480C-1a	R8	1099	C	PL	—	SCARCE	—	

GILLETT & NILES / mortar and pestle / DRUGGISTS / HUDSON, / MICH.

GREEN & WARDSWORTH

CWT	Rarity	Reverse Die	Metal	Edge	VG	VF	EF	Unc
480D-1a	R7	1183	C	PL	15	45	60	110

GREEN & WARDSWORTH / (ornament) / LIVERY / (ornament) / HUDSON .. MICH.

H. HOWE & CO.

CWT	Rarity	Reverse Die	Metal	Edge	VG	VF	EF	Unc
480E-1a	R8	1183	C	PL	20	45	60	100

* H. HOWE & Co. * / DEALER IN / GENERAL, / HARDWARE / HUDSON .. MICH.

PALMER & GOODSALL

CWT	Rarity	Reverse Die	Metal	Edge	VG	VF	EF	Unc
480F-1a	R7	1183	C	PL	20	45	60	100

PALMER & GOODSALL / - * - / HARDWARE / * / DEALERS, / - * - / * HUDSON, MICH. *

TUBBS & SPEAR

CWT	Rarity	Reverse Die	Metal	Edge	VG	VF	EF	Unc
480G-1a	R5	1183	C	PL	20	30	40	100

TUBBS & SPEAR / + * + / GROCERS / (ornament) / HUDSON ... MICH.

Ionia

JAMES KENNEDY

CWT	Rarity	Reverse Die	Metal	Edge	VG	VF	EF	Unc
495A-1a	R2	—	C	PL	4	8	10	15

JAMES. KENNEDY. / Indian head to left / * 1863 * Rv: EXCHANGE INSURANCE / COLLECTION / - - / & U. S. / - - / WAR CLAIM / OFFICE / - - / IONIA MICH

F. SLOAN

CWT	Rarity	Reverse Die	Metal	Edge	VG	VF	EF	Unc
495B-1a	R4	1101	C	PL	8	25	35	55

F. SLOAN / STOVES, / HARDWARE, / IRON, STEEL / & NAILS / IONIA, MICH.

Jackson

S. HOLLAND & SON

CWT	Rarity	Reverse Die	Metal	Edge	VG	VF	EF	Unc
525A-1a	R8	1098	C	PL	—	SCARCE	—	

S. HOLLAND & SON / mortar and pestle / DRUGGISTS / JACKSON, / MICH.

H. S. ISMON

CWT	Rarity	Reverse Die	Metal	Edge	VG	VF	EF	Unc
525B-1a	R5	1098	C	PL	10	40	45	65

H. S. ISMON / DEALER / - IN / STAPLE - / & FANCY / - - / DRY GOODS / JACKSON, MICH

WM. JACKSON

CWT	Rarity	Reverse Die	Metal	Edge	VG	VF	EF	Unc
525C-1a	R3	—	C	PL	4	8	10	25

Wm. JACKSON / x / CLUSIVE / TRADE / IN / * GROCERIES. * Rv: JACKSON HALL / (ornament) / BLOCK / JACKSON, / - . - / * MICH. *

W. JAXON

CWT	Rarity	Reverse Die	Metal	Edge	VG	VF	EF	Unc
525D-2a	R3	1348	C	PL	5	10	12	30

W. JAXON / (ornament) / GROCER, / JACKSON HALL / JACKSON, / MICH. / *** 1863 ***

Jonesville

C. C. BLAKESLEE

CWT	Rarity	Reverse Die	Metal	Edge	VG	VF	EF	Unc
527A-1a	R8	1187	C	PL	—	SCARCE	—	

C. C. BLAKESLEE / mortar and pestle / DRUGGIST. / JONESVILLE, MICH

A. & H. GALE

CWT	Rarity	Reverse Die	Metal	Edge	VG	VF	EF	Unc
527B-1a	R9	1187	C	PL	—	RARE	—	

A. & H. GALE / ******** / MANFRS / OF / AGRICULT.'RL. / --.-- / IMPLEMENTS / (ornament) / ******** / JONESVILLE, M.

H. R. GARDNER & CO.

CWT	Rarity	Reverse Die	Metal	Edge	VG	VF	EF	Unc
527C-2a	R7	1185	C	PL	15	60	90	140

H. R. GARDNER & Co. / WOOLEN / (ornament) / MANUF'RS. / JONESVILLE MICH.

J. S. LEWIS

CWT	Rarity	Reverse Die	Metal	Edge	VG	VF	EF	Unc
527D-1a	R9	1185	C	PL	25	90	125	160

J. S. LEWIS, / (ornament) / HARDWARE / (ornament) / IRON & NAILS, / JONESVILLE ..... MICH.

VAN NESS & TURNER

CWT	Rarity	Reverse Die	Metal	Edge	VG	VF	EF	Unc
527E-1a	R5	1185	C	PL	20	60	80	125

VAN NESS & TURNER / DRY GOODS / (ornament) / * AND * / (ornament) / GROCERIES / JONESVILLE.....MICH.

D. A. WISNER & SON

CWT	Rarity	Reverse Die	Metal	Edge	VG	VF	EF	Unc
527F-1a	R6	1185	C	PL	15	50	70	100

D. A. WISNER & SON / * DRY * / GOODS / * AND * / (ornament) / GROCERIES / * JONESVILLE..MICH. *

Juneau

** See Wisconsin 320A

Kalamazoo

BABCOCK & COBB

CWT	Rarity	Reverse Die	Metal	Edge	VG	VF	EF	Unc
530A-2a	R6	1203	C	PL	8	20	25	50

BABCOCK & COBB / DRY / GOODS / CARPETS / & / CLOTHING / .. * .. / KALAMAZOO.

COBB & FISHER

CWT	Rarity	Reverse Die	Metal	Edge	VG	VF	EF	Unc
530B-2a	R4	1094	C	PL	8	20	25	50

COBB & FISHER / .. * .. / DEALERS / IN / CROCKERY / (ornament) / KALAMAZOO

DAVIS & BATES

CWT	Rarity	Reverse Die	Metal	Edge	VG	VF	EF	Unc
530C-2a	R5	1094	C	PL	8	20	25	50

DAVIS & BATES / ONE / PRICE / CASH / STORE / * KALAMAZOO *

R. R. HOWARD

CWT	Rarity	Reverse Die	Metal	Edge	VG	VF	EF	Unc
530D-1a	R4	1094	C	PL	8	20	25	50

R. R. HOWARD / HARDWARE / CUTLERY & C. / KALAMAZOO / MICH.

KELLOGG & CO.

CWT	Rarity	Reverse Die	Metal	Edge	VG	VF	EF	Unc
530E-1a	R5	1094	C	PL	8	20	25	50

KELLOGG & CO. / MANFR'S / OF / LUMBER / DOORS / BLINDS & SASH / KALAMAZOO

H. S. PARKER & CO.

CWT	Rarity	Reverse Die	Metal	Edge	VG	VF	EF	Unc
530F-2a	R5	1108	C	PL	10	30	50	80

H. S. PARKER & CO. / (line) / HATS / CAPS / (line) / BOOTS / (line) / & SHOES / KALAMAZOO

L. W. PERRIN

CWT	Rarity	Reverse Die	Metal	Edge	VG	VF	EF	Unc
530G-1a	R4	1037	C	R	8	15	25	50

L. W. PERRIN / DRY / GOODS / GROCERIES / & CARPETS / KALAMAZOO

ROBERTS & HILLHOUSE

CWT	Rarity	Reverse Die	Metal	Edge	VG	VF	EF	Unc
530H-2a	R3	1203	C	PL		—	SCARCE	—

ROBERTS & / HILLHOUSE / DRUGGISTS / SIGN / OF / EAGLE & MORTAR / KALAMAZOO, MICH.

Lansing

DAVID EKSTEIN

CWT	Rarity	Reverse Die	Metal	Edge	VG	VF	EF	Unc
560A-2a	R5	1126	C	PL	10	30	40	65

DAVID EKSTEIN / DEALER / IN / GROCERIES / AND / PROVISIONS / LANSING, / MICH.

A. J. VIELE

CWT	Rarity	Reverse Die	Metal	Edge	VG	VF	EF	Unc
560B-2a	R4	1168	C	PL	10	30	40	75

*** A. J. VIELE, *** / BOOKS, / STATIONERY, / PIANOS & / SEWING / MACHINES, / * LANSING, * / MICH.

Lapeer

H. GRISWOLD & CO.

CWT	Rarity	Reverse Die	Metal	Edge	VG	VF	EF	Unc
565A-1a	R5	1024	C	R	8	50	65	100

H. GRISWOLD & CO. / DEALERS / IN / DRY / GOODS / GROCERIES / & C. / LAPEER, MICH.

Lawton

FAIRBANK & SCRIVER

CWT	Rarity	Reverse Die	Metal	Edge	VG	VF	EF	Unc
570A-2a	R6	1098	C	PL	15	40	50	90

FAIRBANK & SCRIVER / STOVES. / (ornament) / HARDWARE / & / CUTLERY / LAWTON. MIC.

Ligonier

** See Indiana 550G

Litchfield

A. BURLESON

CWT	Rarity	Reverse Die	Metal	Edge	VG	VF	EF	Unc
577A-1b	R8	1187	BR	PL		—	RARE	—

A BURLESON / DRY / GOODS, / GROCERIES, / BOOTS & SHOES. / * LITCHFIELD, MICH. *

Lowell

W. R. BLAISDELL

CWT	Rarity	Reverse Die	Metal	Edge	VG	VF	EF	Unc
580A-2a	R8	1101	C	PL		—	RARE	—

W. R. BLAISDELL / STOVES / TIN. / & HARDWARE. / LOWELL. / MICH.

HATCH & CRAW

CWT	Rarity	Reverse Die	Metal	Edge	VG	VF	EF	Unc
580B-3a	R7	1101	C	PL	10	30	45	100

HATCH & CRAW / MANFR'S / - & - / DEALERS IN / FLOUR & GRAIN / LOWELL, / MICH.

Lyons

BAUDER & BUTTON

CWT	Rarity	Reverse Die	Metal	Edge	VG	VF	EF	Unc
587A-1a	R8	1101	C	PL		—	SCARCE	—

BAUDER & BUTTON / WAR / CLAIM / AGENTS / (line) / ATTORNEYS / AT LAW / (ornament) / LYONS, MICH.

A. BUTTON

CWT	Rarity	Reverse Die	Metal	Edge	VG	VF	EF	Unc
587B-1a	R7	1169	C	PL	15	50	75	140

A. BUTTON / WAR / CLAIM ATTORNEY / AND GENERAL / (line) GENERAL (line) / (line) COLLECTING (line) / AGENT. / (ornament) / LYONS, MICH.

L. F. HEATH

CWT	Rarity	Reverse Die	Metal	Edge	VG	VF	EF	Unc
587C-1a	R7	1321	C	PL		—	SCARCE	—

* L. F. HEATH, * / WATCH / MAKER / AND / PHOTOGRAPHER, / LYONS, / (ornament) / * MICH. *

Manchester

VAN DUYN & LYNCH

CWT	Rarity	Reverse Die	Metal	Edge	VG	VF	EF	Unc
588A-1b	R7	1310	BR	PL		—	SCARCE	—

VAN DUYN & LYNCH / DRUGGISTS / AND / GROCERS, / MANCHESTER / MICH.

Maple Rapids

ISAAC HEWITT

CWT	Rarity	Reverse Die	Metal	Edge	VG	VF	EF	Unc
595A-2a	R8	1105	C	PL		—	RARE	—

ISAAC HEWITT / DRY / GOODS / & / GROCERIES. / MAPLE RAPIDS / MICH.

Marshall

ISAAC BEERS

CWT	Rarity	Reverse Die	Metal	Edge	VG	VF	EF	Unc
610A-1a	R9	1098	C	PL		—	SCARCE	—

ISAAC BEERS. / STOVES / * / HARDWARE / . / TOOLS & / TIN WARE / * / MARSHALL, MICH.

C. M. BREWER

CWT	Rarity	Reverse Die	Metal	Edge	VG	VF	EF	Unc
610B-1a	R6	1095	C	PL	4	8	10	40

C. M. BREWER / DEALER / IN / DRY GOODS / GROCERIES & / HARDWARE / MARSHALL, / - * - / MICH.

L. H. ROBINSON

CWT	Rarity	Reverse Die	Metal	Edge	VG	VF	EF	Unc
610C-3a	R7	1018	C	R	4	8	10	30

L. H. ROBINSON / DEALER / IN / GROCERIES / - & - / NOTIONS / MARSHALL, MICH.

Mason

J. W. PHELPS & CO.

CWT	Rarity	Reverse Die	Metal	Edge	VG	VF	EF	Unc
615A-2a	R5	1042	C	R	10	60	75	120

J. W. PHELPS & CO / HARDWARE / TIN & COPPER / - WARE - / DRUGS / & / MEDICINES / MASON, MICH.

Morenci

J. M. PAGE & CO.

CWT	Rarity	Reverse Die	Metal	Edge	VG	VF	EF	Unc
660A-1a	R6	1186	C	PL	8	25	40	75

J. M. PAGE & Co. / DEALERS IN / GENERAL / (ornament) / HARDWARE / * MORENCI, MICH. *

RICHARDS & CO.

CWT	Rarity	Reverse Die	Metal	Edge	VG	VF	EF	Unc
660B-2a	R3	1099	C	PL	8	15	20	45

RICHARDS & CO. / * / DEALERS / IN / DRY GOODS. / HARDWARE / & C. / MORENCI, MICH.

Mussey

E. C. MORSE

CWT	Rarity	Reverse Die	Metal	Edge	VG	VF	EF	Unc
680A-1a	R5	1037	C	R	15	50	75	100

- . - E. C. MORSE - . - / DRY / GOODS / GROCERIES / & C. / MUSSEY

Niles

G. A. COLBY & CO.

CWT	Rarity	Reverse Die	Metal	Edge	VG	VF	EF	Unc
700A-1a	R6	1203	C	PL	8	20	25	50

G. A. COLBY & CO. / WHOLESALE / - * - / GROCERIES / & / BAKERY / NILES. MICH.

H. EASTMAN

CWT	Rarity	Reverse Die	Metal	Edge	VG	VF	EF	Unc
700B-1a	R3	1099	C	PL	8	20	25	45

H. EASTMAN / DEALER / IN / DRY GOODS. / CLOTHING. / BOOTS & (line) / (line) SHOES. (line) / NILES. MICH.

E. S. PARKER

CWT	Rarity	Reverse Die	Metal	Edge	VG	VF	EF	Unc
700C-3a	R6	1098	C	PL	8	30	40	70

(ornament) E. S. PARKER (ornament) / DEALER / IN / HATS. CAPS / & FURS / * (ornament) * / NILES. MICH.

G. W. & H. C. PLATT

CWT	Rarity	Reverse Die	Metal	Edge	VG	VF	EF	Unc
700D-3a	R4	1108	C	PL	8	15	25	50

G. W. & H. C. PLATT / - * - / STOVES. / AND / HARDWARE / NILES, / MICH.

H. G. SLEIGHT

CWT	Rarity	Reverse Die	Metal	Edge	VG	VF	EF	Unc
700E-4a	R4	1101	C	PL	8	15	25	50

H. G. SLEIGHT / DEALER / IN / GROCERIES. / SEEDS / & C. / NILES, MICH.

Owosso

C. E. SHATTUCK

CWT	Rarity	Reverse Die	Metal	Edge	VG	VF	EF	Unc
735A-1a	R5	1122	C	PL	10	25	40	70

C. E. SHATTUCK / DEALER IN / BRICK / - & - / DRAIN TILE / OWASSO, / MICH.

M. L. STEWART

CWT	Rarity	Reverse Die	Metal	Edge	VG	VF	EF	Unc
735B-1a	R5	1127	C	PL	10	25	40	70

* M. L. STEWART, * / WHOLESALE / AND / RETAIL / GROCER, / OWOSSO, / MICH.

Parma

GLAZIER'S PHARMACY

CWT	Rarity	Reverse Die	Metal	Edge	VG	VF	EF	Unc
740A-1a	R3	—	C	PL	8	25	35	55

GLAZIER'S PHARMACY above mortar and pestle. PARMA MIC. below. Rv: * BUY YOUR MEDICINES * / AND / (ornament) / OILS / AT / (ornament) / PAINTS

Paw Paw

J. R. FOOTE

CWT	Rarity	Reverse Die	Metal	Edge	VG	VF	EF	Unc
745A-1a	R7	1099	C	PL	20	65	90	150

J. R. FOOTE / (ornament) / CROCKERY / GLASSWARE / & / GROCERIES / PAW PAW, / MICH.

G. W. LONGWELL

CWT	Rarity	Reverse Die	Metal	Edge	VG	VF	EF	Unc
745B-1a	R8	1102	C	PL		—	SCARCE	—

G. W. LONGWELL / DRUGS / - & - / GROCERIES. / MAIN St. / PAW PAW. MICH

A. SHERMAN & CO.

CWT	Rarity	Reverse Die	Metal	Edge	VG	VF	EF	Unc
745C-1a	R7	1003	C	PL		—	SCARCE	—

A. SHERMAN & CO. / GENERAL MERCHANTS / & / PROPR'S OF / PAW PAW / (ornament) / FLOURING MILLS / PAW PAW. MICH

J. D. SHERMAN

CWT	Rarity	Reverse Die	Metal	Edge	VG	VF	EF	Unc
745D-1a	R6	1105	C	PL	20	65	90	150

J. D. SHERMAN / WHOLESALE / (ornament) / GROCERIES / & / PROVISIONS / PAW PAW, / MICH.

Pontiac

FOX & SMITH

CWT	Rarity	Reverse Die	Metal	Edge	VG	VF	EF	Unc
770A-2a	R3	1210	C	PL	5	15	25	50

FOX & SMITH / PRODUCE & / COMMISSION / MERCHANTS / & DEALERS IN / PLASTER / PONTIAC. MICH.

MORRIS & MESSINGER

CWT	Rarity	Reverse Die	Metal	Edge	VG	VF	EF	Unc
770B-1b	R4	1305	BR	PL	4	8	10	20

MORRIS & MESSINGER / DEALERS / IN / HARDWARE / IRON, STEEL, / NAILS & GLASS. / * PONTIAC *

A. PARKER

CWT	Rarity	Reverse Die	Metal	Edge	VG	VF	EF	Unc
770C-1b	R3	—	BR	PL	15	50	75	125

A. PARKER, / DEALER / IN / (ornament) DRUGS (ornament) / MEDICINES / GROCERIES & / GLASS / (ornament) PONTIAC (ornament) Rv: FRENCH'S HAIR RESTORATIVE / FOR RESTORING GRAY HAIR around bottle with "FRENCH'S" on it.

Saginaw City

WM. BINDER

CWT	Rarity	Reverse Die	Metal	Edge	VG	VF	EF	Unc
845A-1a	R8	1101	C	PL	25	100	125	250

WM. BINDER / (ornament) / DRY GOODS / GROCERIES. / SAGINAW / CITY / * MICH *

EPTING & EATON

CWT	Rarity	Reverse Die	Metal	Edge	VG	VF	EF	Unc
845B-1a	R8	1095	C	PL		—	RARE	—

EPTING & EATON / DEALERS / IN / DRUGS & / MEDICINES. / SAGINAW CITY / MICH.

Salina

GALLAGHER & HESS

CWT	Rarity	Reverse Die	Metal	Edge	VG	VF	EF	Unc
855A-1a	R5	1095	C	PL	10	25	45	85

GALLAGHER & HESS / mortar and pestle / DRUGGISTS. / SALINA, / MICH.

Saranac

W. DARLING

CWT	Rarity	Reverse Die	Metal	Edge	VG	VF	EF	Unc
865A-1a	R8	—	C	PL		—	RARE	—

(ornament) / W. DARLING / (ornament) / SARANAC / (ornament) MICH (ornament) / 1864 (Thirteen stars around.) Rv: Wreath enclosing a boot and seven stars.

Schoolcraft

I. ALLEN & SON

CWT	Rarity	Reverse Die	Metal	Edge	VG	VF	EF	Unc
900A-1a	R8	1094	C	PL		—	SCARCE	—

I. ALLEN & SON / STOVES / & / HARDWARE / SCHOOLCRAFT / MICH.

I. W. PRUSEL & CO.

CWT	Rarity	Reverse Die	Metal	Edge	VG	VF	EF	Unc
900B-1a	R8	1110	C	PL		—	SCARCE	—

I. W. PRUSEL & CO / DRY (line) / (line) GOODS (line) / GROCERIES / BOOTS / & / SHOES / SCHOOLCRAFT

St. Johns

G. W. STEPHENSON

CWT	Rarity	Reverse Die	Metal	Edge	VG	VF	EF	Unc
915A-1a	R5	1310	C	PL	10	40	50	100

G. W. STEPHENSON / GENERAL / * / MERCHANT / St. JOHNS / MICH.

Tecumseh

FISHER & HENDRYX

CWT	Rarity	Reverse Die	Metal	Edge	VG	VF	EF	Unc
920A-1a	R6	1310	C	PL		—	SCARCE	—

FISHER & HENDRYX / DRUGGISTS / AND / GROCERS / CHICAGO ST. / TECUMSEH, / MICH.

DR. E. HAUSE

CWT	Rarity	Reverse Die	Metal	Edge	VG	VF	EF	Unc
920B-3a	R5	1099	C	PL	15	35	50	75

DR. E. HAUSE / (ornament) / DENTIST / TECUMSEH / MICH.

G. T. KETCHAM

CWT	Rarity	Reverse Die	Metal	Edge	VG	VF	EF	Unc
920C-1a	R4	1099	C	PL	8	15	25	60

G. T. KETCHAM / *** / NEWS DEALER / & / (line) / BOOK / (line) / SELLER / (line) / TECUMSEH, MICH

C. S. PATTERSON

CWT	Rarity	Reverse Die	Metal	Edge	VG	VF	EF	Unc
920D-1a	R4	1099	C	PL	10	25	40	60

C. S. PATTERSON / mortar and pestle / DRUGGIST. / TECUMSEH / MICH.

Ypsilanti

E. HEWITT & BRO.

CWT	Rarity	Reverse Die	Metal	Edge	VG	VF	EF	Unc
960A-6a	R3	1094	C	PL	4	8	10	40

E. HEWITT & BRO. / DEALERS / IN / DRY GOODS / & MANFRS / OF BOOTS / & SHOES / YPSILANTI, MICH.

SHOWERMAN & BRO.

CWT	Rarity	Reverse Die	Metal	Edge	VG	VF	EF	Unc
960B-1a	R4	1105	C	PL	4	8	10	40

SHOWERMAN & BRO. / DEALERS / IN / DRY GOODS / CLOTHING / HATS & CAPS / BOOTS & SHOES / YPSILANTI, MICH.

MINNESOTA

Red Wing

A. W. E.

CWT	Rarity	Reverse Die	Metal	Edge	VG	VF	EF	Unc
680A-2a	R7	1272	C	PL		—	RARE	—

A. W. E. / RED WING, / MINN.

Rochester

F. W. ANDREWS

CWT	Rarity	Reverse Die	Metal	Edge	VG	VF	EF	Unc
720A-3a	R7	1168	C	PL	100	175	225	275

F. W. ANDREWS / eagle in glory / DRY GOODS / - & C. - / ROCHESTER, / MINN.

St. Paul

D. C. GREENLEAF

CWT	Rarity	Reverse Die	Metal	Edge	VG	VF	EF	Unc
760A-1a	R8	Blank	C	PL	100	175	225	275

(ornament) / D. C. GREENLEAF / WATCH / MAKER, / ST. PAUL, / * MIN. * / - . -

WHEELER & WILSONS

CWT	Rarity	Reverse Die	Metal	Edge	VG	VF	EF	Unc
760B-1a	R6	1298	C	PL	100	175	225	275

WHEELER & WILSONS / SEWING / MACHINES / F. M. JOHNSON / AGT. / 3d. St. / ST. PAUL, MIN.

Winona

C. BENSON

CWT	Rarity	Reverse Die	Metal	Edge	VG	VF	EF	Unc
980A-1a	R7	1310	C	PL	100	175	225	300

C. BENSON, / DRUGGIST / WINONA, / MINN.

COE & HAYDEN

CWT	Rarity	Reverse Die	Metal	Edge	VG	VF	EF	Unc
980B-1a	R6	—	C	PL	100	175	225	275

COE & HAYDEN / DRY GOODS / * / CROCKERY, / BOOTS, SHOES, / AND / GROCERIES. / THE REGULATOR. Rv: ** THE REGULATOR ** / NO. 2, / SIMPSON / BLOCK, / SECOND ST. / WINONA, / MINN. / * 1863 *

MISSOURI

Ironton

D. PECK & CO.

CWT	Rarity	Reverse Die	Metal	Edge	VG	VF	EF	Unc
400A-1a	R7	1046	C	R		—	RARE	—

D. PECK & CO. / DEALERS / IN / GROCERIES / - DRUGS - / & / MEDICINES / IRONTON, MO.

St. Joseph

JOHN KENMUIR

CWT	Rarity	Reverse Die	Metal	Edge	VG	VF	EF	Unc
880A-1b	R9	—	BR	PL		—	RARE	—

JOHN KENMUIR / . + . / MAN'FG / JEWELER / . + . / ST. JOSEPH. MO

St. Louis

DROVERS HOTEL

CWT	Rarity	Reverse Die	Metal	Edge	VG	VF	EF	Unc
910A-1a	R6	1008	C	PL	20	75	100	150

DROVERS / HOTEL above steer's head in center. 125 NORTH 4' ST / ST LOUIS, MO. below.

LALLEMAND'S

CWT	Rarity	Reverse Die	Metal	Edge	VG	VF	EF	Unc
910B-1a	R8	—	C	R		—	SCARCE	—

USE / LALLEMAND'S / SPECIFIC / SOLD / BY / DRUGGISTS / JNO. H. BLOOD, AGT / 24 FIFTH ST. / ST. LOUIS Rv: LALLEMAND'S / RHEUMATISM / GOUT / - & - / NEURALGIA / SPECIFIC

HENRY JENKENS

CWT	Rarity	Reverse Die	Metal	Edge	VG	VF	EF	Unc
910C-1a	R4	1274	C	PL	10	25	35	45

HENRY JENKENS / WHOLESALE / & / RETAIL / (ornament) / CLOTHIER / ST. LOUIS, MO.

NEW HAMPSHIRE

Concord

A. W. GALE

CWT	Rarity	Reverse Die	Metal	Edge	VG	VF	EF	Unc
120A-1a	R5	—	C	PL	10	25	35	50

A. W. GALE / RESTORATOR / AT / DEPOT / CONCORD, N. H. Rv: *** GOOD FOR *** / * / ONE / CENT / (ornament) / IN GOODS

NEW JERSEY

Atlantic City

NEPTUNE HOUSE

CWT	Rarity	Reverse Die	Metal	Edge	VG	VF	EF	Unc
20A-1a	R2	—	C	PL	4	8	10	15

NEPTUNE / (ornament) / HOUSE / ATLANTIC / CITY / 1863 within circle of thirteen large stars. Rv: SMICK'S within an oak wreath.

NOTE: Comes with extensive obverse die breaks.

Elizabeth Port

JOHN ENGEL

CWT	Rarity	Reverse Die	Metal	Edge	VG	VF	EF	Unc
220A-2a	R3	1214	C	PL	5	12	15	30

JOHN ENGEL / (line) / MERCHANT / (line) / TAILOR / - 52 - / FIRST ST. / ELIZABETH Pt NJ.

Jersey City

TERHUNE BROTHERS

CWT	Rarity	Reverse Die	Metal	Edge	VG	VF	EF	Unc
350A-1a	R2	1215	C	PL	5	12	15	30

TERHUNE BROTHERS / 71 & 73 / (curved lines) / NEWARK AV. / JERSEY CITY / - NJ - / HARDWARE

Newark

J. L. AGENS & CO.

CWT	Rarity	Reverse Die	Metal	Edge	VG	VF	EF	Unc
555A-5a	R3	1214	C	PL	4	6	8	15

J. L. AGENS & Co. / - No. 1. - / (curved lines) / COMMERCE ST. / (curved lines) / NEWARK NJ. / NEWSPAPERS.

CHARLES KOLB

CWT	Rarity	Reverse Die	Metal	Edge	VG	VF	EF	Unc
555B-1a	R3	1014	C	PL	4	6	8	15

CHARLES KOLB / 102 / MARKET ST. / + * + / RESTAURANT.

J. WIGHTMAN

CWT	Rarity	Reverse Die	Metal	Edge	VG	VF	EF	Unc
555C-2a	R3	1016	C	PL	4	8	10	15

J. WIGHTMAN / 188 / WASHINGTON / ST. / NEWARK, N.J.

Perth Amboy

COUTTS & BRO.

CWT	Rarity	Reverse Die	Metal	Edge	VG	VF	EF	Unc
690A-1a	R4	1265	C	PL	4	10	12	20

COUTTS & BRO. / (curved line) / DRY GOODS / - & - / GROCERIES / (curved line) / P. AMBOY, NJ.

Trenton

B. W. TITUS

CWT	Rarity	Reverse Die	Metal	Edge	VG	VF	EF	Unc
885A-1b	R3	—	BR	PL	4	6	8	15

B. W. TITUS / 20 / (ornament) / E. STATE ST. / (ornament) / TRENTON N.J. Rv: DRY GOODS / (ornament) / OIL CLOTHS / (ornament) / CARPETS / (ornament)

Williamstown

BODINE & BROTHERS

CWT	Rarity	Reverse Die	Metal	Edge	VG	VF	EF	Unc
925A-1b	R8	—	BR	PL		—	RARE	—

DUE BEARER IN MDZE AT COUNTER OF OUR STORE * around outer edge. * / ONE CENT / BODINE & / BROTHERS / 1863 in center. Rv: Incuse of obverse.

NEW YORK

Albany

BENJAMIN & HERRICK

CWT	Rarity	Reverse Die	Metal	Edge	VG	VF	EF	Unc
10A-1a	R2	—	C	PL	4	6	8	15

BENJAMIN & HERRICK / FRUIT / DEALERS / ALBANY, N. Y. Rv: REDEEMED AT / 427 / BROADWAY / (ornament) / 1863

NOTE: F of FRUIT touches first N of BENJAMIN on obverse. On the reverse, the top of the 7 is curved.

P. V. FORT & CO.

CWT	Rarity	Reverse Die	Metal	Edge	VG	VF	EF	Unc
10B-1a	R3	—	C	PL	4	6	8	15

* P. V. FORT & CO. * / DEALERS / IN / FRUIT / AND / (ornament) NUTS (ornament) / ALBANY N.Y. Rv: *** REDEEMED *** / (ornament) AT (ornament) / No. 427 / BROADWAY / 1864

JOS. MCBURNEY

CWT	Rarity	Reverse Die	Metal	Edge	VG	VF	EF	Unc
10C-1a	R3	—	C	PL	4	6	8	15

JOs. Mc.BURNEY / * / CIGAR BOX MANUF'R / (ornament) 26 (ornament) / MULBERRY ST. / ** / ALBANY N.Y. Rv: REDEEMED / AT / (ornament) / 26 / MULBERRY ST. / ALBANY N.Y.

N.Y.C.R.R. EX. TRAINS

CWT	Rarity	Reverse Die	Metal	Edge	VG	VF	EF	Unc
10D-1a	R4	—	C	PL	4	8	10	15

- N.Y.C.R.R. EX. TRAINS - / LEAVE / ALBANY / 7-30 & 9 / (ornament) A.M. (ornament) / 12-20 & 6 / * P.M. * Rv: N.Y.C.R.R. EX. TRAINS / LEAVE / BUFFALO / (ornament) 5 & 8 (ornament) / A.M. / 5-45 & 10-55 / * P.M. *

STRAIGHT'S ELEPHANTINE

CWT	Rarity	Reverse Die	Metal	Edge	VG	VF	EF	Unc
10F-1a	R3	—	C	PL	4	10	15	20

STRAIGHT'S ELEPHANTINE / SHOE STORE above elephant in boots to right with rug on its back marked 398. BROADWAY / 1863 below. Rv: * REDEEMED AT MY SHOE STORE * / 398 / BROADWAY / ALBANY / * N.Y. *

JOHN THOMAS, JR.

CWT	Rarity	Reverse Die	Metal	Edge	VG	VF	EF	Unc
10G-1a	R3	—	C	PL	4	6	8	15

JOHN THOMAS Jr. / + / PREMIUM / . / MILLS / + / * COFFEE & SPICES * Rv: REDEEMED / EXCHANGE / & / DEAN ST'S. / 1863 / *** ALBANY N.Y. ***

D. L. WING

CWT	Rarity	Reverse Die	Metal	Edge	VG	VF	EF	Unc
10H	R1	1372	C	PL	4	6	8	15

D. L. WING & CO. / (ornament) 318 (ornament) / ** / BROADWAY / *** / * ALBANY N.Y. *

Almond

H. DARTT

CWT	Rarity	Reverse Die	Metal	Edge	VG	VF	EF	Unc
15A-1a	R4	1090	C	PL	10	25	35	90

H. DARTT / DRY GOODS / GROCERIES / & / EXCHANGE / OFFICE / ALMOND. N.Y.

Belmont

LANGDONS HARDWARE

CWT	Rarity	Reverse Die	Metal	Edge	VG	VF	EF	Unc
77A-1a	R5	1096	C	PL	10	20	30	65

LANGDONS. HARDWARE STORE * / & / EXCHANGE / OFFICE / BELMONT / N.Y.

Binghampton

EVANS & ALLEN

CWT	Rarity	Reverse Die	Metal	Edge	VG	VF	EF	Unc
80A-1a	R3	1368	C	PL	6	12	15	30

EVANS & ALLEN / WATCHES / & / JEWELRY / BINGHAMTON / NY

NOTE: Spelling of BINGHAMPTON.

HERSCHMAN BROS. & CO.

CWT	Rarity	Reverse Die	Metal	Edge	VG	VF	EF	Unc
80B-1a	R3	1368	C	PL	6	12	15	30

HERSCHMAN. BROs. & CO / DRY / GOODS / 20 / COURT. ST / BINGHAMPTON / NY

Brooklyn

BRAUN & SCHELLWORTH'S

CWT	Rarity	Reverse Die	Metal	Edge	VG	VF	EF	Unc
95A-1a	R2	1243	C	PL	4	6	8	15

BRAUN & SCHELLWORTH'S / 132. 134. 136 / COURT St / - * - / BROOKLYN / PAVILION

C. J. HAUCK

CWT	Rarity	Reverse Die	Metal	Edge	VG	VF	EF	Unc
95B-1a	R2	1256	C	PL	4	6	8	15

C. J. HAUCK / 108 / LEONARD St / BROOKLYN, E.D / N.Y.

M. IBERT

CWT	Rarity	Reverse Die	Metal	Edge	VG	VF	EF	Unc
95C-1g	R9	—	L	PL		—	RARE	—

M. IBERT / COR / MONTROSE & / GRAHAM / AVE / BROOKLYN ED Rv: GOOD FOR / 1 / * CENT *

T. IVORY

CWT	Rarity	Reverse Die	Metal	Edge	VG	VF	EF	Unc
95D-1b	R3	1006	BR	PL	4	8	10	15

T. IVORY. / COR. / FULTON & ORANGE / - STs - / BROOKLYN / BILLIARD SALOON.

JOHN JOERGERS

CWT	Rarity	Reverse Die	Metal	Edge	VG	VF	EF	Unc
95E-1a	R2	1256	C	PL	4	6	8	25

JOHN JOERGERS / * / NORTH 2nd St. / BROOKLYN, E.D. / L.I.

DANIEL WILLIAMS

CWT	Rarity	Reverse Die	Metal	Edge	VG	VF	EF	Unc
95F-1a	R2	1006	C	PL	4	6	8	15

DANIEL WILLIAMS / -. - / GROCER / CORNER / COURT & WARREN / STs / BROOKLYN.

Buffalo

JAMES ADAMS & CO.

CWT	Rarity	Reverse Die	Metal	Edge	VG	VF	EF	Unc
105A-1a	R4	1077	C	PL	4	8	10	25

JAMES ADAMS & CO. / TOBACCO / & / CIGARS. / 207 / WASHINGTON / ST / BUFFALO

ALBERGER'S

CWT	Rarity	Reverse Die	Metal	Edge	VG	VF	EF	Unc
105B-1a	R3	1039	C	R	4	8	10	20

ALBERGER'S / MEAT / - / STORE / * BUFFALO *

E. G. BARROWS

CWT	Rarity	Reverse Die	Metal	Edge	VG	VF	EF	Unc
105C-1a	R3	1024	C	R	8	30	45	60

E. G. BARROWS / BRANDIES / WINES & CIGARS / - NO. 6 - / EAST SWAN / ST. / BUFFALO

F. J. BIELER

CWT	Rarity	Reverse Die	Metal	Edge	VG	VF	EF	Unc
105D-1a	R3	1077	C	PL	4	8	10	25

F. J. BIELER / 157 / MAIN ST. / *** / BUFFALO.

T. J. CONRY

CWT	Rarity	Reverse Die	Metal	Edge	VG	VF	EF	Unc
105E-1a	R3	1077	C	PL	4	8	10	25

T J CONRY / PICTURE / *** / FRAMES. / NEWSPAPERS & C / 19 / SENECA St / BUFFALO.

A. M. DUBURN

CWT	Rarity	Reverse Die	Metal	Edge	VG	VF	EF	Unc
105F-1a	R2	1024	C	R	8	25	35	50

A. M. DUBURN / CANAL / TIN SHOP / - NO 29 - / COMMERCIAL / ST. / BUFFALO

L. DANFORTH

CWT	Rarity	Reverse Die	Metal	Edge	VG	VF	EF	Unc
105G-1a	R5	1037	C	R	8	25	35	60

HOWES / SCALES / L. DANFORTH / AGT. / 93 MAIN, ST. / BUFFALO.

W. G. FOX

CWT	Rarity	Reverse Die	Metal	Edge	VG	VF	EF	Unc
105H-1a	R3	1024	C	R	4	10	12	20

W. G. FOX / OYSTERS / FRUITS / & / LIQUORS / 195 MAIN ST. / BUFFALO

GEO. GAGE

CWT	Rarity	Reverse Die	Metal	Edge	VG	VF	EF	Unc
105I-3a	R2	1037	C	R	4	10	12	25

GEO. GAGE / GROCER / 334 / MAIN / ST. / BUFFALO

HOCHSTETTER & STRAUSS

CWT	Rarity	Reverse Die	Metal	Edge	VG	VF	EF	Unc
105J-1a	R3	1024	C	R	4	10	12	30

HOCHSTETTER & STRAUSS / DRY / GOODS / - 280 - / MAIN / ST. / BUFFALO

A. M. JOHNSTON

CWT	Rarity	Reverse Die	Metal	Edge	VG	VF	EF	Unc
105K-1a	R2	1039	C	R	4	10	12	20

A. M. JOHNSTON / GROCER / 52 / MAIN / ST / BUFFALO

JOHN C. POST

CWT	Rarity	Reverse Die	Metal	Edge	VG	VF	EF	Unc
105L-1a	R3	1024	C	R	6	20	30	45

JOHN C. POST / PAINTS / OILS / & / GLASS / NO. 8 SWAN, ST. / BUFFALO

REILLY'S BAZAAR

CWT	Rarity	Reverse Die	Metal	Edge	VG	VF	EF	Unc
105M-1a	R5	1368	C	PL	8	30	45	100

REILLY'S / BAZAAR / 228 / MAIN. ST / BUFFALO. NY

ROBINSON & BALL

CWT	Rarity	Reverse Die	Metal	Edge	VG	VF	EF	Unc
105N-1a	R4	1073	C	R	8	15	25	45

ROBINSON & BALL / GENTS / FURNISHING / GOODS / 275 MAIN ST / BUFFALO

ROWE & CO.

CWT	Rarity	Reverse Die	Metal	Edge	VG	VF	EF	Unc
1050-1a	R3	1042	C	R	6	20	25	45

ROWE & CO / OYSTER / & FOREIGN - / - FRUIT / DEPOT / 197 MAIN, ST. / BUFFALO

S. B. SEWARD

CWT	Rarity	Reverse Die	Metal	Edge	VG	VF	EF	Unc
105P-1a	R5	1040	C	R	8	25	30	45

USE / SEWARD'S / COUGH / - CURE - / S. B. SEWARD / DRUGGIST / BUFFALO

SOHM & ROHMANN

CWT	Rarity	Reverse Die	Metal	Edge	VG	VF	EF	Unc
105Q-2a	R4	1042	C	R	10	50	75	125

SOHM & ROHMANN / BUTCHERS / (ornament) / * / BUFFALO

C. R. WALKER

CWT	Rarity	Reverse Die	Metal	Edge	VG	VF	EF	Unc
105R-1a	R5	1077	C	PL	8	20	25	40

WATSONS NEURALGIA KING: * / C. R. WALKER / 255 / MAIN ST. / *** / BUFFALO

WEBSTER & CO.

CWT	Rarity	Reverse Die	Metal	Edge	VG	VF	EF	Unc
105S-1a	R3	1077	C	PL	6	15	20	30

WEBSTER & CO. / GROCERS / NO. 1 / SENECA / ST. / BUFFALO. N.Y.

Cohoes

ALDEN & FRINK

CWT	Rarity	Reverse Die	Metal	Edge	VG	VF	EF	Unc
140A-1a	R1	—	C	PL	4	6	8	15

** ALDEN & FRINK ** above an Indian head to left in center. - 1863 - below. Rv: ** MERCHANTS ** / (ornament) / 40 / MOHAWK St / (ornament) / COHOES N-Y.

Cooperstown

BINGHAM & JARVIS

CWT	Rarity	Reverse Die	Metal	Edge	VG	VF	EF	Unc
145A-1a	R5	1175	C	PL		—	SCARCE	—

BINGHAM / & / JARVIS / DRUGS, / MEDICINES / PAINTS, OILS & C.

G. L. BOWNE

CWT	Rarity	Reverse Die	Metal	Edge	VG	VF	EF	Unc
145B-1a	R2	—	C	PL	4	8	10	20

G. L . BOWNE / WILL / REDEEM / AT THE / IRON CLAD / COOPERSTOWN, N.Y. Rv: BINGHAM / & / JARVIS / DRUGS, MEDICINES / PAINTS, OILS & C.

Elmira

LOUIS STRAUSS & CO.

CWT	Rarity	Reverse Die	Metal	Edge	VG	VF	EF	Unc
230A-1a	R4	1024	C	R	8	25	35	60

LOUIS STRAUSS & CO. / DRY / GOODS / No. 3 / UNION - / - BLOCK / ELMIRA, N.Y.

Fort Edwards

HARVEY & CO.

CWT	Rarity	Reverse Die	Metal	Edge	VG	VF	EF	Unc
270A-1a	R2	—	C	PL	4	6	8	15

+ HARVEY & CO. + above Indian head to left in center. - 1863 - below. Rv: *********** / (ornament) / GENERAL / STORE. / (ornament) / * FORT EDWARD NY. *

Greenpoint

A. KILLEEN

CWT	Rarity	Reverse Die	Metal	Edge	VG	VF	EF	Unc
330A-5a	R3	1232	C	PL	4	8	10	15

A. KILLEEN / - + - / No 1 & 16 / FERRY / - St - / GREENPOINT.

New York City

ATLANTIC GARDEN

CWT	Rarity	Reverse Die	Metal	Edge	VG	VF	EF	Unc
630A-1A	R2	—	C	PL	4	8	10	15

ATLANTIC GARDEN / 50 / BOWERY, / NEW YORK / 1863. Rv: GRAND CONCERT / EVERY NIGHT. / lyre with oak branches at side in center / ADMISSION / FREE.

CAFE AUTENRIETH

CWT	Rarity	Reverse Die	Metal	Edge	VG	VF	EF	Unc
630B-1a	R1	1075	C	PL	4	6	8	15

CAFE AUTENRIETH / 85 / CHATHAM ST. / N.Y. / 1863.

C. BAHR

CWT	Rarity	Reverse Die	Metal	Edge	VG	VF	EF	Unc
630C-1a	R2	1075	C	PL	4	6	8	15

C. BAHR / COr CLIFF / - AND - / FRANKFORT St. / - / NEW YORK

H. J. BANG

CWT	Rarity	Reverse Die	Metal	Edge	VG	VF	EF	Unc
630D-1a	R2	—	C	PL	4	6	8	15

H. J. BANG, / (ornament) / RESTAURANT / 231 / BROADWAY. Rv: IMPORTER OF / bunch of grapes with the name GLAUBRECHT below them / * RHINE WINES. *

THOS. BENNETT

CWT	Rarity	Reverse Die	Metal	Edge	VG	VF	EF	Unc
630E-1a	R1	—	C	PL	4	6	8	15

THos. BENNETT / N.Y. in wreath in center / 213 FULTON ST. / A. L. HENNING N.Y. in very small letters.

V. BENNER & CH. BENDINGER

CWT	Rarity	Reverse Die	Metal	Edge	VG	VF	EF	Unc
630F-1a	R2	—	C	PL	4	6	8	15

V. BENNER & CH. BENDINGER / Indian head to left with the name L. ROLOFF below / * 1863 * (Eighth feather is below the level of the R in BENDINGER. Rv: IMPORTERS OF WINES & LIQUORS / wine bottle in wreath in center / - No 1 Ave A. -

I. W. BLAIN

CWT	Rarity	Reverse Die	Metal	Edge	VG	VF	EF	Unc
630G-1b	R9	Blank	BR	PL		—	RARE	—

I. W. BLAIN / 10 cts / 16 & 18' / FULTON MARKET N.Y. / 1862

J. L. BODE

CWT	Rarity	Reverse Die	Metal	Edge	VG	VF	EF	Unc
630H-1a	R1	—	C	PL	4	6	8	15

J. L. BODE / mounted stag's head to left / BIRDSTUFFER / 1863 Rv: BOHEMIAN / FANCY / GLASSWORK / - 16 - / N. WILLIAM St / N.Y.

JAS. BRENNAN

CWT	Rarity	Reverse Die	Metal	Edge	VG	VF	EF	Unc
630I-1a	R3	1152	C	PL	4	12	15	25

JAs. BRENNAN / - 37 - / NASSAU St / FOREIGN / - & - / U.S. POSTAGE STAMPS.

BRIDGENS

CWT	Rarity	Reverse Die	Metal	Edge	VG	VF	EF	Unc
630J-2a	R3	1137	C	PL	4	20	30	50

BRIDGENS. / (curved line) / METAL TOKENS / - & - / STORE CARDS / - 189 - / WILLIAM ST. N.Y.

T. BRIMELOW

CWT	Rarity	Reverse Die	Metal	Edge	VG	VF	EF	Unc
630K-1a	R3	1138	C	PL	4	8	10	20

T. BRIMELOW, DRUGGIST, / figure 1 in wreath, surrounding a mortar and pestle which divides the date, 1863 / 432 THIRD AVENUE. N.Y.

BROAS BROS.

CWT	Rarity	Reverse Die	Metal	Edge	VG	VF	EF	Unc
630L-1a	R2	1004	C	PL	4	6	8	15

BROAS BROs above. Wreath around ARMY / AND / NAVY in center. * NEW YORK * below.

BROAS PIE BAKER

CWT	Rarity	Reverse Die	Metal	Edge	VG	VF	EF	Unc
630M-1a	R2	1060	C	PL	4	6	8	15

BROAS PIE BAKER / ONE / COUNTRY / * / 131 41ST ST N.Y.

M. S. BROWN

CWT	Rarity	Reverse Die	Metal	Edge	VG	VF	EF	Unc
630N-2a	R2	—	C	PL	4	6	8	15

M. S. BROWN / 1863 in center of an open wreath with a shield at top center. B of BROWN under point of shield. Rv: EUREKA / . - 2 - . / WARREN ST. / - . - / NEW YORK

W. S. BROWN

CWT	Rarity	Reverse Die	Metal	Edge	VG	VF	EF	Unc
630O-1a	R3	—	C	PL		—	SCARCE	—

W. S. BROWN / 1863 in wreath with shield at top.

CARLAND'S

CWT	Rarity	Reverse Die	Metal	Edge	VG	VF	EF	Unc
630P-1a	R2	—	C	PL	4	6	8	15

CARLAND'S / 95 / BOWERY / COR. OF / HESTER ST. N.Y. Rv: FINE ALE / * / DRAWN / * / FROM WOOD.

NOTE: F of OF under right side of R of BOWERY.

CITY OF NEW YORK

CWT	Rarity	Reverse Die	Metal	Edge	VG	VF	EF	Unc
630Q-1a	R1	1011	C	PL	4	6	8	15

CITY OF NEW YORK / I.O.U. / ONE / CENT / - / * 1863. *

G. A. DEFANDORF

CWT	Rarity	Reverse Die	Metal	Edge	VG	VF	EF	Unc
630R-1j	R9	—	G-S	PL		—	RARE	—

G. A. DEFANDORF / 233 / E. 77th ST. / - / DENTIST. Rv: Same as Obverse.

NOTE: The first letter of the last name is probably a D that wasn't stamped with enough pressure.

TOM CULLEN

CWT	Rarity	Reverse Die	Metal	Edge	VG	VF	EF	Unc
630S-2a	R2	1255	C	PL	4	6	8	15

TOM CULLEN / LIQUORS / 609 / GRAND St N.Y.

J. J. DIEHL

CWT	Rarity	Reverse Die	Metal	Edge	VG	VF	EF	Unc
630T-1a	R2	1011	C	PL	4	6	8	15

J. J. DIEHL UNDERTAKER / 133 / coffin in open wreath / ESSEX St. / (ornament) NEW YORK. (ornament)

CARL DIEM

CWT	Rarity	Reverse Die	Metal	Edge	VG	VF	EF	Unc
630U-1a1	R3	1417	C	PL	4	10	12	25

* CARL DIEM * / (curved line) / CONSTANZER / (curved line) / (curved line) / BRAUERE / (curved line) / 565 & 567 / 4th ST. / NEW YORK.

C. DOSCHER

CWT	Rarity	Reverse Die	Metal	Edge	VG	VF	EF	Unc
630V-3a	R2	1254	C	PL	4	6	8	15

C. DOSCHER 241 WASHn St. N.Y. / bust of Washington to right in center. 1863. below.

FELIX

CWT	Rarity	Reverse Die	Metal	Edge	VG	VF	EF	Unc
630W-1a	R3	1015	C	PL	10	35	50	75

* FELIX * / Hebrew letters for "Kosher" / (two curved lines) / DINING / (two curved lines) / SALOON / (line) / 256 / BROADWAY, / NEW YORK.

FEUCHTWANGER'S COMPOSITION

CWT	Rarity	Reverse Die	Metal	Edge	VG	VF	EF	Unc
630X-1j	R7	—	G-S	R		—	RARE	—

FEUCHTWANGER'S COMPOSITION around. 3 / THREE / CENTS within wreath in center with numeric "3" at top center of wreath. Rv: Large eagle with snake in talons in center and date of 1864 below.

J. FISHER

CWT	Rarity	Reverse Die	Metal	Edge	VG	VF	EF	Unc
630Y-1a	R2	1214	C	PL	4	12	15	25

J. FISHER. / - 254 - / SEVENTH / - AV. - / SEGAR STORE.

FR. FREISE

CWT	Rarity	Reverse Die	Metal	Edge	VG	VF	EF	Unc
630Z-1a	R3	—	C	PL	4	6	8	15

FR. FREISE, LEICHENBESORGER / Indian head to left / 12 AVE. A, / * NEW YORK. *

J. F. GARDNER

CWT	Rarity	Reverse Die	Metal	Edge	VG	VF	EF	Unc
630AA-1a	R4	1015	C	PL	4	8	12	20

J. F. GARDNER / 55 / HENRY / ST. / * N.Y. *

A. GAVRON

CWT	Rarity	Reverse Die	Metal	Edge	VG	VF	EF	Unc
630AB-1a	R2	1006	C	PL	4	6	8	15

A. GAVRON. / - 213 - / BOWERY / - & - / 102 PITT ST. / - NY - / SAUSAGES.

CHARLES GENTSCH

CWT	Rarity	Reverse Die	Metal	Edge	VG	VF	EF	Unc
630AC-1a	R2	—	C	PL	4	6	8	15

* CHARLES GENTSCH * / Indian head to left / * 1863 * Rv: CAFE / RESTAURANT / DU COMMERCE / No 426 / BROADWAY N-Y.

H. D. GERDTS

CWT	Rarity	Reverse Die	Metal	Edge	VG	VF	EF	Unc
630AD-1a	R3	1137	C	PL	4	10	12	20

H. D. GERDTS / BROKER / - & - / COIN DEALER / - 240 - / GREENWICH ST. NY.

G. GRAHAM

CWT	Rarity	Reverse Die	Metal	Edge	VG	VF	EF	Unc
630AE-2a	1263	C	PL	4	6	8	15	

G. GRAHAM, / COR. / HENRY / & MONTGOMERY St. / COR. BLEECKER & / TENTH / St. / LIQUORS.

J. A. C. GRUBE

CWT	Rarity	Reverse Die	Metal	Edge	VG	VF	EF	Unc
630AF-2a	R2	1257	C	PL	4	6	8	15

J. A. C. GRUBE, / SEGARS / AND / TOBACCO. / 7 BOWERY 7 / NEW YORK.

JOHN P. GRUBER

CWT	Rarity	Reverse Die	Metal	Edge	VG	VF	EF	Unc
630AG-1a	R2	1197	C	PL	4	6	8	15

JOHN P. GRUBER / set of balances in center / NEW YORK. below.

NOTE: One with broken die.

A. J. HENNING

CWT	Rarity	Reverse Die	Metal	Edge	VG	VF	EF	Unc
630AH-1a	R4	—	C	PL	8	25	35	65

A. J. HENNING / DIE / SINKER / & / * ENGRAVER * Rv: Wreath enclosing 87 / FULTON ST. / N-Y.

WILLIAM HASTINGS

CWT	Rarity	Reverse Die	Metal	Edge	VG	VF	EF	Unc
630AI-1g	R2	—	L	PL	4	6	8	25

WILLIAM HASTINGS / Indian head to left in center / 1863 below. Rv: Wreath enclosing IM - / PORTED / LIQUORS

CHR. F. HETZEL

CWT	Rarity	Reverse Die	Metal	Edge	VG	VF	EF	Unc
630AJ-1a	R3	1330	C	PL	4	6	8	15

CHR. F. HETZEL / ROOFER / NEW - YORK

HUSSEY'S SPECIAL MESSAGE POST

CWT	Rarity	Reverse Die	Metal	Edge	VG	VF	EF	Unc
630AK-1a	R2	1162	C	PL	4	8	10	15

HUSSEY'S SPECIAL MESSAGE POST / 50 / WILLIAM St. / NEW YORK / - * -

GEORGE HYENLEIN

CWT	Rarity	Reverse Die	Metal	Edge	VG	VF	EF	Unc
630AL-1a	R2	1610	C	PL	4	6	8	15

GEORGE HYENLEIN / * / 23 / CHRYSTIE St. / N.Y.

CHRISTOPH KARL

CWT	Rarity	Reverse Die	Metal	Edge	VG	VF	EF	Unc
630AM-1a	R1	1164	C	PL	4	6	8	15

CHRISTOPH KARL / lyre in wreath in center / 42 AVENUE A, NEW YORK.

H. & M. KAYSER & CO.

CWT	Rarity	Reverse Die	Metal	Edge	VG	VF	EF	Unc
630AMa-1a	R7	1190	C	PL		—	RARE	—

H & M. KAYSER & CO. / IMPORTERS / OF / FANCY GOODS / NEW - YORK

R. T. KELLY

CWT	Rarity	Reverse Die	Metal	Edge	VG	VF	EF	Unc
630AN-1a	R3	1249	C	PL	4	8	10	20

R. T. KELLY / high hat dividing the date 1863 / E. S. / 1319 THIRD AVE. / NEW YORK.

KNOOPS

CWT	Rarity	Reverse Die	Metal	Edge	VG	VF	EF	Unc
630AO-1a	R2	1075	C	PL	4	6	8	15

KNOOPS SEGARS & TOBACCO / 131 / BOWERY / N. Y. / * 1863 *

H. M. LANE

CWT	Rarity	Reverse Die	Metal	Edge	VG	VF	EF	Unc
630AP-5a	R1	1132	C	PL	4	6	8	15

H. M. LANE / LAMPS / KEROSENE OIL & C / 18 / SPRING St. N.Y.

GUSTAVUS LINDENMUELLER

CWT	Rarity	Reverse Die	Metal	Edge	VG	VF	EF	Unc
630AQ-1a	R1	—	C	PL	4	6	8	15

GUSTAVUS LINDENMUELLER / wreath enclosing beer mug / NEW YORK (26 berries in the wreath) (Also thick planchet) Rv: Bust of bearded man to left with name L. ROLOFF below bust. 13 stars and date 1863 around.

CHARLES A. LUHRS

CWT	Rarity	Reverse Die	Metal	Edge	VG	VF	EF	Unc
630AR-1a	R2	—	C	PL	4	6	8	15

CHARLES A. LUHRS / 77 / (ornament) / PIKE SLIP / (two lines) / COR. WATER ST. / (ornament) / NEW YORK. Rv: PIKE SLIP SHADES above wreath enclosing beer glass in center. 1863. below.

C. MAGNUS

CWT	Rarity	Reverse Die	Metal	Edge	VG	VF	EF	Unc
630AS-1b	R3	—	BR	PL	4	8	10	20

C. MAGNUS' NATIONAL PRINTING ESTABLISHMENT. around border. Eagle on shield in center with NEW YORK above eagle.

J. MAHNKEN

CWT	Rarity	Reverse Die	Metal	Edge	VG	VF	EF	Unc
630AT-1a	R2	1006	C	PL	4	6	8	15

J. MAHNKEN / 19 & 22 / WEST ST. / - N_Y - / LIQUORS & SEGARS

B. MALONEY

CWT	Rarity	Reverse Die	Metal	Edge	VG	VF	EF	Unc
630AU-1a	R2	—	C	PL	4	6	8	15

B. MALONEY, / Indian head to left in center / * PROPRIETOR. * Rv: NATIONAL / (ornament) / 499 / THIRD AVENUE / - . - / ** 1863 **

JOHN MATTHEWS

CWT	Rarity	Reverse Die	Metal	Edge	VG	VF	EF	Unc
630AV-1a	R4	—	C	PL	6	25	35	60

JOHN MATTHEWS / MANUFACTURER / OF SODA WATER / APPARATUS / No. 437 FIRST Ave. / NEW-YORK. Rv: Laureated female head to left with MATTHEWS MEDAL around, 1863 at bottom.

H. B. MELVILLE

CWT	Rarity	Reverse Die	Metal	Edge	VG	VF	EF	Unc
630AW-1a	R4	—	C	PL	4	8	10	25

H. B. MELVILLE, / bust of man to left in center / * Agt. 1863. * Rv: JEWELER. / GOOD FOR / ONE / CENT / 76 BLEECKER ST. N.Y.

EDWARD MIEHLING

CWT	Rarity	Reverse Die	Metal	Edge	VG	VF	EF	Unc
630AX-1a	R1	1010	C	PL	4	6	8	15

EDWARD MIEHLING'S / - 85 - / AVE. B. / - N-Y. - / MEAT MARKET.

MILLER'S HAIR DYE

CWT	Rarity	Reverse Die	Metal	Edge	VG	VF	EF	Unc
630AY-1a	R2	—	C	PL	4	10	12	20

USE MILLER'S / 50 / CENTS / N.Y. / HAIR DYE Rv: USE / MILLER'S / 25 / CENTS / HAIR / INVIGORATOR

L. MILLER'S HAIR INVIGORATOR

CWT	Rarity	Reverse Die	Metal	Edge	VG	VF	EF	Unc
630AZ-1a	R4	—	C	PL		—	SCARCE	—

USE / L. MILLER'S / HAIR / INVIGORATOR / NY. Rv: Same incused lettering as obverse.

G. M. MITTNACHT'S EAGLE SAFE

CWT	Rarity	Reverse Die	Metal	Edge	VG	VF	EF	Unc
630BA-2a	R3	—	C	PL	4	6	8	20

G. M. MITTNACHT'S EAGLE SAFE around border with a safe in center and three small stars above safe. Rv: * 23 SPRING ST. * / large chopping block in center / * NEW YORK *

MONK'S METAL SIGNS

CWT	Rarity	Reverse Die	Metal	Edge	VG	VF	EF	Unc
630BB-1a	R3	1000	C	PL	4	6	8	15

MONK'S / *** / METAL / - * - / SIGNS. in a circle of 34 stars with a small eagle below. (Also thick planchet.)

HENRY C. MONTZ

CWT	Rarity	Reverse Die	Metal	Edge	VG	VF	EF	Unc
630BC-1a	R3	—	C	PL	4	8	10	25

HENRY C. MONTZ / bust of man to left in center with initials C.D.H. directly beneath bust / * ORPHEUS HALL. * Rv: A TOKEN / OF / THE WAR / FOR THE / UNION. / 1863.

NEW YORK AND ALBANY

CWT	Rarity	Reverse Die	Metal	Edge	VG	VF	EF	Unc
630BD-1a	R2	1	C	PL	4	6	8	15

NEW-YORK AND ALBANY *** / PEOPLES / *** / LINE / OF / (ornament) / * STEAM BOATS * Rv: (ornament) TIME TABLE (ornament) / LEAVE N.Y. / 6 P.M. / LEAVE ALBANY / + 7 1/2 P.M. +

G. PARSONS

CWT	Rarity	Reverse Die	Metal	Edge	VG	VF	EF	Unc
630BE-2a	R3	1017	C	PL	4	6	8	15

G. PARSONS / 24 / JOHN ST. / N.Y. / * FIREWORKS *

CHES PFAFF

CWT	Rarity	Reverse Die	Metal	Edge	VG	VF	EF	Unc
630BF-1a	R2	—	C	PL	4	6	8	20

CHes PFAFF / (ornament) / RESTAURANT / 647 / BROADWAY, N.Y. Rv: Full length figure of a monk standing to left.

JOHN QUINN

CWT	Rarity	Reverse Die	Metal	Edge	VG	VF	EF	Unc
630BG-5a	R2	1243	C	PL	4	6	8	15

JOHN QUINN / (ornament) / GROCER / COR 26 STs / LEXINGTON AV.

CHRISTIAN RAUH

CWT	Rarity	Reverse Die	Metal	Edge	VG	VF	EF	Unc
630BH-1a	R2	1294	C	PL	4	6	8	15

CHRISTIAN RAUH / large basket of flowers in center / 48 AVE. A, N.Y. / * CONFECTIONER *

FREDERICK ROLLWAGEN, JR.

CWT	Rarity	Reverse Die	Metal	Edge	VG	VF	EF	Unc
630BI-1a	R2	—	C	PL	4	6	8	15

FREDERICK ROLLWAGEN, JR. / Indian head to left in center / 1863 below. Rv: 587 / THIRD AVENUE, / AND / 20 & 21 / CENTRE MARKET, / N.Y.

GREAT FAIR

CWT	Rarity	Reverse Die	Metal	Edge	VG	VF	EF	Unc
630BJ-1a	R4	1138	C	PL		—	RARE	—

BLESSED IS THE GIVER. / GREAT FAIR / FOR THE / (curved line) / SANITARY / (curved line) / COMMISSION / (curved line) / NEW YORK / MAY, 1864.

ED SCHAAF

CWT	Rarity	Reverse Die	Metal	Edge	VG	VF	EF	Unc
630BK-1a	R1	1230	C	PL	4	6	8	15

ED. SCHAAF / ***** / 14 & 16 / ***** / DIVISION ST.

J. SCHORK

CWT	Rarity	Reverse Die	Metal	Edge	VG	VF	EF	Unc
630BL-1g	R8	—	L	PL		—	RARE	—

J. SCHORK / 1863 CH-R 1507 Rv: Clock dial showing 3 o'clock.

JOHN SCHUH'S SALOON

CWT	Rarity	Reverse Die	Metal	Edge	VG	VF	EF	Unc
630BM-1a	R1	1010	C	PL	4	6	8	15

JOHN SCHUH'S / - 88 - / FIRST AVE. / - N_Y - / * SALOON *

GEO. D. SCHMIDT

CWT	Rarity	Reverse Die	Metal	Edge	VG	VF	EF	Unc
630BN-1a	R4	1015	C	PL	4	6	8	15

FIRST AVE. HALL / 96 / (ornament) / BETWEEN / 5th & 6th / STS. / * GEO. D. SCHMIDT *

EDWD. SCHULZE'S RESTAURANT

CWT	Rarity	Reverse Die	Metal	Edge	VG	VF	EF	Unc
630BO-1a	R1	1291	C	PL	4	6	8	15

EDWd. SCHULZE'S / 24 / WILLIAM / STREET / * / * RESTAURANT. *

S. H. SCRIPTURE

CWT	Rarity	Reverse Die	Metal	Edge	VG	VF	EF	Unc
630BP-1h	R5	—	V	PL		—	SCARCE	—

REDEEMABLE / S. H. SCRIPTURE / IN CURRENCY. Rv: GOOD FOR / 4 / * CENTS *. Fourish ends under first C of CURRENCY.

PH. J. SEITER'S MARKET

CWT	Rarity	Reverse Die	Metal	Edge	VG	VF	EF	Unc
630BQ-1b	R1	—	BR	PL	4	6	8	15

** PH. J. SEITER'S ** / Bull's head to left in center / MARKET Rv: REDEEMED / AT / (ornament) / MY MARKET / 102 THIRD AVE. / N.Y.

NOTE: Left ear of bull points to R of SEITER'S. Also thick planchet.

I. SOMMERS

CWT	Rarity	Reverse Die	Metal	Edge	VG	VF	EF	Unc
630BR-1a	R2	1382	C	PL	4	6	8	15

JONES WOOD / - / HOTEL / N.Y. / I. SOMMERS

STAUDINGER'S

CWT	Rarity	Reverse Die	Metal	Edge	VG	VF	EF	Unc
630BS-1a	R2	1375	C	PL	4	6	8	15

* STAUDINGER'S * / 116 / BROADWAY N.Y.

ST. CHARLES BILLIARD ROOMS

CWT	Rarity	Reverse Die	Metal	Edge	VG	VF	EF	Unc
630BT-1a	R3	1075	C	PL	4	6	8	15

St. CHARLES BILLIARD ROOMS / 584 & 586, / 8th. AVE. / * / - NY -

S. STEINFELD

CWT	Rarity	Reverse Die	Metal	Edge	VG	VF	EF	Unc
630BU-1a	R1	—	C	PL	4	6	8	15

S. STEINFELD / coat of arms with sceptre pointing to G of AGENT in center / SOLE AGENT FOR THE U.S. Rv: PRINCIPAL DEPOT / 1863 / OF THE / FRENCH / COGNAC / BITTERS / 70 / NASSAU ST.

STORY & SOUTHWORTH

CWT	Rarity	Reverse Die	Metal	Edge	VG	VF	EF	Unc
630BV-1a	R1	1330	C	PL	4	6	8	15

STORY & SOUTHWORTH / GROCERS / 53 / VESEY St. / - * - / NEW YORK.

STRASBURGER & NUHN

CWT	Rarity	Reverse Die	Metal	Edge	VG	VF	EF	Unc
630BW-1b	R5	1189	BR	PL	10	40	55	125

STRASBURGER & NUHN / IMPORTERS / 65 / MAIDENLANE / NEW YORK

WM. THIERBACH

CWT	Rarity	Reverse Die	Metal	Edge	VG	VF	EF	Unc
630BX-1g	R2	—	L	PL	4	6	8	25

WM THIERBACH 142 ELM ST. / Indian head to left in center / 1863 below. Rv: Wreath enclosing the word GROCER.

C. TOLLNER & HAMMACHER

CWT	Rarity	Reverse Die	Metal	Edge	VG	VF	EF	Unc
630BY-1a	R3	1256	C	PL	4	6	8	15

C. TOLLNER & HAMMACHER / HARDWARE / 209 / * BOWERY, * / * NEW YORK. *

PETER WARMKESSEL

CWT	Rarity	Reverse Die	Metal	Edge	VG	VF	EF	Unc
630BZ-1a	R2	—	C	PL	4	6	8	15

PETER WARMKESSEL / 8 / (ornament) / DUANE St. / NEW YORK. Rv: ESTABLISHED / House with an A. on left and a D. on right, and the name WARMKESSEL across it. The name HORTER is directly beneath the foundation. / 1850 below.

J. WARNER

CWT	Rarity	Reverse Die	Metal	Edge	VG	VF	EF	Unc
630CA-1a	R3	1385	C	PL		—	SCARCE	—

J. H. WARNER / - 104 - / BARCLAY / - ST - / NEW YORK

WM. F. WARNER

CWT	Rarity	Reverse Die	Metal	Edge	VG	VF	EF	Unc
630CB-1a	R3	1006	C	PL	4	6	8	15

Wm. F. WARNER / (ornament) / No 1 / (ornament) / CATHERINE MARKET.

WASHINGTON MARKET

CWT	Rarity	Reverse Die	Metal	Edge	VG	VF	EF	Unc
630CC-4a	R2	1353	C	PL	4	6	8	15

WASHINGTON MARKET / large turkey to left in center / * EXCHANGE *

WASHINGTON RESTAURANT

CWT	Rarity	Reverse Die	Metal	Edge	VG	VF	EF	Unc
630CD-1a	R3	1265	C	PL	4	6	8	15

WASHINGTON / - No. 1 - / BROADWAY, / - N_Y - / RESTAURANT.

JOHN WATSON

CWT	Rarity	Reverse Die	Metal	Edge	VG	VF	EF	Unc
630CE-1a	R3	—	C	PL	4	8	10	20

JOHN WATSON 381 BOWERY, N.Y / Indian head to left in center / 1863 Rv: UNION / - TEA - / STORE enclosed in wreath.

WATSON'S T STORE

CWT	Rarity	Reverse Die	Metal	Edge	VG	VF	EF	Unc
630CF-1g	R7	—	L	PL	30	90	120	200

WATSON'S / T / * STORE * Rv: GOOD FOR / 1 / * CENT *

WHITE HATTER

CWT	Rarity	Reverse Die	Metal	Edge	VG	VF	EF	Unc
630CG-1a	R3	1051	C	PL	4	8	10	20

WHITE / HATTER / 216 / BROADWAY

THOMAS WHITE

CWT	Rarity	Reverse Die	Metal	Edge	VG	VF	EF	Unc
630CH-1a	R1	—	C	PL	4	6	8	15

THOMAS WHITE / Indian head to left in center / (ornament) 1863 (ornament). Rv: BUTCHER / (ornament) / No / 13 & 14 / ABATTOIR / PLACE. / (ornament) / (ornament) WEST 39th St N-Y. (ornament)

WILLIARD & JACKSONS

CWT	Rarity	Reverse Die	Metal	Edge	VG	VF	EF	Unc
630CI-1a	R2	—	C	PL	4	6	8	15

WILLARD & JACKSONS / eagle on shield / OYSTER HOUSE / 532 BROADWAY, N-Y. Rv: Flag and staff on building in open wreath. 1863 on shield below building.

Niagara Falls

M. WALSH & SONS

CWT	Rarity	Reverse Die	Metal	Edge	VG	VF	EF	Unc
640A-1a	R4	1042	C	R	40	90	115	160

M. WALSH & SONS / STAPLE & FANCY / - / DRY / GOODS / NIAGARA FALLS, N.Y.

Ogdensburg

G. IDLER'S MEAT MARKET

CWT	Rarity	Reverse Die	Metal	Edge	VG	VF	EF	Unc
665A-1a	R4	1042	C	R	8	40	55	90

G. IDLER'S / - * - / MEAT / - * - / MARKET / OGDENSBURGH, N.Y.

NOTE: Spelling of OGDENSBURG.

JOHNSON HOUSE

CWT	Rarity	Reverse Die	Metal	Edge	VG	VF	EF	Unc
665B-1a	R4	1042	C	R	6	15	20	50

JOHNSON / HOUSE / - * - / A. M. SHERMAN / PRO. / OGDENSBURGH, N.Y.

NOTE: Spelling of OGDENSBURG.

Oswego

M. L. MARSHALL

CWT	Rarity	Reverse Die	Metal	Edge	VG	VF	EF	Unc
695A-2a	R1	—	C	PL	4	8	10	20

M. L. MARSHALL / fish to left in center / 1863 / * OSWEGO, N.Y. * Rv: TOYS, FANCY GOODS, / * / FISHING / TACKLE / AND / RARE COIN.

Poughkeepsie

EASTMAN NATIONAL BUSINESS COLLEGE

CWT	Rarity	Reverse Die	Metal	Edge	VG	VF	EF	Unc
760A-1d	R7	—	C-N	PL	10	65	85	125

EASTMAN / NATIONAL / BUSINESS / COLLEGE / * POUGHKEEPSIE, N.Y. * Rv: ACTUAL BUSINESS / (ornament) / open book with 1 on left and C on right. / (ornament) / * DEPARTMENT *

Seneca Falls

D. SKIDMORE

CWT	Rarity	Reverse Die	Metal	Edge	VG	VF	EF	Unc
845A-1a	R4	—	C	PL	40	100	130	200

D. SKIDMORE / GOOD FOR ONE / eagle with cigar in beak in center / SENECA FALLS. N.Y. Rv: SKIDMORE'S / HEAD / QUARTERS / 95 FALL ST. / - + - / HOTEL.

Troy

CHARLES BABCOCK

CWT	Rarity	Reverse Die	Metal	Edge	VG	VF	EF	Unc
890A-1a	R3	1013	C	PL	4	8	10	20

CHARLES BABCOCK, JEWELER / enclosed in wreath 72 / CONG (ornament) / ST. / below TROY, N.Y.

OLIVER BOUTWELL

CWT	Rarity	Reverse Die	Metal	Edge	VG	VF	EF	Unc
890B-1b	R1	—	BR	PL	4	6	8	15

OLIVER BOUTWELL / (ornament) / MILLER / (ornament) / * TROY N.Y. * Rv: REDEEMED / (ornament) / AT / MY OFFICE / (ornament) / 1863

FRED A. PLUM

CWT	Rarity	Reverse Die	Metal	Edge	VG	VF	EF	Unc
890C-1h	R6	—	V	PL	15	60	75	100

FRED. A. PLUM. / 1 / * CENT * Rv: GOODYEAR / * / INDIA RUBBER / DEPOT / 190 / RIVER ST. / TROY. N.Y.

W. E. HAGAN

CWT	Rarity	Reverse Die	Metal	Edge	VG	VF	EF	Unc
890D-1h	R6	—	V	PL		—	SCARCE	—

W. E. HAGAN / No. 1 / FIRST ST. / TROY, N.Y. Rv: SODA WATER / 5 / * CENTS *

ROBINSON & BALLOU

CWT	Rarity	Reverse Die	Metal	Edge	VG	VF	EF	Unc
890E-1b	R1	—	BR	PL	4	6	8	15

ROBINSON & BALLOU / (ornament) / GROCERS / (ornament) / * TROY N.Y. * Rv: REDEEMED / AT / (ornament) / OUR STORE / (ornament) / 1863

Utica

DICKINSON COMSTOCK & CO.

CWT	Rarity	Reverse Die	Metal	Edge	VG	VF	EF	Unc
905A-1a	R5	1266	C	PL	15	60	80	110

DICKINSON COMSTOCK & CO. / DRUGGISTS / & / GROCERS / * UTICA N.Y. *

I. J. KNAPP

CWT	Rarity	Reverse Die	Metal	Edge	VG	VF	EF	Unc
905B-1a	R4	1265	C	PL	4	6	8	15

... I. J. KNAPP ... / - No 8 - / LIBERTY St / UTICA / - N.Y - / WINES & LIQUORS.

SHERWOOD & HOPSON

CWT	Rarity	Reverse Die	Metal	Edge	VG	VF	EF	Unc
905C-1a	R3	1233	C	PL	4	6	8	15

SHERWOOD & HOPSON / - + - / (ornament) CHINA (ornament) / EMPORIUM / +++ / * UTICA N.Y. *

Waterloo

HENRY C. WELLES

CWT	Rarity	Reverse Die	Metal	Edge	VG	VF	EF	Unc
940A-1a	R3	1358	C	PL	4	6	8	15

HENRY C. WELLES / DRUGGIST / & / BOOK / SELLER. / * WATERLOO N.Y. *

Watertown

HART'S ARCADE GALLERY

CWT	Rarity	Reverse Die	Metal	Edge	VG	VF	EF	Unc
945A-1a	R3	1407	C	PL	4	10	12	20

WATERTOWN N.Y. / * HART'S * / (ornament) / ARCADE / (ornament) / * GALLERY * / * FOR BEST PICTURES *

Whitehall

E. W. HALL

CWT	Rarity	Reverse Die	Metal	Edge	VG	VF	EF	Unc
985A-1a	R1	—	C	PL	4	6	10	15

TO PURIFY THE BLOOD, / E. W. HALL / WHITEHALL, / N.Y. / USE ATHERTON'S PILLS Rv: TRY ATHERTON'S / WILD / CHERRY / SYRUP / FOR / COUGHS & COLDS

Williamsville

WILLIAMSVILLE EXPRESS

CWT	Rarity	Reverse Die	Metal	Edge	VG	VF	EF	Unc
990A-1a	R6	—	C	R	10	50	75	110

WILLIAMSVILLE / ***** / LEAVES / 8. A.M. / ****** / WILLIAMSVILLE / * EXPRESS * Rv: WILLIAMSVILLE / **** / LEAVES / BUFFALO / 3. P.M. / EXPRESS

Yonkers

E. E. HASSE

CWT	Rarity	Reverse Die	Metal	Edge	VG	VF	EF	Unc
995A-1a	R2	1075	C	PL	4	15	20	30

E. E. HASSE / * / YONKERS / (ornament) / N.Y.

OHIO

Adamsville

STONER & SHROYER

CWT	Rarity	Reverse Die	Metal	Edge	VG	VF	EF	Unc
5A-1a	R3	1048	C	PL	5	15	20	50

STONER & SHROYER / DRY GOODS / ADAMSVILLE / (ornament) / OHIO

Adelphi

D. H. STROUS

CWT	Rarity	Reverse Die	Metal	Edge	VG	VF	EF	Unc
10A-2a	R4	1171	C	PL	10	25	30	60

D. H. STROUS / FLOUR / & / WOOLEN / MANUF'RS / ADELPHI.O.

Ashland

ELLA BUCHANAN

CWT	Rarity	Reverse Die	Metal	Edge	VG	VF	EF	Unc
25A-1bo	R9	Same	BR	R		—	RARE	—

ELLA BUCHANAN / WATCHMAKER / ASHLAND, O.

NOTE: Known over Lincoln political token DeW. AL 1864-37, and also over McClellan political token DeW. GMcC 1864027 (A.N.S.).

Barnesville

N. PATTERSON

CWT	Rarity	Reverse Die	Metal	Edge	VG	VF	EF	Unc
50A-1a	R5	—	C	PL	5	15	20	40

N. PATTERSON / SADDLERY / - * - / HARDWARE / (ornament) / BARNESVILLE / * OHIO. * Rv: LEATHER, / AND / SHOE FINDINGS / WOOL, / SHEEP PELTS, / SHIPPING / FURRS, / & C. & C.

NOTE: FURS spelled with two R's on reverse.

W. A. TALBOT & SON

CWT	Rarity	Reverse Die	Metal	Edge	VG	VF	EF	Unc
50B-2a	R3	1126	C	PL	4	10	12	40

W. A. TALBOT & SON / DRY GOODS / (ornament) / BARNESVILLE / (ornament) / OHIO.

Bellaire

BELLAIRE FERRY TICKET

CWT	Rarity	Reverse Die	Metal	Edge	VG	VF	EF	Unc
60A-1a	R7	1168	C	PL	25	75	90	125

** BELLAIRE ** / (ornament) / FERRY / (ornament) / ** TICKET. **

NOTE: Listed as transportation token, Atwood, Ohio 60A.

J. S. BONBRIGHT

CWT	Rarity	Reverse Die	Metal	Edge	VG	VF	EF	Unc
60B-2a	R4	1123	C	PL	5	15	20	40

* J. S. BONBRIGHT * / HARDWARE / AND / STOVE / DEALER / BELLAIRE / * OHIO. *

RICHARDSON & BRO.

CWT	Rarity	Reverse Die	Metal	Edge	VG	VF	EF	Unc
60C-2a	R6	1180	C	PL	10	20	30	50

RICHARDSON & BRO. / DRY GOODS / NOTIONS / DRUGS AND / MEDICINES / BELLAIRE / OHIO

E. B. WINANS & CO.

CWT	Rarity	Reverse Die	Metal	Edge	VG	VF	EF	Unc
60D-1a	R5	1091	C	PL	5	15	25	40

E. B. WINANS & CO. / DRY GOODS, / (ornament) / NOTIONS, / DRUGS AND / MEDICINES, / BELLAIRE / -- / - OHIO. -

Bellevue

APPLEGATE & CO.

CWT	Rarity	Reverse Die	Metal	Edge	VG	VF	EF	Unc
65A-1a	R5	1181	C	PL	5	15	20	45

CHEAP CASH STORE / (ornament) / APPLEGATE / & Co. / BELLEVUE, O.

P. BRADY

CWT	Rarity	Reverse Die	Metal	Edge	VG	VF	EF	Unc
65B-1a	R7	1122	C	PL	5	15	20	50

P. BRADY, / DEALER / IN / STOVES, TIN / AND HOUSE / FURNISHING / GOODS / BELLEVUE, OHIO.

C. A. WILLARD

CWT	Rarity	Reverse Die	Metal	Edge	VG	VF	EF	Unc
65C-1a	R6	1127	C	PL	5	15	20	45

C. A. WILLARD / * / DRY GOODS / - * - / BELLEVUE, O.

Belmont

O. C. METCALF

CWT	Rarity	Reverse Die	Metal	Edge	VG	VF	EF	Unc
70A-1a	R8	1090	C	PL		—	RARE	—

O. C. METCALF / DRY GOODS / BELMONT / OHIO

Berea

D. E. STEARNS

CWT	Rarity	Reverse Die	Metal	Edge	VG	VF	EF	Unc
74A-1a1	R3	—	C	PL	4	8	10	30

D. E. STEARNS, BEREA, O above. Grindstone in center. 1863 below. Rv: GRINDSTONES / MOUNTED / WITH PATENT / ADJUSTABLE REST / FOR / GRINDING / ALL SIZES / HARVESTER KNIVES

Beverly

P. BURKHOLTER

CWT	Rarity	Reverse Die	Metal	Edge	VG	VF	EF	Unc
76A-1a	R5	1082	C	PL	10	30	40	65

P. BURKHOLTER / DEALER / IN / GROCERIES / PROVISIONS / CONFECTIONARY / * - AND - * / PRODUCE, / BEVERLY, / OHIO.

Birmingham

CRAIG & FOY

CWT	Rarity	Reverse Die	Metal	Edge	VG	VF	EF	Unc
79A-2a	R4	1089	C	PL	8	20	25	45

CRAIG & FOY / (ornament) / DRY GOODS / BIRMINGHAM / -- / * OHIO. *

Bryan

JEFF MILLER

CWT	Rarity	Reverse Die	Metal	Edge	VG	VF	EF	Unc
100A-1a	R3	1326	C	PL	4	8	10	35

JEFF MILLER / DEALER / IN / HARDWARE, / BRYAN, / OHIO.

E. G. SELBY & CO.

CWT	Rarity	Reverse Die	Metal	Edge	VG	VF	EF	Unc
100B-2a	R4	1334	C	PL	4	8	10	25

E. G. SELBY & CO. / DEALERS / IN / HARDWARE / BRYAN, / OHIO.

Cadiz

G. B. BARRETT

CWT	Rarity	Reverse Die	Metal	Edge	VG	VF	EF	Unc
110A-5a	R6	1042	C	R	4	12	15	40

G. B. BARRETT / DEALER / IN / WATCHES - / - CLOCKS / JEWELRY / FANCY GOODS / CADIZ, O.

J. M. ROBINSON

CWT	Rarity	Reverse Die	Metal	Edge	VG	VF	EF	Unc
110B-1a	R6	1018	C	R	4	15	20	35

J. M. ROBINSON / DEALER / IN / HARDWARE / STOVES / FIRE FRONTS & C. / CADIZ, O.

Cambridge

A. C. COCHRAN

CWT	Rarity	Reverse Die	Metal	Edge	VG	VF	EF	Unc
115A-2a	R4	1178	C	PL	5	15	20	40

A. C. COCHRAN above. HARDWARE / DEALER on lock in center. CAMBRIDGE, O. below.

J. J. SQUIER

CWT	Rarity	Reverse Die	Metal	Edge	VG	VF	EF	Unc
115B-6a	R3	1126	C	PL	4	8	10	35

J. J. SQUIER / - * - / DRY GOODS / (ornament) / CAMBRIDGE, O.

Camden

C. CHADWICK

CWT	Rarity	Reverse Die	Metal	Edge	VG	VF	EF	Unc
120A-2a	R6	1229	C	PL	8	20	30	40

C. CHADWICK / DEALER / IN / DRY GOODS / (ornament) / CAMDEN, O.

J. P. FORNSHELL

CWT	Rarity	Reverse Die	Metal	Edge	VG	VF	EF	Unc
120B-1a	R6	1038	C	PL	5	20	25	50

J. P. FORNSHELL / GROCER / & / OYSTER / DEALER / CAMDEN, O.

Canaan

GRIMES & GRINER

CWT	Rarity	Reverse Die	Metal	Edge	VG	VF	EF	Unc
122A-1a	R5	1123	C	PL	10	25	40	60

GRIMES & GRINER / DEALERS / IN / DRY GOODS / NOTIONS & C. / CANAAN, / OHIO.

Canton

J. A. MEYER

CWT	Rarity	Reverse Die	Metal	Edge	VG	VF	EF	Unc
125A-1a1	R5	1028	C	PL	5	20	25	45

J. A. MEYER / WATCHES / CLOCKS / - + - / JEWELRY / CANTON, O.

C. OBERLY

CWT	Rarity	Reverse Die	Metal	Edge	VG	VF	EF	Unc
125B-1a	R6	1122	C	PL	10	25	35	50

C. OBERLY, / DEALER / IN / (curved line) / GROCERIES (curved line) / (curved line) PROVISIONS, / (curved line) / CONFECTIONERY, / WOODEN & WILLOW / WARE, / CANTON, OHIO.

Centerville

JAMES MATHEWS

CWT	Rarity	Reverse Die	Metal	Edge	VG	VF	EF	Unc
135A-1a	R6	1085	C	PL	10	30	40	60

JAMES MATHEWS / DEALER / IN / DRY GOODS, / GROCERIES. / & C. / CENTERVILLE, O.

Chesterville

BARTLETT GOBLE & CO.

CWT	Rarity	Reverse Die	Metal	Edge	VG	VF	EF	Unc
150A-1a	R6	1046	C	R	12	30	40	75

BARTLETT GOBLE & CO / STAPLE & FANCY / = / DRY / GOODS / = / GROCERIES / & C. / CHESTERVILLE, O.

MILES & SPERRY

CWT	Rarity	Reverse Die	Metal	Edge	VG	VF	EF	Unc
150B-1a	R7	1046	C	R	10	25	35	60

MILES & SPERRY / DEALERS IN / DRY / GOODS / - . - / GROCERIES / & C. / CHESTERVILLE, O.

Chillicothe

JOHN BOHN

CWT	Rarity	Reverse Die	Metal	Edge	VG	VF	EF	Unc
160A-1b	R8	1391	BR	R		—	SCARCE	—

JOHN BOHN / (ornament) / CHILLICOTHE, O.

JNO. F. BIER & BRO.

CWT	Rarity	Reverse Die	Metal	Edge	VG	VF	EF	Unc
160B-2a	R4	1123	C	PL	5	15	25	40

JNO. F. BIER & BRO. / DEALERS / - IN - / GROCERIES / BOOTS & SHOES / 101 PAINT / STREET / CHILLICOTHE, O.

JAS. DRISCOLL

CWT	Rarity	Reverse Die	Metal	Edge	VG	VF	EF	Unc
160C-1b	R8	1391	BR	R		—	SCARCE	—

JAS. DRISCOLL / (ornament) / CHILLICOTHE, O.

H. KEIM

CWT	Rarity	Reverse Die	Metal	Edge	VG	VF	EF	Unc
160D-1a	R8	1171	C	PL	10	40	50	125

H. KEIM / GROCER / COR. / FOURTH & HICKORY / STS. / CHILLICOTHE. O.

M. KIRSCH

CWT	Rarity	Reverse Die	Metal	Edge	VG	VF	EF	Unc
160E-1b	R9	—	BR	PL		—	SCARCE	—

PHOENIX HOUSE / No. 155 / SECOND ST / . . / M KIRSCH / PROP / * CHILLICOTHE, O * Rv: GOOD FOR / (ornament) 5 (ornament) / CENTS / - AT - / M. KIRSCH'S / BAR

A. S. KRAMER

CWT	Rarity	Reverse Die	Metal	Edge	VG	VF	EF	Unc
160F-3a	R6	1227	C	PL	8	20	30	45

A. S. KRAMER / DEALER / - IN - / CONFECTIONERY, / TOYS / NOTIONS & C / ALLEN / BLOCK / PAINT ST. / * CHILLICOTHE, O. *

RUFUS MOTTER

CWT	Rarity	Reverse Die	Metal	Edge	VG	VF	EF	Unc
160G-5a	R3	1322	C	PL	4	12	15	30

RUFUS MOTTER / BOOK, / PERIODICAL, / NEWS, CIGAR, / TOBACCO / - AND - / - NOTION - / DEALER, / -- / -- CHILLICOTHE, O. —

T. RUPEL & CO.

CWT	Rarity	Reverse Die	Metal	Edge	VG	VF	EF	Unc
160H-1a	R4	1181	C	PL	4	12	15	25

T. RUPEL & CO / (ornament) / GROCERS / No. 52 / 4th St / CHILLICOTHE, O.

WM. M. SOSMAN

CWT	Rarity	Reverse Die	Metal	Edge	VG	VF	EF	Unc
160I-1a	R4	1125	C	PL	5	20	30	45

* Wm. M. SOSMAN * / BAKER / & / GROCER / CHILLICOTHE / * OHIO. *

A. WALLACE

CWT	Rarity	Reverse Die	Metal	Edge	VG	VF	EF	Unc
160J-1a	R5	1168	C	PL	5	12	15	35

A. WALLACE, / NEWS / DEPOT, / TOBACCO, / CIGARS / & / NOTIONS, / CHILLICOTHE, O.

Cincinnati

M. ADLETA

CWT	Rarity	Reverse Die	Metal	Edge	VG	VF	EF	Unc
165A-4a	R3	1036	C	PL	4	8	10	25

M. ADLETA / 570 / CEN / AVENUE / CINCINNATI

W. ALENBURG

CWT	Rarity	Reverse Die	Metal	Edge	VG	VF	EF	Unc
165B-1a	R7	1386	C	PL	20	90	125	250

W. ALENBURG, / * / No. 622 / CENTRAL / - AVENUE / * / MEAT STORE

B. B. ARMSTRONG

CWT	Rarity	Reverse Die	Metal	Edge	VG	VF	EF	Unc
165C-3a	R6	1042	C	R	4	8	10	30

B. B. ARMSTRONG / BLACK / BEAR / HOTEL / 9' & SYCAMORE / STS. / CINCINNATI

F. M. ASHTON

CWT	Rarity	Reverse Die	Metal	Edge	VG	VF	EF	Unc
165D-1b	R8	—	BR	PL		—	RARE	—

F. M. ASHTON / ----- / WATCH CHECK Rv: - MURDOCK & SPENCER - / 139 / W' FIFTH / STREET / - CINCINNATI - (Obv. Ohio 165DZ-1)

F. ARNOLD

CWT	Rarity	Reverse Die	Metal	Edge	VG	VF	EF	Unc
165E-3a	R3	1038	C	PL	4	8	10	30

GRUHLERS / GARDEN / CONCERT / - SALOON / 470 VINE ST. / F. ARNOLD

J. S. AUSTIN

CWT	Rarity	Reverse Die	Metal	Edge	VG	VF	EF	Unc
165F-1a	R3	1009	C	PL	4	8	10	30

J. S. AUSTIN / DEALER / IN / STAPLES & FANCY / GROCERIES / 5TH & ELM / STS. / CINCINNATI

H. AVERMAAT

CWT	Rarity	Reverse Die	Metal	Edge	VG	VF	EF	Unc
165G-1a	R2	1008	C	PL	4	8	10	25

H. AVERMAAT / DEALER / IN / BUTTER / & / * EGGS * / 315 FINDLAY ST / CIN-CINNATI

S. BACCIOCCO

CWT	Rarity	Reverse Die	Metal	Edge	VG	VF	EF	Unc
165H-3a	R5	1274	C	PL	4	15	20	35

S. BACCIOCCO / CONFECTIONARY / AND / ICE / CREAM / SALOON / --- / 176 FIFTH ST.

E. BACHER

CWT	Rarity	Reverse Die	Metal	Edge	VG	VF	EF	Unc
165I-1a	R6	—	C	PL		—	SCARCE	—

E. BACHER in script on plain planchet. Rv: GOOD / - FOR - / FIVE CENTS / IN / REFRESHMENTS, / UNION SALOON.

R. BATHGATE

CWT	Rarity	Reverse Die	Metal	Edge	VG	VF	EF	Unc
165J-1a	R5	1008	C	PL	4	10	12	25

R. BATHGATE / DEALER / IN / BOOTS, SHOES / & / GROCERIES / 198 W. 6' ST. / CINCINNATI

JOHN BAUER

CWT	Rarity	Reverse Die	Metal	Edge	VG	VF	EF	Unc
165K-2a	R4	1026	C	PL	4	8	10	25

JOHN BAUER / 29 / FRONT / ST. / CINCINNATI

C. H. BEER'S SALOON

CWT	Rarity	Reverse Die	Metal	Edge	VG	VF	EF	Unc
165L-1a	R2	—	C	PL	4	8	10	20

*** C. H. BEER'S / SALOON / (ornament) 55 (ornament) / BROADWAY / CINT'I. O. Rv: (ornament) ALSO / CUTLERY, / . - x - . / NOTIONS / (ornament) / - & C - / (ornament)

B. P. BELKNP

CWT	Rarity	Reverse Die	Metal	Edge	VG	VF	EF	Unc
165M-1a	R6	1346	C	PL	40	90	110	175

TEETH / EXTRACTED / WITHOUT / PAIN, / BY / * B. P. BELKNP. *

NOTE: Probable error in spelling, as believe should be BELKNAP.

DR. BENNETT'S MEDICINES

CWT	Rarity	Reverse Die	Metal	Edge	VG	VF	EF	Unc
165N-9a	R1	1352	C	PL	4	8	10	20

DR. BENNETT'S / - x - / MEDICINES / - / CURE / SICKNESS / AND / **** PAIN. ****

C. H. BENNETT

CWT	Rarity	Reverse Die	Metal	Edge	VG	VF	EF	Unc
165O-2a	R2	1029	C	PL	4	10	12	25

C. H. BENNETT above. Sheaf of wheat in center with STEAM to left and BAKERY to right. 89 COURT ST below.

FRANK BERESFORD

CWT	Rarity	Reverse Die	Metal	Edge	VG	VF	EF	Unc
165P-1a1	R2	—	C	PL	4	10	12	20

FRANK BERESFORD above. Square and compass in center. CINCINNATI below. Rv: BUY YOUR / MEAT / OF / FRANK / BERESFORD / IN / MARKET

F. BILLIODS

CWT	Rarity	Reverse Die	Metal	Edge	VG	VF	EF	Unc
165Q-1b	R7	—	BR	PL		—	RARE	—

DUE THE BEARER / 25 / CENTS / - . - IN - . - / x BEER x / F. BILLIODS / BREWER Rv: JOHN STANTON / + / STAMP / & BRAND / CUTTER / * / CINCINNATI

LEW. BOMAN

CWT	Rarity	Reverse Die	Metal	Edge	VG	VF	EF	Unc
165R-1a	R6	1009	C	PL	4	12	15	35

LEW. BOMAN / SETS A / LUNCH / AT THE / * / BRIGHTON / HOUSE / AT 10 O CLOCK / SUNDAY

A. BRUGGEMANN

CWT	Rarity	Reverse Die	Metal	Edge	VG	VF	EF	Unc
165S-2a	R4	1386	C	PL	4	15	20	45

A. BRUGGEMANN / * / GROCER / COR. / LIBERTY / - / & WALNUT.

J. CAMPBELL

CWT	Rarity	Reverse Die	Metal	Edge	VG	VF	EF	Unc
165T-1a	R5	1023	C	PL	4	8	10	25

J. CAMPBELL / GROCER / - & - / PROVISION / DEALER / 481 JOHN, ST.

CENTRAL COAL OFFICE

CWT	Rarity	Reverse Die	Metal	Edge	VG	VF	EF	Unc
165U-1a	R8	—	C	PL	30	100	125	150

BUY YOUR COAL NOW / - AT - / CENTRAL / COAL OFFICE / - 56 - / * W. FOURTH ST. CIN'TI. * Rv: * GOOD FOR * / portrait to left in center / ONE CENTS WORTH OF COAL.

CHAMBERLAIN BROS.

CWT	Rarity	Reverse Die	Metal	Edge	VG	VF	EF	Unc
165V-4B	R7	1312	BR	R		—	SCARCE	—

*** CHAMBERLAIN BROS, around border. 1 / GLASS / * / SODA / WATER in center.

CIN. & COV. FERRY COMPANY

CWT	Rarity	Reverse Die	Metal	Edge	VG	VF	EF	Unc
165W-1a	R3	1022	C	PL	5	15	20	30

CIN. & COV. / FERRY / COMPANY

CITY HOSIERY STORE

CWT	Rarity	Reverse Die	Metal	Edge	VG	VF	EF	Unc
165X-1a	R5	1021	C	PL	4	8	10	25

CITY HOSIERY STORE / LADIES / - & - / GENTS / FURNISHINGS / & / FANCY GOODS / NO. 12 W. 5' ST

C. E. CLARK'S LIGHTNING HAIR DYEING ROOM

CWT	Rarity	Reverse Die	Metal	Edge	VG	VF	EF	Unc
165Y-2a	R6	1042	C	R	10	25	30	45

* GOOD FOR * / ONE / SHAVE / AT / C. E. CLARK'S / LIGHTNING / HAIR DYEING ROOM / NO. 4 / BURNET HOUSE

COLE'S BAKERY

CWT	Rarity	Reverse Die	Metal	Edge	VG	VF	EF	Unc
165Z-1a	R6	1009	C	PL	4	12	15	35

GOOD FOR / * / ONE / CENT / AT / COLE'S BAKERY

COMMISSION BOOTS & SHOES

CWT	Rarity	Reverse Die	Metal	Edge	VG	VF	EF	Unc
165AA-1a	R5	1008	C	PL	4	12	15	30

COMMISSION / BOOTS / & / SHOES / 154 / MAIN ST. / CINCINNATI

CONN. MUT. LIFE INS. CO.

CWT	Rarity	Reverse Die	Metal	Edge	VG	VF	EF	Unc
165AB-1a	R8	1047	C	R		—	RARE	—

CONN. MUT. LIFE INS. CO. / CAPITAL / OVER / 6000000 / DOLLARS / 1804

CHAS. CONROY

CWT	Rarity	Reverse Die	Metal	Edge	VG	VF	EF	Unc
165AC-1a	R4	1026	C	PL	4	8	10	35

CHAS. CONROY / GROCER / & / LIQUOR / DEALER / 3 & CEN. AVENUE

CONSULERE GENERI

CWT	Rarity	Reverse Die	Metal	Edge	VG	VF	EF	Unc
165AD-2a	R7	—	C	R	10	40	60	85

CONSULERE / GENERI / HOMINUM / HO HI / WHANG / B. C. / 129374 / Three stars on each side in circles. Rv: MAGI GENII / - * - / QUBO / = DAIRI = / WHANG

CONTINENTAL

CWT	Rarity	Reverse Die	Metal	Edge	VG	VF	EF	Unc
165ADa-1b	R9	—	BR	PL		—	RARE	—

(ornament) GOOD FOR (ornament) / 10 / IN DRINKS AT / THE / CONTINENTAL Rv: JOHN STANTON / * / STAMP / BRAND / CUTTER / * / CINCI NATI within beaded circle in center.

CONTINENTAL HOTEL

CWT	Rarity	Reverse Die	Metal	Edge	VG	VF	EF	Unc
165ADb-1b	R9	Blank	BR	PL		—	RARE	—

CONTINENTAL / HOTEL / MONEY / CHECK

NOTE: Same as reverse of OH 165FM-6.

COSTELLO'S TRIMMINGS & FANCY GOODS

CWT	Rarity	Reverse Die	Metal	Edge	VG	VF	EF	Unc
165AE-1a1	R4	1007	C	PL	4	8	10	30

COSTELLO'S / TRIMMINGS / - & - / FANCY GOODS / 138 / * FIFTH ST * / CIN-CINNATI

CRITTENDEN SHADES

CWT	Rarity	Reverse Die	Metal	Edge	VG	VF	EF	Unc
165AF-1a	R6	1056	C	PL	4	25	35	60

* / CRITTENDEN / - + - / SHADES / *

J. M. DAGGERT & CO.

CWT	Rarity	Reverse Die	Metal	Edge	VG	VF	EF	Unc
165AG-1a	R9	1056	C	R		—	RARE	—

BATES / HOUSE / ONE / MEAL / x J. M. DAGGETT & CO. x

GEO. R. DIXON & CO.

CWT	Rarity	Reverse Die	Metal	Edge	VG	VF	EF	Unc
165AH-1a	R3	1007	C	PL	4	8	10	20

GEO. R. DIXON & CO. / SPICE / MILLS / SYCAMORE / BET. 7' & 8' STS. / CIN-CINNATI

J. N. DONIPHAN

CWT	Rarity	Reverse Die	Metal	Edge	VG	VF	EF	Unc
165AI-1a	R5	1032	C	PL	4	12	15	30

J. N. DONIPHAN / 188 / EAST / PEARL / ST. / CINCINNATI.

GARRET T. DORLAND

CWT	Rarity	Reverse Die	Metal	Edge	VG	VF	EF	Unc
165AJ-1a	R3	1008	C	PL	4	8	10	25

GARRET T. DORLAND / IMPORTER / OF / WATCHES / AND / JEWELRY / N.W. COR. MAIN & PEARL / STS. / CINCINNATI

R. DOWNING

CWT	Rarity	Reverse Die	Metal	Edge	VG	VF	EF	Unc
165AK-7b	R9	1370	C	R		—	SCARCE	—

R. DOWNING / PUBLISHER / - OF - / SHEET SONGS / & DEALER IN / OLD / COINS / CINCINNATI

L. ECKERT

CWT	Rarity	Reverse Die	Metal	Edge	VG	VF	EF	Unc
165AL-1a	R5	1019	C	PL	4	8	10	25

L. ECKERT / BOOKBINDER / STATIONER / - & - / FANCY GOODS / N.W. COR. / WALNUT & 13' STS / CINCINNATI

C. W. ELLIS

CWT	Rarity	Reverse Die	Metal	Edge	VG	VF	EF	Unc
165AM-1a	R7	—	C	R	15	50	70	125

C. W. ELLIS / GEN. AGT. / 35 W. 3D ST. / CIN, O / = / DAYTON AGENCY / 44 JEFF. ST. Rv: CONN. MUT. LIFE INS. CO. / CAPITAL / OVER / 6000000 / DOLLARS / 1864

EVANS'

CWT	Rarity	Reverse Die	Metal	Edge	VG	VF	EF	Unc
165AMa-1b	R6	Blank	BR	PL	40	125	150	200

EVENS' / ALL KINDS OF / SEWING - / MACHINES / REPAIRED / 64 / W. 4TH. ST.

EXCELSIOR TOBACCO

CWT	Rarity	Reverse Die	Metal	Edge	VG	VF	EF	Unc
165AMb-1a	R8	1418	C	PL		—	RARE	—

EXCELSIOR / TOBACCO / WORKS / 210 & 212 / ELM ST. CIN. O. / ESTABLISHED / 1835

FENTON & BECK

CWT	Rarity	Reverse Die	Metal	Edge	VG	VF	EF	Unc
165AN-1a	R4	1030	C	PL	4	10	12	25

FENTON & BECK / DAILY / MARKET / N.W. COR. / 6' & PLUM

J. FERGUSON

CWT	Rarity	Reverse Die	Metal	Edge	VG	VF	EF	Unc
165AO-1a	R4	1008	C	PL	4	10	12	25

J. FERGUSON / GROCER / - * - / COR. 9' & VINE STS / CINCINNATI / GOODS DELIVERED / FREE OF CHARGE

E. FIEDLER'S

CWT	Rarity	Reverse Die	Metal	Edge	VG	VF	EF	Unc
165AP-1a	R3	1022	C	PL	4	8	10	25

* E. FIEDLER'S * / BEER / HALL / 206 / VINE, ST.

EMIL FIEDLER

CWT	Rarity	Reverse Die	Metal	Edge	VG	VF	EF	Unc
165AQ-1e	R9	—	W-M	PL		—	RARE	—

EMIL FIEDLER Rv: C3 in a circle of 13 stars.

FIFTH STREET

CWT	Rarity	Reverse Die	Metal	Edge	VG	VF	EF	Unc
165AR-1b	R8	—	BR	R		—	RARE	—

FIFTH STREET / 5 / GARDEN Rv: JAS MURDOCK JR. / 165 RACE ST / CIN'TI

F. FISCHER

CWT	Rarity	Reverse Die	Metal	Edge	VG	VF	EF	Unc
165AS-1a	R5	1036	C	PL	4	8	10	25

F. FISCHER / 214 / VINE / ST. / CINCINNATI

FISLER & CHANCE

CWT	Rarity	Reverse Die	Metal	Edge	VG	VF	EF	Unc
165AT-1a	R8	1047	C	R	20	50	75	100

+ FISLER & CHANCE + above. 1 / GLASS / SODA WATER in center. POLAR below.

W. C. FITHIAN

CWT	Rarity	Reverse Die	Metal	Edge	VG	VF	EF	Unc
165AU-1b	R9	—	BR	PL		—	SCARCE	—

W. C. FITHIAN / *** / PAINTER / & / GRAINER / 420 EIGHTH ST / *** / CINCIN-NATI Rv: - MURDOCK & SPENCER - / 139 / W. FIFTH / STREET / - CINCINNATI - (obv. Ohio 165DZ)

J. W. FITZGERALD

CWT	Rarity	Reverse Die	Metal	Edge	VG	VF	EF	Unc
165AV-1a	R5	1127	C	PL	4	10	12	25

J. W. FITZGERALD / * GROCER * / COR / FIFTH / AND / BROADWAY / CINCIN-NATI.

CHAS. FLACH

CWT	Rarity	Reverse Die	Metal	Edge	VG	VF	EF	Unc
165AW-2a	R5	1026	C	PL	4	10	12	25

CHAS. FLACH / DEALER / IN / PROVISIONS / COR. / MADISON & CANAL / - * - / CINCINNATI.

JAMES FOSTER JR. & CO.

CWT	Rarity	Reverse Die	Metal	Edge	VG	VF	EF	Unc
165AX-1a	R8	1047	C	R		—	RARE	—

* JAMES FOSTER JR. & CO. CINCINNATI around border. * COR. FIFTH & RACE STS. in circle in center.

JOHN FRANK

CWT	Rarity	Reverse Die	Metal	Edge	VG	VF	EF	Unc
165AY-1a	R7	—	C	R	30	85	100	150

JOHN FRANK above eight small circles around ornament in center. Five stars below. Rv: ONE / HALF / PINT / OF / MILK

FROST'S MEDICINE

CWT	Rarity	Reverse Die	Metal	Edge	VG	VF	EF	Unc
165AZ-3a	R5	1046	C	R	4	15	20	45

USE / FROST'S / MEDICINE / SOLD / BY / DRUGGISTS

JOHN GALVAGNI

CWT	Rarity	Reverse Die	Metal	Edge	VG	VF	EF	Unc
165BA-1a	R4	1007	C	PL	4	10	12	25

JOHN GALVAGNI / FANCY - / GOODS / & / * TOYS * / 513 / VINE BET. 14' & 15' / STS. / CINCINNATI

GALWAY SMITH & CO.

CWT	Rarity	Reverse Die	Metal	Edge	VG	VF	EF	Unc
165BAa-1a	R9	—	C	PL	30	75	100	140

BUY YOUR / COAL / FROM / GALWAY SMITH & CO. Rv: GOOD FOR / 1 / CENT / PAYMENT IN COAL / GALWAY SMITH & CO.

L. GEILFUS

CWT	Rarity	Reverse Die	Metal	Edge	VG	VF	EF	Unc
165BB-1a	R5	1247	C	PL	4	25	35	60

L. GELFUS / * / GROCER / - 701 - / ELM ST.

J. GEISER

CWT	Rarity	Reverse Die	Metal	Edge	VG	VF	EF	Unc
165BC-1a	R7	1386	C	PL	30	100	125	200

(ornament) / J GEISER / (ornament)

NOTE: Listed as Marvin 762d. Comes with broken obv. die.

W. GENTSCH

CWT	Rarity	Reverse Die	Metal	Edge	VG	VF	EF	Unc
165BD-1a	R6	1026	C	PL	4	12	15	30

W. GENTSCH / WINE - / & / - BEER / SALOON / 393 VINE, ST.

O. GOFFERY

CWT	Rarity	Reverse Die	Metal	Edge	VG	VF	EF	Unc
165BE-2a	R5	1039	C	R	4	15	20	30

SEGARS / - . - / O. G. / - . - / TOBACCO

R. G.

CWT	Rarity	Reverse Die	Metal	Edge	VG	VF	EF	Unc
165BF-1b	R8	—	BR	PL		—	SCARCE	—

R. G. / 5 (incused lettering) Rv: JAS MURDOCK JR. / 165 RACE ST. / CIN'TI. (incused lettering)

NOTE: May be post-Civil War.

R. GOHS

CWT	Rarity	Reverse Die	Metal	Edge	VG	VF	EF	Unc
165BG-1b	R8	—	BR	PL		—	SCARCE	—

GOOD / FOR 5c (cents) / R. GOHS / CIN. O. Rv: JAS MURDOCK JR. / 165 RACE ST. / CIN'TI. (incused lettering)

NOTE: May be post-Civil War.

J. GROSSIUS

CWT	Rarity	Reverse Die	Metal	Edge	VG	VF	EF	Unc
165BH-1a	R7	1056	C	PL	20	50	70	150

J. GROSSIUS, / * / TINNER. / 33 / COURT ST. / CIN.O.

JACOB GUTH

CWT	Rarity	Reverse Die	Metal	Edge	VG	VF	EF	Unc
165BI-5a	R5	1036	C	PL	4	10	12	30

JACOB GUTH / S.W. COR. / VINE / & / COLUMBIA / STS. / CINCINNATI

CARL HAAS

CWT	Rarity	Reverse Die	Metal	Edge	VG	VF	EF	Unc
165BJ-12a	R2	1020	C	PL	4	10	12	25

CARL HAAS above rabbit in center. 493 VINE, ST below.

NOTE: All specimens show name recut and shifted to the right.

C. HAHNEMANN'S BAKERY

CWT	Rarity	Reverse Die	Metal	Edge	VG	VF	EF	Unc
165BK-1e	R8	—	W-M	PL		—	RARE	—

C. HAHNEMANN'S / * / BAKERY / (ornament) / 549 VINE ST. Rv: C3 in circle of thirteen stars. (Same Rev. as Ohio 165AQ)

W. W. HANLEY

CWT	Rarity	Reverse Die	Metal	Edge	VG	VF	EF	Unc
165BL-1a	R5	1008	C	PL	4	10	12	30

W. W. HANLEY / WHOLESALE / GROCER / 25 / MAIN ST / CINCINNATI

NOTE: MAIN is clearly reengraved over another name. H and L are distinguishable underneath.

HARPEL

CWT	Rarity	Reverse Die	Metal	Edge	VG	VF	EF	Unc
165BM-1a	R5	1009	C	PL	4	10	12	30

HARPEL / * SUPERIOR * / CARD / & / MERCANTILE / PRINTER / S.E. COR. 3RD & VINE ST. / CINCINNATI

C. G. HARTMANN

CWT	Rarity	Reverse Die	Metal	Edge	VG	VF	EF	Unc
165BN-1a	R5	1248	C	PL	10	35	45	85

C. G. HARTMANN, / * / GROCER / 140 / EVERETT ST. / CIN. O.

M. HARTZEL

CWT	Rarity	Reverse Die	Metal	Edge	VG	VF	EF	Unc
165BO-1a	R3	1009	C	PL	4	8	10	25

M. HARTZEL / GROCER / & / COMMISSION / MERC'T / N.W. COR. 3' & ELM / STS. / CINCINNATI

J. HAYES & BRO.

CWT	Rarity	Reverse Die	Metal	Edge	VG	VF	EF	Unc
165BP-1a	R7	1169	C	PL	20	75	100	150

J. HAYES & BRO. above. 5 in center. CENTS below.

HEINMAN'S

** (165BQ) Now listed as MICH. 225AJa

E. HEINZMANN

CWT	Rarity	Reverse Die	Metal	Edge	VG	VF	EF	Unc
165BR-2a	R6	1388	C	PL	6	20	30	65

E. HEINZMANN / * / No. 12 / * / COURT ST.

NOTE: Marvin 727b - This piece comes with broken reverse die.

J. HELMIG

CWT	Rarity	Reverse Die	Metal	Edge	VG	VF	EF	Unc
165BS-2a	R4	1029	C	PL	4	10	12	35

J. HELMIG / GROCER / 708 / FREEMAN / ST. / CINCINNATI

B. HEMPELMAN

CWT	Rarity	Reverse Die	Metal	Edge	VG	VF	EF	Unc
165BT-1a	R3	1019	C	PL	4	8	10	25

B. HEMPELMAN / DEALER / IN / GROCERIES / & / FEED / N.W. COR. / LINN & FINDLAY / STS / CINCINNATI

HERANCOURT'S BREWERY

CWT	Rarity	Reverse Die	Metal	Edge	VG	VF	EF	Unc
165BU-1b	R8	—	BR	PL		—	RARE	—

DUE THE BEARER / * 25 * / CENTS / IN BEER AT / HERANCOURT'S / BREWERY Rv: JOHN STANTON / STAMP / BRAND / CUTTER / CINCINNATI

V. HEYL

CWT	Rarity	Reverse Die	Metal	Edge	VG	VF	EF	Unc
165BV-4a	R3	1026	C	PL	4	10	12	25

FARMERS HOTEL / COR. / COURT / - & - / RACE / STS. / CINCINNATI / V. HEYL

DR. H. H. HILL & CO.

CWT	Rarity	Reverse Die	Metal	Edge	VG	VF	EF	Unc
165BW-2a	R3	1030	C	PL	4	20	25	35

DR. H. H. HILL & CO. / DEALERS / IN / DRUGS / & / MEDICINES / S.E. COR. 5' & RACE / STS / CINCINNATI, O.

B. HINTRICK & C. GLASER

CWT	Rarity	Reverse Die	Metal	Edge	VG	VF	EF	Unc
165BX-1a	R5	1020	C	PL	4	12	15	30

B. HINTRICK & CO. GLASER / 636 & 638 / ELM / ST. / (ornament)

NOTE: Most combinations with this die have a broken obverse die.

GILBERT B. HOTCHKISS

CWT	Rarity	Reverse Die	Metal	Edge	VG	VF	EF	Unc
165BY-1b	R8	1362	BR	PL		—	SCARCE	—

GILBERT B. HOTCHKISS. / - I - / PINT / MILK / (ornament)

J. A. HUGHES

CWT	Rarity	Reverse Die	Metal	Edge	VG	VF	EF	Unc
165BZ-1a	R9	1131	C	PL		—	RARE	—

J. A. HUGHES above. METALIC / CARDS in wreath in center. CINCINNATI, O. below.

NOTE: METALLIC spelled with one L.

P. HUGHES

CWT	Rarity	Reverse Die	Metal	Edge	VG	VF	EF	Unc
165CA-1a	R9	1192	C	R		—	RARE	—

GOOD FOR ONE / - 5 - / CENT / LOAF OF BREAD / P. HUGHES

C. C. HYATT

CWT	Rarity	Reverse Die	Metal	Edge	VG	VF	EF	Unc
165CB-1a	R4	1007	C	PL	4	8	10	30

C. C. HYATT / STAPLE - / - & FANCY / GROCER / COR. / FREEMAN & POPLAR / STS. / * CINCINNATI *

B. JAHR

CWT	Rarity	Reverse Die	Metal	Edge	VG	VF	EF	Unc
165CC-2a	R9	1047	C	R		—	RARE	—

B. JAHR / 549 / VINE STR. / * / CIN'TI. O.

B. JAHR & COMPANY

CWT	Rarity	Reverse Die	Metal	Edge	VG	VF	EF	Unc
165CD-2a	R9	1392	C	PL		—	RARE	—

B. JAHR & CO / * / 549 / VINE ST. / * CIN. O.

NOTE: Obv. die crack on all pieces seen.

H. JOHNSTON

CWT	Rarity	Reverse Die	Metal	Edge	VG	VF	EF	Unc
165CE-1a	R8	1388	C	PL		—	RARE	—

H. JOHNSTON / - / DIE / SINKER / 154 / EVERETT ST / CIN. O.

NOTE: It is assumed this is an error where the H is intended for W. All pieces seen have badly broken reverse die.

W. JOHNSTON

CWT	Rarity	Reverse Die	Metal	Edge	VG	VF	EF	Unc
165CF-1a	R3	1056	C	PL	4	6	8	20

W. JOHNSTON, / * / DIE / SINKER / 154 / EVERETT ST. / CIN. O.

C. KAHN & CO.

CWT	Rarity	Reverse Die	Metal	Edge	VG	VF	EF	Unc
165CG-1a	R7	1056	C	PL	10	40	50	90

C. KAHN & CO., / * / No. 73 / EVERETT ST. / * MEAT * / STORE.

A. KARMAN

CWT	Rarity	Reverse Die	Metal	Edge	VG	VF	EF	Unc
165CH-1a	R4	1247	C	PL	8	25	30	65

A. KARMAN, / * / No. / - 627 - / CENTRAL / AVENUE / CIN. O.

J. KATZENSTEIN

CWT	Rarity	Reverse Die	Metal	Edge	VG	VF	EF	Unc
165CI-2b	R9	1192	BR	R		—	SCARCE	—

o / J. KATZENSTEIN / N.O. / Row of nine dots below.

WARREN KENNEDY

CWT	Rarity	Reverse Die	Metal	Edge	VG	VF	EF	Unc
165CJ-7a	R2	1176	C	PL	4	8	10	20

WARREN KENNEDY, / * / NEWS / DEPOT / 160 / + / VINE ST.

FRANK KERN

CWT	Rarity	Reverse Die	Metal	Edge	VG	VF	EF	Unc
165CK-2a	R4	1029	C	PL	4	8	10	30

FRANK KERN / GROCER / 692 / CEN AVENUE

NOTE: CEN is reengraved and moved to the right.

J. KIRCHENSCHLAGER

CWT	Rarity	Reverse Die	Metal	Edge	VG	VF	EF	Unc
165CL-1a	R7	1295	C	PL	50	100	125	225

GOOD FOR / (ornament) 5 (ornament) / CENTS / AT THE / BAR / J. KIRCHEN-SCHLAGER

J. KIRKER & CO.

CWT	Rarity	Reverse Die	Metal	Edge	VG	VF	EF	Unc
165CM-3a	R5	1352	C	PL	5	10	12	30

* J. KIRKER & CO. * / GROCERS / AND / PRODUCE / (ornament) / DEALERS / CINCINNATI, O

B. KITTEREDGE & CO.

CWT	Rarity	Reverse Die	Metal	Edge	VG	VF	EF	Unc
165CN-2a	R2	—	C	PL	4	8	10	20

* B. KITTEREDGE & Co., 134 MAIN St, CIN, O. * above Liberty head to left in center. 1863 below. Rv: DEALERS IN MILITARY GOODS. above GUNS, PISTOLS / (ornament) / AND / (ornament) / SPORTING in wreath in center. (ornament) APPARATUS (ornament) below.

J. KLEIN

CWT	Rarity	Reverse Die	Metal	Edge	VG	VF	EF	Unc
165CP-2a	R6	1029	C	PL	4	12	15	25

J. KLEIN / - . - / GROCER / 63 / HAMILTON ROAD

JACOB KNAUBER

CWT	Rarity	Reverse Die	Metal	Edge	VG	VF	EF	Unc
165CQ-1a	R3	1007	C	PL	4	10	12	25

JACOB KNAUBER / - . - / BUTCHER / * (ornament) * / CIN. O.

WM. KNECHT

CWT	Rarity	Reverse Die	Metal	Edge	VG	VF	EF	Unc
165CR-4a	R3	1034	C	PL	4	8	10	25

WM. KNECHT / GROCER / 502 / JOHN, ST. / CINCINNATI

JOHN KOCH

CWT	Rarity	Reverse Die	Metal	Edge	VG	VF	EF	Unc
165CS-1a	R5	1026	C	PL	4	8	10	25

JOHN KOCH / * (ornament) * / No. 10 / * (ornament) * / HARRISON ROAD

KOOS RESTAURANT

CWT	Rarity	Reverse Die	Metal	Edge	VG	VF	EF	Unc
165CT-1a	R9	1192	C	R		—	RARE	—

* BEER CHECK * / 5 / KOOS / RESTAURANT

B. KREAGER

CWT	Rarity	Reverse Die	Metal	Edge	VG	VF	EF	Unc
165CU-1a	R4	1026	C	PL	4	8	10	25

B. KREAGER / GROCER / COR. / HOME & SMITH / STS. / CINCINNATI

H. KREBER

CWT	Rarity	Reverse Die	Metal	Edge	VG	VF	EF	Unc
165CV-2a	R6	1177	C	PL	4	8	10	25

*** H. KREBER *** / (ornament) / GROCER / (ornament) / COLUMBIA / - BET. - / ROWE & MILL

A. KRENGEL'S UNION EXCHANGE

CWT	Rarity	Reverse Die	Metal	Edge	VG	VF	EF	Unc
165CW-4a	R4	1026	C	PL	4	8	10	30

A. KRENGEL'S / UNION / EXCHANGE / 218 / VINE, ST.

JACOB KRICK

CWT	Rarity	Reverse Die	Metal	Edge	VG	VF	EF	Unc
165CX-1a	R8	1047	C	R		—	RARE	—

JACOB / (ornament) / KRICK. Ornaments above, below and at sides.

W. K. LANPHEAR

CWT	Rarity	Reverse Die	Metal	Edge	VG	VF	EF	Unc
165CY-3a	R3	1088	C	PL	4	8	10	20

W. K. LANPHEAR above. MANU'FR / OF / METALIC / CARDS in corn wreath in center. CINCINNATI, O. below.

NOTE: METALLIC spelled with one L.

LANPHEAR'S

CWT	Rarity	Reverse Die	Metal	Edge	VG	VF	EF	Unc
165CZ-1b	R1	Blank	BR	PL	4	8	10	25

GOOD FOR / 5 / * CENTS * / IN CIGARS / OR TOBACCO / AT / LANPHEAR'S 133 VINE ST.

NOTE: Struck on a thin planchet.

J. F. LARWELL

CWT	Rarity	Reverse Die	Metal	Edge	VG	VF	EF	Unc
165DA-1a	R8	1046	C	PL		—	SCARCE	—

- (hole at top center) - / *** J. F. LARWELL *** / WATCH / MAKER

S. LASURS

CWT	Rarity	Reverse Die	Metal	Edge	VG	VF	EF	Unc
165DB-1a	R2	1057	C	PL	4	8	10	35

S. LASURS. / + / DEALER IN / RAGS / & METALS. / 26 / 15 ST. CIN. O.

NOTE: Usually comes with heavy rev. die break and sometimes with obv. break.

H. LAZARESS

CWT	Rarity	Reverse Die	Metal	Edge	VG	VF	EF	Unc
165DC-1a	R2	1247	C	PL	4	8	10	25

H. LAZARESS, / DEALER / IN / RAGS & METALS. / - 26 - / 15 ST.

LEAVITT & BEVIS

CWT	Rarity	Reverse Die	Metal	Edge	VG	VF	EF	Unc
165DD-1a	R3	1009	C	PL	4	8	10	25

LEAVITT & BEVIS / GENTS / FURNISHING / & / GOODS / 5TH & VINE / STS. / CINCINNATI

M. LINDERMANN

CWT	Rarity	Reverse Die	Metal	Edge	VG	VF	EF	Unc
165DE-1a	R3	1057	C	PL	4	8	10	25

M. LINDERMANN, / + / COR. / ELM / & HENRY / CHECK MAKER.

H. LOEWENSTEIN

CWT	Rarity	Reverse Die	Metal	Edge	VG	VF	EF	Unc
165DF-5a	R4	1036	C	PL	4	10	12	25

H. LOEWENSTEIN / BUTCHER / - * - / N.W. COR 9TH & JOHN

F. W. LUTZ

CWT	Rarity	Reverse Die	Metal	Edge	VG	VF	EF	Unc
165DG-1a	R7	1298	C	PL		—	RARE	—

F. W. LUTZ / ARTIST.

R. E. MACAULEY

CWT	Rarity	Reverse Die	Metal	Edge	VG	VF	EF	Unc
165DH-1a	R8	—	C	PL		—	RARE	—

GOOD FOR / ONE / (ornament) LOAF (ornament) / - 278 - / FIFTH ST. / R. E. MACAULEY Rv: JOHN STANTON / + / STAMP / BRAND / CUTTER / * / CINCINNATI

R. T. MARKHAM

CWT	Rarity	Reverse Die	Metal	Edge	VG	VF	EF	Unc
165DI-1a	R8	—	C	PL	40	100	160	250

GOOD FOR 5 Ct. / (ornament) / DRINK / AT THE / BAR / R. T. MARKHAM. Rv: *** JOHN'S *** / 5 CENTS / SALOON.

MARSH & MINER

CWT	Rarity	Reverse Die	Metal	Edge	VG	VF	EF	Unc
165DJ-2a1	R3	1022	C	PL	4	8	10	30

MARSH & MINER / VEST / MANUFACTURERS / 207 / WADE,ST. / CINCINNATI

MARTIN'S GROCERY

CWT	Rarity	Reverse Die	Metal	Edge	VG	VF	EF	Unc
165DK-1a	R3	1022	C	PL	4	8	10	25

MARTIN'S / GROCERY / 23 / WATER, ST. / CINCINNATI

W. C. MCCLENAHAN & CO.

CWT	Rarity	Reverse Die	Metal	Edge	VG	VF	EF	Unc
165DL-3a	R6	1124	C	PL	4	10	15	45

* W. C. Mc.CLENAHAN & CO. * / (ornament) / GROCER / N.E. COR. / 4. & / SYCAMORE

T. W. MCDONALD

CWT	Rarity	Reverse Die	Metal	Edge	VG	VF	EF	Unc
165DM-2a1	R3	1008	C	PL	4	10	12	25

T. W. McDONALD / BOOTS / & / SHOES / 299 / CEN. AVENUE / CINCINNATI

L. PHIL MEREDITH & J. N. M'CLUNG'S

CWT	Rarity	Reverse Die	Metal	Edge	VG	VF	EF	Unc
165DN-1a	R8	1344	C	PL		—	RARE	—

L. PHIL. MEREDITH / & J. N. M'CLUNG / DENTISTS / AT / M'CLUNG'S / DENTAL ROOMS / 152 / SIXTH ST. / CINCINNATI, O.

MERCHANTS HOTEL

CWT	Rarity	Reverse Die	Metal	Edge	VG	VF	EF	Unc
165DO-1bo	R9	—	BR	PL		—	RARE	—

MERCHANTS / a string of seventeen beads / * HOTEL * Rv: MURDOCK & SPENCER / 139 / W' FIFTH / STREET / CINCINNATI (Obv. Ohio 165DZ).

NOTE: Struck over McClellan political token.

ADAM METZ

CWT	Rarity	Reverse Die	Metal	Edge	VG	VF	EF	Unc
165DP-2a	R3	1008	C	PL	4	8	10	25

ADAM METZ / (ornament) / BUTCHER / - * - / 957 / CEN. AVENUE

J. & D. METZ

CWT	Rarity	Reverse Die	Metal	Edge	VG	VF	EF	Unc
165DQ-1a	R5	1022	C	PL	4	12	15	25

J & D. METZ / PORK / PACKERS / CINCINNATI

GEO. METZGER

CWT	Rarity	Reverse Die	Metal	Edge	VG	VF	EF	Unc
165DR-1a	R7	1029	C	PL	4	10	25	40

GEO. METZGER / 12 / MILE / - . - / HOUSE

L. MEYER

CWT	Rarity	Reverse Die	Metal	Edge	VG	VF	EF	Unc
165DS-1a	R4	1026	C	PL	4	10	12	35

L. MEYER / * WEST * / END / SALOON / CINCINNATI

MIEDEKING

CWT	Rarity	Reverse Die	Metal	Edge	VG	VF	EF	Unc
165DT-1a	R7	1019	C	PL	4	15	20	35

BUY YOUR / GROCERIES / FROM / MIEDEKING / N.E. COR / 9' & JOHN STS

S. B. MONARCH

CWT	Rarity	Reverse Die	Metal	Edge	VG	VF	EF	Unc
165DU-2a	R9	1393	C	R		—	RARE	—

+ BAR + / 10 / S. B. MONARCH

J. T. MOORE

CWT	Rarity	Reverse Die	Metal	Edge	VG	VF	EF	Unc
165DV-1a	R6	1007	C	PL	4	15	20	40

J. T. MOORE / FRUIT / * DEALER * / 164 / SIXTH ST. / CINCINNATI

MORGAN & FERRY

CWT	Rarity	Reverse Die	Metal	Edge	VG	VF	EF	Unc
165DW-2a	R4	1008	C	PL	4	12	15	30

MORGAN & FERRY / 5 / No. 20 E. 5' ST / CINCINNATI

H. J. MOSER

CWT	Rarity	Reverse Die	Metal	Edge	VG	VF	EF	Unc
165DX-1a	R9	1047	C	R		—	RARE	—

H. J. MOSER, WATCHMAKER * around. A line of five beads enclosed in fourteen stars in center.

JAS. MURDOCK, JR.

CWT	Rarity	Reverse Die	Metal	Edge	VG	VF	EF	Unc
165DY-1b	R8	—	BR	R	4	10	15	30

* JAS. MURDOCK, JR. * / M'F'R' OF / LEAD SEALS, / WIRES / & / PRESSES / 165 RACE ST. CINTI. O. Rv: M'F'T'R OF BAGGAGE CHECKS, WAX SEALS & TICKET STAMPS around. 100 / 10 IN. / WIRES in center.

MURDOCK & SPENCER

CWT	Rarity	Reverse Die	Metal	Edge	VG	VF	EF	Unc
165DZ-3b	R7	—	BR	PL	20	60	75	125

* MURDOCK & SPENCER & / STAMPS / - . - / BRANDS / STENCILS / BAGGAGE CHECKS / & C 139 & C / W. 5' ST. CINCINNATI Rv: Obv. incused.

E. MYERS & CO.

CWT	Rarity	Reverse Die	Metal	Edge	VG	VF	EF	Unc
165EA-4a	R5	1036	C	PL	4	12	15	30

E. MYERS & CO / DEALERS / IN / FOREIGN / FRUIT / & / CONFECTIONERY / 52 MAIN, ST. CIN, O.

H. NIEBUHR

CWT	Rarity	Reverse Die	Metal	Edge	VG	VF	EF	Unc
165EB-3a	R4	1295	C	PL	4	10	12	25

* .H. NIEBUHR * / WINE / & / BEER / SALOON / 223 / CENTRAL AVE.

F. J. NIEMER'S HOTEL

CWT	Rarity	Reverse Die	Metal	Edge	VG	VF	EF	Unc
165EC-2a	R3	1176	C	PL	4	10	12	25

F. J. NIEMER'S / HOTEL / - 262 - / (ornament) / FRONT, ST. / - CIN.O.-

J. H. NOLWER

CWT	Rarity	Reverse Die	Metal	Edge	VG	VF	EF	Unc
165ED-1a	R7	1388	C	PL	20	50	70	125

J. H. NOLWER, / (ornament) / COr. / ELM & - / FINDLEY / (ornament) / GROCER.

R. D. NORRIS

CWT	Rarity	Reverse Die	Metal	Edge	VG	VF	EF	Unc
165EF-1a	R4	1019	C	PL	4	8	10	25

R. D. NORRIS. / DRY / GOODS / 174 / FIFTH, ST.

O'DONOGHUE & NAISH

CWT	Rarity	Reverse Die	Metal	Edge	VG	VF	EF	Unc
165EG-3a	R3	1009	C	PL	4	8	10	25

O'DONOGHUE & NAISH / BOOTS / - & - / SHOES / 164 WEST 5' ST / CINCINNATI

O'REILLY BROS.

CWT	Rarity	Reverse Die	Metal	Edge	VG	VF	EF	Unc
165EH-3a	R6	1023	C	PL	4	12	15	35

O'REILLY BROS. / DRY / GOODS / 112 / FIFTH, ST / CINCINNATI.

B. PANZER

CWT	Rarity	Reverse Die	Metal	Edge	VG	VF	EF	Unc
165EI-1a	R8	—	C	PL		—	RARE	—

* B. PANZER. * above. 5 within circle in center. CENTS. below. Rv: JOS. J. SAYRE / * / DIE / SINKER / 4th & / * / WALNUT CIN. O.

PEEBLES

CWT	Rarity	Reverse Die	Metal	Edge	VG	VF	EF	Unc
165EJ-2a	R2	1008	C	PL	4	8	10	25

PEEBLES / DEALER / IN / STAPLE & FANCY / GROCERIES / 5TH & RACE / STS. / CINCINNATI

PHILIP

CWT	Rarity	Reverse Die	Metal	Edge	VG	VF	EF	Unc
165EK-2a	R3	1036	C	PL	4	12	15	25

PHILIP / - 16 - / WALNUT / ST. / CINCINNATI

J. G. PLEISTEINER

CWT	Rarity	Reverse Die	Metal	Edge	VG	VF	EF	Unc
165EL-1a	R7	1007	C	PL	4	20	25	35

J. G. PLEISTEINER / FANCY / GOODS / & / NOTIONS / 555 VINE ST. / BT. 15' & LIBERTY / CINCINNATI

CHAS. PLUMB

CWT	Rarity	Reverse Die	Metal	Edge	VG	VF	EF	Unc
165EM-1a	R3	1029	C	PL	4	8	10	25

CH'AS. PLUMB / HUCKSTER / MARKET / CINCINNATI

POGUE & JONES

CWT	Rarity	Reverse Die	Metal	Edge	VG	VF	EF	Unc
165EN-2a	R3	1036	C	PL	4	10	12	30

POGUE & JONES / DRY / GOODS / 128 / FIFTH, ST. / CINCINNATI

HENRY PORTER

CWT	Rarity	Reverse Die	Metal	Edge	VG	VF	EF	Unc
165EO-3b	R8	1397	BR	R		—	SCARCE	—

HENRY PORTER / = 95 = / FIFTH / ST. / CINCINNATI

H. RANSICK

CWT	Rarity	Reverse Die	Metal	Edge	VG	VF	EF	Unc
165EP-1a	R8	—	C	PL	40	75	100	150

(ornament) / H. RANSICK / GOOD FOR / 1 / LOAF / (ornament) / 357 W. 5th ST. (ornament) Rv: Similar to Rev. Ohio 905C, but eagle facing left.

H. A. RATTERMAN

CWT	Rarity	Reverse Die	Metal	Edge	VG	VF	EF	Unc
165EQ-2a1	R3	1008	C	PL	4	8	10	25

H. A. RATTERMAN above. Ornament enclosed in a circle of twelve stars within a beaded circle. CINCINNATI below.

NOTE: Comes with broken reverse die.

JOHN RAVY

CWT	Rarity	Reverse Die	Metal	Edge	VG	VF	EF	Unc
165ER-2a	R2	1008	C	PL	4	8	10	20

JOHN RAVY / CONFECTIONER / 185 / - RACE - / STREET / CINCINNATI

I. REES

CWT	Rarity	Reverse Die	Metal	Edge	VG	VF	EF	Unc
165ES-1a	R1	1170	C	PL	4	6	8	15

*** I. REES *** / 401 / CENTRAL / AVE. / CINCINNATI, O.

J. REISS & CO.

CWT	Rarity	Reverse Die	Metal	Edge	VG	VF	EF	Unc
165ET-2a	R4	1386	C	PL	20	100	125	200

J. REIS & CO, / + / Cor. 7th & / - / WALNUT / * / MEAT STORE.

J. F. RESTA

CWT	Rarity	Reverse Die	Metal	Edge	VG	VF	EF	Unc
165EU-1a	R5	1022	C	PL	4	12	15	30

J. F. RESTA / 3' & SMITH / STS / CINCINNATI / SAUSAGE / * MAKER *

A. RICKE

CWT	Rarity	Reverse Die	Metal	Edge	VG	VF	EF	Unc
165EV-5a	R3	1036	C	PL	4	8	10	25

A. RICKE above. Ornament within circle of eleven stars in center. CINCINNATI below.

B. J. RICKING

CWT	Rarity	Reverse Die	Metal	Edge	VG	VF	EF	Unc
165EW-1a	R2	1088	C	PL	4	8	10	30

*** B. J. RICKING *** / (ornament) / GROCER / - 49 - / PLUM ST. / (ornament) / CINTI. O.

GEO. W. RITTER'S MEAT STORE

CWT	Rarity	Reverse Die	Metal	Edge	VG	VF	EF	Unc
165EX-1a	R5	1290	C	PL	4	8	10	30

GEO. W. RITTER'S / MEAT / STORE / 241 / FOURTH ST.

F. H. ROLLINS

CWT	Rarity	Reverse Die	Metal	Edge	VG	VF	EF	Unc
165EY-1b	R7	—	BR	R		—	SCARCE	—

F. H. ROLLINS above. Indian head to left in center. 18, PUBLIC LANDING CIN'TI. O. below. Rv: STATIONERY / PRINTING / - & - / BLANK / BOOKS

YANKEE ROBINSON

CWT	Rarity	Reverse Die	Metal	Edge	VG	VF	EF	Unc
165EZ-1a	R1	—	C	PL	4	6	8	20

YANKEE ROBINSON above portrait of man with gun resting on right shoulder in center. THE GREAT COMEDIAN below. Rv: YANKEE ROBINSON above triangle enclosing hand in center pointing to TRIAD. At sides of triangle, PAST PRESENT FUTURE. BIG SHOW below.

ALBERT ROSS

CWT	Rarity	Reverse Die	Metal	Edge	VG	VF	EF	Unc
165FA-2a	R3	1309	C	PL	4	12	15	30

. ALBERT ROSS, DRUGGIST / CORNER / OF CENTRAL / AVENUE / - & - / 8th STREET / CINCINNATI

ELIS ROUSE'S HAIR PRESERVATIVE

CWT	Rarity	Reverse Die	Metal	Edge	VG	VF	EF	Unc
165FB-1a	R8	1047	C	R		—	RARE	—

ELLIS ROUSE'S / HAIR / PRESERVATIVE / - * - / METROPOLITAN / SHAVING / SALOON

JOHN SACKSTEDER

CWT	Rarity	Reverse Die	Metal	Edge	VG	VF	EF	Unc
165FC-2a	R2	1170	C	PL	4	10	12	30

** JOHN SACKSTEDER, ** / MAN'FR / OF / SEWING / MACHINES / 419 / CEN. AVE. / CIN. O.

SACKSTEDER & MARTIN

CWT	Rarity	Reverse Die	Metal	Edge	VG	VF	EF	Unc
165FD-1b	R5	Blank	BR	PL		—	SCARCE	—

* SACKSTEDER * / & / MARTIN / MANUFACTURERS / CINCINNATI / (ornament) OHIO (ornament).

JOS. J. SAYRE

CWT	Rarity	Reverse Die	Metal	Edge	VG	VF	EF	Unc
165FE-1b	R9	—	BR	PL		—	RARE	—

JOS. J. SAYRE / * / DIE / SINKER / 4th & / WALNUT CIN. O. Rv: * BERRY CHECK * above. GOOD / - * - / FOR within circle in center. ONE BOX below.

CHR. SCHLOENDORN

CWT	Rarity	Reverse Die	Metal	Edge	VG	VF	EF	Unc
165FF-1a	R5	1007	C	PL	4	12	15	30

CHR. SCHLOENDORN / PAPER / HANGINGS / - & - / FANCY GOODS / 492 / MAIN ST. / * CINCINNATI *

G. SCH.

CWT	Rarity	Reverse Die	Metal	Edge	VG	VF	EF	Unc
165FG-1a	R9	1056	C	PL		—	RARE	—

G. SCH, / GROCER / - 646 - / VINE ST / CIN. O.

H. SCHMIDT'S AUCTION & COMMISSION

CWT	Rarity	Reverse Die	Metal	Edge	VG	VF	EF	Unc
165FH-5a	R4	1033	C	PL	4	8	10	25

H. SCHMIDT'S / AUCTION / & / COMMISSION / GOODS / 27 ELDER, ST. / CINCINNATI

L. SCHNEIDER

CWT	Rarity	Reverse Die	Metal	Edge	VG	VF	EF	Unc
165FI-6a	R3	1029	C	PL	4	8	10	20

L. SCHNEIDER / 557 / WALNUT / ST. / CINCINNATI

H. SCHOTT

CWT	Rarity	Reverse Die	Metal	Edge	VG	VF	EF	Unc
165FJ-1b	R9	1391	BR	R		—	RARE	—

H. SCHOTT / 248 / W. LIBERTY / * ST. * / CIN'TI, O

LOT SCOTT

CWT	Rarity	Reverse Die	Metal	Edge	VG	VF	EF	Unc
165FK-1a	R8	1047	C	R		—	RARE	—

I - X - L / * / DAIRY / *** / LOT SCOTT

SCHULTZ & NEGLEY

CWT	Rarity	Reverse Die	Metal	Edge	VG	VF	EF	Unc
165FL-1c	R9	1391	N	R		—	SCARCE	—

* SCHULTZ & NEGLEY * / DRUGGISTS / * / N.E. COR. / * / 5' & MAIN ST / CIN'TI. O.

WM. SENOUR

CWT	Rarity	Reverse Die	Metal	Edge	VG	VF	EF	Unc
165FM-7a	R9	—	C	PL	20	100	125	175

(ornament) / Wm. Senour. in script / (ornament)

N. MENDAL SHAFER

CWT	Rarity	Reverse Die	Metal	Edge	VG	VF	EF	Unc
165FN-1a1	R2	—	C	PL	4	10	12	30

N. MENDAL SHAFER / ATTORNEY / - & - / COUNSELOR / AT / LAW / 57 THIRD ST. / CINCINNATI Rv: THE / FEDERAL / GOVERNMENT / A / NATIONAL - / - CURRENCY / FREE TRADE / AND / HUMAN RIGHTS.

H. E. SHAW

CWT	Rarity	Reverse Die	Metal	Edge	VG	VF	EF	Unc
165FO-2a	R3	1176	C	PL	4	12	15	30

* H. E. SHAW, ** / (ornament) / NEW / - AND - / SECOND HAND / FURNITURE / 18 / EAST 4. ST. / ** CIN. O. **

F. SHEEN

CWT	Rarity	Reverse Die	Metal	Edge	VG	VF	EF	Unc
165FP-8a	R5	1033	C	PL	4	8	10	25

F. SHEEN / GROCERIES / & / BREAD / STUFFS / 70 / E. PEARL, ST.

WM. E. SINN

CWT	Rarity	Reverse Die	Metal	Edge	VG	VF	EF	Unc
165FQ-1b	R7	—	BR	PL		—	RARE	—

Wm. E. SINN / 5 / (ornament) CENTS (ornament) Rv: JOHN STANTON / + / STAMP / BRAND / CUTTER / * / CINCINNATI.

FRANK SMITH

CWT	Rarity	Reverse Die	Metal	Edge	VG	VF	EF	Unc
165FR-3a	R4	1028	C	PL	4	8	10	25

FRANK SMITH / GROCERY / - & - / LIQUOR / STORE / 119 SYCAMORE, ST. / CINCINNATI

J. SMITH'S MEAT STORE

CWT	Rarity	Reverse Die	Metal	Edge	VG	VF	EF	Unc
165FS-6a	R4	1036	C	PL	4	8	10	25

J. SMITH'S / MEAT / STORE / 143 LOCK, ST.

S. & L. SMITH

CWT	Rarity	Reverse Die	Metal	Edge	VG	VF	EF	Unc
165FT-4a	R3	1036	C	PL	4	8	10	25

S. & L. SMITH / * (ornament) * / GROCERS / * (ornament) * / CINCINNATI

F. SNYDER

CWT	Rarity	Reverse Die	Metal	Edge	VG	VF	EF	Unc
165FU-1a	R9	1247	C	PL		—	RARE	—

F. SNYDER / GROCER / 53 / COURT ST. / CIN. O.

CHAS. SPREEN

CWT	Rarity	Reverse Die	Metal	Edge	VG	VF	EF	Unc
165FV-2a	R4	1021	C	PL	4	8	10	30

CHAS. SPREEN / GROCER / & / PRODUCE / DEALER / COR. COURT & LINN, STS.

H. STALKAMP

CWT	Rarity	Reverse Die	Metal	Edge	VG	VF	EF	Unc
165FW-2a	R3	1036	C	PL	4	8	10	25

H. STALKAMP / GROCER / 10 / GREEN, ST / CINCINNATI

JOHN STANTON

CWT	Rarity	Reverse Die	Metal	Edge	VG	VF	EF	Unc
165FX-5a	R5	1042	C	R	4	12	15	30

JOHN STANTON / MANUFACTURER / OF / STORE / * CARDS * / (ornament) / STENCILS / STAMPS & BRANDS / CINCINNATI, OHIO

D. B. STERRET

CWT	Rarity	Reverse Die	Metal	Edge	VG	VF	EF	Unc
165FY-1a	R5	1026	C	PL	4	15	20	35

* D. B. S. * / (ornament) / GROCER / - * - / 541 MAIN, ST.

C. SUTTON'S NEW GROCERY STORE

CWT	Rarity	Reverse Die	Metal	Edge	VG	VF	EF	Unc
165FZ-1a	R3	1026	C	PL	4	12	15	40

C. SUTTON'S / NEW / GROCERY / STORE/ 202 FIFTH, ST

WM. TELL

CWT	Rarity	Reverse Die	Metal	Edge	VG	VF	EF	Unc
165GA-2a	R4	1034	C	PL	4	8	10	25

WM. TELL / HOUSE / 225 / SIXTH, ST. / CINCINNATI

E. TOWNLEY

CWT	Rarity	Reverse Die	Metal	Edge	VG	VF	EF	Unc
165GB-1a	R4	1020	C	PL	4	10	12	25

E. TOWNLEY / HIVES / & / BEES / MOUNT AUBURN / CINCINNATI

VAN WUNDER

CWT	Rarity	Reverse Die	Metal	Edge	VG	VF	EF	Unc
165GC-7a	R5	1045	C	PL	4	15	20	40

BUY MEAT / OF / VAN, WUNDER / IN / MARKET

H. VARWIG'S

CWT	Rarity	Reverse Die	Metal	Edge	VG	VF	EF	Unc
165GD-1b	R7	—	BR	PL		—	SCARCE	—

GOOD / FOR 5 CTS. / IN / BREAD / AT / (ornament) H. HARWIG'S (ornament) / * 151 * / WEST COURT ST. Rv: JOHN STANTON / + / STAMP / BRAND / CUTTER / * / CINCINNATI

NOTE: Struck on thin planchet.

JACOB VOGEL

CWT	Rarity	Reverse Die	Metal	Edge	VG	VF	EF	Unc
165GE-2a	R4	1023	C	PL	4	8	10	25

JACOB VOGEL / BUTCHER / 985 / CEN. AVENUE

WALDO & BRANDON'S EMPORIUM

CWT	Rarity	Reverse Die	Metal	Edge	VG	VF	EF	Unc
165GF-1a	R5	—	C	PL	8	20	25	45

WALDO & BRANDON'S / EMPORIUM / 1863 Rv: DRY GOODS / (ornament) / -AND - / (ornament) / GROCERIES

WEATHERBY'S EMPORIUM

CWT	Rarity	Reverse Die	Metal	Edge	VG	VF	EF	Unc
165GG-1a	R5	1019	C	PL	4	10	12	25

WEATHERBY'S / CHEAP / DRY / GOODS / EMPORIUM / CINCINNATI.

H. C. WEHRMAN

CWT	Rarity	Reverse Die	Metal	Edge	VG	VF	EF	Unc
165GH-2a	R2	1026	C	PL	4	8	10	25

H. C. WEHRMAN / BAKER above. Sheaf of wheat in center. 217 EVERETT, ST. below.

WEIGHELL & SON'S

CWT	Rarity	Reverse Die	Metal	Edge	VG	VF	EF	Unc
165GI-1a	R7	—	C	PL		—	RARE	—

GOOD FOR / 20 / * CENTS * / IN / TOBACCO / AT / WEIGHELL & SON'S Rv: EXCELSIOR / TOBACCO / WORKS 210 & 212 / ELM ST. CIN. O / ESTABLISHED / 1835 (Obv. Ohio 165AMb).

W. W. WERT

CWT	Rarity	Reverse Die	Metal	Edge	VG	VF	EF	Unc
165GJ-6a	R3	1030	C	PL	4	8	10	25

W. W. WERT / AUCTION / & / COMMISSION / BOOTS & SHOES / WHOLESALE / * / RETAIL / 154 MAIN, ST

WILKINSONS

CWT	Rarity	Reverse Die	Metal	Edge	VG	VF	EF	Unc
165GK-1b	R9	—	BR	PL		—	RARE	—

GOOD FOR / 25 / CENTS / AT / WILKINSONS / 110 / WEST 4TH. ST. Rv: REDEEMED / IN / PAR FUNDS / IN SUMS OF / ONE / DOLLAR (Rev. Ohio 165Z-9)

A. B. WILSON

CWT	Rarity	Reverse Die	Metal	Edge	VG	VF	EF	Unc
165GL-1a1	R2	1008	C	PL	4	8	10	25

A. B. WILSON / STAPLE / & / FANCY / GROCER / 224 / W 6TH. ST. / CINCINNATI

H. WIND

CWT	Rarity	Reverse Die	Metal	Edge	VG	VF	EF	Unc
165GM-1a1	R8	1009	C	R		—	SCARCE	—

* GOOD FOR * / 5 / CENTS / (ornament) / H. WIND

WINE STEINER

CWT	Rarity	Reverse Die	Metal	Edge	VG	VF	EF	Unc
165GN-5a	R4	1192	C	PL	4	10	12	25

WINE STEINER / 35 / EAST / THIRD / ST. / CINCINNATI.

JOHN WOESSNER'S JEFFERSON SALOON

CWT	Rarity	Reverse Die	Metal	Edge	VG	VF	EF	Unc
165GO-1a	R3	1007	C	PL	4	10	12	25

JOHN WOESSNER'S / JEFFERSON / SALOON / COR. / 12' & MAIN, STS. / CINCINNATI

G. WOLFER

CWT	Rarity	Reverse Die	Metal	Edge	VG	VF	EF	Unc
165GP-2a	R6	1034	C	PL	4	8	10	30

G. WOLFE / TIN / SHOP / 62 FINDLAY, ST / CINCINNATI

WOOD & HARRISON

CWT	Rarity	Reverse Die	Metal	Edge	VG	VF	EF	Unc
165GQ-1b	R9	—	BR	PL		—	SCARCE	—

WOOD & HARRISON / *** / GOOD FOR / ********* / 10 / CENTS Rv: JOHN STANTON / + / STAMP / BRAND / CUTTER / * / CINCINNATI

WRIGHT

CWT	Rarity	Reverse Die	Metal	Edge	VG	VF	EF	Unc
165GR-1a	R2	1170	C	PL	4	6	8	15

** WRIGHT ** / - * - / CINCINNATI. / - * - / *** 1863 ***

ROBERT WRIGHT

CWT	Rarity	Reverse Die	Metal	Edge	VG	VF	EF	Unc
165GS-8a	R2	1021	C	PL	4	6	8	20

ROBERT WRIGHT / DRY / GOODS / 397 / CEN. AVENUE

NOTE: Comes with reverse die breaks.

H. B. XELAR

CWT	Rarity	Reverse Die	Metal	Edge	VG	VF	EF	Unc
165GT-3a	R1	1274	C	PL	4	6	8	15

** H. B. XELAR ** / WINE / - & - / BEER / SALOON.

STEPHAN YEATMAN

CWT	Rarity	Reverse Die	Metal	Edge	VG	VF	EF	Unc
165GU-2a	R6	1042	C	R	10	30	50	65

S. Y. surrounded by thirteen stars

L. YOUNG

CWT	Rarity	Reverse Die	Metal	Edge	VG	VF	EF	Unc
165GV-2a	R8	1343	C	PL		—	SCARCE	—

L. YOUNG - scrolls above and below.

JOS. ZANDT

CWT	Rarity	Reverse Die	Metal	Edge	VG	VF	EF	Unc
165GW-1a	R9	1274	C	PL		—	RARE	—

JOS. ZANDT / ICE / CREAM / SALOON / 285 / CENTRAL AV.

NOTE: An obvious error, intended for ZANONE.

JOS. ZANONE

CWT	Rarity	Reverse Die	Metal	Edge	VG	VF	EF	Unc
165GX-2a	R8	1172	C	PL		—	SCARCE	—

JOS. ZANONE / ICE / CREAM / SALOON / 285 / CENTRAL AV.

JOHN E. ZELTNER

CWT	Rarity	Reverse Die	Metal	Edge	VG	VF	EF	Unc
165GY-27a	R2	1019	C	PL	4	8	10	20

JOHN E. ZELTNER / NATIONAL / HALL / 400 / VINE ST. / CINCINNATI, O.

Circleville

G. H. FICKARDT & CO.

CWT	Rarity	Reverse Die	Metal	Edge	VG	VF	EF	Unc
168A-5a	R4	1179	C	PL	8	20	25	60

G. H. FICKARDT & CO. / DRUGGISTS / (ornament) / CIRCLEVILLE / (ornament) / OHIO.

J. L. KING

CWT	Rarity	Reverse Die	Metal	Edge	VG	VF	EF	Unc
168B-4a	R5	1331	C	PL	8	20	25	40

J. L. KING / GROCERY / AND / PROVISION / (ornament) / STORE / CIRCLEVILLE, O.

MASON & SON

CWT	Rarity	Reverse Die	Metal	Edge	VG	VF	EF	Unc
168C-1a	R3	1124	C	PL	8	20	25	35

MASON & SON / GROCERS / AND / LIQUOR / (ornament) / DEALERS / CIRCLEVILLE, O.

Clarksburg

FRENCH

CWT	Rarity	Reverse Die	Metal	Edge	VG	VF	EF	Unc
170A-1a	R5	1059	C	PL	10	30	40	90

GROCERIES & NOTIONS / (ornament) SOLD BY (ornament) / ONE / FRENCH / (ornament) / (ornament) / CLARKSBURG, O. (ornament).

JAMES & FRENCH

CWT	Rarity	Reverse Die	Metal	Edge	VG	VF	EF	Unc
170B-1a	R6	1059	C	PL	10	30	40	90

JAMES & FRENCH / HAVE / * IT! * / -.- / CLARKSBURG / -.- / OHIO.

MAUCH & BRADBURY

CWT	Rarity	Reverse Die	Metal	Edge	VG	VF	EF	Unc
170C-1a	R9	1059	C	PL		—	SCARCE	—

GOOD FOR / ONE / CENT / AT / MAUCK & BRADBURY.

NOTE: All of the above from Clarksburg have an Indian head dated 1873, which is assumed to be an error.

Cleveland

A. & H.

CWT	Rarity	Reverse Die	Metal	Edge	VG	VF	EF	Unc
175A-1a	R9	1319	C	R		—	RARE	—

A. & H. surrounded by 36 stars. Circle at top (for hole).

BRATTIN

CWT	Rarity	Reverse Die	Metal	Edge	VG	VF	EF	Unc
175B-1a	R9	1319	C	R		—	RARE	—

BRATTIN - 3 stars at top.

NOTE: The above two pieces attributed to Cleveland by J. Barrett.

C. G. BRUCE

CWT	Rarity	Reverse Die	Metal	Edge	VG	VF	EF	Unc
175C-1a	R2	—	C	PL	4	8	10	20

C. G. BRUCE / AUTHORIZED / WAR / CLAIM / AGENT / 1863 / CLEVELAND, O. Rv: $100 BOUNTY / PENSIONS / BACK PAY / &C. / COLLECTED / & / CASHED

NOTE: A of AGENT between C & L of CLAIM on obverse.

C. CHANDLER

CWT	Rarity	Reverse Die	Metal	Edge	VG	VF	EF	Unc
175D-1a	R4	1180	C	PL	4	8	10	30

C. CHANDLER, / FRUIT / - SEED - / DEALER / CLEVELAND-O.

DECKAND & ENGLEHART

CWT	Rarity	Reverse Die	Metal	Edge	VG	VF	EF	Unc
175E-1a	R3	1098	C	PL	4	10	12	30

DECKAND & ENGLEHART / FASHIONABLE / (ornament) / HATTERS. / CLEVELAND / (ornament) / OHIO.

DUNN, GOUDY & BRO.

CWT	Rarity	Reverse Die	Metal	Edge	VG	VF	EF	Unc
175F-1a	R3	1125	C	PL	4	10	12	30

DUNN, GOUDY & BRO, / (ornament) / GROCERIES / &C. / 149 / ONTARIO ST. / CLEVELAND, O.

D. W. GAGE

CWT	Rarity	Reverse Die	Metal	Edge	VG	VF	EF	Unc
175G-1a	R3	—	C	R	4	8	10	25

D. W. GAGE / AUTHORIZED / -WAR- / CLAIM / AGENT / 1863 / CLEVELAND, O. Rv: $100 BOUNTY / PENSIONS / BACK PAY / &C COLLECTED / & / CASHED (same as Rev. Ohio 165C-7a)

J. H. & A. S. GORHAM

CWT	Rarity	Reverse Die	Metal	Edge	VG	VF	EF	Unc
175H-1a	R4	1178	C	PL	4	10	12	25

J. H. & A. S. GORHAM / GROCERS / MANUFACTURERS / OF / CRACKERS / * AND * / (ornament) / CONFECTIONERY / CLEVELAND, O.

JOHN HAWKINS

CWT	Rarity	Reverse Die	Metal	Edge	VG	VF	EF	Unc
175I-1a	R3	—	C	PL	10	20	25	60

JOHN HAWKINS above bust to right in center. THE LADIES MAN below. Rv: NEWBURGH HOUSE / 226 / ONTARIO ST. / CLEVELAND, OHIO.

J. LANGHORN

CWT	Rarity	Reverse Die	Metal	Edge	VG	VF	EF	Unc
175J-2a	R3	1180	C	PL	4	10	12	30

* * J. LANGHORN * * / MEAT / - * - / STORE / - * - / BANK, ST. CLEVELAND, O.

C. L. MARVIN

CWT	Rarity	Reverse Die	Metal	Edge	VG	VF	EF	Unc
175K-1a	R3	1180	C	PL	4	12	15	30

C. L. MARVIN, / STOVE & / * / GRATE / DEPOT. / 50 / PUBLIC SQUARE / CLEVELAND, O.

T. J. QUINLAN

CWT	Rarity	Reverse Die	Metal	Edge	VG	VF	EF	Unc
175L-1a	R2	—	C	PL	4	10	12	30

* T. J. QUINLAN * / BILL / POSTER / -AND- / DISTRIBUTOR, / 174 / ONTARIO, ST. / CLEVELAND, O. Rv: T. J. QUINLAN, / NEWS / PAPERS, / STATIONERY, / SONGS / AND / YANKEE / * * NOTIONS. * *

I. P. SHERWOOD

CWT	Rarity	Reverse Die	Metal	Edge	VG	VF	EF	Unc
175M-1a	R4	1024	C	R	4	8	10	20

I. P. SHERWOOD / DRY / GOODS / -&- / MILLINERY / CLEVELAND, O.

J. P. SHERWOOD

CWT	Rarity	Reverse Die	Metal	Edge	VG	VF	EF	Unc
175N-1a	R5	1028	C	R	4	8	10	20

J. P. SHERWOOD / DRY / GOODS / & / MILLINERY / CLEVELAND, O.

NOTE: Either the 175M or 175N is an error, but we have not been able to determine which is the correct usage.

CHAS. W. STEARNS

CWT	Rarity	Reverse Die	Metal	Edge	VG	VF	EF	Unc
175O-1a	R2	—	C	R	4	10	12	30

CHAS. W. STEARNS above FOOT / OF / VINEYARD / ST / CLEVELAND on grindstone in center. OHIO below. Rv: GRINDSTONES / FLAGGING / -&- / BUILDING / STONES

TAGES

CWT	Rarity	Reverse Die	Metal	Edge	VG	VF	EF	Unc
175P-1a	R5	—	C	PL	5	20	30	90

* TAGES * / LONDON / YOKE SHIRT. / MANUFY / 243 / SUPERIOR ST. / CLEVELAND. OHIO. Rv: SEND FOR A / CIRCULAR / A PERFECT / -FIT- / GUARANTEED.

WARDS

CWT	Rarity	Reverse Die	Metal	Edge	VG	VF	EF	Unc
175Q-1a	R7	1024	C	PL	30	100	135	200

WARDS / LAKE / SUPERIOR / -LINE- / STEAMER / PLANET / CLEVELAND DETROIT & LAKE SUPERIOR *

NOTE: Probably should be listed in Detroit, as home office was there.

JOS. WELF

CWT	Rarity	Reverse Die	Metal	Edge	VG	VF	EF	Unc
175R-1a	R9	1319	C	R		—	RARE	—

- * - / JOS. WELF / line below. Circle at top (for hole)

WESTERN UNION TELEGRAPH CO.

CWT	Rarity	Reverse Die	Metal	Edge	VG	VF	EF	Unc
175Ra-ie	R10	1862	C-N	PL		—	RARE	—

WESTERN / UNION / TELEGRAPH CO. / CLEVELAND.O. / 1862

NOTE: Incused or planed down 1857 C-N Cent - was stolen from Dr. H. Aqua collection.

GEO. WORTHINGTON & CO.

CWT	Rarity	Reverse Die	Metal	Edge	VG	VF	EF	Unc
175S-4a	R2	—	C	PL	4	12	15	30

GEO. WORTHINGTON & CO. above. HARDWARE / DEALERS inscribed on padlock in center. CLEVELAND, O. below. Rv: TRY / ALLEN'S / BLACKLEAD / COMPOUND / BABBITT / METAL / 1863

Collinsville

P. CARLE & SON

CWT	Rarity	Reverse Die	Metal	Edge	VG	VF	EF	Unc
185A-1a	R3	1019	C	PL	4	15	20	40

P. CARLE & SON / GROCERS / -&- / GRAIN / DEALERS / * COLLINSVILLE, O. *

NOTE: The second C in GROCERS touches the first C and is light. The S is also double cut.

Columbiana

ICENHOUR & CO.

CWT	Rarity	Reverse Die	Metal	Edge	VG	VF	EF	Unc
190A-3a	R5	1313	C	R	10	30	45	70

ICENHOUR & CO / PRODUCE / -C.- / COMMISSION / MERCHANTS / COLUMBIANA, O.

G. KIPP

CWT	Rarity	Reverse Die	Metal	Edge	VG	VF	EF	Unc
190B-1a	R3	1046	C	R	4	8	10	25

G. KIPP / PRODUCE / DEALER. / COLUMBIANA, O.

NOTE: Comes with obverse die breaks.

Columbus

JOHN GRETHER

CWT	Rarity	Reverse Die	Metal	Edge	VG	VF	EF	Unc
200A-2A	R6	1042	C	R	4	12	15	40

JOHN GRETHER / IMPORTER / OF / CHINA / -&- / QUEENSWARE / COLUMBUS, O.

HEINTZ & HENKLE

CWT	Rarity	Reverse Die	Metal	Edge	VG	VF	EF	Unc
200B-3a	R3	1177	C	PL	4	12	15	35

HEINTZ & HINKLE / DEALERS / -IN- / GROCERIES / 136 COR 4TH. / AND / FRIEND / COLUMBUS, O.

J. M. & V. KOERNER

CWT	Rarity	Reverse Die	Metal	Edge	VG	VF	EF	Unc
200C-1a	R3	1082	C	PL	4	8	10	30

J. M. & V. KOERNER, / GROCERS / - * - / S.E. COR. / BROAD / & / FRONT / COLUMBUS, O.

S. T. MARTIN

CWT	Rarity	Reverse Die	Metal	Edge	VG	VF	EF	Unc
200D-2a	R1	1089	C	PL	4	8	10	25

S. T. MARTIN / EATING / HOUSE / 160 / SOUTH FOURTH ST / (ornament)(ornament) / COLUMBUS / * OHIO. *

MERCHANTS EXCHANGE

CWT	Rarity	Reverse Die	Metal	Edge	VG	VF	EF	Unc
200E-1b	R9	—	BR	PL	—	SCARCE		—

MERCHANTS EXCHANGE / (ornament) / COLUMBUS / * OHIO * Rv: Number 10 in a circle of stars.

NOTE: Probably struck about 1870-1875.

WM. H. RESTIEAUX

CWT	Rarity	Reverse Die	Metal	Edge	VG	VF	EF	Unc
200F-2a	R3	1222	C	PL	4	10	12	30

Wm. H. RESTIEAUX, / (ornament) / GROCER / (ornament) / COLUMBUS, O.

H. SCHREINER

CWT	Rarity	Reverse Die	Metal	Edge	VG	VF	EF	Unc
200G-1a	R3	1125	C	PL	5	15	20	35

H. SCHREINER / GROCERIES / AND / PROVISIONS / 169 / EAST / FRIEND ST. / COLUMBUS. O.

MRS. M. A. VAN HOUTEN

CWT	Rarity	Reverse Die	Metal	Edge	VG	VF	EF	Unc
200H-1a	R4	1127	C	PL	8	20	25	50

MRS. M. A. VAN HOUTEN / MILLINER / 68 / E. TOWN ST. / COLUMBUS / OHIO.

WAGNER'S DINING HALL

CWT	Rarity	Reverse Die	Metal	Edge	VG	VF	EF	Unc
200I-3a	R3	1178	C	PL	4	10	12	30

* * WAGNER'S * * / (ornament) / DINING / HALL, / (ornament) / COLUMBUS, O.

WIATT & BRO.

CWT	Rarity	Reverse Die	Metal	Edge	VG	VF	EF	Unc
200J-2a	R5	1176	C	PL	4	15	20	40

WIATT & BRO / (ornament) / BAKERS / -&- / CONFECTIONERS / COLUMBUS, O.

Crestline

JACOB STUMP

CWT	Rarity	Reverse Die	Metal	Edge	VG	VF	EF	Unc
215A-1a	R5	1342	C	PL	20	60	80	100

JACOB STUMP / MERCHANT TAILOR / -&- / READY MADE / CLOTHING, / CRESTLINE, / OHIO.

Dayton

J. C. CAIN

CWT	Rarity	Reverse Die	Metal	Edge	VG	VF	EF	Unc
230A-1a	R5	1083	C	PL	10	15	25	90

J. C. CAIN / (ornament) / NOTIONS, / 305 THIRD ST. / DAYTON, / (ornament) OHIO. (ornament)

J. DURST

CWT	Rarity	Reverse Die	Metal	Edge	VG	VF	EF	Unc
230B-1a	R4	1018	C	R	4	8	10	40

J. DURST / - * (ornament) * - / GROCER / - * (ornament) * - / DAYTON, O.

HENRY KLINE

CWT	Rarity	Reverse Die	Metal	Edge	VG	VF	EF	Unc
230C-1a	R9	Blank	C	PL		—	RARE	—

HENRY KLINE / CLOCKS / WATCHES / & / JEWELRY / DAYTON / O.

RICKEYS

CWT	Rarity	Reverse Die	Metal	Edge	VG	VF	EF	Unc
230D-1a	R5	—	C	R	4	15	25	40

RICKEYS / BOOK STORE / 326 3rd St / DAYTON, O. Rv: BOOKS AND PAPERS / GO TO / RICKEYS. 1863 / CASH PAID FOR RAGS.

S. WILD

CWT	Rarity	Reverse Die	Metal	Edge	VG	VF	EF	Unc
230E-1a	R5	1046	C	R	4	12	15	45

S. WILD / COFFEE / HOUSE / (ornament) / DAYTON, O.

Defiance

RUHL'S PREMIUM STEEL PENS

CWT	Rarity	Reverse Die	Metal	Edge	VG	VF	EF	Unc
240A-1a	R3	1008	C	PL	8	20	30	50

RUHL'S / PREMIUM / STEEL / PENS / DEFIANCE, O.

Delphos

J. W. HUNT

CWT	Rarity	Reverse Die	Metal	Edge	VG	VF	EF	Unc
250A-1a	R4	1037	C	R	8	20	25	50

J. W. HUNT / DRUGGIST / -&- / EXPRESS / AGT. / DELPHOS, O.

Edgerton

D. FARNHAM & CO.

CWT	Rarity	Reverse Die	Metal	Edge	VG	VF	EF	Unc
270A-4a	R5	1223	C	PL	8	15	25	60

D. FARNHAM & CO. / DEALERS / IN / DRY GOODS, / EDGERTON, / * / OHIO.

Elyria

W. B. EAGER

CWT	Rarity	Reverse Die	Metal	Edge	VG	VF	EF	Unc
290A-1b	R2	—	BR	PL	4	8	10	25

W. B. EAGER ELYRIA O. above. Indian head to left in center. WHOLESALE AGT. below. Rv: TRY / ALLEN'S / BLACKLEAD / COMPOUND / BABBITT / METAL 1862

Findlay

BOGER C. KIMMEL

CWT	Rarity	Reverse Die	Metal	Edge	VG	VF	EF	Unc
300A-1bo	R9	Blank	BR	R		—	RARE	—

BOGER C. KIMMEL / (beaded line) / FINDLAY, O.

NOTE: Struck over a McClellan token.

I. BOGER

CWT	Rarity	Reverse Die	Metal	Edge	VG	VF	EF	Unc
300B-1a	R8	1320	C	PL		—	RARE	—

I. BOGER / (ornament) / WATCH MAKER / & / JEWELER / (ornament) / FINDLAY, O.

OSBORNE & BRO.

CWT	Rarity	Reverse Die	Metal	Edge	VG	VF	EF	Unc
300C-1a	R8	1024	C	R	50	150	200	275

OSBORNE & BRO / GROCERS / -&- / PRODUCE / - / DEALERS / FINDLAY, O.

Frazeyburg

E. L. LEMERT

CWT	Rarity	Reverse Die	Metal	Edge	VG	VF	EF	Unc
310A-1a	R6	1037	C	R	10	25	40	75

* E. L. LEMERT * / DRY / GOODS / -&- / GROCERIES / FRAZEYBURG, O.

Fredericktown

BARTLETT & RIGBY

CWT	Rarity	Reverse Die	Metal	Edge	VG	VF	EF	Unc
320A-1a	R6	1046	C	R	8	20	30	60

BARTLETT & RIGHT / DRY / GOODS, / - / GROCERIES. / =&C.= / FREDERICKTOWN, O.

MOSURE BRO & LEMON

CWT	Rarity	Reverse Die	Metal	Edge	VG	VF	EF	Unc
320B-1a	R5	1346	C	PL	8	20	30	50

MOSURE BRO & LEMON / CLOTHING / & / DRY GOODS / FREDERICKTOWN, O.

ROGERS & CASSELL

CWT	Rarity	Reverse Die	Metal	Edge	VG	VF	EF	Unc
320C-1a	R4	1304	C	PL	8	15	20	50

ROGERS & CASSELL / HARDWARE / IRON & NAILS / FREDERICKTOWN / OHIO

S. S. TUTTLE

CWT	Rarity	Reverse Die	Metal	Edge	VG	VF	EF	Unc
320D-3a	R4	1046	C	R	4	10	15	40

S. S. TUTTLE / PRODUCE / COMMISSION / -&- / FORWARDING / MERCHANT / FREDERICKTOWN, O.

Fremont

P. CLOSE

CWT	Rarity	Reverse Die	Metal	Edge	VG	VF	EF	Unc
330A-1a	R4	1087	C	PL	4	12	15	40

P. CLOSE / GROCERIES / WINES / LIQUORS & CIGARS / WHOLESALE / & / RETAIL / FREMONT, O.

DR. E. DILLON & SON

CWT	Rarity	Reverse Die	Metal	Edge	VG	VF	EF	Unc
330B-1a	R5	1310	C	PL	8	25	30	45

DR. E. DILLON & SON / DRUGGISTS, / (mortar and pestle) / FREMONT, / OHIO.

M. DRYFOOS

CWT	Rarity	Reverse Die	Metal	Edge	VG	VF	EF	Unc
330C-1a	R6	1337	C	PL	4	15	20	45

M. DRYFOOS / MERCHANT / TAILOR / AND DEALER IN / READY MADE / CLOTHING, / FREMONT, O.

EMRICH & CO.

CWT	Rarity	Reverse Die	Metal	Edge	VG	VF	EF	Unc
330D-1a	R5	1087	C	PL	8	15	25	40

EMRICH & CO. / (ornament) / DRY GOODS, / CLOTHING / &C. FREMONT, O.

HOOT & MENG

CWT	Rarity	Reverse Die	Metal	Edge	VG	VF	EF	Unc
330E-1a	R4	1317	C	PL	4	15	25	35

HOOT & MENG / MANUFR'S. / AND / DEALERS IN / BOOTS & SHOES, / FREMONT, / OHIO.

D. W. KREBS & CO.

CWT	Rarity	Reverse Die	Metal	Edge	VG	VF	EF	Unc
330F-1a	R5	1085	C	PL	4	12	25	35

D. W. KREBS & CO. / DEALERS / IN / DRY GOODS / CLOTHING / &C. / FREMONT, O.

ROBERTS & SHELDON

CWT	Rarity	Reverse Die	Metal	Edge	VG	VF	EF	Unc
330G-1a	R5	1306	C	PL	4	15	25	50

* ROBERTS & SHELDON , * / DEALERS IN / STOVES, TIN, / -AND- / HARDWARE, / FREMONT, OHIO.

THOMPSON & SPICER

CWT	Rarity	Reverse Die	Metal	Edge	VG	VF	EF	Unc
330H-1a	R6	1302	C	PL	4	15	20	35

THOMPSON & SPICER, / STOVES, / TIN / & HOUSE / FURNISHING / GOODS / FREMONT, / OHIO.

Galion

D. & W. RIBLET

CWT	Rarity	Reverse Die	Metal	Edge	VG	VF	EF	Unc
340A-1a	R4	1333	C	PL	4	12	15	30

D & W. RIBLET above. U. S. shield in center. GALION, OHIO. below.

Gallipolis

J. D. BAILEY

CWT	Rarity	Reverse Die	Metal	Edge	VG	VF	EF	Unc
345A-1a	R8	1037	C	R	10	50	75	175

* J. D. BAILEY * / FANCY / DRY / GOODS / NOTIONS / =&= / GROCERIES / GALLIPOLIS, O.

J. J. CADOT & BRO.

CWT	Rarity	Reverse Die	Metal	Edge	VG	VF	EF	Unc
345B-1a	R5	1122	C	PL	4	15	20	35

J. J. CADOT & BRO. / GROCERS / (ornament) / GALLIPOLIS / * OHIO. *

S. GOETZ

CWT	Rarity	Reverse Die	Metal	Edge	VG	VF	EF	Unc
345C-1c	R8	1391	N	R		—	SCARCE	—

GOOD FOR / 5 CTS / AT / S. GOETZ / COR. GRAPE & / 3. STS / GALLIPOLIS, O.

HENKING, ALLEMONG & CO.

CWT	Rarity	Reverse Die	Metal	Edge	VG	VF	EF	Unc
345D-1a	R8	—	C	R		—	SCARCE	—

HENKING, ALLEMONG & CO / WHOLESALE / GROCERS / GALLIPOLIS / * / -o- RV: (ornament) DRAYAGE (ornament) / 10 / CENTS

Greenville

F. H. HAFER & CO.

CWT	Rarity	Reverse Die	Metal	Edge	VG	VF	EF	Unc
360A-2a	R3	1038	C	PL	4	12	15	35

F. H. Hafer & Co. / STAPLE / & / FANCY / GROCERS / GREENVILLE, O.

T. P. TURPEN

CWT	Rarity	Reverse Die	Metal	Edge	VG	VF	EF	Unc
360B-3a	R7	1042	C	R	10	25	35	50

T. P. TURPEN / GROCER / -&- / TOBACCO / DEALER / GREENVILLE, O.

Hamilton

JOHN DEINZER

CWT	Rarity	Reverse Die	Metal	Edge	VG	VF	EF	Unc
385A-1a	R5	1021	C	PL	4	12	20	35

JOHN DEINZER / FAMILY / GROCERY / NO. / 19 HIGH. ST. / HAMILTON, O.

H. & W. FRECHTLING

CWT	Rarity	Reverse Die	Metal	Edge	VG	VF	EF	Unc
385B-2a	R8	1042	C	R	15	30	45	85

H. & W. FRECHTLING / DEALERS IN / DRY / GOODS / -&- / GROCERIES / HAMILTON, O.

J. F. GOLLER

CWT	Rarity	Reverse Die	Metal	Edge	VG	VF	EF	Unc
385C-1b	R8	—	BR	PL		—	RARE	—

* J. F. GOLLER * / GOOD FOR / 5 / CENTS / HAMILTON, O. Rv: JAS. MURDOCK, JR. / STAMPS / BURNINS / BRAND / AND / STENCILS / (ornament) 139 (ornament) / W. 5 ST. CINCINNATI.

JOHN SCHUBERT

CWT	Rarity	Reverse Die	Metal	Edge	VG	VF	EF	Unc
385D-3a	R4	1021	C	PL	4	10	15	30

JOHN SCHUBERT / HAMILTON / SALOON / HIGH / STREET / HAMILTON, O.

NOTE: L of SALOON cut over another L to the left.

Hillsboro

BLACK & KIBLER

CWT	Rarity	Reverse Die	Metal	Edge	VG	VF	EF	Unc
400A-2a	R4	1332	C	PL	4	12	15	45

* BLACK & KIBLER * / DEALERS / IN / HARDWARE / IRON / & / NAILS. / HILLSBORO. O.

CHANEY & HARRIS

CWT	Rarity	Reverse Die	Metal	Edge	VG	VF	EF	Unc
400B-1a	R8	1122	C	PL	15	40	50	125

* CHANEY & HARRIS * / DEALERS / IN / DRY GOODS / (ornament) / HILLSBORO / -- / OHIO.

O. J. ECKLEY

CWT	Rarity	Reverse Die	Metal	Edge	VG	VF	EF	Unc
400C-1a	R6	1287	C	PL	10	20	30	75

* * O. J. ECKLEY * * / DAILY / MEAT / MARKET / HILLSBORO / * * OHIO. * *

HERRON & AMEN

CWT	Rarity	Reverse Die	Metal	Edge	VG	VF	EF	Unc
400D-1a	R3	1223	C	PL	8	15	25	45

HERRON & AMEN / DRY GOODS / & / NOTIONS / HILLSBORO / OHIO.

GEO. MARCH

CWT	Rarity	Reverse Die	Metal	Edge	VG	VF	EF	Unc
400E-2a	R4	1223	C	PL	4	8	10	30

GEO. MARCH / DEALER / IN / DRY / GOODS / HILLSBORO / OHIO.

NOTE: Comes with obverse die broken.

Jackson

JOHN CHESNU'S EXCHANGE

CWT	Rarity	Reverse Die	Metal	Edge	VG	VF	EF	Unc
415A-2a	R8	1047	C	R		—	RARE	—

JOHN CHESNU'S / (ornament) / EXHCHANGE / - * - / * JACKSON, O. *

NOTE: The name is undoubtedly meant to be CHESTNUT. On obverse die of all varieties, JACKSON is clearly engraved over PORTSMOUTH.

Kenton

J. M. BRUNSON

CWT	Rarity	Reverse Die	Metal	Edge	VG	VF	EF	Unc
420A-1a	R6	—	C	PL	4	15	25	35

J. M. BRUNSON, / DEALER / IN / (ornament) / DRY GOODS, / (ornament) &C. (ornament) / KENTON OHIO. Rv: * FANCY & STAPLE * above. Flag on staff within a circle of stars in center. * DRY GOODS &C. * below.

Lancaster

J. AMBRUSTER

CWT	Rarity	Reverse Die	Metal	Edge	VG	VF	EF	Unc
440A-4a	R4	1084	C	PL	4	15	20	30

J. ARMBRUSTER, / (ornament) / GROCER / LANCASTER / -.- / * OHIO. *

NOTE: ARMBRUSTER is the correct spelling.

J. BLOCK

CWT	Rarity	Reverse Die	Metal	Edge	VG	VF	EF	Unc
440B-1a	R5	1337	C	PL	4	15	25	45

J. BLOCK, AGT. / READY / MADE / CLOTHING / TALMADGE / BLOCK / LANCASTER, O.

CHAS. PAIRAN

CWT	Rarity	Reverse Die	Metal	Edge	VG	VF	EF	Unc
440C-3a	R5	1166	C	PL	4	15	25	50

* CHAS. PAIRAN * / GROCER / AND / LIQUOR / (ornament) / DEALER / LANCASTER, O.

ANDREW REID

CWT	Rarity	Reverse Die	Metal	Edge	VG	VF	EF	Unc
440D-1a	R4	1273	C	PL	8	15	20	40

ANDREW REID, / DRY GOODS / (ornament) / AND / (ornament) / SHOES, LANCASTER, O.

Laurelville

GEO. D. RIEGEL

CWT	Rarity	Reverse Die	Metal	Edge	VG	VF	EF	Unc
445A-1a	R3	1082	C	PL	4	12	15	30

GEO. D. RIEGEL / DRY GOODS / AND / GROCERIES / LAURELVILLE / * OHIO. *

Lima

R. BOOSE

CWT	Rarity	Reverse Die	Metal	Edge	VG	VF	EF	Unc
450A-2a	R3	1091	C	PL	4	8	15	40

* R. BOOSE * / DEALER / IN / DRY GOODS / LIMA, / OHIO. / * * * * * * * *

NOTE: Comes with broken reverse die.

London

JAS. McLAUGHLIN

CWT	Rarity	Reverse Die	Metal	Edge	VG	VF	EF	Unc
470A-2b	R8	—	BR	PL		—	RARE	—

JAS McLAUGHLIN / DEALERS / IN / CIGARS & / TOBACCO / (ornament) / LONDON, OHIO Rv: 10 / CENTS surrounded by 12 stars.

Loudenville

F. SCHUCH

CWT	Rarity	Reverse Die	Metal	Edge	VG	VF	EF	Unc
485A-1a	R5	1082	C	PL	10	30	40	60

F. SCHUCH, / DEALER / IN / GROCERIES/ LOUDENVILLE / -.- / * OHIO. *

Mansfield

H. ENDLY

CWT	Rarity	Reverse Die	Metal	Edge	VG	VF	EF	Unc
505A-1a	R2	1270	C	PL	4	8	10	20

* H. ENDLY, * / DEALER / IN / HATS / AND / CAPS / MANSFIELD, O.

F. B. ORR

CWT	Rarity	Reverse Die	Metal	Edge	VG	VF	EF	Unc
505B-7a	R3	1269	C	PL	4	12	15	30

F. B. ORR. / DEALER IN / HARDWARE / IRON & NAILS / MANSFIELD. O.

Marion

A. E. GRIFFIN

CWT	Rarity	Reverse Die	Metal	Edge	VG	VF	EF	Unc
520A-1a	R5	1083	C	PL	20	65	90	125

* A. E. GRIFFIN * / DENTIST above. Plate of false teeth in center. MARION, / (ornament) / OHIO.

Martinsburg

A. & W. H. BARNES

CWT	Rarity	Reverse Die	Metal	Edge	VG	VF	EF	Unc
530A-1a	R4	1122	C	PL	10	12	20	60

A. & W. H. BARNES / (ornament) / DRY GOODS, / MARTINSBURG, / OHIO.

M. N. DAYTON

CWT	Rarity	Reverse Die	Metal	Edge	VG	VF	EF	Unc
530B-1a	R6	—	C	PL	10	25	35	70

M. N. DAYTON, above. Mortar and pestle in center. MARTINSBURG / OHIO. below. Rv: DEALERS IN / DRUGS / MEDICINES / & / GROCERIES

Massillon

P. G. ALBRIGHT

CWT	Rarity	Reverse Die	Metal	Edge	VG	VF	EF	Unc
535A-3a	R2	1224	C	PL	4	8	10	20

* P. G. ALBRIGHT, * / WHOLESALE / * / AND / RETAIL / GROCER, / * / MASSILLON, O.

J. E. DANGILER

CWT	Rarity	Reverse Die	Metal	Edge	VG	VF	EF	Unc
535B-2a	R2	1169	C	PL	4	8	10	25

J. B. DANGLER / DEALER / -IN- / DRY GOODS / MASSILLON / * OHIO. * / -.-

G. W. LAUGHLIN

CWT	Rarity	Reverse Die	Metal	Edge	VG	VF	EF	Unc
535Ba-1b	R10	Blank	BR	PL		—	RARE	—

* / G. W. LAUGHLIN / JEWELER / (beaded line) / MASSILLON, O.

FRED LOEFFLER

CWT	Rarity	Reverse Die	Metal	Edge	VG	VF	EF	Unc
535C-2a	R2	1130	C	PL	4	8	10	25

FRED LOEFFLER, / RETAIL / GROCER, / MAIN ST. / MASSILLON / OHIO.

H. KNOBLOCH

CWT	Rarity	Reverse Die	Metal	Edge	VG	VF	EF	Unc
535D-2a	R3	1089	C	PL	4	8	10	25

H. KNOBLOCH / -.- / RETAIL / -.- / GROCER ERIE ST. / (ornament) / MASSILLON, OHIO.

Maumee City

H. BURRITT

CWT	Rarity	Reverse Die	Metal	Edge	VG	VF	EF	Unc
540A-1a	R3	1310	C	PL	10	30	40	75

H. BURRITT / DRUGS, / MEDICINES, / OILS, / DYE STUFFS &C. / MAUMEE CITY, / * OHIO. *

MAUMEE AND PERRYSBURG TOOL BRIDGE CO.

CWT	Rarity	Reverse Die	Metal	Edge	VG	VF	EF	Unc
540B-1a	R6	1128	C	PL	25	70	85	135

MAUMEE / AND / PERRYSBURG / TOLL / BRIDGE, CO.

McConnelsville

H. M. COCHRAN

CWT	Rarity	Reverse Die	Metal	Edge	VG	VF	EF	Unc
550A-1a	R4	1331	C	PL	10	25	35	60

H. M. COCHRAN / TOBACCO / MANUFACTURER / McCONNELSVILLE / OHIO / * * 1863 * *

Middleton

P. L. POTTER

CWT	Rarity	Reverse Die	Metal	Edge	VG	VF	EF	Unc
555A-1a	R5	1019	C	PL	8	20	25	45

P. L. POTTER / DEALER / IN / GROCERIES / -&- / QUEENSWARE / MIDDLETOWN, O.

Monroeville

R. G. MARTIN

CWT	Rarity	Reverse Die	Metal	Edge	VG	VF	EF	Unc
560A-5a	R3	1128	C	PL	5	15	20	40

R. G. MARTIN / HARDWARE / (ornament) / STOVES AND / TIN WARE, MONROEVILLE / OHIO.

A. W. PRENTISS

CWT	Rarity	Reverse Die	Metal	Edge	VG	VF	EF	Unc
560B-2a	R4	1169	C	PL	5	15	20	35

A. W. PRENTISS / DRY GOODS, / * / GROCERIES / * / BOOTS & SHOES / MONROEVILLE, O.

Morristown

P. LOCHARY

CWT	Rarity	Reverse Die	Metal	Edge	VG	VF	EF	Unc
565A-2a	R3	1128	C	PL	5	12	20	40

* P. LOCHARY * / - * - / NEW / STORE / (ornament) / MORRISTOWN, O.

Morrow

J. M. DYNES

CWT	Rarity	Reverse Die	Metal	Edge	VG	VF	EF	Unc
570A-1a	R3	1303	C	PL	15	50	65	90

* J. M. DYNES * / DRY GOODS / AND / GROCERIES / AT / AUCTION / * MORROW, OHIO.

E. LEVY

CWT	Rarity	Reverse Die	Metal	Edge	VG	VF	EF	Unc
570B-2a	R5	1178	C	PL	25	85	115	150

* * E. LEVY * * / DRY GOODS, / (ornament) / CLOTHING, / BOOTS, / (ornament) / SHOES &C. / * MORROW, OHIO. *

Mt. Eaton

D. GIAUGUE

CWT	Rarity	Reverse Die	Metal	Edge	VG	VF	EF	Unc
585A-1a	R4	1086	C	PL	10	35	45	70

D. GIAUGUE / DEALER / IN / GROCERIES / -AND- / PROVISIONS / MT. EATON / * O. *

Mussey

NOTE: E. C. Morse, formerly listed as Mussey, Ohio, is actually Mussey Twp., St. Clair Co., Mich. and is now listed as MICH 680A.

Navarre

HALL & FRYMIRE

CWT	Rarity	Reverse Die	Metal	Edge	VG	VF	EF	Unc
597A-1a	R5	1299	C	PL	5	15	25	40

* HALL & FRYMIRE, * / DEALERS / IN / STOVES / -AND- / TIN WARE, / NAVARRE, / OHIO.

Newcomerstown

A. S. TWIFORD

CWT	Rarity	Reverse Die	Metal	Edge	VG	VF	EF	Unc
610A-1a	R4	1310	C	PL	50	150	175	200

* A. S. TWIFORD * / PHOTOGRAPH / ARTIST / AND / DRUGGIST / NEWCOMER-STOWN / (ornament) OHIO. (ornament)

New Lisbon

A. J. BLOCKSOM

CWT	Rarity	Reverse Die	Metal	Edge	VG	VF	EF	Unc
615A-1e	R9	—	W-M	PL		—	RARE	—

A. J. BLOCKSOM / (ornament) / DRUGGIST / (ornament) / NEW LISBON, O.

New London

H. H. ROBINSON

CWT	Rarity	Reverse Die	Metal	Edge	VG	VF	EF	Unc
620A-7a	R3	1045	C	PL	4	10	12	25

H. H. ROBINSON / DRY / GOODS / GROCERIES, / -&- / PRODUCE / NEW LON-DON, B. Co.

G. M. SHAW

CWT	Rarity	Reverse Die	Metal	Edge	VG	VF	EF	Unc
620B-2a	R7	1176	C	PL	10	40	60	80

CHEAP / (curved line) CASH / (curved line) / (curved line) STORE / (curved line) / G. M. SHAW / NEW LONDON / BUTLER, CO. / * OHIO. * / (ornament).

North Hampton

M. HARTMAN

CWT	Rarity	Reverse Die	Metal	Edge	VG	VF	EF	Unc
645A-1a	R4	1046	C	R	5	15	20	50

M. HARTMAN / DRY / =GOODS= / HARDWARE / BOOTS / & / SHOES / NORTH HAMPTON, O.

G. W. McLEAN

CWT	Rarity	Reverse Die	Metal	Edge	VG	VF	EF	Unc
645B-1a	R7	1037	C	R	10	30	45	85

G. W. McLEAN / (ornament) / PRODUCE / DEALER / NORTH HAMPTON, O.

North Liberty

SAM L. BISHOP

CWT	Rarity	Reverse Die	Metal	Edge	VG	VF	EF	Unc
650A-1a	R4	1122	C	PL	10	25	35	50

SAM I. BISHOP, / DEALER / IN / DRY GOODS, / GROCERIES &C. / NORTH LIB-ERTY / OHIO.

NOTE: Comes with broken reverse die.

Norwalk

P. TIMMENS

CWT	Rarity	Reverse Die	Metal	Edge	VG	VF	EF	Unc
670A-3a	R4	1089	C	PL	15	50	65	85

P. TIMMENS / * / GROCERIES & / -.- / PROVISIONS / NORWALK, O.

Oberlin

R. H. BIRGE

CWT	Rarity	Reverse Die	Metal	Edge	VG	VF	EF	Unc
690A-1a	R6	1310	C	PL	10	30	40	70

* R. H. BIRGE * / DRUGS / GROCERIES &C. / SIGN BIG MORTAR / MAIN ST. / OBERLIN O.

FRANK HENDRY

CWT	Rarity	Reverse Die	Metal	Edge	VG	VF	EF	Unc
690B-1a	R6	1089	C	PL	15	50	75	125

FRANK HENDRY / MAN'FR / OF / SPECTACLES & / EYE GLASSES / OBERLIN CO.

Orrville

J. F. SEAS

CWT	Rarity	Reverse Die	Metal	Edge	VG	VF	EF	Unc
695A-3a	R6	1019	C	PL	5	20	25	50

J. F. SEAS / DEALER / IN / HARDWARE / -BOOKS- / PAINTS, OILS / &C. / OR-VILLE, O.

NOTE: The city name should be spelled ORRVILLE - one R is missing

Oxford

McGAW & RICHEY

CWT	Rarity	Reverse Die	Metal	Edge	VG	VF	EF	Unc
710A-2a	R4	1180	C	PL	5	15	25	45

McGAW & RICHEY / DEALERS / IN / DRUGS / BOOKS / AND / WALL PAPER / OXFORD, O.

NEWTON & KUMLERS

CWT	Rarity	Reverse Die	Metal	Edge	VG	VF	EF	Unc
710B-1a	R5	1058	C	PL	10	25	40	80

NEWTON & KUMLERS, / * / DEALERS / -IN- / DRY / GOODS / * / OXFORD O.

Perrysburg

G. BEACH

CWT	Rarity	Reverse Die	Metal	Edge	VG	VF	EF	Unc
725A-2a	R6	1181	C	PL	10	30	40	60

G. BEACH, / * / DRY GOODS, / CLOTHING, / BOOTS SHOES &C. / PERRYSBURG, / * / * OHIO. *

D. KREPS

CWT	Rarity	Reverse Die	Metal	Edge	VG	VF	EF	Unc
725B-1a	R6	—	C	PL	10	25	35	60

D. KREPS / * / DEALER IN / AGRICULTURAL / IMPLEMENTS / & FARM TOOLS / PERRYSBURG, / * OHIO. *

Piqua

DRS. BROWN & DILLS

CWT	Rarity	Reverse Die	Metal	Edge	VG	VF	EF	Unc
730A-8a	R3	—	C	PL	10	20	30	75

* DRS. BROWN & DILLS * / (ornament) / DENTISTS / -- PIQUA / - * - / OHIO. Rv: BRANCH OFFICE, / false teeth / TROY, / - * - / * OHIO. *

FRENCH & SWONGER

CWT	Rarity	Reverse Die	Metal	Edge	VG	VF	EF	Unc
730B-1a	R4	1287	C	PL	10	25	35	90

FRENCH & SWONGER / DAILY / MEAT / .... / MARKET. / PIQUA, O.

MARTIN HOEGNER

CWT	Rarity	Reverse Die	Metal	Edge	VG	VF	EF	Unc
730C-1a	R6	1287	C	PL	10	40	50	100

MARTIN HOEGNER / DAILY / MEAT / MARKET / PIQUA, O.

MARROW & PARKER

CWT	Rarity	Reverse Die	Metal	Edge	VG	VF	EF	Unc
730D-1a	R8	1223	C	PL		—	SCARCE	—

MARROW & PARKER / DEALERS / IN / DRY GOODS / PIQUA, O.

SMART & CO.

CWT	Rarity	Reverse Die	Metal	Edge	VG	VF	EF	Unc
730E-1a	R4	1122	C	PL	5	15	25	40

SMART & CO. / (ornament) / GROCERS, / 1361 / MAIN ST. / * PIQUA, O. *

Pomeroy

W. A. AICHER

CWT	Rarity	Reverse Die	Metal	Edge	VG	VF	EF	Unc
735A-1bo	R9	—	BR	PL		—	RARE	—

* * / W. A. AICHER / (beaded line) / POMEROY. O. Rv: MURDOCK & SPENCER / 139 / * / 5' ST / CIN' O.

NOTE: Struck over a McClellan political card.

J. P. TOU

CWT	Rarity	Reverse Die	Metal	Edge	VG	VF	EF	Unc
735B-5a	R5	1045	C	PL	5	15	25	40

J. P. TOU / GROCER / 104. / FRONT / ST / POMEROY, O.

Portsmouth

BURTON'S EXCHANGE

CWT	Rarity	Reverse Die	Metal	Edge	VG	VF	EF	Unc
745A-1a	R8	1047	C	R	25	80	100	150

BURTON'S / (ornament) / EXCHANGE / (ornament) / PORTSMOUTH, O.

S. W. CUNNING

CWT	Rarity	Reverse Die	Metal	Edge	VG	VF	EF	Unc
745B-3a	R6	1042	C	R	10	25	40	60

S. W. CUNNING / WHOLESALE / LIQUORS / No. 6 / FRONT, ST. / PORTSMOUTH, O.

Putnam

L. WILES

CWT	Rarity	Reverse Die	Metal	Edge	VG	VF	EF	Unc
755A-1a	R6	1126	C	PL	10	35	50	75

* L. WILES * / (ornament) / DRY GOODS / -&C.- / PUTNAM, O.

Ravenna

BUTLER WITTER & CO.

CWT	Rarity	Reverse Die	Metal	Edge	VG	VF	EF	Unc
765A-1a	R3	—	C	PL	5	10	15	35

BUTLER WITTER & CO. / DEALERS / IN / W. R. BUTTER / AND CHEESE / RAVENNA / OHIO. Rv: BUTLER WITTER & CO. / DEALERS / IN / FAMILY / GROCERIES. / 8 PHOENIX / BLOCK / RAVENNA / OHIO.

DR. D. R. JENNINGS

CWT	Rarity	Reverse Die	Metal	Edge	VG	VF	EF	Unc
765B-4a	R3	1344	C	PL	75	150	175	250

* DR. D. R. JENNINGS * / SURGEON / -- / DENTIST, / RAVENNA / * OHIO. *

C. A. PEASE

CWT	Rarity	Reverse Die	Metal	Edge	VG	VF	EF	Unc
765C-1a	R3	1082	C	PL	5	15	20	35

C. A. PEASE, / DEALER / IN / GROCERIES / FRUITS &C. / 4 PHOENIX BLOCK / RAVENA / OHIO.

MRS. REED

CWT	Rarity	Reverse Die	Metal	Edge	VG	VF	EF	Unc
765D-1a	R4	1273	C	PL	10	25	35	65

MRS. REED / (ornament) / MILLINERY / -AND- / FANCY / GOODS / RAVENA / * * * OHIO * * *

WM. WARD

CWT	Rarity	Reverse Die	Metal	Edge	VG	VF	EF	Unc
765E-1a	R3	—	C	PL	8	15	25	40

BUY / YOUR / DRY GOODS / AND GROCERIES / -OF- / WM. WARD / RAVENNA, / OHIO. / 1863 Rv: * * WM. WARD * * / PAYS / THE / HIGHEST / MARKET / PRICE FOR / BUTTER / AND / * * CHEESE. * *

NOTE: THE V of RAVENNA is overcut on A.

Richmond

B. L. CREW

CWT	Rarity	Reverse Die	Metal	Edge	VG	VF	EF	Unc
770A-1a	R5	1028	C	PL	10	25	40	70

B. L. CREW / DRY / GOODS / & / GROCERIES / RICHMOND, O.

Ripley

DUNBAR & WOLFF

CWT	Rarity	Reverse Die	Metal	Edge	VG	VF	EF	Unc
780A-1bo	R9	—	BR	PL		—	RARE	—

DUNBAR & WOLFF / WATCHMAKERS / \xaf \xaf / (beaded line) / RIPLEY. O. Rv: MURDOCK & SPENCER / 139 / * 5' ST / CIN' O.

Sharonville

W. K. McMILLINS

CWT	Rarity	Reverse Die	Metal	Edge	VG	VF	EF	Unc
800A-1a	R6	1028	C	PL	15	35	50	90

W. K. McMILLINS / (ornament) / STORE / (ornament) / SHARONVILLE, O.

Shelby

CUMMINS & ANDERSON

CWT	Rarity	Reverse Die	Metal	Edge	VG	VF	EF	Unc
805A-1a	R7	1037	C	R	5	20	30	45

CUMMINS & ANDERSON / DRY / GOODS / = = / GROCERIES / -&- / MILLINERY / SHELBY, O.

THOS. MICKEY

CWT	Rarity	Reverse Die	Metal	Edge	VG	VF	EF	Unc
805B-1a	R4	—	C	PL	5	12	15	30

* THOS. MICKEY / SHELBY, / OHIO / DRY GOODS, / GROCERIES, / HATS, CAPS / AND MILLINERY GOODS. Rv: * HIGHEST * / CASH / PRICE / PAID / FOR / COUNTRY PRODUCE.

Sidney

FRY & JOHNSTON

CWT	Rarity	Reverse Die	Metal	Edge	VG	VF	EF	Unc
815A-3a	R4	1122	C	PL	10	30	45	85

FRY & JOHNSTON / -.- / DRY GOODS / BOOTS / & SHOES. / SINDEY, O.

JASON McVAY

CWT	Rarity	Reverse Die	Metal	Edge	VG	VF	EF	Unc
815B-1a	R3	1337	C	PL	10	25	30	60

JASON McVAY / ...... / DRY GOODS / BOOTS / SHOES & C / SIDNEY, O.

S. N. TODD

CWT	Rarity	Reverse Die	Metal	Edge	VG	VF	EF	Unc
815C-1a	R7	1316	C	PL		—	SCARCE	—

S. N. TODD & CO. / DRUGGISTS / (ornament) & (ornament) / STATIONERS / SIDNEY, O.

Sonora

WILLIAM LEAS.

CWT	Rarity	Reverse Die	Metal	Edge	VG	VF	EF	Unc
820A-1a	R5	1091	C	PL	10	35	45	95

WILLIAMS LEAS. / CALL / AT THE / CASH / STORE / SONORA. O.

Springfield

W. G. BRAIN

CWT	Rarity	Reverse Die	Metal	Edge	VG	VF	EF	Unc
830A-9a	R3	1034	C	PL	5	15	20	30

W. G. BRAIN / CASH / DRUGGIST / MARKET / ST. / SPRINGFIELD, O.

KAUFMANN & CO.

CWT	Rarity	Reverse Die	Metal	Edge	VG	VF	EF	Unc
830B-1a	R4	1028	C	PL	5	10	15	25

KAUFMANN & CO / CIGARS / -&- / LIQUORS / MARKET / ST / SPRINGFIELD, O.

J. W. LOW

CWT	Rarity	Reverse Die	Metal	Edge	VG	VF	EF	Unc
830C-7a	R3	1046	C	R	5	10	12	25

J. W. LOW / BOOKS / -&- / WALL . PAPER / MARKET / ST. / SPRINGFIELD, O.

LUDLOW & BUSHNELL

CWT	Rarity	Reverse Die	Metal	Edge	VG	VF	EF	Unc
830D-4a	R5	1036	C	PL	5	15	20	40

LUDLOW & BUSHNELL / DRUGGISTS / 85 / MAIN, ST. / SPRINGFIELD, O.

G. W. McLEAN

CWT	Rarity	Reverse Die	Metal	Edge	VG	VF	EF	Unc
830E-1a	R5	1042	C	R	5	15	20	40

G. W. McLEAN / PRODUCE / -.- / DEALER / SPRINGFIELD, O.

MURPHY & BRO.

CWT	Rarity	Reverse Die	Metal	Edge	VG	VF	EF	Unc
830F-3a	R6	1042	C	R	5	15	25	45

MURPHY & BRO. / DRY / GOODS / MARKET / ST / SPRINGFIELD, O.

C. RUNYON

CWT	Rarity	Reverse Die	Metal	Edge	VG	VF	EF	Unc
830G-1a	R7	1037	C	R	5	20	25	60

C. RUNYON / GROCERIES / - * - / MARKET / ST. / SPINGFIELD, O.

NOTE: SPRINGFIELD is spelled SPINGFIELD on this die.

Steubinville

WM. DUNLAP

CWT	Rarity	Reverse Die	Metal	Edge	VG	VF	EF	Unc
835A-2a	R3	1166	C	PL	5	12	15	30

WM. DUNLAP / - * - / DRY GOODS / & GROCERIES / FOURTH ST. / STEUBENVILLE, * OHIO. *

J. H. BRISTOR

CWT	Rarity	Reverse Die	Metal	Edge	VG	VF	EF	Unc
835B-2a	R3	1326	C	PL	5	10	15	30

J. H. BRISTOR / -.- / COR. / FOURTH / AND / MARKET / - * - / STEUBENVILLE, O.

J. W. GRAY

CWT	Rarity	Reverse Die	Metal	Edge	VG	VF	EF	Unc
835C-4a	R2	1181	C	PL	5	10	12	20

J. W. GRAY / GROCERIES / AND / DRY GOODS / COR. ADAMS / & / SIXTH / STEUBENVILLE, O.

J. H. HIND'S NEWS DEPOT

CWT	Rarity	Reverse Die	Metal	Edge	VG	VF	EF	Unc
835D-1a	R5	1166	C	PL	5	12	20	35

J. H. HIND'S, / NEWS / DEPOT / COR 4TH. & MARKET / STEUBENVILLE / * * OHIO. * *

C. M. MAY

CWT	Rarity	Reverse Die	Metal	Edge	VG	VF	EF	Unc
835E-2a	R2	1342	C	PL	5	10	12	30

C. M. MAY / -- / MERCHANT / TAILOR / AND / * CLOTHIER * / STEUBENVILLE / * * OHIO. * *

J. McCAULEY

CWT	Rarity	Reverse Die	Metal	Edge	VG	VF	EF	Unc
835F-1a	R4	1227	C	PL	5	10	12	30

* J. McCAULEY * / - * - / GROCER / FOURTH ST. / STEUBENVILLE / * OHIO. *

D. McCONVILLE

CWT	Rarity	Reverse Die	Metal	Edge	VG	VF	EF	Unc
835G-2a	R4	1178	C	PL	5	10	15	25

* D.McCONVILLE * / DRY GOODS / AND / NOTIONS / - * - / STEUBENVILLE / * OHIO. *

Stryker

JOHN S. KINGSLAND

CWT	Rarity	Reverse Die	Metal	Edge	VG	VF	EF	Unc
840A-1a	R5	1094	C	PL	10	40	50	95

JOHN S. KINGSLAND / & BRO. / (mortar and pestle) / DRUGGISTS. / STRYKER / OHIO.

G. W. HAMBLIN

CWT	Rarity	Reverse Die	Metal	Edge	VG	VF	EF	Unc
840B-2a	R6	1107	C	PL	10	35	50	135

G. W. HAMBLIN / GENERAL / * * * / GOODS / * * * / DEALER / STRYKER, OHIO.

Syracuse

H. BARTELS DRY GOODS

CWT	Rarity	Reverse Die	Metal	Edge	VG	VF	EF	Unc
845A-1a	R5	1046	C	R	10	25	40	70

H. BARTELS / DRY / =GOODS= / GROCERIES / BOOTS / & / SHOES / SYRACUSE, O.

Tiffin

M J. KIRCHNER

CWT	Rarity	Reverse Die	Metal	Edge	VG	VF	EF	Unc
850A-1a	R7	1037	C	R	10	25	35	50

M. J. KIRCHNER / GROCERIES / -- / WASHINGTON / ST. / TIFFIN, O.

SONDER & CARPENTERS CARD

CWT	Rarity	Reverse Die	Metal	Edge	VG	VF	EF	Unc
850B-1b	R3	—	BR	PL	5	10	12	25

SONDER / & / CARPENTERS / CARD within a wreath. Rv: (ornament) WHOLESALE (ornament) / (ornament) / RETAIL / -.- / DRY GOODS / TIFFIN OHIO.

SOUDER & CARPENTER'S

CWT	Rarity	Reverse Die	Metal	Edge	VG	VF	EF	Unc
850C-1b	R3	—	BR	PL	5	10	12	25

SOUDER / + & + / CARPENTER'S / CARD within a wreath. Rv: * DRY GOODS * / ... +++ ... / DEALERS, / *** / TIFFIN, / (scrolled ornament) / OHIO

NOTE: Either 850B or 850C is an error, but the correct spelling is not known.

Tippecanoe

E. C. SAYLOR

CWT	Rarity	Reverse Die	Metal	Edge	VG	VF	EF	Unc
855A-1a	R5	1228	C	PL	10	25	30	75

* E. C. SAYLOR * / DAILY / MEAT / MARKET / - * - / TIPPECANOE, O.

Toledo

C. P. CURTIS

CWT	Rarity	Reverse Die	Metal	Edge	VG	VF	EF	Unc
860A-1a	R3	1085	C	PL	4	8	10	25

C. P. CURTIS / - * - / AUCTION / & COMMISSION / MERCHANT, / 157 SUMMIT ST. / TOLEDO / * OHIO. *

HOUGH & HALL

CWT	Rarity	Reverse Die	Metal	Edge	VG	VF	EF	Unc
860B-1a	R4	1168	C	PL	4	10	12	25

HOUGH & HALL / DRY GOODS / - * - / CARPETS / OIL CLOTHS &C / 23 SUMMIT ST. / TOLEDO, / OHIO.

KETCHAM & BARKER

CWT	Rarity	Reverse Die	Metal	Edge	VG	VF	EF	Unc
860C-1a	R3	1305	C	PL	4	10	12	25

* KETCHAM & BARKER * / (ornament) / DEALERS / -IN- / HARDWARE / STOVES & / TIN WARE / (ornament) / TOLEDO, OHIO.

PLESSNER & SON

CWT	Rarity	Reverse Die	Metal	Edge	VG	VF	EF	Unc
860D-1b	R3	1310	BR	PL	5	20	25	45

PLESSNER & SON / (mortar and pestle) / DRUGGISTS, / 23 / SUMMIT ST./ TOLEDO, OHIO.

Troy

J. HALL

CWT	Rarity	Reverse Die	Metal	Edge	VG	VF	EF	Unc
880A-1a	R3	—	C	PL	10	30	40	80

** J. HALL * * / -- / GRAIN / DEALER / -- / ** TROY, O. * * Rv: RAILROAD / (ornament) / -1863- / (ornament) / WAREHOUSE.

S. K. HARTER

CWT	Rarity	Reverse Die	Metal	Edge	VG	VF	EF	Unc
880B-1a	R7	1332	C	PL	20	65	80	175

* S. K. HARTER * / DEALER / IN / IRON NAILS / HARDWARE / GUNS & PISTOLS / * / TROY, O.

S. E. HUSTLER

CWT	Rarity	Reverse Die	Metal	Edge	VG	VF	EF	Unc
880C-4a	R3	1223	C	PL	5	10	12	30

* * S. E. HUSTLER * * / BROWN'S / OLD / CORNER / -- / * TROY, O. *

JULIAN & CO.

CWT	Rarity	Reverse Die	Metal	Edge	VG	VF	EF	Unc
880D-2a	R3	1320	C	PL	5	15	20	40

JULIAN & CO / (ornament) / WATCHMAKERS / & / JEWELERS / TROY, O.

DAVID KELLY

CWT	Rarity	Reverse Die	Metal	Edge	VG	VF	EF	Unc
880E-5a	R3	1180	C	PL	5	10	12	30

DAVID KELLY / DEALER / IN / -BOOKS,- / STATIONERY / &C. / * TROY, O. *

PEARSON & BRO.

CWT	Rarity	Reverse Die	Metal	Edge	VG	VF	EF	Unc
880F-6a	R3	1228	C	PL	4	8	10	25

PEARSON & BRO. / WHOLESALE / & / RETAIL / GROCERS / TROY, O.

RINEHART & GRAY

CWT	Rarity	Reverse Die	Metal	Edge	VG	VF	EF	Unc
880G-1a	R4	1126	C	PL	10	25	35	65

* RINEHART & GRAY * / CASH / DRUGGISTS / - * - / SUCCESSORS / TO / R. WRIGHT / * TROY, O. *

Uniontown

FAULEY & BRECHBILL

CWT	Rarity	Reverse Die	Metal	Edge	VG	VF	EF	Unc
890A-1a	R5	1091	C	PL	10	35	45	90

FAULEY & BRECHBILL / DRY GOODS / CLOTHING / & / GROCERIES / UNIONTOWN O.

Urbana

C McCARTY

CWT	Rarity	Reverse Die	Metal	Edge	VG	VF	EF	Unc
895A-1a	R8	1047	C	R		—	RARE	—

WASHINGTON / + / HOUSE / C. McCARTY / URBANA / O

WALKER'S ALE DEPOT

CWT	Rarity	Reverse Die	Metal	Edge	VG	VF	EF	Unc
895B-1a	R9	1018	C	R		—	RARE	—

WALKER'S / ALE / DEPOT / URBANA, O.

Van Wert

A. JACOBS

CWT	Rarity	Reverse Die	Metal	Edge	VG	VF	EF	Unc
900A-1a	R7	1342	C	PL	30	90	125	175

A. JACOBS / MERCHANT TAILOR / & / READY MADE / CLOTHING, / VAN WERT, / OHIO.

Wappakoneta

DAVIS & WHITEMAN

CWT	Rarity	Reverse Die	Metal	Edge	VG	VF	EF	Unc
905A-4a	R4	1336	C	PL	5	20	30	70

DAVIS & WHITEMAN / GROCERS / & / COMMISSION / MERCHANTS. / WAPPAKONETA, O.

A. C. MILES

CWT	Rarity	Reverse Die	Metal	Edge	VG	VF	EF	Unc
905B-1a	R4	1325	C	PL	5	25	30	50

A. C. MILES, / GROCERIES / & STATIONERY. / -.- / WAPPAKONETA, O.

SANITARY FAIR

CWT	Rarity	Reverse Die	Metal	Edge	VG	VF	EF	Unc
905C-1b	R7	—	BR	PL		—	SCARCE	—

MEMENTO / OF THE / SANITARY / FAIR / -OF- / WAPAKONETA, O. Rv: Trophy of flags & arms with eagle perched on drum.

NOTE: There is only one P in WAPPAKONETA on this piece.

J. M. TIMMERMEISTER

CWT	Rarity	Reverse Die	Metal	Edge	VG	VF	EF	Unc
905D-1a	R3	1181	C	PL	5	20	30	60

J. M. TIMMERMEISTER / DRY GOODS / -&- / GROCERIES / WAPPAKONETA, O.

Warren

ROBBINS' CARD

CWT	Rarity	Reverse Die	Metal	Edge	VG	VF	EF	Unc
910A-1a	R3	—	C	PL	5	15	20	35

ROBBINS' / CARD within a wreath. Rv: +PHOTOGRAPHIC+ / ALBUMS / (ornament) / 15 / MARKET ST. / * WARREN OHIO *

Wellsville

HOOVER & CAMP

CWT	Rarity	Reverse Die	Metal	Edge	VG	VF	EF	Unc
915A-2a	R4	1322	C	PL	15	60	75	90

HOOVER & CAMP / PIANOS / MELODIANS AND / MUSICAL / MDS. / -- / WELLSVILLE, O.

WM. LAWRENCE

CWT	Rarity	Reverse Die	Metal	Edge	VG	VF	EF	Unc
915B-1a	R3	1178	C	PL	15	35	50	80

WM. LAWRENCE / CLOTHIER / AND / PHOTOGRAPHIC / ARTIST, / WELLSVILLE, O.

West Jefferson

JOHN TRESSLER

CWT	Rarity	Reverse Die	Metal	Edge	VG	VF	EF	Unc
920A-1a	R3	1336	C	PL	5	10	20	40

WEST JEFFERSON Wms. CO. OHIO / JOHN TRESLER / GROCERY / STORE / - * - / * 1863 *

West Newton

C. M. COFFIN

CWT	Rarity	Reverse Die	Metal	Edge	VG	VF	EF	Unc
925A-1a	R6	1037	C	R	5	15	25	55

C. M. COFFIN / * DEALER * / IN / DRY / GOODS / &C. / WEST NEWTON, OHIO.

West Unity

DAVIES & MAXWELL

CWT	Rarity	Reverse Die	Metal	Edge	VG	VF	EF	Unc
930A-1a	R4	1126	C	PL	5	12	15	30

DAVIES & MAXWELL / DEALERS / IN / HARDWARE / -AND- / AGRICULTURAL / MACHINERY / WEST UNITY / OHIO.

W. H. McGREW

CWT	Rarity	Reverse Die	Metal	Edge	VG	VF	EF	Unc
930B-2a	R4	1127	C	PL	5	20	25	45

W. H. McGREW / DRUGGIST / (mortar and pestle) / WEST UNITY, * OHIO. *

S. PIERCE & SON

CWT	Rarity	Reverse Die	Metal	Edge	VG	VF	EF	Unc
930C-2a	R5	1224	C	PL	5	12	15	35

S. PIERCE & SON / DEALERS / IN / DRY GOODS / GROCERIES / &C. WEST UNITY, O.

S. F. SNOW

CWT	Rarity	Reverse Die	Metal	Edge	VG	VF	EF	Unc
930D-3a	R6	1130	C	PL	15	40	50	90

S. F. SNOW / DENTIST / false teeth / WEST UNITY, / * * OHIO. * *

Wilmington

MRS. OWENS & TAYLOR

CWT	Rarity	Reverse Die	Metal	Edge	VG	VF	EF	Unc
935A-4a	R8	1242	C	PL		—	SCARCE	—

MRS. OWENS & TAYLOR / -.- / MILINERY / -AND- / FANCY STORE / SOUTH ST. / NEAR / DEPOT / WILMINGTON, O.

H. PERRIN

CWT	Rarity	Reverse Die	Metal	Edge	VG	VF	EF	Unc
935B-1a	R3	1178	C	PL	8	20	25	40

H. PERRIN / - / HARDWARE, / - / GROCERIES / -&C.- / WILMINGTON. O.

WM. PRESTON

CWT	Rarity	Reverse Die	Metal	Edge	VG	VF	EF	Unc
935C-1a	R4	1347	C	PL	15	40	50	80

CHEAP / (curved line) / CASH / (curved line) / STORE / (curved line) / Wm. PRESTON / WILMINGTON / * * * / * * OHIO * *

T. R. WRAITH

CWT	Rarity	Reverse Die	Metal	Edge	VG	VF	EF	Unc
935D-1a	R5	—	C	PL	5	20	25	45

T. R. WRAITH / (ornament) / HARDWARE / MERCHANT / (ornament) / WHILMINGTON. O. Rv: * * SUGAR * * / -- / MILLS / . / AND / -- / EVAPORATORS.

Woodsfield

J. W. WALTON

CWT	Rarity	Reverse Die	Metal	Edge	VG	VF	EF	Unc
960A-1a	R3	—	C	PL	5	12	15	35

* * J. W. WALTON * * / (ornament) / - * - / GROCER / WOODSFIELD / - * - / * OHIO. * Rv: J. W. WALTON / (ornament) / PENSION / (ornament) / AGENT.

Wooster

P. E. BEACH

CWT	Rarity	Reverse Die	Metal	Edge	VG	VF	EF	Unc
975A-1a	R4	—	C	PL	5	12	15	30

P. E. BEACH above. Silk hat in center. WOOSTER . OHIO below. Rv: * DEALER IN * / HAT, / CAPS / & / FANCY GOODS.

J. R. BOWMAN

CWT	Rarity	Reverse Die	Metal	Edge	VG	VF	EF	Unc
975B-3a	R6	1036	C	PL	5	12	15	30

J. R. BOWMAN / DEALER / IN / WATCHES- / -CLOCKS / & / JEWELRY / WEST LIBERTY ST. / WOOSTER, O.

G. BRUMTER

CWT	Rarity	Reverse Die	Metal	Edge	VG	VF	EF	Unc
975C-3a	R5	1178	C	PL	5	15	20	40

G. BRUMTER / DEALER / IN / GROCERIES / W. LIBERTY ST / WOOSTER, / - OHIO.- / -.-

JAMES B. CHILDS

CWT	Rarity	Reverse Die	Metal	Edge	VG	VF	EF	Unc
975D-1a	R3	1406	C	PL	5	8	10	25

+ JAMES B. CHILDS = . / CLOTHING / HATS, CAPS / & TRUNKS / .WOOSTER OHIO.

J. S. DUDEN

CWT	Rarity	Reverse Die	Metal	Edge	VG	VF	EF	Unc
975E-1a	R3	1126	C	PL	5	20	25	45

J. S. DUDEN / DEALER / IN / GROCERIES / -AND- / PROVISIONS / WOOSTER / OHIO.

SAMUEL GEITGEY

CWT	Rarity	Reverse Die	Metal	Edge	VG	VF	EF	Unc
975F-3a	R4	1303	C	PL	5	12	15	30

* SAMUEL GEITGEY * / DEALER / IN / STOVES AND / TIN WARE / -OF- / - / ALL KINDS / * WOOSTER, O. *

JOHN LEIS

CWT	Rarity	Reverse Die	Metal	Edge	VG	VF	EF	Unc
975G-1b	R7	1343	BR	PL		—	SCARCE	—

JOHN LEIS, / 5 / WOOSTER, O.

S. C. MARTIN

CWT	Rarity	Reverse Die	Metal	Edge	VG	VF	EF	Unc
975H-3b	R8	—	BR	PL		—	SCARCE	—

S. C. MARTIN / .-.-. / WOOSTER, / .-.-. / OHIO. Rv: * * * GOOD FOR * * * / 5 (cents symbol) / IN TRADE

NOTE: Probably struck well after 1890 and perhaps as late as 1910.

MILLER & CO.

CWT	Rarity	Reverse Die	Metal	Edge	VG	VF	EF	Unc
975I-1a	R3	—	C	PL	5	10	12	30

MILLER & CO. / QUEENSWARE / AND / GLASSWARE / NEAR / POST OFFICE / WOOSTER, O. Rv: DEALERS / In (curved line) HOOP (curved line) / (curved line) SKIRTS (curved line) / HATS CAPS / AND / (ornament) / * NOTIONS *

NOLD & CO.

CWT	Rarity	Reverse Die	Metal	Edge	VG	VF	EF	Unc
975J-1a	R5	1-94	C	PL	5	15	20	40

* * * * NOLD & CO. * * * * / DEALERS / IN / PORK / -AND- / BEEF / WOOSTER / OHIO.

JAMES PATRICK

CWT	Rarity	Reverse Die	Metal	Edge	VG	VF	EF	Unc
975K-1a	R2	1123	C	PL	5	10	12	30

JAMES PATRICK / - * - / BUTTER / PACKER / (ornament) / WOOSTER, OHIO.

C. ROTH

CWT	Rarity	Reverse Die	Metal	Edge	VG	VF	EF	Unc
975L-1a	R3	1317	C	PL	5	20	25	35

C. ROTH / -.- / MANUF'R. / AND DEALER / IN BOOTS / AND SHOES / WOOSTER, / OHIO.

ROWE & BROS.

CWT	Rarity	Reverse Die	Metal	Edge	VG	VF	EF	Unc
975M-2a	R2	1320	C	PL	5	15	20	30

ROWE & BRO. / WATCHES, / (ornament) / CLOCKS AND / JEWELRY, / S.E. COR. PUB. / * / SQUARE / WOOSTER, O.

Xenia

F. J. HALLS

CWT	Rarity	Reverse Die	Metal	Edge	VG	VF	EF	Unc
985A-1a	R7	1085	C	PL	30	100	135	190

F. J. HALLS, / WHOLESALE / & / RETAIL / GROCERY & / CONFECTIONARY / STORE, / XENIA, O.

Youngstown

W. & A. J. PACKARD

CWT	Rarity	Reverse Die	Metal	Edge	VG	VF	EF	Unc
990A-1a	R2	—	C	PL	4	8	10	15

W. & A. J. PACKARD above. U.S. shield in center. YOUNGSTOWN, OHIO. below. Rv: WARREN PACKARD / HARDWARE / AND / IRON / WARREN, OHIO.

Zanesville

BARRELL'S WORM CONFECTIONS

CWT	Rarity	Reverse Die	Metal	Edge	VG	VF	EF	Unc
995A-1a	R2	—	C	PL	5	8	12	30

BARRELL'S / - * - / WORM / CONFECTIONS / H. G. O. CARY / ZANESVILLE / OHIO. Rv: CARY'S / CCC / COUGH / CURE with four stars at each side.

H. G. O. CARY

CWT	Rarity	Reverse Die	Metal	Edge	VG	VF	EF	Unc
995B-2a	R1	—	C	PL	5	8	12	30

ADDRESS / (ornament) / H. G. O. CARY / DRUGGIST / AND / -- / CHEMIST / ZANESVILLE, O.

JOSEPH CROSBY

CWT	Rarity	Reverse Die	Metal	Edge	VG	VF	EF	Unc
995C-1a	R4	1125	C	PL	5	10	12	30

JOSEPH CROSBY / GROCER / AND / TEA DEALER / 83 / MAIN ST. / ZANESVILLE. O.

EVERICH & BARTON

CWT	Rarity	Reverse Die	Metal	Edge	VG	VF	EF	Unc
995D-1a	R4	1273	C	PL	5	12	15	40

EVERICH & BARTON / GROCERS / AND / LIQUOR / DEALERS / ZANESVILLE / -.- / * OHIO. *

ALEX R. GRANT & CO.

CWT	Rarity	Reverse Die	Metal	Edge	VG	VF	EF	Unc
995E-1a	R3	1125	C	PL	5	12	20	30

ALEX R. GRANT & CO. / DRY GOODS / (ornament) / ZANESVILLE / -.- / * OHIO. *

G. W. GRIFFEE

CWT	Rarity	Reverse Die	Metal	Edge	VG	VF	EF	Unc
995F-2a	R3	1322	C	PL	5	10	12	30

G. W. GRIFFEE, / NEWS / DEALER / STATIONER / &C. ZANESVILLE, O.

W. B. HARRIS & BRO.

CWT	Rarity	Reverse Die	Metal	Edge	VG	VF	EF	Unc
995G-2a	R4	1083	C	PL	5	12	15	30

W. B. HARRIS & BRO. / DRY GOODS / - * - / GROCERIES / HARDWARE / -&C.- / ZANESVILLE, O.

HERENDEEN & WITTER

CWT	Rarity	Reverse Die	Metal	Edge	VG	VF	EF	Unc
995H-1a	R3	1342	C	PL	5	12	15	35

* HERENDEEN & WITTER * / SINGERS / SEWING / MACHINES / (ornament) / ZANESVILLE / * OHIO. *

JOHN IRWIN

CWT	Rarity	Reverse Die	Metal	Edge	VG	VF	EF	Unc
995I-1a	R6	1082	C	PL	5	15	25	45

JOHN IRWIN / WHOLESALE / -.- / DEALER IN / WINES & LIQUORS / COR. MAIN & SIXTH / ZANESVILLE / * . OHIO * / —

C. W. POTWIN & CO.

CWT	Rarity	Reverse Die	Metal	Edge	VG	VF	EF	Unc
995J-1a	R3	—	C	PL	5	15	20	35

C. W. POTWIN & CO. above. Padlock in center. ZANESVILLE, O. below. Rv: AGRICULTURAL IMPLEMENTS / SADLERY / AND / CARRIAGE / - * - / TRIMMINGS / * * *

WEBSTER, DUMM & CO.

CWT	Rarity	Reverse Die	Metal	Edge	VG	VF	EF	Unc
995K-1a	R4	1178	C	PL	5	12	20	35

WEBSTER, DUMM & CO. / -+- / TOBACCONISTS / (ornament) / ZANESVILLE, O.

PENNSYLVANIA

Allegheny City

WM. CARSON

CWT	Rarity	Reverse Die	Metal	Edge	VG	VF	EF	Unc
13A-1a	R6	1023	C	PL	5	15	20	50

Wm. CARSON / LEATHER / MERCHANT / 46 / OHIO / ST. ALLEGHENY CITY

CITY TEA HOUSE

CWT	Rarity	Reverse Die	Metal	Edge	VG	VF	EF	Unc
13B-1a	R8	1042	C	PL		—	SCARCE	—

CITY / TEA / HOUSE / NO. 20 / DIAMOND / ALLEGHENY, PA.

GREGG & DALZELL

CWT	Rarity	Reverse Die	Metal	Edge	VG	VF	EF	Unc
13C-1A	R5	1028	C	PL	5	15	20	30

GREGG & DALZELL / NATIONAL / PLANNING / MILL / ALLEGHENY CITY

HAHN & RIDDLE

CWT	Rarity	Reverse Die	Metal	Edge	VG	VF	EF	Unc
13D-1a	R8	1042	C	R	5	12	20	30

HAHN & RIDDLE / GROCERS/ DIAMOND / ALLEGHENY, PA.

R. & W. JENKINSON

CWT	Rarity	Reverse Die	Metal	Edge	VG	VF	EF	Unc
13E-4a	R3	1331	C	PL	5	8	10	20

R. & W. JENKINSON, / * / TOBACCO / - / DEALERS / + / ALLEGHANY PA.

NOTE: Spelling error in ALLEGHENY.

JOHN SHERER

CWT	Rarity	Reverse Die	Metal	Edge	VG	VF	EF	Unc
13F-4a	R4	1180	C	PL	5	8	12	25

JOHN SHERER/ TOBACCO / (ornament) / DEALER / * 75 * / -- / FEDERAL ST. / ALLEGHANY CITY.

NOTE: Spelling error in ALLEGHENY.

Bakerstown

JAMES MAINES

CWT	Rarity	Reverse Die	Metal	Edge	VG	VF	EF	Unc
60A-1a	R5	1125	C	PL	8	15	20	45

JAMES MAINES / GALLERY / -x- / MAIN ST. / - * - / - / BAKERSTOWN. PA.

Erie

W. BELL'S EXCHANGE

CWT	Rarity	Reverse Die	Metal	Edge	VG	VF	EF	Unc
360A-1do	R6	—	C-N	PL	30	80	100	200

FOR / BARGAINS / IN / DRY GOODS / GO TO / W. BELL'S / EXCHANGE / ERIE PA

Rv: Reverse of this card is the obverse of U.S. cent of 1859.

NOTE: The reverse of a regular cent was turned down on a lathe and the legend counterstamped.

Honesdale

PETERSEN'S JEWELERS

CWT	Rarity	Reverse Die	Metal	Edge	VG	VF	EF	Unc
464A-1a	R4	1006	C	PL	4	8	10	25

PETERSEN'S / (curve line) / HONESDALE. / SCRANTON. (line) / & PITTSTON. / - PA- / JEWELLERS.

NOTE: Spelling error in JEWELERS.

Lancaster

S. H. ZAHM

CWT	Rarity	Reverse Die	Metal	Edge	VG	VF	EF	Unc
525A-1a	R5	1148	C	PL	20	50	65	90

S. H. ZAHM / DEALER / -IN- / COINS, TOKENS / MEDALS &C / LANCASTER, PA.

Lawrenceville

WM. SMITH

CWT	Rarity	Reverse Die	Metal	Edge	VG	VF	EF	Unc
535A-2a	R4	1180	C	PL	8	20	25	50

Wm. SMITH / (ornament) / GROCER / (ornament) / LAWRENCEVILLE / .- * PA. * -

Meadville

G. C. PORTER & CO.

CWT	Rarity	Reverse Die	Metal	Edge	VG	VF	EF	Unc
615A-1a	R2	—	C	PL	4	6	8	20

* GO TO G. C. PORTER & CO., * above. Indian head to left in center. FOR YOUR DRY GOODS. below. Rv: G. C. PORTER & CO. / CLOTHING & / GENTS FURNISHING / GOODS / MEADVILLE, Pa.

Mount Washington

J. McKAIN

CWT	Rarity	Reverse Die	Metal	Edge	VG	VF	EF	Unc
650A-1a	R2	1389	C	PL	4	6	8	25

J. McKAIN / GROCER / MOUNT / WASHINGTON.

NOTE: Formerly listed under Pittsburgh.

Philadelphia

ADAMS

CWT	Rarity	Reverse Die	Metal	Edge	VG	VF	EF	Unc
750A-1b	R2	—	BR	PL	4	6	8	20

Small helmeted head with ADAMS below within a laurel wreath. Rv: TON HALL / 457 / - * - / NORTH 3'. ST. / PHILA.

M. B. ALLEBACH

CWT	Rarity	Reverse Die	Metal	Edge	VG	VF	EF	Unc
750B-ld	R6	1093	C-N	PL	8	20	30	55

M. B. ALLEBACH (line) / WATCH / MAKER / & JEWELER. / (line) / 126 / N. 2nd St. / PHILADELPHIA.

AMON

CWT	Rarity	Reverse Die	Metal	Edge	VG	VF	EF	Unc
750C-1a	R3	—	C	PL	5	12	15	30

AMON above. Sheaf of wheat in center. 1863 below. Three stars on each side of sheaf of wheat. Rv: * BAKERY * / 1011 / BEACH ST. / PHILA.

BALTZ & STILZ

CWT	Rarity	Reverse Die	Metal	Edge	VG	VF	EF	Unc
750D-1a	R3	1381	C	PL	4	6	8	15

. * . / BALTZ & STILZ. . * . / IMPORTERS of ABOVE. Bunch of grapes in center. WINES / PHILADA. PA. below.

M. F. BEIRN

CWT	Rarity	Reverse Die	Metal	Edge	VG	VF	EF	Unc
750E-1a	R2	1093	C	PL	4	6	8	15

M. F. BEIRN / MAGNOLIA / HOTEL. / 100 So. 8th St / AND / 416 LIBRARY St. / PHILADELPHIA.

M. C. CAMPBELL'S DANCING ACADEMY

CWT	Rarity	Reverse Die	Metal	Edge	VG	VF	EF	Unc
750F-1a	R4	—	C	PL	5	12	15	30

* M. C. CAMPBELL'S DANCING ACADEMY around edge. COR. 8 AND / SP. GARDEN / ST. PHILA. in center. Rv: SKATING / ACADEMY / (ornament) / WASHINGTON / HALL.

CENTRAL NATIONAL

CWT	Rarity	Reverse Die	Metal	Edge	VG	VF	EF	Unc
750G-1a	R6	—	C	PL	5	12	15	30

* CENTRAL NATIONAL * / * / HOME / FOR / D. V. S. Rv: * GOOD FOR * / 5 / CENTS / - / AT STORE.

CHESTNUT & WALNUT PASSENGER R.R. CO.

CWT	Rarity	Reverse Die	Metal	Edge	VG	VF	EF	Unc
750H-1a	R9	1148	C	PL		—	RARE	—

CHESTNUT & WALNUT / ONE / FARE / PASSENGER R. R. CO.

COOMBS

CWT	Rarity	Reverse Die	Metal	Edge	VG	VF	EF	Unc
750I-1a	R3	—	C	PL	5	10	15	35

(ornament) / COOMBS / 1863 within a wreath. Rv: * SECOND ST. EXCHANGE * / 432 / (ornament) / N. SECOND / ... / ST. / PHILA.

R. FLANAGAN's PUNCH

CWT	Rarity	Reverse Die	Metal	Edge	VG	VF	EF	Unc
750J-1a1	R2	—	C	PL	5	10	12	20

* R. FLANAGAN's * / PUNCH above. Goblet in cent 112 to left of goblet stem, 156 to right of goblet stem. NORTH 6th St. below. Rv: PURE COPPER / PREFERABLE / TO / PAPER. / (ornament) / PHILADA.

NOTE: This piece is listed in the 1858 Numis. Soc. of Phila. list, and thus must be pre-Civil War. It is left in merely for historical reasons.

FOX'S CASINO

CWT	Rarity	Reverse Die	Metal	Edge	VG	VF	EF	Unc
750JA-1a	R5	—	C	PL	5	12	15	35

(3 curved lines) / FOX's / (2 curved lines) / (ornament) * (ornament) / (curved lines) CASINO / (curved lines) Rv: -.- / CHESTNUT St. / (ornament) / - * 620 * - / (ornament) / PHILA. / (ornament)

J. HENRY GERCKE

CWT	Rarity	Reverse Die	Metal	Edge	VG	VF	EF	Unc
750K-1a	R6	1133	C	PL	5	20	30	55

J. HENRY GERCKE / WATCHMAKER / AND / JEWELER / 1206 PINE St. PHILA.

NOTE: The same obverse comes with a Masonic temple reverse, but the temple was not built until 1873.

GREAT CENTRAL FAIR

CWT	Rarity	Reverse Die	Metal	Edge	VG	VF	EF	Unc
750L-1a	R1	1135	C	R	4	6	8	15

GREAT / CENTRAL / FAIR / PHILADELPHIA / JUNE 1864

NOTE: There are at least 28 different die combinations and metal varieties of these tokens, most of which cannot be distinguished by the naked eye. See detailed list by M. and G. Fuld, The Numismatist, Sept., 1952 page 887.

NORTH MILITARY HALL

CWT	Rarity	Reverse Die	Metal	Edge	VG	VF	EF	Unc
750M-1a	R2	1377	C	PL	4	6	8	15

* NORTH MILITARY HALL * above. Lyre in center. F. & L. LADNER / 532 N. 3. St. below.

A. LAMBERT

CWT	Rarity	Reverse Die	Metal	Edge	VG	VF	EF	Unc
750N-1a	R4	1092	C	PL	5	10	15	35

A. LAMBERT / COR. 4TH / AND / LIBRARY ST. / PHILADA.

H. MULLIGAN

CWT	Rarity	Reverse Die	Metal	Edge	VG	VF	EF	Unc
750O-1b	R5	—	BR	PL	8	35	50	70

* H. MULLIGAN * above. Watch and chain in center. 444 N. 2nd St. PHILa. below. Rv: IMPORTER / OF / WATCHES / MANUFACTURER OF / JEWELRY / AGENT / FOR / EASTERN JEWELRY.

F. P. ROGERS

CWT	Rarity	Reverse Die	Metal	Edge	VG	VF	EF	Unc
750P-1a	R6	—	C	PL	8	15	20	35

F. P. ROGERS . 937 Sth. 10th. St. PHILADaPa around outer edge. Milk can in center dividing date 1863. Rv: MANUFACTURER / OF / MILK CANS / DAIRY / FIXTURES / ROOFING & GUTTER TIN.

G. J. RUELIUS

CWT	Rarity	Reverse Die	Metal	Edge	VG	VF	EF	Unc
750Q-1a	R3	—	C	PL	4	6	8	15

G. J. RUELING / (ornament) / 319 / - * - / NORTH 4. St. / PHILA. CITY HOTEL above. Building with staff and flag in center. 1863 below.

G. A. SCHWARZ

CWT	Rarity	Reverse Die	Metal	Edge	VG	VF	EF	Unc
750R-1e	R10	1250	W-M	PL		—	RARE	—

G. A. SCHWARZ / 1006 / CHESTNUT / ST. / PHILA:

STEPPACHER

CWT	Rarity	Reverse Die	Metal	Edge	VG	VF	EF	Unc
750S-1a	R2	1381	C	PL	4	6	8	15

STEPPACHER . / (curved line) AGT. / ORLEANS / (curved lines) HOUSE / (curved lines) / 531 / -.- / CHESNUT St. / PHILA.

NOTE: Spelling error in CHESTNUT.

GRANVILLE STOKES

CWT	Rarity	Reverse Die	Metal	Edge	VG	VF	EF	Unc
750-1b	R7	—	BR	R	20	65	90	125

GRANVILLE STOKES above. Eagle in center. 1862 / MERCHANT TAILOR / 609 CHESNUT St. PHILADELPHIA below. Rv: FINE / FASHIONABLE CLOTHING / 1862 / GRANVILLE / STOKES / 609 CHESNUT ST. / PHILADELPHIA.

NOTE: Spelling error in CHESTNUT.

A. B. TAYLOR

CWT	Rarity	Reverse Die	Metal	Edge	VG	VF	EF	Unc
750U-1c	R7	—	N	PL	—	SCARCE	—	

A. B. TAYLOR. / SODA WATER / 1861 / PHILADA: / 1015 CHESTNUT ST. Rv: THE BEST PREPARATIONS / TAYLOR'S / ORILOTE / AND DENTICRETE / FOR THE TEETH.

N. & G. TAYLOR CO.

CWT	Rarity	Reverse Die	Metal	Edge	VG	VF	EF	Unc
750V-1a	R4	—	C	PL	5	10	12	35

N. & G. TAYLOR CO. / 1863 / bust of Washington facing right in center / 303 / BRANCH ST / PHILADELPHIA. Rv: TIN PLATE, / FILES, / METALS, / STEEL, / WIRE, COPPER &C.

UNION VOLUNTEER REFRESHMENT SALOON

CWT	Rarity	Reverse Die	Metal	Edge	VG	VF	EF	Unc
750W-3a	R3	—	C	PL	5	12	15	35

UNION / VOLUNTEER / REFRESHMENT / SALOON / INSTID. / MAY 27, 1861. Rv: SECOND ANNUAL / FAIR / HELD / JUNE 15, 1863.

NOTE: Comes with heavy reverse die cuts.

Pittsburgh

ALLEGHENY VALLEY RAILROAD HOTEL

CWT	Rarity	Reverse Die	Metal	Edge	VG	VF	EF	Unc
765A-1a	R7	1023	C	R	20	75	100	150

ALLEGHENY VALLEY / RAILROAD / HOTEL / OPPOSITE / DEPOT / PITTSBURGH, PA.

F. BEILSTEINE

CWT	Rarity	Reverse Die	Metal	Edge	VG	VF	EF	Unc
765B-2a	R4	1177	C	PL	5	15	20	40

F. BEILSTEINE / BUTCHER / 105 / DIAMOND / MARKET / E. SIDE / PITTSBURG.

NOTE: PITTSBURGH spelled without H.

BUFFUMS

CWT	Rarity	Reverse Die	Metal	Edge	VG	VF	EF	Unc
765C-1a	R2	—	C	PL	5	8	10	20

BUFFUMS / MINERAL / WATER / PITTSBURG Rv: Bottle in center surrounded by 27 crosses.

NOTE: PITTSBURGH spelled without H.

J. A. ECKERT

CWT	Rarity	Reverse Die	Metal	Edge	VG	VF	EF	Unc
765D-2a	R5	1176	C	PL	5	12	15	40

* * * J. A. ECKERT * * * / BUTCHER / 111 / DIAMOND / (ornament) / MARKET / PITTSBURG.

NOTE: PITTSBURGH spelled without H.

JOS. FLEMING

CWT	Rarity	Reverse Die	Metal	Edge	VG	VF	EF	Unc
765E-2a	R3	1026	C	PL	5	12	15	45

JOS. FLEMING / DRUGGIST / COR. MARKET, ST / & THE / DIAMOND / PITTSBURG.

NOTE: PITTSBURGH spelled without H.

W. A. GILDENFENNEY

CWT	Rarity	Reverse Die	Metal	Edge	VG	VF	EF	Unc
765F-1a	R4	1032	C	PL	4	8	10	25

W. A. GILDENFENNY / BOOKS / PAPERS / & / STATIONERY / 45 FIFTH, ST / PITTSBURGH

D. A. HALL & CO.

CWT	Rarity	Reverse Die	Metal	Edge	VG	VF	EF	Unc
765G-1a	R2	1124	C	PL	5	15	20	30

* D. A. HALL & CO. * / TEA / DEALERS / 27 / FIFTH ST. / PITTSBURG

NOTE: PITTSBURGH spelled without H.

J. W. HANNAH

CWT	Rarity	Reverse Die	Metal	Edge	VG	VF	EF	Unc
765H-2a	R6	1177	C	PL	5	20	25	40

J. W. HANNAH / * 81 * / LIBERTY / * ST. * / PITTSBURG, PA.

NOTE: PITTSBURGH spelled without "H".

J. C. & W. H. LIPPINCOTT

CWT	Rarity	Reverse Die	Metal	Edge	VG	VF	EF	Unc
765I-2a	R4	1176	C	PL	5	12	15	30

J. C. & W. H. LIPPINCOTT, / * GROCERS * / No. 19 / DIAMOND. / PITTSBURG, / * PA. *

NOTE: PITTSBURGH spelled without H.

A. LUDEWIG

CWT	Rarity	Reverse Die	Metal	Edge	VG	VF	EF	Unc
765J-1a	R3	—	C	PL	5	12	15	35

A. LUDEWIG, / DEALER IN / TOBACO, SNUFF / AND / (ornament) CIGARS, (ornament) / 310 & 312, / LIBERTY ST, / PITTSBURGH, Pa.

NOTE: Misspelling of TOBACCO with only one "C".

J. W. McCARTHY

CWT	Rarity	Reverse Die	Metal	Edge	VG	VF	EF	Unc
765K-1a	R3	1026	C	PL	10	25	35	50

J. W. McCARTHY / BILL / POSTER / PITTSBURGH

J. McKAIN

NOTE: J. McKain formerly listed as Pittsburgh changed to Mount Washington, Pa.

HENRY MINER

CWT	Rarity	Reverse Die	Metal	Edge	VG	VF	EF	Unc
765M-1b	R2	1364	BR	PL	4	6	8	15

** HENRY MINER ** / NEWS / (ornament) ** (ornament) / DEALER / -.- 71 & 73 FIFTH ST. / PITTSBURGH

PEKIN TEA STORE

CWT	Rarity	Reverse Die	Metal	Edge	VG	VF	EF	Unc
765N-3a	R3	1028	C	PL	5	8	10	25

PEKIN / TEA / STORE / No 50 / ST. CLAIR, ST. / PITTSBURGH

A. C. PENTZ

CWT	Rarity	Reverse Die	Metal	Edge	VG	VF	EF	Unc
765O-1a	R4	1023	C	PL	5	12	15	25

A. C. PENTZ / TIN COPPER & / SHEET IRONWARE / STOVES / 20 / PENN, ST. / PITTSBURGH

PITTOCK NEWS DEALER

CWT	Rarity	Reverse Die	Metal	Edge	VG	VF	EF	Unc
765P-1a	R2	1034	C	PL	4	6	8	15

* PITTOCK * / NEWS / (ornament) / DEALER / PITTSBURGH

JOHN W. PITTOCK

CWT	Rarity	Reverse Die	Metal	Edge	VG	VF	EF	Unc
765Q-2a	R3	1020	C	PL	4	6	8	25

JOHN W. PITTOCK / NEWS / DEALER / OPPOSITE / POST OFFICE / PITTSBURGH

PITTSBURGH DRY GOODS

CWT	Rarity	Reverse Die	Metal	Edge	VG	VF	EF	Unc
765R-2a	R2	1408	C	PL	4	6	8	15

* PITTSBURGH * / (ornament) / DRY GOODS / GROCERIES / -.- / HARDWARE & NOTIONS.

PITTSBURGH GAZETTE

CWT	Rarity	Reverse Die	Metal	Edge	VG	VF	EF	Unc
765S-2a	R3	1176	C	PL	4	8	10	20

PITTSBURGH / (ornament) / GAZETTE / * 84 * / FIFTH, ST.

REYMER & BROS.

CWT	Rarity	Reverse Die	Metal	Edge	VG	VF	EF	Unc
765T-1a	R3	1177	C	PL	4	12	15	30

REYMER & BROS. / CONFECTIONERS / (ornament) / - * - / PITTSBURG / * PA. *

NOTE: PITTSBURGH spelled without H.

SINCLAIR & WILSON

CWT	Rarity	Reverse Die	Metal	Edge	VG	VF	EF	Unc
765U-1a	R4	1177	C	PL	5	15	20	45

SINCLAIR & WILSON / CLOTHING / (ornament) / STORE / * 120 * / (ornament) / MARKET ST. / PITTSBURG.

NOTE: PITTSBURGH spelled without H.

FRANK SNYDER

CWT	Rarity	Reverse Die	Metal	Edge	VG	VF	EF	Unc
765V-2A	R6	1177	C	PL	5	15	20	35

FRANK SNYDER, / TOBACCO / AND / SEGARS / - 43 - / FOURTH ST. / PITTSBURGH.

West Greenville

PACKARD & CO.

CWT	Rarity	Reverse Die	Metal	Edge	VG	VF	EF	Unc
967A-1b	R3	—	BR	PL	4	8	10	30

* PACKARD & CO. * / (ornament) / HARDWARE / & / (ornament) IRON (ornament) / (ornament) / WEST GREENVILLE PA. Rv: * D. B. PACKARD & CO. * / (ornament) / CROCKERY / (ornament) / WEST GREENVILLE PA.

Wilkes Barre

CLARK & CO.

CWT	Rarity	Reverse Die	Metal	Edge	VG	VF	EF	Unc
985A-1a	R9	1319	C	R		—	RARE	—

(ornament) / CLARK & CO. / NO. / beaded line with 12 beads.

NOTE: The only basis for attribution to Wilkes Barre are the notes from the late Joseph Barnett.

RHODE ISLAND

Providence

ARCADE HOUSE

CWT	Rarity	Reverse Die	Metal	Edge	VG	VF	EF	Unc
700A-4a	R3	—	C	PL	4	6	8	15

ARCADE / HOUSE / 62 / BROAD. St / PROVIDENCE. R. I. Rv: H. DOBSON above. UNION / 1864 in center. Wreath below. (OBV RI 700D-1)

BILLIARD ROOM & RESTAURANT

CWT	Rarity	Reverse Die	Metal	Edge	VG	VF	EF	Unc
700B-1a	R8	1374	C	PL		—	RARE	—

Billiard Room / No / 27=31 / Pleasant / Street / - & Restaurant

CHARNLEY

CWT	Rarity	Reverse Die	Metal	Edge	VG	VF	EF	Unc
700C-3a	R3	1374	C	PL	4	6	8	15

* * * * * * * * * * * * * / CHARNLEY / anchor on shield in center / No. 11 ORANGE ST. / PROVIDENCE, R.I.

H. DOBSON

CWT	Rarity	Reverse Die	Metal	Edge	VG	VF	EF	Unc
700D-1a	R9	1285	C	PL		—	RARE	—

H. DOBSON above. UNION / 1864 in center. Wreath below.

FRANK L. GAY

CWT	Rarity	Reverse Die	Metal	Edge	VG	VF	EF	Unc
700E-2a	R2	1264	C	PL	4	6	8	15

FRANK. L. GAY / Bookseller / PROV. / * / R. I. / &. / Stationer. / 140 Westminster St

H. Y. LE FEVRE

CWT	Rarity	Reverse Die	Metal	Edge	VG	VF	EF	Unc
700F-1a	R3	1294	C	PL	8	20	30	90

H-Y. LEFEVRE. PRO: EMPIRE SALOON around. UNION in wreath in center. (thick 2-1/2 mm.)

NOTE: The S and N in SALOON are backwards.

CITY FRUIT STORE

CWT	Rarity	Reverse Die	Metal	Edge	VG	VF	EF	Unc
700G-2a	R2	1159	C	PL	4	6	8	15

CITY FRUIT STORE / -No. 4- / Werbosset / S.t. Prov. R. I. / Redeemed By Phillips

POHLE

CWT	Rarity	Reverse Die	Metal	Edge	VG	VF	EF	Unc
700H-1a	R9	—	C	PL		—	RARE	—

(ornament) POHLE (ornament) above. Bunch of grapes in center. 1863 below. Rv: (ornament) ELMWOOD VINEYARD around. Anchor in wreath in center.

F. W. SHATTUCK

CWT	Rarity	Reverse Die	Metal	Edge	VG	VF	EF	Unc
700I-1a	R7	—	C	PL		—	SCARCE	—

F. W. Shattuck / PROV. / 1864 / (ornament) / R. I. / 13 Weybosset. St. Rv: BURNSIDE above. S in wreath in center. FRUIT STORE below.

TENNESSEE

Clarksville

ANDREW KING

CWT	Rarity	Reverse Die	Metal	Edge	VG	VF	EF	Unc
130A-3a	R8	1047	C	R		—	RARE	—

ANDREW KING / (ornament) / MERCH'T / CLARKSVILLE / (ornament) / * TENN. *

Dedham

N. O. UNDERWOOD

CWT	Rarity	Reverse Die	Metal	Edge	VG	VF	EF	Unc
180A-2b	R7	1082	BR	PL		—	SCARCE	—

N. O. UNDERWOOD / GOOD FOR / 25 / CENTS / DEDHAM / TENN.

Knoxville

BARRY & M'DANNEL

CWT	Rarity	Reverse Die	Metal	Edge	VG	VF	EF	Unc
430A-1b	R7	—	BR	R		—	SCARCE	—

BARRY & M'DANNEL / PREMIUM / CONFECTIONERS / (ornament) * (ornament) / KNOXVILLE / * / TENN. Rv: * ARCTIC * / + / GOOD / FOR / 1 /. GLASS. / SODA WATER

Memphis

COSSITT HILL & CO.

CWT	Rarity	Reverse Die	Metal	Edge	VG	VF	EF	Unc
600A-7a	R6	1424	C	PL	50	150	200	275

COSSITT HILL & CO. / MEMPHIS.

NOTE: This piece, plus Tenn 600B, E and F are described in detail in NUMISMATIC SCRAPBOOK, Sept. 1958. Reference to numbers assigned in that article is given _ F III / 3.

ELLIOTT, VINSON & CO.

CWT	Rarity	Reverse Die	Metal	Edge	VG	VF	EF	Unc
600B-7a	R6	1424	C	PL	50	150	200	275

ELLIOTT, VINSON & CO. / MEMPHIS.

B. E. HAMMAR & CO.

CWT	Rarity	Reverse Die	Metal	Edge	VG	VF	EF	Unc
600C-1a	R7	1042	C	R	50	135	185	250

B. E. HAMMAR & CO. / DRAYAGE / -25- / CENTS / MEMPHIS, TENN.

WM. McDONALD

CWT	Rarity	Reverse Die	Metal	Edge	VG	VF	EF	Unc
600D-1a	R7	1042	C	R	50	135	185	250

WM. / McDONALD / DRYAGE / 25 / CENTS / MEMPHIS, TENN.

STEAMER

CWT	Rarity	Reverse Die	Metal	Edge	VG	VF	EF	Unc
600E-5a	R6	1422	C	PL	50	150	200	275

STEAMER / LANCASTER No. 4

STOCKMAN & CO.

CWT	Rarity	Reverse Die	Metal	Edge	VG	VF	EF	Unc
600F-5a	R6	1422	C	PL	50	150	200	275

STOCKMAN & CO. / 159 MAIN ST. / MEMPHIS.

Nashville

GOLD PEN DEPOT

CWT	Rarity	Reverse Die	Metal	Edge	VG	VF	EF	Unc
690A-1b	R9	Blank	BR	PL		—	RARE	—

* * GOLD PEN / DEPOT / -72- / CHERRY ST. / NASHVILLE, TENN.

HARRIS & PEARL

CWT	Rarity	Reverse Die	Metal	Edge	VG	VF	EF	Unc
690B-1a	R9	1047	C	R		—	RARE	—

HARRIS & PEARL / * * * / NASHVILLE / * / TENN.

D. L. LAPSLEY & CO.

CWT	Rarity	Reverse Die	Metal	Edge	VG	VF	EF	Unc
690C-1a	R9	1047	C	R	—	RARE	—	

D. L. LAPSLEY & CO / * * * / NASHVILLE / * / TENN.

McKAY & LAPSLEY

CWT	Rarity	Reverse Die	Metal	Edge	VG	VF	EF	Unc
690D-2a	R8	1047	C	R	—	RARE	—	

McKay & LAPSLEY / * * (ornament) * * / NASHVILLE / * / TENN.

WALKER & NAPIER

CWT	Rarity	Reverse Die	Metal	Edge	VG	VF	EF	Unc
690E-1a	R8	1047	C	R	—	RARE	—	

WALKER & NAPIER / * (ornament) * / NASHVILLE / TENN.

VIRGINIA

Norfolk

F. PFEIFFER & CO.

CWT	Rarity	Reverse Die	Metal	Edge	VG	VF	EF	Unc
580A-1g	R8	1284	L	PL	75	125	200	350

* F. PFEIFFER & CO. above. VA. within beaded circle in center. NORFOLK below.

WEST VIRGINIA

Charleston

SNOW HILL

CWT	Rarity	Reverse Die	Metal	Edge	VG	VF	EF	Unc
100B-1a	R9	—	C	R	—	RARE	—	

- SNOW HILL - / 5 / CENTS Rv: (ornament) PAYABLE / - IN - / MERCHANDISE

Glen Easton

BASSETT'S CHEAP DRY GOODS

CWT	Rarity	Reverse Die	Metal	Edge	VG	VF	EF	Unc
220A-2a	R7	1126	C	PL	30	90	125	200

BASSETT'S / CHEAP / DRY GOODS / GROCERIES / ETC. / GLEN EASTON / W. VA.

Hartford City

KELLY'S STORE

CWT	Rarity	Reverse Die	Metal	Edge	VG	VF	EF	Unc
260A-1b	R9	1391	BR	R	—	SCARCE	—	

In MERCHANDISE / KELLY'S / STORE / HARTFORD / CITY / - W VA -

Wheeling

BASSETT'S CHEAP DRY GOODS

CWT	Rarity	Reverse Die	Metal	Edge	VG	VF	EF	Unc
890A-5a	R6	1128	C	PL	8	20	30	110

BASSETT'S / CHEAP / DRY GOODS / 35 MAIN ST / WHEELING / W. VA.

JOHN ECKHART

CWT	Rarity	Reverse Die	Metal	Edge	VG	VF	EF	Unc
890B-1a	R5	1126	C	PL	8	20	30	110

JOHN ECKHART / MANUF'R / OF / HOSIERY / &C. / 187 / MAIN ST / WHEELING, / W. VA>

JAS. GRAVES & CO.

CWT	Rarity	Reverse Die	Metal	Edge	VG	VF	EF	Unc
890C-1a	R6	1322	C	PL	8	20	30	130

JAS. GRAVES & CO. / WALL PAPER / AND / NEWS DEALERS / -30- / MUNROE ST / WHEELING / W. VA.

R. C. GRAVES

CWT	Rarity	Reverse Die	Metal	Edge	VG	VF	EF	Unc
890D-2a	R6	1122	C	PL	8	20	30	110

R. C. GRAVES / PERIODICAL / AND / NEWS DEALER / -78- / MARKET ST. / WHEELING, / -.- / W. VA.

D. NICOLL & BRO.

CWT	Rarity	Reverse Die	Metal	Edge	VG	VF	EF	Unc
890E-1a	R7	1126	C	PL	8	30	45	125

* D. NICOLL & BRO. * / VARIETY / * / STORE / 109 / MAIN ST. / WHEELING / W. VA.

J. W. C. SMITH

CWT	Rarity	Reverse Die	Metal	Edge	VG	VF	EF	Unc
890F-1a	R7	1169	C	PL	8	30	45	125

J. W. C. SMITH, / DEALER / IN / LEATHER / AND FINDINGS / 189 MAIN ST / WHEELING, WEST VA.

C. E. STIFEL

CWT	Rarity	Reverse Die	Metal	Edge	VG	VF	EF	Unc
890-G-2a	R6	1178	C	PL	8	30	45	150

C. E. STIFFEL / * / TIN / -AND- / SHEET IRON / -WARE- / WHEELING / * / * W. VA. *

WISCONSIN

Appleton

PARSONS & BARLOW

CWT	Rarity	Reverse Die	Metal	Edge	VG	VF	EF	Unc
30A-2a	R7	1195	C	PL	—	SCARCE	—	

PARSONS & BARLOW / (ornament) / GROCERS / (ornament)/ APPLETON WIS.

Baraboo

PECK & ORVIS

CWT	Rarity	Reverse Die	Metal	Edge	VG	VF	EF	Unc
45A-5A	R5	1246	C	PL	5	15	25	45

(ornament) PECK & ORVIS (ornament) / DRUGGISTS / & / GROCERS, / BARA-BOO, / WIS.

Barton

JOHN REISSE

CWT	Rarity	Reverse Die	Metal	Edge	VG	VF	EF	Unc
50A-1a	R7	1194	C	PL	—	SCARCE	—	

- JOHN REISSE - / DEALER / IN / DRY GOODS / GROCERIES / CLOTHING/ HATS & / - / BARTON. WASH. CO. WIS.

Beaver Dam

F. KRUEGER

CWT	Rarity	Reverse Die	Metal	Edge	VG	VF	EF	Unc
55A-1a	R5	1194	C	PL	8	20	25	50

F. KRUEGER / DRY GOODS, / GROCERIES, / BOOTS & SHOES / HARDWARE / &C. BEAVER DAM, WIS.

A. P. REDFIELD

CWT	Rarity	Reverse Die	Metal	Edge	VG	VF	EF	Unc
55B-1a	R5	1194	C	PL	8	20	30	60

A. P. REDFIELD / HARDWARE / IRON / TIN WARE, / STOVES / NAILS &C. / BEA-VER DAM, WIS.

O. M. WARREN

CWT	Rarity	Reverse Die	Metal	Edge	VG	VF	EF	Unc
55C-1a	R5	1220	C	PL	5	30	40	75

O. M. WARREN / HARDWARE / IRON / TIN WARE / STOVES / NAILS &C. / BEA-VER DAM, WIS.

Beloit

PECK & PRATT

CWT	Rarity	Reverse Die	Metal	Edge	VG	VF	EF	Unc
70A-1a	R8	1209	C	PL		—	SCARCE	—

* PECK & PRATT * / DEALERS / IN / WINES / LIQUORS / & SEGARS / - * - / BELOIT, WIS.

Columbus

PH. CARPELES & CO.

CWT	Rarity	Reverse Die	Metal	Edge	VG	VF	EF	Unc
120A-1a	R3	1194	C	PL	5	15	20	40

PH. CARPELES & CO. / DRY - GOODS / & / GROCERIES / (ornament) / COLUMBUS. WIS.

FRANK HUGGINS

CWT	Rarity	Reverse Die	Metal	Edge	VG	VF	EF	Unc
120B-1a	R5	1194	C	PL	5	15	20	60

FRANK HUGGINS / DRUGS / & / MEDICINES / (ornament) / COLUMBUS, WIS.

D. F. NEWCOMB

CWT	Rarity	Reverse Die	Metal	Edge	VG	VF	EF	Unc
120C-1a	R5	1194	C	PL	5	20	25	65

D. F. NEWCOMB / (ornament) / DRY GOODS / -&- / GROCERIES / (ornament) / COLUMBUS, WIS.

WILLIAMS BRO'S.

CWT	Rarity	Reverse Die	Metal	Edge	VG	VF	EF	Unc
120D-1a	R4	1105	C	PL	5	15	20	60

WILLIAMS BRO'S / CHEMISTS / (mortar and pestle) / & DRUGGISTS / COLUMBUS / WIS.

Cross Plains

C. DAHMEN & SON

CWT	Rarity	Reverse Die	Metal	Edge	VG	VF	EF	Unc
140A-1a	R5	1105	C	PL	10	30	40	100

C. DAHMEN & SON / DEALERS / IN / DRY GOODS / GROCERIES / &C. / CROSS PLAINES / WIS.

East Troy

C. W. SMITH

CWT	Rarity	Reverse Die	Metal	Edge	VG	VF	EF	Unc
185A-2a	R5	1194	C	PL	8	20	25	50

C. W. SMITH / DEALERS / IN / DRY GOODS, / GROCERIES, / HARDWARE & / CROCKERY. / EAST TROY WIS.

Edgerton

C. C. ROOT & BRO.

CWT	Rarity	Reverse Die	Metal	Edge	VG	VF	EF	Unc
190A-1a	R4	1222	C	PL	8	30	45	90

C. C. ROOT & BRO. / DRY GOODS, / CLOTHING, / BOOTS, / SHOES CROCKERY, / GROCERIES / &C. / EDGERTON, / WIS.

Fond du Lac

C. L. ALLING

CWT	Rarity	Reverse Die	Metal	Edge	VG	VF	EF	Unc
220A-1a	R6	1082	C	PL	10	35	45	75

C. L. ALLING / (ornament) / GROCER, / FOND DU LAC, / * WISC. * / -.-

A. R. BRASS

CWT	Rarity	Reverse Die	Metal	Edge	VG	VF	EF	Unc
220B-1a	R6	1127	C	PL	10	30	40	60

A. R. BRASS / -*- / GENERAL / DEALER IN / PRODUCE / FOND DU LAC / * WIS. *

CARPENTER & PIER

CWT	Rarity	Reverse Die	Metal	Edge	VG	VF	EF	Unc
220C-1a	R5	1082	C	PL	5	15	20	45

CARPENTER & PIER. / CALL / AT THE / FARMERS / STORE / FOND DU LAC / WIS.

CLARKE & CARPENTER

CWT	Rarity	Reverse Die	Metal	Edge	VG	VF	EF	Unc
220D-1a	R6	1181	C	PL	5	20	25	60

CLARKE & CARPENTER / DEALERS / IN / DRY GOODS / AND GROCERIES / FOND DU LAC / WIS.

F. FRITZ

CWT	Rarity	Reverse Die	Metal	Edge	VG	VF	EF	Unc
220E-2a	R5	1194	C	PL	5	10	15	50

F. FRITZ / GROCERIES. / CROCKERY / PROVISI= / ONS &C. / FOND DU LAC, WIS.

J. C. LOWELL

CWT	Rarity	Reverse Die	Metal	Edge	VG	VF	EF	Unc
220F-1a	R5	1082	C	PL	10	30	40	85

J. C. LOWELL / DRUGGIST / & / GROCER / FONDULAC, / WIS.

NOTE: Spelling of FOND DU LAC.

T. MASON

CWT	Rarity	Reverse Die	Metal	Edge	VG	VF	EF	Unc
220G-1a	R6	—	C	PL	8	25	30	50

T. MASON / (ornament) / GROCER / FOND DU LAC, / WIS. Rv: T. MASON / - * - / CROCKERY / AND / GLASSWARE.

NYE & YOUMANS

CWT	Rarity	Reverse Die	Metal	Edge	VG	VF	EF	Unc
220H-1a	R2	1128	C	PL	5	15	20	35

NYE & YOUMANS / DEALERS / IN / GROCERIES / & CROCKERY / FOND DU LAC, WIS.

A. T. PERKINS

CWT	Rarity	Reverse Die	Metal	Edge	VG	VF	EF	Unc
220I-1a	R6	—	C	PL	15	45	60	90

A. T. PERKINS / CITY / BAKERY, / FOND DU LAC, / WIS. Rv: A. T. PERKINS / MANUFACTURER / OF / CRACKERS / AND / - * - / CONFECTIONARY.

PERKINS & SMITH

CWT	Rarity	Reverse Die	Metal	Edge	VG	VF	EF	Unc
220J-1a	R6	1089	C	PL	10	20	30	60

* PERKINS & SMITH * / DEALERS / IN / STOVES / AND / TIN WARE / FOND DU LAC / WIS.

C. J. PETTIBONE & CO.

CWT	Rarity	Reverse Die	Metal	Edge	VG	VF	EF	Unc
220K-1a	R5	—	C	PL	8	25	35	50

C. J. PETTIBONE & CO. / DRY GOODS / (ornament) / HOUSE, / FOND DU LAC, / WIS. Rv: BOOTS, / SHOES / -AND- / YANKEE / NOTIONS. / - * -

A. RAYMOND

CWT	Rarity	Reverse Die	Metal	Edge	VG	VF	EF	Unc
220L-2a	R5	1168	C	PL	10	25	35	55

A. RAYMOND / (ornament) / GROCER, / FOND DU LAC / * WIS. * / --

T. S. WRIGHT

CWT	Rarity	Reverse Die	Metal	Edge	VG	VF	EF	Unc
220M-1a	R4	—	C	PL	8	20	30	85

T. S. WRIGHT / - * - / CHEMIST / AND / DRUGGIST, / FONDULAC / WIS. Rv: * T. S. WRIGHT * / -x- / BOOKS / -&- / STATIONERY.

NOTE: Spelling of FOND DU LAC.

Genesee Station

D. L. EDWARDS

CWT	Rarity	Reverse Die	Metal	Edge	VG	VF	EF	Unc
235A-1a	R9	1107	C	PL		—	RARE	—

D. L. EDWARDS / DRY / GOODS & / GROCERIES / GENESEE / STATION / WIS.

Green Bay

A. DETRICH

CWT	Rarity	Reverse Die	Metal	Edge	VG	VF	EF	Unc
250A-1a	R3	1127	C	PL	5	8	10	30

A. DETRICH / DEALER / IN / GROCERIES, / PROVISIONS / LIQUORS &C. / GREEN BAY, / WIS.

HOFFMAN & LEWIS

CWT	Rarity	Reverse Die	Metal	Edge	VG	VF	EF	Unc
250B-1a	R6	1127	C	PL	8	20	25	55

HOFFMAN & LEWIS / MERCHANT / (ornament) / TAILORS, / GREEN BAY, / WIS.

A. KIMBOLL

CWT	Rarity	Reverse Die	Metal	Edge	VG	VF	EF	Unc
250C-1a	R5	1084	C	PL	5	12	15	35

A. KIMBOLL, / DEALER / IN / HARDWARE / GREEN BAY / * WIS. *

PHILIPP KLAUS

CWT	Rarity	Reverse Die	Metal	Edge	VG	VF	EF	Unc
250D-1a	R6	1089	C	PL	10	20	35	85

PHILIPP KLAUS, / YANKEE NOTIONS / AND / TOYS, / GREEN BAY / WIS.

DRS. RHODE & HICKS

CWT	Rarity	Reverse Die	Metal	Edge	VG	VF	EF	Unc
250E-1a	R7	1316	C	PL	20	75	100	160

DRS. RHODE & HICKS / EAGLE / DRUG / STORE, / GREEN BAY / WIS.

F. R. SCHETTLER

CWT	Rarity	Reverse Die	Metal	Edge	VG	VF	EF	Unc
250F-1a	R2	1084	C	PL	5	8	10	35

F. R. SCHETTLER / DEALER / IN / HARDWARE / GREEN BAY / WIS.

SAM. STERN

CWT	Rarity	Reverse Die	Metal	Edge	VG	VF	EF	Unc
250G-1a	R7	1387	C	PL	20	70	90	135

SAM. STERN / MERCHANT / TAILOR / & DEALER IN / CLOTHING, / GREEN BAY, / WIS.

Z. Z. ST. LEWIS

250H See 250I as this is a die cutting error.

J. J. ST. LOUIS

CWT	Rarity	Reverse Die	Metal	Edge	VG	VF	EF	Unc
250I-1a	R8	1168	C	PL	8	15	25	60

J. J. St. LOUIS / DEALER / IN / HARDWARE / GREEN BAY / * WIS. * / - * -

Z. Z. ST. LEWIS

CWT	Rarity	Reverse Die	Metal	Edge	VG	VF	EF	Unc
250I-4a	R5	1168	C	PL	5	15	25	50

Z. Z. St. LEWIS, / DEALER / IN / HARDWARE / GREEN BAY, / * WIS. * / - * -

NOTE: This is a die cutting error.

Hales Corner

J. SIEGEL

CWT	Rarity	Reverse Die	Metal	Edge	VG	VF	EF	Unc
270A-1a	R3	1194	C	PL	10	15	20	65

J. SIEGEL / (ornament) / DRY GOODS / & / GROCERIES / (ornament) / HALES CORNER.

Janesville

E. S. BARROWS

CWT	Rarity	Reverse Die	Metal	Edge	VG	VF	EF	Unc
300A-1a	R4	—	C	PL	15	40	55	95

E. S. BARROWS. / SEEDS / & / FARMING / TOOLS / JANESVILLE, WIS. Rv: STOVES, HARDWARE, IRON &C. (ornament) encircling a plow in center.

L. R. CARSWELL

CWT	Rarity	Reverse Die	Metal	Edge	VG	VF	EF	Unc
300B-1a	R6	1106	C	PL	8	20	35	85

L. R. CARSWELL / CONFECTIONERY / TOYS & / GROCERIES / JANESVILLE, WIS.

CHAPMANS ONE PRICE STORE

CWT	Rarity	Reverse Die	Metal	Edge	VG	VF	EF	Unc
300C-1a	R5	—	C	PL	10	20	30	60

CHAPMANS ONE PRICE STORE. / LAPPINS / BL'K / JANESVILLE / WIS. / (ornament) Rv: DRY GOODS, CLOTHING, BOOTS & SHOES (ornament) / HATS / & CAPS / GROCERIES / &C. / AT / LOW PRICES.

E. CONNELL & CO.

CWT	Rarity	Reverse Die	Metal	Edge	VG	VF	EF	Unc
300D-1a	R5	1106	C	PL	5	15	25	50

E. CONNELL & CO / GROCERIES / LIQUORS / LIME & / WOOD / JANESVILLE, WIS.

M. HARSH

CWT	Rarity	Reverse Die	Metal	Edge	VG	VF	EF	Unc
300E-1a	R7	1205	C	PL	25	90	125	175

M. HARSH / YOUNG / AMERICA CLOTHING / . * . / HOUSE / JANESVILLE, WIS.

H. L. MUTH

300F See 300G

H. L. SMITH

CWT	Rarity	Reverse Die	Metal	Edge	VG	VF	EF	Unc
300G-1b	R8	1111	BR	PL	10	50	70	125

H. L. SMITH / IRON. / HARDWARE. / (line) WAGON (curved lines) / (curved lines) STUFF &C. (curved lines) / padlock / JANESVILLE, WIS.

NOTE: There is a reference for H. L. MUTH, but it is questionable whether this piece actually exists.

Jefferson

PHILIP JOHNSON

CWT	Rarity	Reverse Die	Metal	Edge	VG	VF	EF	Unc
310A-1a	R6	1316	C	PL	10	45	60	80

PHILIP JOHNSON / DRUGS / PAINTS OILS / BOOKS, STATIONERY & C. / JEFFERSON, / WIS. .

JOHN JUNG

CWT	Rarity	Reverse Die	Metal	Edge	VG	VF	EF	Unc
310B-1a	R3	1226	C	PL	8	15	25	45

JOHN JUNG, / DRY GOODS / GROCERIES & / HARDWARE / JEFFERSON, / WIS.

J. F. W. MEYER

CWT	Rarity	Reverse Die	Metal	Edge	VG	VF	EF	Unc
310C-1a	R4	1088	C	PL	10	20	30	55

J. F. W. MEYER / -- / GROCERIES / PROVISIONS / & / NOTIONS, / JEFFERSON, WIS.

D. OSTRANDER

CWT	Rarity	Reverse Die	Metal	Edge	VG	VF	EF	Unc
310D-1a	R6	1298	C	PL	15	40	50	95

D. OSTRANDER / GROCER & / INSURANCE / AGT. / JEFFERSON, WIS.

S. STEINHART

CWT	Rarity	Reverse Die	Metal	Edge	VG	VF	EF	Unc
310E-1a	R6	1337	C	PL	5	20	25	50

S. STEINHART / DRY GOODS / & / GROCERIES / JEFFERSON, WIS.

Juneau

S. H. COLEMAN

CWT	Rarity	Reverse Die	Metal	Edge	VG	VF	EF	Unc
320A-1a	R8	1122	C	PL	30	110	140	250

S. H. COLEMAN / DEALER / -IN- / DRY GOODS / JUNEAU. / -WIS.-

Kenosha

N. A. BROWN'S CREAM ALE

CWT	Rarity	Reverse Die	Metal	Edge	VG	VF	EF	Unc
330A-2a	R7	1108	C	PL	—		SCARCE	—

N. A. BROWN'S / CREAM / ALE / STOCK PORTER / & / KENNET / KENOSHA, WIS.

GERKEN & ERNST

CWT	Rarity	Reverse Die	Metal	Edge	VG	VF	EF	Unc
330B-2a	R7	1105	C	PL	10	30	45	80

GERKEN & ERNST / - * - / DEALERS / IN / GROCERIES / & / PROVISIONS / KENOSHA, WIS.

HOHN SIMMONS & CO.

CWT	Rarity	Reverse Die	Metal	Edge	VG	VF	EF	Unc
330C-1a	R4	1106	C	PL	15	30	40	100

HOHN SIMMONS & CO. / BOOTS / SHOES & / . * . / LEATHER / KENOSHA. WIS.

LYMAN MOWRY & CO.

CWT	Rarity	Reverse Die	Metal	Edge	VG	VF	EF	Unc
330D-1a	R7	1106	C	PL	10	30	50	85

LYMAN & MOWRY & CO. / BOOTS, / SHOES, / & LEATHER. / KENOSHA, WIS.

Kilbourn City (Wisconsin Dells)

J. E. DIXON & SONS

CWT	Rarity	Reverse Die	Metal	Edge	VG	VF	EF	Unc
340A-1a	R7	1205	C	PL	20	50	70	165

J. E. DIXON & SONS / DRY / GOODS, / GROCERIES / (ornament) BOOTS (ornament) / & SHOES (ornament) / KILBOURN CITY. / WJS.

NOTE: Spelling of WIS.

T. HOFFMAN

CWT	Rarity	Reverse Die	Metal	Edge	VG	VF	EF	Unc
340B-1a	R7	1194	C	PL	20	60	75	150

T. HOFFMAN / barrel in center / KYLBOURN CITY. WIS.

NOTE: Spelling of KILBOURN.

La Crosse

MONS. ANDERSON

CWT	Rarity	Reverse Die	Metal	Edge	VG	VF	EF	Unc
360A-1a	R6	1280	C	PL	12	25	30	60

MONS. ANDERSON / DEALER / IN / DRY GOODS, / CLOTHING, / BOOTS SHOES &C. / LA CROSSE, / * WIS. *

GEO. E. STANLEY

CWT	Rarity	Reverse Die	Metal	Edge	VG	VF	EF	Unc
360B-1a	R6	1321	C	PL	10	25	35	75

GEO. E. STANLEY / LA CROSS / WIS. * 1863 * / --

NOTE: Spelling of La Crosse.

Madison

JAS. FR. BODTKER

CWT	Rarity	Reverse Die	Metal	Edge	VG	VF	EF	Unc
410A-1a	R7	1205	C	PL	25	50	85	175

JAS. FR. BODTKER / (ornament) / MADISON. / WIS. / (ornament) / PHOTOGRAPHER

EMIGRANTEN OFFICE

CWT	Rarity	Reverse Die	Metal	Edge	VG	VF	EF	Unc
410B-1a	R3	—	C	PL	12	25	35	60

EMIGRANTEN / OFFICE / KING ST. / MADISON, / * WIS. * Rv: THE ONLY / - * - / NORWEIGEN / NEWS PAPER / PUBLISHED / IN / AMERICA.

R. K. FINDLAY & CO.

CWT	Rarity	Reverse Die	Metal	Edge	VG	VF	EF	Unc
410C-1a	R6	—	C	PL	8	20	25	45

R. K. FINDLAY & CO. / DRUGGISTS / AND / GROCERS, / MADISON, / * WIS. * Rv: THE CELEBRATED / (ornament) / TEA / (ornament) / ESTABLISHMENT.

S. KLAUBER & CO.

CWT	Rarity	Reverse Die	Metal	Edge	VG	VF	EF	Unc
410D-1a	R4	1169	C	PL	5	10	12	40

S. KLAUBER & CO. / DRY GOODS / CLOTHING / & / FURNISHING / GOODS, / MADISON, / WIS.

HUNTLEY & STEENSLAND

CWT	Rarity	Reverse Die	Metal	Edge	VG	VF	EF	Unc
410E-R2	R2	1083	C	PL	5	10	12	40

* HUNTLEY & STEENSLAND * / GROCERIES / * / AND / CROCKERY / - * - / MADISON, / WIS.

J. J. LAWRENCE

CWT	Rarity	Reverse Die	Metal	Edge	VG	VF	EF	Unc
410F-1a	R4	1222	C	PL	5	15	20	50

* J. J. LAWRENCE * / GROCERIES / CROCKERY / & / GLASSWARE / 17 / KING / ST. / MADISON WIS.

MADISON BREWERY

CWT	Rarity	Reverse Die	Metal	Edge	VG	VF	EF	Unc
410G-1a	R5	—	C	PL	15	50	75	175

MADISON BREWERY / MANFR. OF / LAGER BEER / * * * * * / STOCK / * -&- * / CREAM ALE Rv: J. RODERMUND / horse pulling wagon with three barrels / MADISON, WIS.

E. NEWCOMB

CWT	Rarity	Reverse Die	Metal	Edge	VG	VF	EF	Unc
410H-1a	R4	1169	C	PL	8	15	20	45

BUY / YOUR / * MEAT * / -OF- / E. NEWCOMB / MAIN / ST. / MADISON, WIS.

GEORGE V. OTT

CWT	Rarity	Reverse Die	Metal	Edge	VG	VF	EF	Unc
410I-1a	R3	1205	C	PL	10	20	25	80

GEORGE V. OTT / MANFR & DEALER / IN / LEATHER / HIDES & C. / TANNERY / MADISON. WIS.

RAMSAY & CAMPBELL

CWT	Rarity	Reverse Die	Metal	Edge	VG	VF	EF	Unc
410J-1a	R3	1332	C	PL	10	20	30	75

RAMSAY & CAMPBELL / STOVES / TIN, / IRON & / FARMING / TOOLS / MADISON, / * WIS. *

J. RODERMUND

CWT	Rarity	Reverse Die	Metal	Edge	VG	VF	EF	Unc
410K-1a	R7	1105	C	PL	10	20	25	75

J. RODERMUND / DEALER / IN / DRY GOODS / & GROCERIES / MADISON. / WIS.

WM. VOIGHT

CWT	Rarity	Reverse Die	Metal	Edge	VG	VF	EF	Unc
410L-1a	R6	1205	C	PL	10	35	45	80

CAPITOL STEAM BREWERY / BY WM. VOIGHT / MANFR. OF / + ALE & + / (line) LAGER (line) / (line) BEER (line) / MADISON / WIS.

Manitowoc

W. H. HORN

CWT	Rarity	Reverse Die	Metal	Edge	VG	VF	EF	Unc
420A-2a	R4	1194	C	PL	5	10	12	30

W. H. HORN / (ornament) / PRODUCE / DEALER. / (ornament) / MANITOWOC

STUCKE & CO.

CWT	Rarity	Reverse Die	Metal	Edge	VG	VF	EF	Unc
420B-4a	R2	1194	C	PL	5	10	12	30

STUCKE & CO. / (ornament) / PRODUCE / DEALER / (ornament) / MANITOWOC, WIS.

Marshall

I. LIVINGSTON

CWT	Rarity	Reverse Die	Metal	Edge	VG	VF	EF	Unc
435A-1a	R8	1194	C	PL	20	65	85	150

I. LIVINGSTON / (ornament) / DRY GOODS / GROCERIES / &C. / MARSHALL. WIS.

G. W. VOSBURGH

CWT	Rarity	Reverse Die	Metal	Edge	VG	VF	EF	Unc
435B-1a	R5	1194	C	PL	12	40	50	90

G. W. VOSBURGH / (ornament) / HARDWARE, / STOVES, / & TIN. / (ornament) / MARSHALL, WIS.

Mauston

D. CAMPBELL

CWT	Rarity	Reverse Die	Metal	Edge	VG	VF	EF	Unc
450A-1a	R7	1107	C	PL	25	85	110	200

D. CAMPBELL / HARDWARE / & / GROCERIES / MAUSTON / WIS.

Mayfield

E. WIRTH

CWT	Rarity	Reverse Die	Metal	Edge	VG	VF	EF	Unc
460A-2a	R6	1194	C	PL	8	25	40	70

- E. WIRTH - / DEALER / IN / DRY GOODS, / GROCERIES, / CLOTHING, / HATS, / &C. / FIELD, WIS.

Milwaukee

E ASCHERMANN & CO.

CWT	Rarity	Reverse Die	Metal	Edge	VG	VF	EF	Unc
510A-1a	R5	—	C	PL	5	12	15	35

- E. ASCHERMANN & CO. - / Indian on pony / MILWAUKEE Rv: CIGARS & TOBACCO / WHOLESALE / & / RETAIL / 274 / WEST WATER ST.

C. H. BAST

CWT	Rarity	Reverse Die	Metal	Edge	VG	VF	EF	Unc
510B-1a	R5	—	C	PL	5	15	20	80

(ornament) WISCONSIN BREWERY (ornament) / beer keg / CH. BAST Rv: MILWAUKEE above. Six pointed star with beer mug in center dividing the date 1863, with 18 on left and 63 on the right. WISCONSIN below.

PHILIP BEST

CWT	Rarity	Reverse Die	Metal	Edge	VG	VF	EF	Unc
510C-1a	R2	—	C	PL	4	8	10	25

* PHILIP BEST * / mug of beer / 1863 / LAGERBEER Rv: (ornament) EMPIRE BREWERY (ornament) / beer keg with brewers tools of the trade with MARR directly beneath / MILWAUKEE

BEST & CO.'S

CWT	Rarity	Reverse Die	Metal	Edge	VG	VF	EF	Unc
510D-1a	R9	—	C	PL		—	RARE	—

BEST & CO's. / beer keg / BEER HALL Rv: BEER OR CASH / 5 / MIL. / MARKET STREET

NOTE: This is a very crude piece and it is doubtful that it is of Civil War origin.

V. BLATZ

CWT	Rarity	Reverse Die	Metal	Edge	VG	VF	EF	Unc
510E-1a	R2	—	C	PL	4	8	10	25

V. BLATZ on left side of figure of King Gambrinus holding glass of beer. LAGER BEER on right side. Rv; CITY BREWERY / & / MALT HOUSE. / 1863 / MILWAUKEE.

M. BODDEN

CWT	Rarity	Reverse Die	Metal	Edge	VG	VF	EF	Unc
510F-1a	R4	1194	C	PL	4	15	20	30

M. BODDEN / (ornament) / MILWAUKEE, / (ornament) / WISCONSIN.

A. J. COOPER

CWT	Rarity	Reverse Die	Metal	Edge	VG	VF	EF	Unc
510H-1a	R5	1194	C	PL	4	10	12	35

A. J. COOPER / LUMBER / YARD. / EAST WATER ST. / N. OF WALKERS PT / BRIDGE, / MILWAUKEE.

D. J. DOORNINK

CWT	Rarity	Reverse Die	Metal	Edge	VG	VF	EF	Unc
510I-1a	R5	—	C	PL	4	15	20	40

- D. J. DOORNINK - / beehive / 1863 / MILWAUKEE Rv: GROCERIES / (ornament) & (ornament) / DRY GOODS. / COR. OF 10TH / & / CHERRY ST.

A. H. FILNER

CWT	Rarity	Reverse Die	Metal	Edge	VG	VF	EF	Unc
510J-1a1	R8	—	C	R		—	RARE	—

A. H. FILNER. / CORNER / OF 7th & / SHERMAN / STREET, / MILWAUKEE. Rv: GROCERIES & / (ornament) / KEGELBAHN / (ornament) / PROVISIONS

JOSEPH FISCHBEIN

CWT	Rarity	Reverse Die	Metal	Edge	VG	VF	EF	Unc
510K-3a	R5	—	C	PL	4	10	12	35

JOSEPH FISCHBEIN / AGT. / (ornament) 315. (ornament) / WEST / WATER ST. / MILWAUKEE / WIS. Rv: GROCERIES, / (ornament) / PROVISIONS / (ornament) & (ornament) / DRY GOODS / 1863.

NOTE: The 3 in the address has been re-cut over a 1.

WM. FRANKFURTH

CWT	Rarity	Reverse Die	Metal	Edge	VG	VF	EF	Unc
510L-1a	R2	—	C	PL	4	10	12	30

WM. FRANKFURTH. above. Bust of Indian in headdress in center. MILWAUKEE, WIS. below. Rv: * STOVES & HARDWARE. * / center design consists of axe, shovel, hammer and a saw with the words DON'T DESPAIR on the blade / 1863

GOES & FALK

CWT	Rarity	Reverse Die	Metal	Edge	VG	VF	EF	Unc
510M-1a	R2	—	C	PL	4	12	15	30

GOES & FALK / three barrels / 18 on left of barrels and 63 on the right / MILWAUKEE. Rv: WISCONSIN / MALT HOUSE / & / BAVARIA / -BREWERY-

NOTE: This piece is also struck on a thin planchet.

GOLL & FRANK'S RETAIL STORE

CWT	Rarity	Reverse Die	Metal	Edge	VG	VF	EF	Unc
510N-1a	R5	—	C	PL	4	12	15	50

GOLL & FRANK's / RETAIL STORE / 319 / THIRD ST. / MILWAUKEE. / J. H. HANTZSCH / AGT. Rv: (ornament) DRY GOODS (ornament) / FANCY / GOODS, / YANKEE NOTIONS, / FEATHERS / ETC.

C. E. GRAFF

CWT	Rarity	Reverse Die	Metal	Edge	VG	VF	EF	Unc
510O-2a	R4	1194	C	PL	4	15	20	40

C. E. GRAFF / DEALER / IN / ALL KINDS OF / MACHINERY. / (ornament) / MILWAUKEE, WIS.

C. HAMBACH

CWT	Rarity	Reverse Die	Metal	Edge	VG	VF	EF	Unc
510P-1a	R5	1194	C	PL	4	15	20	55

(ornament) / HAMBACH, / (ornament) / MILWAUKEE / (ornament)

T. W. HART

CWT	Rarity	Reverse Die	Metal	Edge	VG	VF	EF	Unc
510Q-1a	R8	—	C	PL		—	SCARCE	—

(ornament) / T. W. HART, / SUPT. / (ornament) Rv: M. W. M. / PLANK ROAD / COMPANY. (ornament)

NOTE: There is no definite proof that this piece is of Civil War vintage or that it was issued in Milwaukee. M. W. M. (Milwaukee, Watertown, Madison).

C. H. HERMAN & CO.

CWT	Rarity	Reverse Die	Metal	Edge	VG	VF	EF	Unc
510R-1a	R6	—	C	PL	4	15	20	60

C. H. HERMANN & CO. / (ornament) / crossed brooms behind a jug / 1863 / MILWAUKEE Rv: BROOM & / STONE / WARE / FACTORY. / 318 / EAST WATER ST.

GEO KANE

CWT	Rarity	Reverse Die	Metal	Edge	VG	VF	EF	Unc
510S-1a	R5	1194	C	PL	10	30	40	80

GEO. KANE / DEALER / IN / FINE FAMILY / GROCERIES / No. 10. / SPRING ST. / MILWAUKEE.

KIRBY LANGWORTHY & CO.

CWT	Rarity	Reverse Die	Metal	Edge	VG	VF	EF	Unc
510T-1a	R6	1108	C	PL		—	SCARCE	—

* THRESHING * / MACHINE / WORKS / KIRBY / LANGWORTHY / & CO / MILWAUKEE / -.- /

A. KLEINSTEIBER

CWT	Rarity	Reverse Die	Metal	Edge	VG	VF	EF	Unc
510U-1a	R6	—	C	PL	4	12	15	25

+ A. KLEINSTEIBER + / 1863 / lady's hat and flowers / MILWAUKEE Rv: MILLINERY / & / FANCY GOODS / 5th / BETW: POPLAR / & / CHESTNUT ST.

CHAS. KLEINSTEUBER

CWT	Rarity	Reverse Die	Metal	Edge	VG	VF	EF	Unc
510V-1a	R4	—	C	PL	5	15	20	45

* CHAs. KLEINSTEUBER * / man's bust to left with 18 on the left and 63 on the right / MECHANIC. Rv: SMALL MACHINERY, / MODELS, / ENGRAVING, / STENCIL= / CUTTING. / No. 24 / TAMARACK ST. / MILWAUKEE.

NOTE: This piece is also struck on a thick planchet (1-1/2 mm) as compared to the regular (2-1/4 mm) and thick 2-3/4 mm.

H. KURT

CWT	Rarity	Reverse Die	Metal	Edge	VG	VF	EF	Unc
510W-1a	R4	1194	C	PL	5	10	12	30

H. KURT / (ornament) / GROCERY / COR. OF / HANOVER & / FLORIDA ST. / (ornament) / MILWAUKEE.

LOUIS KURZ

CWT	Rarity	Reverse Die	Metal	Edge	VG	VF	EF	Unc
510X-1a	R6	1194	C	PL	10	30	35	90

LOUIS KURZ / PICTORIAL / LITHOGRAPHER / (ornament) / MILWAUKEE.

A. LEDERER & CO.

CWT	Rarity	Reverse Die	Metal	Edge	VG	VF	EF	Unc
510Y-3a	R5	1108	C	PL	5	15	20	45

A. LEDERER & CO. / DRY / GOODS / COR / E. WATER / & / MICHIGAN STS./ MILWAUKEE.

M. C. MEYER

CWT	Rarity	Reverse Die	Metal	Edge	VG	VF	EF	Unc
510Z-1a	R4	1194	C	PL	5	12	15	60

M. C. MEYER / (ornament) / M. G. B. PL. ROAD / (ornament) / MILWAUKEE.

A. MILLER & CO.

CWT	Rarity	Reverse Die	Metal	Edge	VG	VF	EF	Unc
510AA-2a	R6	1194	C	PL	5	20	30	50

A. MILLER & CO. / (ornament) / PRODUCE / -&- / COMMISSION / (ornament) / MILWAUKEE, WIS.

FRIEDRICH MILLER

CWT	Rarity	Reverse Die	Metal	Edge	VG	VF	EF	Unc
510AB-1a	R3	—	C	PL	5	10	12	25

FRIEDRICH MILLER / barrel containing tools of trade and heads of barley with 18 to the left and 63 to the right with MARR directly beneath / LAGER BEER / Rv: PLANK ROAD / BREWERY , / (ornament) / MILWAUKEE.

F. MITZLAFF

CWT	Rarity	Reverse Die	Metal	Edge	VG	VF	EF	Unc
510AC-1a	R4	1194	C	PL	5	8	15	35

F. MITZLAFF / (ornament) / GROCER / (ornament) / MILWAUKEE

MOSSIN & MARR

CWT	Rarity	Reverse Die	Metal	Edge	VG	VF	EF	Unc
510AD-1a	R4	1220	C	PL	4	10	12	25

MOSSIN & MARR / (ornament) / (curved lines) / ENGRAVERS / (curved lines) / (ornament) / MILWAUKEE.

CARL PAESCHKE

CWT	Rarity	Reverse Die	Metal	Edge	VG	VF	EF	Unc
510AE-2a	R5	—	C	PL	5	10	12	35

CARL PAESCHKE / (curved lines) / DRY GOODS / -.- / STORE / (Curved lines) / FOND DU LAC / ROAD / MILWAUKEE. Rv: GROCERIES (ornament) / PROVISIONS / (ornament) & (ornament) / DRY GOODS / 1863.

NOTE: This piece is also struck on a think planchet.

PLANER & KAYER'S SEWING MACHINE

CWT	Rarity	Reverse Die	Metal	Edge	VG	VF	EF	Unc
510AF-1a	R4	1194	C	PL	8	25	35	90

PLANER & KAYER'S / SEWING / MACHINE. / COR. OF / MAIN & MASON / ST'S. / MILWAUKEE, WIS.

J. PRITZLAFF & CO.

CWT	Rarity	Reverse Die	Metal	Edge	VG	VF	EF	Unc
510AG-1a1	R4	—	C	R	5	12	15	35

J. PRITZLAFF & CO. / stove / No. 303. 3rd ST. / (ornament) / MILWAUKEE Rv: HARDWARE, / IRON, / NAILS, GLASS, / & STOVES. / 1863

J. SCHEIDHAUER

CWT	Rarity	Reverse Die	Metal	Edge	VG	VF	EF	Unc
510AH-1a	R5	1194	C	PL	10	40	50	90

J. SCHEIDHAUER / MANUFACTURER / OF / SOAP / & / CANDLES. / MILWAUKEE, WIS.

J. B. SCHRAM

CWT	Rarity	Reverse Die	Metal	Edge	VG	VF	EF	Unc
510AI-1a	R3	1194	C	PL	4	10	12	40

J. B. SCHRAM / (ornament) / WHOLESALE / GROCER / (ornament) / MILWAUKEE

SEVERN & JONES

CWT	Rarity	Reverse Die	Metal	Edge	VG	VF	EF	Unc
510AJ-1a	R5	1194	C	PL	4	10	12	60

SEVERN & JONES / (ornament) / PRODUCE / & / COMMISSION / (ornament) / MILWAUKEE, WIS.

C. T. STAMM & SON

CWT	Rarity	Reverse Die	Metal	Edge	VG	VF	EF	Unc
510AK-2a	R5	1194	C	PL	5	10	12	30

C. T. STAMM & SON / STOVES. / TIN / & HARDWARE / REED / ST. / MILWAUKEE

A. H. STEINMANN

CWT	Rarity	Reverse Die	Metal	Edge	VG	VF	EF	Unc
510AL-1a	R3	1194	C	PL	5	12	15	50

A. H. STEINMANN / GROCERIES / DRY GOODS / & / MILLINERY. / CORNER OF 11 & / GALENA St. / MILWAUKEE.

D. STOFFEL

CWT	Rarity	Reverse Die	Metal	Edge	VG	VF	EF	Unc
510AM-1a	R4	1194	C	PL	5	12	15	40

D. STOFFEL / (ornament) / GROCERIES / & / PROVISIONS / 7th STREET / MILWAUKEE.

FRIEDRICH THIELE

CWT	Rarity	Reverse Die	Metal	Edge	VG	VF	EF	Unc
510AN-1a	R6	1194	C	PL	5	10	12	50

FRIEDRICH THIELE / (ornament) / MEAT / MARKET / (oranament)

I. TELLER

CWT	Rarity	Reverse Die	Metal	Edge	VG	VF	EF	Unc
510AO-2a	R4	1194	C	PL	5	10	12	30

(ornament) / I. TELLER, / MILWAUKEE. / (ornament)

NOTE: The R has been re-cut over an E.

H. UPMEYER

CWT	Rarity	Reverse Die	Metal	Edge	VG	VF	EF	Unc
510AP-1a	R3	1155	C	PL	5	10	12	35

H. UPMEYER / (ornament) / JEWELLER / 258 / W. WATER ST. / MILWAUKEE

NOTE: This piece is also struck on a thick planchet.

HERMANN VOIGT

CWT	Rarity	Reverse Die	Metal	Edge	VG	VF	EF	Unc
510AQ-1a	R4	—	C	PL	5	15	20	40

- HERMAN VOIGT - / 1863. / STOVE / MILWAUKEE. Rv: STOVES / & / TIN WARE / 329. / WEST WATER ST.

Neenah

JOHN HUNT

CWT	Rarity	Reverse Die	Metal	Edge	VG	VF	EF	Unc
520A-1a	R4	—	C	PL	5	20	25	50

JOHN HUNT / (ornament) / GROCERIES / & PROVISIONS, / NEENAH, WIS. Rv: McCABE / CORAL / MILLS, / MANASH, / WIS.

C. W. LEAVENS & CO.

CWT	Rarity	Reverse Die	Metal	Edge	VG	VF	EF	Unc
520B-1a	R3	1316	C	PL	5	20	25	60

C. W. LEAVENS & CO. / GROCERIES / NEENAH, / WIS.

Newburg

FRANCKENBERG & KELLER

CWT	Rarity	Reverse Die	Metal	Edge	VG	VF	EF	Unc
530A-1a	R6	1194	C	PL	10	30	40	90

FRANCKENBERG & KELLER / DEALERS / IN / DRY GOODS / GROCERIES / HARD= / WARE. / NEWBURG, WIS.

New Lisbon

J. RAMSEY

CWT	Rarity	Reverse Die	Metal	Edge	VG	VF	EF	Unc
540A-1a	R8	1205	C	PL	20	60	80	200

J. RAMSEY / DRY / GOODS / GROCERIES / & GENERAL / . * . / MERCHANDIZE / NEW LISBON, WIS.

L. C. WESCOTT

CWT	Rarity	Reverse Die	Metal	Edge	VG	VF	EF	Unc
540B-1a	R7	1107	C	PL	20	60	95	200

L. C. WESCOTT / DEALER / IN / HARDWARE / STOVES & / AGRICULTURAL / IMPLEMENTS / NEW LISBON, WIS.

North Prairie

W. H. BOGARDUS

CWT	Rarity	Reverse Die	Metal	Edge	VG	VF	EF	Unc
550A-1a	R5	1194	C	PL	10	40	55	125

W. H. BOGARDUS / DEALER / IN / DRY GOODS, / GROCERIES / HARD= / WARE / NORTH PRAIRIE.

J. REMINGTON SONS

CWT	Rarity	Reverse Die	Metal	Edge	VG	VF	EF	Unc
550B-1a	R8	1106	C	PL		—	RARE	—

J. REMINGTON / SONS. / DRY / GOODS & / GROCERIES / NORTH / PRAIRIE / WIS.

J. SMART

CWT	Rarity	Reverse Die	Metal	Edge	VG	VF	EF	Unc
550C-1a	R7	1205	C	PL		—	RARE	—

J. SMART / STEAM / FLOURING & / PLANING / MILLS / NORTH PRAIRIE, WIS.

Oconomowoc

MRS. J. TATE

CWT	Rarity	Reverse Die	Metal	Edge	VG	VF	EF	Unc
590A-1a	R9	1174	C	PL		—	RARE	—

MRS. J. TATE / (ornament) / MILLINER / (ornament) / OCONOMOWOC.

Oconto Co.

STILES GANG MILLS

CWT	Rarity	Reverse Die	Metal	Edge	VG	VF	EF	Unc
600A-1a	R4	1194	C	PL	10	25	35	100

STILES GANG MILLS / DEALER / IN / LUMBER, / LATH, / & / SHINGLES. / OCONTO CO. WIS.

Oshkosh

G. BOCK

CWT	Rarity	Reverse Die	Metal	Edge	VG	VF	EF	Unc
620A-1a	R6	—	C	PL	15	50	75	110

CITY HOTEL / G. BOCK / PROPRIETOR / OSHKOSH. / WIS. Rv: THE NEAREST / HOTEL / TO / THE / STEAM BOAT / LANDING / FERRY ST.

JOS. BOLES

CWT	Rarity	Reverse Die	Metal	Edge	VG	VF	EF	Unc
620B-1a	R3	1337	C	PL	8	20	25	50

- JOS. BOLES - / MERCHANT TAILOR / AND / DEALER IN / CLOTHING, / OSHKOSH, / WIS.

FRAKER BROS.

CWT	Rarity	Reverse Die	Metal	Edge	VG	VF	EF	Unc
620C-1a	R3	—	C	PL	4	10	12	30

FRAKER BRO'S. / DEALERS / -IN- / BOOTS & SHOES / 51 FERRY ST. / OSHKOSH, WIS. Rv: FRAKER BRO'S. / DEALERS / -IN- / LEATHER, / HIDES, / (ornament) / WOOL & FURS.

ANDREW HABEN & CO.

CWT	Rarity	Reverse Die	Metal	Edge	VG	VF	EF	Unc
620D-3a	R6	1222	C	PL	10	30	40	70

ANDREW HABEN & CO. / DEALERS / -IN- / CLOTHING / OSHKOSH, / WIS.

HASBROUCK & FRANCHER

CWT	Rarity	Reverse Die	Metal	Edge	VG	VF	EF	Unc
620E-1a	R3	1300	C	PL	10	30	40	60

HASBROUCK & FRANCHER / DEALERS / IN / STOVES & / TIN WARE, / OSHKOSH, WIS.

HAY & CLARK

CWT	Rarity	Reverse Die	Metal	Edge	VG	VF	EF	Unc
620F-1a	R5	1178	C	PL	8	20	30	60

HAY & CLARK / DEALERS / IN / HARDWARE / OSHKOSH / * WIS. *

JAENICKE & KLOTZSCH

CWT	Rarity	Reverse Die	Metal	Edge	VG	VF	EF	Unc
620G-1a	R4	1194	C	PL	8	20	30	50

JAENICKE & KLOTZSCH / MANUFACTURERS / -&- / DEALERS / IN LEATHER / HIDES / &C. / OSHKOSH, WIS.

KELLOGG & HUGHES

CWT	Rarity	Reverse Die	Metal	Edge	VG	VF	EF	Unc
620H-1a	R3	1127	C	PL	8	20	30	60

KELLOGG & HUGHES / (ornament) / DRY GOODS / OSHKOSH, / WIS. / * * * * * * * * * * *

LEVY & DUNCAN

CWT	Rarity	Reverse Die	Metal	Edge	VG	VF	EF	Unc
620I-4a	R6	1128	C	PL	10	20	35	60

LEVY & DUNCAN, / DEALERS / IN / CLOTHING / OSHKOSH, / -WIS.- / (ornament)

LINES & RUSSELL

CWT	Rarity	Reverse Die	Metal	Edge	VG	VF	EF	Unc
620J-1a	R3	—	C	PL	10	20	35	70

LINES & RUSSELL / HARNESS / MAKERS, / OSHKOSH, / * WIS. * / Rv: (ornament) / SADDLER / (ornament) / HARDWARE / (ornament)

A. NEFF

CWT	Rarity	Reverse Die	Metal	Edge	VG	VF	EF	Unc
620K-1a	R3	1300	C	PL	8	20	30	50

A. NEFF / DEALER IN / HARDWARE / GROCERIES &C / OSHKOSH, / WIS.

S. B. & J. A. PAIGE

CWT	Rarity	Reverse Die	Metal	Edge	VG	VF	EF	Unc
620L-3a	R5	1178	C	PL	8	20	30	60

S. B. & J. A. PAIGE / GROCERS / (ornament) / OSHKOSH / * WIS. *

H. RANS

CWT	Rarity	Reverse Die	Metal	Edge	VG	VF	EF	Unc
620M-3a	R5	1127	C	PL	8	20	30	60

- * - / H. RANS, / DEALER / -IN- / CLOTHING, / OSHKOSH WIS. / * * * * * * * * *

B. H. SOPER

CWT	Rarity	Reverse Die	Metal	Edge	VG	VF	EF	Unc
620N-1a	R4	1084	C	PL	8	20	30	50

B. H. SOPER, / (ornament) / DEALER / -IN- / FURNITURE / OSHKOSH, / WIS.

ALLEN VOSBURGH & CO.

CWT	Rarity	Reverse Die	Metal	Edge	VG	VF	EF	Unc
620O-1a	R4	—	C	PL	20	60	80	150

ALLEN VOSBURG & CO. / MUSIC / STORE ./ OSHKOSH, WIS. Rv: * * * STEINWAY'S * * * / -.- / PIANOS, / SMITH'S / MELODEONS / -&- / TREMLO / HARMONIUMS.

WM. L. WILLIAMS

CWT	Rarity	Reverse Die	Metal	Edge	VG	VF	EF	Unc
620P-2a	R6	1127	C	PL	10	30	40	70

WM. L. WILLIAMS / CHEMIST / AND / DRUGGIST / 43 FERRY ST / OSHKOSH, / WIS.

Portage City

T. M. McMILLAN

CWT	Rarity	Reverse Die	Metal	Edge	VG	VF	EF	Unc
660A-1a	R7	1205	C	PL	20	75	100	200

T. M. McMILLAN / GROCERIES / & / CROCKERY. / PORTAGE CITY. / WIS.

Port Washington

J. DRUECKER

CWT	Rarity	Reverse Die	Metal	Edge	VG	VF	EF	Unc
680A-1a	R5	1194	C	PL	10	25	35	100

J. DRUECKER / DEALER / IN / DRY GOODS, / GROCERIES, / CLOTHING, / HATS, / &C. / PORT WASHINGTON WIS.

Racine

J. I. CASE & CO.

CWT	Rarity	Reverse Die	Metal	Edge	VG	VF	EF	Unc
700A-2a	R4	1098	C	PL	5	10	12	50

J. I. CASE & CO. / ... * ... / THRASHING / (ornament) / MACHINE / - / MANFR'S / RACINE, WIS.

J. CLOUGH

CWT	Rarity	Reverse Die	Metal	Edge	VG	VF	EF	Unc
700B-2a	R5	1105	C	PL	10	25	35	85

J.CLOUGH / FINE / FAMILY / GROCERIES. / NUTS / &C. / RACINE. WIS.

JOHN ELKINS

CWT	Rarity	Reverse Die	Metal	Edge	VG	VF	EF	Unc
700C-1a	R6	1101	C	PL	5	8	10	45

JOHN ELKINS / DEALER / IN / WATCHES. / JEWELRY. / PIANOS / &C. / RACINE, WIS.

F. ELMLINGER

CWT	Rarity	Reverse Die	Metal	Edge	VG	VF	EF	Unc
700D-1a	R6	1106	C	PL	4	8	10	20

F. ELMLINGER / - * - / MERCHANT / - / TAILOR / . * . / RACINE, WIS.

J. W. ENGLISH

CWT	Rarity	Reverse Die	Metal	Edge	VG	VF	EF	Unc
700E-1a	R5	1105	C	PL	5	15	25	55

* J. W. ENGLISH * / TRUNK / & / HARNESS / DEALER / COR. MAIN & 3d St. / RACINE, WIS.

ERHARDT & RAPS

CWT	Rarity	Reverse Die	Metal	Edge	VG	VF	EF	Unc
700F-1a	R3	1220	C	PL	5	12	15	35

ERHARDT & RAPS / (ornament) / Auctioneers / (ornament) / RACINE. WIS.

NOTE: This piece is also struck on a thick planchet.

THOS. FALVEY

CWT	Rarity	Reverse Die	Metal	Edge	VG	VF	EF	Unc
700G-2a	R5	1105	C	PL	5	10	15	45

THOS. FALVEY / * * * * * * * / MANFR'R / OF / REAPERS & / MOWERS. / RACINE / WIS.

D. H. JONES

CWT	Rarity	Reverse Die	Metal	Edge	VG	VF	EF	Unc
700H-1a	R6	1105	C	PL	10	25	35	80

D. H. JONES / STAPLE & / (ornament) FANCY / DRY GOODS / 136 / MAIN ST. / RACINE, WIS.

J. & H. MILLER

CWT	Rarity	Reverse Die	Metal	Edge	VG	VF	EF	Unc
700I-1a	R7	1105	C	PL	10	25	35	90

* J. & H. MILLER * / DEALERS / IN / BOOTS / -&- / SHOES / * * * * * / RACINE. WIS.

THELEN & DIETERICH

CWT	Rarity	Reverse Die	Metal	Edge	VG	VF	EF	Unc
700J-1a	R7	1108	C	PL		—	SCARCE	—

THELEN & DIETERICH / DEALERS / IN / (curved line) / DRY (curved line) / (curved line) GOODS / (curved line) / & / GROCERIES / RACINE. / WIS.

Ripon

GREENWAY & CO'S

CWT	Rarity	Reverse Die	Metal	Edge	VG	VF	EF	Unc
720A-1a	R8	—	C	R		—	SCARCE	—

GREENWAY & CO'S / RESTAURANT / & / BILLIARD / ROOMS / --- / RIPON, WIS. Rv: GREENWAY'S / IMMENSE / * CONCERT * / HALL / RIPON, / WIS. / SEATS 1000 PEOPLE.

Sauk City

C. NEBEL

CWT	Rarity	Reverse Die	Metal	Edge	VG	VF	EF	Unc
770A-1a	R3	1194	C	PL	5	12	15	40

C. NEBEL / (ornament) / STEAM / MILLS / (ornament) / SAUK CITY, WIS.

Sheboygan

TROWBRIDGE'S

CWT	Rarity	Reverse Die	Metal	Edge	VG	VF	EF	Unc
790A-2a1	R8	1319	C	R		—	RARE	—

TROWBRIDGE'S / WATCH / CLOCK / & / JEWELRY / STORE / SHEBOYGAN, WIS.

Sparta

HAMILTON & CO.

CWT	Rarity	Reverse Die	Metal	Edge	VG	VF	EF	Unc
830A-1a	R5	1107	C	PL	10	25	30	100

HAMILTON & CO. / (ornament) / GROCERS / SPARTA, / WIS.

W. S. NEWTON

CWT	Rarity	Reverse Die	Metal	Edge	VG	VF	EF	Unc
830B-1a	R6	1107	C	PL	10	35	45	100

W. S. NEWTON / DEALER / IN / HARDWARE / & / STOVES / SPARTA, WIS.

Stoughton

T. P. CAMP

CWT	Rarity	Reverse Die	Metal	Edge	VG	VF	EF	Unc
860A-1a	R7	1320	C	PL	15	70	90	125

* T. P. CAMP * / WATCH / MAKER, / STOUGHTON, * WIS. *

DEARBOURN & ROOT

CWT	Rarity	Reverse Die	Metal	Edge	VG	VF	EF	Unc
860B-1a	R6	1222	C	PL	8	20	35	75

DEARBOURN / & / ROOT / GROCERS / STOUGHTON / * WIS. *

H. PETERSON

CWT	Rarity	Reverse Die	Metal	Edge	VG	VF	EF	Unc
860C-1a	R3	1181	C	PL	8	20	25	65

H. PETERSON / DRY GOODS / CLOTHING / BOOTS & SHOES / &C. / -- / STOUGHTON, WIS.

Tomah

EATON & BARNES

CWT	Rarity	Reverse Die	Metal	Edge	VG	VF	EF	Unc
890A-1a	R6	1194	C	PL	8	20	30	80

EATON & BARNS / DEALER / IN / DRY GOODS, / GROCERIES / &C. / TOMAH, WIS.

WM. RUNKEL

CWT	Rarity	Reverse Die	Metal	Edge	VG	VF	EF	Unc
890B-1a	R3	1194	C	PL	8	20	35	80

WM. RUNKEL / (ornament) / DEALER / IN / DRY / GOODS / &C. / TOMAH & NEW LISBON

Two Rivers

R. SUETTINGER

CWT	Rarity	Reverse Die	Metal	Edge	VG	VF	EF	Unc
900A-1a	R4	1194	C	PL	8	15	25	60

R. SUETTINGER / MANUFACT'R / & DEALER / IN / STOVES, TIN & / SHEET IRON / WARE. / TWO RIVERS, WIS.

Waterloo

PH. CARPELES & CO.

CWT	Rarity	Reverse Die	Metal	Edge	VG	VF	EF	Unc
915A-2a	R4	1194	C	PL	5	15	20	45

PH. CARPELES & CO. / DRY- / GOODS / & / GROCERIES. / (ornament) / WATERLOO, WIS

Watertown

H. BELLACK

CWT	Rarity	Reverse Die	Metal	Edge	VG	VF	EF	Unc
920A-1a	R3	1168	C	PL	5	15	20	40

H. BELLACK / DRY GOODS / GROCERIES & / PROVISIONS / WATERTOWN, / WIS.

BERTRAM & CO.

CWT	Rarity	Reverse Die	Metal	Edge	VG	VF	EF	Unc
920B-1a	R4	1317	C	PL	8	25	35	50

BERTRAM & CO. / BOOTS & SHOES / SIGN / OF THE / MAMMOTH / BOOT, / WATERTOWN, WIS.

CORDES & PLATZ

CWT	Rarity	Reverse Die	Metal	Edge	VG	VF	EF	Unc
920C-1a	R3	1084	C	PL	5	12	15	40

CORDES & PLATZ / DRY GOODS / GROCERIES & / LIQUORS, / WATERTOWN, / WIS.

T. DERVIN

CWT	Rarity	Reverse Die	Metal	Edge	VG	VF	EF	Unc
920D-2a	R4	1194	C	PL	5	10	12	45

T. DERVIN / DRY GOODS, / GROCERIES / & / CLOTHING / WATERTOWN WIS.

PATRICK DUFFY

CWT	Rarity	Reverse Die	Metal	Edge	VG	VF	EF	Unc
920E-1a	R5	1194	C	PL	5	15	20	50

PATRICK DUFFY / (ornament) / GROCER. / (ornament) / WATERTOWN, WIS.

FISCHER & ROHR

CWT	Rarity	Reverse Die	Metal	Edge	VG	VF	EF	Unc
920F-1a	R4	1194	C	PL	5	20	25	75

FISCHER & ROHR / (ornament) / CLOTHIERS / WATERTOWN / (ornament) / WIS.

FISCHER & ROHR

CWT	Rarity	Reverse Die	Metal	Edge	VG	VF	EF	Unc
920F-2a	R5	1342	C	PL	5	15	20	40

FISCHER & ROHR / READY / MADE / CLOTHING, / 35 MAIN ST. / WATERTOWN / WIS.

W. C. FOUNTAIN

CWT	Rarity	Reverse Die	Metal	Edge	VG	VF	EF	Unc
920G-1a	R6	1316	C	PL	5	15	20	40

W. C. FOUNTAIN, / DRUGS / PAINTS OILS / BOOKS, / STATIONERY &C. / WATERTOWN, / WIS.

CHAS. GOELDNER

CWT	Rarity	Reverse Die	Metal	Edge	VG	VF	EF	Unc
930H-4a	R5	1341	C	PL	5	15	20	40

* CHAS. GOELDNER, * / MUSICAL / INSTRUMENTS / -AND- / NOTIONS, / WATERTOWN / WIS.

JOHN HEYMANN

CWT	Rarity	Reverse Die	Metal	Edge	VG	VF	EF	Unc
920I-1a	R4	1194	C	PL	10	20	35	60

JOHN HEYMANN / (ornament) / OYSTER / RESTAURANT / & / BEER HALL. / WATERTOWN, WIS.

DANIEL KUSEL

CWT	Rarity	Reverse Die	Metal	Edge	VG	VF	EF	Unc
920J-1a	R3	1194	C	PL	8	20	25	60

DANIEL KUSEL / (ornament) / HARDWARE / (ornament) / WATERTOWN, WIS.

NOTE: This piece is also struck on a thin planchet.

J. MOULTON

CWT	Rarity	Reverse Die	Metal	Edge	VG	VF	EF	Unc
920K-1a	R4	1088	C	PL	8	20	25	40

J. MOULTON / GROCERIES / FLOUR & FEED / WATERTOWN / WIS.

THEODORE RACEK

CWT	Rarity	Reverse Die	Metal	Edge	VG	VF	EF	Unc
920L-1a	R3	1295	C	PL	5	15	20	50

THEODORE RACEK, / RESTAURANT / WATERTOWN, / WIS. / * * * * * * * * *

T. RACEK

CWT	Rarity	Reverse Die	Metal	Edge	VG	VF	EF	Unc
920M-1b	R8	1356	BR	PL	5	10	12	20

GOOD FOR ONE GLASS BEER (ornament) around / (ornament) / T. RACEK / (ornament) / WATERTOWN / WIS.

Waukesha

CHARLES CORK

CWT	Rarity	Reverse Die	Metal	Edge	VG	VF	EF	Unc
930A-1a	R7	1127	C	PL	20	65	90	175

CHARLES CORK / GROCERIES / - * - / CROCKERY / & NOTIONS / WAUKESHA, / WIS.

J. A. DUNBAR

CWT	Rarity	Reverse Die	Metal	Edge	VG	VF	EF	Unc
930B-1a	R6	1127	C	PL	15	55	75	145

J. A. DUNBAR / GROCERIES / PROVISIONS / FRUITS / &C. / WAUKESHA, WIS.

H. W. SHERMAN

CWT	Rarity	Reverse Die	Metal	Edge	VG	VF	EF	Unc
930C-1a	R7	1317	C	PL	15	50	75	120

H. W. SHERMAN AGT. / DRY GOODS / - * - / HATS, / CAPS AND / GROCERIES, / WAUKESHA, / WIS.

Whitewater

GALLT & COLE

CWT	Rarity	Reverse Die	Metal	Edge	VG	VF	EF	Unc
960A-1a	R5	1111	C	PL	8	15	20	50

GALLT & COLE / DRY / GOODS. / GROCERIES. / (line) / BOOTS & (curved line) / SHOES &C / (line)/ WHITEWATER, WIS.

J. S. LATHROP

CWT	Rarity	Reverse Die	Metal	Edge	VG	VF	EF	Unc
960B-1a	R4	1128	C	PL	10	30	40	75

J. S. LATHROP, / GROCERIES / AND / PROVISIONS / WHITEWATER / * WIS. *

J. T. SMITH

CWT	Rarity	Reverse Die	Metal	Edge	VG	VF	EF	Unc
960C-1a	R5	1320	C	PL	5	15	20	60

J. T. SMITH / JEWELER / WHITEWATER / * * WIS. * *

DR. VAN VALKENBURGH

CWT	Rarity	Reverse Die	Metal	Edge	VG	VF	EF	Unc
960D-1a	R5	1310	C	PL	8	20	25	55

DR. VAN VALKENBURGH / DRUGGIST / * / AND / GROCER, / WHITEWATER, / WIS.

A. WAHLSTEDT

CWT	Rarity	Reverse Die	Metal	Edge	VG	VF	EF	Unc
960E-2a	R4	1111	C	PL	8	25	35	70

A. WAHLSTEDT / DRY / GOODS / GROCERIES / & / LIQUORS / WHITEWATER, WIS

STORE CARD PHOTOS

PA 464A-4b PA 750P-5c PA 750La-1a

PA 464A-5b PA 750E-3e PA 750N-1a

PA 464A-6b PA 750E-1a1 PA 765F-2a

PA 615A-1a PA 750E-4e PA 765Q-4a

PA 750B-3a

PA 750B-3b PA 750V-3b

PA 750E-2a

PA 750E-2e PA 750V-5b

CATALOG OF PATRIOTIC CIVIL WAR TOKEN DIE COMBINATIONS

The section which follows details patriotic Civil War tokens, that is, those tokens which passed as currency which do not bear the name of any merchant or other redeemer.

Frequently they bear some of the same dies as used in Civil War Store Cards.

Die numbers 1000 and higher are Civil War Token Society numbers which may be found illustrated on the plates at the beginning of the Civil War Store Card Section.

Die numbers under 600 are Fuld Patriotic die numbers assigned originally by George and Melvin Fuld which are used exclusively on the Patriotic series and find no counterparts in the Store Card series. We have converted all Fuld numbers (under 600) to CWTS numbers (1000 and up) wherever possible.

Plates for some of the Patriotic dies follow, as do certain charts to assist the catalog users with some of the more difficult dies to tell apart - such as the "Dix" and U.S. Flag and "Our Army" die series.

Die Combination	Metal	Rarity	VG	F	VF	Unc
2/270	C	R8				
4/354	L	R7				
5/288	C	R2				
6/268	C	R1				
6A/317	C	R1				
6B/309	C	R1				
6B/310	C	R3				
6C/314	C	R5				
7/313	C	R2				
7/315	C	R2				
7A/316	C	R3				
7A/317	C	R1				
7B/315	C	R5				
8/268	C	R5				
8/309	C	R3				
8/313	C	R2				
8/314	C	R1				
11/298	C	R1				
11/312	C	R3				
12/297	C	R2				
12/351	C	R2				
13/297	C	R2				
14/297	C	R3				
15/319	C	R2				
16/300	C	R3				
16/301	C	R4				
16/353	C	R7				
17/388	C	R2				
19/1271	C	R2				
20/303	C	R3				
20/318	C	R8				
20/384	C	R7				
21/170	C	R10				
23/306	C	R1				
23/1246	C	R3				
24/246	C	R2				
25/418	C	R4				
26/418	C	R2				
27/365	C	R3				
28/303	C	R2				
29/303	C	R2				
36/340	C	R2				
36/1246	C	R3				
36/1275	C	R4				
41/178	WM	R9				
41/240	C	R8				
41/267	WM	R8				
41/337	C	R2				
41/341	C	R9				
41/342	C	R9				
42/336	C	R3				
43/387	C	R4				
43/388	C	R2				
44/350	C	R2				
45/332	C	R1				
46/335	C	R2				
46/339	C	R1				
47/332	C	R1				
48/299	C	R1				
49/343	C	R1				
50/342	C	R3				
51/333	C	R6				
51/334	C	R1				
51/342	C	R1				
51/342A	C	R5				
52/296	C	R4				
52/335	C	R3				
52/342	C	R1				
52/430	C	R3				
53/336	C	R1				
54/179	C	R2				
54/335	C	R5				
54/342	C	R5				
54/343	C	R4				
54/344	C	R3				
55/1175	C	R1				
59/385	C	R2				
59/453	C	R7				
62/367	C	R3				
62A/367	C	R5				
63/366	C	R1				
63/443	C	R2				
64/362	C	R4				
65/371	C	R4				
65A/371	C	R7				
66/370	C	R2				
67/372	BR	R7				
68/308	C	R3				
68/309	C	R1				
68/310	C	R3				
68A/369	C	R3				
69/261	CN	R9				
69/367	CN	R9				
69/369	C	R3				
77/331	C	R4				
79/297	C	R9				
79/351	C	R1				
80/351	C	R3				
81/351	C	R1				
82/351	C	R1				
82/352	C	R1				
83/264	C	R4				
87/356	C	R2				
89/356	C	R2				
90/364	C	R1				
91/303	C	R3				
91/373	C	R7				
91/1275	BR	R8				
91/1276	C	R8				
93/362	C	R2				
93/394	C	R3				
94/363	C	R3				
95/368	C	R2				
96A/131A	C	R8				
97/389	C	R2				
98/291	C	R4				
99/292	C	R3				

See Pricing Table on page 380

Die Combination	Metal	Rarity	VG	F	VF	Unc
100/341	C	R8				
104/263	C	R5				
104/521	C	R9				
107/108	C	R7				
107/1246	BR	R9				
107/1275	C	R1				
108/201	C	R3				
109/442	C	R5				
110/442	C	R1				
110/1246	C	R9				
111/340	C	R3				
111/1246	C	R4				
112/1271	C	R1				
113/1145	C	R9				
113/1244	C	R9				
113/1275	C	R9				
114/1275	C	R9				
117/420	C	R1				
118/418	C	R2				
118/419	C	R4				
119/398	C	R1				
119/1219	C	R9				
119/1253	BR	R8				
125/201	C	R8				
125/249	C	R6				
125/253	C	R9				
125/428	C	R9				
125/1174	C	R9				
125/1244	C	R7				
125/1245	C	R9				
125/1272	BR	R8				
125/1275	C	R8				
125/1353	C	R9				
126/406A	C	R9				
126/1241	C	R9				
126/1244	C	R9				
126/1245	C	R5				
126/1275	C	R9				
128/289	BR	R3				
128/290	BR	R4				
130/142	BR	R10				
130/347	WM	R9				
130/1250	C	R9				
131/217	C	R8				
131/479	C	R8				
131A/349A	C	R8				
132/149	C	R5				
132A/149	C	R5				
133/458	C	R8				
135/440	C	R2				
135/441	C	R2				
135/1219	C	R8				
136/397	C	R1				
137/309	C	R9				
137/395	C	R1				
138A/150	C	R6				
139/1275	C	R9				
141/307	C	R1				
142/347	C	R8				
142/348	C	R9				
142/1193	C	R9				
142/1250	C	R9				
143/261	C	R1				
147/227	C	R8				
147/228	C	R7				
166/1275	C	R4				
167/318	C	R3				
167/1276	C	R7				
168/311	C	R1				
169/213	C	R2				
171/340	WM	R9				
171/428	C	R7				
173/272	C	R1				
174/189	C	R10				
174/272	C	R1				
174/1237	C	R10				
176/1246	C	R1				
177/1244	C	R9				
177/1245	C	R9				
177/1246	C	R2				
177/1275	C	R9				
178/266	C	R3				
178/267	C	R1				
180/341	C	R1				
180/343	C	R4				
180/430	C	R4				
181/343	C	R7				
188/384	C	R2				
188/1276	C	R8				

Die Combination	Metal	Rarity	VG	F	VF	Unc
189/231	C	R10				
189/399	C	R1				
190/1275	WM	R9				
191/443	C	R1				
195/247	C	R8				
195/376	C	R4				
195/1257	C	R3				
201/1244	C	R9				
201/1245	CN	R8				
201/1246	BR	R9				
201/1275	C	R3				
203/412	C	R2				
203/413	C	R3				
204/413	C	R3				
205/410	C	R3				
205/441	C	R9				
207/323	C	R2				
207/324	C	R2				
207/325	C	R4				
207/327	BR	R7				
207/409	C	R1				
207/410	C	R1				
207/412	C	R1				
208/325	C	R1				
208/410	C	R1				
209/409	C	R7				
209/410	C	R3				
209/412	C	R3				
209/414	C	R2				
210/323	C	R1				
210/408	C	R2				
210/413A	BR	R9				
210/415	C	R3				
210/416	C	R4				
212/415	C	R2				
216/293	C	R2				
217/479	C	R7				
219/320	C	R1				
219/323	C	R2				
220/322	C	R1				
220/327	C	R9				
221/324	C	R1				
221/327	C	R3				
222/325	C	R2				
222/328	C	R2				
224/322	C	R1				
224/325	C	R3				
224/326	C	R1				
224/327	C	R8				
225/321	C	R9				
225/327	C	R1				
226/321	C	R4				
230/352	C	R2				
231/352	C	R1				
231/399	C	R10				
232A/403	C	R9				
235/269	C	R2				
236/426	C	R1				
237/423	C	R1				
238/402	C	R4				
238/405	C	R3				
239/421	C	R4				
239/422	C	R2				
240/337	C	R1				
240/341	C	R1				
241/296	C	R9				
241/336	C	R1				
241/337	C	R9				
241/338	C	R2				
242/1255	C	R2				
245/375	C	R3				
247/1256	C	R2				
247/1258	C	R3				
247/1259	C	R5				
249/1246	C	R4				
249/1275	C	R3				
252/1244	C	R9				
252/1245	C	R9				
252/1246	C	R4				
252/1275	C	R8				
253/1244	C	R9				
253/1275	C	R9				
255/1214	C	R1				
255/1265	C	R1				
255/1268	C	R1				
255/1269	C	R1				
256/1214	C	R3				
257/311	C	R3				
258/446	C	R3				

See Pricing Table on page 380

Die Combination	Metal	Rarity	VG	F	VF	Unc
259/445	C	R3				
260/447	C	R7				
276/278	C	R6				
299/350	C	R2				
305/350	C	R9				
332/336	C	R4				
336/337	WM	R9				
337/350	C	R2				
340/428	WM	R9				
428/1275	C	R9				
474/475	C	R8				
478/480	C	R10				
481/482	C	R8				
481/483	C	R8				
481/484	C	R8				
481/485	C	R8				
481/486	C	R8				
481/487	C	R8				
481/488	C	R8				
481/489	C	R8				
481/490	C	R8				
481/491	C	R8				
481/492	C	R8				
481/493	L	R8				
481/493A	C	R8				
481/493B	C	R8				
494/495	C	R9				
496/497	BR	R9				
498/499	Iron	R8				
500/501	BR	R8				
500/504	BR	R8				
500/505	BR	R8				
500/505A	BR	R8				
502/503	BR	R8				
520/521	C	R7				
526/Blank	C	R10				
1000/1132	BR	R8				
1000/1218	C	R7				
1000/1236	C	R1				
1000/1253	C	R7				
1000/1267	C	R1				
1000/1277	C	R3				
1001/273	BR	R6				
1001/464	BR	R9				
1001/465	BR	R9				
1001/465A	BR	R9				
1002/298	C	R2				
1002/312	C	R1				
1003/238	C	R8				
1003/298A	C	R9				
1003/400	C	R8				
1003/404	C	R9				
1003/405	C	R6				
1003/406	C	R5				
1003/407	C	R7				
1003/431	C	R7				
1003/1049	C	R9				
1003/1234	C	R8				
1004/300	C	R2				
1004/302	C	R5				
1004/304	C	R7				
1004/305	C	R9				
1004/337	C	R6				
1004/353	c	R3				
1005/418	C	R3				
1005/442	C	R2				
1006/255	C	R3				
1006/256	C	R2				
1006/1215	C	R1				
1008/473	C	R9				
1008/1279	N	R9				
1009/467	C	R7				
1009/473	C	R7				
1009/1288	C	R8				
1010/439	C	R3				
1015/1230	C	R8				
1015/1249	C	R4				
1016/1132	C	R7				
1016/1218	C	R3				
1016/1251	C	R2				
1017/119	C	R9				
1017/1132	C	R9				
1017/1218	C	R4				
1017/1219	C	R8				
1017/1251	C	R4				
1017/1252	C	R8				
1017/1253	C	R8				
1019/473	BR	R9				
1019/1160	Z	R9				

Die Combination	Metal	Rarity	VG	F	VF	Unc
1019/1192	C	R9				
1019/1279	C	R9				
1019/1282	Z	R10				
1019/1283	C	R9				
1019/1393	BR	R9				
1019/1400	BR	R9				
1019/1401	Z	R9				
1028/1030	C	R5				
1028/1045	C	R9 Reeded				
1030/1045	C	R9 Reeded				
1038/1192	C	R4				
1038/1279	C	R9				
1038/1393	C	R9				
1038/1401	C	R9				
1042/467	C	R8 Reeded				
1042/1370	C	R8 Reeded				
1045/1160	C	R8				
1045/1279	C	R8				
1046/456B	BR	R9 Reeded				
1046/473	C	R9 Reeded				
1046/1313	C	R7 Reeded				
1046/1399	C	R9 Reeded				
1048/1134	C	R8				
1048/1146	C	R9				
1048/1151	C	R9				
1048/1182	C	R9				
1049/431	C	R8				
1051/330	C	R3				
1052/119	C	R9				
1052/440	C	R9				
1052/1132	N	R9				
1052/1218	BR	R9				
1052/1219	C	R3				
1052/440	C	R9				
1053/357	C	R2				
1054/1254	C	R3				
1072/263	C	R9				
1073/161	C	R3				
1073/1175	C	R8				
1073/1236	C	R6				
1073/1277	C	R6				
1974/293	C	R5				
1074/375	C	R4				
1094/1205	C	R7				
1094/1298	C	R9				
1095/1357	C	R7				
1099/1357	C	R7				
1101/1203	N	R10				
1105/1357	C	R7				
1106/276	C	R8				
1106/277	C	R5				
1106/278	C	R5				
1106/1357	C	R6				
1107/265	C	R5				
1107/274	C	R6				
1107/277	C	R5				
1107/278	C	R8				
1122/1226	C	R9				
1124/1131	C	R9				
1127/1341	C	R9				
1132/358	C	R4				
1132/1216	C	R8				
1132/1218	BR	R8				
1132/1219	C	R9				
1132/1236	C	R9				
1132/1251	C	R3				
1132/1252	C	R8				
1132/1253	WM	R8				
1132/1267	C	R9				
1132/1277	C	R9				
1133/1275	C	R4				
1134/477	WM	R9				
1134/1146	WM	R8				
1134/1150	C	R8				
1134/1151	C	R9				
1134/1193	WM	R9				
1135/462	C	R8				
1135/1136	C	R10				
1137/255	C	R9				
1137/256	BR	R6				
1137/1215	CN	R7				
1140/466	L	R9				
1144/177	C	R9				
1144/201	C	R8				
1144/252	C	R9				
1144/1244	C	R7				
1145/177	N	R5				
1145/201	C	R4				
1145/252	C	R9				

See Pricing Table on page 380

Die Combination	Metal	Rarity	VG	F	VF	Unc
1145/253	C	R9				
1145/428	C	R9				
1145/1174	C	R9				
1145/1241	BR	R3				
1145/1244	C	R9				
1145/1245	CN	R6				
1145/1275	C	R9				
1145/1353	C	R9				
1146/130	C	R10				
1146/137A	WM	R9				
1146/142	BR	R9				
1146/347	C	R9				
1146/348	WM	R9				
1146/477	WM	R9				
1146/1150	C	R9				
1146/1151	C	R9				
1146/1193	C	R9				
1146/1250	C	R9				
1147/472	C	R9				
1147/481	C	R9				
1147/1191	C	R9				
1147/1285	C	R9				
1149/430	C	R1				
1150/1193	C	R8				
1151/1193	C	R9				
1151/1215	C	R1				
1151/1250	BR	R9				
1152/255	C	R2				
1152/256	C	R3				
1152/1215	C	R1				
1153/394	C	R1				
1153/1162	L	R9				
1155/1220	C	R4				
1155/1272	C	R7				
1156/469A	C	R9				
1157/1250	C	R9				
1158/1422	C	R8				
1158/1423	C	R8				
1158/1424	C	R8				
1158/1425	C	R8				
1158/1426	C	R8				
1158/1427	C	R8				
1159/472	C	R9				
1159/1191	C	R9				
1159/1285	C	R9				
1161/232	C	R5				
1161/400	C	R3				
1161/401	C	R5				
1161/403	C	R4				
1162/476	C	R9				
1162/1235	L	R8				
1162/1407	C	R9				
1165/400	C	R4				
1165/431	C	R4				
1166/1273	C	R9				
1169/469	C	R8				
1172/1274	C	R9				
1174/1220	C	R7				
1174/1272	C	R5				
1175/338	C	R5				
1182/463	L	R9				
1183/1262	C	R6				
1191/1374	C	R9				
1192/468	BR	R9				
1197/1263	C	R7				
1200/312	C	R1				
1201/352	C	R2				
1202/400	C	R5				
1202/431	C	R5				
1213/520	BR	R9				
1213/1272	BR	R9				
1214/1215	BR	R8				
1216/1251	C	R3				
1216/1253	BR	R9				
1217/1257	C	R5				
1217/1259	C	R2				
1218/1253	C	R9				
1218/1277	C	R9				
1219/440	WM	R9				
1219/1252	WM	R10				
1219/1253	WM	R10				
1220/1272	C	R5				
1221/429	C	R4				
1224/470A	C	R9				
1227/1273	C	R9				
1228/470A	C	R8				
1230/1249	C	R8				
1232/1215	C	R1				
1233/320	C	R2				

Die Combination	Metal	Rarity	VG	F	VF	Unc
1233/323	C	R3				
1234/400	C	R2				
1234/402	C	R9				
1235/415	C	R9				
1235/416	C	R2				
1236/1252	C	R9				
1236/1253	C	R8				
1236/1267	WM	R9				
1237/312	C	R2				
1238/431	C	R4				
1239/291	C	R2				
1239/375A	C	R1				
1239/381	C	R1				
1240/1257	C	R3				
1240/1259	C	R3				
1240/247	C	R3				
1241/252	C	R9				
1241/428	C	R9				
1241/1245	C	R9				
1242/1278	C	R7				
1243/255	C	R1				
1243/1215	C	R1				
1244/428	C	R9				
1244/1275	C	R9				
1245/428	C	R9				
1245/1245	C	R9				
1245/1275	C	R4				
1250/477	WM	R9				
1252/1277	C	R8				
1253/1277	BR	R8				
1264/1374	C	R8				
1265/1215	C	R3				
1268/1215	WM	R8				
1273/1342	C	R10				
1274/1274	C	R9				
1279/452A	BR	R9				
1285/1374	C	R9				
1353/1245	C	R9				
1353/1275	C	R9				
1374/472	C	R9				
1374/480A	C	R9				
1386/1247	C	R5				
1406/471	C	R2				
1407/471	C	R1				
1418/1158	C	R8				
1418/1419	C	R8				
1418/1420	C	R8				
1418/1422	C	R8				
1418/1423	C	R8				
1418/1424	C	R8				
1418/1425	C	R8				
1418/1426	C	R8				
1418/1427	C	R8				
1419/1158	C	R8				
1419/1420	C	R8				
1419/1422	C	R8				
1420/1158	C	R8				
1420/1422	C	R8				
1420/1423	C	R8				
1420/1424	C	R8				
1420/1425	C	R8				
1420/1426	C	R8				
1420/1427	C	R8				
1422/1423	C	R8				
1422/1424	C	R8				
1422/1425	C	R8				
1422/1426	BR	R8				
1422/1427	C	R8				
1423/516	BR	R5				
1423/517	BR	R6				
1423/518	BR	R8				
1423/1424	C	R8				
1423/1425	C	R8				
1423/1426	BR	R4				
1423/1427	C	R8				
1424/1425	C	R8				
1424/1426	C	R8				
1424/1427	C	R8				
1426/516	C	R8				
1426/1427	C	R8				
1919/1253	WM	R10				
1974/293	C	R5				
1974/375	C	R4				

See Pricing Table on page 380

The prices listed in this chart are typical for patriotic Civil War tokens in the grades and rarities listed. Some pieces may command higher or lower prices depending on their popularity.

VALUES FOR COPPER AND BRASS PATRIOTIC CIVIL WAR TOKENS

	GRADES			
RARITY	**VG**	**VF**	**EF**	**UNC**
RI	3.00	6.00	8.00	15.00
R2	3.00	6.00	8.00	15.00
R3	5.00	7.00	10.00	20.00
R4	6.00	10.00	15.00	25.00
R5	8.00	12.00	20.00	35.00
R6	10.00	20.00	35.00	50.00
R7	15.00	35.00	55.00	80.00
R8	20.00	50.00	90.00	125.00
R9	30.00	80.00	135.00	200.00
R10		SPECULATIVE		

Prices are given for copper and brass specimens, as they are the two most common metals used in striking Civil war tokens. Tokens struck in other metals sell at a premium. Those metals generally sell at the price listed in the chart above, plus a percentage premium, listed below:

Copper-nickel	40-80%
German Silver	100-200%
Lead	15-30%
Nickel	50-100%
Silver	100-200%
White Metal	25-50%
Zinc-plated	30-50%
Overstruck on a Copper-nickel cent	50-100%
Overstruck on a U.S. silver dime	300% & up

Silver-plated and gold-plated Civil War tokens sometimes command a premium, but in general sell at the same price as their base metal.

PATRIOTIC DIE PHOTOS

36 45 48 51 59

67 107 117 128 130

136 142 201 209 212

221 237 239 240 241

247 252 255 256

258 259 289 299

PATRIOTIC DIE PHOTOS

332 334 337 340 341

347 350 372 397

414 415 420 422 434

445 446 453 471 474

475 478 480 481 485

489 502 510B 526

PATRIOTIC DIE PHOTOS

1235 1250 NY 105H-2a

NY 630K-3a NY 630Y-1a

NY 630AA-1a NY 630AD-1a

NY 630AQ-3a NY 630BB-7a

PA 464A-4b

TABLE IX*

Key to Flag Tokens ("Dix" obverses) - Dies 203 through 218

Die	Number of stars in flag	Number of bars in flag	Cap shape	End of pole in relation to 1	Shape of right botton end of flag	Position of top right star
203	25	5	Short, round, convex	Even with base	Very slight fold	Opposite 1st bar
204	25	5	Long, thin concave	About midway up side	Almost straight	Between 1st bar and space below
205	25	6	Long, thin concave	Even with base, very close	Moderate bulge	At corner of flag
206	25	6	Long, thin concave	Opposite end of top serif	Slight inward dip	At corner of flag
207	25	6	Long, thin convex	Even with base	Heavy bulge	Opposite 1st bar
			2nd star down & 2nd star in from upper left recut			
208	26	6	Long, thin pointed	Just above base	Almost straight	Slightly below 1st bar
209	25	6	Long, thin pointed	About 1/3 up side	Slight bulge	Opposite 1st bar
210	36	5	Short convex	Even with base	Short inward dip	Slightly below 1st bar
211	36	5	Short convex	Even with base	Short inward dip	Slightly below 1st bar
			Same hub as 210, but no raised rim			
212	30	6	Short convex	Very slight bulge	Opposite 2nd bar	
213	12	5	Thick concave	Divides date	Straight	No stars
			STAND BY THE FLAG around			
214	25	6	Short convex	No date	Heavy bulge	Opposite 2nd bar
			No date, diamond below			
215	25	6	Short convex	No date	Heavy bulge	Opposite 2nd bar
			Same as 215, no diamond			
216	16	5	NO CAP	No date	Irregular	Below 1st bar
			Flag in wreath, 13 stars inside			
217	30	7	NO CAP	No date	Straight	No stars above
			LONG MAY IT WAVE around			
218	20 (?)	6	Stubby cap (?)	Date above flag	Moderate bulge	No stars above
			Warrior with flag over shoulder			

TABLE X*

Key to "The Federal Union Must and Shall Be Preserved"

Die	Position of "I" of IT relation to FEDERAL	Position of "P" of PRE-SERVED in respect to THE and the circle of stars	Remarks
219	Directly below center of "F"	Points to right of last star	"A" of AND points below "T" of IT
220	Directly below center of "F"	Points to right of last star	"A" of AND points to left foot of "M" of MUST
221	Directly below left center of "F"	Points to left foot of "T" of THE	
222	Points to space between "E" of THE & "F" of FEDERAL	Points to left foot of "T" of THE	Die break at foot of "T" of THE. 'E' of BE over 'Y'
223	Identical to 222		Error "BY" instead of "BE"
224	Points of space between "E" of THE & "F" of FEDERAL	Points to center of "T" of THE	
225	Directly below left side of first "E" of FEDERAL	Points to right of last star	
226	Directly below center of "F"	Points to right of last star	Stars at side of SHALL are very large with center consisting of two concentric circles

* Adapted from Fuld, M. and G. ***The Numismatist*** 67:449 (1954)

TABLE XI

Key to Army & Navy in Wreath Dies - "Army & Navy" STRAIGHT

Dies 296 through 319

Die	Point of left sword handle	Point of right sword handle	Position of end of left top leaf	Position of end of right top leaf	Bow shape	Remarks
296	Near left serif of N	Near right side of Y	Slightly to right of A	Over right serif of Y	Open, downward to right	No bow ends
297	Below left serif of N	Slightly to right side of Y	To left center of R	Over right side of M	Closed, downward to left	Sword handles touch leaves
298	To left of N	Below center of Y	Between RM	Over right side of M	Open slightly downward to left	Sword handles touch leaves
298A	To left of N	Below center of Y	Between RM	Over right side of M	Open slightly downward to left	Virtually identical to 298, but with lower relief border and denticles
299	Below left center of N	Below left side of Y	Over center of R	Between MY	Small, no slope	Sword handles merge with leaves
300	Below right side of N	Below center of Y	Over left side of R	Over right side of M	Medium, no slope	Star between wreath
301	To the right of center of N	Below left side of Y	Over left side of R	Over right side of M	Small, no slope	Star between wreath
302	Below left side of N	Below center of Y	Over left side of R	Over right side of M	Medium, no slope	Ends of wreath almost invisible, star
303	Below left side of N	Slightly to right of Y	Over center of R	Between MY	Medium, downward to left	Small star between wreath
304	Below right side of N	Slightly to left of Y	Over left side of R	Slightly to right of center of M	Small, no slope	Crudely struck
305	No swords	No Swords	Over left side of R	Over left side of Y	Double bow	Small star
306	Below left side of N	Slightly to right of Y	Over left side of M	Over right side of M	Medium, slightly to left	Sword handle just touches leaves
307	To left of center of N	Slightly to right of Y	Over left side of R	Between MY	Small, slightly to left	Very small sword handles
308	Far to left of N	To right of Y	Over center of R	Over center of M	Large, slightly to left	3 leaves on end of left top of wreath
309	Far to left of N	Far to right of Y	Over center of R	Over center of M	Open, downward to left	
310	To left of N	To right of Y	Over center of R	To left of center of M	Open, slightly downward to left	Wreath very close to inscription

Table XI — Continued

Die	Point of left sword handle	Point of right sword handle	Position of end of left top leaf	Position of end of right top leaf	Bow shape	Remarks
311	Sword handles turned upwards		Over center of R	Over center of M	Double Bow	ARMY and NAVY slightly curved
312	Below left serif of N	To right of Y	To right center of R	To right center of M	Medium, open downwards to left	
313	Below left serif of N	Slightly to right of Y	Over center of R	Over center of M	Medium, downward to left	Left top of wreath has 2 leaves
314	Slightly to left of N	To right of Y	Over left center of R	Over center of M	Closed, downward to left	
315	To left of N	To right of Y	Over center of R	Over right center of M	Medium, downward to left	Right sword handle merges with leaves
316	To left and even with base of N	To right and even with base of Y	Over center of R	Over left side of M	Large, downward to left	
317	To left of N	Right of Y	Over left side of R	Over center of M	Large, downward to left	
318	Below center of N	Below center of Y	To right side of R	To right side of M	Very small, no slope	
319	To left of center of N	To right of center of Y	To right side of R	To right center of M	Medium, downward to left	

TABLE XII*

Key to "Army and Navy" dies - all dies have "Army and Navy" curved with star between wreath. Dies 320 through 329

Die	Wreath Description	Remarks
320	Left side of wreath has eight berries. Right side has eight acorns	Long prominent ray points to left side of "M" of Army, small ring on anchor
321	Left side of wreath has eight berries. Right side has eight acorns	Left side of wreath made of oak leaves, being different from any others in series
322	Wreath has no berries	Long, prominent ray from star points to right side of "R" of Army
323	Left side of wreath contains eight berries. Right side has no acorns	Anchor rope shows at juncture between wreaths. Prominent ray points between "RM" of Army
324	Left side of wreath contains six berries. Right side has no acorns	Anchor rope shows at juncture between wreaths
325	Wreath has no berries	No prominent ray at star. Ring of anchor very eccentric shape, similar to egg on side
326	Wreath has no berries	Long, prominent ray from star points to upper right arch of the "M" of Army
327	Wreath has no berries	Anchor rope shows at juncture between wreaths. Die break from base of "Y" of Navy to sword handle
328	Left side of wreath contains ten berries. Right side has ten acorns	Anchor rope shows at juncture between wreaths

* Adapted from Fuld, M. and G. ***The Numismatist*** 67:449 (1954)

TABLE XIII

Key to "Not One Cent" reverses. Dies 354 through 385

Die	Position of left side of N of NOT	NOT with or with-out serifs	Number of berries in wreath		Position of berry near C of CENT	Position of berry near base of T of CENT	Remarks
			Left side	Right side			
354	Left side of O	With	No berries			Star rather than bow joining wreath	
355	To left of center of O	Without	10	9	Even with base	Even with base	
356	Over center of O	With	8	8	Almost even with top	Slightly above base	
357	To right side of O	With	7	6	Almost to center	Almost to center	
358	Between O and N	With	10	10	Even with top	Below base	
359	Between O and N	With	10	10	Slightly above bottom	Even with base	
360	To right side of O	With	10	10	1/3 up side	Slightly above base	
361	Between O and N	With	8	8	2/3 up side	Almost to center	H just above bow
362	Between O and N	With	8	10	Even with bottom	2/3 up side	JGW below CENT
363	To left of N	With	8	8	2/3 up side	Even with top	Diamond below CENT
364	To right side of N	With	8	8	Slightly over 1/2 up side	2/3 up side	Eagle's head below CENT
365	To left of center of O	Without	No berries			E far from wreath	
366	To left of center of O	Without	No berries			E almost touches wreath	
367	To right of center of O	With	No berries			NOT large, O is oval	
368	To right side of O	With	No berries			NOT large, O is round	
369	To right side of O	With	No berries			CENT in smaller letters than ONE	
370	To right side of O	With	No berries			NOT far below wreath ends	
371	To right side of O	With	No berries			NOT close to wreath ends	
372	To right side of O	With	No berries			T of NOT almost touches wreath	
373		With	No berries			NOT very high between ends of wreath	

Table XIII — Continued

Die	Position of left side of N of NOT	NOT with or without serifs	Number of berries in wreath		Position of berry near C of CENT	Position of berry near base of T of CENT	Remarks
			Left side	Right side			
374	To far right side of O	Without	7	6	Even with center	None	Star below CENT: star between wreath ends
375	Between O and N	Without	34 total	no bow	Even with center	Slightly above bottom	1863 below CENT, berry between OT of NOT
375A	To far right of O	Without	36 total	no bow	Even with bottom	1/3 up side	1863 below CENT; berry above T of NOT
376	To right of O	With	28 total	no bow	One even with top due below bottom	Slightly below top	E.S. below CENT
377	To right of O	Without	32 total	no bow	1/3 up side	Even with center	L. ROLOFF below CENT. L beneath right side of C
378	Between ON	With	32 total	no bow	1/2 up side	2/3 up side	L. ROLOFF below CENT. L beneath left side of E
379	To right of O	Without	32 total	no bow	Even with bottom	Almost touches die break from base of T	
380	To right of O	Without	32 total	no bow	2/3 up side, slightly below bottom	Even with bottom, even with top	
381	To center of O	Without	44 total	no bow	Even with center	Even with center	
382	To right of O	Without	32 total	no bow	Even with center	Even with base	
383		Without	4	3	Even with bottom	Very near base	Shield below CENT
384	To center of O	With	32 total	no bow	1/3 up side	2/3 up side	Four stars in triangle below CENT
385	To right of center of O	With	No berries			Very crude die, no bow	

TABLE XIV*

Key to "Dix" Token Reverses. Dies 408 through 416

Die	Outer Circle	Position of S of SHOOT below ATTEMPT	Position of T of SPOT above IT	Position of H of HIM
408	Yes	S below AT	T slightly above T of It	To right of S of ATTEMPTS
409	Yes	S slightly to right of first T	T slightly below T of IT	To left of T of TO
410	Yes	S below A	T between I & T of IT	Between S of ATTEMPTS and T of TO
411	Yes	S slightly to left of first T	T opposite I of IT	Between S of ATTEMPTS and T of TO
412	Yes	S below A	T opposite T of IT	Below T of TO
		Inner circle rope-like		
413	Yes	S below A	T slightly below T of IT	Below T of TO
		Almost identical to 412. Inner circle denticles not rope-like		
413A	Yes	S slightly to right of first T	T opposite D of DOWN	Below T of TO
		See Plate XXII		
414	Yes	S slightly to right of A	T opposite R of TEAR	Slightly to right of S of ATTEMPTS
		Die reads SPOOT		
415	No	S slightly to left of A	T between R of TEAR and I of IT	To left of T of TO
416	No	S slightly to right of A	T opposite I of IT	To right of T of TO

U.S. Trade Tokens

1866-1889

A catalog of the private coinage and advertising tokens of an industrializing America, from the close of the Civil War to the centennial of Washington's inaugural.

Special Consultants

Joseph Schmidt
David Schenkman
Steve Tanenbaum
George Fuld
Gregory Brunk
Hank Thoele

Broadway, New York, with the 100's and 200's in foreground, shows the tangle of electrification overhead about 1880. After the great Blizzard of 1888 such wires went underground. This section of Broadway was an emporium for jewelers. (Courtesy New York Historical Society)

THE BUSTLING POST-CIVIL WAR ERA

This section first appeared as a book in 1983. It sold out completely, requiring the publishers to bring out a new revised edition to meet the now-continuous demand from the public, in 1988.

Now this large section is revised again — prices are changed, mistakes corrected, mavericks attributed, footnotes expanded, probable dates of issue narrowed.

It also is much larger, thanks to the generosity of our contributors and the quality of token research in the last five years.

The 1983 book cataloged the 1876 Centennial cards exhaustively. That so few additions in this area have been reported since then, attests to the thoroughness of the initial effort.

The earlier efforts also cataloged a large number of counterstamps — many for the first time. These have grown in legitimacy in the interval, and the present work adds a good many more.

Hundreds of maverick trade checks — including many of the billiard-related type — have been attributed by the efforts of individuals and societies, and these are included. In no segment of token research has the going been more slow — or more satisfying — and readers will discover many of their "unknowns" are now slotted chronologically and geographically.

A good many reported but unverified attributions are also included in special addenda after several Midwestern states, so the user of this reference may be fully informed.

Coverage of picker checks, primarily from Maryland and Delaware, is greatly expanded.

Better quality photographs — and more of them — are interspersed throughout the section. We have added appendices at the back of this book which should open new horizons for the student.

A special feature of the post-Civil War period is the Centennial of the United States celebrations which took place in Philadelphia in 1876. The Centennial spawned a large number of special tokens — made as much for collectors as for the general public — carrying the names of many prominent merchants of the Seventies.

This series is dominated by such stock devices as the Liberty Bell, Libertas Americana medal, Continental Army soldier, Independence Hall, etc. An attractive Abraham Lincoln bust by Bolen was also introduced at about the same time or somewhat earlier.

The so called "Centennial cards" were in many respects a throwback to the Golden Age of token issuance in the late 1850's — they are decorative, and not needed (or used) as money. There are several independent series of 1876 Centennial cards, by Lingg, by Kline, by Bolen, etc., and all of them are covered in this reference.

At the same time, though, the burgeoning needs of trade were calling for an ever-widening issuance of trade tokens, which were utilitarian in appearance and worth a fixed amount — 25 cents, one drink, one shave, one admittance, one cigar, one tune.

In *U.S. Trade Tokens 1866-1889,* the user will discover that it contains pieces of all of these categories:

- Store cards
- Advertising checks
- Work, Job, Picker and Railroad checks and talleys
- Saloon and Billiard tokens
- Checks for value
- Exposition and Festival medalets
- Counterstamped coins
- Other related items

There are a number of post-Civil War series which are **not** included in this book, principally because good references already exist for them and this book is intended to serve the interests of collectors of the many series listed above. Those series not included are:

- Transportation tokens
- Hard Rubber tokens and medals
- Embossed Shell and Mirror cards
- Military and Sutler tokens
- Political campaign tokens (except Store Card mules)

Genealogical Research

A number of basic historical source documents were used to enhance the data included in this section. The facts are presented, whenever possible, after digestion and editing.

Once, five years ago, while going over the notes extracted from the tedious chore of studying aging books and reading microfilm, I said silently to myself, "It's a good thing you've got 49 years of numismatic background. This is hard stuff to absorb."

When one assembles a catalog such as this, one finds the necessity of dealing with names — thousands of them. America is rich in source material, however, so it becomes a matter of examining enough printed material, over enough time, to sift out useful tidbits of information.

The primary source documents include the decennial census records, city directories, county history books, directories of specialized professions, and books containing rosters of certain professions known to be active in token-making or counterstamping: silversmiths, gunsmiths, stencil cutters and sealmakers and daguerreotypers, for example.

We owe a special debt of gratitude to the Mormon Genealogical Library in Salt Lake City, Utah, a repository of more than 60 million family names. Nowhere else in North America can one find such a wealth of census records, graves records, very early city directories and other business directories, land registrations, etc. I spent many days there deeply immersed in the "people history" of our nation.

Many token collectors are amateur historians. Their breadth of knowledge on commercial America might astound professional historians. Some of these who were especially helpful in this section were: Byron Johnson, Gary Pipher, Steve Tanenbaum, Bruce W. Smith, Dave Schenkman, Bob Schuman, Mike Pfefferkorn, Joe Schmidt, Damia Francis, Joseph Levine and Hank Thoele.

Maverick Counterstamps

Counterstamped coins which bear locales of the issuer, or for which the locale has been deduced by research, are included in their proper place under state listings. Those maverick counterstamps which suggest mercantile reasons for their existence, or which have been found on several different coins, appear under the Maverick section if their locale is not known.

All counterstamps have been examined by the author or one of his major collaborators, so their existence is verified, and many of these have been photographed. The listing thus is supplemental to lists published earlier in *The Numismatist* such as those by Gould or Hallenbeck. The accumulations of counterstamps of all these specialists have been examined: Steve Tanenbaum, Frank Kovacs, David Schenkman, John Cheramy, Roy Van Ormer, Hank Spangenberger, Kurt R. Krueger, Rich Hartzog, Dr. Gregory Brunk, Gary Pipher, Chester L. Krause, Byron Johnson, Joseph Schmidt, Stanley L. Steinberg, David Jerdee, Kean Leiker.

Cross-references to the published lists of Dr. Gregory Brunk, Kenneth Hallenbeck, Maurice M. Gould, Stanley Steinberg, Joseph Schmidt, Frank Duffield and others are included throughout the catalog.

One theme that recurs frequently on American counterstamped coins employs certain words, such as CAST STEEL, CAST STEEL WARRANTED, WARRANTED, PATENT, etc. Sometimes these words are accompanied by initials, names, locales or dates.

We believe these terms are associated with the manufacture of firearms, and may have been parts of the punches used to mark lock-plates and other metallic portions of muskets, rifles, revolvers, etc.

These terms also are associated with punches used to mark knives, axes, cutlery or tools. The number of counterstamps using such terms is large enough to admit of other possibilities as well. As time passes, more of these maverick stampings will be attributed by collectors.

It is not likely the "cast steel" type of counterstamp was used for advertising purposes. More likely is that handy coins were used to test the punches — or to create personal pocket pieces for workmen.

"Cast steel warranted" was a common product guarantee of the 19th century.

Author and numismatist Dwight B. Demeritt Jr. of Brooklyn, N.Y., who wrote a book about the gunsmiths of Maine in 1973, observed in a private letter to your author in 1984:

"I noted in that book that Maine gunsmiths seemed to like to advertise by counterstamping United States coins."

He added, "Coins bearing the stamp WARRANTED CAST STEEL may well be the work of gunsmiths. A number of gunsmiths had dies with that phrase which they usually applied to the barrels of their guns."

Numbering System

An entirely new numbering system has been devised for this section. Only a tiny fraction of the pieces catalogued herein were listed in the references by Adams and Miller, and thus an adaptation of the Adams-Miller numbering system was not considered appropriate.

The Rulau numbers used throughout this section constitute a system in which the state and city of issue (where known) are abbreviated as part of the number, and then a numerical system has been applied which takes into account some peculiarities of the 1866-1889 token-issuing period.

Cross-reference in the catalog to the numbers previously assigned to the same tokens by Adams-Miller, Wright, Kappen, Storer, King, Rulau-Fuld, Duffield, Brunk, Schenkman, Lipscomb, Gould and other cataloguers, is extensive. Users of the catalog should have little difficulty in checking with entries on their token envelopes or in their collection ledgers.

Al-Bi 7 identifies the Dude Saloon one drink token of the 1880's issued in Birmingham, Alabama.

Ca-Va 3 identifies the Will J. Shinn counterstamped quarter dollar of Vallejo, Calif., circa 1870's.

Il-Ch 14 indentifies the Dacosta 75-cent token of the 1880's issued in Chicago, Ill.

Special numbers have also been applied to non-local issues (**NL-12,** for example), and to mavericks, those unattributed pieces which plague every collector (**Mv 3,** etc.)

Metals

Brass	copper-zinc alloy, yellowish
Bronze	copper-tin alloy, brownish
Copper	pure copper, reddish
Cupronickel	copper-nickel alloy*
Galvanized Iron	zinc-iron, grayish
German Silver	copper-nickel-zinc alloy*
Gold	gold-copper alloy
Iron	pure iron, grayish
Nickel	pure nickel, magnetic*
Oroide	copper-zinc alloy, golden
Pot Metal	lead-based alloy, dark
Silver	silver-copper alloy
Steel	iron alloy, silvery
Tin	pure tin**
Vulcanite	hardened rubber
White Metal	lead-tin alloy

* It is frequently difficult to tell nickel and its principal alloys apart. New, they all resemble silver and look much alike. Pure nickel is magnetic, however, and only a small amount of impurity removes the magnetic quality. Cupronickel resists tarnish, while German silver (also called nickel-silver, argentan and other names) tarnishes much like silver. The catalog may well be in error in describing some of these nickel-alloy pieces.

** Pure tin is almost never used in token manufacture. Old catalogs frequently refer to "tin" pieces; what is meant is generally silvered white metal.

NOTE: Certain other substances are catalogued herein, namely Leather, Cardboard, Celluloid, Bone, Ivory, Mother-of-Pearl, etc. These terms are self-explanatory and should cause little trouble.

The Role of Aluminum

Very few trade tokens, store cards or medals were made of aluminum prior to 1890. A small number of commemorative medals were struck in the 1880's, and the U.S. Mint used aluminum even earlier for pattern coins and for assay medals.

There is good reason for the sparsity of aluminum used in the period covered by this reference, 1866-1889. In 1854 aluminum was worth $17 an ounce (gold was $20 at the time), but there wasn't a pound of it in the world available for the coining process. By 1859 the only aluminum refinery in the world (in France), had produced a total of 60 pounds of aluminum and was selling it at $17 a pound. It was much more expensive than silver at this time.

In the United States, during the 1860's, or 1870's and early 1880's, aluminum was selling at about $2 an ounce — twice the price of silver. When the first U.S. electrolytic process for refining aluminum began in November, 1888, aluminum was being offered at "several dollars a pound."

Then in 1889 its price stood at $3 a pound; by 1891 it had dropped to $1.50 a pound, and in 1893 to 75 cents per pound. During 1889 the plant was producing 50 pounds a day, but there was almost no market for the metal.

Thus it can be seen that aluminum, expensive before the 1888 breakthrough in refining the metal from its ores, was suitable only for certain medals and a few store cards (such as presentation pieces for employees) before 1889. Almost all the aluminum tokens listed by Dr. Wright, therefore, can be assumed — safely — to emanate from the 1890's, and the number of aluminum pieces included in this section is minimal (some that are included properly belong to the 1890-on period but complete some series or literary thought and thus find space herein.)

Interestingly, by 1910 aluminum had become so cheap — and its novelty had by then worn off — that there was a retreat from its use in preparing medals and store cards, though its use in tokens continued. This situation was not reversed until about 1950, after the aluminum industry had begun an "education " program to induce aluminum's use in almost every conceivable form. A byproduct of the propaganda campaign is that aluminum medals once more became fashionable.

For the collector concerned with "dating" his elusive tokens, the history of aluminum's use is most helpful. The simple rule: If it's aluminum, it's post-1889. (The few exceptions, we trust, are cataloged in these pages.)

DATES OF ISSUE FOR BILLIARD TOKEN DISTRIBUTORS

The list has been expanded to include companies other than strictly billiard supply manufacturers. Included are canning machinery suppliers, manufacturers of saloon fixtures, bagatelle tables, etc. There is no reason to believe these companies actually struck tokens themselves — they probably subcontracted the work for their clients out to tokenmakers in many different cities.

Dates in parentheses are probable dates of issue, not dates the companies were in business under that name. Charles Pick & Co. were in business until 1915 but probably stopped supplying tokens before 1895. The "rarity guide" is to determine comparative availability of the distributors' products.

(Research courtesy of Hank Thoele, Tom Wall, Chicago Historical Society, Wisconsin Historical Society, Active Token Collectors Organization)

COMPARATIVE RARITY GUIDE:

R1 Very Common

R2 Common

R3 Sometimes Available

R4 Difficult to Find

R5 Very Difficult

-0-0-0-0-0-0-0-0-0-0-0-0-0-

BRUNSWICK COMPANIES:

Brunswick Bros., 1875-76, No tokens

Brunswick & Co., 1877-94, R2

J. M. Brunswick Billiard Mfg. Co., 1872-73, No tokens

J. M. Brunswick & Balke Co., Chicago, 1880-84, R1

Brunswick Balke Collender Co., Chicago, 1884-1914, R1

H. W. Collender Co., Chicago, 1875-84, R5

E. Brunswick Billiard Table Co., S.F., 1887-91, R4

OTHER BILLIARDS SUPPLIERS

American Billiard Co., Cincinnati, ca 1895, R5

J. D. Babcock & Co., Syracuse, N.Y., 1900-02, R5

The Ballingal Pool Table Check, ?, R3

Century Table Co., Chicago, ?, R5

Garden City Billiard Co., Chicago, 1882-97, R3

W. H. Griffith & Co., New York, 1880-98, R4

Henry Gunklach & Sons, Cincinnati, 1883-1907, R5

August Jungblut & Co., S.F. 1881-91, R4

Aug. Kern B.S., St. Louis, ?-1911, R3

George Kuehl & Bro., Chicago, 1881-82, R3

George Kuehl Billiard Supplies, Chicago, 1886-1905, R3

Merle & Heaney Mfg. Co., Chicago, 1903-13, R4

The Minn Billiard Co., Milwaukee, 1897-1918, R4

W. Morris, Islington, Birmingham, England, ?, R5

National Billiard Mfg. Co., Cincinnati, 1883-1920 ?, R3 — (A. Gunklach & Co.)

George E. Phelan, New York, ca 1876, R4

R. Rothschild's Sons, Cincinnati, 1881-89, R4

Estate of St. Germain, S.F., 1892, R5

St. Germain Billiard Co., S.F., 1892-1900 ?, —

A. E. Schmidt (billiard tables), St. Louis, 1898-1970's, R1

E. Schmidt (billiard tables), St. Louis, ?, R4

Schulenberg Billiard Tables, Detroit, 1851-1920 ?, R5

D. W. Seely, Elmira, N.Y., ca 1890, R5

Nic Stoll, Chicago, 1886-87, R5

Stoll & Merz, Chicago, 1884-85, R4

Jacob Strahle, San Francisco, 1881-91, R3

Superior Billiard Co., St. Louis, ?, R5

Tivoli Table Co., Chicago, ca 1901, R4

C. Tuckhorn & Co., Chicago, 1880-90, R5

H. Tuckhorn, Chicago, 1893-98, R5

S. Twist, Islington, Birmingham, England, ?, R5

Charles Passow, Chicago, 1876-1905, R3

Charles Passow & Sons, Chicago, 1888-1915, R3

FIXTURES & CANNERY SUPPLIERS

Becker Schnepel B. S. Co. (bakery supplies), St. Louis, ca 1912, R5

Hoole Mfg. Co. (railroad supplies?), New York, 1890's, R5

Kernan Mfg. Co. (sporting goods), Chicago, 1890's-1915, R5

Koken B.S. Co. (barber supplies), St. Louis, 1888-1906, R3

F. Messmer Faucet Co., St. Louis, 1885-91, R5

F. Messmer Mfg. Co. (fixtures), St. Louis, 1892-98, R4

Chas. Pick & Co., Chicago, 1878-92, R2

Porter, Wittgenfeld & Co. (saloon supplies), Cincinnati, ?, R5

A. A. Plastridge (bagatelle), Providence, ?, R3

Sprague Canning Machinery Co., Chicago, 1901-11, R3

Daniel G. Trench & Co., Chicago, 1883-1914, R5

Western Supply Co., Kansas City, ca 1889, R5

GERMAN SILVER KEY CHECKS, ETC. OF THE 1880'S

The mail order firm of Peck & Snyder, 126 Nassau St., New York, listed in its 1886 catalog a group of German silver checks for sale which turn up occasionally stamped with names and cities and sometimes businesses. Since this mail order catalog entry proves conclusively our contention in the first edition that these were early I.D. tags of the 1880's, we are reproducing the designs from the catalog herewith.

These checks were fairly expensive in 1886, 25 cents each (inscribed brass checks were only $2.30 per hundred, for comparison).

Items numbered 72, 74, 75 and 76 are included in several of our catalog entries under New York, Pennsylvania, Texas, etc.

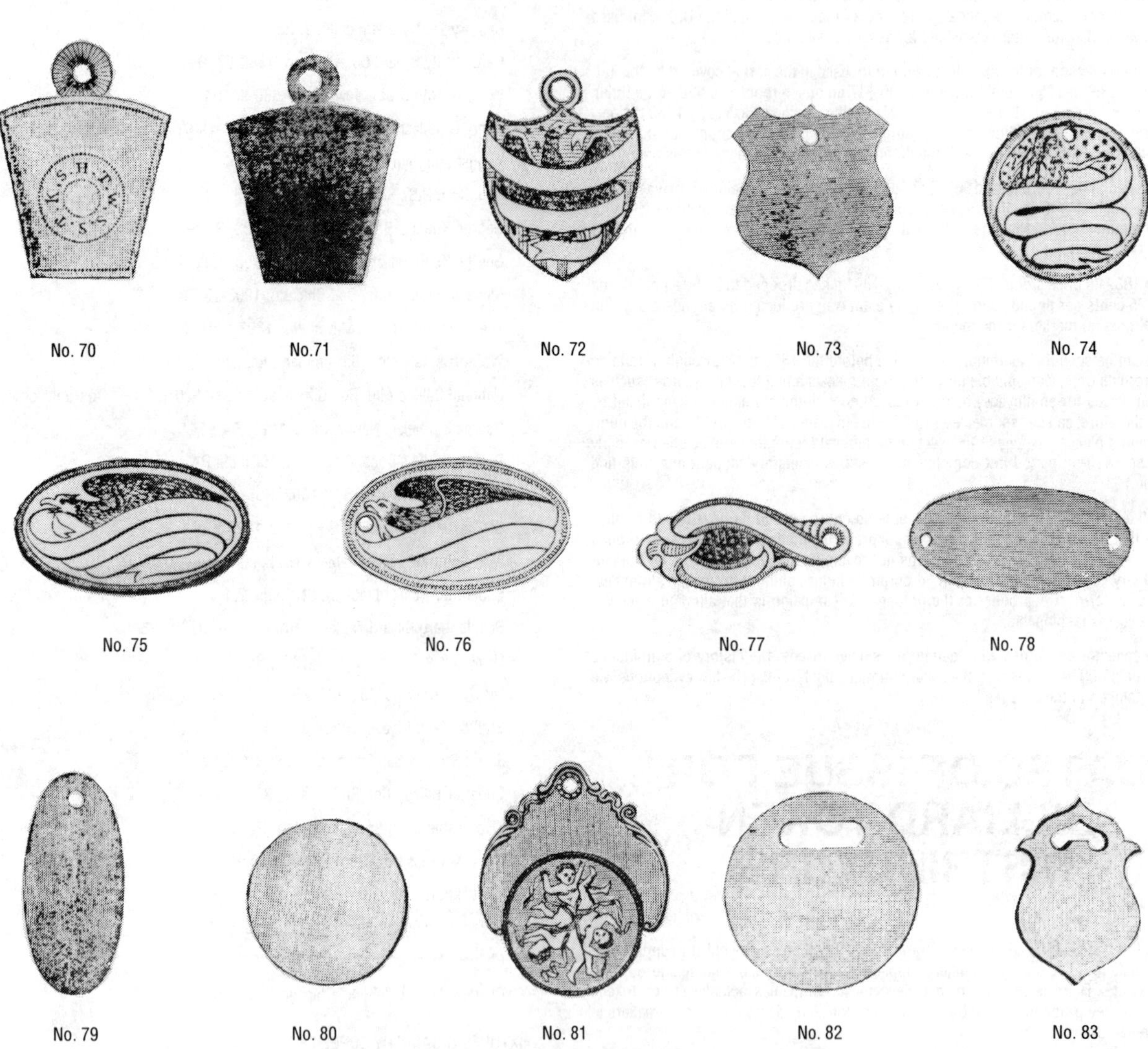

No. 70 No.71 No. 72 No. 73 No. 74 No. 75 No. 76 No. 77 No. 78 No. 79 No. 80 No. 81 No. 82 No. 83

BOTTLES

It is possible to locate collector bottles of products associated with the world of American tokens. A brief description of some of these bottles, and the price one would have to expect to pay for them from antique traders, follows:

AYER'S CHERRY PECTORAL: rectangular, light green glass, 7 inches high (Dr. J.C. Ayer) $30.00

AYER's HAIR VIGOR: peacock blue glass $25.00

AYER'S AGUE CURE: rectangular, aqua glass, 7 inches high $10.00

DRAKE'S PLANTATION BITTERS: cabin-shaped, 4 to 6-log, various $70.00 to $850.00

HOUCK'S PATENT PANACEA, BALTIMORE: open pontil, aqua glass, 6-1/4 inches high $140.00

STEINFELD'S FRENCH COGNAC BITTERS: cabin-shaped, yellow-amber glass $2300.00

UDOLPHO WOLFE'S AROMATIC SCHNAPPS: light green glass $15.00

HALLMARKS OF SILVERSMITHS

Silversmithy was an important fact of American life from about 1670 to 1870, but then mass-produced tableware and flatware gradually replaced the hallmarked works of individual craftsmen. Not many silversmith hallmarks appear on pieces in the 1866-1889 time period.

Still, a few generalizations are in order here.

The following list of symbols and words made up the 'quality marks' in general use by silversmiths, and these sometimes appear counterstamped on coins — alone or with a mark of a craftsman. Words such as COIN, DOLLAR, STANDARD or PURE came into use about 1830 to indicate 'coin silver' — that is, .900 fine, the same as U.S. silver coinage.

STERLING indicated (and still does today) the British silver standard of .925 fine.

The words were used somewhat indiscriminately. Silver objects down to about .800 fine were still marked COIN or PURE, and the words gradually came to indicate pure silver all the way through, rather than silver-plated.

C	Coin silver
COIN	
D	Dollar (coin silver)
DOLLAR	
PREMIUM	(used mostly in New York City)
PURE	
PURE COIN	
PURE COIN SILVER	
PURE SILVER COIN	
RARE	
S	Sterling
STANDARD	(used mostly in Philadelphia)
STERLING	
10:15	(used only in Baltimore)
11 OZ	(used only in Baltimore)

CENTENNIAL DIES

A

B

C

D

E

F

G

H

J

K

L

OV

Memorial Hall

V

W

X

Y

Z

Arrangement of the Centennial Cards

A special feature of this catalog is the inclusion of all those store cards issued before and during the Centennial of the United States in 1876. This grouping of store cards, which has always had special relevance for historically minded collectors, is very perplexing to the novice collector. Partly this is due to the early efforts of Wright, Adams and others to list all the issuers and pieces known to them — mostly without benefit of illustration.

In 1981 Arlie R. Slabaugh cleared up much of the confusion in his booklet on the Lingg-struck cards, and in this reference we are detailing a good number more of Lingg pieces than were included in Slabaugh, as well as cataloguing all those Kline, Bolen and other Centennial-type cards known to the author and his contributors.

The Kline, Bolen and other cards are treated as all other tokens, with full narrative description after each listing. A special arrangement of our own has been adopted for the Lingg cards — those which recur most frequently and which are usually thought of when the term "Centennial cards" is used.

There are 11 obverse dies measuring 23 millimeters (slightly larger than U.S. nickel size); 5 obverse dies measuring 19mm (U.S. cent size); and 1 oval die measuring 25 by 20mm. Each Lingg die is assigned a letter. (A few special obverse dies, SM, SP, etc., are described under their issuer.

Here is a listing of the Lingg Centennial dies; the date shown is the latest date appearing on the die.

	23 Millimeter Dies	
Die A	Libertas Americana	1776
Die B	Liberty Bell, 13 stars	1776
Die C	Liberty Bell, dashes	1776
Die D	Two heads	No date
Die E	Continental soldier	1876
Die F	Maryland arms	No date
Die G	Carpenter's Hall	1774
Die H	Independence Hall	1776
Die J	Public buildings	No date
Die K	Capitol	No date
Die L	Watch	1857
	19 Millimeter Dies	
Die V	Memorial Hall	1876
Die W	Liberty Bell, small letters	1876
Die X	Liberty Bell, large letters	1876
Die Y	Independence Hall	1776
Die Z	New Masonic Hall	No date
	Oval 25 by 20 Millimeter Dies	
Die OV	Independence Hall	1876

There are well over 600 design and metal varieties in this series, plus at least 30 mulings of obverse dies with each other (no issuer name on token). In addition, there are a number of minor die varieties and die striation varieties (not catalogued) which would push this total higher.

Most of the Centennial cards are scarce. It is doubtful if any merchant ordered as many as 1,000 pieces of any one type. Many of the specimens made for collectors by the token-makers were in the 5 to 25 mintage range.

The cards are generally priced in this volume for EF and Unc. only, since few actually received wear. Some did serve as pocket pieces (as they were intended to do) and show much wear, but these are the exceptions. In a few cases, F and VF specimens are priced where they are known to exist.

All Centennial tokens have plain edges and most are well struck up.

The Libertas Americana design (die A) is probably the most common occurring motif in the series. Yet it is also the most sought after by token collectors who are not specialists in the Centennial series. The device is a reduced-size imitation of the DuVivier medal struck at the Paris Mint to honor "American Liberty" on the occasion of the 1776 Declaration of Independence. The flowing hair Liberty head also was captured on the U.S.' earliest Large cent designs in 1793.

As one of America's favorite medallic design concepts, it is only natural that collectors should seek out the Libertas Americana type in preference to the stodgier dies with buildings (G, H, J, K, OV, V, Y and Z) or Liberty Bells (B, C, W and X).

A plate of Lingg Centennial card obverse dies appears here. The cards are listed in this manner under their issuers, and each reverse die (text side) is described under the issuer. In this manner line listings which save space and are easy to use are applied to the Lingg-struck series. (See Lingg & Bro., Philadelphia, for more details on the Centennial cards in the catalog itself.)

ALABAMA

BANK SALOON
Birmingham, Ala.

Rulau	Date	Metal	Size	F	VF	EF	Unc
Al-Bi 3	(1880's)	GS	16mm	—	—	250.	—

BANK SALOON / S. AND L. (AND diagonally right) / BIRMINGHAM / (ornament) / ALA. Rv: 2 1/2. Plain edge. Only 1 specimen known. (Roy J. Wood coll.)

Published here for the first time, this token surfaced only in February, 1994. For history of Bank Saloon, see under Dude Saloon below. S. and L. were the proprietors, Soloman and Levi.

THE DUDE SALOON
Birmingham, Ala.

Rulau	Date	Metal	Size	VG	F	VF	Unc
Al-Bi 7	(1880's)	GS	30mm	—	—	350.	—

Man with top hat and tails standing, walking stick under right arm, left hand flicking ash from a cigar, monocle on the left eye. Above: THE DUDE SALOON. Below: BIRMINGHAM, ALA. Rv: I O U . / (ornament) / . ONE . / (sun) / . DRINK . Plain edge.

There are only five specimens known, one having been sold to an anonymous woman in a Dick Grinolds 1982 sale. Others are owned by L. B. Fauver of California and Roy J. Wood of Alabama, and the American Numismatic Society and George R. Ganter.

The Dude Saloon (open 1871-1907) stood at the southwest corner of Second Ave. and 20th Street near the heart of the business district, in the first three-story brick building built in Birmingham. It was a beautiful and elaborately furnished bar — for men only! It was both saloon and restaurant, and had "boarding" rooms upstairs.

Birmingham in the 1880's was known as the "Pittsburgh of the South" industrially, but it was also called "Bad Birmingham" socially. It had saloons and brothels on most street corners. The homicide rate was high.

In 1886, the biggest boom year of the 19th century, Birmingham had 17 saloons, one brewery, four whiskey warehouses and many brothels. There were less than 25 policemen and vigilante justice was frequent.

The "three best bars" in Birmingham in 1891 were the Dude Saloon, Peerless Saloon and Bank Saloon, the latter on the northwest corner of 1st Ave. and 20th Street, the city's main crossing just a block from the Dude. All this saloon glory ended in 1907, when Birmingham was first voted "dry."

Captain J. B. Webb came to Birmingham from Elyton in 1871, the year the city was founded, and built the Webb Building housing the Dude Saloon. It was an impressive structure overshadowing the city center when it was built. He was backed by the Elyton Land Company.

Today the Webb Building still stands, housing Yogo's Frosty Frozen Yogurt.

(See "Downtown Birmingham, Architectural and Historical Walking Tour Guide," by Marjorie L. White, Birmingham, 1980)

Die-links indicate the token may have been struck by the Heidemann Mfg. Co., San Antonio, Texas.

The Bank Saloon about 1889.

Dude Saloon building in 1980.

J. M. APPLING
Carbon Hill, Ala.

Rulau	Date	Metal	Size	VG	F	VF	Unc
Al-CH 1	(1893)	—	--mm	—	—	25.00	—

J. M. APPLING / CARBON HILL, / ALA. Rv: 5 ¢. (Roy Wood coll.)

Saloon, listed 1893.

J. L. HARTUNG
Eufaula, Ala.

Rulau	Date	Metal	Size	VG	F	VF	Unc
Al-Eu 7	(1875-76)	Brass	24mm	—	—	150.	—

J. L. HARTUNG / GOOD FOR / 10 ¢ / AT BAR / EUFAULA, ALA. (The first and last lines are incused). Rv: MEYER & ILLIG / ST LOUIS in arcs at center. Plain edge. Only 2 known. (Cindy Grellman coll.)

J. L. Hartung operated a saloon in Eufaula, according to the 1876 Bradstreet directory. He does not appear in either the 1870 or 1909 directories. The Grellman specimen appeared in a 1984 Presidential Coin & Antique auction.

J. M. McROHAN
Hayneville, Ala.

Rulau	Date	Metal	Size	F	VF	EF	Unc
Al-Hy 3	(1880's)	GS	**	—	—	20.00	—

** Shield-shaped flan with eye, 23x29mm.
Three folds of scroll across eagle with folded wings. Incused on scroll: J. M. McRohan / Hayneville. / Ala. Rv: Blank. (Elmer Randall coll.)

An early ID tag. McRohan has not yet been traced.

B. M. GREGORY
Mobile, Ala.

Rulau	Date	Metal	Size	VG	F	VF	EF
Al-Mo 12	1872	Silver	39mm	—	—	175.	—

B. M. GREGORY. / MOBILE ALA. / 1872. ctsp on Bolivia silver 1835-PTS-IM 8-sueldos. (John Ford coll.; Brunk 17143)

McLEAN & WINTER
Mobile, Ala.

Rulau	Date	Metal	Size	VG	F	VF	Unc
Al-Mo 16	(1889-90)	—	--mm	—	—	32.50	—

McLEAN & WINTER / 12 1/2 ¢ / IN TRADE / SALOON. (Roy J. Wood coll.)

Tentative attribution. Said to be Mobile circa 1890.

C. L. RUTH
Montgomery, Ala.

Rulau	Date	Metal	Size	VG	F	VF	EF
Al-Mn 8	1889	Brass	26mm	—	—	16.00	30.00

Buildings at center, SOUTHERN EXPOSITION above, 1889 below. Rv: Defiant eagle left perched atop globe, pocket watch in its beak. Above: SOUVENIR / C. L. RUTH / JEWELER. Below: MONTGOMERY, ALA. Plain edge. Issued holed. (ANS coll.)

ARIZONA

NOTE: We are indebted to John T. Hamilton III, Hank Thoele and Bob Temarantz for revising the Arizona token information which appears in this U.S. Trade Tokens section and the Gay Nineties section which follows. Arizona Territory pieces yield some of the highest prices, consistently, at recent public auctions of exonumia.

We thank Peter Spooner for his dictionary of Arizona place names.

R. P. FURROW
Ashfork, Ariz.

Rulau	Date	Metal	Size	VG	F	VF	Unc
Az-AF 1	(1884-85)	Brass	25mm	—	50.00	—	—

Brunswick die BB-8a. Rv: GOOD FOR / 1 / R. P. / FURROW (name in panel) / * DRINK *. Plain edge. (Thoele & Temarantz reports; Brunswick 2127)

Appears only in the 1884-85 gazetteer, under saloons.

FURROW & OLIVER
Ashfork, Ariz.

Rulau	Date	Metal	Size	VG	F	VF	Unc
Az-AF 2	(1884)	Brass	25mm	—	—	285.	—

FURROW & OLIVER / PROPS (all in shadow box). Rv: GOOD FOR / ONE / AT THE / GOLDROOM / DRINK. Plain edge. Unique; discovered in 1993. (Temarantz coll.)

The partnership is listed only 1884. R. P. Furrow seems to be the successor. Ashfork is in Yavapai County.

STEWARTS SALOON
Benson, Ariz.

Rulau	Date	Metal	Size	VG	F	VF	Unc
Az-Be 3	(1880-85)	CN	24mm	500.	—	800.	—

Within central oval surrounded by floreate devices: STEWARTS / SALOON / BENSON / A.T. Rv: GOOD FOR / * 1 * / DRINK / (arc of 19 alternating stars and rosettes). Plain edge. (Hamilton coll.)

Benson, in Cochise County, had its post office established in 1880.

S. R. PIERCE
Bisbee, Ariz.

Rulau	Date	Metal	Size	VG	F	VF	Unc
Az-Bi 4	(1883-84)	Brass	Oct 27mm	—	—	300.	—

Chas. Pick & Co. die. Rv: GOOD FOR ONE DRINK / AT / MINERS / EXCHANGE / BISBEE, / ARIZONA / S. R. PIERCE, PROP. (Temarantz coll.)

J. B. AYARS
Charleston, Ariz.

Rulau	Date	Metal	Size	VG	F	VF	EF
Az-Ch 1	(1882-86)	WM	25mm	700.	—	1200.	—

Pool table in circle. Around: THE J. M. BRUNSWICK & BALKE COS / * CHECK *. Rv: Within close-set circle of stars: GOOD FOR ONE / DRINK / J. B. AYARS / (stars in cruciform) / CHARLESTON, A.T. Plain edge. 3 pieces known.

A.T. = Arizona Territory. Arizona was admitted to the Union in 1912. Charleston is now a ghost town in Cochise County.

A. G. HILL
Clifton, Ariz.

Rulau	Date	Metal	Size	VG	F	VF	Unc
Az-Cf 3	(1884)	CN	25mm	—	—	400.	—

LONE STAR SALOON / (Star) / A. G. HILL / -+- / PROPRIETOR. Rv: GOOD FOR / ONE / DRINK. (Hamilton coll.)

This historic mining town is located at the mouth of Chase Creek at the San Francisco River. Post office opened 1875. Greenlee County.

C. J. HILL
Copper City, Ariz.

Rulau	Date	Metal	Size	VG	F	VF	Unc
Az-CC 3	(1880's)	GS	Sc Oval 29x25mm	—	—	600.	—

I.O.O.F. (Odd Fellows) identity tag with incused inscription on four folds of scroll: C. J. HILL / COPPER. CITY / NO 18 / A. T. Rv: Blank. Unique. (Hamilton coll.)

Copper City was a mining center in Gila County, now a ghost town. Identity tags, while eminently collectible, generally do not command very high prices, but this is the only known numismatic memento of Copper City.

(Elephant)
Fish Creek, Ariz.

Rulau	Date	Metal	Size	VG	F	VF	Unc
Az-FC 1	(1881)	Brass	Sc 29.5mm	—	—	400.	—

Elephant. Around: FISH / CREEK. Rv: GOOD FOR / ONE / DRINK. (Temarantz coll.)

This town no longer exists; the 1877 Postal Guide notes it had no post office.

J. J. D.
(J. J. Donahue)
Flagstaff, Ariz.

Rulau	Date	Metal	Size	F	VF	EF	Unc
Az-Fl 3	(1885-99)	Brass	25mm	350.	—	500.	—

Revolver left, FLAGSTAFF / ARIZONA around. Rv: SENATE / J. J. D. / SALOON. Plain edge. (Hamilton coll.)

Donahue's saloon was listed 1885 through 1914. Arizona adopted Prohibition on Dec. 31, 1914, ending the old era of saloons in the state five years before Prohibition became the law of the land across the United States on January 1, 1920.

C. E. TAYLOR
Globe, Ariz.

Rulau	Date	Metal	Size	VG	F	EF	Unc
Az-Gb 3	(1886-90)	Brass	25mm	—	400.	700.	—

Brunswick die BBC. Rv: GOOD FOR / ONE (in panel) / C. E. TAYLOR / GLOBE. A. T. (name and locale in panel) / DRINK. (Hamilton coll.)

In business 1886-1902.

J. ROSBOROUGH
Hackberry, Ariz.

Rulau	Date	Metal	Size	VG	F	VF	Unc
Az-Ha 1	(1884-97)	Brass	Oct 28mm	—	—	200.	—

(All incused): J. ROSBOROUGH / GOOD FOR / 1 / DRINK / HACKBERRY. Rv: Blank. (Temarantz coll.)

This Mohave County village had 150 people in 1910. Post office established 1878. Now a ghost town.

ALEXANDER BROS.
Indian Hot Springs, Ariz.

Rulau	Date	Metal	Size	VG	F	VF	Unc
Az-In 5	(1893-99)	Brass	31mm	—	200.	400.	—

Large building. Around: INDIAN HOT SPRINGS / Via / Ft. Thomas / ARIZONA. Rv: GOOD / FOR ONE / HEIST / FAMOUS / INDIAN HOT SPRINGS / + ALEXANDER + / BROS. / PROPS. / (tiny) L. H. MOISE S.F. (Hamilton coll.)

Hotel and hot springs were owned and operated by John and A. C. Alexander from 1899 to 1910, according to directories. However, the L. H. Moise signature was used 1893-97. Graham County.

JOE MAYER
Mayer, Ariz.

Rulau	Date	Metal	Size	VG	F	VF	Unc
Az-My 1	(1892-99)	Aluminum	Oval 41x33mm	—	—	300.	—

GOOD FOR / (ornament) / JOE MAYER / (ornament) / ONE MEAL. Rv: Same as obverse. (Hamilton coll.)

In business 1892-1914.

W. M. KRIDER
Mineral Park, Ariz.

Rulau	Date	Metal	Size	VG	F	VF	Unc
Az-MP 1	(1879-87)	Brass	25mm	—	—	400.	—

(All incused): W. M. KRIDER / (Star) / MINERAL PARK. Rv: GOOD FOR / ONE / DRINK. (Temarantz coll.)

This place had a post office 1872-1912 in Mohave County, Arizona. Now a ghost town near Kingman.

D. C. M. CO. STORE
Morenci, Ariz.

Rulau	Date	Metal	Size	VG	F	VF	Unc
Az-Mo 1	(1888-)	Silver	vv	—	—	250.	—

vv Irregular shape, 30 x 35mm.

Building with train in foreground and mountains in background. Around: D. C. M. CO. STORE / MORENCI, ARIZ. Rv: Blank. Issued slotted for use as a fob (?). (John Hamilton coll.)

D. C. M. CO. = Detroit Copper Mines Company. This firm was in business 1888-1916.

J. T. BRICKWOOD
Nogales, Ariz.

Rulau	Date	Metal	Size	VG	F	VF	Unc
Az-No 1	(1883-)	CN	25mm	—	—	250.	—

(Ornament) / * J. T. * / BRICKWOOD / PROP. / (ornament) / Rv: GOOD FOR / 1 (in panel) / EXCHANGE / SALOON (name in oval panel) / * DRINK *. (Hamilton coll.)

Brickwood is listed 1883-1913. The token style is early.

ORO BLANCO STORE
Oro Blanco, Ariz.

Rulau	Date	Metal	Size	VG	F	VF	Unc
Az-OB 1	(1881-85)	Brass	29mm	—	—	500.	—

ORO BLANCO / + (Rosette) + / STORE. Rv: 50 (shaded). Incised, beaded rim on each side. Plain edge. (Hamilton coll.)

Oro Blanco is a ghost town near Arivaca, Santa Cruz County. The store supposedly was open 1881-1910. The Oro Blanco post office, opened 1879, closed 1903, then was open again briefly 1908-15.

Brass 25 cents, 24mm, and 10 cents, square 24mm, are known, each worth $500 in Fine.

BEN. BUTLER
Phoenix, Ariz.

Rulau	Date	Metal	Size	VG	F	VF	Unc
Az-Ph 3	(1892-99)	Aluminum	29mm	—	—	400.	—

View of ruins. Around: SOUVENIR / CASA GRANDE RUINS / (tiny) / KLINKNER. Rv: THE CAPITOL / BEN. / (starburst) / BUTLER. / PHOENIX, ARIZ. Plain edge. (Hamilton coll.)

Listed 1892-1911.

C. E. EMERSON
Pinal, Ariz.

Rulau	Date	Metal	Size	VG	F	VF	EF
Az-Pn 1	(1878)	Brass	35mm	—	—	900.	—

C. E. EMERSON (incuse) / 50 C (relief, in circle) / PINAL, A. T. (incuse). Rv: Blank. Plain edge.

Rulau	Date	Metal	Size	VG	F	VF	EF
Az-Pn 2	(1878)	Brass	28mm	—	—	1200.	—

As last, but 25 C. Apparently unique.

Pinal is a ghost town, in Pinal County. It was a milling town for the Silver King mine ca 1878-91.

P. B. GRAHAM
Pinal, Ariz.

Rulau	Date	Metal	Size	VG	F	VF	EF
Az-Pn 3	(1881-85)	Brass	24mm	—	—	400.	—

(On panel amid ornamentation): R. B. GRAHAM / PROP. Rv: GOOD FOR / -1- / DRINK / AT THE PALACE / *********. Plain edge.

Struck by L. Boche, Chicago.

HARTER & LEWIS
Pinal, Ariz.

Rulau	Date	Metal	Size	VG	F	VF	EF
Az-Pn 4	(1882-83)	Brass	24mm	—	600.	—	800.

On central oval panel surrounded by ornamentation: HARTER & / LEWIS / PINAL. Rv: GOOD FOR / 25 C / DELTA (on panel) / -IN- / TRADE. Plain edge. 2 or 3 pieces known.

HARRY HOLBORN
Pioneer, Ariz.

Rulau	Date	Metal	Size	VG	F	VG	EF
Az-Pi 1	(1882-85)	Brass	24mm	—	—	300.	—

DEALERS IN above crossed bar utensils, within beaded circle. Around: CHAS. PICK & CO. / -CHICAGO. -. Rv: GOOD FOR / -1- / DRINK / -*- / HARRY HOLBORN / (arc of stars). Plain edge. Apparently unique.

Pioneer is now a ghost town. Directories show Holborn was at South Pioneer 1882-83, Pioneer 1883-84 and Casa Grande 1884-85. The post office at Pioneer in Gila County was established 1882 but closed in 1885.

MANN & MARTIN
Pioneer, Ariz.

Rulau	Date	Metal	Size	VG	F	VG	EF
Az-Pi 3	(1883-84)	WM	Oct 28mm	—	—	250.	—

THE J. M. BRUNSWICK / & / BALKE COs. / (pool table). Rv: GOOD FOR / * 1 * / MANN & / MARTIN / * DRINK *. Plain edge.

A. AITKEN
Prescott, Ariz.

Rulau	Date	Metal	Size	VG	F	VF	Unc
Az-Pr 1	(1889-90)	GS	25mm	—	—	800.	—

A. AITKEN / CIGARS / & / TOBACCOS. / PRESCOTT, A. T. Rv: GOOD FOR ONE / 12 1/2 ¢ / CIGAR / AT AITKEN'S / CIGAR STORE. (Kirtley Nov. 1986 sale; Temarantz report)

Alvord Aitken's funeral was published in the 1990 Weiner book, *Prescott, A Pictorial History*. This unique (Rarity 10) token has cataloged as high as $900, but realized $600 in the 1986 Kirtley sale.

Rulau	Date	Metal	Size	VG	F	VF	Unc
Az-Pr 2	(1889-90)	—	25mm	—	—	600.	—

Jacob Strahle billiard die. Rv: A. AITKIN. 3 pieces known. (Hamilton coll.)

Tentative attribution.

J. M. AITKEN

Rulau	Date	Metal	Size	VG	F	VF	Unc
Az-Pr 4	(1891-96)	Brass	24mm	—	—	500.	—

J. M. AITKEN / CIGARS / & / TOBACCO / PRESCOTT, ARIZ. Rv: GOOD FOR / 12 1/2 ¢ / CIGAR. (Temarantz coll.)

It seemed logical to keep the Aitken pieces together, though they bridge the USTT and Gay Nineties periods.

ROBERT BROWN

Rulau	Date	Metal	Size	VG	F	VF	Unc
Az-Pr 6	(1897-)	CN	21mm	—	—	700.	—

PALACE SALOON / * / ROBERT / BROWN / * / PRESCOTT, A. T. / (tiny) MOISE KLINKNER CO. S. F. Rv: GOOD FOR / . / ONE / . / DRINK / (tiny) L. H. MOISE S.F. (Hamilton coll.)

The saloon is listed 1893 through 1912, but the Moise and Klinkner firms did not merge until 1897.

Arizona specialist John T. Hamilton III states: "This great saloon still exists and is worth a visit. The Steve McQueen movie *Rodeo* was filmed there."

GOLDWATER'S

Rulau	Date	Metal	Size	VG	F	VF	Unc
Az-Pr 10	(1888-)	Brass	Sc 26mm	—	—	500.	—

GOLDWATER'S / THE / BEST / ALWAYS / PRESCOTT, / ARIZ. / (tiny) L.A. RUB STAMP CO. Rv: GOOD FOR ANY / BUTTERICK PATTERN / OR DELINEATOR. Only 2 pieces known. (Hamilton coll.)

This was the business of Senator Barry Goldwater's family, a department store 1888-1931. Butterick and Delineator were sewing patterns. In 1964 Barry Goldwater was the Republican presidential candidate.

J. SORG
Prescott, Ariz.

Rulau	Date	Metal	Size	VG	F	VF	Unc
Az-Pr 20	(1881-91)	Brass	Oct 27mm	—	—	350.	—

J. SORG / PRESCOTT / ARIZ. Rv: GOOD FOR / ONE / DRINK / AT THE / UNION SALOON. Plain edge. Unique. (Temarantz coll.)

The Union Saloon was a notorious brothel in Prescott's early days.

BENSON & STEWART
Queen, Ariz.

Rulau	Date	Metal	Size	VG	F	VF	Unc
Az-Qn 1	(1883)	GS	24mm	—	—	200.	—

BENSON / & STEWART / PRO. Rv: GOOD FOR / * 1 * / DRINK / (arc of stars). Plain edge. (Temarantz coll.)

Queen disappeared before 1890. Its site is now in the town of Superior in Pinal County.

SILVER KING HOTEL
Silver King, Ariz.

Rulau	Date	Metal	Size	VG	F	VF	Unc
Az-SK 2	(1880-84)	Brass	Oct 28mm	500.	—	—	—

SILVER KING HOTEL / GOOD FOR / -1- / MEAL / -*-. Rv: Blank. Plain edge. (Temarantz coll.)

Silver King was a mining camp 1877-1912, now totally abandoned, near Superior, Pinal County.

THOMPSON & BOWEN
Silver King, Ariz.

Rulau	Date	Metal	Size	VG	F	VF	Unc
Az-SK 3	(1880-81)	Brass	24mm	—	—	400.	—

GOOD FOR / THOMPSON / & BOWEN (names in oval shadow box) / — A — / * DRINK *. Rv: 25 / CENTS. Plain edge. (Temarantz coll.)

I. E. SOLOMON
Solomonville, Ariz.

Rulau	Date	Metal	Size	VG	F	VF	Unc
Az-Sm 1	(1880's)	Brass	25mm	—	—	800.	—

I. E. SOLOMON / + / -.- / SOLOMONVILLE, ARIZ TY. Rv: GOOD FOR / 1 / * DRINK *. Plain edge. (Hamilton coll.)

Solomon's saloon and store, begun 1880, gradually evolved into Valley National Bank of Arizona, at one time the largest bank in the Rocky Mountain states. VNB is now part of Bank One.

Solomonville's post office opened 1878. Solomon was out of business 1910. The place is a virtual ghost town today, in Graham County.

CHAS. SALARI
Tempe, Ariz.

Rulau	Date	Metal	Size	VG	F	VF	Unc
Az-Tm 3	(1888-90)	Brass	25mm	—	—	800.	—

Brunswick die BBC. Rv: GOOD FOR A DRINK / -AT- / ARLINGTON / HOUSE / TEMPE, A.T. / CHAS. SALARI PROPR. (Hamilton coll.)

Tempe was known as Hayden's Ferry 1872-1879, then Tempe since.

ALHAMBRA
Tombstone, Ariz.

Rulau	Date	Metal	Size	VG	F	VF	Unc
Az-Tm 1	(1881-82)	Brass	21mm	—	50.00	—	—

ALHAMBRA. Rv: GOOD FOR / 12 1/2 ¢ / IN TRADE. Plain edge. (Temarantz coll.)

CAMPBELL & HATCH

Rulau	Date	Metal	Size	VG	F	VF	Unc
Az-Tm 3	(1881-83)	Brass	23mm	—	—	600.	—

(All incused): CAMPBELL & HATCH / GOOD FOR / A / DRINK / 25 C. Rv: Blank. Plain edge. (Temarantz, Hamilton colls.)

Bob Temarantz calls this a "very historic token" because it was in this saloon in 1881 that Virgil Earp, Wyatt's brother, was shot in revenge for the shootout at the O.K. Corral.

ELITE SALOON

Rulau	Date	Metal	Size	VG	F	VF	Unc
Az-Tm 5	(1883-84)	Brass	23.5mm	—	—	200.	—

ELITE / SALOON. Rv: GOOD FOR / ONE / DRINK.

HAEFFNER & SHAUGHNESSY

Rulau	Date	Metal	Size	VG	F	VF	Unc
Az-Tm 6	(1886-90)	Brass	25mm	—	—	900.	—

HAEFFNER & SHAUGHNESSY / GOOD FOR / 1/ DRINK / 12 1/2 ¢ / *. Rv: BILLIARD / -*- / PARLOR / TOMBSTONE / A.T. (Hamilton coll.)

A.T. = Arizona Territory

KEG SALOON

Rulau	Date	Metal	Size	VG	F	VF	Unc
Az-Tm 7	(1880's)	Brass	25mm	—	—	900.	—

KEG / SALOON / TOMBSTONE / A.T. Rv: GOOD FOR / 1/ * DRINK *. (Hamilton coll.)

J. J. McCLELLAND

Rulau	Date	Metal	Size	VG	F	VF	Unc
Az-Tm 9	(1881-83)	Brass	24mm	—	—	900.	—

GOOD FOR / 12 1/2 ¢ / IN / MERCHANDISE / J. J . McCLELLAND (in scroll) / TOMBSTONE, A. T. Plain edge. (Hamilton coll.)

S. TRIBOLET

Tombstone, Ariz.

Rulau	Date	Metal	Size	VG	F	VF	Unc
Az-Tm 12	(1880-95)	Brass	25mm	—	—	800.	—

GOOD FOR / 1/ S. TRIBOLET / TOMBSTONE / A.T. / DRINK. Rv: Brunswick die BB. (Temarantz, Hamilton colls.)

THE FASHION SALOON

Tucson, Ariz.

Rulau	Date	Metal	Size	VG	F	VF	Unc
Az-Tc 1	(1882-97)	Brass	Sq 23mm	1000.	—	—	—

THE FASHION SALOON / TUCSON / A. T. Rv: 12 1/2 / CENTS. Unique. (Temarantz coll.)

ALEX. LEVIN

Rulau	Date	Metal	Size	VG	F	VF	Unc
Az-Tc 2	(1869-87)	Brass	24mm	—	—	1000.	—

Chas. Pick & Co. die. Rv: GOOD FOR ONE BIT / ALEX LEVIN / TUCSON / A.T. / AT THE BAR. Only 2 pieces known.

One Bit = One Real, or 12 1/2 cents. A.T. = Arizona Territory.

PALACE CIGAR STORE

Rulau	Date	Metal	Size	VG	F	VF	Unc
Az-Tc 3	(1883-99)	Brass	Sc 29mm	—	—	700.	—

AT THE / PALACE / CIGAR STORE / TUCSON A.T. Rv: 12 1/2 (large). (Hamilton coll.)

Listed 1883-1901.

GEORGE SICOCAN

Tucson, Ariz.

Rulau	Date	Metal	Size	VG	F	VF	Unc
Az-Tc 4	(1888-89)	Brass	27mm	—	—	650.	—

GOOD FOR ONE DRINK / AT / DEPOT / BEER GARDEN / TUCSON, A.T. Rv: GEORGE SICOCAN / DEALER / IN / WINES / LIQUORS / AND / CIGARS. Plain edge. (Temarantz and Hamilton colls.)

FASHION SALOON

Willcox, Ariz.

Rulau	Date	Metal	Size	VG	F	VF	Unc
Az-Wx 3	(1880-84)	Brass	24.5mm	—	—	200.	—

Brunswick die BB. Rv: GOOD FOR / 1/ DRINK / H. & R. / FASHION SALOON / WILCOX (sic!). (Temarantz, Hamilton colls.)

H. & R. = Harold and Raum.

RECEPTION

Winslow, Ariz.

Rulau	Date	Metal	Size	VG	F	VF	Unc
Az-Wn 1	(1887-91)	Brass	23mm	—	—	700.	—

RECEPTION / GOOD FOR / 1 / DRINK / * WINSLOW, A.T. *. Rv: G. P. on radiant oval, with arc of stars above and below. (Hamilton coll.)

ARKANSAS

HERMAN KAHN CO.

Little Rock, Ark.

Rulau	Date	Metal	Size	F	VF	EF	Unc
Ar-LR 7	(1889-90)	Copper	31mm	—	—	20.00	40.00

HERMAN KAHN CO. / WHOLESALE / AGENTS / * LITTLE ROCK. ARK. *. Rv: Same as reverse of Mi-De 2 (FONTELLA CIGAR). Plain edge. (Craig Whitford coll.; Robinson BY-01)

SNYDER & BRADY

Little Rock, Ark.

Rulau	Date	Metal	Size	VG	F	VF	Unc
Ar-LR 10	(1888)	Brass	24mm	20.00	—	45.00	—

Brunswick die BB. Rv: GOOD FOR / 5 ¢ / SNYDER & BRADY / IN / TRADE. (Thoele report; Robinson EX-05).

Appears only in 1888 directory. Saloon.

GALLAGHER HOUSE

Pine Bluff, Ark.

Rulau	Date	Metal	Size	VG	F	VF	Unc
Ar-PB 2	(1882)	GS	22mm	—	—	50.00	—

GALLAGHER HOUSE / THIRD AVE. / PINE BLUFF, ARK. Rv: I.O.U. / 1 / DRINK / P. GALLAGHER. Plain edge. (Robinson AC-01)

Pat Gallagher operated this hotel and bar on East 3rd in 1882.

S. GUGGENHEIM

Pine Bluff, Ark.

Rulau	Date	Metal	Size	VG	F	VF	Unc
Ar-PB 4	(1889-90)	GS	Sc 29mm	—	—	45.00	—

Brunswick die BBC. Rv: GOOD FOR / 5 ¢ / S. GUGGENHEIM / AT THE BAR. (Thoele report; Robinson AD-05)

The saloon business of Sol Guggenheim appears only in the 1890 directory

A.B.

Uncertain Location

Rulau	Date	Metal	Size	VG	F	VF	EF
Ar-Un 1	(?)	Copper	29mm	—	—	50.00	—

A. B. ARKANSAS ctsp on U.S. Large cent. (Hallenbeck 1.760; Brunk 1067)

CALIFORNIA

BURBANK HOTEL

Burbank, Calif.

Rulau	Date	Metal	Size	VG	F	VF	EF
Ca-Bk 3	(?)	Silver	31mm	—	—	150.	—

BURBANK HOTEL ctsp on obverse of U.S. 1875 Seated Liberty half dollar. BURBANK ctsp on reverse of the coin. (Robert M. Ramsay coll.)

Rulau	Date	Metal	Size	VG	F	VF	EF
Ca-Bk 4	(?)	Silver	35mm	—	—	100.	—

HOTEL / BURBANK ctsp on Saxony 1843-G thaler. (Van Ormer sale 2561)

C. E. MITCHELL

Cloverdale, Calif.

Rulau	Date	Metal	Size	VG	F	VF	Unc
Ca-Cv 3	(1882)	Brass	24mm	—	—	75.00	—

EXPRESS SALOON / C. E. MITCHELL / CLOVERDALE, CAL. Rv: GOOD FOR / ONE / DRINK / OR / CIGAR. (Kappen Clov. 4)

C. Mitchell was listed under liquors in the 1882 edition of *McKenney's Business Directory of the Principal Towns of California* (and other Western states). This directory was discovered by Larry Oller and Kent Johnson.

Mitchell issued other tokens in the 1890's.

F. SPENCER

Cloverdale, Calif.

Rulau	Date	Metal	Size	VG	F	VF	Unc
Ca-Cv 7	(1883-91)	Brass	25mm	—	—	65.00	—

SAMPLE ROOMS / F. SPENCER / PROP'R / CLOVERDALE CAL. / (tiny) JACOB STRAHLE & CO. SAN FRANCISCO, CAL. Rv: GOOD FOR / ONE / DRINK / OR / CIGAR. (Kappen Clov. 13)

SIEBERT & VASSALO

Columbia, Calif.

Rulau	Date	Metal	Size	VG	F	VF	Unc
Ca-CO 7	(1882)	Brass	24mm	—	—	75.00	—

Liberty Head left in central circle, THE J.M. BRUNSWICK & BALKE COS. / .CHECK. around. Rv: GOOD FOR 12 1/2 ¢ / SIEBERT & VASSALO. Plain edge.

Siebert and Vassolo (sic!) ran the Big Tree Saloon in Columbia in 1882.

D. SHERIDAN

Gridley, Calif.

Rulau	Date	Metal	Size	VG	F	VF	Unc
Ca-Gr 3	(1880's)	Brass	24mm	—	—	60.00	—

Brunswick die BB. Rv: GOOD FOR / 1 / DRINK OR CIGAR / D. SHERIDAN / GRIDLEY. (Kappen Grd. 34)

Probably circa 1885 based on BB style.

J. RODGERS

Hanford, Calif.

Rulau	Date	Metal	Size	VG	F	VF	Unc
Ca-Hn 3	(1884-89)	Brass	24.5mm	—	—	75.00	—

Brunswick die BB-7a. Rv: GOOD FOR / * 1 * / DRINK / GEM SALOON / J. RODGERS / PROP. / HANFORD. (Kappen Hanford 18)

C. ANCHARDOQUI

Las Cruces, Calif.

Rulau	Date	Metal	Size	VG	F	VF	Unc
Ca-Lc 1	(?)	Brass	21mm	—	15.00	22.00	—

* / C. ANCHARDOQUI / *. Rv: * GOOD FOR * / 1 / SHEEP SHEAR. Plain edge. (Kappen LC 1)

Sheep shearing tokens used on the Anchardoqui ranch at Las Cruces in Santa Barbara County.

R.A. AYERS

Los Angeles, Calif. (?)

Rulau	Date	Metal	Size	VG	F	VF	Unc
Ca-LA 1	(?)	Copper	29mm	—	30.00	—	—

R.A. AYERS / L.A. ctsp on U.S. 1825 Large cent. (Hallenbeck 1.759; Brunk 1500)

The attribution to Los Angeles is arbitrary, based on the 'L.A.' punch, and needs verification. The initials could have a totally different meaning, for example LA for Louisiana.

BRUNSWICK BILLIARD PARLOR
Los Angeles, Calif.

Rulau	Date	Metal	Size	VG	F	VF	Unc
Ca-LA 3	(ca 1885)	Brass	24mm	—	—	55.00	—

Brunswick die BB. Rv: BRUNSWICK BILLIARD PARLOR / GOOD FOR / 12 1/2 ¢ / IN TRADE / LOS ANGELES. (Kappen LA 163)

Possibly a "showroom" token where Brunswick equipment was sold.

E. FLEUR
Los Angeles, Calif.

Rulau	Date	Metal	Size	VG	F	VF	Unc
Ca-LA 8	(1883-91)	Brass	26.5mm	—	—	65.00	—

UNCLE SAM'S SALOON / E. FLEUR / 406 / N. LOS ANGELES ST. / LOS ANGELES, CAL. / (tiny) J. STRAHLE & CO. S.F. CAL. Rv: GOOD FOR / 10 / CENTS / DRINK. (Kappen LA 1117)

G. LACOUR
Los Angeles, Calif.

Rulau	Date	Metal	Size	VG	F	VF	Unc
Ca-LA 11	(1887-91)	Brass	25mm	—	—	200.	—

GOOD FOR / A 5 ¢ / G. LACOUR / DRINK. Rv: THE E. BRUNSWICK / BILLIARD TABLE / COMPANY / SAN FRANCISCO. (Kappen LA 574)

Rulau	Date	Metal	Size	VG	F	VF	Unc
Ca-LA 12	(?)	Brass	25mm	—	—	25.00	—

GOOD FOR / A 5 ¢ / GEO. LACOUR / DRINK. Rv: F. C. DOUGHERTY / ENGRAVER / 212 W 1ST ST. / L.A. (Kappen LA 575)

Dougherty was the diecutter for this token.

Rulau	Date	Metal	Size	VG	F	VF	Unc
Ca-LA 13	(1890's)	Aluminum	25mm	—	—	7.00	—

G. LACOUR / 367 ALISO ST. / LOS ANGELES, CAL. Rv: GOOD FOR / A 5 ¢ / DRINK. (Kappen LA 573)

George Lacour's saloon tokens are kept together in this section, rather than placing part of them under Gay Nineties.

TEMESCAL PARK HOUSE
Oakland, Calif.

Rulau	Date	Metal	Size	VG	F	VF	Unc
Ca-Oa 5	(ca 1885)	Brass	24mm	—	—	35.00	—

Brunswick die BB. Rv: GOOD FOR / 10 ¢ / TEMESCAL / PARK HOUSE / IN / TRADE. (Kappen Oak. 504)

House = Hotel.

THE TIVOLI
Mendocino, Calif.

Rulau	Date	Metal	Size	VG	F	VF	Unc
Ca-Me 2	(1881-91)	Brass	24mm	—	—	25.00	—

Jacob Strahle die. Rv: GOOD FOR ONE CIGAR / AT / THE TIVOLI / MENDOCINO, CAL. / W. T. WILSON. (Kappen Mendo. 5)

D. N. FRIESLEBEN
Oroville, Calif.

Rulau	Date	Metal	Size	VG	F	VF	EF
Ca-Or 1	(?)	Silver	31mm	—	—	235.	—

D. N. FRIESLEBEN / -o- / OROVILLE, all within oval, ctsp on U.S. 1861 Seated Liberty half dollar. (Brunk 15170)

Oroville is in Butte County. Listed in 1877 Postal Guide.

AMERICAN HOTEL BAR
Petaluma, Calif.

Rulau	Date	Metal	Size	VG	F	VF	Unc
Ca-Pe 1	(ca 1885)	Brass	24mm	—	—	75.00	—

THE J. M. BRUNSWICK & BALKE CO. Rv: GOOD FOR / 1 / DRINK / AMERICAN / PETALUMA. Plain edge. (Brunswick 2009; Kappen Pet. 4)

J.B.
(Jotham Bixby)
Rancho Los Cerritos, Calif.

Rulau	Date	Metal	Size	VG	F	VF	Unc
Ca-RC 1	(1866-81)	Copper	19mm	—	10.00	15.00	—

J B. Rv: Blank. Plain edge. Irregularly round planchet. (Kappen Rancho Los Cerritos 1)

These were sheep shearing tallies used by Jotham Bixby on his Rancho Los Cerritos spread in Los Angeles County, from 1866 to 1881. Los Cerritos was located near present Long Beach.

IKE BERNSTEIN
Redding, Calif.

Rulau	Date	Metal	Size	VG	F	VF	Unc
Ca-Re 1	(1881-91)	Brass	24mm	—	—	40.00	—

Jacob Strahle die. Rv: GOOD FOR ONE DRINK / OR / CIGAR / ELITE / SALOON / IKE BERNSTEIN / REDDING, CAL. (Kappen Red. 19)

THE OFFICE
Redding, Calif.

Rulau	Date	Metal	Size	VG	F	VF	Unc
Ca-Re 2	(1881-91)	Brass	24mm	—	—	25.00	—

Jacob Strahle die. Rv: THE OFFICE / REDDING, CAL.

FRANK A. MILLER
Riverside, Calif.

Rulau	Date	Metal	Size	VG	F	VF	Unc
Ca-Rv 4	(ca 1880)	Tin*	32mm	—	—	55.00	—

* Struck in pure tin. SAMPLE PURE TIN / FROM / TEMESCAL MINE. / COMPLIMENTS / HOTEL GLENWOOD / RIVERSIDE, CAL. / FRANK A. MILLER, PROP. Rv: TIN MINE 12 MILES / FROM / RIVERSIDE / THE / GREATEST ORANGE / GROWING DISTRICT / IN THE / WORLD. Plain edge. (Wright 702)

GEORGE LEE
Rocklin, Calif.

Rulau	Date	Metal	Size	VG	F	VF	Unc
Ca-RK 3	(1883-91)	Brass	26mm	—	—	75.00	—

Billiard table. JACOB STRAHLE & CO. / BILLIARD M'F'R'S / 515 MARKET ST. / SAN FRANCISCO, CAL. Rv: GOOD FOR A DRINK / - OR - / CIGAR / GEORGE LEE / * ROCKLIN, CAL. *. Plain edge. (Wright 588; Kappen Rock. 12)

W. R. WILLIAMS
Rocklin, Calif.

Rulau	Date	Metal	Size	VG	F	VF	Unc
Ca-Rk 11	(1883-91)	Brass	25mm	—	—	65.00	—

Jacob Strahle & Co. die. Rv: GOOD FOR ONE DRINK / AT / W. R. WILLIAMS / SALOON / ROKLIN, (sic!) CAL. (Kappen Rock. 22)

GRUHLER'S SALOON
Sacramento, Calif.

Rulau	Date	Metal	Size	VG	F	VF	Unc
Ca-Sc 4	(1890's)	Brass	24mm	—	—	55.00	—

Brunswick die BB. Rv: GRUHLER'S SALOON / SACRAMENTO. (Brunswick 2146; Kappen Sac. 265)

Rulau	Date	Metal	Size	VG	F	VF	Unc
Ca-Sc 6	(1881-91)	Brass	24mm	—	—	55.00	—

J. Strahle die. Rv: GRUHLER'S SALOON / SACRAMENTO.

These billiard dies were in use in the 1880's. Directory evidence is still lacking.

A. LEONARD

San Benito, Calif.

Rulau	Date	Metal	Size	VG	F	VF	Unc
Ca-SB 5	(1883-91)	Brass	25mm	—	—	60.00	—

Jacob Strahle & Co. die. Rv: GOOD FOR ONE DRINK / (four stars) / -+- / A. LEONARD / (three stars and two dots) / SAN BENITO, CAL. (Kappen S.B. 1)

G. F. BOCHOW

San Diego, Calif.

Rulau	Date	Metal	Size	VG	F	VF	Unc
Ca-SD 1	(1887-89)	Brass	25mm	—	—	250.	—

THE E. BRUNSWICK BILLIARD TABLE CO. Rv: GOOD FOR / 12 1/2 ¢ / G. F. BOCHOW / 1427 H. ST. / BET. 5TH & 6TH. Plain edge. 2 pieces known. (Brunswick 1001)

TILL A. BURNS

San Diego, Calif.

Rulau	Date	Metal	Size	VG	F	VF	Unc
Ca-SD 2	(ca 1885)	Brass	24mm	—	—	50.00	—

Billiard table at bottom. Above: THE / J. M. BRUNSWICK / AND / BALKE CO. Rv: GOOD FOR / 1 / TILL A. BURNS / SAN DIEGO / * DRINK *. Plain edge. (Brunswick 2052)

BROWN BROS. & CO.

San Francisco, Calif.

Rulau	Date	Metal	Size	VG	F	VF	Unc
Ca-SF 7	(1882-86)	Copper	31mm	—	12.50	20.00	40.00

Eagle at center, head turned right, SILVER SAVING SALE above, SOUVENIR below. Rv: BROWN BROS. & CO. / WHOLESALE / MANUFACTURERS / OF / CLOTHING / RETAILING / AT / WHOLESALE / PRICES / 121-123 SANSOME ST. S.F. Plain edge. Two die varieties. (Kappen S.F. 334)

Brown Brothers & Co. (Morris & Lewis Brown and Bernard Bahr Sheideman) were first listed 1868-69 as agents of Oregon Woolen Mills, and capitalists, with offices at the southeast corner of Sansome and Sacramento Sts. In 1870 the address was 4 Battery St.; in 1871, 24 Sansome; 1872-80, 24 and 26 Sansome; after 1880 they were at 121-123 Sansome St., the address on the tokens. When last listed in 1885-86, Ralph Brown had been added to the company's ownership.

W. BUCKLEY

Rulau	Date	Metal	Size	VG	F	VF	EF
Ca-SF 16	(?)	Bronze	23mm	—	—	75.00	—

W. BUCKLEY / S. F. ctsp on U.S. 1864 2-Cent piece. (Brunk 5695)

THE CALIFORNIA INSURANCE CO.

Rulau	Date	Metal	Size	VG	F	VF	Unc
Ca-SF 18	(?)	Silver	29mm	—	—	37.50	—

-THE- / CALIFORNIA / INSURANCE / -CO.- / SAN FRANCISCO. CAL. within beaded circle. Rv: Nine upright bars within beaded circle. On illustrated example, there is incused: 225 - 1 - ST. CLAREMONT - CAL. / STEEVE (sic!) MOORE. Wide dentilated border on each side. Plain edge. Issued holed.

An identity disk of California Insurance Co.

CERCLE FRANCAIS

Rulau	Date	Metal	Size	VG	F	VF	Unc
Ca-SF 20	(1888-1905)	Brass	25mm	—	20.00	—	—

CERCLE / FRANCAIS. Rv: GOOD FOR ONE / 25 ¢ / CIGAR. Plain edge.

The Cercle Francais ("French Club") appears in the directories for 1888 through 1905.

CERCLE M. S.

Rulau	Date	Metal	Size	VG	F	VF	EF
Ca-SF 22	(?)	GS	27.5mm	—	—	40.00	60.00

Eagle with drooping wings on plain field. Rv: CERCLE / 1 / M. * S.

This token was first reported by Schmidt & Owen in TAMS Journal for Oct. 1980, page 192. It is apparently a companion to the Mauduit & Co. 'Cercle de San Francisco' and the Cercle Francais pieces. Just what social or fraternal role these 'cercles' (clubs) served is yet to be discovered.

CHUNG JAN

Rulau	Date	Metal	Size	F	VF	Unc
Ca-SF 25	(ca 1885)	Brass	28mm	15.00	—	—

* / CHUNG / JAN / 1438 1/2 / L. H. MOISE S.F. Rv: Similar to obverse, but from differing die; no signature of token-maker. Plain edge.

Struck by L. H. Moise of San Francisco. The attribution to San Francisco is unverified, but probable. (See *The Numismatist* for Jan. 1951, page 52.)

CORNELL WATCH CO.

Rulau	Date	Metal	Size	F	VF	EF	Unc
Ca-SF 28	1875	S/WM	30.5mm	20.00	30.00	40.00	75.00

Clock face, CORNELL WATCH CO. / SAN FRANCISCO in upper part of face. Rv: TENTH INDUSTRIAL FAIR / SAN FRANCISCO / 1875 / * OF THE MECHANICS INSTITUTE *. Plain edge. (Wright 1379) (Kappen S.F. 576)

Cornell Watch Co. apparently was in business only 1875-1877. Paul Cornell was president and Henry Cox secretary; the works were at West 4th between Bryant and Harrison. R.H. French became secretary in 1877. In the 1877-78 directory, French was listed as secretary of the California Watch Co. at 120 Sutter St.

JOHN DAVIES

Rulau	Date	Metal	Size	VG	F	VF	Unc
Ca-SF 29	(1888-89)	Brass	24mm	—	—	55.00	—

Jacob Strahle & Co. die. Rv: GOOD FOR ONE / 10 ¢ / DRINK / JOHN DAVIES / AUSTRALIAN / EXCHANGE / 309 THIRD STR. (Kappen S.F. 108)

DEUTSCHE FRIEDENSFEIER

Rulau	Date	Metal	Size	F	VF	EF	Unc
Ca-SF 30	1871	Silver	30mm	—	—	—	40.00

Seated Germania facing, with six flags around her. Around: ZUR ERINNERUNG A. D. DEUTSCHE FRIEDENSFEIER. Below: .IN SAN FRANCISCO. Rv: Crossed German flag and sword within oak and olive wreath. Around: EINIGKEIT MACHT STARK. DURCH KAMPF ZUM SIEG. Below: D. 22. MAERZ / 1871. Plain edge. Weight 11.7 grams.

In commemoration of the German peace celebration following the Franco-Prussian war. Dies cut by Albrecht Kuner, the maker of many dies for territorial gold coin issues. (See *The Numismatist*, 1910, page 107.)

Specimens appeared in the Garrett IV sale in 1981 and the Clifford sale in 1982.

(See background notes under Milwaukier Friedens-Feier, Milwaukee, Wis.)

EUREKA (Hotel)

Rulau	Date	Metal	Size	F	VF	EF	Unc
Ca-SF 33	1867	Brass	20mm	—	20.00	—	40.00

(Three rosettes) / EUREKA / * 1867 *. Rv: 5 / CENTS. 11 stars around. Toothed borders on each side. Plain edge. (Kappen S.F. 784)

Rulau	Date	Metal	Size	F	VF	EF	Unc
Ca-SF 34	1867	Brass	20mm	—	20.00	—	40.00

Similar, but 10 / CENTS on reverse. 12 stars around. Plain edge. (Kappen S.F. 785)

Rulau	Date	Metal	Size	F	VF	EF	Unc
Ca-SF 35	1867	Brass	22mm	—	20.00	—	40.00

Similar, but 50 / CENTS on reverse. 11 stars around. Plain edge. (Wright 296; Kappen S.F. 786; Fuld NC-12b)

Eureka Hotel on Sansome Street was under the proprietorship of Jacob Levy, 1864-1868. The attribition is circumstantial.

In 1984, a set of six pieces bearing the obverse die of Ca-SF 33 to 35 surfaced, with differing reverses and in copper, part red uncirculated. The reverses bear numerals, but not the word CENTS. Each measures 20mm, and each piece has a finely reeded edge, unlike 33 to 35.

The numerals appearing on these pieces are: 10, 20, 30, 50, 60 and 500. The appearance casts doubt on the attribution to California. The set of six was housed in a very old 2x2 envelope and was accompanied by a small but select group of rare American tokens. More research is required.

W. FRANK & CO.

Rulau	Date	Metal	Size	VG	F	VF	Unc
Ca-SF 38	(1867-70)	Brass	27mm	100.	200.	400.	500.

Eagle with U.S. shield on its breast at center. Around: THE LARGEST STOCK OF BASKETS AND WILLOW WARE *. Rv: W. FRANK & CO. / JMPORTERS / OF / TOYS AND FANCY / GOODS / SAN FRANCISCO / CAL. Plain edge. (Kappen S.F. 887; Miller Calif. 4)

Rulau	Date	Metal	Size	VG	F	VF	Unc
Ca-SF 39	(1867-70)	WM	27mm	100.	200.	400.	500.

As 4. Plain edge. (Not in Kappen; Miller Calif. 4A)

William Frank & Co. were at 406 and 408 Stockton in 1867. Then at 406 and 408 Battery St. 1868-69, and at 406 Battery St. in 1870.

M. C. HAWLEY & CO.

(See II-Ch 104, Schuttler Wagons, Chicago, Ill.)

N. J. HYMAN

Rulau	Date	Metal	Size	VG	F	VF	Unc
Ca-SF 42	(1876-77)	Copper	32mm	125.	200.	300.	400.

N. J. HYMAN / S.F. CAL / SOLE AGENTS FOR / - HYMAN'S - / ENGLISH BLACK / GARNET JEWELLER / WHOLESALE / & RETAIL / 205 KEARNY ST. Rv: N. J. HYMAN / S.F. CAL / IMPORTER OF WATCHES / * FINE JEWELLERY / FRENCH ENGLISH / JAPANESE & CHINESE / FANCY GOODS / - &C - 205. KEARNY ST. Reeded edge. (Wright 483) (Kappen S.F. 1191; Miller Calif. 5)

Rulau	Date	Metal	Size	VG	F	VF	Unc
Ca-SF 43	(1878)	Copper	32mm	100.	175.	250.	350.

Similar to 5, but the address has been removed from the die. Reeded edge. (Kappen S.F. 1191A; Miller Calif. 5A)

Nathan J. Hyman in 1875 was at the S.W. corner of Montgomery and Pine streets, then 1876-77 at 205 Kearny St. where the tokens were issued. In 1878 he was at 307 Kearny St.

Hyman was a clerk for Joseph Brothers, also token issuers 1854-60, in 1860-61. He was a salesman in 1867.

(Knights Templar)

Rulau	Date	Metal	Size	F	VF	EF	Unc
Ca-SF 44	1883	Copper	15mm	—	15.00	—	25.00

Maltese cross emblem of the Knights Templar. Rv: SAN FRANCISCO / CAL. / -.- / SOUVENIR / -.- / AUG. 1883. Plain edge. (Behringer coll.; Pete Peters Coll.)

Struck by Scovill Mfg. Co., Waterbury Conn.

Rulau	Date	Metal	Size	F	VF	EF	Unc
Ca-SF 44B	1883	Brass	22mm	—	15.00	—	25.00

Obverse as 44. Rv: KNIGHTS TEMPLAR'S / SAN FRANCISCO / CAL. / SOUVENIR (on rect. cartouche) / 20TH TO 25TH / AUGUST / 1883 / TRIENNIAL CONCLAVE. Plain edge. (Peter Fuhrman coll.)

Rulau	Date	Metal	Size	F	VF	EF	Unc
Ca-SF 44C	1883	Copper	42mm	—	—	—	50.00

Similar to 44B. (William Williges coll.)

MAUDUIT & CO.

Rulau	Date	Metal	Size	VG	F	VF	Unc
Ca-SF 45	(?)	WM	27.5mm	250.	350.	750.	1000.

MAUDUIT / ¢ (sic) / COMPNIE. Rv: CERCLE DE SAN FRANCISCO / 1/2 / DOLLAR / (ornament). Plain edge. (Wright 675; Kappen S.F. 465; Miller Calif. 8)

This token was missing from all the great 19th century token collections, Dr. Wright says. Thus far, Mauduit & Co.'s "San Francisco Club" has eluded attribution. Some authorities feel it may be a Latin American token.

NEWMAN BROS.

Rulau	Date	Metal	Size	VG	F	VF	Unc
Ca-SF 50	(1865-66)	Brass	20mm	100.	250.	500.	700.

Liberty head with 13 stars around, COMP. S. MARKE below. Rv: NEWMAN BROS. / IMPORTERS / OF TOYS & / BASKETS / SAN FRANCISCO. Plain edge. (Miller Calif. 8-1/2)

Rulau	Date	Metal	Size	VG	F	VF	Unc
Ca-SF 51	(1865-66)	WM	20mm	100.	250.	500.	700.

As 8 1/2. Plain edge. (Miller Calif. 8-1/2 A)

Thomas and Edward Newman established a brush factory in May 1856 at 74 Sansome St. In 1858 they were at 74 Battery St., then at 303 Battery St. in 1864-65, and at 406 & 408 Battery St. in 1865-66. They imported, manufactured and dealt in brushes. In 1865-66 they also advertised themselves as "importers and jobbers of wood and willow ware, etc." The partnership apparently dissolved in 1868.

The game counter-type tokens are believed to emanate from the 1865-66 period.

WEIL & LEVY

Rulau	Date	Metal	Size	VG	F	VF	Unc
Ca-SF 60	(1864-70)	Brass	22mm	—	—	200.	400.

Spread eagle, U.S. shield on its breast, head turned left, scroll above reads IMPORTERS OF FANCY GOODS. Above: WEIL & LEVY. Below: SAN FRANCISCO. Rv: Laurel wreath, the center blank. Plain edge. (R-F Sca-16; Miller Calif. 12A). Rarity 9.

Rulau	Date	Metal	Size	VG	F	VF	Unc
Ca-SF 61	(1864-70)	Brass	22mm	—	—	200.	400.

Obverse as 60. Rv: Liberty Head left in circle of 11 stars, SP. MARKE below. Plain edge. (Kurth 28; R-F Sca-17; Miller Calif. 12B). Rarity 7.

Rulau	Date	Metal	Size	VG	F	VF	Unc
Ca-SF 62	(1864-70)	Brass	27.5mm	—	—	200.	400.

As 61, but in larger size. Plain edge. (Kurth 29; R-F Sca-18; Miller Calif. 12). Rarity 7.

Rulau	Date	Metal	Size	VG	F	VF	Unc
Ca-SF 63	(1864-70)	Brass	33.5mm	—	—	200.	400.

Similar to 60, but in larger size. Plain edge. (Kurth 30; R-F Sca-19; Miller Calif. 12D). Rarity 8.

Rulau	Date	Metal	Size	VG	F	VF	Unc
Ca-SF 64	(1864-70)	Brass	34mm	—	—	200.	400.

Obverse similar to 60. Rv: WEIL & LEVY below eagle. Plain edge. (R-F Sca-20; Miller Calif. 12C). Rarity 8. (This piece has not been examined)

Meyer Weil and Solomon A. Levy, in partnership as stationers, cutlers and importers 1864-1870, were at the northwest corner of Sacramento and Battery Streets 1864-1865. By 1870 they were at 113 Battery Street. In 1871 the firm name became Weil & Woodleaf.

In the listing above, all the tokens are store card-game counters for use in card games. Ca-SF 60 and 61 are $5 size, Ca-SF 62 $10 size, and Ca-SF 63 and 64 are $20 gold piece size. All are quite rare.

WILL & FINCK CO.

San Francisco, Calif.

Rulau	Date	Metal	Size	F	VF	EF	Unc
Ca-SF 70	1883	Copper	**	—	—	6.00	9.00

** Oval, 37x26mm.
PATENT FARO LAMP / WILL & FINCK CO / 1883 / PHELAN BUILDING S.F. Rv: Intaglio of obverse. Plain edge. Thin flan. Issued holed.

Rulau	Date	Metal	Size	F	VF	EF	Unc
Ca-SF 72	ND	Brass	**	—	—	6.00	9.00

** Unequal hexagon, 40x28mm.
PATENT PENDING / WILL & FINCK / 821 KEARNY ST. / SAN FRANCISCO / HAP. HAZARD OIL LAMP. Rv: Blank. Plain edge. Medium thick flan.

In 1990 a hoard of 20 copper and 30 brass pieces in choice condition surfaced and was purchased by Gregory Brunk. He believes the copper item is a tag which was attached to the firm's oil lamps. The brass piece may be a nameplate of some sort, but probably is an advertising check.

Until 1990 this firm and its tokens were unknown to numismatists.

SEEBACHS CORNER

San Jose, Calif.

Rulau	Date	Metal	Size	VG	F	VF	Unc
Ca-SJ 3	(1882-95)	Brass	Sc 28mm	—	—	60.00	—

GOOD FOR / 5 ¢ / DRINK / SEEBACHS CORNER. Rv: NEW YORK / SALOON / SAN JOSE, CAL. (Kappen S.J. 290)

Henry Seebach is listed under "retail liquor" (a saloon) in the McKenney directory for 1882.

KIFER & FITZPATRICK

Santa Clara, Calif.

Rulau	Date	Metal	Size	VG	F	VF	Unc
Ca-SC 3	(1887-)	Brass	Oval 34.5x19.5mm	—	—	60.00	—

KIFER & FITZPATRICK / SANTA CLARA. Rv: 5 / MODEL SALOON. (Kappen S.C. 20)

In business circa 1887 to 1902.

MERRILL & WRIGHT

Santa Cruz, Calif.

Rulau	Date	Metal	Size	VG	F	VF	Unc
Ca-Sz 7	(1882)	Brass	24.5mm	—	—	75.00	—

Brunswick die BB. Rv: MERRILL & WRIGHT / BANK / EXCHANGE / SANTA CRUZ. (Kappen S. Cruz 10)

Merrill & Wright are listed as liquor dealers in 1882.

GALL & MADDENS

Stockton, Calif.

Rulau	Date	Metal	Size	VG	F	VF	Unc
Ca-St 4	(1874-81)	CN	24mm	—	—	100.	—

Pool table at center, THE J.M. BRUNSWICK / & / BALKE COS above, CHECK below. Rv: GOOD FOR / 1 / DRINK / GALL & MADDENS / STOCKTON, CAL. Plain edge. (Brunswick 2132)

Rulau	Date	Metal	Size	VG	F	VF	Unc
Ca-St 6	(1882)	Brass	25mm	—	—	65.00	—

Liberty head left within central circle, THE J.M. BRUNSWICK & BALKE COS. around, .CHECK. below. Rv: GOOD FOR / 1 / DRINK / J.D. GALL. Plain edge. (Brunswick 2133)

John D. Gall and Frank Madden apparently were in a saloon partnership ca 1874-1881. The 1882 directory lists Gall under retail liquors alone, and Frank Madden issued tokens in his name 1884-92.

FRANK MADDEN

Stockton, Calif.

Rulau	Date	Metal	Size	VG	F	VF	Unc
Ca-St 9	(1884-92)	Brass	24mm	—	—	75.00	—

Brunswick die BBC-10b. Rv: FRANK MADDEN / INDEPENDENT / SALOON / STOCKTON / CAL. (Kappen Stock. 165)

SETH PEYTON

Rulau	Date	Metal	Size	VG	F	VF	Unc
Ca-St 11	(1882-87)	Brass	25mm	—	—	75.00	—

THE BRUNSWICK BALKE / COLLENDER / COMPY. / (Pool table) / CHECK. Rv: SETH PEYTON/ STOCKTON, CAL. (Kappen Stock. 275)

Seth Peyton is listed under liquors in 1882, but the token type is about 1884 on.

SMITH & HAAS

Stockton, Calif.

Rulau	Date	Metal	Size	VG	F	VF	Unc
Ca-St 15	(1884-92)	—	--mm	—	—	75.00	—

Brunswick die BBC-9b. Rv: SMITH & HAAS / 234 / MAIN ST. / STOCKTON / CALA. (Kappen Stock. 313)

BBC-9b die was issued prior to the use of aluminum in Brunswick tokens.

L. ROMER

Suisun, Calif.

Rulau	Date	Metal	Size	VG	F	VF	Unc
Ca-Su 3	(1883-91)	Brass	24.5mm	—	—	125.	—

AUG. JUNGBLUT & CO. / MANUFACTURERS / - OF - / (Pool table) / SAN FRANCISCO, CAL. Rv: L. ROMER / GOOD FOR / 5 ¢ / DRINK / AT / O.K. SALOON SUISUN, CAL. (Kappen Suisun 13)

Jungblut store cards are among the most difficult to locate.

NEW ESS(EX) SALOON

Truckee, Calif.

Rulau	Date	Metal	Size	VG	F	VF	Unc
Ca-Tk 4	(ca 1885)	Brass	25mm	—	—	100.	—

THE J.M. BRUNSWICK & BALKE CO. Rv: GOOD FOR / 1 / NEW ESS SALOON / TRUCKEE, CALIF. Plain edge. (Brunswick 2263)

WILL J. SHINN

Vallejo, Calif.

Rulau	Date	Metal	Size	VG	F	VF	EF
Ca-Va 3	(?)	Silver	25mm	—	—	80.00	—

WILL. J. / SHINN / VALLEJO. ctsp on U.S. 1868-S Liberty Seated quarter. (Dr. Sol Taylor collection; Brunk 36440)

Vallejo, in Sonoma County, is just north of San Francisco, on San Francisco Bay. In 1877 it was in Solano County.

A. ZELLER

(probably California)

Rulau	Date	Metal	Size	VG	F	VF	Unc
Ca-Un 1	(1883-91)	Brass	24mm	—	—	75.00	—

GOOD FOR / A 5¢ / A. ZELLER / * DRINK *. Rv: Pool table in center. AUG. JUNGBLUT & CO. / MANUFACTURERS / - OF - above; SAN FRANCISCO, CAL. below. Beaded rim. Plain edge. (Not in Kappen)

August Jungblut & Co., San Francisco manufacturers of pool tables and supplies, prepared tokens for their clients in the 1881-1891 period. Zeller has not been located.

REPORTED CALIFORNIA BILLIARD TOKENS

Following is a list of unverified attributions for this era. These are given here for informational purposes: (* indicates city name is given on the token)

Name on Token	Possible Locale	Billiard Die	Gazetteer
* Angelo, R.	Pacheco	BBC	?
* Arend, Henry	Chico	St. Germain	(1892-1900)
* Ayers & Smith	Oakland	BB	?
* Ayers, John	Salinas	BBC-11	?
Bailey, J. W.	San Francisco	BB	?
Barney, Growler	San Francisco	J. Strahle	(1881-91)
Bellevue Saloon	San Francisco	J. Strahle	
* Bennett's Saloon, J. F. J.	Soquel	J. Strahle	
* Berryman, A.	Los Gatos	J. Strahle	
Bottomley, Isaac	Oakland	J. Strahle	(1881-91)
* Cerf, L.	San Buenaventura	J. Strahle	

Name on Token	Possible Locale	Billiard Die	Gazetteer
* Chase & Son	San Felipe	J. Strahle	
* Conway, B.	San Francisco	A. Jungblut	(1881-91)
Eilerman, F. A.	Nevada City	BBC	?
Esterline, W. H.	Camino	BBC	?
* Evers, P.	Tres Pinos	J. Strahle	
Felsen Grotte	San Francisco	A. Jungblut	
* Flynn & Tuck	Needles	J. Strahle	
* Groves & Yager	San Bernardino	A. Jungblut	
* Heffner, G.	National City	J. Strahle	(1881-91)
Hoessli's Saloon, C. R.	Princeton	J. Strahle	
* P. H. Lawlor	Fairfield	J. Strahle	?
* Landium Bros.	Peach Tree	J. Strahle	(1883-91)
* Louvre, The	Angel's Camp	St. Germain	
* Rookard, I. S.	Calistoga	J. Strahle	
Selk & Furnhagen	San Francisco	J. Strahle	
* Snow & Craig's	Chico	J. Strahle	
Wornes, R. C.	Monterey	BB	?
Wornes, R. C.	Watsonville	BBC	?
Leon, Y. (Leon Yparraguirre)	Tres Pinos	BBC	?
* Young America Bil'd Hall	San Francisco	J. Strahle	
Zanitta, A.	San Juan	BB	?
* Zotte, A.	Los Banos	A. Jungblut	

COLORADO

FRANK THALER
Animas Forks, Colo.

Rulau	Date	Metal	Size	VG	F	VF	Unc
Co-AF 1	(1884)	GS	24mm	—	—	40.00	—

Brunswick die BB-8b. Rv: GOOD FOR / ONE / FRANK / THALER (name in panel) / * DRINK *. Plain edge. (Brunswick 2350)

T.A. RUCKER
Aspen, Colo.

Rulau	Date	Metal	Size	F	VF	EF	Unc
Co-As 1	(1870's ?)	Silver	31mm	—	—	150.	—

T. A. RUCKER, / ASPEN, COLO. ctsp on U.S. 1844 Seated Liberty half dollar. (Brunk 35343)

EV. LUTH. CHURCH
Brighton, Colo.

Rulau	Date	Metal	Size	VG	F	VF	Unc
Co-Br 1	(1884-1900)	CN	29mm	—	75.00	—	—

Pool table, THE BRUNSWICK BALKE / COLLENDER / COMPY. above, CHECK in exergue. Rv: EV. LUTH. CHURCH / (ornament) / BRIGHTON / COLO. Plain edge. (Brunswick 5201) Scalloped flan.

KNOX BROS.
Canon City, Colo.

Rulau	Date	Metal	Size	F	VF	EF	Unc
Co-Ca 3	(?)	WM	38mm	—	85.00	—	—

Seated female next to a broken column, looking at the sun rising over the sea. A harp at the female's side. All enclosed by a wreath of shamrocks, a star near the wreath's top opening. Rv: KNOX BROS. / KB (monogram) / * CANON CITY COLO. *. Rare. (Wright 1490)

The seated female and sun undoubtedly represents Ireland awaiting deliverance. The Fenian movement was strong in the American West in the 1866-1875 period; this piece might mourn the failure of the two Fenian raids into Canada in 1866 and 1870.

Rulau	Date	Metal	Size	F	VF	EF	Unc
Co-Ca 4	(1890)	Alum	38mm	—	—	100.	—

Obverse as reverse of 3 (Monogram). Rv: GOOD FOR / 12 1/2 ¢ / IN TRADE / AT MY BAR. Plain edge. (ANS coll.)

Knox Brothers were not listed in the 1878 Colorado directory.

Rulau	Date	Metal	Size	F	VF	EF	Unc
Co-Ca 5	1892	Aluminum	38mm	—	—	100.	125.

Obverse as 4. Rv: GRAND LODGE / -OF- / TEXAS / (three interlocked rings) / SAN ANTONIO, TEXAS. / * FEBRUARY 1st 1892 *. Plain edge. (Hartzog coll.)

Co-Ca 5 seems to be an illogical muling, placed here despite its date to keep the Knox Bros. pieces together.

C. C. R. R.
(Colorado Central Railroad)
Central City, Colo.

Wood hauler tokens of the C.C.R.R. in various fractional cord denominations were listed by Dr. P. Whiteley in *The Numismatist* in error. The tokens were actually issues of M.C.R.R. (Michigan Central Railroad), which see.

L.T. NOSSAMAN
Central City, Colo.

Rulau	Date	Metal	Size	VG	F	VF	EF
Co-CC 12	(?)	Silver	28.3mm	—	—	150.	—

L.T. NOSSAMAN / (star) / CENTRAL / (three leaves) CITY, / (star) / (three leaves) COL. TER. (three leaves) ctsp on Spanish-American 1783-Mo-FF 2-reales, which has been broadened by the striking from 27 to 28.3mm. There is also an engraved circle of diamonds struck to form a border around the counterstamping. Holed flan. (Spangenberger coll.; Brunk 29910)

Colorado was a territory only from 1861 to August 1, 1876, when it was admitted to the Union as a state. Nossaman does not appear in the 1878 directory.

O. B.
(Otto Brohm)
Denver, Colo.

Rulau	Date	Metal	Size	F	VF	EF	Unc
Co-De 2	(1886-87)	Brass	24.5mm	—	—	30.00	—

O. B. on oval panel across center, floreate devices above and below. Rv: THE J. M. BRUNSWICK / & / BALKE COS / (pool table) / CHECK. Plain edge. (Larry Oller coll.)

Otto Brohm was a saloon proprietor in Denver, listed in the 1887 Colorado gazetteer. The token was found in Colorado.

JOHN J. MAXEY

(See II-Ch 106, Schuttler Wagons, Chicago, Ill.)

NATIONAL MINING AND INDUSTRIAL EXPOSITION
Denver, Colo.

Rulau	Date	Metal	Size	F	VF	EF	Unc
Co-De 5	1882	Silver	31mm	—	—	—	165.

Mountainous mining scene fills entire field. The scene includes a cutaway of the underground workings. Rv: Buildings across center, small E. JACCARD JEWELRY CO. ST. LOUIS MO. under ground line. Above: NATIONAL MINING. Below: DENVER CO. 1882 / (arm and hammer) / AND INDUSTRIAL EXPOSITION. Plain edge.

The workmanship on this medalet is superb. Probably much more rare than price indicates.

JOSLIN & PARK
Leadville, Colo. and Salt Lake City, Utah

Rulau	Date	Metal	Size	VG	F	VF	Unc
Co-Le-5	(?)	?	--mm	—	—	75.00	—

JOSLIN & PARK / JEWELERS / LEADVILLE, COLO. & SALT LAKE, UTAH.

An advertising whist counter. (Stanley Steinberg 1982 sale number 85, lot 35).

WINDSOR BAR
Durango, Colo.

Rulau	Date	Metal	Size	VG	F	VF	Unc
Co-Dg 3	(1880's)	Brass	23mm	—	—	65.00	—

(All incused): AT WINDSOR BAR / GOOD FOR / ONE / . DRINK . / (ornament). Rv: Blank. (L. Stubler coll.)

Used at the bar in the Windsor Hotel, Durango, in the 1880's.

LEADVILLE, COLO.

Rulau	Date	Metal	Size	F	VF	EF	Unc
Co-Ld 7	1880	Gold	15mm	—	—	Unique	

LEADVILLE. / COLO. / 1880 engraved on obverse of U.S. 1871 gold dollar.

Generally engraved pieces (love tokens) are excluded from this reference, but this Colorado Territory piece provides an exception.

HUBERT MINE
Nevadaville, Colo.

Rulau	Date	Metal	Size	VG	F	VF	EF
Co-Nv 3	(1882-83)	Brass	--mm	—	—	150.	—

(All incused): HUBERT MINE / 1/4 / * CORD *. Rv: Blank. Plain edge.

Rulau	Date	Metal	Size	VG	F	VF	EF
Co-Nv 5	(1882-83)	Brass	--mm	—	—	150.	—

HUBERT MILL (in relief in recessed arc) / 1/3 (incused) / 1/4 CORD (in relief in recessed arc). Rv: Blank. Plain edge.

These are ore haulers' tokens or chips, ore being measured in cords rather than weighed. A " cord" of ore in Gilpin County, Colo. equaled 7 to 10 tons of weight. A quarter cord filled a light wagon; the third cord a somewhat heavier wagon; and a " half cord" wagon had wheels over 50 inches in diameter, and high sideboards.

(See "Numismatic Reminiscences from the Shining Mountains" by Dr. Philip Whitely, in *The Numismatist* for June, 1967) Dr. Whitely attributed both tokens to Cripple Creek in error. The Hubert Mine actually was at Nevadaville near Central City.

The Hubert Mine is listed in 1883 at Nevadaville on Gunnell Hill, Nevada Mining District, one mile from Central City, Colorado. The mine was in Gilpin County. Matthew Balsinger and B. H. Kock had a claim measuring 1,000 by 150 feet.

In the 1883 Colorado Mining Directory, no other Hubert Mine is listed.

Kenneth L. Hallenbeck, who conducted the research on Hubert for this edition of *USTT*, noted that " Cripple Creek really did not get going (as a mining center) until 1891."

J. HILDENBRAND
Pueblo, Colo.

Rulau	Date	Metal	Size	F	VF	EF	Unc
Co-Pu 3	(1887-89)	Brass	25mm	—	—	50.00	—

* GOOD FOR * / 15 C / J. / HILDENBRAND / AT THE BAR. Rv: Numeral 15 in circle of 8 alternating stars and 8 small o's. (Tom Wall coll.)

Saloon, listed in the 1888 and 1889 gazetteers.

JAMES REED
Pueblo, Colo.

Rulau	Date	Metal	Size	VG	F	VF	Unc
Co-Pu 6	(1884)	Brass	25mm	—	—	35.00	—

Chas. Pick & Co. die. Rv: GOOD FOR / 5 ¢ / JAMES REED (name in panel) / IN / TRADE. Only 2 known.

James Reed was listed under saloons in Pueblo 1884; then under saloons and billiard halls in Beaver City, Neb. 1886, and then under saloons in Las Animas, Colo. 1888-89.

Pick supplied eating utensils and glassware to saloons 1878 through 1892. These tokens could have been used in all three towns.

HY. CZARNOWSKY
Silver Plume, Colo.

Rulau	Date	Metal	Size	VG	F	VF	Unc
Co-SP 2	(1884-91)	Brass	25mm	—	75.00	—	—

-.- / CHECK / -.- in central circle, BRUNSWICK & COMPANY. above, CHICAGO. below. Rv: GOOD FOR / 5¢ / HY. CZARNOWSKY / .IN. / TRADE. Plain edge. (Brunswick 19)

Silver Plume is in Clear Creek County, Colo.

REPORTED COLORADO BILLIARD TOKENS

Following is a list of unverified attributions for this era. These are given here for informational purposes: (* Indicates city name on token)

Name on Token	Possible Locale	Billiard Die	Gazetteer
Anderson, J. H.	Denver	BBC	1884
Ashley, C.	Buena Vista	Chas. Pick	1884-88
Bowe's Saloon, John	Leadville	BBC	?
Burke's Saloon	Leadville	BBC	?
Elgin Hotel	Denver	BBC-11	?
Grenfel, Jas. H.	Bald Mountain	BBC	?
* Robert & Chapman	Erie	Chas. Pick	?

CONNECTICUT

WALLACE BARNES

Bridgeport, Conn.

Rulau	Date	Metal	Size	VG	F	VF	EF
Ct-Br 1	(1884-85)	Silver	25mm	—	40.00	—	80.00

WALLACE BARNES curved, ctsp twice on U.S. 1834 or 1847 Liberty Seated quarter. The counterstamp is repeated once on reverse of the coin. (Kurt Krueger coll.; Rulau MV 16; Brunk 2490)

Rulau	Date	Metal	Size	VG	F	VF	EF
Ct-Br 1A	(?)	Silver	38mm	—	—	300.	—

WALLACE BARNES curved, ctsp on South American silver dollar. AYACUCHO PERU ctsp on edge of the coin. (ex-Rulau coll.)

Rulau	Date	Metal	Size	VG	F	VF	EF
Ct-Br 1B	(?)	Copper	29mm	—	—	60.00	—

WALLACE BARNES curved, ctsp on U.S. Large cent (Dates examined: 1798, 1817,1822, 1831, 1834, 1835, 1837, 1839, 1841, 1842, 1843, 1845.)

Some 18 pieces are known to exist, including a 1737 and an unknown date Spanish-American 8-reales silver coin.

In 1885 Wallace Barnes was a Bridgeport maker of clock springs.

COE BRASS MFG. CO.

Rulau	Date	Metal	Size	F	VF	EF	Unc
Ct-Br 3	(1880's)	Brass	21mm	—	—	22.50	—

COE BRASS MFG CO. / No / ****. Rv: GERMAN SILVER (incused). Plain edge. Issued holed. (Charles Ziegler coll.)

Collector Charles Ziegler, York, Pa., possesses a shipping receipt for the Bridgeport Steamboat Co., Bridgeport, Conn., for payment of shipping 20 barrels of copper, $97.28, for Coe Brass Co. The receipt is dated August 1, 1883.

STOEHR'S LAGER BIER

Bridgeport, Conn.

Rulau	Date	Metal	Size	VG	F	VF	EF
Ct-Br 4	(1878-83)	Silver	31mm	—	—	225.	—

DRINK / STOEHR'S / LAGER BIER ctsp on U.S. 1861 S.L. half dollar. (Brunk 38500; Rulau Ne-Om 10)

Rulau	Date	Metal	Size	VG	F	VF	EF
Ct-Br-5	(1878-83)	Silver	25mm	—	—	225.	—

Similar ctsp on U.S. Seated Liberty quarter. Dates examined: 1854, 1877.

Christian Stoehr had a saloon at the corner of Fairfield Ave. and Cannon St. He was a Bridgeport brewer 1878-1883.

These stamps are not connected with Storz Brewing of Omaha, Neb.

PASCAL & GEORGE TICKNOR

Bridgeport, Conn.

Rulau	Date	Metal	Size	VG	F	VF	EF
Ct-Br 7	1871	Silver	31mm	—	100.	—	—

PASCAL & GEORGE / BRIDGEPORT / JULY / . / 1871 / CONN. TICKNOR ctsp on reverse of U.S. 1857 Seated Liberty half dollar, well worn. (B&M Patterson 1985 sale, lot 1693; Brunk 40068)

This piece realized $192.50 in the March 25-26, 1985 Patterson sale.

U.S. RAPID-FIRE GUN & POWDER CO.

Derby, Conn.

Rulau	Date	Metal	Size	VG	F	VF	Unc
Ct-Db 4	(1870's)	Brass	21mm	—	—	20.00	—

U. S. / * / RAPID-FIRE / GUN & POWDER / CO. / DERBY, CONN. Rv: 2 (large, incuse). Plain edge. Issued holed. (Gary Potter coll.)

REMOVAL OF BATTLE FLAGS

Hartford, Conn.

Rulau	Date	Metal	Size	VG	F	VF	Unc
Ct-Ha-8	1879	WM	31mm	—	5.00	8.00	18.00

Building. Above: REMOVAL OF CONNECTICUT BATTLE FLAGS. Below: HARTFORD / SEPT 17TH 1879. Rv: Trophies of war. 1861 1865 on cannon. Above: THE UNION SAVED. Below: Wreath. Plain edge.

ALFRED S. ROBINSON

Rulau	Date	Metal	Size	F	VF	Unc	Proof
Ct-Ha 10	(?)	Copper	28mm	—	—	Unique	

Building of C.G. Day & Co. at 56 Asylum Street, before which are pedestrians and carriages. Rv: ALFRED S. ROBINSON. / BANKER / BROKER / AND / NOTARY PUBLIC / DEALER IN / STOCKS BONDS NOTES / LAND WARRENTS / UNCURRENT MONEY AND / ALL KINDS OF AMERICAN / & FOREIGN / SPECIE / 309 MAIN ST HARTFORD CONN. (The only specimen is in Wadsworth Athenaeum, Hartford). (Miller Conn. 6)

Rulau	Date	Metal	Size	F	VF	Unc	Proof
Ct-Ha 11	1861	Silver	28mm	—	—	250.	400.

Imitation of Higley threepence (standing deer left, VALUE. ME. AS. YOU. PLEASE around, (hand) III (star) below. Rv: ALFRED S. ROBINSON / BANKER / NUMISMATIST & / NOTARY PUBLIC / DEALER IN / STOCKS. BONDS. NOTES. / LAND WARRANTS / UNCURRENT MONEY / & ALL KINDS OF / AMERICAN & FOREIGN / SPECIE / HARTFORD, CONN. 1861. (Miller Conn. 7)

Rulau	Date	Metal	Size	F	VF	EF	Unc
Ct-Ha 12	1861	S/Copper	28mm	—	40.00	70.00	110.

As 11. (Miller Conn. 7A)

Rulau	Date	Metal	Size	F	VF	EF	Unc
Ct-Ha 13	1861	Copper	28mm	—	40.00	70.00	110.

As 11. Mintage: 150. (Miller Conn. 8)

Rulau	Date	Metal	Size	F	VF	EF	Unc
Ct-Ha 14	1861	Brass	28mm	—	40.00	70.00	110.

As 11. (Miller Conn. 9)

Ct-Ha 15 1861 WM 28mm — 25.00 50.00 110.
As 11. Mintage: 150. Two specimens appeared in the Dec. 17, 1981 Springfield sale. (Miller Conn. 10)

Ct-Ha 16 1861 CN 28mm — 40.00 70.00 110.
As 11. (Miller Conn. 11)

Ct-Ha 19 (1860's) WM 41mm — — 20.00 35.00
Bust facing at center, ROBERT FULTON above, BORN 1765 DIED 1815 below. Rv: Steamship at center. Above: (13 stars) / STEAM NAVIGATION / WAS FIRST ESTABLISD (sic) IN THE / UNITED STATES. Below: ON THE / HUDSON RIVER / 1807 / ALFRED S. ROBINSON'S HISTORICAL SERIES NO 2. Plain edge.

Ct-Ha 19A (1860's) Copper 41mm — — 20.00 35.00
As 19, but Copper. Plain edge.

Ct-Ha 19B (1860's) Brass 41mm — — 20.00 35.00
As 19, but Brass. Plain edge.

SOLDIERS & SAILORS MEMORIAL

Rulau	Date	Metal	Size	VG	F	VF	Unc
Ct-Ha 38	1886	WM	32mm	—	—	—	27.50

SOLDIERS & SAILORS MEMORIAL, 1886, HARTFORD, CONN. Signed by G. E. FOWNES. Plain edge.

J. F. WHITAKER

Hartford, Conn.

Rulau	Date	Metal	Size	VG	F	VF	EF
Ct-Ha 80	(?)	Bronze	23mm	—	—	75.00	—

J. F. WHITAKER / H'TF'D CT. ctsp on U.S. 1864 2-cent piece. (Koppenhaver Nov. 1983 sale, lot 15)

LITCHFIELD & CO.

Litchfield, Conn.

Rulau	Date	Metal	Size	G	VG	F	EF
Co-Li 1	(?)	Bronze	23mm	—	—	60.00	—

LITCHFIELD / & CO. in closed arc, ctsp on U.S. 1866 2-cent piece. (Stanley L. Steinberg coll., Malden, Mass.; Brunk 24610)

MIDDLETOWN PLATE & SCALES

Middletown, Conn.

Rulau	Date	Metal	Size	G	VG	F	EF
Ct-Mi 4	1875	CN	22mm	—	—	75.00	—

MIDDLETOWN PLATE & SCALES, U.S.A. ctsp on obverse of U.S. 1867 Shield nickel. 11/1875/17 ctsp on reverse of the coin. (Brunk 27570)

WILCOX CRITTENDEN & CO.

Middletown, Conn.

Rulau	Date	Metal	Size	F	VF	EF	Unc
Ct-Mi 8	(?)	Brass	19mm	—	6.00	—	—

WILCOX, CRITTENDEN & CO., / MIDDLETOWN, / CONN. / *. Rv: JOB GALVANIZING & TINNING / ESTABLISHED / 1847 / (ornament). Plain edge.

Ct-Mi 9 (?) Brass 19mm — 6.00 — —
Obverse as 8. Rv: DIFFICULT WORK TO US / AS SIMPLE AS / THIS PUZZLE / (ornament). Plain edge.

NEW BOSTON

New Boston, Conn.

Rulau	Date	Metal	Size	F	VF	EF	Unc
Ct-NB 3	1874	CN	19mm	—	—	30.00	—

NEW.BOSTON. / JAN. 10 / 1874. ctsp on U.S. 1862 cupronickel Indian cent. (Rulau coll.)

C.W. BETTS

New Haven, Conn.

Rulau	Date	Metal	Size	F	VF	EF	Unc
Ct-NH 3	(1880's)	Copper	32mm	—	200.	—	Rare

C.W. BETTS, NUMISMATIST. Rude impression. (Miller Conn. 16)

Rulau	Date	Metal	Size	F	VF	EF	Unc
Ct-NH 4	(?)	Lead	32mm	—	200.	—	Rare

As 16. (Miller Conn. 17)

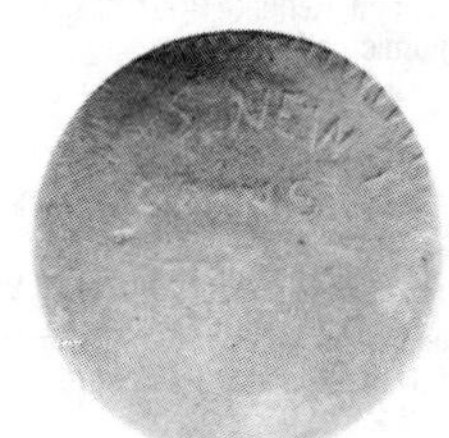

Ct-NH 6 (?) Copper 28mm — 200. — Rare
C.W. BETTS, COINS, MEDALS (etc.). Rude impression. (Miller Conn. 18)

Ct-NH 7 (?) Lead --mm — 200. — Rare
As 18. (Miller Conn. 19)

C.(harles) Wyllys Betts was a collector of great imagination and creativity, who is responsible for a number of Colonial imitations and concoctions. He is best known, though, for his book *American Colonial History Illustrated by Contemporary Medals* (New York, 1894; Quarterman reprint 1972). This book is based upon Betts' manuscript, which was left unfinished at his death in 1887. His brother Frederic H. Betts and nephew Wyllys Rosseter Betts, plus editors Lyman Haynes Low and William T. R. Marvin finished the work and enlivened it with copious footnotes and line illustrations. The 1972 reprint added photographs of many specimens.

Rulau	Date	Metal	Size	F	VF	EF	Unc
Ct-NH 8	(1880's)	—	23mm	—	200.	—	Rare

CHAS WYLLYS / BETTS. Center blank. Rv: Blank. Plain edge. (Kenneth Bressett coll.)

Ct-NH 9	(?)	—	29mm	—	200.	—	Rare

CONNECTICUT / NEW . HAVEN (boss). Ornament at center. Four leaf-like ornaments at bottom. Rv: Radiant shield. (Kenneth Bressett report)

Bressett says that Ct-NH 9 is a modern fantasy made by C. Wyllys Betts. Betts made dozens of imitations of Colonial coins and created other concoctions. His own store cards are quite rare.

P. DOLLAN

Rulau	Date	Metal	Size	VG	F	VF	Unc
Ct-NH 15	(?)	Silver	-mm	—	—	30.00	—

Intricate struck design, with incused legends above and below. Above: P. DOLLAN over (apparent) P. DOOLAN. Below: S. M. A. A. NO 81. Rv: Blank, except for small NEW HAVEN / CONN. Plain edge. (Robert M. Ramsay coll.)

The blank could be a coin of some type with shaved sides. Has the appearance of being a piece with magic connections.

HUSSEY & MURRAY

Rulau	Date	Metal	Size				
Ct-NH 10	(?)	—	31mm	—	250.	—	Rare

HUSSEY & MURRAY / BAKERS / CHOCOLATE / (rosette of dots). Beaded rim. Rv: Intaglio of obverse. Plain edge. (Kenneth Bressett coll.)

Another Betts fantasy concoction, Kenneth Bressett says. As all Betts imitations, it is very scarce and not well known in numismatic circles.

WILCOX
New Haven, Conn.

Rulau	Date	Metal	Size	VG	F	VF	EF
Ct-NH 20	(?)	Copper	29mm	—	—	100.	—

WILCOX / N. HAVEN ctsp on U.S. 1822 Large cent. (Hallenbeck 23.514; Brunk 43345)

Alvan Wilcox was a silversmith in business 1836-1890, according to Kovel (see Bibliography).

J. RAUB
Niantic, Conn.

Rulau	Date	Metal	Size	VG	F	VF	EF
Ct-Ni 3	(1859-61)	Silver	32.5mm	—	—	175.	—

J. RAUB / NIANTIC. C.T. / (mounted Indian right) ctsp on U.S. 1827 Bust half dollar. Rv: J. RAUB / NIANTIC. C.T. / (running dog right) / H. J. I. ctsp on reverse of the coin. (Kirtley Nov. 1991 sale, lot Q026; Brunk 33545)

Joseph L. Raub sold fishing tackle in Niantic, Conn. 1859-64. Then, in Nevada, Ohio in 1874, he obtained patents on a breechloading firearm (Jan. 13) and a cartridge capper (April 7). In the 1876-89 period, he was a gunsmith in New London, Conn., which is near Niantic. This was indeed a multi-talented, mobile man!

E. STILLMAN
Stonington, Conn.

Rulau	Date	Metal	Size	VG	F	VF	EF
Ct-St 4	(?)	Copper	29mm	—	—	90.00	—

E. STILLMAN ctsp on U.S. 1803, 1820 and 1835 Large cents. (Brunk 38420)

Rulau	Date	Metal	Size	VG	F	VF	EF
C5-St 5	(?)	Silver	21mm	—	—	90.00	—

Similar ctsp on Spanish-American 1789 1-real. (Rulau MV 327)

BROWN & BROTHERS
Waterbury, Conn.

Rulau	Date	Metal	Size	VG	F	VF	Unc
Ct-Wb 1	(1880's)	Brass	20mm	—	3.00	5.00	15.00

* BROWN & BROTHERS *. Rv: NO / 7 / (incused) / WATERBURY. CONN. Plain edge. Holed planchet. (Wright 105; MIller Conn 29)

These work checks of Brown and Brothers brass works have various numbers incused on reverse. Wright 105 was No. 9; the specimen shown (No. 7) was in the Byron Johnson collection. A specimen numbered 18, with "U" ctsp on obverse, is in the Rulau collection. Another, stamped SPRING / 3, is in Rulau coll.

The firm was in business 1884-1904.

HOLMES BOOTH & HAYDENS

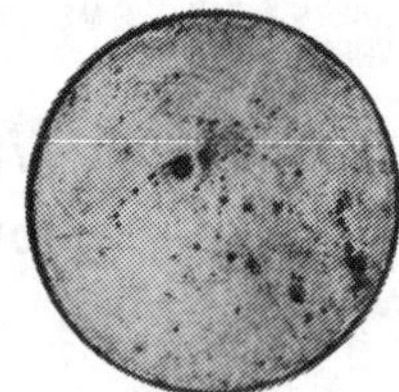

Rulau	Date	Metal	Size	VG	F	VF	Unc
Ct-Wb 10	(?)	German Silver	26mm	3.00	5.00	10.00	18.00

THIS IS / NICKEL SILVER / THE BASE / ON WHICH / HOLMES BOOTH & HAYDENS / PLATE, all amid ornamental flourishes. Rv: Blank. Plain edge. (Wright 458; Miller Conn 31)

Rulau	Date	Metal	Size	VG	F	VF	Unc
Ct-Wb 10A	(?)	GS	26mm	—	—	—	—

Same with reeded edge. (Miller Conn 31A)

Rulau	Date	Metal	Size	VG	F	VF	Unc
Ct-Wb 11	1879	German Silver	26mm	3.00	5.00	10.00	18.00

As Conn 31, but ctsp 1879. (Miller Conn 31B)

Rulau	Date	Metal	Size	VG	F	EF	Unc
Ct-Wb 13	(?)	Copper	20mm	3.00	5.00	15.00	40.00

HOLMES BOOTH & HAYDENS, MFGS. OF LAMP GOODS. (Miller Conn 32)

Rulau	Date	Metal	Size	VG	F	EF	Unc
Ct-Wb 13A	(?)	Brass	20mm	3.00	5.00	15.00	40.00

Similar to 32. (Miller Conn 32A)

Rulau	Date	Metal	Size	VG	F	EF	Unc
Ct-Wb 13B	(?)	German Silver	20mm	3.00	5.00	15.00	40.00

Similar to 32. (Miller 32B)

Rulau	Date	Metal	Size	VG	F	EF	Unc
Ct-Wb 14	(?)	Brass	24mm	—	—	15.00	40.00

HOLMES BOOTH & HAYDENS. Rv: Stamped '38'. (Miller Conn 32C)

Rulau	Date	Metal	Size	VG	F	EF	Unc
Ct-Wb 15	(?)	Copper	24mm	—	—	15.00	40.00

Obverse as last. Rv: Stamped 'E 192'. (Miller Conn 32D)

Ct-Wb 17 (?) Copper 24mm 3.00 5.00 10.00 20.00
* HOLMES BOOTH & HAYDENS / NO. Rv: (All incused): 19 N.G. / COPPER. Plain edge. Issued holed. (Rulau coll.; Miller Conn 32E)

Ct-Wb 18 (?) Brass 24mm 3.00 5.00 10.00 20.00
As Conn 32E, except reverse is incused: N. G. / SPRING. (Miller Conn 32F)

The last four pieces are apparently workmen's or job checks, common to the nonferrous metal works in Waterbury, Conn., especially the brass mills. These were reported by the Fulds in 1951.

Ct-Wb 20 (?) Gilt Brass 24mm — — 10.00 20.00
THE HOLMES, BOOTH / No / & HAYDENS CO. Rv: (All incused): 9 N. G. / HARD. Plain edge. (Miller Conn 32G)

The firm was in business from 1853 to sometime before 1922.

SCOVILL MFG. CO.

Rulau	Date	Metal	Size	F	VF	EF	Unc
Ct-Wb 30	(?)	S/Brass	23mm	3.00	5.00	7.00	10.00

No. / 025 (incuse) / SILVER (on scroll). Rv: SCOVILL / MFG CO *. Plain edge. Issued holed. (Miller Conn 130)

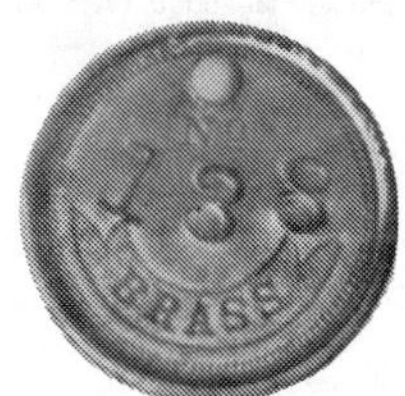

Ct-Wb 31 (?) Brass 23mm 3.00 5.00 7.00 10.00
No. / (incused number) / BRASS (on scroll). Rv: As last. Plain edge. Issued holed. (Numbers examined: 040, 138) (Miller Conn 131)

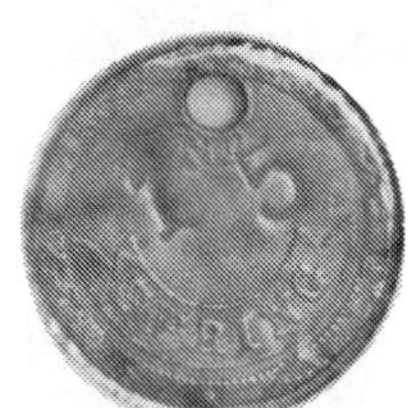

Ct-Wb 32 (?) Brass 23mm 3.00 5.00 7.00 10.00
No. / 15 (incuse) / SPRING (on scroll). Rv: As last. Plain edge. Issued holed. (Lea Hornbeck coll.; Miller Conn 132)

Undoubtedly other counterstamped numerals exist. Though obviously related to the other Connecticut work checks, this item was not reported until 1982.

WATERBURY BRASS CO.

Rulau	Date	Metal	Size	VG	F	VF	Unc
Ct-Wb 40	(?)	Brass	23mm	3.00	5.00	7.00	10.00

WATERBURY*BRASS - Co around empty central space. Rv: 13 stars around empty central space. Plain edge. Holed planchet. (Wright 1209) Known ctsp numerals: 9, 13. (Miller Conn 36)

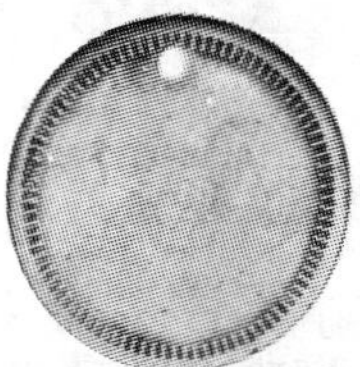

Ct-Wb 41 (?) Brass 23mm 3.00 5.00 7.00 10.00
NO / WATERBURY BRASS CO. around empty central space. Rv: Blank. Dentilated rim on both sides. (Illustrated specimen in Rulau coll. is stamped 13 / N.G. on the obverse). Plain edge. Holed planchet. (Miller Conn 36A)

Ct-Wb 42 (?) Brass 19mm 3.00 5.00 7.00 10.00
Similar to 36A, stamped 10 / HARD. (Krause coll.; Miller Conn 36B)

Ct-Wb 44 (?) Brass 19mm 3.00 5.00 7.00 10.00
* NO * / WATERBURY. CONN. Rv: ***** WATERBURY BRASS CO. Plain edge. Holed planchet. (Miller Conn 37)

These work checks of the Waterbury Brass Company exist with various numerals counterstamped incuse on them. Specimen of Conn36 in Wright and Rulau collections was numbered 13. Specimens of 37 in Rulau coll. are numbered 16, 17 and 18 respectively.

WATERBURY BUCKLE CO.

Rulau	Date	Metal	Size	VG	F	VF	Unc
Ct-Wb 48	ND	Brass	23mm	—	—	15.00	—

WATERBURY BUCKLE CO. / No / 38 (incuse) / PAY CHECK. Rv: Blank. Plain edge. Issued holed. (Gary Potter coll.)

LESLIE S. WHITE

Rulau	Date	Metal	Size	VG	F	VF	EF
Ct-Wb 50	(1888)	CN	22mm	—	—	75.00	—

LESLIE S. WHITE / WATERBURY, CT. ctsp on U.S. 1887 Liberty Head nickel. (Brunk 43070)

Leslie S. White of Waterbury was an engineer.

He worked for the Waterbury Watch Co. in 1881, and for Electrical Appliance Co. in 1887.

L. S. WHITE

Waterbury, Conn.

Ct-Wb 55 (?) Copper 29mm — — 150. —
L. S. WHITE PATENTED / JAN 31 1854 ctsp on U.S. 1848 Large cent. (Brunk 43060)

Ct-Wb 57 (?) Copper 29mm — — 150. —
L. S. WHITE ctsp on U.S. 1851 Large cent. (Brunk 43050)

Leroy S. White was a gifted gunsmith who registered several firearms patents. In addition to the patent mentioned on Ct-Wb 55, he patented a breech-loading rifle on Jan. 6, 1863.

In the 1860's and 1870's he was an officer of Rogers and Brothers, the silverware firm. In 1910 he was president of Electrical Appliance Co.

NO. 3 COPPER
Waterbury, Conn. ?

Rulau	Date	Metal	Size	VG	F	VF	EF
Ct-Wb 5	(1880's)	Brass	23mm	—	—	6.00	—

NO. / .3 / — / 8 / COPPER. Rv: Blank. Dentilated rim on each side. Plain edge. Issued holed.

Assigned to Waterbury on basis that workmanship is the same as that on Waterbury Brass Co. and other similar work checks.

JIM FAIRBANKS
West Meriden, Conn.

Rulau	Date	Metal	Size	VG	F	VF	EF
Ct-WM 4	(?)	Silver	31mm	—	—	150.	—

JIM FAIRBANKS / WEST / MERIDEN / CONN ctsp on U.S. 1875 Seated Liberty half dollar. (Robert M. Ramsay coll.)

DELAWARE

DELAWARE IRON CO.
Delaware

Rulau	Date	Metal	Size	F	VF	EF	Unc
De-Un 1	(?)	Brass	29mm	—	11.00	—	—

DELAWARE / 501 (incused) / * IRON CO. *. Rv: Blank. Plain edge.

L. E. A.
(L. E. Anthony)
Bannister Hall, Del.

Rulau	Date	Metal	Size	F	VF	EF	Unc
De-BH 1	(1878-90)	Brass	Oct 25mm	—	—	—	15.00
	(All incused): L E A / 1. Rv: Blank. Plain edge. (W. T. Miller 210A15-1)						
De-BH 3	(1878-90)	Brass	Sq 25mm	—	—	—	Rare
	As 1, but numeral 4. (Miller A15-4)						
De-BH 4	(1878-90)	Brass	Scal 28mm	—	—	—	Rare
	As 1, but numeral 6. (Miller A15-6)						
De-BH 5	(1878-90)	Brass	**	—	—	—	Rare
	** Figure 8 shaped. As 1, but numeral 8. (Miller A15-8)						
De-BH 6	(1878-90)	Brass	++	—	—	—	Rare
	++ Shield shaped. As 1, but numeral 10. (Miller A15-10)						
De-BH 7	(1878-90)	Brass	**	—	—	—	Rare
	** Clover-leaf shaped. As 1, but numeral 20. (Miller A15-20)						

Numbers 1 through 7 above have centrally holed flans.

L. E. Anthony was a fruit grower at Bannister Hall, near Clayton, Delaware, first listed in 1878. The tokens are all fruit picker checks used on his farm.

About 1897 he was succeeded as a fruit grower by his son, J. W. Anthony, who issued very similar picker checks with the initials J W A incused. Another member of the Anthony family issued checks with the initials H S A incused.

Clayton is in Kent County.

P. F. & CO.
(Peck, Friedel & Co.)
Felton, Del.

Rulau	Date	Metal	Size	F	VF	EF	Unc
De-Fe 1	(1876-77)	Brass	Oct 26mm	—	—	—	Rare
	(All incused): P F & Co. / 1. Rv: Blank. Plain edge. (W. T. Miller 290P5-1)						
De-Fe 2	(1876-77)	Brass	**	—	—	—	Rare
	** Oval 30 x 25mm. As 1, but numeral 5. (Miller P5-5)						
De-Fe3	(1876-77)	Brass	**	—	—	—	Rare
	** Shield shaped, 22 x 25mm. As 1, but numeral 10. (Miller P5-10)						

All these tokens were issued with centrally located holed flans.

Peck, Friedel & Company were fruit packers and fruit growers listed in 1876-77. The owners were C. L. Peck and Jacob Friedel.

A related token issue appeared late in the 1800's (?) with the initials C. F., for Charles Friedel, a local grower.

J. E. SHORT & CO.
Greenwood, Del.

Rulau	Date	Metal	Size	F	VF	EF	Unc
De-Gr 5	(1888-91)	Brass	24mm	—	—	Rare	—

J. E. SHORT & CO. / 1 B. Rv: Blank. Plain edge. (W. T. Miller 350S5)

The 1889 and 1891 directories list J. E. Short & Co. as fruit and vegetable packers. 1 B means 1 Basket, or 1 Bushel (?).

S. H. L.'S SONS
(S. H. Levin's Sons)
Leipsic, Del.

Rulau	Date	Metal	Size	F	VF	EF	Unc
De-Lp 3	(1880-99)	Brass	24mm	—	—	35.00	—

S. H. L'.s SONS / 3 C / LEIPSIC. Rv: Large numeral 3 within surround of long and short rays. Plain edge. (Miller 410L5)

S. H. Levin's Sons began canning fruit and vegetables during the early 1880's. The company last operated in 1913. In 1914 the Levin's Sons cannery was taken over by Richardson & Robbins of Dover, Delaware.

F. F. P. CO.
(Farmers Fruit Preserving Co.)
Rising Sun, Del.

Rulau	Date	Metal	Size	F	VF	EF	Unc
De-RS 1	(1876-77)	Copper	19mm	—	—	—	200.
	(All in relief) 1 / F. F. P. Co / B. Rv: Blank. Plain edge. (W.T. Miller 530F5-1a)						
De-RS 2	(1876-77)	Copper	**	—	—	—	200.
	** Diamond shaped, 23 x 18mm. As 1. (Miller F5-1b)						
De-RS 3	(1876-77)	Copper	++	—	—	—	200.
	++ Heart shaped, 22 x 24mm. As 1, but numeral 10. (Miller F5-10a)						
De-RS 4	(1876-77)	Copper	**	—	—	—	200.
	** Oval 22 x 16mm. As 1, but numeral 10. (Miller F5-10b)						

Farmers Fruit Preserving Company was listed as a fruit cannery 1876-1877. Its head office was in Camden, Del., and the cannery at Rising Sun in Kent County. The B equals Basket? Only one or two of each of these rare tokens is known.

THOMAS DEACON
Wilmington, Del.

Rulau	Date	Metal	Size	F	VF	EF	Unc
De-Wi 3	(1880's)	GS	**	—	—	35.00	—

** Shield-shaped flan with eye, 23 x 29mm. Three folds of scroll across eagle with folded wings. Incused on scroll: THOMAS DEACON. / WILMINGTON / DEL. Rv: (All incused): * / STOVE, TIN, / -&- / SHEET - IRON / MANUF'NG / * / * 118 * / M'K'T. ST. Plain edge. (ANS collection)

EDEN LODGE NO. 34
Wilmington, Del.

Rulau	Date	Metal	Size	F	VF	EF	Unc
De-Wi 5	1888	WM	38mm	—	—	—	15.00

Seal within recessed center, WILMINGTON, DELAWARE. * SEPT. 18TH. 1888. * around. Rv: EDEN LODGE NO. 34 / SEPT. 13. / F L T (each letter in three links of chain) / 1888. * SOUTH TRENTON LODGE NO. 36 *. Plain edge. (Ganter collection)

DISTRICT OF COLUMBIA

A. DITTRICH

Washington, D.C.

Rulau	Date	Metal	Size	VG	F	VF	Unc
DC-Wa 10	1875	Brass	26mm	—	20.00	—	—
	Grecian head with coronet left, 11 stars around, 1875 below. Rv: A. DITTRICH / HATTER / - AND - / FURRIER / 724 / 7TH. ST. / WASHINGTON. D.C. Plain edge. Scarce. (Wright 252)						

KNIGHTS OF THE GOLDEN EAGLE

Rulau	Date	Metal	Size	F	VF	EF	Unc
DC-Wa 17	1888	Brass	25.5mm	—	—	—	20.00
	Capitol at center, ANNUAL CONVOCATION OF SUPREME CASTLE / KNIGHTS OF THE GOLDEN EAGLE above, WASHINGTON / MAY 22. / . 1888. . below. Rv: Laurel wreath around rim surrounds blank center, apparently for inscribing. Plain edge.						

MAYNARD ARMS CO.

Rulau	Date	Metal	Size	F	VF	EF	Unc
DC-Wa 18	(1860's)	Copper	29mm	—	175.	—	—
	MANUFACTURED BY / MASS. ARMS CO. / CHICOPEE FALLS ctsp on obverse of U.S. 1851 Large cent. MAYNARD ARMS CO. / WASHINGTON ctsp on reverse of the coin. (Charles Ziegler Coll., York, Pa.; Brunk 26553)						
DC-Wa 18C	(1860's)	CN	19mm	—	—	50.00	—
	E.R. MAYNARD ctsp on U.S. 1858 Flying Eagle cent. Letter punches match 18. (Kirtley Aug. 1987 sale, lot 131; Brunk 26547)						

Dr. Edward Maynard, a dental surgeon of Washington, invented the Maynard breech-loading percussion carbine, which he had patented in 1856 and 1859. The carbine was manufactured at Massachusetts Arms Co. in Chicopee Falls, Mass. The U.S. purchased 20,202 Maynard carbines during the Civil War.

Earlier, Dr. Maynard had patented the Maynard tape primer for percussion rifles, in 1845. Some 20,000 Remington flintlock muskets were adapted by the U.S. with Maynard primers in 1854-57.

O. U. A. M.
(Order United American Mechanics)

Rulau	Date	Metal	Size	F	VF	EF	Unc
DC-Wa 19	1876	Copper	20.7mm	—	—	—	20.00
	Arm and hammer within square-and-compass. Above: Scroll, on which: HONESTY, INDUSTRY, SOBRIETY. Below: O. U. A. M. Rv: Within open-end wreath: 31ST / ANNIVERSARY / JULY 8TH / 1876. Plain edge. Rare. (Rulau coll., ex-Ellis Edlow)						

Attribution by Ellis Edlow, D.C. specialist. Possibly Massachusetts. The 'O. U. A. M.' evidently was founded in 1845. (See Baker 336)

Rulau	Date	Metal	Size	F	VF	EF	Unc
DC-Wa 20	(1876-83)	Silver	25mm	—	—	—	100.
	Roman mantled bust right, tiny R L on truncation. Around: GEN. GEORGE WASHINGTON. FIRST PRES. U.S. 1789. Rv: O. U. A. M. divided by compass and square; HONESTY INDUSTRY AND SOBRIETY. Plain edge. (Baker 336)						
DC-Wa 20A	(1876-83)	Copper	25mm	—	—	—	25.00
	As 20. (Baker 336)						
DC-Wa 20B	(1876-83)	Brass	25mm	—	—	—	25.00
	As 20. (Baker 336)						
DC-Wa 20C	(1876-83)	Gilt/B	25mm	—	—	—	25.00
	As 20. (Fuld coll.)						

R. L. = Robert Lovett Jr. of Philadelphia.

H. SCHWARZENBERG

Rulau	Date	Metal	Size	VG	F	VF	Unc
DC-Wa 23	(?)	Brass	25mm	—	—	15.00	—
	Harp. A FINE ORCHESTRION WILL PERFORM / EVERY / AFTERNOON / AND / EVENING. Rv: H. SCHWARZENBERG'S / TERRITORIAL / * / HOUSE / 468 / PENN AVE / WASHINGTON, D.C. Plain edge. (Wright 964)						

SOCIETY ARMY OF THE CUMBERLAND

Rulau	Date	Metal	Size	VG	F	VF	Unc
DC-Wa 25	1879	WM	21mm	—	—	—	30.00
	Wreath encloses: THOMAS / 1870. Rv: SOCIETY ARMY OF THE CUMBERLAND / WASHINGTON / CITY / 1879. Plain edge. (Wright 1138)						
DC-Wa 25A	1879	Copper	21mm	—	—	—	30.00
	As 25. Plain edge. 1,000 struck. (Julian UN-2)						

Designed by Charles E. Barber of the U.S. Mint, and struck by Peter L. Krider of Philadelphia.

SOCIETY ARMY OF THE TENNESSEE

Rulau	Date	Metal	Size	F	VF	EF	Unc
DC-Wa 27	1876	WM	19mm	—	—	—	30.00
	Mounted officer at center, McPHERSON above, 1864 in exergue. Tiny G H L at rim at 8 o'clock. Rv: SOCIETY ARMY OF THE TENNESSEE / WASHINGTON / CITY / 1876. Plain edge.						
DC-Wa 27A	1876	Copper	19mm	—	—	—	30.00
	As 27. Plain edge. 3,500 struck. (Julian UN-3)						
DC-Wa 27B	1876	Brass	19mm	—	—	—	30.00
	As 27. Plain edge.						
DC-Wa 27C	1876	Silver	19mm	—	—	—	100.
	As 27. Plain edge.						

The copper pieces were struck at the U.S. Mint. White metal pieces were made by George H. Lovett.

UNION CLUB

Rulau	Date	Metal	Size	F	VF	EF	Unc
DC-Wa 29	(1870's)	Brass	19mm	—	20.00	30.00	—

Monogram EL at center, * UNION CLUB * above, WASHINGTON CITY GARDEN below. Rv: Numeral 10 within open-end wreath, a star in the opening. Plain edge. (Rulau coll., ex-Ellis Edlow)

Apparently a product of F. X. Koehler, the Baltimore diesinker.

WASHINGTON SAENGERBUND

Rulau	Date	Metal	Size	VG	F	VF	Unc
DC-Wa 31	(1880's)	Brass	24mm	—	—	25.00	—

Lyre above open book, on which are letters S B. Around: WASHINGTON SAENGERBUND / D.C. Rv: Large numeral 5 within long and short rays. Plain edge. (Rulau coll. ex-Ellis Edlow)

Saengerbund = Singing league.

W.C. TAX
(Washington City Dog Tax)
Washington, D.C.

Rulau	Date	Metal	Size	F	VF	EF	Unc
DC-Wa 32	1880	CN	**	—	10.00	—	

** Shield-shaped flan 22 x 25.5mm.
Dog W. C. D. C. around: TAX in exergue. Rv: NO. / 1880. (Wright 1211)

There is space on reverse to stamp in a number.

FLORIDA

T. S. R. R.
Yabor City-Tampa, Fla.

Rulau	Date	Metal	Size	VG	F	VF	Unc
Fl-Ya 1	(?)	Copper	**	—	—	150.	—

** Six-sided spade shaped.
(All incused): GOOD FOR / ONE / CORD/ Rv: T. S. R. R. Issued holed. (Kirtley Jan. 1994 San Jose sale, lot 1267)

This piece fetched $127 at public sale in January, 1994. It is previously unpublished.

GEORGIA

INTERNATIONAL COTTON EXPOSITION
Atlanta, Ga.

Rulau	Date	Metal	Size	F	VF	EF	Unc
Ga-At 2	1881	Silver	28.3mm	—	—	25.00	45.00

Seated Commerce left, on a bale of cotton, extending a laurel crown over a factory, 1881. below. Around: INTERNATIONAL COTTON EXPOSITION. / * ATLANTA, GA. *. Rv: Antique locomotive left, PROGRESS below. In outer circle: Ornate wreath with star in opening at top. Plain edge.

PIEDMONT EXPOSITION

Rulau	Date	Metal	Size	F	VF	EF	Unc
Ga-At 4	1889	WM	32mm	—	15.00	—	25.00

Phoenix rising from flames at center, RESURGENS above, * 1864 * ATLANTA, GA. * 1889 * below. Rv: Buildings at center, PIEDMONT EXPOSITION above, MAIN BUILDING / (U.S. shield between four draped flags). There is an ornate border on each side of this medalet. Plain edge.

RESURGENS
Atlanta, Ga.

Rulau	Date	Metal	Size	F	VF	EF	Unc
Ga-AT 8	1865	Brass	14.5mm	—	—	75.00	—

Phoenix rising from flames at center, 1847 RESURGENS 1865 around, ATLANTA, GA. below. Rv: Blank. Plain edge. (Tom Wall coll.)

Resurgens is a Latin word meaning recovering or reawakening and the phoenix rising from its own ashes is a favorite mythical theme used by many governments and movements, including the Greek government in the 1820's and Henri Christophe of Haiti about the same time.

REUNION OF CONFEDERATE VETERANS
Atlanta, Ga. ?

Rulau	Date	Metal	Size	F	VF	EF	Unc
Ga-AT 86	1887	Bronze	38mm	—	—	80.00	—

Davis bust half right. JEFFERSON DAVIS around. Rv: MEMENTO / OF THE / REUNION / OF / CONFEDERATE VETERANS / AT THE / GEORGIA STATE FAIR. / OCT. 26, 1887 — all within wreath. Plain edge. (Kirtley July 1987 sale, lot 305)

GREER LAKE & CO.

Macon, Ga.

Rulau	Date	Metal	Size	VG	F	VF	Unc
Ga-Ma 5	(1870-75)	CN	26mm	—	—	25.00	—

(All incused: I BUY MY / GROCERIES / FROM / GREER LAKE & CO / AND / PAY FOR THEM. Rv: MACON STREET / RAILROAD. Plain edge. Scarce. (Partin 2625U)

This general store is listed 1871 thru 1875. The phrase "I pay for them" seems to be a reference to the practice of company stores of encouraging workers to charge their groceries.

L. MERKEL

Rulau	Date	Metal	Size	VG	F	VF	Unc
Ga-Ma 10	(1875-93)	Brass	23mm	—	—	20.00	—

(All incused): L. MERKEL / 1 / LOAF BREAD. Rv: Blank. Plain edge. (Partin 2625AJ)

Louis Merkel's bakery is listed 1875 thru 1893.

J. NALLE (et al)

Macon, Ga.

Rulau	Date	Metal	Size	VG	F	VF	EF
Ga-Ma 13	(?)	Copper	29mm	—	75.00	—	—

J. NALLE — N. YORK — M. BENEDICT J.A. & S. S. VIRGIN MACON, GEO. ctsp on a U.S. 1835 Large cent. (Brunk 29240)

VANDIVER'S BIJOU SALOON

Rome, Ga.

Rulau	Date	Metal	Size	VG	F	VF	Unc
Ga-Ro 20	(1888-93)	CN	25mm	—	—	65.00	—

VANDIVER'S / – / BIJOU / SALOON / – / ++++ ROME, GA. ++++. Rv: I. O. U. / ONE / ** DRINK **. Plain edge. (Kirtley Oct. 1992 sale, lot 3314; Partin 3270V)

The reverse die appears to be related to Al-Bi 7, the 1880's Dude Saloon token of Birmingham, Ala. J. M. Vandiver appears in the 1893 directory.

ELDORADO SALOON

Savannah, Ga.

Rulau	Date	Metal	Size	VG	F	VF	Unc
Ga-Sa 4	(1870's)	GS	28.2mm	—	—	150.	—

(All incused, and the incused letters enameled black) ELDORADO SALOON / 10 / SAVANNAH, GA. Rv: Blank. Plain edge. (Miller Ga 4)

HAYWOODS SALOON

Savannah, Ga.

Rulau	Date	Metal	Size	VG	F	VF	Unc
Ga-Sa 8	(1870's)	GS	28mm	—	—	150.	—

HAYWOODS SALOON. Numeral 10 in center. (Miller Ga 5)

Rulau	Date	Metal	Size	VG	F	VF	Unc
Ga-Sa 9	(1870's)	GS	28mm	—	—	150.	—

Similar, but numeral 25 in center. (Miller Ga 6)

IDAHO

ANTON PFEIFER

Bonanza, Idaho

Rulau	Date	Metal	Size	VG	F	VF	Unc
Id-Bo 1	1887	Brass	--mm	—	—	1500.	—

(All incused): ANTON . PFEIFER / GOOD FOR / 5 (ornate) ¢ / IN TRADE. Rv: 1887. Plain edge.

This general store appears both under Bonanza and Vienna in Idaho Territory, only in the 1886-87 directory. The Egnew specimen is EF+ with no defects.

Idaho was admitted to statehood July 3, 1890. Both towns had disappeared by WWI. A post office was established in Vienna, then in Alturas County, in 1882.

HEDLUND & OLSON

Burke, Idaho

Rulau	Date	Metal	Size	VG	F	VF	Unc
Id-Bu 2	(?)	Brass	21mm	—	—	10.00	—

HEDLUND & OLSON / (ornament) / BURKE, / — / — IDAHO. Rv: GOOD FOR / — / 12 1/2 ¢ / — / —IN TRADE—. Plain edge. Rarity 7.

HUNT & MOORE

Rulau	Date	Metal	Size	VG	F	VF	Unc
Id-Bu 4	(?)	Brass	21mm	—	5.00	—	—

HUNT & MOORE / (radiant star) / PROPRIETORS. Rv: * GOOD FOR * / 1 / DRINK. Plain edge. (Richard Magnuson coll.)

This token is not listed in the standard Idaho token reference, *Idaho Merchants' Tokens 1865-1970*, by Frank R. Schell. According to R. G. Dun's Business Directory, Hunt & Moore were out of business before 1917.

(Swan) AND ANDERSON

Burke, Idaho

Rulau	Date	Metal	Size	VG	F	VF	Unc
Id-Bu 6	(?)	Brass	21mm	—	—	15.00	—

Swan across top, AND / ANDERSON below. Rv: GOOD FOR / -.- / *ONE* / -.- / DRINK. Plain edge. Recessed dentilated rim on reverse. Rarity 7.

ED. HENNESS

Clark Fork, Idaho

Rulau	Date	Metal	Size	VG	F	VF	Unc
Id-CF 1	(1882)	Brass	--mm	—	—	—	—

Brunswick die BBC. Rv: GOOD FOR 5¢ / ED. HENNESS (in oval panel) / IN TRADE.

General store, 1882 directory. Bonner County.

E. P. BAIRD

Cottonwood, Idaho

Rulau	Date	Metal	Size	VG	F	VF	Unc
Id-Ct 1	(1889-90)	Brass	--mm	—	—	—	—

Brunswick die BB. Rv: GOOD FOR 5 ¢ / E. P. BAIRD (in oval panel) / IN TRADE.

Livery, listed 1889-1893 directories, but the Brunswick-Balke die would indicate the earlier period of issuance.

D. F. OSGOOD

Crystal, Idaho

Rulau	Date	Metal	Size	VG	F	VF	Unc
Id-Cr 3	(1886)	Brass	--mm	—	—	—	—

Brunswick die BB. Rv: GOOD FOR 5 ¢ / D. F. OSGOOD (in oval panel) / IN TRADE.

Hotel and saloon, 1886 directory. This tiny place in Power County had 75 people in 1910.

ANDERSON BROS.

Eagle Rock, Idaho

Rulau	Date	Metal	Size	VG	F	VF	Unc
Id-ER 1	(1886)	Brass	25mm	—	—	150.	—

GOOD FOR / 5 ¢ / ANDERSON BROS. (name in panel) / IN / TRADE. Rv: Pool table in center circle, THE J. M. BRUNSWICK & BALKE COS. around, CHECK below. Plain edge. (Brunswick 2010; Rulau Wa-Br 1)

Specialist Lewis L. Egnew reveals that recent research shows the Anderson Brothers operated in Eagle Rock, then a place in Oneida County, Idaho Territory, in 1886. Andersons were general traders, and a specimen of the token was taken from an Eagle Rock area estate with the Ed. F. Winn token.

The original attribution to Brewster, Wash. was made in "The Brunswick Story" in 1977, but we do not know its basis. We concur with Mr. Egnew, a careful researcher who has used original source documents through years of collecting and study. Thus this reassignment from Washington to Idaho.

Eagle Rock no longer exists. It had a post office in 1877, according to postal guides. Later, Ingle System scrip 5¢ through $1 was issued by Anderson Brothers.

ED. F. WINN
Eagle Rock, Idaho

Rulau	Date	Metal	Size	VG	F	VF	Unc
Id-ER 5	(1882-86)	Brass	--mm	—	—	150.	—

Chas. Pick & Co. die. Rv: GOOD FOR 12 1/2 ¢ / ED. F. WINN (in panel) / IN TRADE. Plain edge.

Saloon, listed in 1882-1886 directories.

JAMES BARD
Gem, Idaho

Rulau	Date	Metal	Size	VG	F	VF	Unc
Id-Gm 1	(1889-90)	GS	24mm	—	—	—	—

Brunswick die BBC-10b. Rv: GOOD FOR / 5 ¢ / JAMES BARD (name in oval panel) / IN TRADE. Plain edge. (Brunswick 5039; Egnew coll.)

Listed in the 1890 directory as a saloon. Bard & Leighty were listed in 1893. Shoshone County.

MARRS & ALLRED
Gooding, Idaho

Rulau	Date	Metal	Size	VG	F	VF	Unc
Id-Gd 3	(?)	Brass	--mm	—	—	800.	—

American eagle, E PLURIBUS UNUM. Rv: GOOD FOR 5 ¢ IN TRADE / MARRS & ALLRED / POOL / BILLIARDS / CIGARS & / CONFECTIONERY. (Egnew report)

J. I. SCHWALBACH
Grangeville, Idaho

Rulau	Date	Metal	Size	VG	F	VF	Unc
Id-Gr 3	(1880-93)	Brass	--mm	—	—	—	—

Brunswick die BB. Rv: GOOD FOR / 5 ¢ / J. I. SCHWALBACH (name in oval panel) / IN TRADE.

Listed as a mill 1880's through 1893 as Jacob Schwalbach. The Brunswick-Balke type is early.

A. C. SMITH
Hailey, Idaho

Rulau	Date	Metal	Size	VG	F	VF	Unc
Id-Ha 5	(1886-96)	Brass	--mm	—	—	150.	—

(Burst of stars) / A. C. SMITH (on oval panel) / (burst of stars). Rv: Brunswick die BBC.

Hotel and saloon, appearing in the 1886, 1893 and 1896 directories.

J. H. WARREN
Hailey, Idaho

Rulau	Date	Metal	Size	VG	F	VF	Unc
Id-Ha 7	(1886)	Brass	--mm	—	—	—	—

GOOD FOR / 12 1/2 ¢ / J. H. WARREN (in oval panel) / IN TRADE. Rv: 12 1/2 ¢ on plain field. Plain edge. (Egnew coll.)

Listed as a market (general produce ?) in 1886 directory.

MINERS BREWERY & BAKERY
Idaho City, Idaho

Rulau	Date	Metal	Size	VG	F	VF	Unc
Id-IC 3	1865	Copper	25mm	200.	350.	800.	—

MINERS BREWERY & BAKERY / IDAHO / CITY / 1865. Rv: Circle of 13 rosettes around: GOOD / FOR 25 Cts. Plain edge.

Only a few pieces are known of what is probably Idaho's earliest token. It was first reported by Robert J. Lindesmith in the Nov. 1962 issue of *TAMS Journal* while your author was the journal's editor, and it has since been learned that it probably was issued about 1870.

C. SNYDER
Julietta, Idaho

Rulau	Date	Metal	Size	VG	F	VF	Unc
Id-Ju 1	(1886)	Brass	24mm	—	—	150.	—

Brunswick die BB-6e. Rv: GOOD FOR / 5 ¢ (in panel) / C. SNYDER (in oval panel) / -IN- / TRADE. Plain edge. (Brunswick 2335)

Grocery, listed in 1886.

A. ZIMMERMANN
Kellogg, Idaho

Rulau	Date	Metal	Size	VG	F	VF	Unc
Id-Ke 5	(1888-96)	Brass	--mm	—	—	45.00	—

Brunswick die BB. Rv: GOOD FOR / 5 ¢ / A. ZIMMERMANN (in oval panel) / AT THE BAR.

Listed as a hotel bar 1888, then as a hotel and bakery 1895-96.

Rulau	Date	Metal	Size	VG	F	VF	Unc
Id-Ke 6	(1888-96)	Brass	--mm	—	—	45.00	—

Brunswick die BBC. Rv: GOOD FOR / 5 ¢ / A. ZIMMERMANN (in oval panel) / IN TRADE.

Tokens Id-Ke 5 & 6 were acquired directly from a Kellogg estate, Egnew reports.

GEORGE MELTZER
Ketchum, Idaho

Rulau	Date	Metal	Size	VG	F	VF	Unc
Id-Kt 3	(1886)	Brass	25mm	—	—	45.00	—

Brunswick die BBC-11. Rv: GOOD FOR / 5 ¢ / GEORGE MELTZER (in oval panel) / IN TRADE. (Brunswick 5476)

There is an apparent diecutter's error in the surname on this token. The livery stable of George Metzler appears spelled that way in directories 1886 through 1893.

HOTEL DE FRANCE
Lewiston, Idaho

Rulau	Date	Metal	Size	VG	F	VF	Unc
Id-Le 2	(?)	Copper	35mm	—	—	40.00	—

(All incused): HOTEL DE FRANCE / ONE / MEAL / LEWISTON, IDAHO. Rv: Blank. Plain edge.

TRIMBLE
Lewiston, Idaho

Rulau	Date	Metal	Size	VG	F	VF	Unc
Id-Le 7	(1889)	GS	--mm	—	75.00	—	—

(Ornaments) / TRIMBLE / (ornaments). Rv: Blank. (Lewis Egnew coll.)

Hank Trimble appears in the 1889 directory. The Egnew specimen was excavated on the site of the former saloon.

J. N. ADAMS
Market Lake, Idaho

Rulau	Date	Metal	Size	VG	F	VF	Unc
Id-ML 1	(1886)	Brass	--mm	—	—	100.	—

Brunswick die BBC. Rv: GOOD FOR / 5 ¢ / J. N. ADAMS (in oval panel) / IN TRADE. (Egnew coll.)

J. N. Adams was engaged in the sale of general merchandise in 1886 in Market Lake, Idaho Territory. His was the only listing for that year in the town. The place had no post office listing 1877-82 and had disappeared by World War I.

J. W. LIEUALLENS BAKERY
Moscow, Idaho

Rulau	Date	Metal	Size	VG	F	VF	Unc
Id-Md 1	(?)	WM	24mm	—	—	15.00	—

(All incused, crude) J. W. LIEUALLENS / -BAKERY-. Rv: ONE / 1 / LOAF. Plain edge.

W. C. DAVIS
Rathdrum, Idaho

Rulau	Date	Metal	Size	VG	F	VF	Unc
Id-Ra 2	(1885)	—	--mm	—	—	—	—

Brunswick die BB. Rv: GOOD FOR / 5 ¢ / W. C. DAVIS (in oval panel) / IN TRADE.

William C. Davis, saloon, listed in 1885-86 gazetteer.

HOTEL LEMHI BAR
Salmon, Idaho

Rulau	Date	Metal	Size	VG	F	VF	Unc
Id-Sa 2	(?)	CN	**	—	—	40.00	—

** Rect. 31 x 19mm.

HOTEL LEMHI / BAR / WM ANDERSON BROS. Rv: GOOD FOR / 12 1/2 ¢/ IN TRADE. Plain edge.

William Anderson still ran this hotel in 1918. Rarity 7.

J. C. MARTINELY
Salmon City, Idaho

Rulau	Date	Metal	Size	VG	F	VF	Unc
Id-SC 4	(1886)	Brass	--mm	—	—	200.	—

(All incused): J. C. MARTINELY / GOOD FOR A DRINK. Rv: Large M. (Egnew coll.)

J. C. Martinely, saloon, listed in 1886 directory. Egnew calls this piece "one of Idaho's most desirable early tokens."

THE NEW RESORT
Shoshone, Idaho

Rulau	Date	Metal	Size	VG	F	VF	Unc
Id-Sh 2	(?)	Brass	29mm	—	—	20.00	—

THE NEW RESORT / (flowers) / SHOSHONE, / -IDA.-. Rv: GOOD FOR. / CENTS / * 12 1/2 * / CENTS / .IN TRADE. Plain edge. Rarity 7.

J. E. REYNOLDS
Shoup, Idaho

Rulau	Date	Metal	Size	VG	F	VF	Unc
Id-Sp 2	(1887-90)	—	--mm	—	—	—	—

(Burst of stars) / J. E. REYNOLDS (in oval panel) / (burst of stars). Rv: GOOD FOR / ONE / DRINK.

Saloon, listed 1887 through 1890.

McCAULEY BROS.
Twin Falls, Idaho

Rulau	Date	Metal	Size	VG	F	VF	Unc
Id-TF 3	(?)	GS	--mm	—	—	100.	—

Brunswick die BB. Rv: GOOD FOR / 5 / McCAULEY / BROS. (name in panel) / CENTS / IN TRADE.

The style is 1880's. This cigar store and confectionery is still listed 1914.

W. H. KRUSE
Vienna, Idaho

Rulau	Date	Metal	Size	VG	F	VF	Unc
Ids-Vi 1	(1886)	Brass	--mm	—	—	—	—

Brunswick die BBC. Rv: GOOD FOR / 5 ¢ / W. H. KRUSE (in oval panel) / IN TRADE.

William H. Kruse, hotel, 1886 directory.

JOE ROGERS
Wardner, Idaho

Rulau	Date	Metal	Size	VG	F	VF	Unc
Id-Wa 2	(1889-91)	Brass	--mm	—	—	25.00	—

Chas. Pick & Co. die. Rv: JOE ROGERS.

Listed only in the 1891 directory.

W. H. PHILLIPS
Weiser, Idaho

Rulau	Date	Metal	Size	VG	F	VF	Unc
Id-We 3	(1880's)	GS	--mm	—	—	250.	—

GOOD FOR / 5 ¢ / W. H. PHILLIPS (in oval panel) / IN TRADE. Rv: NATIONAL BILLIARD MANUF'G CO / (Crossed cuesticks separate N-B-M-Co. Plain edge. Apparently unique.

Rulau	Date	Metal	Size	VG	F	VF	Unc
Id-We 4	(?)	Brass	18.5mm	—	—	35.00	—

W. H. PHILLIPS / * / WEISER, / IDA. Rv: GOOD FOR / 5 ¢ / . IN TRADE . Rarity 7.

Neither Phillips token is previously published. Id-We 4 may postdate 1889.

ILLINOIS

JOHN RHODES
Altamont, Ill.

Rulau	Date	Metal	Size	VG	F	VF	Unc
Il-Al 4	(1882)	—	24mm	—	—	10.00	—

Brunswick die BB-8a. Rv: GOOD FOR / 5 ¢ (in panel) / JOHN / RHODES (name in panel) / -IN- / +) trade (+. Plain edge.

H.N. KENDALL
Alton, Ill.

Rulau	Date	Metal	Size	VG	F	VF	Unc
Il-At 3	(1870's)	Brass	26mm	—	10.00	15.00	—
Il-At 4	(1870's)	Brass	23mm	—	20.00	25.00	—

Il-At 3: H.N. KENDALL / 1 / BREAD. Rv: Blank. Plain edge. Rarity 9. (Wright 542; Schmidt K46)

Il-At 4: H.N. KENDALL & CO. / 1 / BREAD (all incused). Rv: No. Plain edge. Rarity 9. (Schmidt K47)

H.N. Kendall and Co. was primarily a baker of crackers. The building is still standing today, with its brick ovens still in the basement.

A.F. MILLER

Rulau	Date	Metal	Size	VG	F	VF	Unc
Il-At 7	(1889-90)	Alum	23mm	—	—	15.00	—

A.F. MILLER / ALTON / ILLS. Rv: GOOD FOR / 2 1/2 ¢ / IN TRADE. Plain edge. (Schmidt M31)

Augustus F. Miller was a tobacco maker located at 3rd and Langdon in Alton, according to the 1886-87 directory for Alton and Madison County. However, aluminum was not used in tokens before 1888-89 except rarely.

SHURTLEFF COLLEGE

Rulau	Date	Metal	Size	VG	F	VF	Unc
Il-At 11	1867	Bronze	31mm	—	—	12.50	20.00

Male bust facing at center, CHILDRENS PROFESSORSHIP / * 1867 *. Rv: View of college at center, SHURTLEFF COLLEGE CHARTERD 1835. Plain edge. (Schmidt S29)

Shurtleff College became part of Southern Illinois University in the late 1950's.

E.B. YOUNG
Alton, Ill.

Rulau	Date	Metal	Size	VG	F	VF	Unc
Il-At 15	(1889)	Aluminum	23mm	—	15.00	20.00	—

HOPPE'S / CHINA HALL / ALTON, ILL. Rv: (Incuse) E. B. YOUNG / (relief) GOOD FOR / 1 / PINT / MILK. Plain edge. (Schmidt)

Emily B. Young was the proprietor, according to the Bradstreet Directory for 1890. The obverse was one used by several merchants in the area. The city of Alton was named for Alton Easton, son of its founder, Rufus Easton.

COFFEY & HARRISON
Ashley, Ill.

Rulau	Date	Metal	Size	VG	F	VF	Unc
Il-As 3	1881	WM	31mm	7.50	10.00	15.00	—

COFFEY & HARRISON / * (rosette) * / 1881 / ASHLEY, ILL. / * (rosette) *. RV: (FLowers) / 100 / C.B. Plain edge. (Schmidt C58) Rarity 8.

Coffey, Brown & Co. had a general store and a mill, according to the *Bradstreet Directory*. In the 1870 *Bradstreet* this had become Coffey, Brown & Harrison, mill.

CONRAD KEMPEL
Ashton, Ill.

Rulau	Date	Metal	Size	VG	F	VF	Unc
Il-An 2	(1882)	Brass	25mm	—	—	25.00	—

Chas. Pick & Co. die. Rv: GOOD FOR / 5 ¢ / CONRAD / KEMPEL / IN / TRADE. (Thoele coll.)

Saloon, listed in the 1882 gazetteer.

J. B. CALLAN
Aurora, Ill

Rulau	Date	Metal	Size	VG	F	VF	Unc
Il-Au 2	(1884)	Brass	25mm	—	—	15.00	—

Brunswick die BB. Rv: GOOD FOR / 5 ¢ / J. B. CALLAN (in oval panel) / IN / TRADE.

Saloon, listed in 1884.

GATES & TRASK

Rulau	Date	Metal	Size	VG	F	VF	EF
Il-Au 4	(1860's ?)	Copper	29mm	—	—	100.	—

GATES & TRASK ctsp on U.S. 1839 Large cent. (Dr. Sol Taylor collection; Brunk 15780)

MAY & DICKES

Rulau	Date	Metal	Size	VG	F	VF	Unc
Il-Au 6	(1884)	Brass	24.5mm	—	25.00	—	—

Brunswick die BBC-9a. Rv: GOOD FOR (in scroll) / 5 ¢ (in panel) / MAY & / DICKES (names in oval panel) / IN / TRADE (in scroll). Plain edge. (Stubler coll.)

Billiard hall, listed only 1884.

MUSCHLER & WILLIS

Rulau	Date	Metal	Size	VG	F	VF	Unc
Il-Au 7	(1886-90)	Brass	23mm	10.00	15.00	20.00	—

(All incused): MUSCHLER & WILLIS / GOOD FOR / 5¢ / IN TRADE. Rv: Blank. Plain edge. Rarity 8. (Schmidt M80)

George F. Muschler and James H. Willis ran a saloon on North Broadway from 1886 to 1890, selling Schlitz' Milwaukee beer.

JACK SHORT
Aurora, Ill.

Rulau	Date	Metal	Size	VG	F	VF	Unc
Il-Au 12	(1881-1893)	Brass	24mm	12.00	17.00	25.00	—

JACK SHORT AURORA, ILL. / GOOD FOR / 5¢ / IN TRADE. Rv: Large 5. Plain edge. Rarity 8. (Schmidt S36)

John M. Short opened his saloon in 1881 as a "sample room," a commonly used term in those days which fooled no one. In 1887 he moved one block to Fox Street, operating the saloon until his death in 1898.

Earlier, about 1870, Short may have run a saloon with a partner as Short & Evans. Old timers recalled Short's as a fine, clean saloon with a discreet "family entrance" at the rear of the building.

NEWTON WAGON CO.
Batavia, Ill.

Rulau	Date	Metal	Size	VG	F	VF	Unc
Il-Bt 7	(1880's)	Copper	25mm	—	20.00	30.00	—

Wagon and team, NEWTON HIGH GRADE WAGONS. Rv: NOTHING BUT WAGONS SINCE 1854. NEWTON WAGON CO. BATAVIA. ILL. Plain edge. Rarity 6. (Schmidt N19)

The 1890 *Bradstreet Directory* said this firm had $250,000 surplus capital, a great amount in those days. The firm also appears in the 1866 and 1870 directories.

PHILIP ZAHN
Beardstown, Ill.

Rulau	Date	Metal	Size	VG	F	VF	Unc
Il-Bd 6	(1882-88)	GS	Sq 23mm	—	—	20.00	—

Chas. Pick die. Rv: GOOD FOR / 5 ¢ / PHILLIP / ZAHN / In / TRADE.

Saloon, listed 1882 to 1888. Possibly 100 pieces known; a hoard was dispersed in the 1980's. (Information courtesy Tom Wall and Lee Schumacher)

BAKER & THOMAS
Belleville, Ill.

Rulau	Date	Metal	Size	VG	F	VF
Il-Bv 2	(1871)	GS	23mm	—	—	60.00

(All incused): BAKER & THOMAS / DRUGGISTS / BELLEVILLE. Rv: SODA. Plain edge. Only 1 known. (Rich Hartzog coll.)

These druggists appear in the 1871 directory, but have disappeared by the 1878 edition.

AUG. TIEMANN
Belleville, Ill.

Rulau	Date	Metal	Size	VG	F	VF	Unc
Il-Bv 18	(1888)	Brass	24mm	—	—	35.00	55.00

Eagle displayed, head turned left. Rv: ONE DRINK / (Beer stein) / AUG. TIEMANN / (Star) / STERN BIER. Plain edge.

Stern bier = Star beer. Tiemann's saloon appears in the 1888 gazetteer.

P. HAUSCHILD
Benson, Ill.

Rulau	Date	Metal	Size	VG	F	VF	Unc
Il-Be 4	(1880-86)	Brass	26mm	—	15.00	20.00	—

GOOD FOR / 5 ¢/ P. HAUSCHILD / BENSON, ILL. / IN / TRADE. Rv: Goblet and crossed utensils at center, CHAS. PICK & CO. / DEALERS IN above, - CHICAGO - below. Plain edge. (Schmidt H11)

J. E. WHITTLE
Birkner, Ill.

Rulau	Date	Metal	Size	VG	F	VF	Unc
Il-Bi 3	(1888)	Brass	Sc 28mm	—	—	25.00	—

N.B.M. Co. die. Rv: GOOD FOR / 5 ¢ / IN / TRADE / * J. E. WHITTLE *.

A Mrs. J. Whittle, saloon, is listed for 1888, possibly a widow or possibly J. E. was a woman.

J. F. ILLGEN
Bloom, Ill.

Rulau	Date	Metal	Size	VG	F	VF	Unc
Il-Bm 1	(1884)	Brass	24mm	—	35.00	50.00	—

Pool table, three balls and a cuestick, THE J.M. BRUNSWICK / & / BALKE COS. Rv: GOOD FOR / 5¢ / J. F. ILLGEN / BLOOM. ILL. / IN TRADE. Plain edge. Rarity 8. (Schmidt I39; Brunswick 2176)

This is a token of Bloom and not Bloomington, as one might believe.

M. CHATFIELD
Bloomington, Ill.

Rulau	Date	Metal	Size	VG	F	VF	EF
Il-Bl 2	(1853-65)	Silver	27mm	125.	—	175.	—

M. CHATFIELD / BLOOMINGTON / — ILL. — ctsp on Spanish-American 2-reales. Examined: 1821-Mo, 1828, unknown date. (Brunk 7550)

Rulau	Date	Metal	Size	VG	F	VF	EF
Il-Bl 2A	(?)	Silver	25mm	125.	—	175.	—
	Similar ctsp on U.S. 1853 A&R or 1854 Seated Liberty quarter.						
Il-Bl 2B	(?)	Silver	31mm	125.	—	175.	—
	Similar ctsp on U.S. 1854-O Seated Liberty half dollar.						
Il-B1 2D	(?)	Silver	31mm	125.	—	175.	—
	Similar ctsp on U.S. 1853 Arrows S.L. half dollar. (Erwin E. Brauer report)						

Milo Chatfield is listed as a wholesale grocer and tobacco dealer in the 1853 and 1855 directories, but does not appear in the 1866 to 1870 directories. In 1873 he is listed as a carpenter. All these Chatfield pieces may belong to the 1854-55 period, placing them in the *U.S. Merchant Tokens 1845-1860* section.

Chatfield was elected alderman 1855, and became street commissioner 1870. In 1873 he was a carpenter; in 1880 a mail carrier. Disappears from directory in 1886.

H. DOHRMANN
Blue Island, Ill.

Rulau	Date	Metal	Size	VG	F	VF	Unc
Il-Bl 2	(1884)	Brass	25mm	—	—	50.00	—

GOOD FOR 5 CENTS / H. / DOHRMANN / IN TRADE. Rv: STOLL & MERZ / (Pool table) / CHECK. Unique. (Thoele coll.)

Henry Dohrmann appears under saloons in the 1884-85 Polk gazetteer. Stoll & Merz was a short-lived billiard supplier whose store card is very rare.

M. HELBREG & CO.
Blue Island, Ill.

Rulau	Date	Metal	Size	VG	F	VF	Unc
Il-Bl 6	(1882-83)	Brass	25mm	—	—	20.00	—

M. HELBREG & CO / GOOD FOR / A 5 ¢ / DRINK. Rv: Large 5 in circle of stars. (Rouleau coll.)

Saloon, 1882-83 gazetteer.

MICHAEL MORGAN
Braidwood, Ill. ?

Rulau	Date	Metal	Size	VG	F	VF	Unc
Il-Br 3	(1890's)	Brass	25mm	—	—	25.00	—

BBC-7 die. Rv: GOOD FOR / 2 1/2 ¢/ MICHAEL / MORGAN / IN / TRADE. Plain edge. (Thoele coll.: Vacketta N/L)

Michael Morgan's saloon appears in the 1884 directory. Normally the BBC-7 die appears on post-1890 tokens, says Hank Thoele, Green Bay, Wis. specialist in billiard and saloon tokens.

WM. H. SCHUTTER
Cairo, Ill.

Rulau	Date	Metal	Size	VG	F	VF	Unc
Il-Cr 4	(Ca 1863)	Brass	24mm	—	—	50.00	Rare
	Liberty head, 12 stars around. Rv: WM H. SCHUTTER / CAIRO / 10 / CENTS. Plain edge. Rarity 7. (Schmidt S15)						
Il-Cr 4F	(1875-80)	Brass	34mm	—	30.00	45.00	—
	(All incused). Within circle: WM. H. SCHUTTER / NO. 4 / SPRINGFIELD / BLOCK. Rv: 50 / CTS. Plain edge.						
Il-Cr 4G	(1870's)	Brass	25mm	—	30.00	45.00	—
	Indian head left surrounded by stars, 50 C in exergue. Rv: As obverse of 15. Plain edge. (Wright 960)						

This liquor and cigar merchant appears in the 1866-1870 directories. Number 4 appeared in an 1863 numismatic auction.

J. D. BRAHM & CO.
Canton, Ill.

Rulau	Date	Metal	Size	F	VF	EF	Unc
Il-Ca 1	1868	WM	19mm	—	—	30.00	—

Bust left. HORATIO SEYMOUR around, 1868 below. Rv: PENNSYLVANIA CASH STORE / DRY GOODS / CLOTHING / &C. / J. D. BRAHM & CO / CANTON, ILL. Plain edge. (Jim Hartman coll.)

The one known specimen was dug up and has a rough surface. "BRAHM" could be "BEAHM".

H. C. AHRENS
Champaign, Ill.

Rulau	Date	Metal	Size	VG	F	VF	Unc
Il-Cm 1	(1888)	Brass	23mm	—	—	35.00	—

CHECK in fancy lettering within beaded circle. Around: L. BOCHE ENGRAVER & DIE SINKER CHICAGO. / (rosette). Rv: GOOD FOR 5 CENTS IN TRADE / . / H. C. / AHRENS / . (name in circle) / +. Plain edge. (Thoele report)

Saloon, listed only in 1888.

J. O. CONKLIN
Champaign, Ill.

Rulau	Date	Metal	Size	VG	F	VF	Unc
Il-Cm 5	1865	Brass	22mm	—	30.00	35.00	50.00

Dog in center, CHAMPAIGN, ILL. 1865. RV; J. O. CONKLIN 10 / BAR CHECK. Plain edge. Rarity 6. (Schmidt C-52)

Joseph O. Conklin, saloon and eating house, appears in the 1866 *Broadstreet Directory* but has vanished by the 1870 edition.

G. T. ABBEY
Chicago, Ill.

Rulau	Date	Metal	Size	VG	F	VF	Unc
Il-Ch A1	(1860-80)	Silver	25mm	—	—	85.00	—

G. T. ABBEY / CHICAGO, ILL. ctsp on U.S. 1854 S.L. quarter, (Kirtley June 1988 sale, lot 120; Brunk 137)

JOHN BERNERO

Rulau	Date	Metal	Size	VG	F	VF	Unc
Il-Ch B1	(1882-)	GS	25mm	—	—	5.00	—

JOHN BERNERO / -*- / 249 / SO. WESTERN AVE. Rv: GOOD FOR / 2 1/2 ¢ / IN TRADE.

John Bernero is listed under saloons 1882 through 1914.

L. BIGGIO

Rulau	Date	Metal	Size	VG	F	VF	EF
Il-Ch 1	(1886-87)	Copper	29mm	—	—	50.00	—

L. BIGGIO ctsp on U.S. 1951 Large cent. (Rich Hartzog coll.; Brunk 3630)

Lawrence Biggio had a saloon at 30 West Randolph St. listed in the 1887 directory. By 1893 Biggio Brothers' saloon was located at 6 South Canal St.

L. BOCHE

Rulau	Date	Metal	Size	VG	F	VF	Unc
Il-Ch 2	(1880's)	GS	25mm	—	—	25.00	35.00

Owl facing, seated on sword and scepter, all within wreath. L. BOCHE, CHECK M'F'R above, CHICAGO. below. Rv: Large ornate numeral 25 within beaded circle. Plain edge.

Boche struck tokens for firms in eight states, from the late 1870's to about 1905. A 15-cent token is reported.

R. BOEHM

Rulau	Date	Metal	Size	VG	F	VF	Unc
Il-Ch A2	ND	GS	21mm	—	—	30.00	35.00

Within wreaths: Wine bottles and glasses on tray. Rv: R. BOEHM / 536 / W. MADISON / ST. / * CHICAGO *. Rare. (Kirtley May 1991 sale, lot U001)

A. P. BOYNTON

Rulau	Date	Metal	Size	VG	F	VF	EF
Il-Ch B2	(1872)	Silver	18.5mm	100.	—	150.	—
Il-Ch C2	(1872)	Silver	26mm	100.	—	150.	—

Il-Ch B2: A. P. BOYNTON / WATCH MAKER ctsp on U.S. dime. Dates examined: 1837, 1840, 1843, 1845, 1849. 5 pieces known. (Kovacs coll.; Brunk 4760)

Il-Ch C2: Similar ctsp on U.S. quarter. Examined: 1806, 1837. 2 pieces known.

Andrew Parker Boynton was a pocket watch maker, located on 12th Street, Chicago, in 1872. Later he was at 282 1/2 State St.

BRANDS BRG. CO.

Rulau	Date	Metal	Size	F	VF	EF	Unc
Il-Ch A2	(ca 1880-90)	Brass	27mm	—	—	35.00	—

M. BRANDS / BRG. CO. Rv: Blank. Plain edge.

This brewery was owned by the father, Michael Brand, of famed numismatist Virgil M. Brand. Brand Brewing Co., Virgil's business, was a separate entity.

BUHLERT & STEPHANY

Rulau	Date	Metal	Size	VG	F	VF	Unc
Il-Ch 3	1881	Brass	25mm	5.00	10.00	15.00	—

Large star at center, with 1881 on it. Around: BUNDES SANGERFEST / CHICAGO. Rv: BUHLERT & STEPHANY 5 CENTS. Plain edge. Rarity 4. (Schmidt B88)

BUTCHERS N. P. A.

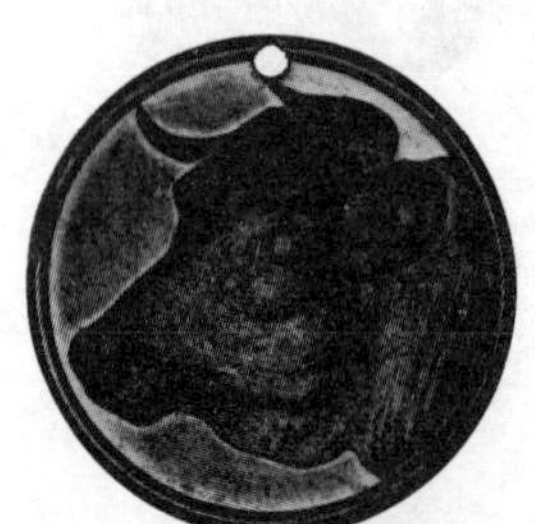

Rulau	Date	Metal	Size	F	VF	EF	Unc
Il-Ch 4	1887	WM	33mm	—	20.00	—	30.00

Bull's head left. Rv: Eagle, shield and plow at lower center. Above: 2.. NATIONAL CONVENTION OF BUTCHERS N. P. A. / CHICAGO MAY 24-27 / 1887. Plain edge.

Il-Ch 5 1887 WM 34mm — 20.00 — 35.00
Butcher and steer standing, facing, in central circle, SOUVENIR above, BUTCHERS CONVENTION below. Rv: CHICAGO / MAY 24-27-87. / UNDER THE / AUSPICES / OF / B.N.P.A. OF U.S. Plain edge.

B.N.P.A. = Butchers National Protective Association.

CANALPORT AVE. POLICE STATION

Rulau	Date	Metal	Size	VG	F	VF	Unc
Il-Ch 6	1886	WM	30mm	—	—	25.00	—

Crossed billy clubs with thongs at center, IN MEMORY OF THE DEDICATION / OF / CANALPORT AVE. above, POLICE STATION. / * AUG. 5. 1886. * below. Rv: (Ornament) / JOHN REHM / -*- / LIEUTENANT / (ornament). Plain edge. Rarity 9. (Schmidt C18)

There are only two specimens known, one of which has a recut 6 in the date. The famous Haymarket Massacre took place May 4, 1886, but anarchist troubles continued into the summer.

CENTENNIAL OF OUR NATION

Rulau	Date	Metal	Size	F	VF	EF	Unc
Il-Ch 7	1889	WM*	37mm	5.00	10.00	15.00	20.00

Naked bust of George Washington left, UNITED STATES OF AMERICA / IN GOD WE TRUST. Rv: THE CENTENNIAL OF OUR NATION CHICAGO COMMEMORATION 1789 APRIL 30. 1889. Plain edge. Issued holed. Rarity 4. Issued with a red, white and blue suspension ribbon. (Schmidt C42)

Rulau	Date	Metal	Size	F	VF	EF	Unc
Il-Ch8	1889	WM*	37mm	—	—	15.00	30.00

* Actually pot metal, a lead alloy. As 7, except E PLURIBUS UNUM replaces CHICAGO COMMEMORATION on obverse. Plain edge. Issued holed. 5 known. (Schmidt C42a)

CHICAGO EXPOSITION

Rulau	Date	Metal	Size	VG	F	VF	Unc
Il-Ch 9	1874	WM	31mm	5.00	9.00	15.00	20.00

Building at center, CHICAGO EXPOSITION. Rv: INTERSTATE - INDUSTRIAL EXPOSITION MEDAL, 1874, SECOND ANNUAL EXPOSITION, CHICAGO. ILLS. Plain edge. Rarity 6. (Schmidt C53)

Il-Ch 10 1875 WM 30mm — — 10.00 20.00
Eagle with wings outstretched, points down, 13 stars around, 1875 below. Rv: Building at center, THIRD ANNUAL above, CHICAGO / . / EXPOSITION MEDAL below. Plain edge. Rarity 8. (Schmidt C57)

Il-Ch 11 1876 WM 30mm — — 10.00 20.00
Building at center, CENTENNIAL EXPOSITION above, * 1876 * / OF CHICAGO. below. Rev: Eagle at center, head turned left, HAPPY / .-. below, all within central circle. Around: EAT GUNTHER'S CANDY / * AND YOU WILL BE *. Plain edge. Rarity 7. (Schmidt C40)

Reverse of an 1876 shell card . Worth $65 VF. (Slabaugh coll.)

THE CHICAGO HERALD

Rulau	Date	Metal	Size	F	VF	EF	Unc
Il-Ch 12	1889	WM	37mm	—	20.00	25.00	40.00

Man standing, leaning against high-front-wheel bicycle, THE CHICAGO HERALD above, CHAMPION below. Rv: SOUVENIR / OF / TOM ROE'S / BICYCLE TOUR / SAN FRANCISCO / TO CHICAGO / 1889 (on plaque) / SEPT. 21 - DEC. 3 / ON A / "LIGHT CHAMPION". Plain edge. Rarity 7. (Schmidt C61)

About 20 pieces known, including six Unc.

CHICAGO SCALE CO.

Rulau	Date	Metal	Size	VG	F	VF	EF
Il-Ch 13	(?)	Silver	25mm	—	50.00	—	—

CHICAGO SCALE CO. ctsp on both sides of U.S. 1854 Seated Liberty quarter. The punch is too large for the coin and is continued on the opposite side. (Van Ormer sale 2573; Brunk 7620)

S.D. CHILDS & CO.

Rulau	Date	Metal	Size	VG	F	VF	Unc
II-Ch 14	(1875-85)	GS	24mm	—	15.00	20.00	—

Eagle at center, head turned left. E PLURIBUS UNUM above, CHILDS, CHICAGO below. Rv: Mounted Indian left at top, large 5 ¢ at center, fan-shaped ornament at bottom. Plain edge. Rarity 7. (Schmidt C76)

Rulau	Date	Metal	Size	VG	F	VF	Unc
II-Ch 15	(1880's)	Brass	32mm	6.50	9.00	12.50	20.00

Indian head right, superimposed on a pelt pierced by an arrow. S.D. CHILDS & CO. above, *** CHICAGO. *** below. Rv: THIS COIN / MADE BY / S.D. CHILDS & CO. / 200 CLARK ST. / CHICAGO. Reeded edge. Rarity 6. (Schmidt (C70)

Rulau	Date	Metal	Size	VG	F	VF	Unc
II-Ch 16	(1880's)	Gilt/B	32mm	6.50	9.00	12.00	25.00

Indian bust in full headdress right, S.D. CHILDS & CO. above, *** CHICAGO *** below. Rev: Same as 15. Reeded edge. Rarity 6. (Schmidt C72)

Rulau	Date	Metal	Size	VG	F	VF	Unc
II-Ch 16F	(1880's)	Gilt/B	32mm	6.50	9.00	12.00	25.00

Obverse as 16 (Indian bust right). Rv: ADVERTISING NOVELTIES / COINS / CHARMS / FOBS / BUTTONS / ****. Reeded edge. Rarity 6. (Schmidt C74)

COLES & OSTRANDER

Rulau	Date	Metal	Size	VG	F	VF	Unc
II-Ch 16K	(1886)	GS	25mm	—	10.00	—	—

COLES & OSTRANDER / -228- / SO. CLARK / * ST. * / CHICAGO. Rv: CELEBRATED / -*- / OLD / * CROW *. (Thoele coll.)

Coles & Ostrander appear under saloons in the 1886 gazetteer. Celebrated Old Crow was apparently a whiskey brand.

W. M. COLLINS

Rulau	Date	Metal	Size	VG	F	VF	Unc
II-Ch 16R	(1880-84)	Brass	25mm	—	—	35.00	—

Brunswick die BB-4. Rv: GOOD FOR / 5 ¢ / W. M. COLLINS (in panel) / IN / TRADE / (ornament). Plain edge.

Collins is listed as a Chicago saloonkeeper in the 1880 and 1884 directories. The early Brunswick token type fits neatly within those dates. Later, by 1889, Collins may have relocated his business to Clear Lake, Iowa.

CUDDY

Rulau	Date	Metal	Size	VG	F	VF	EF
II-Ch 16T	(1886-87)	Copper	28mm	—	—	75.00	—

CUDDY / 80 ctsp on worn copper coin. (Brunk 10230)

Rulau	Date	Metal	Size	VG	F	VF	EF
II-Ch 16U	(1886-87)	Copper	28mm	—	—	75.00	—

CUDDY / 40 ctsp on U.S. 1837 Large cent. (Partrick coll.)

J. Cuddy and Co. were commission merchants at 62 Water St. listed in the 1887 directory. These items may have been used as tally or work checks.

DACOSTA'S

Rulau	Date	Metal	Size	VG	F	VF	Unc
II-Ch 17	(1880's ?)	Brass	24mm	—	—	15.00	30.00

DACOSTA'S / ESTABLISHED / 1877 / *.*.*.*.* / .+. CHICAGO .+. Rv: Large numeral 75 within circle formed of alternating stars and ornate crosses. Plain edge. Rarity 7. (Schmidt D17)

DALLEMAND & CO.

Rulau	Date	Metal	Size	F	VF	EF	Unc
II-Ch 18	(1888-95)	Aluminum	40mm	—	5.00	—	15.00

Large D&C monogram within central circle, small TRADE MARK below. Around: DALLEMAND & CO. / * CHICAGO. *. Rv: CREAM (in script) / PURE RYE / RICH AND MELLOW. Plain edge. (Wright 225; Schmidt D20)

Rulau	Date	Metal	Size	F	VF	EF	Unc
II-Ch A18	(1888-95)	Alum	38mm	—	5.00	—	15.00

Obverse as 18. Rv: CREAM (script) / RICH AND MELLOW. Plain edge.

W. DEAKIN

Rulau	Date	Metal	Size	VG	F	VF	EF
II-Ch 19	1863	Copper	29mm	—	—	350.	—

W. DEAKIN / DEALER IN BOOKS & COINS / 131 WELLS ST / CHICAGO 1863 ctsp on planed-down early English copper coin. (Brunk 11165)

The only piece known, sold 1975 for $125, was dug up 1973. The 1863 date is contemporary with issuance. He does not appear in 1866-70 directories.

DOUGLAS MONUMENT ASSOCIATION

Rulau	Date	Metal	Size	F	VF	EF	Unc
II-Ch 20	1866	WM	34mm	—	25.00	45.00	60.00

Naked bust left of Stephen A. Douglas, three stars below bust. Around: BORN APRIL 23. 1813. DIED JUNE 8. 1861. Rv: DOUGLAS MONUMENT ASSOCIATION / CORNER STONE / LAID (on tablet) / SEPTEMBER 6. / 1866 / *. Plain edge. Rarity 9. (Schmidt D70)

G. D. DUNHAM

Rulau	Date	Metal	Size	VG	F	VF	Unc
II-Ch A20	(?)	Silver	34mm	—	—	125.	—

G. D. DUNHAM / CHICAGO ctsp on obverse of Bank of England 1814 3-shilling token. CHICAGO ctsp on reverse of the coin. (Krueger 3572; Brunk 12375)

The famous numismatist William Forrester Dunham was from Chicago, but whether G.D. Dunham was an ancestor must be researched.

P.C. DUNN SALOON

Rulau	Date	Metal	Size	VG	F	VF	Unc
II-Ch 21	(1876-83)	Copper	29mm	—	—	200.	—

P.C. DUNN / SALOON / CHICAGO / ILLS. ctsp on U.S. 1851 Large cent. (Rich Hartzog coll.;Brunk 12440)

Peter C. Dunn appears in the 1876 and 1883 directories.

WM. ELSER

Rulau	Date	Metal	Size	VG	F	VF	Unc
II-Ch B21	(?)	CN	24mm	—	—	15.00	—

GOOD FOR ONE DRINK / 5 ¢ / Wm / ELSER / +. Rv: Ornate numeral 5 at center. Around: L. BOCHE CHECK MANUFR 166 RANDOLPH ST. CHICAGO. Plain edge.

F. & M. (and) J.R.M.

Rulau	Date	Metal	Size	VG	F	VF	Unc
II-Ch 22	(1874-84)	Brass	24mm	—	25.00	—	—

Liberty Head left in beaded circle. Around: THE J.M. BRUNSWICK & BALKE COS. / .CHECK. Rv: GOOD FOR / 5 ¢ / F. & M. / 170 S. CLARK ST. Plain edge. (Brunswick 2113)

Rulau	Date	Metal	Size	VG	F	VF	Unc
II-Ch 22C	(1874-84)	Brass	24mm	—	—	25.00	—

Pool table in central beaded circle. Around: THE J.M. BRUNSWICK & BALKE COS. / CHECK. Rv: GOOD FOR / * 5 ¢ * / J.R.M. (on scroll) / .-. 170 CLARK ST. / (19 alternating dots and stars). Plain edge. (Brunswick 2182)

The attribution to Chicago is tentative.

FIRST INTERNATIONAL MILITARY ENCAMPMENT

Rulau	Date	Metal	Size	VG	F	VF	Unc
II-Ch 23	1887	WM	29mm	—	—	15.00	25.00

Mounted officer at center, tents at left, soldiers at attention at right. Rv: INTERNATIONAL MILITARY ENCAMPMENT AT CHICAGO. ILL. U.S.A. SOUVENIR OCTOBER 1887. Plain edge. Rarity 6. (Schmidt F30)

Rulau	Date	Metal	Size	VG	F	VF	Unc
II-Ch 23B	1887	Gilt/B	32mm	5.00	10.00	15.00	25.00

Soldier in kneeling rifle position within central circle, INTERNATL MILITARY ENCAMPMENT CHICAGO OCT. / 1887 around. Rv: Crossed rifles as supporters and military helmet as crest surround shield, on which a sentry guards tents. Plain edge.

COL. JAMES FISK JR.

Rulau	Date	Metal	Size	VG	F	VF	Unc
II-Ch 23F	(1871)	Brass	23mm	7.50	10.00	15.00	25.00

Bust right, tiny A. WILLEMIN under truncation. Around: COL. JAMES FISK JR. Rv: Railroad engine to right, RELIEF FOR above, CHICAGO. below. Plain edge. (Bruce Smith coll.)

Col. James Fisk Jr. (1834-1872) was a partner of financier Jay Gould. Together they attempted to corner the gold market in 1869, bringing on the Panic of '69 and, after Fisk's death, the grim Panic of 1873 was an offshoot result, some say.

In this token, however, Fisk is a hero. He donated use of his railroad trains to carry food, medical supplies and other goods to survivors of the Great Chicago Fire of 1871. Smith reports he has owned three specimens, all of which have been holed. The Unc. price above would pertain to an unpierced specimen.

Nearly 5,000 tokens were issued, some from a reengraved die. As late as 1950 in Chicago, these were still considered "junk box" items. Specimens exist in silvered brass and copper.

FRENCH PALACE

Rulau	Date	Metal	Size	VG	F	VF	Unc
II-Ch 24	(1880's)	CN	24mm	—	—	30.00	—

FRENCH PALACE / 5 / 81 UNION ST. Rv: Blank. Plain edge.

The Rich Hartzog collection specimen has a pedigree back to 1915, ex-Morris Thacker, Benjamin Odesser, Joseph Schmidt, Hartzog. The establishment may have been a bawdy house.

GARDEN CITY BILLIARD TABLE CO.

Rulau	Date	Metal	Size	VG	F	VF	EF
Il-Ch A24	(1880's ?)	Brass	25mm	—	—	15.00	—

THE / GARDEN CITY / (ornament) / BILLIARD / (ornament) / TABLE CO. / CHICAGO. Rv: GOOD FOR / 5 ¢ / PALACE / IN / TRADE. Plain edge.

J.W. GEHRIG

Rulau	Date	Metal	Size	VG	F	VF	EF
Il-Ch 25	(1878-83)	Silver	31mm	150.	—	250.	—

J.W. GEHRIG PHOTOGRAPHER. ctsp in a circle on U.S. 1849 or 1877 Liberty Seated half dollar.

Gehrig appears in the 1872 and 1883 directories.

GENIN THE HATTER

Rulau	Date	Metal	Size	VG	F	VF	Unc
Il-Ch 26	1872	GS	24mm	25.00	35.00	—	—

Hat with buckled band, 1872. Rv: GENIN THE HATTER / 175 W. MADISON ST. / CHICAGO. Plain edge. Thin planchet. Rarity 7. (Schmidt G20)

Genin in 1853 had a store at 214 Broadway in New York, next door to Barnum's American Museum.

GILES BRO. & CO.

Rulau	Date	Metal	Size	VG	F	VF	Unc
Il-Ch 27	1883	WM	32mm	—	—	15.00	30.00

Locomotive, SOUVENIR NATL. R.R. EXPOSITION / CHICAGO 1883. Rv: Pocket watch within wreath at center. Around: GILES BRO. & CO. WATCHES, DIAMONDS. Plain edge. Rarity 7. (Schmidt G35)

GRAND CENTRAL CLOTHING HOUSE

Rulau	Date	Metal	Size	VG	F	VF	Unc
Il-Ch 28	(1870-90)	GS	24mm	—	—	5.00	15.00

GRAND CENTRAL / ONE PRICE / CLOTHING HOUSE / 142 & 144 / STATE ST. / CHICAGO. Rv: THIS MEDAL / GOOD FOR / ONE DOLLAR / ON EACH / TWENTY DOLLARS / PURCHASED AT / 142 & 144 STATE ST . / CHICAGO. Thick planchet. Plain edge. Rarity 2. (Wright 398; Schmidt G60a)

Rulau	Date	Metal	Size	VG	F	VF	Unc
Il-Ch 28A	(1870-90)	Brass	24mm	—	—	30.00	—

As 28. Plain edge. Rarity 9. (Schmidt G60)

Rulau	Date	Metal	Size	VG	F	VF	Unc
Il-Ch 28B	(1870-90)	Copper	24mm	—	—	40.00	—

As 28. Plain edge. Rarity 8.

GREAT SANITARY FAIR

Rulau	Date	Metal	Size	F	VF	EF	Unc
Il-Ch A28	1865	Silver	24mm	—	—	75.00	—

Eagle, wings folded, on U.S. Shield. Around: ARMY OF THE AMERICAN EAGLE / (tiny) / P. A. MEYER. Rv: MEDAL OF HONOR (in scroll) / No 16 (incuse script) / AWARDED / AT THE / GREAT SANITARY FAIR / IN CHICAGO 1865 / To Roderick S. Owen (incuse, script) / FOR PATRIOTIC SERVICES. Plain edge.

GRENIER'S LYCEUM

Rulau	Date	Metal	Size	F	VF	EF	Unc
Il-Ch 29	(1880's)	Brass	24mm	—	10.00	15.00	20.00

* GRENIER'S LYCEUM * / VARIETY / .-. / PALACE / -*- GOLD MINE / -NO 1-. Rv: * GRENIER'S GARDEN * / CHICAGO'S / -*- / GREATEST / -RESORT- / GOLD MINE / NO 2. Plain edge. Rarity 2. (Schmidt G75)

Rulau	Date	Metal	Size	F	VF	EF	Unc
Il-Ch 29A	(1880's)	Copper	24mm	—	12.50	16.00	20.00

As 29. Plain edge. Rarity 5. (Schmidt G75a)

Rulau	Date	Metal	Size	F	VF	EF	Unc
Il-Ch 29B	(1880's)	Nickel	24mm	—	12.50	16.00	25.00

As 29. Plain edge. Rarity 6. (Schmidt G75b)

Grenier's Lyceum and Grenier's Garden were entertainment houses of the 1880's. The text's use of "gold mine" (of entertainment) is unusual.

HANNAH AND HOGG

Rulau	Date	Metal	Size	VG	F	VF	Unc
Il-Ch 30	(1870-90)	GS	24mm	2.00	3.00	7.50	15.00

Scotch thistle with three blooms. Rv: HANNAH / AND (on ribbon) / * HOGG *. Thin planchet. Plain edge. (Wright 421; Schmidt H12)

Rulau	Date	Metal	Size	VG	F	VF	Unc
Il-Ch 30A	(1870-90)	Copper	24mm	—	—	11.50	25.00

As 30. Plain edge. (Schmidt H12a)

Rulau	Date	Metal	Size	VG	F	VF	Unc
Il-Ch 31	(1870-90)	GS	24mm	2.00	3.00	5.00	10.00

Scotch thistle with one blossom. Rv: HANNAH / AND (on ribbon) / * HOGG *. Thick planchet. Plain edge. (Schmidt H12b)

II-Ch 32	(1880-99)	GS	24mm	2.00	3.00	5.00	10.00

Scotch thistle with three blooms above HANNAH / * HOGG (all in script) / 222 & 224 CLARK ST. / -151- / RANDOLPH ST. / HOTEL BREVOORT / STOCK EXCHANGE / FISHER BUILDING / 83 MADISON ST. / CHICAGO. in eight lines. Thin planchet. Plain edge. There are five die varieties of this piece. (Miller III 13; Schmidt H12c to H12g)

Schmidt H12c Variety

II-Ch 33	(1880-99)	GS	24mm	—	—	5.00	10.00

As 32, but centrally holed planchet. Plain edge. There are three major obverse die varieties of this token, with differing thistle arrangements; all are Rarity 3. (Schmidt H12h to H12j)

Hannah and Hogg were proud Scotsmen who used their national flower, the thistle, liberally on their tokens. They operated a chain of saloons in Chicago for about 40 years before 1919 - many in choice locations as II-Ch 32 above indicates.

Each Hannah and Hogg piece catalogued here was worth 2 1/2 Cents in trade, it is theorized.

In 1918, Hannah & Hogg Inc. were listed in the R.G. Dun directory as being in the wholesale wine and liquor business. But the business had changed hands in 1914. Both Hannah and Hogg were dead by 1919.

All Hannah and Hogg taverns had a stone man at the entrance-way. It was at once their symbol, trademark and advertisement.

The name still graces a rather poor grade of whiskey sold in Chicago and environs.

ILLINOIS MILITARY & MECHANICAL TRAINING SCHOOL

Rulau	Date	Metal	Size	F	VF	Unc	Proof
II-Ch 50	1887	SWM	30mm	—	—	25.00	—

Building across center; ILLINOIS MILITARY / & / MECHANICAL above; TRAINING SCHOOL / FOR / POOR / BOYS / CHICAGO. Rv: Within central circle: SOUVENIR / 1837 1887 / (ornament) / (star). Plain edge. Issued holed at top for suspension from red ribbon.

The 1837 date is puzzling. The school was founded in the 1850's. Such schools did exaggerate their founding date to add to prestige.

F.A. JENSCH

Rulau	Date	Metal	Size	F	VF	EF	Unc
II-Ch 53	1857	Copper	25mm	—	5.00	10.00	20.00

Mounted bell inscribed: F.A. JENSCH / BELL FOUNDER / CHICAGO, ILL. Above: MADE TO ORDER FROM 1 TO 50,000 LBS. In exergue: ESTAB'D 1857. Rv: F.A. JENSCH / BELL / FOUNDER / (ornament) / 105 S. WELLS ST. / CHICAGO. Plain edge. (Miller III 18; Schmidt J28b)

II-Ch 54	1857	Brass	25mm	—	10.00	15.00	30.00

As 53. Plain edge. (Miller III 19; Schmidt J28)

II-Ch 54A	1857	S/Br	25mm	—	10.00	—	30.00

As 53. Plain edge. (Schmidt J28c)

II-Ch 55	1857	WM	25mm	—	20.00	25.00	40.00

As 53. Plain edge. (Wright 508; Miller III 20; Schmidt J28d)

II-Ch 56	1857	Copper	25mm	—	30.00	—	50.00

Similar to 53, but no address on reverse. Bell is smaller, and no 'ESTAB'D 1857' on obverse. (Miller III 20A; Schmidt J28e

Probably issued in the 1865-1880 period. The date 1857 refers to the firm's founding.

LYCEUM THEATRE

Rulau	Date	Metal	Size	VG	F	VF	Unc
II-Ch 60	(1870-90)	GS	24mm	2.00	3.50	5.00	10.00

LYCEUM THEATRE / FINEST / VAUDEVILLE / HOUSE / ON EARTH / CHICAGO. Rv: LAUGHING HEADQUARTERS / BURLESQUE/ NOVELTY / MINSTRELS / SPECTACULAR / COMEDY. Thin planchet. Plain edge. There are three varieties, all Rarity 5. (Schmidt L92)

MALLORY COMMISSION CO.

Rulau	Date	Metal	Size	F	VF	EF	Unc
II-Ch 61	(?)	Bronze	37mm	—	25.00	37.50	—

Steer left, MALLORY COMMISSION CO. above, tiny S.D. CHILDS & CO. CHICAGO. below. Rv: LIVE STOCK COMMISSION / CHICAGO / KANSAS CITY / SO. ST. JOSEPH / SO. OMAHA / SIOUX CITY / SO. ST. PAUL / . ESTABLISHED 1862. Plain edge.

II-Ch 61c	(?)	Bronze	37mm	—	25.00	37.50	—

Similar to last, but LIVE STOCK COMMISSION above steer on obverse. Rv: Similar to last, but first line reads: MALLORY COMMISSION CO. Flourishes have been added throughout legend. Plain edge.

JOHN MANION

Rulau	Date	Metal	Size	VG	F	VF	Unc
IL-Ch A61	(1886-87)	CN	24mm	—	—	25.00	—

Brunswick die BB-4. Rv: GOOD FOR / 5 ¢ / JOHN MANION (on panel) / IN / TRADE / (ornament). (Thoele coll.)

Saloon, appearing in the 1887 directory.

N. MATSON & CO.

Rulau	Date	Metal	Size	VG	F	VF	Unc
Il-Ch 62	(1870's)	Silver	26mm	—	15.00	20.00	—

N. MATSON & CO. / JEWELERS / 117 / LAKE ST. / CHICAGO ILL. Rv: JEWELRY / (Counterstamped numeral) / CHECK. Reeded Edge. Rarity 8. (Schmidt Chicago M12)

The specimen in the collection of James H. Holtel, Nelsonville, Ohio, is stamped with the numeral '499' on reverse. Only five pieces are known.

Matson & Hoes, jewelry, appears in the 1866 directory. N. Matson & Co. is listed in 1870.

McCAULEY BROS.

Rulau	Date	Metal	Size	VG	F	VF	Unc
Il-Ch A62	(1885-87)	CN	25mm	—	—	20.00	—

Brunswick die BB-6b. Rv: Stars encircled: GOOD FOR / 10 ¢ / McCAULEY / BROS / IN TRADE.

John and Wiliam McCauley had a saloon at 123 West Randolph listed in the 1885 and 1887 directories. The token was apparently struck by L. Boche.

McCORMICK & DOYLE

Rulau	Date	Metal	Size	VG	F	VF	Unc
Il-Ch 63	(1885-90)	Brass	24.5mm	—	—	20.00	—

Chas. Pick & Co. die. Rv: GOOD FOR / 5 ¢ / McCORMICK / & DOYLE (names in cross-hatched panel) / IN TRADE / AT THE BAR. Unique.

John H. McCormick and Michael Doyle, saloon, 3701 Butterfield, listed in city directory 1885-1890.

22 NORD-AMER. SANGERFEST

Rulau	Date	Metal	Size	F	VF	EF	Unc
Il-Ch 64	1881	WM	30mm	—	10.00	12.50	20.00

Woman with lyre standing half right. Around: DER MENSCHHEIT WURDE IST IN EURE HAND GEGEBEN, BEWAHRT SIE. Rv: Within wreath: 22 / NORD-AMER. / SANGERFEST / CHICAGO. / 1881 / JUNI 29. JULY 3. Plain edge.

Commemorated the 22nd North American Singing Festival in Chicago in 1881. The 19th century German immigrants retained their cultural ties with Germanism through singing festivals, turner (gymnastic) fests and other events honored on medalets and tokens.

B. F. NORRIS & CO.

Rulau	Date	Metal	Size	F	VF	EF	Unc
Il-Ch 65	(1876)	Gilt/B	39mm	—	15.00	22.50	35.00

B. F. NORRIS & CO / CENTENNIAL / (eagle) / PERPETUAL / POCKET / PAT APPL'D FOR / CALENDER (sic!) / WHOLESALE JEWELERS CHICAGO ILLS. Rv: Revolving perpetual calendar. Plain edge. R8. (Schmidt N55)

Rulau	Date	Metal	Size	F	VF	EF	Unc
Il-Ch 65A	(1876)	Gilt/Cop	39mm	—	15.00	22.50	35.00

As last. R8. (Wright 765; Schmidt N55a)

Joseph Schmidt, Illinois specialist, reports strong collector demand for pocket calendars. As a Centennial year item, this type is especially desirable.

A successor firm, B. F. Norris, Allister & Co., issued a pocket calendar for the Columbian Exposition in 1893.

NORTHWESTERN DENTAL INFIRMARY

Rulau	Date	Metal	Size	VG	F	VF	Unc
Il-Ch 66	(1870-90)	GS	24mm	—	—	15.00	30.00

NORTH WESTERN / * / DENTAL / INFIRMARY / CHICAGO / OPERA HOUSE. / Rv: ALL WORK FREE / SMALL / * CHARGE * / FOR / MATERIAL. Thin planchet. Plain edge.

N. W. SHOW CASE MFG. CO.

Rulau	Date	Metal	Size	VG	F	VF	Unc
Il-Ch 69	(1872)	GS	23mm	—	—	5.00	15.00

Curved front showcase, RE ESTABLISHED above, AT / 59 & 61 S. CANAL ST. / CHICAGO. Rv: NICKEL / FROM THE / RUINS / OF THE / N.W. SHOW CASE MF'G CO. / OCT. 9TH. Thin planchet. Plain edge. Rarity 6. (Wright 1544; Schmidt N57)

Four square miles of Chicago, including the business district, were destroyed by a great fire on Oct. 8-9, 1871. Canal St. lies along the south branch of the Chicago River and this area was thoroughly burned out, the flames even leaping the river northeastward and dying out only when they reached the lake on the north side.

Rulau	Date	Metal	Size	VG	F	VF	Unc
Il-Ch 70	(1870's)	CN	21mm	—	—	4.00	10.00

Large 10 C. at center. Around: N. W. SHOWCASE MF'G CO. / 59 & 61 SO CANAL ST. CHICAGO. Rv: RE'D'M'BLE IN SUMS NOT EX'C'D'G 10 PR CT ON PURCHASE / GOOD FOR / 10 C. / IN MDSE. Plain edge. Rarity 4. (Schmidt N58)

PALMER HOUSE

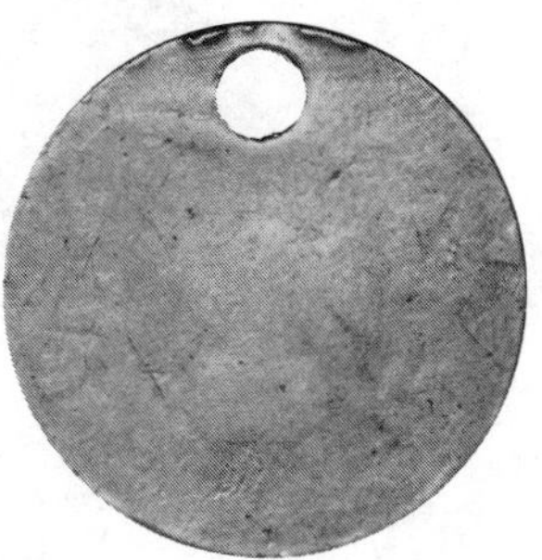

Rulau	Date	Metal	Size	VG	F	VF	Unc
Il-Ch 71	(1880-93)	CN*	38mm	—	—	22.50	—

* Cupronickel, with black enameled letters. (All incused): PALMER HOUSE / 10¢ / 66 / BARBER SHOP. Rv: Blank. Plain edge. Issued holed. Only 5 pieces known.

Rulau	Date	Metal	Size	VG	F	VF	Unc
Il-Ch 72	(1880's)	Brass	26mm	—	—	20.00	—

Crossed billiard cues within central circle, N-B-M-C in angles. Around: NATIONAL BILLIARD MFG. CO. Rv: PALMER HOUSE / GOOD FOR / 5 C / IN TRADE / * BAR *. Plain edge.

PETER SCHUTTLER

Rulau	Date	Metal	Size	F	VF	EF	Unc
Il-Ch 100	1876	Brass	32mm	—	5.00	10.00	25.00

Manufacturing plant at center, THE PIONEER WAGON WORKS / OF THE WEST. above, ESTABLISHED ↙ - 1843 - / PETER SCHUTTLER CHICAGO. below. Rv: Wagon at center, * MFR. OF FARM, FREIGHT & SPRING WAGONS * / FIRST PREMIUM above, PARIS 1867 / PHILADELPHIA / .1876. / FACTORY 45 W. MONROE ST. CHICAGO below. Plain edge. (Schmidt S20). There are four die varieties.

Rulau	Date	Metal	Size	F	VF	EF	Unc
Il-Ch 100A	1876	Brass	32mm	—	15.00	25.00	35.00

As 100, but thick planchet. Plain edge. (Schmidt S20a)

Rulau	Date	Metal	Size	F	VF	EF	Unc
Il-Ch 100B	1876	S/Brass	32mm	—	15.00	25.00	40.00

As 100. Plain edge. (Schmidt S20b)

Rulau	Date	Metal	Size	F	VF	EF	Unc
Il-Ch 100C	1876	WM	32mm	—	5.00	10.00	40.00

As 100. Plain edge. (Schmidt S20c). Thick flan.

Rulau	Date	Metal	Size	F	VF	EF	Unc
Il-Ch 101	(1876)	WM	32mm	—	—	—	100.

Bearded bust left, BORN 1811 vertically at left, DIED 1865 vertically at right. PETER SCHUTTLER SR. above, * FOUNDER OF THE SCHUTTLER WAGON WORKS * below. Rv: As obverse of Il-Ch 100. Plain edge. (David Schenkman coll.)

This piece is unlisted by all catalogers and is, so far, unique. The reverse is the same as the obverse of Il-Ch 100.

BRANCH AGENCY TOKENS

Most of these tokens used an obverse die similar to Il-Ch 100, with minor die variations. Some reverse dies substituted "dealer in agricultural implements" for "first premium," etc. The name of the agent is inscribed with the city of issue. All agency store cards are 33mm, plain edge, Rarity 7 through Rarity 10.

Rulau	Date	Metal	Agent	F	VF	EF	Unc
Il-Ch 104	1876	Brass	**	—	20.00	25.00	40.00
	** M.C. Hawley & Co., San Francisco.						
Il-Ch 104A	1876	WM	**	20.00	25.00	40.00	60.00

Rulau	Date	Metal	Agent	F	VF	EF	Unc
Il-Ch 106	(1876)	Brass	**	—	20.00	25.00	40.00
	** John J. Maxey, Denver, Col						
Il-Ch 106A	(1876)	WM	**	—	25.00	40.00	50.00

Rulau	Date	Metal	Agent	F	VF	EF	Unc
Il-Ch 108	1876	Brass	**	—	35.00	50.00	125.
	** Thos. C. Carson, Iowa City, IA						

Rulau	Date	Metal	Agent	F	VF	EF	Unc
Il-Ch 110	1876	Brass	**	—	17.00	25.00	35.00
	** Smith & Keating, Kansas City, Mo.						
Il-Ch 112	1876	Brass	**	—	17.00	25.00	35.00
	** Dodd & Co. Portland, Or.						
Il-Ch 114	1876	Brass	Austin, Tx.	—	—	200.	—
Il-Ch 115	1876	Brass	**	—	17.00	22.50	33.00
	** A.B. Tabor, Dallas Tx.						
Il-Ch 115A	1876	WM	**	—	25.00	40.00	60.00

Il-Ch 116	1876	Brass	**	—	17.00	22.50	33.00

** Byers Bros., Sherman, Tx.

Il-Ch 117	1876	Brass	**	—	17.00	22.50	50.00

** George A. Lowe, Salt Lake City, Ut.

Il-Ch 117A	1876	WM	**	—	—	—	Unique
Il-Ch 118	1876	Brass	**	—	45.00	75.00	100.

** Herman Haas, Cheyenne, Wy

SCHUTTLER & HOTZ

Rulau	Date	Metal	Size	F	VF	EF	Unc
Il-Ch 120	1878	Copper	34mm	—	10.00	15.00	25.00

Obverse similar to 100, with minor differences. The 1843 is larger. Rv: Wagon at center, * SCHUTTLER & HOTZ, MANUFACTURERS OF THE * / FIRST PREMIUM. PARIS 1867. / PHILADELPHIA 1876 / PARIS 1878 above, ESTABLISHED / 1843 / OFFICE 45 W. MONROE ST. / CHICAGO, ILL. / OLD RELIABLE SCHUTTLER WAGON below. Plain edge. Thick planchet. (Schmidt S22)

Il-Ch 122	(1889)	Aluminum	34mm	—	10.00	15.00	25.00

Obverse similar to 120, with minor differences. Rv: Wagon right, its right side wheels appearing tilted inward. Above: FIRST PREMIUM. Below: WHEREVER EXHIBITED; all within central circle. Around: SCHUTTLER & HOTZ, MANUFACTURERS OF . / THE OLD RELIABLE SCHUTTLER WAGON. Plain edge. (Schmidt S23)

Il-Ch 123	(1889)	Aluminum	34mm	—	5.00	10.00	25.00

As 122, but wheels on reverse appear normal. Plain edge. (Schmidt S23a)

SEA'S MILLINERY DEPT.

Rulau	Date	Metal	Size	VG	F	VF	Unc
Il-Ch 73	1885	WM	--mm	—	—	10.00	20.00

Eagle with U.S. shield on its breast at center, SEA'S MILLINERY DEPT. around, 1885. below. Rv: SEA'S / MILLINERY / DEPT. / SOUVENIR / OF THE OPENING / 20TH SEASON. Plain edge.

SELZ

Rulau	Date	Metal	Size	F	VF	EF	Unc
Il-Ch A73	(1876)	Bronze	**	—	15.00	—	—

** Bell-shaped, 36 x 37.8mm.
SELZ / LIBERTY BELL MEDAL / 1776 / AWARDED FOR / PROFICIENCY IN / SCHOLARSHIP AND DEPORTMENT / BY / SELZ. CHICAGO. Rv: DONATED BY / (sunburst) / SELZ, CHICAGO. Plain edge. (Rulau coll.)

Morris Selz.

E.H. STEIN

Rulau	Date	Metal	Size	VG	F	VF	Unc
Il-Ch 74	(1866-69)	Nickel	21mm	—	—	40.00	—

E.H. STEIN / $1.00 / STORE / CITY OF PARIS / 83. S. CLARK. ST (all lettering incuse). Rv: Blank. Plain edge. 2 known. (Rulau-Miller III 107)

The address could fix this concern as early as 1845. The "City of Paris" was a block in Chicago which boasted many shops handling the exotic wares of the world before and during the Civil War. The token's crudeness seemed to indicate a date before 1860, and thus it was included in our 1845-60 reference.

Joseph Schmidt, the Illinois token expert, points out that Stein was at 83 Clark St. as late as 1871-1876. David Schenkman thought this piece dates from about 1870.

The 1869 Chicago directory may have cleared up the matter. It lists "E.H. Stein, proprietor of City of Paris One Dollar Store" at 81 So. Clark, probably another entrance to the same building. So we are reassigning the token to this 1866-1889 reference.

E.H. Stein does not appear in either the 1859 or 1865 directories.

ROBERT TARRANT

Rulau	Date	Metal	Size	F	VF	EF	Unc
Il-Ch 75	(1889?)	Alum	38mm	—	25.00	35.00	50.00

Steamboat to left, MARINE ENGINE above, WORKS in exergue. Tiny CHILDS CHICAGO below exergue line. Rv: COMPLIMENTS / —OF— / ROBERT TARRANT / CHICAGO / —.— / 52 TO 56 ILLINOIS ST. Plain edge. Rarity 8. (Wright 1091; Schmidt T10)

TERRILL BROS.

Rulau	Date	Metal	Size	VG	F	VF	EF
Il-Ch 76	(1885)	Brass	29mm	—	—	40.00	—

(All incused): TERRILL BROS., 196 & 198 S. WATER ST., 50 1 COOP. Rv: Blank. Plain edge. 2 known. (Schmidt T20)

Terrill Brothers became defunct by 1896.

DANIEL G. TRENCH & CO.

Rulau	Date	Metal	Size	F	VF	EF	Unc
Il-Ch 77	(1883-93)	Brass	20mm	—	9.00	15.00	—

DANIEL G. TRENCH & CO. / CANNING / FACTORY / OUTFITTERS / * / CHICAGO. Rv: Blank. Plain edge. (Schmidt T33)

The Trench store card was muled with many other tokens of the period. This is the only known piece mentioning Trench alone.

C. TUCKHORN

Rulau	Date	Metal	Size	VG	F	VF	Unc
Il-Ch C77	(1880-90)	Brass	--mm	—	20.00	—	—

C. TUCKHORN / & CO. / BILLIARD & POOL / TABLES / 35 .5TH AVE. / CHICAGO. Rv: GOOD FOR / 5 C / (blank tablet) / -IN- / * TRADE *. Plain edge. (Thoele report)

Tuckhorn was active as a manufacturer of billiard tables 1880 through 1890, and distributed billiard checks to his clients. The piece above is a stock die sample piece; the blank tablet would include the name or initials of the customer.

VAUGHAN'S SEED STORE

Rulau	Date	Metal	Size	F	VF	EF	Unc
Il-Ch 78	1887	CN	31mm	5.00	10.00	15.00	20.00

Six-story building at center, VAUGHAN'S SEED STORE above, CHICAGO below. Rv: + 3RD ANNUAL MEETING + / SAF / COMPLIMENTS / OF / J. C. VAUGHAN / 1887. Plain edge. Rarity 7. (Wright 1186; Schmidt V10)

Dr. Wright called this piece rare in 1901! SAF = Society of American Florists. There are two die varieties.

WALDRON'S PRESCRIPTION STORE

Rulau	Date	Metal	Size	F	VF	EF	Unc
Il-Ch 79	(1885)	Brass	25mm	—	—	75.00	—

Eagle facing, head turned left. WALDRON'S PRESCRIPTION STORE around, .CHICAGO. below. Rv: GOOD FOR ONE GLASS OF SODA WATER / AT / WALDRON'S / RANDOLPH / & / FIFTH AVE. / —.— / .CHICAGO. Plain edge. 2 known. (Schmidt W12)

FRED WOLF
Chicago, Ill.

Rulau	Date	Metal	Size	VG	F	VF	Unc
Il-Ch	(1887)	—	Oct 26mm	—	—	15.00	—

NBMCo die. Rv: FRED WOLF / GOOD FOR / 5 ¢ / * IN TRADE *.

Saloon, listed in 1887.

ST. PATRICKS PARISH
East St. Louis, Ill.

Rulau	Date	Metal	Size	VG	F	VF	Unc
Il-ES 8	(?)	Brass	23mm	—	—	25.00	—

ST. PATRICKS PARISH / 5 ¢ / E ST L. Rv: EXCELSIOR / 113 / OLIVE / ST. / ST. LOUIS. Plain edge.

CONCORDIA
Elgin, Ill.

Rulau	Date	Metal	Size	VG	F	VF	Unc
Il-El 3	(1885)	Brass	25mm	—	10.00	20.00	30.00

Indian head left within central beaded circle. Around: L. BOCHE ENGRAVER, DIE SINKER & MANUF'R OF CHECKS, 166 RANDOLPH ST. CHICAGO. Rv: CONCORDIA / * / ELGIN / ILLS. surrounded by circle of 35 stars. Plain edge. (Schmidt C58)

ELGIN NATIONAL WATCH CO.

The Elgin National Watch Co. gave away attractive 30mm white metal tokens with their watches. Most were identical, except that an incuse watch movement number has been placed on reverse, and the watch model name is included on many of the pieces following the word NAME. Though many thousands of these tokens must have been issued, they are not particularly common in numismatic channels and we suspect that a great many of them are still resting in homes among other old oddments.

Rulau	Date	Metal	Size	F	VF	EF	Unc
Il-El 5	(1870's)	WM	30mm	5.00	9.00	15.00	25.00

Winged nude man with scythe and large Elgin watch striding right, THE ELGIN NATIONAL WATCH COMPANY OF ELGIN ILLS / * INCORPORATED 1865 *. Rv: ELGIN NATIONAL WATCH CO / THIS / CERTIFIES THAT / LEVER MOVEMENT / NO. 205091 (numerals incused; these change on each token) / ENGRAVED / MANF'D ELGIN, ILLS. / WAS MANUFACTURED BY US / OF THE BEST MATERIALS / AND IS / WARRANTED / A GOOD / TIME-KEEPER. Plain edge. (Schmidt Not Listed)

II-El 6 (1870's) WM 30mm 3.00 5.00 8.00 15.00
Obverse as 5. Rv: As 5, except fifth and sixth lines of central legend read: NAMED / ELGIN NAT. WATCH CO. instead of: ENGRAVED / MANF'D ELGIN, ILLS. Plain edge. Rarity 5. (Wright 287; Miller Ill. 42; Schmidt E27)

II-El 6 is the most readily available token in this series. The following varieties are the same as II-El 6 except that they bear one of 13 watch model names in the sixth line on reverse, following NAMED on the fifth line. Each variety is Rarity 5 or 6, apparently, ranging in price about $5 to $10 more than comparable conditions in II-El 6. (Other watch model names may exist)

II-El 6A T.M. AVERY (reverse watch name)
II-El 6B GAIL BORDEN
II-El 6C H.Z. CULVER
II-El 6D DEXTER ST.
II-El 6E CHAS. FARGO
II-El 6F W.H. FERRY
II-El 6G LADY ELGIN
II-El 6H M.D. OGDEN
II-El 6I B.W. RAYMOND
II-El 6J J.T. RYERSON
II-El 6K H.H. TAYLOR (Miller III 43)
II-El 6L C.M. WHEELER

II-El 7 (1870's) SB 16mm — — — Rare
"Trademark" on pedestal, on which stands winged nude Father Time similar to that on II-El 5 and 6. Rv: Intaglio of obverse. Plain edge. Rarity 8. (Schmidt E29) A bangle?

Rulau	Date	Metal	Size	VG	F	VF	Unc
II-El 8	1873	WM	30mm	5.00	7.00	10.00	35.00

Exposition building in center, CHICAGO EXPOSITION above, 1873 / * below. Tiny V.S. WEBER below ground. Rv: Clock face in center, hands at 3:02 1/2 position. Around: MADE BY THE NATIONAL ELGIN WATCH CO / * IN EXPOSITION BUILDING *. Thick planchet. Plain edge. Rarity 6. (Schmidt C50)

II-El 9 1873 WM 30mm — 10.00 25.00 50.00
As 8, but CONTRIBUTION TO 1873 / YELLOW FEVER SUFFERERS added to reverse. Clock hands at 3:38 position. Plain edge. Rarity 6. (Schmidt C50a)

Rulau	Date	Metal	Size	F	VF	EF	Unc
II-El 10	1874	WM	30mm	3.00	7.00	15.00	25.00

Exposition building, CHICAGO EXPOSITION above, 1000 FT. LONG 240 FT. W. / * 1874 * / * below. Tiny V.S. WEBER CHICAGO below ground. Rv: As obverse of II-El 5 (Winged nude Father Time). Plain edge. Rarity 6. (Schmidt C53)

Rulau	Date	Metal	Size	VG	F	VF	Unc
II-El 11	(1875)	WM	30mm	—	—	7.00	20.00

Obverse as II-El 5. Rv: Building at center, THIRD ANNUAL above, CHICAGO / EXPOSITION MEDAL below. Plain edge. Rarity 6. (Schmidt C55)

II-El 14 (1898-1930) Brass 31mm 2.00 3.50 5.00 10.00
Winged Father Time right, holding aloft a large watch, and ELGIN ADVENTURERS' CLUB across the standing figure's legs - all within a clock face. Rv: (8 stars) / THIS IS TO / CERTIFY THAT / A. RUSSELL (incused; or another name) / IS A CHARTER / MEMBER / IF FOUND PLEASE RETURN TO THE ELGIN NATIONAL WATCH CO. ELGIN, ILL. Plain edge. Issued holed.

Dr Wright in 1898 called the figure on II-El 5 "Father Time," but the more familiar figure of Father Time today does appear on the last token listed above, II-El 14. The figure on 5 is unique to Elgin — a compelling representation.

The Chicago Exposition tokens perhaps should have been listed under Chicago in this catalog, but we preferred to keep all the Elgin National Watch Co. pieces together. Non-Elgin exposition pieces may be found under Chicago.

ELGIN TURNVEREIN

Rulau	Date	Metal	Size	VG	F	VF	Unc
II-El 16	(1880's)	Brass	Oct 23mm	—	—	15.00	25.00

Owl facing, perched on crossed torch and sword, all within wreath. Above: L. BOCHE, CHECK M ' F ' R. Below: CHICAGO. Rv: ELGIN / —.— / TURN / —.— / VEREIN within corded circle. Plain edge. (Schmidt E32)

FREJA

Rulau	Date	Metal	Size	VG	F	VF	Unc
II-El 18	(1880's)	Brass	25mm	—	20.00	25.00	—

Obverse as II-El 3, the Concordia token (Indian head left, L. BOCHE). Rv: FREJA / ELGIN / ILL. surrounded by stars. Plain edge. (Schmidt F70)

SVEA SOCIETY

Elgin, Ill.

Rulau	Date	Metal	Size	VG	F	VF	Unc
II-El 40	(1885)	Brass	27mm?	—	10.00	15.00	—

Three stars in relief within depressed circular center. SVEA SOCIETY / ELGIN (All incused): around. Rv: Blank. Plain edge.

Rulau	Date	Metal	Size	VG	F	VF	Unc
Il-El 42	(1885)	Brass	27mm?	—	10.00	15.00	—

Blank depressed circular center. (All incused): SVEA HALL / ELGIN around. Rv: Blank. Plain edge.

Svea = Swedish. Both pieces are in Rich Hartzog coll. The Svea Society was large; a hoard of tokens could exist.

P. HERMAN JR.

Freeburg, Ill.

Rulau	Date	Metal	Size	VG	F	VF	Unc
Il-Fr 5	(1880's)	Brass	28mm	—	—	15.00	—
	10 / ¢ within central circle, P. HERMAN JR. above, FREEBURG, ILL. below. Rv: Blank. Plain edge. (Tom Wall coll.)						
Il-Fr 6	(1880's)	Brass	33mm	—	—	15.00	—
	Similar, but 25 / ¢. Plain edge.						
Il-Fr 7	(1880's)	Brass	36mm	—	—	15.00	—
	Similar, but 50 / ¢. Plain edge.						

Rulau	Date	Metal	Size	VG	F	VF	Unc
Il-Fr 8	(1880's)	Brass	39mm	—	—	30.00	—
	Similar, but $ 1. Plain edge. (Rulau coll.)						

G. STODDARD

Galena, Ill.

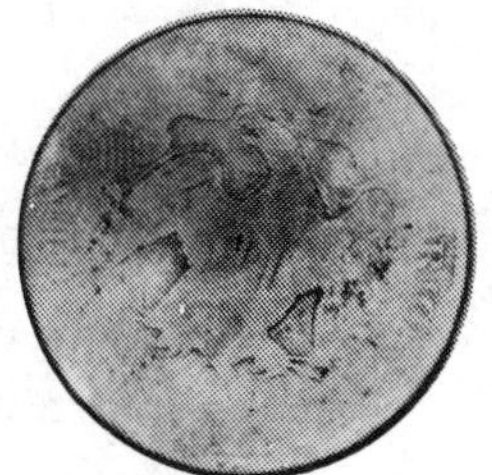

Rulau	Date	Metal	Size	VG	F	VF	EF
Il-Ga 3	(1878)	Silver	31mm	—	200.	—	300.
	G. STODDARD / GALENA ctsp on U.S. 1876 or 1877-CC Seated Liberty half dollar. (Thoele coll.; Brunk 38480)						
Il-Ga 4	(1878)	Silver	18mm	—	200.	—	—
	Similar ctsp on U.S. 1876 S.L. dime.						

Gideon Stoddard was a ship's carpenter and steamboat captain.

JOHN HAAKE

Germantown, Ill.

Rulau	Date	Metal	Size	VG	F	VF	Unc
Il-Gm 4	(1885-88)	Brass	23mm	—	12.00	—	—
	JOHN HAAKE (incused) / GOOD FOR / 5 ¢ / DRINK. Rv: F. MESSMER / FAUCET CO. / ST. LOUIS. (Alpert Feb. 1989 sale, lot 238)						

John Haake is listed as a saloon proprietor in the 1888 gazetteer. The Messmer Faucet Co. was a predecessor of Messmer Mfg. Co. The latter was in business 1885-98.

BOLL & HOERETH

Hecker, Ill.

Rulau	Date	Metal	Size	VG	F	VF	Unc
Il-He 1	(1889-90)	Brass	Oct 23mm	—	7.50	10.00	—
	BOLL & HOERETH / -*- / (ornament) / * HECKER, ILLS. *. Rv: GOOD FOR / $1.00 (in circle) / IN MERCHANDISE *. (Tom Wall coll.)						
Il-He 2	(1889-90)	Brass	23mm	—	7.50	10.00	—
	As last, but 50 ¢.						

Similar, round 23mm brass tokens in 25¢, 10¢ and 5¢ denominations exist, all valued at same prices at quoted above. According to the Bradstreet directory for 1890, this was a general store in this small Monroe County village (pop. 200 in 1910).

G. BUSSE

Hyde Park, Ill.

Rulau	Date	Metal	Size	VG	F	VF	Unc
Il-HP 1	(1888)	Brass	25mm	—	—	25.00	—
	Early Chas. Pick die. Rv: GOOD FOR / 5 ¢ / G. BUSSE (on panel) / IN / * TRADE *. Plain edge. (Thoele coll.)						

J. K. BROWN

Kensington, Ill.

Rulau	Date	Metal	Size	VG	F	VF	Unc
Il-Ke 1	(1884)	Brass	25mm	—	—	12.50	—
	GOOD FOR / 5 ¢ / IN TRADE / AT BAR / J. K. BROWN. Rv: Blank. (Thoele coll., ex-Weinberg)						

J. K. Brown's saloon and billiard hall is listed by the 1884 gazetteer. Token made by L. Boche?

SHERMAN & BARK

Kensington, Ill.

Rulau	Date	Metal	Size	VG	F	VF	Unc
Il-Ke 3	(1886)	CN	25mm	—	—	25.00	—
	THE / BRUNSWICK / – BALKE – / COLLENDER CO / (Pool table). Rv: GOOD FOR / 5 ¢ / IN TRADE / SHERMAN / & BARK / KENSINGTON / COR / 115TH & / FRONT ST. Plain edge.						

Saloon, listed 1886.

T.B. ROWIN
Kirkland, Ill.

Rulau	Date	Metal	Size	VG	F	VF	Unc
Il-Kk 3	(1880's)	Brass	24mm	—	30.00	50.00	—

Female head left in central circle, THE J.M. BRUNSWICK & BALKE COS. around, CHECK. below. Rv: GOOD FOR / 5¢ / T.B. ROWIN / KIRKLAND / IN / TRADE / *. Plain edge. (Schmidt R74)

KNIELING & SCHILD
Lakeview, Ill.

Rulau	Date	Metal	Size	VG	F	VF	Unc
Il-Lk 5	(1888)	Brass	24mm	—	—	11.00	—

(All incused): KNIELING & SCHILD / GOOD FOR / * 5 ¢ * / DRINK / LAKEVIEW. Rv: Blank. (Thoele coll.)

Knieling & Schild are listed under saloons in Wright's Grove, Ill. in the 1888-89 gazetteer. Lakeview post office was established Jan. 1869 but closed May 1879, and was served from nieghboring Wright's Grove office though remaining a separate community. Both Lakeview and Wright's Grove were absorbed by Chicago 1890.

J. F. PIERCE
Leland, Ill.

Rulau	Date	Metal	Size	VG	F	VF	Unc
Il-Le 3	(1860)	Copper	29mm	—	—	30.00	—

J. F. PIERCE ctsp on U.S. 1850 or worn Large cent. (Brunk 32070)

Pierce was a gunsmith, listed in the 1860 directory. The attribution is tentative.

JOHN BERNER
Lyons, Ill.

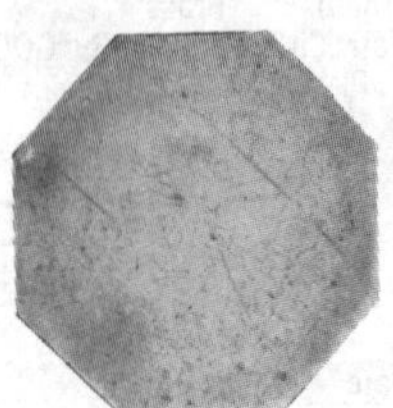

Rulau	Date	Metal	Size	VG	F	VF	Unc
Il-Ly 3	(1880's)	Nickel	Oct 25mm	—	—	20.00	—

(All incused): JOHN BERNER / GOOD FOR / 5 ¢ / * DRINK * / LYONS. Rv: Blank. Plain edge. Only 3 known.

BLANCHARD HOUSE
Monmouth, Ill.

Rulau	Date	Metal	Size	VG	F	VF	EF
Il-Mn 3	(1858-70)	Copper	29mm	100.	—	150.	—

BLANCHARD HOUSE / MONMOUTH / ILL ctsp on U.S. 1847 Large cent. Five specimens known.

Rulau	Date	Metal	Size	VG	F	VF	EF
Il-Mn 4	(1858-70)	Silver	27mm	125.	—	175.	—

Similar ctsp on Spanish-American 1786-Mo or 1793 or 1809 2-reales. (Gould 321; Brunk 3990)

Rulau	Date	Metal	Size	VG	F	VF	EF
Il-Mn 4A	(1858-70)	Silver	27mm	125.	—	175.	—

Similar ctsp on Spanish-American Carlos III 2-reales. Also there is a small 'E' incused below. (Frank Kovacs coll.)

Rulau	Date	Metal	Size	VG	F	VF	EF
Il-Mn 5	(1858-70)	Silver	25mm	125.	—	175.	—

Similar ctsp on U.S. 1853 or 1854 or worn S.L. quarter. 4 pieces known.

Rulau	Date	Metal	Size	VG	F	VF	EF
Il-Mn A5	(1858-70)	Silver	32.5mm	—	—	200.	—

Similar ctsp on U.S. 1826 Bust half dollar.

These pieces are probably related to the 1865 token of the Edward Blanchard bar, Il-Mn 6. Note that Blanchard used some coins already obsolete as money for his counterstamps.

Edward Blanchard appears as a saloonkeeper in the 1858, 1866 and 1870 " Bradstreet Directories."

ED. BLANCHARD

Rulau	Date	Metal	Size	VG	F	VF	Unc
Il-Mn 6	1865	Brass	22mm	—	25.00	35.00	60.00

Horse. ED BLANCHARD — BAR CHECK. Rv: Dog. MONMOUTH, ILLS. — 1865. (Wright 1340; Schmidt B37)

J. W. GAUL
Monmouth, Ill.

Rulau	Date	Metal	Size	VG	F	VF	Unc
Il-Mn 9	(?)	Brass	25mm	20.00	25.00	40.00	75.00

Elephant standing right. Rv: J. W. GAUL / * 5 * / MONMOUTH, ILLS. Plain edge. Rarity 6.

Compare this elephant with that on Maverick number MV 450 in this book. While resembling each other, they are definitely from different dies. The John W. Gaul restaurant was still in business in 1918.

C. WOODYATT
Morrison, Ill.

Rulau	Date	Metal	Size	VG	F	VF	Unc
Il-Mr 3	(1882)	Brass	25mm	—	—	8.00	—

(All incused): C. WOODYATT / GOOD FOR / 5 ¢ / IN TRADE / (horned ornament). Rv: POOL CHEEK (sic!) / MORRISON. Plain edge. The only known specimen is holed at 5 o'clock.

Charles Woodyatt, billiard hall, 1882 gazetteer.

W. S. STITELY
Mount Carroll, Ill.

Rulau	Date	Metal	Size	VG	F	VF	Unc
Il-MC 7	(?)	Brass	24mm	—	—	10.00	—

(All incused): W. S. STITELY / GOOD FOR / 5 ¢ / LOAF OF BREAD / MT. CARROLL ILL. Rv: Blank. Plain edge. Beaded, incised rim on both sides.

Rulau	Date	Metal	Size	VG	F	VF	Unc
Il-MC 7A	(?)	Alum	24mm	—	—	10.00	—

As 7. Plain edge. (Probably 1890's)

ADRIAN WEGER
Murphysboro, Ill.

Rulau	Date	Metal	Size	VG	F	VF	Unc
Il-Mu 4	(1888)	Brass	25mm	—	—	35.00	—

GOOD FOR / 5 ¢ / ADRIAN / WEGER / IN / TRADE. Rv: 5 within circle of 16 stars. (Thoele coll., ex-Weinberg)

Saloon, listed in 1888 gazetteer.

M. WACHTER
O'Fallon, Ill.

Rulau	Date	Metal	Size	VG	F	VF	Unc
Il-Of 7	(1880-87)	Brass	23mm	—	—	15.00	—

(Incuse) M. WACHTER / (relief) GOOD FOR / (relief) 5 C / (relief) DRINK / (incuse) ornament. Rv: (All relief) F. MESSMER / —.— / FAUCET CO. / —.— / ST. LOUIS. Plain edge. 5 known. (Schmidt W10)

Rulau	Date	Metal	Size	VG	F	VF	Unc
Il-Of 9	(1880-87)	Br	Sc 23mm	—	—	15.00	—

(Incuse) M. WACHTER / (relief) GOOD FOR / (relief) 5 ¢ / (relief) LOAF BREAD. Rv: Blank. Plain edge. Rarity 8. (Schmidt W12)

JOHN PARCHEN

Ohio, Ill.

Rulau	Date	Metal	Size	VG	F	VF	Unc
Il-Oh	(1888-89)	Brass	25mm	—	—	25.00	—

Brunswick die BB-7a. Rv: GOOD FOR / 5 ¢ (in panel) / JOHN / PARCHEN (name in panel) / AT BAR.

This token has previously been thought to be from Dakota Territory, but is more properly attributed to the city of Ohio, Ill. (See ATCO journal for July 1993, pg. 8)

L. STEVENSON

Ohio, Ill.

Rulau	Date	Metal	Size	VG	F	VF	Unc
Il-Oh 3	(1888)	Brass	xx	—	—	15.00	—

xx Heart-shaped flan, 24x27mm.
(All incused): L. STEVENSON / GOOD FOR / 5 C monogram / . IN TRADE . Rv: Blank. (Vacketta N/L)

Billiards, in 1888 gazetteer. The town of Ohio is in Bureau County.

WASHINGTON CENTENNIAL SOUVENIR

Olney, Ill.

Rulau	Date	Metal	Size	VG	F	VF	EF
Il-Oy 5	1889	WM*	37mm	—	—	25.00	60.00

*Actually pot metal, a lead alloy. Obverse as Il-Ch 7 (Washington bust left). Rv: As Il-Ch 7, but WASHINGTON CENTENNIAL SOUVENIR at top and PUBLIC SCHOOL OLNEY, ILL. at bottom. Plain edge. Issued holed with a red ribbon for suspension. (Harvey Gamer coll.)

The one known specimen was discovered in late 1983.

F. X. MAYER

Oregon, Ill.

Rulau	Date	Metal	Size	VG	F	VF	Unc
Il-Or 5	(1880's)	Br	Oct 26mm	—	—	15.00	—

F. X. MAYER / (stylized flower) / OREGON / ILL. Rv: GOOD FOR / 5 / CENTS / -AT- / *** X.'S. ***. Plain edge.

Mayer was in business 1880-1895, and evidently his place was known as 'X's' after his middle initial. (Likely his name was Francis Xavier Mayer - common among German Catholics).

BOWMAN

Ottawa, Ill.

Rulau	Date	Metal	Size	VG	F	VF	EF
Il-Ot 2	(1870-81)	Silver	31mm	—	—	300.	—

BOWMAN / PHOTOGRAPHER / OTTAWA. ILL. ctsp on U.S. 1860 Liberty Seated half dollar. (Bill Rodgers collection; Schmidt B57; Brunk 4650)

Rulau	Date	Metal	Size	VG	F	VF	EF
Il-Ot 3	(1870-81)	Silver	31mm	—	—	200.	—

Similar ctsp on U.S. 1857 Liberty Seated half dollar.

Rulau	Date	Metal	Size	VG	F	VF	EF
Il-Ot 4	(1870-81)	Silver	25mm	—	—	150.	—

Similar ctsp on U.S. 1856 quarter.

Rulau	Date	Metal	Size	VG	F	VF	EF
Il-Ot 5	(1870-81)	Silver	19mm	—	—	150.	—

BOWMAN ctsp on U.S. 1835 dime. (Brunk 4640)

Rulau	Date	Metal	Size	VG	F	VF	EF
Il-Ot 6	(1870-81)	Silver	31mm	—	—	300.	—

BOWMAN / OTTAWA, ILL ctsp on Canada 1870 half dollar. (Brunk 4645)

W. E. Bowman, born in Pennsylvania Apr. 28, 1834, studied photography in 1857 under Dewitt Rawson and settled in LaSalle, Ill. in 1865. His photography won him six silver medals at state fairs. The counterstamps date from 1870-1881, most likely.

BRUNKER

Rulau	Date	Metal	Size	VG	F	VF	Unc
Il-Ot 8	(1860's)	Silver	25mm	—	—	200.	—

BRUNKER / OTTAWA ctsp on U.S. 1853. Arrows & Rays S.L. quarter.

Peter Brunker was an Ottawa gunsmith in business from 1840 to 1882. He made percussion half-stock weapons, according to the magazine *Muzzle Blasts* for April, 1943. Brunker is listed in Frank Sellers' *American Gunsmiths* (1983) on page 44.

The counterstamp is made from his punch for marking weapons.

CHILD & BRO.

Rulau	Date	Metal	Size	VG	F	VF	EF
Il-Ot 9	(1866-76)	Silver	31mm	125.	—	150.	—

CHILD & BRO / OTTAWA ILL ctsp on U.S. Liberty Seated half dollar. Examined: 1853, 1854-0, 1855, unknown dates. (Brunk 7630) (Seven specimens known.)

Rulau	Date	Metal	Size	VG	F	VF	EF
Il-Ot 10	(1866-76)	Silver	25mm	—	—	150.	—

Similar ctsp on U.S. 1853, 1854, 1858, or 1859 Seated Liberty quarter. 7 known.

Rulau	Date	Metal	Size	VG	F	VF	EF
Il-Ot 12	(1866-76)	Silver	38mm	—	—	250.	—

Similar ctsp on U.S. 1865-0 Seated Liberty silver dollar.

Child & Brother are listed as shoemakers in the 1866, 1870, 1871 and 1876 directories.

M. KEIM

Ottawa, Ill.

Rulau	Date	Metal	Size	VG	F	VF	Unc
Il-Ot 20	(1884)	Brass	25mm	—	—	8.00	—

(All incused): GOOD FOR / 5 ¢ / M. KEIM. Rv: Blank.

Saloon, in the 1884 gazetteer.

O. L. LEWIS

Pana, Ill.

Rulau	Date	Metal	Size	VG	F	VF	Unc
Il-Pa 3	(1893)	Brass	25mm	—	—	25.00	—

Brunswick die BBC-10b. Rv: GOOD FOR / 2 1/2 ¢ / O. L. LEWIS / IN / TRADE. (Tom Wall coll.)

Billiard hall, 1893 directory.

KINGMAN & CO.

Peoria, Ill. & St. Louis, Mo.

Rulau	Date	Metal	Size	VG	F	VF	Unc
Il-Pe 6	1885	WM	31mm?	—	—	20.00	35.00

Plough at center, KINGMAN & CO. / WHOLESALE above, FARM / MACHINERY / PEORIA, ILL. * ST. LOUIS, MO. below. Rv: HIGHEST AWARD / FOR / BEST DISPLAY / AT / ST. LOUIS FAIR, 1885. (Wright 554)

Kingman, Hotchkiss & Co., farm implements, appears in 1870 directories.

CENTENNIAL OF OUR NATION

Peru, Ill.

Rulau	Date	Metal	Size	F	VF	EF	Unc
Il-Pu 4	1889	WM*	37mm	—	—	20.00	50.00

*Actually pot metal, a lead alloy. Obverse same as Il-Ch 7 (Washington bust left). Rv: As Il-Ch 7, but .PERU, ILLS. COMMEMORATION. at bottom in place of CHICAGO COMMEMORATION. Plain edge. Issued holed. 2 known. (Schmidt C42)

The Schmidt specimen, the finest known, is shown above. The Phil Klabel specimen has been dug up. (See same issuer under Chicago and Springfield). This type could have been issued for other towns as well.

F. W. WEISHEIT

Peru, Ill.

Rulau	Date	Metal	Size	VG	F	VF	Unc
Il-Pu 10	(1884-88)	Brass	24mm	—	—	35.00	—

CHAS. PICK & CO / DEALERS IN / (bar utensils) / CHICAGO. Rv: GOOD FOR / 5 C / F. W. / WEISHEIT / IN / TRADE. Plain edge. (Thoele coll.)

F.W. Weisheit appears in the 1884, 1886 and 1888 gazetteers under saloons.

R. I. A.
(Rock Island Arsenal)

Rock Island, Ill.

Rulau	Date	Metal	Size	VG	F	VF	Unc
Il-RI 4	1882	Copper	40mm	—	—	150.	200.

Crossed cannon at center, bomb above, W at left, P at right, RIA below. Rv: NO 1882. Plain edge. An incused numeral is added on reverse; the illustrated specimen is 2587. (Curto AR 17)

(See James J. Curto's article on the Rock Island Arsenal in *The Numismatist* for May 1975.

Rulau	Date	Metal	Size	VG	F	VF	Unc
Il-RI 5	1882	Copper	40mm	—	—	150.	200.

Obverse similar to 4 above. Rv: No / 1882 (The 'o' of No is lower case; the date is much larger than on 4.) The Hartzog specimen is incused with numeral 3905. Reeded edge. (Curto N/L)

A. H. HENNIS

Sandwich, Ill.

Rulau	Date	Metal	Size	VG	F	VF	Unc
Il-Sa 3	(1888)	Brass	Oct 27mm	—	—	25.00	—

GOOD FOR 5 CENTS / -A. H. - / HENNIS / (ornament). Rv: GEO. KUEHL & BRO. / BILLIARD / -.- / CLOTHS / -&- / SUPPLIES / (Rosette) CHICAGO. (Rosette).

Listed under billiards in 1888 gazetteer. Middle initial not confirmed.

AUGUST RADKE

Savanna, Ill.

Rulau	Date	Metal	Size	VG	F	VF	Unc
Il-Sv 3	(1888)	Brass	24mm	—	—	25.00	—

N-B-M-Co within crossed cuesticks in central circle. Around: NATIONAL BILLIARD MAN'FG CO. / CIN, O. Rv: GOOD FOR / A 5 C / AUGUST / RADKE (last three lines in shaped cartouche) / DRINK. Plain edge.

Saloon, listed 1888.

H. S. M.
(H. S. Moody)

Shawneetown, Ill.

Rulau	Date	Metal	Size	VG	F	VF	Unc
Il-Sh 4	(1878-83)	Brass	31mm	—	10.00	15.00	—

H. S. M. / SHAWNEETOWN, ILS. Rv: Blank. Plain edge. Rarity 9. (Schmidt H9)

H. S. Moody appears in the 1878 and 1883 directories.

CENTENNIAL OF OUR NATION

Springfield, Ill.

Rulau	Date	Metal	Size	VG	F	VF	Unc
Il-Sp 3	1889	WM*	37mm	—	—	25.00	40.00

* Actually pot metal, another lead alloy.
Obverse same as Il-Ch 7 (Washington bust left). Rv: As Il-Ch 7, but SPRINGFIELD, ILL. COMMEMORATION at bottom in place of CHICAGO COMMEMORATION. Plain edge. Issued holed with a red, white and blue ribbon for suspension. 3 known. (Schmidt C42)

For similar pieces of the same issue, see under Chicago and Peru, Ill.

ILLINOIS WATCH CO.

Springfield, Ill.

Rulau	Date	Metal	Size	VG	F	VF	Unc
Il-Sp 9	(?)	WM	28mm	—	—	20.00	30.00

Clock face. In upper area: I W C. Rv: ILLINOIS WATCH Co / —— / KEY / — & — / STEM WIND / WATCHES / —— / SPRINGFIELD. Plain edge.

EMIL DEVIC

Spring Valley, Ill.

Rulau	Date	Metal	Size	VG	F	VF	Unc
Il-SV 3	(1888)	Brass	24mm	—	—	25.00	—

(All incused): EMIL DEVIC / GOOD FOR / 5 ¢ / IN TRADE. Rv: Blank. (Thoele coll., ex-Bill White)

Emil Devic, saloon, listed in 1888-89 *Illinois State Gazetteer.*

KITTINGERS

Upper Alton, Ill.

Rulau	Date	Metal	Size	VG	F	VF	Unc
Il-Ua 2	(1880-1900)	Brass	Sc, 23mm	—	15.00	25.00	—

KITTINGERS / 1 / LOAF. Rv: EXCELSIOR, 113 OLIVE ST., ST. LOUIS. Plain edge. Rarity 8. (Schmidt K32)

Daniel B. Kittinger had a grocery store in Upper Alton, at College Avenue near Manning Street, in the 1880's and 1890's.

The Excelsior firm in St. Louis struck his tokens.

PETER CARLSON

Utica, Ill.

Rulau	Date	Metal	Size	VG	F	VF	Unc
Il-Ut 3	(1880)	Brass	Oct 26mm	—	—	10.00	—

(All incused): PETER CARLSON / GOOD FOR / 5 ¢ / DRINK / AT BAR / UTICA, ILLS. Rv: Blank. Plain edge. Only 4 specimens known.

C. E. HENSEN

Virden, Ill.

Rulau	Date	Metal	Size	VG	F	VF	Unc
Il-Vi 3	(1880's)	Brass	25mm	—	—	15.00	25.00

Rooster left, C. E. HENSEN above, VIRDEN, ILL. below. Rv: Large 15 within circle of 16 alternating stars and rosettes, each of 5 points. Plain edge.

W. C. McDONALD

Virginia, Ill.

Rulau	Date	Metal	Size	VG	F	VF	Unc
Il-Vg 5	(?)	CN	25mm	—	17.50	25.00	—

W. C. McDONALD / BILLIARD / * / PARLOR / VIRGINIA ILL. Rv: GOOD FOR 5 CENTS / UNCLE BEN ? . * . / * CIGAR * / + 5 + / O IN TRADE O. Plain edge. (Hartzog coll.)

A. NESBIT

Whitehall, Ill.

Rulau	Date	Metal	Size	VG	F	VF	Unc
Il-Wt 3	(1870's)	Brass	25mm	—	11.00	18.00	—

(All incused): A. NESBIT / 10¢ / BREAD. Rv: Blank. Plain edge. Rarity 9. (Schmidt N20; Tom Wall coll.)

Archibald Nesbit, born in Ireland, traveled extensively before settling in Whitehall (which was once known as Loafer's Grove). Nesbit's bakery was operated in the 1870's.

PETER HEIM

Wright's Grove, Ill.

Rulau	Date	Metal	Size	VG	F	VF	Unc
Il-WG 3	(1884-87)	Brass	25mm	—	—	6.00	—

GOOD FOR / A 5 ¢ / PETER HEIM (in cross-hatched panel) / DRINK. Rv: 5 (large, shaded). Probably unique.

Peter Heim's saloon appears in the 1884 and 1886 gazetteers.

Wright's Grove was known as Wrightwood before 1875. The Wright's Grove post office was established Nov. 1875 and closed March 1889. Wright's Grove and its sister community, Lakeview, were annexed to Chicago 1890.

JOSEPH SACHSEL

Rulau	Date	Metal	Size	VG	F	VF	Unc
Il-WG 6	(1886-89)	Brass	25mm	—	—	6.00	—

GOOD FOR / 5 ¢ / JOSEPH / SACHSEL (name in oval cross-hatched panel) / IN / TRADE. Rv: Large 5 in circle of alternating stars and moons. Only 1 piece known.

Saloon, listed 1886 and 1889 gazetteers.

ERNST STADE

Wright's Grove, Ill.

Rulau	Date	Metal	Size	VG	F	VF	Unc
Il-WG 8	(1888-89)	Brass	25mm	—	—	35.00	—

Brunswick die BBC-10a. Rv: GOOD FOR / 5 ¢ / ERNST / STADE (name in oval panel) / IN / TRADE. Unique. (Thoele coll.)

Ernst Stade was listed under billiard halls in the 1888-89 gazetteer.

HAYWARD'S BILLIARD PARLOR

Illinois ?

Rulau	Date	Metal	Size	VG	F	VF	Unc
Il-Un 1	(1880-86)	Brass	25mm	—	15.00	20.00	—

HAYWARD'S BILLIARD PARLOR / GOOD FOR / 15¢ / AT BAR. Rv: Crossed goblet, tongs and ladle. Above: CHAS. PICK & CO. / DEALERS IN. Below: (Diamond) CHICAGO. (diamond). Plain edge. All devices and lettering incused.

Charles Pick & Company was a manufacturer of supplies for billiard parlors, restaurants, etc. Its tokens, unlike those of the Brunswick and other billiard supply houses, are less often encountered. Pick made tokens for concerns in 11 states and Canada, using at least 13 different stock dies in the 1880-1895 period. That used here is the oldest type, circa 1880-86.

INDIANA

L. M. H.
(L. M. Howar)
Alexandria, Ind.

Rulau	Date	Metal	Size	VG	F	VF	Unc
In-Ax 3	(?)	Brass	28.2mm	—	—	10.00	—

(All incused): L. M. H. Rv: GOOD FOR / 5 / AT BAR. Incised, beaded rim on each side. Plain edge. (Joseph Zaffern coll.)

Alexandria is in Clay County, Indiana.

C. S. HILDEBRAND & CO.
Crawfordsville, Ind.

Rulau	Date	Metal	Size	VG	F	VF	Unc
In-Cr 3	(?)	Brass	23mm	—	—	90.00	—

O / C.S. HILDEBRAND / — & CO — / WATCHMAKERS / — / & / JEWELERS / CRAWFORDSVILLE, IND. Rv: JAMES MURDOCK, JR. / STAMPS / BURNING / BRANDS / AND / STENCILS / 139 / W. 5TH ST., CINCINNATI. Plain edge. (Wright 452; Miller Ind 1)

ALBERT MUHLEISEN
Crawfordsville, Ind.

Rulau	Date	Metal	Size	VG	F	VF	Unc
In-Cr 7	(1884-90)	Brass	Sq 23mm	—	5.00	—	—

GOOD FOR / 5 C / ALBERT / MUHLEISEN / IN / TRADE. Rv: Blank. (Alpert Feb. 1989 sale, lot 177)

Saloon proprietor Albert Muhleisen appears in the 1884, 1887 and 1890 gazetteers.

CHRISTIAN ENTEMANN
Fort Wayne, Ind.

Rulau	Date	Metal	Size	VG	F	VF	Unc
In-Fo 5	(1881-90)	Brass	--mm	—	—	30.00	—

Brunswick die BB-3. Rv: GOOD FOR / 10 C / CHRIST / ENTEMANN. Plain edge. (Thoele coll.; Koppenhaver June 1987 sale, lot 699)

Saloon, lised in gazetteers for 1881 thru 1890.

W. H. LINDLAG

Rulau	Date	Metal	Size	VG	F	VF	Unc
In-Fo 9	(1883-87)	GS	25mm	—	—	25.00	—

Brunswick die BB-6d. Rv: GOOD FOR / 5 C / W. H. LINDLAG / -IN- / TRADE. (Bill Hamm coll.)

Saloon, listed in gazetteers for 1884 and 1887 in Fort Wayne.

Rulau	Date	Metal	Size	VG	F	VF	Unc
In-Fo 9C	(1883-87)	GS	25mm	—	—	25.00	—

As In-Fo 9, but M ctsp above pool table, possibly for a change in owners. (Thoele coll.)

JOHN T. WAGNER

Rulau	Date	Metal	Size	VG	F	VF	Unc
In-Fo 15	(1886-87)	Brass	25mm	—	—	20.00	—

GOOD FOR / 5 C / JOHN / T. / WAGNER surrounded by circle of stars. Rv: Large numeral 5. Plain edge. (Thoele report)

Saloon, listed in 1887 *State Gazetteer.*

M. S. WICKLIFFE
Fort Wayne, Ind.

Rulau	Date	Metal	Size	VG	F	VF	Unc
In-Fo 17	(1886-87)	Brass	25mm	—	—	7.00	—

GOOD FOR / 5 C / M. S. / WICKLIFFE / IN / TRADE. Rv: Large numeral 5 in circle of 16 stars. Plain edge. (Thoele report)

Saloon, listed in 1887 *State Gazetteer.*

F. H. THOMAS
Galveston, Ind.

Rulau	Date	Metal	Size	VG	F	VF	EF
In-Gv 1	(1880-99)	GS	**	—	—	—	20.00

** Oval, 33.6 by 19mm.

Eagle atop U.S. shield on right, four folds of a scroll at left. On the folds: (incused) RETURN TO / F. H. THOMAS, / GALVESTON / IND. Rv: (All incused): DEALER IN / GENERAL / MERCHANDISE / ESTABLISHED / 1865. Plain edge. Issued holed. (Rulau coll.)

This may be a fob for a key ring, of very old workmanship. This is of the same type as the H. Cockerel piece of Clarksville, Texas (see Tx-Cv 3).

INDIANA STATE FAIR
Indianapolis, Ind.

Rulau	Date	Metal	Size	VG	F	VF	Unc
In-Ip 3	1873	WM	29mm	—	—	20.00	—

Building. Above: EXPOSITION BUILDING. In exergue: INDIANAPOLIS / (winged wheel). Rv: INDIANA STATE FAIR / o AND EXPOSITION. o around circle of 22 stars. Within the starred circle: SEPT. 10. / 1873. / TO OCT. 10. Plain edge. (Kirtley report)

GEO. J. MAYER CO.

Rulau	Date	Metal	Size	VG	F	VF	Unc
In-Ip 5	(1885)	Brass	27mm	—	—	50.00	75.00

GEO. J. MAYER / MAKERS OF / CHECKS / ... / INDIANAPOLIS, IND. Rv: GOOD FOR / 1 / CATALOGUE / AT OUR OFFICE. Plain edge.

Mayer made hundreds of cannery checks for Indiana and for the East Coast canneries. The firm was active 1885-1958 and later.

ZACARIAH MILTON

Rulau	Date	Metal	Size	VG	F	VF	Unc
In-Ip 6	(1870-90)	Silver	25mm	—	—	80.00	—

ZACARIAH MILTON / F. L. T. / INDIANAPOLIS, IND. ctsp on Canada 25-cents, date worn off. (Brunk 27970)

JOHN WEILACHER

Rulau	Date	Metal	Size	VG	F	VF	Unc
In-Ip 8	(1880-82)	Brass	29mm	—	—	15.00	—

JOHN WEILACHER / - 5 - / CENTS / BILLIARDS / 33 / N. PENN ST. Rv: within circle: C. C. NOYES / MAKER / -27- / S. MERIDIAN ST. / INDIANAPOLIS. IND. Plain edge. (Wright 1718: CWT Ind 460AA)

Weilacher is listed as a saloon operator at 33 No. Penn St. 1878-87 and then at East Washington St. 1887 on. He was in the saloon business in Indianapolis from about 1876 until 1910.

C. C. Noyes, who had worked 1878-79 with John Stanton of Cincinnati, was in the token-making business in Indianapolis 1880-86, but at 27 So. Meridian only 1880-82.

(Research by Bill Hamm, Bloomington, Ind.)

WHITNEY SEWING MACHINE

Indianapolis, Ind.

Rulau	Date	Metal	Size	VG	F	VF	Unc
In-Ip 9	1874	WM	29mm	7.50	10.00	15.00	30.00

Buildings across center, tiny CHAS. H. COX. at right under ground line. Above: EXPOSITION BUILDINGS. Below: INDIANAPOLIS. / *. Rv: Within wreath at center: INDIANA / STATE FAIR / & / EXPOSITION / * / 1874. Around: * BUY THE WHITNEY SEWING MACHINE & GET FOR THIS $10. Plain edge. (Brunk coll.)

Struck by Charles H. Cox of Indianapolis, who was in business 1860-1881.

B. W. SMITH & CO.

Lafayette, Ind.

Rulau	Date	Metal	Size	VG	F	VF	Unc
In-La 6	1882	Brass	25mm	—	—	10.00	—

Man cutting tree at right, bison charging left, sun rising over mountains in background. DOG TAG / 1882 above. Rv: Number 183 in relief on open book; B. W. SMITH & CO. / LAFAYETTE. / IND. below. Plain edge. Issued holed. (Wright 995)

Dr. Wright's piece was numbered '89'.

Rev. B. Wilson Smith, in business 1879-90, made these tags in 1882 and 1883.

E. D. YORK

Lafayette, Ind.

Rulau	Date	Metal	Size	VG	F	VF	EF
In-La 20	(1880's)	Silver	22mm	—	—	175.	—

E. D. YORK, -*- / Messenger, / Am. Expr. Co., / -*- / Lafayette, Ind. *engraved* on shaved flan of a U.S.20-cent piece (issued only 1875-78). (Harvey Gamer coll.)

HENRY ZAHRT

La Porte, Ind.

Rulau	Date	Metal	Size	VG	F	VF	Unc
In-Lp 7	(1879-82)	Brass	26mm	—	—	8.00	—

GOOD FOR / 5 ¢ / H. ZAHRT (all incused). Rv: Blank. (Thoele coll., ex-Weinberg)

BILL'S PLACE

Middlebury, Ind.

Rulau	Date	Metal	Size	VG	F	VF	Unc
In-Mi 2	(1885-91)	Brass	24mm	—	—	27.50	—

Geo. Kuehl die. Rv: BILL'S PLACE / NO. 3 / MIDDLEBURY, IND. (Wagaman M-4800)

C. S. STEEL

Mishawaka, Ind.

Rulau	Date	Metal	Size	VG	F	VF	EF
In-Mk 7	(?)	Copper	29mm	—	—	75.00	—

C. S. STEEL / MISHAWAKA ctsp on U.S. Large cent. (Hallenbeck 19.771)

P. A. FOLLMAR

Monterey, Ind.

Rulau	Date	Metal	Size	VG	F	VF	Unc
In-Mn 1	(1889-90)	WM	24mm	—	—	25.00	—

THE BRUNSWICK BALKE / COLLENDER / COMPY. / (Pool table) / CHECK (Brunswick die 10B). Rv: GOOD FOR / 5 C / P. A. FOLLMAR / (ornament) / IN TRADE. Plain edge. (Bill Hamm coll.)

Follmar is listed under saloons in the 1890 gazetteer.

W. W. BONGE

Montpelier, Ind.

Rulau	Date	Metal	Size	VG	F	VF	Unc
In-Mo 1	(1889-90)	Brass	25mm	—	—	25.00	—

THE BRUNSWICK BALKE / COLLENDER / COMPY. / (Pool table) / CHECK. Rv: GOOD FOR / 5 C/ W. W. BONGE / B-IN-B / TRADE. Plain edge. (Thoele collection)

Rulau	Date	Metal	Size	VG	F	VF	Unc
In-Mo 3	(1887-90)	Brass	Scal 27mm	—	—	22.50	30.00

NATIONAL BILLIARD MFG CO / N B M Co / (Crossed cue sticks) / CIN O. Rv: GOOD FOR / 5 C / W. W. BONGE / IN / TRADE. Second and third lines in beaded, shaped cartouche. (Hamm coll., ex-Thoele)

Washington W. Bonge saloon.

The obverse of In-Mo 1 is Brunswick die BBC-11, frequently referred to in this reference book.

Bonge was in business at least 1887-1890 in Montpelier.

J. F. BAKER

New Albany, Ind.

Rulau	Date	Metal	Size	VG	F	VF	Unc
In-NA 1	(1886-87)	GS	25mm	—	—	25.00	—

Brunswick die BB-8a. Rv: GOOD FOR / 5 C / J. F. BAKER / IN / TRADE. Plain edge.

Saloon, listed in 1887 *State Gazetteer.*

T. W. STEPHENS

Perrysville, Ind.

Rulau	Date	Metal	Size	VG	F	VF	Unc
In-Pe 3	(1882)	Brass	25mm	—	—	25.00	—

Brunswick die BB-6a. Rv: GOOD FOR / 5 ¢ / T. W. STEPHENS (in oval cross-hatched panel) / IN / TRADE. Only 1 piece known. (Thoele coll.)

T.W. Stephens, saloon, 1882 Polk gazetteer.

J. F. MACKE

Richmond, Ind.

Rulau	Date	Metal	Size	VG	F	VF	Unc
IN-Ri 5	(1883-84)	—	--mm	—	—	40.00	—

Chas. Pick & Co. die. Rv: Description not available. (Thoele report)

Listed in 1884 *State Gazetteer.*

Most of the high price of attributed billiard tokens of the 1880's and 1890's is due to the fact of *attribution* - a painfully slow process by dedicated collectors burning midnight oil over old directories, atlases and gazetteers. An unattributed billiard token of this era is worth well under $10.00, but that price doubles, trebles or quadruples after verified attribution.

MAGGIE E. FISH

Sharpsville, Ind.

Rulau	Date	Metal	Size	VG	F	VF	EF
In-Sh 1	1870	Silver	31mm	—	—	15.00	—

MAGGIE E. FISH / SHARPSVILLE, / IND. / MARCH 4TH, 1870 / (star) ctsp on U.S. 1858-O Seated Liberty half dollar. (Van Ormer sale 2644; Brunk 14205)

Made from individual letter punches in upper and lower case letters by J. W. Fuller, the Sharpsville, Pennsylvania jeweler (which see).

Brunk assigns this piece to Pennsylvania and it is possible "Ind." means something other than Indiana. The 1887 Postal Guide lists a Sharpsville in Tipton County, Ind. however.

J. H. R.
(J. H. Ritzler)

South Bend, Ind.

Rulau	Date	Metal	Size	VG	F	VF	Unc
In-SB 1	(1899-1900)	Brass	23mm	—	—	5.00	—

(All incuse) J. H. R. / GOOD FOR / 5¢. Rv: (All incuse) D. ARMSTRONG / MAKER. Plain edge. (Coll. John Cheramy, Victoria, Canada)

Saloon, listed in 1900 Dun reference. David Armstrong was a South Bend maker of rather crude incuse tokens 1882-1916.

FRANK HEINIG & BRO.

Terre Haute, Ind.

Rulau	Date	Metal	Size	VG	F	VF	Unc
In-TH	(1868-73)	Copper	27mm	—	—	25.00	—

Eagle displayed, U.S. shield on its breast. Around: FRANK HEINIG & BRO. / (illegible). Rv: UNION STEAM BAKERY / GOOD / FOR ONE / FIVE / CENT / LOAF OF BREAD. Plain edge.

Fred F. Heinig and his older brother Charles F. Heinig were born in Germany. They immigrated in 1853. Both brothers served in the Union army in the Civil War.

Fred moved to Terre Haute and opened a bakery in 1864. Charles joined as junior partner in 1866. By 1872 it was described: "The Union Steam Bakery and Candy Manufactory of Frank Heinig & Brother is one of the largest and most complete establishments of the kind in the state."

The business dissolved in 1876 after a bankruptcy.

Fred Heinig continued in business as a baker until some time before 1894, when he became a travel agent.

(Research by Bill Hamm, Bloomington, Ind.)

CHAS. F. RAKER

Vincennes, Ind.

Rulau	Date	Metal	Size	VG	F	VF	Unc
In-Vn 3	(1870-76)	Brass	19mm	—	—	50.00	—

CHAS. F. RAKER / DEALER / IN / DRY GOODS / & / GROCERIES / VINCENNES, IND. Rv: Large numeral 10 at center, 12 stars around, CENTS below (Fuld die 1394). Plain edge. (Fuld Ind 930A-1b)

Rulau	Date	Metal	Size	VG	F	VF	Unc
In-Vn 4	(1870-76)	Brass	19mm	—	—	50.00	—

Obverse as last. Rv: Large numeral 25 at center, 11 stars around, CENTS below. (Fuld die 1399). Plain edge. (Fuld Ind 930A-2b)

Both above tokens for years had been thought to be Civil War tokens. Directory evidence shows they could not be.

Raker began in business about 1870. He arrived in Vincennes from Germany in 1860, but is listed as a grocer for the first time only in the 1870 Dun directory and the 1870 gazetteer; the earliest he could have begun business as a grocer would have been 1869.

Raker was born in 1840; it is probable that the 21-year-old German immigrant in 1861 entered the Union army. (Research by Bill Hamm, Blommington, Ind.)

J. WILLIS COTTON

Walkerton, Ind.

Rulau	Date	Metal	Size	VG	F	VF	EF
In-Wa 3	1875	Copper	29mm	—	—	225.	—

J.W. COTTON, WALKERTON, IND. / 1875 ctsp on U.S. 1845 Large cent. Rv: GOOD HEALTH IS MORE WEALTH THAN MUCH MONEY on coin's reverse. (Brunk 9740)

Rulau	Date	Metal	Size	VG	F	VF	EF
In-Wa 3A	1875	Copper	28mm	—	—	225.	—

Similar ctsp on Essequibo & Demerary 1813 half stiver, KM-9.

Rulau	Date	Metal	Size	VG	F	VF	EF
In-Wa 4	1875	Copper	29mm	—	—	100.	—

WILLIS COTTON, WALKERTON, IND. / 1875 ctsp on U.S. 1845 Large cent obverse. Rv: INDUSTRY AND ECONOMY SHOULD GO HAND IN HAND on coin's reverse. (Brunk 9750)

P. HUFFMAN

Warsaw, Ind.

Rulau	Date	Metal	Size	VG	F	VF	EF
In-Ww 4	(?)	Silver	39mm	—	—	150.	—

P. HUFFMAN / WARSAW, INDIANA ctsp on Spanish-American 1809-Mo 8-reales. (Gould 98; Hallenbeck coll.; Brunk 20580)

Huffman came from Ohio to Indiana.

PETER GROSS

Winamac, Ind.

Rulau	Date	Metal	Size	VG	F	VF	EF
In-Wi 1	(1883-87)	Brass	25mm	—	—	30.00	—

Brunswick-Balke-Collender die. Rv: Description not available. (Thoele report)

The Peter Gross saloon is listed in the 1884 and 1887 gazetteers. Later, in 1901, he was at Dubuque, Iowa.

INDIANA ASBURY UNIVERSITY

Indiana

Rulau	Date	Metal	Size	VG	F	VF	Unc
In-Un 2	1866	Brass	30mm	—	—	12.50	—

Male bust in clerical garb to right, CENTENNIAL MEDAL above, 1866 below. Rv: INDIANA / ASBURY / UNIVERSITY within wreath. Outside wreath: SUNDAY SCHOOL CENTENARY CHAIR. Plain edge. Issued holed.

REPORTED INDIANA BILLIARD TOKENS

The following unverified attributions have been reported for this era. They are listed here for informational purposes: (* Indicates city name on token)

Name on Token	Possible Locale	Billiard Die	Gazetteer
F. J. Barr	South Bend	BB-7a	1880-84
Syl Beals	Hammond	BBC-10a	1887
Syl Beals	Bourbon	BBC-10a	1890
D. Behrens	Michigan City	Chas. Pick	1882
C. L. Brown	Leesburg	Chas. Pick	1884
Frank Disher	Mitchel	B-2b	1887-95
H. Dols	Milltown	Messmer Fauc.	1880's
Falvey & Wagner	Kewanna	B-2e	1884
Jacob Green	Cromwell	B & Co.	1884-87
A. Hofer	Berne	BB-6d	1882
Thomas Jacobs	Markle	BBC-7	1887-91
J. C. Kuhn	Plymouth	BB-7a	1882-87
Ed Laws	Crown Point	BB-6a	1882-95
* Jacob Maas	Kokomo	Chas. Pick	1890
C. F. Miller	Logansport	BBC	1887
T. S. Pickens	Orleans	Chas. Pick	1884
F. W. Pottmeyer	Logansport	BBC-11	?
* Royal Center Canning	Royal center	D. Trench	1883-1914
* H. C. Sparks	Markle	BBC-10b	1890
Mrs. Wm. Stauss	Jeffersonville	BB-6d	1887
Mike Walsh	LaFayette	BBC-4	1884
Jas. Weaver	Sheldon	Chas. Pick	1884-90
Jas. Weaver	Hillsboro	Chas. Pick	1887

IOWA

J. ALDERSON
Alta, Iowa

Rulau	Date	Metal	Size	VG	F	VF	Unc
Ia-Al 1	(1887-92)	Brass	25mm	—	—	25.00	—

Brunswick die BBC-9b. Rv: GOOD FOR / * 5 ¢ * / J. ALDERSON (name in panel) / IN / * TRADE *. (Thoele coll.)

James Alderson, billiard hall, listed 1887-1892. Listed as a "temperance saloon" in 1890!

C. W. SHEPHERD
Algona, Iowa

Rulau	Date	Metal	Size	VG	F	VF	Unc
Ia-Ag 4	(1886-87)	Brass	25mm	—	—	20.00	—

Brunswick die BBC-11. Rv: GOOD FOR / 5 C / C. W. / SHEPHERD / IN / TRADE. Plain edge. (TAMS maverick 11877)

Billiard hall listed in the 1887 *Polk's State Gazetteer.*

This token appeared in *TAMS Journal* for August, 1987, page 146.

J. H. FRAHM
Audubon, Iowa

Rulau	Date	Metal	Size	VG	F	VF	Unc
Ia-Au 4	(1888-89)	Brass	25mm	—	—	25.00	—

Brunswick die BB-8a. Rv: GOOD FOR / 5 C / JOHN H. / FRAHM / IN / TRADE. Plain edge. (Thoele report)

Billiards, listed in 1886-1889 *Polk's State Gazetteer.* John H. Frahm.

J. D. KUNEY
Brush Creek, Iowa

Rulau	Date	Metal	Size	VG	F	VF	Unc
Ia-BC 3	(1884)	Brass	25mm	—	—	30.00	—

Brunswick die BB-8a. Rv: GOOD FOR / 5 ¢ / J. D. KUNEY (in oval cross-hatched panel) / IN / TRADE. Only 1 piece reported.

Billiard hall, Polk's 1884-87 gazetteers.

M. V. HAMILTON
Carroll, Iowa

Rulau	Date	Metal	Size	VG	F	VF	Unc
Ia-Ca 3	(1883-84)	—	--mm	—	—	25.00	—

Brunswick die BB-7a. Rv: Description not available. (Thoele report)

Appears only in the 1884-86 gazetteers.

C. P. REINHART
Carroll, Iowa

Rulau	Date	Metal	Size	VG	F	VF	Unc
Ia-Ca 5	(1910)	Brass	24mm	—	—	20.00	—
	Brunswick die BBC-11. Rv: GOOD FOR / 5 CENTS / C. P. REINHART.						
Ia-Ca 6	(1910)	Brass	24mm	—	—	25.00	—
	Obverse as reverse of 5. Rv: Blank.						
Ia-Ca 7	(?)	Brass	--mm	—	—	30.00	—
	C. P. / REINHART / CARROLL, IA. Rv: Blank.						

The three tokens above were lots 529-531 in the Paul Koppenhaver sale of June 4, 1988.

Rulau	Date	Metal	Size	VG	F	VF	Unc
Ia-Ca 9	(1880's)	Brass	24mm	—	—	30.00	—

Brunswick die BBC-8. Rv: GOOD FOR / 5 C / C. P. REINHART / CARROLL, IOWA. Plain edge. (Brunswick 5601; Koppenhaver June 1987 sale, lot 731)

Ia-Ca 5 is a hoard token; some 50 pieces are on the market. Reinhart's billiard hall was in business until 1914.

G. BITZER
Cedar Rapids, Iowa ?

Rulau	Date	Metal	Size	VG	F	VF	Unc
Ia-CR 1	(?)	—	--mm	—	—	35.00	—
	G. BITZER ctsp on 1867 Cedar Rapids, Iowa bridge token, Atwood 150B. (Brunk 3800)						
Ia-CR 2	(?)	CN	20mm	—	—	35.00	—
	Similar ctsp on Jamaica 1882-H farthing. (Brunk report)						
Ia-CR 3	(?)	Bronze	20mm	—	—	35.00	—
	Similar ctsp on Norway 1876 2-ore, KM-353.						

Cedar Rapids city directories for 1877-1890 do not list Bitzer, nor does the index to the *Cedar Rapids Gazette* for this period. Brunk advances the theory that these may be work tallies.

The attribution to Iowa is based solely on the token on which a counterstamp appears, perhaps too thin a basis. The time of issue seems to be the 1880's.

FRANK HORAK
Cedar Rapids, Iowa

Rulau	Date	Metal	Size	VG	F	VF	Unc
Ia-CR 11	(1884-87)	Brass	25mm	—	—	25.00	—

Brunswick die BB-7A. Rv: GOOD FOR / 5 C / FRANK / HORAK / AT BAR. (Thoele coll.; Ferguson 900)

Saloon, listed in the 1875 thru 1887 gazetteers. He was also a grocer.

A. SWAN
Cedar Rapids, Iowa

Rulau	Date	Metal	Size	VG	F	VF	Unc
Ia-CR 30	(1882-83)	Brass	Scal 30mm	—	6.50	—	—

(All incused): GOOD FOR / 5 ¢ / DRINK / A. SWAN. Rv: Blank.

Andrew Swan, saloon, listed in 1882-83 gazetteer.

CRESTON BLUE GRASS PALACE
Creston, Iowa

Rulau	Date	Metal	Size	VF	F	VF	EF
Ia-CR 3	1889	WM	25.5mm	—	—	15.00	25.00

Castle with turrets at center, pennons flying. Tiny P. L. KRIDER CO. PHILA. in exergue. Rv: Bale at center, sheaf of wheat at each side, all at center. Around: CRESTON BLUE GRASS. PALACE. Below: * 1889 *. Plain edge. Rarity 7. (Formerly Rulau Oh-Cn 3)

Struck by the P. L. Krider firm in Philadelphia.

Creston, the seat of Union County, is in the heart of Iowa's blue grass country. It was designated the headquarters of the Blue Grass League of Southwest Iowa in 1889, and a turreted Blue Grass Palace was erected. Eighteen counties cooperated to build this structure and a similar one in 1890 - both entirely covered with blue grass.

In the late 1880's and early 1890's regional exhibitions of agriculture and industry were popular in Iowa. In addition to the Blue Grass Palace in Creston, there was a Corn Palace in Sioux City (which see in this reference), a Coal Palace in Ottumwa, and a Mineral Palace in Colo. An article on the Coal Palace appreared in 1983 in the *TAMS Journal,* written by Thomas P. Garnder, Keokuk, Iowa.

(Creston information from *American Guide Series: Iowa* (1938; page 529)

The token above was listed erroneously under Creston, Ohio earlier.

CHRIST. BOYSCHOU
Davenport, Iowa

Rulau	Date	Metal	Size	VG	F	VF	Unc
Ia-Da 2	(1887)	Brass	24.5mm	—	—	25.00	—

Brunswick die BBC-11. Rv: GOOD FOR / 5 ¢ / CHRIST. BOYSCHOU / IN / TRADE. Plain edge. (Norris Wahl coll.)

Christian Boyschou, billiards and saloon, appears in the 1882, 1884 and 1887 gazetteers. At a later date, he moved to Chicago; he appears under saloons in the Chicago Lakeside directory for 1902.

G. GRUHL
Davenport, Iowa

Rulau	Date	Metal	Size	VG	F	VF	Unc
Ia-Da 7	(1889)	Brass	23mm	—	—	40.00	—

Geo. Kuehl billiard die. Rv: GOOD FOR / 5 ¢ / G. * GRUHL * / * AT THE BAR *. Plain edge. (Jack Glass coll.)

Gustav Gruhl is listed under saloons in the 1889 gazetteer.

F. C. SEYMOUR
Des Moines, Iowa

Rulau	Date	Metal	Size	VG	F	VF	Unc
Ia-Dm 7	(1881)	—	--mm	—	—	25.00	—

Chas. Pick & Co. die. Rv: GOOD FOR / 10 ¢ / F. C. SEYMOUR / IN / TRADE. (Rouleau coll., ex-Egnew)

F. C. Seymour, saloon, 1881 gazetteer.

C. CANNON
Dubuque, Iowa

The counterstamped pieces of grocer Cannon have been determined to be from the 1856-62 period and are now listed in our *U.S. Merchant Tokens 1845-1860* reference.

DUBUQUE HIGH BRIDGE
Dubuque, Iowa

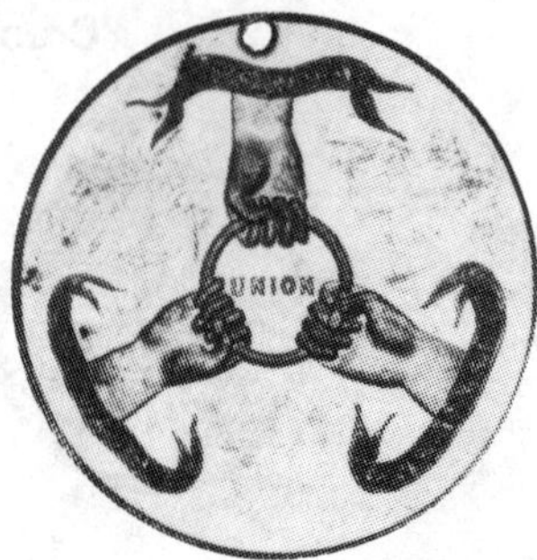

Rulau	Date	Metal	Size	VG	F	VF	Unc
Ia-Du 4	1887	WM	41mm	—	—	30.00	45.00

Aerial view of bridge across Mississippi River, ships passing underneath. Around: DUBUQUE HIGH BRIDGE / * OPENED NOV. 29, 1887. *. Rv: Three hands labeled IOWA, ILLINOIS, WISCONSIN grasp ring within which is: UNION. Plain edge.

H. HARTMAN
Dubuque, Iowa

Rulau	Date	Metal	Size	VG	F	VF	Unc
Ia-Du 9	(1889)	—	--mm	—	—	25.00	—

Brunswick die BB-7a. Rv: GOOD FOR / 5 ¢ / H. HARTMAN / IN / TRADE. (Rouleau coll., ex-Egnew)

Henry Hartman, saloon, 1889 gazetteer.

FRANK CONRAD
Dyersville, Iowa

Rulau	Date	Metal	Size	VG	F	VF	Unc
Ia-Dy 1	(1882)	Brass	24mm	—	—	45.00	—

Check in ornamental script within beaded circle. Around: THE J. W. BRUNSWICK & BALKE COs. / + (Brunswick die BB-3). Rv: GOOD FOR / 5 ¢ / FRANK / CONRAD. (name within panel) / IN / (scroll) TRADE (scroll) / -.- . (Jack Glass attribution; Brunswick 2080)

Conrad appears in the 1882 *Iowa Gazetteer* under saloons only in 1882. Earlier (1877) the same man, or another by the same name, kept a saloon in Manistee, Mich., but BB-3 type tokens were not supplied before 1880-81.

OTTO BRUMM
Garnavillo, Iowa

Rulau	Date	Metal	Size	VG	F	VF	Unc
Ia-Gv 1	(1884)	—	--mm	—	—	30.00	—

Brunswick die BB-6a. Rv: GOOD FOR / 5 ¢ / OTTO BRUMM / IN / TRADE. (Rouleau coll., ex-Egnew)

O. Brumm, saloon, 1884 gazetteer. Garnavillo, in Clayton County, had 1910 pop. of 368.

D. S. ATKINSON
Glidden, Iowa

Rulau	Date	Metal	Size	VG	F	VF	Unc
Ia-Gd 1	(1884)	—	Oct --mm	—	—	30.00	—

Brunswick die BB-3. Rv: GOOD FOR / 5 ¢ / D. S. ATKINSON / IN / TRADE. (Rouleau coll., ex-Egnew)

D. S. Atkinson, saloon, 1884 gazetteer.

H. G. WELLS
Greely, Iowa

Rulau	Date	Metal	Size	VG	F	VF	Unc
Ia-Gy 5	(1884)	Brass	25mm	—	—	30.00	—

Brunswick die BB-8b. Rv: GOOD FOR / 5 ¢ / H. G. WELLS (in oval cross-hatched panel) / IN / * TRADE *.

Billiard hall, 1884 *Iowa State Gazetteer.*

J. W. BROWN
Griswold, Iowa

Rulau	Date	Metal	Size	VG	F	VF	Unc
Ia-Gr 1	(1884-86)	Brass	--mm	—	—	10.00	—

Brunswick die BB-8b. Rv: GOOD FOR / 5 ¢ / J. W. BROWN (in panel) / IN / TRADE. (Robert Cruise coll.)

J. W. Brown appears as a billiard hall proprietor from 1884 through 1908. The token itself is early, probably issued before 1886.

J. BOEHM
Holstein, Iowa

Rulau	Date	Metal	Size	VG	F	VF	Unc
Ia-Ho 2	(1887)	Brass	24.5mm	—	—	30.00	—

Brunswick die BB-6a. Rv: GOOD FOR / 5 ¢ / J. BOEHM / IN / TRADE. (Norris Wahl coll.)

Joseph Boehm, billiard hall, 1887 gazetteer.

CITTIE MACLIN
Indianola, Iowa

Rulau	Date	Metal	Size	VG	F	VF	EF
Ia-In 3	(?)	Silver	38.1mm	—	100.	—	150.

CITTIE / MACLIN. / PROP. / I. T. CARTER / INDIANOLA, IA. ctsp on U.S. 1884 Morgan dollar. (Partrick coll., ex-Fuld; Brunk 25610)

Indianola is in Warren County, Iowa.

THOS. C. CARSON
Iowa City, Iowa

(See Il-Ch 108, Schuttler Wagons, under Chicago, Illinois. The popular Schuttler Wagon firm generally had one exclusive sales agent in each major retail area, and some of them issued tokens)

G. H. BECKER
Lake Park, Iowa

Rulau	Date	Metal	Size	VG	F	VF	Unc
Ia-LP 2	(1887)	Brass	Oct 25mm	—	—	25.00	—

Brunswick die BBC-6a. Rv: GOOD FOR / 5 C / G. H. BECKER / LAKE PARK, IA. Plain edge. (Koppenhaver report)

A. GILBERTSON
Lansing, Iowa

Rulau	Date	Metal	Size	F	VF	EF	Unc
Ia-Ln 2	(1883-84)	Brass	25mm	—	—	25.00	—

Brunswick die BB-3. Rv: GOOD FOR / 5 ¢ / A. GILBERTSON / * IN * / * TRADE *. (Thoele report)

Albert Gilbertson saloon, listed in the 1884-86 gazetteers.

J. M. RATCLIFF
Marengo, Iowa

Rulau	Date	Metal	Size	VG	F	VF	Unc
Ia-Mg 8	(1887-89)	—	--mm	—	—	40.00	—

Brunswick die BB-6b. Rv: GOOD FOR / 5 ¢ / J. M. RATCLIFF / IN / TRADE. Only 2 pieces known. (Rouleau coll., ex-Egnew)

Billiard hall in 1887 and 1889 gazetteers.

JOHN KUEHNE
Marion, Iowa

Rulau	Date	Metal	Size	VG	F	VF	Unc
Ia-Ma 5	(1884)	Brass	24.5mm	—	—	30.00	—

Brunswick die B-2e. Rv: GOOD FOR / 5 ¢ / JOHN KUEHNE / IN / TRADE. (Norris Wahl coll.)

John Kuehne's saloon appears in the 1884-85 gazetteer.

GEORGE ALBRAND
Moscow, Iowa

Rulau	Date	Metal	Size	F	VF	EF	Unc
Ia-Mw 1	(1885-88)	—	--mm	—	—	25.00	—

Brunswick die BB-6c. Rv: Description not available. (Thoele report)

Listed in the 1882 and 1888 gazetteers.

A. KOHN & CO.
McGreger, Iowa

1876 Centennial Tokens

Reverse type 1: A. KOHN & CO. / (star) / CLOTHING / HALL / HATS & CAPS / McGREGER, IOWA. (All 23mm; plain edge)

Rulau	Obv	Rev	Metal	F	VF	EF	Unc
Ia-Mc 3	G (Miller Iowa 1)	1	WM	—	—	—	100.
Ia-Mc 3 A	G (ANS coll.)	1	Copper	—	—	—	100.
Ia-Mc 3 B	G (ANS coll.)	1	Brass	—	—	—	100.

KRIMES
Mt. Carmet, Iowa

Rulau	Date	Metal	Size	F	VF	EF	Unc
Ia-MC 3	(1884-90's)	Brass	--mm	—	15.00	—	—

Brunswick die BBC-8. Rv: GOOD FOR / 5 ¢ / KRIMES / MT. CARMET. Plain edge. (Brunswick 5397)

JOHN LUTZ
Ogden, Iowa ?

Rulau	Date	Metal	Size	VG	F	VF	Unc
Ia-Og 2	(1887)	Brass	Oct 27mm	—	—	125.	—

THE H. W. COLLENDER CO.s / (Pool table) / CHECK. Rv: GOOD FOR 5 CENTS IN TRADE / JOHN / LUTZ / +. Plain edge. (Collender die C-2; Thoele coll., ex-Rouleau, Egnew)

This token illustrates the extreme difficulty in attributing mavericks even when their issuer can be traced through directories. John Lutz moved his business often, as these listings attest:

1877 Bay City, Mich., Saloon
1883 Cincinnati, Ohio, Saloon
1884 Waterloo, Ill., Saloon
1884 Chicago, Ill., Saloon
1887 Ogden, Iowa, Billiard hall
1888-1895 McDill, Wis., Hotel and Saloon

Collender merged with Brunswick-Balke in 1884, but the Collender (and the BB) dies were used for a time after the merger, to save money. So only Ogden, Iowa fits the general pattern, though Collender issued tokens as early as 1875.

Tentative attribution.

J.B. ADLON
Oskaloosa, Iowa

Rulau	Date	Metal	Size	VG	F	VF	EF
Ia-Os 1	1876	Silver	26mm	—	—	150.	—

J.B. ADLON. / 1876. / OSKLOOSA ctsp on 1853 Arrows and Rays quarter dollar. (Krause coll.; Brunk 417)

The attribution to Oskaloosa, Iowa is now verified. J. B. Adlon, a jeweler, appears in the 1871 directory.

CHAS. BLATTNER
Oskaloosa, Iowa

Rulau	Date	Metal	Size	VG	F	VF	Unc
Ia-Os 4	(1887)	Brass	24mm	—	—	25.00	—

C h e c k in circle, J. M. BRUNSWICK & BALKE COs. around. (Brunswick die BB-6a). Rv: GOOD FOR / 5 C / CHAS. / BLATTNER / IN / * TRADE *. (Hosek coll.)

Blattner's billiard hall appears in the 1887 gazetteer. Earlier, 1881-84 he had been at Pella, Iowa.

Rulau	Date	Metal	Size	VG	F	VF	Unc
Ia-Os 5	(1887)	Brass	24mm	—	—	20.00	—

Brunswick die BBC-11. Rv: Similar to Ia-Os 4. (Jack Glass coll.)

J. W. DINSMORE
Prairie City, Iowa

Rulau	Date	Metal	Size	VG	F	VF	Unc
Ia-Pr 3	(1884-92)	Brass	Sc --mm	—	—	7.50	—

J. W. DINSMORE. Rv: Blank. (Rouleau coll., ex-Egnew)

J. W. Dinsmore, saloon 1884, billiard hall 1892.

W. H. BECK
Sioux City, Iowa

Rulau	Date	Metal	Size	VG	F	VF	EF
Ia-SC 4	1890	WM	37mm	—	—	10.00	—

SIOUX CITY CORN PALACE / * 1890 *. Rv: W. H. BECK'S / — CORN PALACE — / SOUVENIR. Plain edge. (Stanley L. Steinberg 1984 sale)

Beck was a jeweler.

Rulau	Date	Metal	Size	VG	F	VF	EF
Ia-SC A4	1889	Brass	25mm	—	—	6.00	—

Building. SIOUX CITY CORN PALACE around, 1889 in exergue. Rv: Ear of corn. Around: W. H. BECK'S SOUVENIR / * WE ARE THE PEOPLE *. (Jack Glass coll.)

CORN PALACE
Sioux City, Iowa

Rulau	Date	Metal	Size	VG	F	VF	Unc
Ia-SC 5	1887	Gilt Brass	26mm	—	—	10.00	20.00

Building, CORN PALACE around, SIOUX CITY in exergue. Rv: . IOWA . DAKOTA . / SOUVENIR / (sunburst) / OF THE / HARVEST / FESTIVAL / OCT. 1887 / . / MINNESOTA . NEBRASKA. Plain edge. Issued holed.

Rulau	Date	Metal	Size	F	VF	EF	Unc
Ia-SC 7	1888	Gilt Brass	25mm	—	—	5.00	15.00

Building at center, CORN PALACE above, SIOUX CITY, IA. below. Rv: SOUVENIR / OF / THE CORN PALACE / CITY OF THE WORLD / 1888., all within flourishes. Plain edge.

Rulau	Date	Metal	Size	F	VF	EF	Unc
Ia-SC 8	1888	Gilt Brass	25mm	—	—	10.00	20.00

Indian head left, KING CORN on its headband. Above: SECOND ANNUAL HARVEST FESTIVAL. Below: SOUVENIR / + 1888 +. Rv: Building at center, CORN PALACE above. SIOUX CITY in exergue. Plain edge.

Rulau	Date	Metal	Size	F	VF	EF	Unc
Ia-SC 9	1888	SWM	30mm	—	—	10.00	20.00

Liberty head in Phrygian cap right, ears of corn at either side. SIOUX CITY on headband. M on truncation of bust. Rv: Corn Palace in center, . CORN PALACE . above, SEP. 24. OCT. 6. 1888. below. Plain edge. Issued holed.

Rulau	Date	Metal	Size	F	VF	EF	Unc
Ia-SC 11	1888	Gilt Brass	30mm	—	—	15.00	30.00

Building at center, SIOUX CITY above, CORN PALACE below. Rv: Two cornstalk wreaths around: IOWA / MINNESOTA / NEBRASKA / DAKOTA / —.— / 1888. Dentilated rim on each side. Plain edge.

Rulau	Date	Metal	Size	F	VF	EF	Unc
Ia-SC 13	1888	Gilt Brass	26mm	—	—	10.00	15.00

Corn Palace at center, CORN PALACE SIOUX CITY above, 1888 in exergue. Rv: Ear of corn upright, on which is superimposed a winding ribbon. On five folds of the ribbon: THE / EIGHTH / WONDER / OF THE / WORLD. Plain edge. Issued holed.

Rulau	Date	Metal	Size	F	VF	EF	Unc
Ia-SC A13	1888	Brass	25mm	—	—	10.00	12.50

Building at center, CORN PALACE SIOUX CITY above, SEP. 24. OCT. 6. / 1888. in exergue. Rv: Ear of corn in a crown at center, THE EIGHTH WONDER OF / THE WORLD above, CORN IS KING below. Plain edge.

Rulau	Date	Metal	Size	F	VF	EF	Unc
Ia-SC 14	1889	Gilt Brass	26mm	—	—	5.00	15.00

Corn Palace within central circle, SIOUX CITY CORN PALACE around, . 1889 . below. Rv: Crossed ears of corn surrounded by wreath. CORN IS KING around. Plain edge. Issued holed.

Rulau	Date	Metal	Size	F	VF	EF	Unc
Ia-SC 15	1889	Bronze	26mm	—	—	10.00	15.00

Female statue bearing torch and cornstalk. Rv: Building. Around: CORN PALACE SIOUX CITY / 1889. Plain edge.

Corn Palace tokens bearing dates 1890 and 1891 are also reported. Apparently all Corn Palace pieces were originally issued as badges suspended from ribbons, or intended for such use. A typical 1891 issue follows.

Rulau	Date	Metal	Size	F	VF	EF	Unc
Ia-SC 18	1891	Gilt Brass	26mm	—	—	5.00	15.00

Building, SIOUX CITY CORN PALACE above, 1891 in exergue. Rv: Crossed ears of corn between sprays, CORN IS KING around. Plain edge. Issued holed.

B. DAVIDSON & CO.

Sioux City, Iowa

Rulau	Date	Metal	Size	VG	F	VF	EF
Ia-SC 25	1888	Gilt Brass	22mm	—	—	20.00	30.00

Ear of corn through a crown at center, COMPLIMENTS OF / B. DAVIDSON & CO. around. Rv: Corn Palace at center, CORN PALACE SIOUX CITY above, SEP. 24. OCT. 6 / 1888. in exergue. Plain edge. Issued holed. (ANS coll.)

Ben Davidson & Co. at 14th & Pierce Streets in later years became Davidson's Department Store.

WM. FREES

Spencer, Iowa

Rulau	Date	Metal	Size	VG	F	VF	Unc
Ia-Sp 2	(1883-89)	Brass	26mm	—	—	25.00	—

Brunswick die BB-3. Rv: Description not available. (Thoele report)

Listed in the 1884 thru 1889 gazetteers.

CASPER BENESK

Spillville, Iowa

Rulau	Date	Metal	Size	VG	F	VF	Unc
Ia-Sv 1	(1877-94)	Brass	24mm	—	—	50.00	—

—.—/ CHECK / —.— within central circle. Around: BRUNSWICK & COMPANY. / CHICAGO. Rv: GOOD FOR / 5 ¢ / CASPER BENESK. Plain edge. (Brunswick page 16, no number)

Rulau	Date	Metal	Size	VG	F	VF	Unc
Ia-Sv 3	(1874-84)	Brass	24mm	—	30.00	—	—

Brunswick die BB-8a. Rv: Similar to Ia-Sv 1. Plain edge. (Koppenhaver June 1987 sale, lot 718)

THOS. BARTON

Strawberry Point, Iowa

Rulau	Date	Metal	Size	VG	F	VF	Unc
Ia-SP 1	(1884)	—	--mm	—	—	25.00	—

Brunswick die BB-7a. Rv: GOOD FOR / 5 ¢ / THOS. BARTON / IN / TRADE.

Barton ran a saloon and billiard hall in Strawberry Point 1884. By 1888 he was listed as a saloonkeeper in Volga, Iowa.

WM. CRABB

Swan, Iowa

Rulau	Date	Metal	Size	VG	F	VF	EF
Ia-Sw 1	(1883-84)	Brass	24mm	—	—	30.00	—

Brunswick die BB-6a. Rv: Description not available. (Thoele report)

Listed in the 1884 gazetteer.

PUTZEL'S CLOTHING HALL

Winterset, Iowa

1876 Centennial Tokens

Reverse type 1: PUTZEL'S / (star) / CLOTHING / HALL / HATS CAPS / WINTERSET, IOWA. (All 23mm; plain edge)

Rulau	Obv	Rev	Metal	F	VF	EF	Unc
Ia-Wi 3	H (Miller 2)	1	WM	—	—	—	100.
Ia-Wi 3A	H (ANS coll.)	1	Brass	—	—	—	100.

THEO A. ALLEN

Iowa

Rulau	Date	Metal	Size	F	VF	EF	Unc
Ia-Un 1	(1880's)	GS	**	—	—	35.00	—

** Shield-shaped flan with eye, 23x29mm.
Three folds of scroll across eagle with folded wings. Incused on scroll: THEO. A. ALLEN / D & St. P. R. R / IOWA. Rv: PATd. DEC 29, 1868 in arc across top. Incused on plain field. Compass-Square-G. (Elmer Randall coll.)

D & St. P. R. R = Denver & St. Paul Railroad. For a very similar item, se De-Wi 3 under Wilmington, Del.

The blank ID tag is type 72 of the Peck & Synder 1886 catalog.

(L) AWRENCE BRO (S).

Iowa

Rulau	Date	Metal	Size	VG	F	VF	EF
Ia-Un 3	(?)	Copper	28mm	—	—	30.00	—

(L)AWRENCE BRO(S) / IOWA 3 ctsp on U.S. Hard Times store card of Wm. H. Milton, Boston, Mass. of the 1830's (Low 265). The L and S are missing, but inferred from the text. Reverse is ctsp with numeral 58 and indecipherable markings. (John Cheramy coll.; Brunk 24040)

The counterstamp is somewhat uneven and partially double struck, thus not completely legible. It has been asserted without evidence that the Lawrence Brothers, 1950's-1960's numismatic publishers of Anamosa, Iowa were responsible. We think this unlikely.

REPORTED IOWA BILLIARD TOKENS

The following unverified attributions have been reported for this era. They are listed here for informational purposes:

Name on Token	Possible Locale	Billiard Die	Gazetteer
August Adams	Volga	BBC ?	1887
Chas. Bahning	Dyersville	Geo. Kuehl	1890
Thos. Barton	Strawberry Point	BB-7a	1884
W. F. Bosten	Muscatine	B-2b	1889
Hugh Chambers	Lake City	BB-4	1882-89
Hugo C. Fabricius	Reinbeck	BBC-11	1892
Wm. T. Foust	Cherokee	Geo. Kuehl	1882-83
J. G. Gallagher	West Bend	BBC-9b	1884
Oss. Hollowell (Austin Hollowell)	Keokuk	BB	1887
James Junk	Sioux City	BB-7a	1881
G. S. Kendall	Alton	BB-4	1883-84
J. W. Loudon	Fontanelle	Chas. Pick	1881-82
Mayes & Tappe	Muscatine	BBC-9a	1887
J. W. Nolan	Marengo	Kuehl & Bro.	1882
J. W. Nolan	Van Horne	BBC	1886
Oakes (Thomas J. Oakes)	Fairfield	BB	1882
Walter Payne	Vinton	Chas. Pick	1884
John Schmitz	Halbur	BB-6c	1887-90
John Vaughn	Glidden	B-2e	1884-87
John Vaughn	Glidden	BB-6a	1884-87

KANSAS

J. P. BAUMANN

Chanute, Kas.

Rulau	Date	Metal	Size	VG	F	VF	Unc
Ks-Ch 1	(1882)	—	--mm	—	—	35.00	—

J. P. BAUMANN / COLONIAL. Rv: GOOD FOR / 10 ¢ / ONE DRINK. (Rouleau coll.)

Billiard hall, 1882 gazetteer.

SWENSON BROTHERS

Cleburne, Kansas

Rulau	Date	Metal	Size	VG	F	VF	Unc
Ks-Cl 5	1888	Brass	**	—	—	10.00	—

** Oct 22.5mm. Triangle with large 1 inside, at center.
Around: SWENSON BROTHERS / A 1888 D. Rv: Triangle with 1 inside, GOOD FOR above, MDSE. below. Plain edge. Two die varieties (large dots and small dots).

Rulau	Date	Metal	Size	VG	F	VF	Unc
Ks-Cl 6	1888	Brass	21mm	—	—	10.00	—

Similar, but 5. Plain edge.

Rulau	Date	Metal	Size	VG	F	VF	Unc
Ks-Cl 10	1888	Alum	39mm	—	—	15.00	—

Similar, but large S inside each triangle, and 500 on three sides around it. Plain edge.

Aluminum was still a somewhat 'noble' metal in 1888, accounting for its use on the $5 denomination. (See "The Swenson Brothers" by Kent Johnson in *TAMS Journal* for Oct. 1977).

These tokens could have been issued later than the date they bear.

G. M. HOOVER

Dodge City, Kas.

Rulau	Date	Metal	Size	VG	F	VF	Unc
Ks-DC 3	(1884)	Brass	24.5mm	—	—	35.00	—

GOOD FOR / ONE / G. M. HOOVER / * DRINK *. Rv: 15 within circle of alternating stars and dots.

J. C. WHITNEY

Irving, Kas.

Rulau	Date	Metal	Size	VG	F	VF	Unc
Ks-Ir 7	(1888)	Brass	25mm	—	—	40.00	—

Brunswick die B-2e. Rv: GOOD FOR / 5 ¢ / J. C. WHITNEY (in cross-hatched panel) / IN / TRADE. About 5 pieces known. (Brunswick 78)

J. Whitney, billiard hall, 1888-89 gazetteer.

MILLARD & COOPER

Lawrence, Kas.

Rulau	Date	Metal	Size	F	VF	EF	Unc
Ks-Lw 7	(1885-86)	Brass	25mm	—	—	40.00	—

THE / J. M. BRUNSWICK / AND / BALKE CO / (Pool table) . Rv: GOOD FOR / 5 C / MILLARD / & COOPER / IN / TRADE. Plain edge. (Thoele coll.)

Millard & Cooper were pool hall proprietors listed in the 1886 gazetteer under Lawrence, Kansas.

MOAK BROS.

Lawrence, Kas.

Rulau	Date	Metal	Size	VG	F	VF	Unc
Ks-Lw 9	(1884-89)	—	--mm	—	—	40.00	—

Brunswick die BB-6a. Rv: GOOD FOR / 5 ¢ / MOAK BROS. / IN / TRADE. (Rouleau coll.,ex-Egnew)

Moak Brothers billiard hall appears in the 1884, 1886 and 1888 gazetteers under Lawrence, also in the 1888 directory under Wichita. A. J. Moak appears under Lawrence, billiard hall, in 1891.

THAD. WHIPPO

Marysville, Kansas

Rulau	Date	Metal	Size	F	VF	EF	Unc
Ks-Ma 8	(1886-89)	Brass	25mm	—	—	40.00	—

(Brunswick die B-2E) Rv: THAD. / WHIPPO. (Thoele coll.)

Thad. Whippo is listed as a billiard hall proprietor 1886 to 1889.

J. COTTER

Ottawa, Kas.

Rulau	Date	Metal	Size	VG	F	VF	Unc
Ks-Ot 2	(1888)	Brass	25mm	—	—	40.00	—

Brunswick die B-2b. Rv: GOOD FOR / 2 1/2 ¢ / J. COTTER (in cross-hatched panel) / IN / TRADE. Only 1 piece reported. (Thoele coll.)

Julius Cotter, billiard hall, 1888-89 gazetteer.

RALPH CECIL

Stark, Kansas

Rulau	Date	Metal	Size	VG	F	VF	Unc
Ks-St 1	(?)	Bronze	19mm	—	—	50.00	—

RALPH CECIL / M. W. A. / STARK, KANS. ctsp on U.S. Indian cent. (Keystone State Numismatics coll., ex-Sol Taylor)

Court House Square, Lexington, Kentucky, 1887.

KENTUCKY

H. K. MITCHELL
Franklin, Ky.

Rulau	Date	Metal	Size	VG	F	VF	EF
Ky-Fr 1	(?)	Silver	38mm	—	—	200.	—
	H. K. MITCHELL / — DRUGGIST / — / — FRANKLIN, KY. — ctsp on U.S. 1880 Morgan silver dollar. (Van Ormer 2760; Koppenhaver June 1979 sale, lot 236; Brunk 28093)						

HARNESS & CLAY
Hopkinsville, Ky.

Rulau	Date	Metal	Size	VG	F	VF	Unc
Ky-Ho 1	(?)	Gilt/B	23mm	—	—	100.	—
	HARNESS & CLAY / PHARMACISTS / — / HOPKINSVILLE / KY. Rv: — / 5 ¢/ SODA. / —. Rim of beaded dots on both sides. Plain edge. Square planchet. (Miller Ky. 1/2A)						

SHELTON'S CURD HOUSE
Lexington, Ky.

Rulau	Date	Metal	Size	VG	F	VF	EF
Ky Lx 7	ND	Silver	31mm	—	—	300.	—
	SHELTON'S (curved) / LEX. KY. ctsp on U.S. 1858-0 Seated Liberty half dollar. (Kirtley Dec. 1990 list)						
Ky-Lx 7A	ND	Silver	25mm	—	—	200.	—
	Similar ctsp on U.S. 1853 or 1856 S.L. quarter. 4 pieces known. (Brunk 36350)						
Ky-Lx 8	ND	Silver	31mm	—	—	300.	—
	SHELTON'S (curved) / LEX. KY. / CURD HOUSE ctsp on U.S. 1858 S.L. half dollar. (Krueger 3562; Brunk 36355). CURD HOUSE is from a separate punch with larger letters than those in the first two lines.						

Robert B. Shelton and William P. Curd managed the Curd House on Water Street near the railway depot, a hotel, restaurant and livery stable, from 1854 on.

LEX. KY.

Rulau	Date	Metal	Size	VG	F	VF	EF
Ky-Lx 35	ND	Bronze	23mm	35.00	—	—	—
	LEX. KY. ctsp on U.S. Shield 2-cent piece, worn. (Kirtley Nov. 6, 1990 sale, lot A636)						
Ky-Lx 36	ND	Copper	29mm	—	—	20.00	—
	Similar ctsp on U.S. 1835 Large cent. (Brunk 24450)						
Ky-Lx 37	ND	Silver	27mm	30.00	—	50.00	—
	Similar ctsp on Spanish-American 2-reales. Examined: 1708, 1813.						

H. WILSON

Rulau	Date	Metal	Size	VG	F	VF	EF
Ky-Lx 10	(?)	Silver	30mm	—	—	100.	—
	H. WILSON LEX. KY. ctsp on Canada 1870 Queen Victoria half dollar. (Cheramy coll.; Brunk 43730)						

WINCHESTER
Lexington, Ky.

Rulau	Date	Metal	Size	VG	F	VF	EF
Ky-Lx 12	(?)	Silver	31mm	—	—	100.	—
	WINCHESTER, LEX. KY ctsp on U.S. 1838 Bust half dollar. (Brunk 43850)						

COOK & SLOSS
Louisville, Ky.

Rulau	Date	Metal	Size	VG	F	VF	Unc
Ky-Lo 4	(1870's)	Brass	26mm	—	—	40.00	75.00
	Exposition buildings, LOUISVILLE INDUSTRIAL EXPOSITION. Rv: COOK & SLOSS, JEWELERS, LOUISVILLE. Plain edge. (Miller Ky. 5)						
Ky-Lo 5	(1870's)	Brass	26mm	—	—	40.00	75.00
	Railroad locomotive right, spewing smoke, PROGRESS above. Rv: As 5. Plain edge. (Miller Ky. 6)						

John W. Cook and Simon R. Goodman comprised Cook & Goodman, jewelry and watches, 128 Third Street, between Jefferson and Green, in the 1865 and 1866 directories. The 1869 directory reveals the name was changed to Cook, Goodman & Co. when the original partners admitted Levi Sloss.

DEPPEN'S HATTERS

Rulau	Date	Metal	Size	VG	F	VF	Unc
Ky-Lo 7	1888	Alum	23mm	—	—	10.00	20.00
	Flowers over entire field. Across center is a bar inscribed: LOUISVILLE, KY. Around: COMMERCIAL AND FLORAL CELEBRATION / 1888. Rv: DEPPEN'S / HATTERS / ** / CLOTHIERS / HABERDASHERS / xx / TAILORS / * LOUISVILLE *. Plain edge. (Wright 242)						

J. HART

Rulau	Date	Metal	Size	VG	F	VF	Unc
Ky-Lo 9	(?)	Silver	25mm	—	—	75.00	—
	J. HART / LOU. KY. ctsp on U.S. 1856 S.L. quarter. (Lot 015 in H. Joseph Levine sale of June 27, 1987)						

HOWE MACHINE CO.

Rulau	Date	Metal	Size	VG	F	VF	Unc
Ky-Lo 10	(1870's)	Brass	26mm	—	20.00	40.00	75.00
	Bust right within circle. Around: THE HOWE MACHINE CO. Below: * ELIAS HOWE JR. *. Rv: Railroad locomotive right, spewing smoke from its chimney. Above: PROGRESS. Plain edge. (Wright 1461; Miller Ky. 15)						
Ky-Lo 11	(?)	WM	26mm	—	—	40.00	75.00
	As 10. Plain edge. (Miller Ky. 15A)						
Ky-Lo 12	(?)	Brass	26mm	—	—	40.00	75.00
	Exposition buildings, LOUISVILLE INDUSTRIAL EXPOSITION. Rv: Large $10 at center. Inscription: BUY A HOWE MACHINE FOR CASH & RECEIVE FOR THIS / AT 166 FOURTH ST., LOUISVILLE, KY. Plain edge. (Miller Ky. 16)						
Ky-Lo 13	(?)	Brass	26mm	—	—	50.00	90.00
	Obverse as reverse of Ky 10 (Locomotive). Rv: As 16. Plain edge. (Wright 1462; Miller Ky. 17)						
Ky-Lo 14	(1870's)	Brass	26mm	—	—	10.00	20.00
	Obverse as 12 (Exposition buildings). Rv: As 10 (Locomotive). Plain edge. Muling: no name on token. (Miller Ky. 18)						

The Exposition Buildings or Locomotive stock dies were also used on other Louisville cards — of F. S. Kirtland, Cook & Sloss, Preuser & Wellenvoss, and J. W. Quest.

In the 1880's Louisville moved to rebuild the shattered industry of the South following the Civil War and was greatly aided in this by the extension of the Louisville & Nashville Railroad, referred to on the tokens as 'PROGRESS'.

The Howe series of tokens seems to have been issued by G. W. Scovill, Louisville agent for Howe's Sewing Machines, who was listed at 133 4th Street in the 1869 directory.

JEWELL & BEDDO

Rulau	Date	Metal	Size	VG	F	VF	Unc
Ky-Lo 16	(1870's)	Brass	26mm	—	—	50.00	90.00
	Railroad locomotive right, spewing smoke, PROGRESS above, single star in exergue. Rv: JEWELL & BEDDO. / JEWELERS / * / MASONIC TEMPLE, / —*— / LOUISVILLE, KY. Plain edge. (ANS coll.)						

F. S. KIRTLAND

Rulau	Date	Metal	Size	VG	F	VF	Unc
Ky-Lo 17	(1870's)	Brass	26mm	—	—	50.00	90.00
	Exposition buildings, LOUISVILLE INDUSTRIAL EXPOSITION. Rv: F. S. KIRTLAND / * / CLOTHING / N. E. COR. FOURTH / & JEFFERSON / * / LOUISVILLE, KY. Plain edge. (Miller Ky. 20)						
Ky-Lo 18	(?)	Brass	26mm	—	—	50.00	90.00
	Railroad locomotive right, spewing, PROGRESS above. Rv: As 17. Plain edge. (Wright 558; Miller Ky. 21)						

LOUISVILLE EXPOSITION

Rulau	Date	Metal	Size	VG	F	VF	EF
Ky-Lo A18	1885	WM	35mm	—	—	10.00	20.00
	Female facing, arms outstretched, females on either side, sitting. Implements around — anvil, wheel, shield, artist's palette, etc. All within recessed center. Rv: Building, LOUISVILLE, KY. above, 1885 / EXPOSITION in exergue. Plain edge.						

McBURNIE

Rulau	Date	Metal	Size	F	VF	EF	Unc
Ky-Lo 19	1883	G/Bronze	14mm	—	—	50.00	90.00
	High heeled shoe at center, COMPLIMENTS OF McBURNIE / LOUISVILLE, KY. Rv: View of grounds at Southern Exposition, 1883. Plain edge. (Hartzog Aug. 13, 1983 sale, lot 200)						

PREUSER & WELLENVOSS

Rulau	Date	Metal	Size	VG	F	VF	Unc
Ky-Lo 20	(1870's)	Brass	26mm	—	—	40.00	75.00

Exposition buildings, LOUISVILLE INDUSTRIAL EXPOSITION. Rv: Hat. PREUSER & WELLENVOSS / 56 MARKET ST. BET. 2ND & 3RD ST / * LOUISVILLE KY. *. Plain edge. (Wright 847; Miller Ky. 27)

Ky-Lo 21	(1875-76)	Brass	26mm	—	—	40.00	75.00

Railroad locomotive right, spewing smoke, PROGRESS above. Rv: As 27. Plain edge. (Miller Ky. 28)

George Preuser and Henry Wellenvoss are listed as hat and cap merchants at 52 West Market Street, between 2nd and 3rd Streets, in the 1865, 1866 and 1869 directories.

The address on the token is 56 Market Street, possibly a new building erected in the 1870's. This address appears in the 1876 directory.

J. W. QUEST

Rulau	Date	Metal	Size	VG	F	VF	Unc
Ky-Lo 24	(1870's)	Brass	25mm	—	—	50.00	90.00

Buildings, LOUISVILLE INDUSTRIAL EXPOSITION. Rv: J. W. QUEST / BOOTS & SHOES / (boot) / 80 WEST MARKET ST. / LOUISVILLE, KY. Plain edge. (Miller Ky. 30)

Ky-Lo 25	(1870's)	Brass	25mm	—	—	15.00	30.00

Locomotive spewing smoke right, PROGRESS above. Rv: As Ky. 30. Plain edge. (Wright 864; Miller Ky. 31)

J. W. Quest is first met with in the 1866 directory, where he is listed as a clerk for John H. Quast, boots and shoes, at 113 4th Street. Quest's residence then was at the southwest corner of Jefferson and 6th. The Quast listing is repeated in the 1869 directory.

Quest's business must date from the 1870's.

SOUTHERN EXPOSITION

Rulau	Date	Metal	Size	VG	F	VF	Unc
Ky-Lo 30	1883	Bronze	28mm	—	—	10.00	20.00

Aerial view of exposition building complex, mountains in background. Rv: SOUTHERN EXPOSITION / AUG. 1ST 1883 / SOUVENIR (on scroll) / 100 DAYS / LOUISVILLE, KY. Plain edge.

Ky-Lo 32	1883	S/WM	32mm	—	15.00	—	30.00

Two men shaking hands within a shield, ribbon below reads: UNITED WE STAND DIVIDED WE FALL. Below: SOUTHERN EXPOSITION, LOUISVILLE, KENTUCKY. Rv: Building across center, OPENS AUG. 1ST 1883 above, CONTINUES / ONE HUNDRED DAYS below. Plain edge.

Ky-Lo 33	1883	Gilt/Br	25.5mm	—	—	Scarce	—

Exposition building on central panel. Above: Locomotive in circular wreath. Below: Two men shaking hands in circular wreath. Rv: Within wreath: SOUTHERN / EXPOSITION / LOUISVILLE / KY. / 1883. Intermittently reeded edge. (Leon Lindheim coll.)

Intermittent reeding is most unusual at this early period. The reeds occur in groups of four, each group separated by a smooth area. This would have been a costly extra at the time — adding little if anything to the medalet's appearance.

Rulau	Date	Metal	Size	VG	F	VF	Unc
Ky-Lo 34	1883	Bronze	15mm	—	—	12.50	20.00

Aerial view of exposition grounds, LOUISVILLE above, tiny CED below. Rv: SOUVENIR / SOUTHERN / (rosette flanked by sprays) / EXPOSITION / 1883. (Zaffern coll.; Behringer coll.)

Struck by Scovill Mfg. Co., Waterbury, Conn.

WAYT DENTAL CO.

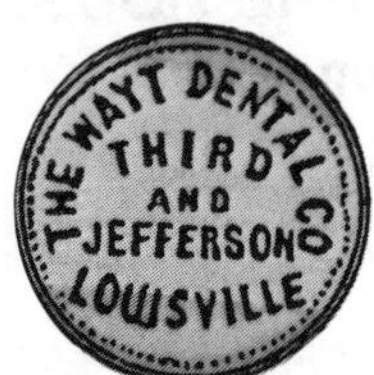

Rulau	Date	Metal	Size	VG	F	VF	Unc
Ky-Lo 35	(?)	GS	25mm	—	—	75.00	—

THE WAYT DENTAL CO / THIRD / AND / JEFFERSON / LOUISVILLE. Rv: FOUR EXPERIENCED / DENTISTS / AND A KIND / —AND— / EFFICIENT / LADY / ATTENDANT. (Wright 1133)

GEORGE WOLF

Louisville, Ky.

Rulau	Date	Metal	Size	VG	F	VF	Unc
Ky-Lo 40	(1866-75)	WM	--mm	—	—	40.00	75.00

View of bridge. Rv: GEORGE WOLF, JEWELER. Plain edge. (Miller Ky 35)

George Wolf was a partner in Wolf & Durringer, dealers in watches, clocks and jewelry, corner 5th and Market, 1865-69. He was also a partner in George Wolf & Son with Henry Wolf, watchmakers and jewelers, 196 Preston, 1866-95. The latter firm can be found listed through the 1895 directory.

F. B.

Newport, Ky.

Rulau	Date	Metal	Size	VG	F	VF	Unc
Ky-Ne 3	(?)	Br	Sq. 23.5mm	—	—	20.00	—

— * — / F. B. / NEWPORT, KY. / (ornament), all within central circle. Rv: - * - / POST OFFICE / — * — / EXCHANGE / — * — / UNSER FRITZ / — * — / I. (All arranged in diamond shape.) There is a beaded border on each side. Plain edge.

P. H. KEEN

Newport, Ky.

Rulau	Date	Metal	Size	VG	F	VF	EF
Ky-Ne 8	ND	Copper	29mm	—	—	75.00	—

P. H. KEEN / NEWPORT / KY / + ctsp on U.S. 1854 Large cent. P. KEEN ctsp on reverse of coin. (Rulau coll., ex-Tanenbaum; Brunk 22358)

Individual letter-punches.

C. A. DEUSER
Owensborough, Ky.

Rulau	Date	Metal	Size	VG	F	VF	Unc
Ky-Ow 2	(1883)	Brass	23mm	—	—	6.00	—
	(All incused): C. A. DEUSER / GOOD FOR / 5 C / . AT BAR . / (Star). Rv: Blank.						

One C. Deuser kept a saloon in 1883, according to Hank Thoele. Thoele has been unable to confirm the middle initial.

J. BLUM
Paducah, Ky.

Rulau	Date	Metal	Size	VG	F	VF	Unc
Ky-Pd 3	(?)	Brass	--mm	—	—	30.00	—
	NATIONAL BILLIARD MANF'G CO. / (Crosses cues separate N-B-M-Co) / CINCINNATI. Rv: PALMER HOUSE / J. BLUM / * PADUCAH, KY.						

W. M. CRUMP
Rocky Hill Station, Ky.

Rulau	Date	Metal	Size	VG	F	VF	Unc
Ky-Rh 1	(1883)	Brass	25mm	—	—	8.00	—
	GOOD FOR / 5 ¢ / W. M. CRUMP (in panel) / IN / TRADE. Rv: Large 5 in circle of asterisks. (ATCO Maverick 2125; Thoele coll.)						

W. M. Crump appears under saloons in the 1883 gazetteer. This Edmunson County village had 138 people in 1910.

JOHN H. JENKINS
Silver Grove, Ky.

Rulau	Date	Metal	Size	VG	F	VF	EF
Ky-Si 4	(?)	Silver	31mm	—	150.	—	250.
	JOHN H. JENKINS / SILVER GROVE ctsp on U.S. 1865-S Liberty Seated half dollar. (Gould 33; Brunk 21610)						

There is a Silver Grove in Campbell County near the Ohio River, a suburb of Newport, upriver from Cincinnati. No Silver Grove, however, appeared in the 1877 Postal Guide anywhere in the U.S.A.

NORTH JELLICO COAL CO.
Wilton, Ky.

Rulau	Date	Metal	Size	VG	F	VF	Unc
Ky-Wi 2	1888	Nickel	--mm	—	15.00	25.00	—
	Crossed pick and shovel at center, NORTH JELLICO COAL CO. around, * 1888 * below. Rv: 25.						
Ky-Wi 3	1888	Nickel	--mm	—	15.00	25.00	—
	As 6, but 10.						
Ky-Wi 4	1888	Nickel	--mm	—	15.00	25.00	—
	As 6, but 5.						

This company was in operation until 1928. After 1903 it had up to 579 employees. Wilton is in Knox County.

There are also $1 and 50-cent tokens in nickel, and a whole set in copper.

REPORTED KENTUCKY BILLIARD TOKENS

Following is a listing of unverified attributions for this era. These are given here for informational purposes:

Name on Token	Possible Locale	Billiard Die	Gazetteer
J. Q. Adams	Lexington	BBC-11	1896
C. A. Meyerratkin	Covington	BBC-3	1896
T. Schmidt	Newport	BB-3	1883
J. Wenderoth	Newport	BBC-3b	1896
T. H. Williams	Newport	BB-6a	1883

LOUISIANA

CHARLES H. RICHARDSON
Baton Rouge, La.

Rulau	Date	Metal	Size	VG	F	VF	EF
La-BR 7	(1868?)	Silver	27mm	—	—	225.	—
	CHARLES H. RICHARDSON / BATON ROUGE, LA. ctsp on Spanish-American 2-reales.						
La-BR 8	(?)	Silver	38mm	300.	—	450.	—
	Similar ctsp on U.S. 1860 Liberty Seated dollar. (Gould 6; Brunk 34190)						
La-BR 9	(?)	Silver	38mm	—	—	150.	—
	Similar ctsp on U.S. 1867 Liberty Seated dollar. (Gould 6)						
La-BR 11	(?)	Silver	25mm	200.	—	300.	—
	RICHARDSON / BATON ROUGE, LA. ctsp on several different, unspecified coins. (Brunk 34185)						
La-BR 13	(?)	Copper	29mm	100.	—	150.	—
	RICHARDSON ctsp on U.S. 1829 Large cent. (Brunk 34170)						

This latter stamp is also reported on a Spanish-American 1747 1-real coin.

G. W. BENNETT
Bennettville, La.

Rulau	Date	Metal	Size	F	VF	EF	Unc
La-Be 1	1871	GS	30mm	65.00	135.	—	Rare
	(All lettering incuse). G. W. BENNETT / GOOD FOR / x 25¢ x / IN GOODS / BENNETTVILLE, LA. 1871. Rv: Same as obverse. Plain edge.						
La-Be 2	1871	GS	32mm			V.	Rare
	As 1, but 50¢. Plain edge.						
La-Be 3	1871	GS	38.6mm			V.	Rare
	As 1, but $1oo. Plain edge.						

This was a general store in Rapides Parish, probably associated with sugar plantations, which closed in 1905. Bennettville was located between Bunkie and Cheneyville. It is possible that 5 and 10-cent tokens were issued, but none have been reported.

At present only one or two specimens of each token are known. The 25-cent piece illustrated (Alan Weinberg coll., ex-Rulau, Fuld) is in VF-plus condition.

Rulau	Date	Metal	Size	F	VF	EF	Unc
La-Be 6	(?)	Brass	23mm	—	50.00	—	—
	(All incused): GOOD FOR / 10 ¢ / IN GOODS / G. W. BENNETT. Rv: Blank. Plain edge.						
La-Be 7	(?)	Brass	23mm	—	50.00	—	—
	As last, but 25 ¢. Plain edge.						
La-Be 8	(?)	Brass	23mm	—	50.00	—	—
	As last, but 50 ¢. Plain edge.						
La-Be 9	(?)	Brass	23mm	—	50.00	—	—
	As last, but $1. on second line. Plain edge.						

Possibly issued somewhere in the 1880-1905 period. The earlier issue of this general store operator, dated 1871, is listed as La-Be 1 through 3. All four above specimens in collection of Cindy Grellman, Lake Mary, Fla.

La-Be 6 through 9 could postdate the 1866-89 period.

J. MURDOCH, FRANKLIN PL'T.
Hard Times Landing, La.

Rulau	Date	Metal	Size	VG	F	VF	Unc
La-HT 1	(1882-93)	Brass	23mm	—	40.00	—	—
	FRANKLIN PL'T. / J. MURDOCH. / NOT / TRANSFERABLE. Rv: Numeral 5. Plain edge. Apparently unique. (Tylenda 3894 A-05)						

Dun directories for 1882 and 1893 list J. Murdoch as planter and general store proprietor. Unlisted in Tylenda, but assigned number shown.

Rulau	Date	Metal	Size	VG	F	VF	Unc
La-HT 2	(1882-93)	Brass	Oct 26mm	—	40.00	—	—
	As 1, but 25¢. (Ty. 3894 A25)						

L. J. CHAUVIN
Houma, La.

Rulau	Date	Metal	Size	VG	F	VF	Unc
La-Hm 3	(?)	Brass	32.5mm	—	—	30.00	—

L. J. CHAUVIN / GENERAL / —.— / HOUMA, LA. Rv: GOOD FOR / * 50 * / IN TRADE. Incised, dentilated rim on each side. Plain edge. (Rulau coll.)

JULIUS LEVIN & CO.
Levin, La.

Rulau	Date	Metal	Size	VG	F	VF	Unc
La-Lv 1	(1880-95)	Brass	23mm	—	—	100.	—
	JULIUS LEVIN & CO. (incuse) / GOOD FOR / 5 C / IN MDSE. / LEVIN, LA. (incuse). Rv: W. H. HASKELL / 713 OLIVE ST. / ST. LOUIS. Plain edge.						
La-Lv 4	(1880-95)	Brass	28mm	—	—	100.	—
	Similar, but 1.00. Plain edge.						

Julius Levin operated a sawmill at what is known today as Tioga in Rapides Parish.

J. L. WILLIAMS
Mansfield, La.

Rulau	Date	Metal	Size	F	VF	EF	Unc
La-Mn 5	(1876)	Brass	Oct 25mm	—	30.00	—	—

J. L. WILLIAMS / SAMPLE / ROOM. Rv: GOOD FOR / 10 C / IN TRADE. Plain edge. Apparently unique. (Tylenda 5509 E-10)

The only known specimen was dug up in Mansfield. The Dun directory reveals that J. L. Williams ran a saloon in 1876. Not in Tylenda, but assigned number shown above.

ALF J. MAYER
Marksville, La.

Rulau	Date	Metal	Size	VG	F	VF	Unc
La-Ma 4	(1880)	Brass	--mm	—	—	40.00	—
	ALF. J. MAYER, / . . . . . . / —*— / MARKSVILLE / — LA. —. Rv: MERCHANDISE / 25 / CHECK. Plain edge.						
La-Ma5	(1880)	Brass	Oct. --mm	—	—	40.00	—
	Similar, but 10 instead of 25. Plain edge.						

GEO. L. MAYER
Marksville, La.

Rulau	Date	Metal	Size	VG	F	VF	Unc
La-Ma 9	(1880's)	Brass	30mm	—	—	40.00	—

GOOD FOR MERCHANDISE / GEO. L. / MAYER / — . — / MARKSVILLE / LA. Rv: 1oo. Beaded rims on both sides. Plain edge.

Rulau	Date	Metal	Size	G	VG	F	EF
La-Ma 13	(1880's)	Brass	Oc. 23mm	5.00	10.00	25.00	—

GOOD FOR MERCHANDISE / GEO. L. / MAYER / —.— / MARKSVILLE / LA. Rv: Large 10. Plain edge.

In 1918 there was a firm, Mayer Brothers, in the auto and supply business in Marksville, Avoyelles Parish, which may have been a successor firm. In 1918 Marksville had 1,076 people.

HENRY KLINE
Monroe, La.

Rulau	Date	Metal	Size	VG	F	VF	Unc
La-Mo 3	(1889-93)	GS	29mm	—	—	75.00	—

COMMERCIAL / SALOON / HENRY KLINE, / PRO. / MONROE, LA. Rv: I O U / ONE / DRINK. Plain edge. (Tylenda 5936 G)

Listed in 1893 directory.

CASSIDY'S
New Orleans, La.

Rulau	Date	Metal	Size	VG	F	VF	Unc
La-No 8	(1880's ?)	Brass	31mm	—	13.50	22.50	—

CASSIDY'S / $5.00 / 174 / GRAVIER ST. Rv: Blank. (Wright 146)

COTTON CENTENNIAL EXPOSITION

Rulau	Date	Metal	Size	F	VF	EF	Unc
La-NO 12	1884	Silver	23.9mm	—	20.00	—	—

Shield and crescent before cotton bale, cotton plant etc. NEW ORLEANS on crescent. Small A. B. GRISWOLD & Co below. Around: COTTON CENTENNIAL EXPOSITION / + 1884-5 +. Rv: Blank. The illustrated specimen has monogram CAE (?) engraved on reverse. Issued with loop. Weight: 4.57 grams.

CRESCENT CITY ATHLETIC CLUB

Rulau	Date	Metal	Size	F	VF	EF	Unc
La-No 15	1883	?	--mm	—	40.00	—	—

Building at center, CRESCENT CITY ATHLETIC CLUB above, AMPHITHEATER below. Rv: Two men boxing. HALL VS. FITZSIMMONS / $40,000 / MARCH 8TH, 1883. Plain edge. (Wright 1383)

The token description in Wright is incomplete.

Robert Fitzsimmons (called "Bob" or "Ruby Robert") was born in Helston, Cornwall, England, June 4, 1862, and died in Chicago, Oct. 22, 1917. He became world boxing champion in three separate weight divisions, middleweight, light heavyweight and heavyweight (respectively in 1891, 1903 and 1897). Born in Cornwall, he grew up in New Zealand and emigrated to America in 1890 after visiting there in 1883. He won the middleweight championship from Nonpareil Jack Dempsey (13 rounds) in New Orleans, Jan. 14, 1891. He won the heavyweight championship from Jim Corbett (14 rounds) in Carson City, Nev. on March 17, 1897 (resigning his middleweight crown). He lost the heavyweight crown to James J. Jeffries (11 rounds) at Coney Island, N.Y., June 9, 1899.

Fitzsimmons won the light heavyweight crown at the age of 41 when he defeated George Gardner (20 rounds) in San Francisco, Nov. 25, 1903. He lost this crown in a knockout (13 rounds) in San Francisco on Dec. 20, 1905 by Jack O'Brien. Fitzsimmons weighed only about 170 pounds in his fighting career but had the chest and shoulder development of a much larger man.

GEORGE J. DORR

Rulau	Date	Metal	Size	VG	F	VF	Unc
La-NO 17	(1885)	Silver	38.1mm	—	50.00	—	—

GEORGE J. DORR / COTTON CENTENNIAL / NEW ORLEANS engraved in three lines on U.S. 1885-O Morgan silver dollar. (Joe Schmidt coll.)

The World's Industrial and Cotton Centennial Exposition took place in New Orleans from Dec. 16, 1884 through May 31, 1885. The Dorr piece may well be a personal memento, but it was thought best to include it.

A. FATTERS

Rulau	Date	Metal	Size	VG	F	VF	Unc
La-NO 20	(?)	Brass	23mm	—	—	30.00	—

Pool table at center, POOL above, CHECK below. Rv: A. FATTERS / GOOD FOR / 5 ¢ / DRINK / NEW ORLEANS. Plain edge.

Anthony Fatter's billiard parlor was located at 841 Royal St. from the 1880's to about 1907.

MARDI GRAS

Rulau	Date	Metal	Size	F	VF	EF	Unc
La-NO 25	1884	Gilt Brass	16mm	12.50	17.50	25.00	40.00

NEW ORLEANS / 1884 / FEBRUARY. Rv: MARDI GRAS / (ornament) / SOUVENIR. Plain edge.

NORTH, CENTRAL AND SOUTH AMERICAN EXPOSITION

Rulau	Date	Metal	Size	F	VF	EF	Unc
La-NO 29	1886	S/WM	31.5mm	—	—	20.00	55.00

Building across center, THE MAIN BUILDING above, 1378 BY 905 FEET / (U.S. shield flanked by four flags). Globe at center showing Western Hemisphere, 1885 at North Pole and 1886 at South Pole. Around all: NORTH, CENTRAL & SOUTH * AMERICAN EXPOSITION / * NEW ORLEANS *. Plain edge.

ROBINSON MUSEUM & THEATRE

Rulau	Date	Metal	Size	VG	F	VF	Unc
La-NO 33	1884	WM	24mm	—	—	150.	—

ROBINSON MAMMOTH / MUSEUM & THEATRE. / ONE / DIME. Rv: OPENING SOUVENIR / PRESENTED BY / E. ROBINSON / PROPRIETOR, / NEW ORLEANS / LA. / OCT. 30, 1884. Loop attached. Plain edge.

Rulau	Date	Metal	Size	VG	F	VF	Unc
La-NO 33A	1884	Brass	24mm	—	—	150.	—

As 33. (Grellman coll.)

Rulau	Date	Metal	Size	VG	F	VF	Unc
La-NO 33B	1884	S/Brass	24mm	—	—	150.	—

As 33. (Grellman coll.)

SOUVENIR OF THE CARNIVAL

Rulau	Date	Metal	Size	F	VF	EF	Unc
La-NO 39	(1880-90)	Brass	30mm	25.00	—	—	—

Coat of arm. Rv: SOUVENIR OF THE CARNIVAL. NEW ORLEANS. Issued with loop.

WORLD'S INDUSTRIAL AND COTTON CENTENNIAL EXPOSITION

New Orleans, La.

Rulau	Date	Metal	Size	F	VF	EF	Unc
La-NO 48	1884	Brass	23.7mm	—	—		20.00

Buildings at center, WORLD EXPOSITION / NEW ORLEANS above, MAIN BUILDING / 1884-1885 below. Rv: Crossed hammer, pick and shovel against anvil, wheel to lower right, all within crude wreath. Plain edge. (Hartzog coll.)

Rulau	Date	Metal	Size	F	VF	EF	Unc
La-NO 50	1885	WM	21mm	—	—	5.00	20.00

Large 5-pointed star above exposition building, all within starred wreath. Rv: Bale of cotton within circular laurel wreath at center. THE WORLDS INDUSTRIAL / AND COTTON CENTENNIAL above; * EXPOSITION * / * NEW ORLEANS . 1884 1885 * below. Plain edge. (Grellman coll.)

Rulau	Date	Metal	Size	F	VF	EF	Unc
La-NO 52	1885	Brass	26mm	—	—	12.50	18.50

Defiant eagle standing above three shields, stars and rays around. Above: WORLDS INDUSTRIAL AND COTTON CENTENNIAL. In a cartouche below: 1884-5 / EXPOSITION / NEW ORLEANS. Rv: SOUVENIR at center, wreath around. Plain edge. (Grellman coll.)

Rulau	Date	Metal	Size	F	VF	EF	Unc
La-NO 52A	1885	Nickel	26mm	—	—	—	25.00

As 52. (Ganter coll.)

Rulau	Date	Metal	Size	F	VF	EF	Unc
La-NO 55	1885	WM	31.5mm	—	—	5.00	25.00

Pelican feeding its young at center, FROM DEC. 16. 1884 TO above, MAY 31, 1885 below. All within a wreath of corn, cotton, tobacco, etc. Around the rim: THE WORLDS INDUSTRIAL AND COTTON CENTENNIAL EXPOSITION / NEW ORLEANS. Rv: Building across center, 1378 BY 905 FEET under the ground line. Above: THE MAIN BUILDING. Below: U.S. shield flanked by flags. Plain edge. (Grellman coll.)

Rulau	Date	Metal	Size	F	VF	EF	Unc
La-NO 57	1885	WM	31.5mm	—	5.00	—	30.00

Building across center, THE MAIN BUILDING above, NEW ORLEANS / 1884 ' 85 / (crescent) below. Rv: Within wreath: SOUVENIR / OF THE / WORLDS / INDUSTRIAL / AND / COTTON / EXPOSITION. Plain edge.

There are at least 10 other medalets under 35mm honoring this exposition, plus another 11 larger pieces in the So-Called Dollars category not listed in this reference. Those listed here are representative of the store card-sized pieces commemorating this important event, which brought New Orleans back to world attention after its Civil War and Reconstruction decline.

E. L. CHARROPPIN

Port Allen, La.

Rulau	Date	Metal	Size	VG	F	VF	Unc
La-PA 2	1882	Brass	28mm	—	100.	Rare	—

Bottle at center, E. L. CHARROPPIN, above, PORT ALLEN, LA. below. Rv: Star at center, VELVET BOWEN above, 1882 below. Plain edge.

Charroppin's general store was in business from the 1870's to about 1900. 'Velvet Bowen' was a brand of whiskey. Port Allen is in West Baton Rouge Parish.

L. A. RIVIERE

Thibodaux, La.

Rulau	Date	Metal	Size	VG	F	VF	Unc
La-Th 3	(1876-89)	Brass	25mm	—	—	40.00	—

L. A. RIVIERE / -.- / DEALER / -IN- / GROCERIES / LIQUORS / & FEED / -*- THIBODAUX, LA. -*-. Rv: GOOD FOR / -*- / 25 / CTS / * IN TRADE *. Plain edge. Apparently unique. (Tylendia 8337 T-25; Grellman coll.)

L. A. Riviere, dealer in dry goods, groceries, etc., appears in the 1876, 1882 and 1893 directories - though by the latter year the style has become L. A. Riviere & Co. Not in Tylenda, but assigned number shown above by Edmund Tylenda and Cindy Grellman.

JNO. KANE

Vidalia, La.

Rulau	Date	Metal	Size	VG	F	VF	Unc
La-Vi 1	(1881-82)	Brass	23mm	—	50.00	—	—

(All incused): JNO. KANE / (5-pointed Star) / VIDALIA. Rv: Blank. Incised, beaded rim on each side. Plain edge. Apparently unique. (Tylenda 8708 D; Grellman coll.)

John Kane, agent, is listed in the 1882 directory as proprietor of a saloon.

CHAS. WISE

Waterproof, La.

Rulau	Date	Metal	Size	VG	F	VF	Unc
La-Wt 1	(1888-90)	Brass	28mm	—	—	50.00	—

CHAS. WISE, / (Flowers) / WATERPROOF. Rv: GOOD FOR * / ONE / *** / DRINK. Plain edge.

Charles Wise was listed as a general merchant in Waterproof (Tensas Parish) in the 1890 and 1893 business directories.

F. A. DUNN

Wilson, La.

Rulau	Date	Metal	Size	VG	F	VF	Unc
La-Wi 2	(?)	Brass	24mm	—	—	40.00	—

F. A. DUNN / GOOD FOR / 1 / SHAVE / WILSON LA. Rv: In small circle: AUG. KERN B. S. CO. / ST. LOUIS. (Wright 270)

The August Kern firm in St. Louis made many of the nation's "shave checks." Wilson is in East Feliciana Parish. The 1910 population was 762.

F. MARINO

Louisiana

Rulau	Date	Metal	Size	VG	F	VF	Unc
La-Mr 3	1889	Silver	31mm	—	150.	—	—

F. MARINO. / LA / BELLE / SALOON. 1889 ctsp on U.S. 1858-O Seated Liberty half dollar. (Donald G. Partrick collection; Brunk 26030)

MAINE

L. W. HUNT

Augusta, Maine

Rulau	Date	Metal	Size	VG	F	VF	EF
Me-Au 2	1881	Silver	31mm	—	—	85.00	—

L W HUNT / AUGUSTA / ME ctsp on obverse of Ecuador 1855 4-reales, KM-37. Rv: 1881 ctsp on reverse of the coin. (Stanley Steinberg report; Brunk 20763)

N. H. BRAGG & SON

Bangor, Maine

Rulau	Date	Metal	Size	VG	F	VF	EF
Me-Ba 2	(1867-70)	Copper	29mm	—	100.	—	175.

N. H. BRAGG & SON / BANGOR ME. ctsp on U.S. 1845 Large cent. (Hallenbeck 2.759; Miller Me 1; Brunk 4990)

Norris H. Bragg and Sumner Basford arrived in Bangor from Dixmont, Maine in 1854 and opened a store at 4 Broad Street retailing iron, steel and blacksmith goods. This was called Bragg & Basford. Bragg had been a blacksmith for 20 years in Dixmont before moving to Bangor.

In 1863 Bragg bought out Basford and the business continued as Norris H. Bragg. In January 1867 he admitted his son N. E. Bragg to the business which became known as N. H. Bragg & Son, still at 4 Broad Street and now advertising itself as dealers in Cumberland coal, bar iron, steel, spokes, wheels, anvils, axles, sledges, hammers, blacksmith bellows, Rhode Island horseshoes, malleable iron, castings, etc.

Norris Bragg died in May 1867, leaving the business to his 25-year-old son, who conducted it alone until 1871. In 1871 N. E. Bragg admitted his brother C. F. Bragg, just 21, as a partner, and the business became N. H. Bragg & Sons. By 1875 the Bragg firm had expanded to include an agency for the Philadelphia portable forge and blower then used by "every class of metalworker throughout the country." They also sold Archibald cast iron hubbed wagon wheels, and Worcester & Hunt's drilling machines.

N. H. Bragg & Sons Inc. are listed as being in the wholesale iron business in 1918.

The counterstamps were probably issued in 1867 to announce the new business name, and in any event no later than 1871.

N. H. BRAGG & SON,

DEALERS IN

Cumberland Coal,

BAR IRON AND STEEL,

Spokes, Wheels, Bent Rims, Anvils and Vises, Screw Plates, Sledges and Hammers, Smiths' Bellows, Rhode Island Horse Shoes, Wagon Axles, Nuts and Washers, Side and Elliptic Springs, Rasps and Files, Lever Punches, Carriage Bolts, Malleable Iron, Castings, etc.,

No. 4 Broad Street, Bangor, Me.

Bragg ad in the 1869-70 Bangor city directory.

B. PARKER

Rulau	Date	Metal	Size	VG	F	VF	EF
Me-Ba 10	(1862-69)	Copper	29mm	25.00	—	40.00	—

B. PARKER ctsp on U.S. Large cent. Dates examined: 1823, 1827, 1831, 1837, 1839, 1840, 1843, 1844, 1845, 1846, 1847, 1848, 1850, 1851, 1853, 1856, 1857 F. E. About 210 pieces known. (Duffield 1431; Hallenbeck 16.500; Brunk 30945)

Rulau	Date	Metal	Size	VG	F	VF	EF
Me-Ba 11	(1862-69)	Copper	29mm	—	—	40.00	—

Similar ctsp on U.S. 1853 Large cent, with additional ctsp on each side: A: S. Mc P. (Kovacs coll.)

Ben Parker had a brass foundry and metalworking business at 3 Columbia St. in the 1862-69 period and probably earlier. He made stencils for marking lumber, and had a sideline business of countermarking Large cents (and other coins) with people's names or initials for his customers.

Collector Walter B. Gould of Bangor, who knew Parker when Gould was a youth, once possessed 200 Large cents with the B. PARKER stamp upon them. Parker made the T.J.S. - marked cents for Thomas J. Stewart of Bangor (which see).

F. J. PHILBROOK

Rulau	Date	Metal	Size	VG	F	VF	EF
Me-Ba 13	(1871-90)	Copper	29mm	—	—	40.00	—

F. J. PHILBROOK ctsp on U.S. Large cent, date worn off. (Brunk 31953)

Francis J. Philbrook was a gunsmith and machinist in Bangor 1871-1890. He was involved in several partnerships: Staples & Philbrook, 1874, with Charles G. Staples; and Philbrook & Payne, 1878-1884. In 1877 he patented a fishing reel.

C. V. RAMSDELL

Rulau	Date	Metal	Size	G	VG	F	EF
Me-Ba 14	(1855-67)	Copper	29mm	—	—	40.00	—

C.V. RAMSDELL ctsp on U.S. 1850 Large cent. (Partrick coll.; Brunk 33450)

Charles V. Ramsdell was a general gunsmith 1855-1886. He was part of C.V. & J.W. Ramsdell 1867-70 and Ramsdell & Neal 1871-86.

T. J. S.
(Thomas J. Stewart)

Rulau	Date	Metal	Size	VG	F	VF	EF
Me-Ba 17	(1862-69)	Copper	29mm	—	—	45.00	—

T. J. S. ctsp on U.S. 1839 Large cent. (Duffield 1451; Hallenbeck 20.251; Brunk 39183)

Rulau	Date	Metal	Size	VG	F	VF	EF
Me-Ba 18	(1862-69)	Copper	29mm	—	—	30.00	—

T. J. STEWART ctsp on U.S. Large cent. (Hallenbeck 19.757; Brunk 38310)

Rulau	Date	Metal	Size	VG	F	VF	EF
Me-Ba 19	(1862-69)	Bronze	23mm	—	—	50.00	—

T. J. S. ctsp on obverse of U.S. 1864 2-cent piece. J. W. ROBY ctsp on reverse of coin.

Thomas J. Stewart manufacturered birch bark shooks from 1850 on, which he exported to the Mediterranean area for oranges and lemons. The T.J.S. counterstamp was his business mark for the shooks.

The stencils for Stewart's mark were made by metalworker Ben Parker of Bangor (which see).

Stewart died Feb. 6, 1890. His firm at that time ran 16 mills manufacturing shooks, barrels, spool timber, staves, and acting as commission merchants.

C. A. STRANGE (et al)

Rulau	Date	Metal	Size	VG	F	VF	EF
Me-Ba 33	(1866-69)	CN	22mm	—	75.00	—	—

C. A. STRANGE / W. C. WEBBER / M. W. MUNRO ctsp on U.S. 1866 Shield nickel. (John W. Gregg coll., St. Clair, Mich.)

This may have been a test piece for Strange. The other two names have turned up alone on counterstamped coins; at present they are unknown as personalities.

Rulau	Date	Metal	Size	VG	F	VF	EF
Me-Ba 34	(1866-69)	Copper	29mm	—	75.00	—	—

C. A. STRANGE / J. W. STRANGE / W. C. WEBBER ctsp on U.S. 1818 Large cent. (Brunk 38690/38720/42330)

J. W. STRANGE and
C. A. STRANGE
Bangor, Maine

Rulau	Date	Metal	Size	VG	F	VF	EF
Me-Ba 20	(1859-71)	Copper	29mm	—	—	90.00	—

J. W. STRANGE ctsp on U.S. 1846 Large cent. (Brunk 38720)

Rulau	Date	Metal	Size	VG	F	VF	EF
Me-Ba 21	(1859-71)	Copper	29mm	—	—	150.	—

J. W. STRANGE / STEEL / LETTER / CUTTER / BANGOR, MAINE ctsp on U.S. 1826 Large cent. (Brunk 38725)

Rulau	Date	Metal	Size	VG	F	VF	EF
Me-Ba 22	(1866-69)	Copper	29mm	—	35.00	—	50.00

C. A. Strange ctsp on U.S. Large cents. 8 specimens known. Dates examined: 1803, 1805, 1837, 1842, 1846, 1851, 1853, 1856. (Duffield 1431; Hallenbeck 19.761; Brunk 38690)

Rulau	Date	Metal	Size	VG	F	VF	EF
Me-Ba 24	(1866-69)	CN	19mm	—	40.00	—	60.00

Similar ctsp on U.S. 1857 Flying Eagle, or Indian cents dated 1861 or 1864.

Rulau	Date	Metal	Size	VG	F	VF	EF
Me-Ba 27	(1866-69)	CN	22mm	—	40.00	—	—

Similar ctsp on U.S. Shield nickel. Dates examined: 1866, 1868.

Jirah W. Strange and his son, C. A. Strange, had a brass foundry, diesinking and stencil making business in Bangor, on Central Street. They manufactured brass candlesticks, andirons, etc.

The Stranges countermarked copper cents and other coins, some of them artistically, often in small script letters. Some of their products include: HUNT & MOORE: C. A. SWIFT / C. BIGNAL; W. WILLY / S. S., and their own pieces.

J. W. Strange apparently also conducted a letter-cutting, machinist and britannia ware business in Taunton, Mass. 1859-71.

Collector Walter B. Gould of Bangor in 1921 wrote: "In the 1850's and 60's it seems to have been a common practice to mutilate, mark and hole coins. There was no law against it, and the mutilated coins...were equally as desirable as the perfect and clumsy coins of the period." In the 1860's Gould personally knew two of the countermarkers of Bangor — Ben Parker of 3 Columbia St. and J. W. Strange of Central St., both metalworkers and brass founders.

W. C. WEBBER
Bangor, Maine ?

Rulau	Date	Metal	Size	VG	F	VF	EF
Me-Ba 42	(1860's)	Silver	32.5mm	35.00	—	55.00	—

W. C. WEBBER ctsp on U.S. Bust half dollars. Examined: 1812, 1832. (Brunk 42330)

The stamping was done by C. A. Strange of Bangor, which see.

SAGADAHOCK HOUSE
Bath, Maine

Rulau	Date	Metal	Size	G	VG	F	EF
Me-Bt 2	(?)	Silver	31mm	—	—	50.00	—

SAGADAHOCK HOUSE ctsp on U.S. 1876 half dollar. (Gould 41; Brunk 35560)

For many years this Gould-listed counterstamp defied all efforts at attribution, partly because Maurice Gould listed the stamp as SAGADA HOCKHOUSE instead of SAGADAHOCK HOUSE. Your author admits he never learned what a "hockhouse" might have been.

In 1987, while perusing a marvelous old book which came into my possession, the 1839 edition of John Hayward's *The New England Gazetteer.* I learned that Sagadahock, an Indian name, was the name once used to describe the area at the mouth of the Kennebec River.

According to the *Gazetteer,* in 1607 a group of colonists of the Plymouth Company chartered by King James I of England landed at Sagadahock (the mouth of the Kennebec). The colony of 108 men was led by Captain George Popham and Captain Raleigh Gilbert and landed in August on the coast near the island of Monheagan. The colony did not prosper and was abandoned in one year.

Years later, in 1630, Biddeford was settled, and then Saco in 1631. Originally they were united, but later became separate cities in York County, Maine.

Dr. Gregory Brunk finally located this 19th century hotel in Bath, Maine.

W. R. FIELD
Brunswick, Maine

Rulau	Date	Metal	Size	VG	F	VF	Unc
Me-Br 3	(?)	WM	28mm	—	—	90.00	—
	W. R. FIELD / . BRUNSWICK . ME . . around empty circle. MAINE CENTRAL DINING ROOM / . around empty central circle. Numeral 75 incused on each side. Plain edge. Rare.						

W. PLACE

Charleston, Maine

Rulau	Date	Metal	Size	VG	F	VF	EF
Me-Ch 3	(1862-79)	Copper	29mm	60.00	—	90.00	—
	W. PLACE ctsp on U.S. Large cent. Dates examined: 1818, 1834, 1838. Only 3 known. (Brunk 32270)						
Me-Ch 4	(1862-79)	Copper	29mm	65.00	—	90.00	—
	W. PLACE ctsp on reverse of U.S. 1818 Large cent. XIX STEEL BACK ctsp on opposite side of the coin,						

William S. Place was a percussion gun maker of Charleston, Maine, from 1862 to 1879. The marks are some of his lockplate markings. (References: Frank Sellers, and Arcadi Gluckman)

CHESTER GREENWOOD & CO.

Farmington, Maine

Rulau	Date	Size	VG	F	EF	Unc	
Me-Fa 1	(1873-89)	Brass	24mm	5.00	7.50	12.50	20.00
	CHESTER GREENWOOD & CO. / MFERS. / FARMINGTON, MAINE. Rv: IF YOU WANT THE / BEST / GET / GREENWOODS / EAR PROTECTORS / FOR 25 CTS / EVERYWHERE. (Miller Me 4)						

Chester Greenwood invented the earmuff at age 15 in 1873. His company's tokens are one of the most easily available of 19th century Maine pieces.

(Rooster)

Lewiston, Maine

Rulau	Date	Metal	Size	VG	F	VF	EF
Me-Le 3	ND	CN	22mm	125.	—	175.	—
	(Rooster) / LEWISTON / ME. ctsp on U.S. 1867 or 1869 Shield nickel. LEWISTON / ME. ctsp on opposite side of the coin. (Kirtley Oct. 1990 price list; Brunk 24443)						

ORONO

Orono, Maine

Rulau	Date	Metal	Size	VG	F	VF	EF
Me-Oo 1	(?)	Copper	29mm	—	30.00	—	—
	ORONO ctsp with interlocking leters in cross form on both sides of U.S. 188- Large cent. (Dwight B. Demeritt collection, Brooklyn, N.Y.)						

Orono is a university town.

G. L. BAILEY

Portland, Maine

Rulau	Date	Metal	Size	VG	F	VF	EF
Me-Po 1	(1865-1905)	Silver	32.5mm	200.	—	300.	—
	G. L. BAILEY / (flintlock pistol) / ctsp on U.S. Bust type half dollar. (Gould 3; Brunk 1830)						

Gilbert L. Bailey was a sporting goods dealer in business from 1849 to 1904. He held 21 patents on reloading tools, door checks, fishing reels and a secret ballot box.

Rulau	Date	Metal	Size	VG	F	VF	EF
Me-Po 2	(?)	Copper	29mm	60.00	—	90.00	—
	Similar ctsp on U.S. Large cent. Examined: 1833, 1839.						

G. L. BAILEY & J. W. SAWYER

Rulau	Date	Metal	Size	G	VG	F	EF
Me-Po 4	(1850)	Copper	29mm	—	—	200.	—
	G. L. BAILEY / J. W. SAWYER ctsp on U.S. 1839 Large cent. (Collection S. L. Steinberg, Malden, Mass.)						

Gilbert L. Bailey and Joshua W. Sawyer were gunsmiths. Sawyer was in business 1844-1850.

E. K. BOOTHBY

Portland, Maine

Rulau	Date	Metal	Size	VG	F	VG	EF
Me-Po 5	(1858-80)	Copper	29mm	—	—	50.00	—
	E. K. BOOTHBY ctsp on U.S. Large cent. Examined: 1828, 1852. (Brunk 4350)						

Edward K. Boothby was a manufacturer of airguns from 1858 to 1899. (See Frank M. Sellers' "American Gunsmiths").

U.S. coins counterstamped D. S. BOOTHBY, dated 1864-75, are reported. They may be connected. One David Boothby was a gunsmith in Livermore, Maine 1870-84.

J. T. BROWN

Portland, Maine

Rulau	Date	Metal	Size	VG	F	VF	EF
Me-Po 6	1867	Silver	38mm	—	—	80.00	—
	J. T. BROWN / PORTLAND CO. 1867 ctsp on Mexico 1866 Maximilian peso. (Brunk 5520)						

The Portland Company, organized 1846, became one of New England's largest foundries. It made locomotives and heavy machinery during most of the 19th century, as well as cannon and ironclad gunboats in the Civil War.

CENTENNIAL ANNIVERSARY

Portland, Maine

Rulau	Date	Metal	Size	VG	F	VF	Unc
Me-Po 7	1886	WM	37.5mm	—	—	30.00	—
	Whale-supported, eagle crested arms, RESURGAM on scroll below. Around: CENTENNIAL ANNIVERSARY OF PORTLAND, MAINE / HELD JULY 4-6 1886. Rv: Within wreath: INCORPORATED / — / AS A TOWN / JULY 4, / 1786. Plain edge. (Zaffern coll.)						

G. A. R. 19 ANNUAL ENCAMPMENT

Rulau	Date	Metal	Size	F	VF	EF	Unc
Me-Po 8	1885	Bronze	27mm	—	—	15.00	30.00
	Grant head left above laurel sprays, ULYSSES S. GRANT above. Rv: CAMP / GRANT / PORTLAND MAINE / 19, ANNUAL / ENCAMPMENT / G . A . R / JUNE 24 25 1885. Plain edge.						
Me-Po 9	1885	Bronze	25mm	—	—	15.00	30.00
	Civilian bust right, GENERAL U.S. GRANT around. Rv: As Me-Po 8. Plain edge.						

The G.A.R. (Grand Army of the Republic) was the principal veterans' organization of the Union forces following the Civil War. This campout took place 20 years after the Civil War ended, while the bulk of the veterans were still vigorous and at the peak of their influence in life.

ULMER & HEER
Portland, Maine

Rulau	Date	Metal	Size	VG	F	VF	EF
Me-Po 20	(1869)	Copper	23mm	—	—	60.00	—

ULMER & HEER (curved) / — / PORTLAND. ME. ctsp on U.S. 1865 Shield 2-cent piece. (PCAC July 1993 sale, lot 101; Brunk 40825)

Ulmer & Heer was a cutlery manufacturing firm established in Portland in 1869. The logotype matches that used on its cutlery wares.

A. D. SWEETSIR
Scarborough, Maine

Rulau	Date	Metal	Size	VG	F	VF	EF
Me-Sb 3	(1862-69)	Copper	29mm	—	25.00	—	45.00
	A. D. SWEETSIR ctsp on U.S. Large cent. Examined: 1821, 1824, 1825, 1828, 1833, 1836, 1837, 1838, 1843, 1845, 1847, 1848, 1853. At least 18 specimens known. (Tanenbaum coll.; Duffield 1431; Hallenbeck 19.766; Brunk 39100)						
Me-Sb 4	(1862-69)	Copper	28mm	—	—	50.00	—
	Similar ctsp on New Brunswick 1854 halfpenny, KM-3.						
Me-Sb 5	(1862-69)	Silver	25mm	—	35.00	—	55.00
	Similar ctsp on U.S. 1855 Seated Liberty quarter. (Koppenhaver Nov. 1983 sale)						

William Swoger attributed these marks in 1991 to Alvin D. Sweetsir of Scarborough, Maine, whose occupation has not been determined. See "An Introduction to Genealogical Numismatic Research" by Swoger in the *TAMS Journal* for June, 1991.

M. B. CYPHERS
Skowhegan, Maine

Rulau	Date	Metal	Size	VG	F	VF	EF
Me-Sk 1	(1859-68)	Silver	18mm	—	—	175.	—
	M. B. Cyphers (upper & lower case incuse letters) ctsp on U.S. 1854 Seated Liberty dime.						
Me-Sk 1A	(1859-68)	Silver	19mm	—	—	175.	—
	M. B. Cyphers (upper & lower case letters) ctsp on U.S. 1832 Bust dime. (Brunk 10500; Rulau coll., ex-Gamer)						

Cyphers was a gunsmith in Skowhegan 1859-1868. He relocated in Greenville, Mich. 1870-1906. It is believed his known counterstamps were issued in Maine.

(Research courtesy Dwight B. Demeritt and Frank Sellers.)

JOSEPH LESSOR
Waterville, Maine

Rulau	Date	Metal	Size	VG	F	VF	Unc
Me-Wa 3	(1874-84)	CN	--mm	—	75.00	—	—

Brunswick-Balke die. Rv: JOSEPH LESSOR / 5. (Kirtley Feb. 1991 price list)

Previously unpublished, this pool maverick is one of the few ever traced to Maine.

A. S. RICHMOND
Winthrop, Maine

Rulau	Date	Metal	Size	VG	F	VF	EF
Me-Wi 6	(?)	Copper	29mm	—	—	150.	—

A. S. RICHMOND / WINTHROP, ME. ctsp on U.S. 1853 Large cent. (Tanenbaum coll.; Brunk 34220)

A. S. Richmond is listed in the 1866 edition of *Bradstreet's Directory* as being in the shoe business.

F. QUEBE
York, Maine

Rulau	Date	Metal	Size	F	VF	EF	Unc
Me-Yo 1	(1865)	WM	22.5mm	—	—	—	2 Known

Washington head right, HUGHES on truncation of bust. Rv: Wide depressed rim around edge; raised central area blank. Within depressed rim: F. QUEBE / (three dots) YORK ME (three dots). Plain edge. (Miller Me 7)

Struck by J. A. Hughes, diesinker of Cincinnati, Ohio.

G. F. FISHER
(Maine ?)

Rulau	Date	Metal	Size	VG	F	VF
Me-Un 1	1879	Copper	29mm	—	175.	—

1879 / G. F. FISHER is ctsp on a U.S. Large cent which has previously been ctsp DR / SHATTUCK'S / WATER CURE / WATERFORD / ME. (Brunk 14245)

One G. Frederick Fisher was a Washington, D.C. gunsmith 1864-67.

C. A. FRENCH
Sandy Point, Maine

Rulau	Date	Metal	Size	VG	F	VF	EF
Me-SP 1	1878	Silver	38.1mm	—	75.00	—	—

C. A. FRENCH / SANDY POINT. / MAINE. / NOV. 28 / 1878 ctsp on U.S. 1878 Morgan silver dollar. (Brunk 15110; PCAC July 1993 sale, lot 929)

MARYLAND

W. R. BAKER
Annapolis, Md.

Rulau	Date	Metal	Size	VG	F	VF	Unc
Md-An 2	(1870's)	Brass	25mm	—	10.00	15.00	—
	Coronet Liberty head left, four stars on coronet, within a wreath, a star above. Rv: W. R. BAKER / * / FRUIT / — *1* — / PACKER / * / ANNAPOLIS, MD. Plain edge. (Miller Md 1; Duffield 3)						
Md-An 4	(1870's)	Brass	18mm	—	—	15.00	—
	Eagle. Rv: As 2, no denomination. Plain edge. (Miller Md 1A)						

PEGGY STEWART
Annapolis, Md.

Rulau	Date	Metal	Size	VG	F	VF	Unc
Md-An 20	1875	WM	24mm	—	—	35.00	—

Ship. Above: PEGGY STEWART, Below: ANNAPOLIS / OCTOBER 19 1774. Rv: Bust left. Around: MARTHA WASHINGTON / BALTO. FEB. 22 1875. Plain edge.

The brig 'Peggy Stewart' arrived at Annapolis harbor with a cargo of tea and other goods on Oct. 14, 1774, and its owner paid the hated duty on tea. Following an angry meeting of patriots Oct. 19, the ship and its cargo were burned to the waterline.

This act was said to "out-Boston Boston" and the Peggy Stewart became a symbol of the independence struggle in Maryland.

(See "Burning of the 'Peggy Stewart'" by Millard Hajek in *Maryland TAMS Journal* for November 1988.)

J. H. R.
(John Henry Robinson)
Anne Arundel County, Md.

The 1874-1885 picker checks of this issuer are catalogued under *U.S. Merchant Tokens 1845-1860*, which see.

L. R. S.
(Larkin R. Shipley)
Anne Arundel County, Md.

The 1874-1885 picker checks of this issuer are cataloged under *U.S. Merchant Token 1845-1860*, which see.

A.C. CO.
(Aughinbaugh Canning Co.)
Baltimore, Md.

Rulau	Date	Metal	Size	VG	F	VF	Unc
Md-Ba 118	(1882-88)	Copper	19.3mm	—	—	7.00	—

(Wavy line) / A.C. Co. / (wavy line). Rv: 1 / BKT. Plain edge. Rarity 5.

F.A. Waidner & Co. were oyster, fruit and vegetable packers at 2307-2311 Boston St., established in 1879. In 1882 Waidner was incorporated with the Aughinbaugh Canning Co., with C.R. Aughinbaugh, manager. The oysters and fruit of this company had an enviable reputation in Europe for uniform good quality, and more than 500 employees were working. In 1886, more than 3,500,000 cans of oysters, fruits and vegetables were processed, and exports were made to Australia, Mexico, South America, Canada and all over the U.S. By 1918 Aughinbaugh was a subsidiary of Torsch Packing Co.

The tokens were "shucker checks" for oysters.

L. A.
(Louis Asbeck)

Rulau	Date	Metal	Size	F	VF	EF	Unc
Md-Ba 1	(1870-78)	Brass	20mm	—	5.00	7.50	—

MYSTIC / L. A. Rv: Numeral 5 within wreath, star at wreath opening at top. Plain edge. (Miller Md 4; Dufield 2)

Louis Asbeck was the proprietor of the Mystic Restaurant at 13 So. Eutaw St. from 1864 through 1878.

W. S. AHERN & J. F. BROADBENT

Rulau	Date	Metal	Size	VG	F	VF	Unc
Md-Ba AA1	(1860's)	Brass	20mm	—	—	Scarce	—

W. S. AHERN & J. F. BROADBENT. / * / OYSTER / & FRUIT / PACKERS / *. Rv: No description available. Plain edge. (R. Lee Barton report)

Oyster packers and fruit canners. Directories from 1870-1899 do not list this firm.

(ANCHOR) HOTEL

Rulau	Date	Metal	Size	F	VF	EF	Unc
Md-Ba A1	(1890's)	Gilt Brass	33mm	—	—	8.00	12.00

Anchor at center, —MEAL CHECK— above, —HOTEL— / 610 & 612 E. PRATT ST. below. Rv: Large numeral 25 within rays. Plain edge. (Courtesy Walt Alcott, Quartz Hill, Calif.)

There are later issues of this hostelry in aluminum. Possibly issued early 1900's.

B. L.
(Baltimore Liederkranz)

Rulau	Date	Metal	Size	VG	F	VF	Unc
Md-Ba 2	(1870's)	Brass	20mm	—	3.00	5.00	10.00

Script monogram B.L. Rv: Numeral 5 in oak and olive wreath, star at top opening. Plain edge. (Miller Md 5; Duffield 4)

Rulau	Date	Metal	Size	VG	F	VF	Unc
Md-Ba 2C	(1870's)	GS	20mm	3.00	5.00	8.50	11.00

As last, but numeral 25. Plain edge. (Miller Md 6; Duffield 5)

The Baltimore Liederkranz, organized 1836, was the oldest of many German singing societies in Baltimore. In 1899 it was merged with the Germania Maennerchor. The B.L. headquarters were at 274 (later 661) West Lexington St.

Baltimore building addresses were completely renumbered in 1886.

H. C. B.
(Charles Betch)

Rulau	Date	Metal	Size	VG	F	VF	Unc
Md-Ba 4	(1870's)	Brass	21mm	—	—	3.50	—

H. C. B. in an arc incused at center of blank field. Rv: Blank. Beaded, incised rim on each side. Plain edge. Rarity 5.

Charles Betch was an oyster packer located at McElderberry's Wharf in Baltimore in the 1870's. His tokens were oyster shucker's checks.

BALTIMORE

Rulau	Date	Metal	Size	VG	F	VF	EF
Md-Ba 5	1868	Copper	29mm	—	—	25.00	—

BALTIMORE 1868 ctsp on U.S. Large cent. (Hallenbeck 2.507; Brunk 2250)

BALTIMORE FESTIVAL

Rulau	Date	Metal	Size	F	VF	EF	Unc
Md-Ba 6	1881	WM	25mm	—	5.00	—	15.00

Statue, BALTIMORE FESTIVAL. Rv: Bird, ORIOLE, 1881. Issued holed. Plain edge.

Rulau	Date	Metal	Size	F	VF	EF	Unc
Md-Ba 6A	1882	WM	35mm	—	5.00	10.00	20.00

Crested and supported city arms, BALTIMORE FESTIVAL above, 1882 below. Rv: Bird in flight to left with elf-like figure astride it. Below: ORIOLE. Plain edge. (Hibler-Kappen 592)

BALTIMORE ORIOLE CELEBRATION

Rulau	Date	Metal	Size	F	VF	EF	Unc
Md-Ba 6C	1882	WM	32.5mm	—	5.00	6.00	11.00

Statue atop memorial. Rv: Oriole flying left at center, BALTIMORE ORIOLE . CELEBRATION above, + SEP. 12. 13. 14. 1882. + below. Plain edge. (Brunk coll.)

S. S. BARNES & CO.

Rulau	Date	Metal	Size	F	VF	EF	Unc
Md-Ba 9	(1867-68)	Brass	21mm	—	—	20.00	30.00

Two oyster shells within a circle of 16 stars. Rv: S. S. BARNES & CO. / OYSTER PLANTERS & / PACKERS / ELLICOTS WHARF / CR WEST & / JACKSON ST / BALTIMORE, MD. Plain edge. (Miller Md 10; Duffield 9)

S. S. Barnes and Co. were in the oyster planting and packing business only from 1867 to 1868. Nothing can be learned from the directories about Barnes in the 1869-74 period, but he was part of the firm of Hunt, Barnes & Co. at 66 Boston St. 1875-1879.

The token is of superb workmanship, one of the most attractive shucker checks of Maryland.

WM. BELT & CO.

Rulau	Date	Metal	Size	VG	F	VF	Unc
Md-Ba 6J	(1876)	Brass	29mm	—	—	30.00	40.00

Eagle displayed, U.S. shield on its breast, 10 stars above, arrows, palm branch and scroll below. Rv: WM. BELT & CO. / MANUFACTURERS / —OF— / CUT SOLES / SIDE & SCRAP LEATHER / FOR SALE / —37— / S. CALVERT ST BALTO. MD. Plain edge. (Miller Md 12; Duffield 11)

William Belt and Co. was formed in 1876 by William Belt and Samuel C. Donaldson. In 1877-1878 Belt conducted the business alone at 52 Light St. The token was cut by F. X. Koehler of Baltimore.

THE B. C. BIBB STOVE CO.

Rulau	Date	Metal	Size	F	VF	EF	Unc
Md-Ba 7	(1889)	Brass	25mm	3.00	5.00	8.00	15.00

Cook stove at center, .THE B. C. BIBB STOVE CO. / BALTIMORE, MD around. Rv: ESTABLISHED 1851 / THE / B. C. BIBB STOVE CO / FIREPLACE HEATERS / COOKSTOVES RANGES / FURNACES &C. / (ornament) / BALTIMORE MD. Plain edge. (Wright 1103; Duffield 12; Miller Md. 13)

Rulau	Date	Metal	Size	F	VF	EF	Unc
Md-Ba 8	(1889)	Copper	25mm	—	5.00	10.00	20.00

As 7. Plain edge. (Duffield 12; Miller Md. 14)

Bentley C. Bibb and H. P. Robbins formed a partnership to manufacture stoves in 1851. It was Bibb & Robbins 1851-1855; Bibb & Co. 1855-1877; Bibb & Son 1877-1889, and B. C. Bibb Stove Co. 1889 to 1918 or later. Bentley C. Bibb died June 23, 1894, aged 79. From 1851 until 1907 or later its location was the same - 39-41 Light St. (renumbered 107-109 in 1886).

BOHEMIAN CEMETERY

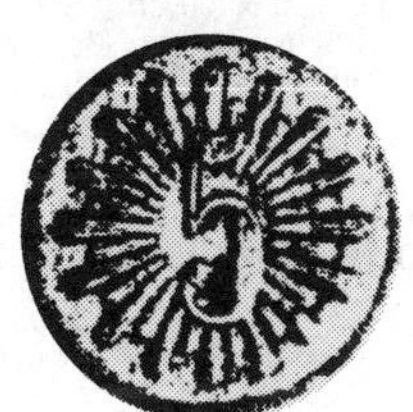

Rulau	Date	Metal	Size	VG	F	VF	Unc
Md-Ba A8	(1884)	Brass	25mm	—	—	Scarce	—

FOR BENEFIT / OF / BOHEMIAN / CEMETERY. Rv: Large radiant numeral 5. Plain edge. (Schenkman S60-B205-5)

The Bohemian National Cemetery (Cesky Narodni Hrbitov) was dedicated Sept. 17, 1884. The tokens were used as scrip to purchase food and drink in the picnic area adjacent to the burial grounds. A 15-cent token is also reported in this series.

Possibly issued 1890-1900.

H. S. BURGES

Rulau	Date	Metal	Size	VG	F	VF	EF
Md-Ba 125	(?)	Copper	29mm	25.00	—	40.00	—

H. S. BURGES ctsp on U.S. Large cents. Dates examined: 1803, 1805, 1807, 1817, 1818, 1820, 1822, 1825, 1827, 1828, 1829, 1831, 1832, 1835, 1837, 1838, 1839, 1840, 1842, 1843, 1844, 1845, 1846, 1847, 1848, 1849, 1850, 1851, 1852, 1853, 1854, 1855, 1857, unknown dates. At least 86 pieces known. (Brunk 5930; Rulau MV 36; Gould 10)

Rulau	Date	Metal	Size	VG	F	VF	EF
Md-Ba 126	(?)	CN	19mm	30.00	—	50.00	—

Similar ctsp on U.S. 1858 Flying Eagle cent. 2 known.

Rulau	Date	Metal	Size	VG	F	VF	EF
Md-Ba 127	(?)	Silver	19mm	—	—	50.00	—

Similar ctsp on U.S. 1830 Bust dime.

Rulau	Date	Metal	Size	VG	F	VF	EF
Md-Ba 128	(?)	Silver	32.5mm	—	—	65.00	—

Similar ctsp on U.S. 1817 Bust half dollar.

Burges was a silver plater. He was a prolific counterstamper. One of his stamped Large cents was earlier stamped by photographer C. W. King (Brunk 22910)

GEO. D. BROOKS

Rulau	Date	Metal	Size	VG	F	VF	Unc
Md-Ba C8	(1870's?)	Brass	19mm	—	—	Scarce	—

GEO. D. BROOKS / 100 / CANS / . CANTON CAN WORKS . Rv: No description available. Plain edge. (R. Lee Barton report)

Manufacturers of tin cans for the Baltimore canning industry.

CALF HIDE ASSOC.

Rulau	Date	Metal	Size	VF	F	VF	Unc
Md-Ba 9	(?)	Brass	24mm	—	—	15.00	—

CALF HIDE ASSOC. (relief) / * 10 (incuse) / OF BALTO. CITY (relief). Rv: CLASS (relief) / D (incuse) /180 (incuse). Plain edge. (Wright 140)

CARROLLTON CLOTHING HOUSE

Rulau	Date	Metal	Size	VG	F	VF	Unc
Md-Ba 10	1876	Brass	25mm	—	—	27.50	—

Liberty head left, wearing coronet bearing four stars, 1876 in exergue. Rv: THE CARROLLTON / 171 / W BALTO ST. / NEXT TO THE / CARROLLTON / HOTEL / CLOTHING HOUSE. Plain edge. (Wright 1661; Miller Md 23; Duffield 20)

The Carrollton Clothing House, as such, does not appear in any of the directories. In that of 1876, and in that year only, is found: 'G. C. Norris, retail clothing, 171 W. Baltimore St.' This would indicate Norris' years of activity were limited to 1875-76.

Dr. Wright called this piece rare in 1900, and Frank G. Duffield did not dispute this claim in 1907. The Fulds, in the 1950's, knew of only two specimens, including their own. The die work is that of J. F. W. Dorman.

CASINO NO. 3

Rulau	Date	Metal	Size	VG	F	VF	Unc
Md-Ba 16	(1870-75)	Brass	19mm	—	—	20.00	40.00

Eagle with outstretched wings at center, CASINO NO. 3. above, * BALTO * below. Rv: Numeral 5 within wreath, star in opening at top. Plain edge. (Miller Md) Rarity 6.

Rulau	Date	Metal	Size	VG	F	VF	Unc
Md-Ba 17	(1870-75)	Copper	19mm	—	—	20.00	40.00

Obverse as last. Rv: Similar to last, but numeral 10. Plain edge. (Miller Md 25). Rarity 6.

Rulau	Date	Metal	Size	VG	F	VF	Unc
Md-Ba 18	(1870-75)	GS	19mm	—	—	20.00	40.00

Similar to last, but numeral 25. Plain edge. (Miller Md 24; Duffield 21). Rarity 6.

The Casino Clubrooms were located at 216 (later 1122) Hartford Ave. and served as headquarters for a political club during the 1870-75 period. The significance of 'No. 3' has not been learned. The striking is by J. F. W. Dorman.

G. D. CLARIDGE & CO.

Rulau	Date	Metal	Size	VG	F	VF	Unc
Md-Ba 20	1875	Brass	--mm	—	—	25.00	—

Liberty head, 1875 below. Rv: G. D. CLARIDGE & CO / DEALERS IN / DAIRY / PRODUCTS / BALTIMORE. (Wright 1366)

CONCORDIA

Rulau	Date	Metal	Size	F	VF	EF	Unc
Md-Ba 11	(1870's)	Copper	22mm	—	5.00	7.50	15.00

Eagle with drooping wings, head turned right, shield on breast, 17 stars above. Rv: CONCORDIA / 5 / .BALTIMORE. (Wright 185; Duffield 31; Miller Md. 39)

Rulau	Date	Metal	Size	F	VF	EF	Unc
Md-Ba 12	(1870's)	Brass	22mm	—	5.00	7.50	15.00

Similar to 11, but numeral 10 on reverse. (Miller Md. 40)

Rulau	Date	Metal	Size	F	VF	EF	Unc
Md-Ba 13	(1870's)	CN	22mm	—	5.00	15.00	20.00

Similar to 11, but numeral 25 on reverse. (Duffield 32; Miller Md. 41)

Rulau	Date	Metal	Size	F	VF	EF	Unc
Md-Ba 14	(1870's)	—	22mm	—	—	25.00	50.00

Similar to 11, but numeral 50 on reverse. (Russ Sears report)

The Concordia German Association was founded 1847 at Western Hall, corner Howard and Lexington Streets. In 1865 its new home — Concordia Opera House and Hall — opened at corner Eutaw and German Streets. The Concordia Opera House burned down June 10, 1892, and the association passed out of existence. In 1868 Charles Dickens gave readings there.

COX

Rulau	Date	Metal	Size	VG	F	VF	Unc
Md-Ba 15	(1870)	Copper	19.5mm	—	—	22.50	30.00

Eagle with drooping wings atop mound of olive branches, 12 stars around. Rv: COX within circular wreath tied with a bow at bottom. Dentilated rims on both sides.

DORMAN'S STENCIL & STAMP WORKS

Rulau	Date	Metal	Size	F	VF	EF	Unc
Md-Ba 22	(1869-71)	Brass	24mm	5.00	7.50	10.00	25.00

J. F. W. DORMAN / — / MAN'F'R OF / PRINTING / — PRESSES — / 21 GERMAN ST. / —*— / BALTIMORE. Rv: DORMAN'S STENCIL & STAMP WORKS / 25 / BALTIMORE . (Duffield 35; Miller Md. 44)

Rulau	Date	Metal	Size	F	VF	EF	Unc
Md-Ba 23	(1869-71)	SB	20mm	—	5.00	10.00	15.00

Obverse similar to 22, but PRINTING PRESSES on two scrolls. Rv: Large numeral 5 surrounded by rays. (Duffield 36; Miller Md. 45)

Rulau	Date	Metal	Size	F	VF	EF	Unc
Md-Ba 25	1875	Brass	20mm	—	5.00	8.00	15.00

Liberty head in coronet left, 1875 below, 13 stars around. Rv: DORMAN'S STENCIL / & / STAMP / WORKS / 19 / GERMAN ST. / BALTIMORE. (Wright 267; Duffield 33; Miller Md. 42)

Rulau	Date	Metal	Size	F	VF	EF	Unc
Md-Ba 26	1875	Brass	20mm	—	5.00	8.00	15.00

As 25, but 19 GERMAN ST. in larger letters. (Duffield 34; Miller Md. 43)

John F. W. Dorman was proprietor of Dorman's Stencil & Stamp Works 1874-1891. This firm was known as Dorman & Thomas 1866-1869 (Dorman and James S. Thomas); J. F. W. Dorman & Co. 1869-1871 (Dorman and William F. Sutz); United States Mfg. Co. 1871-1878, and The J. F. W. Dorman Co. 1891-1918 or later.

The above tokens were issued on the occasion of Dorman occupying his new building at 19 German Street in 1875.

John F. W. Dorman was born in Warsaw, Kentucky in 1836, later moving to St. Louis, where he engaged in several trades. Before the Civil War he was an actor and was associated with others in managing other actors. During the war he was a sutler, and for a time was confined in the Confederates' Libby Prison.

In 1866 in partnership with J. S. Thomas, he opened a stencil cutting and rubber stamp manufacturing business in Baltimore, at 97 West Lombard St. Thomas withdrew in 1869 and William F. Sutz became a partner. The name United States Manufacturing Co. was adopted in 1870 and this was continued until 1879, when Dorman began manufacturing printing presses. In 1874 he erected a large 5-story building at 19 German St., where his enterprises were located until his death on March 26, 1893.

After Dorman's death the business was conducted by a stock company in the Equitable Building at 121 East Fayette St., until that building burned about 1904.

Both the United States Manufacturing Co. and Dorman's Stencil & Stamp Works were in business at the same time in the 1870-1879 period. Dorman was president and principal stockholder of both firms.

(For full information on Dorman, see "The Tokens and Medals Relating to Numismatists and Coin Dealers" in *The Numismatist* for 1905, by Albert R. Frey.)

WM. L. ELLIS & CO.

Rulau	Date	Metal	Size	F	VF	EF	Unc
Md-Ba 28	(1865-70)	Nickel	19mm	—	—	40.00	60.00

Square, compass and G at center, WM. L. ELLIS & CO. around, 6-pointed star below. Rv: 10 / GALL'S at center, 13 stars around. Plain edge.

William L. Ellis was a ship's carpenter at Orleans near Broadway through 1864. In 1865 he formed William L. Ellis & Co., moving to Orleans between Broadway and Ann on Fells Point. The oyster packing firm consisted of Ellis and F.M. Ketchum. The business lasted until 1888.

D. E. F. & CO.
(David E. Foote & Co.)

Rulau	Date	Metal	Size	VG	F	VF	Unc
Md-Ba 29	(1870's)	Brass	Scal 28mm	—	—	25.00	—

(All incused): D. E. F. & CO / MD / 4. Rv: Blank. Incised, beaded rim on each side.

Oyster packers.

G. FALKENSTEIN

Rulau	Date	Metal	Size	F	VF	EF	Unc
Md-Ba 30	(1870's)	Brass	20mm	4.00	6.00	9.00	15.00

Tree at center, GREENWOOD PARK / G. FALKENSTEIN around. Rv: Numeral 10 within wreath. (Duffield 39; Miller Md. 47 1/2)

Rulau	Date	Metal	Size	F	VF	EF	Unc
Md-Ba 31	(1870's)	Brass	20mm	4.00	6.00	9.00	15.00

As 30. (Miller Md. 48)

Rulau	Date	Metal	Size	F	VF	EF	Unc
Md-Ba 32	(1870's)	Brass	—	4.00	6.00	9.00	15.00

As 30, but numeral 5 on reverse. (Miller Md. 49)

Rulau	Date	Metal	Size	F	VF	EF	Unc
Md-Ba 33	(1870's)	GS	20mm	4.00	6.00	9.00	15.00

Similar to 30, but numeral 25 on reverse. (Wright 304; Duffield 40; Miller Md. 50)

George Falkenstein operated a restaurant at 32 East Pratt St. 1867-70, then at Gay and Frederick Streets 1870-90. The Greenwood Park Brewery was located at Belair Road and Oliver St. J. F. W. Dorman cut these tokens.

FOUNDING OF THE CITY

Rulau	Date	Metal	Size	F	VF	EF	Unc
Md-Ba 35	1880	Brass	32mm	—	5.00	8.00	15.00

Facing bust of Calvert, * GEORGE CALVERT * above, THE FIRST LORD OF BALTIMORE below. Rv: Monument at center. 150TH ANNIVERSARY OF THE FOUNDING OF THE CITY / 1730 1880 / OCT. 11TH / OF / * BALTIMORE *. Plain edge.

Rulau	Date	Metal	Size	F	VF	EF	Unc
Md-Ba 35B	1880	Brass	31mm	2.00	3.00	3.50	5.00

Monument and bust, GEORGE CALVERT. Rv: 150TH ANNIVERSARY OF THE FOUNDING OF THE CITY, 1730-1880. Plain edge.

FREE POOL
(Joseph Beard Jr.)

Rulau	Date	Metal	Size	VG	F	VF	Unc
Md-Ba 36	(1883-85)	CN	25mm	—	—	15.00	25.00

(All incused): Elephant at center, FREE above, POOL below. Rv: 33 & 35 / E. BALTIMORE.

CHAS. W. GEEKIE

Rulau	Date	Metal	Size	F	VF	EF	Unc
Md-Ba A36	(1860's)	S/WM	23mm	—	—	400.	—

Two decanters flank fouled anchor, 13 stars in field, LADIES BLUSH above. Rv: * CHAS. W. GEEKIE * / 5 / — / NO. 123 / BALTIMORE ST / *. Plain edge. (Miller Md 57; Duffield 46; Wright 367; H. R. Storer 37)

Rulau	Date	Metal	Size	F	VF	EF	Unc
Md-Ba A36a	(1860's)	GS	23mm	—	—	400.	—

As last. Plain edge. (Miller Md 58)

Rulau	Date	Metal	Size	F	VF	EF	Unc
Md-Ba B36	(1860's)	S/WM	23mm	—	—	400.	—

Similar to last, but '10' at center. Plain edge. (Miller Md 59)

Rulau	Date	Metal	Size	F	VF	EF	Unc
Md-Ba C36	(1860's)	GS	23mm	400.	—	—	—

As last. Plain edge. Only 1 known. (Russ Sears report)

C. W. & F. S. GEEKIE

Rulau	Date	Metal	Size	F	VF	EF	Unc
Md-Ba D36	(1870's)	WM	23mm	—	1000.	—	—

Obverse same as Md-Ba A36, the Chas. W. Geekie card. Rv: Similar to Md-Ba A36, but C. W. & F. S. GEEKIE replaces CHAS. W. GEEKIE. Plain edge. (Wright 367A). This piece has not been examined by the author: Known only from Dr. Wright's description.

Charles W. Geekie was born in Scotland in 1819. He came to northern New York in 1837 with his father. Charles Geekie was connected with large hotels in New York, Philadelphia, St. Louis, New Orleans and Chicago before settling in Baltimore in 1860.

He was in the wholesale and retail liquor business at 123 West Baltimore St. 1860-76. In 1876 he moved to Kent County, Md., to engage in raising stock. He returned to Baltimore 1882, opening a wholesale liquor business at 6 So. Charles St. He moved this to 3 No. Liberty St. in 1884, conducting the business there until his death, Oct. 7, 1892.

The liquor business at 123 W. Baltimore St. was continued for a few years after 1876 by Geekie's sons, Charles W. and Frederick S. Geekie.

GERMANIA MAENNERCHOR

Rulau	Date	Metal	Size	F	VF	EF	Unc
Md-Ba L36	(1870s)	Copper	22mm	—	—	20.00	—

Harp enclosed in wreath, GERMANIA MAENNERCHOR / BALT. around. Rv: Numeral 5 within wreath. (Wright 373)

10 and 25-cent tokens also are known; similar prices.

GOSMAN & CO.

Rulau	Date	Metal	Size	F	VF	EF	Unc
Md-Ba 37	(1868-78)	GS	22mm	5.00	10.00	20.00	45.00

Urn fountain at center, GOSMAN & CO. around, * BALTO. * below. Rv: Numeral 10 within wreath. Plain edge. (Wright 391; Miller Md 63; Duffield 52)

Adam J. Gosman appears as a druggist in 1858 at 194 East Fayette St. In 1860 he moved to 66 No. Eden. Then in 1863-64 he was at Gay and Baltimore Sts., the address of the well-established MacKenzie & Co. drug firm, which he succeeded in 1865, establishing a "family medicine and prescription store."

The name Gosman & Co. was announced in 1868 when he became associated with another token-issuing druggist, John J. Myer (which see), who had joined MacKenzie & Co. in 1856. The address now was 191 Madison Ave. (Myer kept his own business at Fremont and Townsend 1873-78 though associated with Gosman.)

GREENWOOD PARK

Rulau	Date	Metal	Size	VG	F	VF	Unc
Md-Ba 40	(1870's)	Brass	16mm	—	—	9.00	20.00
	Numeral 5 on reverse. (Miller Md. 64 1/2)						
Md-Ba 41	(1870's)	Brass	19mm	—	—	9.00	20.00
	Numeral 10 on reverse. (Miller Md. 64 1/2A)						

Rulau	Date	Metal	Size	VG	F	VF	Unc
Md-Ba 43	(1870's)	Brass	23mm	—	—	200.	300.

Tree with spreading branches separates G --- B. Rv: GREENWOOD PARK / 25 / BALTO. Beaded rim on each side. Plain edge.

The G.B. equals George Bauernschmidt. George Fuld dates this piece to the late 1870's.

This piece appeared as lot 4402 in the Chesterfield sale in Indianapolis, April 3-4, 1981. It is obviously related to the later (1867-1875) George Falkenstein tokens of the Greenwood Park Brewery (Miller 47 1/2) — all using the tree with spreading branches motif.

The 25-cent denomination realized $300 in the 1983 AB&R sale.

GREISENHEIM

Rulau	Date	Metal	Size	F	VF	EF	Unc
Md-Ba 44	1885	Bronze	32mm	—	—	15.00	—

Building at center, GREISENHEIM above, BALTIMORE / 1885. below. Rv: ZUM ANDENKEN / AN DIE / EIN WEIHUNG / DES DEUTSCHEN / GREISENHEIM / IM MAI / 1885 / GEGRUNDET JUNI 30, 1881. Plain edge. Issued holed.

The word 'Greisenheim' means 'Home for the Aged'. The reverse legend translates: 'In memory of the consecration of the German Home for the Aged, May 1885, Founded June 30, 1881'.

JOEL GUTMAN & CO.

Baltimore, Md.

Rulau	Date	Metal	Size	VG	F	VF	Unc
Md-Ba 45	(1886-99)	GS	20mm	—	—	6.00	—

JOEL GUTMAN & CO. / DRY GOODS / -.- / 112 TO 122 / N. EUTAW ST. Rv: 10 (large, rays from behind). (Duffield 55)

Gutman was in business 1886 through 1907, at least.

CHAS. W. HAMILL & CO.

Rulau	Date	Metal	Size	F	VF	EF	Unc
Md-Ba 46	1880	S/WM	29mm	—	8.00	15.00	25.00

Morgan-type Liberty head left, F. X. KOHLER on truncation of neck. Around: CHAS. W. HAMILL & CO. MF. SILVER PLATED WARE. Rv: Baltimore Monument at center, 150TH ANNIVERSARY BALTIMORE CITY around, OCTOBER / 1880 below. Plain edge. (Wright 417; Miller Md 67)

Rulau	Date	Metal	Size	F	VF	EF	Unc
Md-Ba 46A	1880	Gilt/WM	29mm	—	—	—	50.00

As 46. Plain edge.

The head is a remarkably close copy of the Morgan silver dollar's head. The Morgan dollar had been introduced only two years earlier at this point and was still a popular novelty.

H. J. HORN & CO.

Rulau	Date	Metal	Size	VG	F	VF	Unc
Md-Ba 47	(1870's)	Brass	19mm	—	—	25.00	—

H. J. HORN & CO. / 5 / BALTIMORE. Rv: No description available. Plain edge. (R. Lee Barton report)

Oyster packers.

SAMUEL JACKSON

Rulau	Date	Metal	Size	VG	F	VF	EF
Md-Ba 49	(?)	Copper	29mm	—	—	75.00	—

SAMUEL / JACKSON / BALTIMORE ctsp on U.S. Large cent. (Hallenbeck 10.504)

JOHNS HOPKINS COLORED ORPHAN ASYLUM

Rulau	Date	Metal	Size	VG	F	VF	Unc
Md-Ba 51	(1870's)	Brass	20mm	—	—	60.00	—

JOHNS HOPKINS / INCORPORATED / * / 1867 / COLORED ORPHAN ASYLUM. Rv: Thick rod extending almost across diameter, with 14 thick rays emanating from it. Plain edge. (B.A. Robinson Jr. coll., Joppatowne, Md.)

The owner, Bern Robinson, was able to learn only that the building became a hospital about 1937. What purpose the token served is not known.

An aluminum piece of this design with numeral '5' is known. A "10" has been reported.

KENSETT

Rulau	Date	Metal	Size	F	VF	EF	Unc
Md-Ba 55	(1865-75)	Brass	24mm	3.00	5.00	8.00	15.00

(Ornament) / KENSETT / (ornament). Rv: Same as obverse. (Wright 545; Duffield 68; Miller Md. 80)

Thomas Kensett, founder of Kensett & Co., was born in Cheshire, Conn. on Feb. 12, 1814. He came to Baltimore in 1840 and established an oyster and fruit packaging business, using a secret process invented by his father in 1819. At first he was on York Street, then in 1852 he erected a large building on West Falls Avenue, where the business remained. In 1855 Ira B. Wheeler became a partner of Thomas Kensett for a short time. Kensett died Aug. 6, 1877. The business was carried on by his sons and nephews.

FRANCIS X. KOEHLER

Rulau	Date	Metal	Size	F	VF	EF	Unc
Ma-Ba 63	(ca 1878)	Brass	27mm	—	—	150.	Rare

Imitation of Morgan Liberty head left, tiny F X KOHLER below truncation, 13 stars around. Rv: FRANCIS X. KOEHLER / ENGRAVER / & / DIESINKER / * / BALTIMORE. Plain edge. (ANS coll.)

Francis Xavier Koehler was born in Schwabisch Gmund, Wurttemberg, on Oct. 8, 1818. His mother was an engraver of jewelry in Schwabisch Gmund, from whom he learned the art. Later he went to Stuttgart where he apprenticed as a goldsmith and die cutter. He was employed in Stuttgart until 1850.

He emigrated to Baltimore in 1850 and entered business with silver plater Jacob Seeger for about a year. In 1851 he began business as a manufacturing jeweler and die cutter on New Church St. near Sharp. In 1853 he moved to 124 W. Fayette St., and in 1854 to 140 W. Fayette St., remaining there until 1863.

In 1863 he expanded his diecutting business and ceased the manufacture of jewelry, moving to Liberty and Marion Streets, and later to 11 No. Liberty St. where he stayed until 1869. In 1869 he moved to 54 German St. and in 1879 to 20 German St. He retired in 1885 and died March 22, 1886.

His output of medals and tokens is impressive and he was a close friend of U.S. Mint engraver Anthony C. Pacquet who frequently stayed at the Koehler home. Koehler was active in Baltimore German groups and was vice president of the Concordia German Association for many years.

An article on his life and works appeared in the September 1916 *The Numismatist*, written anonymously. At that time and for many years afterward the Koehler store card, Md-Ba 63, was unknown to the collecting world.

J. G. KRAFT & CO.

Rulau	Date	Metal	Size	VG	F	VF	Unc
Md-Ba A63	(1860-80's)	Brass	--mm	—	15.00	—	—

J. G. KRAFT & CO., OYSTER AND FRUIT PACKERS. Rv: 5 within rays. (Schenkman K-191)

LIX

Rulau	Date	Metal	Size	VG	F	VF	Unc
Md-Ba 64	(1883-86)	CN	20mm	—	—	35.00	70.00

LIX within oak wreath. Rv: 5 at center of a circle of 13 6-pointed stars. Plain edge. (Duffield 76)

Rulau	Date	Metal	Size	VG	F	VF	Unc
Md-Ba 64A	(1883-86)	CN	20mm	—	—	35.00	—
	As last, but numeral 10. (Robert Lindesmith coll.)						
Md-Ba 64B	(1883-86)	CN	20mm	—	—	35.00	—
	As last, but numeral 25. Rare. (Robert Lindesmith coll.)						
Md-Ba 64F	(1883-86)	CN	20mm	—	—	50.00	—
	As last, but numeral 100. Rare.						

Julius G. Lix was the steward for the Baltimore Club in the years 1883 through 1886. Lix could not have been unaware that his name LIX, spelled all in capital letters on this handsome token, also stood for the Roman numeral '59'.

The cards are scarce. Though 64 was listed by Duffield, it was not listed by Adams or Miller. Numbers 64A and 64B are catalogued here for the first time. All have fine workmanship, possibly by Francis X. Koehler.

The Baltimore Club was at 187 No. Charles St. (renumbered to 905 No. Charles St. in 1886).

LYON-HALL & CO.

Rulau	Date	Metal	Size	F	VF	EF	Unc
Md-Ba 65	(1884-94)	Brass	25mm	50.00	—	75.00	—

CHINA - LYON-HALL & CO. - JAPAN / BALTIMORE ctsp on border of China 1-cash coin of Ch'ing dynasty. Rv: CHINA-INDIA-JAPAN / MATTING IMPORTERS. ctsp on opposite side border of the coin. Plain edge. About 35 are known. (Brunk; 25455)

Lyon & Co. (J. Crawford Lyon and William A. Lyon) traded in carpets at 236 W. Baltimore St. from 1881 on. In 1884 they admitted John W. Hall and the business became Lyon-Hall & Co. and began trading in imports.

They moved to 8 W. Baltimore St. in 1887 and to 105 Hopkins Place in 1890 and to 6 South St. in 1892. John W. Hall withdrew in 1895 and the name became Lyon Bros. (still J. Crawford and William A. Lyon), importers of matting, fur rugs and linoleum.

Great quantities of the cheap Chinese cash (face value only 1/10 cent) were imported by Chinese-Americans for gambling pieces and as decorations for wicker sewing baskets, etc., so these coins provided a convenient and cheap flan for Lyon-Hall's advertising tokens.

Specimens examined have been 1-cash of Chia Ch'ing (1796-1820), Tientsin Mint, and Ch'ien Lung (1736-95), Peking Board of Revenue Mint and Chengtu Mint. These cash types were once exceedingly common.

T. J. M. & CO.
(Thomas J. Myer & Co.)

Rulau	Date	Metal	Size	VG	F	VF	Unc
Md-Ba A65	(1870's)	Brass	21mm	—	—	Scarce	—

T. J. M. & CO. / (Radiant 5-pointed star) / -*-. Rv: No description available. Plain edge. (R. Lee Barton report)

Oyster packers.

MABLEY & CAREW

Rulau	Date	Metal	Size	F	VF	EF	Unc
Md-Ba B65	(?)	WM	38mm	—	—	20.00	27.50

MABLEY & CAREW'S / (Monument) / LEGAL GUARANTEE. Rv: WE GUARANTEE / THAT / THE GOODS BOUGHT OF US ARE / AS REPRESENTED AND LOWER IN / PRICE THAN THE SAME QUALITY / CAN BE BOUGHT ELSEWHERE SHOULD / YOU BECOME DISSATISFIED AT ANY / TIME WE WILL EXCHANGE THE / GOODS REFUND YOUR MONEY / OR GIVE YOU A REBATE / IN HARD CASH / MABLEY & CAREW. Plain edge. (Wright 640)

MARYLAND EXPOSITION

Rulau	Date	Metal	Size	F	VF	EF	Unc
Md-Ba D65	1889	Aluminum	38mm	—	—	—	25.00

Mustached male bust left. Around: HON. FERDINAND C. LATROBE. / * FIVE TIMES MAYOR. Rv: Building. Around: MARYLAND EXPOSITION / CITY HALL / BALTIMORE. SEPT. 9-14. 1889. Plain edge. (Dillingham coll.)

MARYLAND INSTITUTE

Rulau	Date	Metal	Size	F	VF	EF	Unc
Md-Ba E65	1872	WM	24mm	—	—	22.50	—

Building. Above: INSTITUTED 1847. In exergue: INCORPORATED / 1848. Rv: MARYLAND INSTITUTE. / 25TH / ANNUAL / EXHIBITION / OCT. 1872 / (ornament) / BALTO. MD. Plain edge.

Maryland Institute, specializing in mechanical arts, was founded 1825 and burned down 1835. It was reorganized 1848 and erected its own building (shown on the medalet) in 1851 on Marsh Market Place. This too was destroyed by fire 1904 and two new buildings were erected.

L. McMURRAY & CO.

Rulau	Date	Metal	Size	F	VF	EF	Unc
Md-Ba 66	(1860-69)	Brass	19mm	—	—	40.00	100.
	L. McMURRAY & CO. / 5 / CENT / CHECK. Rv: Numeral 5 surrounded by rays. Plain edge.						
Md-Ba 67	(1870-80)	Brass	20mm	—	—	10.00	15.00
	L. Mc. M. / & CO. / *. Rv: Numeral 5 within circular wreath. Plain edge.						
Md-Ba 67A	(1870-80)	Copper	20.5mm	—	—	10.00	15.00
	As last, but slightly larger flan. Plain edge.						

L. McMurray and Co. (Louis McMurray, Charles E. Houghton and A.B. Ellis), oyster and fruit packers, were located at 1, 3, 5 and 7 Cross St. from 1860 to 1870.

The Baltimore directories listed the firm as L. Mc.M. & Co. at 254-256 West Biddle St. 1870-1889. At the same time, Louis McMurray & Co. was listed at 1-7 Cross St., 1870-89. After 1889 the companies became vegetable packers; a branch packed corn in Frederick, Md. The company does not appear in the 1890 directory.

None of these McMurray checks (used for tallying oyster shucking, etc.) were listed in Wright, Adams-Miller or Duffield.

Baltimore had 27 oyster and fruit packers in 1860, 85 in 1871, 101 in 1879, 110 in 1881, 86 in 1889, and only 15 in 1890. The demise of oyster packing affected most packer firms by ending their business lives; McMurray switched to vegetable canning.

By 1918 McMurray was no longer listed in either Baltimore or Frederick. A Frederick City Packing Co., fruit and vegetable packers, was listed in 1918, but there may be no connection.

(See "The Canning Industry in Baltimore" by M. and G. Fuld in *Token Collector's Pages* (Boston, 1972, pages 125-129) for an excellent exposition on this subject.

J.J. MEYER & CO.
(Actual name: Myer)

Rulau	Date	Metal	Size	F	VF	EF	Unc
Md-Ba 69	(1873-78)	GS	22mm	15.00	25.00	—	50.00

Urn fountain at center, J.J. MEYER & CO. above, .BALTO. below. Plain edge. (Miller Md 89A)

Myer's name is misspelled on the token. For details, see under Gosman & Co., Baltimore.

B. MOMENTHY

Rulau	Date	Metal	Size	VG	F	VF	Unc
Md-Ba 70	(1870)	Copper	20mm	—	10.00	—	—

B. MOMENTHY / FAYETTE HALL / BALTIMORE. Rv: Numeral 5 within wreath. Plain edge. (Miller Md 91; Duffield 85)

Rulau	Date	Metal	Size	VG	F	VF	Unc
Md-Ba 70C	(1870)	Brass	20mm	—	10.00	—	—

Obverse as 70. Rv: Similar to 70, but no numeral at center. (Miller Md 92)

Bruno Momenthy was proprietor about 1870 of Fayette Hall (also known as Central Hall) at 28 No. Gay St.

Bruno Momenthy (the same man, or a successor ?) was listed in 1917-1918 as a "wholesale liquor dealer and restaurateur" in the *R.G. Dun Business Register.*

MOORE & BRADY

Rulau	Date	Metal	Size	VG	F	VF	Unc
Md-Ba 71	(1875)	Brass	24mm	12.00	16.00	22.00	45.00

Coronet Liberty head left, four stars on coronet, circle of stars around. Rv: Raised rectangle at center (a can?) between ornaments, MOORE & BRADY above, BALTIMORE below. Plain edge. (Miller Md 95; Duffield 88; Schenkman M194)

Rulau	Date	Metal	Size	VG	F	VF	Unc
Md-Ba 71B	(1875)	Brass	24mm	—	16.00	22.00	45.00

As 71, but ctsp on obverse: #3 Y (probably for 'Number 3 Yard'). Plain edge. (Miller Md 96)

Rulau	Date	Metal	Size	VG	F	VF	Unc
Md-Ba 72	(1875)	Brass	18mm	—	15.00	20.00	30.00

MOORE & BRADY / * / FIVE / * / BALTIMORE. Rv: Blank. Plain edge. (Miller Md 96A; Duffield 89)

George W. Moore formed Geo. W. Moore & Co. in 1872 at 54 No. High St., oyster packers. In 1875 he admitted James H. Brady and the firm became Moore & Brady, located at the foot of Montgomery St. Francis X. Koehler struck their tokens. The business survived to 1906 or later.

For complete data, see "Maryland Canning Tokens" by Jane Sears in Winter 1987 *Maryland TAMS Journal.*

NEW YORK CLOTHING HOUSE

Rulau	Date	Metal	Size	F	VF	EF	Unc
Md-Ba 79	1889	WM	39.5mm	7.00	10.00	15.00	25.00

Monument separates SEPT. 12. — SEPT. 12. / 1814. — 1889. Around: ANNIVERSARY / * BATTLE OF NORTH POINT. *. Rv: SOUVENIR (on scroll) / OF THE / NEW YORK / CLOTHING / HOUSE / BALTIMORE, MD. Plain edge. (Miller Md 101; Duffield 90)

New York Clothing House was established in 1875. In 1887 it relocated at 102 East Baltimore St. It was still in business in 1918, owned by the Rosenfeld Brothers.

NONPAREIL

Rulau	Date	Metal	Size	F	VF	EF	Unc
Md-Ba 80	(1867-70)	Nickel	20mm	—	5.00	10.00	20.00

Liberty head in Phrygian cap left, 13 stars around. Small PJH below head. Rv: NONPAREIL / * 5 * / BALTIMORE. (Wright 762; Miller Md. 99)

Rulau	Date	Metal	Size	F	VF	EF	Unc
Md-Ba 81	(1867-70)	Nickel	20mm	—	5.00	12.00	20.00

As 80, but ctsp B.A. (Miller Md. 100)

Struck by Peter H. Jacobus of Philadelphia. The Nonpareil Association was a social club from 1867 to 1870, headquartered at the corner of Bond and Bank Streets. The French word "nonpareil" means matchless, or unparalleled.

WM. NUMSEN & SONS

Rulau	Date	Metal	Size	VG	F	VF	Unc
Md-Ba 83	(1870's)	Brass	24mm	—	—	8.00	20.00

Coronet Liberty head left within wreath. Rev: Large radiant N at center, WM NUMSEN & SONS around, ornament below. Plain edge.

Rulau	Date	Metal	Size	VG	F	VF	Unc
MD-Ba 84	(1870's)	Brass	21mm	—	—	4.00	20.00

Large N in chief of U.S. shield, at center, palm wreath around. Rv: W. N. / & / SONS within circle of 13 6-pointed stars. Plain edge. (Wright 1259; Miller Md 102)

Probably both tokens were struck by Dorman in Baltimore.

William Numsen & Sons Inc. were still in the oyster and fruit packing business in Baltimore in 1918. They had a branch at Asbestos in Carroll County, and other branches. In 1918 there was another Baltimore firm, Numsen & Davis, vegetable packing and canned goods. N&D had a branch at Benedict in Charles County.

Numsen, Carroll & Co. were at 18 Light Street in 1876. Established 1847, they were oyster and fruit packers.

O'NEILL & CO.

Rulau	Date	Metal	Size	VG	F	VF	Unc
Md-Ba 200	(1869-73)	CN	25mm	—	—	20.00	25.00

O'NEILL & CO. / * 1 * / GAL. / CANTON. Rv: REDEEMABLE / * / FROM / SHUCKERS / * / ONLY. Plain edge. (Miller Md 106; Duffield 95; Wright 788)

Canton was the southeastern section of Baltimore, between Patterson Park and the harbor, Boston Street being the main thoroughfare.

O'Neill and Co. was formed in 1869 by James H. O'Neill, F. Wehr and H. Wehr. The Wehrs withdrew in 1870. The business was at 112 Boston St. until 1873, when it apparently ended its corporate life.

This is one of the most explicit shucker checks of Baltimore as regards redemption. Dr. Wright called it rare in 1898.

ORDER OF THE IRON HALL

Rulau	Date	Metal	Size	F	VF	EF	Unc
Md-Ba 201	1889	Lead	36mm	—	—	12.50	—

Safe at center, $1000 / 76 on its front. SEVENTH ANNIVERSARY — NNER BRANCH NO. 76 above, BALTO, MD. APR. 8, 1889 below. Rv: Bust of man at center, ORDER OF THE IRON HALL above, F. D. SOMERBY SUPREME JUSTICE below. Plain edge.

Collector William E. Hamm, Bloomington, Ind., a specialist in Iron Hall memorabilia, points out that Iron Hall tokens also originated in Indiana and in Washington, D.C., as well as other locations.

PATAPSCO FRUIT BUTTER CO.

1876 Centennial Tokens

Reverse type 1: * PATAPSCO FRUIT BUTTER CO. * / NO. 27 / SOUTH / * / LIBERTY ST / BALTIMORE, / MD. (All 23mm; plain edge)

Rulau	Obv	Rev	Metal	F	VF	EF	Unc
Md-Ba 205	A	1	WM	5.00	8.00	15.00	40.00
	(Wright 795; Miller Md 113; Duffield 100						
Md-Ba 206	B	1	WM	5.00	8.00	15.00	40.00
	(Miller 109; Duffield 97)						
Md-Ba 206	A B	1	Copper	—	—	17.50	55.00
Md-Ba 206	B B	1	Brass	—	—	20.00	55.00
Md-Ba 207	D	1	WM	—	—	17.50	40.00
Md-Ba 208	E	1	WM	—	—	15.00	40.00
	(Miller 114; Duffield 101)						
Md-Ba 209	F	1	WM	—	—	15.00	40.00
	(Miller 115; Duffield 102)						
Md-Ba 210	G	1	WM	—	—	15.00	40.00
	(Miller 112; Duffield 99)						
Md-Ba 211	H	1	WM	—	—	15.00	40.00
	(Miller 110; Duffield 98)						
Md-Ba 211	A H	1	Brass	—	—	20.00	55.00
	(Miller 111)						
Md-Ba 212	J	1	WM	—	—	20.00	40.00
	(Miller 117)						
Md-Ba 213	K	1	WM				
	Not confirmed						

The Patapsco Fruit Butter Co. apparently existed under that name only in the Centennial year, 1876. It comprised Mrs. L.F. Munder and Maurice P. Munder. It was a subsidiary of C.F. Munder & Brother, confectioners, at the same address, 27 So. Liberty St., which advertised that year it was "also proprietors of the Patapsco Fruit Butter Co."

Charles F. Munder, a baker and confectioner, founded the parent firm about 1820. From 1856 to 1878 it was known as C.F. Munder & Bro. The firm, at the same address for 58 years, was dissolved in 1878.

PLATT & CO.

Rulau	Date	Metal	Size	F	VF	EF	Unc
Md-Ba 216	(1875)	Brass	19mm	—	—	22.50	—

PLATT & CO / 3/ * BALTO *. Rv: Same as obverse. (Wright 839 1/2; Miller Md 121). Also known in copper.

Rulau	Date	Metal	Size	F	VF	EF	Unc
Md-Ba 216A	(1875)	Brass	19mm	—	—	22.50	—

As 216, but numeral 5. (Duffield 104; Miller Md 119)

Platt & Co. was organized in 1864 on the south side of the Basin, adjoining the city yard. Landra Beach Platt was the founder. These were oyster shucker checks.

POST OFFICE

Rulau	Date	Metal	Size	F	VF	EF	Unc
Md-Ba 220	1889	Gilt/B	25.5mm	—	—	—	15.00

Building at center, POST OFFICE BALTIMORE, MD. above, DEDICATED SEP. 12, 1889 below. Rv: Sailing war vessels at sea bombarding fortress in foreground. Above: BOMBARDMENT OF FORT McHENRY. Below: 1814. Plain edge.

PRICE BROS.

Rulau	Date	Metal	Size	VG	F	VF	Unc
Md-Ba 85	1866	CN	19.4mm	—	—	25.00	—

Oyster at center, ONE GALLON above, * OYSTERS * below. Rv: PRICE BROS. / 1866 / * BALTO. *. Plain edge. Rarity 6. (Miller Md. 122; Wright 848; Duffield 105)

Rulau	Date	Metal	Size	VG	F	VF	Unc
Md-Ba 86	1866	CN	19.4mm	—	—	25.00	—

Obverse as last. Rv: PRICE BROS. & CO. / 1866 / * BALTO. *. Plain edge. Rarity 6. (Miller Md. 123; Wright 849; Duffield 123)

John S. and Joseph Price were members of the firm of Price Brothers, oyster and fruit packers, at the foot of Cross Street, from 1866-1869. The 1866 date in the first instance is probably the date of issue as well as the establishment date of the firm; the second token was probably issued one or more years later.

PRINGSHEIM

Rulau	Date	Metal	Size	VG	F	VF	Unc
Md-Ba 87	(1865-66)	S/Brass	15mm	—	—	35.00	—

Cylindrical object within circle of 12 stars at center, PRINGSHEIM above, BALTIMORE below. Rv: ONE / WHITE within wreath. Plain edge. (Miller Md 124; Duffield 107)

"One White" equaled "One Beer." Moritz Pringsheim about 1865-66 was a brewer of Berlin White Beer. He was also proprietor of a Restaurant at 16 So. Frederick St.

P.J. REID

Rulau	Date	Metal	Size	VG	F	VF	Unc
Md-Ba 89	(1885-90)	CN	30mm	3.00	5.00	10.00	—

(All incuse) P.J. REID / 65 (numeral very large). Rv: Blank. Plain edge. (Miller Md 129; Duffield 110)

Patrick J. Reid ran a restaurant at 2 McClellan St. from 1885 to 1890. Probably other incuse numerals exist, but none have been reported. This piece may be quite scarce.

SCHUTZEN PARK

Rulau	Date	Metal	Size	F	VF	EF	Unc
Md-Ba 90	(?)	Copper	20mm	2.50	4.00	7.50	20.00

Crossed rifles above a target. No wreath. SCHUTZEN PARK BALTO. around. Rv: Large 5 in wreath, star at top. (Duffield 121; Miller Md. 141)

Rulau	Date	Metal	Size	F	VF	EF	Unc
Md-Ba 91	(?)	Copper	20mm	5.00	8.00	10.00	20.00

Obverse as 141. Rv: Blank. (Miller Md. 141A)

6 BALTM.

Rulau	Date	Metal	Size	VG	F	VF	EF
Md-Ba 94	(?)	Copper	23mm	—	—	25.00	—

6 (four dotted lines) / BALTM. ctsp on U.S. Half cent. Dates examined: 1797, 1825, 1834, 1854. (Brunk 2260)

The four dotted lines in the ctsp represent either a fireplace grate or an oyster crate. If the latter, this might be a work check.

JOHN A. SHRIVER CO.

Rulau	Date	Metal	Size	VG	F	VF	EF
Md-Ba 92	(?)	Brass	23mm	—	—	—	15.00

Eagle. Rv: JOHN L. SHRIVER / BROS / 307 / W PRATT / ST. (Wright 982)

SMITH & WICKS

Rulau	Date	Metal	Size	VG	F	VF	Unc
Md-Ba 95	(1870's)	Brass	18mm	—	—	25.00	—

Seated Liberty, 11 stars above (imitation of U.S. dime). Rv: Central circular design, SMITH & WICKS above, . BALTO . . below. Plain edge. (John Cheramy coll.)

On the specimen reported, the counterstamped initials A K appear on obverse.

SOC. DEM. T. UNION

Rulau	Date	Metal	Size	VG	F	VF	Unc
Md-Ba 96	(?)	Brass	19mm	—	—	20.00	—

Owl above scroll inscribed: S.D.T. / BALT. Rv: SOC. DEM. / T. UNION / 5. (Wright 1014)

L. C. SPENCER & CO.

Rulau	Date	Metal	Size	VG	F	VF	Unc
Md-Ba A96	(?)	CN	22mm	—	—	20.00	—

Shield, L. C. SPENCER & CO. *. Rv: Oyster, ONE GALLON. Plain edge. (Wright 1024)

GEO. P. STEINBACH

Rulau	Date	Metal	Size	VG	F	VF	Unc
Md-Ba 200	(?)	Brass	33.5mm	—	85.00	150.	250.

Liberty head left, LIBERTY on her coronet. Around: JMPORTER OF TOYS & FANCY GOODS / *. Rv: American eagle displayed, and radiant oval of stars as crest. Around: GEO. P. STEINBACH / * BALTIMORE, MD. *. Reeded edge. About 4 pieces known. (Kurth; Rulau-Fuld; Fauver 163a & b; Wright 1047)

Rulau	Date	Metal	Size	VG	F	VF	Unc
Md-Ba 201	(?)	Brass	27.5mm	—	16.00	35.00	70.00

Similar to 200, in smaller format. More than 75 pieces known. Reeded edge. (Kurth; Rulau-Fuld, Fauver 162a & kpa)

Varieties of both pieces are known. Steinbach imported these counters from Lauer of Nuremberg, Germany. Both are close imitations of U.S. $20 and $10 gold coins.

TEUTONIA CLUB

Rulau	Date	Metal	Size	VG	F	VF	Unc
Md-Ba C96	(1870's)	Brass	25mm	—	—	25.00	—

TEUTONIA / O / CLUB / O / BALTO CO. Rv: Numeral 25 within wreath. (Wright 1098). A "5" is also known; similar price.

CHAS. TREUSCH

Rulau	Date	Metal	Size	F	VF	EF	Unc
Md-Ba 97	(1868-70)	Brass	20mm	—	4.00	9.00	20.00

Liberty head in Phrygian cap left; small P.H.J. below truncation of neck. 13 stars around. Rv: CHAS. TREUSCH / 5 / * BALTIMORE *. (Wright 1160; Duffield 145; Miller Md. 170)

Rulau	Date	Metal	Size	F	VF	EF	Unc
Md-Ba 98	(1868's-70)	Lead	--mm	—	15.00	—	—

Flower with 12 petals. Rv: As reverse of 97. (Duffield 146; Miller Md. 171)

Struck by Peter H. Jacobus of Philadelphia. Charles Treusch began business 1868 as an oyster and fruit packer. Previously for several years he had been a member of the firm of Treusch, Schoenberg & Co. He died Feb. 9, 1903, having been born in Germany in 1828.

ROBERT TURNER & SON

Rulau	Date	Metal	Size	G	VG	F	EF
Md-Ba 105	(1867)	Silver	38mm	—	—	125.	—

ROBERT TURNER & SON ctsp on U.S. 1867 silver dollar reverse. (Gould 7; Duffield 147; Brunk 40620; Miller Md 172)

Robert Turner was engaged in the flour, feed and lime business at 43 So. Frederick St. In 1867 Harry F. Turner, a son, was admitted to the business, which may have been honored by this counterstamp. The firm survived to 1907 or later. In 1918 Turner & Owens, commission merchants, were apparent successors.

It is possible this item exists only as an embossed shell card, not a counterstamped coin.

U.S. MANF/G. CO.

Rulau	Date	Metal	Size	VG	F	VF	Unc
Md-Ba 110	1872	GS	20mm	—	8.00	15.00	27.50

U.S. MANF'G CO / STEEL / STAMPS , / STENCILS &C / 97 / W. LOMBARD ST. / BALTIMORE. Rv: MARYLAND INSTITUTE / 25TH / EXHIBITION / OCT. 1872. BALTO. MD. Plain edge. (Wright 1172; Duffield 149; Miller Md 174)

Rulau	Date	Metal	Size	VG	F	VF	Unc
Md-Ba 110A	1872	Brass	20mm	—	8.00	15.00	27.50

As 110. Plain edge. (Miller Md 175)

Rulau	Date	Metal	Size	VG	F	VF	Unc
Md-Ba 111	1872	Brass	20mm	—	—	10.00	30.00

As 110A, but ctsp with numeral '5'. Plain edge. (Duffield 149; Miller Md 176)

See J.F.W. Dorman under Baltimore in this reference.

UBV MONOGRAM
Baltimore, Md.

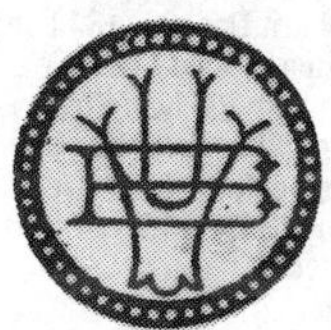

Rulau	Date	Metal	Size	VG	F	VF	Unc
Md-Ba 108	(1875)	Brass	21mm	—	—	Scarce	—

Unusual UBV monogram. Incised, beaded rim. (Millard W. Hajek report)

UBV = Unkel Braesig Verein, a German singing society formed in 1875.

Rulau	Date	Metal	Size	VG	F	VF	Unc
Md-Ba 109	(1875)	CN	21mm	—	—	—	—

As 108. (Russ Sears report)

F.A. WAIDNER & CO.

Rulau	Date	Metal	Size	VG	F	VF	Unc
Md-Ba 115	(1879-82)	Copper	23.5mm	—	—	10.00	—

F.A. WAIDNER & CO. / (ornament) around blank center. Rv: Blank. Plain edge. Rarity 8.

GEO. W. WEBB & CO.
Baltimore, Md.

Rulau	Date	Metal	Size	VG	F	VF	EF
Md-Ba 120	(1870's)	Copper	21mm	—	—	75.00	—

GEO. W. WEBB & CO / ·*· / BALTO. ctsp on Oldenburg 1865-B 3-schwaren. Also on same side (obverse) is another stamp, C. S. RAIT and an illegible mark. (Van Ormer sale 2871)

American counterstamps on minor coins of the Grand Duchy of Oldenburg in Germany are virtually unknown, but the 3-schwaren might have circulated as an undersized American 2-cent piece. The U.S. 2-cent piece measures 23mm.

George W. Webb & Co. in 1871 was located at Light and Baltimore Streets. They dealt in silverware.

PACKING AND CANNING WAGES

In Baltimore in the 1882-1885 period, these wages for a steady expert female worker prevailed: (Based on a 12-hour day)

June peas (shucked)	**6 cents per gallon (20 gallons per day) or $1.20 per day**
Strawberries (capped)	**1 cent per box (80 boxes per day) or 80 cents per day**
Tomatoes (peeled)	**5 cents per 12-quart bucket (28 buckets per day) or $1.40 per day**
Peaches (peeled)	**25 cents per box (6 boxes per day) or $1.50 per day**
Apples or Pears (peeled)	**Same as Peaches**

Female cannery workers made about $4.50 per week.

Male workers made more, depending on the nature of the work. Processor $3.50 per day, capper $2 per day, can varnishers $1.25 per day. Female can labelers received only 10 cents an hour, or $1.20 per 12-hour day.

E.J.H.
(Edward J. Hines)
Bodkin Point, Md.

Rulau	Date	Metal	Size	VG	F	VF	Unc
Md-Bo 3	(1880's)	Brass	**	—	—	5.00	—

** Oct 19mm.

E.J.H stamped on plain flan with recessed rim all around. Rv: Blank, but recessed rim. Plain edge.

Edward James Hines III (1822-1926), used these picker checks about the 1880's and perhaps later.

W. & SON
(Wallace & Son)
Cambridge, Md.

Rulau	Date	Metal	Size	VG	F	VF	Unc
Md-Ca 8	(1880's)	Brass	29.5mm	—	3.50	4.50	7.00

(All incused): W & SON / 4. Rv: Blank. Incised, dentilated rim on each side. Plain edge.

Rulau	Date	Metal	Size	VG	F	VF	Unc
Md-Ca 8A	(1880's)	Brass	29.5mm	—	—	3.50	5.50

As last, but incused on blank with incised, beaded rim on both sides instead of the dentilated variety of 8.

James Wallace & Son were in the cannery business in Dorchester County 1870-1919. Established on Cambridge Creek, they were the pioneer oyster, fruit and vegetable packers in the county. From 1904 on the firm was known as Wallace Packing Co. In the early days they had two buildings (one 95 by 50 feet and another 95 by 145 feet) and several hundred feet of wharf.

James Wallace died in 1903 and the business was taken over by James and Brent Waddell and John G. Mills. In 1919 Phillips Packing Co. bought the firm and it became Factory D of the giant Phillips canning enterprise.

Other W & Son checks are reported, a round brass piece, 19mm, numeral 5, and octagonal brass piece, 24mm, numeral 9. All the Wallace tokens were used as shucker or packer checks to record the labors of its workers (Burton D-159)

One of the earliest packers on the eastern shore of Maryland was Colonel James Wallace (1818-1887), who associated his son James (II) (1850-1903) in the business with him. In 1896 the company's capacity had risen to 25,000 cans a day. Their labels included ABBSCO BRAND (named for an Indian tribe) and PRIDE OF CAMBRIDGE.

Apparently a good-sized hoard came on the market, as pieces of Md-Ca 8 could still be obtained in average condition in 1993 for as little as $2. (Dick Grinolds report)

R. L. & CO.
(Rice Lamotte & Co.)
Chestertown, Md.

Rulau	Date	Metal	Size	VG	F	VF	Unc
Md-Ch 1	(1888-89)	Brass	23mm	—	—	Scarce	—

R. L. & Co. (relief) / 25 (incuse) / CHESTERTOWN (relief). Rv: No description available. Plain edge. (Burton K-47)

This was a cannery operation. The token was struck from dies.

S. H. GIBSON & SON
Crisfield, Md.

Rulau	Date	Metal	Size	VG	F	VF	Unc
Md-Cr 8	(1880's)	Brass	25.5mm	—	—	25.00	—

S. H. GIBSON & SON / OYSTER PACKERS / G/ 1 CALL. / CRISFIELD, MD. Rv: Blank. (Miller Md 184; Duffield 50)

This token was given to workers for one gallon of oysters shucked. The checks were redeemed each day for money.

MILLIGAN & SON
Crisfield, Md.

Rulau	Date	Metal	Size	F	VF	EF	Unc
Md-Cr 12	1875	Brass	20mm	5.00	10.00	—	25.00

Coronet Liberty head left, 1875. Rv: MILLIGAN & SON / 1 GAL. Plain edge. (Miller Md-184a)

E.W. Milligan and Son were oyster packers. This shucker's check is for one gallon of oysters.

EMMANUEL CHOIR
Cumberland, Md.

Rulau	Date	Metal	Size	VG	F	VF	Unc
Md-Cm 3	(?)	Brass	--mm	—	—	35.00	—

EMMANUEL CHOIR, / 5 / CUMBERLAND, MD. Rv: Blank, but dentilated rim. Plain edge. (Kirtley Sept. 1988 sale, lot 97)

H. A. R.
(Harry A. Roe)
Denton, Md.

Rulau	Date	Metal	Size	VG	F	VF	Unc
Md-De 8	(1887)	Brass	**	—	—	10.00	—

** Oct 22.5mm.
(All incused): H. A. R. (Burton C-168)

At least six varieties of this canner's checks are known, including round ones, and one lettered: O / H. A. ROE / I.

Harry A. Roe was the first canner of fruits and vegetables in Denton, county seat of Caroline County on Maryland's eastern shore. Roe also made cans.

Denton Cannery at West Denton was continued under his son.

W. S. P.
(W. S. Potter)
East New Market, Md.

Rulau	Date	Metal	Size	VG	F	VF	Unc
Md-EN 3	(1877)	Brass	**	—	—	6.50	—

** Scal 22mm.
(All incused): W. S. P. / 10. Incised beaded rim. (Burton D-126)

Dorchester County cannery checks.

BEALL BAUSH & CO. (and) JOHNSON BROS.
Frostburg, Md.

Rulau	Date	Metal	Size	VG	F	VF	Unc
Md-Fr 2	(1870's)	Brass	29mm	—	—	—	—

Eagle displayed, U.S. shield on its breast, head turned left, olive branch and arrows in its talons. Rv: BEALL BAUSH & CO. / PAY TO BEARER / $2 (incused) / JOHNSON BROS. Plain edge. (*TAMS Journal* for Oct. 1990, pgs. 161-162)

Struck by John F. Wesley Dorman of Baltimore.

Beall Baush & Co. were established in the 1870's as a general store, remaining in business until the 1890's. Johnson Brothers was a lumber company formed in the 1870's and it changed its name circa 1900-05 to J. Johnson & Son. Both firms appear in the 1882 Maryland business directory.

The tokens were apparently issued as scrip (advances on pay) to Johnson Brothers' employees, who could redeem them for goods at the Beall Baush store. Frostburg is in Allegany County in western Maryland, west of Cumberland.

MACGILL & MOORE
Hagerstown, Md.

Rulau	Date	Metal	Size	VG	F	VF	Unc
Md-Ha 7	(1889-90)	Brass	18mm	—	—	15.00	40.00

Eagle with U.S. shield on breast. Rv: Radiate numeral 3 at center, MACGILL & MOORE above, HAGERSTOWN, MD. below Plain edge. Thin flan. (Miller Md 188A)

Rulau	Date	Metal	Size	VG	F	VF	Unc
Md-Ha 8	(1889-90)	Brass	20mm	—	—	15.00	40.00

Liberty head. Rv: Similar, but radiate numeral 5. Plain edge. (Duffield 78; Miller Md 188)

R.E.O.
(Robert E. Owens)
Hanover, Md.

Rulau	Date	Metal	Size	VG	F	VF	Unc
Md-Hn 3	(1889)	Fiber	23mm	—	—	3.75	—

R.E.O. / 1 stamped on plain flan. Rv: Blank. Thick flan. Plain edge. The fiber flans are colored red.

E.K.
(Egbert Kelly)
Harmans, Md.

Rulau	Date	Metal	Size	VG	F	VF	Unc.
Md-Hr 3	(1885)	Brass	21mm	—	5.00	—	—

E.K. / 2 stamped in center, beaded rim around. Rv: Blank, but beaded rim. Plain edge.

Rulau	Date	Metal	Size	VG	F	VF	Unc.
Md-Hr 4	(1890's)	Brass	20mm	—	5.00	—	—

E.K. / 1 stamped in center, recessed dentilated rim. Rv: Blank, but recessed dentilated rim. Plain edge.

Rulau	Date	Metal	Size	VG	F	VF	Unc.
Md-Hr 5	(1890's)	Brass Oc	19mm	—	5.00	—	—

E.K. / 5 stamped in center, recessed rim around. Rv: Blank, but recessed rim. Plain edge.

Rulau	Date	Metal	Size	VG	F	VF	Unc.
Md-Hr 6	(1890's)	Brass Oc	19mm	—	5.00	—	—

E.K. / 10. Similar to last. Plain edge.

Egbert J. Kelly was born in 1863 and died in 1945.

H.N.K.
(Hezron N. Kelley)
Harmans, Md.

The 1874-1880 picker checks of this issuer are catalogued in *U.S. Merchant Tokens 1845-1860*, which see.

A. A. S.
(Adam A. Shipley)
Harmans, Md.

Rulau	Date	Metal	Size	VG	F	VF	Unc
Md-Hr 20	(1880's)	Brass	28mm	—	—	6.00	—

A.A.S. monogram / 500. Rv: Blank. Plain edge. Incised, beaded rim on each side.

Rulau	Date	Metal	Size	VG	F	VF	Unc
Md-Hr 21	(1880's)	Brass	**	—	—	3.00	—

**Scal 22mm.
A. A. S. / 1. Rv: Blank. Incised, beaded rim on each side. Plain edge.

Rulau	Date	Metal	Size	VG	F	VF	Unc
Md-Hr 22	(1880's)	Brass	**	—	—	3.00	—

**Scal 22mm.
Same, but numeral 2, 5 or 10.

Rulau	Date	Metal	Size	VG	F	VF	Unc
Md-Hr 23	(?)	Brass	**	—	—	3.00	—

**Oct 29mm.
A A S. Rv: 20 / BU. Incised, beaded rim on each side. Plain edge. (20 bushels)

Rulau	Date	Metal	Size	VG	F	VF	Unc
Md-Hr 24	(?)	Brass	**	—	—	3.00	—

**Oct 29mm.
Same, but numerals 5 or 10.

Rulau	Date	Metal	Size	VG	F	VF	Unc
Md-Hr 26	(?)	Brass	**	—	—	3.00	—

**Oct 25mm.
A. A. S. Rv: 1/4 / BU. Plain rims. Plain edge. (1/4 bushel)

Rulau	Date	Metal	Size	VG	F	VF	Unc
Md-Hr 28	(?)	Brass	**	—	—	3.00	—

**Oct 25mm.
Same, but numerals 1 or 2 1/2.

Adam Alexander Shipley was born Dec. 28, 1844 and died Feb. 24, 1915. He farmed at Harmans, Md., near what is now Ridge Road.

In November, 1987 his descendant, Blodwin Shipley Potee, turned over a few remaining picker checks of A. A. Shipley to the Anne Arrundell County Historical Society.

NOTE: The initials A.A.S. also stand for another A.A. County farmer who issued picker checks, Alfred Asbury Stinchcomb (1845-1915), who farmed at Pasadena, Md. Some of the above checks may later be attributed to him!

J. O.
(Joshua Owens)
Jessup, Md.

Rulau	Date	Metal	Size	VG	F	VF	Unc
Md-Je 4	(1888)	Brass	20.5mm	—	—	6.00	—

(All incused): J. O. / 2. Rv: Blank. Plain edge. There are two varieties, with large 2 and small 2. The large 2 has a straight base; the small 2 a curly base. (Rulau coll.)

Joshua Owens farmed at Race Road in Jessup. He had these picker checks stamped in 1888, according to family records. There are five denominations known.

A nephew, Harry Owens, farmed at Smith Station, Md. and used the picker checks of his uncle, counterstamped on the reverse H. O. The H. O. stamping may also be found on the reverse of A. C. W. (Arthur Cromwell Whittemore) checks of Brandon Shores, Md.

T. H. G.
(T. Herbert Goslin)
Linkwood, Md.

Rulau	Date	Metal	Size	VG	F	VF	Unc
Md-Li 3	(1875-83)	Brass	23mm	—	—	—	—

(All incused): T H G / 2. (Burton D-54)

Dorchester County cannery checks.

T.F.B.
(Thomas F. Bottomley)
Magothy, Md.

Rulau	Date	Metal	Size	VG	F	VF	Unc
Md-Mg 1	(1880's ?)	Brass Sc	22mm	—	4.00	—	—

T.F.B. / 1 1/2 stamped at center. Rv: Blank. Recessed beaded rim on each side. Plain edge.

Md-Mg 2	Similar, 7 1/2	Octagonal, 22mm
Md-Mg 3	Similar, 10	Round, 23mm
Md-Mg 4	Similar, 15	Round, 23mm
Md-Mg 5	Similar, 20	Octagonal, 22mm
Md-Mg 6	Similar, 30	Scalloped, 25mm
Md-Mg 7	Similar, 75	Round, 29mm (dentilated, non-recessed rim)

Thomas F. Bottomley farmed on Fortsmall Wood Road, Magothy. Robert Wesley Chard, another chit issuer, apparently was his illegitimate son.

A. W. M.
(Andrew W. Murphy)
Secretary, Md.

Rulau	Date	Metal	Size	VG	F	VF	Unc
Md-Se 7	(1880's)	Brass	21mm	—	—	5.50	—

(Ornament) / A. W. M. / (ornament). Rv: Large numeral 1 at center of rays. Dentilated rim on each side. Plain edge.

This is an oyster shucker's check for one gallon. It was probably redeemed for about 20 cents. The token was struck by J. F. W. Dorman of Baltimore.

WESLEY CANNING CO.
Snow Hill, Md.

Rulau	Date	Metal	Size	VG	F	VF	Unc
Md-SH 3	(1900?)	Brass	**	—	—	7.00	—

** Oct 26mm.
WESLEY / CANNING / CO. Rv: 1 BKT. Plain edge. (Rulau coll.)

BKT = Bucket.

G. & S.
(Gadd & Sudler)
Sudlersville, Md.

Rulau	Date	Metal	Size	VG	F	VF	Unc
Md-Sd 3	(1874)	Brass	22mm	—	—	Rare	—

G & S. Rv: No description. Dentilated rim on each side. Plain edge. Unique? (Burton QA-25)

A. J. Gadd and Dr. Arthur E. Sudler established the Gadd & Sudler Cannery in 1874, canning OUR CHOICE fruits and vegetables. In 1898 the name became A. J. Gadd & Co. Sudlersville is in Queen Anne's County on the eastern shore.

B. F. SHRIVER & CO.
Union Mills, Md.

Rulau	Date	Metal	Size	VG	F	VF	Unc
Md-UM 5	(1870's)	Brass	18mm	—	—	15.00	40.00

Eagle with shield on its breast, head facing right. Rv: B. F. SHRIVER & CO. / 2 1/2 within beaded circle / UNION MILLS, MD. Dentilated rim on each side. Plain edge.

Rulau	Date	Metal	Size	VG	F	VF	Unc
Md-UM 6	(1870's)	Brass	18mm	—	—	—	—

As Md-UM 5, but numeral 3 at center of reverse. Plain edge.

Both tokens struck by J. F. W. Dorman of Baltimore. In collection of Jim Hirtle, Westminster, Md.

J.S.H.
(John S. Hawkins)
Wellhams, Md.

Rulau	Date	Metal	Size	VG	F	VF	Unc
Md-Wm 4	(1880's)	Brass	20mm	—	5.00	—	—

J.S.H / 1 stamped on plain flan with recessed, dentilated rim. Rv: Blank, but recessed rim. Plain edge.

John Sterling Hawkins Sr. (1865-1894) farmed at Wellhams, Maryland, in Anne Arundel County.

B. F. SHRIVER & CO.
Westminster, Md.

Rulau	Date	Metal	Size	F	VF	EF	Unc
Md-Ws 6	(1870's)	GS	25mm	5.00	10.00	15.00	30.00

Liberty head within wreath. Rv: Large numeral 5, radiant, at center, B. F. SHRIVER & CO., WESTMINSTER, MD. around. Plain edge. (Miller Md 189; Duffield 129)

Rulau	Date	Metal	Size	F	VF	EF	Unc
Md-Ws 7	(1870's)	WM	20mm	8.00	12.00	20.00	30.00

Obverse as 6. Rv: Similar to 6, but numeral 3. Plain edge. (Miller Md 190)

SOVEREIGNS OF INDUSTRY
Woodberry, Md.

Rulau	Date	Metal	Size	VG	F	VF	Unc
Md-Wb 3	1876	Brass	25mm	—	—	5.00	15.00

Coronet Liberty head left, four stars in its coronet. Eleven stars around. Rv: SOVEREIGNS OF INDUSTRY, EXCELSIOR COUNCIL / WOODBERRY, MD. Incused numeral at center within beaded circle. (Numerals examined: 1). Plain edge. (Miller Md 191; Duffield 137)

Rulau	Date	Metal	Size	VG	F	VF	Unc
Md-Wb 4	1876	Lead	25mm	—	—	5.00	15.00

As 3. (Numerals examined: 15). Plain edge.

Probably an identification check for a society. Woodberry was incorporated into Baltimore 1888.

W. P. CO.
Maryland ?

Rulau	Date	Metal	Size	VG	F	VF	Unc
Md-Un 1	(?)	Brass	24mm	—	—	7.00	—

(All incuse) W. P. CO / PEELERS / CHECK. Rv: Blank. Incised, dentilated rim on both sides. Plain edge.

PICKER CHECKS OF ANNE ARUNDEL COUNTY, MD.

The following list of initials covers known picker chit issuers from 1853 to 1945. It was compiled with the aid of the Anne Arundel County Historical Society in Maryland, and Maryland Token and Medal Society.

JFA	Joseph Frank Andrzojewski — MILLERSVILLE (born 1888, died 1970)
JSA & Co	James S. Armiger & Co. — SOLLEY ROAD
JCA	Josiah C. Armiger — STONEY CREEK and BODKIN CREEK (born 1843, died 1928)
RHA	Richard Henry Arnold — Mountain Rd., A.A. County
B	Unidentified
GB	George Benning — GALESVILLE (tomatoes)
BBB	Basil B. Benson (aluminum)
JSB	James S. Benson (ca 1910)
JB	John Blackowicz — DISCUS MILL ROAD ("Smitty")
JB	Johann Blob — DORSEY ROAD (born 1889, died 1963)
MB	Maximilian Blob — JESSUPS (born 1883, died 1969)
ALB	Arthur L. Boone — JACOBSVILLE
CB	Charles Boone — JACOBSVILLE (born 1858, died 1951)
CB JR	Charles Boone Jr. — JACOBSVILLE
CFB	Christian Frederick Ballman — BROOKLYN (born 1864 died 1949)
LMB	L. M. Boyer (?) — SEVERN
JMB	Joseph M. Brian — LINTHICUM
GHB	George H. Brice — ST. MARGARETS
CWB	Charles Wesley Brown — MAGO VISTA (born 1850, died 1921)
GMB	G. Milton Bensen (brass)
HB	Henry Brooks — CEDAR HILL (black farmer)
HCB	Henry Clay Bourke — SEVERNA PARK (born 1859, died 1945)
JRB JR	James Rufus Benson Jr. — MARLEY CREEK (born 1893, died 1930)
MAB	Mahlon A. Benson (brass) HANOVER
MB	Mahlon Benson — HARMANS
TFB	Thomas F. Bottomley — MAGOTHY
UWB	Ulysses W. Brooks — GLEN BURNIE (married 1877) and Urias Brooks (born 1877, died 1964)
WB	William Brossius — CROWNSVILLE
JFB	Johann Freidrich Bussey — SEVERN (born 1855, died 1924)
G F BECK	Not located
C & BRO	Frank Chairs & Brother — MARLEY
C & BRO	Cook (or Curren) and Brothers — PASADENA
BSC	Basil Smith Cromwell — FERNDALE
CC	Charles Clark — PASADENA
ELC	Emory Luther Cromwell — FERNDALE
FC	Franklin Chairs (?)
FPC	Frank(lin) P. Chairs — PASADENA
FWC	Frederick W. Cook (no number quantities on checks)
GTC	George T. Chaney — ODENTON (married 1905)
JC	Jefferson Cook — PASADENA
JWC	John Wesley Clark — SEVERN (Reese Road)
MC	Monroe Cook — PASADENA
PAC	Plummer Arthur Clark — FORT MEADE (checks used until 1917)
RSC	Richard Stanley Cole
RWC	Robert Wesley Chard — BODKIN CREEK
STC OF J	Sedwick Thomas Cromwell of John — GLEN BURNIE (born 1862, died 1950)
TMC	Thomas M. Cole — HARMANS (1870-80) Samuel Vinton Clark (1880-1918) Gilbert H. Clark & Bros. (1918-45) (all above used same checks 75 years)
WLC	William Landy Cook — GIBSON ISLAND (from 1908) (born 1886, died 1968)
WSC	William Shipley Crisp — BROOKLYN (born 1886, died 1919)
D. BROS	Unidentified
AJD	Andrew J. Disney — HANOVER
MD	Mahlon Disney — Mountain Rd., A. A. County
WD	William C. Dotson Daniel C. Dotson (born 1831, died 1927)
WPD	William Paul Disney — SEVERN
EA	Unidentified
JFE	John F. Ellison — PASADENA
OE	O. Elzey — DORSEY
JF	Unidentified
JHF	Joseph Henry Frantum Jr.

RTF Richard Thomas Ford — LINTHICUM
CMG Charles Milton Green — MILLERSVILLE (died 1937)
JHG John G. Gischel — Ritchie Hwy., A.A. County (born 1867, died 1953)
RWG Robert Wesley Griffith — GLEN BURNIE (born 1849, died 1925)
SLG Samuel L. Gaylor — Ridge Rd., A.A. County
WG William Gunther — Old Annapolis Rd., A.A. County
WTG Unidentified
ASH Albert Sydney Johnston Hammond (born 1863, died 1932) MARLEY CREEK (now COUNTRY CLUB ESTATES)
C & RTH Clarence Hammond (born 1882, died 1928) Richard Thomas Hammond (born 1883, died 1909) (together, Old Ordnance Rd., A.A. County)
CHH Charles H. Hodges — MARLEY CREEK
DH Unidentified
EHH Egbert H. Hawkins — HARMANS (born 1893, died 1919)
EJH Edward James Hines III — BODKIN CREEK (born 1822, died 1926)
EJH JR. Edward James Hines Jr. — BODKIN CREEK
HH Harbert Hammond — MARLEY CREEK 1900-18 REISTERTOWN 1918-on (born 1875, died 1953)
HRH Rezin Howard Hammond (born 1864, died 1928) CEDAR FARM (now Benson-Hammond House, AACHS)
JAH John Asbury Hancock — BODKIN POINT (born 1837, married 1861; tokens used 1853-61 for strawberries. Farm called "Hancock's Resolution" at Bayside Beach
JEH Unidentified
JH James Hawkins
JSH John Sterling Hawkins Sr. — WELLHAMS (born 1865, died 1894)
JTH John Thomas Hammond (born 1838, died 1909) and John Thomas Hammond (II) (born 1872, died 1940) (now ORDNANCE DEPOT & G.S.A.)
MH Marmaduke Hamilton
PH & B Peter Hahn & Brother — PASADENA
RWH Richard Walter Hawkins
WSH William Shipley Hammond — Old Ordnance Rd., A.A.C. (born 1866, died 1924)
JEA Unidentified
JWA Unidentified
J & N Zechariah Johnson & John Neidert — PASADENA
EGJ Elmer G. Jubb — PASADENA
EJ Enos Jeffrey
FJ Fletcher Joyce — MILLERSVILLE and ODENTON
GAJ George Albert Jenkins — PASADENA (born 1892, died 1960)
GGJ Gustavius G. Jenkins — JACOBSVILLE (died 1915)
JCJ James Clinton Jacobs — SEVERN (born 1882, died 1967)
ZJ Zechariah Johnson — PASADENA
BAK Benjamin A. Klug — Mountain Rd., A.A. County
EK Egbert J. Kelly — HARMANS (born 1863, died 1945)
HNK Hezron Nehemiah Kelly — HARMANS (born 1818, died 1880)
HSK Hiram S. Kelly — HARMANS (born 1859, died 1932)
TRK Unidentified
WDK W. D. Klingelhofer — Mountain Rd., A.A. County
JML or JLM J. M. Lowman — ODENTON
SL Sweetser Linthicum — LINTHICUM
WL Wesley Linthicum — Mountain Rd., A.A. County
G McP or G Mc George McPherson — McPHERSON STATION (now LINKS FARM)
AGM A. G. Meyers — New Cut Rd., A.A. County
BFM Benjamin Franklin Mewshaw — BROOKLYN (born 1880, died 1928)
FM or F. MEWSHAW Franklin Mewshaw — BROOKLYN (born 1845, died 1903) Listed in 1878 AA Co. Atlas. Mewshaw also ctsp. checks of Wm. Remmey
GFM Unidentified
HJM Henry Jackson Myers — SEVERNA PARK
JLM J. M. Lowman — ODENTON
JM John Meek — JACOBSVILLE
JM & CO Unidentified
JLM J. M. Lowman — ODENTON
LM Lewis Myers
RHM Richard Henry Maynard — ODENTON (born 1864, died 1918) (Anne Arundel County dump now on this site)
CAN Charles Adam Neidert — ELVATON
JEN J. E. Nunn — SEVERN
HO Harry Owens — SMITH STATION (ELMHURST) (born 1891, died 1969)
JO Joshua Owens — HANOVER
REO Robert Edward Owens — HANOVER (checks used 1889 only)
TO Tomas Osborne — SEVERNA PARK
ALBERT James Albert Portaskewicz (surname changed to Albert)
ACP Alpheus Clinton Pumphrey — HANOVER
BCP Unidentified
BFP Benjamine Franklin Pumphrey — MILLERSVILLE
BFP/BP = big peas
BFP/LP = little peas
CBP Charles B. Pumphrey — MARLEY CREEK
JRP John Randolph Parker — ANNE ARUNDEL CO. (Crain Hwy) (born 1846, died 1912) Farmed and kept store 3rd district. Had store checks. Married at 40 to Sarah A. Meyers (1866-1939). Family used store checks to ca 1920.
KP Knollie (Nollie) Pumphrey — FERNDALE
NCP Nathan C. Pumphrey — W. Furnace Branch Rd., A.A.C. (born 1821, died 1891) (checks later used by Carl Shipley?)
NP Nelson S. Phelps — Welhams Cross Rd., A.A. County (in 1878 A.A. County Atlas) (son born 1894 ?)
OCP Oden C. Pumphrey — (peas, berries) (1900)
OSP Unidentified
RDP Rufus Dallas Phelps — BROOKLYN (in 1878 Atlas) (born 1845, died 1918)
RHP Richard H. Pumphrey — PASADENA
RLP Robert Lee Pumphrey — PASADENA
RNP Roland Nelson Phelps — GLEN BURNIE (born 1873, died 1953)
STP Sedwick Thomas Pumphrey — FERNDALE (born 1864, died 1929)
TCP Thales Cornelius Pumphrey — FERNDALE (checks used 1885-1938) (born 1862, died 1942)
TOP Thomas Octavia Pumphrey — MILLERSVILLE (1841-1909)
TP Thomas Pumphrey — PUMPHREY'S STATION (born 1824, died 1909)
WWP W.W. Phelps
AQ A. Queen — QUEENSTOWN
MQ Mahlon Queen — QUEENSTOWN
R Unidentified
BTR Benjamin T. Ray — HARMANS (born 1846, died 1921)
EWWR Ernest W. W. Ruths
JBR Joseph Benson Ray — SEVERN and HANOVER (1881-1962)
JHR John Henry Robinson — NORTH LINTHICUM (born a slave Nov. 21, 1844, freed 1864. Married a slave, Della Queen. Farmed at River Road.)
RR on WD A son of W. C. Dotson
WR or W. REMMY or WR / FM William Remmey — BROOKLYN (born 1856, died 1927) Franklin Mewshaw — BROOKLYN (which see) (after 1900)
AAS Adam Alexander Shipley — HARMANS (born 1844, died 1915)
AAS Alfred Asbury Stinchcomb — PASADENA (born 1848, died 1915)
ACS August Carl Schmidt — PASADENA
BHS Basil Hamilton Smith — SEVERN (born 1884, died 1960)
CLS Charles L. Solley — SOLLEY (born 1860, died 1921)
CVB SMITH Charles Van Buren Smith — HANOVER
D St Daniel Stoll — SNOW HILL (large tin checks) Farm taken for Beltway 1969. In 1878 Atlas
ELS Elza Lee Stewart — GLEN BURNIE PARK
EVS Edward V. Spriggs (1860-1884). Had no checks.
FOS Frank Orlando Spriggs.
FS Frank Sewell — Ridge Rd., A.A. County
GBS George Bandell Stinchcomb — MANHATTAN BEACH (born 1848, died 1915)
GCS George G. Schmidt — PASADENA
HJS Henry J. Smith — SEVERN
H St Herman Stoll — BROOKLYN
JCS Joshua Cromwell Stewart — GLEN BURNIE PARK
JES John Edward Stoll — LINTHICUM (born 1863, died 1947)
JFS John Franklin Shipley of Othc — McPHERSON STATION (born 1858)
JS Joe Sewell — MATHEWS TOWN
JS John Smith
JS John Stewart — HANOVER
JWS John Wilson Shipley — WELLHAMS (used 1902-03 only) (born 1865, died 1952)
LRS Larkin Rudolphus Shipley — HARMANS (born 1841, died 1890) Tokens used 1874-1940
L SCHR Louis Schramm Sr. — PASADENA (tin checks, marked 1 BOX STRAWBERRIES)
MFS Mary Frances Spriggs — ARNOLD (born 1848, died 1934)
MS Michael Sroka — HANOVER
NS Nick Simms
RLS Richard Luther Shipley — SHIPLEY (born 1849, died 1923)
ROS Roderick Octavius Shipley — HANOVER (born 1848, died 1922)
THS Theodore H. Stinchcomb — Mountain Rd., A.A. County
TSS Unidentified
WAS William Abner Shipley — 'BACHELOR'S HOPE' (born 1845, died 1907)
WES or ES William Elbridge Shipley (tokens used 1890-1930) (born 1870, died 1930) — Ridge Rd., A.A. County
WJS William J. Schmidt — PASADENA
BFT Benjamin F. Thomas — HAMMONDS LANE
CRT Carroll R. Thomas — GAMBRILS

JFT	James Frank Turner
LCT	Louis C. Tepper — Newcut Rd., A.A. County
LJT	John Linton Tubbs (known as Linton Tubbs) (born 1830 died 1930) Checks always used 'LJT'
SST	Sewell Summerfield Tracey — MARLEY CREEK
ACW	Arthur Cromwell Whittemore — GREENLAND BEACH (born 1865, died 1943) "Brandon Shores"
ACW	A Cromwell Whittemore — GLEN BURNIE (1900-1947)
CRW	Charles Ritchie Winterson — HANOVER
CW	A. Cromwell Whittemore — GLEN BURNIE (1900-1947)
EBW	Eden B. Watts — SEVERN
EW	Ernest Wesley — (now FRIENDSHIP PARK)
FW	Frank Wimmer — GLEN BURNIE
GW	George Wiegand — PLEASANT PLAINS FARMS (1900)
HEW	Harry Emil Wagner — ADMIRAL (now FORT MEADE) (born 1882, died 1956)
JAW	John August Wagner — SEVERN (born 1849, died 1913)
JBW	Jno. B. Wells (peas) (1900)
JPW	James P. Watts — Admiral (now FORT MEADE)
JW	James Wade — SEVERN
PSW	Penrhyn Stanley Watts — FORT MEADE and SEVERN (born 1890, died 1970)
SSW	Summerfield S. Wheeler — Solley Rd., A.A. County
STW	Samuel T. Wilson — MAGO VISTA
WEW	William Eben Watts
WTW	William T. Watts — Ridge Rd., A.A. County
WW	William Ware (a Black) — Off Ritchie Hwy, A.A.C.
NW/B	William Ware & Brother
HY	Henry Yealdhall — WOODLAND HEIGHTS

For additional reading consult "Builder Uncovers Tin Box Containing Servants' Checks Used by Pumphrey," by Melvin Fuld, in *Coin World* for March 9, 1966, page 46. Also see "Anne Arundel County Farmers' Picker Checks," by Ora Pumphrey Smith, Severna Park, Md., 3rd ed., 1989; "The Pickers of Anne Arundel County," by Mrs. Chipman W. Cunningham, Severna Park, Md., ca 1980; and "View from a Commission Merchant" by J. Thomas Pumphrey, ca 1988.

Continuing research into this intriguing specialty is published in the column "Checken Fer Pickers" by Will Mumford in issues of the *Maryland Tams Journal* (Baltimore). The issue of Winter 1989 is especially enlightening.

We are indebted to the following members of the Anne Arundel County Historical Society for information contained in the above alphabetized listing: Ora P. Smith, JoAnn Coe Stoll, Mrs. Chipman Cunningham. The county which spawned these picker checks is Anne Arundel County, Maryland, south of Baltimore — named after Lady Ann Arrundell, wife of Cecil Calvert, Lord Baltimore.

According to classified ads appearing in 1900 editions of Annapolis' *Evening Capital*, certain agents were designated to accept picker checks and these then would be redeemed by farmers such as George Wiegand and Oden C. Pumphrey. These agents were: Charles Weiss, Edward Weiss, Mrs. Herold, M. M. Smith and Charles Mulhmister. Another farmer, Jno. B. Wells, warned he would not redeem pea picker checks if they were "traded for," presumably by merchants.

MASSACHUSETTS

NEEDHAM & CHAPLIN

Adams, Mass. ?

Rulau	Date	Metal	Size	F	VF	EF	Unc
Ma-Ad 2	(1885)	Brass	24mm	—	—	20.00	—

Brunswick die BB-2. Rv: NEEDHAM & CHAPLIN / (crossed cues and balls) / POOL. (Thoele coll.)

John Needham and William Chaplin were listed as "liquor dealers" (saloonkeepers) in the 1885 edition of *New England Business Directory & Gazetteer*. They were listed as separate proprietors, not partners. The partnership itself still needs to be established. Tentative attribution.

A.P. KNOWLES

Ashland, Mass.

Rulau	Date	Metal	Size	VG	F	VF	EF
Ma-As 4	1873	Copper	29mm	125.	—	175.	—

MADE BY A. P. KNOWLES / ASHLAND, MASS. / STENCILS, STEEL STAMPS, KEY CHECKS / 1873 ctsp on U.S. 1845 Large cent. (Koppenhaver Aug. 1982 sale; Brunk 23320; Rulau Mass 535)

It is likely that Knowles was himself a counterstamper of coins for other parties, as this business seemed to flourish in New England in the 1850's and 1860's.

G. GERRY

Athol, Mass.

Rulau	Date	Metal	Size	VG	F	VF	EF
Ma-At 1	(?)	Copper	29mm	—	50.00	—	100.
	G. GERRY / ATHOL MASS. ctsp on U.S. Large cent. Examined: 1830, 1836, 1843, 1846, 1847, 1852, 1854. 7 pieces known. (Hallenbeck 7.511; Brunk 16000)						
Ma At 2	(?)	Copper	29mm	—	50.00	—	100.
	G. GERRY ctsp on U.S. Large cent. Examined: 1795, 1836, 1847. (Tanenbaum coll.; Brunk 15990)						

George Gerry founded his textile mill in 1853. He died in 1876 and his son succeeded.

In 1918 George Gerry & Son, machinery manufacturers, were successors. Athol is in Worcester County. This remained a family business until 1981.

BEDFOR(D) MILLS FLOUR

Bedford, Mass. ?

Rulau	Date	Metal	Size	VG	F	VF	EF
Ma-Be 1	(?)	Silver	18mm	—	—	100.	—
	CALL FOR / BEDFOR(D) / MILLS / FLOUR ctsp on U.S. Seated Liberty dime, date worn off. The legend is partly off the flan. (Rulau coll.)						
Ma-Be 2	(1880's)	Silver	38mm	—	150.	—	—
	BEDFORD MILLS ctsp on U.S. 1880 Morgan silver dollar. (Brunk 3037)						

Bedford is in Middlesex County.

AMERICAN STEAM GAUGE (?)

Boston, Mass.

Rulau	Date	Metal	Size	VG	F	VF	Unc
Ma-Bo 1	(?)	Brass	29mm	—	—	Rare	—

(All incuse) AMERIC / STEAM GAU / BOSTO. Rv: 56. Incuse dentilation around each rim. Plain edge. Issued holed.

The letters on obverse run off the planchet. This may be a tool check or a time check.

BERNARD & FRIEDMAN

Rulau	Date	Metal	Size	F	VF	EF	Unc
Ma-Bo 12	(?)	Cop.	22x26mm	—	5.00	10.00	18.00

Shield of arms at center (Shield divided per bend; in chief three horseshoes; in base three nails). Above: BERNARD & FRIEDMAN.; below: BOSTON. Rv: BERNARD & FRIEDMAN. / TITAN / CALF / BOSTON. Plain edge. Horseshoe-shaped flan. (Wright 1337)

In 1918 The Bernard Co. were leather makers.

BOSTON ATHLETIC ASSOCIATION

Rulau	Date	Metal	Size	F	VF	EF	Unc
Ma-Bo A12	1887	S/Nickel	**	3.00	—	—	—

** Irreg 30 mm.

Coat of arms (partially enameled), BOSTON ATHLETIC ASSOCIATION, 1887. Rv: Blank. Plain edge. Issued with loop. (Dick Grinolds report)

Probably a watch fob.

BOSTON NUMISMATIC SOCIETY

Rulau	Date	Metal	Size	F	VF	EF	Unc
Ma-Bo 13	1873	Brass	31mm	—	—	—	40.00
	Both sides of New England shilling above pine tree on a hill, INSTITUTED / 1860 above, all within central circle. Around, in two concentric circles: PRESIDENCY OF ULYSSES S. GRANT / **** 1873 **** / BOSTON NUMISMATIC SOCIETY / INCORPORATED 1870. Rv: Society seal in central circle. Around, in two concentric circles: TWIN DELVERS IN THE GARDEN OF HISTORY / (ISAAC F. WOODS / MEMORIAL SERIES) / N. E. HISTORIC GENEALOGICAL / * SOCIETY *. Plain edge. (Wright 89)						
Ma-Bo 13A	1873	S/Brass	31mm	—	—	—	40.00
	As last. Plain edge.						
Ma-Bo 13B	1873	Copper	31mm	—	—	—	40.00
	As last. Plain edge.						
Ma-Bo 13C	1873	Silver	31mm	—	—	—	75.00
	As last. Plain edge. (Ganter coll.)						

Isaac F. Wood's memorial series. This is the same I. F. Wood of New York who issued the Cogan "English Daddy" pieces of Brooklyn, N.Y. (See NY-Bk 7 through 10)

These pieces are known counterstamped - for example with 'D. No. 2'.

M. L. BRADFORD & CO.

Rulau	Date	Metal	Size	VG	F	VF	Unc
Ma-Bo A13	(1865-70)	WM	27mm	22.50	30.00	40.00	60.00
	M.L. BRADFORD & CO. / CUTLERY / AND / HARDWARE. Rv: Beaded oval encloses numeral 413 incuse. Inscribed: 142 WASH. ST. / BOSTON, MASS. (Wright 1344; Miller 25A). Issued holed.						
Ma-Bo B13	(1865-70)	Copper	27mm	—	—		V. Rare
	As B13. (Storer 228; Miller 25B)						

BRADFORD & ANTHONY

Rulau	Date	Metal	Size	VG	F	VF	Unc
Ma-Bo E13	(1870's)	GS	32mm	18.00	30.00	55.00	85.00
	BRADFORD & ANTHONY. / 374 WASHINGTON ST. / BOSTON. / 103. Rv: (Tiny) J. ROBBINS / BOSTON. Plain edge. Centrally holed flan. (The '374' has been added after '186' was lined out). (Miller 500)						

Martin L. Bradford & Co., cutlery, was at 178 Washington Street in 1863. (142 Washington on tokens).

Martin L. Bradford & Nathan Anthony, hardware, were at 178 Washington Street in 1863. (374 and 186 Washington on tokens).

Martin L. Bradford was located at 142 Washington Street, in the first building north of Old South Church, in 1870. In a panoramic sketch of the east side of Washington Street, Bradford (on the street floor) shared the 3-story building with: Benjamin W. Gage (street floor); Fowler & Wells and M. E. Walcott (second floor); Propeller Signs and Clapp's Paint Depot (third floor).

In the 1863 directory Bradford is located at 178 Washington. Thus Mass. 25A and 25B are post-merchant era - probably 1865-70. They sold, among other things, skates.

HENRY W. BURR & CO.

Rulau	Date	Metal	Size	VG	F	VF	Unc
Ma-Bo 14	(1870's)	WM	31mm	—	—	—	Rare
	HENRY W. BURR & CO / RUBBER / GOODS / OF EVERY / DESCRIPTION / AT WHOLESALE & RETAIL. Rv: BOSTON RUBBER EMPORIUM / NO. 37 / MILK ST. / * / BOSTON / MASS. Plain edge. (Tanenbaum coll.)						

This token is normally molded in hard rubber. Only one white metal example has been seen.

L.J. COLBY

Rulau	Date	Metal	Size	VG	F	VF	EF
Ma-Bo 15	(?)	Silver	24mm	30.00	—	60.00	—
	(5-pointed star in circle) / L.J. COLBY in circle / (5-pointed star in circle) / BOSTON MASS in circle — ctsp on reverse of England 1817 Shilling. (Tanenbaum coll.; Van Ormer sale 2598; Brunk 8730)						

HENRY COOK

Rulau	Date	Metal	Size	F	VF	EF	Unc
Ma-Bo 19	(1861-2)	Copper	43mm	—	25.00	35.00	50.00
	Scroll inscribed CONSTITUTION. NO SURRENDER OF THE FORT SUMTER OF THE NORTH. Thirteen stars. Under scroll: THE GIFT OF OUR PATRIOT SIRES / WE NEVER WILL / SURRENDER / TO / TRAITORS AND REBELS. Rv: Wreath around: HENRY COOK / MONEY BROKER / AND DEALER IN / RARE AND ANTIQUE / COINS / MEDALS / AUTOGRAPHS / CURIOSITIES, RELICS / &C &C / NO. 74 FRIEND ST., / BOSTON. Plain edge. (Wright 205; Miller Mass 28)						
Ma-Bo 19A	(1861-2)	WM	43mm	—	25.00	35.00	57.50
	As last. Plain edge. (Miller Mass 29)						
Ma-Bo 20	(1860's)	Copper	28mm	600.	—	—	—
	Eagle on apothecary's mortar (Haviland Stevenson card, Miller SC 3). Rv: HENRY COOK, MONEY BROKER. Only 2 pieces known. (Woodward Oct. 25, 1886 sale, lot 1342)						

J. COOK

Rulau	Date	Metal	Size	VG	F	VF	EF
Ma-Bo-21	(?)	Copper	28mm	—	25.00	—	35.00
	(U.S. eagle in circular indent) / (Indian as on Massachusetts cent in oval indent) / J. COOK ctsp on Canada halfpenny token of Starr & Shannon, Halifax. (Storer 307)						
Ma-Bo 21A	(?)	Copper	29mm	—	—	—	35.00
	Similar ctsp on U.S. 1816 Large cent. (Brunk 9400)						

GEORGE FERA

Rulau	Date	Metal	Size	F	VF	EF	Unc
Ma-Bo 22	1864	Copper	27mm	—	30.00	—	75.00
	SOLDIERS' FAIR DEC. 1864. SPRINGFIELD MASS. within laurel wreath. Rv: GEORGE FERA / * STUDIO BUILDING * / MERRIAM (tiny) Plain edge. (Miller Mass 42)						
Ma-Bo 23	1864	WM	27mm	—	—	—	75.00
	As Ma-Bo 22. (Miller Mass 43)						
Ma-Bo 24	(1867-71)	Copper	27mm	—	30.00	—	75.00
	APOLLO GARDENS / 576 / WASHINGTON ST. / GOOD FOR / 6 / CENTS. / * HESS & SPEIDEL * (reverse of Mass 4). As reverse of (Ma-Bo 22.) Plain edge. (Miller Mass 44.)						

The regular Fera store cards appear in the 1845-1860 section. These are mulings made in the 1867-71 period.

FOREIGN EXHIBITION

Rulau	Date	Metal	Size	F	VF	EF	Unc
Ma-Bo 26	1883	WM	29mm	—	—	35.00	—
	Four 18th century gentlemen gathered around a table for a signing ceremony. Above: TREATY OF PEACE BETWEEN GREAT BRITAIN AND THE UNITED STATES / SEPT 3D. Below: SIGNED AT / PARIS FRANCE. / .1783. Rv: . FOREIGN EXHIBITION . / OPENED / SEPTEMBER 3D. / 1883. / BOSTON, MASS. U.S.A. Plain edge.						

This medalet honors the centennial of the Paris Treaty, by which the United States achieved formal recognition of its independence.

HAPGOOD

Rulau	Date	Metal	Size	VG	F	VF	EF
Ma-Bo 28	(1863-64)	Copper	29mm	—	—	35.00	—
	HAPGOOD BOSTON ctsp on U.S. 1823 Large cent. (Hallenbeck 8.501; Brunk 18170)						

Joab Hapgood was a gunsmith in Boston 1847-1864.

HESS & SPEIDEL, APOLLO GARDENS

Rulau	Date	Metal	Size	F	VF	EF	Unc
Ma-Bo 30	(1860's)	Copper	27mm	—	—	Ex. Rare	
	Lincoln bust right. ABRAHAM LINCOLN above. BORN FEB. 12, 1809. below. Tiny MERRIAM under bust. Rv: APOLLO GARDENS / 576 / WASHINGTON ST. / GOOD FOR / 6 / CENTS. / * HESS & SPEIDEL *. Plain edge. (Miller Mass 9; De-Witt AL 1860-45 (F)						
Ma-Bo 31	(1860's)	WM	27mm	—	—	Ex. Rare	
	As last. Plain edge. (Miller Mass 10)						
Ma-Bo 33	(1870's)	WM	27mm	—	—	Ex. Rare	
	Obverse as last (Lincoln). Rv: Apollo bust right, within oak wreath. APOLLO. above. Plain edge. (Schenkman B1; Miller Mass 10A)						
MA-Bo 34	(1860's)	WM	27mm	—	—	35.00	100.
	Obverse as reverse of Miller Mass 9 (HESS & SPEIDEL card). Rv: Card of George Fera, Studio Building. Plain edge. (Miller Mass 11)						
Ma-Bo 36	(1870's)	WM	27mm	—	—	50.00	100.
	George Washington bust left, J.A. BOLEN under truncation. WASHINGTON above. Rv: As obverse of last (HESS & SPEIDEL card). Plain edge. (Miller Mass 12)						
Ma-Bo 37	(1870's)	Copper	27mm	—	—	50.00	75.00
	As last. Plain edge. (Miller Mass 12A)						

Rulau	Date	Metal	Size	F	VF	EF	Unc
Ma-Bo 39	1862	Copper	27mm	—	—	35.00	100.
	Obverse as reverse of Miller Mass 9 (HESS & SPEIDEL card). Rv: MADE FROM COPPER / - TAKEN FROM - / THE RUINS OF / - THE - / TURPENTINE WORKS / NEWBERN / - N.C. - /DESTROYED BY THE / REBELS / MERRIAM (tiny) / MARCH 14, 1862. Plain edge. (Miller Mass 15; Schenkman B10)						

Rulau	Date	Metal	Size	F	VF	EF	Unc
Ma-Bo 41	1864	Copper	27mm	—	—	—	Rare
	Washington head right within oak branches, WASHINGTON above. Rv: MADE FROM A COPPER BOLT / TAKEN FROM / - THE - / WRECK OF THE / FRIGATE CONGRESS / - BY - / G.W. WILLIAMS / - / CO. C. 25. REG. M.V. / JAN. 1. 1864. Plain edge. (Schenkman B28)						
Ma-Bo 43	(1870's)	Copper	27mm	—	—	35.00	100.
	Obverse as reverse of Miller Mass 9 (HESS & SPEIDEL card). Rv: As reverse of George Fera card (PARTIES SUPPLIED). Plain edge. (Miller Mass 16)						
Ma-Bo 44	(1870's)	WM	27mm	—	—	35.00	100.
	As last. Plain edge. (Miller Mass 17)						
Ma-Bo 46	(1870's)	CN	27mm	—	—	—	100.
	Beardless Lincoln bust right, ABRAHAM LINCOLN above, BORN FEB. 12, 1809. below. Tiny MERRIAM BOSTON below truncation. Rv: Obverse as reverse of Miller Mass 10A (Apollo bust). Plain edge. (Miller Mass 17A; King 598; DeWitt AL 1860-45(E)						

HEUBLEIN'S

Rulau	Date	Metal	Size	VG	F	VF	Unc
Ma-Bo 47	(?)	Silver/Br	27mm	—	—	—	—
	(All incused): HEUBLEIN'S / (numeral) / LUNCH ONLY. Rv: Same as obverse. Plain edge. (Storer 469)						

INTERNATIONAL MARITIME EXHIBITION

Rulau	Date	Metal	Size	VG	F	VF	Unc
Ma-Bo 50	1889-90	Silver	25mm	—	—	15.00	30.00
	A ship, MARITIME EXHIBITION above, BOSTON MASS below. Rv: Buildings, INTERNATIONAL / MARITIME / EXHIBITION / 1889-90. Plain edge. (Wright 661)						
Ma-Bo 51	1889-90	G/Silver	25mm	—	—	15.00	30.00
	As last. (Stanley Steinberg 1982 sale)						

MASONIC TEMPLE

Rulau	Date	Metal	Size	VG	F	VF	EF
Ma-Bo 55	1864	Silver	31mm	—	—	—	100.
	BOSTON/ENCAMPMENT ctsp on obverse of U.S. 1864. Seated Liberty half dollar. TAKEN FROM THE RUINS OF MASONIC TEMPLE / APRIL 6" 1864. ctsp on reverse of the coin. All ctsp letters are in script.						

Rulau	Date	Metal	Size	VG	F	VF	EF
Ma-Bo 57	1864	Silver	31mm	—	—	—	100.
	Similar ctsp to last, but HAMILCAR RICE in script added to obverse, on 1864 Liberty Seated half dollar.						

Rulau	Date	Metal	Size	VG	F	VF	EF
Ma-Bo 59	1864	Silver	31mm	—	—	—	100.
	S. N. FURBER / MASONIC HALL BT. / APRIL 5TH / 1864 (all in script) ctsp on U.S. 1864 Liberty Seated half dollar.						
Ma-Bo 59C	1864	Silver	31mm	—	—	—	190.
	ALVIN ADAMS JR. BOSTON / ENCAMPMENT ctsp on obverse of U.S. 1864 Seated Liberty half dollar. Rv: TAKEN FROM THE RUINS OF MASONIC TEMPLE / APRIL 6TH 1864 ctsp on reverse of the coin. (B&M Patterson 1985 sale, lot 1229)						
Ma-Bo 59D	1864	Silver	31mm	—	—	—	190.
	PRESENTED TO / SIR KT. R H CARLETON BY SIR KT. D.W.W. / BOSTON ctsp on obverse of U.S. 1864 S.L. half dollar. Rv: TAKEN FROM THE RUINS OF MASONIC TEMPLE / APRIL 6TH 1864 ctsp on reverse of the coin. (B&M Emery/ Nichols 1984 sale, lot 1564)						

All these counterstamps, which resemble engravings, were done by the same fine hand in excellent style. All are on new, or near-new coins. The first three reposed in personal collection of Kurt R. Krueger, Iola, Wis. in 1982; ex-Maurice M. Gould collection.

The Boston Masonic Hall burned April 5, 1864. From the inscription, it would appear these then-new half dollars were salvaged from the ruins the next day. What purpose these souvenirs served is conjecture at this point, though it seems likely they were a fund-raising receipt of some kind to rebuild the hall. Just who Hamilcar Rice, S.N. Furber, Alvin Adams Jr., etc., are must also be determined, but it seems safe to assume they were Masons of the Civil War period.

It has been suggested that the United States Mint played a role in the preparation of these marked half dollars.

St. Andrew's Royal Arch Chapter was founded Aug. 12, 1769. Paul Revere was made a Mason in Massachusetts in 1760; he was Master of this lodge 1770-71, 1777-79 and 1780-82. Later Revere was Grand Master of the Grand Lodge of Massachusetts 1794-97. Bronze medals were struck in 1894 for the 125th anniversary of this lodge (King 153). Two volumes of the history of this lodge were published in 1882 by Alfred F. Chapman.

Rulau	Date	Metal	Size	VG	F	VF	EF
Ma-Bo 60	1867	WM	31mm	—	—	—	20.00
	Temple at center, MASONIC TEMPLE above, BOSTON below. Rv: NEW MASONIC TEMPLE / (radiant seeing eye) / DEDICATED / JUNE 24. A. L. 5867 / CHAS. C. DAME / (square and compass) / GRAND MASTER. Plain edge. (Schenkman C12-C13)						

JOS. H. MERRIAM

Rulau	Date	Metal	Size	F	VF	EF	Unc
Ma-Bo 65	(1860)	Copper	32mm	—	—	50.00	75.00
	Daniel Webster. Rv: As reverse of Miller Mass 58. Plain edge.						
Ma-Bo 66	(1860)	Brass	32mm	—	—	50.00	75.00
	As Ma-Bo 65. Plain edge. (Miller Mass 60)						
Ma-Bo 67	(1860)	WM	32mm	—	—	50.00	75.00
	As Ma-Bo 65. Plain edge. (Miller Mass 61)						
Ma-Bo 69	(1860)	Copper	32mm	—	—	50.00	75.00
	Albert Edward, Prince of Wales. Rv: As Ma-Bo 65. Plain edge. (Miller Mass 62)						
Ma-Bo 70	(1860)	Brass	32mm	—	—	50.00	75.00
	As 69. Plain edge. (Miller Mass 63)						
Ma-Bo 71	(1860)	WM	32mm	—	—	50.00	75.00
	As 69. Plain edge. (Miller Mass 64)						

Rulau	Date	Metal	Size	F	VF	EF	Unc
Ma-Bo 72	(1860)	Copper	32mm	—	—	Unique	
	Head of Everett left, EDWARD EVERETT above, BORN APRIL 11, 1794. below. Rv: As Ma-Bo 65. Plain edge. (Springfield sale, Dec. 17, 1981)						
Ma-Bo 72A	(1860)	WM	32mm	—	—	—	100.
	Same as last. (Schenkman C-7)						

Rulau	Date	Metal	Size	F	VF	EF	Unc
Ma-Bo 73	(1860)	Copper	32mm	—	—	50.00	75.00
	Bust of Merriam left, LABOR OMNIA VICIT above. Rv: As 65. Plain edge. (Miller Mass 65)						
Ma-Bo 74	(1860)	Brass	32mm	—	—	50.00	75.00
	As 73. Plain edge. (Miller Mass 66)						
Ma-Bo 75	(1860)	WM	32mm	—	—	50.00	75.00
	As 73. Plain edge. (Miller Mass 67)						
Ma-Bo 77	1859	Copper	32mm	—	—	20.00	50.00
	Bust of Sayers left, THOMAS SAYERS / CHAMPION OF ENGLAND 1859. Rv: As 65. Plain edge. (Wright 693A; Miller Mass 68)						

Rulau	Date	Metal	Size	F	VF	EF	Unc
Ma-Bo 78	1859	Copper	32mm	—	—	20.00	50.00
	Bust of Heenan right, JOHN C. HEENAN / CHAMPION OF AMERICA 1859. Rv: As 65. Plain edge. (Wright 693; Miller Mass 69)						
Ma-Bo 79	(1860)	WM	32mm	—	—	20.00	50.00
	Bust of Apollo. Rv: As 65. Plain edge. (Miller Mass 68A)						

Rulau	Date	Metal	Size	VG	F	VF	Unc
Ma-Bo 81	1862	Copper	27mm	—	—	—	Rare
	Washington head in wreath right, WASHINGTON above (obverse of Mass 55). Rv: MADE FROM COPPER / — TAKEN FROM — / THE RUINS OF / — THE — / TURPENTINE WORKS / NEWBERN / —N.C.— / DESTROYED BY THE REBELS / MARCH 14, 1862 (reverse of Miller Mass 15). Rarity 9. (Baker 622)						

Merriam store cards of the 1859-1860 period may be found in *U.S. Merchant Tokens 1845-1860.* Those true store cards of the Civil War period appear in *Civil War Store Cards* by the Fulds.

E. R. MORSE

Rulau	Date	Metal	Size	VG	F	VF	EF
Ma-Bo 83	(?)	Copper	29mm	—	200.	—	—
	E. R. MORSE / UNION ST. / BOSTON ctsp on U.S. 1802 Large cent. (Hallenbeck 13.752; Brunk 28520)						

NATIONAL PEACE JUBILEE

Rulau	Date	Metal	Size	F	VF	EF	Unc
Ma-Bo 88	1869	G/Br	28mm	—	5.00	10.00	15.00

Large building at center. Above: NATIONAL PEACE JUBILEE / LET US HAVE / PEACE. Below: COLISEUM / BOSTON JUNE 17. 69. Rv: U.S. eagle displayed, UNITED STATES above, THE BIRTH PLACE OF FREEDOM below. Plain edge. (Wright 1371)

Rulau	Date	Metal	Size	F	VF	EF	Unc
Ma-Bo 89	1869	G/Br	28mm	—	5.00	10.00	15.00

Obverse as last. Rv: P.S. GILMORE, / STATISTICS / LENGTH 500 FT / WIDTH 300 FT / HEIGHT 100 FT / LUMBER 2000000 / NAILS 23 TONS / GAS PIPE 25000 FT / SEATS 50000 / *** ORIGINATOR. ***. Plain edge.

H. M. RICHARDS & CO.

Rulau	Date	Metal	Size	F	VF	EF	Unc
Ma-Bo 94	(1879)	N/Steel*	31mm	—	—	300.	—

* The steel token has nickel plating on the edge and rim and on all lettering. The field is enameled black.

H. M. RICHARDS & CO. / MANUFRS OF / JEWELRY, / SOCIETY & / MILITARY / BADGES, / EMBLEMS &C. / *7 GREEN ST. BOSTON. *. Rv: * PAY AT * / 50 / THE COUNTER. Plain edge.

According to the patent application accompanying the only known specimen of this token, Hervey M. Richards of North Attleboro, Mass. (the same man who manufactured Hard Times tokens more than 40 years earlier) on June 29, 1878 filed this token with his application for a new design of "lunch and baggage checks." Patent No. 218.577 was granted Aug. 12, 1879.

In 1918 in Attleboro a probable successor firm, W. E. Richards Co., were manufacturing jewelers.

C. W. RICHARDSON

Rulau	Date	Metal	Size	VG	F	VF	EF
Ma-Bo 95	(?)	Silver	25mm	—	—	75.00	—

C. W. RICHARDSON, BOSTON ctsp on U.S. 1853 Arrows & Rays Seated Liberty quarter. (Brunk 34200)

JOHN ROBBINS

In 1863 Robbins was a manufacturer of brass, copper and white metal baggage checks, and also railroad lanterns, according to the city directory for that year. He was located at 42 Kneeland.

R & CO.
(Rueter & Company)

Rulau	Date	Metal	Size	VG	F	VF	EF
Ma-Bo D95	(?)	Brass	**	—	—	—	—

** Scal --mm.

H. S. B. / GOOD OF DRINK / R & CO. Rv: Blank. Plain edge. (Storer 471)

H.S.B. = Highland Spring Brewery.

Rueter & Co., Inc., brewers, were still in business 1918.

RUETER & ALLEY

Rulau	Date	Metal	Size	VG	F	VF	EF
Ma-Bo E95	(1870's)	Brass	30mm	400.	700.	1200.	—

Crossed broom, shovel and malt-spade, *R. — & — A. * above; H — S — B below. Rv: HIGHLAND SPRING BREWERY / (ornament) / RUETER / - & - ALLEY, / (ornament) / BOSTON. Rare. (Miller 85)

Rulau	Date	Metal	Size	VG	F	VF	EF
Ma-Bo F95	(1870's)	S/Brass	30mm	—	—	—	Ex. Rare

As E95. (Wright 921; Miller 86)

Rulau	Date	Metal	Size	VG	F	VF	EF
Ma-Bo G95	(1870's)	Copper	30mm	—	—	—	Ex.Rare

As E95. (Al Zaika coll.; Storer report)

In *The Numismatist* for September, 1914, the editor illustrated this token and asked for assistance in attributing it. If any assistance was forthcoming, it was never published. Dr. Benjamin P. Wright about 1900 called it, "one of the rarest American cards."

RUETER & CO.

Rulau	Date	Metal	Size	VG	F	VF	EF
Ma-Bo H95	(1880's)	Copper	29mm	—	—	—	1200.

Obverse similar to 85, but beaded circle encircles tools. *R. — & — CO.* replaces *R. — & — A.* In small letters below: SEMPER IDEM (ever the same). Rv: Within beaded circle: RUETER / & / COMPANY. Around: HIGHLAND SPRING BREWERY / BOSTON. Plain edge. (Miller 85A)

The Rueter companies have long been mystery firms to token collectors, but they are at last positioned properly in this reference. Earlier it had been thought they were Early or Hard Times pieces.

No Rueter is listed in Boston census reports for 1820, 1830, 1840 or 1850, or in the Boston directories for 1860 or 1863. However the 1888 directory lists Rueter & Co., Highland Spring Brewery, at Heath corner of Terrace.

The Rueter & Alley pieces probably were issued first.

In 1950 coin dealer John LeBlanc of Boston offered two or three different of these tokens for $50 each but could locate no takers, according to Steve Tanenbaum of New York. Maurice M. Gould of Boston never owned these pieces, Tanenbaum points out.

F. W. SNOW

Rulau	Date	Metal	Size	VG	F	VF	EF
Ma-Bo 96	(?)	Bronze	31mm	—	—	75.00	—

F. W. SNOW BOSTON ctsp on Great Britain 1865 Victoria penny. (Brunk 37450)

It is possible that the F. SNOW counterstamp on an 1851 Large cent, Hallenbeck 19.750; (Brunk 37440) is connected with this issuer.

Francis W. Snow, gold pen manufacturer, was located at 95 1/2 Washington Street in 1863.

T. P. SPITZ

Rulau	Date	Metal	Size	VG	F	VF	EF
Ma-Bo 97	(?)	GS	**	—	—	—	Scarce

** Oval 35 x 21.5mm.

Eagle. On three scrolls: T. P. SPITZ / 28 PORTER ST. / BOSTON. Rv: Blank. (Wright 1029)

STATE HOUSE CAFE

Rulau	Date	Metal	Size	VG	F	VF	EF
Ma-Bo 98	(1870's)	CN	**	—	—	—	Rare

** Square, 37x37mm.

STATE HOUSE / 10 / CAFE. Rv: JOHN ROBBINS M.F.R. CO. / BOSTON MASS. Plain edge. (Wright 1634)

Robbins made tokens from at least 1863 on. (See Robbins under Boston).

THROUGH THE FIRE

Rulau	Date	Metal	Size	VG	F	VF	EF
Ma-Bo 100	1872	Bronze	23mm	—	—	45.00	—

THROUGH . THE FIRE./ BOSTON./ NOV./ 9 / 1872. ctsp on U.S. 1867 2-cent piece. (Brunk 4440)

The great fire of 1872 destroyed much of the heart of Boston.

Rulau	Date	Metal	Size	VG	F	VF	EF
Ma-Bo 101	1872	CN	22mm	—	—	40.00	—

GREAT. FIRE / AT / BOSTON / NOV 9. ctsp on shaved obverse of U.S. Shield nickel. 1872 ctsp on reverse of the coin. (Kirtley June 1988 sale, lot 106)

Rulau	Date	Metal	Size	VG	F	VF	EF
Ma-Bo 102	1872	Bronze	23mm	—	—	45.00	—

BOSTON / NOV / 9-72 / FIRE ctsp on U.S. 1868 Shield 2-cent piece. (Brunk 4430)

Rulau	Date	Metal	Size	VG	F	VF	EF
Ma-Bo 103	1872	Bronze	23mm	—	—	45.00	—

GREAT FIRE BOSTON / NOV 9 / 1872 ctsp on U.S. Shield 2-cent piece. (Brunk 4435)

All the Great Fire souvenirs are from the same letter punches, Brunk points out.

YOUNGS HOTEL

Boston, Mass.

Rulau	Date	Metal	Size	VG	F	VF	Unc
Ma-Bo 120	(?)	Brass	28mm	—	—	—	—

(All incused): YOUNGS HOTEL HALL & WHIPPLE / 75 / C / BOSTON. Rv: Same as obverse. Plain edge. (Storer 818)

HARVARD BANJO CLUB

Cambridge, Mass.

Rulau	Date	Metal	Size				
Ma-Cm 4	1886	Copper	**	—	100.	—	—

** Oct. 42mm.
-HARVARD BANJO CLUB- / H - B - C in angles formed by crossed banjo and guitar / 1886. Rv: Blank. (Design is in circular border). (Kirtley Aug. 1987 sale, lot 152)

Charles Kirtley called this a die splasher in his 1987 catalog. The photo appears to indicate a complete medal, however, ready for engraving on its blank reverse. The piece is rare.

F. G. WINNETT

Cambridge, Mass.

Rulau	Date	Metal	Size	VG	F	VF	Unc
Ma-Cm 7	(ca 1873)	CN	**	2.00	3.50	5.00	11.50

** Oval 35x19mm.
Eagle. Inscribed: F.G. WINNETT / 25 MILL ST. / CAMBRIDGE / MASS. Rv: Blank. Plain edge. (Wright 1731)

Frederick G. Winnett is listed as a clerk at Rhoades' at 17 Brattle Square in the 1873 directory. Winnett boarded at 25 So. Mill St. that year.

'Rhoades' was the provisions store of Solomon Rhoades.

The Winnett piece must be an identification tag of some kind. Although Dr. Wright's piece has not been examined, it may be the same stock type as Tx-Cv 3 (which see under Clarksville, Texas).

ROBINSON & HEATH

Chicopee, Mass.

Rulau	Date	Metal	Size	VG	F	VF	Unc
Ma-Cp 4	(1880's)	Br	**	—	35.00	45.00	—

** Oct 26mm.
Indian head left in central circle. Around: L. BOCHE, ENGRAVER, DIE SINKER & MANUF'R OF CHECKS, 166 RANDOLPH ST. CHICAGO. Rv: GOOD FOR 5 CENTS / ROBINSON / & / HEATH / ... / CHICOPEE / MASS / * IN TRADE *. Plain edge. (Hartzog coll.)

Boche introduced the Indian head stock die about 1885. (See a similar card under Concordia, Elgin, Ill.)

CHELSEA M. E. CHURCH

Chelsea, Mass.

Rulau	Date	Metal	Size	F	VF	EF	Unc
Ma-Ch 3	1883	WM	27.8mm	—	15.00	20.00	25.00

Facade of building, CHELSEA M. E. CHURCH above. 1843 1883 in exergue. Rv: Within wreath: IN MEMORY / OF / DEBT PAYING / BY / THE SCHOOL / MAY '83. Plain edge. (Rulau MV 42K)

M.E. = Methodist Episcopal.

MASS. ARMS CO.

Chicopee Falls, Mass.

Rulau	Date	Metal	Size	VG	F	VF	EF
Ma-CF 3	(1860-66)	Copper	29mm	100.	—	150.	—

MANUFACTURED BY / MASS. ARMS CO. / CHICOPEE FALLS ctsp on U.S. Large cent. Examined: 1842, 1851, 1857. (Hallenbeck 13.502; Brunk 26430)

Rulau	Date	Metal	Size	VG	F	VF	EF
Ma-CF 6	(1860's)	Silver	31mm	—	—	225.	—

Similar ctsp on U.S. Liberty Seated 1857 half dollar (Kurt Krueger coll.)

Rulau	Date	Metal	Size	VG	F	VF	EF
Ma-CF 7	(1860's)	Copper	29mm	—	—	225.	—

Similar ctsp on U.S. Colonial coin.

The counterstamp is the stamp used to mark Smith breech-loading percussion carbines made by the firm during the Civil War. Massachusetts Arms Co. was incorporated March 5, 1850; the Smith carbine was patented 1856-1857. The firm also made Maynard and Greene carbines and Wesson and Leavitt revolvers. The business failed after the war and was taken over Feb. 1, 1876 by Lamb Knitting Machine Co.

Both Horace Smith and Daniel Wesson of the famed Smith & Wesson arms firms were early associates.

F. BLODGETT
Gardner, Mass.

Rulau	Date	Metal	Size	VG	F	VF	EF
Ma-Gr 2	(?)	Copper	29mm	—	—	75.00	—

F. BLODGETT / GARDNER, MASS. ctsp on U.S. Large cent. (Hallenbeck 2.545; Brunk 4050)

ROGERS & BRO.
Gloucester, Mass.

Rulau	Date	Metal	Size	VG	F	VF	Unc
Ma-Gc 7	(?)	Brass	19mm	—	10.00	—	20.00

Closed hand emitting electric discharges. ROGERS & BRO TRIPLE PLATE. Rv: Blank. Plain edge. (Wright 910)

J. S. Rogers & Brother were manufacturing jewelers.

F. L. BLINN
Haverhill, Mass.

Rulau	Date	Metal	Size	VG	F	VF	Unc
Ma-Hv 2	(1880's?)	Brass	--mm	—	—	20.00	—

F. L. BLINN / Large ornate 5 / HAVERHILL. Rv: Large ornate 5 at center, rayed 5-pointed star above and below. Dentilated rim on each side. Plain edge. (Jim Hirtle coll., Westminster, Md.)

Blinn reputedly ran a cigar store.

J. C. TILTON
Haverhill, Mass. (?)

Rulau	Date	Metal	Size	VG	F	VF	EF
Ma-Hv 18	ND	Silver	19mm	40.00	—	65.00	—

Large X in relief within shaded circular depression above: J. C. TILTON in relief within rectangular depression, ctsp on Spanish-American 1-real or U.S. dime (?), worn smooth. 3 pieces known. (Rulau coll., ex-Fauver and Steinberg; Brunk 40175)

J. C. Tilton was a shoe manufacturer in Haverhill, Mass. The attribution is doubtful.

Both the circular and rectangular depressions are from prepared punches such as those used by silversmiths and other metalsmiths, but Tilton has not been located in any metalworker listing.

W. A. CHENEY
Holyoke, Mass.

Rulau	Date	Metal	Size	VG	F	VF	Unc
Ma-Hy 3	1874	Bronze	31mm	—	—	60.00	—

W. A. CHENEY / HOLYOKE MASS ctsp on reverse of Great Britain 1863 penny. MAY 16 74 ctsp on obverse of coin. (Dwight Demeritt collection)

ARLINGTON COOP. ASSN.
Lawrence, Mass.

Rulau	Date	Metal	Size	VG	F	VF	Unc
Ma-Ar 1	1884	Brass	29mm	—	—	—	—

ARLINGTON COOP. ASSN. / LAWRENCE, MASS. / INC. JULY 8, 1884. Rv: 10. Plain edge. (Storer 1131)

PIERCE'S ROSETTA HAIR TONIC
Lowell, Mass.

Rulau	Date	Metal	Size	VG	F	EF	Unc
Ma-Lo 15	(?)	Silver	27mm	150.	—	225.	—

GOOD FOR / A BOTTLE / PIERCE'S / ROSETTA / HAIR TONIC ctsp on Spanish-American 2-reales. Dates examined: 1772, 1797, 1810, 1820, 1821. (Gould 340; Brunk 32060)

Rulau	Date	Metal	Size	VG	F	EF	Unc
Ma-Lo 16	(?)	Silver	27mm	—	—	225.	—

Similar ctsp on Mexico 1826-Mo 2-reales. (Rulau MV 257A)

(Also see Dr. Darby under Boston, Mass. for Gould 325, which is a combination counterstamp of Dr. Darby and Pierce's Rosetta Hair Tonic on a Spanish-American 2-reales.)

Dr. George Pierce was a patent medicine dealer of Lowell, Mass.

W. A. C.

Rulau	Date	Metal	Size	VG	F	VF	Unc
Ma-Lo 4	1876	WM	25mm	—	—	10.00	—

Female seated right, in her hand a distaff for spinning. SHE SEEKETH / WOOL AND FLAX AND WORKETH WILLINGLY WITH HER HANDS 1776. Rv: Large monogram. W.A.C. at center. ART IS THE HAND MAID OF HUMAN GOOD / LOWELL 1876. Plain edge. (Wright 1194)

A. LAWRENCE
Lowell, Mass.

Rulau	Date	Metal	Size	VG	F	VF	EF
Ma-Lo 8	(?)	CN	19mm	—	—	150.	—

A. LAWRENCE / DENTIST / LOWELL ctsp on U.S. 1857 Flying Eagle cent. (Brunk 24050)

Lawrence practiced dentistry in Lowell 1841-1872.

DR. RIDGE'S FOOD
Malden, Mass.

Rulau	Date	Metal	Size	VG	F	VF	Unc
Ma-Md 10	1872	WM	32mm	—	—	65.00	—

* DR. RIDGE'S FOOD FOR * / (embossed) 4 — 1 — 2 — 3 (At four compass points) / (raised boss, for spinning) / INFANTS & INVALIDS. Rv: WORLD'S PEACE JUBILEE & MUSICAL FESTIVAL / DR. RIDGE'S FOOD FOR / (raised boss) / INFANTS & INVALIDS / * 1872 *. Plain edge. (Wright 896 variety: Horatio Storer 3025 or 3026). Rarity 9.

In *Medicina in Nummis*, Dr. Storer mentions three varieties of this very early spinner token, one of which is 34mm in diameter.

Dr. Ridge's was America's first baby food, appearing long before Gerber's or Pablum were heard of. It was manufactured at first in Malden and later in Palmer, Mass.

John Woolrich was born 1837 in Handley, Cheshire, England, and apprenticed as a chemist in Chester. In 1860 at age 23 he emigrated to Halifax, Nova Scotia and established a leading pharmaceutical business there. He married Louisa Woodill of Halifax in 1862.

In 1872 Woolrich obtained the manufacturing and distribution rights in the U.S. for Ridge's Baby Food, an English patented preparation, and he joined others in a venture in Malden, Massachusetts. Dr. Ridge's Food was made of pure wheat grains which had been subjected to a process which made it easily digestible and nutritious for babies and invalids. Woolrich thus became the first person in the United States to venture into the baby food business.

In 1874 the factory was moved to Palmer, Mass., where railroads could ease distribution. Woolrich & Co.'s plant, known as Ridge's Food Factory, was located in a large frame building resembling a residence at the corner of Pine and Thorndike Streets. In 1877 Woolrich himself settled in Palmer, building a posh residence, Tushingham Cottage, on a hill on Thorndike Street overlooking his factory.

In 1895 Woolrich sold both the business and the residence to G. M. Atkins and S. H. Hellyar, and he retired. After that the business gradually faded away as others, more aggressive, entered the baby food business.

(Information courtesy Robert H. L. Russell, Palmer, Mass., and the article by Marion Lis, "Baby Food Industry Had Infancy Here" in *The Journal Register* for Jan. 10, 1985)

ESSEX COUNTY CLUB
Manchester, Mass.

Rulau	Date	Metal	Size	VG	F	VF	Unc
Ma-Mn 3	(?)	Silver	35mm	—	—	—	—

Goat, courant to left, in central circle. Around: ESSEX COUNTY CLUB / MANCHESTER . MASS. Rv: Blank. Plain edge. (Storer 1243)

Rulau	Date	Metal	Size	VG	F	VF	Unc
Ma-Mn 5	(?)	Bronze	**	—	—	—	—

** Irreg 36mm.

Golfer left on crossed pine boughs, trees in the background. Around: ESSEX COUNTY CLUB. Rv: Blank. Plain edge. (Storer 1244)

The Essex County Club was a country club featuring golf as a main attraction. The bronze piece above was struck by N. G. Wood & Sons.

Probably both pieces are membership medalets, on which the member's name could be engraved.

The term "courant" is an heraldic one meaning "prancing" and usually used with horses. It is distinguished from "rampant" (fully erect on hind legs, usually used with lions); courant indicates the forelegs are above the ground but not nearly so upright as in the term rampant.

Goats were occasionally used as the heraldic symbols for golfing clubs of Massachusetts on their membership medals. For example the clubs in Albemarles, Brookline and Hoosik-Whisick featured a goat on their membership pieces. It would be interesting to trace the deprivation of this usage; the goat is not normally thought of as one of the "noble" animals (lion, horse, eagle, bull) frequently used to adorn medals and coins.

TOWLE SILVERSMITHS

Newburyport, Mass.

Rulau	Date	Metal	Size	F	VF	EF	Unc
Ma-Nw 5	(?)	Silver	25.2mm	—	—	100.	—

(All incuse, script lettering): Towle Silversmiths / (stylized walking rampant lion right) / Sterling / 900 / Newburyport Massachusetts. Rv: Blank. Plain edge. (Fred Borgmann coll.)

The weight of this piece is 3.23 grams and its specific gravity 9.78, indicating silver purity of about .575.

It is difficult to assess this token's purpose, but it clearly emanates from the firm begun by Towle and Jones in 1857 which became in 1940 Towle Manufacturing Company. They were major manufacturers of silverware and later of silverplated ware.

PALMER, MASS.

Rulau	Date	Metal	Size	VG	F	VF	EF
Ma-Pa 1	(?)	Silver	38mm	25.00	—	50.00	—

PALMER, MASS. ctsp on U.S. 1879 Morgan silver dollar. (Koppenhaver Aug. 1982 sale; Brunk 30810)

NOVELTY CHECK CO.

North Attleboro, Mass.

Rulau	Date	Metal	Size	VG	F	VF	Unc
Ma-At 6	1879	CN	28.5mm	—	—	100.	—

* NOVELTY * / CHECK / CO. / PAT. AUG / 12 '79 / NO. ATTLEBORO, MASS. Rv: PAY AT / 40 * THE COUNTER *. Reeded edge. Rare. (Dick Balbaton coll.)

The card is enameled black. It is non-magnetic.

CHARLES ALBERT COPELAND

Peabody, Mass.

Rulau	Date	Metal	Size	F	VF	EF	Unc
Ma-Pe 2	1871	Silver	38mm	—	—	200.	—

CHARLES ALBERT COPELAND / BORN / MARCH / 2ND amid flourishes engraved on planed-off reverse of U.S. 1871 Seated Liberty dollar. (William Swoger coll.; Brunk 9507)

Copeland was born March 2, 1871 in Peabody, and lived and died in the same city, according to Swoger.

There was no Copeland in business in Peabody in 1918, according to the Dun directory. He would have been 47 at the time.

G. S. GATES

Rutland, Mass.

Rulau	Date	Metal	Size	VG	F	VF	EF
Ma-Ru 5	(?)	Silver	25mm	—	—	75.00	—

G. S. GATES / RUTLAND, MASS. ctsp on U.S. 1875 Liberty Seated quarter dollar. (Gould 82; Brunk 15820)

BEE HIVE

Salem, Mass.

Rulau	Date	Metal	Size	VG	F	VF	Unc
Ma-Sa 3	(?)	WM	28.5mm	—	—	20.00	—

BEE HIVE / 5. Rv: Same as obverse. Plain edge.

Attributed by association with a business card with which it was discovered. The card reads: FRANK COUSINS — BEE HIVE — SALEM, MASS. — XMAS & NEW YEAR GIFTS.

BICYCLE TOURNAMENT

Springfield, Mass.

Rulau	Date	Metal	Size	F	VF	EF	Unc
Ma-Sp 2	1883	WM	35mm	—	—	25.00	35.00

Bearded male bust right, BICYCLE TOURNAMENT above, SEPT. 18-19-20 / — 1883 — below. Rv: Ornate shield of arms at center. Inscription around: SPRINGFIELD. / ORGANIZED A TOWN MAY 14. 1636 O.S. ** A CITY MAY 25. 1852. Plain edge. (Lot 1340, Brand 1984 sale; not in Storer)

J. A. BOLEN

NOTE: Restrikes of some Bolen rarities exist, which are undectable from originals.

Rulau	Date	Metal	Size	F	VF	EF	Unc
Ma-Sp 4	1862	Copper	28.3mm	—	—	—	150.

Boy with flag riding a flying eagle, YOUNG AMERICA around, 1862 below. Border of dots and stars around rim. Rv: J. A. BOLEN / DIE SINKER / AND / MEDALIST / SPRINGFIELD, MASS. Plain edge. Only 75 struck. (Wright 127; Miller Mass 101)

Rulau	Date	Metal	Size	F	VF	EF	Unc
Ma-Sp 5	1862	Brass	28.3mm	—	—	—	150.

As 4. Plain edge. Only 75 struck. (Miller Mass 102)

Rulau	Date	Metal	Size	F	VF	EF	Unc
Ma-Sp 6	1862	Silvered	28.3mm	—	—	—	150.

As 4. Plain edge. (Miller Mass 102A)

Rulau	Date	Metal	Size	F	VF	EF	Unc
Ma-Sp 7	1862	Copper	28.3mm	—	—	75.00	100.

Obverse as 4. Rv: Building with flag flying, tiny J. A. BOLEN on truncation. Below: U.S. / ARSENAL. Plain edge. (Miller Mass 101A)

Rulau	Date	Metal	Size	F	VF	EF	Unc
Ma-Sp 8	1862	WM	28.3mm	—	—	75.00	100.

As 7. Plain edge. (R. B. White collection). This piece was not recorded by Adams or Miller.

Ma-Sp 10 (1950) Copper 29mm — 35.00 — —
J. A. BOLEN ctsp on U.S. 1848, 1851 or worn Large cent. Also, J. A. BOLEENN ctsp in mirror-image in smaller letters on same side of cent. Plain edge. (R. B. White collection; Brunk 4170)

Rulau	Date	Metal	Size	VG	F	VF	EF
Ma-Sp 11	(1950)	Copper	29mm	—	35.00	—	—

J. A. BOLEN. / J. A. BOLEN. ctsp on U.S. early Large cent, date worn off.

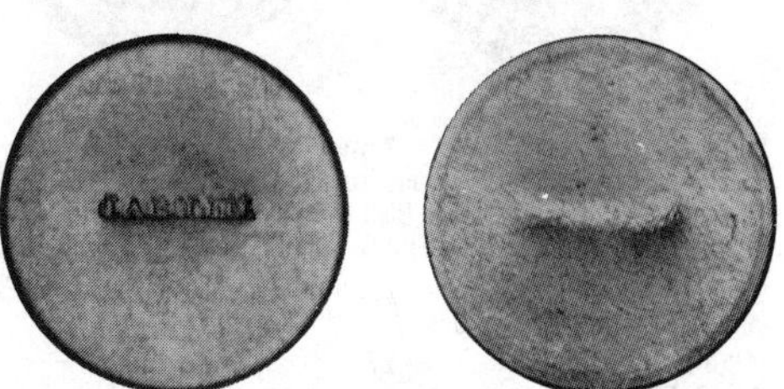

Rulau	Date	Metal	Size	F	VF	EF	Unc
Ma-Sp 12	(1950)	Alum	28.7mm	—	—	35.00	—

J. A. BOLEN ctsp on blank aluminum disc. Plain edge. (R. B. White collection)

The three counterstamps above appear to be test pieces by Bolen to test his name punches, as used on the truncations of various tokens which he signed. There are two specimens of the aluminum disc in the R. B. White collection, and several others elsewhere.

NOTE REGARDING Ma-Sp 10, 11 and 12, the Bolen counterstamps:

An old Boston coin dealer, Harold Whiteneck, who had a shop downtown, told Kenneth Hallenbeck that his brother possessed a group of genuine Bolen punches and "punched up" some U.S. Large cents, with which he teased counterstamp specialist Maurice M. Gould, then head of Copley Coin Co. in Boston. The dealer, Whiteneck, in 1955, moved to Fort Lauderdale, Fla.

The counterstamps are fantasy or sport strikes; they will remain listed here, with appropriate remarks, since the Bolen punches apparently were original and their products, thus, desirable.

Some original Bolen punches were sold in the 1977 auction of Maurice Gould's estate, and another appeared in a 1990 Bowers & Merena sale.

Ma-Sp 14 (1862) Copper 28.3mm — — — 100.
Obverse as reverse of Ma-Sp 7 (U.S. Arsenal). Rv: U.S. ARMORY / * / ESTABLISHED / BY / ACT OF CONGRESS / IN APRIL, / 1794. / SPRINGFIELD, MASS. Plain edge.

Ma-Sp 14A (1862) Brass 28.3mm — — — 75.00
As 14. Plain edge. 75 struck.

Ma-Sp 15 (1862) Copper 28.3mm — — — Rare
Similar to Ma-Sp 14, except that sun appears at upper left of obverse, above the armory. Plain edge. Only 5 struck.

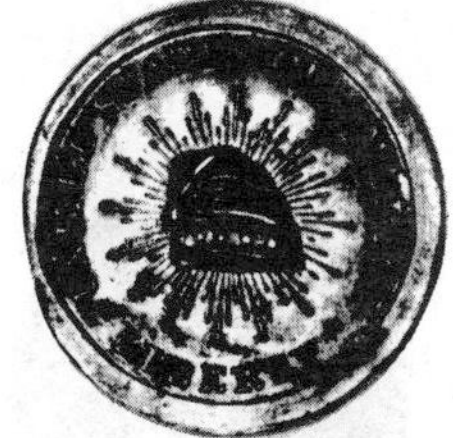

Ma-Sp 16 (1862) Copper 28.3mm — — — 75.00
Obverse as reverse of 7 (U.S. Arsenal). Rv: Liberty cap within rays. Around: UNITED STATES OF AMERICA / * LIBERTY *. Plain edge. (Wright 1173)

Ma-Sp 16A (1862) WM 28.3mm — — — 100.
As 16. (Ken Kershaw coll.; Midge Hall, England)

Ma-Sp 17 (1862) Brass 28.3mm — — — 100.
Obverse as 14 (Arsenal). Rv: As reverse of 18 (Bolen store card). Plain edge.

Ma-Sp 17A (1862) WM 28.3mm — — — 100.
As 17. Plain edge.

Ma-Sp 18 (1862) Brass 28.3mm — — — 100.
Obverse: U.S. ARMORY / * / ESTABLISHED / BY / ACT OF CONGRESS / IN APRIL, / 1794. / SPRINGFIELD, MASS. Rv: As reverse of Ma-Sp 4 (J. A. BOLEN / DIE SINKER). Plain edge. (Wright 1171; Springfield 1981 sale, lot 4508)

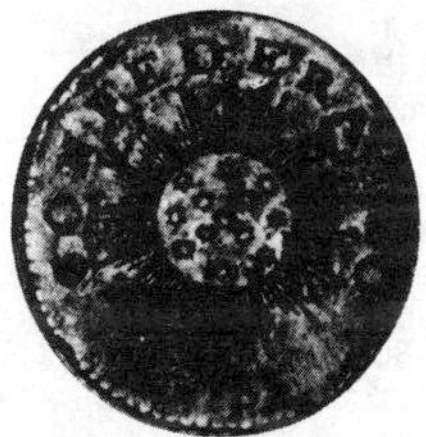

Ma-Sp 20 (1862) Copper 28.3mm — — Unique
Confederatio cent imitation. Rv: As Ma-Sp 4 reverse.

Ma-Sp 22 (1864) Brass 28mm — — — 350.
J. A. BOLEN, / (ornament) / DIE SINKER AND MEDALIST. SPRINGFIELD, MASS. Rv: Radiant Phrygian (Liberty) cap at center, UNITED STATES OF AMERICA around, * LIBERTY * below. Plain edge. (Miller Mass 102B)

Only known specimen of 22 sold Oct. 30, 1982 in New York Public Library sale, lot 2718, for $352.

Ma-Sp 24 1864 Oroide 28mm — — — 200.
Bearded bust of Bolen left, a rosette at either side. J. A. BOLEN, above, 1864 below. Rv: As reverse of 22 (Liberty cap). Only 25 struck. (Miller Mass 103)

Ma-Sp 25 1864 Copper 28mm — — — 200.
As 24. Plain edge. (Fuld NC-9a). Rarity 9.

Mad-Sp 26 1864 Silver 28mm — — — Unique
As 24. Plain edge. (Fuld NC-9f)

NOTE: Some authorities question whether there is any difference between Ma-Sp 24 and 25. Bolen himself did not recognize the difference between Oroide and Copper. Specialist Michael E. Hallihan of Ayer, Mass., believes the Oroide distinction was made by a dealer to hype sales from a catalog he produced.

Ma-Sp 28 1864 Copper 28mm — — — 200.
Obverse similar to 24, but smaller date and lettering. Rv: STAMP. CUTTER, / (ornament) / DIE. SINKER, / AND / MEDALIST. / SPRINGFIELD, MASS. Plain edge. Only 25 struck. (Miller Mass 105; Fuld NC-8a). Rarity 8.

Ma-Sp 29 1864 Brass 28mm — — — 250.
Same as 28. Plain edge. (Miller Mass 105A)

Ma-Sp 30 1865 Copper 28mm — — — 100.
Obverse similar to Ma-Sp 24, but 1865 date. Rv: As reverse of Ma-Sp 28. Plain edge. Only 10 struck. (Miller Mass 106)

Ma-Sp 31 1865 WM 28mm — — — 100.
As 30. Plain edge. Only 10 struck. (Miller Mass 107)

Ma-Sp 32 1865 WM 28mm — — — 150.
Obverse similar, but TWO STRUCK & DIE DESTROYED added. Plain edge. Only 2 struck. (Miller Mass 108)

Ma-Sp 34 1865 Oroide 27mm — — — 100.
Bearded bust of Bolen left, J. A. BOLEN. at left, 1865. at right. Rv: Within oak wreath: DIE / SINKER / &c. / SPRINGFIELD / MASS / B. (tiny). Plain edge. Only 50 struck. (Miller Mass 109)

Ma-Sp 35 1865 WM 27mm — — — 100.
As 34. Plain edge. Only 50 struck. (Miller Mass 110)

Ma-Sp 36 (?) Silver 27mm — — — Unique
Head of Bolen to left, tiny BOLEN under bust. J. A. BOLEN around. Rv: DIE SINKER &C. (same as Bolen number 21). Plain edge. Only 1 struck. (Miller Mass 111)

Ma-Sp 37 (?) Copper 27mm — — — 100.
As 36. Plain edge. Only 15 struck. (Miller Mass 112)

Ma-Sp 38 (?) Brass 27mm — — — 100.
As 36. Plain edge. Only 15 struck. (Miller Mass 113)

Ma-Sp 39 (?) WM 27mm — — — 100.
As 36. Plain edge. Only 15 struck. (Miller Mass 114)

Ma-Sp 40 1865 Silver 27mm — — Ex. Rare
Obverse as Ma-Sp 34 (bust left, 1865). Rv: As reverse of Ma-Sp 41 (Libertas Americana). Plain edge. Only 2 struck.

Ma-Sp 41 1867 Silver 27mm — — — Unique
Bearded bust of Bolen left, J. A. BOLEN, at left, 1867 at right. Rv: LIBERTAS AMERICANA. Plain edge. Only 1 struck. (Miller Mass 115; Bolen 32)

Ma-Sp 42 1867 Brass 27mm — — — Unique
As 41. Plain edge. Only 1 struck. (Miller Mass 116)

Ma-Sp 43 1867 Copper 27mm — — — 100.
As 41. Plain edge. (Miller Mass 116A)

Ma-Sp 43D 1867 WM 27mm — — — Unique
As 41. Plain edge. Only 1 struck. The location of this piece in any collection is not known; it was listed as Mule-3 in Bolen's own catalog.

Ma-Sp 44 1867 Copper 27mm — — — 100.
Obverse as 41 (Bolen left, 1867). Rv: As reverse of 34 (DIE SINKER in wreath). Plain edge. Only 14 struck. (Springfield 1981 sale, lot 4508)

Ma-Sp 45 1867 WM 27mm — — — 100.
Same as 44. Plain edge. Only 2 specimens known. (Springfield 1981 sale, lot 4508)

Ma-Sp 45A 1867 Brass 27mm — — Unique
As Ma-Sp 44. Plain edge. Only 1 struck.

Ma-Sp 47 1869 Silver 27mm — — — Unique
Bearded bust of Bolen left, J. A. BOLEN, at left, 1869. at right. Rv: As reverse of 34 (DIE SINKER in wreath). Plain edge. Only 1 struck. (Miller Mass 117; Bolen 217)

Ma-Sp 48 1869 Copper 27mm — — — 100.
As 47. Plain edge. Only 28 struck. (Miller Mass 118)

Ma-Sp 49 1869 Brass 27mm — — — 100.
As 47. Plain edge. Only 20 struck. (Miller Mass 119)

Ma-Sp 50 1869 WM 27mm — — — 150.
As 47. Plain edge. Only 3 struck. (Miller Mass 120)

Ma-Sp 52 1869 Silver 27mm — — — 250.
Obverse as 47. Rv: As obverse of Ma-Sp 56 (THE PYNCHON HOUSE). Plain edge. (Miller Mass 123)

Ma-Sp 53 1869 Copper 27mm — — — 100.
As 52. Plain edge. (Miller Mass 124)

Ma-Sp 54 1869 Brass 27mm — — — 100.
As 52. Plain edge. (Miller Mass 125)

Ma-Sp 56 (1869) Brass 27mm — — 20.00 40.00
View of the Old Pynchon House from the left side. Rv: THE PYNCHON HOUSE. / CALLED / THE OLD FORT. / BUILT BY / JOHN PYNCHON, / IN 1660. / TAKEN DOWN / IN 1831. / SPRINGFIELD. MASS. Plain edge. Only 45 struck.

Ma-Sp 56A (1869) Copper 27mm — — 20.00 40.00
As 56. Plain edge. 95 struck.

Ma-Sp 56B (1869) WM 27mm — — 30.00 50.00
As 56. Plain edge.

Ma-Sp 56C (1869) Silver 27mm — — — 150.
As 56. Plain edge. Only 10 struck.

Bolen was active as a diesinker from 1861 to 1891.

J. CUMMINGS

Rulau	Date	Metal	Size	VG	F	VF	EF
Ma-Sp 58	(?)	Copper	33mm	—	—	35.00	—

J. CUMMINGS / SPRINGFIELD MASS ctsp on Canada 1857 Bank of Upper Canada penny token, Breton 719.

MOORE BROTHERS

Rulau	Date	Metal	Size	F	VF	EF	Unc
Ma-Sp 60	(1870)	WM	27mm	—	—	100.	150.

MOORE BROTHERS / PHOTOGRAPHIC / ARTISTS. / OPP / COURT SQUARE / MAIN ST. / SPRINGFIELD, MASS. Rv: PHOTOGRAPHS / MADE / AND FINISHED / IN ANY / DESIRED / STYLE OR SIZE. Plain edge. Only 400 struck. (Wright 720; Storer 1683; Miller Mass 128)

Ma-Sp 61 (1870) Copper 27mm — — — 200.
As 60. Only 5 struck. (Miller Mass 126)

Ma-Sp 62 (1870) Brass 27mm — — — 300.
As 60. Supposedly only 1 struck. (Miller Mass 127)

All were struck by J. A. Bolen of Springfield, Mass

L. C. RODIER

Rulau	Date	Metal	Size	VG	F	VF	Unc
Ma-Sp 63	1873	Brass	29mm	—	—	35.00	—

Large 5-pointed star. Around: L. C. RODIER'S PATENT — NOV 18. 73. (Stanley Steinberg 1982 sale)

Louis C. Rodier was a gunsmith. In 1862 and in 1873 he obtained rifle patents. In 1873 the firm was called Rodier & Bates.

SOLDIERS' FAIR

Rulau	Date	Metal	Size	F	VF	EF	Unc
Ma-Sp 65	1864	WM	27mm	—	—	—	200.

Washington bust left, J. A. BOLEN under truncation. WASHINGTON above. Rv: SOLDIERS' / FAIR / DEC. / 1864. / SPRINGFIELD, MASS. (all within oak wreath). Plain edge. 350 struck. (Schenkman B5)

Rulau	Date	Metal	Size	F	VF	EF	Unc
Ma-Sp 65A	1864	Copper	27mm	—	—	—	Rare

As 65. Plain edge. Only 2 struck.

Rulau	Date	Metal	Size	F	VF	EF	Unc
Ma-Sp 65B	1864	CN	27mm	—	—	—	Rare

As 65. Plain edge. (Ganter coll.)

Rulau	Date	Metal	Size	F	VF	EF	Unc
Ma-Sp 67	(1870's)	SC	27mm	—	—	150.	—

Obverse as Miller Mass 17A (Beardless Lincoln right). Rv: As last. Plain edge. (DeWitt AL 1860-45(C); King 514)

Rulau	Date	Metal	Size	F	VF	EF	Unc
Ma-Sp 68	(1870's)	Copper	27mm	—	—	10.00	25.00
Ma-Sp 68A	(1870's)	Silver	27mm	—	—	—	250.

Ma-Sp 68: Obverse as Ma-Bo 33 reverse (Apollo head). Rv: As last. (Schenkman B-3)

Ma-Sp 68A: As 68. Plain edge. (Storer 1700)

Rulau	Date	Metal	Size	F	VF	EF	Unc
Ma-Sp 68F	(1867-71)	WM	29mm	—	—	—	250.

Obverse as rev. of Ma-Sp 65. Rv: PARTIES / -+- / SUPPLIED / -- / AT SHORT / -*- / NOTICE. Plain edge. Ex. Rare.

68F is an illogical muling of Soldiers' Fair and George Fera (Boston) store cards, made from original Merriam dies in the 1867-71 period.

SPRINGFIELD ANTIQUARIANS

Springfield, Mass.

Rulau	Date	Metal	Size	VG	F	VF	Unc
Ma-Sp 69	1866	Copper	28mm	—	—	—	40.00

Eagle perched on shield, to right, MASSACHUSETTS above, 1866 below. Rv: SPRINGFIELD / ANTIQUARIANS / * / JAS PARKER, / WM. H BOWDOIN, / C. B. NEWELL, / J. A. BOLEN, / J WHITCOMB, / D. K. LEE, / WM. CLOGSTON. Only 14 struck. (Wright 1034)

Rulau	Date	Metal	Size	VG	F	VF	Unc
Ma-Sp 70	1866	WM	28mm	—	—	—	Unique

As last. Only 1 struck.

Struck by James A. Bolen of Springfield.

Rulau	Date	Metal	Size	VG	F	VF	Unc
Ma-Sp 70A	1866	Brass	28mm	—	—		Unique
Ma-Sp 70B	1866	Silver	28mm	—	—	—	300.

Ma-Sp 70A: As 69. Only 1 struck.

Ma-Sp 70B: As 69. Only 2 struck.

Rulau	Date	Metal	Size	VG	F	VF	Unc
Ma-Sp 72	1866	Copper	28mm	—	—	V. Rare	

Obverse as 69. Rv: LEXINGTON, / APRIL 19, 1775. / ******* / BALTIMORE, / APRIL 19, 1861., all within floreate circle. Plain edge.

Rulau	Date	Metal	Size	VG	F	VF	Unc
Ma-Sp 72A	1866	Brass	28mm	—	—	—	Unique
Ma-Sp 72B	1866	WM	28mm	—	—	—	Unique
Ma-Sp 72C	1866	Silver	28mm	—	—	—	Ex. Rare

Ma-Sp 72A: As 72. Plain edge.

Ma-Sp 72B: As 72. Plain edge.

Ma-Sp 72C: As 72. Plain edge.

C. H. HASKELL

West Townsend, Mass.

Rulau	Date	Metal	Size	VG	F	VF	EF
Ma-WT 1	1861	Brass	28mm	—	—	—	Ex.Rare

Spread eagle, WAR OF 1861 / UNITED STATES around. Rv: (All incused): C. H. HASKELL / PALM LEAF / HAT / MANUFTR / WEST . TOWNSEND MS. Plain edge. (Storer 1763)

This is a most unusual item - a Civil War dog tag (soldier's identity tag) turned into a store card advertisement for a manufacturer! Only a single copy is known at this time.

DEUTSCHER LIEDERKRANZ

Webster, Mass.

Rulau	Date	Metal	Size	VG	F	VF	Unc
Ma-Wb 1	(?)	Brass	**	—	—	—	—

** Scal 25mm.

In circle of stars: A lyre. DEUTSCHER LIEDERKRANZ. Rv: Blank. Plain edge. (Storer 1740)

Deutscher Liederkranz = German Singing Circle.

In the final quarter of the 19th century, German singing groups all over America issued tokens, sometimes as membership badges and occasionally as "good fors." Liederkranz is sometimes rendered as "Gesangverein = Singing Society" or by another German idiom.

T. W. S. JOZEFA

Rulau	Date	Metal	Size	VG	F	VF	Unc
Ma-Wb 3	(?)	Brass	29mm?	—	—	25.00	—

(All incused): T W. S. JOZEFA. / WEBSTER. / MASS. Rv: (?). Plain edge.

TURNVEREIN

Webster, Mass.

Rulau	Date	Metal	Size	VG	F	VF	Unc
Ma-Wb 20	(?)	WM	**	—	—	—	—

** Oval 26x19mm.

TURNVEREIN / VORWAERTS / WEBSTER, MASS. Rv: Blank. Plain edge. (Storer 1741)

A turnverein was a German athletic and fraternal group - part of the worldwide Turners' movement. VORWAERTS = Forward, their motto.

ALLEN'S PATENT
(E. Allen & Co.)
Worcester, Mass.

Rulau	Date	Metal	Size	VG	F	VF	Unc
Ma-Wc 1	(1856-71)	Copper	29mm	—	—	75.00	—

ALLEN'S PATENT / 1845 ctsp on U.S. Large cent. (Brunk 630)

Allen & Wheelock and its successor, E. Allen & Co., both located in Worcester, Mass., used the term ALLEN'S PATENT to mark many of the rifles, pistols and "pepperbox" revolvers they made in the 1856-71 period. Ethan Allen's many patents were obtained in 1837, 1845, 1855, 1857, 1858, 1860, 1865 and 1868 — and the patent dates also were stamped into the metal parts of guns.

Ethan Allen (no relation to the Revolutionary War hero) began manufacturing in 1831 in the hamlet of Milford, Mass. Knives were his product — knives of all kinds, shoemaker tools and other devices for cutting. Later in 1831 he moved to North Grafton, Mass. and began his gunmaking career by producing a "cane gun" patented by Dr. Roger Lambert.

The 1837 patent covered a "tube hammer" pocket pistol, a forerunner of his famed pepperbox pistols. Ethan Allen (1806-71) was personally involved in all these firms:

E. Allen 1831-37
Allen & Thurber 1837-54
Allen Thurber & Co. 1854-56
Allen & Wheelock 1856-65
E. Allen & Co. 1865-71

His two sons-in-law, Henry C. Wadsworth and Sullivan Forehand, took over the firm in 1871 under the Forehand & Sullivan name.

(Reference: "Flayderman's Guide to Antique American Firearms" by Norm Flayderman, Northbrook, Ill., 1980)

C. V. FROHSINN

Rulau	Date	Metal	Size	VG	F	VF	Unc
Ma-Wc A2	(?)	WM	23mm	—	—	—	—

C. V. FROHSINN . / 5 / WORCESTER . MASS. Rv: Blank. Plain edge. (Storer 1793)

FISKE & GODDARD

Rulau	Date	Metal	Size	VG	F	VF	Unc
Ma-Wc 2	(?)	Copper	**	—	—	—	—

** Oval 38x26mm.
FISKE & GODDARD / WATCH MAKERS / & / JEWELERS / 195 MAIN ST. / UNION BLOCK / WORCESTER . MASS. Rv: Blank. Plain edge. (Storer 1792)

L. D. GODDARD

Rulau	Date	Metal	Size	VG	F	VF	Unc
Ma-Wc 3	(?)	Brass	27mm	—	—	—	—

(All incused): L. D. GODDARD / WATCHMAKER / 195 MAIN ST. / UNION BLOCK / WORCESTER . MASS. Rv: Blank. Plain edges. (Storer 1794)

Both the Fiske & Goddard and L. D. Goddard pieces are watchmaker's checks, used in the 19th century to keep track of customer's watches taken in for repair.

Goddard was a grand old name in Worcester manufacturing jewelry circles. L. Goddard & Son were active about 1830; D. Goddard & Son about 1845; D. Goddard & Co. circa 1845-1850. Neither L. D. Goddard nor Fiske & Goddard have as yet been traced, but the name Goddard disappears from Worcester directories before World War I. Tentatively we are assuming an 1870-90 provenance for these checks.

H. HALE

Rulau	Date	Metal	Size	VG	F	VF	EF
Ma-Wc 4	(?)	CN	19mm	—	—	20.00	—

H. HALE ctsp on U.S. 1857 Flying Eagle cent. (Brunk; 17760)

Ma-Wc 5	(?)	Silver	31mm	—	—	30.00	—

Similar ctsp on U.S. 1855 Seated Liberty half dollar.

A.J. Hale of Bristol, Conn. and Worcester, Mass., was a gunsmith active in the 1837-1852 period. His mark is encountered on pistols. This attribution is very tentative.

D. A. HAWKINS

Rulau	Date	Metal	Size	VG	F	VF	Unc
Ma-WC 6	(?)	Copper	29mm	—	—	50.00	—

D. A. HAWKINS . / WORCESTER . MASS ctsp on U.S. Large cent. (Storer 1795)

F. M. LAMB

Rulau	Date	Metal	Size	VG	F	VF	Unc
Ma-WC 8	(?)	Brass	26mm	—	—	—	—

HARRINGTON CORNER / F. M. LAMB / WATCH MAKER / 275 Main St. / WORCESTER MASS. Rv: Blank. Plain edge. (Storer 1798)

Watchmaker's check, probably circa 1870-90.

PHENYO C. CO.

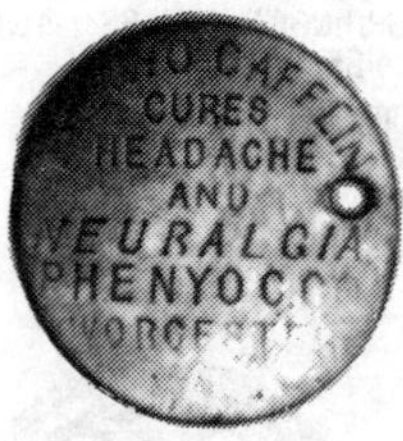

Rulau	Date	Metal	Size	VG	F	VF	Unc
Ma-Wc 12	(1880's ?)	Brass	28mm	—	—	10.00	—

(All incused): PHENYO CAFFEIN / CURES / HEADACHE / AND / NEURALGIA / PHENYO C. CO / WORCESTER / MASS. Rv: Blank. Plain edge. (Wright 822)

Ma-Wc 13	(1880's ?)	Brass	25mm	—	—	17.50	—

(All incused): CHILIAN PUZZLE / REMOVE / THE RING / AND / PUT IT ON / AGAIN. Rv: Blank. Plain edge.

These two brass tags were on either end of an advertising puzzle given out by the Phenyo Caffein people. The puzzle consisted of a metal ring plus a series of wood dowels linked together with metal straps. Stanley L. Steinberg, Malden, Mass., says: "For some reason the PUZZLE tag is rarely found. It seems that many found the puzzle hard to do and were frustrated enough to destroy all but the PHENYO tag. The PHENYO tag also circulated as an advertising token."

The only known complete puzzle with tags is in the collection of Jerry Slocum, Beverly Hills, Calif.

O.P. SHATTUCK

Rulau	Date	Metal	Size	VG	F	VF	EF
Ma-Wc 15	(1876)	Silver	38mm	350.	—	500.	—

SMOKE O.P. SHATTUCK'S / CIGARS ctsp on U.S. 1871 Liberty Seated silver dollar. (Gould 56; Van Ormer sale 2839; Miller 132; Brunk 36200)

Ma-Wc 16	(1876)	Silver	25mm	200.	—	300.	—

Similar ctsp on U.S. 1854 or 1858 S.L. quarter. (B&M Patterson 1985 sale, lot 1675; Van Ormer sale 2838; Miller 132M)

Oliver P. Shattuck's "Twin Brothers" cigar manufactory was at 369 Main St. in Worcester in 1876. These pieces earlier were thought to have been issued in Maine or New Hampshire.

Oliver's son Edson Shattuck succeeded him in cigar making early in the 20th century.

O. F. STEBBINS (AND)
J. RICE

Rulau	Date	Metal	Size	VG	F	VF	Unc
Ma-Wc 17	(?)	Brass	Sq 25mm	—	—	—	—

(All incused): O. F. STEBBINS J. RICE WORCESTER / (numeral). Rv: Blank. Plain edge. (Storer 1820)

STOCKWELL & PRATT

Ma-Wc 18	(?)	WM	19mm	—	—	—	—

(All incused): STOCKWELL / & PRATT / OPTICIANS. Rv: (All incused): WORCESTER / - / 330 / - / MAIN ST. Plain edge. (Storer 1821)

TOUGAS & DUPREY
Worcester, Mass.

Rulau	Date	Metal	Size	VG	F	VF	EF
Ma-Wc 20	(1869-71)	Copper	29mm	—	—	150.	—
	TOUGAS & DUPREY / WORCESTER / MASS. ctsp on reverse of U.S. 1853 Large cent. (Tanenbaum collection)						

Louis Tougas and Eli Duprey made cutters and dies at 9 Cypress St., 1869-1871.

G. O. CURRIER
Massachusetts

Rulau	Date	Metal	Size	VG	F	VF	EF
Ma-Un 1	(1860's)	CN	19mm	—	—	50.00	—
	G. O. CURRIER ctsp on U.S. 1857 Flying Eagle cent. (Brunk 10310)						
Ma-Un 2	(1860's)	Copper	28mm	—	—	50.00	—
	Similar ctsp on New Brunswick 1861 cent.						

There are two possibilities: George Ornello Currier (born 1836) of Lynn, Mass., and George Odin Currier (1842-1924) of Boston.

MICHIGAN

G. R. & I. R. R.
Michigan

Rulau	Date	Metal	Size	VG	F	VF
Mi-NL 3	(?)	Copper	33mm	—	100.	1 Known
	G. R. & I. R. R. 1/2 CORD NO. 16. Thick planchet. Plain edge. (James J. Curto coll.)					
Mi-NL 4	(?)	Copper	28mm	—	100.	1 Known
	Similar, but 1/4 CORD NO. 16. Thick planchet. Plain edge. (James J. Curto coll.)					
Mi-NL 5	(?)	Brass	28mm	—	100.	1 Known
	Same as last (1/4 CORD). Thin planchet. Plain edge. (James J. Curto coll.)					

Assigned here tentatively. The unidentified railway could be something like 'Grand Rapids & Ionia R.R.' or 'Grand Rapids & Indiana R.R.'. However, Curto and others, including Clyde Drewing, feel it could be in Canada, since the token sizes equate with the penny and halfpenny of the 1850's and 1860's.

M. C. R. R.
(Michigan Central Railroad)
Michigan

Rulau	Date	Metal	Size	VG	F	VF	EF
Mi-NL 15	(?)	Brass	25mm	—	—	75.00	—
	M. C. R. R. / 109 (incused). Rv: 1/8 / CORD. Milled border on each side. Plain edge.						
Mi-NL 16	(?)	Brass	27mm	—	—	75.00	—
	As 15, but 1/4 / CORD. Plain edge.						

Rulau	Date	Metal	Size	VG	F	VF	EF
Mi-NL 17	(?)	Brass	27mm	—	—	75.00	—
	M. C. R. R. / 103 (incused). Rv: 1/2 / CORD. Plain edge. Number 9 and 50 also known.						
Mi-NL 18	(?)	Brass	--mm	—	—	100.	—
	As 15, but 1 / CORD. Plain edge.						

Probably issued in the 1860's. (See "Woodburning Engine Fuel Tokens" by Clyde J. Drewing in *The Numismatist* for July, 1964)

M. S. & N. I. R. R.
(Michigan Southern & Northern Indiana Railroad)
Michigan

Rulau	Date	Metal	Size	VG	F	VF	EF
Mi-NL 22	(1863-69)	Copper	25mm	—	—	—	75.00
	M. S. & N. I. R. R. / (ornament) / E & N/ DIV / (ornament). Rv: 1/2 / CORD / 78 (incuse). Stars around rim on each side. Plain edge. (Drewing type 1) (The incuse numeral is the engine number; '78' was the 'E. M. Gilbert,' built by the MS& NIRR locomotive works. Other engine numbers known on this token: 7 'Pony'; 31 'Toledo'; 45 'South Bend'; 48 'Ontario'; 55 'Michigan'; 65 'E. Morrison'; 67 'J. Stroyer'; 68 'A. Havemeyer'; 72 'Falcon'; 81 'R. Gardner'; 87 'Monitor')						
Mi-NL 23	(1863-69)	Brass	25mm	—	—	—	75.00
	Same. Only known with engine numbers 7, 69 and 87. Plain edge. (Drewing type 1)						
Mi-NL 25	(1863-69)	Copper	23mm	—	—	—	75.00
	As last, but 1/4 / CORD / 24 (incuse) on reverse. Plain edge. (Drewing type 1) (Engine numbers known: 24, 77)						
Mi-NL 26	(1863-69)	Copper	25mm	—	—	—	Ex. Rare
	As last (1/4 / CORD), but ctsp W. O. EBERSOL. Plain edge. (Drewing type 1). This could have been an engine name, or the name of an engineer.						

NOTE: E & N DIV = Eastern and Northern Division.

Rulau	Date	Metal	Size	VG	F	VF	EF
Mi-NL 30	(1863-69)	Copper	23mm	—	75.00	—	—
	M. S. & N. I. R. R. / W. D. Rv: 1/2 / CORD / 20 (incused). Plain edge. (Drewing type 2) (Engine numbers known: 20 'Gov. Marcy'; 23 'Arab'; 33 'New Castle'; 35 Prairie'; 48 Ontario'; 60 'Missouri'; 84 'M. L. Sykes Jr.'; 88 'Dictator')						

Rulau	Date	Metal	Size	VG	F	VF	EF
Mi-NL 32	(1863-69)	Copper	23mm	—	—	75.00	—
	As last, but 1/4 / CORD / 5 (incused) on reverse. Plain edge. (Drewing type 2) (Engine numbers known: 5 'J. M. Coffee Jr.'; 20 'Gov. Marcy'; 61 'Pacific'; 22 'Oceola')						
Mi-NL 34	(1863-69)	Copper	29mm	—	—	75.00	—
	As last (W. D. 1/2 CORD), but no engine number and in larger size. Plain edge. (Drewing type 3)						

NOTE: W. D. = Western Division.

The Michigan Southern and Northern Indiana Railroad had stations at Elkhart and Kendallville, Ind.; Wauseon, Ohio; Lenawee Junction, Adrian and Coldwater, Mich. The "wood up" stations, where cords of wood were stored by the people who received these tokens for their work, were less than 60 miles apart.

The railroad kept money on deposit at various banks to redeem the tokens. They were worth from 90 cents to $1.25 per full cord.

The railroad's predecessor issued a shareholder report in 1850 and the railroad itself issued another in 1863 which gave numbers and names of all engines in use, as well as who built them, and the costs of fuel and maintenance.

The Michigan Southern Railway Co. and Northern Indiana Railway Co. merged in 1855 to form the MS&NIRR. In 1869 this line took over the Lake Shore Railway Co. and became the Lake Shore & Michigan Southern Railroad (LS&MSRR). In 1918 it was part of the New York Central system.

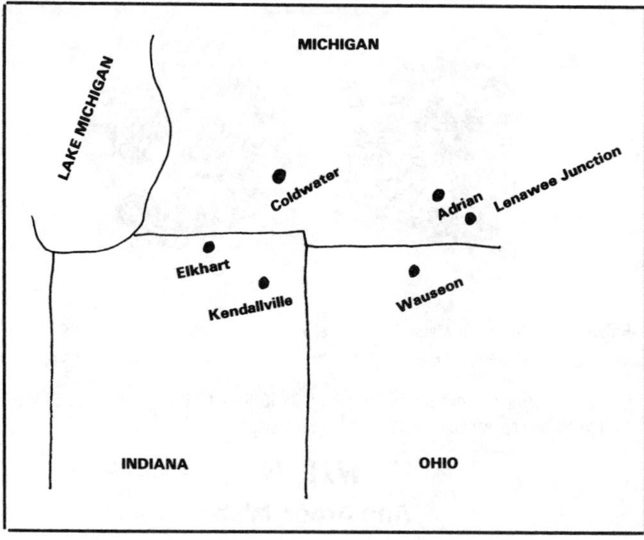

Map of the communities served by the M.S.&N.I.R.R.

ALBION COLLEGE
Albion, Michigan

Rulau	Date	Metal	Size	VG	F	VF	EF
Mi-Ab 1	1884	WM	35mm	—	—	15.00	—

Building within central circle. Above: ASBURY CENTENARY LIBRARY ASSOCIATION. Below: ** ALBION * 1884 * COLLEGE **. Rv: Rev. Coke administering oath to kneeling Asbury within central circle, ASBURY at left, COKE at right. Around: FRANCIS ASBURY ORDAINED BISHOP OF THE METHODIST EPISCOPAL CHURCH DEC 27 / 1784. Plain edge. (Brunk coll.)

Rulau	Date	Metal	Size	VG	F	VF	EF
Mi-Ab 1A	1884	Silver	35mm	—	—	35.00	—

As Mi-Ab 1. Plain edge. (Bill Swoger coll.) The first medalet was listed under Indiana in error in the First Edition of this reference, with number In-Un 4. Albion College is in Albion, Michigan.

Rulau	Date	Metal	Size	VG	F	VF	Unc
Mi-Ab 3	1866	WM	30mm	—	—	15.00	—

John Wesley bust right. Around: HUNDREDTH YEAR OF AMERICAN METHODISM / . 1766-1866 . Rv: In central circle, sunrays shine down on globe, LUX FIAT. below. In concentric circles around: SUNDAY SCHOOL CENTENARY MEDAL / . ALBION COLLEGE . / * ALBION. MICH. * / (spray) . Plain edge. Issued holed for wear. (Zaffern coll.)

Lux fiat = Light does it.

Francis Asbury was born Aug. 20, 1745 at Handsworth, Staffordshire, England. A preacher, he emigrated to America in 1771 and soon became John Wesley's general assistant in the Methodist Church. He favored American independence and became a citizen of Delaware in 1778. In 1784 he was elected superintendent of the Methodist Church in America and its first bishop consecrated in this country. It is due to his diligent travel as head of the church that it grew from 3 to 412 congregations by the time of his death March 31, 1816, at Spottsylvania, Va.

JOHN G. FOX
Albion, Mich.

Rulau	Date	Metal	Size	VG	F	VF	Unc
Mi-Ab 6	(1888-89)	Brass	**	—	—	25.00	—

** Scal 29mm.
Chas. Pick die. Rv: GOOD FOR / 5 C / JOHN G. FOX (on panel) / IN / TRADE.

Fox' saloon appears only in 1888 and 1889 directories.

W. L. H.
Ann Arbor, Mich.

Rulau	Date	Metal	Size	VG	F	VF	EF
Mi-AA 3	(1870's?)	Bronze	19mm	—	—	20.00	—

MIKE DWYER
Big Rapids, Mich.

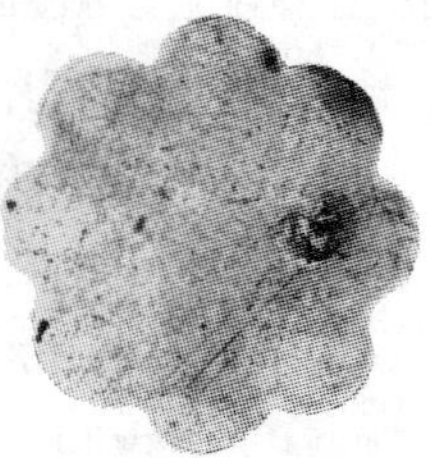

Rulau	Date	Metal	Size	VG	F	VF	Unc
Mi-BR 1	(1887-89)	Brass	**	—	—	10.00	—

** Scal 29mm.
(All incused): MIKE DWYER / 5 C / IN TRADE / (ornament). Rv: Blank. (Thoele coll.)

Saloon, listed in 1888-89 directories.

P. E. BALLOU
Blendon, Mich.

Rulau	Date	Metal	Size	VG	F	VF	EF
Mi-Bn 1	(1870's)	CN	22mm	225.00	—	300.	—

P. E. BALLOU / PHRENOLOGIST ctsp on U.S. 1871 Shield nickel. (Brunk 2220)

Rulau	Date	Metal	Size	VG	F	VF	EF
Mi-Bn 2	(1870's)	Bronze	23mm	225.	—	300.	—

Similar ctsp on U.S. Shield 2-cent piece. Examined: 1865, 1870. (Rulau MV 11A)

Rulau	Date	Metal	Size	VG	F	VF	EF
Mi-Bn 3	(1870's)	Bronze	19mm	225.	—	300.	—

Similar ctsp on U.S. Indian cent. Examined: 1866, unknown dates. 3 specimens known. (Duffield 1391)

Rulau	Date	Metal	Size	VG	F	VF	EF
Mi-Bn 4	(1870's)	Copper	29mm	225.	—	300.	—

Similar ctsp on U.S. 1846 Large cent. (Kirtley 1989 list number 33)

A phrenologist is one who analyzes character and development of the faculties by studying the shape and protuberances of the skull. The prime advocate of phrenology was O. S. Fowler, who published much on this quasi-medical discipline about 1870.

Perry E. Ballou was born in Monroe, Mass. about 1833, one of seven children of Leavitt Ballou (born in Monroe in Oct. 1807) and Betsey (Bisbee) Ballou. Sons Clark A., Oscar and Perry E. were among the seven children.

Leavitt Ballou moved his family to Blendon, Mich. about 1845, where he farmed. Later Oscar Ballou farmed adjacent to his father.

Clark A. Ballou worked as an artisan at the Remington rifle factory in Ilion, N.Y. for a time.

For a number of years Perry E. Ballou was a traveling lecturer on phrenology and related subjects. After receiving his medical degree 1881, he settled down to the practice of homoeopathic medicine and phrenology in West Millwood, Ohio.

Perry had his brother Clark prepare a die to counterstamp small-denomination coins which were given away at his lectures as an advertisement. The issuance must have been limited, because only 8 pieces have been reported to date, even though this stamp has been known in numismatic circles for 70 or 80 years.

Blendon was a tiny place with a post office in 1877 in Ottawa County. By 1918 Blendon apparently was gone. South Blendon had a grocery store and population of 45.

C. RUGGLES
Bronson, Mich.

Rulau	Date	Metal	Size	VG	F	VF	EF
Mi-Br 3	(1880's)	CN	22mm	—	100.	—	—

C. RUGGLES / BRONSON, MICH. ctsp on obverse of U.S. Shield nickel. WANTED / OLD / COINS / & / RELICS ctsp on other side. (William Swoger report; Brunk 35283)

Charles Ruggles (1852-1930) was a harness maker in Bronson in 1870's, in partnership with a younger brother. He was a collector of coins and antiques, and probably stamped more coins than that recorded above.

JAKE HOBSON
Caro, Mich.

Rulau	Date	Metal	Size	VG	F	VF	Unc
Mi-Ca 2	(1889)	Brass	25mm	—	—	8.50	—

GOOD FOR / 5 ¢ / JAKE / HOBSON / IN / * TRADE *. Rv: 5 in circle of 16 rosettes. Plain edge. (Zaffern coll.)

WM. AMERHEIM
Detroit, Mich.

Rulau	Date	Metal	Size	VG	F	VF	Unc
Mi-De 1	(1875-81)	Brass	21mm	—	15.00	40.00	—

Star in center. DAS LEBEN IST / DOCH SCHON. Rv: WM. AMERHEIM / 3 C / DETROIT. Plain edge. (Haseltine sale 1347)

Rulau	Date	Metal	Size	VG	F	VF	Unc
Mi-De 1C	(1875-81)	Brass	24mm	—	15.00	40.00	—

Similar to last, but 5 C. Plain edge. (Wright 41; Haseltine sale 1348; Rulau Det 1)

Das leben ist doch schon = Living is very beautiful.

Both tokens were offered in the John W. Haseltine sale of Dec. 12-13, 1881, thus must have been issued 1881 or earlier. Mi-De 1C was listed in our Tokens of the Gay Nineties but is now removed to this section. (Research courtesy Robert Lindesmith)

Haseltine spelled the surname as AMRHEIN, but Dr. Wright examined the 1C token and described it precisely. We accept Wright's spelling until a specimen can be examined.

BROWN BROTHERS

Rulau	Date	Metal	Size	F	VF	EF	Unc
Mi-De 2	(?)	Copper	31mm	2.50	3.50	4.50	6.00

BROWN BROTHERS / THE / CIGAR / MAKERS / * DETROIT *. Rv: THIS CHECK WILL BE REDEEMED BY ANY DEALER * / GOOD FOR / ONE / FONTELLA / CIGAR. Plain edge. (Miller Mich 1)

Rulau	Date	Metal	Size	F	VF	EF	Unc
Mi-De 3	(?)	CN	31mm	—	—	6.50	—

BROWN BROTHERS / LAFLORDE / FONTELLA / 5 ct / CIGARS / DETROIT. Rv: Large 5 at center, border of scallops. Plain edge.

BUEHLER D. CORNELL

Rulau	Date	Metal	Size	VG	F	VF	EF
Mi-De 4	(?)	Copper	29mm	—	—	50.00	—

BUEHLER D. CORNELL / DETROIT ctsp on U.S. Large cent. (Hallenbeck 2.769; Brunk 9650)

DET. LOCK AND VRITY. WKS.

Rulau	Date	Metal	Size	VG	F	VF	Unc
Mi-De 7	(?)	Bronze	25mm	—	—	125.	—

DET. LOCK AND VRITY. WKS. / DETROIT, MICH. ctsp on Great Britain 1861 halfpenny. (Frederick Montgomery coll., Wayne Mich.; Brunk 11478)

Detroit Lock and Variety Works.

R. GRAVIER

Rulau	Date	Metal	Size	VG	F	VF	Unc
Mi-De 8	(?)	Brass	19.5mm	—	—	20.00	—

(All incused): R. GRAVIER / 68 / GRATIOT ST / -o- / DETROIT. RV: LIQUOR / DEALER. Plain edge.

GRIESHABER

Rulau	Date	Metal	Size	VG	F	VF	Unc
Mi-De 9	(?)	Bronze	19mm	—	—	35.00	—

GRIESHABER (curved) / DETROIT (curved) in dotted oval cartouche, ctsp incuse on U.S. 1871 Indian cent. (Paul Cunningham coll.)

J. CHR. JACOBS

Rulau	Date	Metal	Size	VG	F	VF	Unc
Mi-De 10	(?)	Brass	18.5mm	—	—	20.00	—

(All incused): J. CHR. JACOB. / DETROIT. Rv: Blank. Plain edge. (Paul Cunningham coll.)

Johann Christian Jacob?

MABLEY & COMPANY
Detroit, Mich.

Rulau	Date	Metal	Size	F	VF	EF	Unc
Mi-De 11	1889	Brass	44mm	—	15.00	20.00	—

Building, 1889-90 in exergue, all within circle. Around: TWO MEDALS WERE AWARDED / * MABLEY & COMPANY BY THE DETROIT EXPOSITION ASS'N *. Rv: Buildings within two overlapping oval frames. Around: MABLEY & COMPANY / -- / DETROIT. / 12 STORES & 62 / DEPARTMENTS / THE / MEDAL / WINNERS / * THE LARGEST RETAIL ESTABLISHMENT IN MICHIGAN *. Plain edge. Issued with loop. (Thomas Casper coll.)

C. W. MARTIN

Rulau	Date	Metal	Size	VG	F	VF	Unc
Mi-De 12	(?)	Silver	38mm	—	—	100.	—

C W MARTIN (curved) / DETROIT / MICH / 1911 BURLINGAME AVE (curved) ctsp on France 5-francs of Louis Philippe I. (Brunk 26135)

MICHIGAN STOVE CO.

Rulau	Date	Metal	Size	F	VF	EF	Unc
Mi-De 13	1885	Wood	44mm	—	—	—	100.

GARLAND / STOVES / AND / RANGES on flaming grate in central circle. Around: COMPLIMENTS (on cartouche) / MICHIGAN STOVE Co. / DETROIT . CHICAGO . BUFFALO (all on panel). Rv: THE WORLD's INDUSTRIAL / AND / COTTON / CENTENNIAL / EXPOSITION / (ornament) / -. 1885 .- /* NEW ORLEANS *. Rare.

A. NIEPER

Rulau	Date	Metal	Size	VG	F	VF	Unc
Mi-De 15	(1875-81)	Brass	24mm	—	15.00	40.00	—

Camel. Rv: Large 5 at center. Around: * A NIEPER. DETROIT. MICH. Plain edge. (Haseltine sale 1346)

Rulau	Date	Metal	Size	VG	F	VF	Unc
Mi-De 16	(1875-81)	Brass	21mm	—	15.00	40.00	—

Similar to last, but 3 at center. Plain edge. (Wright 759; Rulau Det 40)

Mi-De 15 appeared in the John W. Haseltine auction of Dec. 12-13, 1881, and thus the pieces must have been issued in 1881 or earlier. Number 16 was listed by Dr. Wright, and by your author in *Tokens of the Gay Nineties*, but is now removed to this section. (See Wm. Amerheim above for simlar tokens).

A. F. SMITH
Detroit, Mich.

Rulau	Date	Metal	Size	VG	F	VF	EF
Mi-De 25	(1875-80)	Silver	24.3mm	—	—	85.00	—

A. F. SMITH, (curved) / -0- / DETROIT MICH. (curved) ctsp on planed-off reverse of U.S. 1874 Seated Liberty quarter. Linked diamond shapes make up border around the counterstamp. (Rulau coll., ex-W. Swoger; Brunk 36927)

Andrew F. Smith & Co. were manufacturers and wholesalers of boots and shoes about 1875-88, first at 25 Jefferson Ave. and then at 90 Woodward. They succeeded Stephen F. Smith & Co. at the Woodward address.

Stephen F. Smith & Co. had been at 76 Woodward 1855-70. In 1889 Andrew F. Smith was out of the boot and shoe business and was a travel agent at 22 Selden Ave. and later at 794 2nd Ave.

Prepared from a punch, this counterstamp apparently was intended for advertising purposes. Only a single specimen has been reported to date.

DETROIT, MICH.

Rulau	Date	Metal	Size	VG	F	VF	EF
Mi-De 50	(?)	Copper	28mm	—	—	20.00	—

DETROIT ctsp on Canada 1852 token, Breton 719. (John Cheramy coll.; Brunk 11483)

L. A. GLESTON & CO.

Kalamazoo, Mich.

Rulau	Date	Metal	Size	VG	F	VF	EF
Mi-Ka 3	(1880)	Silver	38mm	—	—	80.00	—

KALAMAZOO (curved) / L A GLESTON & CO / SPRING, WORKS (curved) ctsp on U.S. 1879 Morgan silver dollar. (Kovacs coll., ex-Tanenbaum)

Michigan Bureau of History revealed that Gleston & Co. was incorporated July 15, 1874, but never submitted annual reports. Frank Kovacs determined that there is no relation to the Kalamazoo Spring Co., formed 1957 and absorbed by Peterson Spring Co. 1986.

The only known specimen of the stamp has the logo applied unevenly and many letters do not appear.

JOHN LOSCH

East Saginaw, Mich.

Rulau	Date	Metal	Size	VG	F	VF	Unc
Mi-ES 2	(1880-82)	Brass	23mm	—	—	20.00	—

(All incused): JOHN LOSCH / GOOD FOR / 5 ¢ / AT BAR / E. SAGINAW. Rv: Blank. Plain edge. (Coll. John Cheramy, Victoria, Canada)

John Losch saloon was listed in the 1881 and 1882 gazetteers. It had disappeared by the 1885 gazetteer.

F. S. POSTAL

Evart, Mich.

Rulau	Date	Metal	Size	VG	F	VF	Unc
Mi-Ev 2	(1886-87)	GS	25mm	—	—	35.00	—

Brunswick die BBC-9b. Rv: GOOD FOR / 10 C / F. S. POSTAL / IN TRADE. Plain edge. (Thoele coll.)

Listed in the 1887 gazetteer.

F. F. EMMER

Grand Rapids, Mich.

Rulau	Date	Metal	Size	F	VF	EF	Unc
Mi-GR 4	(1884-89)	Brass	25mm	—	—	10.00	—

TEMPERANCE POOL ROOMS / GOOD FOR / 5 C / IN TRADE / F. F. EMMER. Rv: Numeral 5 within circle of stars. Plain edge. (Thoele report)

F. F. Emmer was listed under pool halls in the 1885 thru 1889 gazetteers. Presumably a "temperance" pool hall was one which dispensed no alcoholic beverages.

4 PENINSULAR SAENGERFEST

Grand Rapids, Mich.

Rulau	Date	Metal	Size	F	VF	EF	Unc
Mi-GR 9	1881	WM	30.4mm	—	15.00	—	—

Standing robed female playing lyre, tiny L. BOCHE beneath her left foot. Around: DER MENSCHHEIT WURDE 1ST IN EURE HAND GEGEBE V. BEWAHRT SIE. Rv: Within wreath: 4 / PENINSULAR / SAENGERFEST / AUG. 81 / GRAND RAPIDS MICH. Plain edge.

JOHNNIE H. HAMILTON

Ionia, Mich.

Rulau	Date	Metal	Size	VG	F	VF	EF
Mi-Lo 5	(?)	Silver	31mm	—	—	100.	—

JOHNNIE H. HAMILTON. (curved) / (compass-square-G) / IONIA. / MICH. ctsp on U.S. 1839 S.L. half dollar. (Krause coll.; Brunk 17967)

Hamilton undoubtedly was a Mason, as that symbolism is expressed on this piece. The counterstamp is well made, but might be personal rather than business-related.

M.B. TOUTLOFF

Ishpeming, Mich.

Rulau	Date	Metal	Size	VG	F	VF	Unc
Mi-Is 4	(1880-96)	Brass	25mm	—	—	30.00	—

Pool table at bottom, THE J.M. BRUNSWICK / & / BALKE COS. Rv: GOOD FOR / 5¢ / M.B. TOUTLOFF / IN TRADE. Plain edge. (Brunswick 2353)

N. H. ECKLER

Jackson, Mich.

Rulau	Date	Metal	Size	VG	F	VF	Unc
Mi-Ja 2	(1881-89)	Brass	Sq 24mm	—	—	25.00	—

Chas. Pick. & Co. die. Rv: GOOD FOR / 5 ¢ / N. H. ECKLER (in a panel) / IN / TRADE. Only 1 piece known. (Thoele coll.)

Noah H. Eckler was listed under saloons in the 1881 through 1889 gazetteers.

J.J. DEAL

Jonesville, Mich.

Rulau	Date	Metal	Size	VG	F	VF	Unc
Mi-Jo 3	(?)	Gold/Ld*	**	—	—	40.00	—

* Lead, gold-plated. ** 57 x 22mm.

Parallelogram shaped. J.J.DEAL / --- / JONESVILLE, MICH. Rv: Blank. Plain edge. (Wright 237)

J. W. WHITEFORD

Lake City, Mich.

Rulau	Date	Metal	Size	VG	F	VF	Unc
Mi-LC 1	(1886-88)	Brass	25mm	—	—	30.00	—

Brunswick die BB-8a. Rv: GOOD FOR / 5 C / J. W. WHITEFORD / IN / TRADE. Plain edge.

Saloon, listed in the 1887-88 gazetteers.

J. B. TOUPIN
Lake Linden, Mich.

Rulau	Date	Metal	Size	VG	F	VF	Unc
Mi-LL 3	(1888-89)	Brass	**	—	—	30.00	—

** Scal, 26mm.
CHAS. PICK & CO. / DEALERS IN / (crossed utensils) / CHICAGO. Rv: GOOD FOR / 5 C / J. B. TOUPIN / IN / TRADE. Plain edge.

This check was listed by Ore Vacketta in July, 1983 as a dubious Chicago token. The J. B. Toupin saloon appears in the 1889 gazetteer.

W. H. RAYNER
Mason, Mich.

Rulau	Date	Metal	Size	VG	F	VF	EF
Mi-MS 3	(?)	Bronze	23mm	—	35.00	—	55.00

W. H. RAYNER / -- / MASON. ctsp on U.S. 1865 2-cent piece. (Rulau coll.; Brunk 33643)

Rulau	Date	Metal	Size	VG	F	VF	EF
Mi-MS 5	(?)	Silver	31mm	—	35.00	—	55.00

Similar ctsp on U.S. 1877 S.L. half dollar. (Koppenhaver report)

A possible successor firm, Robbins B. Rayner, was in the coal, cement and roofing business circa 1917. Mason, in Ingham County, had 1,742 people in World War I.

F. A. STANLEY
Millington, Mich.

Rulau	Date	Metal	Size	VG	F	VF	EF
Mi-MI 2	(1888-90)	Brass	25mm	—	—	30.00	—

Brunswick die B-2a. Rv: GOOD FOR / 5 C / F. A. / STANLEY / IN / TRADE. Plain edge.

Billiard hall, listed in 1888-90 gazetteers.

FRANK X. VOGEL
Muskegon, Mich.

Rulau	Date	Metal	Size	VG	F	VF	Unc
Mi-Mg 7	(1889)	Brass	25mm	—	—	15.00	—

GOOD FOR / 5 ¢ / FRANK / X. VOGEL / IN / TRADE. Rv: 5 in circle of 16 stars. Plain edge. (Thoele coll., ex-Weinberg)

C. O. BROWN
Olivet, Mich.

Rulau	Date	Metal	Size	VG	F	VF	EF
Mi-Ov 2	(?)	CN	18mm	—	30.00	—	—

C. O. BROWN OLIVET MICH. ctsp on U.S. 1873 nickel 3-cent piece. (Brunk 5380)

JOS. JOHNSTON
Port Huron, Mich.

Rulau	Date	Metal	Size	VG	F	VF	Unc
Mi-PH 3	(1885)	Brass	25mm	—	—	15.00	—

Brunswick die BBC-2a. Rv: GOOD FOR / 5 ¢ (in panel) / JOS. JOHNSTON (in oval panel) / -IN- / TRADE.

J. STREETER
Richmond, Mich.

Rulau	Date	Metal	Size	VG	F	VF	EF
Mi-Rc 3	1874	GS	23.7mm	—	—	15.00	—

Liberty with flag above three folds of ribbon, on which are: J. Streeter / Richmond. / Mich. Rv: (All incused): BORN MAY. 27. 1840. / Hastings Co. ONT. (square & compass) / (star) 1874. Plain edge. (Zaffern coll.)

Masonic ID tag of a Canadian-born Richmond person of substance.

HENRY STEPHENS & CO.
St. Helen, Mich.

Rulau	Date	Metal	Size	VG	F	VF	EF
Mi-SH 3	(1870's?)	Copper	30mm	—	—	50.00	—

Eagle displayed, U.S. shield on its breast, scroll below. Rv: HENRY STEPHENS & CO. / GOOD FOR / 10 C / IN M'D'SE / ST. HELEN MICH.

The obverse die also is used on the "Gold Region" tokens of J. W. & Co., which see under Mavericks.

FREE DOW
Sandbeach, Mich.

Rulau	Date	Metal	Size	VG	F	VF	Unc
Mi-Sa 2	(1885)	Brass	Oct 26mm	4.50	9.00	—	—

GOOD FOR / 5 C / FREE DOW / AT THE BAR. Rv: 5 in a circle of stars. (Alpert Feb. 1989 sale, lot 144)

Free Dow's billiard hall appears in the 1885 Michigan gazetteer.

FOLLETT HOUSE
Ypsilanti, Mich.

Rulau	Date	Metal	Size	VG	F	VF	Unc
Mi-Yp 1	(1881)	Brass	25mm	—	—	25.00	—

Chas. Pick & Co. die. Rv: GOOD FOR / 5 ¢ / FOLLETT / HOUSE (name in cross-hatched panel) / IN / TRADE.

Zell's United States Business Directory for 1881 listed this hotel.

REPORTED MICHIGAN BILLIARD TOKENS

The following unverified attributions have been reported for this era. They are listed here for informational purposes:

Name on Token	Possible Locale	Billiard Die	Gazetteer
Boehm & Miller	East Saginaw	Chas. Pick	1881-82
M. Blau	Calumet	BBC-9b	1889
Wm. Budde	Sebewaing	Chas. Pick	1889
Ed Casey	Cheboygan	BBC ?	1887
The Courtwright	Newaygo	Chas. Pick	1885-1903
J. Doran	Marquette	B-3	1889
Neil Johnson	Saginaw	Chas. Pick	1887-1901
Lundeberg & Co.	Calumet	BBC-10b	1885
Gilbert Moblo	East Jordan	B-2e	1887-89
Conrad Orth	Detroit	B-2a	1881
Wm. Perkins	Detroit	—	1885
P. Raquet	East Saginaw	BB-3	1881-89
J.C. Shaw	Imlay City	BB-6a	1885
E.E. Whitney	Kalamazoo	—	1885
W.H. Wilson	Muskegon	B-2e	1889
John S. Wimble	St. Johns	BBC-11	1885
J. Wuerthner	Manchester	Kuehl & Bro.	1881-85

MINNESOTA

VAN DYKE & LARSON
Alexandria, Minn.

Rulau	Date	Metal	Size	VG	F	VF	Unc
Mn-Al 7	(1882)	Brass	25mm	—	35.00	—	—

Brunswick die BB-4. Rv: GOOD FOR / 10 ¢ / VAN DYKE / & LARSON / IN / TRADE / (ornament). (McFerran coll.)

Saloon, listed in the 1882 gazetteer.

A.E. RYAN
Barrett, Minn.

Rulau	Date	Metal	Size	VG	F	VF	Unc
Mn-Bt 3	(1880)	Brass	19mm	—	—	10.00	—

A. E. RYAN / GENERAL MERCHANDISE / BARRETT, MINN. Rv: GOOD FOR / 5 / CTS IN TRADE. Plain edge. (Fuld NC-6b; Barnett-H&G 4635)

Although Joseph Barnett called this a Civil War token, it was shown it could not be. The first homestead in Barrett was erected in 1868.

W. P. DINON
Bird Island, Minn.

Rulau	Date	Metal	Size	VG	F	VF	Unc
Mn-Bl 1	(1882-98)	Brass	26mm	—	—	6.50	—

W. P. DINON. Rv: GOOD FOR / 5 ¢ / IN TRADE./

William P. Dinon is listed under hotels 1882-1889 and under saloons 1882-1898. Tokens are readily available.

W. M. REMPEL
Butterfield, Minn.

Rulau	Date	Metal	Size	VG	F	VF	Unc
Mn-Bu 2	(1886-92)	Brass	24mm	—	—	25.00	—

Brunswick die B & Co. Rv: GOOD FOR / 5 ¢ / W. W. REMPEL / IN / TRADE. (McFerran coll.)

William W. Rempel, saloon, listed 1886 through 1892.

F. NELSON
Carlton, Minn.

Rulau	Date	Metal	Size	VG	F	VF	Unc
Mn-Ca 1	(1888-93)	Brass	25mm	—	25.00	—	—

GOOD FOR / 5 ¢ / F. NELSON / AT THE BAR. Rv: Large 5.

Frederick Nelson, saloon, listed 1888-1893. The only known specimen was dug on the former site by Wade Renstrom.

J. BEIERSTETTEL
Chaska, Minn.

Rulau	Date	Metal	Size	VG	F	VF	Unc
Mn-Ck 1	(1888-89)	Brass	25mm	—	—	25.00	—

THE / BRUNSWICK / BALKE / COLLENDER CO. / (Billiard table). Rv: GOOD FOR / 5 ¢ / J. BEIERSTETTEL / AT BAR. (Loperfido coll.)

John Beierstettel, saloon, listed 1888-1889.

ARTHUR D. BAKER
Deer Creek, Minn.

Rulau	Date	Metal	Size	VG	F	VF	Unc
Mn-DC 1	(1886-90)	Brass	23mm	—	—	10.00	—

(All incused): ARTHUR D. BAKER / GOOD FOR / 10 C / IN TRADE / DEER CREEK. Rv: Blank. Plain edge.

This was a general store 1886-1890.

KRAUSE AND STAHLBUSH
Duluth, Minn.

Rulau	Date	Metal	Size	VG	F	VF	Unc
Mn-Du 2	(1886)	Brass	24mm	—	—	10.00	—

KRAUSE / AND / STAHLBUSH / DULUTH / MINN. Rv: GOOD FOR / 5 C / IN / TRADE. Plain edge.

This was a saloon.

L. MURAY
Duluth, Minn.

Rulau	Date	Metal	Size	VG	F	VF	Unc
Mn-Du 7	(1882-89)	Brass	Oct 26mm	—	—	11.00	—

(All incused): L. MURAY / GOOD FOR / 5 ¢ / CIGAR / DULUTH MINN. Rv: Blank. (McFerran coll.)

Louis Muray, hotel and saloon, 124 West Superior St., listed 1882-1889.

THE NEW BODEGA

Rulau	Date	Metal	Size	VG	F	VF	Unc
Mn-Du 9	(?)	GS	29mm	—	—	30.00	—

Barrel. Below: 12 1/2 ¢. Rv: THE NEW BODEGA / 205 / W. SUPERIOR / ST. / DULUTH, MINN. Several pieces known. Plain edge.

Bodega (Spanish) means winery.

M. NORRIS
Duluth, Minn.

Rulau	Date	Metal	Size	VG	F	VF	Unc
Mn-Du 11	(1882-89)	GS	24mm	—	—	11.00	—

M. NORRIS / DULUTH, MINN. Rv: GOOD FOR / 5 ¢ / IN TRADE. (McFerran coll.)

Michael Norris, saloon, is listed 1882 through 1889.

D. MOES
Farmington, Minn.

Rulau	Date	Metal	Size	VG	F	VF	Unc
Mn-Fa 7	(1885-86)	Brass	24.5mm	—	—	35.00	—

Chas. Pick die (small utensils, + at either side). Rv: GOOD FOR / (5 ¢) / AT D. MOES (MOES straight) / -IN- / * TRADE *. Type 1.

Rulau	Date	Metal	Size	VG	F	VF	Unc
Mn-Fa 9	(1885-86)	Brass	24.5mm	—	—	35.00	—

Chas. Pick die (large utensils, 1 at either side). Rv: GOOD FOR / 5 ¢ / AT D. MOES (MOES curved) / IN / * TRADE *. Type 2.

Dominic Moes is listed as a saloon keeper in the 1882-1886 gazetteers.

J. K. O'BRIEN
Fergus Falls, Minn.

Rulau	Date	Metal	Size	F	VF	EF	Unc
Mn-Fe 4	1881-84)	GS	25mm	—	—	35.00	—

Chas. Pick die. Rv: GOOD FOR / J. K. O'BRIEN / A / DRINK. Plain edge.

Saloon, listed in the 1882 and 1884 gazetteers. James K. O'Brien.

G. A. KROPP
Gaylord, Minn.

Rulau	Date	Metal	Size	F	VF	EF	Unc
Mn-Gy 3	1886	Aluminum	38mm	—	9.00	12.00	—

EST 1886 / THIS IS A / POCKET PIECE / FROM / G. A. KROPP / THE JEWELER / GAYLORD, MINN. Rv: WHEN YOU BUY A / WATCH / AT OUR / REGULAR LOW PRICES / FROM $15.00 UP / I WILL ACCEPT / ONE OF THESE CHECKS / AS A / $2.00 PAYMENT. Plain edge. Several pieces known.

Gustav A. Kropp's jewelry business was established 1886 and is last listed 1912. Probably issued early 1890's.

W. TIMM
Gaylord, Minn.

Rulau	Date	Metal	Size	VG	F	VF	Unc
Mn-Gy 9	(1888-89)	Brass	24mm	—	—	9.00	—

(All incused): GOOD FOR / W. TIMM / AT THE BAR. Rv: Blank. (McFerran coll.)

William Timm, saloon, listed 1888-1889.

A. H. REED
Glencoe, Minn.

Rulau	Date	Metal	Size	VG	F	VF	EF
Mn-Gl 1	(1886-90)	Brass	21mm	—	—	10.00	—

A. H. REED. Rv: GOOD FOR / 1 / QUART / MILK. Plain edge.

A. H. Reed used these tokens in the 1886-1890 period in his general store.

Axel Reed won the Medal of Honor in the Civil War.

D. O'DONNELL
Hawley, Minn.

Rulau	Date	Metal	Size	VG	F	VF	Unc
Mn-Hw 7	(1886-87)	Brass	--mm	—	—	20.00	—

Brunswick die BBC-9a. Rv: GOOD FOR / 5 ¢ / D. / O'DONNELL (name in panel) / IN / TRADE. (Robert Cruise coll.)

Daniel O'Donnell's saloon is listed 1886-1887.

BRAHS & CO.
Henderson, Minn.

Rulau	Date	Metal	Size	VG	F	VF	Unc
Mn-Hn 2	(1888-)	Brass	Oct 26mm	—	—	11.00	—

(All incused): BRAHS / & / CO. Rv: GOOD FOR / 5 ¢ / AT BAR. About 4 pieces reported.

Brahs Brothers, saloon, listed 1888 through 1902.

HUDERLE & JANECKY
Hutchinson, Minn.

Rulau	Date	Metal	Size	VG	F	VF	Unc
Mn-Ht 5	(1888-93)	Aluminum	23mm	—	—	9.00	—

HUDERLE & JANECKY, / HUTCHINSON / MINN. Rv: GOOD FOR / 5 ¢ / AT BAR. (McFerran coll.)

John H. Huderle and Mary Janecky are listed under saloons only in 1888.

J. WOOLSTENCROFT
Heron Lake, Minn.

Rulau	Date	Metal	Size	VG	F	VF	EF
Mn-HL 2	(1887-88)	—	--mm	—	—	35.00	—

Brunswick die BB-8b. Rv: J. WOOLSTENCROFT / 5 C. (Brunswick 2386)

John Woolstencroft ran a billiard hall, says the 1888 directory.

JULIUS BURKART
Hokah, Minn.

Rulau	Date	Metal	Size	VG	F	VF	Unc
Mn-Ho 2	(1882-84)	Brass	24mm	—	—	20.00	—

Brunswick & Balke die. Rv: GOOD FOR / 5 C / JULIUS / BURKART / IN / TRADE. (Hosek coll.)

Burkart's billiard hall appears in the 1882 and 1884 gazetteers.

H. SIEMERING
Le Sueur, Minn.

Rulau	Date	Metal	Size	VG	F	VF	Unc
Mn-Ls 3	(1882-98)	Brass	24mm	—	—	9.00	—

H. SIEMERING, / LE SUEUR / MINN. Rv: GOOD FOR / 5 ¢ / AT BAR. (McFerran coll.)

Herman Siemering, saloon, listed 1882 through 1898.

WALKER WEISEL
Le Sueur, Minn.

Rulau	Date	Metal	Size	VG	F	VF	Unc
Mn-Ls 7	(1888)	GS	26mm	—	—	22.50	—

(Knight's armor) / K. P. / F. C. B. / WALKER WEISEL. / AGENT / C. ST. P. M. & O. RY. Plain edge. (McFerran coll.)

K. P. = Knights of Pythias. C. St. P. M. & O. Ry. = Chicago, St. Paul, Milwaukee & Omaha Railway (later Chicago, Milwaukee, St. Paul & Pacific Railroad).

HENRY WILLIAMS
Long Prairie, Minn.

Rulau	Date	Metal	Size	VG	F	VF	Unc
Mn-LP 1	(1885-86)	Brass	**	—	—	20.00	—

** Oct 28mm.

Pool table, THE J. M. BRUNSWICK / & / BALKE CO'S. Rv: GOOD FOR / 5 C / HENRY / WILLIAMS / IN / TRADE. Plain edge.

Directories list Henry Williams as a saloonkeeper 1882-1909. The Brunswick-Balke check type used on this token was issued only 1874-1884, though there was some overlap of B-B named checks after the Brunswick-Balke-Collender type was issued beginning in 1884. It seems reasonable, therefore, to conclude that 1886 was the date of issue of the Henry Williams check, which helped to launch his pool and billiard business.

DAVID SLOAN
Mallory, Minn.

Rulau	Date	Metal	Size	VG	F	VF	Unc
Mn-Ma 2	(1885-87)	Brass	25mm	—	—	15.00	—

Brunswick die BBC-11. Rv: GOOD FOR / 5 C / DAVID / SLOAN / IN / TRADE. Plain edge.

Saloon, listed in the 1886-87 gazetteer.

C. J. KLINE
Mankato, Minn.

Rulau	Date	Metal	Size	VG	F	VF	Unc
Mn-Mk 1	(1886)	Brass	24mm	—	—	30.00	—

Obverse as the Long Prairie token, Mn-LP 1. Rv: GOOD FOR / 5 C / C. J. KLINE / MANKATO / IN / TRADE. Plain edge.

C. J. Kline ran a hotel 1882-1909. Mrs. C. J. Kline is listed as a hotel proprietor in 1912. (See remarks under Long Prairie)

K. ASLESEN
Minneapolis, Minn.

Rulau	Date	Metal	Size	VG	F	VF	Unc
Mn-Mi 2	(1880-95)	Brass	23mm	—	—	8.00	—

ONE BREAD / 5 ¢ / K. ASLESEN. Rv: E. R. WILLIAMSON / MAKER / 202 HENN. AVE. / MINNEAPOLIS. (McFerran coll.)

Knud Aslesen, grocery and bakery, 1880-1920.

CURRAN'S CIGAR STORE

Rulau	Date	Metal	Size	VG	F	VF	Unc
Mn-Mi 5	(1880-84)	Brass	**	—	—	10.00	—

** Oct 21mm.

CURRAN'S / CIGAR STORE / 308 / HENNEPIN AVE. Rv: GOOD FOR / 5 C / IN TRADE. Plain edge.

Morris E. Curran is listed as a cigar purveyor only 1880-1884.

G. D.

Rulau	Date	Metal	Size	VG	F	VF	Unc
Mn-Mi-6	(1874-84)	Brass	24mm	—	—	30.00	—

Pool table at bottom. Above, among flourishes: THE J. M. BRUNSWICK / & / BALKE COS. Rv: GOOD FOR / 5¢ / G. D. / MINNEAPOLIS. Plain edge. (Brunswick 2128)

WM. DONALDSON & CO.

Rulau	Date	Metal	Size	VG	F	VF	Unc
Mn-Mi 7	1886	Brass	25mm	—	—	8.00	—

Building, MINNEAPOLIS EXPOSITION above. 1886 below. Rv: WM DONALDSON & CO. / GLASS BLOCK / (store building) / STORE. Plain edge. (Wright 261)

R. H. DWYER

Rulau	Date	Metal	Size	VG	F	VF	Unc
Mn-Mi 7F	(1888-96)	Brass	25mm	—	—	12.50	—

R. H. DWYER . MINNEAPOLIS / MINN. Rv: 12 1/2. Plain edge. (Loperfido coll.)

Robert H. Dwyer, saloon, 1888-1896, 318 2nd Avenue So.

JAMES FORD

Rulau	Date	Metal	Size	VG	F	VF	Unc
Mn-Mi 8	1886	Brass	20mm	—	—	9.00	—

Mustached male bust left, small T.C. on truncation. Around: JAMES FORD MINNEAPOLIS / 1886. Rv: 2-1/2. Plain edge.

W. E. GERRISH

Rulau	Date	Metal	Size	VG	F	VF	Unc
Mn-Mi 9	(1880-86)	Brass	21mm	—	—	10.00	—

ANDRUS BL'D'G / CIGAR STORE / W. E. GERRISH / PROP. Rv: GOOD FOR / 5 C / IN TRADE. Plain edge. About 4 known.

Directories list W. E. Gerrish as a cigar purveyor 1880-1886.

O. GOEBEL

Rulau	Date	Metal	Size	VG	F	VF	Unc
Mn-Mi 9F	(1884-85)	Brass	Sc 29mm	—	—	12.50	—

(All incused): O. GOEBEL. Rv: GOOD FOR / 5 ¢ / AT THE BAR / (McFarran coll.)

Saloon, listed 1884-85.

L. R. GORMAN

Rulau	Date	Metal	Size	VG	F	VF	Unc
Mn-Mi 9G	(1882-84)	Brass	24mm	—	—	25.00	—

Brunswick die BB. Rv: GOOD FOR / 5 ¢ / L. R. GORMAN / IN / TRADE. (McFerran coll.)

Saloon, listed 1882-1884.

JOHN MARSCH

Rulau	Date	Metal	Size	VG	F	VF	Unc
Mn-Mi A9	(1887-89)	Brass	25mm	—	—	8.00	—

GOOD FOR / 5 C / JOHN MARSCH / IN TRADE. Rv: Large numeral 5. Plain edge. (Thoele report)

MINNEAPOLIS EXPOSITION

Rulau	Date	Metal	Size	VG	F	VF	Unc
Mn-Mi 10	1886	WM	35mm	—	—	10.00	15.00

Liberty head right, its Phrygian cap entwined in garland of wheat and corn. Wreath of wheat and corn below and partly around. Rv: Building at center, tiny 1886 on the ground line. Above: MINNEAPOLIS EXPOSITION. On truncation of the ground: Initials F. M. W. Plain edge.

MINNEAPOLIS INDUSTRIAL EXPOSITION

Rulau	Date	Metal	Size	VG	F	VF	Unc
Mn-Mi 12	1886	Brass	30.5mm	—	—	8.50	15.00

Building at center, tiny N.W. STAMP WORKS below ground line. MINNEAPOLIS INDUSTRIAL above, * / EXPOSITION. in exergue. Rv: MINNEAPOLIS INDUSTRIAL / AUGUST 23 / SOUVENIR (ornate) / OCTOBER 2 / —.— / —1886— / EXPOSITION. Plain edge. Issued holed.

Rulau	Date	Metal	Size	VG	F	VF	Unc
Mn-Mi 13	1887	CN	37mm	—	—	—	20.00

Building, INDUSTRIAL EXPO., MINNEAPOLIS, MINN. 1887. Rv: Street scene. MINNEAPOLIS, MINN. / NICOLLET AVE. / ILLUMINATION.

JAS. MORRISON

Rulau	Date	Metal	Size	VG	F	VF	Unc
Mn-Mi 14	(1887-89)	Brass	25mm	—	—	20.00	—

Brunswick die B-2e. Rv: GOOD FOR / 5 C / JAS. MORRISON / IN / TRADE. Plain edge.

James Morrison's saloon appears in the 1886-89 gazetteers, at 219 S. 3rd St.

POEHLER'S

Rulau	Date	Metal	Size	VG	F	VF	Unc
Mn-Mi 20	(?)	Brass	**	—	—	20.00	—

** Oct 28x28mm.

POEHLER'S / STORE in relief within curving depressions. 50 stamped incuse over incuse 1 ¢ between the curving depressions. Rv: P stamped incuse. Relief beaded rims within border depressions. Plain edge.

Rulau	Date	Metal	Size	VG	F	VF	Unc
Mn-Mi 22	(?)	Brass	30mm	—	—	20.00	—

Similar, but 100. Plain edge.

Poehler's does not appear in the *Atlas of Minnesota*, or the 1880 Minneapolis city directory.

PRINTERS FOUNDRY

Minneapolis, Minn.

Rulau	Date	Metal	Size	VG	F	VF	EF
Mn-Mi 25	(?)	Silver	38mm	—	—	110.	—

PRINTERS / FOUNDRY / MINNEAPOLIS ctsp on U.S. 1881 Morgan silver dollar. (PCAC July 1993 sale, lot 095)

W. YOUN

Northfield, Minn.

Rulau	Date	Metal	Size	VG	F	VF	Unc
Mn-No 7	(?)	GS	23mm	—	—	15.00	—

(All incused): (Shield) / W. YOUN, / MAKER, / NORTHFIELD, MINN. Rv: Blank. (McFerran coll.)

Though possibly important, nothing is known of this token.

A. BELINA

Owatonna, Minn.

Rulau	Date	Metal	Size	VG	F	VF	Unc
Mn-Ow 1	(1884-85)	Brass	24.5mm	—	—	35.00	—

Brunswick die BB-8b. Rv: GOOD FOR / 5 ¢: / A. BELINA (in cross-hatched oval panel) / IN / TRADE. Unique. (Thoele coll.)

Anton Belina, saloon, 1884-85 gazetteer.

C. BOWER

Rulau	Date	Metal	Size	VG	F	VF	Unc
Mn-Ow 2	(1882-84)	Brass	25mm	—	—	35.00	—

Brunswick die BB-6a. Rv: GOOD FOR / 5 ¢ / C. BOWER (in panel) / IN / TRADE / *.

GANSER & GLAESER

Owatonna, Minn.

Rulau	Date	Metal	Size	VG	F	VF	Unc
Mn-Ow 5	(1883-86)	Brass	Sq 24mm	—	—	40.00	—

Chas. Pick & Co. die. Rv: GOOD FOR / 5 ¢ / GANSER & / GLAESER / IN / TRADE. (McFerran coll.)

Ganser & Glaeser are listed under billiards 1878-1883 and saloons 1886.

W. W. BUTCHARD

Rice Point, Minn.

Rulau	Date	Metal	Size	VG	F	VF	Unc
Mn-Rp 1	(1882)	Brass	24.5mm	—	—	25.00	—

Brunswick die BB-8a. Rv: GOOD FOR / 5 ¢ (in panel) / W. W. / BUTCHARD (name within oval panel) / -IN- / * TRADE *. Plain edge.

Saloon, listed 1882.

IRVING W. FOX

Rochester, Minn.

Rulau	Date	Metal	Size	VG	F	VF	Unc
Mn-Ro 4	(?)	Silver	25mm	—	125.	—	—

IRVING. W. FOX / ROCHESTER, / MINN. ctsp on U.S. 1876 quarter dollar. (Hartzog coll.)

D. J. McCARTHY

Rulau	Date	Metal	Size	VG	F	VF	Unc
Mn-Ro 7	(1885-94)	Brass	25mm	—	—	20.00	—

Billiard table, THE / J. M. BRUNSWICK / AND / BALKE CO above. Rv: GOOD FOR / 5 C / D. J. / MC CARTHY / IN / TRADE. Plain edge.

E. A. SCHWARTZ

Rochester, Minn.

Rulau	Date	Metal	Size	VG	F	VF	Unc
Mn-Ro 10	(1886-90)	CN	24mm	—	—	30.00	—

E. A. SCHWARTZ, / C / (crossed cue sticks) / ROCHESTER, MINN. Rv: Large 5. Plain edge.

Edward A. Schwartz ran this saloon 1886-1893.

C. KAERWER

St. Cloud, Minn.

Rulau	Date	Metal	Size	VG	F	VF	Unc
Mn-SC 3	(1886-88)	Brass	29mm	—	—	12.50	—

(All incused): / GOOD FOR / ONE 5 ¢ LOAF / BREAD. / C KAERWER. Rv: Blank. (McFerran coll.)

Charles F. Kaerwer, baker and confectioner, listed 1886-1888.

E. M. HOFF

St. Hilaire, Minn.

Rulau	Date	Metal	Size	VG	F	VF	Unc
Mn-SH 2	(1888-89)	Brass	23mm	—	—	35.00	—

GOOD FOR / 5 ¢ / E. M. / HOFF / AT THE BAR. Rv: GEO. KUEHL BILLIARD SUPPLIES / CHECK / CHICAGO.

Eric M. Hoff, saloon, 1886-1889.

CONRAD SCHUMM

St. Michael, Minn.

Rulau	Date	Metal	Size	VG	F	VF	Unc
Mn-SM 5	(1888-89)	Brass	24mm	—	—	9.00	—

(All incused): CONRAD SCHUMM / GOOD FOR / 5 ¢ / IN TRADE. Rv: Blank.

Saloon, listed 1888-1889.

P. J. DREIS

St. Paul, Minn.

Rulau	Date	Metal	Size	VG	F	VF	Unc
Mn-SP 2	(1888-96)	Brass	26mm	—	—	12.50	—

P. J. DREIS, / PRESCRIPTION / (Mortar and pestle) / PHARMACIST / 465 ST. PETER ST. Rv: GOOD FOR / 5 ¢ / IN TRADE. (Dean Montour coll.)

P. Jos. Dreis, drugs, listed 1888-1896.

ICE PALACE & WINTER CARNIVAL

St. Paul, Minn.

Rulau	Date	Metal	Size	F	VF	EF	Unc
Mn-SP 4	(1887)	GS	31mm	—	—	10.00	15.00

Castle-like building surrounded by battlemented wall, flags and pennons flying, tiny NORTHW. -- ST. WORKS under ground. At bottom: ST. PAUL. Rv: Crossed snowshoes, toboggan, etc. at center. Around: THE ICE PALACE & WINTER CARNIVAL; below: SOUVENIR. Plain edge. Issued holed at top for suspension from light blue ribbon.

Rulau	Date	Metal	Size	F	VF	EF	Unc
Mn-SP 6	1887	Gilt/B	**	—	—	—	10.00

** Sq. 15mm.

Castle-like building at center, tiny N.W. STAMP WKS underground. Above: ST. PAUL ICE PALACE WINTER CARNIVAL. Below: 1887. Rv: Burning flame on long pole superimposed over crossed snowshoes and a sled. All arranged in diamond shape. Plain edge. Looped for suspension.

Rulau	Date	Metal	Size	F	VF	EF	Unc
Mn-SP 8	1886	WM	31mm	—	—	15.00	—

Castle-like building, tiny L. BOCHE CHICAGO under ground. Below: ICE PALACE. Rv: SOUVENIR OF ST. PAUL'S FIRST WINTER CARNIVAL / AND ICE PALACE / (radiant cinquefoil) / 1886 / VAL (star) SOU. Plain edge. (Denton Curtis coll.)

Rulau	Date	Metal	Size	F	VF	EF	Unc
Mn-SP 9	1886 *	Brass	15mm	—	1.50	2.25	3.00

View of Ice Palace. Rv: FEB. / 1886 / ST. PAUL ICE CARNIVAL. Plain edge. Issued holed.

* Replicas of this piece were struck in 1946!

Rulau	Date	Metal	Size	F	VF	EF	Unc
Mn-SP 11	1887	Brass	15mm	—	3.50	—	—

View of Ice Palace, ICE PALACE around. Rv: SOUVENIR / OF THE / 1887 / ICE / CARNIVAL. Plain edge. Issued holed.

Rulau	Date	Metal	Size	F	VF	EF	Unc
Mn-SP 12	1888	WM	39mm	—	—	15.00	20.00

Liberty head. Rv: Ice Palace. Around: ST. PAUL ICE PALACE / 1888. Plain edge.

NOTE: There are other medalets of the St. Paul Ice Carnivals of 1886-1887, mostly in the 31mm size in WM or brass.

A. H. S.
(Adam H. Stahl)

St. Paul, Minn.

Rulau	Date	Metal	Size	VG	F	VF	Unc
Mn-SP 30	(1886-89)	Brass	25mm	3.50	6.00	8.50	—

Brunswick die BBC-11. Rv: * GOOD FOR * / 5 ¢ / A. H. S. (in panel) / AT THE BAR.

Adam H. Stahl appears in St. Paul directories 1882-83 as a grocer and then 1886-89 as a saloonkeeper at Rice & Charles Streets. The latter site is the token's place of use, apparently.

About 1985 a jar of up to 50 of these tokens was found in Hudson, Wisconsin, depressing their price. More than that are known, however, according to specialists.

G. W. BUNCE & CO.

St. Peter, Minn.

Rulau	Date	Metal	Size	VG	F	VF	Unc
Mn-Ss 2	(1891)	Aluminum	25mm	—	—	12.50	—

Liberty head. Around: G. W. BUNCE & CO. ST. PETER, MINN. Rv: GOOD FOR / 5 / CENTS / IN TRADE. Plain edge. (McFerran coll.)

Bunce's grocery appears only in the 1886 directory, but the use of aluminum for "good for" trade pieces did not commence until about 1891. This token is very attractive.

PETER HANKS

Shakopee, Minn.

Rulau	Date	Metal	Size	VG	F	VF	Unc
Mn-Sh 3	(?)	Brass	Oct 25mm	—	—	20.00	—

Brunswick die BBC-7. Rv: GOOD FOR / 5 ¢ / PETER / HANKS (name in oval panel / IN / TRADE.

J. M. MERTZ

Shakopee, Minn.

Rulau	Date	Metal	Size	VG	F	VF	Unc
Mn-Sh 7	(1886-98)	Brass	25mm	—	—	20.00	—

Brunswick die BBC. Rv: GOOD FOR / 5 ¢ / J. M. MERTZ / IN / TRADE. (McFerran coll.)

John Mertz, saloon, listed 1886-1898.

FITZGERALD & CO.

Stillwater, Minn.

Rulau	Date	Metal	Size	VG	F	VF	Unc
Mn-St 2	(1888-89)	Brass	Oct 25mm	—	—	25.00	—

Brunswick die BB. Rv: GOOD FOR 5 ¢ / FITZGERALD / & CO. / IN / TRADE.

Richard Fitzgerald is listed under saloons 1882-1886, then D. R. Fitzgerald 1888. The listing changes to Fitzgerald & Co. 1889-1894. It is difficult to determine just when the name "Fitzgerald & Co." started to be used, but we'd estimate 1888-89.

NEW IDEA

Rulau	Date	Metal	Size	VG	F	VF	Unc
Mn-St 8	(1876-90)	GS	23mm	—	—	20.00	—

NEW IDEA / STILLWATER / MINN. / 112 NO. MAIN ST. Rv: P. D. / 2 1/2 / CENTS. Plain edge. About 4 known.

Rulau	Date	Metal	Size	VG	F	VF	Unc
Mn-St 9	(1876-90)	GS	25mm	—	—	25.00	—

Similar to 8, from differing die, with comma after STILLWATER. Rv: Similar to 8. (McFerran coll.)

Platzi S. Deragisch, saloon, is listed 1876 through 1903.

PACIFIC SALOON

Rulau	Date	Metal	Size	VG	F	VF	Unc
Mn-St 12	(1889)	Aluminum	Oct 23mm	—	—	7.50	—

PACIFIC SALOON / STILLWATER, / MINN. Rv: GOOD FOR / 5 ¢ / AT BAR. (Loperfido coll.)

John W. Schroeder is listed as proprietor of the Pacific Saloon 1887-1889, but the token could be from the 1890's.

ZWOLFTE MINNESOTA SANGER-FEST

Rulau	Date	Metal	Size	F	VG	EF	Unc
Mn-St 30	1883	Silv/Br	30mm	—	25.00	—	—

Lyre within wreath. Rv: ZUR ERINNERUNG / AN DAS / ZWOLFTE MINNESOTA / SANGER-FEST. / STILLWATER / 8. 9. UND 10. SEPTEMBER 1883. Plain edge. Issued with slot for suspension. (Gene Johnson coll.)

S. B.
(Sam Bloom)

Stillwater, Minn.

Rulau	Date	Metal	Size	VG	F	EF	Unc
Mn-St 3	(1868-80)	Bronze	19mm	—	10.00	15.00	—

S B ctsp on reverse of U.S. Indian cent. Numeral 5 ctsp on obverse of the coin. (Dates examined: 1868, 1871, 1875, 1876.)

Rulau	Date	Metal	Size	VG	F	EF	Unc
Mn-St 4	(1868-80)	Bronze	23mm	—	10.00	15.00	—

S B ctsp on obverse of U.S. Shield 2-cent piece. Numeral 10 ctsp on reverse of the coin. (Dates examined: 1864.)

Sam Bloom was a lumberman who allegedly used these counterstamped coins as counters in his logging business in the 1860's and 1870's near Stillwater, Minnesota. (Research courtesy Capt. David Jerdee, Papillion, Neb.)

This attribution is very dubious. Brunk could not confirm it, and the pieces may be mavericks.

ED. McDONALD

Villard, Minn.

Rulau	Date	Metal	Size	VG	F	VF	EF
Mn-Vi 1	(1886-89)	Brass	25mm	—	—	30.00	—

Brunswick die BBC-11. Rv: GOOD FOR / 5 C / ED. / McDONALD / IN / TRADE. Plain edge. (McFerran collection)

Ed. McDonald was listed under saloons in Villard in the 1886 thru 1889 gazetteers. Later (1898-1909) he ran a saloon in Long Prairie, Minn. It is possible McDonald continued use of these checks over a long period at several locations.

J. HOHMAN

Waconia, Minn.

Rulau	Date	Metal	Size	VG	F	VF	EF
Mn-Wc 1	(1883-85)	Brass	24mm	—	—	9.00	—

(All incused): J. HOHMAN. Rv: BOTTLE / 5 / CHECK. Plain edge.

John Hohman is listed under saloons in the 1884-85 Minnesota-Dakota-Montana business directory.

VANZANT & WILLIAMS

Wadena, Minn.

Rulau	Date	Metal	Size	VG	F	VF	Unc
Mn-Wd 3	(1883)	Brass	24mm	—	—	35.00	—

Brunswick die BB-4. Rv: GOOD FOR / 5 ¢ / VANZANT & / WILLIAMS / IN / TRADE. Plain edge. 2 pieces known. (Kruesel, McFerran colls.)

The 1883 Dun directory lists E. L. Vanzant and A. Williams as sellers of liquors, though not in partnership.

EACO
(Everett & Augenbaugh Co.)

Waseca, Minn.

Rulau	Date	Metal	Size	F	VF	EF	Unc
Mn-Wc 3	(?)	Copper	**	—	20.00	—	30.00

** Irregular, 35mm.

Winged horse Pegasus. Rv: MAKE GOOD BREAD / EVERY TIME / EACO / WINGED HORSE / FLOUR / WASECA, MINN. / (tiny) THE GREENDUCK CO. CHICAGO. (McFerran coll.)

Everett & Augenbaugh's flour mill was established 1886. It was last listed 1927.

AMERICAN HOTEL

Winona, Minn.

Rulau	Date	Metal	Size	VG	F	VF	EF
Mn-Wn 1	(ca 1875 ?)	CN	22mm	—	—	70.00	—

AMERICAN / WINONA, MINN / HOTEL ctsp on U.S. 1864, 1866, 1867, 1868, 1869, 1872, 1873, 1874 Shield nickels. The counterstamp is struck from a die, not hand punched.

This hotel was in business 1872 until it burned down 1886. It was also known as Wale's Hotel.

A new hotel was built 1888 at 704-706 West 5th, which closed 1904.

GRIESEL BROS.

Rulau	Date	Metal	Size	VG	F	VF	Unc
Mn-Wn 5	(1886)	Brass	20mm	—	—	7.00	—

GRIESEL BROS. Rv: GOOD FOR / 5 ¢ / IN TRADE. (Dave Schulz coll.)

Saloon, listed 1886.

A. KRALL

Rulau	Date	Metal	Size	VG	F	VF	Unc
Win 7	(1889)	Brass	25mm	—	—	10.00	—

(All incused): A. KRALL / GOOD FOR / 5 ¢ / DRINK / WINONA, MINN. Rv: Blank. Plain edge. (McFerran coll.)

This saloon appears in 1889. It reappears 1902-04 at 926 West 5th Street.

LUDWIG'S HOTEL

Rulau	Date	Metal	Size	VG	F	VF	Unc
Mn-Wn 10	(1880's)	Bronze	19mm	—	—	20.00	—

Brunswick die BB. Rv: LUDWIG'S HOTEL. (Dave Schulz coll.)

Hotel, saloon and billiard hall owned by John Ludwig.

C. MILLER

Rulau	Date	Metal	Size	VG	F	VF	Unc
Mn-Wn 12	(1880's)	Brass	Oct 20mm	—	—	8.00	—

GOOD FOR / 5 ¢ / C. MILLER / IN / TRADE. Rv: Large 5 in circle of stars.

Charles Miller's saloon was at the corner of 2nd and Walnut Streets.

C. O. ROESNER

Rulau	Date	Metal	Size	VG	F	VF	Unc
Mn-Wn 14	(1885)	Brass	21mm	—	—	8.00	—

C. O. ROESNER. Rv: GOOD FOR ONE / 5 ¢ / DRINK / OR CIGAR. (Dave Schulz coll.)

Saloon, listed 1885 only.

JOHN SAILSBURY

Rulau	Date	Metal	Size	VG	F	VF	Unc
Win 16	(?)	Brass	Oct 26mm	—	—	35.00	—

Brunswick die BB. Rv: GOOD FOR / JOHN / SAILSBURY / 1 / DRINK. Plain edge.

Rulau	Date	Metal	Size	VG	F	VF	Unc
Win 17	(1870's)	GS	19mm	—	—	30.00	—

NO. 19 / MAIN ST. / WINONA, / MINN. Rv: GOOD FOR / 5 Cts. / AT THE BAR. Plain edge. (In John W. Haseltine auction catalog of Dec. 16-17, 1880)

Rulau	Date	Metal	Size	VG	F	VF	Unc
Win 17A	(?)	Brass	19mm	—	—	11.00	—

As 17.

Rulau	Date	Metal	Size	VG	F	VF	Unc
Win 18	(?)	Brass	21mm	—	—	12.50	—

As 17, but 10 Cts. (McFerran coll.)

Though 17 thru 18 bear no name, they are tokens of John Sailsbury's saloon and restaurant, active in Winona in the 1880's and 1890's.

(Research by Robert J. Lindesmith, Dayton, Wash.)

SCROTH & AHRENS

Rulau	Date	Metal	Size	VG	F	VF	Unc
Mn-Wn 19	(1870-89)	Brass	20mm	—	—	12.50	—

SCROTH / & / AHRENS. Rv: Stylized S.

Rulau	Date	Metal	Size	VG	F	VF	Unc
Mn-Wn 20	(1870-89)	Brass	22mm	—	—	12.50	—

SCROTH / & / AHRENS. Rv: Large 10. (Dave Schulz coll.)

Diecutter's error on both tokens; the name should be Schroth & Ahrens. They were sash and door makers at corner 4th and Ewing Streets.

H. J. TROOST

Rulau	Date	Metal	Size	VG	F	VF	Unc
Mn-Wn 21	(1889)	Silver	25mm	—	40.00	—	—

H. J. / TROOST / NO. 16, 2' ST. / WINONA, / MINN. *engraved* on shaved reverse of U.S. 1858 S.L. quarter. (Richard McFerran coll.)

Troost & Co. were listed as liquor dealers in the 1889 gazetteer.

WINONA NATIONAL CARNIVAL

Winona, Minn.

Rulau	Date	Metal	Size	VG	F	VF	Unc
Mn-Wn 23	1886	Brass	16mm	—	—	15.00	—

WINONA'S / NATIONAL / CARNIVAL / 1886 - 7. Rv: Blank. (Calvin Woods coll.)

S. THOENI

Wykoff, Minn.

Rulau	Date	Metal	Size	VG	F	VF	Unc
Mn-Wy 2	(1886-94)	Brass	Oct 25mm	—	—	15.00	——

Brunswick die BBC. Rv: GOOD FOR / 5 ¢ / S. THOENI / IN / TRADE. (McFerran coll.)

Simson Thoeni's saloon is listed 1886-1894.

FRED DOELTZ

Young America, Minn.

Rulau	Date	Metal	Size	VG	F	VF	Unc
Mn-Yn 1	(1882-89)	Brass	24mm	—	—	35.00	—

THE J. M. BRUNSWICK & BALKE COS / (pool table) / CHECK. Rv: GOOD FOR / 5 ¢ / FRED / DOELTZ / IN TRADE. (McFerran coll.)

Saloon and hotel, listed 1882-1889.

ADDITIONAL MINNESOTA BILLIARD TOKENS

Following is a listing of verified attributions for this era. These are given here for informational purposes: (* before name means city given on token!)

Name on Token	Possible Locale	Billiard Die	Gazetteer
* C. Anderson	Osakis	BBC ?	1886-88
Anderson Bros.	Duluth	BB-6a	1888
J.G. Brantberg	St. Paul	BB ?	1886-89
Nic. Clemens	St. Charles	BB-7a	1882-89
* Chas. Conaty	Lanesboro	Chas. Pick	1882-84
Fenstermaker & Neal	Breckinridge	BB-7b	1884
John Fey	Ortonville	Chas. Pick	1886-94
Louie Frank	Preston	BB ?	1884
B.P. Hammer	Montevideo	B-2e	1882
William Heidenreich	Shakopee	Chas. Pick	1882-96
* Highland & Murphy	Sauk Center	BBC-9b	1886-89
John Lundberg	Duluth	BBC-11	1886-94
Thomas Mehegan	Benson	BB-7b	1884
A.C. Merrill	Minneapolis	Bruns & Co.	1886
* P. Mohrbacher	Cologne	BB ?	1882-1900
M.C. Milliman	Pipestone	BB-8a	1886
* Newton House	Red Wing	Chas. Pick	1882-90
Math. Offermann	Redwood Falls	BB-4	1875-86
Paulson & Kittelson	Canby	BBC-11	1888
* C. Peterson	St. Paul	BB ?	1882-1919
Frank Roemer	New Prague	Chas. Pick	1886-98
J.X. Rosskopf	New Ulm	BBC ?	1886-87
St. James	Red Wing	BBC ?	1875-date
Nels Sandell	Jordan & St. Paul	BB-7b	1882-93
Chas. Siebert	Minneapolis	Garden City	1886-88
Sparks & Holbrook	New Richland	BB ?	1884-86
T. Tornou	Potsdam	Chas. Pick	1884-89
S. Thoeni	Wykoff	BBC ?	1884-94
Jno. Trenheuser	Mankato	Chas. Pick	1888-1900
J. Utterburg & Co.	Barnesville	BB-4	1882-89
Louis Vasaly	Little Falls	BB-4	1886
John Wellman	Lake City	BBC-10b	1884-88

MISSISSIPPI

VIC TROLIO

Canton, Miss.

Rulau	Date	Metal	Size	VG	F	VF	Unc
Ms-Cn 9	(1880's?)	Silver	18mm	—	45.00	60.00	100.

TAKE ME / (sunburst) / BACK TO / (sunburst) / VIC TROLIO. Rv: — / CANTON, / (sunburst) / — MISS. — / (sunburst) / SOLID SILVER / —. Plain edge. Very rare. (Rulau coll.)

J. D. JEWELL

Silver Lake, Miss.

Rulau	Date	Metal	Size	F	VF	EF	Unc
Ms-SL 2	(?)	—	--mm	25.00	—	100.	150.

IN MERCHANDISE / AT / J. D. JEWELL / —&— / . BRO'S . / STORE / SILVER LAKE MISS. Rv: ********** / 10 / CENTS. Plain edge. (Miller Miss 1A)

Rulau	Date	Metal	Size	F	VF	EF	Unc
Ms-SL 3	(?)	WM	20mm	25.00	—	100.	150.

As 2, but 25 / CENTS. (Miller Miss 1)

Rulau	Date	Metal	Size	F	VF	EF	Unc
Ms-SL 4	(?)	—	--mm	25.00	—	100.	150.

As 2, but 50 / CENTS. (Miller Miss 1B)

Rulau	Date	Metal	Size	F	VF	EF	Unc
Ms-SL 5	(?)	Brass	--mm	30.00	—	100.	150.

As 2, but 1 / DOLLAR. (Miller Miss 1C)

Rulau	Date	Metal	Size	F	VF	EF	Unc
Ms-SL 6	(?)	Nickel	22mm	—	—	100.	150.

As 2, but 5 / DOLLARS. (Miller Miss 1D; in ANS coll.)

We have been unsuccessful thus far in locating Silver Lake, Miss., looking through postal guides, business registers etc. from the 1877 through 1918 period.

T. V. DUNN

Meridian, Miss.

Rulau	Date	Metal	Size	F	VF	EF	Unc
Ms-Me 1	1870	Silver	25mm	—	—	35.00	—

T.V. DUNN / MERIDIAN MISS ctsp with single letter punches on U.S. 1860 S.L. quarter. On opposite side, CITY POLICE / JUNE 1870 is ctsp. (Van Ormer 2626; ex-Hartzog May 1978 sale, lot 192; Brunk 12450)

CLARKE & CO.

Vicksburg, Miss.

Rulau	Date	Metal	Size	VG	F	VF	Unc
Ms-Vi 1	(1880's)	GS	22mm	—	—	—	200.

Eagle left, landing on a drum surrounded by flags, rifles, cannon balls and rays. Rv: CLARKE & CO. / BOOKSELLERS / GOOD FOR / * 7 1/2 ¢ * / PAPER / + VICKSBURG, MISS. +. Reeded edge. (Fuld coll.)

The token's obverse is the same as that of the Wapakoneta, Ohio, Sanitary Fair and the Dunlap & Florer, Osage traders, in the 1860-70 decade. George Fuld surmises that this piece was made about 1890, but we think it likely it was struck in Cincinnati by James Murdock Jr. using an old Civil War die, earlier than 1890. Directory evidence is lacking.

However, Clarke & Co. were still listed in 1917-18 as booksellers and stationers. This is an interesting example of re-use of old dies to fill customer orders. The 7 1/2-cent denomination is very unusual.

CROOM & HILL

Vicksburg, Miss.

Rulau	Date	Metal	Size	VG	F	VF	Unc
Ms-Vi 3	(1870's)	GS	30mm	—	—	40.00	—

CROOM & HILL, HOTEL DIXIE. Rv: Numeral 50. (Miller Miss 2)

PRENTIS HOUSE

Vicksburg, Miss.

Rulau	Date	Metal	Size	VG	F	VF	Unc
Ms-Vi 8	(1870's?)	Brass	**	—	—	50.00	—

** Oval, 43 x 26mm.
PRENTIS HOUSE/ 100 / VICKSBURG. Rv: Blank. Plain edge. (Wright 845)

MISSOURI

THE F. B. P. & M. CO.

Fallback, Mo.

Rulau	Date	Metal	Size	F	VF	EF	Unc
Mo-Fb 2	(1880)	Brass	21mm	—	—	30.00	—

THE F. B. P. & M. CO. / FALLBACK. Rv: Large 5 ¢ . Plain edge. Only 2 known.

One piece brought $20 in a 1973 sale by Joseph Schmidt of Illinois. No recent sales.

L. S. HARRIS

Holden, Mo.

Rulau	Date	Metal	Size	VG	F	VF	EF
Mo-Ho 1	(1880-99)	GS	**	—	—	20.00	—

** Oval 34x20mm.
Angry eagle left, atop four folds of a scroll. On scroll, incuse, is: L. S. HARRIS / TAILOR / HOLDEN / MO. Rv: Blank. Plain edge. Holed at left as issued. (Elmer Randall coll.)

Identification tag.

BULLENE MOORE EMERY & CO.

Kansas City, Mo.

Rulau	Date	Metal	Size	VG	F	VF	Unc
Mo-Kc 2	(1880's)	**	31mm	50.00	—	75.00	—

** Celluloid, cream border and lettering on red field.
(Ornament) BULLENE, MOORE, EMERY & CO, (ornament) / 5 (large, ornate). Rv: Same as obverse. (Tom Wall coll.)

THE CONSOLIDATED KANSAS CITY SMELTING & REFINING CO.

Kansas City, Mo.

Rulau	Date	Metal	Size	F	VF	EF	Unc
Mo-KC 3	1889	Silver	38mm	—	25.00	40.00	70.00

Jugate male busts right, C. KURTZ on truncation, 1889 under truncation. Around: * THE CONSOLIDATED KANSAS CITY SMELTING & REFINING CO. TO THE AMERICAN CONGRESS GREETING. Rv: Two standing females joining hands, each holding a pole topped by a Liberty cap. Around: RECIPROCITY * THE UNITED AMERICAS * COMMERCE / LOS AMERICAS UNIDAS *. Plain edge. (Hibler & Kappen 731)

This company operated mostly in Mexico. It is well known to collectors through its large number of surviving bills of exchange, drafts and other paper numismatica issued from a number of Mexican sites. In its day the firm was a giant in silver and non-ferrous metal refining, in an era when unbridled American business had deep control over much of Mexico's economy, and powerful friends in the U.S. Congress, as this piece indicates. The portraits are those of Presidents Benjamin Harrison of the U.S. and Porfirio Diaz of Mexico.

Rulau	Date	Metal	Size	F	VF	EF	Unc
Mo-Kc 3A	1889	Aluminum	38mm	—	—	35.00	50.00

As 3. The aluminum strikes may have been made later, about 1891.

H.C. DE SOLLAR

Kansas City, Mo.

Rulau	Date	Metal	Size	VG	F	VF	EF
Mo-KC 5	(?)	Silver	31mm	40.00	—	75.00	—

H.C. De SOLLAR. / Kansas City. ctsp on U.S. Liberty Seated Half dollar (date worn off). Tanenbaum coll.; Brunk 11470)

De Sollar does not appear in 1870 directories. The stamp is crude.

FREDERICK FRANCK

Rulau	Date	Metal	Size	VG	F	VF	Unc
Mo-KC 6	(?)	Brass	27mm	—	—	35.00	—

FREDERICK FRANCK, / (ornament) / BILLIARDS / (ornament) / KANSAS CITY, MO. Rv: 5 (large, stippled). Plain edge. (Tom Wall coll.)

NATIONAL AGRICULTURAL EXPOSITION

Rulau	Date	Metal	Size	F	VF	EF	Unc
Mo-KC 7	1887	Brass	38mm	—	—	15.00	20.00

Female on globe points to Kansas City. Around: KANSAS CITY / SOUVENIR. Rv: NATIONAL AGRICULTURAL / EXPOSITION / —1887— / OPENS SEP. 15. / (ornament) / CLOSES OCT. 30. Plain edge. (Gene Johnson coll.)

Rulau	Date	Metal	Size	F	VF	EF	Unc
Mo-KC 8	1887	WM	30mm	—	10.00	—	20.00

Building at center, NATIONAL above, AGRICULTURAL / EXPOSITION / (beehive at center of laurel sprays). Rv: THE / NATIONAL / + 1887 + / AGRICULTURAL / ..*.. / EXPOSITION / KANSAS CITY, / MO. Plain edge. (Brunk coll.)

SMITH & KEATING

(See Il-Ch 110, Schuttler Wagons, under Chicago, Illinois in this section)

SMITH & RIEGER

Rulau	Date	Metal	Size	VG	F	VF	Unc
Mo-KC 11	(1880's)	Brass	25mm	10.00	15.00	25.00	40.00

SMITH & RIEGER, / (ornament) / HATTERS / 554 / MAIN ST. / + / KANSAS CITY, MO. Rv: RECEIVABLE / FOR / 5 / CENTS / IN MERCHANDISE / ON ONE DOLLARS PURCHASE. Plain edge. (Miller Mo 42)

Not in 1870 *Bradstreet Directory.*

STROUSE & BROS.

1876 Centennial Tokens

Reverse type 1: VISIT / STROUSE & BROS. / THE / PEOPLE'S / CLOTHIERS / 428 MAIN ST. / KANSAS CITY, MO. (All 19mm, plain edge. None were listed by Wright, Miller or other cataloguers)

Rulau	Obv	Rev	Metal	F	VF	EF	Unc
Mo-KC 25	W	1	WM	—	—	25.00	60.00
Mo-KC 26	X	1	WM	—	—	25.00	60.00
Mo-KC 26A	X	1	Bronze	—	—	25.00	75.00
Mo-KC 27	Y	1	Bronze	—	—	25.00	75.00
Mo-KC 28	Z	1	WM	—	—	25.00	60.00
Mo-KC 28A	Z	1	Bronze	—	—	25.00	75.00

Strouse & Bros. do not appear in the 1881 directory.

WESTERN SUPPLY CO.

Kansas City, Mo.

Rulau	Date	Metal	Size	VG	F	VF	Unc
Mo-KC 40	(ca 1880's)	Brass	Sq 33mm	—	15.00	—	—

(All incused): WESTERN SUPPLY / CO. / -x- / KANSAS CITY / MISSOURI. Rv: Blank. Plain edge. (Joseph Schmidt coll.)

J. C. DILLON

Kirksville, Mo.

Rulau	Date	Metal	Size	F	VF	EF	Unc
Mo-Kk 1	(?)	CN	22mm	—	—	100.	—

J. C. DILLON / KIRKSVILLE, / MO ctsp on shaved reverse of U.S. 1868 Shield nickel. LIVERY STABLE ctsp on obverse of the coin. (Van Ormer sale 2621; Brunk 11690)

STAR SALOON

La Clede, Mo.

Rulau	Date	Metal	Size	VG	F	VF	EF
Mo-LC 4	1866	**	27mm	—	—	150.	—

** Nickel alloy.

Coronet Liberty head left, 13 stars around, 1866 below. Rv: GOOD FOR ONE DRINK / AT THE / STAR / * SALOON * / LA CLEDE, MO.

One of the two known copies appeared in the Springfield sale in Dec., 1981, as lot 4563. It is now in the Weinberg coll.

WILSON & CRECY

Lamar, Mo.

Rulau	Date	Metal	Size	VG	F	VF	Unc
Mo-Lm 3	(1885-86)	Brass	25mm	—	—	35.00	—

Brunswick die BBC-1. Rv: GOOD FOR / 5 ¢ / WILSON / & CRECY (names in oval panel) / IN / TRADE. (Thoele coll.)

Crecy & Wilson (sic!) are listed under saloons in the 1885-86 Polk gazetteer. The BBC-1 die was short-lived and a rare die type.

J. B. GUM

Mount Vernon, Mo.

Rulau	Date	Metal	Size	VG	F	VF	EF
Mo-MV 2	(?)	CN	22mm	—	—	150.	—

J. B. GUM / WATCHMAKER & JEWELER / NO. 13 / MT. VERNON, MO. ctsp on U.S. 1867 Rays type Shield nickel. (Brunk 17380)

Jacob B. Gum, jeweler, was still in business in 1918. He does not appear in 1870 or 1881 directories.

JOHN KENMUIR
St. Joseph, Mo.

Rulau	Date	Metal	Size	F	VF	EF	Unc
Mo-SJ 6A	(1873-81)	CN	19mm	—	175.	325.	525.

JOHN KENMUIR / * / WATCH / MAKER / FELIX ST. / * / + ST. JOSEPH MO. +. Rv: JOHN KENMUIR / .+. / MAN'FG / JEWELER / --+-- / ST. JOSEPH MO. Plain edge. (Zaffern coll.; ex.rare)

Rulau	Date	Metal	Size	F	VF	EF	Unc
Mo-SJ 6	(1873-81)	Brass	19mm	—	150.	300.	500.

As last. (Fuld Mo 880A). 5 to 10 pieces known.

Brass token has been listed erroneously as a Civil War token, which may account for its high price. It is clearly post-CW and may be overvalued here. Only 3 nickel pieces are known.

John Kenmuir was born in Lisburn, Ireland in 1831. He apprenticed in his father's manufacturing jewelry business in County Down and emigrated to America 1850. He became a manufacturing jeweler in New York and was successful. In 1863 he relocated in Leavenworth City, Kansas and became a retail clock and watch dealer.

In 1873 he moved to St. Joseph, Mo., establishing his business on Felix between 5th and 6th Streets. He was still located there in 1881. Kenmuir established the Bell telephone in St. Joseph in 1874.

NATIONAL RAILWAY ELECTRIC & INDUSTRIAL EXPOSITION
St. Joseph, Mo.

Rulau	Date	Metal	Size	F	VF	EF	Unc
Mo-Jo 15	1889	WM	38mm	—	7.50	15.00	30.00

Building, NATIONAL RAILWAY ELECTRIC & INDUSTRIAL EXPOSITION. around, SEPT. 3RD / 1889 / * in exergue. Rv: Twelve ears of corn and KORN KING within central circle, ST. JOSEPH EXPOSITION / 1889 around. Plain edge.

ANHEUSER-BUSCH
St. Louis, Mo.

Rulau	Date	Metal	Size	F	VF	EF	Unc
Mo-SL 3	1880	CN	29mm	—	—	50.00	—

(All designs and lettering incused). Eagle on shield facing left, through large letter A, 1880 below. Rv: ANHEUSER-BUSCH / ST LOUIS. Plain edge.

(See *TAMS Journal* for Dec. 1977, page 241)

Rulau	Date	Metal	Size	VG	F	VF	Unc
Mo-SL 2	1880	Copper	21mm	5.00	7.50	10.00	25.00

Large A superimposed on eagle and shield, 1880 below. Rv: ANHEUSER-BUSCH / BREW'G * / ASS'N / *. Plain edge. (Miller Mo 1)

Rulau	Date	Metal	Size	VG	F	VF	Unc
Mo-SL 2A	1880	Brass	21mm	3.00	5.00	8.00	20.00

As 2. Plain edge. (Wright 25)

J. BURNS

Rulau	Date	Metal	Size	VG	F	VF	EF
Mo-SL 4	(?)	Silver	31mm	—	—	Rare	—

ST. LOUIS / J. BURNS ctsp on U.S. 1859-0 Seated Liberty half dollar. Two separate punches. (PCAC Dec. 1990 sale, lot 128)

DEUTSCH FRANZOSISCHEN KRIEG

Rulau	Date	Metal	Size	F	VF	EF	Unc
Mo-SL 8	1871	Copper	31mm	—	—	10.00	20.00

Germania with shield and palm standing on Rhine bank, rising sun in background. DURCH EINHEIT ZUR FREIHEIT (Through unity to freedom). Rv: Oak wreath encloses: ZUR ERINNERUNG AN DEN DEUTSCH FRANZOSISCHEN KRIEG 1870 & 1871 ST. LOUIS, MO. (In commemoration of the German French War). C. STUBENRAUCH FECIT ST. LOUIS in tiny letters under Germania on obverse. Plain edge. Weight 15.21 grams.

Rulau	Date	Metal	Size	F	VF	EF	Unc
Mo-SL 8A	1871	WM	31mm	—	—	15.00	30.00

As 8. Plain edge.

Rulau	Date	Metal	Size	F	VF	EF	Unc
MI-SL 8B	1871	Iron	31mm	—	—	15.00	30.00

As 8. Plain edge.

Rulau	Date	Metal	Size	F	VF	EF	Unc
Mo-SL 9	1871	WM	31.4mm	—	—	15.00	30.00

Similar to last, but stems on wreath are not tied together as on copper version, and there is no ribbon. Designer signature reads: C. STUBENRAUCH FECIT. Plain edge. Weight 16.35 grams.

Karl Stubenrauch was mint engraver and medalist in the Grand Duchy of Hesse-Darmstadt 1839-1848, at Darmstadt Mint. He emigrated to the U.S. and about 1850 settled in St. Louis to take up his trade. Later in the 1850's he formed the Stubenrauch & Weber partnership.

For background, see Milwaukier Friedens-Feier, Milwaukee, Wis., in this volume.

FOURTH ST. OPERA HOUSE

Rulau	Date	Metal	Size	VG	F	VF	Unc
Mo-SL 10	(?)	Brass	Oct 27mm	—	—	15.00	—

FOURTH ST. OPERA HOUSE / *** / J.S. EDWARDS ***** / PROP. / *** / ST. LOUIS, MO. Rv: Large 5 at center of circle of nine stars, CENTS below. (Wright 282).

GUS'

Rulau	Date	Metal	Size	VG	F	VF	Unc
Mo-SL 11	(?)	Brass	Oct 24mm	—	—	15.00	—

GUS' / 2 1/2 ¢ / 7' CHOUTEAU AVE. Rv: Blank. Plain edge. (Wright 407)

HASKELL ENGRAVING CO.

Rulau	Date	Metal	Size	F	VF	EF	Unc
Mo-SL 12	(1884)	WM	23mm	—	—	200.	—

Blaine and Logan busts jugate to right, BLAINE at left, LOGAN right. Rv: HASKELL ENGRAVING CO / (rosette) / MEDALS / CHECKS / BADGES / (rosette) / 216 PINE STREET ST LOUIS. Plain edge. Very rare; published here for the first time.

CONRAD KELLERSMAN

Rulau	Date	Metal	Size	VG	F	VF	Unc
Mo-SL 13	1876	WM	25.5mm	—	—	40.00	—

Bearded head left, CONRAD KELLERSMAN 14' & HOWARD. ST. LOUIS around, 1876 below. Rv: Within wreath: GOOD / FOR ONE / 5 / CENT DRINK. Star at wreath opening at top.

This token is superbly executed, in regal European coinage fashion. First published in Missouri Numismatic Society's Journal.

M. & ST. L. PACKET CO.
St. Louis, Mo. (?)

Rulau	Date	Metal	Size	VG	F	VF	Unc
Mo-SL 15	(?)	Brass	21mm	—	35.00	60.00	100.

Liberty head, M. & ST. L. PACKET CO. around, BAR below. Rv: GOOD FOR ONE DRINK / 10. (TAMS maverick 9796)

Rulau	Date	Metal	Size	VG	F	VF	Unc
Mo-SL 16	(?)	Brass	22mm	—	35.00	60.00	100.

Indian head, M. & ST. L. PACKET CO. around, BAR below. Rv: GOOD FOR ONE DRINK / 20. (Alpert sale, Oct. 1981, number 7)

Memphis & St. Louis Packet Co. ? Attribution by Bruce W. Smith, Fort Wayne, Ind.

MAURICE & HENRY

Rulau	Date	Metal	Size	VG	F	VF	EF
Mo-SL 17	(?)	Silver	18mm	—	—	50.00	—

MAURICE & HENRY / ST. LOUIS ctsp on U.S. 1872 Seated Liberty dime. (Kovacs coll.; Brunk 26500)

MERMOD & JACCARD JEWELRY CO.

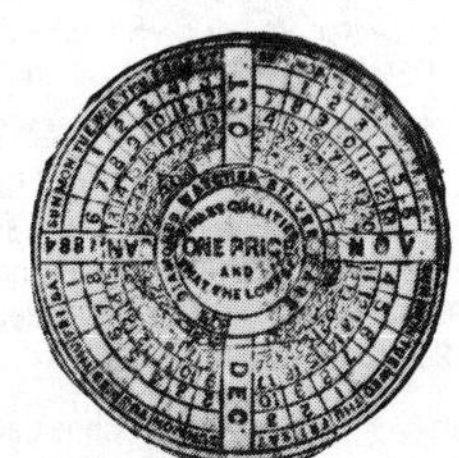

Rulau	Date	Metal	Size	F	VF	EF	Unc
Mo-SL 20	1884	WM	30mm	—	7.00	12.00	35.00

Large building within circle. Inscription inside circle: WE CORDIALLY INVITE YOU TO VISIT OUR MAGNIFICENT ESTABLISHMENT. Outside circle: MERMOD & JACCARD JEWELRY CO. / FOURTH AND LOCUST STS. ST. LOUIS. Rv: Circular 1884 calendar. At center: DIAMONDS WATCHES SILVERWARE / FIRST QUALITIES / ONE PRICE / AND / THAT THE LOWEST. Plain edge.

HENRY MICK

Rulau	Date	Metal	Size	VG	F	VF	Unc
Mo-SL 22	(1877-94)	Brass	23mm	—	—	25.00	—

GOOD FOR / 5 ¢ / HENRY MICK. Rv: BRUNSWICK / * / & CO. in circular form, small, at center of field. Plain edge. (Brunswick page 16, no number)

Henry Mick, brewer, appears in the 1870 directory.

H.T. MOTT

Rulau	Date	Metal	Size	F	VF	EF	Unc
Mo-SL 23	(?)	Brass	23mm	—	20.00	25.00	30.00

Man's high boot inscribed MOTTS BIG; NO. 610 N. B'WAY. Rv: H.T. MOTT / KEEP 10¢ THIS / IN TRADE / ST. LOUIS. Plain edge.

ST. L. & O. R.
(St. Louis & Ohio Railroad)

Rulau	Date	Metal	Size	VG	F	VF	EF
Mo-SL 24	1868	Silver	21mm	—	50.00	—	—

E. T. MILLER / FIREMAN / ST. L. & O. R. / 1868 ctsp on worn Spanish-American 1-real. (PCAC July 1993 sale, lot 092)

ST. BERNARD DOLLAR STORE

Rulau	Date	Metal	Size	F	VF	EF	Unc
Mo-SL A25	(1870's)	Brass	25mm	—	—	40.00	—

ST. BERNARD / DOLLAR STORE / 406 N. 4TH. ST. / * / ST. LOUIS. Rv: SOMETHING / NEW / EVERY DAY / AT / (ornament) OVER (ornament). Plain edge. (ANS coll.)

ST. LOUIS EXPOSITION & MUSIC HALL

Rulau	Date	Metal	Size	F	VF	EF	Unc
Mo-SL B25	1889	S/WM	37.6mm	—	—	35.00	50.00

Building. Around: ST. LOUIS EXPOSITION & MUSIC HALL / * SEP. 4 TO OCT. 19. 1889 *. Supported Missouri arms within raised border of 42 stars. Plain edge. (Hartzog coll.)

ST. LOUIS SAENGERFEST

Rulau	Date	Metal	Size	F	VF	EF	Unc
Mo-SL 26	1872	WM	25mm	—	10.00	18.00	27.50

Building, SAENGERFEST HALL above, 1872 / ST. LOUIS below. Rv: WM. HAGEMANN / DEN / SAENGERN / NORDAMERICA'S / JUNY 1872 / ST. LOUIS. Plain edge.

Rulau	Date	Metal	Size	F	VF	EF	Unc
Mo-SL 27	1872	WM	28mm	—	5.00	7.50	12.50

Woman at harp to left, ST. LOUIS JUNE 1872 around. Tiny C. STUBENRAUCH ENG. in exergue. Rv: Building, 18TH NATIONAL above, SAENGERFEST in exergue. Plain edge. Mounted for suspension from blue ribbon.

Rulau	Date	Metal	Size	F	VF	EF	Unc
Mo-SL 28	1888	Brass	23mm	—	3.00	5.00	10.00

Lyre within wreath. Rv: A REMEMBRANCE / OF THE / SAENGERFEST / AT / ST. LOUIS / * / JUNE 1888. Plain edge.

Saengerfest = A German singing festival.

C.G. SANDERS

Rulau	Date	Metal	Size	VG	F	VF	Unc
Mo-SL 29	(1873-78)	WM	25mm	75.00	100.	150.	300.

Four-mule team pulling cart loaded with wood toward right, CHEAP FUEL in exergue. Rv: C.G. SANDERS / DEALER IN / WOOD COAL / & KINDLING /3127 & 3129 / EASTON AVE / ST. LOUIS, MO. Plain edge. (Miller Mo 28)

Charles G. Sanders first appears in the city directories in 1867 as a measurer. By 1869 he had become a wood dealer. In 1872 he was at Franklin Ave. and Leffingwell, and he added coal to his inventory. In 1873 he moved to 3127 Easton. In 1878 the firm became Charles G. Sanders & Co. as he admitted Eugene F. Pushon as partner. In 1883 the addresses are given as 3137 & 3139 Easton. In 1890 Sanders is listed as a broker and apparently retired from the fuel business.

The token must date from the 1873-1878 period, before the "& Co." was added to the firm name, yet after relocation at 3127 Easton. This token was listed with a question mark as to its dating in the 1st edition of my *U.S. Merchant Tokens 1845-1860*. This is now resolved and this very rare piece is attributed to the 1866-1889 era.

F. L. SCHMID

St. Louis, Mo.

Rulau	Date	Metal	Size	VG	F	VF	Unc
Mo-SL 29F	(?)	Brass	vv	—	—	100.	125.

vv Barrel-shaped, 23x17mm.
Billiards table. Around: BILLIARD / SALOON. Rv: GOOD FOR / ONE DRINK / (bung) / F. L. SCHMID / ST. LOUIS. (Tom Wall coll.)

This is a beautifully designed token. The obverse is arranged horizontally, the reverse vertically. Surprisingly, Unc. specimens are known.

SCHNAIDER'S GARDEN

Rulau	Date	Metal	Size	VG	F	VF	Unc
Mo-SL 30	(1885)	GS	33mm	—	20.00	40.00	65.00

View of buildings and gardens. At base in tiny letters: W. W. WILCOX CHICAGO. Rv: SCHNAIDER'S / (ornament) / GARDEN / (ornament) / ST. LOUIS, MO. Plain edge. (Wright 949)

Rulau	Date	Metal	Size	VG	F	VF	Unc
Mo-SL 30A	(1885)	Copper	33m	—	—	Unique	—

As 30. Plain edge.

Rulau	Date	Metal	Size	VG	F	VF	Unc
Mo-SL 30B	(1885)	Brass	33mm	—	25.00	45.00	80.00

As 30. Plain edge.

Struck by W. W. Wilcox of Chicago.

Rulau	Date	Metal	Size	VG	F	VF	Unc
Mo-SL 31	(1880's)	Brass	20mm	6.00	10.00	20.00	30.00

Gothic S within open-end wreath. Rv: SCHNAIDER'S / 5 / GARDEN. Plain edge. Small 5.

Rulau	Date	Metal	Size	VG	F	VF	Unc
Mo-SL 31A	(1880's)	Brass	21mm	6.00	10.00	20.00	30.00

Similar to 31, but larger numeral 5.

Rulau	Date	Metal	Size	VG	F	VF	Unc
Mo-SL 32	1886	WM	39mm	—	—	15.00	30.00

Knights Templar emblem, a Maltese cross with a radiant cross-through-crown at center. IN - HOC - SIGNO - VINCES on arms of cross. Rv: SCHNAIDER'S GARDEN SOUVENIR / 23" / TRIENNIAL / K.T. / CONCLAVE / * ST. LOUIS. SEPT. 1886. *. Plain edge.

Joseph Schnaider, born in the Grand Duchy of Baden in 1832, learned the brewing art in Europe before emigrating to St. Louis in 1854. He became foreman of the Philadelphia Brewery on Morgan Street 1854-56. In 1856 he established his own business as a partnership, the Green Tree Brewery, on Second Street. This moved 1863 to larger quarters on Sidney Street, but Schnaider sold out in 1865.

Then in 1865 he built Joseph Schnaider's Brewery on Chouteau Avenue between Mississippi and Armstrong. Connected with it was Schnaider's Garden, a pleasure garden of the kind so common in Germany but then an innovation in St. Louis. The Garden became famous throughout the country for its high class musical and other entertainments and proved exceedingly profitable.

The whole business incorporated in 1879 under the name Joseph Schnaider Brewing Co. Schnaider died at age 49 in Heidelberg, Germany in 1881, where he had traveled to recover his shattered health. He left a wife and seven children. The business was continued by the company until 1889, when it was absorbed by St. Louis Brewing Assn., which closed the brewery a few years later.

SOUTH MISSION SABBATH SCHOOL

Rulau	Date	Metal	Size	F	VF	EF	Unc
Mo-SL 32F	1867	Silver	25mm	—	20.00	30.00	40.00

Building within central circle, SOUTH MISSION SABBATH SCHOOL / * ST. LOUIS MO. * around. Rv: JULY 7 1867 above radiant book, on which is inscribed: THE WAY / OF LIFE. Reeded edge. (Hartzog coll.)

The illustrated specimen is struck over a U.S. 1857 Seated Liberty quarter.

JOEL SWOPE

1876 Centennial Tokens

Reverse type 1: JOEL SWOPE'S / ONE / PRICE / SHOE HOUSE / —*— / 311 N. 4TH ST. / ST. LOUIS. (All 23mm, plain edge)

Rulau	Obv	Rev	Metal	F	VF	EF	Unc
Mo-SL 33	A	1	WM	—	—	15.00	45.00
	(Miller Mo 36A; Wright 1082)						
Mo-SL 34	B	1	WM	—	—	15.00	45.00
Mo-SL 34A	B	1	Brass	—	—	—	60.00
Mo-SL 35	E	1	WM	—	—	15.00	45.00
Mo-SL 35A	E	1	Brass	—	—	—	60.00
	(Miller Mo 36)						
Mo-SL 36	F	1	WM	—	—	—	45.00
	(Springfield 1981 sale, lot 4548)						
Mo-SL 37	G	1	WM	—	—	—	45.00
Mo-SL 38	H	1	WM	—	—	—	45.00
Mo-SL 39	J	1	WM	—	—	15.00	45.00
Mo-SL 40	K	1	WM	—	—	—	45.00

It is possible Die D (Two heads) may exist, but it has not been seen.

Seen above is Swope's "Shoe Buggy", a 19th century promotion of great effectiveness.

Swope, Levy & Co., wholesalers in boots and shoes, was established in 1865 by Joel Swope and Joseph and David Levy, at 41 No. Main St., St. Louis. In 1867 they moved to 124 No. Main St. In 1868 a new partnership was formed by Joel Swope and his brother Isaac, the latter a former Civil War sutler; this was Swope & Brother at 1012 Broadway 1868-1870.

In 1871 Joel Swope became sole proprietor, at 2012 Broadway. Later addresses of Joel Swope's were 1016 Broadway (1872); 112 No. 4th (1873-75); 311 No. 4th, the address on the tokens (1876-80). About 1881 the business became Joel Swope & Bro. when another brother, Meier Swope, joined Joel. In 1887 the firm moved to 311 No. Broadway. Joel Swope died in 1901.

Meier Swope became head of the firm, which was renamed Swope Shoe Company in 1902. It is still known by this name in business today.

C. THIET

St. Louis, Mo.

Rulau	Date	Metal	Size	VG	F	VF	Unc
Mo-SL 60	(1880's)	Brass	23mm	—	15.00	25.00	—

C. THIET. Rv: C. THIET / MODOC / ST. LOUIS. Plain edge.

Charles Thiet's Modoc Saloon is listed at 704 So. 4th St. in the 1881 directory.

SHIBBOLETH LEAD MINING CO.

Shibboleth, Mo.

Rulau	Date	Metal	Size	VG	F	VF	Unc
Mo-Sh 1	(1880's)	Brass	20mm	—	—	75.00	—
	SHIBBOLETH L.M. CO. (incuse) / 5 ¢ . Rv: S.L.M. (incuse). Plain edge.						
Mo-Sh 2	(1880's)	Brass	30mm	—	—	75.00	—
	(All incuse) SHIBBOLETH LEAD MINING CO. / $1oo. Rv: Blank. Plain edge. (Wright 979)						

The value of token study to history is demonstrated by these pieces. Without them, the saga of a town and an industry might be lost.

Type 1 appeared in a lumber camp token book recently as an unattributed item. Type 2 was called "extremely rare" by Dr. Wright in 1898. A third type of S.L.M. Co. token is reported by Mike Pfefferkorn of St. Louis, but no description is available.

Lead was discovered at Shibboleth in 1811. Mining commenced then and was conducted sporadically by various owners until at least the 1880's. A town grew up around the mines, but it had largely disappeared by 1900.

The U.S. Postal Guides for 1877-81 reveal it did not have a post office at that time. The town still appears in census records, but it is not shown on any 20th century maps. It is located in Washington County, 1.5 miles northwest of Cadet.

C. H. & CO.
(Columbia Hunt & Co.)

Webb City, Mo.

Rulau	Date	Metal	Size	VG	F	VF	Unc
Mo-Wb 2	(1882-84)	Brass	24mm	—	25.00	—	—

DRINK / 12 1/2 / C / C. H. & CO. Rv: Blank. Plain edge. (Elmer E. Randall coll.)

Columbia & Hunt was a partnership of the brothers J. C. and Charles Columbia of Webb City and Lon Hunt of Columbus, Kansas. The enterprise was a large billiard and pool hall opened about 1882.

SPRAGUE & BLODGETT

Missouri

Rulau	Date	Metal	Size	G	VG	F	EF
MO-Un 7	(1877)	Silver	31mm	—	150.	—	250.

SPRAGUE & BLODGETT'S / ADMIT / ONE / GEORGIA MINSTRELS ctsp on U.S. Liberty Seated half dollar. Dates examined: 1862, 1863, 1873-Arrows, 1874, 1876. (Gould 64; Brunk 37710) Only 10 pieces known.

The attribution to Missouri might be logical. For comparison, Daniel Emmett's Virginia Minstrels played primarily in New York.

An admission check to a minstrel show. Sprague & Blodgett's Georgia Minstrels first performed in Missouri in 1876.

The troupe included James Bland, Billy Kersands, Sam Lucas and others.

REPORTED MISSOURI BILLIARD TOKENS

The following is a listing of unverified attributions for this era. These are given here for informational purposes:

Name on Token	Possible Locale	Billiard Die	Gazetteer
R. A. Bruns	Kansas City	BB-7a	1888-89
D. Crump	Memphis	BBC-7	1893-98
Gold Dust Saloon	Merceline	Chas. Pick	1893
Henry Hertz	St. Louis	B-2e	1893
M. Hilgert	St. Joseph	BBC	1891
Kaess	St. Louis	BB-3	1883
Thos. McNamara	St. Louis	BB-6a	1883
Pat Pierce	Chillicothe	BBC-10b	1885
J. H. Simms	Huntsville	BB-8a	1883-84
W. H. Tripp	Milan	BBC-9a	1885
J. T. Turner	Linneus	Geo. Kuehl	1885
A. H. Witt	Carthage	BBC-13	1891-98
Chas. Zeppenfeld	Osage City	BB-8a	1883

MONTANA

GREEN'S BUFFET

Butte, Mont.

Rulau	Date	Metal	Size	VG	F	VF	Unc
Mt-Bu 4	(?)	Copper	28mm	25.00	35.00	45.00	75.00

Mine headgear and building, THE ANACONDA above, BUTTE below. Rv: BEST IN THE WEST / —.— / 12 1/2 ¢ / —.— / GREEN'S BUFFET. Plain edge.

A. L. Green, saloon, 1906-10.

J. HARVEY MCCARTHY

Rulau	Date	Metal	Size	VG	F	VF	Unc
Mt-Bu 8	(1886-96)	—	--mm	—	—	50.00	—

GOOD FOR / 25 ¢ / J. HARVEY MCCARTHY CO. IN / TRADE. Rv: BBC die.

Still listed 1896, saloon.

C. GILROY

Rulau	Date	Metal	Size	VG	F	VF	Unc
Mt-Bu 6	(1888)	—	--mm	—	—	25.00	—

Chas. Pick & Co. die. Rv: C. GILROY.

CHARLES SCHMIDT

Rulau	Date	Metal	Size	VG	F	VF	Unc
Mt-Bu 9	(?)	Brass	Scal 25mm	—	—	30.00	—

CHARLES SCHMIDT / 2 / SO. MAIN, / BUTTE. Rv: GOOD FOR / 2 1/2 C / IN TRADE. Plain edge. (Rulau coll.)

SILVER BOW CLUB

Butte, Mont.

Rulau	Date	Metal	Size	VG	F	VF	Unc
Mt-Bu 20	(?)	GS	27mm	—	—	15.00	—

A. W. O. Rv: Blank. Plain edge. (Wright 32; Rulau MV 305)

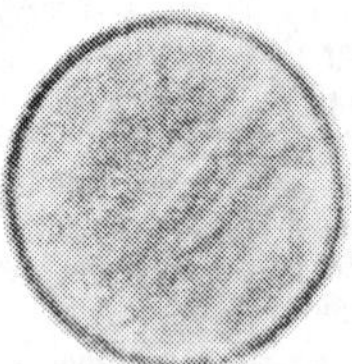

Rulau	Date	Metal	Size	VG	F	VF	Unc
Mt-Bu 21	(?)	GS	24mm	—	—	25.00	—

SILVER / * BOW * / CLUB. Rv: Blank. Plain edge. (Lewis Egnew coll.)

Rulau	Date	Metal	Size	VG	F	VF	Unc
Mt-Bu 22	(?)	GS	25mm	—	—	25.00	—

SILVER BOW / 20 / CLUB. Rv: A. W. O. across center, three stars above and three below. Plain edge. (Wright 984; Rulau MV 307)

The initials A.W.O. stand for A. W. Osburn, the proprietor in the 1890's or earlier. Dr. Wright reported both 1 and 3 in 1898; he mistakenly referred to 1 as 'Silver Draw Club'. (Attribution by Lewis L. Egnew, Port Townsend, Wash., and George Gould, Montana)

Rulau	Date	Metal	Size	VG	F	VF	Unc
Mt-Bu 24	(1884-1900)	Brass	25mm	—	—	80.00	—

Billiard table at bottom. Above: THE / BRUNSWICK / - BALKE - / COLLENDER CO. Rv: A.W.O. SILVER BOW CLUB. Plain edge. (Brunswick 5008)

The club named on this token is the same as that issuer of Dr. Wright's numbers 32 and 984, and the description in Wright for 32 which says "A.O.W." should read "A.W.O.".

Rulau	Date	Metal	Size	VG	F	VF	Unc
Mt-Bu 25	(?)	GS	Oct 26mm	—	—	80.00	—

(All incused): SILVER BOW / CLUB. Rv: A. W. O. Incised rim around obverse only. Probably issued 1870's or 1880's.

P. F. RILEY

Elkhorn, Mont.

Rulau	Date	Metal	Size	VG	F	VF	Unc
Mt-Ek 2	(1884-99)	—	25mm	—	—	45.00	—

Brunswick die BBC-11. P. F. / RILEY / ELKHORN, MONTANA. Plain edge. (Thoele report)

N. P. EXC.

Grantsdale, Mont.

Rulau	Date	Metal	Size	VG	F	VF	EF
Mt-Gr 1	(?)	Silver	31mm	—	—	125.	—

N.P. EXC. GRANTSDALE, MONT. ctsp on U.S. 1870 Seated Liberty half dollar. (Brunk 29180)

Rulau	Date	Metal	Size	VG	F	VF	EF
Mt-Gr 2	(?)	Bronze	19mm	—	—	85.00	—

N. P. EX. CO. ctsp on U.S. 1875 Indian cent. (Brunk 29170)

Rulau	Date	Metal	Size	VG	F	VF	EF
Mt-Gr 4	(?)	Bronze	23mm	—	—	125.	—

N. P. EX. CO. / SEAL & PRESS CO. ctsp on U.S. Shield 2-cent piece. ROCKFORD, DAK. ctsp on opposite side of coin. (Brunk 29175)

Rulau	Date	Metal	Size	VG	F	VF	EF
Mt-Gr 6	1876	Silver	**	—	—	—	125.

** Oct 21mm.

Rayed lantern at center of crossed pickaxe and shovel, engraved at center of ornate border. Rv: ______ / N. P. SILV. MINE / __ . __ ctsp across center of reverse. Script G.W.P. engraved at top, 1876, engraved below, all within ornate rim. Plain edge. Weight 48.5 grams.

This silver charm may be shareholders souvenir of a silver mine. The piece appeared as lot 1723 in the March 25-26, 1985 Bowers & Merena sale of the Patterson collection, where it realized $90.20.

Little is known of the N. P. Exchange and Silver Mine of Grantsdale, Mont. and Rockford, Dakota Territory. Neither place had a post office under those names in the 1877-82 period, though Rockford had one later (1899-1906).

The mine was located at Ravalli, 3 miles from Hamilton, and Grantsdale was named for H. H. Grant. A post office called Skalkaho was opened 1872 to serve the area, and this became Ravalli in 1888. Now served from Missoula.

The possibility that the Grantsdale pieces may be fantasies is discounted by this cataloger and his advisers. The prices quoted above are based on actual sales, but are probably lower than they will be in the near future. (Research courtesy Lea Hornbeck)

BATES & BONER

Helena, Mont.

Rulau	Date	Metal	Size	VG	F	VF	Unc
Mt-He 2	(1888)	Brass	20mm	—	—	50.00	—

Chas. Passow billiard die. Rv: BATES & BONER. (Rouleau coll.)

Bates & Boner, saloon, 1886-87 gazetteer.

SCHWAB & ZIMMERMAN

Helena, Mont.

Rulau	Date	Metal	Size	VG	F	VF	Unc
Mt-He 20	(1880-95)	CN	25mm	—	—	75.00	—

COSMOPOLITAN HOTEL / - BAR - / SCHWAB / AND / ZIMMERMAN / PROPRIETORS / HELENA, MONTANA. Rv: * GOOD FOR * / 12 1/2 ¢ / S AND Z / IN / * TRADE *. Plain edge. (Wright 947)

D. M. CROWLEY

Lewistown, Mont.

Rulau	Date	Metal	Size	VG	F	VF	Unc
Mt-Le 4	(1890's)	Alum	25mm	—	—	100.	—

Horse standing left, ZODIAC in exergue. Rv: D. M. CROWLEY / GOOD FOR / ONE DRINK / AT THE BAR / LEWISTOWN, MONT. Plain edge. (Wright 211)

Daniel M. Crowley, saloon, appears in 1896 directory.

P. W. LEWIS
Poplar Creek, Mont.

Rulau	Date	Metal	Size	VG	F	VF	Unc
Mt-PC 1	(1870-85)	Brass	33mm	—	—	500.	—

P. W. LEWIS / (ornament) / TRADER / POPLAR / CREEK / M.T. Rv: * GOOD FOR * / $1.00 / IN MERCHANDISE. Plain edge. (Dick Grinolds coll.)

Montana became a territory in 1864 and a state in 1889.

M.T. = Montana Territory.

J. CONNELLY
Shonkin, Mont.

Rulau	Date	Metal	Size	VG	F	VF	Unc
Mt-Sh 1	(1888)	Brass	25mm	—	—	Rare	—

(Brunswick die BB-7A). Rv: GOOD FOR / 5 C / J. / CONNELLY / IN TRADE. Plain edge. (Thoele coll.)

Joseph Connelly ran a saloon in 1888, according to directories.

BROUGHTON & MEDLIN
Walkerville, Mont.

Rulau	Date	Metal	Size	VG	F	VF	Unc
Mt-Wa 2	(1892)	Brass	--mm	—	—	50.00	—

Brunswick die B-2c. Rv: BROUGHTON & MEDLIN. Only 2 pieces known.

Appears under saloons in the 1892 gazetteer. In the 1896 directory, Jos. Broughton Co., general merchandise, appears.

REPORTED MONTANA BILLIARD TOKENS

Following is a listing of unverified attributions for this era. These are given here for informational purposes:

Name on Token	Possible Locale	Billiard Die	Gazetteeer
Board of Trade	Great Falls	BBC-11	?
Byrds Saloon	Dupuyear	BBC-9b	1888-89
J. H. Foy	Ashley	B & Co.	1888
Grein, Foskett & Co. (F. Foskett & R. N. Greig)	Anaconda	B & Co.	1892-96
H. A. M. (H. A. Melot ?)	Castle	BBC-11	?
F. B. McCleery	Stuart	BBC	1888-92
Wm. Moore	Butte	BBC	1886
Wm. Moore	Hecla	BBC	1888
J. H. Vanderbeck	Virginia City	Chas. Pick	1882

NEBRASKA

C. W. SHEPHERD
Ansley, Neb.

Rulau	Date	Metal	Size	VG	F	VF	Unc
Ne-An 3	(1888)	GS	25mm	—	—	7.50	—

C. W. SHEPHERD / - (Ornament) - / ********. Rv: 12 1/2 (large) within circle of 10 stars. (Thoele coll., ex-Bill White)

C. W. Shepherd was also at Algona, Iowa (1886-87) where he apparently used a 5-cent token bearing a BBC-11 obverse. The 12 1/2-cent denomination seems more "western," but both tokens could in fact have been used in Ansley.

S. SAGENDORF
Atkinson, Neb.

Rulau	Date	Metal	Size	VG	F	VF	Unc
Ne-At 3	(1881-82)	Brass	25mm	—	—	40.00	—

(Brunswick die BB-4). Rv: GOOD FOR / 5 C / S. SAGENDORF / IN / TRADE. Plain edge. (Hosek coll.)

A saloon and pool hall listed in 1882.

ROE
Beatrice, Neb.

Rulau	Date	Metal	Size	VG	F	VF	EF
Ne-Be 9	(?)	Bronze	23mm	—	50.00	—	—

ROE. / BEATRICE / NEB ctsp on U.S. 1869 2-cent piece. The letters of ROE. and NEB are crude and irregular, but BEATRICE may have been incused from a letter-punch. NIFMY ctsp on reverse of coin. (Frank Kovacs coll.; Brunk 34810)

E. E. S.
(E. E. Sponable)
Beatrice, Neb.

Rulau	Date	Metal	Size	VG	F	VF	Unc
Ne-Be 13	(1875-84)	CN	**	—	—	35.00	—

** Oct 25mm.

Pool table at center within beaded circle. Around: THE H. W. COLLENDER COS. Below: * CHECK *. Rv: Circle of 25 stars near rim. Within central circle: E. E. S. / BEATRICE / NEBR. Plain edge. (Brunswick 4003)

N. D. COMBS
Brownville, Neb.

Rulau	Date	Metal	Size	VG	F	VF	Unc
Ne-Br 2	(1884)	Brass	24mm	—	—	40.00	

CHAS. PICK & CO. / DEALERS IN / (Crossed goblet, ladle and icetongs) / * CHICAGO *. Rv: GOOD FOR / 5 C / N. D. COMBS (on panel) / -AT THE- / * BAR *. Plain edge. (George Hosek coll.)

Combs is listed under saloons in the 1884 gazetteer. (Research courtesy of Hank Thoele)

FRANK HART
Dannebrog, Neb.

Rulau	Date	Metal	Size	VG	F	VF	Unc
Ne-Db 1	(?)	Brass	--mm	—	—	35.00	—

Brunswick die BB. Rv: FRANK HART, DANNEBROG. (Thoele report)

E. T. HANNA
Dawson, Neb.

Rulau	Date	Metal	Size	F	VF	EF	Unc
Ne-Da 1	(1885-86)	Brass	25mm	—	—	40.00	—

THE BRUNSWICK BALKE / COLLENDER / COMPY. / (Pool table) / CHECK. Rv: GOOD FOR / 5 C / E. T. HANNA (on panel) / IN / * TRADE *. Plain edge. (Thoele coll.)

E. T. Hanna is listed under billiards in Dawson, Nebraska in the 1886 gazetteer.

HOWARD BROS.
Firth, Neb.

Rulau	Date	Metal	Size	VG	F	VF	Unc
Ne-Fi 3	(1884)	Brass	24mm	—	—	15.00	

Brunswick die BB-8A. Rv: GOOD FOR / 5 C / HOWARD / BROS / IN / TRADE. (Thoele coll., ex-Weinberg)

The only known specimen was excavated and then cleaned.

WM. KLEFFEL
Fremont, Neb.

Rulau	Date	Metal	Size	VG	F	VF	Unc
Ne-Fr 3	(1879-84)	Brass	25mm	—	—	20.00	—

Brunswick die BB-6A. Rv: GOOD FOR / 12 1/2 C / AT / WM. KLEFFEL / IN / TRADE. (George Hosek coll.)

Kleffel is listed as a billiard hall proprietor 1879 and a saloonkeeper 1884.

E. KUEN
Fremont, Neb.

Rulau	Date	Metal	Size	VG	F	VF	Unc
Ne-Fr 5	(1882-83)	Brass	--mm	—	—	35.00	—

Brunswick die BB-6a. Rv: GOOD FOR / 5 ¢ / E. KUEN (in panel) / IN / TRADE. (Cruise coll.)

Saloon, listed 1882-1883.

HINKEL & WENZEL
Hampton, Neb.

Rulau	Date	Metal	Size	VG	F	VF	Unc
Ne-Hm 3	(1884)	Brass	--mm	—		35.00	—

Brunswick die BB-6a. Rv: GOOD FOR / 5 ¢ / HINKEL / & WENZEL (names within panel) / AT THE / BAR. (Robert Cruise coll.)

The spelling under saloons in the 1884 gazetteer is given as Hankel & Wencel, but the directories often misspelled surnames in the 19th century. Both Thoele and Cruise agree this is a proper attribution.

T. P. QUICK
Lincoln, Neb.

Rulau	Date	Metal	Size	VG	F	VF	Unc
Ne-Li 10	(1879-87)	Brass	24.5mm	—	—	20.00	—

Crossed pool cues and rack of balls, POOL CHECK above. Rv: GOOD FOR / 15 C / T. P. QUICK (on shaded panel) / IN / * TRADE *. Plain edge. 10 to 15 pieces are known. (Thoele coll.)

T. P. Quick ran a pool hall and saloon listed in directories 1879 through 1887.

W. A. GRENHOW
Omaha, Neb.

Rulau	Date	Metal	Size	VG	F	VF	EF
Ne-Om 7	(?)	Silver	33mm	—	50.00	—	—

W. A. GRENHOW / OMAHA ctsp on worn Prussia vereinsthaler of Friedrich Wilhelm IV, ca 1857-61, KM 152. (Brunk 17133)

E. PICKARD

Rulau	Date	Metal	Size	VG	F	VF	Unc
Ne-Om 10	(1883-86)	GS	25mm	—	—	30.00	—

THE / J. M. BRUNSWICK / AND / BALKE CO / (Pool table). Rv: GOOD FOR / 5 C / E. PICKARD / IN / TRADE. Plain edge. (Thoele coll.)

Eugene Pickard is listed under pool halls and saloons in Omaha in the 1884 and 1886 gazetteers.

J. TREITSCHKE
Omaha, Neb.

Rulau	Date	Metal	Size	F	VF	EF	Unc
Ne-Om 15	(?)	Brass	24mm	—	7.50	—	—

J TREITSCHKE / GOOD FOR / 5 C / AT BAR / OMAHA. Rv: Blank. Plain edge. (Wright 1158)

A. CABON
Pierce, Neb.

Rulau	Date	Metal	Size	VG	F	VF	Unc
Ne-Pi 2	(1884)	Brass	24.5mm	—	—	40.00	—

Brunswick die BB-4. Rv: GOOD FOR / 5 ¢ / A. CABON (in panel) / IN / TRADE. (Cruise coll.)

In directories 1882-1885. Anton Cabon, billiard hall and saloon.

HAHN & McCLINTOCK
St. Edward, Neb.

Rulau	Date	Metal	Size	VG	F	VF	Unc
Ne-St 3	(1899-)	Brass	25mm	—	—	30.00	—

Eagle with folded wings perched on a cannon. Rv: GOOD FOR / 5 ¢ / IN TRADE / (ornament) / HAHN & McCLINTOCK. Plain edge. (Robert Cruise coll.)

Drug store, listed 1899 through 1902.

A. D. WHITE
St. Edward, Neb.

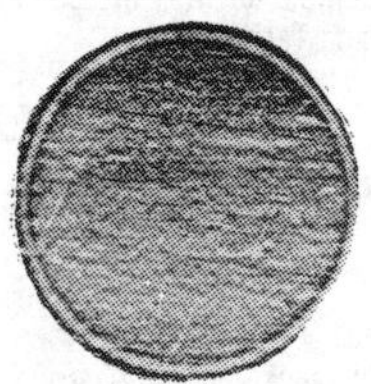

Rulau	Date	Metal	Size	VG	F	VF	Unc
Ne-St 7	(1886-99)	Brass	24mm	—	—	12.50	—

(All incused): A. D. WHITE / GOOD FOR / A / 5 ¢ / CIGAR / THE DRUGGIST. (Cruise coll.)

Drug store, listed 1886 through 1902.

JOHN JANECEK
Schuyler, Neb.

Rulau	Date	Metal	Size	F	VF	EF	Unc
Ne-Sc 1	(1882-84)	Brass	25mm	—	—	40.00	—

THE J. M. BRUNSWICK / — & — / BALKE COS / (Pool table) (Brunswick type BB-8A). Rv: GOOD FOR / -5- / CENTS / JOHN JANECEK / *********. Plain edge. (Robert Cruise coll.)

According to the Wolfe Gazetteer, John Janecek was proprietor of a saloon and billiard hall in Schuyler 1882 to 1884.

VERBA & MILOTA
Schuyler, Neb.

Rulau	Date	Metal	Size	VG	F	VF	Unc
Ne-Sc 9	(1884-92)	Brass	--mm	—	—	25.00	—

Brunswick die BBC-10a. Rv: GOOD FOR / 5 ¢ / VERBA / & MILOTA (names within panel) / IN / TRADE. Plain edge. (Robert Cruise coll.)

Wenzel Milota, saloon, appears in Schuyler in the 1886, 1890, 1893 and 1895 directories, and Thomas Verba, grocery, in the 1894 and 1897 directories. No Verba and Milota partnership has been traced. Cruise, a Nebraska specialist, feels this is a solid attribution; Hank Thoele is less certain of the location to Schuyler.

J. S. MONTZ
Tecumseh, Neb.

Rulau	Date	Metal	Size	VG	F	VF	Unc
Ne-Te 3	(1886-88)	—	--mm	—	—	12.00	—

GOOD FOR / 5 ¢ / J. S. MONTZ / AT / THE BAR. Rv: 5. (Rouleau coll., ex-Egnew)

J. S. Montz saloon, listed in 1886 and 1888 gazetteers.

W. H. HOAG
Tekamha, Neb.

Rulau	Date	Metal	Size	VG	F	VF	Unc
Ne-Tk 3	(1886)	Brass	Oct 26mm	—	—	15.00	—

GOOD FOR / 10 ¢ (in panel) / W. H. HOAG (in oval panel) / IN / TRADE. Rv: 10 (large) in circle of alternating stars and dots. (Robert Cruise coll.)

Saloon, listed only in 1886.

J. T. HILTON
Waco, Neb.

Rulau	Date	Metal	Size	F	VF	EF	Unc
Ne-Wa 1	(1884-86)	Brass	25mm	—	—	40.00	—

THE / J. M. BRUNSWICK / CO. / (Pool table). Rv: GOOD FOR / 5 C / J. T. HILTON (on panel) / IN / TRADE. (Robert Cruise coll.)

J. T. Hilton operated a pool hall in 1884 and a saloon in 1886, according to research by Hank Thoele. The obverse type is Brunswick BB-7A.

FRED KRUEGER
Wisner, Neb.

Rulau	Date	Metal	Size	VG	F	VF	Unc
Ne-Ws 3	(1886)	Brass	24mm	—	—	25.00	—

Brunswick die BBC-9b. Rv: GOOD FOR / 5 ¢ / FRED / KRUEGER (name within panel) / IN / TRADE. (Cruise coll.)

Saloon, listed only in 1886.

GRAY & CO.
Wymore, Neb.

Rulau	Date	Metal	Size	VG	F	VF	Unc
Ne-Wy 2	(1882)	GS	24.5mm	—	—	40.00	—

Brunswick die BB-6b. Rv: GOOD FOR / 5 ¢ / GRAY & CO / IN / TRADE. (Norris Wahl coll.)

Gray & Co., billiard hall, listed in *Wolfe's Nebraska State Gazetteer* for 1882.

GEO. W. SPRAGUE
York, Neb.

Rulau	Date	Metal	Size	VG	F	VF	Unc
Ne-Yo 3	(1884)	CN	24mm	—	—	27.50	—

THE / J. M. BRUNSWICK / AND / BALKE CO / (Pool table). Rv: GOOD FOR / 10 ¢ / GEO. W. / SPRAGUE / IN / TRADE. Plain edge. (George Hosek coll.)

In the 1884 gazetteer, Sprague is listed under billiards.

C. O. WILCOX & CO.
York, Neb.

Rulau	Date	Metal	Size	VG	F	VF	Unc
Ne-Yo 7	(1886)	Brass	24mm	—	—	30.00	—

THE / BRUNSWICK / -BALKE- / COLLENDER CO / (pool table). Rv: GOOD FOR / 5 ¢ / C. O. WILCOX / & CO. / IN / * TRADE *. (George Hosek coll.)

C. O. Wilcox & Co. appears under billiards in the 1886 R. G. Dun directory.

REPORTED NEBRASKA BILLIARD TOKENS

Following is a listing of unverified attributions for this era. These are given here for informational purposes:

Name on Token	Possible Locale	Billiard Die	Gazetteer
H. W. Bartlett & Co.	Campbell	BBC-11	?
Curtis & Job	Scotia	BB	1884
Duryee & Ashmore	Plum Creek	BBC-9b	1884
Geo. E. Gray	Bloomfield	BBC-8	?
N. A. Hagenstein	Scribner	BB-7a	1884
L. Haggander	Hooper	BBC-11	1886-91
W. Toliver	Elba	BBC-11	1886
H. Wachendorf	Talmage	BB-8b	1890
Henry Zohn	Pierce	BB-8a	1884-86

NEVADA

H. LEWIS
Aurora, Nev.

Rulau	Date	Metal	Size	VG	F	VF	Unc
Nv-Au 2	(?)	Celluloid	Rect -x-mm	—	—	150.	—

Rectangular flan, size not known, white.
GOOD FOR ONE DRINK / H. LEWIS / AURORA, NEV. Rv: DRINK / JESSE MOORE / A. A. / WHISKEY / (tiny) THE WHITEHEAD & HOAG CO. NEWARK, N.J. Only 2 pieces known. (HSD AD-2)

Aurora was county seat of Esmeralda County in the 1870's, but it is now in Mineral County.

BERNARD & HILL
Carlin, Nev.

Rulau	Date	Metal	Size	VG	F	VF	Unc
Nv-Ca 1	(1879-93)	Brass	Oct 26mm	—	—	75.00	—

Chas. Pick & Co. die. Rv: BERNARD & HILL / GOOD FOR / 12 1/2 / CENTS / AT THE BAR / CARLIN, NEV. Plain edge. 4 pieces reported. (HSD Cd-1)

HIGHFIELD BROS.
Carlin, Nev.

Rulau	Date	Metal	Size	VG	F	VF	Unc
Nv-Ca 6	(1887-91)	Brass	24mm	—	—	50.00	—

HIGHFIELD BROS. / GOOD FOR / 12 1/2 ¢ / AT THE BAR / CARLIN. Rv: THE E. BRUNSWICK / BILLIARD / TABLE / COMPANY / SAN FRANCISCO. Only 1 known. (HSD Cd-7)

The traditional use of the Spanish "bit" denomination (one real, or 12 1/2 cents) died hard in the West. Technically, the use of foreign coins ended in the U.S. in 1857, but it was into the early 20th century that Western tokens were still using bit (1/8 dollar) values.

MONARCH SALOON
Carson City, Nev.

Rulau	Date	Metal	Size	VG	F	VF	Unc
Nv-CC 4	(1874-84)	Brass	25mm	—	—	100.	—

Pool table within beaded central circle, THE J. M. BRUNSWICK & BALKE COS. around, CHECK below. Rv: GOOD FOR / 1 / MONARCH SALOON / CARSON CITY / DRINK. (Large M and S in Monarch Saloon.) Plain edge. 4 pieces known. (Brunswick 2252; HSD Cf-27a)

Rulau	Date	Metal	Size	VG	F	VF	Unc
Nv-CC5	(1874-84)	Brass	25mm	—	—	100.	—

As 4, but N in SALOON is backward. Word CITY is dropped. Plain edge. 2 known. (Brunswick 2253; HSD Cf-27b)

A 1907 directory said this place was opposite the V & T depot. Later Monarch Saloon tokens bore the name of proprietor Eli Barkley.

H. MAU & CO.
Eureka, Nev.

Rulau	Date	Metal	Size	VG	F	VF	Unc
Nv-Eu 3	(1881-88)	Brass	Sc 25mm	—	—	75.00	—

(All incused): H. MAU / & CO. Rv: GOOD FOR / 1 / DRINK. Unique. (HSD Ef-8a)

Rulau	Date	Metal	Size	VG	F	VF	Unc
Nv-Eu 4	(1881-88)	Brass	Sc 25mm	—	—	75.00	—

(All incused): H. MAU / & CO. Rv: Blank. Unique. (HSD Ef-8b)

Rulau	Date	Metal	Size	VG	F	VF	Unc
Nv-Eu 6	(1880's)	Brass	25mm	—	—	75.00	—

ONE / H. MAU & CO / DRINK. Rv: SMOKE / H. PLAGEMANN / & CO's / CIGARS. 4 pieces known. (HSD Ef-8c)

Rulau	Date	Metal	Size	VG	F	VF	Unc
Nv-Eu 8	(1880's)	Brass	25mm	—	—	100.	—

Brunswick die BBC. Rv: GOOD FOR / ONE / H. MAN (sic!) / DRINK. 2 pieces known. (HSD Ef-8d)

Henry Mau ran the San Francisco Brewery, a Eureka saloon, and other businesses, from 1881 until he died in 1888.

JELLERSON & MARTELL

Glenbrook, Nev.

Rulau	Date	Metal	Size	VG	F	VF	Unc
Nv-Gb 3	(?)	GS	24mm	—	—	300.	—

GOOD FOR ONE DRINK / AT / JELLERSON / & / MARTELL / GLENBROOK, NEV. Rv: Brunswick die BBC-11. 3 pieces reported. (HSD Gh-2)

Rulau	Date	Metal	Size	VG	F	VF	Unc
Nv-Gb 4	(?)	Brass	25mm	—	—	85.00	—

GOOD FOR / ONE / F. S. JELLERSON / DRINK. Rv: Brunswick die BBC-11. Unique. (HSD Gh-1)

These are, possibly, Gay Nineties issues. Glenbrook's post office opened 1882.

MONROE HOUSE BAR

Pyramid, Nev.

Rulau	Date	Metal	Size	VG	F	VF	Unc
Nv-Py 1	(1886)	Brass	--mm	—	—	100.	—

Brunswick die BB. Rv: MONROE HOUSE / 5 / BAR. Only 1 known. (HSD Pi-1)

The 1886 directory lists a Monroe Bros. Hotel at Pyramid, a place which existed in Washoe County about 34 miles north of Reno.

JOS. SCHRECK

Sweetwater, Nev.

Rulau	Date	Metal	Size	VG	F	VF	Unc
Nv-Sw 3	(1886)	—	24mm	—	—	200.	—

Brunswick die BBC-8. Rv: GOOD FOR / 5 ¢ / JOS. SCHRECK / IN / TRADE. Only 1 known. (HSD Sr-1)

J. Schreck, hotel, is listed at Sweetwater in the 1886 directory.

E. G. & S. M. COMPANY

Wadsworth, Nev.

Rulau	Date	Metal	Size	VG	F	VF	EF
Nv-Wa 3	(?)	Silver	38mm	—	—	250.	—

E. G. & S. M. COMPANY ctsp on U.S. 1872 Liberty Seated dollar. The letters are small and arched. (Gould 3; Brunk 12730)

Rulau	Date	Metal	Size	VG	F	VF	EF
Nv-Wa 4	(?)	Silver	38mm	—	—	250.	—

Similar ctsp on U.S. 1900 Morgan dollar. (Rulau MV 77A)

The "E. G." = Eugene Griswold, who ran a general store and produced bicarbonate of soda in Wadsworth. In the 1901 *Dun Directory* Griswold is shown to have outlets in Chico and San Francisco, Calif.

A previous owner of Nv-Wa 3 had indicated Virginia City, Nev. as its site. "E. G. & S. M. Company" was apparently a partnership. These pieces belong under *Tokens of the Gay Nineties.*

YANKEE BLADE

Yankee Blade, Nev.

Rulau	Date	Metal	Size	VG	F	VF	EF
Nv-YB 1	(1863-66)	Silver	25mm	—	—	200.	—

YANKEE BLADE ctsp on U.S. 1853 Arrows & Rays S.L. quarter. (Gould 96; Rulau MV 423)

Yankee Blade was a mining camp about 4 miles north of Austin which grew up because of silver strikes in 1863. The camp was named for a New England newspaper, *The Yankee Blade.*

Silver mines were developed in Emigrant and Yankee Blade canyons. They were very active in 1864 and a stage company set up here. There was a stockade and about 30 adobe or stone structures.

Water was struck inadvertently in the mines in late 1866 or early 1867, and the mines were never reopened.

The attribution is tentative, and results from information gleaned by Douglas B. McDonald of Reno, Nevada. (See Helen S. Carlson's "Nevada Place Names, A Geographical Dictionary." and Stanley W. Paher's "Nevada Ghost Towns and Mining Camps."

Mr. McDonald advances the theory that the counterstamp may have been associated with silver ingots marked at an assay office, but he could find no evidence in reading the only contemporary area newspaper, the *Reese River Reveille* of Austin, Nevada.

NEW HAMPSHIRE

T. WM. ABBOT

Concord, N.H.

Rulau	Date	Metal	Size	VG	F	VF	EF
NH-Co 1	(?)	CN	19mm	—	—	150.	—

T. Wm. ABBOT / (fouled anchor) / MILLVILL / WORKS / CONCORD / N.H. ctsp on U.S. 1863 Indian cent.

In 1868 there were two Concord manufacturers who may be connected - Abbot, Downing & Co., carriage and sleigh mfrs., and Badger & Abbot, machinery mfrs.

KEARSARGE HOUSE

Conway, N.H.

Rulau	Date	Metal	Size	VG	F	VF	EF
NH-Cn 3	(?)	Bronze	24mm	—	—	60.00	—

KEARSARGE / HOUSE in two lines ctsp on U.S. 2-cent piece of the 1864-72 period. (Brunk 22340)

In 1868, the Kearsarge House, a hotel in Conway, N.H., was owned by S. D. Thompson, according to the New Hampshire Business Directory for that year.

M. G. DAY

Cornish, N.H. ?

Rulau	Date	Metal	Size	VG	F	VF	EF
NH-Cr 3	(?)	Copper	28mm	—	—	45.00	—

M. G. DAY / CORNISH I ctsp on Canada 1857 halfpenny token, Breton 720 (the 'I' is a broken letter, probably the left leg of an N or M. (Larry Laevens coll., Brantford, Ont.)

Assigned tentatively to Cornish, N.H. There is also a Cornish in Maine. There is no Cornish in Canada.

C.D. ROBINSON

Epping, N.H.

Rulau	Date	Metal	Size	VG	F	VF	Unc
NH-Ep 1	(1884-1900)	Brass	24mm	—	—	100.	—

Large pool table. Above: THE / BRUNSWICK / —BALKE— / COLLENDER CO. Rv: GOOD FOR / 5 ¢ / C. D. / ROBINSON / EPPING N.H. / IN / TRADE. Plain edge. (Brunswick 5613)

J. BROWN
Fremont, N.H.

Rulau	Date	Metal	Size	VG	F	VF	EF
NH-Fr 2	(1860-72)	Copper	29mm	100.	—	150.	—

J. BROWN / FREMONT, N.H. ctsp on U.S. Large cent. Examined: 1849, 1853. (Brunk 5500)

Rulau	Date	Metal	Size	VG	F	VF	EF
NH-Fr 3	(1860-72)	CN	19mm	—	—	150.	—

Similar ctsp on U.S. 1858 Flying Eagle cent.

Rulau	Date	Metal	Size	VG	F	VF	EF
NH-Fr 6	(1860-72)	Copper	29mm	90.00	—	125.	—

J. BROWN ctsp on U.S. Large Cent. Examined: 1846, 1850, worn date. (Brunk 5490)

John Brown & Sons were gunsmiths in Fremont, N.H., according to the *New Hampshire Business Directory* for 1868. John F. Brown was a gunsmith from 1845 to his death in 1895.

John Brown's Rifle Factory was a recruiting office for Union sharpshooters in the Civil War. The son, Andrew, was in charge of the business from at least 1873 on.

Fremont received its name in 1854; previously it was called Poplin.

G. N. DEMOND
Gorham, N.H.

Rulau	Date	Metal	Size	VG	F	VF	EF
NH-Go 4	(?)	Silver	25mm	—	—	100.	—

G. N. DEMOND / GORHAM, NEW HAMPSHIRE ctsp on U.S. 1878 Liberty Seated quarter dollar. (Gould 79; Brunk 11370)

KEMP
Lisbon, N.H.

Rulau	Date	Metal	Size	VG	F	VF	EF
NH-Li 3	ND	Copper	29mm	—	—	100.	—

KEMP / LISBON. N. ctsp incuse on worn U.S. Large cent of 1800-03 type. LISBON. N.H. ctsp on reverse of the coin. (Gaylor Lipscomb coll.)

L. R. Kemp was a stove dealer and tinsmith in Lisbon listed in 1868. Lisbon, in Grafton County, had 1,886 people that year. Tentative attribution.

R. J. P. GOODWIN
Manchester, N.H.

Rulau	Date	Metal	Size	VG	F	VF	EF
NH-Ma 4	(?)	Silver	25mm	—	—	75.00	—

R. J. P. GOODWIN, MANCHESTER, N.H. ctsp on Canada 1870 Victoria quarter dollar. (Brunk 16530)

Richard J. P. Goodwin is listed as a physician in Manchester in 1868 in the *New Hampshire Business Directory*. At that time, the city had 20,107 people.

FETE PATRONALE DES CANADIENS FRANCAIS
Nashua, N.H.

Rulau	Date	Metal	Size	F	VF	EF	Unc
NH-Na 2	1888	WM	39mm	—	—	—	—

Standing female holding pennon. Around: FETE NATIONALE DES CANADIENS FRANCAIS / NASHUA, N.H. / 26, 27, 28 JUN. / 1888. Rv: Shield of arms of New Hampshire. Plain edge. (Bruce Cox coll., Wakefield, Mich.)

NASHUA, N.H.

Rulau	Date	Metal	Size	VG	F	VF	EF
NH-Na 4	(?)	Copper	29mm	60.00	—	90.00	—

NASHUA N.H. ctsp on U.S. Large cent. Examined: 1832, 1851. (Charles Dobie coll., Toronto, Canada; Brunk 29273)

Rulau	Date	Metal	Size	VG	F	VF	EF
NH-Na 6	(?)	Copper	29mm	—	—	150.	—

NASHUA, N.H. / PATENT / (Eagle) ctsp on U.S. Large cent (Brunk 29275)

Nashua Manufacturing Co., in business 1841 on, was a maker of locks, guns, axes, hoes, plows and other tools. It is the likely issuer. Another possibility is Nashua Lock Co.

F. W. EMERY
Peterborough, N.H.

Rulau	Date	Metal	Size	VG	F	VF	EF
NH-Pe 3	(1868)	Copper	29mm	30.00	—	45.00	—

F. W. EMERY ctsp on U.S. 1846 or 1851 Large Cent. (Brunk 13340)

Emery was a jeweler and dealt in clocks, watches, silverware etc.

The attribution is tentative. New Hampshire was a veritable hotbed of counterstamping activities at this time.

P. S. & P. R. R. CO. (Portland, Saco and Portsmouth Railroad)
Portsmouth, N.H.

Rulau	Date	Metal	Size	VG	F	VF	EF
NH-Po 5	(?)	Copper	29mm	—	—	75.00	—

P. S. & P. R. R. ctsp in one line on U.S. 1848 Large cent. (Alfred D. Hoch coll.; Brunk 30585)

W. N. BERRY
Rye, N.H.

Rulau	Date	Metal	Size	VG	F	VF	EF
NH-Ry 3	(?)	Bronze	19mm	—	75.00	—	—

W. N. BERRY / RYE, N.H. ctsp on U.S. 1875 Indian cent. (Van Ormer sale 2538; Brunk 3500)

NEW JERSEY

ASBURY PARK
Asbury Park, N.J.

Rulau	Date	Metal	Size	VG	F	VF	EF
NJ-As 1	(1877-78)	Silver	18mm	50.00	—	75.00	—

ASBURY PARK, N.J. ctsp on U.S. Seated Liberty dime. Dates examined: 1872, 1873, 1876, 1876-CC, 1877. About 17 pieces reported. (Van Ormer sale 2515, 2516; Brunk 1180)

Rulau	Date	Metal	Size	VG	F	VF	EF
NJ-As 3	(1877-78)	Silver	31mm	—	—	90.00	—

Similar ctsp on U.S. Seated Liberty half dollar. Dates examined: 1873. Only 5 pieces reported. (Brunk report)

Rulau	Date	Metal	Size	VG	F	VF	EF
NJ-As 4	(1877-78)	Copper	29mm	—	—	45.00	—

Similar ctsp on U.S. 1838 Large cent.

Rulau	Date	Metal	Size	VG	F	VF	EF
NJ-As 5	(1877-78)	Bronze	19mm	—	—	45.00	—

Similar ctsp on U.S. 1875 Indian cent.

James A. Bradley, a New York City brush salesman, developed 500 acres of wilderness near Queen Grove into a summer camp for temperance advocates, after 1870. This became Asbury Park, in Monmouth County.

The stamp is found with stamps of Bradley & Smith (Brunk 4830) and TIFFANY & CO. (Brunk 40130), which see under New York City, or below.

The 1877 Postal Guide reveals that Asbury Park, N.J. had the same name in the 1877-80 period when these counterstamps must have been applied.

BRADLEY & SMITH
Asbury Park, N.J.

Rulau	Date	Metal	Size	VG	F	VF	EF
NJ-As 3	(?)	Silver	31mm	—	—	150.	—

BRADLEY & SMITH / BRUSHES, N.Y. ctsp on obverse of U.S. 1873 Arrows S.L. half dollar. ASBURY PARK, N.J. ctsp on reverse of the coin. (Brunk 1180/4830)

Six of these pieces are known, three with ASBURY PARK, N.J. on reverse and three without. See notes under NJ-As 5.

APPLEGATES PALACE OF FLYING ANIMALS

Atlantic City, N.J.

Rulau	Date	Metal	Size	VG	F	VF	Unc
NJ-AC 3	(1889-90)	Brass	29mm	12.50	16.00	25.00	75.00

Two donkeys facing in opposite directions, star below. WHEN SHALL WE THREE MEET AGAIN. is around. Rv: APPLEGATES / (ornament) / PALACE / — OF — / FLYING ANIMALS. Plain edge. (Wright 40; Miller Pa 22)

Recent evidence assigns a date to this piece. A similar donkey die, but only 19mm in diameter, was used in the late 1840's on the Durkee & Co. omnibus tokens of New York City. The Applegate tokens postdate the CW era.

One Pennsylvania diesinker's token (Pa-Ph 373) has the same two-donkey motif, indicating the probability that Sinkler & Davey struck the Applegate token.

Sinkler & Davey were in business in the late 1880's, according to David Gladfelter, a collector of diesinker tokens who owns one of these pieces (ex-Schenkman). They used the donkey die only 1889-90, apparently.

A "palace of flying animals" or "flying horses" is an old name for a merry-go-round. Probably Adams, Raymond et al assigned these pieces to Philadelphia in the mistaken belief they were associated with the 1876 Applegates Galleries tokens.

Rulau	Date	Metal	Size	VG	F	VF	Unc
NJ-AC 6	(1884-89)	Brass	Scal 29mm	—	—	45.00	—

APPLEGATE'S / (ornament) /. PALACE. Rev: Large numeral 5. (Damia Francis coll.)

John R. Applegate, an Atlantic City, N.J., Boardwalk photographer, built a pier there at Tennessee Avenue and the Boardwalk in 1883. It was a double decker with an amusement pavilion at the far end. The pier was operated for seven seasons under Applegate's management.

APPLEGATE'S ON THE BEACH

Rulau	Date	Metal	Size	VG	F	VF	Unc
NJ-AC 11	(1884-89)	WM	17mm	—	—	35.00	—

APPLEGATE'S / ON / THE / BEACH. Rv: Blank (intaglio of obverse). (Miller Pa 27)

Rulau	Date	Metal	Size	VG	F	VF	Unc
NJ-AC 12	(1884-89)	Brass	25mm	—	—	200.	Rare

A WALK ON / APPLEGATE'S / 5 / PIER. Rv: A RIDE ON / APPLEGATE'S / 5 / CAROUSAL. Plain edge. (Miller Pa 27A)

The series of cards issued by Applegate span a good number of years. Wayte Raymond felt AC-3 was issued well before 1850, but this seems erroneous. Its scalloped companion, discovered only in 1977 by Rich Hartzog, is obviously much later. Another unrelated series, APPLEGATES GALLERIES (Adams Pa 23 to 25; Wright 29), was issued in 1876 in Philadelphia.

Lionel Rudduck possessed both specimens above and attributed them to Atlantic City, N.J. - not Philadelphia.

CHARLES McGLADE MANSION

Rulau	Date	Metal	Size	F	VF	EF	Unc
NJ-AC 20	1888	WM	25mm	—	—	10.00	—

SOUVENIR / CHARLES McGLADE / MANSION / ATLANTIC CITY / 1888. Rv: SOUVENIR / CONSTANTINE CARPENTER / DANCING / ACADEMY / PHILADELPHIA / 1888. Plain edge.

YOUNG & CO.

Rulau	Date	Metal	Size	VG	F	VF	Unc
NJ-AC 31	(?)	WM	26mm	—	—	20.00	30.00

Lady on horseback, YOUNG & CO. Rv: Large star, MERRY GO ROUND. Plain edge. (Wright 1293)

YOUNG'S AMUSEMENT CO.

Rulau	Date	Metal	Size	VG	F	VF	Unc
NJ-AC 33	(?)	RV	25mm	—	—	20.00	40.00

Lady on horseback, ATLANTIC CITY above. Rv: Shoreline scene, YOUNG'S AMUSEMENT CO. / MERRY GO / ROUND. Plain edge.

YOUNG & McSHEA

Atlantic City, N.J.

Rulau	Date	Metal	Size	VG	F	VF	Unc
NJ-AC 36	(1885)	Brass	26mm	—	—	20.00	30.00

Lady on horseback, ATLANTIC CITY above. Rv: Lighthouse; ship sailing; YOUNG & McSHEA'S / MERRY GO / ROUND. Plain edge. (Wright 1295)

Rulau	Date	Metal	Size	VG	F	VF	Unc
NJ-AC 38	1888	Brass	25mm	—	—	20.00	35.00

Similar to last, but date 1888 added. Rv: Similar to last.

Rulau	Date	Metal	Size	VG	F	VF	Unc
NJ-AC 39	(?)	RV	25mm	—	15.00	25.00	40.00

Similar to last, but Gothic lettering and no date.

Rulau	Date	Metal	Size	VG	F	VF	Unc
NJ-AC 40	(?)	BV	25mm	—	15.00	25.00	40.00

As last. Plain edge.

In general, we have avoided listing hard rubber store cards, but make an exception in the various Young series.

John Lake Young added much to the color of Atlantic City: Bathhouses, Young's Hotel (later the Mayflower), Young's Ocean Pier (originally Applegate's, later Central Pier), Young & McShea's merry-go-round, Bleak House, Young's Apartment Hotel, Young's Million Dollar Pier.

Born in 1853 near Atlantic City, by 1885 he was a lifeguard and policeman there. In 1885 he and Stewart R. McShea, a retired Pennsylvanian, became partners in a carousel on the Boardwalk. McShea was a most religious man and was opposed to Sunday amusement activity. The city also frowned on such frivolity.

To keep the merry-go-round in the limelight seven days a week, they bought more than 100 records, mostly hymns, for the organ; and enough hymnals for one for each double seat on the carousel. The idea caught on and visitors flocked to sing hymns and ride the merry-go-round on Sundays.

BORDENTOWN HOUSE

Bordentown, N.J.

Rulau	Date	Metal	Size	F	VF	EF	Unc
NJ-Bo 1	(?)	Brass	28mm	—	—	25.00	—

(All incuse) BORDENTOWN HOUSE 5 in circle. Rv: Blank.

Bordentown House was one of the best known hotels in New Jersey during the days of the old Camden & Amboy Railroad. It was opened to the public in 1832.

BURLINGTON CO. AGRICULTURAL FAIR

Burlington, N.J.

Rulau	Date	Metal	Size	F	VF	EF	Unc
NJ-Bu 1	1886	WM	38mm	—	15.00	—	—

Farmer standing, with plow, livestock, farm and farmhouse. Rv: Within wreath: BURLINGTON / CO. / AGRICULTURAL / FAIR / OCT. 11 / 1886. Plain edge. (Zaika coll.)

Burlington is the county seat of Burlington County, New Jersey.

KAIGHN'S AVE. PALACE

Camden, N.J.

Rulau	Date	Metal	Size	VG	F	VF	Unc
NJ-Cm 6	(1880's ?)	Brass	Oct 27mm	—	—	50.00	—
	KAIGHN'S AVE. PALACE OF FLYING / ANIMALS / 409-11-13 / KAIGHN AVE / CAMDEN, N.J. Rv: Incused numeral 164.						

The term "palace of flying animals" was used to describe a merry-go-round in the early days. Applegate's Palace of Flying Animals was a well-known merry-go-round enterprise in Atlantic City, N.J. (though its tokens were thought for long to be from Philadelphia). The term apparently grew up when the earliest merry-go-rounds were said to have "flying horses."

F. MESTER

Camden, N.J.

Rulau	Date	Metal	Size	VG	F	VF	Unc
NJ-Cm 9	(1882-85)	Brass	24mm	—	—	25.00	—
	Brunswick die BBC-9a. Rv: GOOD FOR / 5 ¢ (in panel) / F. MESTER (in oval panel) / IN / TRADE.						

Saloon, listed in 1882 and 1885 directories.

STOCKTON HOTEL

Cape May, N.J.

Rulau	Date	Metal	Size	F	VF	EF	Unc
NJ-CM 4	1871	WM	33mm	—	—	5.00	15.00
	STOCKTON / HOTEL / CAPE MAY / N.J. Rv: CHILDRENS / (scene) / BALL / 1871. Issued holed, suspended from a gold-plated scroll reading STOCKTON. Plain edge. (Kurt Krueger Sept. 7, 1983 sale, lot 1232)						
NJ-CM 5	1876	WM	18mm	—	5.00	10.00	15.00
	Bust of George Washington. Rv: CHILDREN'S / BALL / STOCKTON / HOTEL / CAPE MAY N.J. / 1876.						
NJ-CM 6	(?)	S/WM	33mm	—	—	6.25	15.00
	View of hotel. Around: STOCKTON HOTEL / CAPE MAY / N.J. Rv: Diamond-shaped ornaments above and below: SOUVENIR in a wavy line. Issued holed. (Al Zaika coll.)						

WHITNEY BROS.

Glassboro, N.J.

Rulau	Date	Metal	Size	F	VF	EF	Unc
NJ-Gb 4	1869	Copper	19mm	—	—	12.00	30.00
	Demijohn at center, WHITNEY GLASS WORKS around, * * * / (leaf) N.J. (leaf) below. Rv: DUE BEARER IN M'DSE AT OUR STORE / ONE CENT / WHITNEY BROS / 1869. Plain edge. (Miller NJ 19)						
NJ-Gb 5	1869	Brass	19mm	—	—	8.00	20.00
	As 4. Plain edge. (Wright 1240; Miller NJ 20)						
NJ-Gb 6	1869	WM	19mm	—	—	15.00	40.00
	As 4. Plain edge. Thin flan. (Miller NJ 21)						
NJ-Gb 7	1869	WM	19mm	—	—	15.00	40.00
	As 6, but Thick flan. (Miller NJ 22)						

Rulau	Date	Metal	Size	F	VF	EF	Unc
NJ-Gb 7A	1869	WM	19.5mm	—	—	15.00	40.00
	Obverse similar to 7, but N.J. upside down, and no stars or leaves flanking it. 3mm thick. (Peter Fuhrman coll.)						
NJ-Gb 8	1869	CN	19mm	—	—	14.50	40.00
	As 4. Plain edge. (Miller NJ 22A)						
NJ-Gb 9	1869	Silver	19mm	—	—	—	250.
	As 4. Plain edge. (Miller NJ 18)						
NJ-Gb 11	(1869)	Copper	19mm	—	—	—	100.
	Obverse as 4 (demijohn). Rv: Eagle with U.S. shield on breast (Fuld CW die 1182). Plain edge. (Fuld NC-29a). Rarity 9.						
NJ-Gb 12	(1869)	WM	19mm	—	—	—	100.
	As 11. Plain edge. (Fuld NC-29e). Rarity 9.						
NJ-Gb 13	(1869)	Silver	19mm	—	—	—	350.
	As 11. Plain edge. (Fuld NC-29f). Rarity 9.						
NJ-Gb 15	(1869)	Brass	19mm	—	—	—	200.
	Benjamin Franklin bust in fur cap left, stars around. Rv: As obverse of 4 (demijohn). Plain edge. Rarity 9.						
NJ-Gb 16	(1869)	WM	19mm	—	—	—	200.
	As 15. Rarity 9.						

This firm also issued cent-denomination tokens dated 1852 (Miller NJ 16 and 17).

NJ-Gb 15 and 16 were lot 170 in the July 11-12, 1894 sale by S.H. & H. Chapman of the famous collection of Isaac F. Wood of Rahway, N.J.

NOTE: The obverse die featuring the demijohn occurs in five separate die varieties. These are detailed by Damia R. Francis in the August 1969 issue of *TAMS Journal.*

HOBOKEN ACADEMY

Hoboken, N.J.

Rulau	Date	Metal	Size	F	VF	EF	Unc
NJ-Ho 5	1886	WM	31mm	—	—	40.00	—
	Building. Around: HOBOKEN ACADEMY / * INAUGURATED 1861 *. Rv: ZUR ERINNERUNG / AND DIE FEIER / * / DES 25. JAHRIGEN / BESTEHENS / D. 11 FEBRUAR / (Scroll) 1886 (Scroll). Plain edge. (Kirtley Dec. 1989 sale, lot 2195)						

Zur erinnerung (etc.) = In commemoration of the jubilee of the 25th anniversary on Feb. 11, 1886.

PHIL. KRAMER

Hoboken, N.J.

Rulau	Date	Metal	Size	VG	F	VF	Unc
NJ-Ho 10	(1885)	Brass	**	—	—	35.00	—

** Oct 27mm.
Chas. Pick die. Rv: GOOD FOR / 5 ¢ / PHIL. / KRAMER / AT THE BAR.

BASFORD & GLENN

Jersey City, N.J.

Rulau	Date	Metal	Size	VG	F	VF	Unc
NJ-JC 2	(?)	Aluminum	24mm	—	—	15.00	—

BASFORD & GLENN / —*— / 2 1/2 / —*— / — 5 EXCHANGE PLACE J.C. Rv: Macy & Jenkins / - - - / OLD / CLUB HOUSE / — . / — WHISKEY / . (Wright 43)

THE BOSTON

Rulau	Date	Metal	Size	VG	F	VF	Unc
NJ-JC 4	(?)	Brass	31mm	—	—	10.00	35.00

Radiant sun at center, a scroll above and below. Scrolls read: THE BOSTON / ONE PRICE. Rv: B.O.P.C.H. / (ornament) / 42 & 44 / NEWARK AVE. / (ornament) / JERSEY CITY. (Wright 1104)

Wright called this piece very rare about 1899. It was probably issued some time after the Civil War.

B.O.P.C.H. = Boston One Price Clothing House.

DIXON CRUCIBLE CO.

Rulau	Date	Metal	Size	VG	F	VF	Unc
NJ-JC 7	1876	Graphite	63mm	—	—	125.	200.

DIXON'S / CARBURET OF IRON / STOVE (POT) POLISH / AMERICAN GRAPHITE / PENCILS / CENTENNIAL 1876 EXHIBITION. Rv: Bound group of graphite rods at center. DIXON CRUCIBLE CO. / ESTABLISHED / 1827 above; ORESTES CLEVELAND / PRESIDENT. / JERSEY CITY, N.J. (Wright 260)

Called the "rarest type of 1876 Centennial piece extant," this specimen is struck in graphite. Only a few pieces survive. The illustrated specimen was lot 2704 in the Bowers & Ruddy 1981 ANA sale. Dr. B.P. Wright in 1899 considered this piece rare.

JERSEY CITY SUNDAY SCHOOLS

Jersey City, N.J.

Rulau	Date	Metal	Size	F	VF	EF	Unc
NJ-JC 18	1876	WM	28mm	—	5.00	10.00	15.00

Washington head left, * IN GOD WE TRUST. * above, 1776. CENTENNIAL. 1876. below. Rv: 21ST / ANNIVERSARY / OF THE / JERSEY CITY / SUNDAY / SCHOOLS / MAY 21 / 1876, all within palm wreath. Plain edge. (There is a small P on the edge of the bust) (Baker 372)

Rulau	Date	Metal	Size	F	VF	EF	Unc
NJ-JC 18A	1876	Bronze	28mm	—	5.00	10.00	15.00

As 18. (Baker 372)

Rulau	Date	Metal	Size	F	VF	EF	Unc
NJ-JC 18B	1876	Silver	28mm	—	—	—	100.

As 18. (Baker 372)

ALFRED R. SHREVE

Mount Holly, N.J.

Rulau	Date	Metal	Size	F	VF	EF	Unc
NJ-MH 3	(1863-69)	Brass	25.5mm	—	—	10.00	35.00

A shield, inscribed with a monogram formed by the letters A.R.S. Rv: ALFRED R. SHREVE / DEALER / IN / HARDWARE / PAINTS / OILS & C / MOUNT HOLLY / N.J. (Miller NJ 23)

Rulau	Date	Metal	Size	F	VF	EF	Unc
NJ-MH 4	(1863-69)	Copper	25.5mm	—	—	10.00	35.00

As NJ 23. (Wright 981; Miller NJ 24)

Rulau	Date	Metal	Size	F	VF	EF	Unc
NJ-MH 5	(1863-69)	WM	25.5mm	—	—	10.00	35.00

As NJ 23.

Rulau	Date	Metal	Size	F	VF	EF	Unc
NJ-MH 6	(1863-69)	WM	25.5mm	—	—	10.00	35.00

As NJ 25, but Thick flan.

BALDWIN & SMITH

Newark, N.J.

Rulau	Date	Metal	Size	VG	F	VF	EF
NJ-Ne 2	(?)	Copper	29mm	—	—	100.	—

BALDWIN & SMITH NEWARK ctsp on U.S. 1849 Large cent. (Brunk 2070)

D. A. PIONIER JUBILAUM

Rulau	Date	Metal	Size	F	VF	EF	Unc
NJ-Ne 7	1883	WM	24mm	—	—	20.00	—

1863 / D. A. / PIONIER / JUBILAUM / NEWARK, N.J. / 1883. Rv: Pioneer and scene.

The German American Pioneers Society issued this token in 1883. D. A. = Deutsch Amerikanische.

BUNDES TURN FEST

Rulau	Date	Metal	Size	F	VF	EF	Unc
NJ-Ne 4	1885	S/WM	38mm	—	—	13.50	20.00

BUNDES TURN FEST DES N. A. T. B. NEWARK, N.J. / STF monogram with crossed swords and owl's head at top / (wreath) / 1885. Rv: Bearded male bust left, tiny MEYERS & WENTHE below. Wreath border. Issued with loop. (Al Zaika coll.)

FEIGENSPAN'S LAGER

Newark, N.J.

Rulau	Date	Metal	Size	F	VF	EF	Unc
NJ-Ne 12	(1870's)	Copper	--mm	—	—	150.	—

DRINK / FEIGENSPAN'S / LAGER ctsp on copper disc.

Rulau	Date	Metal	Size	F	VF	EF	Unc
NJ-Ne 13	(1870's)	Silver	25mm	—	—	300.	—

DRINK / FEIGENSPAN'S / LAGER ctsp on U.S. Seated Liberty quarters. Examined: 1838, 1855, 1875, 1876, unknown date. 6 known. (Brunk 13930)

Rulau	Date	Metal	Size	F	VF	EF	Unc
NJ-Ne 15	(1875-80)	Silver	31mm	—	—	300.	—

Similar ctsp on U.S. 1875-1876 Seated Liberty half dollars. (Herbert Weiss coll., Cranford, N.J.)

C. Feigenspan & Co., brewers, advertised Enport Lager Beer in an ad in the 1875 *Boyd's New Jersey State Business Directory*. The brewery was at Belmont Avenue in Newark. The firm's New York City office then was at 70 Cortlandt St.

In the three-line counterstamp, DRINK / FEIGENSPAN'S appears to be one die, while LAGER appears to be a separate die.

Christian Feigenspan Inc. is still in business. It was founded in 1869.

CARPENDER

New Brunswick, N.J.

Rulau	Date	Metal	Size	VG	F	VF	EF
NJ-NB 4	(?)	Copper	29mm	—	—	25.00	—

CARPENDER ctsp on U.S. 1834 Large cent. 2 known. (Brunk 6850)

Carpender was a wallpaper manufacturer in New Brunswick, N.J., according to Stanley L. Steinberg.

SMITH'S HOTEL

New Brunswick, N.J.

Rulau	Date	Metal	Size	VG	F	VF	Unc
NJ-NB 11	(?)	Bronze	25mm	—	—	300.	—

GOOD FOR / 5 CENTS AT / oo / SMITH'S / HOTEL, ctsp on shaved side of unrecognizable coin. (Spangenberger Oct. 1983 sale, lot 83; Brunk 36895)

Similar stamps are known on all these coins, worth $300 each; Spanish-American 1779 2-reales; Mexico 1828 2-reales; Spanish-American 1774 1-real; Mexico 1828 1-real; France copper.

Located at 222 Burnet St., this house was long known as the Bull's Head.

MRS. J. SCHVERLICHOVSKY

Perth Amboy, N.J.

Rulau	Date	Metal	Size	VG	F	VF	Unc
NJ-PA 6	(?)	Brass	18mm	—	—	15.00	—

Fouled anchor at center, MRS. J. SCHVERLICHOVSKY around P. A. N. J. below. Rv: GOOD FOR / * 5 ¢ * / IN TRADE. Plain edge.

N.G. OF N.J. (National Guard of New Jersey)

Sea Girt, N.J.

Rulau	Date	Metal	Size	F	VF	EF	Unc
NJ-SG 3	1889	Brass	25mm	—	5.00	—	15.00

New Jersey state seal. Rv: ENCAMPMENT / OF / 1ST BRIGADE / N.G. OF N.J. / AT / SEA GIRT 1889.

Rulau	Date	Metal	Size	F	VF	EF	Unc
NJ-SG 3A	1889	S/WM	25mm	—	5.00	—	15.00

As 3. Issued holed. (Zaika coll.)

Rulau	Date	Metal	Size	F	VF	EF	Unc
NJ-SG 4	1890	Brass	25mm	—	5.00	—	15.00

New Jersey state seal. Rv: ENCAMPMENT OF 2ND BRIGADE / N.G. OF N.J. / AT / SEA GIRT 1890.

WM. LINDE

Summit, N.J.

Rulau	Date	Metal	Size	VG	F	VF	Unc
NJ-Sm 3	(?)	Bronze	25mm	—	—	100.	—

Clockface, on center of which is: WM. LINDE / — EXPERT — / WATCHMAKER / JEWELRY & SILVER WARE / SUMMIT. / N.J. Rv: Lord's prayer, wreath at left. Plain edge.

J. H. W.

Trenton, N.J.

Rulau	Date	Metal	Size	VG	F	VF	Unc
NJ-Tr 6	(?)	Bronze	19mm	—	—	30.00	—

TRENTON, N.J. / J. H. W. ctsp on U.S. 1865 Indian cent. (Zaika coll.)

J. T. KINNEY

Trenton, N.J.

Rulau	Date	Metal	Size	VG	F	VF	Unc
NJ-Tr 8	(1880's ?)	—	38mm	—	—	100.	—

Copy of a U.S. 1842 Seated Liberty silver dollar. Rv: J.T. KINNEY. 23 W. STATE ST., TRENTON, N.J. DEALER IN CROCKERY & GLASS. (Koppenhaver June 1988 sale, lot 265)

N.J.N.G. 9TH REGT. C CO. (New Jersey National Guard, 9th Regiment 'C' Company)

New Jersey

Rulau	Date	Metal	Size	F	VF	EF	Unc
NJ-Un 1	1881	WM	30mm	—	—	—	20.00

Large Armory building at center, COMMEMORATIVE OF THE ARMORY FAIR / DEC 1881 above; 9TH REGT. / N.J.N.G. in exergue. Rv: Fancy monogram CCo at center, wreath and circle entirely around. Plain edge.

Rulau	Date	Metal	Size	F	VF	EF	Unc
NJ-Un 2	1881	Brass	30mm	—	—	—	20.00

As last. Plain edge. (Wright 203)

(See page 192, *TAMS Journal* for October 1972)

The location of Company C's Armory has not been traced.

REPORTED NEW JERSEY BILLIARD TOKENS

Following is a listing of unverified attributions for this era. These are given for informational purposes:

Name on Token	Possible Locale	Billiard Die	Gazetteer
J. Gaffney	Trenton	BB-2	1882-85
F. Schussler	Jersey City	BB-2	1882
C. Zimmer	Plainfield	BB-2	1885

NEW MEXICO

CHAS. E. BONSALL

Albuquerque, N.M.

Rulau	Date	Metal	Size	VG	F	VF	Unc
NM-Aq 2	(1886)	CN	24mm	—	—	150.	—

Pool table in central circle, THE J.M. BRUNSWICK & BALKE COS. around, CHECK below. Rv: CHAS. E. BONSALL, 12 1/2 ¢, ALBUQUERQUE, N.M. Plain edge. (Brunswick 2036)

REESE & LOEBENE

Albuquerque, N.M. ?

Rulau	Date	Metal	Size	VG	F	VF	Unc
NM-Aq 7	(1884)	Brass	25mm	—	—	35.00	—

Chas. Pick & Co. die. Rv: GOOD FOR / * 1 * / REESE & / LOEBENE (names in panel) / DRINK. Unique. (Thoele coll.)

Polk's Rocky Mountain Gazetteer for 1884-85 shows saloons owned by "Reese & Loebner" at Albuquerque and at Copper, N.M. Toelel believes that Loebene is a misspelling by the diecutter, or else Loebner a printing error. Tentative attribution.

RYNERSON & ARMIJO

Las Cruces, N.M.

Rulau	Date	Metal	Size	F	VF	EF	Unc
NM-Lc 3	(1900-05)	Aluminum	32mm	—	—	500.	—

Rooster crowing left, on ground. Around: A PRIZE FOR THE LARGEST. Rv: GOOD FOR ONE DRINK / AT THE / * / EXCHANGE (on scroll) / * / SALOON / RYNERSON & ARMIJO / LAS CRUCES, N.M. Plain edge. (John T. Hamilton III coll.)

JOHN HESS

Raton, N.M.

Rulau	Date	Metal	Size	VG	F	VF	Unc
NM-Ra 1	(1884)	Brass	--mm	—	—	40.00	—

Brunswick die BB-5. Rv: JOHN HESS.

Billiards, 1884 gazetteer.

TERTIO MILLENNIAL ANNIVERSARY

Santa Fe, N.M.

Rulau	Date	Metal	Size	F	VF	EF	Unc
NM-SF 4	1883	S/WM	32mm	—	—	—	75.00

Eagle with serpent in its claw standing on a cactus, the date MDCCCL (1850) beneath, all radiant within a shield and above a scroll which is lettered CRESCIT EUNDO. At left: 1550. At right: 1883. Around all: TERTIO MILLENNIAL ANNIVERSARY * SANTA FE N. M. JULY 2, TO AUG 3, . Rv: Old Spanish structure. In exergue: SAN MIGUEL / CHAPEL. Plain edge. (Brunk coll.)

Rulau	Date	Metal	Size	F	VF	EF	Unc
NM-SF 4A	1883	Bronze	32mm	—	—	40.00	65.00

As 4. Plain edge. (Kirtley Aug. 1987 sale, lot 270)

Rulau	Date	Metal	Size	F	VF	EF	Unc
NM-SF 6	1883	S/WM	35mm	—	—	—	75.00

Facing bust. Around: MOST REVD. J. B. LAMY ARCHBISHOP OF NEW MEXICO. Rv: Old Spanish chapel, SAN MIGUEL below, in central circle. Around: TERTIO MILLENNIAL ANNIVERSARY SANTA FE NEW MEXICO / . 1550 . 1883. Plain edge.

The phrase "Tertio Millennial Anniversary" on these pieces refers to a "one-third millennium," or 333 years - 1550 to 1883. Santa Fe was founded in 1550 by the Spaniards; its name translates "Holy Faith." Spaniards claim to have penetrated the area in 1550.

DAUM'S LIQUOR STORE

Socorro, N.M.

Rulau	Date	Metal	Size	VG	F	VF	Unc
NM-So 1	(1882)	Brass	24mm	—	50.00	—	—

Brunswick die BB-6a. Rv: GOOD FOR / * / * / DRINK / = AT = / DAUM'S LIQUOR STORE. (R. B. Worthington coll.)

There is a Daum's Liquor House listed at Socorro in 1882. Tentative attribution.

W. H. PYBURN

New Mexico ?

Rulau	Date	Metal	Size	VG	F	VF	Unc
NM-Un 1	(1880's)	Brass	25mm	—	—	25.00	—

Brunswick die BB-4. Rv: GOOD FOR / 12 1/2 ¢ / IN TRADE / W. H. PYBURN.

Uncertain attribution.

NEW YORK

JAMES ACKROYD & SONS

Albany N.Y.

Rulau	Date	Metal	Size	VG	F	VF	Unc
NY-Ab1	(?)	Copper	26mm	—	—	—	—

Tools. JAMES ACKROYD & SONS / BROADWAY AT TIVOLI / ALBANY, N.Y. / EST. 1857.

ALBANY (N.Y.)

Rulau	Date	Metal	Size	VG	F	VF	EF
NY-Ab 2	(?)	Bronze	19mm	—	—	60.00	—

ALBANY ctsp on U.S. 1875 Indian cent.

Rulau	Date	Metal	Size	VG	F	VF	EF
NY-Ab 2A	(?)	Copper	29mm	—	30.00	—	45.00

Similar ctsp on U.S. Large cent. Examined: 1837, 1849, date not known. (Brunk 530)

Rulau	Date	Metal	Size	VG	F	VF	EF
NY-Ab 3	(?)	Silver	18.5mm	—	—	65.00	—

Similar ctsp on U.S. 1838 dime.

Rulau	Date	Metal	Size	VG	F	VF	EF
NY-Ab 3A	(?)	Silver	27mm	—	—	65.00	—

Similar ctsp on Spanish-American 2-reales. Examined: 1770, 1774.

Brunk believes the Albany Agricultural Works, founded in the 1840's as makers of agricultural implements and tools, may be the issuer.

S. CLARK

Rulau	Date	Metal	Size	G	VG	F	EF
NY-Ab 4	(?)	Copper	29mm	—	—	—	—

S. CLARK ctsp on U.S. 1846 Large cent. (Brunk 8140)

R.S. Clark was a rifle maker of Albany, New York. Doubtful attribution.

S. GLOCK

Rulau	Date	Metal	Size	VG	F	VF	EF
NY-Ab 8	(?)	CN	19mm	50.00	—	100.	—

S. GLOCK / 27 GANSE-VOORT ST. / ALBANY, N.Y. ctsp on U.S. 1857-58 Flying Eagle cent.

There was an S. Glock listed in the 1818 city directory as a furnace man; there may be a connection.

C.E. HORN

Rulau	Date	Metal	Size	VG	F	VF	EF
Ny-Ab 11	(1879)	CN	19mm	—	50.00	—	—

C.E. HORN 58 COLUMBIA STREET ALBANY, N.Y. ctsp on obverse of U.S. 1858 Flying Eagle cent. WILL STAMP ANY NAME & ADDR ON A KEY CHECK FOR 25 CTS. ctsp on reverse of the coin. (Owen & Schmidt 1747)

This could be an important key to understanding counterstamped coins in the post-Civil War period. The 25-cent fee seems excessive by the price standards of that day. Issued by Clarence E. Horn, a grocer.

G.O.

Albany, N.Y.

Rulau	Date	Metal	Size	VG	F	VF	EF
NY-Ab 21	(?)	Copper	29mm	—	—	35.00	—

G.O. / ALBANY / NY ctsp on U.S. 1843 Large cent. (Brunk 15415)

J. GAFFNEY

Amsterdam, N.Y. and Trenton N.J.

Rulau	Date	Metal	Size	VG	F	VF	Unc
NY-Am 2	(1882-85)	Brass	24mm	—	—	25.00	—

THE / J. M. BRUNSWICK & BALKE (curved) / CO / MONARCH / CUSHIONS / NEW YORK. Rv: J. GAFFNEY.

The obverse die is Brunswick die BB-2, apparently struck by New York City diesinker McNamara.

Gaffney appears in Amsterdam in 1882, then in Trenton 1882 through 1885. The tokens likely were used at both sites.

LOCKWOOD SEWING SCHOOL

Auburn, N.Y.

Rulau	Date	Metal	Size	VG	F	VF	Unc
NY-Au 11	(1865-79)	WM	31mm	—	—	10.00	—

AUBURN / N.Y. within circular wreath at center. Around and below: LOCKWOOD SEWING SCHOOL. Rv: 24-pointed star device with blank circle at center. Plain edge. (John Stribhei coll.)

The Lockwood school is supposed to have been active in the 1860's or 1870's.

T. KNOX

Rulau	Date	Metal	Size	VG	F	VF	EF
NY-Au 7	(1872)	Copper	29mm	—	100.	—	150.

T. KNOX / AUBURN, N.Y. ctsp on U.S. 1848 or 1854 Large cent. (Tanenbaum collection; Brunk 23350)

T. Knox & Brother is listed as being in the boot and shoe business in Auburn in 1872, in *Bradstreet's Register.*

PETER SIMMONS

Auburn, N.Y.

Rulau	Date	Metal	Size	VG	F	VF	EF
NY-Au 40	1881	Brass	32mm	—	—	85.00	—

PETER SIMMONS / (ornament) / AUBURN. N.Y. / 1881 ctsp on planed-off reverse of Peter Schuttler token, Il-Ch 100. Date 1881 is ctsp twice on obverse of the 1876 token. (Charles Ziegler coll.)

ST. JULIAN

Binghamton, N.Y.

Rulau	Date	Metal	Size	F	VF	EF	Unc
NY-Bi 9	(?)	Brass	27mm	—	—	12.00	—

(Incused) ST. JULIAN / * 5 * / CENTS. Rv: Blank. Plain edge. (S. L. Steinberg 1984 sale)

St. Julian Cafe was a late 19th century institution in Binghamton, N.Y.

SHEAK, ROGERS & CO.

Binghamton, N.Y.

Rulau	Date	Metal	Size	VG	F	VF	Unc
NY-Bi 11	(1883-84)	Lead	19mm	6.00	11.00	15.00	—

SHEAK, ROGERS & CO. / *. Rv: BINGHAMTON, / N.Y. / (ornament). Plain edge.

Sheak, Rogers & Co. (Andrew G. Sheak, Peter F. Sheak and Richard J. Rogers) were cigar manufacturers at 172 Washington St. and appear in Binghamton directories under that name only in 1883 and 1884. It is possible this name could have been adopted as early as 1882.

This firm traces an interesting assortment of predecessors and successors. The firm seems to trace its lineage to Michael A. Sheak in 1870; he was the principal in Sheak & Mayo, flour, feed and wholesale provisions, at 98 Washington St. 1870-77. In the latter year it became M. A. Sheak & Co. (L. M. Bowers, principal), wholesale provisions and groceries, same address. In 1879-81 the principal was Andrew G. Sheak.

The switch to the cigar manufacturing business (later the business that grew explosively in Binghamton, especially 1895-1911) occurred about 1882-83 under the Sheak, Rogers & Co. name.

In 1885 the cigar business (same address) became Sheak, Keeler & Co. (Andrew G. Sheak, Peter F. Sheak and M. J. Keeler). The former partner began his own cigar manufactory, R. J. Rogers Co., 130 State St., 1885.

In 1887 Sheak, Keeler & Co. relocated at 123 State St. In 1888 it became Sheak, Keeler Manufacturing Co. (A. G. Sheak, M. J. Keeler, L. S. Carter and H. B. Darrow). During 1889-90 Andrew G. and Peter F. Sheak seem to reenter the cigar business themselves under those names, at 123 State St. But the business must have ended then, because in 1891 A. G. Sheak is listed as a 'commercial traveler' (salesman) and P. F. Sheak as a 'clerk bds.' (possibly boardinghouse clerk), and these listings continue through 1895.

Then in 1896 appears R. E. Curtis Medicine Co. with A. G. Sheak as manager, and it is still so listed in 1904. Meanwhile Rogers' firm had become Barlow, Rogers & Simpson and, as Barlow, Rogers & Co. survived to 1901. In the latter year it became part of the American Cigar Co. (All Sheak-Rogers research by Gary Pipher, Johnson City, N.Y.)

J. F. TOZER
Binghamton, N.Y.

Rulau	Date	Metal	Size	VG	F	VF	Unc
NY-Bi 19	(1871)	Silver	38.1mm	350.	—	550	—

J. F. TOZER ctsp on U.S. 1871 Seated Liberty silver dollar. (Brunk 40370; B&M Nov. 1993 sale)

Rulau	Date	Metal	Size	VG	F	VF	Unc
NY-Bi 19A	(1871)	Silver	32.5mm	100.	—	150.	—

Similar ctsp on U.S. 1836 Bust half dollar.

Rulau	Date	Metal	Size	VG	F	VF	Unc
NY-Bi 19B	(1871)	Silver	16mm	60.00	—	90.00	—

Similar ctsp on U.S. 1832 Bust half dime.

Junius F. Tozer was a watchmaker, jeweler and silversmith listed in directories on Court Street 1859-1871. He had been a Civil War hero. NY-Bi 19 fetched $550 in the Bowers & Merena 1993 auction cited.

F. OLVERT
Black River, N.Y.

Rulau	Date	Metal	Size	VG	F	VF	Unc
NY-BR 1	(ca 1880)	Copper	--mm	—	—	35.00	—

F. OLVERT. / BLACK. / RIVER. N.Y. ctsp crudely with single letter-punches on England 1873 penny. (Charles Kirtley Aug. 1987 sale, lot 126)

TIVOLI
Boonville, N.Y.

Rulau	Date	Metal	Size	F	VF	EF	Unc
NY-Bo 6	(?)	Copper	22mm	—	2.00	—	—

Eagle on a shield. Rv: TIVOLI / 5 ¢ / BOONVILLE. (Wright 1150)

BROOKLYN SINGLE TAX CLUB
Brooklyn, N.Y.

Rulau	Date	Metal	Size	F	VF	EF	Unc
NY-Bk 5	(?)	CN	26mm	—	—	—	—

Numeral 10 at center, BROOKLYN SINGLE TAX CLUB around. Rv: Same as obverse. (All lettering incuse). Plain edge. (Wright 103)

BROOKLYN AND NEW YORK BRIDGE

Rulau	Date	Metal	Size	F	VF	EF	Unc
NY-Bk 3	1883	WM	31mm	—	—	—	25.00

Bridge, ships in water, oval seals on crossed branches below. A MONUMENT TO / AMERICAN GENIUS above, FINIS CORONAT OPUS below. Rv: A / SOUVENIR / TO / COMMEMORATE THE / OPENING OF THE / BROOKLYN / AND / NEW YORK / BRIDGE / MAY 24TH 1883. Tiny COPYRIGHT SECURED. Plain edge.

EDWARD COGAN

Rulau	Date	Metal	Size	F	VF	EF	Unc
NY-Bk 7	(1866-75)	WM	26mm	—	—	300.	—

THE / ENGLISH / "DADDY / OF THE / AMERICAN / COIN TRADE". Rv. "YOURS FAITHFULLY (script) / (monogram) / "A FOINE OULD / BROOKLYN GINTLEMAN / OF A PEPPERY / TURN OF MOIND, / HE GITS HIS / EBENAZUR UP AND / THIN HE GOES IT / BLOIND". (Miller NY 8A)

Rulau	Date	Metal	Size	F	VF	EF	Unc
NY-Bk 8	(1866-75)	Silver	26mm	—	—	750.	—

As 7. (Wright 1109; Miller NY 8). 2 known.

Rulau	Date	Metal	Size	F	VF	EF	Unc
NY-Bk 9	(1866-75)	Copper	26mm	—	—	—	150.

As 7. (Miller NY 8B)

Rulau	Date	Metal	Size	F	VF	EF	Unc
NY-Bk 9A	(1866-75)	Brass	--mm	—	—	—	600.

As 7 (long verse). Only 2 known; Slabaugh & Steinle colls.

Rulau	Date	Metal	Size	F	VF	EF	Unc
NY-Bk 10	(1866-75)	WM	26mm	—	—	—	250.

Similar to 7, but reverse inscription ends with MOIND. (Miller NY 7)

Rulau	Date	Metal	Size	F	VF	EF	Unc
NY-Bk 10A	(1866-75)	Brass	26mm	—	—	—	1000.

As 10. Only known specimen is in the Stewart Witham coll.

Enlargement

In the 1872 directory, Cogan appears as a broker at 100 William St. His home that year was at 408 State.

Coin dealer Edward Cogan moved from Philadelphia to Brooklyn in 1865.

These tokens were reportedly issued by Isaac F. Wood of New York to honor his friend, Cogan. It is supposedly Wood's monogram - Ici. - which appears on the pieces. According to Elizabeth Steinle, So. Charleston, W. Va., a Cogan specialist, that still requires verification.

"Yours faithfully" is the closing Cogan used on all his correspondence.

Wood was a very active collector of the 1860's and 1870's. He produced the Boston Numismatic Society Medal (MA-Bo 13 in this book), and was a dedicated collector of 1876 Centennial tokens. It is not certain when he made the Cogan pieces.

All the Cogan "Daddy" pieces are rare. NY-Bk 8 in silver is known in only 2 copies. One known specimen, in the Elizabeth Steinle collection, is ex-Doughty, Edgar Adams, F.C.C. Boyd and John Ford. The other is in the Witham coll.

The provenance of the Steinle specimen of NY-Bk 10 is Doughty, Boyd, Ford. The Steinle specimen of NY-Bk 7 is Edward Cogan, Cogan family, then Steinle; it is reported here for the first time. Mrs. Steinle acquired her specimen of NY-Bk 9, also unpublished, from Thomas Delorey. Another NY-Bk 9 is in the Witham coll.

CONEY ISLAND JOCKEY CLUB

Rulau	Date	Metal	Size	F	VF	EF	Unc
NY-Bk 14	1880	WM	**	—	—	25.00	60.00

** Oval, 29 by 37mm.

Jockey riding racehorse right, 1880 / TIFFANY & CO. below, all within central oval. Around: CONEY ISLAND JOCKEY CLUB / .*. Rv: MEMBERS PASS NOT TRANSFERABLE. around empty central oval. At center an incused number. Plain edge. (Illustrated specimen, the Woodring-Fuld piece, is numbered 307). Rarity 7.

Rulau	Date	Metal	Size	F	VF	EF	Unc
NY-Bk 15	1881	WM	**	—	—	25.00	60.00

** Oval, 29 x 37mm.

Similar to 14, but 1881. Plain edge. (Miller NY 12A)

Rulau	Date	Metal	Size	F	VF	EF	Unc
NY-Bk17	1883	WM	**	—	—	25.00	60.00

** Oval, 29 x 37mm.

Similar to 14, but 1883 on panel. Plain edge. (Wright 186; Miller NY 12)

A. FREY
Brooklyn, N.Y.

Rulau	Date	Metal	Size	VG	F	VF	Unc
NY-Bk 19	(1882)	Brass	24mm	—	—	25.00	—

Brunswick die BB-2. Rv: (All incused): A. FREY / 5 (large) (crossed cues and four balls). (Rulau Mn-La 3)

Adam Frey, liquor dealer (saloon), was at 198 Scholes in 1882. This token relocated from Minnesota in last edition.

GREEN POINT PRESBYTERIAN SUNDAY SCHOOL

1876 Centennial Tokens

Reverse type 1: Wreath encloses: GREEN POINT / (ornament) / PRESBYTERIAN / SUNDAY / SCHOOL / JUNE 7TH / 1876. (All 23mm; plain edge)

Rulau	Obv	Rev	Metal	F	VF	EF	Unc
NY-Bk 21	B	1	Brass	—	—	—	Rare

(Wright 404)

This token has not been located in any collection. Other varieties may exist.

L.I.P. & B.A. No. 1

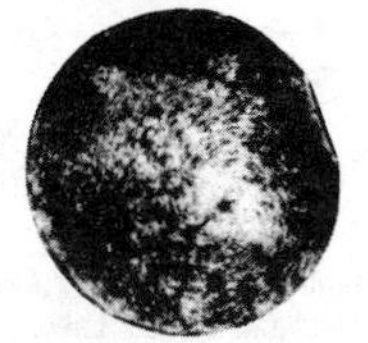

Rulau	Date	Metal	Size	VG	F	VF	Unc
NY-Bk 27	(1880's)	CN	22mm	—	—	75.00	—

Sailing ship within central circle. Around: L.I.P. & B.A. / No 1 OF BKLYN & N.Y. Rv: Blank. Plain edge. (N.Y. Public Library sale, Oct. 30, 1982)

Just what the Long Island Protective and Benevolent Association Number 1 of Brooklyn and New York was must be traced, but from the token's provenance in the New York Public Library collection it can be assumed to be some sort of laborers' group.

ROLLER SKATING ASSOCIATION

Rulau	Date	Metal	Size	VG	F	VF	Unc
NY-Bk 40	1876	Brass	24mm	—	—	15.00	40.00

Shoe on a roller skate, ROLLER SKATING ASSOCIATION, 1876. Rv: BROOKLYN RINK / SKATE / CHECK / * 1. Plain edge. (Miller NY 16; Wright 102)

NY-Bk 40A	1876	N/Brass	24mm	—	—	20.00	45.00

As 40. Plain edge.

NY-Bk 40B	1876	WM	24mm	—	—	20.00	45.00

As 40. Plain edge.

NY-Bk 41	1876	Copper	24mm	—	—	25.00	60.00

Obverse as last. Rv: MC CORMICK'S PARK / SKATE / CHECK. Plain edge. (Miller NY 17)

ROXBEE & PRITCHITT

Rulau	Date	Metal	Size	VG	F	VF	EF
NY-Bk 43	(?)	Copper	29mm	40.00	—	100.	—

ROXBEE & PRITCHITT / BROOKLYN ctsp on each side of U.S. 1828 Large cent. (Tanenbaum coll.; Brunk 35190)

WILLIAMSBURGH BREWING CO.

Brooklyn, N.Y.

Rulau	Date	Metal	Size	VG	F	VF	Unc
NY-Bk 51	(1875)	Brass	23mm	10.00	20.00	35.00	75.00

Liberty head. Rv: WILLIAMSBURGH BREWING CO. / LIMITED, / 1 / GLASS / ***. Plain edge. (Miller NY 18)

FIREMENS CONVENTION

Buffalo, N.Y.

Rulau	Date	Metal	Size	VG	F	VF	Unc
NY-Bf 8	1886	S/WM	35mm	—	—	40.00	—

Fireman's hat before firefighting tools: Axe, ladder, nozzle, etc. Rv: Within circular wreath: AUG. / 17-20 / 1886. Around: FIREMENS CONVENTION HELD AT BUFFALO, N.Y. Plain edge. (Peters coll.)

GLOBE CLOTHIERS

Buffalo, N.Y.

Rulau	Date	Metal	Size	F	VF	EF	Unc
NY-Bf 10	1885	WM	37mm	—	—	65.00	—

Bust, GENERAL U.S. GRANT. Rv: GLOBE CLOTHIERS / SENECA ST. OPP. POST OFFICE / BUFFALO / 1885 / N.Y. Plain edge. Issued holed.

IN MEMORY OF OUR SOLDIERS & SAILORS

Rulau	Date	Metal	Size	VG	F	VF	Unc
NY-Bf 12	1884	S/WM	30mm	—	—	25.00	—

Monument. Around: IN MEMORY OF OUR SOLDIERS & SAILORS. Rv: UNVEILED / * / JULY THE 4th / * 1884 * / BUFFALO / N.Y. Plain edge. (Peters coll.)

INTERNATIONAL FAIR

Rulau	Date	Metal	Size	F	VF	EF	Unc
NY-Bf 14	1888	S/WM	34mm	—	15.00	30.00	40.00

Building. Around: INTERNATIONAL / FAIR. Rv: BUFFALO, N.Y. SEPT. 4th TO 14th. (ornaments) / 1888 / (ornaments) / *****. Plain edge.

PRATT & LETCHWORTH CO.

Rulau	Date	Metal	Size	VG	F	VF	Unc
NY-Bf 16	(1889)	Aluminum	20mm	15.00	17.00	20.00	—

PL monogram at center. Around: PRATT & LETCHWORTH CO., INC. Rv: GOOD FOR / ¢ 5 ¢ / IN TRADE. Plain edge. Small letters; cent sign repeated twice.

NY-Bf 17	(1890's)	Aluminum	20mm	15.00	17.00	20.00	—

Obverse as last. Rv: GOOD FOR / 5 ¢ / IN TRADE. Larger letters; single cent sign. (Norman Peters coll.)

Pratt & Letchworth were manufacturers of steel and malleable iron castings. In 1918 their R. G. Dun credit rating was the highest given.

The 1880-89 listings gave 329-331 Washington St. as an address. A store (company store?) is listed 1890 at 189 Tonawanda St.

A.F. WENDT

Buffalo, N.Y.

Rulau	Date	Metal	Size	F	VF	EF	Unc
NY-Bf 22	(?)	Brass	26mm	5.00	7.50	10.00	35.00

COMPLIMENTS / OF / A.F. WENDT / 36 / MAIN ST. Rv: Blank. Plain edge. (Wright 1720)

SAGE'S CANDY COIN

Buffalo, N.Y.

Rulau	Date	Metal	Size	VG	F	VF	EF
NY-Bf 18	(1874)	Silver	26mm	50.00	—	100.	—

SAGE'S / CANDY / COIN ctsp on U.S. 1871 or 1874 Liberty Seated quarter dollar. 19 pieces reported. (Gould 54; Brunk 35565; Van Ormer 2828; Rulau MV 289)

NY-Bf 19	(1874)	Silver	31mm	50.00	—	100.	—

Similar ctsp on U.S. 1871 or 1874 Liberty Seated half dollar. 13 pieces reported. (Gould 38; Van Ormer 2829)

NY-Bf 20	(1874)	Silver	38mm	200.	—	400.	—

Similar ctsp on U.S. 1871 or 1874 Trade dollar. 4 pieces known. (Gould 22; Van Ormer 2830)

R. V. Pierce of Buffalo sold various patent medicines under the names Dr. Pierce or Dr. Sage.

EWD. D. BEDFORD

Cambria, N.Y.

Rulau	Date	Metal	Size	VG	F	VF	EF
NY-Cb 1	(?)	CN	19mm	—	—	50.00	—

EWD W. BEDFORD (curved) / CAMBRIA. (curved) / N.Y. ctsp on shaved reverse of U.S. 1858 Flying Eagle cent. (Norman Peters coll.; Brunk 3040)

Cambria was a tiny place (pop. 60) in Niagara County in 1910. The "EWD" could be a diecutter's error for "EDW", but it could be deliberate.

CENTRAL EXCHANGE

Camillus, N.Y. ?

Rulau	Date	Metal	Size	VG	F	VF	Unc
NY-Ca 1	(1880's)	CN	29mm	—	—	40.00	—

(All incused): CENTRAL EXCHANGE / 20 / CAMILLE FOREST. Rv: Same as obverse. (TAMS Maverick 9266)

This token is too similar in style to Delmonico (NY-NY 61-61A) and John Ronan (NY-NY 266) to be coincidental, thus the tentative attribution to 1880's New York state.

It also resembles C. R. Hartson, Cooperstown, N.Y. (Coo 2 in Gay Nineties section). Camillus is in Onondaga County.

CHASE MILLS

Chase Mills, N.Y.

Rulau	Date	Metal	Size	VG	F	VF	Unc
NY-CM 8	(?)	Bronze	23mm	—	40.00	—	—

CHASE — / MILLS ctsp on U.S. 1864 Shield 2-cent piece. (B&M Patterson 1985 sale, lot 1680)

NY-CM 9	(?)	Bronze	19mm	—	40.00	—	—

Similar ctsp on U.S. 1868 Indian cent. (Brunk 7545)

WM. C. PARKER

Chase Mills, N.Y.

Rulau	Date	Metal	Size	VG	F	VF	Unc
NY-CM 1	(?)	Bronze	23mm	—	—	100.	—

CHASE — / WM. C. PARKER / MILLS. ctsp on reverse of U.S. 1865 2-cent piece. WM. C. PARKER ctsp on obverse of the coin. (Tanenbaum coll.; Brunk 31040)

W. V. FINN

Chateaugay, N.Y.

Rulau	Date	Metal	Size	VG	F	VF	Unc
NY-Ch 3	(1882)	Brass	25mm	—	15.00	—	—

Brunswick die BBC-9a. Rv: GOOD FOR / 5 C / W. V. FINN / IN TRADE. Plain edge. (Thoele report)

Dubious attribution. Billiard hall proprietors by the same name were traced in this time period in Amery, Wis. and in Clear Lake, Wis.

S. B. UNDERILL

Chenango Forks, N.Y.

Rulau	Date	Metal	Size	VG	F	VF	Unc
NY-CF 1	(?)	Silver	31mm	—	—	Rare	—

(All script) S. B. Underill / Carriage Maker / Chenango Forks / N. Y. within ornate border, engraved on shaved reverse of U.S. 1856 Seated Liberty half dollar. Possibly unique. (Gary Pipher coll.)

Though this piece is made as a love token would be, it seems to have a merchant connotation. Carriage makers were one trade which advertised via counterstamped coins in the 1850-1880 period. It was thought better to include it than exclude it from this reference.

FIREMEN'S TOURNAMENT

Cobleskill, N.Y.

Rulau	Date	Metal	Size	VG	F	VF	Unc
NY-Cb 3	1884	WM	30mm	—	—	8.00	—

Fireman's hat, ladder, pike, axe and hose at center, FIREMEN'S TOURNAMENT above, COBLESKILL, NY AUG. 21, 1884 below. Rv: COBLESKILL, / ONEONTA / NORWICH, / COOPERSTOWN, / DELHI, / BAINBRIDGE, / FORT PLAIN, / SCHENEVUS, / SCHOHARIE. Plain edge. Issued holed.

All the towns named on reverse are in New York state.

OQUAGA HOUSE

Deposit, N.Y.

Rulau	Date	Metal	Size	VG	F	VF	Unc
NY-Dp 4	(?)	GS	25mm	—	—	30.00	50.00

OQUAGA / * / DEPOSIT / & / N.Y. / HOUSE. Rv: ** GOOD FOR ** / * 5 C * / OQUAGA / * / HOUSE. Plain edge. (Wright 791)

YOUNG MEN'S ASSOCIATION

Dunkirk, N.Y.

Rulau	Date	Metal	Size	F	VF	EF	Unc
NY-Du 5	ND	WM	38mm	—	—	—	25.00

SOUVENIR in fancy type at center of wreath. Rv: GRAND FAIR & CARNIVAL / * THE * / YOUNG MEN'S / (ornament) / ASSOCIATION / — / DUNKIRK, / — N.Y. —. Plain edge. (ANS collection)

BUTLER & BEE

East Bay, L.I., N.Y.

Rulau	Date	Metal	Size	F	VF	EF	Unc
NY-Eb 1	1860(80s)	Copper	31mm	—	—	2 Known	

Imitation of Large cent. Excellently-designed Coronet Liberty head left, LIBERTY on band. Around in crude letters: BUTLER & BEE 76 E. BAY. Below: 1860. Rv: Mirror image of obverse, but struck, not intaglio. Plain edge. (R. Henry Norweb coll.)

A C. Wyllys Betts fantasy concoction, says Kenneth E. Bressett. (See C.W. Betts under New Haven, Conn.)

H. KNICKMAN

East New York, N.Y.

Rulau	Date	Metal	Size	VG	F	VF	Unc
NY-Ea 6	(1880's)	GS	25mm	—	—	4.50	—

Liberty holding long star-spangled pennon. On four of the pennon's folds are: H. KNICKMAN / PLANK ROAD / E. N.Y. / L.I. Plain edge. Issued holed. (Fuld N.Y.-114.104.1-TR-18-GS-15 1/2-bd. no. 4, ed. no. 1-r)

This is an identification disc. Because of the PLANK ROAD wording, it was once thought to be a transportation system tag, but this is merely an address. (See also a similar disc of C.J. Lyons, Susquehanna, Pa.)

C. KLAPPROTH

Elmira, N.Y.

Rulau	Date	Metal	Size	VG	F	VF	Unc
NY-Em 7	(1882)	Brass	24mm	—	—	25.00	—

Brunswick die BB-2. Rv: C. KLAPPROTH.

ROBERTS DYE WORKS

Elmira, N.Y.

Rulau	Date	Metal	Size	VG	F	VF	EF
NY-Em 12	(1888-89)	Bronze	21mm	15.00	—	25.00	—

ROBERTS / DYE WORKS / 436 / E WATER ST / ELMIRA, N.Y. ctsp on Great Britain farthings. (Dates examined: 1860, 1868, 1869, 1874, 1875, 1878, 1879, 1880, 1883, 1884, 1885, 1886, 1887, 1888, 1889). Some farthings were new when stamped. At least 58 pieces known. (Brunk 34615)

Rulau	Date	Metal	Size	VG	F	VF	EF
NY-Em 14	(1888-90)	Bronze	25mm	—	12.50	—	25.00

Similar ctsp on Great Britain 1890 halfpennies. 29 pieces known. (Most coins seen have mint luster.)

Rulau	Date	Metal	Size	VG	F	VF	EF
NY-Em 16	(1888-89)	Bronze	31mm	—	—	—	27.50

Similar ctsp on Great Britain 1889 penny. 4 pieces known.

William Roberts Jr. is listed in the 1890 *Bradstreet Directory* as a dyer, but he does not appear in the 1900, 1902 or 1905 editions. Supposedly the business closed in 1891. Since a number of mint-fresh 1888-1890 coins were used, it seems reasonable to conclude most counterstamps were applied in 1889-1890.

"According to the 1855 city directory, William Roberts was a tailor at 213 Water Street. By the time of the 1880-1882 *Elmira City Directory* the name of the business was changed to that of his son, William Roberts, Jr. It appears to have closed in 1891. The 1880-1882 advertisement for the firm reads:

"William Roberts, Jr., Queen City Steam Dyeing and Scouring Works. Ladies' shawls, cloaks and dresses dyed and finished in a superior manner in the dress or in the piece. Feather and glove dyeing especially. Gents' clothing scoured, dyed and pressed to look equal to new."

Roberts stamped a number of English bronze coins which he probably intended to give away in the year 1890 and 1891, but he went out of business before most of them could be dispersed. A hoard of the countermarks was apparently discovered in the 1970s, and at first it was speculated that these might be recent fantasies. However, Charles W. Foster reported such a piece in 1954 in the *Numismatic Scrapbook Magazine.* Many of the coins are in Extremely Fine condition, although it is common to find weakly struck countermarks."

Dr. Brunk records the observation of 58 English farthings, 29 English halfpennies, and four English pennies.

M. METZGER

Herkimer, N.Y.

Rulau	Date	Metal	Size	VG	F	VF	EF
NY-He 3	(?)	Bronze	23mm	—	25.00	—	—

M. METZGER / HERKIMER ctsp on U.S. 1864 2-cent piece. (B&M Hoke Green 1985 sale, lot 2405; Brunk 27505)

J.B. WARREN

Ithaca, N.Y.

Rulau	Date	Metal	Size	VG	F	VF	EF
NY-It 11	(?)	Copper	29mm	—	—	40.00	—

J.B. WARREN / ITHACA, N.Y. ctsp on U.S. Large cent. (Hallenbeck 23.525; Brunk 41910)

H. V. PERRY

Jamestown, N.Y.

Rulau	Date	Metal	Size	VG	F	VF	Unc
NY-Jm 5	1866	Bronze	23mm	—	—	75.00	—

H. V. PERRY / JAMESTOWN / N.Y. / 1866 ctsp on U.S. 1865 2-cent piece's shaved reverse. (Tanenbaum coll.; Brunk 31765)

Perry is listed as a gunsmith in the 1866 *Bradstreet Directory.* Perry was located in Jamestown ca 1866-1897.

A manufacturer of percussion rifles, he had been in Fredonia, N.Y. 1850-55 and Pomfret, N.Y. 1858-62, then Ellicott, N.Y. 1863-65.

A.D. SHARPE

Jamestown, N.Y.

Rulau	Date	Metal	Size	F	VF	EF	Unc
NY-Jm 8	(1884)	Brass	15mm	—	35.00	45.00	—

Bearded bust left, JAS G. BLAINE, all within laurel wreath. Rv: A.D. SHARPE / PEOPLES / DRY GOODS / STORE / 30 / MAIN ST. / JAMESTOWN, N.Y. Plain edge. Thin flan. Rarity 7. (Miller NY 34)

Rulau	Date	Metal	Size	F	VF	EF	Unc
NY-Jm 9	(1884)	Brass	15mm	—	45.00	60.00	—

Bust right, GROVER CLEVELAND, all within laurel wreath. Rv: As reverse of NY-Jm 8. Plain edge. Thin flan. Rarity 8. (Miller NY 34A)

BLACK RIVER AND UTICA RAIL ROAD COMPANY

Jefferson County, N.Y.

Rulau	Date	Metal	Size	VG	F	VF	Unc
NY-Jf 1	(?)	C/Lead	57mm	—	—	Ex. Rare	

In central circle: Landscape. Hotel in left foreground, antique train unloading freight in right foreground. Black River is shown where it empties into Lake Ontario at Dexter (?). Two vessels are seen on the river. Around, in circular "collar": BLACK RIVER AND UTICA RAILROAD COMPANY. / =*** =, Rv: Blank. Plain edge. (Wright 59)

Dr. Wright in 1898 believed his piece to be unique.

H.E. HART

Keeseville, N.Y.

Rulau	Date	Metal	Size	VG	F	VF	EF
NY-Ke 4	(?)	Bronze	23mm	—	75.00	—	—

H.E. HART / KEESEVILLE, N.Y. ctsp on U.S. 1868 2-cent piece. (Koppenhaver Aug. 1982 sale; Brunk 18470)

HENRY BALTHASAR

Lancaster, N.Y.

Rulau	Date	Metal	Size	VG	F	VF	Unc
NY-La 2	(1883-84)	Brass	24.5mm	—	20.00	35.00	—

HENRY BALTHASAR / 5 / LANCASTER, N.Y. Rv: GOOD FOR / 5 cts / AT / * THE BAR *. Plain edge. (Norman Peters coll.)

Sample room and billiard hall at West Main and Railroad Streets, 1883-1888. Later directories (1889-90) list him as a "bartender," perhaps working for others.

C. RIVINIUS

Morrisania, N.Y.

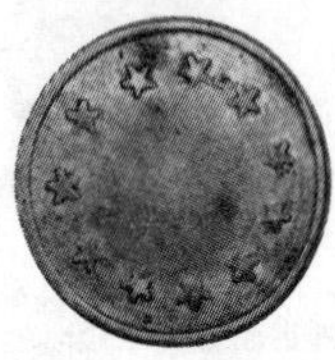

Rulau	Date	Metal	Size	VG	F	VF	Unc
NY-Mr 1	(1860-80)	Brass	22mm	—	—	Very Rare	

C. RIVINIUS / 1 (with circle). Rv: Circle of 11 5-pointed stars. Plain edge. (Miller NY 40)

Rulau	Date	Metal	Size	VG	F	VF	Unc
NY-Mr 2	(1860-80)	Brass	22mm	—	—	Very Rare	

C. RIVINIUS / 1. Rv: 6-pointed star at center, border of 11 each alternating teeth and dots. Plain edge.

Morrisania is now part of the Bronx, New York City.

GEO. H. BOCK

Mount Vernon, N.Y.

Rulau	Date	Metal	Size	VG	F	VF	Unc
NY-MV 1	(1884-99)	—	24mm	—	—	25.00	—

GEO. H. BOCK / MT. VERNON / NEW YORK. Rv: Brunswick die BBC-11. (Thoele report)

JENNIE MAXWELL

Newfane, N.Y.

Rulau	Date	Metal	Size	VG	F	VF	EF
NY-Nf 2	(?)	Bronze	23mm	—	—	50.00	—

JENNIE MAXWELL. (curved) / NEWFANE / N.Y. ctsp on U.S. 1864 2-cent piece. (Norman G. Peters coll.)

Newfane is in Niagara County.

ASBRO

New York, N.Y.

Rulau	Date	Metal	Size	VG	F	VF	EF
NY-NY 1	(?)	Silver	38mm	—	—	150.	—

ASBRO (curved) / N.Y. ctsp on France 1868-BB 5-francs. Also, word STERLING is ctsp incuse within a rectangular depression on the same side of the coin. (Kean Leiker collection, Garden Grove, Calif.; Brunk 1175)

This seems to be the mark of a silversmith or manufacturing silverware firm, yet it has not been traced to date. The 'Asbro' may be a name, or a contraction for "A. S. Brothers."

C. AUSTIN

Rulau	Date	Metal	Size	VG	F	VF	Unc
NY-NY 2	(1870's)	Brass	26.7mm	100.	200.	300.	500.

Standing elephant left, JUMBO under ground line. C. AUSTIN, ENGRAVER, above, .30 E. 14. ST. NEW YORK . below. Rv: GO TO / C. AUSTIN, / ENGRAVER, / FOR / BANGLES / 30 E. 14TH ST. / (UP STAIRS) / NEW YORK. Plain edge. (Wright 31; Miller NY 49)

The only specimens seen have had heavy die breaks on the obverse.

"Jumbo" was P.T. Barnum's prized elephant, purchased in England.

S.B. & CO.

Rulau	Date	Metal	Size	VG	F	VF	EF
NY-NY 3	(?)	Copper	29mm	—	—	50.00	—

S.B. & CO. / NEW YORK ctsp on U.S. 1848 Large cent. (Tanenbaum coll.; Brunk 35423)

Rulau	Date	Metal	Size	VG	F	VF	EF
NY-NY 4	(?)	Copper	29mm	—	—	25.00	—

S. B. & CO ctsp on U.S. 1832 Large cent. (Brunk 35420)

BALT. & OHIO R.R.

Rulau	Date	Metal	Size	VG	F	VF	Unc
NY-NY 6	(?)	Brass	29mm	4.75	9.00	14.00	30.00

Horseshoe at center, HERE'S / LUCK enclosed within it. Above: BALT. & OHIO R.R. Below: OFFICE / 315 BROADWAY, N.Y. Rv: CHICAGO, CINCINNATI, ST. LOUIS, PITTSBURGH / VIA / WASHINGTON (on scroll) / TO. Plain edge. (Wright 64)

Rulau	Date	Metal	Size	VG	F	VF	Unc
NY-NY 6A	(?)	Copper	29mm	—	—	10.00	30.00

As 6. Plain edge.

Rulau	Date	Metal	Size	VG	F	VF	Unc
NY-NY 6B	(?)	Silver	29mm	—	—	50.00	100.

As 6. Plain edge.

P.T. BARNUM

Rulau	Date	Metal	Size	F	VF	EF	Unc
NY-NY 10	1870's	Copper	40mm	—	—	400.	

Building at center, above which flies a flag labeled MUSEUM. Building inscribed AMERICAN MUSEUM on two sides. In exergue: P.T. BARNUM / PROPRIETOR. Above the building: NEW YORK. Rv: Head of Barnum in medallion. Inscribed: PHINEAS T. BARNUM. Flags and scrollwork. Flag on left reads: AMERICAN MUSEUM, NEW YORK. Inscription: THIS IMMENSE ESTABLISHMENT / CONTAINS 500,000 CURIOSITIES / INCLUDING BIRDS, BEASTS, INSECTS / FOSSILS, MINERALS, MARINE SPECIMENS, INDIAN IMPLEMENTS, SUITS OF ARMOR, STATUARY, COINS, MEDALS / CHOICE PAINTINGS, RARE ENGRAVINGS, GRAND COSMORAMA, AEREAL GARDEN / AND LECTURE ROOM IN WHICH RICH / DIVERSIFIED AND TALENTED / ENTERTAINMENTS ARE GIVEN / UNSURPASSED IN THE WORLD. ADMISSSON TO THE WHOLE / ONLY 25 CENTS. Plain edge. (Miller NY 58)

Rulau	Date	Metal	Size	F	VF	EF	Unc
NY-NY 11	1870's	WM	40mm	—	—	400.	

As 10. (Wright 63; Miller NY 59)

Both above struck by Allen & Moore, Birmingham, England.

Rulau	Date	Metal	Size	F	VF	EF	Unc
NY-NY 15	1881	Brass	27mm	—	—	200.	—

Two busts jugate, facing right. GEN'L AND MRS. TOM THUMB / * SOUVENIR 1881 * Rv: P.T. BARNUM'S / GREATEST SHOW / ON / EARTH / UNITED WITH / THE / GREAT LONDON CIRCUS. (Wright 1427)

The famous P.T. Barnum's museum was located on Broadway, corner of Ann Street, and was the scene of many of Barnum's triumphs. Adams states that the copper piece is "Ex. Rare." One white metal piece in the Fuld collection was purchased by a previous owner in 1900 who paid $6.50 for it at auction. His notation was that in white metal it was very rare at that time. Another WM piece appeared in the 1988 Levine-Magriel sale, lot 127.

"Tom Thumb," (Charles S. Stratton) was a midget made famous by Barnum.

Rulau	Date	Metal	Size	F	VF	EF	Unc
NY-NY 17	1881	Brass	27mm	—	—	65.00	—

'Chang-Yu-Sing' in Chinese characters in central circle. Around: CHANG THE GREAT CHINESE GIANT. / * SOUVENIR 1881 *. Rv: Same as NY-NY 15. Plain edge.

Chang was a real giant, more than 8 feet tall. Born in Peking in 1847, his name was Chang Yu-sing. He provided an excellent counter balance of physical properties to the tiny Tom Thumb in Barnum's shows.

There are several other tokens of Tom Thumb, not directly connected to Barnum's American Museum. (See "Some Tokens of the Greatest Show on Earth," in *The Numismatist* for March 1919.

An interesting Barnum piece is listed below:

Rulau	Date	Metal	Size	VG	F	VF	Unc
NY-NY 19	(ca 1852)	Brass	22mm	6.00	11.00	20.00	30.00

Coronet Liberty head left, 13 stars around. Rv: Stratton standing alongside two books to emphasize his tiny size. Above: GENERAL TOM THUMB. Below: 15 LBS. WEIGHT. Plain edge. (This is a game counter struck in England to use as a U.S. $5 gold piece in games, and for advertising.)

BENEDICT BROS.

Rulau	Date	Metal	Size	VG	F	VF	Unc
NY-NY 25	(1866-81)	Silver	23mm	—	—	25.00	

Helmeted goddess head right, ROMA. Rv: BENEDICT BROS. / 169 & 171 / BROADWAY / N.Y. / * STERLING *. Plain edge. The flan is irregularly round in imitation of an ancient Roman coin.

The brothers were Edwin P., Fredric P. and Read Benedict. They were in business after 1853 to the 1890's. They sold watches and jewelry. They do not appear in the 1853 or 1898 directories. They are listed at 171 Broadway in the 1866 through 1890 directories, then at 171B Broadway in 1893.

BLOOMINGDALES

Rulau	Date	Metal	Size	VG	F	VF	Unc
NY-NY 30	(1880's)	Brass	28mm	20.00	32.50	50.00	—

Struck rim of relief dots within recessed line on each side. Incused on obverse: BLOOMINGDALES / 637. Rv: Blank. Plain edge. Issued holed. Rare.

Probably a work tally for employees of Bloomingdale's department store. The stock die type of the rim design is typical of the 1880's. If a work tally, it would have been in use as a timekeeping device before introduction of the time clock system.

Lyman G. Bloomingdale (1841-1905) was a merchant in Leavenworth, Kansas at the outbreak of the Civil War. He enlisted in the Union Army when war broke out, serving honorably until 1865. Ignoring conventional mercantile wisdom in Manhattan, he and his brother Joseph B. Bloomingdale opened a small department store at the corner of 56th St. and 3rd Ave. on the upper east side in 1872. It was an instant success.

About 1895 Bloomingdale Brothers erected a gigantic new store on Third Avenue between 59th and 60th Streets. Its five floors and two basement levels and rooftop greenhouse became a wonder of the mercantile world, earning it its slogan: "All cars transfer to Bloomingdale's" — a reference to the fact that streetcars serving Third, Lexington, 59th and 60th brought thousands of buyers each day to the store. Joseph Bloomingdale retired in 1896.

Upon Lyman Bloomingdale's death in 1905 he was succeeded by his three sons, Samuel J., Hiram C. and Irving J. Bloomingdale. The store received another huge boost in popularity with the opening in 1909 of the Queensbury Bridge which brought Long Islanders direct to Bloomingdale Plaza and the store.

Bloomingdale created the Bloomingdale Bros. Employes Mutual Aid Society in 1881, one of the best organized and most beneficial societies of its kind — providing free vacations at Far Rockaway for female employes in a time when Manhattan sweatshops and bad working conditions were the norm. Rest areas, lunchroom, free medical care during working hours — were some of the BBEMAS amenities at the turn of the century.

BOYD'S BATTERY

Rulau	Date	Metal	Size	F	VF	EF	Unc
NY-NY 33	1878	**	30.5mm	—	100.	125.	175.

** Ring of gilt brass encircles and binds 12 small, varicolored metal rounds which in turn surround a 6-scalloped 18mm copper centerpiece. The centerpiece has a gilt brass center-plug. The 'battery' contains 15 separate metal pieces securely adhering to each other, made of gilt brass. German silver, copper etc. (All incused: BOYD'S / o BATTERY o. Rv: PATENTED / JAN. 17 1878. Plain edge.

J. C. Boyd sold the 'battery' to agents around the country for 50 cents, according to his contemporary advertising. Retail price was probably about $1. Supposedly the battery's electric current purified the blood when it was worn around the neck. Since there are open spaces between the 12 small rounds, no loop was needed for attachment to a thin chain.

The 8 1/2 by 7 1/4 inch black-on-blue advertising broadside reproduced here (worth $60 VF) reveals it was called "Boyd's Miniature Galvanic Battery."

Though many of these pieces must have been made, they seem not to have survived in any numbers. They are quite scarce in numismatic circles, always sought, and increasing in price.

J.M. BRADSTREET AND SONS and BRADSTREET, HOFFMAN & CO.

Rulau	Date	Metal	Size	VG	F	VF	Unc
NY-NY 35	1862	Silver	34mm	—	—	—	500.

J.M. BRADSTREET AND SONS * / 247 B'WAY N.Y. / B.R. OFFICE / IN / BOSTON - BALT / PHILA. - L'VILLE / PITTS. - CHICO. / CIN. / DET / ST. LOUIS / IMPROVED / MERCANTILE AGENCY. Rv: BRADSTREET HOFFMAN & CO - 247 BROADWAY / COLLECTOR OF CLAIMS / IN / ALL PARTS / OF THE / UNITED STATES / AND / BRITISH PROVINCES / JULY 4, 1862. (Miller NY 80)

Rulau	Date	Metal	Size	VG	F	VF	Unc
NY-NY 36	1862	Copper	34mm	—	—	80.00	175.

As 35. (Wright 134; Miller NY 81)

Rulau	Date	Metal	Size	VG	F	VF	Unc
NY-NY 37	1862	Brass	34mm	—	—	80.00	175.

As 35. (Wright 133; Miller NY 82)

Rulau	Date	Metal	Size	VG	F	VF	Unc
NY-NY 39	1862	Brass	34mm	—	—	—	Rare

Clothed, bearded bust of Lincoln left, on plain field. Rv: As reverse of 35. (BRADSTREET HOFFMAN). Plain edge. (King 560)

These firms were predecessors of Dun & Bradstreet, the credit rating agency.

H. BROWN BRO. & CO.

Rulau	Date	Metal	Size	F	VF	EF	Unc
NY-NY 43	(1876)	WM	16mm	5.00	10.00	15.00	40.00

Liberty Bell. Rv: H. BROWN BRO. & CO. / BOYS & / CHILDREN'S / CLOTHING / 314 GRAND ST. / NEW YORK. Plain edge. (Miller NY 134)

Rulau	Date	Metal	Size	F	VF	EF	Unc
NY-NY 44	(1873-74)	WM	26mm	15.00	22.50	30.00	100.

Clothed, bearded Lincoln bust right, LINCOLN above. Tiny BOLEN under bust. Rv: As 43, in larger size. Plain edge. (King 608; Miller NY 135)

Rulau	Date	Metal	Size	F	VF	EF	Unc
NY-NY 45	(1875)	WM	25mm	5.00	10.00	15.00	50.00

American flag. Rv: As 44. Plain edge. (Miller NY 136)

Rulau	Date	Metal	Size	F	VF	EF	Unc
NY-NY 46	(1875)	Copper	29mm	—	—	—	Rare

As 45, but struck over U.S. Large cent. Possibly unique.

CASWELL, MASSEY & CO.

Rulau	Date	Metal	Size	F	VF	EF	Unc
NY-NY 48	(?)	GS	24mm	—	20.00	—	—

(All incused): CASWELL, MASSEY & CO. / 1121 / BROADWAY / N—Y. / +. Rv: PRESCRIPTION / (numeral) / * CHECK *. Plain edge. (Numerals examined: 425, 858, 980)

CITY OF NEW YORK AIR SHIP

Rulau	Date	Metal	Size	F	VF	EF	Unc
NY-NY 50	(1880)	Bronze	35mm	—	75.00	100.	175.

Balloon with large gondola, small windmill and paddle, CITY OF NEW YORK across the inflated balloon. Around: GREAT AIR SHIP CITY OF NEW YORK. Rv: DIAMETER / 150 FEET. / HEIGHT, 200 FEET. / WEIGHT WITH OUTFIT / 3 1/2 TONS. / LIFTING POWER, / 22 TONS. / CAPACITY / OF / GAS ENVELOPE, / 375,000 CUBIC FEET. Plain edge. (N.Y. Public Library sale, Oct. 30, 1982)

Rulau	Date	Metal	Size	F	VF	EF	Unc
NY-NY 50A	(1880)	WM	35mm	—	35.00	40.00	75.00

As 50. Plain edge.

Rulau	Date	Metal	Size	F	VF	EF	Unc
NY-NY 50B	(1880)	Silver	35mm	—	—	—	250.

As 50. Plain edge.

L. COHEN

Rulau	Date	Metal	Size	VG	F	VF	EF
NY-NY 51	(1880's)	Copper	31mm	—	—	50.00	—

O. B. A. / L. COHEN / 1637 LEX'N / AV. N.Y. ctsp on obverse of Great Britain 1875 copper penny. Crosshatches are ctsp to obscure the Latin legends. (ANS coll.)

THE COMMERCIAL EXCHANGE

Rulau	Date	Metal	Size	VG	F	VF	Unc
NY-NY 52	(1880's)	GS	26.5mm	—	—	25.00	—

(All incuse) THE COMMERCIAL EXCHANGE / REGISTERED / —.— / No 35333 / EXPIRES 1896 / —.— / 265 & 267 / —.— / + BROADWAY. N.Y. +. Rv: Blank. Plain edge. (Rulau coll.)

The serial number, and the digital '6' in 1896, have been punched in separately from the other incuse lettering. Probably rare.

H. CONRIED

Rulau	Date	Metal	Size	VG	F	VF	Unc
NY-NY 53	(1870's)	Silver	25mm	—	—	300.	—

COMPLIMENTS OF / H. CONRIED / IRVING PLACE THEATRE ctsp on U.S. 1876-S Seated Liberty quarter. (Tanenbaum coll.)

From the late 1870's.

COOPER & DEMAREST

Rulau	Date	Metal	Size	VG	F	VF	EF
NY-NY 54	(1853-56)	Copper	29mm	—	100.	—	—

COOPER & DEMAREST / 222 CANAL ST ctsp on U.S. 1848 Large cent. (Brunk 9490; Rulau MV 62)

James C. Cooper and Garret Brinckerhoff Demarest were daguerreotypers in business at 222 Canal St. 1853-56 at least.

J. CROOKES

Rulau	Date	Metal	Size	F	VF	EF	Unc
NY-NY 56	(?)	Copper	29mm	—	—	40.00	—

J. CROOKES / N.Y. ctsp on each side of U.S. 1844 Large cent. (Rulau coll.)

DALY'S 5TH AVE. THEATRE

Rulau	Date	Metal	Size	F	VF	EF	Unc
NY-NY 60	1876	Silver	**	—	—	175.	225.

** Rec., 76x28mm.
DALY'S 5TH. AVE. THEATRE / 200TH PERFORMANCE OF / PIQUE. / -.- / FRIDAY, JUNE 23RD.. 1876. / LADY'S / TICKET. / PIQUE. / RETAIN THIS CHECK. Rv: (hallmark: dog, anchor, Gothic 'G') / STERLING / GORHAM & CO. / SILVERSMITHS / UNION SQUARE. Plain edge. (Wright 224; Springfield 1981 sale, lot 4561)

Less than 6 pieces are known, including the Brand and Springfield collections' specimens. It is possible the B.P. Wright specimen and Springfield piece are one and the same.

Sterling silver (.925 fine) souvenir tickets for ladies for "Pique's" 200th performance at Daly's Fifth Avenue Theatre.

DEAN

1876 Centennial Tokens

Reverse type 1: (All inscriptions curved) * DEAN * / CAKES / AND / CONFECTIONERY / 17 UNION SQUARE NEW YORK. (All 23mm, plain edge)

Reverse type 2: (One straight and four curved lines) DEAN / —— / CAKES / — / AND / — / CONFECTIONERY / 17 UNION SQUARE NEW YORK. (All 23mm, plain edge)

Rulau	Obv	Rev	Metal	FG	VF	EF	Unc
NY-NY 700	A (Miller NY 194)	1	WM	5.00	8.00	15.00	40.00
NY-NY 701	B (Miller NY 196; Wright 236)	1	WM	5.00	8.00	15.00	40.00
NY-NY 701 A	B	1	Brass	—	—	15.00	40.00
NY-NY 702	D	1	WM	—	—	15.00	40.00
NY-NY 703	E (Miller NY 197)	1	WM	—	—	15.00	40.00
NY-NY 703 A	E (Miller NY 198)	1	Copper	—	—	—	45.00
NY-NY 704	F (Miller NY 199)	1	WM	—	—	20.00	45.00
NY-NY 705	G	1	WM	—	—	20.00	45.00
NY-NY 705 A	G (Miller NY 195)	1	Copper	—	—	—	45.00
NY-NY 706	H (Miller NY 200)	1	Copper	—	—	20.00	45.00
NY-NY 707	K	1	WM	—	—	20.00	45.00
NY-NY 709	A (Miller NY 201)	2	WM	5.00	8.00	15.00	40.00
NY-NY 709A	A (ANS collection)	2	Copper	—	—	—	55.00
NY-NY 710	B (Miller NY 202)	2	WM	—	10.00	15.00	40.00
NY-NY 711	E (Miller NY 203)	2	WM	—	—	15.00	40.00
NY-NY 711 A	E (Miller NY 204)	2	Copper	—	—	20.00	45.00
NY-NY 712	F (Miller NY 205)	2	WM	—	—	20.00	45.00
NY-NY 713	G (Levine-Magriel 1988 sale, lot 915)	2	WM	—	—	—	45.00
NY-NY 713 A	G	2	Copper	—	—	—	45.00
NY-NY 714	H (Miller NY 206)	2	Copper	—	—	20.00	45.00

There may be more unreported Dean die combinations, but the Slabaugh book of 1981 was updated by Steve Tanenbaum in 1983 before this compilation was attempted.

Charles A. Dean was a manufacturer of specialties in fine cakes and confectionery and served weddings and parties, according to the May 1, 1876 edition of *Trow's New York City Directory.*

DELMONICO

Rulau	Date	Metal	Size	VG	F	VF	Unc
NY-NY 61	(1877-84)	S/Brass	28mm	15.00	20.00	30.00	40.00

DELMONICO / A (numeral) A / 112 BROADWAY. Rv: Same. (Numerals seen: 15, 45) (Miller NY 207)

Rulau	Date	Metal	Size	VG	F	VF	Unc
NY-NY 61A	(1877-84)	S/Brass	28mm	—	—	45.00	—

As 61, but numeral 100 on each side.

Lorenzo Delmonico and Peter A. Delmonico in 1844-1849 operated two thriving businesses — a restaurant at 2 South William Street and a hotel at 25 Broadway.

The tokens with the 112 Broadway address were issued 1877-1884 by the partnership. A specimen appeared in the April 1884 Levick sale (lot 2176). In the 1870's the partnership had become Lorenzo D., Charles D. and Siro P. Delmonico.

DEUTSCHEN HOSPITALS

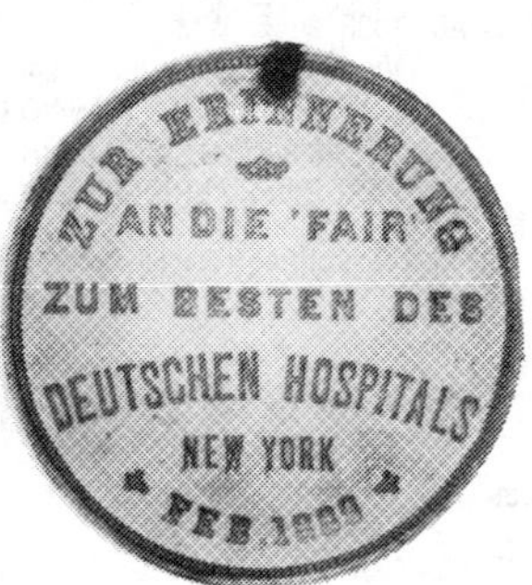

Rulau	Date	Metal	Size	VG	F	Unc	Proof
NY-NY A61	1889	WM	40mm	—	—	30.00	30.00

Building at center, DEUTSCHEN *+* HOSPITALS around. Tiny C. L. CHAPELLE on truncation of ground. Rv: ZUR ERINNERUNG / (ornament) / AN DIE 'FAIR' / ZUM BESTEN DES / DEUTSCHEN HOSPITALS / NEW YORK / + FEB. 1889 +. Plain edge. Issued holed. (Lots 1272-1274, Brand 1984 sale)

Collector Virgil Brand bought 60 remainders of this medal in proof and these were dispersed in June, 1984. It was issued in connection with a fair for the German hospitals in New York City.

DRITTES AMERICANISCHES BUNDESSCHIESSEN

Rulau	Date	Metal	Size	F	VF	EF	Unc
NY-NY C61	1868	Silver	38mm	—	—	250.	350.

Supported New York arms, tiny F. B. Smith, F. under truncation. Around: DRITTES AMERICANISCHES BUNDESSCHIESSEN ABGEHALTEN IN NEW-YORK. / 1868. Rv: Target on breast of headless eagle, crossed rifles in its talons. Circle of 5-pointed stars around. (Kirtley Oct. 1988 sale, lot 660)

The German legend translates: Third American League Shooting (fest) held in New York, 1868. The shooting medals were struck by F. B. Smith and Horst, New York City medalists.

DRIVING CLUB OF NEW YORK

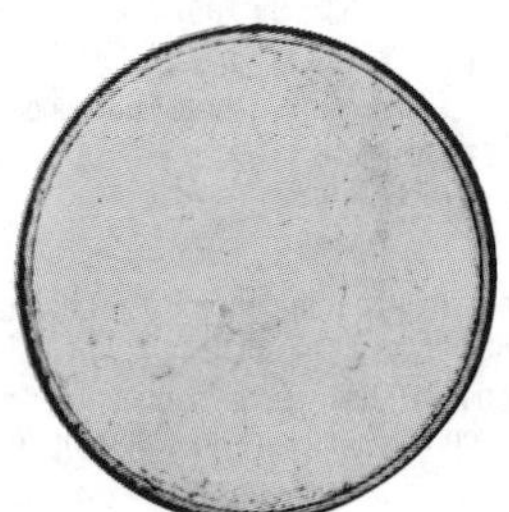

Rulau	Date	Metal	Size	VG	F	VF	Unc
NY-NY 62	1885	Silver	34mm	—	—	Rare	—

THE DRIVING CLUB OF NEW YORK / MEMBER / (Horse galloping to left) / .1885. Rv: Blank. Plain edge. Thick flan. (Tanenbaum coll.)

Apparently this was a jockey club.

EAST RIVER BRIDGE

Rulau	Date	Metal	Size	F	VF	EF	Unc
NY-NY A62	1883	WM	37mm	—	—	25.00	35.00

View of the bridge connecting Brooklyn and New York. Above: "TWO CITIES AS ONE" (Gothic text) / NEW YORK / & BROOKLYN. Tiny C E D at lower right. Rv: Wreath encloses: SOUVENIR (on scroll) / OF THE / OPENING / — OF THE — / EAST RIVER / BRIDGE / MAY 24TH / 1883 / 1867 — 1883. Plain edge.

The East River Bridge quickly became known as the Brooklyn Bridge after its 1883 dedication.

THE EGYPTIAN OBELISK

Rulau	Date	Metal	Size	F	VF	EF	Unc
NY-NY 63	1880	Copper	34mm	—	—	—	20.00

Obelisk at center, THE EGYPTIAN OBELISK above, WAS TRANSPORTED FROM EGYPT AND / ERECTED IN CENTRAL PARK, NEW YORK, 1880 below. Rv: CORNER STONE LAID BY THE GRAND LODGE F.A.M. STATE OF N.Y. / OCTOBER 9, 1880. Plain edge.

Rulau	Date	Metal	Size	F	VF	EF	Unc
NY-NY 63A	1880	Gilt Brass	34mm	—	—	—	20.00

Same as last. Plain edge.

Rulau	Date	Metal	Size	F	VF	EF	Unc
NY-NY 63B	1880	WM	34mm	—	—	—	22.50

Same as last. Plain edge.

(See "Egyptian Obelisk Explained" by Terry Trantow, in *TAMS Journal* for Dec., 1978)

GEO. EHRET

Rulau	Date	Metal	Size	VG	F	VF	Unc
NY-NY 64	(1870's)	Brass	23mm	—	25.00	50.00	75.00

Coronet Liberty head left. Rv: GEO. EHRET / 1 / * GLASS *. Plain edge. (Miller NY 231)

JOHN EICHLER

Rulau	Date	Metal	Size	VG	F	VF	Unc
NY-NY 66	(1870's)	Brass	23mm	—	25.00	50.00	75.00

Coronet Liberty head left. Rv: JOHN EICHLER / 1 / * GLASS *. Plain edge. (Miller NY 233)

FARMERS' AND MECHANICS' LIFE INSURANCE CO.

Rulau	Date	Metal	Size	F	VF	EF	Unc
NY-NY 70	1869	Silver	32mm	—	—	100.	250.

Bust facing left, FARMERS AND MECHANICS LIFE INSURANCE CO. / NEW YORK / 1869. Rv: ONE HUNDRED THOUSAND DOLLARS / DEPOSITED / * / WITH THE / ** / NEW YORK STATE / INSURANCE / DEPARTMENT / -.- / 'I AM INSURED'. (Wright 305; Miller NY 234)

Rulau	Date	Metal	Size	F	VF	EF	Unc
NY-NY 71	1869	Brass	32mm	10.00	16.00	25.00	50.00

As 70. (Miller NY 235)

Rulau	Date	Metal	Size	F	VF	EF	Unc
NY-NY 72	1869	Copper	32mm	10.00	16.00	25.00	50.00

As 70. (Miller NY 236)

Rulau	Date	Metal	Size	F	VF	EF	Unc
NY-NY 73	1869	WM	32mm	12.50	20.00	30.00	60.00

As 70. (Miller NY 237)

407 B.WAY

Rulau	Date	Metal	Size	VG	F	VF	EF
NY-NY 80	(?)	Silver	24mm	—	—	25.00	—

407 B.WAY / N.Y. ctsp on U.S. 1857 Liberty Seated quarter. (Tanenbaum coll.)

A very interesting counterstamp. It will require a great deal of luck to ascertain which merchant located at number 407 Broadway issued this piece. It probably dates from the late 1860's, or later.

FRANKLIN & CO.

Rulau	Date	Metal	Size	F	VF	EF	Unc
NY-NY 85	1876	Copper	· 25mm	4.00	10.00	15.00	50.00
	Liberty Bell, rayed eagle above, seven stars left, six right. CENTENNIAL / 1776 - 1876. Rv: FRANKLIN & CO. / BOYS' & / CHILDREN'S / OUTFITTING / UNION SQUARE, N.Y. Plain edge. (Wright 343; Miller NY 266A)						
NY-NY 85A	1876	Brass	25mm	—	—	—	50.00
	As 85. Plain edge. Thick flan.						
NY-NY 86	1876	WM	25mm	4.00	10.00	15.00	50.00
	As 85. Plain edge. (Miller NY 266)						
NY-NY 88	(1873-74)	Copper	26mm	15.00	22.50	30.00	50.00
	Clothed, bearded bust of Lincoln right, LINCOLN above. Under the bust: BOLEN. Rv: As reverse of 85. Plain edge. (Miller NY 267)						
NY-NY 89	(1873-74)	Brass	26mm	15.00	22.50	30.00	50.00
	As 88. Plain edge. (King 606; Miller NY 267A)						
NY-NY 90	(1873-74)	WM	26mm	—	—	35.00	60.00
	As 88. Plain edge. (King 606; Miller NY 267B)						

FREDERICK'S PHARMACY

1876 Centennial Tokens

Reverse type 1: GOOD FOR / * / 1 GLASS OF / SODA WATER / AT FREDERICKS / PHARMACY / COR. 60TH ST. / & SECOND AVE. N.Y. (All 23mm; plain edge)

Rulau	Obv	Rev	Metal	F	VF	EF	Unc
NY-NY 720	A	1	WM	5.00	8.00	15.00	40.00
	(Miller NY 268)						
NY-NY 720 A	A	1	Copper	—	—	20.00	45.00
	Also in Bronze.						
NY-NY 720 B	A	1	Brass	—	—	—	45.00
NY-NY 721	B	1	WM	—	8.00	15.00	40.00
	(Miller 269)						
NY-NY 721 A	B	1	Copper	—	—	—	45.00
NY-NY 721 B	B	1	Brass	—	—	—	45.00
NY-NY 722	D	1	Copper	—	—	—	50.00
	(Miller 272)						
NY-NY 723	E	1	WM	—	—	15.00	40.00
	(Miller 271)						
NY-NY 723 A	E	1	Copper	—	—	20.00	45.00
	(Miller 272)						
NY-NY 723 B	E	1	Brass	—	—	—	45.00
NY-NY 724	F	1	WM	—	—	20.00	45.00
	(Miller 273A; Wright 344)						
NY-NY 724 A	F	1	Copper	—	—	—	45.00
	(ANS collection)						
NY-NY 725	G	1	WM	—	—	—	50.00
NY-NY 725 A	G	1	Bronze	—	—	—	50.00
NY-NY 726	H	1	WM	—	—	15.00	40.00
NY-NY 726 A	H	1	Copper	—	—	—	45.00
NY-NY 727	J	1	Copper	—	—	—	50.00
NY-NY 728	K	1	Copper	—	—	20.00	45.00
	(Miller 274)						

FRIEDENSFEIER IM JAHRE 1871

Rulau	Date	Metal	Size	F	VF	EF	Unc
NY-NY 92	1871	WM	38mm	—	—	37.50	—
	Standing warrior Germania with shield and sword, left, with sunrise over the (Vosges?) mountains in background, all within central circle. Around: DIE WACHT IN DEN VOGESEN. / (ornament). Rv: Within wreath: ZUR ERINNERUNG / AN DIE / FRIEDENSFEIER / IM JAHRE 1871 / NEW YORK. Plain edge. (Fred Borgmann coll.)						

For an explanation of the Friedensfeier (Peace Jubilee), see Milwaukier Friedens-Feier under Milwaukee, Wis.

This Germania is somewhat different than on other 1871 Peace medalets, and she is called not Die Wacht am Rhein (The Watch on the Rhine), but Die Wacht in den Vogesen (The Watch in the Vosges).

CHAS. D. GLADDING

Rulau	Date	Metal	Size	VG	F	VF	EF
NY-NY 93	1861	Silver	31mm	40.00	—	60.00	—
	CHAS. D. GLADDING (curved) / 1861 ctsp on U.S. 1854-O with Arrows Liberty Seated half dollar. (Dr. Sol Taylor collection, Orange, Calif.; Brunk 16297)						

General merchandise in 1860's.

GLOBE FIRE INS. CO.

Rulau	Date	Metal	Size	F	VF	EF	Unc
NY-NY 95	1876	Copper	25mm	4.00	10.00	15.00	50.00
	Liberty Bell. Rv: Globe at center, showing Western Hemisphere. Above: GLOBE FIRE INS. CO. Below: 176 BROADWAY N.Y. Plain edge. (Miller NY 281)						
NY-NY 96	1876	Brass	25mm	4.00	10.00	15.00	50.00
	As 95. Plain edge. (Miller NY 280)						
NY-NY 97	1876	WM	25mm	4.00	10.00	15.00	40.00
	As 95. Plain edge. (Miller NY 282)						
NY-NY 98	(1876)	Copper	25mm	4.00	10.00	15.00	50.00
	American flag, LONG MAY IT WAVE and 13 stars around. Rv: As 95. Plain edge. (Miller NY 283)						
NY-NY 99	(1876)	Brass	25mm	4.00	10.00	15.00	50.00
	As 98. Plain edge. (Miller NY 284)						
NY-NY 100	(1876)	WM	25mm	4.00	10.00	15.00	40.00
	As 98. Plain edge. (Wright 384; Miller NY 284A)						
NY-NY 101	(1873-74)	WM	25mm	10.00	20.00	50.00	100.
	Clothed, bearded bust of Lincoln right, LINCOLN above, tiny BOLEN beneath bust. Rv: As 95. Plain edge. (King 609; Miller NY 285)						

Types 95 and 98 are also known in bronze at same price range.

GLOBE FIRE CO.
JOHN M. HAZLETT

Rulau	Date	Metal	Size	VG	F	VF	EF
NY-NY 103	(1870's)	Silver	38.1mm	—	—	—	80.00

JOHN M. HAZLETT. / GLOBE FIRE CO / MAY 22d. 1820 engraved on obverse of U.S. 1871 Seated Liberty dollar. (Kurt Krueger Sept. 7, 1983 sale, lot 1275; Bill Carey coll., Getzville, N.Y.)

GREAT UNION PACIFIC TEA CO.

1876 Centennial Tokens

Reverse type 1: GREAT UNION PACIFIC / 1 lb. / COFFEE (curved) / * TEA CO. *. (All 23mm; plain edge)

Reverse type 2: 557 8TH AVE. COR. 38TH ST. / 1 lb. / COFFEE (straight) / * 368 GRAND ST. *. (All 23mm; plain edge)

Reverse type 2E. As 2, but 368 GRAND erased on die. (All 23mm; plain edge)

Reverse type 3: GREAT UNION PACIFIC TEA CO. / (numeral) / *. Large letters; small numeral. (All 23mm; plain edge)

Reverse type 4: Similar to 3. Large letters; medium sized numeral. (All 23mm; plain edge)

Reverse type 5: Similar to 3. Large letters; large numeral. (all 23mm; plain edge)

Reverse type 6: GREAT UNION PACIFIC TEA COMPANY. / (numeral) / *. Small letters; medium sized numeral. (All 23mm; plain edge)

Reverse type 7: 557 8TH AVE. COR. 38TH ST. / (numeral) / * 368 GRAND ST. *. Medium sized numeral. (All 23mm; plain edge)

Reverse type 7E: As 7, but 368 GRAND erased on die. (All 23mm; plain edge)

Reverse type 8: GREAT UNION PACIFIC / 2 lb. / COFFEE. (This die is reported but has not been examined)

Rulau	Obv	Rev	Metal	F	VF	EF	Unc
NY-NY 730	A	1	WM	—	—	15.00	40.00
NY-NY 730	A A	1	Copper	—	—	—	45.00
NY-NY 730 B	A	1	Brass	—	—	—	45.00
NY-NY 730 F	B	1	WM	—	—	15.00	40.00
NY-NY 730 J	E	1	WM				
	Not confirmed (Miller Pa 186)						
NY-NY 731	G	1	WM	—	—	15.00	40.00
	Thick flan. (Miller Pa 182)						
NY-NY 731 A	G	1	WM	—	—	—	40.00
	Thin flan.						
NY-NY 731 B	G	1	Copper	—	—	—	45.00
NY-NY 732	A	2	Brass	—	—	—	50.00
NY-NY 732 F	G	2E	WM	—	22.50	—	—
NY-NY 733	G	3	WM	—	—	15.00	40.00
	Numeral 13. (Miller Pa 183)						
NY-NY 734	H	4	WM	—	—	15.00	40.00
	Numeral 20.						
NY-NY 735	G	5	WM	—	—	15.00	40.00
	Numeral 15. (Miller Pa 184)						
NY-NY 735 A	G	5	WM	—	—	15.00	40.00
	Numeral 18. (Miller Pa 185)						
NY-NY 736	A	6	WM	—	—	—	40.00
	Numeral 18.						
NY-NY 737	G	7	WM	—	—	15.00	40.00
	Numeral 13.						
NY-NY 737 A	G	7	WM	—	—	15.00	40.00
	Numeral 20.						
NY-NY 738	G	7E	WM	—	22.50	—	—
	Numeral 15.						
NY-NY 739	B	8	WM			Not confirmed	
	(Wright 402)						

This series is easily the most confusing and least understood of any of the Centennial card issuers. Even its location is confusing. Dr. Wright did not attribute to locale, but both Edgar Adams and Donald Miller assigned the issuer to Philadelphia. Arlie R. Slabaugh assigned it to New York City, as embossed shell cards of this issue are reported with the New York address. However, the Great Union Pacific Tea Co. does not appear under either Philadelphia or New York in directories we have searched!

We settled on New York, with the concurrence of Steve Tanenbaum, who assembled enough of these pieces to make some sense of the series, but we will continue searching for some sort of directory verification.

In the section above, we've listed 10 separate dies (including two erasures on dies), and there well may be more. The list above is the most complete ever published, but we believe it to be representative rather than complete. Certainly many more die combinations and metal variations must have been issued, and it is likely these pieces were given out widely to customers, though all seem scarce today. Perhaps a hoard exists.

W. D. GRIMSHAW

Rulau	Date	Metal	Size	F	VF	EF	Unc
NY-NY 105	1867	S/WM	39mm	40.00	60.00	80.00	100.

Stamping press at center, STAMPED OCT. 1867 above, BY COMPRESSED AIR HAMMER below. Rv: W. D. GRIMSHAW / THOS. PROSSER / & SON / 15 GOLD ST. / NEW YORK / PAT. JAN. 10. 1865. MAY 21. 1867. Plain edge. (Miller NY 291; Wright 405)

A HAPPY NEW YEAR

Rulau	Date	Metal	Size	F	VF	EF	Unc
NY-NY 108	1883	GS	21mm	—	—	6.50	—

Witch seated on broomstick right, WE ALL HAVE OUR HOBBIES below. Rv: On folds of a scroll: A / HAPPY / NEW YEAR / 1883. (Thoele coll.)

Engraver George Hampden Lovett of New York used the 'Witch-Hobbies' motif extensively on his store cards and medalets of about 1860. He was in business 1848-1890.

We are tentatively assigning this piece as a result to New York City.

HALLE DES C. T. V.

Rulau	Date	Metal	Size	F	VF	EF	Unc
NY-NY 107	1887	WM	32mm	—	—	25.00	—

Bearded man's bust left, within oak wreath. Under truncation of bust, in tiny letters: G. LEYERS NEWARK / N. Rv: Within wreath: + ZUR + / ERINNERUNG / AN DIE / GRUND-STEIN / LEGUNG / DER HALLE DES / C. T. V. / NEW YORK SEP. 5. '87 / (symbol). The "symbol" is a capital S intertwined around a Maltese cross, crossed scepter and sword behind. Plain edge. Issued holed. (Rulau coll.)

The reverse legend translates: In commemoration of the cornerstone laying of the hall of the C. T. V., New York, Sep. 5, 1887. C.T.V. is not known at this point, but the 'T.V.' probably stands for Turnverein (Turners Union), a German gymnastic-social movement.

T. HOAG

1876 Centennial Tokens

Reverse type 1: T. HOAG / WATCHES. / CLOCKS & (on scroll) / JEWELRY (on scroll) / 1373 BROADWAY / NEW YORK. (All 23mm; plain edge)

Rulau	Obv	Rev	Metal	F	VF	EF	Unc
NY-NY 740	A (Wright 1454; Miller NY 341)	1	WM	5.00	8.00	12.50	30.00
NY-NY 741	B (Miller 342)	1	WM	—	8.00	12.50	30.00
NY-NY 742	E (Miller 343)	1	WM	—	—	12.50	30.00
NY-NY 742 A	E (Miller 344)	1	Copper	—	—	17.50	40.00
NY-NY 743	F (Miller 345)	1	WM	—	—	15.00	35.00
NY-NY 744	G (Miller 346A)	1	WM	—	—	15.00	40.00
NY-NY 745	H	1	WM	—	—	—	45.00
NY-NY 745 A	H (Miller 346)	1	Copper	—	—	—	45.00
NY-NY 746	K (Miller 346B)	1	WM	—	—	15.00	40.00

Thomas Hoag appears in the 1876 directory.

HOEFT

Rulau	Date	Metal	Size	VG	F	VF	EF
NY-NY 115	(?)	Copper	29mm	—	—	75.00	—

HOEFT / 256 / CHERRY ST. / N.Y. ctsp on U.S. Large cent. (Hallenbeck 8.756;Brunk 19805)

H. W. HOOPS

1876 Centennial Tokens

Reverse type 1: H. W. HOOPS / OLD / CONFECTIONERY / 370 BOWERY / NEW YORK. (All 23mm; plain edge)

Rulau	Obv	Rev	Metal	F	VF	EF	Unc
NY-NY 750	A (Miller NY 351)	1	WM	5.00	8.00	12.50	30.00
NY-NY 751	B (Miller 352)	1	WM	—	—	12.50	30.00
NY-NY 751	AB (Miller 353)	1	Copper	—	—	—	40.00
NY-NY 751	BB	1	Brass	—	—	—	40.00
NY-NY 752	E (Miller 354)	1	WM	—	—	12.50	30.00
NY-NY 753	F (Miller 355)	1	WM	—	—	15.00	40.00
NY-NY 754	G	1	WM	—	8.00	15.00	40.00
NY-NY 755	K	1	WM	—	—	—	40.00

He does not appear in the 1876 directory. A candy maker, Herman Hoops, at 270 8th Ave., does appear. There may be a connection.

HUDNUT'S MINERAL

Rulau	Date	Metal	Size	F	VF	EF	Unc
NY-NY 117	(1869-81)	CN	--mm	—	15.00	—	40.00

HUDNUT'S MINERAL. Rv: Blank. (Miller NY 360)

Alexander Hudnut & Co. appears in 1869 as a drug store at 218 Broadway. He was here at least until 1881.

The book *Centennial - American Life in 1876* by W. P. Randel says: "Hudnut's Fountain in the Herald Building dispensed as many as 3,500 glassfuls of iced soda water on a hot day ...The $50,000 price tag for the soft drink concession at the exhibition was a measure of the popularity of the stuff."

HUYLER'S

1876 Centennial Tokens

Reverse type 1: HUYLER'S / —*— / OLD FASHIONED / MOLASSES (on scroll) / CANDY. (on scroll) / 31 EIGHTH AVE. / AND / 869 B.WAY N.Y. (All 23mm; plain edge)

Rulau	Obv	Rev	Metal	F	VF	EF	Unc
NY-NY 760	A (Miller NY 361)	1	WM	—	—	12.50	30.00
NY-NY 761	B Thick flan. (Wright 1466; Miller 362)	1	WM	—	—	12.50	30.00
NY-NY 761 A	B Thin flan.	1	WM	—	—	12.50	30.00
NY-NY 761 B	B	1	Brass	—	—	20.00	45.00
NY-NY 762	E Thick flan. (Miller 363)	1	WM	—	—	12.50	30.00
NY-NY 762 A	E Thin flan.	1	WM	—	—	12.50	30.00
NY-NY 762 B	E	1	Copper	—	—	15.00	35.00

David Huyler, baker, 31 8th Ave., appears in the 1876 directory.

Rulau	Obv	Rev	Metal	F	VF	EF	Unc
NY-NY 763	F (Miller 365)	1	WM	—	—	15.00	40.00

NY-NY 764	G	1	WM	—	—	15.00	40.00
NY-NY 765	H (Miller 366)	1	WM	—	—	12.50	30.00
NY-NY 765	A H (Miller 367)	1	Copper	—	—	15.00	40.00

Huyler's also had a branch operation in Philadelphia. This famous candy maker later had special tokens at the 1904 St. Louis World's Fair.

IRISH REPUBLIC

Rulau	Date	Metal	Size	VG	F	VF	Unc
NY-NY-A117	1866	Brass	29mm	—	—	150.	300.

Sailing ship left, dividing large F — B, IRISH above, REPUBLIC below. Rv: Clasped hands above sunrise. IRELAND / 18 (shamrock) 66 above, AMERICA below. Six stars on left, seven on right. Issued holed. (Wright 494; Rulau MV 153; Forrer V, 484-485)

This token is connected with the Fenian raid on Canada in May, 1866. FB equals Fenian Brotherhood. The centers of Irish agitation after the Civil War were Boston and New York.

John O'Neil was born in Ireland in 1834 and died in Omaha in Jan. 1878. He served as a Union soldier for three years, resigning in 1864 and established a pension agency in Nashville, Tenn. In 1866 he was appointed by his Irish compatriots to command the Fenian forces that invaded Canada. He invaded with a force of 1,500 men, and took control of Fort Erie. Grant arrived the next day in Buffalo with orders that no additional Fenians be allowed to cross, and with no ammunition or supplies O'Neil was forced to retreat to the U.S. Seven hundred Fenians were arrested, and after an abortive attempt to invade again in 1870, he was imprisoned for several months. He later attempted to establish an Irish colony in Nebraska.

Forrer reports that a New York die sinker by the name of Sewell (the medals strangely resemble the work of Scovill Mfg. Co. of Waterbury, Conn.) issued the badges shown above to members of the brotherhood. He states that the organization was set up as a Republic, and shows an illustration of the identical badge, with a suspension ribbon. After the abortive attempt of 1870, the Home Rule and Land League movements practically superseded the Fenian. The name was taken from an ancient military organization called Fionna Eirinn, said to have been instituted in Ireland in 300 B.C.

"The Irish Republic" was also a journal, published at 84 Washington St., Chicago, Ill.

Rulau	Date	Metal	Size	VG	F	VF	Unc
Ny-NY B117	(1870's)	Copper	19mm	—	—	200.	—

American eagle with shield on its breast, wings drooping, above nest of chicks. Star at either side of eagle's head; letters F -- B separated by nest. Around: ** PROTECTION ***. Rv: Blank. (L. B. Fauver coll.)

Fauver says the symbolism is of the U.S. eagle protecting the Irish "republican chicks."

He also reveals that A117 can be found with either a silver wash or gold wash, possibly used to denote rank. Other Fenian Brotherhood numismatica which exist are enameled pins of the 1880's and celluloid pinbacks after 1896.

S. JANE'S STORE

Rulau	Date	Metal	Size	VG	F	VF	EF
NY-NY 118	(?)	Silver	25mm	—	—	100.	—

s. j jane's / store / n.y. (all lower case letters) ctsp on U.S. 1873 w/Arrows quarter. (Joseph Schmidt coll.; Brunk 21540)

The first 'j' is probably a mistaken extra punch.

JEFFERSON INSURANCE COMPANY

Rulau	Date	Metal	Size	F	VF	EF	Unc
NY-NY 126	(1873-74)	WM	26mm	15.00	22.50	50.00	100.

Clothed, bearded bust of Lincoln right, LINCOLN above. Tiny BOLEN under bust. Rv: JEFFERSON / INSURANCE / COMPANY / CAPITAL $200,000 / SURPLUS 300,000 / 111 BROADWAY / NEW YORK. Plain edge. (King 607; Miller NY 372)

NY-NY 127	(1873-74)	Brass	26mm	—	—	—	—

As 126. Plain edge. (Miller NY 372B)

NY-NY 129 B	1876	Copper	25mm	5.00	10.00	15.00	50.00

Liberty Bell and 13 stars, CENTENNIAL above, 1776 1876 below. Rv: As 126. Plain edge. (Wright 505; Miller NY 372A)

NY-NY 129 A	1876	WM	25mm	5.00	10.00	15.00	40.00

As 129. Plain edge.

NY-NY 131	(1876)	WM	25mm	10.00	15.00	22.50	50.00

Thomas Jefferson, JEFFERSON. Rv: As 126. Plain edge. (Miller NY 372C)

WILLIAM R. JENKINS

1876 Centennial Tokens

Reverse type 1: WILLIAM R. JENKINS / STATIONER, / —.— / PRINTER / & BOOKSELLER / NO. 839 / SIXTH AVE. N.Y. (All 23mm; plain edge)

Rulau	Obv	Rev	Metal	F	VF	EF	Unc
NY-NY 770	A (Miller NY 373)	1	WM	5.00	8.00	14.00	30.00
NY-NY 771	B (Wright 506; Miller 374)	1	WM	—	—	14.00	30.00
NY-NY 771 A	B Also in Bronze.	1	Copper	—	—	17.50	40.00
NY-NY 771 B	B	1	Brass	—	—	20.00	45.00
NY-NY 772	E (Miller 375)	1	WM	—	—	14.00	30.00
NY-NY 773	F (Miller 376)	1	WM	—	—	17.50	40.00
NY-NY 774	G	1	Copper	—	—	20.00	45.00
NY-NY 775	H (Miller 377A)	1	WM	—	—	17.50	40.00
NY-NY 775 A	H (Miller 377)	1	Copper	—	—	—	45.00
NY-NY 776	J	1	WM	—	—	—	40.00

K. KNIGHT

Rulau	Date	Metal	Size	VG	F	VF	EF
NY-NY 135	(?)	Copper	29mm	—	—	75.00	—

K. KNIGHT / 5 BAXTER ST. / NEW YORK ctsp on U.S. Large cent. (Hallenbeck 11.751; Brunk 23270)

Several specimens were in the Maurice M. Gould collection, but unfortunately the dates on the coins were not recorded.

RUD. KOHLER

Rulau	Date	Metal	Size	VG	F	VF	Unc
NY-NY 137	(1876)	WM	25mm	—	50.00	—	—

RUD. KOHLER / 70 / 5TH / AVE / NYC ctsp on reverse of flattened Traphagen Hunter centennial token, Rulau NY-NY 851. (Tanenbaum coll.)

Kohler was a dealer in coins and coin books.

TH. KRUGER

Rulau	Date	Metal	Size	F	VF	EF	Unc
NY-NY 139	1876	WM	24mm	—	20.00	50.00	75.00

Spread eagle, BEER TICKET / 1876. Rv: GOOD FOR ONE GLASS OF BEER / AT / 440 B'WAY / RESTAURANT 285 CANAL ST., LUNCH ROOM / 564 B'WAY. / LAGER BEER / STATION / TH. KRUGER-. (Wright 569)

P.L. & CO.
(Pierre Lorillard & Co.)

Rulau	Date	Metal	Size	F	VF	EF	Unc
NY-NY 155	1876	Copper	37mm	7.50	10.00	20.00	30.00
	Monogram PL & CO within laurel wreath, 1876 breaking wreath at bottom. Rv: Large numeral 50 in circle of stars. (Miller NY 479)						
NY-NY 156	1876	GS	37mm	7.50	10.00	20.00	30.00
	As 155. (Wright 629; Miller NY 480)						
NY-NY 157	1876	Brass	25mm	7.50	10.00	15.00	30.00
	As 155, but numeral 10. (Miller NY 481)						
NY-NY 157A	1876	GS	25mm	—	—	15.00	30.00
	As 157. (Levine-Magriel 1988, lot 982)						

Rulau	Date	Metal	Size	F	VF	EF	Unc
NY-NY 158	1876	GS	20mm	4.00	6.00	10.00	30.00
	Obverse as 155. Rv: Large numeral 5 in circle of 12 stars. (Miller NY 482)						
NY-NY 158A	1876	Brass	20mm	—	—	10.00	30.00
	As 158.						

Rulau	Date	Metal	Size	F	VF	EF	Unc
NY-NY 159	1876	GS	17mm	4.00	6.00	10.00	30.00
	Obverse as 155. Rv: Large numeral 1 in circle of 10 stars. (Miller NY 483)						
NY-NY 160	1876	Brass	17mm	4.00	6.00	10.00	30.00
	As 159.						

P. (Pierre) Lorillard & Co., the famous cigarette, cigar and chewing tobacco manufacturers, are now (since 1968) a division of Loews Corporation. They are located at 200 East 42nd St. in New York City. Some of their better known cigarette brands were Old Gold, Kent, True, Newport and Spring.

Complete denomination sets in brass and GS may exist.

LAFAYETTE RESTAURANT

Rulau	Date	Metal	Size	VG	F	VF	Unc
NY-NY 154	(1876)	Brass	17.5mm	—	25.00	35.00	—
	LAFAYETTE / Large ornament 5 / * RESTAURANT *. Rv: Same as obverse. Plain edge. (Pipher coll. ex-Fuld, Katen)						

Rulau	Date	Metal	Size	VG	F	VF	Unc
NY-NY A154	(1876)	Brass	21mm	—	25.00	35.00	—
	As last, but 10. Plain edge. (Pipher coll.)						

Rulau	Date	Metal	Size	VG	F	VF	Unc
NY-NY B154	(1876)	Brass	26.5mm	—	30.00	40.00	—
	As last, but 50. Plain edge. (Wright 573; Presidential Coin sale, April 1977; Pipher coll.)						

DAVID H. LANE

Rulau	Date	Metal	Size	F	VF	EF	Unc
NY-NY 145	1875	WM	26mm	—	—	50.00	100.
	Abraham Lincoln, by Bolen. Rv: RECORDER OF DEEDS / * / 1875 / * / * DAVID H. LANE *. Plain edge. (Miller NY 416)						
NY-NY 147	1875	Brass	26mm	—	—	15.00	50.00
	U.S. flag, 13 stars around, LONG MAY IT WAVE. Rv: As last. Plain edge. (Miller NY 416A; Wright 576)						
NY-NY 147	Aî1875	Bronze	26mm	—	—	15.00	50.00
	As 147.						

Rulau	Date	Metal	Size	F	VF	EF	Unc
NY-NY 149	1876	Bronze	26mm	—	—	15.00	50.00
	Radiant eagle perched atop Liberty Bell. Around: ******* CENTENNIAL *******. Below: 1776 1876. Rv: As last. Plain edge. (Miller NY 416B)						
NY-NY 149A	1876	Brass	26mm	—	—	15.00	50.00
	As 149. Plain edge.						
NY-NY 149B	1876	WM	26mm	—	—	15.00	40.00
	As 149. Plain edge.						
NY-NY 149C	1876	Copper	26mm	—	—	15.00	50.00
	As 149. Plain edge.						
NY-NY 150	1876	Copper	26mm	—	—	Unique	
	As last, but overstruck on a cut-down Large cent. The ONE CENT is clearly visible on the bell side. Struck in proof. (Bowers & Ruddy Nov. 1982 sale)						

PH. J. LAUBER'S RESTAURANT

Rulau	Date	Metal	Size	VG	F	VF	Unc
NY-NY 161	(?)	Copper	30mm	—	40.00	50.00	—
	ONE / DOLLAR within wreath at center, *** PH. J. LAUBER'S *** / RESTAURANT, around. Rv: Same as obverse. Plain edge. Centrally holed flan. (Pipher collection)						

Rulau	Date	Metal	Size	VG	F	VF	Unc
NY-NY 162	(1876)	Brass	17mm	—	15.00	22.50	—
	PH. J. LAUBER'S / Large ornate 5 / * RESTAURANT *. Rv: Same as obverse. Plain edge. (Pipher coll.)						

J. H. LESTER

Rulau	Date	Metal	Size	VG	F	VF	EF
NY-NY 163	(?)	Bronze	23mm	—	—	10.00	—
	J. H. LESTER / 483 BROADWAY / N.Y. ctsp on U.S. 1867 Shield 2-cent piece. (B&M Patterson 1985 sale, lot 1662; Brunk 24343)						

FRITZ LINDINGER

Rulau	Date	Metal	Size	VG	F	VF	Unc
NY-NY 153	(1880-86)	CN	25mm	—	—	8.50	—

MUTUAL CAFE / 45 / LIBERTY ST. / NEW YORK. Rv: FRITZ LINDINGER / 2 1/2 / 45 LIBERTY ST. Plain edge. (John Stribhei coll.)

Rulau	Date	Metal	Size	VG	F	VF	Unc
NY-NY 154	(?)	CN	--mm	—	—	8.00	—

CAFE LINDINGER / 56 & 58 LIBERTY ST. / NEW YORK. Rv: 2 1/2. (Koppenhaver June 1988 sale, lot 810)

R.H. MACY & CO.

Rulau	Date	Metal	Size	F	VF	EF	Unc
NY-NY 173	1876	Copper	28mm	10.00	20.00	30.00	100.

Large star, numeral '7' on it. Above: R.H. MACY & CO. N.Y. Below: SODA WATER. Rv: Cupid with monkey wrench protecting soda water apparatus from a bear's attack. Tiny K. MULLER F. under Cupid and bear. JOHN MATTHEWS NEW YORK around, 1876 in exergue. Plain edge. Thick flan. (Miller NY 512)

Rulau	Date	Metal	Size	F	VF	EF	Unc
NY-NY 174	1876	Copper	27mm	10.00	20.00	30.00	100.

As 173, but 5, 14, 18 or 36 on star instead of '7'. Plain edge. Thick flan. (Wright 645; Miller NY 513)

The reverse of both cards is that of John Matthews of New York, NY-NY 190 and 191 (which see).

MANHATTAN WATCH CO.

NOTE: There are two obverse dies and two reverse dies of these tokens. Obverse (watch face) Type A has a short minute hand. Type B has a long minute hand, the hand pointing past the numerals in the border. The illustration is of Type A.

The only difference in the reverse die is the address. Type 1 reads 234 BROADWAY, N.Y. Type 2 reads 16 PARK PLACE, N.Y.

All the Manhattan Watch Co. tokens have been made as imitation watches with a "stem winder." On a great many surviving pieces, these stem winders have been filed off, leaving the round token. To be considered in 'Unc.' condition, full stem winder must be present.

Rulau	Date	Metal	Size	F	VF	EF	Unc
NY-NY 177	(?)	Copper	31mm	5.00	10.00	15.00	40.00

Obverse A, reverse 1. Watch face, MANHATTAN on upper part of face. Rv: MANHATTAN WATCH CO. / 3/5 / SIZE OF / WATCH. / GOLD PLATE / $6.00 / NICKEL / $5.00 / + 234 BROADWAY, N.Y. +. Plain edge. (Wright 657; Miller NY 518)

Rulau	Date	Metal	Size	F	VF	EF	Unc
NY-NY 177A	(?)	Brass	31mm	5.00	10.00	15.00	45.00

As 177. Plain edge. (Miller NY 519)

Rulau	Date	Metal	Size	F	VF	EF	Unc
NY-NY 177B	(?)	GS	31mm	5.00	10.00	15.00	40.00

As 177. Plain edge. (Miller NY 520)

Rulau	Date	Metal	Size	F	VF	EF	Unc
NY-NY 178	(?)	Brass	31mm	5.00	10.00	15.00	40.00

Obverse A, reverse 2. Short minute hand; 16 PARK PLACE, N.Y. Plain edge.

Rulau	Date	Metal	Size	F	VF	EF	Unc
NY-NY 178A	(?)	GS	31mm	5.00	10.00	15.00	40.00

As 178. Plain edge.

Rulau	Date	Metal	Size	F	VF	EF	Unc
NY-NY 179	(?)	GS	31mm	7.50	15.00	25.00	60.00

Obverse B, reverse 2. Long minute hand; 16 PARK PLACE, N.Y. Plain edge.

Rulau	Date	Metal	Size	F	VF	EF	Unc
NY-NY 181	(?)	Gilt/GS	31mm	—	—	25.00	—

As 177, but ctsp 'MOSER' on lower part of watch face.

Rulau	Date	Metal	Size	F	VF	EF	Unc
NY-NY 181C	(?)	GS	31mm	—	—	25.00	—

As 177, but ctsp 'E. HOWARD' on lower part of watch face. (Pipher coll.)

Edward Howard appears in the 1890 directory as an advertising agent and dealer in cotton waste. In the 1902 directory he is still listed as an ad agent but there is also a listing for the Edward Howard Clock Co. It is possible this counterstamp comes from the 1900 period, though the token appeared 20 years earlier.

Rulau	Date	Metal	Size	F	VF	EF	Unc
NY-NY 182	(?)	GS	31mm	—	—	25.00	—

As 177, but ctsp 'TODD / THE / JEWELER' on watch face.

It is believed additional counterstamp varieties similar to 181 and 182 will surface. These apparently were distributors of the Manhattan Watch Co. products.

MANN BROTHERS

Rulau	Date	Metal	Size	F	VF	EF	Unc
NY-NY 183	(1880's?)	Gilt Brass	31mm	—	—	15.00	25.00

Bearded face right dominates the left side. To right: MANN BROTHERS / GRAND & / ORCHARD / NEW YORK. Rv: HONEST GOODS / —— / CLOTHIERS / (rosette) / —HATTERS— / —.— / FURNISHERS / —.— / * HONEST VALUE *. Plain edge. Issued holed. (ANS coll.)

MARTINKA & CO.

Rulau	Date	Metal	Size	F	VF	EF	Unc
NY-NY 185	(1875)	S/Br	31mm	30.00	50.00	—	60.00

Magician standing on a globe, MUNDUS VULT DECIPI: DECIPIATUR. Rv: MARTINKA & CO / MANUFACTURERS / OF / FINE MAGICAL / APPARATUS / NEW-YORK / (wreath). Reeded edge.

Martinka Co. may have reissued these tokens as late as 1921.

JOHN MATTHEWS

NOTE: Tokens of this design, 1863, are catalogued as Civil War tokens, Fuld NY 630-AV-la (Miller NY 523 to 526B)

Rulau	Date	Metal	Size	F	VF	EF	Unc
NY-NY 190	1876	Copper	28mm	6.00	10.00	20.00	40.00

Obverse similar to 1863 token illustration, but MATTHEWS' SODA WATER APPARATUS. above, 1876. below. Rv: Cupid with monkey wrench protecting soda water apparatus from a bear's attack. Tiny K. MULLER F. under Cupid and bear. JOHN MATTHEWS NEW YORK around, 1876 in exergue. Thick planchet. (Wright 674; Miller NY 525)

NY-NY 191	1876	Bronze	28mm	5.00	7.00	9.00	12.50

As 190. (Distinguishing between copper and bronze specimens is very difficult.) (Miller NY 526)

NY-NY 195	1876	Bronze	28mm	—	—	—	20.00

Obverse as reverse of 190. Rv: Blank, but '18' incused.

NY-NY 196	1876	Bronze	28mm	—	—	—	70.00

As 195, but '40,' '135,' '149,' '180' or '225' incused.

NY-NY 197	1876	Bronze	28mm	—	—	—	70.00

Obv. as 195. Rv: Large star at center, SODA WATER below. '96' incused on star. Plain edge. Thick flan.

NY-NY 197A	1876	Bronze	28mm	—	—	—	70.00

As 197, but numerals are in *relief.* (Numerals examined: 6, 7, 18)

NY-NY 199	1882	S/Cop.	45mm	15.00	30.00	50.00	75.00

Head to right, JOHN MATTHEWS / 1808-1870. Rv: Similar to reverse of 190, 1882 in exergue. (Miller NY 527)

John Matthews founded his soda water apparatus manufactory in 1832. He held many U.S. patents.

METROPOLITAN INSURANCE COMPANY

Rulau	Date	Metal	Size	F	VF	EF	Unc
NY-NY 205	1865	Copper	27mm	5.00	10.00	15.00	30.00

Sailing vessel to right, METROPOLITAN above, INSURANCE COMPANY below. Rv: MARINE & FIRE. / CAPITAL / $300,000 / SURPLUS / $458.321. / 108 BROADWAY / NEW YORK / 1865. (Miller NY 577)

NY-NY 206	1865	Brass	27mm	5.00	10.00	15.00	30.00

As 205. (Miller NY 578)

NY-NY 207	1865	Copper	--mm	5.00	10.00	15.00	30.00

Similar to 205, but CAPITAL / $1,000,000. (Miller NY 575)

NY-NY 208	1865	Brass	--mm	5.00	10.00	15.00	30.00

As 207. (Miller NY 576)

NY-NY 210	1866	Copper	31mm	5.00	8.00	14.00	30.00

Obverse as 205. Rv: Similar, but legend reads: MARINE & FIRE. / CAPITAL, / $1,000,000 / ASSETS, / $1,650,000 / 108 & 110 BDWAY / NEW YORK / 1866 / DEALERS MAY PARTICIPATE IN PROFITS. Plain edge. (Miller NY 579)

NY-NY 211	1866	Brass	31mm	5.00	8.00	14.00	30.00

As 205. Plain edge. (Miller NY 580)

H. J. MEYER

Rulau	Date	Metal	Size	VG	F	VF	Unc
NY-NY 212	1880	N/Br	31mm	—	—	Rare	—

H. J. MEYER / ESTABLISHED / COMMISSION / (Star) / MERCHANT / 1880 / 275 WASHINGTON ST. N. Y. CITY. Rv: BUTTER * CHEESE * EGGS / POULTRY / * (Star) * / ETC. / *. Plain edge. (Tanenbaum coll.)

MORTON HOUSE BAR

Rulau	Date	Metal	Size	VG	F	VF	Unc
NY-NY 213	(ca 1880)	Brass	29mm	—	—	25.00	—

MORTON HOUSE BAR / 10 / UNION SQUARE. Rv: Same as obverse. Plain edge. Issued holed. (Paul Bosco April 1989 sale, lot 148)

N.Y., N.H. & H. R.R.

Rulau	Date	Metal	Size	F	VF	EF	Unc
NY-NY 214	(?)	Brass	39mm	—	—	15.00	—

N.Y., N.H. & H. R.R. Rv: Blank. Plain edge. (Stanley Steinberg 1984 sale)

Railroad tag of the New York, New Haven and Hartford Railroad?

NELSON & CO.

Rulau	Date	Metal	Size	VG	F	VF	Unc
NY-NY 215	(ca 1885)	S/Brass	28.5mm	—	—	45.00	—

(All incused): * NEW-YORK * / 10 / NELSON & CO. Rv: * NELSON & CO * / 10 / NEW-YORK. Plain edge. (ANS coll.)

NEW YORK TURNVEREIN

Rulau	Date	Metal	Size	F	VF	EF	Unc
NY-NY 222	1875	Bronze	32mm	—	20.00	—	—

Crossed sword and torch tied with a bow, eagle perched above, at center. Above: NEW-YORK TURNVEREIN. Below: GEGR: JUNI 6. 1850. Rv: BAHN / FREI within wreath at center, ZUR ERINNERUNG AN DIE 25 JAHR. STIFTUNGSFEIER around, 1875 below. Plain edge. (Larry Laevens coll.)

Issue by the New York Turnverein (New York Turners' Union), founded June 6, 1850, on the occasion of its 25th anniversary in 1875. The words 'Bahn Frei' on reverse signify that entry was free.

PARISIAN VARIETIES

Rulau	Date	Metal	Size	G	VG	F	VF
NY-NY 230	(1876)	Silver	31mm	—	75.00	100.	150.

PARISIAN / VARIETIES / 16. ST. & B'WAY N.Y. in three lines ctsp on U.S. Seated Liberty half dollar. Examined: 1854, 1858, 1865, 1866, 1873, 1874, 1875, unknown dates. At least 33 pieces known. (Duffield 1500; Gould 39; Miller NY 627; Brunk 30900)

Rulau	Date	Metal	Size	G	VG	F	VF
NY-NY 231	(1876)	Silver	33mm	—	—	100.	150.

Same ctsp on U.S. Bust type half dollar. (Gould 47)

Rulau	Date	Metal	Size	G	VG	F	VF
NY-NY 234	(1876)	Silver	39mm	—	200.	—	300.

Same ctsp on U.S. 1876 Trade dollar. (Gould 47)

Rulau	Date	Metal	Size	G	VG	F	VF
NY-NY 236	(1876)	Silver	27mm	—	100.	—	150.

Same ctsp on Spanish-American 2-reales. (Gould 115)

Parisian Varieties was an erotic show of nubile young ladies which opened Sept. 15, 1875 and last advertised on Oct. 21, 1876. The *New York Times* reported it was formerly Robinson Hall, and in its Sept. 19, 1875 edition Parisian Varieties advertised it wanted to hire "fifty handsome young ladies." In a *Times* ad of Oct. 18, 1876, it advertised that the Varities offered "sensational legs on the brain or Satan's vendue." (See *The Numismatist* for June 1993, pg. 728, for research by Robert D. Leonard)

W. E. PARK

Rulau	Date	Metal	Size	F	VF	EF	Unc
NY-NY 241	(?)	Silver	19mm	—	90.00	—	—

W. E. PARK / N.Y. GEN. ctsp on Great Britain sixpence, date worn off.

Rulau	Date	Metal	Size	F	VF	EF	Unc
NY-NY 241A	(?)	Bronze	19mm	—	90.00	—	—

Similar ctsp on U.S. Indian cent.

PARK THEATRE

Rulau	Date	Metal	Size	F	VF	EF	Unc
NY-NY 240	1875	WM	43mm	—	30.00	—	50.00

Accolated bust left, PRESENTED BY MR. & MRS. WM. J. FLORENCE. Rv: Wreath, within which: PARK THEATRE / DECEMBER 13, 1875 / 100DTH / NIGHT / OF THE / MIGHTY / DOLLAR. (Wright 797; Springfield 1981 sale, lot 4561)

For earlier tokens of a famous theater by this name, see the Early American Tokens section.

PARKER HOUSE LUNCH

New York, N.Y. ?

Rulau	Date	Metal	Size	VG	F	VF	Unc
NY-NY 242	(1870's)	CN	29mm	—	—	—	—

PARKER HOUSE LUNCH / 45 . Rv: Same as obverse. Plain edge. (Kirtley Dec. 13, 1988 sale, lot 662)

Similar to the Ronan and Delmonico pieces, which see under New York City.

PARMELEE, WEBSTER & CO.

Rulau	Date	Metal	Size	F	VF	EF	Unc
NY-NY 243	1868	Silver	21mm	—	—	—	100.
	Bust of Grant right. Rv: PARMELEE, WEBSTER & CO. / 155 JANE ST. / PURE / 10 / ALUMINUM. Plain edge. (Miller NY 628)						
NY-NY 243A	1868	Copper	21mm	—	10.00	20.00	40.00
	As 243. (Miller 629)						
NY-NY 243B	1868	Brass	21mm	—	10.00	20.00	40.00
	As 243. (Miller 630)						
NY-NY 243C	1868	WM	21mm	—	10.00	20.00	40.00
	As 243. (Miller 631)						
NY-NY 243D	1868	Alum	21mm	—	—	—	Rare
	As 243. (Tanenbaum coll.)						

PEPER & OHLHAVERS

New York, N.Y.

Rulau	Date	Metal	Size	VG	F	VF	Unc
NY-NY 880	(?)	GS	29mm	—	—	14.00	—
	(All incused): PEPER & OHLHAVERS / 5 / 1201 3RD AVE. Rv: Same as obverse. (Thoele coll.)						

Peper and Ohlhavers operated saloons at multiple N.Y.C. locations 1890-1894 (including one at 3rd Avenue), but the date they were at 1201 3rd has not been pinpointed.

GEO. E. PHELAN

1876 Centennial Tokens

Reverse type 1: GEO E. PHELAN / BILLIARD / (billiard table) / TABLES / 36 E. 14TH ST. N.Y. (All 23mm; plain edge)

Rulau	Obv	Rev	Metal	F	VF	EF	Unc
NY-NY 780	A	1	WM	—	—	12.50	30.00
	(Miller NY 635)						
NY-NY 780 A	A	1	Copper	—	—	17.50	40.00
NY-NY 780 B	A	1	Brass	—	—	17.50	40.00
	(Wright 821)						
NY-NY 781	B	1	WM	—	—	12.50	30.00
	(Miller 636)						
NY-NY 781 A	B	1	Copper	—	—	17.50	40.00
	Also in Bronze.						
NY-NY 782	E	1	WM	—	—	12.50	30.00
	(Miller 637)						
NY-NY 782 A	E	1	Copper	—	—	17.50	40.00
	(Miller 638)						
NY-NY 782 B	E	1	Brass	—	—	20.00	45.00
NY-NY 783	F	1	WM	—	—	17.50	40.00
	(Miller 639)						
NY-NY 784	G	1	Copper	—	—	20.00	45.00
	Also in Bronze.						
NY-NY 785	H	1	Copper	—	—	20.00	45.00
	Also in Bronze.						

Phelan later became part of the H. W. Collender Co. firm of billiard table manufacturers and thus, in 1884, part of the Brunswick-Balke-Collender Co. (now the Brunswick Corp.)

These are the first known North American tokens to depict a billiard table.

PHOTOGRAPHIC TIMES

Rulau	Date	Metal	Size	F	VF	EF	Unc
NY-NY 245	1889	WM	48mm	—	100.	150.	—
	Bust of Daguerre left, signature C. L. CHAPPELLE under truncation. SOUVENIR OF THE SEMI-CENTENNIAL OF PHOTOGRAPHY / AUGUST 1889. Rv: PRESENTED BY PHOTOGRAPHIC TIMES, N.Y., 1839 — 1889. Plain edge. Though issued without a hole, these usually occur holed. (Gary Pipher report; Johnson & Jensen sale catalogs)						

PIC-NICK & SOMMERNACHTSFEST

Rulau	Date	Metal	Size	F	VF	EF	Unc
NY-NY 250	1876	WM	26mm	—	—	50.00	100.
	Clothed, bearded bust of Lincoln right, LINCOLN above, tiny BOLEN beneath bust. Rv: (In 11 lines): PIC-NICK & SOMMERNACHTSFEST / ABGEHALTEN VON / UNION SAENGERBUND, PH. / ZU EHREN DES / MARSCHNER / MAENNERCHOR N.Y. / MONTAG / 14 AUG. 1876 / AUF / REISTLE'S SAENGERPARK / AD. 25 CTS. Plain edge. (King 612; Miller Pa 399)						
NY-NY 251	1876	Copper	26mm	—	10.00	20.00	40.00
	Liberty Bell. Rv: As 250. Plain edge. (Miller Pa 399A)						
NY-NY 251A	1876	WM	26mm	—	—	—	40.00
	As 251. Plain edge. (Lindesmith coll.)						
NY-NY 251B	1876	Brass	26mm	—	—	—	40.00
	As 251. Plain edge. (Lindesmith coll.)						
NY-NY A251	1876	WM	26mm	—	—	20.00	40.00
	American flag blowing left, LONG MAY IT WAVE above, 13 stars to right below. Rv: As 250. Plain edge.						

Attributed in error to Philadelphia, Pa. by Adams and Miller.

W. PIMMEL

1876 Centennial Tokens

Reverse type 1: * NEW YORK SEWING MACHINE HEADQUARTERS / W. PIMMEL / GENL. AGT. / 191 / GRAND ST. N.Y. (All 23mm; plain edge)

Rulau	Obv	Rev	Metal	F	VF	EF	Unc
NY-NY 790	A	1	WM	—	—	14.00	30.00
	(Miller NY 640)						
NY-NY 791	B	1	WM	—	—	14.00	30.00
	(Miller 641)						
NY-NY 791 A	B	1	Copper	—	—	17.50	40.00
NY-NY 791 B	B	1	Brass	—	—	—	40.00
	(Wright 851)						
NY-NY 792	E	1	WM	—	—	14.00	30.00
	Miller 642)						
NY-NY 793	F	1	WM	—	—	17.50	40.00
	(Miller 643)						
NY-NY 794	G	1	WM	—	—	17.50	40.00
NY-NY 795	H	1	WM	—	—	17.50	40.00
NY-NY 796	J	1	WM	—	—	20.00	45.00
NY-NY 796 A	J	1	Copper	—	—	—	45.00
NY-NY 796 B	J	1	Brass	—	—	—	45.00

F. PRENTICE

Rulau	Date	Metal	Size	VG	F	VF	Unc
NY-NY 255	1867	Silver	32mm	—	35.00	80.00	150.
	Mine buildings at center, F. PRENTICE. MINING 26 PINE ST. around, * NEW YORK * below. Rv: FIRST PRODUCT / BY / MILL PROCESS / IN THE / PAH-RANAGAT / MINING DISTRICT / NEVADA / JANY. 1867. (Wright 1582; Fonrobert 2627; Miller NY 644)						

PRUDEN'S

1876 Centennial Tokens

Reverse type 1: AT / PRUDEN'S / 66 W. 13TH ST. N.Y. / OPP. MACY'S / SCRAP PICTURES / & FIRE WORKS / — A — / SPECIALTY. (All 23mm; plain edge)

Rulau	Obv	Rev	Metal	F	VF	EF	Unc
NY-NY 800	A (Miller NY 646)	1	WM	5.00	8.00	12.50	30.00
NY-NY 800 A	A	1	Copper	—	—	20.00	45.00
NY-NY 800 B	A	1	Brass	—	—	20.00	45.00
NY-NY 801	B (Miller NY 647)	1	WM	—	—	12.50	30.00
NY-NY 801 A	B (Wright 854)	1	Brass	—	—	20.00	45.00
NY-NY 802	E (Miller 648)	1	WM	—	—	12.50	30.00
NY-NY 803	F (Miller 649)	1	WM	—	—	20.00	45.00
NY-NY 804	G	1	WM	—	—	20.00	45.00
NY-NY 805	H	1	WM	—	—	20.00	45.00
NY-NY 805 A	H (Miller 650)	1	Copper	—	—	22.50	50.00

Isaac C. Pruden, wholesale confectioner, appears at 66 West 13th St. in the 1876 directory.

BANCROFT, REDFIELD & RICE

Rulau	Date	Metal	Size	VG	F	VF	Unc
NY-NY 260	(?)	Lead	23mm	—	—	—	V. Rare

BANCROFT. REDFIELD & RICE. NEW YORK between ornamental dashes. Rv: Blank. (Miller NY 56)

Rulau	Date	Metal	Size	VG	F	VF	Unc
NY-NY 261	(?)	WM	23mm	135.	—	—	—

Similar to 56, but NEW YORK in field. Rv: Blank. (Miller NY 56A)

Apparently a predecessor firm to Redfield & Rice, or in some other way related to it.

REDFIELD & RICE

Rulau	Date	Metal	Size	VG	F	VF	Unc
NY-NY 259	(1867-)	Lead	23mm	—	—	Rare	—

REDFIELD & RICE. NEW YORK with a star between two flowers above and below the text. Small eagle in exergue. Rv: Blank. (Miller NY 655)

Redfield & Rice were silversmiths and manufacturers of silver plated ware in New York from about 1867 on. About 1904 Redfield & Rice merged with Apollo Silver Co. and Shepard & Rice to form a new company, Bernard Rice's Sons. The latter firm used the APOLLO SILVER CO. / (fleur-de-lis) and also the QUADRUPLE PLATE / R / (sunrise) logos on its silver plated ware.

RICE

Rulau	Date	Metal	Size	VG	F	VF	EF
NY-NY 265	(1849-54)	Copper	29mm	100.	—	150.	—

RICE / 194 CANAL ST. ctsp on U.S. Large cent. (Hallenbeck 18.511; Brunk 34040)

Samuel N. Rice, daguerreotyper, was at 194 Canal St. 1849-1854. Also known on a silver half-real.

S.W. RICHARDS

Rulau	Date	Metal	Size	VG	F	VF	Unc
NY-NY C265	(?)	Brass	26mm	—	—	35.00	—

Ancient helmeted head right, in high relief. Rv: S. W. RICHARDS, (curved) / 66 W. 23 ST. N.Y. (curved). (Denton Curtis coll.)

JOHN RONAN

Rulau	Date	Metal	Size	VG	F	VF	Unc
NY-NY 266	(1882-85)	CN	29mm	—	—	Rare	—

(All incused): JOHN RONAN / C 10 C / 589 B'WAY. Rv: Same as obverse. Plain edge. (Hartzog coll.)

This piece is similar to that of the Delmonico Brothers, NY 207.

Rulau	Date	Metal	Size	VG	F	VF	Unc
NY-NY 267	(1882-85)	CN	29.5mm	—	—	Rare	—

(All incused): JOHN RONAN / B 25 B / 589 B'WAY. Rv: Same as obverse. Plain edge. (Hartzog coll.)

John Ronan was at 589 Broadway in 1882-1885.

GEO. P. ROWELL & CO.

1876 Centennial Tokens

Reverse type 1: GEO. P. ROWELL & CO. / NEWSPAPER / ADVERTISING / 41 PARK ROW N.Y. (All 23mm; plain edge)

Rulau	Obv	Rev	Metal	F	VF	EF	Unc
NY-NY 810	A (Wright 918; Miller NY 737)	1	WM	—	—	12.50	30.00
NY-NY 810 A	A	1	Brass	—	—	—	45.00
NY-NY 811	B Thick flan. (Miller 736)	1	WM	—	—	12.50	30.00
NY-NY 811 A	B Thin flan.	1	WM	—	—	15.00	40.00
NY-NY 811 B	B (Miller 735)	1	Copper	—	—	15.00	40.00
NY-NY 811 C	B	1	Brass	—	—	—	45.00
NY-NY 812	C	1	WM	—	—	20.00	45.00
NY-NY 813	D	1	WM	—	—	20.00	45.00
NY-NY 814	E (Miller 738)	1	WM	—	—	12.50	30.00
NY-NY 815	F (Miller 739)	1	WM	—	—	15.00	40.00
NY-NY 816	G	1	WM	—	—	15.00	40.00
NY-NY 817	H	1	WM	—	—	15.00	40.00
NY-NY 817 A	H (Miller 741)	1	Copper	—	—	20.00	45.00
NY-NY 818	J (Miller 740)	1	WM	—	—	20.00	45.00
NY-NY 819	K	1	WM	—	—	15.00	40.00
NY-NY 820	*	1	WM	—	—	—	50.00

* Muling of the Theo. J. Harbach card, Philadelphia, with the Rowell card.

H.G. SAMPSON

Rulau	Date	Metal	Size	F	VF	EF	Unc
NY-NY 269	1876	Silver	42mm	—	—	—	500.

Signing of Declaration of Independence, THE / DECLARATION / OF INDEPENDENCE / 1776. Rv: Linen marker at center, inscribed N.G. SAMPSON. Above: H.G. SAMPSON, DEALER IN RARE AMERICAN & FOREIGN COINS, MEDALS & STAMPS. / COR. BROADWAY & FULTON ST. NEW YORK / 1876 / CENTENNIAL / LINEN MARKER / WHOLESALE & RETAIL. Below: MANUFACTORY, / * 91 BUSHWICK AV., BROOKLYN. * / E.D. Plain edge. (Miller NY 770)

Rulau	Date	Metal	Size	F	VF	EF	Unc
NY-NY 269A	1876	Copper	42mm	—	—	—	150.

As 269. Plain edge. (Miller 771)

NY-NY 269B	1876	Brass	42mm	—	—	—	150.

As 269. Plain edge. (Miller 772)

NY-NY 269C	1876	WM	42mm	—	—	—	150.

As 269. Plain edge. (Wright 933; Miller NY 773)

NY-NY 270	1876	Silver	42mm	—	—	—	500.

Bust of Washington right at center, TO COMMEMORATE THE 100TH ANNIVERSARY OF THE above, DECLARATION OF / INDEPENDENCE below. Ornate border around all. Rv: As reverse of 269. Plain edge (Miller NY 774)

NY-NY 270A	1876	Copper	42mm	—	—	—	150.

As 270. Plain edge (Miller 775)

NY-NY 270B	1876	Brass	42mm	—	—	—	

150.As 270. Plain edge. (Miller 776)

NY-NY 270C	1876	WM	42mm	—	—	—	150.

As 270. Plain edge. (Miller 778)

N. J. SCHLOSS & CO.

Rulau	Date	Metal	Size	F	VF	EF	Unc
NY-NY A270	1889	Gilt/C	32mm	—	6.00	11.00	16.50

Seated man and woman above Paris view, EXPOSITION UNIVERSELLE above. Rv: Fame blowing trumpet, REPUBLIQUE / FRANCAISE at left. On a tablet below the allegorical figure is: N. J. SCHLOSS & CO. Plain edge. (This was MV 295 in first edition of this catalog, under Mavericks)

NY-NY B270	(1878?)	Brass	36mm	—	4.00	9.00	14.00

George Washington bust right within central beaded circle. Around: * GEORGE WASHINGTON * / COMMANDER IN CHIEF. Rv: N. J. SCHLOSS & CO. BOYS CLOTHING / IN / COMMEMORATION / OF THE / DEPARTURE / OF THE / CONTINENTAL / ARMY / JUNE 13 / 1778 / * NEW YORK *. Plain edge. (Wright 946)

Rulau	Date	Metal	Size	VG	F	VF	Unc
NY-NY D270	(?)	Brass	Sq 31.5mm	—	—	—	—

Rv: Buffalo Bill Cody mounted right, with rifle. BUFFALO / BILL. Kirtley Oct. 1992 sale, lot 3328)

SCHMITT & KOEHNE

Rulau	Date	Metal	Size	VG	F	VF	Unc
NY-NY 271	(1870's)	Brass	23mm	—	—	150.	—

Coronet Liberty head left. Rv: SCHMITT & KOEHNE / 1 / * GLASS *. Plain edge. Only 3 known.

Schmidt & Koehne ran the Central Park Brewery.

CHAS. SCHOELLER

Rulau	Date	Metal	Size	VG	F	VF	EF
NY-NY 272	(?)	Copper	29mm	—	—	50.00	—

CHAS. SCHOELLER N.Y. ctsp on U.S. 1837 Large cent. (Hallenbeck 19.517; Brunk 35810)

WILLIAM G. SCHULZE

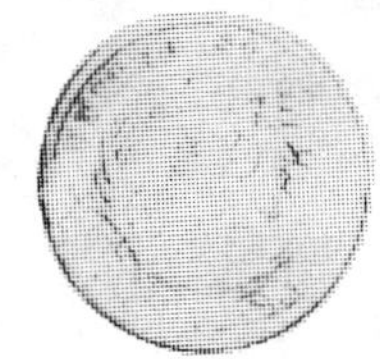

Rulau	Date	Metal	Size	VG	F	VF	EF
NY-NY 273	(?)	Bronze	23mm	—	—	75.00	—

WM. G. SCHULZE / MAKER / NEW YORK ctsp on U.S. 1864 Shield 2-cent piece. (B&M Patterson 1985 sale, lot 1664; Brunk 35830)

The above item, which realized $66 in the March 25-26, 1985 sale, shows evidence on reverse of a similar punch being applied in a 50% larger font of type.

J.W. SCOTT & CO.

Rulau	Date	Metal	Size	F	VF	EF	Unc
Pa-Ph 829	(1870's)	WM	30.6mm	—	125.	175.	325.
	Confederate shield within wreath at center, Liberty cap as crest, CONFEDERATE STATES OF AMERICA above, = HALF DOL. = below. Rv: 4 ORIGINALS STRUCK BY ORDER / OF / C.S.A / IN / NEW ORLEANS / 1861 / ******* / REV. SAME AS / U.S. / (FROM ORIGINAL DIE, SCOTT). Only 500 struck.						

Scott struck this token from the original Confederate half dollar reverse die, muling it with a special die of his own. The token has long been listed in R.S. Yeoman's *A Guide Book of United States Coins* (Red Book) under Confederate States of America.

1876 Centennial Tokens

Reverse type 1: 100 Y'RS OF NAT. IND. / 16 Y'RS / BUSINESS IN / COINS & STAMPS / —*— / J.W. SCOTT & CO. / 146 / FULTON ST. N.Y. (All 23mm; plain edge. Some Scott WM Centennial tokens were issued holed; value 15% less)

Rulau	Obv	Rev	Metal	F	VF	EF	Unc
NY-NY 830	A	1	WM	4.00	7.50	10.00	20.00
	(Miller NY 801)						
NY-NY 830 A	A	1	Copper	—	—	12.50	25.00
	(Miller 799)						
NY-NY 830	B A	1	Brass	—	—	15.00	30.00
	(Miller 800)						
NY-NY 831	B	1	WM	—	—	14.00	26.00
	(Miller 788)						
NY-NY 831 A	B	1	Copper	—	—	15.00	30.00
	(Miller 786)						
NY-NY 831 B	B	1	Brass	—	—	17.50	32.50
	(Miller 787)						
NY-NY 832	E	1	WM	—	—	14.00	26.00
	(Miller 796)						
NY-NY 832 A	E	1	Copper	—	—	15.00	30.00
	Also in Bronze. (Miller 797)						
NY-NY 832 B	E	1	Brass	—	—	17.50	35.00
	(Miller 795)						
NY-NY 833	F	1	WM	—	—	15.00	30.00
	(Miller 791)						
NY-NY 833 A	F	1	Copper	—	—	17.50	35.00
	Also in Bronze. (Miller 789)						
NY-NY 833 B	F	1	Brass	—	—	20.00	40.00
	(Miller 790)						
NY-NY 834	G	1	Copper	—	—	17.50	35.00
	Also in Bronze.						
NY-NY 834 A	G	1	Brass	—	—	20.00	40.00
	(Miller 798)						
NY-NY 835	H	1	WM	—	—	15.00	30.00
	(Miller 794)						
NY-NY 835 A	H	1	Copper	—	—	17.50	35.00
	Also in Bronze. (Miller 792)						
NY-NY 835 B	H	1	Brass	—	—	20.00	40.00
	(Miller 793)						
NY-NY 836	J	1	Copper	—	—	20.00	40.00
	Also in Bronze.						
NY-NY 837	K	1	WM	—	—	15.00	30.00
NY-NY 837 A	K	1	Copper	—	—	17.50	35.00
NY-NY 837 B	K	1	Brass	—	—	20.00	40.00

John W. Scott started his stamp and coin business in New York in 1860. Until at least World War I the Scott firm remained a giant in the coin business, and the name survives today in the Scott line of stamp catalogs (now published by others).

The Scott Centennial tokens are among the most common of these cards. They apparently were made in large variety and good quantity for distribution to customers. Since recipients were collectors, they tended to remain in numismatic channels.

Other varieties than those listed here may exist.

H. SEYMOUR CUTLERY CO.

Rulau	Date	Metal	Size	F	VF	EF	Unc
NY-NY 277	(?)	CN	19mm	—	—	85.00	—
	H. SEYMOUR / CUTLERY CO. / -PATD.- (all within oval) ctsp on U.S. 1857 Flying Eagle cent. (B&M Taylor sale, March 1987, lot 1300; Brunk 35865)						
NY-NY 278	(?)	Bronze	19mm	—	—	60.00	—
	H. SEYMOUR & CO. / PAT. N.Y. ctsp on U.S. 1874 Indian cent. (Brunk 36064)						

SEITZ BROS.

Rulau	Date	Metal	Size	VG	F	VF	Unc
NY-NY 275	(1870's)	Brass	23mm	7.50	20.00	30.00	—
	SEITZ BROS. ONE BIER. Rv: Female head. Plain edge. (Miller NY 807)						

GEO. B. SHARP

Rulau	Date	Metal	Size	VG	F	VF	EF
NY-NY 279	(?)	Bronze	19mm	75.00	—	125.	—
	GEO. B. SHARP / 45 / GOLD STREET / NEW YORK ctsp on U.S. Indian cent. Examined: 1865, 1871, 1874. (Brunk 36170)						

W.G. SINCLAIR

Rulau	Date	Metal	Size	VG	F	VF	EF
NY-NY 280	(?)	Copper	29mm	—	—	90.00	—
	W.G. SINCLAIR / N.Y. ctsp on U.S. 1819 Large cent. (Tanenbaum coll.; Brunk 36660)						
NY-NY 281	(?)	Copper	29mm	60.00	—	90.00	—
	W. G. SINCLAIR ctsp on U.S. 1847 or worn Large cent. (Brunk 36650)						
NY-NY 282	1847	Copper	29mm	75.00	—	100.	—
	W. G. SINCLAIR / 1847 ctsp on U.S. Large cent. (Brunk 36655)						
NY-NY 282A	1847	Silver	27mm	—	—	100.	—
	Similar ctsp on Spanish-American 1816 2-reales.						

William Sinclair is listed as a watchmaker at 21 Chatham St. in 1834. By 1839 he and his son were so listed, the father at 80 Chatham and the son at 90 Chatham.

All these stamps probably belong in the Merchant Token section.

R. SMITH

Rulau	Date	Metal	Size	F	VF	EF	Unc
NY-NY 290	(1870's)	Pewter	23mm	—	—	—	Scrc
	Side-buttoned boot, * CUSTOM WORK * above; CORK SOLES / — * — / A SPECIALTY below. Rv: R. SMITH / BOOTS / — & — / SHOES / 564 BROADWAY, N.Y. Thick planchet. Plain edge. (Wright 1005)						

SMITH & SEWARD

Rulau	Date	Metal	Size	VG	F	VF	Unc
NY-NY 291	(1889-90)	WM	31.5mm	—	15.00	22.50	30.00
	Running horse. Rv: SMITH & SEWARD / MANUFACTURERS / OF / MEDALS / COINS / BADGES / 92 FULTON / 130 & 132 WILLIAM ST. / NEW YORK. Plain edge. (Miller NY 822)						
NY-NY 292	(1889-90)	Alum	31.5mm	—	—	20.00	26.00
	Crowned lion rampant left holding a battle axe, all within a wreath. Rv: As 291. Plain edge. (Wright 1010; Miller NY 821)						

Smith & Seward were successors to Smith & Horst, which earlier had been F. B. Smith & Hartmann and still earlier Bale & Smith. The line of succession in this important 19th century diesinking and minting firm went back to Richard Trested. Thus:

Richard Trested 1821-29 (James Bale his apprentice)
Wright & Bale 1829-33 (Charles Cushing Wright and James Bale)
James Bale 1833-35
Bale & Smith 1835-48 (James Bale and Frederick B. Smith)
Smith & Hartmann 1848-65 (F. B. Smith and Herman Hartmann)
Smith & Horst 1865-? (F. B. Smith and Horst)
Smith & Seward ?-1890's (F. B. Smith and Seward)

STELLING

Rulau	Date	Metal	Size	VG	F	VF	EF
NY-NY 295	(1870's)	Silver	25mm	—	150.	—	300.
	STELLING / 31 / OLD SLIP ctsp on U.S. 1854 or 1857 Seated Liberty quarter dollar. (Schenkman collection; Brunk 38150)						

John Stelling is listed as a liquor dealer at 31 Old Slip during the early 1870's.

HENRY C. STIELER

Rulau	Date	Metal	Size	VG	F	VF	Unc
NY-NY 297	1876	Brass	18mm	—	25.00	35.00	—

HENRY C. STIELER / Large ornate 5 / * 1876 *. Rv: Same as obverse. Plain edge. (Gary Pipher coll.)

STINER TEA COMPANY

Rulau	Date	Metal	Size	F	VF	EF	Unc
NY-NY 300	(1876)	WM	39mm	—	—	20.00	50.00
	Independence Hall, INDEPENDENCE HALL / 1776. Rv: 77 79 81 84 86 / * VESEY ST. N.Y. * / STINERS / N.Y. & CHINA / TEA / COMPANY. / M.H. MOSES & CO. / PROP'S. Plain edge. (Miller NY 838)						
NY-NY 301	(1876)	Copper	39mm	—	—	20.00	50.00
	As 300. (Miller NY 838A) Also known in Bronze.						
NY-NY 302	(1876)	Brass	39mm	—	—	20.00	50.00
	As 300.						
NY-NY 303	(1876)	Alum	39mm	—	—	—	250.
	As 300. Aluminum was a very rare metal at this time. Unique?						
NY-NY 304	(1876)	Leather	39mm	—	—	—	200.
	As 300.						
NY-NY 307	(1876)	Brass	39mm	—	—	20.00	50.00
	Liberty Bell, THE LIBERTY BELL above. Below: LEVITICUS XXV PROCLAIM LIBERTY THROUGH THE LAND UNTO ALL THE INHABITANTS THEREOF * . Rv: As 300. Plain edge. (Wright 1057)						
NY-NY 308	(1876)	Copper	39mm	—	—	20.00	50.00
	As 307.						
NY-NY 308A	(1876)		39mm	—	—	30.00	60.00
	As 307.						
NY-NY 309	(1876)	Bronze	39mm	—	—	20.00	50.00
	As 307.						

This firm was founded in 1840 and also issued tokens in the Merchant period before the Civil War. A Joseph Stiner & Co. Inc. were in the business of groceries, etc. in 1918.

A group of five Stiner Tea Co. pieces in proof, including the aluminum specimen, 303, and another piece struck on leather, 304, was offered by Morty Zerder, New York, in April 1982 for $1,000.

NY-NY 301 is also known in bronze.

In the 1872 directory, Joseph Stiner and Co., tea dealers, are listed in Brooklyn, N.Y., at 255 Grand and at Myrtle Ave. corner Prince.

TIFFANY & CO.

Rulau	Date	Metal	Size	F	VF	EF	Unc
NY-NY 312	(1880's)	Bronze	23mm	—	60.00	—	—
	TIFFANY / & / CO. (tiny punch) ctsp on U.S. 2-cent piece. Examined: 1864, 1868, 1880. (Van Ormer sale 2886' Brunk 40130)						
NY-NY 312A	(1880's)	Copper	29mm	—	60.00	—	—
	Similar ctsp on U.S. 1826 Large cent.						
NY-NY 312C	(1880's)	Bronze	23mm	—	60.00	—	—
	TIFFANY & CO. E. P. ctsp on U.S. 1886 S.L. dime. (Brunk 40140) (E. P. = Electroplate)						
NY-NY 313	(1870's)	Silver	31mm	—	—	100.	—
	TIFFANY & CO., N.Y. ctsp on U.S. 1873 S.L. half dollar. (Brunk 40150)						
NY-NY 313B	(1870's	Bronze	23mm	—	60.00	—	—
	Similar ctsp on U.S. 1868 Shield 2-cent piece.						
NY-NY 313L	(1870's)	Silver	31mm	—	—	450.	—
	TIFFANY & CO. / ASBURY PARK, N.J. / BRADLEY & SMITH BRUSHES, N.Y. ctsp on U.S. 1873 Seated Liberty half dollar. (Brunk 40150/1180/4380)						

Tiffany & Company have been silversmiths and jewelers in New York since 1853, succeeding an earlier firm, Tiffany & Young (1837-53). Charles Tiffany was succeeded by his famous son Louis Comfort Tiffany in 1892. Under L. C. Tiffany (1892-1928), "Tiffany's" became synonymous with the finest in glass, bronze, jewelry, ceramics and silverplate.

All its counterstamps are small.

TRAPHAGEN, HUNTER & CO.

1876 Centennial Tokens

Reverse type 1: TRAPHAGEN, HUNTER & CO. / LEADING CLOTHIERS / FINE GOODS / AT / LOWEST / PRICES / 398, 400 & 402 / BOWERY, N.Y. (All 23mm; plain edge)

Reverse type 2: Similar, but crude lettering. (All 23mm; plain edge)

Rulau	Obv	Rev	Metal	F	VF	EF	Unc
NY-NY 850	A	1	WM	5.00	8.00	11.00	20.00
	(Miller NY 915)						
NY-NY 850 A	A	1	Brass	—	—	14.00	30.00
NY-NY 851	B	1	WM	—	—	12.50	25.00
NY-NY 851 A	B	1	Brass	—	—	20.00	40.00
NY-NY 852	D	1	WM	—	—	15.00	30.00
NY-NY 853	E	1	WM	—	—	12.50	25.00
NY-NY 853 A	E	1	Copper	—	—	15.00	30.00
	(Miller 918)						
NY-NY 854	F	1	WM	—	—	15.00	30.00
NY-NY 855	G	1	WM	—	—	14.00	30.00
	(Miller 917)						
NY-NY 856	H	1	WM	—	—	15.00	30.00
NY-NY 856 A	H	1	Copper	—	—	17.50	40.00
	(Miller 916)						
NY-NY 857	K	1	WM	—	—	15.00	30.00
	(Wright 1155; Miller 915A)						
NY-NY 860	A	2	WM	—	—	15.00	30.00
NY-NY 861	H	2	WM	—	—	15.00	30.00
NY-NY 862	K	2	WM	—	—	15.00	30.00

TRUCK DRIVERS B & P ASSOCIATION

New York, N.Y. ?

Rulau	Date	Metal	Size	VG	F	VF	Unc
NY-NY 325	(1880's)	CN	25mm	—	—	75.00	—

Prancing horse to left within central beaded circle. Around: TRUCK DRIVERS B & P ASSOCIATION. There is a numeral, 176, stamped at bottom. Rv: Blank. Plain edge. (N.Y. Public Library sale, Oct. 30, 1982)

The Truck Drivers Benevolent and Protective Association was apparently an insurance-linked society serving early teamsters. This may have been a fraternal badge.

TRUESDALE

Rulau	Date	Metal	Size	VG	F	VF	EF
NY-NY 330	(?)	Copper	29mm	—	—	—	—

TRUESDALE / N-YORK ctsp on U.S. Large cent. (Hallenbeck 20.756; Brunk 40555)

THE UNION COFFEE CO. LIMITED

Rulau	Date	Metal	Size	VG	F	VF	Unc
NY-NY 340	(1880's)	WM	40mm	—	10.00	25.00	40.00

Female head right, ALAROMA BUNOLA around, MARY ANDERSON below. Rv: UCCo monogram at center, THE UNION COFFEE CO. LIMITED around, * NEW YORK * below. Plain edge.

Rulau	Date	Metal	Size	VG	F	VF	Unc
NY-NY 340B	(1880's)	WM	40mm	—	—	—	—

As 340, but differing head, same name (!), and KOCH & C on truncation of neck. Plain edge. (Jeff Rock coll.)

Rulau	Date	Metal	Size	VG	F	VF	Unc
NY-NY 341	(1880's)	WM	40mm	—	10.00	25.00	40.00

Female head left, ALAROMA BUNOLA around, ADELINA PATTI below. Rv: As last. Plain edge. (Wright 1132)

Rulau	Date	Metal	Size	VG	F	VF	Unc
NY-NY 342	(1880's)	WM	40mm	—	10.00	25.00	40.00

As 341, but ADA REHAN depicted. Plain edge.

Rulau	Date	Metal	Size	VG	F	VF	Unc
NY-NY 343	(1880's)	WM	40mm	—	10.00	25.00	40.00

As 341, but CLARA MORRIS depicted. Plain edge.

Rulau	Date	Metal	Size	VG	F	VF	Unc
NY-NY 344	(1880's)	WM	40mm	—	10.00	25.00	40.00

As 341, but ELLEN TERRY depicted. Plain edge.

Alaroma and Bunola may have been brand names of the coffee U.C. Co. sold.

The Union Coffee Co. Ltd. of New York also issued tokens in hard rubber in the 1890's depicting presidents of the U.S. These also mention Alaroma and Bunola. (See *TAMS Journal* for Oct. 1977, page 182)

Arlie R. Slabaugh reports that these actress advertising pieces also exist in bronze. Possibly all were struck by Koch in New York.

U.C.C. also issued a hard rubber piece depicting Buffalo Bill.

Adelina Patti, the singer, was born in 1843. Ada Rehan played at Daly's Theatre. Patti, then 10, appeared in concert at Tripler's Hall at 677 Broadway, on Sept. 22, 1853.

Adelina Patti-Nicolini owned Craig-y-nos Castle in Wales (see outside back cover of *TAMS Journal* for June 1977)

One contributor reports seeing 25 different U.C. tokens in metal and various colors of hard rubber, but has no details.

VALENTINE & COMPANY

Rulau	Date	Metal	Size	F	VF	Unc	P-L
NY-NY 350	1882	Alum	35mm	—	—	10.00	35.00

VALENTINE & COMPANY / * / NEW YORK / CHICAGO / BOSTON / PARIS / ESTABLISHED / 1832. Rv: THE STANDARD FOR QUALITY / * / VALENTINES VARNISHES (these two words share the VA, N and ES in two lines) / INCORPORATED / 1882. Plain edge. (Wright 1180)

Probably issued about 1900.

ARNOLD VOGT

Rulau	Date	Metal	Size	VG	F	VF	Unc
NY-NY 353	(1882)	Brass	23mm	—	—	25.00	—

Brunswick die BB-2, ctsp C. M. Rv: ARNOLD VOGT / GOOD (5 on beer stein) FOR. All incused. Plain edge. (Thoele coll.)

Arnold Vogt is listed under liquor dealers at 68 Rivington in the 1882 gazetteer.

J.W.

Rulau	Date	Metal	Size	VG	F	VF	EF
NY-NY 360	(?)	Copper	29mm	—	—	50.00	—

J.W. N-Y in relief within rectangular depression ctsp on U.S. 1820 Large cent. (Tanenbaum coll.; Brunk 21335)

The counterstamp appears to be a silversmith's hallmark of New York City.

WASHINGTON INAUGURAL CENTENNIAL

Rulau	Date	Metal	Size	F	VF	EF	Unc
NY-NY 362	1889	WM	26mm	—	—	25.00	40.00

Washington bust right, encircled by thick ornate border. Rv: — — / WASHINGTON / * / INAUGURAL / CENTENNIAL / * 1789 . 1889 * / NEW YORK CITY. Plain edge.

Rulau	Date	Metal	Size	F	VF	EF	Unc
NY-NY 362F	1889	G/Brass	20mm	—	—	12.50	22.50

Washington head right, GEO. WASHINGTON FIRST PRES'T U. S. around, . 1789 . below. Rv: * CENTENNIAL OF HIS INAUGURATION / NEW YORK / APRIL 30, / 1889. Plain edge.

Rulau	Date	Metal	Size	F	VF	EF	Unc
NY-NY 362H	1889	S/WM	24mm	—	—	12.50	22.50

Washington head right within concentric circles of stars and rope. Around: CENTENNIAL INAUGURAL CELEBRATION, NEW YORK / APRIL 30 1889. Rv: Building at center. Around: WHERE HE WAS INAUGURATED FIRST PRESIDENT OF THE U.S. / APRIL 30. 1789 / FEDERAL HALL / WALL ST. / N.Y. Plain edge.

HORACE WATERS & SONS

Rulau	Date	Metal	Size	F	VF	EF	Unc
NY-NY 364	1876	WM	24mm	5.00	6.50	8.00	25.00

Organ of ornate design at center, small cross above organ and around: WATERS' CENTENNIAL CONCERTO ORGAN. .1876. below. Rv: HORACE WATERS & SONS / 481 / BROADWAY / NEW YORK. / PIANOS / & / ORGANS. Plain edge. (Wright 1207; Miller NY 941)

Rulau	Date	Metal	Size	F	VF	EF	Unc
NY-NY 365	1876	WM	24mm	5.00	6.50	8.00	35.00

As 941, but no cross above organ, which is of a different type. (Miller NY 942)

HUGO WELLENKAMP

Rulau	Date	Metal	Size	VG	F	VF	Unc
NY-NY 370	(1863)	Brass	27mm	150.	200.	250.	350.

HUGO WELLENKAMP / COLOSSEUM / x 53 BOWERY. N.Y. x Rv: Blank (intaglio of obverse). All lettering incuse. (Miller NY 946)

Adams lists two pieces, 946 and 947, and says of 947 "Same, inscription, but different die. Brass."

There is little known of this piece or the issuer. It was not listed in the original list of New York City store cards issued in 1885, 1886 and 1887 Coin Collectors Journal. However these pieces were used in the Civil War period as several pieces are from the collection assembled and sold by Doctor George R. Bond on July 18, 1863 and stated by him to be used during the Civil War.

The Fulds were fortunate to have tokens classified by Adams as his 946 and 947. These pieces all are struck by an incuse punch. The planchets are crude, each one being different thickness and some of the edges are rough. It is believed that the punch used in striking these pieces consisted of a slot into which the word COLOSSEUM was inserted. The piece used was no doubt a very crude affair and the pressure used was varied giving different appearances to the pieces. Adams 946 is very thin. There are five minor varieties. Wellenkemp was at 57 1/2 Bowery in 1862 and 53 Bowery in 1863.

E. WELTECK

Rulau	Date	Metal	Size	VG	F	VF	Unc
NY-NY 373	(1876)	Brass	23mm	—	—	—	1 Known.

Coronet Liberty head left. Rv: E. WELTECK / N.Y. / 92 CLINTON ST. Plain edge.

Ernest Welteck operated a beer parlor or a brewery.

I.F.W. (Isaac F. Wood)

Rulau	Date	Metal	Size	F	VF	EF	Unc
NY-NY 395	1877	Brass	21mm	—	—	17.00	27.50

Military bust of Grant right, GENERAL U.S. GRANT around, PRESS 1869 TO '77 (on scroll) below. Rv: TO HIM THAT HATH SHALL BE GIVEN / CIVIS EDINBURGENSIS / AUG. / 31. 1877 / HER / YOUNGEST / BURGESS / I.F.W. / DES. Plain edge.

Rulau	Date	Metal	Size	F	VF	EF	Unc
NY-NY 395A	1877	Copper	21mm	—	—	17.00	27.50

As 395. Plain edge.

Designed by Isaac F. Wood of New York City. The dies were cut by George Hampden Lovett of the same city. Wood is also responsible for the Cogan "English Daddy" pieces of Brooklyn, N.Y., and the Boston Numismatic Society medalet, both catalogued in this reference.

There is an entire series of these pieces that are a pun on Grant's name, e.g. "A civic Grant."

J.G. WILSON

Rulau	Date	Metal	Size	VG	F	VF	EF
NY-NY 380	(?)	Copper	29mm	—	—	55.00	—

J.G. WILSON / GAS FILTER / 30 CENTRE ST. / N.Y. ctsp on U.S. 1850 Large cent. (Hallenbeck 23.539; Brunk 43750)

WOLFE'S SCHIEDAM SCHNAPPS

Rulau	Date	Metal	Size	F	VF	EF	Unc
NY-NY 390	(1868)	WM	26mm	5.00	10.00	15.00	35.00

WOLFES SCHIEDAM SCHNAPPS / FOR SALE / BY ALL / GROCERS / & / DRUGGISTS / *. Rv: DEW OF THE ALPS / AGENT / 22 / BEAVER ST. / NEW YORK. Plain edge. (Wright 1732; Miller NY 956)

At 22 Beaver St. in 1868.

ALFRED WOODHAM

Rulau	Date	Metal	Size	VG	F	VF	EF
NY-NY 393	(?)	Copper	29mm	—	—	35.00	—

ALFRED WOODHAM / NEW YORK ctsp on U.S. 1851 Large cent. (Kovacs coll.)

Y. & CO. (Yuengling & Co.)

Rulau	Date	Metal	Size	F	VF	EF	Unc
NY-NY 400	(1870's)	Brass	22mm	12.00	25.00	50.00	75.00

Liberty head of type of 1857 Large cent, left. Rv: Y & CO. / * 1 * / GLASS. Plain edge. (Miller NY 1006)

Yuengling & Co. were brewers in New York City and this token was good for one glass of their beer.

ZELTNER & CO.

New York, N.Y.

Rulau	Date	Metal	Size	F	VF	EF	Unc
NY-NY 415	(1870's)	Brass	22mm	—	—	17.50	—

Obverse as NY-NY 400 (Y. & CO. Liberty head). Rv: ZELTNER & CO. / * 1 * / GLASS. Plain edge. (Fuld coll.)

Rulau	Date	Metal	Size	F	VF	EF	Unc
NY-NY 415A	1870's	Brass	22mm	—	—	25.00	—

Obverse as 415. Rv: HENRY ZELTNER / * 1 * / GLASS. Plain edge. (Levine-Magriel 1988 sale, lot 1168)

Henry Zeltner and Co. had its brewery at 3rd Avenue and 170th Street in Morrisania (now The Bronx) from 1860 to 1891.

F. C. JOSLIN

North Bay, N.Y.

Rulau	Date	Metal	Size	VG	F	VF	EF
NY-No 1	(?)	Silver	15.5mm	—	—	35.00	—

F. C. JOSLIN / NORTH BAY / N.Y. (in arcs) ctsp on U.S. 1859 Seated Liberty half dime. (Partrick coll.; Brunk 22167)

W.P. DAVIS

North Bloomfield, N.Y.

Rulau	Date	Metal	Size	VG	F	VF	EF
NY-NB 1	(?)	CN	19mm	—	—	225.	—
	W.P. DAVIS / ENGINE CALENDER / & / TILE / MACHINE / MANFR / NO. BLOOMFIELD N.Y. ctsp on reverse of U.S. 1863 Indian cent. Letter 'C' incused six times on obv. of coin. (Tanenbaum coll.)						
NY-NB 2	(?)	Bronze	19mm	—	—	225.	—
	Similar ctsp on U.S. 1875 Indian cent. (Brunk 11030)						

M.L. MARSHALL

Oswego, N.Y.

NOTE: Tokens of this 1862 design are Civil War store cards now listed in the Civil War section.

Morgan L. Marshall also issued 1860-dated tokens in the Merchant era and smaller, 1863-dated pieces in the Civil War period.

OSWEGO STARCH FACTORY

Oswego, N.Y.

Rulau	Date	Metal	Size	VG	F	VF	Unc
NY-Os 20	1873	CN	28mm	25.00	40.00	75.00	100.
	Cornstalk in center, OSWEGO STARCH FACTORY around, 1873. below. Rv: Eagle with drooping wings at top, ONE / BARREL FEED / T.K. in three lines below. Plain edge. Very rare.						

In 1842 Thomas Kingsford invented a process of extracting starch from Indian corn or maize, and became the first person to put into successful operation the method of preparing "corn starch." He incorporated the Oswego Starch Factory in Oswego, N.Y. in 1848. By the 1870's, when the token was issued, the firm had become known as T. Kingsford & Son, Oswego Starch Factory.

A booklet published by the firm in 1876 in connection with the Centennial observances in Philadelphia, where Oswego Corn Starch (edible) and Oswego Silver Gloss Starch (for laundry) won medals, reveals that Dr. S. Willard was president of the firm at that time. Other officers included Nelson Beardsley, vice president, and A.G. Beardsley, secretary and treasurer. Thomson Kingsford was listed among the directors.

The T.K. on the 1873 token stands for Thomas Kingsford. The 'One Barrel Feed' denomination was for semi-liquid "feed starch" used as cattle feed. The token is apparently quite scarce, the author having examined only six different pieces in more than 12 years.

The Oswego Starch Factory appears in the 1890 *Bradstreet Directory,* where it is revealed it had a paid-in capital of $500,000. In 1890 T. Kingsford & Son Inc. is listed as a manufacturer of starches, also. In 1899 Thomson Kingsford formed U.S. Starch Co. from his firm and many smaller ones. In 1900 U.S. Starch Co. and its rival, National Starch Co., united under the latter name. The Oswego branch of National Starch Co. appears in the 1905 and 1909 directories under T. Kingsford & Son. In 1923 it closed.

PHOENIX KNIFE CO.

Phoenix, N.Y.

Rulau	Date	Metal	Size	VG	F	VF	EF
NY-Px 7	(1886)	Silver	18mm	—	—	100.	—
	PHOENIX KNIFE / CO. / PHOENIX, N.Y. ctsp on U.S. 1884 Seated Liberty dime. (Gary Pipher coll.; Brunk 32000)						

The Phoenix Knife Co. was no longer lised in the 1890 *Bradstreet Directory,* though a Central City Knife Co. is, which might be connected.

H. H. BARNARD

Rochester, N.Y.

Rulau	Date	Metal	Size	VG	F	VF	EF
NY-Ro 2	(1863-77)	Copper	18mm	—	—	45.00	—
	H. H. BARNARD ctsp on each side of U.S. 1863 Civil War token of Liberty head / Army & Navy type. (Brunk 2415)						

Henry H. Barnard (1816-78) was a dealer in paints, oils, hardware etc. at 4 Front Street in Rochester. In 1877 he patented a shot cartridge. He died the next year.

SARGENT & GREENLEAF

Rochester, N.Y.

Rulau	Date	Metal	Size	F	VF	EF	Unc
NY-Ro 9	1871	S/Brass	29mm	—	—	35.00	—
	(All incuse) SARGENT & GREENLEAF / PAT'D / SEP. 18. 1860 / JAN. 9. 1866 / AUG. 28. 1866 / JULY 14. 1857 / EX. 7 YEARS / JULY 14. 1871 / ROCHESTER. N.Y. Rv: Blank. Plain edge.						

Sargent & Greenleaf were manufacturers of locks. Presumably the patent dates on the token are for S&G locks. The company is still in business making locking mechanisms for safes.

These pieces were from the lock mechanism on safes, on the cover where combinations were changed, says Norman G. Peters. They could be pried off the old safes.

ROCKAWAY STEEPLE CHASE

Rockaway, N.Y.

Rulau	Date	Metal	Size	VG	F	VF	Unc
NY-Rk 4	1885	Silv/Cop	Irreg 36mm	—	—	50.00	—
	Jockey on horseback clears a hurdle. Around: ROCKAWAY STEEPLE CHASE / MEMBERS BADGE 1885. Rv: Fancy RSA script monogram. Numeral 52 incused below. Issued holed. (Wright 908)						

ROME BRASS & COPPER CO.
Rome, N.Y.

Rulau	Date	Metal	Size	VG	F	VF	Unc
NY-Rm 14	(?)	Brass*	25mm	3.50	5.00	6.50	15.00

* These pieces occur in both Brass and Copper.

NO (backward N) near top center above blank central space; ROME. BRASS & COPPER. CO. around. (Number stamped in center). Rv: ROME. NEW. YORK. along bottom rim. Dentilated rims on each side. Plain edge. Issued holed. (Counterstamps examined: 02; 3; 3 (large); 3 / NG; 4 / SPRING; 9 / SPRING; 10; 10 (Rev: 6); 11 / SPRING; 12; 12 / SOFT; 14; 14 / SPRING; 14 / N.G. / HARD; 16; AR 16 (Rev: G. H, EDG); 18; 19; 20; 20 / B AND / SOFT; 22; 23 / SPRING; 24; 161; 0335) (Rulau-Miller NY 2089)

Rulau	Date	Metal	Size	VG	F	VF	Unc
NY-Rm 15	(?)	Copper	25mm	—	5.00	6.50	15.00

Similar to 14, but N of NO is normal. There is no counterstamped numeral. Plain edge. Issued holed.

Though dates of use of these workmen's or job checks are still not known, it seems probable they were in use after, rather than before, the Civil War.

In 1899 the Rome Brass & Copper Co. had two mills, one for brass and one for copper, in Rome, according to city maps of that year. One rolling mill, for brass, was at Dominick and Bouck Streets, along the Mohawk River. The copper mill and its outbuildings were on both sides of the Black River Canal.

It is probable the work checks were in use in the 1860's or 1870's. They greatly resemble those of the Rome Iron Works, and the work checks in use in Connecticut at the same time period.

ROME IRON WORKS
Rome, N.Y.

Rulau	Date	Metal	Size	VG	F	VF	Unc
NY-Rm 20	(1868-90)	Brass*	24mm	4.50	7.00	9.00	25.00

* These pieces occur in either Brass or Copper.

NO / (blank space) / ROME IRON WORKS. Rv: ROME NEW YORK. Plain edge. Issued holed. Issued without counterstamp.

Rulau	Date	Metal	Size	VG	F	VF	Unc
NY-Rm 22	(1868-90)	Brass*	24mm	4.50	7.00	9.00	—

As 20, but with various counterstamps applied. Specimens examined: 3; 5; 5 / MARKET; 9; 10 / HARD; 10 / SPRING; 14; 15 / SPRING; 16; 17; 18; 19; 20 / SPRING; 21 / SOFT; 22 / NG; 30 / N.G. (Wright 913 was number 17)

* These pieces occur in either Brass or Copper. Several specimens were examined with numbers 14, 16 and 18, in both metals.

Rome Iron Works was founded in 1868. It was still so named in the 1891 *Americanized Encyclopaedia Britannica*. The same firm, called Rome Iron Mills, Inc., manufactures chain link fences today at 416 Canal Street in Rome. It had 125 employees in 1980, but work is seasonal. It is owned by the Oliver family today.

S. A. TELLER
Schenectady, N.Y.

Rulau	Date	Metal	Size	VG	F	VF	Unc
NY-Sy 7	(1882)	Brass	24mm	—	—	25.00	—

Brunswick die BB-2. Rv: S. A. TELLER.

New York City diesinker McNamara struck the distinctive die BB-2, used in Eastern locales.

J. T. SMITH
Schuylerville, N.Y.

Rulau	Date	Metal	Size	VG	F	VF	EF
NY-Sc 2	(?)	CN	19mm	30.00	—	45.00	—

J. T. SMITH ctsp on U.S. Indian Head cent. Examined: 1859, 1863, 1872. (Brunk 37180)

Rulau	Date	Metal	Size	VG	F	VF	EF
NY-Sc 3	(?)	CN	22mm	40.00	—	60.00	—

Similar ctsp on U.S. 1868 or 1869 Shield nickel.

Rulau	Date	Metal	Size	VG	F	VF	EF
NY-Sc 4	(?)	Silver	25mm	—	—	15.00	—

Similar ctsp on U.S. 1854 or 1858 quarter.

This counterstamp has also been reported on an 1876 Half dollar and an 1871 Silver dollar and a wide variety of other coins.

Brunk believes these may be issues of jeweler Joseph T. Smith of Schuylerville, N.Y.

D. SKIDMORE
Seneca Falls, N.Y.

Rulau	Date	Metal	Size	F	VF	EF	Unc
NY-SF 7	(?)	Silver	20mm	—	—	—	—

An eagle with a cigar in its beak, GOOD FOR ONE above the cigar. Around: D. SKIDMORE / SENECA FALLS, N.Y. Rv: SKIDMORE'S / HEAD / QUARTERS / 95 FALL ST. HOTEL. (Wright 990)

Wright called this rare in 1898.

TOM REED
Silver Springs, N.Y.

Rulau	Date	Metal	Size	VG	F	VF	Unc
Ny-Ss 1	(?)	Silver	38.1mm	—	—	75.00	—

TOM REED / SILVER SPRINGS / NEW YORK ctsp in individual letter punches on U.S. 1888 Morgan silver dollar. (PCAC July 1993 sale, lot 929)

This piece fetched $40.70 in the cited 1993 sale.

FIREMAN'S CONVENTION
Syracuse, N.Y.

Rulau	Date	Metal	Size	F	VF	EF	Unc
NY-Sy 6	1885	WM	24mm	—	30.00	—	—

Fire engine, FIREMANS * CONVENTION *. Rv: SYRACUSE / SOUVENIR / AUG. 11-14, 1885. Plain edge. (Wright 1085)

Z. FURMAN

Rulau	Date	Metal	Size	VG	F	VF	Unc
NY-Sy 7	(1882)	Brass	Scal 25mm	—	—	20.00	—

Z. FURMAN / GOOD (5 on beer glass) FOR. Rv: McNAMARA / 64 FULTON ST. (All incused). Plain edge.

Z. B. Furman is listed under liquors in the 1882 Sampson Davenport & Co. gazetteer.

S.M. HENRY
Syracuse, N.Y.

Rulau	Date	Metal	Size	F	VF	EF	Unc
NY-Sy 9	(?)	Brass	**	—	15.00	—	—

** Oval, 32 x 19mm.

Eagle and scrollwork. S.M. HENRY / 484 BASTABLE / CITY. Rv: Blank. Plain edge. (Wright 1451)

The Bastable Block is in Syracuse, N.Y.

CENTENNIAL ANNIVERSARY
Troy, N.Y.

Rulau	Date	Metal	Size	F	VF	EF	Unc
NY-Tr 3	1889	WM	35mm	—	10.00	—	—

Dock scene within circle at center, around: TO COMMEMORATE THE CENTENNIAL AT TROY, N.Y. / ILIUM FUIT TROJA EST ... Rv: Sheaf at center, around: CENTENNIAL / ANNIVERSARY. Plain edge. (Randy Partin coll., Winter Haven, Fla.)

J H
(John Hinkson)
Utica, N.Y.

Rulau	Date	Metal	Size	F	VF	EF	Unc
NY-Ut 6	(?)	Brass	24mm	—	—	—	—

J 5 H / R. Rv: Blank. Plain edge. (Wright 510)

John Hinkson was a saloon proprietor, according to Dr. B. P. Wright in 1898.

J. E. H. KELLY

Rulau	Date	Metal	Size	VG	F	VF	Unc
NY-Ut 9	(?)	GS	**	—	—	—	2 Known

** Oval, 35 x 21mm.

Eagle facing left. Three scrolls beneath: J. E. H. KELLY / KELLY'S HOTEL / UTICA, N.Y. Rv: Blank. Plain edge. (Wright 541)

D. MARC(HISI)

Rulau	Date	Metal	Size	VG	F	VF	Unc
NY-Ut 10	(?)	Silver	18mm	—	—	—	—

D. MARC in relief within toothed rect. depression, ctsp on U.S. 1843 S.L. dime. The impression is incomplete on both ends — the letters showing are merely the central characters in a hallmark. The 'D' is actually just the rightward arc; the upright is missing and this may be another letter entirely. (Partrick coll., ex-S. Steinberg; Brunk 25970)

Tentatively assigned to the Marchisi family of silversmiths of Utica, N.Y. Joseph Marchisi (1802-1874) and Frank W. W. Marchisi (born 1832) are two identified members of the family. They were active in Utica circa 1845-1868.

W.I. MARTIN
Utica, N.Y.

Rulau	Date	Metal	Size	VG	F	VF	Unc
NY-Ut 11	(?)	Copper	35mm	—	—	—	—
	(All incused): MARTINS / 5 / 130 GENESEE ST. Plain edge.						
NY-Ut 12	(?)	GS	29mm	—	—	—	—
	W.I. MARTIN / UTICA / N.Y. / 130 GENESEE ST. Rv: Same as obverse. Plain edge.						
NY-Ut 13	(?)	GS	29mm	—	—	—	—
	W.I. MARTIN / 10 / 130 GENESEE ST. Rv: Same. Plain edge.						
NY-UT 14	(?)	GS	29mm	—	—	—	—
	Similar to 13, but 20. Plain edge.						
NY-Ut 15	(?)	GS	29mm	—	—	—	—
	Similar to 13, but 75. Plain edge.						

D. D. KNAPP
Waverly, N.Y.

Rulau	Date	Metal	Size				
NY-Wv 4	(?)	Bronze	23mm	—	—	40.00	—

D. D. KNAPP, WAVERLY, N.Y. / 10 (circular) ctsp on U.S. 1866 Shield 2-cent piece. (Charles Kirtley Aug. 1987 sale, lot 134; Brunk 23167)

WM. SEDGWICK
Waverly, N.Y.

1876 Centennial Tokens

Reverse type 1: WM. SEDGWICK / WATCHMAKER / — * — / WAVERLY, N.Y. / LOOK WELL TO YOUR TIME. (All 19mm; plain edge)

Rulau	Obv	Rev	Metal	F	VF	EF	Unc
NY-Wv 8	X	1	WM	—	7.50	15.00	40.00
	(Miller NY 1067)						
NY-Wv 8A	X	1	Copper	—	—	15.00	40.00
	(Miller 1067A; Wright 971)						
NY-Wv 8B	X	1	Brass	—	—	15.00	40.00
NY-Wv 9	Y	1	WM	—	10.00	17.50	45.00
NY-Wv 9A	Y	1	Copper	—	—	17.50	45.00
	Also in Bronze.						
NY-Wv 10	V	1	Brass	—	—	30.00	55.00

These are the easiest to obtain of the 19mm tokens in the Centennial series, though all 19mm pieces are difficult in relation to the 23mm tokens.

W. H. EASON
Whitehall, N.Y.

Rulau	Date	Metal	Size	VG	F	VF	Unc
NY-Wh 3	(1880's)	Brass	24mm	—	—	25.00	—

Brunswick die BB-2. Rv: W. H. EASON. (Thoele report)

DEUTSCHLAND'S FRIEDENSFEIER
Williamsburgh, N.Y.

Rulau	Date	Metal	Size	F	VF	EF	Unc
NY-Wm 4	1871	Copper	35.4mm	—	—	—	—

Germania with sword and shield standing on a bluff overlooking the Rhine River, a circle of dots around all. Rv: Small Iron Cross at top. Below: DEUTSCHLAND'S FRIEDENSFEIER WILLIAMSBURGH 10TEN APRIL 1871 (Germany's peace celebration). Plain edge. Weight 14.5 grams.

Designed by Emil Sigel, New York.

Williamsburgh was annexed to Brooklyn in 1855; Brooklyn became a part of New York in 1898. Long after its annexation by Brooklyn, Williamsburgh was still known by that name to its residents and others.

(See Milwaukier Friedens-Feier, Milwaukee, Wis., in this reference.)

A. BELL
Yonkers, N.Y.

Rulau	Date	Metal	Size	VG	F	VF	Unc
NY-Yk 1	(1880's)	Copper	29mm	—	—	300.	—

(All retrograde) YONKES / (script) A. Bell / 1854 amid flourishes, in relief, ctsp on U.S. 1819 Large cent. (The plate token from the Benjamin Betts sale, 1898; it sold in a 1977 auction for $115.). Probably unique. (Miller NY 1069; Miller NY 2323; Brunk 3155)

We have no evidence, but this piece's provenance and its appearance suggest it may have been another of the fantasy concoctions of C. Wyllys Betts (see examples under his name in New Haven, Conn.), and thus we assign an 1880's date to its creation.

Thanks to the kindness of Kenneth Bressett, we examined film negatives of many of Betts' concoctions from the Norweb, ANS and other holdings — all made, presumably, for his own amusement and all rare or unique. Those resembling store cards are included in this reference (see C.W. Betts and Hussey & Murray, New Haven, Conn., and Butler & Bee, East Bay, L.I., N.Y.)

J.W. GASPER
New York (?)

Rulau	Date	Metal	Size	VG	F	VF	Unc
NY-Un 11	(?)	Brass	24mm	—	—	8.00	—

NEW YORK / —*— / BAKERY. / —*— / J.W. GASPER. Rv: GOOD FOR / — 1 — / LOAF / OF / BREAD. Plain edge.

Possibly Canadian.

BULKHEAD

Rulau	Date	Metal	Size	VG	F	VF	Unc
NY-Un 16	(1890)	Brass	25mm	—	—	65.00	—

(All incused): GOOD FOR / 5 ¢ / AT BULKHEAD. Rv: D. W. SEELY / MAKER / DEALER IN BILLIARD / & POOL TABLES / -.- / ELMIRA, N.Y. Plain edge. Only 1 piece known. (Thoele coll., ex-Lou Sutton)

The Bulkhead may have been a New York state saloon. D. W. Seely's cards are among the rarest of billiard tokens.

W. S. HUBBELL
New York ?

Rulau	Date	Metal	Size	VG	F	VF	Unc
NY-Un 12	(1880's)	Brass	24mm	—	—	25.00	—

(All incused): W. S. HUBBELL / 5 (Pool table) / POOL (on the table). Rv: Brunswick die BB-2.

New York City diesinker McNamara apparently made this token. His efforts are being found in the New York City vicinity.

N.Y. & N.E.R.R
New York ?

Rulau	Date	Metal	Size	VG	F	VF	EF
NY-Un 20	(?)	CN	19mm	—	50.00	—	—

N.Y. & N.E.R.R / .MAL (?) & PRESS CO in relief ctsp on reverse of U.S. 1861 Indian cent. Large '72' or '135' in relief on obv. of coin. (The uncertain word in ctsp is struck partly off the flan and is indistinct)

Rulau	Date	Metal	Size	VG	F	VF	EF
NY-Un 21	(?)	Copper	28mm	—	35.00	—	—

Similar ctsp on Canada bank token.

New York and New England Railroad, Engine No. 72 and 135?

J. OSTRANDER

New York ?

Rulau	Date	Metal	Size	VG	F	VF	Unc
NY-Un 25	(1880's)	Brass	24mm	—	—	20.00	—

Brunswick die BB-2. Rv: (All incused): J. OSTRANDER / 5 (large) (Crossed cues and four balls).

Made by McNamara, probably for an East Coast location.

N. Y. N. G. 7TH REGT. (New York National Guard, 7th Regiment)

New York

Rulau	Date	Metal	Size	F	VF	EF	Unc
NY-NL 1	1875	Copper	30mm	—	—	15.00	—

Battle of Bunker Hill Centennial 1775-1875. NYNG 7TH REGT. VISIT.

Rulau	Date	Metal	Size	F	VF	EF	Unc
NY-NL 2	1875	WM	32mm	—	—	25.00	—

Obverse as NY-NL 1. Rv: Script monogram NG, PRO PATRIA ET GLORIA above, all within central circle. Around, in two concentric lines: TO COMMEMORATE THE VISIT OF THE / 7TH REGT. NAT. GUARD / STATE OF N.Y. / TO BOSTON JUNE 17, 1875. Plain edge. (Jim Hirtle coll., Westminster, Md.)

REPORTED NEW YORK STATE BILLIARD TOKENS

The following maverick tokens all use Brunswick die BB-2, which reads: THE / J. M. BRUNSWICK & BALKE (curved) / CO / MONARCH / CUSHIONS / NEW YORK, and is supposed to have been cut in the early 1880's by New York City diesinker McNamara. The name is given as it appears on each token.

These pieces have not yet been located in directories, but the information is furnished here for collector use:

	Name on Token	
John Balz	J. Harris	McGrath & Smith
Barton & Co.	A. Jones	W. S. McKinney
H. E. Bowman	A. O. Kane	O. H. Myer
Cedar Park Hotel	N. Kempf	S. J. Omphalius
C. H. Fowler	J. Krebs	G. G. Passage
A. A. Harpending	Wm. Mann	P. Staeker
		Van Epps & Cook

NORTH CAROLINA

TUCKASEEGE MFG. CO.

Gaston County, N.C.

Rulau	Date	Metal	Size	F	VF	EF	Unc
NC-Gs 3	(1880's)	CN	25.5mm	50.00	80.00	—	—

TUCKASEEGE / (ornament) / M'F'G CO / (ornament) / GASTON CO., N.C. Rv: Large 25 within rays. (Wright 1164)

W. BONITZ

Goldsboro, N.C.

Rulau	Date	Metal	Size	VG	F	VF	Unc
NC-Go 1	(1870's)	Brass	20mm	—	—	60.00	—

W. BONITZ / * / .. x .. / * / GOLDSBORO, N.C. Rv: Numeral 5 surrounded by a wreath, a star in the opening at top. Plain edge.

John Henry William Bonitz, born 1839 in Zellerfeld, Germany, came to Goldsboro 1859, buying out the general store of one Hernglaus. His brother Julius Augustus Bonitz joined him in April, 1861, and the pair also operated a printing business. Julius became a newspaperman after the Civil War, removing to Wilmington, N.C. in 1887. In the early 1870's William, as J.H.W. Bonitz was known, built the Bonitz Hotel but this burned in 1872. In 1876 he opened a restaurant, and then The Arlington (a hotel) in 1882, also known as Bonitz House. Before 1900 William moved to Wilmington, where he ran another hotel and where he died in 1913. The token is probably the work of Koehler of Baltimore.

NORTH DAKOTA

BAER FRANKLIN & BLATT

Sturgis, N. D.

Rulau	Date	Metal	Size	VG	F	VF	Unc
ND-St 1	(?)	—	--mm	—	—	200.	—

Brunswick die BBC-11. Rv: BAER, FRANKLIN & BLATT / STURGIS, D. T.

W. H. BELL

Thompson, N.D.

Rulau	Date	Metal	Size	VG	F	VF	EF
ND-Tm 1	(1884-89)	Brass	25mm	—	100.	—	—

THE / BRUNSWICK / — BALKE — / COLLENDER CO. / (pool table). Rv: GOOD FOR / 5 C / W. H. BELL / IN / TRADE. Plain edge.

Issued in Dakota Territory, according to Hank Thoele. BBC tokens were first issued in 1884 when the partnership was formed. Thompson is in Grand Forks County, North Dakota, but the Postal Guide for 1877 does not list it. Thompson is a very small place — even in 1918 it had only 350 people. North Dakota was made a state in November, 1889.

REPORTED NORTH DAKOTA BILLIARD TOKENS

Following is a listing of unverified attributions for Dakota Territory in what is now North Dakota, for this era. These are given here for informational purposes:

Name on Token	Possible Locale	Billiard Die	Gazetteer
Daily & Falahy	Conway (Walsh County)	BBC-10b	1886-88
H. N. Eddie	Larimore (Grand Forks Co.)	BB-8a	1884
H. N. Eddie	Grand Forks (Grand Forks Co.)	BB-8a	1884-87
Wm. Franklin	Grafton (Walsh County)	Chas. Pick	1884
Peter Haas	Jamestown	BBC	1888
Headquarters	Wahpeton	C. Passow	?
H. C. Jewell	Carpio	BBC-11	1900's
R. Pohl	Jamestown	BB-8b	1884
Shedian House	Bismarck	BB	?

OHIO

GOODYEAR WELT

Akron, Ohio
and Toronto, Canada

Rulau	Date	Metal	Size	VG	F	VF	EF
Oh-Ak 3	(1890's)	Alum	38mm	—	10.00	15.00	—

Scroll entwines grid-marked globe, on which: TRADE / GOODYEAR WELT / MARK / (tiny) C.L.C. Around: * CALL FOR GOODYEAR WELT AND TURNED * / SHOES. Rv: Hand extended upward, on which: FLAX / TRADE MARK. Around, in two concentric circles: SHOES SEWED WITH BARBOUR'S LINEN THREAD WILL NOT RIP / THE BEST FOR SHOP OR FAMILY USE. Plain edge. (Leroux 995X; McColl 129)

Rulau	Date	Metal	Size	VG	F	VF	EF
Oh-Ak 4	(1890's)	Alum	38mm	—	12.50	20.00	—

Obverse as last, except outer inscription reads: NO GOODYEAR WELT SHOES GENUINE WITHOUT THIS TRADE MARK. Rv: As Oh-Ak 3 (Hand, etc.). (Wright 387)

These tokens are claimed both by Canada and the U.S. as, respectively, Canadian and American tokens. Leroux and McColl considered them Canadian because they were distributed by Goodyear Welt's branch in Toronto. Dr. Wright and others have considered them American as they were also distributed in this country.

Oh-Ak 4 is apparently scarcer than 3, based on the number of specimens seen.

W. G. BARNARD

Bellaire, Ohio

Rulau	Date	Metal	Size	VG	F	VF	EF
Oh-Br 1	(1880's)	Brass	19mm	—	—	35.00	—

W. G. BARNARD / COAL / WORKS / * BELLAIR. O. *. Rv: 20 / BUSHELS. Plain edge. (Lot 1354, Brand 1984 sale)

Rulau	Date	Metal	Size	VG	F	VF	EF
Oh-Br 2	(1880's)	Brass	19mm	—	—	35.00	—

Obverse as last. Rv: 200 / BUSHELS. Plain edge. (OH MK-1 in coal scrip reference)

William G. Barnard was active in the 1880's.

A. L. BARON

Bellaire, Ohio

Rulau	Date	Metal	Size	VG	F	VF	EF
Oh-Br 6	1867	Copper	28mm	—	—	55.00	—

A L BARON / DEC / 3 / 1867 ctsp on shaved copper coin, probably a U.S. Large cent. BELLAIRE / OHIO ctsp on shaved opposite side of the coin. The stampings are deep and clear, and all lines but two are curved. However, the letter-punches seem individual, so that the piece may be a personal one. (Krause coll.; Brunk 2512)

C. A. HESCHE

Bucyrus, Ohio

Rulau	Date	Metal	Size	VG	F	VF	Unc
Oh-Bu 3	(1883-88)	Brass	23.5mm	—	—	25.00	—

Crossed goblet, ladle and icetongs in circle. Around: CHAS. PICK & Co. CHICAGO. Rv: GOOD FOR / . 5 C . / C. A. / HESCHE / (Rosette) IN TRADE (Rosette). Plain edge. (Thoele coll; Lipscomb N/L)

Hesche's saloon appears in the 1883 and 1888 gazetteers. The Pick die is one of the earliest used by the company, if not the earliest.

DARINGER & DERR

Canal Dover, Ohio

Rulau	Date	Metal	Size	VG	F	VF	EF
Oh-CD 1	(1883)	Brass	--mm	—	—	15.00	—

Brunswick die BB-6e. Rv: DARINGER & DERR.

JNO. C. HELWIG

Canal Dover, Ohio

Rulau	Date	Metal	Size	VG	F	VF	EF
Oh-CD 4	1876	Silver	31mm	—	—	85.00	—

JNO. C. HELWIG / C. DOVER, O. / 1876 ctsp on U.S. 1876 Seated Liberty half dollar. (Brunk 19140)

Canal Dover is in Tuscarawas County.

DIEBOLD SAFE & LOCK CO.

Canton, Ohio

Rulau	Date	Metal	Size	VG	F	VF	EF
Oh-Cn 3	1871	Brass	27mm	—	—	25.00	35.00

DIEBOLD SAFE & LOCK CO / — / PATENTED / MAY 23, 1871 / — / CANTON, O (all incused). Rv: Blank. Plain edge.

J. KIRCHENSCHLAGER

Chillicothe, Ohio

Rulau	Date	Metal	Size	VG	F	VF	Unc
Oh-Ch 8	(1870's)	Copper	19mm	—	—	—	40.00

Beer stein within wreath (Fuld die 1295). Rv: GOOD FOR / * 5 * / CENTS / AT THE / BAR / J. KIRCHENSHLAGER. Plain edge. (Fuld Ohio 165CL; Lipscomb CH 6430)

Gaylor Lipscomb reports this token is not a Civil War issue, despite its inclusion as such in catalogs over a long period of time. Hetrich-Guttag and Fuld listed it erroneously under Cincinnati.

There are later tokens of this same Chillicothe issuer, probably from the late 1890's. We concur with the Lipscomb findings on Kirchenschlager's tokens.

M. KIRSCH

Chillicothe, Ohio

Rulau	Date	Metal	Size	VG	F	VF	Unc
Oh-Ch 11	(1870)	Brass	22mm	—	—	—	35.00

* PHOENIX HOUSE * / NO. 155 / SECOND ST / ** / M KIRSCH / PROP / CHILLICOTHE, O. Rv: GOOD FOR / —5— / CENTS / —AT— / M. KIRSCH'S / BAR. Plain edge. (Fuld Ohio 160E; Lipscomb CH 6440)

This piece is not a Civil War store card, though listed as such (with reserve) by George Fuld.

SAM'L ACH CO.

Cincinnati, Ohio

Rulau	Date	Metal	Size	VG	F	VF	EF
Oh-Ci 1	(1886)	Brass	Oct 22mm	—	—	7.50	—

SAM'L / ACH / CO. Rv: 2 1/2 amid ornaments. (Emmett Ey coll.)

Wholesale millinery located at 141 and 143 Race Street in 1886.

ATLANTIC BILLIARD HALL

Rulau	Date	Metal	Size	VG	F	VF	Unc
Oh-Ci 2	(1880-86)	Brass	22mm	—	—	10.00	—

ATLANTIC / —*— / H. W. C. / —*— / * BILLIARD HALL *. RV: Large numeral 5 in circle of 16 stars. In tiny letters below: JAS. MURDOCK JR. 165 RACE ST CINTI O. Reeded edge.

Rulau	Date	Metal	Size	VG	F	VF	Unc
Oh-Ci 4	(1880's)	Brass	22mm	—	—	6.50	—

ATLANTIC / * BILLIARD / — / * HALL * / (crossed cue sticks and four balls) / ED. L. LINZ. Rv: Nine stars in an arc above: 5 / CENTS. Plain edge.

In 1889 the Atlantic Billiard Hall, connected with an Atlantic Garden at the same location, was at 245 Vine Street. It was a combination restaurant, saloon and billiard parlor.

'H. W. C.' and Ed. L. Linz were apparently proprietors of the establishment. Dates are estimates.

ULRICH BAUER

Rulau	Date	Metal	Size	VG	F	VF	EF
Oh-Ci 6	(1881)	Brass	22mm	—	—	13.50	—

MADISON PIKE / ULRICH / BAUER / E. WALNUT HILLS / OPP. CINNAMON ST. Rv: GOOD FOR / 5 / CENTS / AT THE BAR / (tiny) JAS. MURDOCK JR. 165 RACE ST. CIN'TI. O. Reeded edge. (Lipscomb CI 0865; Emmett Ey coll.)

This saloon appears in the 1881 directory, according to Emmett Ey. Lipscomb reports it also is listed in the 1909 directory. The style is early.

BELLEVUE HOUSE

Rulau	Date	Metal	Size	VG	F	VF	Unc
Oh-Ci 7	(1876-80)	Copper	--mm	—	—	10.00	—

BELLEVUE HOUSE / CINCINNATI O. Rv: 16 stars in a circle. Plain edge.

Bellevue House was at the head of the Bellevue Inclined Plane railway, which opened for traffic in 1876. Bellevue House was still in business in 1889.

(See Lookout House for a discussion of the resorts on the hills)

Rulau	Date	Metal	Size	VG	F	VF	Unc
Oh-Ci 8	(1870-74)	Brass	22mm	—	15.00	—	—

BELLEVUE HOUSE / 5 / CINCINNATI, O. Rv: Large 5 in circle of 16 stars / (tiny) JAS. MURDOCK JR. 139 W. 5TH CIN'TI, O. (Emmett Ey coll.)

BILLIGHEIMER'S BILLIARD HALL

Rulau	Date	Metal	Size	VG	F	VF	Unc
Oh-Ci 9	(1880-88)	Copper	22mm	—	—	9.50	—

BILLIGHEIMER'S / BILLIARD / HALL / NOS. 210 & 212 / VINE ST / CINCINNATI, O. Rv: Large 5 in circle of 16 stars. Below: Tiny JAS. MURDOCK JR. 165 RACE ST. CIN O. Plain edge.

Rulau	Date	Metal	Size	VG	F	VF	Unc
Oh-Ci 9C	(1880-88)	Copper	22mm	—	—	12.50	—

Obverse as last. Rv: Four-leaf clover in circle of 24 stars. Plain edge.

Rulau	Date	Metal	Size	VG	F	VF	Unc
Oh-Ci 9E	(1886)	Brass	Oct 19mm	—	—	10.00	—

BILLIGHEIMER / 462 & 464 / VINE ST. / CIN. O. Rv: BILLIARDS / 5 / BOWLING / (tiny) JAS. MURDOCK JR. 165 RACE ST CIN. O. (Lipscomb CI 0955; Emmett Ey coll.)

Billigheimer appears at this address in the 1886 directory.

Rulau	Date	Metal	Size	VG	F	VF	Unc
Oh-Ci 10	(1888-89)	CN	22mm	—	—	9.50	—

THE TIEMAN / BILLIARD / HALL / 210 & 212 VINE ST / CIN. O. / D. L. BILLIGHEIMER. Rv: Same as 9 (5 in circle of 16 stars). Plain edge.

David (or Dave) L. Billigheimer was in business with a billiard hall and saloon from 1880 to 1895 at 210 and 212 Vine St. In 1889 he was also operating another saloon at the southeast corner of John and 9th.

The tokens were struck by Murdock.

E. J. BRAUNEIS

Rulau	Date	Metal	Size	VG	F	VF	Unc
Oh-Ci 12	(1880's)	Brass	24mm	—	—	10.00	—

E. J. BRAUNEIS * / * 5 / CINCINNATI, O. Rv: ZOOLOGICAL * / 5 / GARDEN *. Plain edge. (Wright 51)

BURNS FOLZ & SONS

Rulau	Date	Metal	Size	VG	F	VF	Unc
Oh-Ci 14	(?)	Brass	26mm	—	20.00	30.00	70.00

BURNS FOLZ & SONS / GOOD / FOR ONE / 2 / HORSE LOAD / * CINCINNATI OHIO *. Rv: U.S. shield encircled by 16 stars. Plain edge. (Wright 124)

This firm has not been traced. However, in 1889 there was one Amos Burns, contractor for unloading boats, at the southeast corner of 2nd and Broadway, who likely is connected.

This is undoubtedly a drayage check.

RESORTS ON THE HILLS

Closely connected with the development of the inclined plane railways of Cincinnati were the famous resorts and beer gardens atop the hills which these special railways served. On the east on Mount Adams was Highland House, the largest; on the north Lookout House atop Jackson Hill, served by the Mount Auburn Inclined Plane Railway; also on the north Bellevue House served by the Bellevue Inclined Plane Railway, and on the west Price Hill House served by the Price Hill Inclined Plane Railway.

In 1877, historian Henry Howe wrote, "At the summit of these planes are immense beer gardens with mammoth buildings, where on stifling summer nights the city hive swarms out thousands upon thousands of all classes and nationalities, who thus come together and alike yield to the potent influences of music and lager."

LOOKOUT HOUSE

Rulau	Date	Metal	Size	VG	F	VF	Unc
Oh-Ci 30	(1872-76)	Brass	22mm	—	—	10.00	—

GEO. KEMMETER & CO. / (leaf) 5 (Leaf) / CINCINNATI / * / * O *. Rv: LOOKOUT / . / HOUSE / * 5 * / JACKSON HILL. (Miller Oh 17)

Rulau	Date	Metal	Size	VG	F	VF	Unc
Oh-Ci 31	(1872-76)	GS	22mm	—	—	12.50	—

As last, but numeral 20 on each side. (Miller Oh 18)

Lookout House, one of Cincinnati's hilltop resorts and beer gardens, was at the northwest corner of Locust and Mount in Mount Auburn. It was atop Jackson Hill, north of the downtown section of Cincinnati. (Mount Auburn was annexed to Cincinnati in 1870.)

Lookout House was still in business in 1889. The Mount Auburn Inclined Plane railway was opened in 1872, easing the burden of citizens to reach the summit of Jackson Hill and the Lookout House.

J. B. NEEB

Rulau	Date	Metal	Size	VG	F	VF	Unc
Oh-Ci 35	(1870's)	CN	**	—	—	20.00	—

** Oval, 25 x 18mm.

MOUNT AUBURN / —.— / GARDEN / —.— / * CINCINNATI *. Rv: * J. B. NEEB * / 5 / CENTS / * IN TRADE *. Plain edge.

PRICE HILL HOUSE

Rulau	Date	Metal	Size	VG	F	VF	Unc
Oh-Ci 40	(1875-80)	Brass	Oct., 20mm	—	12.50	20.00	—

Eagle. Below, in tiny letters: JAS. MURDOCK JR. 165 RACE ST., CINT'I, O. Rv: PRICE HILL HOUSE / 5 / CENTS. / JOHN ROLF'S. Plain edge. (Wright 1602)

Price Hill House was at the top of the Price Hill Inclined Plane railway northwest of Cincinnati's downtown section. John Rolf later (1889) operated a saloon at the northwest corner of 8th and Matson Place on Price Hill.

Price Hill Inclined Plane railway was opened in 1875.

CINCINNATI INDUSTRIAL EXPOSITION

Rulau	Date	Metal	Size	F	VF	EF	Unc
Oh-Ci 50	1870	WM	26mm	—	—	15.00	22.50

Exposition building (Saengerfest Hall) at center, date 1870 below. Around: * CINCINNATI INDUSTRIAL EXPOSITION. Rv: UNDER THE AUSPICES / OF THE / CHAMBER, / OF / COMMERCE / —o— / BOARD OF TRADE / & OHIO MECHANICS' / INSTITUTE. Plain edge.

(See Russ Rulau's "The Early Tokens of the Queen City, Cincinnati," in the *TAMS Journal* for April 1974.)

The very first Cincinnati Industrial Exposition is honored on this token. It was held Sept. 21 through Oct. 22, 1870, with 300,000 persons in attendance. The exposition building occupied the site of the future Music Hall in Cincinnati.

Rulau	Date	Metal	Size	F	VF	EF	Unc
Oh-Ci 52	1871	WM	26mm	—	—	15.00	22.50

Buildings at center, INDUSTRIAL / 1871 above, EXPOSITION / . / CINCINNATI below. Rv: CHAMBER OF COMMERCE / BOARD / OF TRADE / OHIO MECHANICS / INSTITUTE / TOTAL EXHIBITING / SPACE / 289,094. FEET. Plain edge.

Rulau	Date	Metal	Size	F	VF	EF	Unc
Oh-Ci 52A	1871	WM	26mm	—	—	—	—

As 52. Reeded edge.

The second Cincinnati Industrial Exposition, also on the site of the future Music Hall, was held Sept. 6 through Oct. 8, 1871. Though well attended, the exposition lost $14,000 which had to be repaid by its guarantors.

Rulau	Date	Metal	Size	VG	F	VF	Unc
Oh-Ci 53	1871	WM	26mm	—	—	15.00	—

Obverse as 52. Rv: UNDER THE AUSPICES OF THE / CHAMBER / OF / COMMERCE / . . . . / 145000 / FT / BOARD OF TRADE / & OHIO MECHANICS / INSTITUTE. Plain edge.

Rulau	Date	Metal	Size	F	VF	EF	Unc
Oh-Ci 54	1872	WM	31mm	—	—	15.00	22.50

CINCINNATI / 1872 / (view of exposition) / INDUSTRIAL / EXPOSITION. Rv: Monogram CIE in central circle. Lettered scroll below. In two concentric lines around: BOARD OF TRADE CHAMBER OF COMMERCE / & OHIO MECHANICS INSTITUTE. Reeded edge.

Rulau	Date	Metal	Size	F	VF	EF	Unc
Oh-Ci 55	1872	WM	31mm	—	—	—	—

Obverse similar to 54. Rv: Very large monogram CIE within 4-lobed cartouche at center. Inscription around: THE ARTS. SPACE EIGHT ACRES / OF MANUFACTURES BY . . . . Reeded edge.

Rulau	Date	Metal	Size	F	VF	EF	Unc
Oh-Ci 56	1872	WM	31mm	—	—	15.00	22.50

Obverse as 54. Rv: Very large monogram CIE within 4-lobed cartouche at center. Inscription around: THE ARTS. SPACE EIGHT ACRES / OF MANUFACTURES BY . . . . Reeded edge.

Rulau	Date	Metal	Size	F	VF	EF	Unc
Oh-Ci 56C	1872	WM	31mm	—	—	15.00	22.50

Obverse as 54. Rv: Within wreath: OHIO / — / MECHANICS / — INSTITUTE. Around: BOARD OF TRADE, CHAMBER OF COMMERCE. Plain edge.

Rulau	Date	Metal	Size	F	VF	EF	Unc
Oh-Ci 57	1873	?	28.5mm	—	—	25.00	—

Obverse similar to last, but legends differ. CINCINNATI INDUSTRIAL above, * EXPOSITION * / —*— / 1873 below. Tiny W. W. SPENCER CINCINNATI along lower rim. Rv: Ohio River bridge at center, COVINGTON & CINCINNATI / BRIDGE above, * LENGTH 2200 FT. * / MAIN SPAN 1020 FT. / HIGTH (sic) 100 FT / —o— / COST $2000000. Plain edge.

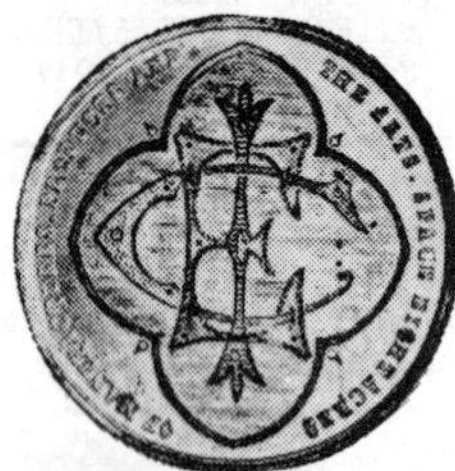

Rulau	Date	Metal	Size	F	VF	EF	Unc
Oh-Ci 58	1873	?	28.5mm	—	—	—	—

Obverse as 55, but date 1873. Rv: As reverse of 56 (CIE monogram in 4-lobed cartouche). Plain edge.

Rulau	Date	Metal	Size	F	VF	EF	Unc
Oh-Ci 59	1873	Gilt/B	28.5mm	—	—	11.00	17.50

* CINCINNATI * / (view of exposition) / —INDUSTRIAL— / 1873. / EXPOSITION. Rv: SEAL OF CINCINNATI / JUNCTAJUVANT / (scales above crossed sword and caduceus) / * 1873. * Plain edge.

The fourth exposition was held September 3 to October 4, 1873 on the site of the future Music Hall. Another financial failure, it needed $15,000 to meet its obligations.

Oh-Ci 60 1874 ? 31mm — — 10.00 15.00
Obverse similar to 57, but date 1874. Rv: Female personification of Knowledge with arms outstretched, facing. Above: MANUFACTURERS PRODUCTS & THE ARTS. In exergue: CT monogram (for diesinker C. Theiler).

Oh-Ci 61 1879 WM 31mm — — 10.00 15.00
Music Hall at center, tiny MURDOCK CIN'TI below the ground line. Above: CINCINNATI INDUSTRIAL. Below: * EXHIBITION * / (beehive at center of branches). Rv: Names of sponsoring groups and 15 commissioners crowded in the field.

Oh-Ci 61A 1879 Copper 31mm — — 13.00 18.00
As 61.

Oh-Ci 63 1881 WM 31mm — — — —
Obverse as 61. Rv: Similar to 61, but date 1881 and some names are changed. (This token was struck by Murdock on the exposition grounds.).

Oh-Ci 64 1883 WM 31mm — — — —
Obverse as 61 (Music Hall). Rv: ELEVENTH / CINCINNATI / INDUSTRIAL / 1883 / EXPOSITION / OF / MANUFACTURES, INVENTIONS / ART / PRODUCTS.

Oh-Ci 65 1884 WM 31mm — — — —
Obverse as 61 (Music Hall). Rv: CINCINNATI / INDUSTRIAL / EXPOSITION / TWELFTH NATIONAL / EXHIBIT / OF / INDUSTRY & ART.

Oh-Ci A65 1884 Brass 26mm — — — —
Buildings at center. In exergue: CINCINNATI / INDUSTRIAL / EXPOSITION. Rv: Same as reverse of Oh-Ci 65. Plain edge.

Oh-Ci 66 1884 GB 25mm — — 8.00 11.00
TWELFTH / CINCINNATI (on scroll) / INDUSTRIAL (on scroll) / EXPOSITION. / 1884. Rv: LORD'S PRAYER / (Lord's prayer within central circle) / SMALLEST EVER COINED. Tiny MURDOCK — CINCINNATI at sides. Plain edge.

This piece is very similar to Murdock's reverse for the Langdon Bakery 'Widow's Mite' token (which see under Cincinnati). But the Langdon piece is much smaller!

Oh-Ci 67 1888 AC Oct 29mm — — 15.00 22.50
CENTENNIAL EXPOSITION / AT CINCINNATI O. U.S. A JULY 4 TO OCT. 27 (Statue in center with dates 1788-1888) Rv: A SOUVENIR / OF THE / EXPOSITION / IN COMMEMORATION OF THE SETTLEMENT OF THE OHIO VALLEY AND THE CENTRAL STATES (old Fort Washington in center) Octagonal.

Made by Murdock.

Oh-Ci 67A 1888 WM 29mm — — 15.00 22.50
Octagonal.

CRELLIN'S PLACE

Rulau	Date	Metal	Size	VG	F	VF	Unc
Oh-Ci 69	(1889-91)	Copper	19mm	—	—	6.50	—

GOOD FOR / * 5 ¢ * / CRELLIN'S PLACE. Rv: Large 5 in circle of 16 stars. Plain edge. (Lipscomb CI 1695)

William F. Crellin kept a saloon at the northeast corner of 6th and Culvert from the late 1880's to about 1909.

CREW'S PYRAMIDAL RAILWAY

Rulau	Date	Metal	Size	F	VF	EF	Unc
Oh-Ci 70	1871	WM	26mm	—	—	20.00	35.00

CREW'S PYRAMIDAL RAILWAY AT / INDUSTRIAL EXPOSITION / (car) / CIN O' / 1871. / AS A / STEAM CAR. Rv: CREW'S PYRAMIDAL RAILWAY / AT/INDUSTRIAL/EXPOSITION / (car) / CIN. O — 1871 / AS A / VELOCIPEDE. Plain edge. (Wright 213; Miller Oh 6)

Oh-Ci 71 1871 WM 26mm — — 25.00 40.00
Obverse as Oh-Ci 52 (buildings). Rv: As Oh-Ci 68 (velocipede). Plain edge.

Oh-Ci 71A 1871 Copper 26mm — — — 50.00
As 69. Plain edge.

Rulau	Date	Metal	Size	VG	F	VF	Unc
Oh-Ci 72	1871	WM	26mm	—	—	—	40.00

Obverse as 71. Rv: Similar to obverse of 70 (ear, edge on to viewer).

LOUIS DOLL'S GARDEN

Rulau	Date	Metal	Size	VG	F	VF	Unc
Oh-Ci 73	(1886)	Brass	26mm	—	5.00	—	—

LOUIS DOLL'S GARDEN / 5 ¢ / IN TRADE/. Rv: Blank. (Emmett Ey coll.)

Saloon, listed in 1886 at 520 Walnut St.

THEO. M. FOUCAR

Rulau	Date	Metal	Size	VG	F	VF	Unc
Oh-Ci 75	(1904-13)	Brass	25mm	—	—	8.00	—

THEO. M. FOUCAR. / * * * / 5 / 429 WALNUT / *. Rv: Large 5 in circle at center, eight stars around. (R-F Soh-2; Lipscomb C1 2305)

Theo. M. Foucar appears in Cincinnati directories of 1889, 1909 and 1918 as a saloon-keeper and liquor dealer. By 1889 Foucar's saloon was at 49 Main St.

The token was made by Gregg G. Wright.

CHAS. FRISCHE

Rulau	Date	Metal	Size	VG	F	VF	Unc
Oh-Ci 76	(1886)	Brass	21mm	—	—	30.00	—

CHAS. FRISCHE / SALOON / N. W. COR. LINN / & LIBERTY / STS / CIN'TI. Rv: (9 stars) / 5 / CENTS / (tiny) JAS. MURDOCK JR. 165 RACE ST. CIN'TI. O. (Emmett Ey coll.)

Saloon, in 1886 directory.

GALT HOUSE

Rulau	Date	Metal	Size	VG	F	VF	Unc
Oh-Ci 78	(?)	Copper	29mm	—	—	150.	—

GALT / HOUSE ctsp on U.S. 1857 Large cent. Brunk 15590; Rulau MV 107)

This token has been attributed to the Galt House hotel in St. Joseph, Utah, which issued paper scrip and has been consigned to the Maverick section of the post-CW era.

We have now decided it must have emanated from the famed Galt House of Cincinnati, at the corner of 6th and Main Streets.

Vulcanite tokens of the Galt House were issued in 32mm size by proprietor George Weber, listed by Lipscomb as C1 2415, very rare.

GERMANIA HOUSE

Rulau	Date	Metal	Size	VG	F	VF	Unc
Oh-Ci 80	(ca 1889)	Brass	24mm	—	—	9.50	—

J. M. KEIBER PRO / * / 89 & 91 / SYCAMORE ST. / * / GERMANIA HOUSE. Rv: Large 5 in circle of 16 stars. Plain edge. (Wright 538; Lipscomb C1 3540)

Germania House is listed at 89 Sycamore in the 1889 directory.

GRAND HOTEL
(A. G. Corre Hotel Co.)

Rulau	Date	Metal	Size	F	VF	EF	Unc
Oh-Ci 81	1879	WM	39mm	—	—	25.00	35.00

Music Hall at center, + SEVENTH CINCINNATI + / INDUSTRIAL above, EXPOSITION / * 1879 * / MANUFACTURES, PRODUCTS AND THE ARTS below. Rv: CINCINNATI'S / THE A. G. CORRE HOTEL CO. / GOOD / —FOR— / ONE MEAL / AMERICAN / PLAN / . . .TER'S / GRAND HOTEL. Plain edge.

Rulau	Date	Metal	Size	F	VF	EF	Unc
Oh-Ci 82	1879 (80's)	WM	39mm	—	—	—	15.00

Obverse as 81. Rv: MADE / FROM / ORIGINAL / DIE. Plain edge.

The second piece is probably a Murdock diesinker advertising token made after 1879.

GRAY'S BANKRUPT STORE

Rulau	Date	Metal	Size	VG	F	VF	Unc
Oh-Ci 83	(1870's)	GS	19mm	12.50	20.00	40.00	—

AT GRAY'S / —**— / BANKRUPT / —**— / *STORE*. Rv: A wreath encloses GOOD FOR / TEN CENTS. Around: Tiny JAS. MURDOCK, JR., 165 RACE ST., CIN., O. (Wright 401; Miller Oh 16)

HAVLIN BARBER SHOP
Cincinnati, Ohio (?)

Rulau	Date	Metal	Size	VG	F	VF	Unc
Oh-Ci 88	(1866-71)	Brass	26mm	—	—	7.50	—

THE HAVLIN / SHINE / — 10 — / CENTS / BARBER SHOP. Rv: (In central circle: JOS. J. SAYRE / —*— / MAKER / S.E. COR. / 4TH / & WALNUT STS. Cin. O. Plain edge.

HERMAN H. HEYNE

Rulau	Date	Metal	Size	VG	F	VF	Unc
Oh-Ci 91	(1897-1900)	Brass	26mm	—	—	12.50	—

HERMAN H. HEYNE * / (star) / CINCINNATI, O., *. Rv: Large numeral 5 in circle of 31 stars. Plain edge. (Wright 448)

Cigar maker.

HOTEL SAVOY

Rulau	Date	Metal	Size	VG	F	VF	Unc
Oh-Ci 93	(1897-1909)	Brass	25mm	12.00	20.00	25.00	—

Rampant lion right, holds scroll reading HOTEL / SAVOY. Below: 2 1/2 (in circle) / CINCINNATI (on scroll). Rv: U.S. shield within circle of 16 6-pointed rosettes. Plain edge. Very scarce. (Lipscomb C1 3165)

EDWARD HUGO

Rulau	Date	Metal	Size	VG	F	VF	Unc
Oh-Ci 94	(1880-88)	Brass	25mm	—	—	8.00	—

Large monogram EH at center, EDW. HUGO above, WARNER & VICTOR. below. Rv: Large 5 in circle, eight stars around. At bottom: Tiny WRIGHT & SON. (Lipscomb C1 3210)

Still in business 1913.

JOS. KAMP

Rulau	Date	Metal	Size	VG	F	VF	Unc
Oh-Ci 97	(1886)	Copper	22mm	10.00	—	—	—

JOS. KAMP / (Jug) / 283 VINE ST. Rv: Large 5 within circle of 16 stars / (tiny) JAS. MURDOCK JR 165 RACE ST. CIN. O. (Lipscomb CI 3515; Emmett Ey coll.)

This saloon is listed in the 1886 directory.

KRAFT & BAUER

Rulau	Date	Metal	Size	VG	F	VF	Unc
Oh-Ci 99	(1904)	Copper	25mm	—	—	9.50	—

KRAFT & BAUER / COLONNADE / 522 VINE ST. Rv: Large 5 in circle, eight stars around. (Lipscomb C1 3735)

Wright struck this token.

LANGDON BAKERY

Rulau	Date	Metal	Size	VG	F	VF	Unc
Oh-Ci 101	(ca 1884)	Brass	13mm	—	—	5.00	8.50

LANGDON BAKERY / WIDOWS / MITE / *CINCINNATI *. Rv: LORD'S PRAYER / (Lord's prayer within a central circle) / SMALLEST EVER COINED. Tiny MURDOCK — CINCINNATI at sides. Plain edge.

Rulau	Date	Metal	Size	VG	F	VF	Unc
Oh-Ci 101A	(1890)	Alum	13mm	—	—	7.00	10.50

As 101. Plain edge.

Sol. Langdon and Son Co., 23-33 Lock St., in 1889 were listed as wholesale bread, cake and cracker bakers. Langdon must have been a numismatist — the "widow's mite" is a tiny copper piece (a lepton) of Biblical times in Palestine, the Bible donation of an old widow.

LICENSED CINCINNATI

Rulau	Date	Metal	Size	VG	F	VF	Unc
Oh-Ci 108	1866	Brass	19mm	—	—	15.00	—

LICENSED / NO. ---- / CINCINNATI, O. / 18 + 66. Rv: Within central circle: MURDOCK & SPENCER / 139 / W FIFTH / STREET / CINCINNATI. Plain edge. Rarity 6. (Fuld NC-11b) Issued holed at top. Also issued with numeral stamped after NO.; in the case of the illustrated specimen 3495.

A Cincinnati dog tag of 1866.

Rulau	Date	Metal	Size	VG	F	VF	Unc
Oh-Ci 109	1871	Brass	**	—	—	50.00	—

** Irregularly oval in shape, somewhat resembling a shoe sole.
LICENSED / No. (incused numeral) / CINCINNATI, 1871. Rv: Within circle: JAS. MURDOCK JR. / STAMPS / BURNING / BRANDS / STENCILS / 139 / W. 5' ST. CINCINNATI. (Emmett Ey coll.)

A Cincinnati dog tag of 1871.

ED L. LINZ

Rulau	Date	Metal	Size	VG	F	VF	Unc
Oh-Ci 110	1882	Copper	26mm	—	—	10.00	—

Male bust within border of stars, 1882 under truncation of bust. Rv: GANO BILLIARD HALL / ED L. LINZ / (crossed cuesticks and balls) 252 VINE ST / CINCINNATI, O. (Lipscomb CI 3995; Emmett Ey coll.)

See Oh-Ci 4 for another Linz token.

LION BUGGY CO.

Rulau	Date	Metal	Size	F	VF	EF	Unc
Oh-Ci 20	(?)	Brass	34mm	7.50	11.50	—	—

Facing lion head, LION BUGGY CO. below. RV: Anchor, with anchor rope around in wreath fashion. Plain edge. (Rulau MV 185)

Small (18-19mm) brass buttons with the Lion Buggy Company's lion's-head emblem were also issued, and these bear the firm's location in Cincinnati — leading to the discovery of just where LBC should be placed geographically. A Madison, Wis. coin dealer enabled us to remove this listing from the first edition's maverick section.

Rulau	Date	Metal	Size	F	VF	EF	Unc
Oh-Cii 21	(1890's)	Brass	34mm	7.50	11.50	—	—

Obverse as 20. Rv: As 20, but Anchor / Buggy Co. appears on the anchor. Along bottom rim: (tiny) W & H Co. Newark N.J. Plain edge. (William Passick coll.)

T. LOVELL

Rulau	Date	Metal	Size	VG	F	VF	Unc
Oh-Ci 114	(1870's)	CN	25mm	—	—	12.50	—

(Ornament) THIS IS (ornament) / THE METAL / THAT / T. LOVELL'S / FORKS & SPOONS / ARE / .PLATED ON. Rv: Blank. Reeded edge. (Wright 622)

Rulau	Date	Metal	Size	VG	F	VF	Unc
Oh-Ci 116	(1870's)	CN	25mm	—	—	14.00	—

Obverse as last. Rv: (All incuse) 5TH & RACE / (ornament) / CIN. O. Reeded edge.

Thomas Lovell was a silverware and jewelry manufacturer.

MABLEY & CAREW

Rulau	Date	Metal	Size	F	VF	EF	Unc
Oh-Ci 119	(1888)	WM	39mm	—	—	22.50	30.00

Music Hall at center, CENTENNIAL above, SOUVENIR below. Rv: * MABLEY & CAREW * / —.— / SHOES / CLOTHING / HATS. / —.— / OPP. FOUNTAIN, CIN. PLAIN EDGE.

Mabley & Carew department store, still opposite Davidson Fountain in downtown Cincinnati, merged with a larger store chain in the 1970's.

CHRISTIAN MOERLEIN BREWING CO.

Rulau	Date	Metal	Size	VG	F	VF	Unc
Oh-Ci 121	1881	Brass	21mm	—	—	40.00	—

THE CHRISTIAN MOERLEIN BREWING CO. (circular) / 1881. Rv: GOOD FOR / 1 / GLASS BEER / (tiny) JAS. MURDOCK JR 165 RACE ST CIN'TI O. (Emmett Ey coll.)

NELSON'S BUSINESS COLLEGES

Cincinnati, Ohio and Springfield, Ohio

Rulau	Date	Metal	Size	VG	F	VF	Unc
Oh-Ci 125	(1870-85)	GS	18.5mm	—	—	20.00	—

NELSON'S / BUSINESS / —.— / COLLEGES / CINCINNATI / AND / * SPRINGFIELD, O. * . Rv: Large numeral 5 within circle of 15 stars. Dentilated rim on each side. Plain edge. Rarity 9.

Rulau	Date	Metal	Size	VG	F	VF	Unc
Oh-Ci 127	(1870-85)	Brass	18.5mm	—	—	—	10.00

Obverse as last. Rv: Large numeral 1 within circle of 16 stars. Below, in tiny letters: JAS MURDOCK 165 RACE ST. CIN O. Dentilated rim on each side. Plain edge. Rarity 8.

Rulau	Date	Metal	Size	VG	F	VF	Unc
Oh-Ci 128	(1870-85)	GS	26mm	—	—	20.00	—

Obverse as 125. Rv: Large 50 within circle of 14 stars. (Emmett Ey coll.)

In 1876, Horatio Nelson's college in Cincinnati was at the southeast corner of 4th and Vine Streets, downtown.

In 1870, Nelson's College issued a series of "college currency" scrip notes signed by Richard Nelson, president.

OCEAN HOUSE

Rulau	Date	Metal	Size	F	VF	EF	Unc
Oh-Ci 129	1883	GS	21.6mm	—	—	15.00	25.00

Clasped hands, —5— / C. SCHMELZ above, 1883 below. Rv: OCEAN HOUSE / 446 & 448 / ELM ST. / * CIN. O. *. Plain edge. (Tanenbaum coll.; Lipscomb C1 5719)

E.L. PAYTON

Rulau	Date	Metal	Size	VG	F	VF	Unc
Oh-Ci 132	(1881)	GS	22mm	—	—	15.00	—

E.L. PAYTON / 159 / RACE ST., CIN., O. Rv: TWO DRINKS / 2 1/2 / FOR / TWENTY-FIVE CENTS. (Wright 806; Lipscomb C1 5008)

JNO. POST

Rulau	Date	Metal	Size	VG	F	VF	Unc
Oh-Ci 140	(1883-88 ?)	Brass	24.5mm	—	—	15.00	—

(All incused): JNO. POST / GOOD FOR / 5 C / DRINK / (ornament). Rv: Blank. Dentilated rim on each side. Plain edge. (Lipscomb N/L)

John Post reputedly was a saloonkeeper circa 1883-88. Reputedly Chicago.

HENRY PROBASCO

Rulau	Date	Metal	Size	F	VF	EF	Unc
Oh-Ci 138	1871	Nickel	26mm	17.50	22.50	30.00	37.50

DAVIDSON FOUNTAIN / (fountain spewing water and showing six statuary groups) / PATENT PENDING. Rv: TO THE / —o— / PEOPLE / — OF — / CINCINNATI / 1871. / TYLER HENRY/ DAVIDSON. PROBASCO. (all within circle). Reeded edge. (Wright 231)

The Tyler Davidson fountain, on the 5th Street Esplanade, was donated to the city of Cincinnati by Henry Probasco, in honor of his brother-in-law, Tyler Davidson. It still stands. The bronze fountain was unveiled October 6, 1871, during the Second Cincinnati Industrial Exposition (Sep. 6-Oct. 8, 1871). The statue cost $200,000; the 400 by 60 foot esplanade another $75,000.

Standing 38 feet high, the fountain contains 24 tons of bronze and 85 tons of porphyry. Central statue on top is the "Genius of Water." It was cast at Royal Bavarian Bronze Foundry, Munich, by Ferdinand von Mueller.

Probasco, penniless in youth, was a patron of arts and literature, whose magnificent chateau in the Clifton section was the envy of the Prince of Wales, Jenny Lind, Charles Dickens, Thackeray and singer Christine Nilsson, all of whom visited it. His painting collection was valued at $200,000.

It is a little known fact that Probasco declared bankruptcy December 13, 1897.

Tyler Davidson was a leading Cincinnati hardware and cutlery merchant. In the 1857 directory Tyler Davidson & Co. was at 140 and 142 Main St.

L. RAUCH'S BAKERY

Rulau	Date	Metal	Size	VG	F	VF	Unc
Oh-Ci 141	(1867)	Brass	Oct 22mm	—	—	75.00	—

(Ornaments) / L. RAUCH'S / BAKERY / (ornaments). Rv: Within circle: MURDOCK & SPENCER 139 W. 5TH STREET CINCINNATI. Plain edge. (Emmett Ey coll.)

Listed in 1867 *Williams Directory.*

REINHART BROS.

Rulau	Date	Metal	Size	VG	F	VF	Unc
Oh-Ci 143	(?)	CN	34mm	—	—	20.00	—

(All lettering incuse on both sides). REINHART BROS. / 5 / 463 VINE ST. Rv: MUSICAL / EXCHANGE. Plain edge. (Lipscomb C1 5310)

LOUIS REINHART

Rulau	Date	Metal	Size	VG	F	VF	Unc
Oh-Ci 144	(1886)	Brass	Oct 19mm	—	—	10.00	—

LOUIS REINHART / 78 / W/ 6TH / ST / CINCINNATI, O. Rv: Large 5 within circle of 16 stars / (tiny) JAS. MURDOCK JR. 165 RACE ST. CIN'TI, O. (Lipscomb CI 5320; Emmett Ey coll.)

Saloon, listed in 1886 *Williams Directory.*

YANKEE ROBINSON

Rulau	Date	Metal	Size	VG	F	VF	EF
Oh-Ci 180	(1869-70)	Silver	31mm	—	200.	—	300.

FREE TICKET TO / YANKEE / ROBINSONS / QUADRUPLE - SHOW ctsp on U.S. Seated Liberty Half dollar. Examined: 1843, 1853, 1854, 1854-O), 1855. 13 pieces known. (H-G 7840; Fuld NC-20f; Brunk 34720)

Oh-Ci 178	(1869-70)	Silver	32.5mm	—	200.	—	—
	Similar ctsp on U.S. 1806 Bust Half dollar.						
Oh-Ci-179	(1869-70)	Same on U.S. quarter		—	300.	—	—

Melvin and George Fuld (in "Token Collector's Page" in *The Numismatist* for Aug. 1955) published this counterstamp and attributed it to Cincinnati, based on the fact that Civil War tokens HG 7841 to 7850, undated and dated 1863, are assigned there. It is interesting to note that Fuld's illustrated piece, and the piece illustrated here — which are clearly not the same piece — are 1854-O Arrows halves. Another piece in the Tanenbaum collection is also an 1854-O Arrows half. Surely this is more than coincidence!

Fayette "Yankee" Robinson billed himself as "The Great Comedian" on his 1863 CW token. He also issued post-Civil War tokens dated 1869 (Fuld 165EZ-14a to 165EZ-16a).

These counterstamped half dollars were some form of admission check. Fifty cents was a good bit of money in the 1860's. Robinson's travelling circus routinely toured the South.

Born 1818, Robinson died in 1884.

C. SEAMER

Rulau	Date	Metal	Size	VG	F	VF	Unc
Oh-Ci 149	(1880's)	Brass	23mm	—	5.00	—	—
	C. SEAMER. Rv: W. W. SPENCER / STENCILS SEALS STAMPS / 153 W. 5TH ST. CIN. O. (Emmett Ey coll.)						

Saloon was located at 164 West 6th Street in 1884 and 1886 directories.

WILLIAM W. SPENCER

Rulau	Date	Metal	Size	F	VF	EF	Unc
Oh-Ci 150	1870	Copper	26mm	—	—	25.00	50.00
	Building, CINCINNATI INDUSTRIAL EXPOSITION. Rv: WM. W. SPENCER. Thick flan. Reeded edge. (Miller Oh 29)						
Oh-Ci 151	1870	WM	26mm	—	—	25.00	50.00
	As Ohio 29. Reeded edge. (Miller Oh 30)						

William W. Spencer was born in Cork, Ireland in 1839. He died before 1911. Spencer worked for diesinker John Stanton 1857-1866, before going into partnership with James Murdock Jr. The Murdock & Spencer firm actually was formed in 1864 as Spencer still worked with Stanton, and it lasted under that name to 1869, located at 139 West 5th St.

William W. Spencer had his own diesinking and engraving and letter cutting business from 1870 until 1909.

G. STADLER

Rulau	Date	Metal	Size	VG	F	VF	Unc
Oh-Ci 166	(1886)	Brass	Oct 23mm	—	—	10.00	—
	5 ¢ / DRINK / AT THE BAR / G. STADLER. Rv: (Logo) JAS. MURDOCK JR 165 RACE ST. (Emmett Ey coll.)						

Saloon, listed in 1886 at 133 Browne Street, Gabriel Stadler, proprietor.

THOMAS & ROBINSON

Rulau	Date	Metal	Size	F	VF	EF	Unc
Oh-Ci 165	1870	WM	26mm	—	—	15.00	22.50
	Exposition building at center, date 1870 below. Around: * CINCINNATI INDUSTRIAL EXPOSITION. Rv: THOMAS & ROBINSON / PUNCHING / DROP / & / MONOGRAM PRESSES, / 222 W & DIES 2D ST. CINCINNATI. Plain edge. (Wright 1140; Miller Oh 31)						

See Cincinnati Industrial Exposition for 1870 in this reference.

J.H. STEVES

Rulau	Date	Metal	Size	VG	F	VF	Unc
Oh-Ci 167	(1884)	Brass	**	—	25.00	—	—
	** Oval 24 x 17mm. * J.H. STEVES / —.. 5 ..— / *. Rv: DAYTON / (ornament) / * HOUSE * / (ornament) / 327 W. 6 ST. Plain edge. Scarce. (Wright 1053; Rulau Oh-Da 22)						

Jacob H. Steves operated a saloon at 327 West 6th St. in 1884.

WALTONS BITTERS

Rulau	Date	Metal	Size	VG	F	VF	EF
Oh-Ci 168	1870's	Silver	31mm	175.	—	250	—
	WE RECOMMEND / WALTONS /BITTERS ctsp on U.S. 1829, 1851, 1853, 1855-O 1858-O half dollar. (Krause coll.; Brunk 41670)						
Oh-Ci 169	(?)	Silver	31mm	—175.	—	250.	—
	Similar ctsp on U.S. 1859, 1861, 1872, 1878 half dolalr. (Gould 43)						

Samuel W. Walton of Cincinnati prepared this patent medicine."Bitters" were usually just flavored alcohol, as "medicines" were exempt from liquor taxes.

WEHRLE HOUSE

Rulau	Date	Metal	Size	VG	F	VF	Unc
Oh-Ci 169F	(1884)	Brass	Oval 28x24mm	—	—	12.00	—
	5 ¢ / DRINK / WEHRLE HOUSE / EUROPEAN . PLAN. Rv: (Logo) JAS. MURDOCK JR 165 RACE ST. CIN'TI. (Emmett Ey coll.)						

Hotel, listed 1884 at 6th and Walnut Streets.

WRIGHT & SON

Rulau	Date	Metal	Size	VG	F	VF	Unc
Oh-Ci 170	(?)	Brass	21mm	—	—	7.50	—
	WRIGHT & SON / —o— / 119 / OPERA PL. / —o— / CINTI. O. Rv: WE / MAKE / -o- / CHECKS. Plain edge.						

Gregg G. Wright was located at 119 Opera Place, admitting his son to the business in the 1880's. In 1889 Gregg G. Wright & Son were at 50 Longworth. Later they were at 20-22 Opera Place. Relocated at 119 Opera Place 1906. From 1909-1949 the firm was known as Gregg G. Wright & Sons.

ZANONI & BACCIOCCO

Cincinnati, Ohio

Rulau	Date	Metal	Size	VG	F	VF	Unc
Oh-Ci 210	(1870-81)	Brass	22mm	—	15.00	25.00	50.00
	ZANONI & / BACCIOCCO. / CHESS & / WHIST / CLUB / 234 / W. 7' ST CIN'TI. O. RV: Large 5 in circle of 16 stars / (tiny) JAS. MURDOCK JR. 165 RACE ST. CIN. O. Plain edge. (Emmett Ey coll.; Rulau-Fuld Soh-1; Miller Ohio 35; Kurth 81H)						

Joseph Zanoni and Dominic Bacciocco apparently became partners circa 1870, with the address 234 West 7th Street used by Zanoni 1870 to 1889 at least, while Bacciocco in 1870 was at northwest corner 3rd and Smith.

Oh-Ci 210 may not be connected with the ice cream saloon tokens of the Civil War period dated 1863 issued by, respectively, Joseph Zanone and S. Bacciocco. Zanone apparently remained a confectioner under the style J. Zanone & Brother at 60 West 5th St. until 1889 or later.

J. L. KING

Circleville, Ohio ?

Rulau	Date	Metal	Size	F	VF	EF	Unc
Oh-Cc 4	(1863-66?)	Silver	25mm	—	100.	—	—
	J. L. KING ctsp on U.S. 1856-O Seated Liberty quarter. (Koppenhaver Nov. 1983 sale, lot 572; Brunk 22933)						

It is possible this is the same J. L. King who issued 1863-dated Civil War tokens. King had a grocery and provision store. (See Fuld Ohio 168B-1a thru 168B-7a)

C. W. BRANDT

Cleveland, Ohio

Rulau	Date	Metal	Size	VG	E	VF	Unc
Oh-Cl 1	(1883-89)	Brass	25mm	—	10.00	—	—
	Brunswick die BB-6d. Rv: GOOD FOR / 5 C / C. W. BRANDT / IN / TRADE. Plain edge.						

C.C.C. & I. RY.
(Cleveland, Columbus, Cincinnati & Indianapolis Railway)
Cleveland, Ohio

Rulau	Date	Metal	Size	VG	F	VF	EF
Oh-Cl 3	(1866-70)	Brass	32mm	—	—	—	2 Known
	(All incused): NO. 134. / C.C.C. & I. RY. Rv: 1 TON near top. Plain edge.						

Possibly a coal token. Compare with the "woodburner" railway tokens listed in this catalog under Crestline, Ohio.

The Cleveland, Columbus & Cincinnati Railroad Co. was chartered March 14, 1836. The Galion to Sidney, Ohio line was completed in April 1853. Paper checks in the Rulau collection prove it was still called the CC&CRR in 1864-1865, when E.S. Flint was superintendent.

Rulau	Date	Metal	Size	VG	F	VF	EF
Oh-Cl 4	(1866-70)	Brass	24mm	—	—	Rare	—
	(All incused): CCC & I RY / 55. Rv: 1/8 / CORD. Plain edge. Thick flan. (Tom Wehner coll., Wapakoneta, Ohio)						

This is a wood burner token, not known to Clyde Drewing (see Bibliography).

COLUMBUS, OHIO

Rulau	Date	Metal	Size	VG	F	VF	EF
Oh-Co 3	(?)	Silver	25mm	—	—	35.00	—
	COLUMBUS, O. ctsp on each side of U.S. 1876 Seated Liberty quarter. (Brunk 9000)						
Oh-Co 4	(?)	Bronze	19mm	—	—	35.00	—
	Similar ctsp on U.S. 1864 Indian cent.						

G. A. R.

Rulau	Date	Metal	Size	VG	F	VF	Unc
Oh-Co 5	1888	WM	37.8mm	—	—	20.00	—
	Supported Ohio arms. Around: TWENTY SECOND ANNUAL ENCAMPMENT G. A. R. / * COLUMBUS, SEP. 1888 *. Rv: Sailor, soldier, woman, child and Miss Liberty between flags and trophies. Around: FRATERNITY CHARITY LOYALTY / * 1861 . VETERAN / 1866 *. Plain edge. (Zaffern coll.)						

G. A. R. = Grand Army of the Republic.

LICENSED

Rulau	Date	Metal	Size	VG	F	VF	Unc
Oh-Co 6	1882	Brass	23mm	—	—	20.00	—
	LICENSED / NOV. / 1882. Rv: COLUMBUS, O. / 1634. Plain edge. Issued holed. (The word LICENSED is in relief, all others are incused)						
Oh-Co 6A	1882	Brass	23mm	—	—	20.00	—
	Similar to 6, but SEP. / 1882 and stamped serial number 1169. Plain edge. Issued holed.						

Probably these are dog tags.

OHIO TOOL CO.

Rulau	Date	Metal	Size	VG	F	VF	EF
Oh-Co 7	(?)	Copper	29mm	—	—	40.00	—
	OHIO TOOL CO. / WARRANTED / CAST / STEEL / Ohio Tool Co. (all lines curved) ctsp on U.S. Large cent. (Charles Dobie coll., Toronto, Canada)						
Oh-Co 7E	(?)	Copper	29mm	—	—	40.00	—
	OHIO TOOL CO. ctsp on U.S. Large cent. (Brunk 30135)						

The firm was established in 1823. It manufactured tools from 1840's to 1880's using prison-supplied labor, when these tokens emanated. It ceased operations 1920.

W.B. POTTS

Rulau	Date	Metal	Size	VG	F	VF	EF
Oh-Co 8	(?)	Copper	29mm	—	—	50.00	—
	W.B. POTTS / COL. O. ctsp on U.S. 1851 Large cent. (Schenkman collection; Brunk 32617)						

HART SCHRADER

Rulau	Date	Metal	Size	VG	F	VF	Unc
Oh-Co 10	(1889)	Brass	22mm	—	—	9.00	—
	HART SCHRADER / AG'T in cartouche / (ornament) / No. 65 / * SOUTH HIGH ST. *. Rv: 2 1/2 within circle of 12 6-pointed rosettes. Below: (tiny) JAS. MURDOCK, JR. 165 RACE ST. CIN'TI. (Lipscomb N/L)						
Oh-Co 11	(1889)	Brass	22mm	—	—	20.00	—
	Obverse as last, but SAMPLE ROOM in place of large ornament. Rv: As last. (Lipscomb CO4750)						

Sample room was a euphemism for saloon. There are several later Hart Schrader tokens at 67 and 71 So. High St., including one in aluminum. The later issues are probably 1890's.

W. R. C.
(Women's Relief Corps)
Columbus, Ohio

Rulau	Date	Metal	Size	F	VF	EF	Unc
Oh-Co 16	1888	Bronze	33mm	—	—	12.00	18.00
	Female bust in high collar three quarters left, signature below: KATE B. KENWOOD (?). Rv: VI NATIONAL CONVENTION / —.— / COLUMBUS / —OHIO— / SEPT. 1888 / -.- / W. R. C. Plain edge.						

The W.R.C. was an organization associated with the Grand Army of the Republic (G.A.R.).

WOOD ENG. NO.
(Pittsburgh, Fort Wayne & Chicago R.R.)
Crestline, Ohio

Rulau	Date	Metal	Size	F	VF	EF	Unc
Oh-Cs 8	(1856-70)	Br	**	—	125.	—	—

** 25 to 31mm.
All incused): WOOD / ENG. NO. 59 / 1 CORD. Rv: Blank. Plain edge. (Drewing type 4) (Engine numbers known: 46, 48, 59)

Rulau	Date	Metal	Size	F	VF	EF	Unc
Oh-Cs 9	(1856-70)	Br	**	—	125.	—	—

** 28 to 29mm.
Similar to last, but 1/2 CORD. Rv: Blank. Plain edge. (Drewing type 4) (Engine numbers known: 12, 20, 116, 126, 129, 130 over 170, 147, 147 over 177)

Rulau	Date	Metal	Size	F	VF	EF	Unc
Oh-Cs 10	(1856-70)	Br	25 to 27mm	—	125.	—	—

Similar to last, but 1/4 CORD. Rv: Blank. Plain edge. (Drewing type 4) Engine numbers known: 5, 8, 14, 17, 54, 59, 116, 153, 167)

(See "Woodburning Engine Fuel Tokens" by Clyde J. Drewing in *The Numismatist* for July, 1964)

Rulau	Date	Metal	Size	F	VF	EF	Unc
Oh-Cs 11	(1960's ?)	Brass	27mm	—	—	—	—

The illustrated specimen is a possible fantasy created in the 1960's to bilk collectors. It is far too well made to compare with numbers 8, 9 and 10.

THE RESORT
Cumminsville, Ohio

Rulau	Date	Metal	Size	VG	F	VF	Unc
Oh-Cm 3	(1870's)	Brass	24mm	—	—	15.00	—

GOOD FOR / 5 ¢ / THE RESORT / CUMMINSVILLE / —IN— / TRADE. Rv: Large ornate numeral 5. Plain edge.

Cumminsville was annexed to Cincinnati in 1873, though local residents continued to use the name for a time. Cumminsville had been settled in 1790 as Ludlow Station.

PONY HOUSE
Dayton, Ohio

Rulau	Date	Metal	Size	VG	F	VF	Unc
Oh-Da 12	(1879-87)	Brass	27mm	—	50.00	65.00	100.

Pony prancing right at center, PONY HOUSE above, SOUTH JEFFERSON ST. below. Rv: Large 2 1/2 ¢ within central circle, JAMES RITTY above, *DAYTON, O. * below. Plain edge.

Rulau	Date	Metal	Size	VG	F	VF	Unc
Oh-Da 14	(1895-1900)	Brass	29mm	—	35.00	50.00	65.00

Obverse similar, but 125 S. JEFFERSON ST. below. Rv: Large 2 1/2 ¢ within beaded central circle, DAYTON above, OHIO below. Plain edge.

Rulau	Date	Metal	Size	VG	F	VF	Unc
Oh-Da 16	(1900-19)	Brass	26mm	—	6.00	8.00	10.00

PONY HOUSE / 125 / SOUTH / JEFFERSON / ST. / DAYTON, OHIO. Rv: GOOD FOR / * 5 ¢ * / IN TRADE. Plain edge.

James (Jake) Ritty opened his first saloon in Dayton in 1871, and then in 1882 operated the Pony House, a saloon and gambling emporium. It was a noted rendezvous. It was between 4th and 5th Streets. Ritty in 1879 invented the cash register and started the company that became the National Cash Register Co. in Dayton. Ritty sold the cash register manufacturing business to John and Frank Patterson in 1884.

William Timmerman issued the second token above. He owned the Pony House after Ritty sold it in 1895. But on Nov. 24, 1913, Timmerman was refused a license under Ohio's new liquor law and was forced to close down.

However, a William F. Timmerman had a liquor business in Dayton in 1918, so he may have managed the Pony House's reopening later.

The third type of brass check (without a pony vignette) was issued after 1900, either by Timmerman or a successor. These checks probably were used until Prohibition began, on Jan. 1, 1920. In the "dry" years 1920-1933, the Pony House became the Pony House Stag Hotel.

(See "The Pony House Checks, Dayton, Ohio" by Waldo C. Moore, in *The Numismatist* for June 1914.)

The Pony House is still in existence, in a sense. In 1967 the bar's fixtures were saved from the wrecking ball on South Jefferson St. and moved to 225 East 6th St., where they were installed, along with other antique Dayton fixtures, in Jay's Seafood Restaurant and Kitchen Door — part of Dayton's restored "old town" called the Oregon District. Your author dined there in July, 1993 and examined many Ritty mementos.

J.B. KENYON
Delta, Ohio

Rulau	Date	Metal	Size	VG	F	VF	EF
Oh-Dt 1	(1880)	Silver	25mm	—	—	75.00	—

J.B. KENYON DELTA, OHIO ctsp on U.S. 1857 Seated Liberty quarter. (Brunk 22610)

James B. Kenyon, born 1857, was a railroad engineer who moved to Montana ca 1880, dying there while building a railroad bridge.

JESSE A. CORWIN SKATING RINK
Eaton, Ohio

Rulau	Date	Metal	Size	VG	F	VF	EF
Oh-Ea 3	1887	GS	23mm	—	20.00	—	—

Four folds of a scroll obscure lower part of U.S. shield. On the scroll, incuse, is: JESSE. A. CORWIN / SKATING RINK MA' / EATON' / OHIO'. Rv: 1887 incused on plain field. Plain edge. Issued holed. (Rulau coll.)

Probably an identification disc.

W. PACKARD
Elyria, Ohio

Rulau	Date	Metal	Size	VG	F	VF	EF
Oh-Ey 5	(?)	Silver	25mm	150.	—	250.	—

W. PACKARD / ELYRIA O. ctsp on U.S. 1854 Arrows Liberty Seated quarter dollar. (Tanenbaum coll.; Brunk 30640)

Rulau	Date	Metal	Size	VG	F	VF	EF
Oh-Ey 7	(?)	Silver	31mm	175.	—	250.	—

W. PACKARD / ELYRIA, O. ctsp on U.S. 1865 Liberty Seated half dollar. (Gould 40)

There was a W. H. Packard in the jewelry business in 1918, possibly a kinsman.

W. H. STRICKLER
Delaware, Ohio

Rulau	Date	Metal	Size	VG	F	VF	Unc
Oh-De 3	(1883)	Brass	25mm	—	—	25.00	—

Brunswick die BB-6d. Rv: GOOD FOR / 5 ¢ / W. H. STRICKLER (in oval panel) / - IN - / TRADE. (Stubler coll.)

Billiard hall, listed in 1883.

H. G. GROSS
Florida, Ohio

Rulau	Date	Metal	Size	VG	F	VF	Unc
Oh-Fd 1	(?)	CN	Oct --mm	—	—	55.00	—

(All incuse): H. G. GROSS / 5 / FLORIDA. Rv: H. RICE MAKER / DAYTON. Plain edge. (Kirtley report)

Once claimed for the state of Florida, but now correctly attributed.

KARG WELL
Findlay, Ohio

Rulau	Date	Metal	Size	VG	F	VF	Unc
Oh-Fi 5	1887	Brass	31.5mm	—	20.00	30.00	45.00

Derrick, well house and pipe with jet of gas burning, 12 000 000 CUBIC left, FEET DAILY right, KARG WELL below — all within central circle. Around: THIS MEDAL IS MADE OF ALUMINUM PRODUCED BY NATURAL GAS FROM FINDLAY CITY *. Rv: SOUVENIR OF THE ANNIVERSARY / OF THE / APPLICATION / OF / NATURAL GAS / TO THE / MECH'L ARTS / . . . / * FINDLAY, OHIO, JUNE 8, 9, 10, 1887. Plain edge. (Wright 532)

This piece should also exist in aluminum, according to the legend, but we have not seen it in that metal.

Dr. Wright thought his brass piece was a die trial, but that seems to be the normal striking. The author once possessed two pieces in brass.

Findlay was a boom center of oil and gas production in the 1880's. The city is also noted as the birthplace of the song, "Down by the Old Mill Stream," written by Tell Taylor after fishing in the Blanchard River near Misamore Mill. Laid out in 1821, Findlay became a city in 1887.

C. W. WOLF
Forgy, Ohio

Rulau	Date	Metal	Size	VG	F	VF	Unch
Oh-Fo 3	(?)	Brass	23mm	—	—	15.00	—

Radiant outline star within beaded circle. Around: MADE BY THE WADSWORTH ENGRAVING CO. SPRINGFIELD, O. / -.-. Rv: C. W. Wolf / 5 amid flourishes / (Star) FORGY, O. (Star). Plain edge. (Lipscomb FO3010)

Forgy is in Clark County.

V. GILCREST
Hamilton, Ohio

Rulau	Date	Metal	Size	VG	F	VF	Unc
Oh-Hm 3	(1870)	Brass	31mm	—	—	20.00	—

Youth standing, facing, at center, dividing RED -- TRUNK, all within beaded circle. Around: * V. GILCREST *. Below: HAMILTON, OHIO. Rv: Early 19th century coach drawn by two horses toward left. Above: RED TRUNK CLOTHING / HOUSE. Plain edge. (National Collectibles Expo sale, Aug. 21, 1982, lot 2623)

These are watch fobs with loop removed.

MASON'S EAGLE BREWERY
Hamilton, Ohio

Rulau	Date	Metal	Size	VG	F	VF	Unc
Oh-Hm 18	(1889)	Brass	29mm	40.00	—	100.	—

MASON'S in large semi-script letters across center, a rayed star above and below. Rv: EAGLE / —*— / BREWERY. Beaded border near rim on each side. Plain edge. Only 2 specimens known.

Issued by Martin Mason in 1889 to advertise his acquisition of the Eagle Brewing Company that year. Mason had purchased an interest in the brewery in 1887, and bought out its principal, H. P. Deuscher, in 1889.

Mason operated the brewery under that title 1889-1896. In the latter year it was incorporated as a stock company as The Martin Mason Brewing Company, with minority interests held by his younger brothers, William and Charles Mason.

The owner of the only known specimens, William H. Schlosser of Hamilton, Ohio, is a great-nephew of Martin Mason and is the grandson of William "Will" Schlosser, son-in-law of Mason, who purchased controlling interest in the brewery in 1901 from Lillie Mason, mother of his wife Sue.

The Eagle Brewery was founded in 1852 by Samuel Beck and John Koeninger. In 1854 it passed to John Schalk and Jacob Stahl, and Stahl became sole owner in 1855. In 1869 Stahl sold out to Henry Eger, who was unsuccessful and sold out in 1881. After passing through a receivership, the brewery was acquired in 1882 by H. P. Deuscher.

Along with all other (legal) breweries, Mason's stopped making beer Dec. 31, 1919 with the coming into effect of Prohibition. In 1924 the plant was sold to its foreman, John Kiessling, who wanted to produce bottled soft drinks. The plant was located on South C Street.

The Eagle Brewery made only draft beer, never bottled, and sold its quality product through its own tap room in Hamilton and other saloons in Butler County, and at public events in the area. It was always a relatively small operation.

Distribution of the advertising tokens was probably limited to a brief period and, since these are maverick pieces without location, it is not surprising they are rare today — missing from all major Ohio token collections. Their publication here may uncover some more specimens, however.

JAS. McLAUGHLIN
London, Ohio

Rulau	Date	Metal	Size	VG	F	VF	Unc
Oh-Ln 4	(1875-80)	Brass	19mm	—	—	—	—

JAS McLAUGHLIN / DEALERS / IN / CIGARS & / TOBACCO / (ornament) / LONDON, OHIO. Rv: Large numeral 10 at center, 12 stars around, CENTS below. Plain edge. (Fuld NC-2b; H&G 8542). Rarity 8.

Rulau	Date	Metal	Size	VG	F	VF	Unc
Oh-Ln 5	(1875-80)	WM	19mm	—	—	—	—

As last. Reeded edge. Rarity 8. (Fuld NC-2e)

Rulau	Date	Metal	Size	VG	F	VF	Unc
Oh-Ln 6	(1875-80)	Silver	19mm	—	—	—	—

As last. Reeded edge. Rarity 9. (Fuld NC-2f)

This token was long thought to be a Civil War issue, but its die work could not have emanated before 1875.

JAMES BUDD
Mifflin, Ohio

Rulau	Date	Metal	Size	VG	F	VF	Unc
Oh-Mf 1	(1883)	Brass	23mm	—	—	25.00	—

(All incused): JAMES BUDD./ Rv: GOOD FOR / 5 ¢ / AT THE BAR. Plain edge. Only 2 known. (ATCO March 1993 sale; Lipscomb coll., ex-Mark Hertzer)

D. V. WHERRY
Mt. Gilead, Ohio

Rulau	Date	Metal	Size	VG	F	VF	EF
Oh-MG 3	(?)	Silver	38.1mm	75.00	—	—	—

D. V. WHERRY / MT. GILEAD. / OHIO ctsp on U.S. 1860 Seated Liberty silver dollar. (Brunk 42870; PCAC July 1993 sale, lot 1100)

WM. HUGHES
Portsmouth, Ohio

Rulau	Date	Metal	Size	VG	F	VF	Unc
Oh-Po 4	(1883-88)	Brass	25mm	—	—	15.00	—

Brunswick die BBC-3. Rv: * GOOD FOR * / 5 ¢ / Wm. HUGHES (in panel) / -IN- / * TRADE *. Plain edge.

J. F. STRONG
Republic, Ohio

Rulau	Date	Metal	Size	VG	F	VF	Unc
Oh-Re 5	(1883-85)	Brass	Oct 27mm	—	—	35.00	—

Geo. Kuehl & Bro. die. Rv: GOOD FOR / 5 ¢ / J. F. / STRONG / * IN TRADE *. (Stubler coll.)

Rulau	Date	Metal	Size	VG	F	VF	Unc
Oh-Re 5A	(1888)	Brass	Oct 27mm	—	—	35.00	—

Similar to 5, from diff. dies.

Rulau	Date	Metal	Size	VG	F	VF	Unc
Oh-Re 6	(1883-89)	Brass	--mm	—	—	25.00	—

Brunswick die BB-6d. Rv: J. F. STRONG.

Jerome F. Strong, saloon, listed 1883 through 1897. Kuehl & Bro. supplied tokens only to 1885; in 1886 this became Kuehl Billiard Supplies.

W. L. RUTTER
Salem, Ohio

Rulau	Date	Metal	Size	VG	F	VF	Unc
Oh-Sa 8	(1882-88)	Brass	24mm	—	—	14.00	—

(All incused): W. L. RUTTER / 10. Rv: W. J. DAVIS / WONDMAR. Plain edge. (Thoele report)

W. L. Rutter's saloon appears in the 1883 and 1888 gazetteers.

Diesinker Davis is presently unknown.

SALEM COMMANDERY 42, K.T.
Salem, Ohio

Rulau	Date	Metal	Size	VG	F	VF	Unc
Oh-Sa 9	1889	Gilt/B	25.5mm	—	—	—	15.00

Crowned Maltese cross at center, crossed swords behind it. On a small circle at the cross' center is a radiant slanting cross with IN HOC SIGNO VINCES. around it. Above: .SALEM, OHIO. Below: SALEM COMMANDERY NO. 42. K.T. Rv: PILGRIMAGE / OF / SALEM COMMANDERY / NO. 42 K.T. / TO / TRIENNIAL CONCLAVE / WASHINGTON / OCTOBER 1889. Plain edge. Issued holed. (Jim Hartman coll.)

K. T. = Knights Templar.

JOHN McKINNEY
Scott, Ohio

Rulau	Date	Metal	Size	VG	F	VF	Unc
Oh-Sc3	(1880's)	Brass	25mm	—	—	40.00	—

(All incused): JOHN MCKINNEY / SCOTT / OHIO. Rv: W. M. M. / GOOD FOR / 5 C / AT BAR. Incised, beaded rim on each side. Plain edge. (Lipscomb N/L)

O. B. B.
South Lebanon, Ohio

Rulau	Date	Metal	Size	VG	F	VF	Unc
Oh-SL 1	(1884-99)	Brass	25mm	—	—	30.00	—

O. B. B. / SOUTH LEBANON, O. Rv: Brunswick die BBC-3. (Lipscomb SO 5020)

NELSON'S LADIES BUSINESS COLLEGE
Springfield, Ohio

Rulau	Date	Metal	Size	VG	F	VF	Unc
Oh-Sp 7	(1870-85)	Brass	19mm	—	—	—	10.00

NELSON'S LADIES / 1 / BUSINESS / COLLEGE. Rv: Numeral 1. Plain edge. Rarity 5. (Lipscomb CI 4640)

Rulau	Date	Metal	Size	VG	F	VF	Unc
Oh-Sp 9	(1883-84)	CN	19mm	—	—	—	—

NELSON'S LADIES BUSINESS / 10 / COLLEGE. Rv: Numeral 10 / (tiny) HOEFLE & DRESSELL, 179 RACE ST., CIN. O. Plain edge. Rarity 8. (Lipscomb SP 2550)

Rulau	Date	Metal	Size	VG	F	VF	Unc
Oh-Sp 11	(1883-84)	CN	29.5mm	—	—	—	—

As last, but numeral 50 on each side. Plain edge. (Ralph Burry coll., Sidney, B.C., Canada)

Rulau	Date	Metal	Size	VG	F	VF	Unc
Oh-Sp 8	(1883-84)	GS	21mm	—	—	15.00	—

Similar to 9, but 5 on each side.

Nelson's Business Colleges were located in Cincinnati and Springfield, Ohio. See Nelson's Business College under Cincinnati in this volume.

Hoefle & Dressell were diesinkers in business only 1883-1884.

SQUIRREL HUNTERS REUNION
Springfield, Ohio

Rulau	Date	Metal	Size	VG	F	VF	Unc
Oh-Sp 22	1880	Brass	25mm	—	—	25.00	—

U.S. shield within circle of 16 rosettes. Rv: MEMORIAL / OF THE / SQUIRREL / HUNTERS / REUNION (last two words on shaped panel) / SPRINGFIELD, O. / SEPT. 30. / 1880. Dentilated rim on each side. Plain edge.

The Squirrel Hunters were a militia-type group assembled to defend Cincinnati from Confederate raiders in the Civil War. Probably issued holed for suspension from a ribbon.

Struck by James Murdock Jr. at 165 Race St., Cincinnati, says Emmett M. Ey.

H. HINLEIN
Steubenville, Ohio

1876 Centennial Tokens

Reverse type 1: H. HINLEIN / CLOTHING / HOUSE / HATS & CAPS. / STEUBENVILLE, OHIO. (All 23mm, plain edge.)

Rulau	Obv	Rev	Metal	F	VF	EF	Unc
Oh-Sb 3	D	1	WM	—	—	275.	—

The only known specimen appeared in Charles Kirtley's Sept. 1991 fixed price list. Never before published, it is from the first new issuer of Centennial cards discovered in some 5 years.

JOHN B. MYERS
Tiffin, Ohio

Rulau	Date	Metal	Size	VG	F	VF	Unc
Oh-Tf 3	(1889)	**	36mm	12.50	20.00	—	—

** Black printing on yellow cardboard.

THIS CHECK IS GOOD FOR / IN GOODS / AT THE STORE OF / JOHN B. MYERS, / DEALER IN / GENERAL MERCHANDISE / TIFFIN, / OHIO. / TWENTY-FIVE CENTS. Rv: Large 25 on ornate cartouche at center. TWENTY-FIVE CENTS above, NOT TRANSFERABLE below. (Rulau coll.)

In 1889 Myers was a dealer in groceries and general merchandise at 16 Sycamore, Tiffin.

TOLEDO MFG. CO.
Toledo, Ohio

Rulau	Date	Metal	Size	VG	F	VF	EF
Oh-To 6	(?)	CN	22mm	—	—	45.00	—

TOLEDO MFG. CO. ctsp on U.S. Shield nickel, date not legible. (Shield nickels were issued 1866-1883)

Rulau	Date	Metal	Size	VG	F	VF	EF
Oh-To 7	(?)	Bronze	23mm	—	—	45.00	—

Similar ctsp on U.S. 1865 2-cent piece. (Brunk 40280)

THE TROY BUGGY WORKS CO.

Troy, Ohio

Rulau	Date	Metal	Size	F	VF	EF	Unc
Oh-Tr 7	(ca 1885)	Gilt/C	22mm	—	6.00	11.00	20.00

Open carriage at center, "I'M IT" / NO. 31 above, THE / YOUNG MAN'S BUGGY below. Rv: Within wreath with a radiant star in top opening: THE / — TROY / BUGGY — / WORKS CO. / TROY, O. Plain edge.

J. H. SNYDER

Uhrichsville, Ohio

Rulau	Date	Metal	Size	VG	F	VF	Unc
Oh-Uh 3	(1880-81)	Brass	19mm	—	—	14.00	—

Pool table. Around: GOOD FOR FIVE CENTS / IN TRADE AT BAR. Rv: J. H. SNYDER / 5 / .*. (Lipscomb N/L)

This pool hall appears in the 1881 gazetteer.

G. W. COLLINS

Urbana, Ohio

Rulau	Date	Metal	Size	F	VF	EF	Unc
Oh-Ur 1	(1858)	Silver	25mm	200.	—	300.	—

G. W. COLLINS / URBANA. O. ctsp on U.S. 1853 or 1854 Arrows S.L. quarter. (Hartzog coll.; Brunk 8900)

G. W. Collins had a photographic studio at 154 Scioto St. in 1858.

BURNETT HOUSE ANNEX

Wapakoneta, Ohio

Rulau	Date	Metal	Size	VG	F	VF	EF
Oh-Wp 2	(?)	CN	27mm	—	—	—	—

Flan perforated with large numeral 5 at center. Around: BURNETT HOUSE ANNEX, WAPAKONETA OHIO. Rv: MADE BY THE WADSWORTH ENGRAVING CO. SPRINGFIELD, O. Plain edge. (Wright 117)

The Burnett House does not appear in the 1857 *Williams' Ohio State Register.*

WILBERFORCE UNIVERSITY

Wilberforce, Ohio

Rulau	Date	Metal	Size	F	VF	EF	Unc
Oh-Wi 8	1884	Copper	28mm	—	—	—	—

Lamp and open book in central circle. Around: WILBERFORCE UNIVERSITY / WISDOM / IS MORE PRECIOUS / THAN RUBIES / ENDOWMENT DAY / MAY 1884. Rv: Lord's prayer. Plain edge. (Bruce Cox coll., Wakefield, Mich.)

The university was named for the great English abolitionist, William Wilberforce (1759-1833), who was a member of Parliament for Hull 1780-1825. The Act of 1807 which he pursued abolished the slave trade, and he lived just long enough to see slavery itself abolished in the British Empire in 1833.

DR. W. H. ALLEN

Youngstown, Ohio

Rulau	Date	Metal	Size	VG	F	VF	EF
Oh-Yg 3	(?)	Silver	25mm	—	—	200.	—

USE DR. W. H. ALLEN'S / SWEET WORM WAFERS, / YOUNGSTOWN, / OHIO. / PRICE $1.00. / SOLD BY / ALL DRUGGISTS. ctsp on U.S. 1876 Liberty Seated quarter dollar. (Gould 70; Van Ormer sale 2505; Brunk 740)

THE BOSTON STORE

Youngstown, Ohio

Rulau	Date	Metal	Size	VG	F	VF	Unc
Oh-Yg 7	(1884)	Brass	12.5mm	Rare	—	115.	—

Bust left within wreath. Around: JAS. G. BLAINE. Rv: COMPLIMENTS OF / THE / BOSTON STORE / YOUNGSTOWN / OHIO. Plain edge. (Stewart Witham coll.; Kirtley Feb. 1991 price list)

This piece has been reported in 15mm diameter.

A. J. G.

Ohio ?

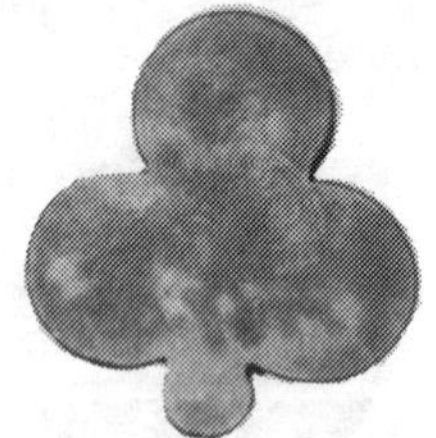

Rulau	Date	Metal	Size	VG	F	VF	Unc
Oh-Un 2	(1880-1900)	Br	**	—	5.00	—	—

** Cloverleaf shaped, 25.5 x 28.5mm.

5 / A. J. G. / (flower). Rv: J. J. SAYRE / MAKER / - 36 - / W FOURTH ST. / CINCINNATI O. Plain edge. (Wright 1303)

The maker, Joseph J. Sayre, was located at 34 and 36 West 4th Street in Cincinnati at least 1889-1909, and probably earlier as well. He was at the southeast corner of 4th and Walnut Streets 1863-1868 and probably longer.

HART'S BAKERY

Ohio ?

Rulau	Date	Metal	Size	VG	F	VF	Unc
Oh-Un 3	(1880's ?)	WM	**	—	—	5.00	—

** Scal, 26.5mm.

(All incused): HART's / BAKERY / H. RICE / MAKER / DAYTON, O. Rv: GOOD FOR / 5 C / LOAF. Plain edge. (Ralph Burry coll., Sidney, B.C., Canada)

WM. URLAU & BRO.
(Ohio ?)

Rulau	Date	Metal	Size	VG	F	VF	Unc
Oh-Un 4	(?)	Brass	24mm	—	—	—	—

Large 5-pointed star at center, WM. URLAU & BRO. above, 181 DOUGLAS ST. below. Rv: ******* / 1 / LOAF OF BREAD / JAS. MURDOCK, JR., 165 RACE ST., CIN. O (Wright 1170)

ADDITIONAL OHIO BILLIARD CHECKS

Following is a listing of verified attributions for this era. These are given here for informational purposes:

Name on Token	Possible Locale	Billiard Die	Gazetteer
Frank Bruns	St. Henry's	NBM Co.	1883-91
H. Cavanaugh	Salem	BBC-2c	1888
Diringer Bros.	Tiffin	BBC-2a	1888
Michael Folatico	Sandusky	BB-6d	1888
Albertus Grubbs	Germantown	BBC-2a	1888
William Guenther	Cleveland	BB-6a	1883
E. R. Hirbe	Norwalk	BBC-2a	1888
John Hulf	Elyria	BBC-2a	1888-91
W. H. Kanode	Logan	BB-6d	1883
John Kissell	Canal Winchester	BB ?	1883
J. G. Lauby	Bryan	BBC-9a	1889
F. Mollenkopf	Nevada	BB-3	1883
Thos. Nolan	Mingo Junction	BBC-9b	1888
H. B. Ramsay	Columbiana	BB-6c	1883
J. Richter	Defiance	NBM Co.	1883
J. Rist	Coalton	BBC-2c	1888
Schnorrenberg	Steubenville	BBC-2a	1883
W. Weisser	Cleveland	BBC-3	1881-88
J. W. West 2 1/2 ¢	Uhrichsville	BBC-2a	1883-88

OKLAHOMA

W. H. DARBY
Muskogee, Okla.

Rulau	Date	Metal	Size	VG	F	VF	Unc
Ok-Mk 3	(1880)	Br	**	—	—	80.00	—

** Sc, 28mm.
W. H. DARBY / MUSKOGEE I. T. and in a field within a circular depression. GOOD FOR / 5 / CTS /
IN TRADE. Reverse: blank. Plain edge. Rarity 8.

The center of this token is incused with raised lettering while the name and the city are incused. From the workmanship this piece was stamped with name and city on a planchet that was pre-stamped with the center devices. This type of planchet is well known and the design was made by a number of die sinkers. Because this is, no doubt, a company store of sorts, there must have been other denominations issued but none have been seen by the author.

Darby could not have been an Indian trader or his name would have been listed in Congressional testimony records.

NATURA TRADING CO.
Natura, Okla.

Rulau	Date	Metal	Size	VG	F	VF	Unc
Ok-Na 3	(?)	Brass	--mm	—	—	150.	—

Brunswick die BBC-6b. Rv: NATURA TRADING CO.

This firm was still in business in 1918, when the recorded population of this tiny Okmulgee County place was only 8!

G. & B. CITY SALOON
Oklahoma City, Okla.

Rulau	Date	Metal	Size	VG	F	VF	Unc
Ok-Oc 5	(1874-84)	Brass	24mm	—	—	40.00	—

Pool table at lower center, THE J. M. BRUNSWICK / & / BALKE COS. above, CHECK below. Rv: GOOD FOR / ONE / G. & B. / CITY SALOON / * DRINK *. Plain edge.

ORIENT BAR
Oklahoma City, Okla.

Rulau	Date	Metal	Size	VG	F	VF	Unc
Ok-Oc 12	(1889-91)	Brass	25mm	—	—	20.00	—

ORIENT BAR / * / 109 / GRAND AVE. Rv: 2 1/2 ¢. Plain edge.

The Orient Bar was listed in the 1890-91 issue of the Oklahoma Gazetteer.

OREGON

W. & H.
(Wintjen & Helms)
Jacksonville, Ore.

Rulau	Date	Metal	Size	VG	F	VF	Unc
Or-Ja 1	(1881-96)	Brass	--mm	—	—	400.	—

Brunswick die BBC-7. Rv: W & H.

Wintjen & Helms saloon, listed in 1881, 1883 and 1896 directories. Jacksonville had 800 people in 1883.

DAMMASH & HANNEMAN
Portland, Ore.

Rulau	Date	Metal	Size	VG	F	VF	Unc
Or-Po 2	(1886)	Brass	Scal 28mm	—	—	25.00	—

GOOD FOR / 5 ¢ / DAMMASH & / HANNEMAN (in cross-hatched oval panel) / IN / TRADE. Rv: Large 5 in circle of alternating stars and moons. (Thoele coll.)

Saloon, listed in 1886 directory.

DODD & CO.

(See Il-Ch 112, Schuttler Wagons, under Chicago, Illinois in this section. Dodd was the Schuttler branch agency for this trade area)

LADD & TILTON

Enlarged

Rulau	Date	Metal	Size	VG	F	VF	EF
Or-Po 1	1871	Gold	27mm	—	—	20,000.	—

LADD & TILTON. / 1871 ctsp on Oregon Exchange Company 1849 $10 gold coin. (Brunk 23660)

The gold in this territorial coin is pure, native Oregon gold.

Ladd & Tilton Bank was organized in 1859, probably the first bank to serve the Oregon country. Ladd & Tilton Bank merged into U.S. National Bank of Portland in 1925.

One specimen of Or-Po 1 was placed in the cornerstone of the Masonic Grand Lodge of Oregon in 1871. This specimen fetched $6695 in the May 21-24, 1964 Pacific Northwest Numismatic Association auction in Portland, then resold immediately for close to $10,000. In October, 1963 another piece, the Walton specimen, realized $10,500 at auction.

Research courtesy Rex Gibson, former manager of Ladd & Bush branch of USNB of Portland; Columbia Coin Co. Inc.; Walla Walla Coin Co.; Terry Trantow, and John Cheramy of Vancouver, Canada.

Ladd & Tilton began mercantile partnership 1851 in Portland, buying out Wakeman Dimon & Co. Tilton withdrew 1854.

NORTH PACIFIC INDUSTRIAL EXPOSITION

Rulau	Date	Metal	Size	VG	F	VF	Unc
Or-Po 5	1889	WM	32mm	—	75.00	—	—
Or-Po 6	1889	WM	32mm	—	75.00	—	—

Or-Po 5: Building. Around: NORTH PACIFIC / INDUSTRIAL / EXPOSITION. Rv: (Wreath) / PORTLAND, OR. / SEP. 26. TO OCT. 26 / 1889. Plain edge. (Richard McFerran coll.)

Or-Po 6: Obverse as 5. Rv: (Wreath) / PORTLAND. / OREGON. / SEPT. 26 / TO / OCT. 26. 1889. Plain edge.

PORTLAND, OREGON

Portland, Ore.

Rulau	Date	Metal	Size	F	VF	EF	Unc
Or-Po 8	1883	WM	24mm	—	—	75.00	—

Locomotive, SEPT. 8TH 1883. below. Rv: PORTLAND OREGON / (two hands shaking / ST. PAUL MINN. Plain edge. (Richard McFerran coll.)

H. BEAUDRY

St. Paul, Ore.

Rulau	Date	Metal	Size	VG	F	VF	Unc
Or-SP 1	(1896)	Brass	--mm	—	—	400.	—

Brunswick die BBC-11. Rv: H. BEAUDRY.

H. Beaudry saloon listed only in 1896, when St. Paul had 100 population.

PENNSYLVANIA

GESANGVEREIN FROHSINN

Altoona, Pa.

Rulau	Date	Metal	Size	VG	F	VF	Unc
Pa-Al 3	1865	Brass	22mm	—	—	15.00	—

Lyre at center of a semi-circle of stars, GESANGVEREIN . FROHSINN / ——. Rv: G. D. / 1865 (at center of open-topped wreath) / * / S. Plain edge. (Jim Hartman coll.)

Hartman does not explain the basis for his assignment of this piece to Altoona, Pa. Over the years the Rulau collection has contained about four specimens of this piece in VF-EF, which had been thought to be German music hall tokens.

M. R. & M. CLUB

Altoona, Pa.

Rulau	Date	Metal	Size	VG	F	VF	Unc
Pa-Al 5	(1870's)	Brass	19mm	—	—	20.00	—

M. R. & M. / CLUB. / ALTOONA, PA. Rv: Large numeral 5 within wreath, star at the top. Plain edge. (Jim Hartman coll.)

Probably struck by J. F. W. Dorman of Baltimore. Also see similar items - Eintracht under Tyrone, Pa., and C. Zimmerman under Johnstown, Pa.

BELLEFONTE IRON CO.

Bellefonte, Pa.

Rulau	Date	Metal	Size	VG	F	VF	Unc
Pa-Be 3	1870	Copper	29mm	—	60.00	—	—

(All incused and retrograde!) BELLEFONTE / INCORPORATED / 1870 / IRON CO ctsp on planed-off obverse of U.S. Large cent. Brunk 3200)

This counterstamp cent could have been used as a seal.

Tool checks or talleys from this firm are also reported, but have not been examined.

NEWMAN'S CLOTHING HOUSE

Bellefonte, Pa.

1876 Centennial Tokens

Reverse type 1: (Description needed)

Rulau	Obv	Rev	Metal	F	VF	EF	Unc
Pa-Be 20	A	1	WM	—	—	20.00	45.00
Pa-Be 21	B (Miller Pa 2)	1	WM	—	—	20.00	45.00
Pa-Be 22	F	1	WM	—	—	20.00	45.00
Pa-Be 23	G	1	WM	—	—	20.00	45.00
Pa-Be 23A	G	1	Copper	—	—	22.50	50.00
Pa-Be 23B	G	1	Brass	—	—	22.50	50.00

C. E. ANDERSON

Butler, Pa.

Rulau	Date	Metal	Size	VG	F	VF	EF
Pa-Bu 1	1867	Silver	25mm	—	—	40.00	—

C. E. ANDERSON / BUTLER, PA. / -*- / 1867. ctsp on shaved obverse of U.S. Seated Liberty quarter. (Van Ormer sale 2511; Brunk 925)

Made from individual letter punches, this item is probably a "dog tag" personal-type token.

W. J. PATTERSON

Concord, Pa.

Rulau	Date	Metal	Size	VG	F	VF	EF
Pa-Co 7	1870	Silver	25mm	—	35.00	—	—

W. J. PATTERSON. / 1870 on cartouche / CONCORD ERIE. CO. / PA. ctsp on shaved rev. of U.S. 1853 S.L. quarter. (Ralph Thompson coll., Bismarck, N.D.; Brunk 31335)

This piece is pierced and has a decorative border engraved around the shaved rim.

JAMES HORRIGAN

Corry, Pa.

Rulau	Date	Metal	Size	VG	F	VF	Unc
Pa-Cy 1	(?)	Silver	39mm	—	—	300.	—

U. S. HOTEL / JAMES HORRIGAN / CORRY, PENNA ctsp on Norway 1865 speciedaler, KM-325. (Arthur Newmark coll.)

The coin itself is quite rare, worth $400 or more in VF. The counterstamped piece fetched $286 in the PCAC July 1993 sale, lot 79.

K. T.
(Knights Templar)
Easton, Pa.

Rulau	Date	Metal	Size	F	VF	EF	Unc
Pa-Ea 6	1889	Gilt Brass	33mm	—	15.00	25.00	—

Ornate Maltese cross with crossed swords behind with inscription on it: EASTON / HUGH DE PAYENS / PA. / NO. 19 / COMMANDERY / KT. Rv: 36TH / ANNUAL CONCLAVE / OF THE / GRAND COMMANDERY / OF K.T. / OF PENNSYLVANIA / EASTON / MAY. 28. 1889. Plain edge.

ENCAMPMENT OF N. G. P.
Gettysburg, Pa.

Rulau	Date	Metal	Size	F	VF	EF	Unc
Pa-Gt 5	1884	S/WM	35mm	—	—	30.00	45.00

Four soldiers practicing rifle firing, tents in background. Rv: Pennsylvania arms, crested and supported, within central circle. Around: ENCAMPMENT OF N. G. P. AT GETTYSBURG / . 1884 . Plain edge.

Unusually handsome medalet. N.G.P. = National Guard of Pennsylvania.

STAR BREWING CO.
Greensburg, Pa.

Rulau	Date	Metal	Size	VG	F	VF	Unc
Pa-Gr 5	(?)	Brass	**	—	—	8.00	—

** Oct --mm.

STAR BREWING CO. / OF / GREENSBURG, / PA. / -.-. Rv: GOOD FOR / 5 C / HOTEL MERCHANTS. Heavy beaded border on each side. (Kirtley report)

HARRISBURG MAENNERCHOR
Harrisburg, Pa.

Rulau	Date	Metal	Size	VG	F	VF	Unc
Pa-Hb 4	(1880-90)	S/Lead	19.5mm	—	—	12.50	—

Harp. Rv: HARRISBURG / (ornament) / MAENNERCHOR. Plain edge. (Wright 430)

Maennerchor = Men's Choir.

COLUMBIA HOTEL
Johnstown, Pa.

Rulau	Date	Metal	Size	VG	F	VF	Unc
Pa-Jn 3	(1875-85)	Brass	19mm	—	—	—	—

COLUMBIA HOTEL / WM. / BOCK / PROP / JOHNSTOWN PA. Rv: * GOOD FOR * / * 5 * / CENTS / IN TRADE. Dentilated rim on each side. Plain edge. Rarity 9. (Fuld NC-4b; H&G 9285)

Long thought to be a Civil War token, this piece was issued a decade or more later.

C. ZIMMERMAN
Johnstown, Pa.

Rulau	Date	Metal	Size	VG	F	VF	Unc
Pa-Jn 27	(1870's)	Brass	22mm	—	—	25.00	35.00

CZ (script monogram) at center, C. ZIMMERMAN above, JOHNSTOWN, PA. below. Rv: GOOD FOR / 5 / CENTS / (small) KOEHLER. Plain edge. (Jim Hartman coll.)

Struck by Francis X. Koehler, the Baltimore tokenmaker. This piece bears a close resemblance to Eintracht of Tyrone, Pa. and M. R. & M. Club of Altoona, Pa. tokens, which see.

Charles Zimmerman was born in 1814 at Bieden Kopf, Hesse Darmstadt, Germany. In 1837 he married Christina Fronheiser and a few years later the Zimmermans and their relatives emigrated to the United States. Sailing to Baltimore, they took a stagecoach to Columbia, Md., then traveled by canal boat to Johnstown, Pa.

At this time there were only seven families residing in Johnstown. Zimmerman worked odd jobs and remodeled a barn for his family to live in. Setting up a cabinet shop on Locust Street, he made spinning wheels. Zimmerman's business grew and in 1841 he moved to Main Street. The business was destroyed by fire 1852.

Soon after Zimmerman bought property on Main Street and established a hotel and grocery. He was appointed a notary public, and became an agent for North German Lloyd Steamship Co., which provided much business at his hotel from travelers to and from Europe. Zimmerman was well educated, especially in German and American history.

He joined the local militia, was a member of many fraternal organizations and helped erect the first German Lutheran Church in Johnstown. He died in 1888, one of Johnstown's earliest leading German citizens.

In the 1866 Dun directory Zimmerman is listed as a saloonkeeper. The George T. Swank directory, the first for Johnstown, lists him as a hotelkeeper at 251-253 Main St. His token probably was used to purchase a mug of beer and it is one of the earliest trade checks of this area. Diesinker Francis X. Koehler in Baltimore produced many tokens from the Civil War to the 1870's.

L. K.
Lancaster, Pa.

Rulau	Date	Metal	Size	VG	F	VF	Unc
Pa-La 6	(1870-80)	Brass	19mm	—	6.00	10.00	—

LANCASTER / L. K. / —.— PA. —.—. Rv: Blank. Dentilated rim on both sides. Plain edge. (Jim Hartman coll.)

Rulau	Date	Metal	Size	VG	F	VF	Unc
Pa-La 6A	(1870-80)	Brass	17.5mm	—	—		Scarce

As 6, but comma (not period) after R of LANCASTER. Comma is low.

Rulau	Date	Metal	Size	VG	F	VF	Unc
Pa-La 6B	(1870-80)	Brass	18mm	—	—		Scarce

As 6A, but comma is high.

Rulau	Date	Metal	Size	VG	F	VF	Unc
Pa-La 7	(1870-80)	Brass	19mm	—	6.00	10.00	—

Obverse as 6. Rv: Eagle. Plain edge.

Rulau	Date	Metal	Size	VG	F	VF	Unc
Pa-La 8	(1870-80)	Brass	20mm	—	—	—	—

LANC. / L. K. Raised rim as on Pa-La 6. Rv: Blank, no raised rim. (Robert M. Ramsay coll., Lancaster, Pa.)

Local Lancaster collectors disagree over the meaning of 'L. K.' Many feel it means Lieder Kranz, a local German social club. Others say it means Lancaster Kindergarten — an old school, now out of business, for the private instruction of children of prosperous families.

D. B. ALEXANDER

Lewistown, Pa.

Rulau	Date	Metal	Size	VG	F	VF	EF
Pa-Lw 1	1868	Silver	23mm	—	—	50.00	—

D. B. ALEXANDER / * 1868 * / LEWISTOWN, PA. ctsp on Great Britain 1842 silver shilling, date worn. (Koppenhaver June 1987 sale, lot 232; Brunk 570)

P. H. CAMPBELL

Mt. Union, Pa.

Rulau	Date	Metal	Size	VG	F	VF	EF
Pa-MU 3	1869	Copper	29mm	—	—	100.	—

P. H. CAMPBELL / XXX / STENCIL CUTTER / 1869 / MT. UNION, PA. ctsp on U.S. 1854 Large cent. (Hallenbeck 3.512; Brunk 6670)

This may well be an advertising check for counterstamping services, since "stencil cutters" of this period are known to have counterstamped coins, especially Large cents, to the order of their customers.

Peter H. Campbell (1830-1872) was a druggist, jeweler and carpenter. In 1867 he signed the petition to charter Mt. Union borough.

ADOPTION OF THE FEDERAL CONSTITUTION

Philadelphia, Pa.

Rulau	Date	Metal	Size	F	VF	EF	Unc
Pa-Ph 1	1887	Gilt/Bs	22mm	—	—	8.00	15.00

Independence Hall. Around: CENTENNIAL CELEBRATION. / 1887 / (dot). Rv: Ten segments make up an archway. On the arch's segments are: C-O-N-S-TI-TU-T-I-O-N. Inside arch: SEP. / 17. In exergue: 1787, Around: ADOPTION OF THE FEDERAL CONSTITUTION. Plain edge. (Rulau coll.)

J. W. AHN'S CONFECTIONERY

1876 Centennial Tokens

Reverse type 1: J. W. AHN'S CONFECTIONERY 1342 RIDGE AVE., PHILA. (All 19mm; plain edge)

Rulau	Obv	Rev	Metal	F	VF	EF	Unc
Pa-Ph 801	W	1	WM	—	—	12.50	30.00
Pa-Ph 801 A	W	1	Copper	—	—	—	45.00
Pa-Ph 802	Y (Miller Pa 16)	1	WM	—	—	11.50	25.00
Pa-Ph 802 A	Y	1	Brass	—	—	15.00	40.00
Pa-Ph 803	Z (Miller 15)	1	WM	—	—	15.00	40.00
Pa-Ph 804	V	1	WM	—	—	17.50	45.00
Pa-Ph 804 A	V (Miller 18)	1	Copper	—	—	20.00	50.00
Pa-Ph 804 B	V (Miller 17)	1	Brass	—	—	20.00	50.00

AMERICAN LIFE INSURANCE CO.

1876 Centennial Tokens

Reverse type 1: AMERICAN / LIFE / INSURANCE CO. / WALNUT ST. / S. E. COR. 4TH, PHILADELPHIA. (All 23mm; plain edge)

Rulau	Obv	Rev	Metal	F	VF	EF	Unc
Pa-Ph 810	A (Miller Pa 11)	1	WM	4.00	8.00	11.00	20.00
Pa-Ph 810 A	A	1	Copper	—	—	12.50	25.00
Pa-Ph 810 B	A (Miller 12)	1	Brass	—	—	15.00	35.00
Pa-Ph 811	B (Miller 13)	1	WM	4.00	8.00	11.00	20.00
Pa-Ph 811 A	B	1	Copper	—	—	12.50	25.00
Pa-Ph 811 B	B	1	Brass	—	—	15.00	35.00
Pa-Ph 812	D	1	WM	—	—	16.50	37.50
Pa-Ph 813	E	1	WM	—	—	12.50	25.00
Pa-Ph 813 A	E (Miller 9)	1	Copper	—	—	15.00	30.00
Pa-Ph 813 B	E (Wright 17)	1	Brass	—	—	15.00	35.00
Pa-Ph 814	F (Miller 14)	1	WM	—	—	20.00	45.00
Pa-Ph 815	G	1	WM	—	—	15.00	35.00
Pa-Ph 815 A	G (Also in Bronze.)	1	Copper	—	—	17.50	37.50
Pa-Ph 815 B	G	1	Brass	—	—	15.00	35.00
Pa-Ph 816	H (Miller 10)	1	WM	—	—	15.00	35.00
Pa-Ph 816 A	H	1	Copper	—	—	17.50	37.50
Pa-Ph 816 B	H (Miller 10A)	1	Brass	—	—	17.50	37.50
Pa-Ph 817	J	1	WM	—	—	17.50	37.50
Pa-Ph 818	K	1	WM	—	—	17.50	37.50

APPLEGATE'S GALLERIES

1876 Centennial Tokens

Reverse type 1: APPLEGATE'S GALLERIES VINE & 8TH STS. PHILA. (All 23mm; plain edge)

Rulau	Obv	Rev	Metal	F	VF	EF	Unc
Pa-Ph 830	A	1	WM	—	—	15.00	40.00
Pa-Ph 831	D	1	WM	—	—	15.00	40.00
Pa-Ph 832	H	1	Brass	—	—	20.00	45.00
Pa-Ph 833	K (Miller Pa 22)	1	WM	—	—	17.50	45.00

James R. Applegate was a photographer. One token listed by Adams and Miller as Pa 26 cannot be identified to the listing above and has not been examined. It could exist, or could be a misdescription in some early catalog. It is a WM piece described as "blank reverse" and "small size."

C. C. ASHBY

Rulau	Date	Metal	Size	VG	F	VF	EF
Pa-Ph 2	(?)	Silver	15mm	—	90.00	—	—

C. C. ASHBY / PHILA. ctsp on France 1853-A 20-centimes. (Frank Kovacs coll.; Brunk 1210)

Rulau	Date	Metal	Size	VG	F	VF	EF
Pa-Ph 2A	(?)	Copper	29mm	—	—	80.00	—

Similar ctsp on U.S. 1798 Large cent.

Rulau	Date	Metal	Size	VG	F	VF	EF
Pa-Ph 2D	(?)	Silver	14mm	—	90.00	—	—

C. C. ASHBY ctsp on U.S. 1852 silver 3-cent piece. (Steinberg sale 100 of 1983, lot 32; Jeff Rock coll.; Brunk 1200)

Rulau	Date	Metal	Size	VG	F	VF	EF
Pa-Ph 2F	(?)	Silver	38mm	—	—	300.	—

C. C. ASHBY / PHILA. ctsp on each side of U.S. 1847 Seated Liberty silver dollar. (Van Ormer sale, lot 2517)

Rulau	Date	Metal	Size	VG	F	VF	EF
Pa-Ph 2G	(?)	Silver	27mm	—	—	90.00	—

Similar ctsp on Spanish-American 1773 2-reales.

BINGHURST & KIRBY

Rulau	Date	Metal	Size	VG	F	VF	EF
Pa-Ph 9	(?)	Copper	29mm	—	—	70.00	—

BINGHURST & KIRBY / PHILAD. / CAST STEEL ctsp on U.S. 1817 Large cent. (Hallenbeck 2.540; Brunk 3690)

S. O. OR C. BUNTING

Rulau	Date	Metal	Size	VG	F	VF	EF
Pa-Ph 11	(?)	Silver	18mm	—	—	80.00	—

S. O. OR C. BUNTING / PHIL ctsp on unrecognizable dime-sized world minor coin. (Joseph Schmidt coll., Dundee, Ill.; Brunk 5853)

The only known specimen was unearthed in Philadelphia with a metal detector.

Rulau	Date	Metal	Size	VG	F	VF	EF
Pa-Ph 12	(?)	Silver	20mm	—	—	80.00	—

S. A. BUNTING PHILA ctsp on worn Spanish-American 1-real. (Dave Schenkman coll.; ex-Joseph Schmidt)

BURR & WITSIL

1876 Centennial Tokens

Reverse type 1: BURR & WITSIL / MANUF's. / OF / METALLIC / BUSINESS CARDS / MEDALS, &C, / 1029 / CHESTNUT ST. / PHILA. (All 23mm; plain edge)

Rulau	Obv	Rev	Metal	F	VF	EF	Unc
Pa-Ph 840	A (Miller Pa 67)	1	WM	5.00	8.00	12.50	25.00
Pa-Ph 840 A	A	1	Copper	—	—	—	40.00
Pa-Ph 840 B	A (Wright 123)	1	Brass	—	—	17.50	35.00
Pa-Ph 841	B (Miller 66)	1	WM	—	—	12.50	25.00
Pa-Ph 841 A	B Also in Bronze.	1	Copper	—	—	15.00	30.00
Pa-Ph 841 B	B	1	Brass	—	—	—	35.00
Pa-Ph 842	D	1	WM	—	—	15.00	30.00
Pa-Ph 843	E (Miller 70A)	1	WM	—	—	12.50	25.00
Pa-Ph 843 A	E (Miller 70)	1	Copper	—	—	15.00	30.00
Pa-Ph 844	F (Miller 71)	1	WM	—	—	15.00	30.00
Pa-Ph 844 A	F	1	Brass	—	—	—	35.00
Pa-Ph 845	G	1	WM	—	—	15.00	30.00
Pa-Ph 845 A	G Also in Bronze.	1	Copper	—	—	17.50	35.00
Pa-Ph 845 B	G (Miller 69)	1	Brass	—	—	20.00	40.00
Pa-Ph 846	H (Miller 63)	1	Copper	—	—	17.50	35.00
Pa-Ph 847	J (Miller 65)	1	WM	—	—	15.00	30.00
Pa-Ph 847 A	J	1	Copper	—	—	17.50	35.00
Pa-Ph 848	K (Miller 62)	1	WM	—	—	15.00	30.00

WM. BURWELL & BRO.

1876 Centennial Tokens

Reverse type 1: WM. BURWELL & BRO. / CARRIAGE MOUNTERS / AND / COACH GOODS GENERALLY / PHILA., PA. (All 23mm; plain edge)

Rulau	Obv	Rev	Metal	F	VF	EF	Unc
Pa-Ph 850	A (Miller Pa 72; Wright 1354)	1	WM	—	—	12.50	20.00
Pa-Ph 850 A	A	1	Copper	—	—	15.00	30.00
Pa-Ph 850 B	A	1	Brass	—	—	17.50	35.00
Pa-Ph 851	B (Miller 73)	1	WM	—	—	12.50	20.00
Pa-Ph 851 A	B	1	Brass	—	—	—	35.00
Pa-Ph 852	D	1	WM	—	—	16.50	32.50
Pa-Ph 853	E (Miller 74)	1	WM	—	—	12.50	20.00
Pa-Ph 853 A	E Also in Bronze.	1	Copper	—	—	15.00	30.00
Pa-Ph 854	F (Miller 75)	1	WM	—	—	17.50	35.00
Pa-Ph 855	G	1	WM	—	—	16.50	32.50
Pa-Ph 856	H (Miller 76)	1	WM	—	—	15.00	30.00

CASSIDY'S OLD ESTABLISHED STORE

1876 Centennial Tokens

Reverse type 1: CASSIDY'S / OLD ESTABLISHED STORE / WATCHES / & / JEWELRY / NO. 8 STH. SECOND ST., / PHILADA. (All 23mm; plain edge)

Rulau	Obv	Rev	Metal	F	VF	EF	Unc
Pa-Ph 860	A (Miller Pa 79)	1	WM	5.00	8.00	12.50	25.00
Pa-Ph 861	B (Miller 80)	1	WM	—	—	12.50	25.00
Pa-Ph 861 A	B	1	Brass	—	—	15.00	30.00
Pa-Ph 862	D	1	WM	—	—	15.00	30.00
Pa-PH 863	E (Miller 78)	1	WM	—	—	12.50	25.00
Pa-Ph 864	F (Miller 77)	1	WM	—	—	17.50	35.00
Pa-Ph 865	G (Miller 81)	1	WM	—	—	15.00	30.00
Pa-Ph 866	H	1	WM	—	—	15.00	30.00
Pa-Ph 866 A	H Also in Bronze.	1	Copper	—	—	20.00	40.00
Pa-Ph 867	*	1	WM	—	—	—	60.00

* Muling of the Lingg & Bro. type 1 store card of Philadelphia with the Cassidy card.

William W. Cassidy began business in 1837 so that by the 1870's he could rightfully claim to being the "old established store."

Lingg & Brother bought out the Cassidy business in mid-1875, continuing it at 8 South 2nd Street, while keeping their own business going at 304 South 2nd Street. It is probable that only a few of these cards were actually issued by Cassidy (die A, Libertas Americana, die D, conjoined heads, etc.), while others were sold by Lingg to collectors. The purchase also accounts for the Cassidy-Lingg muling, Pa-Ph 867.

The Cassidy purchase enabled Lingg to advertise that they had been established in 1837.

JACOB CAUFFMAN

Rulau	Date	Metal	Size	VG	F	VF	Unc
Pa-Ph 13	(1870's)	WM	26mm	—	—	85.00	—

JACOB CAUFFMAN / 253 / W 4th ST / PHILA. Rv: Blank, no rim. (Kirtley June 1990 sale, lot 1945)

THE CENTENARY

Rulau	Date	Metal	Size	F	VF	EF	Unc
Pa-Ph 14	1876	Brass	26mm	—	—	12.50	20.00

Crude bust left, GEORGE WASHINGTON around, * 1876 * below. Rv: Scrawny eagle displayed and scroll above U.S. shield. Around: IN MEMORY OF THE CENTENARY. Plain edge. (Baker 407)

This piece is made in the style and fabric of British game counters of the 1790's, even to the crude workmanship and thin flan. We feel it must have been a deliberate counter imitation, possibly from Philadelphia for the Centennial celebrations there. Baker thought this piece had a French origin.

CENTENNIAL ADVERTISING MEDAL CO.

Rulau	Date	Metal	Size	F	VF	EF	Unc
Pa-Ph 15	(1875)	Copper	19mm	—	7.50	11.50	25.00

Nude Washington bust right, 12 stars around. Rv: CENTENNIAL ADVERTISING MEDAL CO / 1029 / CHESTNUT / ST. / PHILADA. Plain edge. Rarity 6. (Baker 524; Fuld NC-10a; Miller Pa 85)

Rulau	Date	Metal	Size	F	VF	EF	Unc
Pa-Ph 16	(1875)	Brass	19mm	—	7.50	11.50	25.00

As 15. Plain edge. R-6. (Fuld NC-10b; Miller Pa 85A)

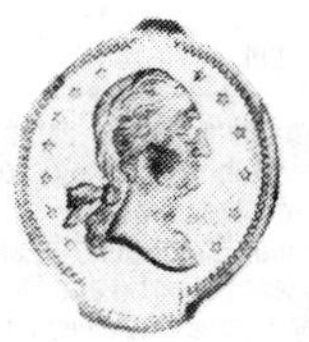

Rulau	Date	Metal	Size	F	VF	EF	Unc
Pa-Ph 16E	(1875)	Brass	19mm	—	—	—	45.00

As 16, but struck in a broken collar. (Hartzog Aug. 13, 1983 sale, lot 227)

Rulau	Date	Metal	Size	F	VF	EF	Unc
Pa-Ph 17	(1875)	Brass	19mm	—	—	—	45.00
	As 16, but on Trial flan. Plain edge. R-8. (Fuld NC-10-B1; Miller Pa 85B)						
Pa-Ph 18	(1875)	WM	19mm	—	—	17.50	35.00
	As 15. Plain edge. R-8. (Fuld NC-10e; Miller Pa 86)						
Pa-Ph 19	(1875)	CN	19mm	—	—	17.50	35.00
	As 15. Plain edge. (Fuld not listed).						

This firm resurrected a Civil War token die of Washington for its obverse. The company was set up to strike medals honoring the expected Centennial of the United States in 1876.

JOHN H. CLAY

Rulau	Date	Metal	Size	F	VF	EF	Unc
Pa-Ph 22	(?)	S/Cop	25mm	—	—	15.00	27.50

Old-fashioned steamer fire engine, VETERAN above, PHILADELPHIA in exergue. Rv: COMPLIMENTS / OF / JOHN H. CLAY / PHILADELPHIA / PA., all within wreath. Plain edge. (Hartzog 1980 sale)

WM. COVERT

1876 Centennial Tokens

Reverse type 1: WM. COVERT / NEWS / EXCHANGE / THEATER, OPERA & MINSTREL TICKETS / ESTAB. 1860 / CONTINENTAL HOTEL / PHILA. / U.S. (All 23mm; plain edge)

Rulau	Obv	Rev	Metal	F	VF	EF	Unc
Pa-Ph 870	A	1	WM	—	8.50	12.50	20.00
	(Miller Pa 104)						
Pa-Ph 871	B	1	WM	—	—	12.50	20.00
	(Miller 107; Wright 1380)						
Pa-Ph 871 A	B	1	Copper	—	—	17.50	40.00
	(Miller 108)						
Pa-Ph 871 B	B	1	Brass	—	—	—	40.00
	Thick flan.						
Pa-Ph 871 C	B	1	Brass	—	—	—	40.00
	Thin flan.						
Pa-Ph 872	D	1	WM	—	—	15.00	35.00
Pa-Ph 873	E	1	WM	—	—	12.50	25.00
	(Miller 106)						
Pa-Ph 873 A	E	1	Bronze	—	—	—	40.00
Pa-Ph 874	F	1	WM	—	—	17.50	40.00
	(Miller 105)						
Pa-Ph 875	G	1	WM	—	—	15.00	35.00
Pa-Ph 876	H	1	WM	—	—	15.00	35.00
Pa-Ph 877	K	1	WM	—	—	—	40.00

I. L. CRAGIN & CO.

1876 Centennial Tokens

Reverse type 1: ASK YOUR GROCER (etc.). (All 23mm; plain edge)

Reverse type 2: MAKE YOUR GROCER / GET / DOBBINS / ELECTRIC SOAP / THE BEST / OF ALL / I. L. CRAGIN & CO. / PHILADA. PA. (All 23mm; plain edge)

Rulau	Obv	Rev	Metal	F	VF	EF	Unc
Pa-Ph 880	A	1	WM	—	—	20.00	45.00
	(Miller Pa 109)						
Pa-Ph 883	A	2	WM	5.00	8.00	13.50	25.00
	(Wright 210; Miller 113)						
Pa-Ph 884	B	2	WM	—	—	15.00	40.00
	(Miller 111)						
Pa-Ph 885	E	2	WM	—	—	15.00	40.00
	(Miller 112)						
Pa-Ph 886	F	2	WM	—	—	17.50	40.00
	(Miller 110)						
Pa-Ph 887	G	2	WM	—	—	15.00	40.00
Pa-Ph 888	H	2	Copper	—	—	17.50	45.00
Pa-Ph 889	K	2	WM	—	—	17.50	40.00

Isaiah L. Cragin & Company were soap manufacturers, established in 1867. Dobbins Electric Soap was a laundry soap named after John B. Dobbins of Philadelphia, who first manufactured it, using a formula obtained from a Frenchman.

The "electric" in the soap's name made use of the popular interest in the mysteries and powers of electricity and implied that the soap was powerful and fast. After Cragin purchased Dobbins' rights the soap was advertised widely. It apparently had a high ph (alkalinity) to give it "sting."

Cragin also had a branch in Boston. He must have had some arrangement with Rudolph Schroder of Altona, Germany to distribute "Dobbins Electrische Seife" in that country.

D. BROS

1876 Centennial Tokens

Reverse type 1: Large D / BROS. (All 23mm; plain edge. Not known to Adams or Miller)

Rulau	Obv	Rev	Metal	F	VF	EF	Unc
Pa-Ph 26	J	1	WM	—	—	25.00	50.00

CHAS. A. DANA

Rulau	Date	Metal	Size	VG	F	VF	Unc
Pa-Ph 27	1876	Silver	31mm	—	—	20.00	55.00
	Bearded male bust left, DEDICATED TO CHAS. A. DANA above, 1776 PHILA. 1876 / EDITOR OF THE NEW YORK "SCUM". Rv: THE CHINESE STINK-POT OF AMERICAN JOURNALISM / HARMLESS / BUT / OH! SO FOUL!! / PHEW! Plain edge.						
Pa-Ph 27A	1876	Copper	31mm	—	—	—	35.00
	As 27. Plain edge.						

Strong satire against Charles Anderson Dana (1819-97), editor of the *New York Sun* from 1868 until his death in 1897. In 1849-62 he had been managing editor of the *New York Tribune*, an antislavery paper. He and George Ripley edited the *New American Cyclopaedia* (16 vols., 1858-63). He was assistant secretary of War in Lincoln's cabinet 1863-64. He authored a number of books.

It would be interesting to learn the identity of the publisher of this satirical piece, which was reported by George Fuld (see *Token Collector Pages*, page 214).

THOMAS DE PUY

Philadelphia, Pa.

1876 Centennial Tokens

Reverse type 1: THOMAS DE PUY / CARPET DEALER / *--- 37 S. SECOND ST. * --- PHILADA. (All 23mm; plain edge)

Rulau	Obv	Rev	Metal	F	VF	EF	Unc
Pa-Ph 890	A	1	WM	—	—	12.50	25.00
	(Miller Pa 114)						
Pa-Ph 891	B	1	WM	—	—	12.50	25.00
	(Wright 241; Miller 116A)						
Pa-Ph 891 A	B	1	Copper	—	—	15.00	35.00
	(Miller 116)						
Pa-Ph 891 B	B	1	Brass	—	—	15.00	35.00
	(Miller 117)						
Pa-Ph 892	C	1	WM	—	—	15.00	30.00
Pa-Ph 892 A	C	1	Copper	—	—	17.50	32.50
Pa-Ph 892 B	C	1	Brass	—	—	17.50	32.50
Pa-Ph 893	E	1	WM	—	—	12.50	25.00
	(Miller 120)						
Pa-Ph 894	F	1	WM	—	—	17.50	32.50
	(Miller 115)						
Pa-Ph 895	G	1	WM	—	—	12.50	25.00
	(Miller 121)						
Pa-Ph 896	H	1	WM	—	—	15.00	30.00
	(Miller 119)						
Pa-Ph 897	K	1	WM	—	—	15.00	30.00
	(Miller 118)						

DICKESON'S COIN & MEDAL SAFE (EVANS & WATSON)

Rulau	Date	Metal	Size	VF	EF	Unc	Proof
Pa-Ph 30	(1869 ?)	Silver	34mm	—	—	175.	300.

Houdon head of Washington right, tiny R.L. on truncation of neck. GEORGE WASHINGTON above, * SECURITY * below. Rv: Ornate double-door safe at center. Above: DICKESON'S COIN & MEDAL SAFE / EVANS & WATSON. Below: * MAKERS. * / 304 CHESTNUT ST. PHILADELPHIA. Less than 10 struck. (Baker 530; Miller Pa 142)

Rulau	Date	Metal	Size	VF	EF	Unc	Proof
Pa-Ph 31	(1869 ?)	Copper	34mm	—	50.00	85.00	—

As 30. (Miller Pa 143)

Rulau	Date	Metal	Size	VF	EF	Unc	Proof
Pa-Ph 32	(1869 ?)	Brass	34mm	—	50.00	85.00	—

As 30. (Miller Pa 144)

Rulau	Date	Metal	Size	VF	EF	Unc	Proof
Pa-Ph 33	(1869 ?)	WM	34mm	—	60.00	85.00	—

As 30. (Miller Pa 145)

Rulau	Date	Metal	Size	VF	EF	Unc	Proof
Pa-Ph 35	1869	WM	34mm	—	60.00	85.00	—

Military bust left, FOR GOV. MAJ. GEN. J. W. GEARY 1869. Tiny W. H. KEY under bust. Rv: AS 30. (Miller Pa 145 1/2)

Rulau	Date	Metal	Size	VF	EF	Unc	Proof
Pa-Ph 36	1869	CN	34mm	—	35.00	85.00	—

As 35. (Miller Pa 146)

Rulau	Date	Metal	Size	VF	EF	Unc	Proof
Pa-Ph 38	(1869)	?	33mm	—	35.00	85.00	—

Bust of Andrew Johnson left, ANDREW JOHNSON above, PRESIDENT U.S. below. Rv: As 30. Plain edge. (DeWitt AJOHN 1866-1(A); Miller Pa 146 1/2)

Rulau	Date	Metal	Size	VF	EF	Unc	Proof
Pa-Ph 40	(1872)	?	33mm	—	—	100.	—

Bust of Ulysses S. Grant right within an almost complete circle of 31 stars (slightly open at top). Within the circle of stars, at left: GENERAL, and at right: U.S. GRANT. Grant's epaulette carries four stars. Rv: As 142. Plain edge. (DeWitt USG 1872-3(A); Miller Pa 146 1/2A)

Rulau	Date	Metal	Size	VF	EF	Unc	Proof
Pa-Ph 44	(?)	Copper	33mm	—	35.00	75.00	—

Imitation of Sommer Islands shilling reverse. Rv: As 30. (Miller Pa 147)

Rulau	Date	Metal	Size	VF	EF	Unc	Proof
Pa-Ph 45	(?)	Brass	33mm	—	35.00	75.00	—

As 44. (Miller Pa 148)

Rulau	Date	Metal	Size	VF	EF	Unc	Proof
Pa-Ph 46	(?)	WM	33mm	—	45.00	75.00	—

As 44. (Miller Pa 149)

Rulau	Date	Metal	Size	VF	EF	Unc	Proof
Pa-Ph 47	(?)	CN	33mm	—	45.00	75.00	—

As 44. (Wright 250; Miller Pa 150)

Rulau	Date	Metal	Size	VF	EF	Unc	Proof
Pa-Ph 50		Copper	33mm	—	40.00	75.00	—

Same reverse. Obv: Hog, imitation of obverse of Sommer Island shilling. Copper. Scarce. (Miller Pa 151)

Rulau	Date	Metal	Size	VF	EF	Unc	Proof
Pa-Ph 51		Brass	33mm	—	40.00	75.00	—

Same. Brass Scarce. (Pa 152)

Rulau	Date	Metal	Size	VF	EF	Unc	Proof
Pa-Ph 52		WM	--mm	—	45.00	75.00	—

Same. White metal. Scarce (Pa 153)

Rulau	Date	Metal	Size	VF	EF	Unc	Proof
Pa-Ph 53		CN	--mm	—	45.00	75.00	—

Same. Copper-nickel. Scarce. (Pa 154)

NOTE: The tokens listed as Adams-Miller Pa 155 through Pa 161A are mulings with no name of the issuer upon them. Numbers 155 to 158 combine the imitation Sommer Islands obverse (hog) and reverse (ship) dies to make the famous Dickeson struck copies of the Sommer Islands shilling. The balance mule the Sommer Islands with Washington dies. None are store cards and thus are not listed here.

Dr. Montroville Wilson Dickeson (1813-1882) was best known for his *American Numismatic Manual* published in Philadelphia in 1859. Though a doctor of medicine, most of his years were spent in the study of antiquities and archeology.

He is well known as a maker of struck copies of American colonial coins, among them the Sommer Islands shilling above, and the 1776 Continental dollar. Kenney (in *Struck Copies of Early American Coins,* says the Sommer Islands shilling copies were made in Philadelphia in the 1850's, though we believe this was later. The Continental dollar copies were produced in 1876 for the Centennial Exposition. Most likely Robert Lovett Jr. prepared the dies for the Sommer Islands shilling copies, and their derivative store cards.

J. H. DIEHL

Rulau	Date	Metal	Size	F	VF	EF	Unc
Pa-Ph 58	(1880's)	CN	8mm	—	—	20.00	27.50

Four-leaf clover. Rv: J. H. DIEHL / 19 NO 9 ST. / * / PHILADELPHIA. Plain edge. (Tanenbaum collection) (Miller Pa. 264D)

FEELY

Rulau	Date	Metal	Size	F	VF	Unc
Pa-Ph 70	(1889-90)	Copper	19mm	—	200.	—

Two donkeys at center, star below. WHEN SHALL WE THREE MEET AGAIN is around. Rv: *FEELY* / 5 / 6TH & CALLOWHILL.

For a discussion of the two-donkey die, see under Applegates Palace of Flying Animals. Two of these pieces were published by H. Joseph Levine in 1980-1981 for the first time.

A James Feely & Son were wagon builders in 1918, as was a John Feely, possibly both descendant firms.

J. H. FERGUSON

Philadelphia, Pa. ?

Rulau	Date	Metal	Size	G	VG	F	EF
Pa-Ph 73	(?)	Copper	29mm	—	15.00	—	25.00

J. H. FERGUSON ctsp on U.S. Large cent. Examined: 1847, 1848, 1854, unknown date. 4 pieces known. (Brunk 14040)

Rulau	Date	Metal	Size	G	VG	F	EF
Pa-Ph 73A	(?)	Silver	25mm	—	—	40.00	—

Similar ctsp on U.S. 1853-A&R quarter.

The attribution, by Stanley L. Steinberg, Malden, Mass., is doubtful. Ferguson was a Philadelphia silversmith.

FIRST REGIMENT, FAIR & BAZAAR

Rulau	Date	Metal	Size	F	VF	EF	Unc
Pa-Ph 76	1884	Gilt Brass	26mm	—	9.00	16.00	20.00

Armory at center, FAIR & BAZAAR above, NOV. 15.-29. / 1884. below. Rv: Pennsylvania arms within central circle, crested and supported. Around: STRUCK IN THE ARMORY OF THE FIRST REGIMENT; at bottom a keystone with NG monogram on it. Plain edge. (Rulau coll.)

An issue of the First Regiment, Pennsylvania National Guard. The workmanship is excellent, leading to the conclusion U.S. Mint machinery may have been used.

1ST REGT. INFANTRY N.G.P.

Rulau	Date	Metal	Size	VF	EF	Unc	Proof
Pa-Ph 77	1884	Bronze	33mm	—	8.00	15.00	30.00

Washington head right, GEORGE WASHINGTON around. Rv: Crest of the First Regiment at center. Around: 1ST REGT. INFANTRY N.G.P. ORGAND. APRIL 19, 1861 / ARMORY DEDICATED / * FEB. 22. 1884 *. Plain edge. (Baker 377)

N.G.P. = National Guard of Pennsylvania.

DR. D. L. FLEMING

1876 Centennial Tokens

Reverse type 1: DR. D.L. FLEMING / 635 / VINE ST. / N.E. COR. 7TH ST., PHILADA. (All 23mm; plain edge)

Obverse die SP: DR. N.B. LEIDY / BLOOD / PURIFIER / 217 N. 6TH ST., PHILA., PA. (All 25mm; plain edge)

Rulau	Obv	Rev	Metal	F	VF	EF	Unc
Pa-Ph 77	E	1	WM	—	—	35.00	60.00
Pa-Ph 77A	E	1	WM	—	—	—	60.00
Pa-Ph 78	K (Miller Pa 166)	1	WM	—	—	30.00	45.00
Pa-Ph 79	SP	1	WM	—	—	35.00	70.00

A double medical card. (Wright 329; Miller 166A)

FRANKLIN FIRE CO. NO. 12

Rulau	Date	Metal	Size	F	VF	EF	Unc
Pa-Ph 85	1872	Silver	46mm	—	—	600.	—

Head of Washington left on plain field. Rv: Plain field with corded rim, engraved in four lines with many flourishes: FRANKLIN FIRE CO. / NO. 12 / 1792 TO 1872 / GEORGE W. PALMER. (Baker S-531)

The entire strike of these pieces at the U.S. Mint consisted of 29 specimens in silver. A similar specimen illustrated in the Baker-Fuld revision is inscribed to Edward P. Turner. The engraver is not known.

FRIES, MALSEED & HAWKINS

1876 Centennial Tokens

Reverse type 1: *** FRIES, MALSEED & HAWKINS *** / 8TH & MARKET / CLOTH / HOUSE / S.E. COR. / PHILADA. (All 23mm; plain edge)

Rulau	Obv	Rev	Metal	F	VF	EF	Unc
Pa-Ph 900	A	1	WM	—	—	15.00	40.00
Pa-Ph 901	C (Miller Pa 169)	1	WM	—	—	15.00	40.00
Pa-Ph 901	A C (Miller 167)	1	Copper	—	—	17.50	45.00
Pa-Ph 901	B C (Wright 349; Miller 168)	1	Brass	—	—	17.50	45.00
Pa-Ph 902	H (Miller 170)	1	WM	—	—	15.00	40.00

See also Malseed & Hawkins, another Centennial card issuer. It still has to be determined what the relationship between these two firms was.

J. HENRY GERCKE

1876 Centennial Tokens

Reverse type 1: J.H. GERCKE * / 1206 / PINE ST. / PHILADA., PA. / WATCHES / CLOCKS / JEWELRY. (All 23mm; plain edge)

Reverse type 2: J. HENRY GERCKE / WATCHMAKER / AND / JEWELER / .1206 PINE ST. PHILA. (All 19mm; plain edge)

Obverse type SM: Bust of George Washington right, 13 stars around. (All 19mm; plain edge)

Rulau	Obv	Rev	Metal	F	VF	EF	Unc
Pa-Ph 95	A (Miller Pa 173)	1	WM	5.00	8.50	12.50	25.00
Pa-Ph 96	B (Wright 370; Miller 172)	1	WM	—	—	12.50	25.00
Pa-Ph 97	E (Miller 174)	1	WM	—	—	12.50	25.00
Pa-Ph 98	F (Miller 175)	1	WM	—	—	15.00	35.00
Pa-Ph 99	H (Miller 176 and 177)	1	WM	—	—	12.50	25.00
Pa-Ph 102	Y	2	WM	—	—	15.00	40.00
Pa-Ph 103	Z (Fuld NC-14e)	2	WM	—	—	12.50	30.00
Pa-Ph 103 A	Z (Fuld NC-14a; Miller Pa 176A)	2	Copper	—	—	12.50	30.00
Pa-Ph 103 B	Z (Fuld NC-14b)	2	Brass	—	—	12.50	30.00
Pa-Ph 104	SM (Fuld Pa 750K-1e)	2	WM	—	—	20.00	45.00
Pa-Ph 104 A	SM (Fuld Pa 750K-1a; Baker 536)	2	Copper	—	—	20.00	45.00
Pa-Ph 104 B	SM (Fuld Pa 750K-1b)	2	Brass	—	—	20.00	45.00

It was once thought that J. Henry Gercke was a Civil War store card issuer, but he was not in business during the war. The CWT connection is recorded in the "Fuld" numbers given above. Numbers 103 through 104b may have been made by Centennial Advertising Medal Co. in 1876.

GERMAN AMERICAN BICENTENNIAL

Rulau	Date	Metal	Size	F	VF	EF	Unc
Pa-Ph 107	1883	WM	32mm	—	—	20.00	—

Eagle perched on U.S. shield, flags, etc., all radiant. Around: GERMAN. AMERICAN. BI-CENTENNIAL. PHILADELPHIA / . OCTOBER 6 1883 . Rv: 3-leaf clover at center, VINUM. LINUM. ET. TETRINUM around — all within central circle. Outside: GERMAN. TOWN. / . OCTOBER VI MDCLXXXIII. Plain edge.

Pa-Ph 108	1883	WM	35mm	—	—	40.00	60.00

Jugate heads of Columbia and Germania right. Around: GERMAN AMERICAN BI-CENTENNIAL-TOWN on scroll above arms; 1683 1883 on tablets; clover; VINUM LINUM ET TEXTRINUM on scroll. Plain edge.

J.W. GILBERT

1876 Centennial Tokens

Reverse type 1: J.W. GILBERT'S / BELL SHIRT / S.E. COR. / 9TH & VINE ST. / * PHILA * / MEN'S WEAR A SPECIALTY. (All 23mm; plain edge)

Rulau	Obv	Rev	Metal	F	VF	EF	Unc
Pa-Ph 910	A	1	WM	—	—	15.00	30.00
Pa-Ph 911	B (Wright 378; Miller Pa 178)	1	WM	—	—	15.00	30.00
Pa-Ph 912	H	1	WM	—	—	15.00	30.00

GOODMAN BROS. & CO.

Rulau	Date	Metal	Size	F	VF	EF	Unc
Pa-Ph 110	(1889)	C/Lead	34mm	—	—	175.	—

Boy and girl dancing. Rv: GOODMAN BROS. & CO. / MAKERS OF THE BEST / —.—/ . CHILDRENS CLOTHING . / —.— / IN AMERICA. / * PHILADELPHIA. *. Plain edge. Issued with loop. Ex. rare. (Tanenbaum coll.)

GRAND COMMANDERY K.T.

Rulau	Date	Metal	Size	F	VF	EF	Unc
Pa-Ph 117	1887	Gilt/B	25.5mm	—	—	—	15.00

Male bust with handlebar mustache, facing three-quarters right. Around: RIGHT EMINENT GRAND COMMANDER. Rv: Slanting cross through crown at top. Below, in seven lines: 34TH ANNUAL CONCLAVE / OF THE / GRAND COMMANDERY K.T. / OF PENNSYLVANIA / MAY 24-25 / 1887. Plain edge. Issued holed.

K.T. = Knights Templar.

H. C. HALL

Rulau	Date	Metal	Size	F	VF	EF	Unc
Pa-Ph 118	(1880's)	Bronze	19mm	—	—	60.00	—

H. C. HALL / 823 ARCH ST. / PHILA. ctsp on U.S. 1880 Indian cent. (Charles Kirtley Aug. 1987 sale, lot 133; Brunk 17820)

SHAMGAR S. HAND

1876 Centennial Tokens

Reverse type 1: SHAMGAR S HAND / NOTARY PUBLIC / AND / REAL ESTATE / AGENT / PHILA. / -- N.W. COR. 4TH & PINE STS. -- . (All 23mm; plain edge)

Rulau	Obv	Rev	Metal	F	VF	EF	Unc
Pa-Ph 920	A (Miller Pa 465)	1	WM	5.00	8.00	12.50	25.00
Pa-Ph 921	B	1	WM	—	—	12.50	25.00
Pa-Ph 921 A	B	1	Copper	—	—	14.00	30.00
Pa-Ph 921 B	B (Wright 419)	1	Brass	—	—	14.00	30.00
Pa-Ph 922	C (Miller 464)	1	WM	—	—	12.50	25.00
Pa-Ph 922	A C Also in Bronze. (Miller 462)	1	Copper	—	—	15.00	32.50
Pa-Ph 922	B C (Miller 463)	1	Brass	—	—	15.00	32.50
Pa-Ph 923	E (Miller 466)	1	WM	—	—	12.50	25.00
Pa-Ph 924	F (Miller 467)	1	WM	—	—	15.00	32.50
Pa-Ph 925	G	1	WM	—	—	14.00	30.00
Pa-Ph 926	H (Miller 468)	1	WM	—	—	14.00	30.00

HARBACH (BROTHERS) THEO. J. HARBACH

1876 Centennial Tokens

Reverse type 1: HARBACH'S / ORIGINAL / WALNUT / CANDY / 36 N. 8 STREET, PHILADA. (All 23mm; plain edge)

Reverse type 2: THEO. J. HARBACH / MANUFACTURER / OF / ADVERTISING / MEDALS / 809 FILBERT ST., PHILA. PA. (All 23mm; plain edge)

Rulau	Obv	Rev	Metal	F	VF	EF	Unc
Pa-Ph 930	A	1	Copper	—	—	15.00	40.00
Pa-Ph 930 A	A (Miller Pa 187A)	1	Brass	—	—	17.50	45.00
Pa-Ph 930 B	A	1	WM	—	—	20.00	50.00
Pa-Ph 931	B (Miller 187)	1	WM	—	—	12.50	25.00
Pa-Ph 932	C	1	WM	—	—	12.50	27.50
Pa-Ph 932 A	C	1	Copper	—	—	15.00	40.00
Pa-Ph 935	A	2	WM	—	8.00	15.00	40.00
Pa-Ph 936	B (Wright 1441)	2	WM	—	—	15.00	40.00
Pa-Ph 936 A	B	2	Brass	—	—	20.00	45.00
Pa-Ph 937	C	2	WM	—	—	15.00	40.00
Pa-Ph 937 A	C	2	Copper	—	—	20.00	45.00
Pa-Ph 938	D	2	WM	—	—	15.00	40.00
Pa-Ph 938 A	D	2	Brass	—	—	20.00	45.00
Pa-Ph 939	G	2	WM	—	—	15.00	40.00
Pa-Ph 940	H	2	WM	—	—	15.00	40.00

The Harbach series is a very confusing one. The Harbach Brothers, Theodore J. and Horatio, sold Harbach's Original Walnut Candy and Harbach's Christmas Tree Ornaments. Theodore J. Harbach also manufactured medallic business cards. The Harbachs used both the Lingg and the Kline Centennial card dies in preparing their own store cards, and as a result the Adams-Miller and other numbering systems are very confused.

The present Harbach listings may not be complete, either.

HARBACH'S CHRISTMAS TREE ORNAMENTS

Rulau	Date	Metal	Size	F	VF	EF	Unc
Pa-Ph 120	(1876)	WM	25mm	6.00	9.00	15.00	30.00

U. S. Flag. Rv: HARBACH'S CHRISTMAS TREE ORNAMENTS. Plain edge. (Miller Pa. 190)

HARBACH'S ORIGINAL WALNUT CANDY

Rulau	Date	Metal	Size	F	VF	EF	Unc
Pa-Ph 123	(1876)	WM	25mm	6.00	9.00	15.00	30.00

A black walnut at center, six stars on left, seven stars on right, ESTABLISHED above, 1842 in exergue. Rv: HARBACH'S / ORIGINAL / WALNUT / CANDY / 36 N. 8 STREET, PHILADA. Plain edge. (Wright 423; Miller Pa. 186A)

Rulau	Date	Metal	Size	F	VF	EF	Unc
Pa-Ph 125	(1876)	WM	25mm	6.00	9.00	15.00	30.00

Liberty Bell surmounted by eagle, CENTENNIAL above. Rv: Similar to 123, but from differing die. Plain edge. (Miller Pa. 188)

HART'S

1876 Centennial Tokens

Reverse type 1: **** BUY YOUR **** / TEAS / AT / —*— / HART'S / ***** / 7TH & CALLOWHILL / PHILA. / & RECEIVE A PRESENT. (All 23mm; plain edge)

Rulau	Obv	Rev	Metal	F	VF	EF	Unc
Pa-Ph 950	A	1	WM	—	—	15.00	40.00
	(Miller Pa 199)						
Pa-Ph 951	B	1	WM	—	—	15.00	40.00
	(Wright 432)						
Pa-Ph 951 A	B	1	Copper	—	—	16.50	40.00
	(Miller 198)						
Pa-Ph 951 B	B	1	Brass	—	—	17.50	45.00
Pa-Ph 952	E	1	WM	—	—	15.00	40.00
	(Miller 200)						
Pa-Ph 953	F	1	WM	—	—	17.50	45.00
	(Miller 201)						
Pa-Ph 954	B	1	WM	—	—	16.50	40.00
Pa-Ph 955	H	1	WM	—	—	16.50	40.00
Pa-Ph 956	K	1	Copper	—	—	17.50	45.00

HUGHES HOUSE

1876 Centennial Tokens

Reverse type 1: HUGHES HOUSE / 686 / * N. BROAD ST. * / ** / PHILA., CHRIS. HUGHES, PROP. (All 23mm; plain edge)

Rulau	Obv	Rev	Metal	F	VF	EF	Unc
Pa-Ph 960	A	1	WM	—	—	15.00	40.00
	(Miller Pa 206)						
Pa-Ph 961	B	1	WM	—	—	15.00	40.00
	(Miller 207)						
Pa-Ph 961 A	B	1	Brass	—	—	20.00	45.00
Pa-Ph 962	D	1	WM	—	—	16.50	40.00
Pa-Ph 963	E	1	WM	—	—	16.50	40.00
	(Miller 208; Wright 479)						
Pa-Ph 964	F	1	WM	—	—	17.50	45.00
Pa-Ph 965	G	1	WM	—	—	16.50	40.00
Pa-Ph 966	H	1	WM	—	—	16.50	40.00
Pa-Ph 967	J	1	WM	—	—	16.50	40.00
Pa-Ph 968	K	1	WM	—	—	17.50	45.00

INTERNATIONAL EXHIBITION

Rulau	Date	Metal	Size	F	VF	EF	Unc
Pa-Ph 155	1876	Brass	24mm	—	—	15.00	27.50

View of Philadelphia, MEMORIAL MEDAL above, 1776 in exergue. Rv: STRUCK WITHIN / THE / INTERNATIONAL / EXHIBITION / 1876. Plain edge.

Rulau	Date	Metal	Size	F	VF	EF	Unc
Pa-Ph 155 A	1876	Bronze	24mm	—	—	15.00	27.50

As 155. Plain edge.

Rulau	Date	Metal	Size	F	VF	EF	Unc
Pa-Ph 156	1877	S/Brass	18mm	—	5.00	10.00	25.00

Floreate struck border around rim of each side, obverse bearing the date 1877. The center, blank, is incused with legends, described next. Obverse: STRUCK IN THE / MAIN BUILDING / OF THE INTERNATIONAL / EXHIBITION, / PHILA. / ON THE FIRST STEAM / COINING PRESS / USED BY THE / U.S. MINT. Reverse: The Lord's prayer. Reeded edge. Piece is thicker than the silver dime.

Also reported in gilt brass.

Rulau	Date	Metal	Size	F	VF	EF	Unc
Pa-Ph A156	1876	GS	15mm	—	5.00	10.00	25.00

STRUCK IN THE / MAIN BUILDING / OF THE INTERNATIONAL / EXHIBITION, / PHILA. / ON THE FIRST STEAM / COINING PRESS / USED BY THE / U.S. MINT. Rv: Lord's Prayer within central circle. Reeded edge.

Rulau	Date	Metal	Size	VG	F	Unc	Proof
Pa-Ph 157	1876	WM	29mm	—	—	20.00	—

Building across center, THE INTERNATIONAL EXHIBITION OF / PHILADELPHIA above, MEMORIAL HALL / A CENTENNIAL OF THE / NATION / 1776-1876 below. Rv: Radiant heraldic eagle, scroll below. Along rims in tiny letters: — J. SCHWERDTNER F. and C. KRAUSE EDITEUR. Plain edge. Issued with eyelet for suspension. (Lots 1275-1277 of Virgil Brand 1984 sale)

Rulau	Date	Metal	Size	F	VF	EF	Unc
Pa-Ph 158	1876	SWM	27.5mm	—	—	20.00	30.00

Martha Washington bust left within laurel wreath. THE 100TH YEAR OF OUR INDEPENDENCE / 1876. Rv: MARTHA / WASHINGTON / MEMORIAL / MEDAL on four folds of a ribbon, all within laurel wreath. Plain edge.

Virgil Brand purchased proof remainders (60 pieces) of this medalet, and these were dispersed in June, 1984.

KELLY'S

1876 Centennial Tokens

Reverse type 1: WEEKLY PAYMENTS TAKEN / ON / FURNITURE / CARPETS &C / AT / KELLY'S / *** / 142 & 144 N 9TH ST / * PHILA *. (All 23mm; plain edge)

Rulau	Obv	Rev	Metal	F	VF	EF	Unc
Pa-Ph 970	A	1	WM	—	—	15.00	40.00
	(Miller Pa 243)						
Pa-Ph 970 A	A	1	Copper	—	—	16.50	40.00
	(Miller 242)						
Pa-Ph 971	B	1	WM	—	—	15.00	40.00
	Thick flan.						
Pa-Ph 971 A	B	1	WM	—	—	15.00	40.00
	Thin flan.						
Pa-Ph 971 B	B	1	Copper	—	—	16.50	40.00
	(Miller 244)						
Pa-Ph 971 C	B	1	Brass	—	—	17.50	45.00
Pa-Ph 972	E	1	WM	—	—	15.00	40.00
	(Miller 246)						

Pa-Ph 972 A	E	1	Copper	—	—	17.50	45.00
Pa-Ph 973	F (Miller 247)	1	WM	—	—	20.00	50.00
Pa-Ph 974	G	1	WM	—	—	16.50	40.00
Pa-Ph 974 A	G (Miller 245)	1	Copper	—	—	17.50	45.00
Pa-Ph 975	H (Miller 241)	1	WM	—	—	17.50	45.00
Pa-Ph 975 A	H (Wright 540; Miller 240)	1	Copper	—	—	20.00	50.00
Pa-Ph 976	K	1	WM	—	—	17.50	45.00

KEY & CO.

Rulau	Date	Metal	Size	F	VF	EF	Unc
Pa-Ph 170	(1860's)	WM	29mm	—	—	20.00	35.00
	Accolated heads of Queen Victoria and Prince Albert, dolphins at base of necks. Around: VICTORIA D. G. BRIT. REG. F. D. ALBERTUS PRINCEPS CONJUX. In exergue: MDCCCLI. Rv: Large open letters K E Y across token contain legend: ORNAMENTAL / MEDAL & SEAL / DIE SINKERS / &C &C / 329 ARCH ST / PHILA. Plain edge. (Wright 547; Miller Pa 265)						
Pa-Ph 170 A	(1860's)	Brass	29mm	—	—	20.00	35.00
	As 170. Plain edge. (Miller 266)						
Pa-Ph 170 B	(1860's)	Copper	29mm	—	—	20.00	35.00
	As 170. Plain edge. (Miller 267)						

This series bears the Roman numerals for the date 1851, yet could not have been struck that early. Key is listed at 329 Arch St. in the 1863 directory, but at 123 Arch St. in the 1850 volume. The significance of the 1851 date is not known at this time; Victoria and Albert were married in 1840. In 1851 Prince Albert opened the Crystal Palace Exhibition in London, the world's first "world's fair."

Pa-Ph 171	(?)	WM	29mm	—	—	14.00	25.00
	Edwin Forrest bust right, EDWIN FORREST around. Rv: As 170 (large K E Y). Plain edge. (Miller Pa 268)						

Pa-Ph 172	(?)	WM	29mm	—	—	14.00	20.00
	Edwin Forrest bust in toga right, no inscription. Rv: As 170. Plain edge. (Miller 269)						
Pa-Ph 173	(?)	WM	29mm	—	—	20.00	32.50
	George Washington head left. Rv: As 170. Plain edge. (Miller 271A)						
Pa-Ph 173 A	(?)	Brass	29mm	—	—	—	32.50
	As 173. Plain edge. (Miller 271)						
Pa-Ph 174	(?)	WM	29mm	—	—	20.00	32.50
	Gen. Peter Lyle. Rv: As 170. Plain edge. (Miller 274)						
Pa-Ph 174 A	(?)	Brass	29mm	—	—	—	32.50
	As 174. Plain edge. (Miller 272)						
Pa-Ph 174 B	(?)	Copper	29mm	—	—	—	32.50
	As 174. Plain edge. (Miller 273)						
Pa-Ph 175	1860	WM	28mm	—	—	35.00	60.00
	Abraham Lincoln right, R L PHILA below truncation. Rv: As 170. Plain edge. (DeWitt AL 1860-51 (A); Miller 265B; King 600). Struck ca. 1864.						
Pa-Ph 175 A	1860	CN	28mm	—	—	35.00	60.00
	As 175. (Dewitt AL 1860-51 (A); Miller 265A)						

Pa-Ph 176	1864	WM	28mm	—	—	—	60.00
	McClellan bust left, MAJ. GEN. GEO. B. McCLELLAN around. Rv: As 170. Plain edge. (DeWitt G McC 1864-24 (A); Miller Pa 267A)						
Pa-Ph 177	(1868)	?	28mm	—	—	35.00	60.00
	Bust right, tiny W.H. KEY F. below truncation. Around: HORATIO SEYMOUR. Rv: As 170. Plain edge. (DeWitt HS 1868-8 (A); Miller 274A)						
Pa-Ph 178	(1872)	?	28mm	—	—	—	60.00
	Grant bust left, tiny KEY.F. below truncation. PRESIDENT U.S. GRANT around, four 6-pointed stars below. Rv: F.C. KEY & SONS / DIE SINKERS & MEDALISTS / 329 / ARCH ST. / PHILADELPHIA, star to right and left. Plain edge. (DeWitt USG 1872-8 (A); Miller Pa 274B)						
Pa-Ph 179	(1860's)	Brass	29mm	—	—	35.00	60.00
	Surrender of General Lee. Rv: As 170. Plain edge. (Miller Pa 285)						
Pa-Ph 179 A	(1860's)	Copper	29mm	—	—	—	60.00
	As 179. Plain edge. (Miller 284)						
Pa-Ph 180	(1860's)	Brass	29mm	—	—	—	80.00
	Cedar Mountain to Reams Station. 28 battles. Rv: As 170. Plain edge. (Miller Pa 285 1/2)						

Pa-Ph 181	1869	Copper	38mm	—	—	—	95.00.
	NATIONAL SEMI CENTENNIAL / (Radiant eye) / ANNIVERSARY / OF / ODD FELLOWSHIP / HELD AT / PHILADELPHIA / (three interlocked rings) / APRIL 26, 1869. Rv: Within laurel wreath: MEDAL / DIE SINKERS / 329 / ARCH ST. / PHILADA. At left: F.C. KEY; at right: & SONS. Plain edge.						
Pa-Ph 181 A	1869	WM	38mm	—	—	—	200.
	As 181. Plain edge. (Miller Pa 263)						

NOTE: F.C. Key and Son were apparently at 123 Arch St. from about 1849 until 1861 or 1862. The firm appears in the 1863 city directory at 329 Arch St. They appear in the 1850 *Philadelphia Business Directory* at 129 Arch St.

Pa-Ph 181 G	(?)	Copper	38mm	—	—	—	125.
	Man striding toward mountain, intent on climbing, bearing pennant on pole reading: I NEVER SAY CANT. In exergue, tiny W.H. KEY F. Rv: As 181. Plain edge. (Tanenbaum coll.)						

Rulau	Date	Metal	Size	F	VF	EF	Unc
Pa-Ph 181 K	1863	Silver	38mm	—	—	—	275.

Crested, supported Philadelphia shield of arms at center, PENNSYLVANIA VOLUNTEERS above, GETTYSBURG / JULY 3, 1863. in exergue. Rv: As 181. Plain edge. (Tanenbaum coll.)

Rulau	Date	Metal	Size	F	VF	EF	Unc
Pa-Ph 181 M	1861	Silver	38mm	—	—	—	500.
	Bust left, THOMAS WILDEY above, BORN JAN. 15, 1783 / DIED OCT. 19, 1861. below. Tiny W H KEY F below truncation of shoulder. Rv: As 181. Plain edge. Only 2 specimens known. (One specimen appeared in the Levick sale, May 26, 1884; another, possibly the same one, in the Bowers & Ruddy Garrett sales 1980-81)						
Pa-Ph 181 N	1861	Copper	38mm	—	—	—	75.00
	As 181M. Plain edge. (Miller Pa 258)						
Pa-Ph 181 P	1861	WM	38mm	—	—	—	100.
	As 181M. Plain edge. (Miller Pa 250)						

Rulau	Date	Metal	Size	F	VF	EF	Unc
Pa-Ph 181 S	1864	Silver	38mm	—	—	—	Rare
	Military bust right, tiny W. H. KEY below truncation. MAJ. GEN. G. K. WARREN around, 1864 below. Rv: Same as 181. Plain edge. (ANS collection)						
Pa-Ph 182	(?)	Brass	29mm	—	—	20.00	35.00
	WE ALL HAVE OUR HOBBIES. Rv: As 170. Plain edge. (Miller Pa 275)						
Pa-Ph 182 A	(?)	Copper	29mm	—	—	20.00	35.00
	As 182. (Miller 276)						
Pa-Ph 182 B	(?)	WM	29mm	—	—	20.00	35.00
	As 182. (Miller 277)						
Pa-Ph 184	(?)	Brass	29mm	—	—	20.00	35.00
	DEDICATED TO COIN COLLECTORS. Rv: As 170. Plain edge. (Miller 278)						
Pa-Ph 184 A	(?)	Copper	29mm	—	—	20.00	35.00
	As 184. (Miller 279)						
Pa-Ph 184 B	(?)	WM	29mm	—	—	20.00	35.00
	As 184. (Miller 280)						
Pa-Ph 186	(?)	Brass	29mm	—	—	20.00	35.00
	Cupid. Rv: As 170. Plain edge. (Miller Pa 281)						
Pa-Ph 186 A	(?)	Copper	29mm	—	—	20.00	35.00
	As 186. (Miller 282)						
Pa-Ph 186 B	(?)	WM	29mm	—	—	20.00	25.00
	As 186. (Miller 283)						

WM. H. KEY (and) J.H. DIEHL

Rulau	Date	Metal	Size	F	VF	EF	Unc
Pa-Ph 188	(1869-80)	Copper	23mm	—	—	25.00	50.00
	Grecian head left, inscribed LIBERTY. Rv: WM. H. KEY / ENGRAVER / NO. 12 STH 37TH ST / PHILADELPHIA (sideways across token) / J. H. DIEHL / MANUFACTURER OF / MEDALS / NO. 728 CHESTNUT ST.,. Plain edge. (The Key and Diehl halves of the reverse read upside down in relation to each other). (Wright 251 and 549; Miller Pa 264)						
Pa-Ph 62	(1870's)	WM	24mm	8.50	11.50	15.00	25.00
	As 264. Plain edge. (Wright 251; Miller Pa. 264A)						

J.H. Diehl is listed at 728 Chestnut St. from 1869 to 1880.

G. KILBRIDE

1876 Centennial Tokens

Reverse type 1: G. KILBRIDE / CHEMIST & / DRUGGIST / ***** / 20TH & CHESTNUT STS / ** PHILADA **. (All 23mm; plain edge)

Rulau	Obv	Rev	Metal	F	VF	EF	Unc
Pa-Ph 980	A	1	WM	—	—	15.00	40.00
	(Wright 553; Miller Pa 254)						
Pa-Ph 981	B	1	WM	—	—	15.00	40.00
	(Miller 253)						
Pa-Ph 962	E	1	WM	—	—	15.00	40.00
	(Miller 255)						
Pa-Ph 982 A	E	1	Copper	—	—	17.50	45.00
	(Miller 256)						
Pa-Ph 983	F	1	WM	—	—	20.00	50.00
	(Miller 257)						
Pa-Ph 984	G	1	WM	—	—	17.50	45.00
Pa-Ph 985	H	1	WM	—	—	17.50	45.00
	(Miller 251)						
Pa-Ph 985 A	H	1	Copper	—	—	20.00	50.00
	(Miller 252)						
Pa-Ph 986	K	1	WM	—	—	17.50	45.00
	(Miller 250)						
Pa-Ph 986 A	K	1	Copper	—	—	20.00	50.00
	(Miller 249)						

JOHN W. KLINE

Rulau	Date	Metal	Size	F	VF	EF	Unc
Pa-Ph 200	(1876)	Brass	25mm	—	10.00	15.00	50.00
	Head of William Penn. Rv: JOHN W. KLINE 212 SOUTH 8TH ST / MANUFACTURER OF / MEDALS / TOKENS, CARDS, &C / IMPORTER & DEALER IN / COINS / MEDALS / SHELLS MINERALS / ENGRAVINGS / AND CURIOSITIES / PHILADELPHIA. Plain edge. (Miller Pa. 286)						
Pa-Ph 201	(1876)	Copper	25mm	—	10.00	15.00	50.00
	As 200. Plain edge. (Miller Pa. 287)						
Pa-Ph 202	(1876)	WM	25mm	—	10.00	15.00	50.00
	As 200. Plain edge. (Miller Pa. 288)						
Pa-Ph 202 A	(1876)	WM	25mm	—	10.00	15.00	50.00
	As 202, but thin planchet. Plain edge. (Miller Pa. 289A)						
Pa-Ph 203	(1876)	Silver	25mm	—	—	—	200.
	As 200. Plain edge. (Miller Pa. 289)						

Rulau	Date	Metal	Size				Unc
Pa-Ph 203 A	(1876)	Alum	26mm	—	—	—	85.00

As 200. Plain edge. (Lindesmith coll., ex-Kabealo 1958)

Rulau	Date	Metal	Size				Unc
Pa-Ph 205	(1876)	Copper	25mm	—	—	—	50.00

Liberty head with flowing hair left, LIBERTAS AMERICANA above, 4 JUIL 1776 in exergue. Rv: As 200. Plain edge.

Rulau	Date	Metal	Size				Unc
Pa-Ph 206	(1876)	Brass	25mm	—	—	—	50.00

As 205. Thick planchet. Plain edge. (Miller Pa. 289B)

DIETRICH KNOPPEL

1876 Centennial Tokens

Reverse type 1: DIETRICH KNOPPEL / MANUFACTURER / OF / FINE / AND / PLAIN / CONFECTIONERY / 1506 MARKET ST., PHILA. (All 23mm; plain edge)

Rulau	Obv	Rev	Metal	F	VF	EF	Unc
Pa-Ph 990	A	1	Copper	—	—	17.50	45.00
Pa-Ph 991	B (Wright 1488)	1	WM	—	—	15.00	40.00
Pa-Ph 992	D	1	WM	—	—	16.50	40.00
Pa-Ph 993	E	1	WM	—	—	15.00	40.00
Pa-Ph 993 A	E	1	Copper	—	—	16.50	40.00
Pa-Ph 994	F	1	WM	—	—	17.50	45.00
Pa-Ph 995	G	1	WM	—	—	16.50	40.00
Pa-Ph 995 A	G	1	Copper	—	—	17.50	45.00
Pa-Ph 996	H	1	WM	—	—	16.50	40.00
Pa-Ph 996 A	H	1	Copper	—	—	17.50	45.00
Pa-Ph 997	J	1	WM	—	—	16.50	40.00
Pa-Ph 997 A	J	1	Copper	—	—	17.50	45.00
Pa-Ph 998	K	1	WM	—	—	16.50	40.00
Pa-Ph 998 A	K	1	Copper	—	—	17.50	45.00

This issuer was unlisted by Adams, Miller and others, though catalogued by Wright. It was reported in 1981 in Arlie R. Slabaugh's book *American Centennial Tokens and Medals* and, in Dec. 1981, in the Springfield sale, lot 4553.

FREDERICK KNOPPEL

1876 Centennial Tokens

Reverse type 1: FRED'K KNOPPEL / MANUFACTURER / OF / FINE / CONFECTIONERY / 1208 ARCH ST., PHILA. (All 23mm; plain edge)

Rulau	Obv	Rev	Metal	F	VF	EF	Unc
Pa-Ph 210	A (Miller Pa 290)	1	WM	5.00	8.50	15.00	40.00
Pa-Ph 210 A	A	1	Copper	—	—	—	50.00
Pa-Ph 211	B (Wright 1489)	1	WM	—	—	15.00	40.00
Pa-Ph 211 A	B	1	Brass	—	—	20.00	50.00
Pa-Ph 212	C	1	WM	—	—	—	50.00
Pa-Ph 213	D (Miller 292)	1	Copper	—	—	20.00	50.00
Pa-Ph 214	E (Miller 293)	1	WM	—	—	15.00	40.00
Pa-Ph 215	F (Miller 291)	1	WM	—	—	17.50	45.00
Pa-Ph 216	G	1	WM	—	—	16.50	40.00
Pa-Ph 216 A	G	1	Copper	—	—	—	50.00
Pa-Ph 217	H	1	WM	—	—	16.50	40.00
Pa-Ph 217 A	H	1	Copper	—	—	—	50.00
Pa-Ph 218	J	1	WM	—	—	16.50	40.00
Pa-Ph 218 A	J	1	Copper	—	—	—	50.00
Pa-Ph 219	K	1	Copper	—	—	—	50.00

JOHN LEAK

Rulau	Date	Metal	Size	VG	F	VF	Unc
Pa-Ph 999	(?)	—	--mm	20.00	40.00	60.00	—

JOHN LEAK. MANUFACTURER AND ENGRAVER &C. 223 N. SECOND ST. Rv: Blank. (Miller 294 1/2)

D. LEWIS

Rulau	Date	Metal	Size	VG	F	VF	Unc
Pa-Ph A219	(?)	WM	25mm	—	—	—	100.

Picket gate at center, D. LEWIS, above, 2313 / N. 8TH ST. / GENERAL IRON WORKER below. Rv: Over-sidewalk awning at center, D. LEWIS, above, 2326 GERMANTOWN AV. below. Plain edge. (ANS coll.)

LINGG & BRO.

1876 Centennial Tokens

Reverse type 1: LINGG & BRO. 304 SO. 2ND ST. / WATCHES / * / AND / * / JEWELRY / * PHILA. *. Beaded inner circle. (All 23mm; plain edge)

Reverse type 2: LINGG & BRO. / WATCHES / * / AND / * / JEWELRY / 304 S. SECOND ST. PHILA. No inner circle. (All 23mm; plain edge)

Reverse type 3: As type 2, but LINGG & BRO. across center. (All 23mm; plain edge)

Reverse type 4: LINGG & BRO. On scroll: COMMEMORATION JULY 5, 1875. (All 23mm; plain edge)

Reverse type 5: Oval flan. LINGG & BRO / WATCHES / AND / JEWELRY / 304 S. SECOND ST. / PHILA. (All 25 by 20mm; plain edge)

Rulau	Obv	Rev	Metal	F	VF	EF	Unc
Pa-Ph 220	A	1	WM	5.00	8.00	15.00	40.00
Pa-Ph 220 A	A Thick flan 7.33/64ths inch.	1	WM	—	—	—	45.00
Pa-Ph 220 B	A (Miller Pa 300)	1	Copper	—	—	15.00	40.00
Pa-Ph 221	H (Miller 299)	1	Copper	—	—	15.00	40.00
Pa-Ph 222	L (Miller 298)	1	WM	—	—	14.00	40.00
Pa-Ph 222 A	L Also in Bronze. (Miller 296)	1	Copper	5.00	8.50	15.00	40.00
Pa-Ph 222 B	L Supposedly only 5 struck. (Wright 608; Miller 297)	1	Brass	—	—	—	75.00
Pa-Ph 224	A (Miller 301)	2	WM	5.00	8.00	14.00	40.00
Pa-Ph 225	B (Miller 303)	1	WM	—	—	14.00	40.00
Pa-Ph 226	D (Miller 302)	2	WM	—	—	15.00	40.00

Rulau	Obv	Rev	Metal	F	VF	EF	Unc
Pa-Ph 227	E (Miller 306)	2	WM	—	—	14.00	40.00
Pa-Ph 228	F (Miller 307)	2	WM	—	—	15.00	40.00
Pa-Ph 229	G (Miller 305)	2	WM	—	—	15.00	40.00
Pa-Ph 230	H (Miller 309)	2	WM	—	—	14.00	40.00
Pa-Ph 230 A	H (Miller 309A)	2	Copper	—	—	20.00	45.00
Pa-Ph 230 B	H (Miller 308)	2	Brass	—	—	17.50	45.00
Pa-Ph 231	J (Miller 304)	2	WM	—	—	15.00	40.00
Pa-Ph 232	L	2	WM	—	—	14.00	40.00
Pa-Ph 232 A	L	2	Copper	—	—	15.00	40.00
Pa-Ph 232 B	L	2	Brass	—	—	15.00	40.00
Pa-Ph 234	A (Miller 312)	3	WM	5.00	8.50	17.50	40.00
Pa-Ph 234 A	A	3	Copper	—	—	20.00	45.00
Pa-Ph 234 B	A	3	Brass	—	—	20.00	45.00
Pa-Ph 235	B (Miller 313B)	3	WM	—	—	14.00	40.00
Pa-Ph 236	D (Miller 311)	3	WM	—	—	14.00	40.00
Pa-Ph 237	E (Miller 313A)	3	WM	—	—	14.00	40.00
Pa-Ph 238	F (Miller 313C)	3	WM	—	—	14.00	40.00
Pa-Ph 239	G (Miller 310)	3	WM	—	—	14.00	40.00
Pa-Ph 240	H	3	WM	—	—	14.00	40.00
Pa-Ph 241	J (Miller 313)	3	WM	—	—	14.00	40.00
Pa-Ph 243	A (Miller Pa 317)	4	WM	—	—	17.50	40.00
Pa-Ph 243 A	A	4	Copper	—	—	20.00	45.00
Pa-Ph 243 B	A	4	Brass	—	—	20.00	45.00
Pa-Ph 244	E	4	WM	—	—	17.50	40.00
Pa-Ph 244 A	E (Miller 315)	4	Copper	—	—	20.00	45.00
Pa-Ph 244 B	E (Miller 314)	4	Brass	—	—	20.00	45.00
Pa-Ph 245	H	4	WM	—	—	17.50	40.00
Pa-Ph 245 A	H	4	Copper	—	—	20.00	45.00
Pa-Ph 245 B	H (Miller 316)	4	Brass	—	—	20.00	45.00
Pa-Ph 246	OV	5	WM	—	—	—	100.

NOTE: More than 30 mulings of obverses with each other are known. One, a muling of die A with die J in White Metal, was listed as Miller 301A. Such mulings are worth $12.50 in EF and $30.00 in Unc. See Slabaugh's reference for varieties.

ALSO NOTE: Die striations plague the Centennial series. They are not detailed in this reference.

1876 Centennial Tokens

Reverse type 6: LINGG & BRO. / 304 / S. SECOND ST. / WATCHES / AND / JEWELRY. (All 19mm; plain edge)

Reverse type 7: WE MAKE / THIS STYLE OF CARD / FOR / $9 PER 1000 / AT / 1029 CHESTNUT ST / PHILADA. No name on tokens. (All 19mm; plain edge)

Rulau	Obv	Rev	Metal	F	VF	EF	Unc
Pa-Ph 248	X	6	WM	—	7.00	10.00	20.00
Pa-Ph 248 A	X	6	Copper	—	—	10.00	20.00
	Also in Bronze. (Miller Pa 308A)						
Pa-Ph 248 B	X	6	Brass	—	—	15.00	25.00
Pa-Ph 249	Y	6	WM	—	—	15.00	25.00
Pa-Ph 249 A	Y	6	Bronze	—	—	15.00	25.00
Pa-Ph 250	V	6	WM	—	—	17.50	30.00
Pa-Ph 252	W	7	WM	—	—	10.00	20.00
Pa-Ph 253	X	7	WM	—	—	10.00	20.00
Pa-Ph 254	Y	7	WM	—	—	10.00	20.00
Pa-Ph 255	Z	7	WM	—	—	15.00	25.00
Pa-Ph 255 A	Z	7	Copper	—	—	15.00	25.00

Rulau	Date	Metal	Size	F	VF	EF	Unc
Pa-Ph A255	1882	Brass	31mm	—	—	15.00	25.00

Indians and Colonials signing treaty beneath a tree. Rv: 1682 / LINGG & BRO. WATCHES 1882 JEWELRY. PHILADELPHIA. / BI-CENTENNIAL / PENN'S / OCT. 23-28 / TREATY / CELEBRATION. / 1882. Plain edge. (Randy Partin report)

LINGG & CO.

1876 Centennial Tokens

Reverse type 1: LINGG & CO. / MANUFACTURERS / OF / METALLIC / BUSINESS CARDS / MEDALS / TOKENS &C / 1029 CHESTNUT ST. PHILADA. (All 23mm; plain edge)

Reverse type 2: Similar, but Oval flan, 25 by 20mm, plain edge.

Rulau	Obv	Rev	Metal	F	VF	EF	Unc
Pa-Ph 256	A (Miller Pa 323)	1	WM	5.00	8.00	15.00	40.00
Pa-Ph 256 A	A	1	Copper	—	—	20.00	45.00
Pa-Ph 256 F	A	1	**	—	—	—	100.
	** Purple fiber.						
Pa-Ph 257	B (Miller 318)	1	WM	5.00	8.00	15.00	40.00
Pa-Ph 257 A	B (Miller 320)	1	Copper	—	—	20.00	45.00
Pa-Ph 257 B	B (Miller 319)	1	Brass	—	—	17.50	40.00
Pa-Ph 258	C (Miller 318A)	1	WM	—	—	15.00	40.00
Pa-Ph 258 A	C	1	Copper	—	—	20.00	45.00
Pa-Ph 258 B	C	1	Brass	—	—	20.00	45.00
Pa-Ph 258 F	D	1	WM	—	—	20.00	45.00
Pa-Ph 259	E	1	WM	—	—	15.00	
	40.00(Miller 324)						
Pa-Ph 259 A	E	1	Copper	—	—	20.00	45.00
Pa-Ph 260	F (Wright 608; Miller 326)	1	WM	—	—	20.00	45.00
Pa-Ph 260 A	F	1	Copper				Not Confirmed
Pa-Ph 261	G	1	WM	—	—	15.00	40.00
Pa-Ph 261 A	G	1	Copper	—	—	20.00	45.00
Pa-Ph 262	H (Miller 322)	1	WM	—	—	15.00	40.00
Pa-Ph 262 A	H	1	Copper	—	—	20.00	45.00
Pa-Ph 262 B	H	1	Brass	—	—	20.00	45.00
Pa-Ph 262 F	K (Miller 321)	1	WM	—	—	20.00	45.00
Pa-Ph 262 G	K	1	Copper	—	—	20.00	45.00
Pa-Ph 263	OV (Miller 326A)	2	WM	—	—	80.00	100.

Joseph Lingg began business during the Civil War as a dealer in watches and jewelry at 1219 Prune St., Philadelphia. In the early 1870's the firm became Lingg & Bro. as Frederick Lingg joined his brother (becoming the dominant partner). They were at 1206 Pine St. and at 304 So. Second St. — the latter the address on the tokens. They apparently consolidated at the Second St. address.

About 1873 they established (or bought out) a token and medal manufacturing business at 1029 Chestnut St. Their first medalet was the 19mm (U.S. cent size) piece for the New Memorial Hall (die Z). About 1874 they produced the 23mm "double head" piece (die D) which reads I ALWAYS BUY THERE above the smiling face and I WILL IN FUTURE above the frowning face.

All the other Lingg stock obverse dies, probably produced from 1874 to 1875, were of Centennial themes. Lingg must have had some distribution arrangement with Theodore J. Harbach, the confectioner, who arranged for many other confectioners to use the cards. The Harbach token-maker cards probably were struck by Lingg.

During 1875 the Linggs sold their interest in the medallic business, and bought out Cassidy's jewelry business — probably selling to Burr & Witsil. Later this became the Centennial Advertising Medal Co., which supplied Lingg die combinations and off-metal strikes for collectors 1876-77.

It is not known why the Maryland coat of arms appears on die F. Only one issuer in Maryland, the Patapsco Fruit Butter Co. of Baltimore, used Centennial cards. Perhaps it was a mistake and the Pennsylvania arms were intended. Public Buildings, die J, is the Philadelphia City Hall, begun 1872 and completed 1901.

DR. W. H. LOBE

Rulau	Date	Metal	Size	F	VF	EF	Unc
Pa-Ph 264	(?)	WM	24mm	—	15.00	30.00	50.00

DR. W. H. LOBE / MEDICAL OFFICES / 329 / N. FIFTEENTH ST. / PHILADA. Rv: OFFICE / HOURS / 11 AM to 2 / AND / 7 to 10 PM. (Wright 613; Miller Pa. 326 1/2)

COUNT & COUNTESS MAGRI

Rulau	Date	Metal	Size	VG	F	VF	Unc
Pa-Ph 265	1885	WM	31mm	—	—	—	40.00

MAGRI above a man and woman standing at center. Around border: PRESENTED BY THE COUNT & COUNTESS C.A. BRADENBURGH & CO. M'GRS. Reverse: in eleven lines, 9th & ARCH ST. MUSEUM PHILA. THE FAVORITE FAMILY RESORT FIRST APPEARANCE BEFORE PUBLIC OF COUNT AND COUNTESS MAGRI FORMERLY MRS. TOM THUMB AFTER THEIR WEDDING TOUR OF EUROPE MON. SEPT. 14, 1885. C.A. BRADENBURGH PRO & M'GR. Beaded border. Plain edge. Rarity 7. (Wright 646)

Mrs. Tom Thumb (Lavinia Warren) married Count Magri after the death of her famous husband. (See P. T. Barnum under New York City)

MALSEED & HAWKINS

1876 Centennial Tokens

Reverse type 1: * MALSEED & HAWKINS * / S.E. COR. / CLOTH / HOUSE / 8TH & MARKET STS. / *** PHILADA. ***. (All 23mm; plain edge)

Rulau	Obv	Rev	Metal	F	VF	EF	Unc
Pa-Ph 270	A (Miller Pa 357)	1	WM	5.00	8.00	15.00	40.00
Pa-Ph 271	B Thick flan. (Miller 358)	1	WM	—	—	15.00	40.00
Pa-Ph 271 A	B Thin flan.	1	WM	—	—	15.00	40.00
Pa-Ph 271 B	B	1	Brass	—	—	20.00	45.00
Pa-Ph 272	E (Miller 359)	1	WM	5.00	8.00	15.00	40.00
Pa-Ph 273	F (Miller 360)	1	WM	—	—	17.50	45.00
Pa-Ph 274	J	1	WM	—	—	17.50	45.00
Pa-Ph 275	K (Miller 362)	1	WM	—	—	20.00	45.00
Pa-Ph 275 A	K (Miller 361)	1	Copper	—	—	20.00	45.00
Pa-Ph 275 B	K (Wright 653; Miller 361A)	1	Brass	—	—	20.00	45.00

See also Fries, Malseed & Hawkins under Philadelphia in this reference.

MASON & CO.

Rulau	Date	Metal	Size	F	VF	EF	Unc
Pa-Ph 290	1870	WM	19mm	—	20.00	25.00	45.00

Washington bust facing, BORN FEB. 22, 1732 above, DIED DEC. 14, 1799 below. Rv: MASON & CO. / 1870 / COIN & STAMP / --- / DEALERS. / 139 / NO. 9TH ST. PHILA. Plain edge. (Baker 559; Fuld NC-16e; Miller Pa 363). Rarity 6. 100 struck.

Rulau	Date	Metal	Size	F	VF	EF	Unc
Pa-Ph 290A	1870	Silver	19mm	—	—	—	200.

As 290. Plain edge. Only 2 struck.

Rulau	Date	Metal	Size	F	VF	EF	Unc
Pa-Ph 291	1870	Copper	19mm	—	10.00	15.00	45.00

As 290. Plain edge. (Baker 559; Wright 671; Fuld NC-16a) RARITY 6. 100 struck.

Rulau	Date	Metal	Size	F	VF	EF	Unc
Pa-Ph 292	1870	Brass	19mm	—	10.00	15.00	45.00

As 290. Plain edge. (Fuld NC-16b; Miller Pa 365) 100 struck.

Rulau	Date	Metal	Size	F	VF	EF	Unc
Pa-Ph 293	1870	Nickel	19mm	—	—	35.00	60.00

As 290. (Miller Pa 366) Only 20 struck.

Rulau	Date	Metal	Size	F	VF	EF	Unc
Pa-Ph 295	1870	WM	19mm	—	—	200.	300.

Lincoln bust right, ABRAHAM LINCOLN around, 1864 below. Rv: As reverse of Pa 290. (DeWitt AL 1864-74 (B).) Tiny K below bust. (King 638) The 'K' is for diesinker William H. Key of Philadelphia. Only 2 struck.

Rulau	Date	Metal	Size	F	VF	EF	Unc
Pa-Ph 296	1870	Brass	19mm	—	—	200.	300.

As 295. Plain edge. Only 2 struck.

Rulau	Date	Metal	Size	F	VF	EF	Unc
Pa-Ph 298	1870	WM	19mm	—	—	200.	300.

Benjamin Franklin bust left. Rv: As 290. Only 2 struck.

Rulau	Date	Metal	Size	F	VF	EF	Unc
Pa-Ph 299	1870	Brass	19mm	—	—	200.	300.

As 298. Only 2 struck.

Mason listed the mintages for his store cards in his journal. The order was executed by Warner and the dies cut by Key.

By 1872 Mason had moved to 907 Chestnut St.

MELVIN & SOEDER

Rulau	Date	Metal	Size	F	VF	EF	Unc
Pa-Ph 300	(1880's)	Brass	32mm	—	—	35.00	—

MELVIN & SOEDER / COMMISSION / MERCHANTS / 334 S. FRONT ST / PHILA. Rv: Large numeral 50 at center, dot at either side, five ornaments above and five below. Plain edge. (ANS coll.)

D. M. MURPHY

1876 Centennial Tokens

Reverse type 1: D. M. MURPHY / (large numeral) / 2ND & CHRISTIAN STS. (All 23mm; plain edge)

Reverse type 2: D. M. MURPHY / 1 lb. COFFEE / 2ND & CHRISTIAN STS. (All 23mm; plain edge)

Rulau	Obv	Rev	Metal	F	VF	EF	Unc
Pa-Ph 276	G Numeral 13.	1	WM	—	—	17.50	45.00
Pa-Ph 276B	G Numeral 15. (Wright 738; Miller 374)	1	WM	—	—	17.50	45.00
Pa-Ph 276 D	G Numeral 20. (Miller 375)	1	WM	—	—	17.50	45.00
Pa-Ph 278	A (Miller 376)	2	WM	—	—	17.50	45.00
Pa-Ph 279	G (Miller 377)	2	WM	—	—	17.50	45.00

These pieces are very similar in style to those of the Great Union Pacific Tea Company, which see.

NATIONAL UNION LEAGUE

Rulau	Date	Metal	Size	F	VF	EF	Unc
Pa-Ph 300	1863	Silver	26mm	—	—	25.00	75.00

Facing bust of Van Buren, MARTIN VAN BUREN above, .THE PEOPLES CHOICE. below. Rv: Shield within wreath, 1863 below. Around: NATIONAL UNION LEAGUE / OF / THE / UNITED STATES. Plain edge. (DeWitt MVB-C (1).

Rulau	Date	Metal	Size	F	VF	EF	Unc
Pa-Ph 301	1863 As last.	Copper	26mm	—	—	25.00	75.00
Pa-Ph 302	1863 As last.	Brass	26mm	—	—	25.00	75.00
Pa-Ph 303	1863 As last.	WM	26mm	—	—	25.00	75.00

All struck by William H. Key of Philadelphia. The shield side has been muled with many other tokens. The obverse die is Low 57 retouched.

UNION LEAGUE

Rulau	Date	Metal	Size	F	VF	EF	Unc
Pa-Ph 306	1863	WM	34mm	—	—	—	35.00

Scroll lettered E PLURIBUS UNUM across U.S. shield at center, separating 1776 — 1863. UNION LEAGUE / JULY 4TH above; PHILADELPHIA. below, Rv: Blank. Plain edge. Rarity 5. (Fuld NC-25e)

Rulau	Date	Metal	Size	F	VF	EF	Unc
Pa-Ph 307	1863	Silver	34mm	—	—	—	100.

As last. Plain edge. Rarity 8. (Fuld NC-25f)

Rulau	Date	Metal	Size	F	VF	EF	Unc
Pa-Ph 309	1863	WM	31mm	—	—	—	50.00

U.S. shield above wreath at center, UNION LEAGUE above, * 1863 * below. Rv: LANCASTER / * PENNA. *. Plain edge. Rarity 7. (Fuld NC-26e)

An illogical muling.

NEW MASONIC TEMPLE

Rulau	Date	Metal	Size	F	VF	EF	Unc
Pa-Ph 311	1873	WM	38.2mm	—	15.00	20.00	25.00

Building at center, NEW MASONIC TEMPLE above, PHILADELPHIA below. Rv: All-seeing eye above square and compass at center, DEDICATED SEPTEMBER 26 A.D. 1873. A. L. 5873 around, small diamond flanked by dots at bottom. Plain edge.

NINTH PRECINCT HOUSE

Rulau	Date	Metal	Size	F	VF	EF	Unc
Pa-Ph 315	(1880's)	WM	22mm	—	—	15.00	40.00

Masonic symbol, with the ribbon bearing a legend: HONESTY, INDUSTRY, SOBRIETY, above, and below: O.V.A.M. Rv: NINTH PRECINCT / HOUSE / 126 CALLOWHILL ST. / PHILADA. / S.H. SMITH, PRO. Plain edge. (Coll. Jeff Rock, Santee, Calif.)

Rulau	Date	Metal	Size	F	VF	EF	Unc
Pa-Ph 315A	(1880's)	Copper	22mm	—	—	—	—

As 315. Plain edge. (Ganter coll.)

98TH ANNIVERSARY OF AMERICAN INDEPENDENCE

Rulau	Date	Metal	Size	F	VF	EF	Unc
PA-Ph A315	1874	S/WM	25mm	—	—	—	25.00

U.S. flag in breeze to left, above arc of 13 stars, LONG MAY IT WAVE. Rv: 98TH ANNIVERSARY OF AMERICAN INDEPENDENCE. / JULY / 4 / 1874. Plain edge.

This token helps to date the other U.S. flag-type mulings with various store cards. This design evidently was issued in early 1874, two years before the 1876 celebrations.

JOHN O'HARE

Rulau	Date	Metal	Size	F	VF	EF	Unc
Pa-Ph C315	(?)	Silver	25mm	—	—	45.00	—

JOHN O'HARE / PHILA. / * PA. * / * within circle of stars and dashes ctsp on U.S. Seated Liberty quarter. (Krueger 3560; Brunk 30115)

PENNSYLVANIA STATE AGRICULTURAL FAIR

Rulau	Date	Metal	Size	F	VF	EF	Unc
Pa-Ph 320	1880	Gilt/Br	25.3mm	—	12.50	20.00	35.00

At center a standing ram faces right, and a ewe left, while a baby lamb reclines right. In exergue: PHILA. SEP. / 1880. On scroll above is incused: INTRL. SHEEP & WOOL SHOW. Rv: Arms of Philadelphia are within a masonry capital. Atop the capital are a cow and her young bull offspring. At left: PENNSYLVANIA / STATE. At right: AGRICULTURAL / FAIR. Plain edge.

Rulau	Date	Metal	Size	F	VF	EF	Unc
Pa-Ph 320A	1880	Gold	25mm	—	—	—	Rare

As 320. A proof specimen of 320A was lot 1235 in the 1984 Virgil Brand sale. It weighed 162.1 grains.

The workmanship on this medalet is outstanding, indicating it is probably a U.S. Mint product. This is one of the most beautiful medalets or tokens included in this catalog. Quite scarce; seldom seen by veteran collectors. Perhaps about 30 pieces traceable.

PENN MUTUAL LIFE INS. COMPANY

1876 Centennial Tokens

Reverse type 1: PENN MUTUAL / LIFE / INS. COMPANY / 921 / CHESTNUT ST. / PHILA. (All 23mm; plain edge)

Rulau	Obv	Rev	Metal	F	VF	EF	Unc
Pa-Ph 316	A (Miller Pa 386)	1	WM	—	—	15.00	35.00
Pa-Ph 316 F	B (Miller 384)	1	WM	—	—	15.00	35.00
Pa-Ph 316 G	B (Miller 383)	1	Copper	—	—	17.50	40.00
Pa-Ph 316 H	B	1	Brass	—	—	20.00	45.00
Pa-Ph 317	E (Miller 387)	1	WM	—	—	15.00	35.00
Pa-Ph 317 A	E	1	Copper	—	—	17.50	40.00
Pa-Ph 317 B	E	1	Brass	—	—	20.00	45.00
Pa-Ph 317 F	F (Wright 812; Miller 385)	1	WM	—	—	20.00	42.50
Pa-Ph 318	G (Miller 388)	1	WM	—	—	15.00	35.00
Pa-Ph 318 F	H	1	WM	—	—	20.00	45.00
Pa-Ph 319	K (Miller 389)	1	WM	—	—	20.00	42.50

This company is still active in the insurance business.

PFAELZER BROS.

1876 Centennial Tokens

Reverse type 1: PFAELZER BROS. / WHOLESALE / JEWELRY / 421 MARKET ST. PHILADA. (All 23mm; plain edge)

Rulau	Obv	Rev	Metal	F	VF	EF	Unc
Pa-Ph 321	A	1	WM	—	—	15.00	40.00
Pa-Ph 322	B (Wright 818)	1	WM	—	—	15.00	40.00
Pa-Ph 322 A	B	1	Copper	—	—	20.00	50.00
Pa-Ph 322 F	E	1	WM	—	—	15.00	40.00
Pa-Ph 323	F	1	WM	—	—	17.50	45.00
Pa-Ph 323 A	F	1	Copper	—	—	20.00	50.00
Pa-Ph 324	H	1	WM	—	—	17.50	45.00
Pa-Ph 324 A	H (Miller Pa 392)	1	Copper	—	—	20.00	50.00
Pa-Ph 324 B	H	1	Brass	—	—	20.00	55.00
Pa-Ph 325	J	1	WM	—	—	17.50	45.00

PHILADELPHIA RIFLE CLUB

Rulau	Date	Metal	Size	F	VF	EF	Unc
Pa-Ph 326	1871	Brass	26mm	—	—	—	35.00
	Target at center, letter V and eagle above. Rv: 25TH / ANNIVERSARY / PHILADELPHIA / RIFLE CLUB / AUGUST / 1871. Plain edge. (Wright 825)						

This club was organized in 1846, one of the earliest rifle organizations in the country. This also exists in silver, $100 in Unc.

A. PICARD

1876 Centennial Tokens

Reverse type 1: A. PICARD / WATCHES / AND / JEWELRY / 805 ARCH ST., PHILAD'A. (All 23mm; plain edge)

Rulau	Obv	Rev	Metal	F	VF	EF	Unc
Pa-Ph 701	A (Miller Pa 403)	1	WM	5.00	8.00	14.00	30.00
Pa-Ph 701 A	A	1	Copper	—	—	17.50	40.00
Pa-Ph 702	C (Miller 401)	1	WM	—	—	14.00	30.00
Pa-Ph 702 A	C	1	Copper	—	—	17.50	40.00
Pa-Ph 702 C	C (Miller 400)	1	Brass	—	—	17.50	40.00
Pa-Ph 703	E (Miller 403B)	1	WM	—	—	15.00	35.00
Pa-Ph 703 A	E	1	Copper	—	—	17.50	40.00
Pa-Ph 704	F (Miller 403A)	1	WM	—	—	20.00	45.00
Pa-Ph 705	G	1	WM	—	—	20.00	45.00
Pa-Ph 705 A	G	1	Copper	—	—	20.00	45.00
Pa-Ph 706	H (Miller 402)	1	WM	—	—	17.50	40.00
Pa-Ph 706 A	H	1	Copper	—	—	20.00	45.00
Pa-Ph 707	K (Miller 403C)	1	WM	—	—	20.00	45.00

PILGRIMAGE OF SAN FRANCISCO CLUB

Rulau	Date	Metal	Size	F	VF	EF	Unc
Pa-Ph 327	1883	Brass	31mm	—	—	25.00	35.00
	Cross-through-crown superimposed over Maltese cross at center. Around: PILGRIMAGE OF SAN FRANCISCO CLUB TO TRIENNIAL CONCLAVE / . 1883 . Rv: Standing pilgrim with staff facing at center. Around, in three lines: PHILADELPHIA ST. JOHN'S KADOSH ST. ALBAN CORINTHIAN AND / KENSINGTON COMMANDERIES KNIGHTS TEMPLAR. / PHILA. PA. Plain edge.						

JACOB RECH

Rulau	Date	Metal	Size	F	VF	EF	Unc
Pa-Ph 330	(1873-74)	WM	26mm	—	—	50.00	100.
	Clothed, bearded bust of Lincoln right, LINCOLN above, tiny BOLEN beneath bust. Rv: JACOB RECH / FIRST CLASS / CARRIAGE / & WAGON / BUILDER / COR. OF / GIRARD AVE. & 8TH ST / PHILADELPHIA. Plain edge. (King 611; Miller Pa 404)						
Pa-Ph 332	1876	Brass	26mm	—	—	50.00	100.
	Bust of Hayes half right, R.B. HAYES above, 1876 below. Rv: As 330. (DeWitt RBH 1876-11; Miller Pa 404A)						
Pa-Ph 333	1876	WM	26mm	—	—	50.00	100.
	As 332. Plain edge. (DeWitt RBH 1876-11)						
Pa-Ph 335	(1876)	Copper	25mm	—	—	20.00	50.00
	American flag blowing to left, LONG MAY IT WAVE above, 13 stars to right below. Rv: As 330. Plain edge. (Wright 1590)						
Pa-Ph 335A	(1876)	WM	25mm	—	—	—	100.
	As 335.						
Pa-Ph 337	(1876)	Copper	26mm	—	—	20.00	50.00
	Liberty bell. Rv: As 330.						

Rech was in business at the same locale in 1872.

J. REED

1876 Centennial Tokens

Reverse type 1: J. REED * ONE PRICE CLOTHING * / S. E. COR. / SECOND / & / SPRUCE / STS. / PHILAD. (All 23mm; plain edge)

Rulau	Obv	Rev	Meta	F	VF	EF	Unc
Pa-Ph 710	A 25.00(Miller Pa 408)	1	WM	5.00	8.00	12.50	
Pa-Ph 711	B	1	WM	—	—	12.50	25.00
Pa-Ph 712	C (Miller 405)	1	WM	—	—	14.00	30.00
Pa-Ph 712 A	C Also in Bronze. (Miller 406)	1	Copper	—	—	17.50	40.00
Pa-Ph 712 B	C	1	Brass	—	—	20.00	45.00
Pa-Ph 713	D	1	WM	—	—	14.00	30.00
Pa-Ph 714	E (Miller 409)	1	WM	—	—	12.50	25.00
Pa-Ph 715	F (Wright 873; Miller 410)	1	WM	—	—	17.50	40.00
Pa-Ph 716	G	1	WM	—	—	14.00	30.00
Pa-Ph 717	H (Miller 407)	1	WM	—	—	17.50	40.00

Jacob Reed's Sons was established in 1824 and is still in business as a men's wear outlet. A new building was erected in 1879, shown in the next token, Pa-Ph 340, which is not part of Reed's Centennial series.

JACOB REED'S SONS

Rulau	Date	Metal	Size	VG	F	VF	Unc
Pa-Ph 340	1879	WM	24mm	—	—	15.00	40.00
	A building. OUR NEW STORE / 1879. Rv: JACOB REED'S / SONS / CLOTHIERS / 2ND / & SPRUCE STS / PHILA. / ESTABLISHED 1824. Plain edge. (Wright 874)						

Rulau	Date	Metal	Size	F	VF	EF	Unc
Pa-Ph 341	1883	WM	34mm	—	—	—	27.50
	Jugate Columbia and Germania heads right, GERMAN AMERICAN BI-CENTENNIAL around, OCT. 6. below. Rv: GERMANTOWN (on scroll) / COMPLIMENTS / OF / JACOB REED'S SONS / —.— / CLOTHIERS / —.— / PHILADELPHIA / 1683 (on tablet) 1883 (on tablet) / (3-leaf clover) / VINUM LINUM ET TEXTRINUM (on scroll). Plain edge. (H&K 597)						

RETAIL GROCERS ASSOCIATION

Rulau	Date	Metal	Size	F	VF	EF	Unc
Pa-Ph 342	1888	WM	38mm	—	—	—	—
	Interior of old grocery store, very well executed. Around: RETAIL GROCERS ASSOCIATION OF PHILADELPHIA * / ORGANIZED 1886 / INCORPORATED 1887. Rv: Within wreath: AUG. 9th / 1888. Around: THIRD ANNUAL JUBILEE / *****. Plain edge. (Ganter coll.)						

N. H. RICE

1876 Centennial Tokens

Reverse type 1: CONTINENTAL / CLOTHING HALL / N. H. RICE / PROP. / 930 MARKET ST. / PHILADA., PA. (All 23mm; plain edge)

Rulau	Obv	Rev	Metal	F	VF	EF	Unc
Pa-Ph 720	A (Miller Pa 413)	1	WM	—	—	14.00	30.00
Pa-Ph 720 AA		1	Copper	—	—	15.00	40.00
Pa-Ph 721	B (Wright 882; Miller 414)	1	WM	—	—	14.00	35.00
Pa-Ph 721 AB		1	Brass	—	—	20.00	45.00
Pa-Ph 722	E (Miller 411)	1	WM	—	—	14.00	35.00
Pa-Ph 723	F (Miller 412)	1	WM	—	—	15.00	40.00
Pa-Ph 724	G (Miller 415)	1	WM	—	—	14.00	30.00
Pa-Ph 725	H	1	WM	—	—	15.00	40.00
Pa-Ph 726	J	1	WM	—	—	17.50	40.00
Pa-Ph 727	K	1	WM	—	—	15.00	40.00

E. LUCIEN RICHIE

Rulau	Date	Metal	Size	F	VF	EF	Unc
Pa-Ph 343	(1876 ?)	WM	24mm	—	—	35.00	—

Building. In exergue: ART GALLERY. Rv: E. LUCIEN RICHIE / ATTORNEY / AND / COUNSELLOR / 704 / WALNUT ST. / PHILADELPHIA. Plain edge. (Wright 890)

Wright in 1898 called this a Centennial card, but the obverse die matches no known Centennial design. We have not examined the piece.

T. ROWLAND & BROTHERS

Rulau	Date	Metal	Size	VG	F	VF	EF
Pa-Ph 348	(?)	Copper	29mm	—	—	75.00	—

T. ROWLAND & / BROTHERS / PHILADA ctsp on U.S. Large cent. (Hallenbeck 18.764; Brunk 35170)

SAUSSER, DANGLER & CO.

1876 Centennial Tokens

Reverse type 1: SAUSSER / DANGLER & CO. / FINE / SEWED SHOES / 412 TO 420 / SOUTH 13TH ST. / PHILA. (All 23mm; plain edge)

Rulau	Obv	Rev	Metal	F	VF	EF	Unc
Pa-Ph 730	A (Wright 1613; Miller Pa 438)	1	WM	—	—	15.00	40.00
Pa-Ph 731	B (Miller 440)	1	WM	—	—	15.00	40.00
Pa-Ph 732	E (Miller 439)	1	WM	—	—	15.00	40.00
Pa-Ph 733	F (Miller 441)	1	WM	—	—	17.50	42.50
Pa-Ph 734	G	1	WM	—	—	17.50	42.50
Pa-Ph 735	H (Miller 442)	1	WM	—	—	17.50	42.50
Pa-Ph 736	J	1	Copper	—	—	20.00	45.00

C. SCHMIDT

Rulau	Date	Metal	Size	VG	F	VF	Unc
Pa-Ph A348	(?)	Copper	23.5mm	—	—	12.50	—

C. SCHMIDT ctsp on each side of a U.S. 1853 or 1854 Half cent. (Stanley Steinberg 1982 sale; Brunk 35790)

JOHN G. SCHMIDT

1876 Centennial Tokens

Reverse type 1: JOHN G. SCHMIDT. / 1236 / POPLAR ST. / (an awl) / PHILADELPHIA / LEATHER / FINDINGS &C. (All 23mm; plain edge)

Obverse die SM: SOLE LEATHER / CALF / & GOAT SKINS. / LASTING. / MACHINE SILK / THREAD / TOOLS, UPPERS / OIL &C. (All 23mm; plain edges)

Rulau	Obv	Rev	Metal	F	VF	EF	Unc
Pa-Ph 352	C	1	Brass	—	—	20.00	45.00
Pa-Ph 353	H	1	WM			Not confirmed	
Pa-Ph 353 A	H	1	Brass	—	—	20.00	45.00
Pa-Ph 354	J (Miller Pa 447)	1	WM	7.50	10.00	15.00	40.00
Pa-Ph 354 A	J (Miller 446)	1	Brass	5.00	8.50	20.00	45.00
Pa-Ph 356	SM (Miller 445)	1	WM	—	—	15.00	40.00
Pa-Ph 356 A	SM (Miller 444)	1	Copper	—	—	25.00	45.00
Pa-Ph 356 B	SM (Wright 947; Miller 443)	1	Brass	5.00	8.50	15.00	25.00

NOTE: Pa-Ph 356B was the regular store card of Schmidt, probably issued before the other tokens were conceived. This is an interesting series, with more varieties probably awaiting discovery.

JOS. SCHOENEMAN & CO.

Rulau	Date	Metal	Size	VG	F	VF	Unc
Pa-Ph 361	(1889)	WM	36mm	—	—	—	150.

Two men in tights boxing, bare-knuckle style. Rv: JOS. / SCHOENEMAN / & CO. / PHILADELPHIA within flourishes. Plain edge. (Wright 951) Scarce

Wright reports this piece in aluminum, which needs comfirmation.

Rulau	Date	Metal	Size	VG	F	VF	Unc
Pa-Ph 362	(1889)	WM	36mm	—	—	—	150.

Batter awaiting baseball as an infielder watches from background. The uniform styles are Gay Nineties or earlier. Rv: Same as last. Plain edge. Scarce

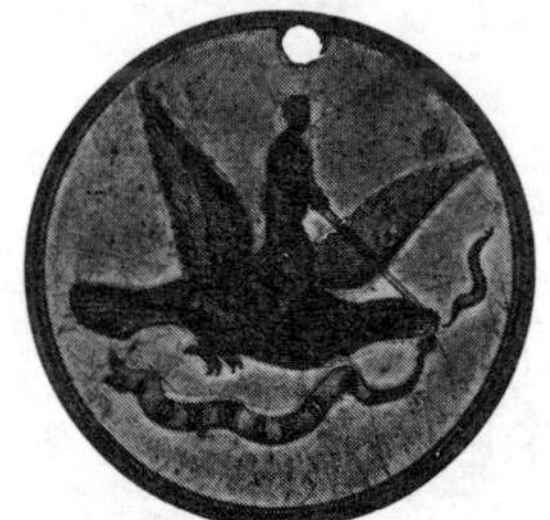

Rulau	Date	Metal	Size	VG	F	VF	Unc
Pa-Ph 363	(1889)	WM	36mm	—	—	—	150.

Standing man riding the back of a gigantic eagle, flying right, from whose beak a ribbon reading ONWARD trails. Rv: As 361. Plain edge. (Brunk coll.)

SCHOENEMAN LANGSTADTER & CO.

Rulau	Date	Metal	Size	VG	F	VF	Unc
Pa-Ph 364	(1889)	WM	36mm	—	—	—	150.

Obverse as 362 (baseball game). Rv: SCHOENEMAN / LANGSTADTER / & CO. / (ornament) — PHILADELPHIA. Plain edge. (Wright 952)

Rulau	Date	Metal	Size	F	VF	EF	Unc
Pa-Ph 364F	(1889)	C/Lead*	34mm	—	—	200.	—

* Copper-plated lead. Boy falling forward off old-fashioned high front wheel bicycle which has hit a stone, as a girl watches. Rv: SCHOENEMAN / LANGSTADTER & CO / PHILADELPHIA. Plain edge. Ex. rare. (Tanenbaum coll.; Ganter coll.)

A possible successor firm, William C. Schoeneman & Son, were in the wholesale fancy goods and toys business in 1918.

C. B. SCOTT & CO.

1876 Centennial Tokens

Reverse type 1: C. B. SCOTT & CO. / MANUFR'S / AND / DEALERS IN / FURNITURE / NO. 33 / SO. SECOND ST. / PHILA. (All 23mm; plain edge)

Rulau	Obv	Rev	Metal	F	VF	EF	Unc
Pa-Ph 740	A (Miller Pa 449)	1	WM	—	—	15.00	40.00
Pa-Ph 740 A	A (Wright 967; Miller 450)	1	Brass	—	—	20.00	45.00
Pa-Ph 741	B (Miller 454)	1	WM	—	—	15.00	40.00
Pa-Ph 741 A	B	1	Copper	—	—	17.50	40.00
Pa-Ph 742	E (Miller 453)	1	WM	—	—	15.00	40.00
Pa-Ph 743	F (Miller 455)	1	WM	—	—	17.50	40.00
Pa-Ph 744	G	1	WM	—	—	17.50	40.00
Pa-Ph 745	H (Miller 452)	1	WM	—	—	17.50	40.00
Pa-Ph 745 A	H	1	Copper	—	—	20.00	45.00
Pa-Ph 745 B	H (Miller 451)	1	Brass	—	—	20.00	50.00
Pa-Ph 746	J	1	WM	—	—	20.00	45.00

2ND REGIMENT N.G. PA.

Rulau	Date	Metal	Size	F	VF	EF	Unc
Pa-Ph 372	1879	Bronze	19mm	—	15.00	—	35.00

Crested shield of arms at center. Eagle, wings folded, head left, is the crest. Arms are those of the Pennsylvania National Guard. On a scroll below: NON SIBI SED PATRIAE (not for self but for country). Around: 2ND REGIMENT N. G. PA. / * 1840. — 1879. *. Rv: Crested, supported shield of arms of Philadelphia at center. Around: COMMEMORATION OF THE FAIR / * NOV. 10. 1879 *. Reeded edge.

Rulau	Date	Metal	Size	F	VF	EF	Unc
Pa-Ph 372A	1879	Silver	19mm	—	—	—	42.50

As 372. Reeded edge. (George Ganter coll.)

Presumably the Pennsylvania National Guard was organized in 1840. This neat, well made cent-sized medalet may be a product of the U.S. Mint.

JOHN H. SERVER

1876 Centennial Tokens

Reverse type 1: JOHN H. SERVER / TOBACCO / CIGARS / AND / VARIETY STORE / 1646 S. 11TH ST. PHILA. (All 23mm; plain edge)

Rulau	Obv	Rev	Metal	F	VF	EF	Unc
Pa-Ph 750	A (Wright 1626; Miller Pa 457)	1	WM	—	—	15.00	40.00
Pa-Ph 751	B (Miller 456)	1	WM	—	—	15.00	40.00
Pa-Ph 751 A	B	1	Brass	—	—	20.00	45.00
Pa-Ph 752	D (Miller 461)	1	WM	—	—	15.00	40.00
Pa-Ph 752 A	D	1	Brass	—	—	20.00	45.00
Pa-Ph 753	E (Miller 458)	1	WM	—	—	15.00	40.00
Pa-Ph 754	F (Miller 459)	1	WM	—	—	20.00	45.00
Pa-Ph 755	G	1	WM	—	—	17.50	40.00
Pa-Ph 756	H (Miller 460)	1	WM	—	—	17.50	40.00
Pa-Ph 757	K (Miller 460A)	1	WM	—	—	20.00	45.00

SHOO FLY

Rulau	Date	Metal	Size	VG	F	VF	EF
Pa-Ph 371	(1885)	Copper	29mm	—	60.00	—	90.00

SHOO / FLY ctsp on U.S. Large cent. (Hallenbeck 19.505; Rulau Z83; Brunk 36495)

Rulau	Date	Metal	Size	VG	F	VF	EF
Pa-Ph 371 B	(1885)	Copper	30mm	—	60.00	—	—

Similar ctsp on France 1855-A 10-centimes of Napoleon III. (Larry Laevens coll.)

Rulau	Date	Metal	Size	VG	F	VF	EF
Pa-Ph 371 E	(1885)	Silver	25mm	—	75.00	—	125.

Similar ctsp on U.S. 1856 Seated Liberty quarter. (Duffield 1501; Rulau Z84)

The Shoo Fly Mfg. Co. apparently started in 1885, when it is likely these counterstamped advertising pieces were made. Shoo Fly is a registered trademark (in the U.S.) of the company. Shoo Fly was called "the animals' friend"; it was a liquid preparation to keep insects off cows, etc.

The Farm Journal of Philadelphia for August 1913 and June 1916 carried this ad:

Shoo-Fly The Animal's Friend

Trade Mark reg. U.S. Pat. Off.

For keeping flies and many other insects off of animals — in barn or pasture — longer than any imitation. Used and endorsed since 1885 by leading dairymen.

$1 worth saves $20.00 in milk and flesh on each cow in a single season. Excellent for galls. Allays itching. Aids in keeping animals from irritating sores by rubbing or stamping. Excellent for lice and mites in poultry houses.

$1.25 ($1.50 west of Mississippi River) will bring you enough Shoo-Fly to protect 10 cows 2 weeks, also our 3-tube gravity sprayers, express prepaid. Money back if not satisfactory. Name Express office. Book FREE.

Special terms to agents.

Shoo-Fly Mfg. Co., Dept. B, 1310 N. 10th St. Phila.

Editor knows from experience Shoo-Fly is O.K.

(Research courtesy Larry Laevens, Brantford, Canada)

SINKLER & DAVEY

Rulau	Date	Metal	Size	F	VF	Unc
Pa-Ph 373	(1889-90)	Brass	29mm	150.	200.	—

Two donkeys are at center, star below. WHEN SHALL WE THREE MEET AGAIN is around. Rv: SINKLER & DAVEY / * / MANUF'S OF / FANCY METAL WORK / LABEL, CHECKS & / FANCY LETTERS. -- / 609 CALLOWHILL ST. / (arrow) PHILAD'A (arrow). Plain edge. (Miller Pa 474 1/2)

Sinkler & Davey were diesinkers in business in Philadelphia in the late 1880's. The same obverse die (two donkeys) was used on the Applegate tokens of Atlantic City and Feely tokens of Philadelphia, and a very similar one (in reduced size) was used on the Durkee & Co. omnibus checks in New York in the 1840's. The Durkee piece may have been the model for the S&D pieces.

A successor firm, William Davey's Son, was in the stamped metal goods business in 1918.

Harry Sinkler and William H. Davey, diesinkers, are listed at the 609 Callowhill St. address only in the 1890 directory, which means they were there, probably, 1889-1890.

Therefore these pieces must be placed in the 1889-90 date frame, or just at the outer edge of our coverage in this section.

G. B. SOLEY

Rulau	Date	Metal	Size	F	VF	EF	Unc
Pa-Ph 375	(1876)	**	37mm	—	—	50.00	65.00

** Golden colored cardboard.

Independence Hall at center, tiny G. B. SOLEY PHILA. below ground line. Above: BIRTH PLACE OF AMERICAN; below: INDEPENDENCE / 1776. Rv: G. B. SOLEY, 1205 CHESTNUT ST. PHILA. / MANUFACTURER / OF / (sprig) MEDALS. (sprig) / —.— / THE LORD'S PRAYER / IN SMALLEST SPACE / EVER STRUCK ON METAL. / —.— / PAPER & METALLIC / ADVERTISING / CARDS. Plain edge.

JOHN STILZ & SON

1876 Centennial Tokens

Reverse type 1: JOHN STILZ & SON / * / FINEST / CLOTHING / HOUSE / S. E. COR. 7 & MARKET / PHILADA. (All 23mm; plain edge)

Rulau	Obv	Rev	Metal	F	VF	EF	Unc
Pa-Ph 760	A	1	WM	5.00	8.00	12.50	30.00
	(Wright 1046; Miller Pa 492)						
Pa-Ph 760 A	A	1	Copper	—	—	14.00	37.50
	(Miller 491)						
Pa-Ph 760 B	A	1	Brass	—	—	16.50	40.00
Pa-Ph 761	B	1	WM	—	—	12.50	30.00
	(Miller 493)						
Pa-Ph 762	C	1	WM	—	—	15.00	37.50
Pa-Ph 763	E	1	WM	—	—	14.00	37.50
	(Miller 495)						
Pa-Ph 764	F	1	WM	—	—	15.00	40.00
	(Miller 496)						
Pa-Ph 765	H	1	WM	—	—	14.00	37.50
	(Miller 494)						
Pa-Ph 766	K	1	WM	—	—	15.00	40.00
	(Miller 497)						

DR. STOUGHTON

1876 Centennial Tokens

Reverse type 1: TEETH / $5 to $15 / PER SET / FILLING 75C to $1. / EXTRACTING 25C / DR. STOUGHTON / 1117 / VINE ST. (All 23mm; plain edge)

Rulau	Obv	Rev	Metal	F	VF	EF	Unc
Pa-Ph 383	A	1	WM	—	—	20.00	45.00
Pa-Ph 384	B	1	WM	—	—	20.00	45.00
Pa-Ph 385	E	1	WM	—	—	20.00	45.00
Pa-Ph 386	F	1	Copper	—	—	25.00	55.00
Pa-Ph 386 A	F	1	Brass	—	—	25.00	55.00
Pa-Ph 387	G	1	WM	—	—	22.50	50.00
Pa-Ph 388	K	1	WM	—	—	22.50	50.00
	(Wright 1066; Miller Pa 502)						

These tokens provide a schedule of big-city dentist fees in 1876. The 25-cent extraction was without benefit of painkiller.

THEATRE CHESTNUT STREET

Rulau	Date	Metal	Size	VG	F	VF	EF
Pa-Ph 377	(?)	Brass	30mm	—	—	Rare	—

(All incused): THEATRE / CHESTNUT / STREET in ornate lettering. Rv: (Engraved in script) Mifs Cushman. on plain field. Raised dentilated border on each side. Plain edge. Holed, as issued. (Woodward 54th sale, Dec. 28, 1882, lot 650 of the Maas collection; Garrett III 1985 by Numismatic Fine Arts)

The 'Mifs' stands for 'Miss'. Theater pass. Report and photo by David R. Sear.

JAS. THORNTON

1876 Centennial Tokens

Reverse type 1: JAS. THORNTON'S / LOOKING GLASS / PICTURE FRAME / AND / BRACKET DEPOT / S. W. COR. 11 AND LOCUST ST., PHILA. (All 23mm; plain edge)

Rulau	Obv	Rev	Metal	F	VF	EF	Unc
Pa-Ph 770	A	1	WM	—	—	12.50	30.00
	(Wright 1144; Miller Pa 521)						
Pa-Ph 771	B	1	WM	—	—	12.50	30.00
	(Miller 520)						
Pa-Ph 771 A	B	1	Copper	—	—	15.00	35.00
	(Miller 519)						
Pa-Ph 771 B	B	1	Brass	—	—	17.50	40.00
Pa-Ph 772	D	1	WM	—	—	15.00	35.00
Pa-Ph 773	E	1	WM	—	—	15.00	35.00
	(Miller 522)						
Pa-Ph 774	F	1	WM	—	—	17.50	40.00
	(Miller 523)						
Pa-Ph 775	G	1	WM	—	—	15.00	35.00
Pa-Ph 776	H	1	WM	—	—	15.00	35.00
Pa-Ph 777	J	1	WM	—	—	15.00	35.00
Pa-Ph 778	K	1	WM	—	—	17.50	40.00
Pa-Ph 778 A	K	1	Brass	—	—	20.00	45.00
	(Miller 519A)						

S. C. UPHAM

1876 Centennial Tokens

Reverse type 1: S. C. UPHAM. PERFUMER. (All 19mm; plain edge)

Rulau	Obv	Rev	Metal	F	VF	EF	Unc
Pa-Ph 780	X	1	WM	—	—	20.00	50.00
Pa-Ph 781	Y	1	WM	—	—	20.00	50.00

S. C. Upham is well known to paper money collectors for his facsimiles of Confederate States notes. These tokens were not known to Wright, Adams, Miller and other cataloguers.

U.S. MINT EMPLOYEES

Rulau	Date	Metal	Size	F	VF	EF	Unc
Pa-Ph 390	1879	Brass	25mm	3.00	6.50	8.50	13.00

Bust left, ULYSSES S. GRANT. Tiny M on truncation of bust. Rv: Supported Philadelphia arms in center circle. STRUCK AND DISTRIBUTED IN THE MUNICIPAL PARADE (diamond) / BY THE EMPLOYES (sic!) OF THE U.S. MINT / . PHILA. DEC. 16. 1879. Plain edge.

Rulau	Date	Metal	Size	F	VF	EF	Unc
Pa-Ph 390 A	1879	Gold	25mm	—	—	—	2 Known

As 390. Plain edge.

Rulau	Date	Metal	Size	F	VF	EF	Unc
Pa-Ph 393	1882	Brass	25mm	2.00	4.00	6.00	12.00

Facing bust in colonial hat, PENN 1682. Rv: Supported Pennsylvania arms in center circle. DISTRIBUTED BY EMPLOYES (sic) OF U.S. MINT DURING THE CELEBRATION. / OF PENNSYLVANIA'S BICENTENNIAL. / . OCT. 24, 1882. Plain edge.

Rulau	Date	Metal	Size	F	VF	EF	Unc
Pa-Ph 393 A	1882	Gold	25mm	—	—	3 Known	—

As 393. Plain edge.

Rulau	Date	Metal	Size	F	VF	EF	Unc
Pa-Ph 393 B	1882	Silver	25mm	—	—	—	—

As 393. Plain edge.

Rulau	Date	Metal	Size	F	VF	EF	Unc
Pa-Ph 396	1887	Brass	25mm	3.00	6.50	8.00	12.00

Bust of U.S. Mint Director Snowden right, A. LOUDON SNOWDEN / o MARSHAL o. Rv: CENTENNIAL OF THE CONSTITUTION / STRUCK / & DISTRIBUTED / IN THE / CIVIC & INDUSTRIAL / PROCESSION / SEPT. 15. / .1787-1887. Plain edge.

JOHN E. VALLEE

1876 Centennial Tokens

Reverse type 1: JOHN E. VALLEE / LOCKSMITH, BELL HANGER / 1934 / GERMANTOWN AVE. (All 23mm; plain edge)

Reverse type 2: JOHN E. VALLEE / BELL HANGER / 2313 / N. EIGHTH ST. / PHILA. (All 23mm; plain edge)

Rulau	Obv	Rev	Metal	F	VF	EF	Unc
Pa-Ph 785	A	1	WM	—	—	15.00	40.00
	(Miller Pa 526)						
Pa-Ph 786	B	1	WM	—	—	15.00	40.00
	(Miller 527)						
Pa-Ph 786 A	B	1	Brass	—	—	20.00	45.00
Pa-Ph 787	C	1	WM	—	—	15.00	45.00
Pa-Ph 788	D	1	WM	—	—	17.50	40.00
	(Miller 529A)						
Pa-Ph 789	E	1	WM	—	—	15.00	40.00
	(Miller 528)						
Pa-Ph 790	F	1	WM	—	—	20.00	45.00

Pa-Ph 791	G	1	WM	—	—	17.50	40.00
	(Miller 525)						
Pa-Ph 792	H	1	WM	—	—	17.50	40.00
	(Miller 524)						
Pa-Ph 793	J	1	Copper	—	—	20.00	45.00
	(Miller 529B)						
Pa-Ph 795	A	2	WM	—	—	15.00	40.00
	(Wright 1181 ?)						
Pa-Ph 796	B	2	WM	—	—	15.00	40.00
Pa-Ph 796 F	G	2	WM	—	—	17.50	45.00
Pa-Ph 797	H	2	WM	—	—	17.50	45.00
Pa-Ph 797 F	J	2	WM	—	—	17.50	45.00
Pa-Ph 798	K	2	WM	—	—	17.50	45.00

VICTORIA CORDAGE WORKS

Rulau	Date	Metal	Size	F	VF	EF	Unc
Pa-Ph 400	(1880's)	GB	25mm	3.00	4.00	5.00	10.00

Wheat stalks within a crown. TRADE MARK below. Rv: + BINDER TWINE + / VICTORIA / (radiant sun) / CORDAGE / WORKS / (radiant sun) / PHILADELPHIA / AND CORDAGE. Plain edge. (Wright 1190)

C.A. WALTHER

1876 Centennial Tokens

Reverse type 1: LIBRARY ST. HALL / 412 LIBRARY ST. / PHILA. / --- / CHOICE / WINES & BEERS. / C. A. WALTHER, PROPR. (All 23mm; plain edge. Not catalogued by Slabaugh)

Rulau	Obv	Rev	Metal	F	VF	EF	Unc
Pa-Ph 405	J	1	WM	—	—	—	100.
Pa-Ph 406	K	1	WM	—	—	13.50	25.00
	(Wright 1714; Miller Pa 529 1/2)						

WANAMAKER & BROWN

Rulau	Date	Metal	Size	F	VF	EF	Unc
Pa-Ph 410	(1880's)	Brass	25mm	2.00	3.00	4.50	10.00
	U.S. flag, WANAMAKER & BROWN below. Rv: Huge building at center, tiny P.L. KRIDER on exergue line. BOYS CLOTHING above, OAK HALL in exergue. Plain edge. (Wright 1201; Miller Pa 532)						
Pa-Ph 411	(1880's)	S/Br	25mm	2.50	3.50	5.00	10.00
	As 410, Plain edge. (Miller Pa 532A)						
Pa-Ph 411 A	(1880's)	Copper	25mm	—	—	—	—
	As 410. Plain edge.						

Struck by Peter L. Krider of Philadelphia.

John Wanamaker (1838-1922) and Nathan Brown founded Wanamaker & Brown, clothiers, in 1861. Brown died in 1868. The firm, under William H. Wanamaker, was still in business in 1918, under the same name.

The extensive token issues of John Wanamaker Stores begin after 1890 and are catalogued in our new reference, *Tokens of the Gay Nineties.*

There are about 50 such pieces known.

CHARLES K. WARNER

Rulau	Date	Metal	Size	F	VF	EF	Unc
Pa-Ph 435	(?)	Copper	--mm	8.00	14.00	18.00	50.00
	Small bust of George Washington. Rv: 28 battles. (Miller Pa 533)						
Pa-Ph 435 A	(?)	Brass	--mm	8.00	14.00	18.00	50.00
	As 435. (Miller Pa 534)						
Pa-Ph 435 B	(?)	WM	--mm	8.00	14.00	22.00	50.00
	As 435. (Miller Pa 535)						

Rulau	Date	Metal	Size	F	VF	EF	Unc
Pa-Ph 437	(1862-63)	Copper	26mm	—	—	30.00	75.00
	Facing bust of Van Buren, MARTIN VAN BUREN. above, .THE PEOPLES CHOICE. below. (Obverse die of Low 57, retouched.) Rv: CHAS. K. WARNER / DEALER IN / AMERICAN & / FOREIGN / COINS / & MEDALS / 326 CHESTNUT ST., PHILA. Plain edge. (DeWitt MVB-C(3)) Only 15 struck. (Miller Pa 535A)						
Pa-Ph 437 A	(1862-63)	Brass	26mm	—	—	30.00	75.00
	As 437. 15 struck. (Miller Pa 535B)						
Pa-Ph 437 B	(1862-63)	WM	26mm	—	—	30.00	75.00
	As 437. 15 struck. (Miller Pa 535C)						
Pa-Ph 439	(?)	Copper	26mm	8.00	14.00	18.00	50.00
	General Peter Lyle. Rv: As 535A. Plain edge. (Miller Pa 536)						
Pa-Ph 439 A	(?)	Brass	26mm	8.00	14.00	18.00	50.00
	As 439. (Miller Pa 537)						
Pa-Ph 439 B	(?)	WM	26mm	8.00	14.00	22.00	50.00
	As 439. (Miller Pa 538)						
Pa-Ph 440	(?)	Copper	26mm	8.00	14.00	18.00	50.00
	THE CONSTITUTION & THE UNION. Rv: As 437. Plain edge. (Miller Pa 539)						
Pa-Ph 440 A	(?)	Brass	26mm	8.00	14.00	18.00	50.00
	As 440. (Miller Pa 540)						
Pa-Ph 440 B	(?)	WM	26mm	8.00	14.00	22.00	50.00
	As 440. (Miller Pa 541)						

Rulau	Date	Metal	Size	F	VF	EF	Unc
Pa-Ph 442	(1863)	Copper	26mm	—	—	30.00	75.00
	General U.S. Grant military bust left, tiny W.H.K. below truncation. Around: LIEUT. GEN. U. S. GRANT. Rv: C. K. WARNER / (eagle) / NUMISMATIST, / 326 / CHESTNUT ST. / - / PHILADELPHIA. Plain edge. Only 15 struck. (Miller Pa 542)						
Pa-Ph 442 A	(1863)	Brass	26mm	—	—	30.00	75.00
	As 442. (Miller Pa 543)						
Pa-Ph 442 B	(1863)	WM	26mm	—	—	30.00	75.00
	As 442. (Miller Pa 544)						
Pa-Ph 443	(1865)	Copper	26mm	—	—	30.00	75.00
	Surrender of General Lee. Rv: As 437. Plain edge. (Miller Pa 545)						
Pa-Ph 443 A	(1865)	Brass	26mm	—	—	30.00	75.00
	As 443. (Miller Pa 546)						
Pa-Ph 443 B	(1865)	WM	26mm	—	—	30.00	75.00
	As 443. (Miller Pa 547)						
Pa-Ph 445	(1868)	Copper	26mm	—	—	25.00	60.00
	Bust of Horatio Seymour. Rv: As 437. Plain edge. (Miller Pa 548)						
Pa-Ph 445 A	(1868)	Brass	26mm	—	—	25.00	60.00
	As 445. (Miller Pa 549)						
Pa-Ph 445 B	(1868)	WM	26mm	—	—	25.00	60.00
	As 445. (Miller Pa 550)						
Pa-Ph 446	1862	Copper	26mm	—	—	30.00	75.00
	Monitor, 1862. Rv: As 437. Plain edge. (Miller Pa 551)						
Pa-Ph 446 A	1862	Brass	26mm	—	—	30.00	75.00
	As 446. (Miller 552)						
Pa-Ph 446 B	1862	WM	26mm	—	—	30.00	75.00
	As 446. (Miller 553)						
Pa-Ph 448	1860('65)	Copper	27mm	—	—	50.00	100.
	Bust of beardless Lincoln right, tiny R L PHILA under truncation of the bust. ABM: LINCOLN, REP. CANDIDATE FOR PRESIDENT around, 1860 below. Rv: Washington bust right within two-line inscription: CHAS. K. WARNER / DEALER IN / AMERICAN & / FOREIGN / MEDALS / 728 CHESTNUT ST., * PHILAD*. Plain edge. (King 601; DeWitt AL 1860-51(B); Miller Pa 554)						
Pa-Ph 448 A	1860('65)	Brass	27mm	—	—	50.00	100.
	As 448. (King 601; DeWitt AL 1860-51(B); Miller 555)						
Pa-Ph 448 B	1860('65)	WM	27mm	—	—	50.00	100.
	As 448. (King 601; DeWitt AL 1860-51(B); Miller 556)						

The dies for 448-448B were cut by Robert Lovett Jr. of Philadelphia. It is possible they were contemporary with the date 1860 and belong in *U.S. Merchant Tokens 1845-1860,* but until evidence suggests otherwise we believe they are post-Civil War products of coin dealer Warner.

Pa-Ph 450 (1863) Copper 26mm 8.00 14.00 18.00 50.00
THE UNION MUST AND SHALL BE PRESERVED around. Head of Washington on flags, Rv: As 442. Plain edge. (Miller Pa 557)

Pa-Ph 450 A 1863 Brass 26mm 8.00 14.00 18.00 50.00
As 450. (Miller 558)

Pa-Ph 450 B 1863 WM 26mm 8.00 14.00 22.00 50.00
As 450. (Miller 559)

Pa-Ph 451 1863 Copper 26mm — — 30.00 75.00
General George B. McClellan. Rv: As 442. Plain edge. Only 15 struck. (Miller Pa 560)

Pa-Ph 451 A (1863) Brass 26mm — — 30.00 75.00
As 451. 15 struck. (Miller 561)

Pa-Ph 451 B (1863) WM 26mm — — 30.00 75.00
As 451. 15 struck. (Miller 562)

Pa-Ph 452 (1864) Copper --mm — — 30.00 75.00
Different head of McClellan than on 560. Rv: As 437. Plain edge.

Pa-Ph 452 A (1864) Brass --mm — — 30.00 75.00
As 452. (Miller 564)

Pa-Ph 452 B (1864) WM --mm — — 30.00 75.00
As 452. (Miller 565)

Pa-Ph 454 (?) Copper --mm — — 20.00 50.00
Victoria and Albert of England. Rv: As 437. Plain edge. (Miller Pa 566)

Pa-Ph 454 A (?) Brass --mm — — 20.00 50.00
As 454. (Miller 567)

Pa-Ph 454 B (?) WM --mm — — 25.00 60.00
As 454. (Miller 568)

Pa-Ph 455 1870 Copper 26mm — — 25.00 60.00
U.S. flag at center, LONG MAY IT WAVE around. Rv: As 535A. Plain edge. (Miller Pa 569A)

Pa-Ph 455 A 1870 Brass 26mm — — 25.00 60.00
As 455. (Miller 569)

Pa-Ph 455 B 1870 WM 26mm — — 25.00 60.00
As 455. (Wright 1204; Miller Pa 569B)

Pa-Ph 457 1863 Copper 26mm — — 25.00 60.00
Shield within a wreath. Around: NATIONAL UNION LEAGUE / OF / THE / 1863 / UNITED STATES. Rv: As 437. Plain edge. Only 15 struck. (Wright 1546; Miller Pa 569C)

Pa-Ph 457 A 1863 Brass 26mm — — 25.00 60.00
As 457. Plain edge. (Fuld NC-28b)

Pa-Ph 457 B 1863 WM 26mm — — 25.00 60.00
As 457. Plain edge. (Fuld NC-28e)

Pa-Ph 457 C 1863 CN 26mm — — — 60.00
As 457. Plain edge. (Fuld NC-28d)

Charles K. Warner and his brother William H. Warner were sons of medalist John S. Warner, who was active as a medalist 1823-1868. Charles and William were jewelers, medalists and coin dealers until the early 20th century.

Pa-Ph 458 1864('69) Copper 28mm — — 50.00 100.
Nude bust of Washington right, surrounded by two-line circular inscription: CHAS. K. WARNER, DEALER IN AMERICAN / & FOREIGN MEDALS / 728 CHESTNUT ST. / * PHILADA *. Rv: Clothed, bearded bust of Lincoln left. Around: ABRAHAM LINCOLN PRESIDENT OF THE U.S. Below: 1864. Under Lincoln's shoulder: W. H. KEY. Plain edge. (King 591; Miller Pa 800)

Pa-Ph 458 A 1864('69) Brass 28mm — — 50.00 100.
As 458. Plain edge. (King 591; Miller 801)

Pa-Ph 458 B 1864('69) WM 28mm — — 50.00 100.
As 458. Plain edge. (King 591; Miller 802)

Pa-Ph 459 1864 Brass 28mm — — 50.00 100.
Obverse as reverse of 458 (Lincoln). Rv: C. K. WARNER / NUMISMATIST / 326 / CHESTNUT ST. / PHILADELPHIA. Plain edge. (King 592; Miller Pa 803)

Pa-Ph 459 A 1864 CN 28mm — — 50.00 100.
As 459. Plain edge. (King 592; Miller 804)

Pa-Ph 461 1864 Brass 28mm — — 50.00 100.
Clothed, bearded bust of Lincoln left, within a circle of 31 stars. Around: ABRAHAM LINCOLN PRESIDENT OF THE U.S. ****. Below: 1864. Under Lincoln's bust: W. H. KEY. Rv: C. K. WARNER / (small eagle displayed) / NUMISMATIST / 326 CHESTNUT ST. / PHILADELPHIA. Plain edge. (King 595; Miller Pa 806)

Pa-Ph 461 A 1864 WM 28mm — — 50.00 100.
As 461. Plain edge. (King 595; Miller Pa 807)

Pa-Ph 461 B 1864 Copper 28mm — — 50.00 100.
Obverse as obverse of Pa 800 (Washington). Rv: As obverse of 461 (Lincoln in circle of 31 stars). Plain edge. (King 596; Miller Pa 809)

It is interesting to note that King's compilation, published in *The Numismatist* in 1924, was available to but apparently not fully consulted by Donald Miller in his 1962 updating of Edgar Adams' 1920 store card catalog, as Pa-Ph 458 to 461B were not mentioned. We assigned numbers 800-809. It is believed the Warner listing in the present reference catalog also fails to list all extant varieties.

Charles K. Warner was born March 29, 1845, the son of medalist John S. Warner. Charles Warner established his coin and medal business at 326 Chestnut St., Philadelphia, in 1861. During 1862-1863 he commissioned W. H. Key to strike a series of patriotic store cards bearing portraits of Van Buren, Lincoln, McClellan, Washington, etc., with his store card on the other side. Only 15 of each type were struck, and these were not sold in his coin dealership, but presented to friends. In late 1863 his store card die was modified and he continued his wide-ranging patriotic cards.

In 1869 he moved to 728 Chestnut St., where he continued issuing special store cards until 1871.

(See Albert R. Frey's "The Tokens and Medals Relating to Numismatists and Coin Dealers" in *The Numismatist* for 1903-1907).

A. J. WEIDENER

1876 Centennial Tokens

Reverse type 1: A. J. WEIDENER / 36 SO. 2ND ST., PHILA. / (ornament) / LAMPS / BRONZES & / SILVER PLATED / WARE. (All 23mm; plain edge)

Rulau	Obv	Rev	Metal	F	VF	EF	Unc
Pa-Ph 480	A (Miller Pa 570)	1	WM	—	—	15.00	40.00
Pa-Ph 481	B (Miller 571)	1	WM	—	—	15.00	40.00
Pa-Ph 481 A	B	1	Brass	—	—	20.00	45.00
Pa-Ph 482	E (Miller 572)	1	WM	—	—	15.00	40.00
Pa-Ph 483	F (Miller 573)	1	WM	—	—	17.50	40.00
Pa-Ph 484	G	1	WM	—	—	17.50	40.00
Pa-Ph 485	H (Miller 570A)	1	WM	—	—	17.50	40.00

WHITMAN & SON

1876 Centennial Tokens

Reverse type 1: WHITMAN & SON / CHOCOLATE / CONFECTIONS / BON BONS / TWELFTH & MARKET ST. / PHILA. (All 23mm; plain edge)

Rulau	Obv	Rev	Metal	F	VF	EF	Unc
Pa-Ph 488	A (Miller Pa 577)	1	WM	5.00	8.50	15.00	40.00
Pa-Ph 489	B (Wright 1242; Miller 576)	1	WM	—	—	15.00	40.00
Pa-Ph 489 A	B	1	Copper	—	—	17.50	42.50
Pa-Ph 489 B	B	1	Brass	—	—	20.00	45.00
Pa-Ph 490	E (Miller 578)	1	WM	—	—	17.50	42.50
Pa-Ph 491	F (Miller 575)	1	WM	—	—	17.50	42.50

Rulau	Obv	Rev	Metal	F	VF	EF	Unc
Pa-Ph 492	G	1	WM	—	—	17.50	42.50
Pa-Ph 493	H	1	WM	—	—	17.50	42.50
	(Miller 575A)						
Pa-Ph 494	K	1	WM	—	—	20.00	45.00

The Whitman Sampler is still being produced. Stephen F. Whitman & Son, confectioners, were located at the southwest corner of 12th and Market, the 1872 directory reports.

F. G. WILLIAMS & CO.

1876 Centennial Tokens

Reverse type 1: DR. WILLIAMS / ANTI / DYSPEPTIC / ELIXIR / F. G. WILLIAMS & CO. / 1301-03 / MARKET ST., PHILA. (All 23mm; plain edge)

Rulau	Obv	Rev	Metal	F	VF	EF	Unc
Pa-Ph 495	A	1	WM	—	—	17.50	40.00
	(Wright 1728; Miller Pa 580)						
Pa-Ph 496	B	1	WM	—	—	17.50	40.00
	(Miller 581)						
Pa-Ph 497	E	1	WM	—	—	17.50	40.00
	(Miller 582)						
Pa-Ph 497	FF	1	WM	—	—	20.00	45.00
	(Miller 583)						
Pa-Ph 498	G	1	WM	—	—	20.00	45.00
Pa-Ph 498	FH	1	WM	—	—	20.00	45.00
	(Miller 579A)						
Pa-Ph 498	GH	1	Copper	—	—	22.50	50.00
	(Miller 579)						

WILSON & FENIMORE

1876 Centennial Tokens

Reverse type 1: WILSON & FENIMORE / ARTISTIC / PAPER / HANGINGS / 915 / MARKET ST. / PHILA. (All 23mm; plain edge)

Rulau	Obv	Rev	Metal	F	VF	EF	Unc
Pa-Ph 499	A	1	WM	—	—	20.00	45.00
	(Wright 1729; Miller Pa 583 1/2)						

WOOD'S MUSEUM

Rulau	Date	Metal	Size	F	VF	EF	Unc
Pa-Ph 500	(?)	Gold/WM	23mm	—	1500.	—	—

WOODS / MUSEUM ctsp on White Metal imitation, once gold plated, of the Oregon Exchange Company 1849 $5 gold piece. (Brunk 44300)

Two or three specimens are thought to exist, according to Don Kagin in *Private Gold Coins and Patterns of the United States,* where this is termed a trial piece for regular Oregon Exchange Co. gold coins. George Fuld advances the theory this was an exhibition item in Wood's Museum. One specimen appeared in the Clifford sale, March 18-20, 1982.

Rulau	Date	Metal	Size	F	VF	EF	Unc
Pa-Ph 502	(1876)	Brass	26mm	4.50	8.50	15.00	40.00
	Liberty head left, LIBERTAS AMERICANA / 4 JUIL. 1776. Rv: COL. WOOD'S MUSEUM N. W. 9TH & ARCH / 500000 / + / CURIOSITIES / GOOD / PERFORMANCE / + IN + LECTURE ROOM / PHILADELPHIA. Plain edge. (Miller Pa 585)						
Pa-Ph 503	(1876)	Copper	26mm	4.50	8.50	15.00	22.50
	As 502. Plain edge. (Miller Pa 585A)						
Pa-Ph 504	(1876)	WM	26mm	4.50	8.50	15.00	40.00
	As 502. Plain edge. (Miller Pa 586)						
Pa-Ph 506	(1876)	Copper	26mm	—	—	20.00	45.00
	Liberty Bell and 13 stars, LIBERTY BELL above, 1776 below. Rv: As 502. Plain edge. (Wright 1271; Miller Pa 586A)						

R. & G. A. WRIGHT

Philadelphia, Pa.

Rulau	Date	Metal	Size	VG	F	VF	Unc
Pa-Ph 510	(1871-72)	Silver	14mm	—	—	Ex. Rare	
	An ornament at center. R. & G. A. WRIGHT / PHILA. Rv: GOLD / MEDAL / PERFUMERY. (Wright 1276)						

Dr. Wright noted that this was the smallest card in his collection.

R. and G. A. Wright, perfumers, were located at 624 Chestnut, the 1872 directory reports.

YATES & CO.

1876 Centennial Tokens

Reverse type 1: YATES & CO. / POPULAR / CLOTHIERS / LEDGER BUILDING / 6TH & / CHESTNUT STS. (All 23mm; plain edge)

Rulau	Obv	Rev	Metal	F	VF	EF	Unc
Pa-Ph 530	D	1	WM	—	12.50	20.00	45.00
	(Wright 1290; Miller Pa 588 1/2)						

A. C. Yates and Co. also issued store cards in the Merchant period (1845-60) from Philadelphia and from Syracuse, N.Y. They were an extremely popular clothing firm in the 19th century.

W. A. BUNTING & SON

Pittsburgh, Pa.

Rulau	Date	Metal	Size	F	VF	EF	Unc
Pa-Pt 2	1876	Aluminum	31mm	—	—	35.00	80.00
	Building across center, TRADESMENS INDUSTRIAL above, INSTITUTE / * / 1876. Rv: W. A. BUNTING & SON / SEAL — / ENGRAVING / STEEL — STAMPS (on scroll) / STENCILS / & C. / PITTSBURGH. Plain edge.						

An early and rare use of aluminum, still then a novelty.

GREAT NORTHERN EXPOSITION

Rulau	Date	Metal	Size	F	VF	EF	Unc
Pa-Pt 7	1883	Brass	21mm	—	10.00	13.00	20.00
	Building, PITTSBURGH above. Rv: THE GREAT / NORTHERN / * / EXPOSITION/ 1883. (Wright 1114)						

GUSKY'S CLOTHIERS HATTERS

Rulau	Date	Metal	Size	F	VF	EF	Unc
Pa-Pt 9	1887	WM	38mm	—	40.00	50.00	—
	St. George slaying the dragon at center. Around: SEMI-CENTENNIAL QUEEN'S JUBILEE, PITTSBURGH, PA. Below: SONS OF ST. GEORGE / JUNE 20. 1887. Rv: Within oak wreath: PRESENTED / BY / GUSKYS' / THE ONE PRICE / CLOTHIERS HATTERS / FURNISHERS / & SHOE DEALERS / 300 TO 400 / MARKET ST. / PITTSBURGH. PA. Plain edge. (Brunk coll.)						

An exceptionally handsome piece, unsigned, but possibly the work of Quint in Philadelphia. Queen Victoria ascended the throne of England in 1837 and this piece commemorates the 50th anniversary of that event.

F. A. HEISLEY

Rulau	Date	Metal	Size	F	VF	EF	Unc
Pa-Pt 12	(?)	Copper	29mm	—	—	60.00	—
	PITTSBURGH / F. A. HEISLEY ctsp on U.S. 1845 Large cent. (Brunk 19060)						

PITTSBURGH EXPOSITION

Rulau	Date	Metal	Size	F	VF	EF	Unc
Pa-Pt 24	1878	Silver	35mm	—	—	—	45.00
	Building across center, PITTSBURGH EXPOSITION / SOCIETY above, EXPOSITION / OF / 1878 below. Rv: Within circular wreath at center: FOUNDED / JUNE 14TH / 1878. Around: WESTERN PENNSYLVANIA NUMSIMATIC SOCIETY / PITTSBURGH, PA. Plain edge. Mintage: 7.						
Pa-Pt 24A	1878	Bronze	35mm	—	—	—	30.00
	As 24. Mintage: 25.						
Pa-Pt 24B	1878	Brass	35mm	—	—	—	30.00
	As 24. Mintage: 15.						
Pa-Pt 24C	1878	S/WM	35mm	—	—	—	35.00
	As 24. Mintage not known.						
Pa-Pt 25	1879	Silver	35mm	—	—	—	45.00
	Building across center, PITTSBURGH EXPOSITION above, SOCIETY / 1879 / W.P.N.S. No 2 below. Rv: Same as reverse of 24. Plain edge. Mintage: 17.						
Pa-Pt 25A	1879	Bronze	35mm	—	—	—	30.00
	As 25. Mintage: 25.						
Pa-Pt 25B	1879	Brass	35mm	—	—	—	30.00
	As 25. Mintage: 25.						
Pa-Pt 25C	1879	S/WM	35mm	—	—	—	35.00
	As 25. Mintage not known.						

Estimates of surviving numbers were furnished in 1987 by Lawrence C. Dziubek of the WPNS. No record of the numbers struck has survived.

Both medal series were issued by Western Pennsylvania Numismatic Society as official souvenirs of the Pittsburgh Exposition. A history of the WPNS written by William W. Woodside and Wayne K. Homren was included in the 1987 booklet issued by the society for its members, and all medallic issues of the society (in 1878, 1879, 1928, 1928-1963 restrikes, and 1978) are included.

PHOSPHOR BRONZE

Rulau	Date	Metal	Size	VG	F	VF	EF
Pa-Pt 15	1872	Copper	28mm	—	50.00	—	—

(Elephant standing left) / Phosphor=Bronze (script) / PAT. MAY 23. 71 / NOV. 14. 71 / APR. 8. 72 ctsp on one side of a worn-smooth unrecognizable coin. Holed flan. Plain edge. (Harvey Gamer coll.; Brunk 32020)

Rulau	Date	Metal	Size	VG	F	VF	EF
Pa-Pt 16	1871	Copper	28mm	—	50.00	—	—

(Elephant standing left) / Phosphor=Bronze (script) / PAT. MAY 23. 71 / NOV. 14. 71 ctsp on U.S. Large cent? ((Brunk 32015)

Rulau	Date	Metal	Size	VG	F	VF	EF
Pa-Pt 17	1872	Copper	28mm	—	50.00	—	—

(Elephant standing left) / Phosphor=Bronze (script) / PAT. MAY 23. 71 / NOV. 14. 71 / AUG. 20. 72 ctsp on U.S. Large cent? (Brunk 32025)

Rulau	Date	Metal	Size	VG	F	VF	EF
Pa-Pt 18	ND	Copper	28mm	30.00	—	50.00	—

(Elephant left) / Phosphor=Bronze / No 7 STUBS / SPRING ctsp on blank disk.

Rulau	Date	Metal	Size	VG	F	VF	EF
Pa-Pt 19	ND	Copper	27mm	30.00	—	50.00	—

(Elephant left) / Phosphor=Bronze / No 12 / B&S / SPRING ctsp on blank disk.

Rulau	Date	Metal	Size	VG	F	VF	EF
Pa-Pt 20	(?)	Bronze	26.7mm	—	—	35.00	—

(All incused): ELEPHANT BRAND / PHOSPHOR=BRONZE (script) / (elephant standing left) / "PHOSPHOR BRONZE" / REG. U.S. PAT. OFF. Rv: Blank. Plain edge. Issued holed. (Rulau MV 256D)

These are all probably tags attached to a bronze alloy roll of wire or spring. They were manufactured by Charles J. A. Dick of Pittsburgh in and after 1872. "Phosphor Bronze" was patented in the U.S. in 1871 by two Belgians, George M. Levi and Charles M. Kunzel.

Phosphor Bronze was 82.5% copper, 15% tin and 2.5% phosphorus.

SONS OF ST. GEORGE

Pittsburgh, Pa.

Rulau	Date	Metal	Size	F	VF	EF	Unc
Pa-Pt 40	1887	Svd WM	37.8mm	—	—	35.00	45.00

Mounted St. George left, slaying the dragon. Around: SEMI-CENTENNIAL QUEEN'S JUBILEE PITTSBURGH, PA. / SONS OF ST. GEORGE / JUNE 20. 1887. Rv: SOUVENIR in fancy letters within oak wreath. Plain edge.

Queen Victoria mounted the British throne in 1837. The Sons of St. George was apparently a British-oriented organization.

RAINBOW FIRE CO.

Reading, Pa.

Rulau	Date	Metal	Size	F	VF	EF	Unc
Pa-Re 8	1873	WM	32mm	—	—	22.50	—

Old water-pumper engine. Around: CENTENNIAL ANNIVERSARY RAINBOW FIRE CO. MARCH 17TH 1873. Rv: RAINBOW FIRE CO / INSTITUTED / MARCH 17TH / 1773 / READING PA. (Levine Dec. 1981 sale)

SCRANTON STOVE WORKS

Scranton, Pa

Rulau	Date	Metal	Size	F	VF	EF	Unc
Pa-Sc 7	1886	Brass	25.5mm	3.00	5.00	7.00	15.00

Scroll inscribed DOCKASH MEDAL at center, around: THE SCRANTON STOVE WORKS / SCRANTON PA. Rv: Globe on a grate inscribed DOCKASH. Around: DOCKASH RANGE WORLD HUNT SOUVENIR 1886. (Wright 1127; Miller Pa 593)

THIRTEENTH REGIMENT N. G. PA.

Scranton, Pa.

Rulau	Date	Metal	Size	F	VF	EF	Unc
Pa-Sc 14	1880	WM	28mm	—	—	—	30.00

Bearded male bust in Civil War uniform left, THIRTEENTH REGIMENT N.G.PA. above, ORGANIZED SEPT. 23. 1878. below. Rv: Armory at center, COMMEMORATIVE OF THE ARMORY FAIR / APRIL 1880 above, SCRANTON CITY / GUARD / ORG. AUGUST 14. 1877 below. Plain edge.

The Pennsylvania National Guard's 13th Regiment apparently grew out of the Scranton City Guard. Undoubtedly there are other Pennsylvania N.G. medalets and tokens than those included in this volume.

J. W. FULLER

Sharpsville, Pa.

Rulau	Date	Metal	Size	VG	F	VF	EF
Pa-Sh 3	(1870)	CN	22mm	75.00	—	125.	—

J. W. FULLER / JEWELER ctsp on U.S. Shield nickel. Dates examined: 1866, 1867, 1869, unknown date. (Rulau Wi-Mi 15; Van Ormer sale 2652; Brunk 15290)

Rulau	Date	Metal	Size	VG	F	VF	EF
Pa-Sh 4	(1870)	CN	22mm	75.00	—	125.	—

J. W. FULLER / JEWELER / SHARPSVILLE ctsp on U.S. Shield nickel. Dates examined: 1866, 1867, 1868, 1869. 6 pieces known. (Van Ormer sale 2651; Brunk 15300)

The style of lettering on these pieces is the same as that on the Maggie Fish piece of Sharpsville, leading to the conclusion that Fuller prepared all of the counterstamps.

Pa-Sh 3 had been attributed to Wisconsin or Indiana in earlier editions of this reference.

Rulau	Date	Metal	Size	VG	F	VF	EF
Pa-Sh 5	(1870)	CN	22mm	—	—	125.	—

J. W. FULLER / JEWELER / SHARPSVILLE PA ctsp on U.S. 1868 Shield nickel. (Brunk 15300)

This town was called Sharpsville Furnace until 1874, when it became an independent borough called Sharpsville in Mercer County.

The town was named after James Sharp, who surveyed it. Fuller was a jeweler; his only daughter died in the 1940's (Brunk research)

SIMON & OPPENHEIMER

Sunbury, Pa.

1876 Centennial Tokens

Reverse type 1: SIMON & OPPENHEIMER, CLOTHING. (All 23mm; plain edge)

Rulau	Obv	Rev	Metal	F	VF	EF	Unc
Pa-Sb 5	A	1	WM	—	—	25.00	50.00
Pa-Sb 6	G	1	WM	—	—	25.00	50.00
	(Miller Pa 594)						
Pa-Sb 6A	G	1	Brass	—	—	—	60.00

C. J. LYONS
Susquehanna, Pa.

Rulau	Date	Metal	Size	VG	F	VF	Unc
Pa-Sq 3	(ca. 1882)	GS	25mm	—	—	4.00	6.50

Liberty holding long star-spangled pennon. On three of the pennon's folds are: C. J. LYONS / SUSQUEHANNA / P.A. Rv: Blank. Dentilated rims on each side. Plain edge. Issued holed.

This is a stock identification disc. It is of the same type as the H. Knickman of East New York, N.Y., reported by the Fulds in The Numismatist (which see). Many of these are known.

J. W. CLARK
Tunkhannock, Pa.

Rulau	Date	Metal	Size	VG	F	VF	EF
Pa-Tu 3	(?)	CN	22mm	—	75.00	—	

J. W. CLARK / TUNKHANNOCK PA ctsp on U.S. 1866 with Rays Shield nickel. (Brunk 8080)

E. T.
(Eintracht)
Tyrone, Pa.

Rulau	Date	Metal	Size	F	VF	EF	Unc
Pa-Ty 2	(1870's)	Copper	20mm	5.00	10.00	15.00	40.00
	Similar to Pa-Ty 3 below, but numeral 5 on reverse. Plain edge.						
Pa-Ty 3	(1870's)	GS	20mm	5.00	10.00	15.00	40.00
	ET (script monogram) at center, EINTRACHT * above, TYRONE, PA. below. Rv: Large numeral 10 within wreath. Star above. Plain edge. (Wright 284; Miller Pa 595)						
Pa-Ty 3A	(1870's)	Brass	20mm	5.00	10.00	15.00	40.00
	As 3. Plain edge. (Fuld coll.)						

These tokens probably struck by J. F. W. Dorman in Baltimore.

737
York, Pa.

Rulau	Date	Metal	Size	VG	F	VF	Unc
Pa-Yk 1	(?)	Alum	24mm	—	—	11.00	—

Brunswick die BBC. Rv: * GOOD FOR * / 5 ¢ / - 737 - (in panel) / IN TRADE.

Bakery Union Local 737 was in York, Pa.

O. R. DAVIS
York, Pa.

Rulau	Date	Metal	Size	F	VF	EF	Unc
Pa-Yk 2	(?)	Silver	25mm	—	—	85.00	—

O. R. DAVIS / YORK, PA. ctsp on U.S. 1853-A&R Seated Liberty quarter. (Van Ormer 2615; Brunk 10960)

(HE)NRY POURCELLE
Pennsylvania ?

Rulau	Date	Metal	Size	VG	F	VF	Unc
Pa-Un 1	(1870's)	Silver	15.5mm	—	—	35.00	—

NRY POURCELLE PA / P ctsp on U.S. 1872 S.L. half dime. (Partrick coll.)

SOUTH PENN HOSE COMPANY
Pennsylvania

Rulau	Date	Metal	Size	VG	F	VF	Unc
Pa-Un 2	1865	Copper	**	—	Rare	—	—
	** Oval 20 x 24mm. Old fashioned hose cart, SOUTH PENN above, HOSE CO. below. Rv: Hose coiled around holder. Around: x INST. MARCH 27, 1846 INC'D MARCH 28 1865. Plain edge. (Wright 1019)						
Pa-Un 2A	1865	Silver	**	—	Rare	—	—
	** Oval 20 x 24mm.As 2. Plain edge.						

RHODE ISLAND

O. H. HYER
Johnston, R.I.

Rulau	Date	Metal	Size	VG	F	VF	Unc
RI-Jo 3	(1885)	Brass	24mm	—	—	35.00	—

(All incused): O. H. HYER / GOOD / 5 ¢ (large) / FOR / IN TRADE. Rv: Brunswick die BB-2. (Thoele coll., ex-Tom Wall)

Otis H. Hyer was a billiard hall proprietor appearing in the 1885 *New England Business Directory and Gazetteer.* It is believed that New York City diesinker McNamara made this token.

GEORGE FINCK
Providence, R. I.

Rulau	Date	Metal	Size	F	VF	EF	Unc
RI-Pr 7	(1876)	WM	22mm	25.00	35.00	50.00	75.00
	George Washington head left, 13 stars around, 1776 below. Rv: ROCHESTER HOTEL / GEORGE / FINCK / PROVIDENCE R. I. Plain edge. (Miller RI 3)						
RI-Pr 8	(1876)	Brass	22mm	30.00	45.00	60.00	90.00
	As 7. Plain edge. (Wright 320; Miller RI 3A).						
RI-Pr 9	(1876)	Copper	22mm	35.00	45.00	60.00	90.00
	As 7. Plain edge.						

GORHAM MFG. CO.

Rulau	Date	Metal	Size	VG	F	VF	Unc
RI-Pr 11	(1860's)	CN	22mm	—	—	90.00	—
	GORHAM. MFG. CO / PATENT 1861 ctsp on U.S. 1866 Shield nickel. (Brunk 16610)						
RI-Pr 12	(1860's)	Silver	25mm	—	—	100.	—
	GORHAM CO. / (anchor) / 0605 SILVER ctsp on U.S. 1853-S Seated Liberty quarter. (Brunk 16600)						

Silversmith Jabez Gorham (born in 1792) established a silverware empire that still exists today, in Providence, Rhode Island. At age 21 he became associated with the silversmith firm of George C. (G.) Clark in Providence, and this lasted 1813-24. Meanwhile he also was associated with silversmith William Hadwen of Nantucket Island, Mass. and Providence, 1816-28.

In 1825 Gorham formed his own company, Gorham & Beebe with Stanton Beebe, 1825-31. This was supplanted by Gorham & Webster (Henry L. Webster) 1831-41. About 1835 there was a short-lived partnership, Gorham, Webster & Price. There had been another corporate title, Gorham Silver Co. briefly in 1831.

In 1842 Gorham ended the Webster connection and admitted his son John Gorham to the business, now restyled Gorham & Son. This became J. Gorham & Son later that year and this was the business title 1842-47.

In 1847 the firm assumed its present name, Gorham Manufacturing Co., and this business was extensively engaged in making "coin silver" (solid .900 fine silver) tableware and fancy services. In 1863 its highly successful line of silverplated ware commenced, and branch operations later were started in New York, Chicago and San Francisco. The New York minting establishment became noteworthy in the 1890's as the striker of so-called Bryan silver money and souvenir pesos of the Cuban revolutionary government.

Gorham's silverplate is usually found marked: G M Co / (anchor in shield) / E P (for Extra Plating). The earlier silverware may be found marked with relief logos such as: GORHAM & WEBSTER, GORHAM WEBSTER & PRICE, J. GORHAM or J GORHAM & SON.

There were a number of Gorham-related silver enterprises not in the direct line from Jabez Gorham in 1813. These included Gorham & Thurber in Providence circa 1850; John Gorham 1814, Miles Gorham 1790-1847, Richard Gorham 1806-41 and Shethear & Gorham 1806 on, all in New Haven, Conn.

A. A. PLASTRIDGE

Providence, R. I.

Rulau	Date	Metal	Size	VG	F	VF	Unc
RI-Pr 15	Late 1860s	WM	27mm	—	—	50.00	75.00

A. A. PLASTRIDGE / (incused numeral) / MERRIAM / PROV. R. I. Rv: WHAT CHEER / (incused numeral) / EATING HOUSE. Plain edge. (Schenkman B48; R-F Srh-2; Miller RI 19)

Rulau	Date	Metal	Size	VG	F	VF	Unc
RI-Pr 17	(1870)	WM	27mm	—	10.00	15.00	22.50

Shield at center, within which is R. D. / 6. BY A. A. PLASTRIDGE above, PROV. R. I. below. Rv: Shield at center, within which is 12 / G. WHAT CHEER above, BAGATELLE TABLES below. Plain edge. (Wright 839; R-F Srh-1; Miller RI 20)

The first piece, RI-Pr 15, was cut by Joseph H. Merriam of Boston. There is no indication on RI-Pr 17 that Merriam prepared these dies, but it seems logical to suppose that this might be so. Both upper and lower dies of RI 17 (in excellent condition) were in the posssession of the author for about 15 years prior to 1978, when they were sold to David T. Alexander of Mahopac, N.Y.

Bagatelle is a modification of billiards, played on an oblong board or table. An ordinary billiard cue and nine balls, one black, four red, and four white, are used. The black ball having been placed on the upper spot, the players "string" for the lead, the winner being the one who plays his ball into the highest hole.

SOUTH CAROLINA

E. HENDERSON PACKING CO.

Beaufort, S.C.

Rulau	Date	Metal	Size	VG	F	VF	Unc
SC-Be 3	(ca 1889 ?)	Alum	Sc, 23mm	—	—	15.00	—

(All incused): Large 2 1/2 at center, E. HENDERSON PACKING CO. around. Rv: Same as obverse. Incised, beaded rim on each side. Plain edge.

HUNT PKG. CO.

Beaufort, S.C.

Rulau	Date	Metal	Size	VG	F	VF	Unc
SC-Be 5	(1880's)	Brass	20mm	—	—	15.00	—

HUNT PKG. CO. / SHUCKING / CHECK / BEAUFORT S.C. Beaded rim. Rv: Blank. Plain edge.

Hunt Packing Company was a shrimp packing plant and this piece was used as a production tally during the late 1800's and possibly until about 1905. The style of check is typical of the mid-1880's.

L. PEARLSTIN

Branchville, S.C.

Rulau	Date	Metal	Size	VG	F	VF	Unc
SC-Br 1	(1886)	Brass	--mm	—	—	35.00	—

Brunswick die BB-6a. Rv: L. PEARLSTIN.

Appears in the 1886 gazetteer.

J. C. SEEGERS & CO.

Columbia, S.C.

Rulau	Date	Metal	Size	VG	F	VF	EF
SC-Co 4	(1870's)	GS	27mm	—	—	20.00	30.00
	Barrel. J. C. SEEGERS & CO. Rv: Numeral 25. Plain edge. (Miller SC 14)						
SC-Co 5	(1870's)	Brass	27mm	—	—	20.00	30.00
	As 4, but numeral 10. Plain edge.						

This piece was catalogued with reserve in *U.S. Merchant Tokens 1845-1860*. It has since been determined that it postdates the Civil War.

J. N. POOLE

Greenville, S.C.

Rulau	Date	Metal	Size	VG	F	VF	Unc
SC-Gr 4	(1870's)	Brass	19mm	—	—	30.00	—

Liberty head within wreath. Rv: J. N. POOLE / 5 / GREENVILLE, S.C.

RICHARD F. MASON

Laurens, S. C.

Rulau	Date	Metal	Size	VG	F	VF	Unc
SC-La 5	1888	Brass	33mm	—	—	75.00	—
	RICHARD F. MASON / DEALER / IN / WATCHES, CLOCKS, / JEWELRY, SILVERWARE / SPECTACLES ETC. / - / REPAIRING A SPECIALTY / TERMS CASH / LAURENS, SO. CA. Rv: MASON'S WATCH & JEWELRY / REPAIR SHOP / WATCH CHECK / 1888 / LAURENS, SO. CA. Plain edge.						
SC-La 6	1888	Brass	33mm	—	—	75.00	—
	As last, but counterstamped with various numbers between words REPAIR SHOP and WATCH CHECK on reverse. Plain edge.						

Mason accounted for items left with him for repair by use of these checks. This token was written up by Melvin and George Fuld in *The Numismatist* in the early 1960's.

WM. L. BRADLEY

Stono, S.C.

Rulau	Date	Metal	Size	VG	F	VF	Unc
SC-St 1	1879	Copper	24mm	—	—	—	Rare

* BULOW STORE * / GOOD FOR / 25 / CENTS / WM. L. BRADLEY. Rv: * THIS CHECK * / NOT / 1879 / TRANSFERABLE. Plain edge. (Wright 94; Rulau MV 22)

Rulau	Date	Metal	Size	VG	F	VF	Unc
SC-St 2	1879	Copper	33mm	—	—	—	Rare

* BULOW STORE * / GOOD FOR / 50 / CENTS / WM. L. BRADLEY. Rv: As 22. Plain edge. (Steinberg 1982 sale)

Rulau	Date	Metal	Size	VG	F	VF	Unc
SC-St 7	1879	Copper	20.5mm	—	—	Rare	—

* BULOW STORE * / GOOD FOR / + 10 + / CENTS. / WM. L. BRADLEY. Rv: Ornate rosette. Around: NOT TRANSFERABLE / * 1879 *. Plain edge. (Rulau MV 23C)

Rulau	Date	Metal	Size	VG	F	VF	Unc
SC-St 8	1879	Copper	30.5mm	—	—	Rare	—

As 23C, but + 50 / CENTS. Plain edge. SC-St 7 and 8 appeared in a Stanley Steinberg Sept. 1985 sale, lots 37-38, and are from completely different dies than SC-St 1 and 2)

According to a book on South Carolina tokens by Tony Chibbaro, the Bulow Store was located at Stono, Charleston County. Neither Stono nor Bulow had post offices in 1877.

SC-St 1 has been known in numismatic circles for a century, but the others much more recently. The issues are extremely rare. They are all now confidently attributed to South Carolina — the only other possibility specified in earlier editions of this reference was Bulow, Volusia County, Florida, a turpentine processing community.

SOUTH DAKOTA

CONSTITUTIONAL PROHIBITION ORGANIZATION

South Dakota

Rulau	Date	Metal	Size	F	VF	EF	Unc
SD-NL 1	1889	Copper	25.5mm	—	—	15.00	25.00

South Dakota state arms, CONSTITUTIONAL PROHIBITION ORGANIZATION. Rv: Fountain, FOR GOD, HOME & NATIVE LAND / SOUTH DAKOTA / 1889. Plain edge.

Rulau	Date	Metal	Size	F	VF	EF	Unc
SD-NL 2	1889	Brass	25.5mm	—	—	15.00	25.00

As last. Plain edge.

The state went "dry" after 1889.

N. RINGROSE

Aberdeen, S.D.

Rulau	Date	Metal	Size	VG	F	VF	Unc
SD-Ab 2	(1884)	CN	24mm	—	—	1200.	—

N. RINGROSE, 10 ¢, ABERDEEN, D.T. Rv: THE J.M. BRUNSWICK & BALKE CO. Plain edge. (Brunswick 2302)

D.T. = Dakota Territory.

M. RINGROSE

Casselton, S.D.

Rulau	Date	Metal	Size	VG	F	VF	Unc
SD-Ca 4	(1880-84)	CN	25mm	—	—	90.00	—

CHAS. PICK & CO. / DEALERS IN / (bar utensils) / — CHICAGO. —. Rv: GOOD FOR / 10 C / IN TRADE / = AT = / BAR / M. RINGROSE. PROP. Plain edge. (Thoele coll.)

P.M. Ringrose saloon is listed in 1884.

ATWATER & BARGESSER

Chamberlain, S.D.

Rulau	Date	Metal	Size	VG	F	VF	Unc
SD-Ch 1	(1886)	Brass	24mm	—	—	1000.	—

ATWATER & BARGESSER / 10 ¢ / CHAMBERLAIN / DAKOTA. Rv: GOOD FOR / 10 / CENTS / IN TRADE. (Rouleau coll.)

Saloon, listed in 1886 Bradstreet directory.

OLIVER McELROY

Chamberlain, S.D.

Rulau	Date	Metal	Size	VG	F	VF	Unc
SD-Ch 3	(1884-88)	Brass	25mm	—	—	95.00	—

Chas. Pick die. Rv: GOOD FOR / ONE / OLIVER / McELROY / DRINK. Plain edge. (Thoele coll., ex-Weinberg)

Oliver McElroy is listed under Dakota Territory as a saloon and billiard hall in the 1884, 1886 and 1888 gazetteers.

CLEVELAND TIN MINING COMPANY

Deadwood, S.D.

Rulau	Date	Metal	Size	VG	F	VF	Unc
SD-Dd 1	1888	Tin*	39mm	—	—	125.	—

* Pure tin, cast.
CLEVELAND TIN MINING CO. / BLACK / HILLS / DAKOTA / * 1888 *. Rv: OFFICES DEADWOOD & NEW YORK CITY . / NIGGER / HILL / TIN. Plain edge.

Rulau	Date	Metal	Size	VG	F	VF	Unc
SD-Dd 2	1890	Tin**	33mm	—	—	75.00	—

** Pure tin, struck.
OFFICES DEADWOOD & NEW YORK CITY . / CLEVELAND / TIN / MINING / COMPANY. Rv: NIGGER HILL TIN BEAR GULCH 1890 / BLACK / HILLS. Plain edge. (Wright 196)

SD-Dd 1, the piece dated 1888, appeared in Melvin and George Fuld's article on U.S. tin mining tokens and medals in *The Numismatist*, but has not been listed elsewhere, apparently. Both these tokens are quite rare; tin does not survive well.

DAKOTA COMMANDERY NO. 1

Deadwood, S.D.

Rulau	Date	Metal	Size	F	VF	EF	Unc
SD-Dd 3	1880	Tin	33mm	—	—	125.	—

Cross through crown at center. DAKOTA COMMANDERY NO. 1. / VINCIT OMNIA VERITAS (truth conquers all) above; CONSTITUTED / AUG. 19, 1880. / * DEADWOOD. DAK. * . Rv: Mining buildings, MADE OF BLACK HILLS TIN / HOMESTAKE above, WM. McMAKIN & CO. / TERRAVILLES S.D. below. (Last two lines of legend uncertain)

This piece is rare. Not listed in the Fuld's article on tin medals and tokens in *The Numismatist.*

The Homestake mine at Lead, S.D., the U.S.'s largest gold mine, was opened 1877 and is still in operation. Lead, tin and other metals are byproducts.

Rulau	Date	Metal	Size	F	VF	EF	Unc
SD-Dd 4	1880	Tin	33mm	—	—	—	—

As 3, except signature is: J. W. FREEMAN, LEAD S.D. and last two lines of legend (tiny): read: WATERS & SCOTT / LEAD S.D. (Rouleau coll.)

Waters & Scott were the medalet's makers.

JNO. GROSS
Freeman, S.D.

Rulau	Date	Metal	Size	VG	F	VF	Unc
SD-Fm 3	(1886)	Brass	25mm	450.	—	650.	—

JNO. GROSS / (Star) / FREEMAN / D.T. Rv: GOOD FOR / 5 ¢ / IN / TRADE. (Bill Rouleau coll.)

A holed specimen recently fetched $450, Rouleau says. The 1886 gazetteeer lists Gross under hotel and saloon.

PETER STEIN
Ipswich, S.D.

Rulau	Date	Metal	Size	F	VF	EF	Unc
SD-Ip 1	(1885-88)	Brass	25mm	—	—	20.00	—

GOOD FOR / 5 C / PETER STEIN / IN / TRADE. Rv: Blank. Plain edge.

Saloon in Ipswich, D.T., 1886-88 listings. Then removed to Oshkosh, Wis. 1888-91 listings.

M. JACOBS
Lead City, S.D.

Rulau	Date	Metal	Size	F	VF	EF	Unc
SD-Ld 2	(1882)	Brass	24mm	—	1200.	—	—

M. JACOBS, ONE DRINK, LEAD CITY, D.T. Rv: Pool table in central circle, THE J.M. BRUNSWICK & BALKE COS. around, CHECK below. (Brunswick die BB-6a). Plain edge. (Brunswick 2184)

D.T. = Dakota Territory.

A. B. HOUTS
Madison, S.D.

Rulau	Date	Metal	Size	F	VF	EF	Unc
SD-Ma 2	(1881-87)	Brass	24mm	—	—	85.00	—

GOOD FOR / 5 ¢ / A. B. / HOUTS / IN / * TRADE *. Rv: Blank. Plain edge. (Thoele report)

A. B. Houts ran a billiard parlor and saloon in Madison, Dakota Territory, listed in the 1882, 1884 and 1887 gazetteers. In 1888-89 he was proprietor of a saloon in Sioux Falls, D.T. He disappears from the directories after 1889.

S. BOATMAN'S SALOON
Miller, S.D.

Rulau	Date	Metal	Size	VG	F	VF	Unc
SD-Ml 1	(1882-89)	Brass	23mm	—	—	450.	—

(All incused): S. BOATMAN'S / SALOON / GOOD FOR / 10 / CENTS / AT / BAR. Rv: Blank. (Rouleau coll.)

Sanford Boatman ran a saloon at Arno and Main Streets in Miller, Dakota Territory from March 29, 1882 to Oct. 10, 1889, according to the newspaper *Miller Press* of the day. Specialist Bill Rouleau paid $450 for this token. South Dakota became a state 1889 and went "dry" in 1890.

E. A. SWAN
Parker, S.D.

Rulau	Date	Metal	Size	VG	F	VF	EF
SD-Pa 1	1883	Silver	31mm	—	—	400.	—

E A SWAN / LIVERY MAN / PARKER DAK / 1883 ctsp on U.S. 1834 Bust half dollar (Overton 101 variety). Possibly unique. (Stewart Witham coll., Ohio; Brunk 38970)

L. L. SHURTLEFF
Pierre, S.D.

Rulau	Date	Metal	Size	VG	F	VF	Unc
SD-Pi 3	(?)	Brass	--mm	—	—	900.	—

Chas. Pick & Co. die. Rv: L. L. SHURTLEFF / PIERRE, DAK.

SAFLOWER
Rapid City, S.D.

Rulau	Date	Metal	Size	VG	F	VF	EF
SD-Ra 3	1888	Silver	38.1mm	—	—	1100.	—

SAFLOWER (curved) / 1888 / RAPID CITY / DAK ctsp on U.S. 1882 Morgan silver dollar obverse. (Bill Rouleau coll.)

The owner recently paid $1000 for this unique, unpublished piece.

G. W. COLLINS
Ree Heights, S.D.

Rulau	Date	Metal	Size	F	VF	EF	Unc
SD-RH 1	(1884-85)	Brass	24mm	—	—	40.00	—

THE J. M. BRUNSWICK / & / BALKE COS. / (pool table). Rv: GOOD FOR / 5 C / G. W. / COLLINS / -IN- / * TRADE *. Plain edge. (Thoele coll.)

Hank Thoele attributes this piece to saloon and billiard hall proprietor G.W. Collins of Ree Heights, Hand County, Dakota Territory, circa 1884-1885.

P. REITER
Sioux Falls, S.D.

Rulau	Date	Metal	Size	VG	F	VF	EF
SD-SF 3	(1886-88)	Brass	25mm	—	—	95.00	—

Crossed goblet, icetong and ladle, DEALERS IN above, all within central circle. Around: CHAS. PICK & CO. / * CHICAGO *. Rv: GOOD FOR / 5 C / P. REITER / IN / TRADE. Plain edge. (Thoele coll.)

This Peter Reiter saloon appears in 1886 and 1888 directories. He moved to Chicago 1891.

Charles Pick & Co. made tokens for its clients 1878-1892 only, according to researcher Hank Thoele. Some authorities claim Pick made tokens until 1915, but this has not been substantiated; after 1900 the Brunswick-Balke-Collender Co. dominated the saloon-and-billiard token field.

JNO. Q. HOUTS
Sioux Falls, S.D.

Rulau	Date	Metal	Size	VG	F	VF	EF
SD-SF 1	(1884-87)	CN	24mm	—	—	85.00	—

Chas. Pick & Co. die. Rv: GOOD FOR / 5 ¢ / JNO. Q. HOUTS (on scroll) / IN / * TRADE *. (Hosek coll.; Thoele report)

J. Q. Houts is listed as a saloon proprietor in Sioux Falls 1884-87. His namesake A. B. Houts is listed in that same city in 1888-89 (see under Madison, S.D.).

By 1891 J. Q. Houts' saloon was relocated in West Superior, Wis.

FRANKLIN BAER & BLATT
Sturgis, S.D.

Rulau	Date	Metal	Size	VG	F	VF	Unc
SD-St 1	(1880's)	Brass	Oct 21mm	—	—	1000.	—

Brunswick die BBC-10 var. Rv: FRANKLIN BAER / -&- / BLATT / (ornament) / STURGIS, / D.T. Plain edge.

Sales records at $1000 in 1990's have been established.

HARMON & CO.
Sturgis, S.D.

Rulau	Date	Metal	Size	VG	F	VF	Unc
SD-St 3	(1880's)	Cardboard	32mm	—	—	150.	—

THIS CHECK IS GOOD FOR / IN GOODS / AT THE STORE OF / HARMON & CO. / STURGIS / CITY DAK. / TWO DOLLARS. Rv: TWO DOLLARS / $ 2 / NOT TRANSFERRABLE.

Printed cardboard round. (Bill Rouleau coll.)

M. DEMENDE
Yankton, S.D.

Rulau	Date	Metal	Size	VG	F	VF	EF
SD-Ya 1	(1884-88)	Brass	24mm	—	—	95.00	—

CHAS. PICK & CO / DEALERS IN / (bar utensils) / CHICAGO. Rv: GOOD FOR / 5 C / M. DEMENDE / IN / TRADE. Plain edge. (Thoele coll.)

Michael Demende was listed under saloons in Yankton, Dakota Territory, in the 1884, 1886 and 1888 R. L. Polk gazetteers.

DONALDSON & BLOOM
Yankton, S.D.

Rulau	Date	Metal	Size	VG	F	VF	EF
SD-Ya 3	(1885-86)	Brass	25mm	—	—	95.00	—

Brunswick die BB-7a. Rv: GOOD FOR / 5 C / DONALDSON / & BLOOM / IN / TRADE. Plain edge. (ATCO maverick 1145; Dick Worthington coll.)

Listed in the 1886 gazetteer.

J. H. ABBOTT
South Dakota

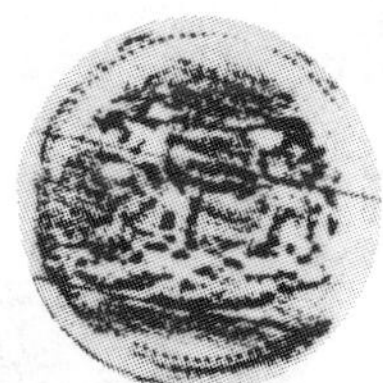

Rulau	Date	Metal	Size	VG	F	VF	Unc
SD-Un 1	(1887)	Brass	25mm	—	—	450.	—

Steer standing left, on ground. Rv: GOOD FOR / 5 ¢ / J. H. ABBOTT (in oval panel) / IN / * TRADE *. (Bill Rouleau coll.)

REPUTED DAKOTA TERRITORY BILLIARD TOKENS

It is tempting for researchers to 'territorialize' their maverick billiard tokens. South Dakota became a state only in 1889.

The following unverified attributions are presented as a matter of information:

Name on Token	Possible Locale	Billiard Die	Gazetteer
Becker & Medinger	Mitchell	BB-8a	1886
F.W. Bennett	Miner & Diana	BB-7b	1884-86
John Goeres	White Lake	BB	1886
Hart Bros.	Aberdeen	BB-7a	1884-87
Lannon & Ricker	Madison	Chas. Pick	1882
John Z. Lewis	Clark	BB-6a	1886
C. C. Maxwell	Watertown	BB-3	1882-86
Mosier & Laube	Huron	Chas. Pick	1882-84
T. Ostenson	Kindred	BB	1882
O.M. Oyhus	Aberdeen	BB ?	1886
H.C. Smith	Deadwood	Chas. Pick	1884
Snider & Johnson	Volga	—	1884
N. Sturgis	Britton	BBC-10b	1886
O.A. Swanson	Warner	BB-7b	1884
Thull & Heim	Salem	BBC-11	1888

TENNESSEE

D.P. HENDERSON & CO.
Chattanooga, Tenn.

Rulau	Date	Metal	Size	F	VF	EF	Unc
Tn-Ch 4	(1880's)	Nickel	30mm	—	—	40.00	—

D.P. HENDERSON / & CO. / BOOK SELLERS, / —*— / STATIONERS, / - AND - / NEWS DEALERS. Rv: CHATTANOOGA / * 7 1/2 * / TENN. Plain edge.

Struck by James Murdock Jr. in Cincinnati. (See *The Numismatist* for Sept., 1978, page 1841)

COAL CREEK COAL CO.
Coal Creek, Tenn.

Rulau	Date	Metal	Size	VG	F	VF	Unc
Tn-Cc 2	1884	Brass	--mm	—	—	20.00	—

COAL CREEK COAL CO. / 25 / * 1884 *. Rv: * C.C.C.C. * / 25 / IN MERCHANDISE / (tiny) HOEFLE & DRESSELL 179 RACE. ST. CIN. O. Plain edge.

T.C. & CO.
Memphis, Tenn.

Rulau	Date	Metal	Size	VG	F	VF	Unc
Tn-Me 6	(?)	Brass	26mm	—	—	200.	250.

T.C. & CO. NO. 230. Rv: 50 DRAYAGE. (Miller Tenn 45)

DODD & WOLFE

Rulau	Date	Metal	Size	VG	F	VF	Unc
Tn-Me 10	(?)	?	--mm	—	—	200.	250.

DODD & WOLFE / 25 / DRAYAGE / MEMPHIS. Rv: Blank. (Wright 1398; Miller Tenn 8A)

A drayage check.

FARGASON, CORDES & CO.

Rulau	Date	Metal	Size	VG	F	VF	Unc
Tn-Me 13	(1865-69)	Brass	22mm	—	—	200.	250.

FARGASON, CORDES & CO / DRAYAGE / MEMPHIS — 50. Rv: MURDOCK & SPENCER / 139 / 5TH ST / CIN. O. (Wright 309; Miller Tenn 9)

Rulau	Date	Metal	Size	VG	F	VF	Unc
Tn-Me 15	(1865-69)	Brass	22mm	—	—	200.	250.

Similar to Tenn 9, but '25' instead of '50'. (Miller Tenn 10)

Drayage checks. Dated on the basis of the Murdock & Spencer signature, which was in use with the 139 5th St. address only in the 1864-1869 period. These pieces have never been listed as Civil War tokens.

W.H. & CO.

Rulau	Date	Metal	Size	VG	F	VF	Unc
Tn-Me 18	(?)	Brass	--mm	—	—	200.	250.

W.H. & CO., MEMPHIS. (Miller Tenn 52)

A drayage check. No information available.

HALLER & ELLIS

Rulau	Date	Metal	Size	VG	F	VF	Unc
Tn-Me 20	(?)	?	--mm	—	—	200.	250.

No description available. (Miller Tenn 26)

A.O. HARRIS & CO.

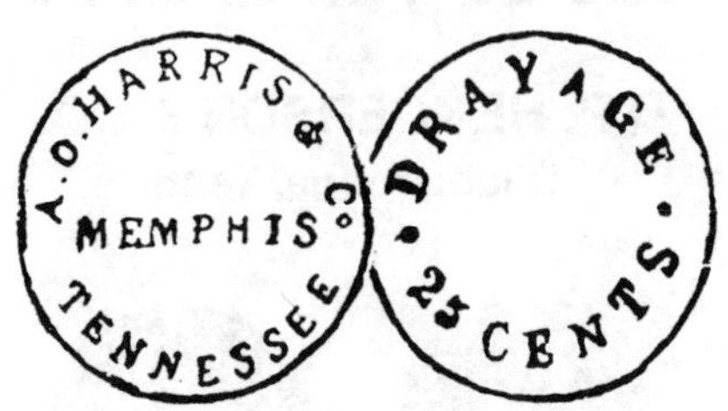

Rulau	Date	Metal	Size	VG	F	VF	Unc
Tn-Me 22	(?)	Brass	28mm	—	—	75.00	150.
	A.O. HARRIS & CO. / MEMPHIS / TENNESSEE. Rv: DRAYAGE / . 25 CENTS . Plain edge. (Wright 427; Miller Tenn 27A)						
Tn-Me 24	(?)	Brass	26mm(?)	—	—	75.00	150.
	Similar to Tenn 27A, but '50' instead of '25'. (Miller Tenn 27)						

Drayage checks. The entire field of Tennessee drayage checks needs research to date the issuing firms better. The checks seem to span the Merchant, Civil War and post-CW eras, and need refinement before any of them can be placed with certainty into any era.

MEGIBBEN & BRO.

Rulau	Date	Metal	Size	VG	F	VF	Unc
Tn-Me 28	(?)	Brass	22mm	—	—	200.	250.
	MEGIBBEN & BRO. / MEMPHIS. 50 / DRAYAGE. (Miller Tenn 29)						

Drayage check.

J.M. MERRILL & CO.

Rulau	Date	Metal	Size	VG	F	VF	Unc
Tn-Me 30	(?)	Brass	--mm	—	—	200.	250.
	J.M. MERRILL & CO. 25 CENTS. (Miller Tenn 30)						

C. MULLER & BRO.

Rulau	Date	Metal	Size	VG	F	EF
Tn-Me 33	(1860)	Silver	31mm	350.	—	500.
	C. MULLER & BRO / MEMPHIS. TENN. / IMPRVD. / SPECTACLES / MANUFACTURER ctsp in five lines on U.S. 1855-O Half dollar. (Brunk 28820)					
Tn-Me 34	(?)	Silver	31mm	350.	—	500.
	Similar ctsp on U.S. 1856-O or 1858-O Half dollar					

In 1860 the Mullers were jewelers, opticians and watchmakers located at 341 Main St.

By 1918 a successor firm, C. Muller & Co., were in the grocery and meat business.

NEVILS & ROSE

Rulau	Date	Metal	Size	VG	F	VF	Unc
Tn-Me 37	(?)	Brass	25mm	—	—	200.	250.
	NEVILS & ROSE, MEMPHIS. 50 DRAYAGE. (Miller Tenn 35) A drayage check.						
Tn-Me 36	(?)	Brass	25mm	—	—	200.	250.
	As 37, but 25.						

PAUL & CROCKETT

Rulau	Date	Metal	Size	VG	F	VF	Unc
Tn-Me 40	(?)	?	--mm	—	—	200.	250.
	No information available. (Miller Tenn 36)						

J.W. SHEERER & CO.

Rulau	Date	Metal	Size	VG	F	VF	Unc
Tn-Me 45	(?)	Brass	30.5mm	—	—	35.00	60.00
	J.W. SHEERER & CO * / 25 (in circle). Rv: DRAYAGE / 25 (in circle) / * CENTS *. Plain edge. (Miller Tenn 37)						
Tn-Me 46	(?)	Brass	30.5mm	—	—	35.00	60.00
	Similar, but '15'. (Miller Tenn 38)						
Tn-Me 47	(?)	Brass	30.5mm	—	—	35.00	60.00
	Similar, but '20'. (Miller Tenn 39)						

Rulau	Date	Metal	Size	VG	F	VF	Unc
Tn-Me 48	(?)	Brass	30.5mm	—	—	35.00	60.00
	Similar, but '25'. (Wright 977; Miller Tenn 40)						
Tn-Me 48A	(?)	S/Br	30.5mm	—	—	35.00	60.00
	As 48. (Miller Tenn 40A)						
Tn-Me 49	(?)	Brass	30.5mm	—	—	35.00	60.00
	Similar, but '50'. (Miller Tenn 41)						

The Sheerer pieces seem always to occur in sets, and are seldom encountered worn.

SOUTHWORTH & KNIGHT

Rulau	Date	Metal	Size	VG	F	VF	Unc
Tn-Me 54	(?)	Brass	26mm	—	—	200.	250.
	SOUTHWORTH & KNIGHT. 25 DRAYAGE. (Miller Tenn 43A)						
Tn-Me 56	(?)	Brass	26mm	—	—	200.	250.
	Similar to 43A, but '50'. (Miller Tenn 43)						

N. H. STARK (?)

Rulau	Date	Metal	Size	VG	F	VF	Unc
Tn-Me 58	(?)	Brass	38mm	—	—	30.00	—
	(All incused): N. H. STARK / MEMPHIS / (eagle displayed) / TENN. / 25. Rv: Intaglio of obverse. Plain edge. (ANS collection)						

WESTERN FOUNDRY

Directory evidence seems to counter the Fulds' claim that these pieces are Civil War store cards. Rather, they seem to be pre-Civil War.

Curtis & Knapp's Western Foundry appears in the 1857 directory, at Poplar near the river. It does not appear in the 1859, 1860, 1865, 1866, 1867, 1868 or 1869 directories.

Therefore we are moving these pieces from our *USTT* (1866-89) to *USMT* (1845-60) sections.

WILSON, LAIRD & CO.

Rulau	Date	Metal	Size	VG	F	VF	Unc
Tn-Me 63	(?)	Brass	26mm	—	—	200.	250.
	WILSON, LAIRD & CO., MEMPHIS. 25 DRAYAGE. (Miller Tenn 49)						
Tn-Me 65	(?)	Brass	26mm	—	—	200.	250.
	Similar, but '50'. (Miller Tenn 48)						

J.M. WISWELL & CO.

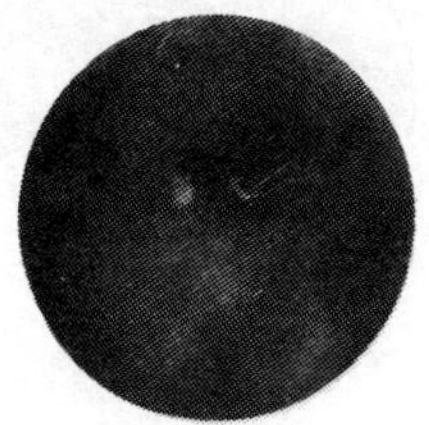

Rulau	Date	Metal	Size	VG	F	VF	Unc
Tn-Me 67	(?)	Brass	28mm	—	—	200.	250.

J.M. WISWELL & CO. / 25 CENTS. Rv: Blank. (Miller Tenn 47)

M. WOLF

Rulau	Date	Metal	Size	VG	F	VF	Unc
Tn-Me 70	(?)	Brass	26mm	—	—	200.	250.
	M. WOLF, DRAYAGE CHECK. 25. (Miller Tenn 50)						
Tn-Me 72	(?)	Brass	26mm	—	—	200.	250.
	Similar, but '50'. (Miller Tenn 51)						

AMMIN'S BROS.

Nashville, Tenn.

Rulau	Date	Metal	Size	VG	F	VF	Unc
Tn-Na 1	(?)	Br.	Oct 27mm	—	—	30.00	—

AMMIN'S BROS. / 1 QUART / NASHVILLE, TENN. Rv: Blank. Plain edge. (Wright 16)

FIRST REGT. TENN. VOLUNTEERS

Rulau	Date	Metal	Size	VG	F	VF	Unc
Tn-Na 7	(1883 ?)	WM	32mm	—	—	40.00	—

FIRST REGT. TENN VOLUNTEERS INFT. C.S.A. / REUNION / NASHVILLE / TENN. Rv: Crossed rifles in wreath, around: OCT. 8, 1862 / OCT. 8. 1863. Plain edge. Issued holed for suspension. (Kirtley July 1987 sale, lot 304)

HOTEL NASHVILLE

Rulau	Date	Metal	Size	VG	F	VF	Unc
Tn-Na 10	(1860-80)	GS	15.5mm	—	85.00	100.	—

(Six-linked chain) / — . — / HOTEL / (sunburst) / NASHVILLE. Rv: 2 1/2. Plain edge. (Rulau coll.)

McKAY & LAPSLEY

McKay & Lapsley issued 1863 and 1864-dated Civil War tokens, and a related firm, D.L. Lapsley & Co. of Nashville, also issued Civil War store cards. (Respectively Fuld 690D-1a to 10d and 690C-1a to 6a). The McKay & Lapsley pieces were listed as Miller Tenn 60 1/2 and 60 1/2 A.

McKay & Lapsley were barbers, at 28 North College, circa 1863-66. David Lapsley continued in business as a barber at 33 North College, circa 1867-69.

The D. L. Lapsley & Co. store cards (Fuld 690C-1a to 6a) may well be post-Civil War in provenance, perhaps as late as 1867. We are not listing them here, however.

MILITARY TOURNAMENT

Rulau	Date	Metal	Size	VF	EF	Unc	Proof
Tn-Na 15	1883	Bronze	39mm	—	—	—	30.00

Sentry standing, facing, before two tents. Rv: Crossed rifles and wreath, NASHVILLE / MAY 21 / 1883 - all within central circle. Around: IN COMMEMORATION OF THE MILITARY TOURNAMENT *. Plain edge. (Byron Johnson coll.)

R.H. SINGLETON

Rulau	Date	Metal	Size	F	VF	EF	Unc
Tn-Na 25	(1866-68)	Copper	21.5mm	—	150.	200.	250.
	Bearded Lincoln bust left, A NATION'S BENEFACTOR around, five stars below. Rv: R.H. SINGLETON / BOOKSELLER / * * * / STATIONER & / JOB PRINTER / P.O. / BUILDING / NASHVILLE. TENN. Plain edge. (King 628; Miller Tenn. 61F)						
Tn-Na 26	(1866-68)	Brass	21.5mm	—	—	200.	250.
	As 25. Plain edge. (Wright 987; King 628; Miller Tenn. 61A)						
Tn-Na 27	(1866-68)	CN	21.5mm	—	—	250.	300.
	As 25. Plain edge. Very rare. (King not listed; Miller Tenn. 61)						

Singleton appears in every directory from 1865 through 1869, indicating he was in business at least 1864-69. In fact, he was the publisher of the city's 1865 directory, known as *Singleton's Nashville Business Directory for 1865*, but this was the only edition he published.

He was a wholesale and retail bookseller and stationer, located in the Post Office Building, and he stocked photo albums, gold pens, silver pencils, pocket knives, combs, mirrors and other objects.

N.L. TARBOX & CO.

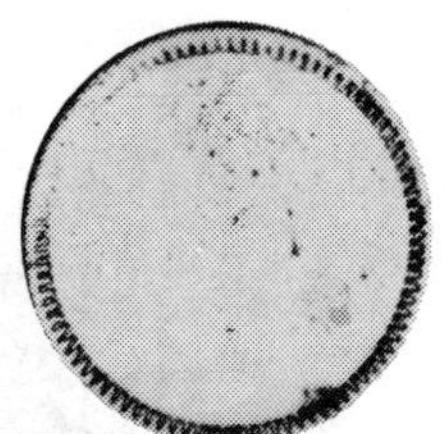

Rulau	Date	Metal	Size	F	VF	EF	Unc
Te-Na 40	(1864)	Brass	20mm	—	—	—	Rare

O / GOLD PEN / DEPOT / - 72 - / CHERRY ST. / ** NASHVILLE. TENN. **. Rv: Blank. (Fuld Tenn 690A-1b). One specimen is known struck over an 1864 Lincoln campaign medalet. This piece was in an auction before 1886.

Some Tarbox tokens may not be Civil War store cards, despite their inclusion in CW catalogs.

E. L. Tarbox & Co., gold pen depot, was located at 72 No. Cherry St., 1864-66. E. L. Tarbox' variety store was on the south side of Church, between Summer and Cherry.

N. L. Tarbox, E. L.'s younger brother, clerked in the store 1865-66. In 1866 or 1867 N. L. was admitted as a partner and the business became known as E. L. Tarbox & Brother, watchmakers, jewelers and repairers, at 52 Union. This lasted to 1868.

One L. G. Tarbox in 1867-68 was cashier at the National Savings Company of Nashville.

The N. L. Tarbox & Co. tokens thus seem to be no earlier than 1869.

TENNESSEE HISTORICAL SOCIETY

Nashville, Tenn.

Rulau	Date	Metal	Size	F	VF	EF	Unc
Tn-Na 42	1880	WM	41mm	—	—	—	30.00

Multitowered building with pennants flying, NASHVILLE CENTENNIAL EXPOSITION / 1780-1880 around. Rv: Equestrian statue left, ANDREW / JACKSON / (crossed sprays) on base. In outer circle: TENNESSEE HISTORICAL SOCIETY / (crossed sprays). Plain edge. (Hibler-Kappen 591)

PINK BENNETT

Union City, Tenn.

Rulau	Date	Metal	Size	F	VF	EF	Unc
Tn-UC 3	(?)	Brass	24mm	—	—	25.00	—

(All incused): Star within circle at center, PINK BENNETT above, UNION CITY, TENN. below. Rv: Blank. Plain edge. (Wright 1336)

JELLICO MT. COAL & COKE CO.

Wooldridge, Tenn.

Rulau	Date	Metal	Size	F	VF	EF	Unc
Tn-Wo 3	1883	GS	22mm	—	30.00	40.00	—
	JELLICO MT COAL & COKE CO. / 5 / MERCHANDISE / * 1883 *. Rv: 5 in circle of 16 stars. Dentilated rim on each side. Plain edge. (Caldwell 9J)						
Tn-Wo 4	1883	GS	--mm	—	30.00	40.00	—
	Similar, but 10.						
Tn-Wo 5	1883	GS	27mm	—	30.00	—	—
	Similar, but 25.						
Tn-Wo 6	1883	GS	--mm	—	30.00	—	—
	Similar, but 50.						
Tn-Wo 7	1883	GS	38mm	—	30.00	—	—
	Similar, but 100.						

Struck by J.W. Murdock & Co. of Cincinnati, Ohio. Supposedly one set in aluminum also exists but it has not been seen.

(See *The Numismatist*) for Nov. 1920, article by John H. Snow, and Dec. 1920, response by H.C. Ezekiel.)

BURNETT HENDRIX & CO.

Tennessee (?)

Rulau	Date	Metal	Size	F	VF	EF	Unc
Tn-Un 1	(?)	Brass	27mm	—	—	200.	250.
	(All incused): DRAYAGE / 25 / BURNETT HENDRIX & CO. Rv: (Small) T. W. MOREHOUSE / J. CITY N.J. Plain edge. (ANS coll.)						

TEXAS

THE HARBOR

Aransas Harbor, Texas

Rulau	Date	Metal	Size	VG	F	VF	Unc
Tx-AH 1	(?)	Brass	25mm	—	—	30.00	—
	(All incused): ARANSAS HARBOR BAR. / GOOD FOR / 12 1/2 ¢ / DRINK. Rv: Blank. Plain edge. (Wright 33)						

Rulau	Date	Metal	Size	VG	F	VF	Unc
Tx-AH 4	(?)	—	31mm	—	—	45.00	—
	Sidewheeler ship right, SOUVENIR OF above, THE FUTURE GREAT below. Rv: LET US GO TO / —+— / THE HARBOR / —+— / ARANSAS HARBOR, TEX. Plain edge. (ANS collection)						

BISMARCK SALOON

Austin, Texas

Rulau	Date	Metal	Size	VG	F	VF	Unc
Tx-Au 3	(1880's)	CN	29mm	—	—	40.00	—
	Facing military bust of Otto von Bismarck at center, BISMARCK above, SALOON below. Rv: Blank. Plain edge.						

Rulau	Date	Metal	Size	VG	F	VF	Unc
Tx-Au 4	(?)	CN	29mm	—	—	100.	—
	Obverse as last. Rv: HENRY RIBBECK across center, scrollwork above and below. (Elmer Randall coll.)						

Henry Ribbeck, a German immigrant, won a lottery prize after arriving in Austin and used the several thousand dollars to go into the saloon business. The Bismarck was named after the Imperial German chancellor (1862-90) who became immensely popular after the German Empire was founded in 1871.

Author William Sidney Porter (O. Henry) frequented the Bismarck, whittling a spot in one table to "mark his place" and this table is now in the O. Henry historical collection at Austin History Library. Later Ribbeck sold his saloon to one Zerchousky.

Even later Ribbeck founded the New Bismarck Saloon, and for a time there were two Bismarck watering holes in Austin, but the tokens are of the original Bismarck. It is believed Zerchousky issued the type without Ribbeck's name. (Information courtesy William Fowler, Austin, Texas)

JULES BORNEFELD

Rulau	Date	Metal	Size	VG	F	VF	Unc
Tx-Au 5	(1877-96)	Brass	21mm	—	—	40.00	—
	Race horse standing left, PALACE SALOON / PAROLE above, * AUSTIN, TEXAS * below. Rv; JULES BORNEFELD / GOOD / FOR ONE / DRINK / (star at center of two branches). Plain edge. (Wright 1342)						
Tx-Au 5A	(1877-96)	Copper	—	—	—	27.50	—
	As 5. Plain edge.						
Tx-Au 5B	(1877-96)	Silver	—	—	—	60.00	—
	As 5. Plain edge.						

Jules Bornefeld ran the Palace Saloon at 901 Congress as early as 1877, continuing its operation until 1896. 'Parole' is a brand of rye whiskey, not the horse's name (as Dr. Wright thought).

There were a number of trial pieces of this token struck in various metals.

COSMOPOLITAN

Austin, Texas

Rulau	Date	Metal	Size	VG	F	VF	Unc
Tx-Au 8	(1883-88)	GS	31mm	—	—	45.00	—
	State Capitol building at center, COSMOPOLITAN above, AUSTIN / TEXAS in exergue. Rv: Old main building of University of Texas at center, GOOD FOR ONE DRINK above. Plain edge. (Wright 207)						
Tx-Au 9	(1883-88)	Brass	31mm	—	—	45.00	—
	Same as last.						
Tx-Au 10	(1888)	Aluminum	31mm	—	—	45.00	—
	Same as last.						

Used at the Cosmopolitan Bar in the 1883-1888 period, these beautiful tokens were made by Heidemann Mfg. Co. in San Antonio. They must have had a souvenir use in addition to their utilitarian use, which would account for their appearing in three different metals.

Aluminum did not become commercially available for token-making until 1888.

C.G. FRENZEL

Rulau	Date	Metal	Size	VG	F	VF	Unc
Tx-AU 12	(1881-89)	Brass	--mm	—	—	25.00	—

R. Rothschild's die. Rv: GOOD FOR / 5 C / C G FRENZEL / IN TRADE. Plain edge. (Dick Worthington coll.)

NEFF & DUFF

Rulau	Date	Metal	Size	VG	F	VF	Unc
Tx-Au 15	(1885-86)	CN	30mm	—	—	80.00	—

Longhorn steer's head facing within central circle. IRON FRONT above, * AUSTIN TEXAS * below. Rv: (ornament) / NEFF & DUFF / (ornament). Plain edge. (Wright 1547)

The Iron Front was the most famous of the Austin saloons, which catered to the thirsty cowboys who drove cattle to markets. The saloon was established in 1866 by Jobe and Robinson and it operated under different proprietors on the same spot until 1919.

John B. Neff and H.H. Duff were the proprietors only in 1885-1886.

The last proprietor of the Iron Front, Thomas A. "Lon" Martin, who ran the place 1905-1919, also issue a token, a cupronickel, 21mm 5-cent piece outside the scope of this work. It is worth $12.50 in VF.

W.B. NEWTON

Rulau	Date	Metal	Size	VG	F	VF	Unc
Tx-Au 17	(1880's)	GS	29mm	—	—	75.00	—

Elephant left on field of ground, WHITE above, AUSTIN, TEXAS below. Rv: W.B. NEWTON / (blank center) / * PROPRIETOR *. Plain edge.

ST. LOUIS SALOON

Rulau	Date	Metal	Size	VG	F	VF	Unc
Tx-Au 20	(1879-94)	Rubber *	29mm	—	—	35.00	—

* Red Vulcanite. BILLIE & CHARLIE / DEALERS IN / IMPORTED AND / DOMESTIC / LIQUORS & CIGARS / AUSTIN, TEXAS. Rv: GOOD FOR / * / ONE DRINK / AT THE / ST. LOUIS / SALOON. Plain edge.

Charles Marshall and William J. Sutor operated the St. Louis Saloon from 1879 through 1894. The token probably was issued in the early 1880's.

William J. (Billy) Sutor later was proprietor of the Hotel Sutor Bar in Austin.

T.A. SCOTT & CO.

Austin, Texas

Rulau	Date	Metal	Size	VG	F	VF	Unc
Tx-Au 22	(1886-88)	Brass	31mm	—	—	25.00	—

Radiant sun at center of large five-pointed star. Letters T-E-X-A-S appear in angles of the outline star. Rv: DRISKILL HOTEL BAR / T.A. SCOTT & CO. / GOOD FOR / — 1 — / DRINK / * AUSTIN, TEX. *. Plain edge.

T.A. Scott was the first proprietor of the Driskill's bar when this famous Austin hostelry opened in 1886.

The Driskill reopened in Sept. 1972, celebrating the event with a wooden token, GOOD FOR ONE FREE DRINK.

M.E. ANDERSON

Bastrop, Texas

Rulau	Date	Metal	Size	VG	F	VF	Unc
Tx-Bp 1	(ca 1882)	CN	Oct., 26mm	—	—	35.00	—

GOOD FOR / * 1 * / M.E. / ANDERSON / * DRINK * (all within round beaded circle, with panels and flourishes present). Rv: Blank. Plain edge.

M.E. Anderson was listed as a saloonkeeper in the 1882 *Texas Gazetteer.*

MIDWAY SALOON

Beeville, Texas

Rulau	Date	Metal	Size	VG	F	VF	Unc
Tx-Be 3	(?)	Aluminum	30mm	—	—	45.00	—

THE MIDWAY / —.— / SALOON / —.— / BEEVILLE, TEXAS. Rv: GOOD FOR / 5¢ / AT BAR. There is a recessed beaded circle inside the rim on each side. Plain edge.

G.F. MILLS

Beeville, Texas

Rulau	Date	Metal	Size	VG	F	VF	Unc
Tx-Be 5	(1880's)	Brass	28mm	—	12.50	—	—

(ornament) GOOD FOR (ornament) / 1 / SHAVE / o / G.F. MILLS (all incused). Rv: Blank. There is a recessed beaded circle inside the rim. Plain edge.

G.F. Mills owned and operated a barber shop in Beeville prior to 1890.

Comparison of this token with that of Lehm's Saloon of Brenham, Texas, reveals the basic blank checks were made by the same maker.

SARG SANDERS & CO.

Belton, Tex.

Rulau	Date	Metal	Size	VG	F	VF	Unc
Tx-Bt 4	(1881-82)	Brass	25mm	—	—	55.00	—

Chas. Pick die. Rv: SARG SANDERS & CO. / BELTON, TEX. Plain edge.

JEFF BREAZEALE'S SALOON

Burnet, Texas

Rulau	Date	Metal	Size	VG	F	VF	Unc
Tx-Bu 1	(1884-94)	Brass	--mm	—	—	35.00	—

BB die. Rv: 12 1/2 C / GOOD FOR 1 / DRINK AT / JEFF BREAZEALE'S / SALOON. Plain edge. (Dick Worthington coll.)

EVANS & LA MOTTE

Boerne, Texas

Rulau	Date	Metal	Size	VG	F	VF	Unc
Tx-Bo 4	(1880's)	Brass	23mm	—	—	12.50	—

EVANS & LA MOTTE / BOERNE. (all incused). Rv: Blank. Plain edge.

LaMotte was listed as a saloonkeeper in the 1882 *Texas Gazetteer.*

LA VALLEE SALOON

Boerne, Texas

Rulau	Date	Metal	Size	VG	F	VF	Unc
Tx-Bo 8	(1884-97)	Brass	23mm	—	—	12.50	—

(All incused). LAVALLEE / GOOD FOR / 5 / CENTS / AT BAR / SALOON. Rv: Blank. Plain edge.

L.N. LaVallee operated his saloon in Boerne at least from 1884 to 1897.

CHAMBER OF COMMERCE SALOON

Brackett, Texas

Rulau	Date	Metal	Size	VG	F	VF	Unc
Tx-Bk 2	(1880's)	Nickel	31mm	—	—	60.00	—

CHAMBER OF COMMERCE / SALOON / BRACKETT, TEXAS. Rv: I. O. U. / ONE / DRINK. Plain edge. (Koppenhaver June 1987 sale, lot 182)

LEHM'S SALOON

Brenham, Texas

Rulau	Date	Metal	Size	VG	F	VF	Unc
Tx-Bm 3	(1880)	Brass	28mm	—	—	25.00	—

LEHM'S / GOOD FOR / 5 / CENTS / AT BAR / SALOON (all incused). Rv: Blank. There is a recessed beaded circle inside the rim. Plain edge.

Bernhard Lehman owned and operated this saloon prior to 1882.

CHARLOTTE H. MILLER

Brownsville, Texas

Rulau	Date	Metal	Size	VG	F	VF	EF
Tx-Br 4	(?)	Silver	32.5mm	—	—	300.	—

CHARLOTTE H. MILLER / BROWNSVILLE / TEX. ctsp. on U.S. 1830 Bust type half dollar. (Brunk 27710)

J.L. BARNES

Bryan, Texas

Rulau	Date	Metal	Size	VG	F	VF	EF
Tx-By 2	(1880-1900)	Silver	26mm	—	—	400.	—
Tx-By 3	(1880-1900)	Silver	31mm	—	—	450.	—

Tx-By 2: J.L. BARNES / SALOON / BRYAN TEX. cstp on U.S. 1853 Liberty Seated quarter. 2 known. (Gould 6; Brunk 2460)

Tx-By 3: Similar ctsp. on U.S. 1858-O and 1873-Arrows and 1874 Liberty Seated half dollars. (Schenkman collection; Van Ormer 2527, 2528)

C. ANCHICKS

Calvert, Texas

Rulau	Date	Metal	Size	VG	F	VF	Unc
Tx-Cv 1	(?)	CN	22mm	—	—	225.	—

C. ANCHICKS / (star) / CALVERT, TEX. on obverse; GOOD FOR ONE DRINK ctsp on reverse of U.S. 1868 Shield nickel. (Van Ormer sale 2510; Koppenhaver Nov. 1983 sale, lot 423; Brunk 920)

H. COCKEREL

Clarksville, Texas

Rulau	Date	Metal	Size	VG	F	VF	Unc
Tx-Ck 3	(1880-99)	CN	**	—	—	25.00	—

** Oval 34.2 x 19.1mm.

Eagle atop U.S. shield above four folds of a scroll. On scroll, incuse, is: H. COCKEREL, / CLARKSVILLE / RED RIVER CO. / TEX. Rv: Blank. Plain edge. Holed at left as issued.

Apparently an identification tag of early vintage.

S

Colorado, Texas

Rulau	Date	Metal	Size	VG	F	VF	EF
Tx-Co 2	(1877-85)	Brass	24mm	—	—	40.00	—

Eagle displayed at center, E. PLURIBUS UNUM above, COLORADO, TEXAS. below. Rv: Large radiant 'S' within circle of alternating stars and dots.

The use of this token is unknown. It could be a merchant's token.

A Texas Ranger camp was established at Colorado in 1877, the first white settlement. A commissary could have served the camp.

NIC. CONSTANTINE'S SALOON

Corpus Christi, Texas

Rulau	Date	Metal	Size	VG	F	VF	Unc
Tx-CC 4	(?)	CN	30mm	—	—	45.00	—

NIC. CONSTANTINE'S / —.— / SALOON / CORPUS CHRISTI / TEX. Rv: GOOD FOR / ONE / * DRINK *. Plain edge.

COTTON EXCHANGE

Cuero, Texas

Rulau	Date	Metal	Size	VG	F	VF	Unc
Tx-Cu 1	(?)	Brass	--mm	—	—	25.00	—

National Billiard Mfg. Co. die. Rv: COTTON EXCHANGE / H. F. HARDT.

H. F. Hardt operated the Cotton Exchange in Cuero, DeWitt County. The attribution is tentative.

CONSOLIDATED STEEL & WIRE CO.

Dallas, Texas

Rulau	Date	Metal	Size	F	VF	EF	Unc
Tx-Da 3	1895	Brass	26mm	—	20.00	—	—

CONSOLIDATED STEEL & WIRE CO / TEXAS STATE FAIR / (Star) / DALLAS / 1895 / CHICAGO, Rv: BAKER PERFECT / BARB / WIRE / (Length of barbed wire) / LIGHTEST / MADE 290 Lbs. PER MILE. Plain edge. (Kirtley report)

Consolidated Steel & Wire Co. also issued tokens for Chicago (consult Index).

A. B. TABOR

Dallas, Texas

(See II-Ch 115, Schuttler Wagons, under Chicago, Illinois in this reference)

FRANK C. BLAINE

Del Rio, Texas

Rulau	Date	Metal	Size	VG	F	VF	Unc
Tx-DR 3	(1880's)	CN	30mm	—	45.00	100.	Rare

Longhorn steer's head facing in circle, tiny W.W. WILCOX at base of neck. CATTLE EXCHANGE above, * DEL RIO, TEXAS. * below. Rv: FRANK / C. / BLAINE. Plain edge.

Rulau	Date	Metal	Size	VG	F	VF	Unc
Tx-DR 4	(1890's)	Brass	21mm	—	—	12.50	—

FRANK C. BLAINE / DEL RIO, / TEX. Rv: GOOD FOR / 5¢ / IN TRADE. Plain edge.

The Cattle Exchange has not yet been identified. It may be a saloon.

COW BOY'S SALOON

Doans, Texas

Rulau	Date	Metal	Size	VG	F	VF	Unc
Tx-Dn 2	(?)	CN	25mm	—	—	60.00	—

Steer standing on a mound. Rv: Stars and dots form border, within which: COW BOY'S / SALOON / DOANS, TEX. Plain edge.

Also known as Doan's Store or Doan's Crossing, Doans was located in Wilbarger County on the Red River, where the Dodge City or Western Trail crossed into Oklahoma. It is said that 6,000,000 cattle crossed the Red River at this point.

A.S. CHRISTIAN

Elgin, Texas

Rulau	Date	Metal	Size	VG	F	VF	Unc
Tx-El 4	(1880's)	Brass	19mm	—	—	17.50	—

A.S. CHRISTIAN / ELGIN, TEXAS. Rv: GOOD FOR / 5¢ / AT THE BAR. Plain edge.

Elgin was founded in 1872.

Christian was probably Elgin's earliest saloonkeeper. The token was issued before 1890.

ACME (SALOON)

El Paso, Texas

Rulau	Date	Metal	Size	VG	F	VF	Unc
Tx-EP 1	(1881)	CN	25mm	—	—	12.50	—

Oval at center, within which: N.F. NEWLAND / PROP. Rose above, diamond below. Rv: GOOD FOR / 1 / ACME / * DRINK *. Plain edge.

N.F. Newland was proprietor of the Acme Saloon at its first location on South El Paso Street, about 1881.

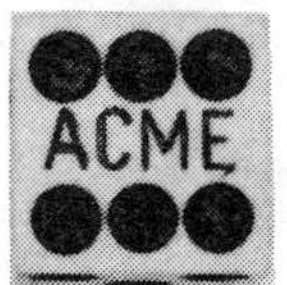

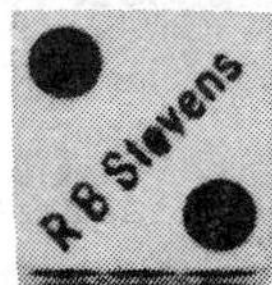

Rulau	Date	Metal	Size	VG	F	VF	Unc
Tx-EP 3	(1895)	Ivory	**	—	—	Rare	—

** Cube (Die) 16x16mm.

Single die of six sides used in Acme's dice games. On 6-pip side: ACME. On 2-pip side: R B STEVENS. On 1-pip side: GOOD FOR / DRINK.

R.B. Stevens was proprietor of the Acme Saloon. These dice tokens were in use there on August 19, 1895, when John Wesley Hardin was gunned down from behind by "Old John" Selman. Newspaper reports say Hardin was shaking dice at the Acme bar for drinks, and as he raised his dice cup for a toss, El Paso chief constable Selman shot him in the back of the head without warning. Selman was charged with murder but was acquitted; his attorney was Albert Fall, who in the Roaring Twenties became a central figure in the Teapot Dome scandal.

John Wesley Hardin (1853-1895) was known as one of the fastest gunfighters in the Southwest. He once outdrew Wild Bill Hickock in Abilene in 1871, though no gunfight resulted and the two drank together and became friends. He is reputed to have killed 40 men in his outlaw career. He killed two Union troopers at Richmond Bottoms, Texas, during the Civil War while only 12.

He became the leader of the Taylor faction against the Suttons in the Gonzales-DeWitt Counties war in 1872-1874, and killed in that war Sheriff J.W. Morgan of Cuero, gunfighter Jack Helm, and Deputy Sheriff Charles Webb of Brown County. He was reputed to have planned the murders of clan leader Bill Sutton and rancher Gabe Slaughter at Indianola.

Texas Ranger John Duncan found Hardin in hiding at Polland, Alabama and sent for Captain John Armstrong of the Rangers. They arrested Hardin in August 1877 aboard a train and Hardin served 17 years in Huntsville State Prison for the "murder" of Webb, even though witnesses said Webb attempted to shoot Hardin in the back.

Hardin was pardoned in the spring of 1894. Having studied law in prison, he opened a law office in Gonzales in Oct. 1894. In early 1895 he moved to El Paso and became a criminal lawyer. During a love affair with the wife of rustler Martin McRose he became morose and began drinking. Hardin slighted the name of policeman "Young John" Selman after Selman had arrested his mistress Mrs. McRose for carrying a gun; the tirade coming after a saloon drinking bout.

Selman's father, then the chief constable of El Paso though himself a former outlaw, shot and killed Hardin from behind in the Acme Saloon without warning. Bartender Frank Patterson told police Selman shot Hardin in the back of the head; a photograph of Hardin's body in the El Paso morgue shows bullet wounds in the right chest and right upper arm, and his face seems unmarred except for dark spots on the left eye.

COBWEB BILLIARD HALL

Rulau	Date	Metal	Size	VF	F	VF	Unc
Tx-EP 5	(1874-84)	Brass	25mm	—	—	30.00	—

Brunswick die BB-6a. Rv: COBWEB BILLIARD HALL / GOOD FOR / 1 / DRINK / W. F. / VANSTON. Plain edge.

W. F. Vanston has been traced in El Paso in directories of this period.

B. DOWELLS

Rulau	Date	Metal	Size	VG	F	VF	EF
Tx-EP 7	(?)	Silver	25mm	125.	—	225.	—

B. DOWELLS / SALOON ctsp on U.S. 1854-O quarter dollar obverse. EL PASO ctsp on reverse of coin. (All lettering is crude, as though a single-letter die punch was used laboriously) (Brunk; 12060)

Ben Dowell was the first mayor of El Paso.

THE OPHIR

Rulau	Date	Metal	Size	VG	F	VF	Unc
Tx-EP 14	(1880's)	CN	24mm	—	—	17.50	—

(All legends incuse). The OPHIR / 106 (in circle) / EL PASO TEX. Rv: Within central circle: GOOD FOR / 12 1/2 / ¢ / IN TRADE. Ornament above, AT THE OPHIR below. Plain edge.

THE PARLOR

El Paso, Texas

Rulau	Date	Metal	Size	VG	F	VF	Unc
Tx-EP 18	(1888)	GS	33mm	—	25.00	—	—

Court house at center, EL PASO COURT HOUSE above, star below. Rv: Church at center. Above: GOOD FOR 1 DRINK AT THE PARLOR / EL PASO / TEX. Below: OLD CHURCH AGE 270 YEARS / PASO DEL NORTE, MEX. Plain edge.

Rulau	Date	Metal	Size	VG	F	VF	Unc
Tx-EP 19	(1889)	Aluminum	33mm	—	15.00	—	—

Same as last. Plain edge.

Rulau	Date	Metal	Size	VG	F	VF	Unc
Tx-EP 20	(1890)	Aluminum	33mm	—	15.00	—	—

Obverse as last. Rv: As last, except text under church reads: OLD CHURCH BUILT 1618 / JUAREZ, MEX.

The Paso del Norte Church was built in 1618, dating the first token exactly. Probably the third type saw the greater use as a drink check.

S. B. MOSSER & CO.

Encinal, Texas

Rulau	Date	Metal	Size	VG	F	VF	Unc
Tx-En 3	(?)	Brass	25mm	—	—	40.00	—

BBC die. Rv: GOOD FOR / ONE / BIT IN TRADE / S. B. MOSSER / & CO. / ENCINAL. Plain edge. (Dick Worthington coll.)

See also S. B. Mosser & Co. under San Antonio, Texas.

B & B WHITE ELEPHANT
Fort Worth, Texas

Rulau	Date	Metal	Size	VG	F	VF	Unc
Tx-FW 4	(1874-84)	Brass	24mm	—	—	55.00	—

Pool table. Above: THE / J.M. BRUNSWICK / AND / BALKE CO. Rv: GOOD FOR / 5¢ / IN TRADE / WHITE / ELEPHANT / B & B / FORT WORTH. Plain edge. (Brunswick 2381)

THE MINT
Fort Worth, Texas

Rulau	Date	Metal	Size	VG	F	VF	Unc
Tx-FW 12	(1874-84)	Brass	25mm	—	—	25.00	—

BB die. Rv: GOOD FOR / 5 C / AT THE / MINT. Plain edge.

AUG. CAMERON
Fredericksburg, Texas

Rulau	Date	Metal	Size	VG	F	VF	Unc
Tx-Fr 3	(1885)	GS	28mm	—	—	37.50	—

State capitol. Rv: AUG. CAMERON / CAPITOL / —*—- / —SALOON— / GOOD FOR / 10 CENTS / DRINK / * FREDERICKSBURG, TEXAS. *. Plain edge. Rarity 8. (Wright 1358).

BEACH HOTEL
Galveston, Texas

Rulau	Date	Metal	Size	VG	F	VF	Unc
Tx-Ga 2	(1880's)	GS	29mm	—	7.50	—	—

BEACH HOTEL / 15 / GALVESTON / large 15 (the last incused). Rv: Similar, but incused; no counterstamped numeral 15. Plain edge.

The Beach Hotel burned down in 1889.

INTER STATE DRILL
Galveston, Texas

Rulau	Date	Metal	Size	F	VF	EF	Unc
Tx-Ga 8	1886	S/WM	36.5mm	—	75.00	—	—

Uniformed mounted officer tipping his cap, within horseshoe, McGRUDER below. Rv: Large 5-pointed star within wreath (the "Lone star"). Around: SOUVENIR INTER STATE DRILL / * GALVESTON. AUG. 5. 86. *. Plain edge. (Norman Peters coll.)

PALACE SALOON
Gonzales, Texas

Rulau	Date	Metal	Size	VG	F	VF	Unc
Tx-Gn 7	(1880's)	Nickel	**	—	—	40.00	—

**Scal 29mm.

PALACE SALOON / W. A. / CARDWELL, PROP. Rv: GOOD FOR / 12 1/2 C / IN TRADE. Plain Edge. (Koppenhaver June 1987 sale, lot 183)

LATRAITE
Houston, Texas

Rulau	Date	Metal	Size	VG	F	VF	Unc
Tx-Ho 3	(1892)	CN	30mm	—	—	40.00	—

Building at center, POST OFFICE above, HOUSTON, TEX. below. Rv: LATRAITE on ornamental scroll across center. At bottom, in small letters: THE HEIDEMANN MFG. CO. S.A. TEX. Plain edge. (Wright N/L)

Jean Pierre Latreyte was born in Pau, France, May 22, 1849. At 16 he emigrated to New Orleans, working there in a saloon 1865-1871. In 1871 he moved to Houston and became a bartender at Kiam's Saloon at Travis and Preston Streets. He opened his own saloon on Congress Avenue across from the courthouse in 1875. In 1879 he opened the Sample Room Saloon on Congress and Fannin Streets.

Latreyte (now John Peter Latreyte) watched his wife Marie Matilde die in 1879. In 1882 he married a 26-year-old widow and bought into her father's hardware business. In 1891 the new post office was completed on the Sample Room's block, and in 1892 Latreyte ordered the handsome tokens depicting the new post office from Heidemann Mfg. Co. in San Antonio. He was divorced in 1894, and died while on a trip to Bourne, Texas, June 20, 1901. He had five daughters.

The Latreyte piece, though struck in 1892, belongs with the rest of the Heidemann-produced Texas pictorial tokens and thus is included in this book.

For a full treatment on Latreyte, see "Latreyte and the Sample Room Saloon" by Ernest Beerstecher, in *TAMS Journal* for August, 1977.

G. ERICHSON

Rulau	Date	Metal	Size	VG	F	VF	EF
Tx-Ho 2	(?)	Silver	31mm	—	—	100.	—

G. ERICHSON / HOUSTON / TEXAS ctsp on U.S. 1858-O Seated Liberty half dollar. (Kovacs coll.; Brunk 13497)

OPERA HOUSE WINE ROOM
Houston, Texas

Rulau	Date	Metal	Size	VG	F	VF	Unc
Tx-Ho 12	(?)	GS	28mm	—	—	—	—

(All incused): OPERA HOUSE / 15 / WINE ROOM. Rv: PAY THE / 15 / CASHIER. Plain edge.

Rulau	Date	Metal	Size	VG	F	VF	Unc
Tx-Ho 13	(?)	GS	28mm	—	—	—	—

As 12, but numeral 20 replaces the 15 on each side. Plain edge. (Wright 790)

Rulau	Date	Metal	Size	VG	F	VF	Unc
Tx-Ho 14	(?)	GS	28mm	—	—	Rare	—

As 12, but numeral 350 replaces the 15 on each side. Plain edge.

Dr. B.P. Wright sold a specimen of 12 on April 15, 1897 to another collector with a tag stating it was rare and from Houston. This piece was sold later to Melvin and George Fuld, who published it in *The Numismatist* in their Token Collector's Pages.

The '350' piece, number 14, was reported by Fowler and Strough in *The Trade Tokens of Texas, Supplement*, Feb. 1979.

THE RANCH
Kerrville, Texas

Rulau	Date	Metal	Size	VG	F	VF	Unc
Tx-Kr 4	(1880's)	CN	31mm	—	—	25.00	—

Steer's head at center, THE RANCH above, KERRVILLE, TEX. below. Rv: GOOD FOR / 12 1/2 ¢ / DRINK / CHAS. BARLEMANN. Plain edge.

Rulau	Date	Metal	Size	VG	F	VF	Unc
Tx-Kr 6	(?)	Brass	24mm	—	—	12.50	—

THE RANCH / (star) / KERRVILLE, TEXAS. Rv: 5¢. Plain edge.

ROSENTHAL'S
La Grange, Texas

Rulau	Date	Metal	Size	VG	F	VF	Unc
Tx-Lg 7	(1890's)	Alum	--mm	—	—	35.00	—

Brunswick die BBC-8. Rv: GOOD FOR / 5 C / ROSENTHAL'S. Plain edge.

Attribution by Paul Koppenhaver, Van Nuys, Calif.

WHITE ELEPHANT
Lampasas, Texas

Rulau	Date	Metal	Size	VG	F	VF	Unc
Tx-Lm 15	(1880)	GS	29mm	—	—	Rare	—

Elephant standing left, WHITE above, ELEPHANT below. Rv: * WHITE ELEPHANT / (star at center of falling rays) / LAMPASAS / —*— / * TEXAS *. Plain edge. Rarity 9.

BOTICA LA MALINCHE
Laredo, Texas

Rulau	Date	Metal	Size	VG	F	VF	Unc
Tx-La 2	(?)	GS	19mm	—	—	25.00	—

Mortar and pestle at center, BOTICA LA MALINCHE above, LAREDO, TEX. below. Rv: GOOD FOR / 6 1/4 / MEX. / IN TRADE. Plain edge.

'6 1/4 Mex.' was one-half real, or 6 1/4 cents U.S.

LAREDO BEER GARDEN
Laredo, Texas

Rulau	Date	Metal	Size	F	VF	EF	Unc
Tx-La 7	(?)	GS	25mm	—	—	12.50	—

LAREDO / BEER / GARDEN. Rv: GOOD FOR / ONE / BEER. Plain edge.

Rulau	Date	Metal	Size	F	VF	EF	Unc
Tx-La 8	(1889-90)	Alum	35mm	—	17.00	30.00	—

Building at center, ANHEUSER BUSCH ST. LOUIS BEER above, LAREDO / * BEER GARDEN * below. Rv: Flying eagle with shield in its talons before a large letter A. Around: GOOD FOR ONE DRINK. Plain edge.

ALGONA BAR

Llano, Texas

Rulau	Date	Metal	Size	VG	F	VF	Unc
Tx-Ln 1	(1880's)	CN	30mm	—	—	45.00	—

Clasped hands at center, THE ALGONA / BAR above, LLANO, / TEXAS. below. Rv: GOOD FOR / —*— / 12 1/2 ¢ / —*— / DRINK. Plain edge.

TOM'S SALOON

Llano, Texas

Rulau	Date	Metal	Size	VG	F	VF	Unc
Tx-Ln 6	(1874-84)	Brass	25mm	—	—	50.00	—

Brunswick die BB-8a. Rv: TOM'S SALOON. Plain edge. (Thoele report)

J.H.M. & B.
(J.H. Muenster & Brother)

Luling, Texas

Rulau	Date	Metal	Size	VG	F	VF	EF
Tx-Lu 7	(1882)	Brass	23mm	—	—	17.50	—

J.H.M. & B. / GOOD FOR / A / DRINK. Rv: Blank. Plain edge.

Rulau	Date	Metal	Size	VG	F	VF	EF
Tx-Lu 9	(1880's)	Brass	23mm	—	—	17.50	—

GOOD FOR / 1 / DRINK / J H M. & BRO. Rv: LULING. Plain edge. (All lettering incuse)

Rulau	Date	Metal	Size	VG	F	VF	EF
Tx-Lu 10	(1880's)	Brass	23mm	—	—	17.50	—

As last, but blank reverse. Plain edge.

The Muensters operated saloons in Luling for several generations. J.H. Muenster & Brother are located there in 1882. D.C. Muenster is placed there in 1890 and 1897. S.A. Muenster operated there in 1914.

Luling was called the "the toughest town in Texas," as were Dallas, Langtry, Jacksboro, Old Tascosa and others from time to time.

Rulau	Date	Metal	Size	VG	F	VF	EF
Tx-Lu 12	(1890's)	Aluminum	24mm	—	—	17.50	—

D.C. MUENSTER / LULING, TEX. Rv: GOOD FOR / 5 / CENTS / IN TRADE. Plain edge.

A. B. FRALEY

Marshall, Texas

Rulau	Date	Metal	Size	VG	F	VF	Unc
Tx-Ms 1	1873	Silver	34mm	—	—	150.	—

A. B. FRALEY / MARSHALL, / TEXAS. / 1873 ctsp on Prussia 1848 thaler. (Donald Partrick coll.; Brunk 14970)

JOSEPH LIPARI

Mexia, Texas

Rulau	Date	Metal	Size	VG	F	VF	Unc
Tx-Mx 2	(1881-82)	CN	24mm	—	—	25.00	—

Pool table. Above: THE J.M. BRUNSWICK / & / BALKE COS. Below: CHECK. Rv: GOOD FOR / * 1 * / JOSEPH LIPARI / DRINK. Plain edge. (Brunswick 2216)

Appears in the 1882 Texas Gazetteer.

GEO. B. BERRY & CO.

Mobeetie, Texas

Rulau	Date	Metal	Size	VG	F	VF	Unc
Tx-Mb 3	(1880's)	CN	Oct, 27mm	—	—	Rare	—

Elephant right on mound. Rv: GOOD FOR ONE DRINK / (radiant star) / GEO. B. BERRY & CO. / (radiant star) / MOBEETIE, TEXAS. Plain edge.

Mobeetie ("Sweetwater" in Indian) was the first settlement in the Texas Panhandle. First known as Hidetown by buffalo hunters, it was established 1874 as a trading post one mile from Fort Elliott.

George B. Berry came from Kansas and opened a saloon and dance hall. Bat Masterson and Temple Houston, son of Sam Houston, both lived in Mobeetie in the early days. Bat killed his first man here in a fight over a girl.

Temple Houston, born 1860 in the governor's mansion, became in 1878 (at 18) district attorney over the vast Panhandle.

BANK EXCHANGE

Palestine, Texas

Rulau	Date	Metal	Size	VG	F	VF	Unc
Tx-Pa 1	(1874-84)	CN	25mm	—	—	25.00	—

Pool table at bottom, THE / J. M. BRUNSWICK / AND / BALKE CO. within flourishes above. Rv: GOOD FOR / 1 / AT BANK / EXCHANGE / DRINK. Plain edge.

Rulau	Date	Metal	Size	VG	F	VF	Unc
Tx-Pa 2	(ca 1880)	Brass	25mm	—	—	V. Rare	

Liberty head to left surrounded by a wreath. Rv: Large numeral 1 in center, REDEEMED AT BANK EXCHANGE around. (Wright 56)

Assigned to Palestine on the basis of name similarity. The term "Bank Exchange" was widely used in Texas at this period.

J. J. MURPHY

Palestine, Texas

Rulau	Date	Metal	Size	VG	F	VF	Unc
Tx-Pa 4	(1880's)	GS	30mm	—	—	200.	—

Texas state capitol building. Rv: J. J. MURPHY, / GOOD FOR / *12 1/2 ¢ * / AT THE / RUBY / PALESTINE, TEXAS. Plain edge.

W. W. CAMP

Pecos, Texas

Rulau	Date	Metal	Size	VG	F	VF	Unc
Tx-Pc 2	(1880's)	Br.	Oct, 27mm	—	—	Rare	—

Steer at center, W. W. CAMP above, PECOS, TEXAS below. Rv: 12 1/2. Plain edge.

Pecos was established in 1881 as a stop on the Texas & Pacific Railroad. It gained early fame as a hangout for fast-draw gunmen, rough and ready cowboys, numerous saloons, and the world's first rodeo (held in 1883). It is now a trading center for a large West Texas area supported by oil, irrigated farming and tourism.

W. J. H. UMLAND

Round Top, Texas

Rulau	Date	Metal	Size	VG	F	VF	Unc
Tx-RT 7	(1874-82)	Brass	23mm	—	—	22.00	—

Pool table at center, THE J. M. BRUNSWICK & BALKE CO. above, o CHECK o below. Rv: GOOD FOR / 5 ¢ / W. J. H. / UMLAND / o IN TRADE o. Plain edge. 25-30 pieces known.

Rulau	Date	Metal	Size	VG	F	VF	Unc
Tx-RT 8	(1874-82)	Brass	24mm	—	—	30.00	—

Similar, but THE J. M. BRUNSWICK / & BALKE COS. above pool table, nothing below it. Rv: As last. Plain edge.

Umland drove a freight wagon on the old New Orleans-San Antonio road and later operated a saloon at Round Top, one of the primary stops on the route. When the railroad bypassed Round Top in the early 1880's, he moved to Carmine and opened a general mercantile business with his son-in-law, E. W. Hoppe, (Hoppe later issued tokens at Carmine).

H. E. V. ROSENBERG

Round Top, Texas

Rulau	Date	Metal	Size	VG	F	VF	Unc
Tx-RT 10	(1874-84)	CN	24mm	—	—	12.50	—

Pool table at bottom, THE J. M. BRUNSWICK / & / BALKE COS above within flourishes. Rv: GOOD FOR / 5 ¢ / H. E. / v. ROSENBERG / IN / * TRADE *. Plain edge. (Brunswick 2306)

The way the small "v." appears before Rosenberg, it must indicate the proprietor's name was H. E. von Rosenberg. He has not yet been traced.

FRED SCHMIDT

San Angelo, Texas

Rulau	Date	Metal	Size	VG	F	VF	Unc
Tx-Sn 7	(?)	Brass	29mm	—	—	Rare	—

Steer's head facing three-quarters right, DROP ME AT THE PARLOR SALOON above, FRED SCHMIDT below. Rv: Courthouse view, SAN ANGELO, TEXAS below. Plain edge.

Tx-Sn 9 (?) Brass 30mm — — Rare —
Longhorn steer head facing three-quarters right, LONGEST HORNS / IN THE / WORLD above, EIGHT FEET FROM TIP TO TIP below. Rv: Horse at left, cowboy tying roped "dogie" at right. FRED SCHMIDT above, SAN ANGELO, TEXAS below. Plain edge.

THE ALAMO
San Antonio, Texas

Rulau	Date	Metal	Size	VG	F	VF	Unc
Tx-SA 1	(1889)	GS	32mm	—	—	45.00	—

Alamo at center, CRADLE OF TEXAS LIBERTY above, ALAMO in exergue. Rv: Post office building at center, POST OFFICE above, SAN ANTONIO, TEX. below. Plain edge. (Gary Pipher coll.)

This is a muling of the Alamo die used on Tx-SA 225 (the White House Saloon piece) and on Tx-SA 72 (the Peter Jonas piece) with the Post Office die used on Tx-SA 107 (the Nentwig's Bar piece). It is undoubtedly a Heidemann Mfg. Co. product, possibly for general use in San Antonio.

ALBERT'S SALOON

Rulau	Date	Metal	Size	VG	F	VF	Unc
Tx-SA 2	(1880's)	GS	32mm	—	60.00	100.	—

Mounted elk's head with 17-point antlers at center, ALBERT'S above, SALOON below. Rv: Ram's head facing, its horns and ears framing 'I O U'. Below: ONE DRINK OR CIGAR. Plain edge. (Wright N/L)

Tx-SA 4 (?) WM 31mm 25.00 32.50 42.00 75.00
The Alamo at center, ALBERT'S SALOON above, THE ALAMO below. Rv: Mission at center, THE MISSION CONCEPCION above, SAN ANTONIO, / TEX. below. Plain edge.

Tx-SA 5 (?) GS 31mm — — 35.00 80.00
As Tx-SA 4. Plain edge.

Tx-SA 7 (1889) Alum. 31mm 15.00 30.00 40.00 65.00
Mounted 78-point buck elk's head above large 5-pointed star, with T-E-X-A-S on the five points of the star. Above: ALBERT'S / — * — / SALOON. Rv: View of the Alamo at center, CRADLE OF TEXAS LIBERTY above, ALAMO in exergue. Plain edge. (Wright 12)

Tx-SA 8 (?) CN 19mm — — 22.50 —
Large 6-pointed Star of David at center, ALBERT'S above, SALOON below. Rv: GOOD FOR / * 2 1/2 ¢ / IN TRADE. Plain edge.

Tx-SA 9 (?) Brass 20mm — — 17.50 —
(All incuse) ALBERT'S 2 1/2. Rv: Blank. Plain edge.

Regarding Tx-SA 7, a 78-point elk's antlers was the greatest number known in Fredrich's day.

Albert Fredrich kept his well-known Albert's Saloon on Dolorosa Street. Albert's was the predecessor of another saloon, the Buckhorn, called San Antonio's most famous saloon. Fredrich, who was proud of his Jewishness at a time when this was soft-pedaled in tough Texas saloons, was the proprietor of the Buckhorn and Albert's Saloon. The Buckhorn ultimately was removed to the Lone Star Brewery grounds, where it is once more in operation as an attraction.

Tx-SA 11 (?) CN 23mm — — 25.00 —
(All incused): BUCK HORN / GOOD FOR / 12 1/2 / CENTS / AT BAR / SALOON. Rv: Blank. Plain edge.

Tx-SA 12 (?) Brass 30mm — — 27.50 35.00
Longhorn steer at center, TEXAS LONG-HORN STEER above, OLD TEX / AT THE BUCKHORN below. Rv: View of the Alamo at center, THE ALAMO above, BUILT IN / 1718 / SAN ANTONIO, TEXAS. Plain edge.

EMIL BEHRENS

Rulau	Date	Metal	Size	F	VF	EF	Unc
Tx-SA 14	(1889-90)	CN	25mm	—	6.00	9.50	—

Winged Cupid riding a swan left, TRADE MARK in exergue, all within central circle. Above: * EMIL BEHRENS C.E. *. Below: PATENT ATTORNEY. Rv: SAN ANTONIO / ELECTROPLATING / WORKS / EMIL BEHRENS & CO. / MANUFACTURERS OF / LIGHT MACHINERY / MODELS & / EXPERIMENTAL / WORKS.

Emil Behrens, civil engineer, was listed in the 1889-1890 San Antonio city directory as a civil, mechanical and electrical engineer, patent attorney, and draftsman. His token is very handsome.

BELL & BROTHERS

Rulau	Date	Metal	Size	VG	F	VF	EF
Tx-SA 16	(1868)	Bronze	19mm	—	—	450.	—

BELL & BROS / (ornamentation) / SAN-ANTONIO / TEXAS ctsp on U.S. 1864 Indian cent. (Brunk 3150)

Tx-SA 17 (?) CN 22mm — — 500. —
Similar ctsp on U.S. 1867 Shield nickel.

Samuel Bell (1798-?) arrived in San Antonio 1851 and set up as a jeweler and silversmith. This became Bell & Brothers in 1863 and by 1885 was the city's leading jeweler.

J. BOSSHARDT

Rulau	Date	Metal	Size	VG	F	VF	Unc
Tx-SA 19	(1883-85)	Brass	23mm	—	12.50	20.00	—

(All incused): GOOD FOR / 5 / CENTS / AT BAR / J. BOSSHARDT. Rv: Blank. Plain edge.

John Bosshardt was operating the Eureka Saloon at the corner of Navarro and Commerce Streets as early as 1883. He advertised a "free lunch every day."

JIM BRADY & CO.

Rulau	Date	Metal	Size	VG	F	VF	Unc
Tx-SA 22	(?)	CN	24mm	—	—	40.00	—

JIM BRADY & CO. / OFFICE BAR / MAIN PLAZA. / Rv: I. O. U. / 12 1/2 ¢ / SAN ANTONIO, TEX. Plain edge.

Tx-SA 24 (?) CN 25mm — — 40.00 —
JIM BRADY'S / OFFICE BAR / MAIN PLAZA. Rv: I. O. U. / 12 1/2¢ / SAN ANTONIO, TEX. Plain edge. (Wright 92)

JOHN BRADY

Rulau	Date	Metal	Size	VG	F	VF	Unc
Tx-SA 26	(?)	GS	30mm	—	35.00	50.00	—

JOHN BRADY'S / (star) / PARLOR BAR / —.— / SAN ANTONIO, / TEXAS. Rv: I.O.U. / —+— / ONE / —+— / .***. DRINK .***. Plain edge.

FRANK BROWN

Rulau	Date	Metal	Size	VG	F	VF	Unc
Tx-SA 28	(?)	Brass	25mm	—	10.00	15.00	—

(All incused): FRANK BROWN / GOOD FOR / 5 LBS. / ICE / SAN ANTONIO. Rv: Blank. Plain edge. (Wright 1347)

BUFFET BAR

Rulau	Date	Metal	Size	VG	F	VF	Unc
Tx-SA 30	(?)	CN	23mm	—	—	40.00	—

View of the Alamo inside a star, all within a wreath. Rv: 121 / W. COMMERCE / BUFFET / BAR / SAN ANTONIO, TEX. / U.S.A. Plain edge.

ELITE SALOON

Rulau	Date	Metal	Size	VG	F	VF	Unc
Tx-SA 38	(1880's)	GS	31mm	—	35.00	50.00	85.00

Soldiers attacking the Alamo at center, ELITE SALOON above, FALL OF THE / ALAMO / 1836 below. Rv: Building with tall tower at center, GOOD FOR ONE DRINK above, GOV. TOWER / SAN ANTONIO, TEX. below. Plain edge. (Wright 1405)

In this unusually detailed token by the Heidemann Mfg. Co., Pres. Santa Ana's army can be seen attacking toward the Alamo in the distance. It is one of the finest of the many fine Texas pictorial tokens of this period.

ELLSWORTH & BUCK

Rulau	Date	Metal	Size	VG	F	VF	Unc
Tx-SA 40	(1880's)	CN	32mm	—	—	60.00	—

Mission at center, MISSION SAN JOSE. above, FOUNDED 1720. below. Rv: CATARACT BAR / * 21 * / SOLEDAD STR. / 12 1/2 / ELLSWORTH & BUCK. Plain edge. (Wright 291)

FRED'S

Rulau	Date	Metal	Size	VG	F	VF	Unc
Tx-SA 43	(1880's)	CN	33mm	—	—	45.00	—

Large building at center, CITY HALL above, — * — / SAN ANTONIO, TEX. below. Rv: FRED'S on ornate scroll across center. Plain edge. (Wright N/L)

J. L. FURTNER

Rulau	Date	Metal	Size	VG	F	VF	Unc
Tx-SA 45	(1880's)	CN	31mm	—	—	40.00	—

MAVERICK HOTEL / (star) / BAR / SAN ANTONIO / TEX. Rv: GOOD FOR ONE DRINK / OR / CIGAR / AT / J. L. FURTNER'S. Plain edge. (Wright 1422)

GUADALUPE HOTEL

Rulau	Date	Metal	Size	VG	F	VF	Unc
Tx-SA 47	(?)	Brass	23mm	—	10.00	—	—

GUADALUPE / HOTEL / GOOD FOR / 5 / CENTS / AT BAR. Rv: Blank. Plain edge.

Rulau	Date	Metal	Size	VG	F	VF	Unc
Tx-SA 48	(?)	Brass	23mm	—	12.50	—	—

GUADALUPE HOTEL / 5 (in central circle) / BAR. Rv: Blank. Plain edge. (Wright 363)

Rulau	Date	Metal	Size	VG	F	VF	Unc
Tx-SA 49	(?)	Brass	23mm	—	10.00	—	—

GUADALUPE / 5 ¢ / HOTEL. Rv: Blank. Plain edge.

Rulau	Date	Metal	Size	VG	F	VF	Unc
Tx-SA 50	(?)	Brass	28mm	—	12.50	—	—

GUADALUPE / 10 ¢ / HOTEL. Rv: Blank. Plain edge.

Rulau	Date	Metal	Size	VG	F	VF	Unc
Tx-SA 52	(?)	Brass	28mm	—	12.50	—	—

GUADALUPE / GOOD FOR / ONE DRINK / HOTEL. Rv: Blank.

THE HEIDEMANN MFG. CO.

Rulau	Date	Metal	Size	VG	F	VF	Unc
Tx-SA 55	(1880's)	CN	33mm	—	—	100.	200.

Same as obverse of Tx-SA 43 (City Hall, Fred's). Rv: THE HEIDEMANN MFG. CO / MAKERS / OF / RUBBER STAMPS / ETC / BADGES / CHECKS / SAN ANTONIO, TEX. Plain edge.

D. & A. HEINEN

Rulau	Date	Metal	Size	VG	F	VF	Unc
Tx-SA 57	(1889)	Alum	30mm	—	—	25.00	35.00

Facing military bust of Travis at center, W.B. TRAVIS above, HERO OF THE ALAMO below. Tiny COPY TD under truncation of bust. Rv: Alamo at center, THE MANHATTAN / D & A HEINEN above, THE ALAMO / ALAMO PLAZA & HOUSTON ST below. Plain edge.

Rulau	Date	Metal	Size	VG	F	VF	Unc
Tx-SA 59	(?)	Alum	23mm	—	—	25.00	—

Obverse as reverse of 57 (The Alamo). Rv: GOOD FOR / CENTS 5 / AT BAR. Plain edge.

HENRY'S BUCK HORN SALOON

Rulau	Date	Metal	Size	VG	F	VF	Unc
Tx-SA 60	(?)	Brass	22mm	—	—	12.50	—

HENRY'S / (steer head inverted) / BUCK HORN / (steer head) / SALOON. Rv: 5. (Kirtley Sept. 1992 sale, lot 1410)

HORNER'S

Rulau	Date	Metal	Size	VG	F	VF	Unc
Tx-SA 62	(1880's)	GS	25mm	—	—	65.00	—

Crow perched on branch left, OLD above, WHISKEY below. GOOD FOR ONE / DRINK / AT / HORNER'S / * / SAN ANTONIO, TEX. Plain edge. (There are three varieties of this token). (Wright 1460)

Rulau	Date	Metal	Size	VG	F	VF	Unc
Tx-SA 63	(1880's)	GS	**	—	—	65.00	—

** Oval, 25 x23mm.
Obverse as 62. Rv: GOOD FOR ONE / DRINK / AT HORNER'S. Plain edge.

JONAS GARDEN

Rulau	Date	Metal	Size	VG	F	VF	Unc
Tx-SA 70	(1882)	Brass	23mm	—	—	17.50	—

JONAS GARDEN / GOOD FOR / 5 / CENTS / AT BAR. Rv: Blank.

Peter Jonas was operating Jonas Garden at 601 Austin Street in San Antonio in 1882.

Rulau	Date	Metal	Size	VG	F	VF	Unc
Tx-SA 72	(1890)	Alum	32mm	—	—	45.00	Rare

Side view of courthouse, BEXAR CO. COURT HOUSE around, PETER JONAS JR. below. Rv: View of the Alamo at center, CRADLE OF TEXAS LIBERTY above, ALAMO in exergue. Plain edge. (Wright 1475)

KLINGLER'S THEATRE

Rulau	Date	Metal	Size	VG	F	VF	Unc
Tx-SA 75	(1880's)	CN	25mm	—	—	35.00	—

KLINGLER'S / (large 5-pointed star) / THEATRE. Rv: Large 5 in circle of 6-pointed stars. Plain edge.

Rulau	Date	Metal	Size	VG	F	VF	Unc
Tx-SA 77	(1880's)	Brass	Oct, 25mm	—	—	35.00	—

Similar, but 25. Plain edge.

Klingler's Theatre was contemporary with The Fashion, The Vaudeville, etc., popular in the 1880's and 1890's. Heidemann Mfg. Co. probably made these tokens.

LITTLE CORNER SALOON

Rulau	Date	Metal	Size	VG	F	VF	Unc
Tx-SA 80	(?)	CN	24mm	—	18.50	35.00	—

LITTLE CORER (sic) SALOON / GOOD FOR / 5 / CENTS / AT BAR. Rv: Blank. Plain edge. (Wright 611)

'Corner' was misspelled and few tokens were made, according to Dr. Wright, writing about 1898.

G. LUBRECHT

Rulau	Date	Metal	Size	VG	F	VF	Unc
Tx-SA 81	(?)	Brass	25mm	—	—	40.00	—

THE / BRUNSWICK / BALKE / COLLENDER CO. / (pool table). Rv: GOOD FOR / 5 C / G. / LUBRECHT / IN / TRADE. Plain edge. (Dick Worthington coll.)

This token has also been reported as being from New Braunfels, Texas, Circa 1884.

McDERMOTT'S SUNSET SALOON

Rulau	Date	Metal	Size	VG	F	VF	Unc
Tx-SA 83	(1880's)	GS	30mm	—	—	30.00	—

Sunburst at upper center, SUNSET SALOON above, 521 AUSTIN ST. / (ornament) / SAN ANTONIO, TEX. below. Plain edge.

Mc (ILVAINE) & PRATT

Rulau	Date	Metal	Size	VG	F	VF	Unc
Tx-SA 85	(1880's)	GS	30mm	—	—	40.00	—

(All incused): GOOD FOR / o / ONE DRINK / Mc & PRATT / (ornament) / SAN ANTONIO. Rv: Blank. Plain edge.

Rulau	Date	Metal	Size	VG	F	VF	Unc
Tx-SA 86	(1880's)	Brass	30mm	—	—	40.00	Rare

As 85. Plain edge. (Wright 1519)

Rulau	Date	Metal	Size	VG	F	VF	Unc
Tx-SA 88	(1880's)	GS	28mm	—	—	70.00	—

Horse's head right. Rv: R. E. McILVAINE / —*— / 254 / W. COMMERCE / ST. / —*— / SAN ANTONIO, TEX. Plain edge. (Wright 1517)

It is believed the 'Mc' of Mc & Pratt is R. E. McIlvaine.

MENGER HOTEL BAR

Rulau	Date	Metal	Size	VG	F	VF	Unc
Tx-SA 92	(?)	CN	24mm	—	—	30.00	—

MENGER HOTEL / BAR / SAN ANTONIO, TEX. Rv: GOOD FOR / ONE / DRINK. Plain edge. (Wright 1520)

F.I. MEYER

Rulau	Date	Metal	Size	VG	F	VF	Unc
Tx-SA 95	(1889)	Alum	30mm	—	—	Rare	—

Eagle perched with wings upraised atop globe, across which is a scroll reading IN VINO VERITAS. Above: F.I. MEYER. Below: ALAMO PLAZA. Rv: Building at center, U.S. POST OFFICE above, SAN ANTONIO / TEXAS in exergue. Plain edge. (Wright 1522)

MIKE & JOE'S SALOON

Rulau	Date	Metal	Size	VG	F	VF	Unc
Tx-SA 98	(?)	CN	25mm	—	—	25.00	—

MIKE & JOE'S / (star) / SALOON / SAN ANTONIO / TEX. Rv: GOOD FOR / ONE / 12 1/2 / CENTS / DRINK. Plain edge.

MISSION GARDEN SALOON

Rulau	Date	Metal	Size	VG	F	VF	Unc
Tx-SA 100	(?)	CN	24.5mm	—	—	40.00	—

MISSION / -.- / * GARDEN * / -.- / SALOON. Rv: GOOD FOR / ONE / BEER OR CIGAR. (Kirtley Sept. 1992 sale, lot 1409)

S.B. MOSSER

Rulau	Date	Metal	Size	VG	F	VF	Unc
Tx-SA 101	(1880 ?)	CN	25mm	—	22.50	35.00	—

S.B. MOSSER & CO / 28 / MILITARY / PLAZA / SAN ANTONIO / TEX. Rv: GOOD FOR ONE DRINK / AT THE / REGISTER. Plain edge.

Rulau	Date	Metal	Size	VG	F	VF	Unc
Tx-SA 103	(1880's ?)	CN	25mm	—	25.00	35.00	—

GOOD FOR ONE DRINK / (star) / AT THE / REGISTER / *. Rv: Large 6 1/4 ¢ within circle of stars and small circles. Plain edge. Scarce.

NENTWIG'S BAR

Rulau	Date	Metal	Size	VG	F	VF	Unc
Tx-SA 107	(1888)	GS	31mm	—	—	75.00	—

Post office building at center, POST OFFICE above, SAN ANTONIO, TEX. below. Rv: Scroll across center. On scroll: NENTWIG'S / BAR. At lower rim: (small) THE HEIDEMANN MFG. CO. S.A. TEX. Plain edge. Rarity 7.

A. ORFILA

Rulau	Date	Metal	Size	VG	F	VF	Unc
Tx-SA 111	(1875)	CN	24mm	—	35.00	—	—

Coronet Liberty head left within palm wreath. Rv: * GOOD FOR * / — I — / DRINK — / (ornament) / — A. ORFILA — Plain edge. (Wright 1566)

Made by J.F.W. Dorman, Baltimore.

MONROE PRATT

Rulau	Date	Metal	Size	VG	F	VF	Unc
Tx-SA 115	(1880's)	GS	28mm	—	—	47.50	80.00
	Lady riding horse sidesaddle. Rv: MONROE PRATT / 12 1/2 ¢ / SAN ANTONIO, TEXAS. Plain edge.						
Tx-SA 116	(1880's)	GS	32mm	—	—	60.00	—
	Lady sitting sidesaddle on horseback, toward left. Rv: MONROE PRATT, / —*— / ONE / DRINK / —*— / * SAN ANTONIO, TEXAS. *. Plain edge.						
Tx-SA 117	(1880's)	Brass	32mm	—	—	100.	—
	As last. Plain edge. (Wright 1581)						

PROFESSOR SALOON

Rulau	Date	Metal	Size	VG	F	VF	Unc
Tx-SA 119	(1880's)	CN	31mm	—	—	60.00	—
	Large star at upper center, PROFESSOR above, SALOON / SAN ANTONIO / TEXAS in three lines below. Rv: (Ornament) GOOD (ornament) / FOR ? ONE / — * — / (ornament) DRINK (ornament). Plain edge. (Wright 1584)						

RHEINER & GAUL

Rulau	Date	Metal	Size	VG	F	VF	Unc
Tx-SA 130	1880-1900	Brass	24mm	—	—	15.00	—
	R. & G. / 2 1/2. Rv: Blank. Plain edge.						
Tx-SA 132	1880-1900	CN	21mm	—	—	15.00	—
	R. & G. / PROP'RS. Rv: GRAND CENTRAL / POOL / CHECK. Plain edge.						
Tx-SA 133	(1880's)	CN	24mm	—	—	30.00	—
	MISSION / (ornament) / * GARDEN * / (ornament) / SALOON. Rv: GOOD FOR / ONE / * BEER * / — OR — / CIGAR. Plain edge. (Wright 1526)						
Tx-SA 134	1880-1900	CN	21mm	—	—	30.00	—
	RHEINER & GAUL / —.— / MISSION / GARDEN. Rv: GOOD FOR / 5¢/ — IN — / * TRADE *. Plain edge. (Wright 1596)						

Mission Garden was located at 315 So. Alamo Street and was one of the "theatres" that provided amusements for the citizenry in the 1880's and 1890's. There is strong evidence linking the two R. & G. tokens to Rheiner & Gaul.

RHEINER'S SALOON

Rulau	Date	Metal	Size	VG	F	VF	Unc
Tx-SA 136	(1890's)	Alum	Sc, 28mm	—	—	—	20.00
	RHEINER'S / SALOON / DULLNIGS / CORNER. Rv: GOOD FOR / 2 1/2 ¢ / AT THE BAR. This scalloped piece has four lobes. Plain edge.						

This piece is likely from a period later than that covered, but it should not be disassociated from the earlier Rheiner pieces.

S.A. LIGHT

Rulau	Date	Metal	Size	VG	F	VF	Unc
Tx-SA 140	(1880's)	Brass	**	—	—	50.00	—
	** Oct 23mm. Large rosette at center, S.A. above, LIGHT below. Rv: Large fraction 3/4 takes up almost entire reverse. Plain edge.						

The San Antonio Light is a newspaper. In 1979, when the supplement to The Trade Tokens of Texas appeared in the *TAMS Journal*, the authors noted that no one at the paper had any idea what these pieces had been used for.

The beading around this stock-die type of crude brass token seems to indicate mid-1880's venue, though it could have been later. The odd denomination (if that's what the 3/4 is) would indicate some sort of tally for newsboys. The piece is probably very rare.

A.B. SAMUELS

Rulau	Date	Metal	Size	VG	F	VF	Unc
Tx-SA 145	(1880's)	GS	31mm	—	—	65.00	—
	Large star at upper center, A.B. SAMUELS around, SAN ANTONIO, / TEXAS. below. Rv: GOOD FOR ONE DRINK / - AT - / SILVER / KING / .-. Plain edge. (Wright 1610)						

Rulau	Date	Metal	Size	VG	F	VF	Unc
Tx-SA 147	(1880's)	CN	31mm	—	—	75.00	95.00
	Horse's head left within horseshoe, SALOON on scroll beneath. Rv: SAMUELS & CO. / -.- / SOUTH / FLORES / ST. / -.- / SAN ANTONIO, TEX. Plain edge. (Wright 1611)						

A. SCHOLZ

Rulau	Date	Metal	Size	VG	F	VF	Unc
Tx-SA 150	(1880's)	GS	28mm	—	—	50.00	—
	Ornate two-story building at center, A. SCHOLZ, / PALM GARDEN above, * / SAN ANTONIO, TEX. below. Plain edge. (Wright 1618)						

Rulau	Date	Metal	Size	VG	F	VF	Unc
Tx-SA 152	(?)	Brass	24mm	—	—	7.50	—
	A. SCHOLZ on scroll across center. Rv: GOOD FOR / 5¢ / IN TRADE. Plain edge.						

Rulau	Date	Metal	Size	VG	F	VF	Unc
Tx-SA 154	(?)	Brass	24mm	—	—	25.00	—
	A. SCHOLZ'S / GOOD FOR / 5 / CENTS / AT BAR / SALOON. Rv: Blank. Plain edge.						

Rulau	Date	Metal	Size	VG	F	VF	Unc
Tx-SA 156	(?)	Brass	21mm	—	—	25.00	—

Small palm trees on mound at bottom. Above: SCHOLZ PALM GARDEN / SAN / ANTONIO / TEX. Rv: Large numeral 5 at center. Plain edge.

Tx-SA 158	(1880's)	BV	28mm	—	—	Rare	—

A. SCHOLZ / SAN ANTONIO. Rv: GOOD FOR / 5 CENT / DRINK. Plain edge.

Tx-SA 160	(1890's)	Alum	21mm	—	—	20.00	—

SHOLZ (sic) PALM GARDEN / SAN / ANTONIO / TEX. Rv: GOOD FOR / 2 1/2 ¢ / IN TRADE. Plain edge.

SOUTHERN HOTEL BAR

Rulau	Date	Metal	Size	VG	F	VF	Unc
Tx-SA 164	(1880's)	GS	32mm	—	25.00	35.00	60.00

The Alamo at center, SOUTHERN HOTEL BAR / SAN ANTONIO / TEXAS above, THE ALAMO in exergue. Rv: Mission at center, GOOD FOR ONE DRINK above, MISSION SAN JOSE below. Plain edge. (Wright 1018)

Tx-SA 165	(1880's)	BV	32mm	—	—	80.00	—

As last, but in vulcanite. Plain edge.

DICK STRAYHORN

Rulau	Date	Metal	Size	VG	F	VF	Unc
Tx-SA 168	(1880's)	CN	31mm	—	—	35.00	

Large diamond-shaped device at center, word THE on it. Above: NOTHING BUT THE BEST. Below: 312 WEST COMMERCE ST. Rv: DICK STRAYHORN (radiant) / (ornament) / PROPRIETOR / SAN ANTONIO / TEX. / *. Plain edge. (Wright 1640)

ERNST STREMMEL

Rulau	Date	Metal	Size	VG	F	VF	Unc
Tx-SA 170	(?)	Alum	24mm	—	—	40.00	—

Bust of Bismarck right, FURST OTTO VON BISMARCK around. Rv: BISMARCK SALOON / 5 / SAN ANTONIO / TEXAS / * ERNST STREMMEL. Plain edge.

CARL STUBENRAUCH

Rulau	Date	Metal	Size	VG	F	EF	Unc
Tx-SA 173	(1875-85)	Bronze	28mm	—	—	50.00	—

Stubenrauch bust left, CARL STUBENRAUCH GENERAL ENGRAVER & DIE SINKER around, SAN ANTONIO TEX. below. Rv: Female personification of Freedom with cornucopia leaning against a medal press. Around: MEDALS OF ALL KINDS MANUFACT'D. Plain edge.

Carl Stubenrauch had been a court engraver in Germany before emigrating to St. Louis in the 1850's. He came to San Antonio in 1875 and became the area's leading engraver, designing many beautiful tokens and medals there, and teaching his talented pupil Charles Simmang to do the same. He died about 1899.

SUE LEE FASHION THEATRE

Rulau	Date	Metal	Size	VG	F	VF	Unc
Tx-SA 175	(1884-90)	Brass	25mm	—	—	35.00	—

SUE LEE / * FASHION * / THEATRE. Rv: Large numeral 25 encircled by 16 alternating stars and rosettes. Plain edge.

The Fashion became San Antonio's leading entertainment palace after the killing of Ben Thompson and King Fisher in 1884 put a damper on The Vaudeville.

The Sue Lee Restaurant was a short distance away, at 3 No. Flores Street. This token probably was good at both places.

TWO BROTHERS SALOON

Rulau	Date	Metal	Size	VG	F	VF	Unc
Tx-SA 190	(?)	Brass	23mm	—	—	25.00	—

TWO BROTHERS / GOOD FOR / 5¢ / AT BAR / SALOON (all incused). Rv: Blank. Plain edge.

Tx-SA 192	(1880's)	Brass	24mm	—	—	30.00	—

Clasped hands at center, TWO BROTHERS SALOON above, SAN / ANTONIO / TEX below. Rv: NO /5. Plain edge.

Tx-SA 193	(1889)	Alum.	Oct 27mm	—	—	25.00	—

Clasped hands at center, TWO BROTHERS BAR above, SAN ANTONIO / TEXAS below. Rv: NO. / 5. Plain edge.

Tx-SA 195	(1880's)	Brass	29mm	—	—	25.00	—

Clasped hands at center, TWO BROTHERS / SALOON above, SAN ANTONIO / TEXAS below. Rv: NUMBER / 1. Plain edge.

Tx-SA 197	(?)	Brass	21mm	—	—	Scarce	—

Star at center, TWO BROTHERS above, BAR below. Rv: Blank. Plain edge.

Tx-SA 199	(1880's)	GS	30mm	—	—	35.00	—

Clasped hands across center, TWO BROTHERS / -+- / SALOON above, SAN ANTONIO / -*- / TEXAS. below. Rv:] GOOD [/ FOR / ONE / (ornament) /] DRINK [. Plain edge. (Wright 1695)

Tx-SA 201	(?)	Brass	21mm	—	—	20.00	—

TWO BROTHERS / SALOON. Rv: Large numeral 10. Plain edge.

Tx-SA 203	(?)	Brass	21mm	—	—	10.00	—

TWO BROTHERS / CAFE. Rv: Large numeral 10. Plain edge.

The Two Brothers issues present a confusing welter of types. They are listed here, but not necessarily in the order in which they were issued; that will require far more study.

VAN'S CAVE

Rulau	Date	Metal	Size	VG	F	VF	Unc
Tx-SA 206	(?)	CN	26mm	—	—	25.00	—

(All incused): VAN'S CAVE / GOOD FOR / ONE DRINK / (ornament) / SAN ANTONIO/ Rv: Blank. Plain edge.

VAUDEVILLE THEATRE

Rulau	Date	Metal	Size	VG	F	VF	Unc
Tx-SA 208	(1880's)	Brass	24mm	—	—	20.00	—

VAUDEVILLE / 25 / THEATRE. Rv: Large 25 at center, encircled by alternating stars and diamonds. Plain edge.

VOLLMER SALOON

Rulau	Date	Metal	Size	VG	F	VF	Unc
Tx-SA 210	(1885-86)	Brass	23mm	—	—	15.00	—

VOLLMER / GOOD FOR / 5 / CENTS / AT BAR / SALOON. Rv: Blank. Plain edge.

J.J. Vollmer ran a saloon at 635 Medina, according to the 1886 city directory.

WHITE (ELEPHANT)

Rulau	Date	Metal	Size	VG	F	VF	Unc
Tx-SA 215	(1880-1900)	CN	25mm	—	—	50.00	—

Elephant left at center, WHITE above, SAN ANTONIO, / TEXAS below. Rv: Large numeral 15 within central circle, GOOD FOR ONE DRINK around, * CENTS * below. Plain edge.

Rulau	Date	Metal	Size	VG	F	VF	Unc
Tx-SA 217	(1880's)	Copper	25mm	—	—	75.00	—

As obverse of last (Elephant). Rv: The Three Graces standing nude at center, MONTAGNY below the ground under them. Plain edge. (Wright 1231)

Rulau	Date	Metal	Size	VG	F	VF	Unc
Tx-SA 217 A	(1880's)	WM	25mm	—	—	Rare	—

As 217. Plain edge.

It is not known whether Montagny is the designer of the token, or the proprietor of the White Elephant.

WHITE HOUSE SALOON
San Antonio, Texas

Rulau	Date	Metal	Size	VG	F	VF	Unc
Tx-SA 225	(1890's)	Alum	31mm	—	—	60.00	—

The Alamo at center, CRADLE OF TEXAS LIBERTY above, ALAMO in exergue. Rv: TAKE ME TO / THE / WHITE HOUSE / SALOON / SAN ANTONIO, TEX. Plain edge. (Wright N/L)

TORIBIO GUERRA Y HNO.
San Diego, Texas

Rulau	Date	Metal	Size	VG	F	VF	Unc
Tx-SD 1	(1886)	Brass	24mm	—	45.00	70.00	—

TORIBIO GUERRA Y HNO. around a large 6-pointed star. Rv: BUENO POR / 10 / CENTAVOS / DE EFECTOS (good for 10 cents of goods). Plain edge. (David Henkle coll.)

At first sight, this would appear to be a Latin American token of typical fabric. It is not.

The R. G. Dun direcotry for San Diego, the Duval County seat in Texas, July 1882, lists: "Guerra, Toribio GS H 3." San Diego is near Corpus Christi. GS = general store. H 3 = Dun credit rating for the business.

Then Bradstreet directory for San Diego issued in 1886 has this entry: "Guerra, Toribio & Bro. Gen'l Store P C." Hno. (Hermano) = Brother.

Thus it seems Guerra took in a brother as partner in or soon before 1886. The San Diego population in 1886 was given as 2,500, yet it boasted 12 general stores in the directory!

KLINE'S
Seguin, Texas

Rulau	Date	Metal	Size	VG	F	VF	Unc
Tx-Sg 3	(1882)	Brass	23mm	—	—	15.00	—

KLINE'S / GOOD FOR / 5 / CENTS / AT BAR / SALOON. Rv: Blank. Plain edge.

Kline appears in the 1882 *Texas Gazetteer*.

HUGO STARCKE
Seguin, Texas

Rulau	Date	Metal	Size	VG	F	VF	Unc
Tx-Sg 6	(1880's)	Brass	29mm	—	—	15.00	—

HUGO / STARCKE. Rv: GOOD FOR / 5¢ / IN TRADE / AT BAR. (AT BAR is incused). Plain edge.

Hugo Starcke ran the Sunset Saloon in Seguin in the 1880's.

BYERS BROS.
Sherman, Texas

(See Il-Ch 116, Schuttler Wagons, under Chicago, Illinois in this section)

COW BOY SALOON
Spanish Fort, Texas

Rulau	Date	Metal	Size	VG	F	VF	Unc
Tx-Sp 2	(1880's)	CN	24mm	—	—	50.00	—

Longhorn steer left, head facing. Rv: GOOD FOR / - A - / COW BOY / SALOON / * DRINK *. Plain edge.

Spanish Fort was an Indian village and French trappers' supply point as early as 1819.

The Cow Boy Saloon was the last oasis for thirsty cowboys coming up the Chisholm Trail, before crossing the Red River into Indian Territory (Oklahoma).

(See Doans - Doan's Crossing - on the Western, or Dodge, Trail, where a similar token was used.)

IRON FRONT SALOON
Temple, Texas

Rulau	Date	Metal	Size	VG	F	VF	Unc
Tx-Tm 3	(?)	Brass	21mm	—	—	30.00	—

THE IRON FRONT SALOON - TEMPLE, TEX. Rv: 12 1/2. Plain edge. (Koppenhaver June 1987 sale, lot 184)

CRYSTAL SALOON
Waco, Texas

Rulau	Date	Metal	Size	VG	F	VF	Unc
Tx-Wa 4	(1874-84)	CN	24mm	—	—	25.00	—

Pool table. Above: THE J.M. BRUNSWICK / & / BALKE COS. Below: CHECK. Rv: GOOD FOR / * 1 * / CRYSTAL SALOON / * DRINK *. Plain edge. (Brunswick 2088)

CLUB JUVENTUD
Texas

Rulau	Date	Metal	Size	VG	F	VF	EF
Tx-Un 1	1874	Silver	27mm	—	—	600.	—

(Five stars in upward arc) / CLUB / Juventud / Bronsvilens / 1874 ctsp on Mexico 1854-Mo-GC 2-reales. (Kurt Krueger Aug. 23, 1988 sale, lot 2322)

We assume Bronsvilens is a surname, since there was no U.S. place of this name listed in the 1877 Postal Guide. The consignor said this piece was from Texas.

Is Bronsvilens a Latinized Brownsville?

REPORTED TEXAS BILLIARD TOKENS

The following pieces are reported as attributed to Texas but not verified. They are cataloged here as a reader service.

(* Indicates city name is on the token)

Name on Token	Reported Locale	Obv. Die	Gazetteer
Tony Bruggeman	San Antonio	BBC	?
Cain & Shaper	San Angelo	BB-8b	?
Cobweb Billiard Hall	El Paso	BB-6a	?
T. Fenton	Atascosa	BB-5a	1884
C. H. French	Victoria	BB-7a	1884
Geo. Gardner	Jacksboro	Koken B.S.	?
W. L. Grumbles	Holland	BBC	?
* Wm. Hancord	Ruttersville	BBC-11	?
Hart & Bond	San Antonio	BBC-9b	?
Otto Heilig	New Braunfels	BBC-9b	1884
* W. T. Holderness & Co.	Valentine	Chas. Pick	?
Hotel Pickwick Bar	Fort Worth	BB-8a	?
L. F. Jecker	Victoria	BB	1882-1914
G. S. Jenkins	Bastrop	BB-8a	?
* Kearly & Mayes	Cleburne	BBC-11	1900
D. Kerns	San Antonio	BBC-9a	1886
Kuhfus & Beseler	Boerne	BBC-11	1897
G. Lubrect	New Braunfels	BBC-9b	1884
W. H. Miller	Electra	BBC-8	1910
* J. E. Moore	Blossom	BBC-8	1897
S. B. Mosser	San Antonio	BBC-10a	?
* S. B. Mosser & Co	Encinal	BBC-9b	?
Wm. Neese	Warrenton	BBC-9b	?
H. Ochs	Fredericksburg	BB-7b	1878-97
J. Oltmann	Schulenberg	BBC-9b	?
* Pendleton & Co	Mobeetie	Chas. Pick	?
Ranch Saloon	San Antonio	Messmer Fauc.	?
Ottomar Schubert	Austin	BB-7a	1890
Schulenburg Turn Verein	Schulenburg	BBC	?
W. F. Vanston	El Paso	BB-6a	?
* The Vault	El Paso	BBC	?
Jim Ware's Saloon	McKinney	BBC-9a	1890
H. H. Weller	Skidmore	NBM Co.	1897
* White Elephant	Fort Worth	BB	?
Williamson & Farish	San Marcos	BB-6a	1884
A. A. Woehler	Brenham	BBC-11	1900
N. E. Woodruffs	Belton	BB-7a	?
Chas. W. Zenker	San Angelo	Chas. Pick	1890-1910

UTAH

MODEL DAIRY
Ogden, Utah

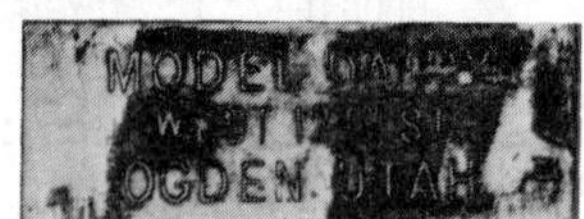

Rulau	Date	Metal	Size	VG	F	VF	Unc
Ut-Og 5	(ca 1898)	WM	**	—	175.	250.	—

** Rec., 38 x 14mm.
Grasshopper left, in high relief. Rv: (All incused): MODEL DAIRY / WEST 12TH ST / OGDEN UTAH. Plain edge. (Wright 1528)

Rulau	Date	Metal	Size	VG	F	VF	Unc
Ut-Og 6	(ca 1898)	WM	**	—	—	—	100.

** Rec., 38 x 14mm.
Obverse as 5. Rv: Blank. Die trial.

Rarity 8 - only about 7 or 8 pieces exist. The Fuld-Rulau specimen is pictured.

The die trial was sold by Stanley L. Steinberg in 1982 list number 87, lot 124.

The grasshopper on the token represents the "Mormon Cricket" or locust, scourge of Utah's territorial period, yet a well-known symbol to the Mormons of that day. It indicated its issuer was a Latter-Day Saints church member.

The first Polk directory for Ogden was in 1890, and there were six dairies in the city or its environs that year but none called Model Dairy.

The Polk directory refers to an earlier directory, but it could not be located. (Research courtesy Donald T. Schmidt, director of library-archives division, Mormon Church historical department, Salt Lake City.)

Model Dairy first appears in the 1899 directory, owned by Oscar B. Madson, in Marriott, a suburb. Then it is in Ogden 1900-1924. Madson died Jan. 10, 1928.

D. N. ADAMSON
Pleasant Grove, Utah

Rulau	Date	Metal	Size	VG	F	VF	Unc
Ut-Pl 1	(1900)	—	--mm	—	—	50.00	—

Brunswick die BBC-11. Rv: D. N. ADAMSON.

GALT HOUSE
St. Joseph, Utah

The counterstamped Large cent listed under this heading in the earlier editions may now be found under Cincinnati, Ohio, which see.

JACOB ALT
Salt Lake City, Utah

Rulau	Date	Metal	Size	VG	F	VF	Unc
Ut-SL 1	1876	Silver	22x23mm	—	—	475.	—

Salt Lake City 1876 / (beer mug, wine bottle, glass). Rv: Jacob ALT / (compass-G-square). Piece is shield-shaped. Unique.

Saloonkeeper listed from 1876 to 1904.

CLASBEY & HOGLE

Rulau	Date	Metal	Size	VG	F	VF	Unc
Ut-SL 2	(1877-84)	Brass	24mm	—	—	700.	—

(All incuse) CLASBEY & HOGLE / GOOD FOR / A / DRINK / SALT LAKE CITY. Rv: Blank. Unique.

Saloonkeepers.

D. A. & M. SOCIETY (Deseret Agricultural & Manufacturing Soc.)

Rulau	Date	Metal	Size	F	VF	EF	Unc
Ut-SL 3	1879	Gold	27mm	—	—	800.	—

(All incused): D. A. & M. SOCIETY / (Beehive) / Chartered 1856. Rv: (All incused): Awarded to / JOHN R. WINDER. / Roadster Mare "Polly" / & Colt "Prince Albert." / S. L. CITY, U.T. / Oct. 1879. Reeded edge. (All engraved on shaved sides of U.S. $10 gold piece, to serve as a gold award medal.) (Lot 296 in Kirtley Oct. 1985 sale; Dr. Sol Taylor coll.)

U.T. = Utah Territory. Utah became a state in 1890.

The Deseret A.&M. Society was founded in 1856 to put on shows of local farming produce and livestock and was a forerunner of the Utah State Fair. John Rex Winder was a local assessor who had a fine stable of horses. Division 3 at the 1879 fair was "Roadsters" and Winder entered the sorrell Polly and her colt Prince Albert, who took gold medal (first) award under the section "best mare with colt." It was common then to engrave a gold coin rather than to issue a struck gold medal.

GARFIELD BEACH

Rulau	Date	Metal	Size	F	VF	EF	Unc
Ut-SL 6	1889	GS	32mm	—	35.00	50.00	—

Mormon tabernacle at center, TABERNACLE above, SALT LAKE CITY. below. Rv: Bathing scene in Great Salt Lake, pavilion in background. GARFIELD BEACH above, 1889 below. Plain edge. (Rich Hartzog report)

LEVIBERG'S PARLOR SALOON

Salt Lake City, Utah

Rulau	Date	Metal	Size	F	VF	EF	Unc
Ut-SL 7	(1880-86)	GS	24mm	—	—	225.	—

Cup with bar utensils. CHAS. PICK & CO. / CHICAGO / DEALERS IN (in circle). Rv: LEVIBERG'S / PARLOR / SALOON / (small star) / SALT LAKE CITY. Plain edge. 3 known.

One piece brought $25 in a 1975 sale by Joseph Schmidt of Illinois. No recent sales.

Charles Pick & Co., manufacturer of supplies for billiard parlors, restaurants, etc., used this stock type in the 1880-86 period. Pick used some 13 stock dies over the 1880-1895 period in which it operated in 11 states and Canada.

GEORGE A. LOWE

Salt Lake City, Utah

(See Il-Ch 117, Schuttler Wagons, under Chicago, Illinois in this section. Lowe was the Schuttler branch agency for the Salt Lake City trade area)

VERMONT

B. B. BOWEN

Bethel, Vt.

Rulau	Date	Metal	Size	VG	F	VF	EF
Vt-Be 1	(?)	Copper	29mm	—	—	50.00	—

B.B. BOWEN ctsp on U.S. 1848 Large cent. (Brunk 4580)

Benjamin B. Bowen was a gunsmith in Bethel, Vermont, 1849-1881. The attribution is tentative.

HOWE'S IMPROVED

Brandon, Vt.

Rulau	Date	Metal	Size	VG	F	VF	EF
Vt-Br 2	(1870's)	Copper	29mm	—	—	75.00	—

HOWE'S / IMPROVED ctsp on U.S. 1848 Large cent. (Brunk 20310)

Howe's Improved Scales were manufactured by the Brandon Manufacturing Co., Brandon, Vt. This company and its agents in New York and Boston issued a large number of embossed shell cards in the 1867-1876 period (see numbers Rulau 318 to 324b in the *TAMS Journal* for April, 1961) but this is the first counterstamp reported for the firm.

E. M. GLYNN

Clarendon, Vt.

Rulau	Date	Metal	Size	VG	F	VF	EF
Vt-Cl 1	(1871-85)	Copper	29mm	75.00	—	125.	—

E. M. GLYNN, GUNSMITH ctsp on U.S. Large cent. Dates examined: 1819, 1849. (Duffield 1402; Hallenbeck 7.509; Rulau Z33)

Rulau	Date	Metal	Size	VG	F	VF	EF
Vt-Cl 2	(1871-83)	Copper	28mm	75.00	—	125.	—

Similar ctsp on Canada copper token. 2 known. (Brunk report; Rulau Z33A)

Edward M. Glynn was a maker of percussion half-stock weapons in Clarendon from 1871 through 1885. His counterstamped cents have been known to collectors since early in the 20th century, yet until now remained mavericks.

Glynn appears in the 1983 reference by Sellers, *American Gunsmiths.*

PATENT

Windsor, Vt.

Rulau	Date	Metal	Size	VG	F	VF	EF
Vt-Wi 4	(?)	Silver	27.5mm	100.	—	200.	—

WINDSOR. VT. / PATENT/ ctsp on U.S. 1806 Draped Bust quarter dollar. (Collection of Dean M. Ryder, Madison, Wis.; Brunk 43870)

A. W. WHITNEY

Woodstock, Vt.

Rulau	Date	Metal	Size	VG	F	VF	EF
Vt-Wo 4	(?)	Copper	28mm	—	—	125.	—

A. W. WHITNEY / WOODSTOCK. VT. ctsp on Netherlands East Indies 1823 1/2-stuiver. (Brunk 43220)

A. W. Whitney was a toolmaker.

P. A. WHITNEY (and) C. A. WOODBURY

Woodstock, Vt.

Rulau	Date	Metal	Size	VG	F	VF	EF
Vt-Wo 6	1862	Copper	29mm	75.00	—	125.	—

P. A. WHITNEY / C. A. WOODBURY / WOODSTOCK / 1862 Vt. ctsp on U.S. 1847 Large cent. (Kurt Krueger coll.; Brunk 43240)

Rulau	Date	Metal	Size	VG	F	VF	EF
Vt-Wo 7	(1869)	Bronze	23mm	—	—	125.	—

P. A. WHITNEY / WOODSTOCK, VT. / 1869 ctsp on U.S. 1865 2-cent piece. IBrunk 43230)

Whitney has not been traced, but Crayton A. Woodbury was a Woodstock gunsmith 1865-1893. Woodbury held several patents for magazine guns, issued in 1880, 1889 and 1893, jointly with Mark F. Richardson. Woodbury apparently had a branch operation in Sherborne, Vt. about 1875.

VIRGINIA

MANSION HOUSE

Alexandria, Va. ?

Rulau	Date	Metal	Size	VG	F	VF	Unc
Va-Al 6	(?)	WM	16mm	—	—	300.	—

Circular wreath at center, MANSION HOUSE around. Rv: Large numeral 5 within radiant circular wreath, all rays on outside of wreath. Plain edge.

Rulau	Date	Metal	Size	VG	F	VF	Unc
Va-Al 7	(?)	WM	17mm	—	300.	—	—

Obverse similar to last. Rv: Numeral 10 within circular wreath. Plain edge.

Rulau	Date	Metal	Size	VG	F	VF	Unc
Va-Al 8	(?)	Brass	25mm	—	50.00	—	—

MANSION HOUSE / 30 / BAR. Rv: Blank. Plain edge.

It is not known if the above three tokens emanate from the famous Mansion House in Alexandria, Virginia, but it seems likely. All three pieces were discovered only in 1988, appearing in Charles Kirtley's sale of Sept. 10 that year as lots 34, 35 and 38, respectively.

E. PIEPENBRING
Alexandria, Va.

Rulau	Date	Metal	Size	F	VF	Unc
Va-Al 10	Late 1860's	Brass	21mm	10.00	20.00	65.00

E. PIEPENBRING / KOEHLER / * / ALEXDR. / VA. Rv: GOOD FOR / 2 / CENTS / KOEHLER. Plain edge. (Schenkman 1040AH2; Miller Va 1A)

Rulau	Date	Metal	Size	F	VF	Unc
Va-Al 11	Late 1860's	Brass	21mm	10.00	20.00	65.00

Similar to 1A, but 3 / CENTS. Plain edge. (Miller Va 1)

Edward Piepenbring was a confectioner in the late 1860's. By 1870 he was out of business. These cards probably appeared in the 1866-1869 period.

F. H. (and) M. P.
Bear Island, Va.

Rulau	Date	Metal	Size	VG	F	VF	EF
Va-Bl 1	1863	CN	19mm	—	65.00	—	—

. BEAR ISLAND / F H / M P / JULY / 4 / 1863 ctsp on planed-off reverse of U.S. 1863 Indian Head cent. (Kurt Krueger coll.; Brunk 2940)

This personal piece must have some Civil War connection. July 4, 1863 was the day following the bitter three-day Battle of Gettysburg, July 1, 2 and 3, 1863. General Robert E. Lee began his retreat to Virginia on July 4, 1863, from Pennsylvania.

Bear Island is in Fairfax County, Virginia, not far from the site of the Battles of Bull Run or from the District of Columbia. It is near Lee Manor and Vienna. Bear Branch is a river rising near Vienna and flowing southward.

COLE & FLINN
Danville, Va.

Rulau	Date	Metal	Size	F	VF	Unc
Va-Da 3	(1876)	S/WM	23mm	—	40.00	75.00

Bell at center, LIBERTY BELL above, 1776 below. Rv: COLE & FLINN / ONE / SODA / * DANVILLE, VA. Plain edge. (Schenkman 2040D; Miller Va 2)

Issued during the Centennial of the United States celebrations.

DIAMOND SALOON
Lynchburg, Va.

Rulau	Date	Metal	Size	F	VF	Unc
Va-Ly 3	1875	Brass	20mm	—	75.00	—

Coronet Liberty head left, 13 stars around, 1875 below. Rv: DIAMOND SALOON / 5 (in diamond) / 65, 9TH ST. / LYNCHBURG, VA. Plain edge. (Schenkman 3180I5; Miller Va 3; Kirtley Oct. 1992 sale, lot 3338)

Struck by the Dorman Stencil & Stamp works, Baltimore, Md.

OFFICE RESTAURANT
Lynchburg, Va.

Rulau	Date	Metal	Size	F	VF	Unc
Va-Ly 7	1875	Brass	20mm	—	40.00	—

Coronet Liberty head left, 13 stars around, 1875 below. Rv: OFFICE RESTAURANT / 5 (in circle) / 106, MAIN ST. / LYNCHBURG, VA. Plain edge. (Schenkman 3180AD5)

Struck by Dorman Stencil & Stamp Works, Baltimore, Md.

PIEDMONT CLUB
Lynchburg, Va.

Rulau	Date	Metal	Size	F	VF	Unc
Va-Ly 9	(1870-85)	GS	19mm	—	30.00	—

Union shield at center, * PIEDMONT CLUB * / LYNCHBURG VA. around. Rv: Numeral 10 within wreath, star at top, bow at bottom. Plain edge. (Wright 830; Schenkman 3180AF10; Miller Va 4)

This token was struck by Francis X. Koehler of Baltimore, Md.

JOSEPH KLEPPER
Norfolk, Va.

Rulau	Date	Metal	Size	F	VF	Unc
Va-No 5	1875	Lead	20mm	—	30.00	—

Coronet Liberty head left, 13 stars around, 1875 below. Rv: JOSEPH KLEPPER / 5 (on sunburst) / NORFOLK. VA. Plain edge. (Schenkman 3680AV5)

Rulau	Date	Metal	Size	F	VF	Unc
Va-No 6	1875	Brass	20mm	—	30.00	—

Similar, but numeral 10 on reverse. (Schenkman 3680AV-10)

Joseph Klepper opened a restaurant at 139 Church St. about 1870. By 1882 his business occupied 139 thru 145 Church St., and included a billiard hall and orchestrion. In 1889 he owned a hotel, and later went into the real estate business. He died Dec. 20, 1896.

Klepper's tokens were made by Dorman Stencil & Stamp Works of Baltimore, Md.

S.H. MARKS & CO.
Petersburg, Va.

1876 Centennial Tokens

Reverse type 1: S.H. MARKS & CO. / * WHOLESALE * / AND / RETAIL / CONFECTIONERS / PETERSBURG, VA. (All 23mm; plain edge)

Rulau	Obv	Rev	Metal	F	VF	EF	Unc
Va-Pe	A	1	WM	—	—	15.00	40.00
	(Miller Va 15; Schenkman 3960Wa)						
Va-Pe 1A	A	1	Copper	—	—	17.50	50.00
	(Schenkman 3960Wb)						
Va-Pe 1B	A	1	Brass	—	—	17.50	50.00
	(Miller 15A; Schenkman 3960Wc)						
Va-Pe 2	B	1	WM	—	—	15.00	40.00
	(Miller 17; Schenkman 3960Xa)						
Va-Pe 2A	B	1	Brass	—	—	20.00	50.00
	(Wright 663' Schenkman 3960Xb)						
Va-Pe 3	E	1	WM	—	—	17.50	40.00
	(Schenkman 3960Y)						
Va-Pe 4	F	1	WM	—	—	17.50	40.00
	(Schenkman 3960Y; Miller 17A)						
Va-Pe 5	G	1	WM	—	—	17.50	40.00
	(Schenkman 3960AB)						
Va-Pe 6	H	1	WM	—	—	17.50	40.00
	(Schenkman 3960AA)						

S.H. Marks and Co., wholesale and retail confectioners, were located at 129 No. Sycamore St. They went out of business in the 1890's. Most varieties of this series were struck for collectors, in very limited numbers.

JAMES E. WOLFF
Petersburg, Va.

Rulau	Date	Metal	Size	VG	F	VF	Unc
Va-Pe 12	1863	GS	26mm	—	—	—	100.
	JAMES E. WOLFF / (tall hat) / NO. 17 / SYCAMORE ST. / PETERSBURG, VA. Rv: Shield. UNION LEAGUE 1863. (Miller Va 26)						
Va-Pe 13	1863	WM	26mm	—	—	—	100.
	As 12. Normal planchet. (Miller Va 27)						
Va-Pe 14	1863	WM	26mm	—	—	—	100.
	As 12. Thin planchet. (Miller Va 27A)						
Va-Pe 15	(?)	GS	26mm	—	—	—	100.
	Obverse as 12. Rv: Flag (Miller Va 28)						
Va-Pe 16	(?)	WM	26mm	—	—	—	75.00
	As 12. (Miller Va 28A)						
Va-Pe 17	(?)	GS	26mm	—	—	—	75.00
	As 12 (Miller Va 29)						
Va-Pe 18	1864	Copper	26mm	—	—	—	150.
	Obverse as 12. Rv: Abraham Lincoln. (DeWitt AL 1864-31A) (Schenkman 3960AQa; Miller Va 29[a])						
Va-Pe 19	1864	WM	26mm	—	—	—	150.
	As 18. (King 612; Miller Va 29A)						

Regular Wolff store cards were issued in the 1850's and appear in my 1845-1860 reference. Items listed above are mulings from the 1867-71 period.

J. L. WISSIN
Portsmouth, Va.

Rulau	Date	Metal	Size	VG	F	VF	EF
Va-Po 5	(?)	Copper	29mm	—	—	100.	—

J.L. WISSIN PORTSMOUTH VA ctsp on U.S. Large cent. (Hallenbeck 23.513; Brunk 44050)

N. Y. COREL

Rappahannock Station, Va.

Rulau	Date	Metal	Size	VG	F	VF	EF
Va-Ra 1	(1870's?)	Copper	--mm	—	—	90.00	—

N. Y. / COREL / RAPAHANNOCK STATION (curved) in three separate punches ctsp on worn Russia copper coin. (Kirtley Nov. 1990 sale, lot A669; Brunk 9555)

The 1877 Postal Guide reveals there was a Rappahannock Station in Fauquier County in northern Virginia. It was no longer listed in 1918.

R. E. LEE MONUMENT

Richmond, Va.

Rulau	Date	Metal	Size	VG	F	VF	EF
Va-Ri 6	1887	S/WM	35mm	—	—	35.00	50.00

Bearded bust facing 3/4 left. Above: GENERAL R. E. LEE. Rv: Mounted statue left. Around: LAYING OF CORNER STONE OF . R. E. LEE MONUMENT RICHMOND. VA. / OCT. 27. 1887. Plain edge. (Hartzog coll.)

R. McNAMEE

Rulau	Date	Metal	Size	VG	F	VF	EF
Va-Ri 8	(1870)	Silver	32.5mm	—	300.	—	—

R McNAMEE / RICHD VA. ctsp on U.S. 1805 Bust type half dollar. (Schenkman collection; Brunk 27180)

Robert McNamee was a dealer in surgical instruments listed in the 1870 Bradstreet directory.

R.A. PATTERSON & CO.

Rulau	Date	Metal	Size	VG	F	VF	Unc
Va-Ri 10	1881	Brass	25mm	—	20.00	30.00	—

Two-horse carriage right, RICHMOND / VA. below. Around: CHEW SHELLROAD TOBACCO / M'F'D BY R.A. PATTERSON & CO. Rv: Within central wreath: FIRST / AWARD / OF / MERIT. Around: INTERNATIONAL COTTON EXPOSITION / ATLANTA GA. 1881. Plain edge.

PIZZINI

1876 Centennial Tokens

Reverse type 1: PIZZINI, / NAPOLEON / OF / CONFECTIONERS / 807 BROAD ST. RICHMOND, VA. (All 23mm; plain edge)

Rulau	Obv	Rev	Metal	F	VF	EF	Unc
Va-Ri 11	A	1	WM	—	—	20.00	45.00
	(Wright 835; Schenkman 4180AY; Miller Va 36E)						
Va-Ri 12	B	1	WM	—	—	20.00	45.00
Va-Ri 12A	B	1	Brass	—	—	20.00	45.00
	(Miller 37A; Schenkman 4180AW)						
Va-Ri 13	C	1	WM	—	—	20.00	45.00
	(Miller 36C; Schenkman 4180AV)						
Va-Ri 14	D	1	WM	—	—	20.00	45.00
	(Miller 36A; Schenkman 4180BE)						
Va-Ri 15	E	1	WM	—	—	20.00	45.00
	(Miller 37; Schenkman 4180BA)						
Va-Ri 16	F	1	WM	—	—	20.00	45.00
	(Miller 36B; Schenkman 4180BC)						
Va-Ri 17	G	1	WM	—	—	20.00	45.00
	(Schenkman 4180BB)						
Va-Ri 18	H	1	WM	—	—	20.00	45.00
	(Schenkman 4180AZ)						
Va-Ri 19	J	1	WM	—	—	20.00	45.00
	(Miller 36D; Schenkman 4180BD)						
Va-Ri 20	K	1	WM	—	—	20.00	45.00
	(Miller 36; Schenkman 4180AX)						

Most varieties of these Centennial store cards were struck in very small quantities for collectors. Any significant demand would raise their price, as Virginia is a popular state with today's collectors.

G. SAUER

Rulau	Date	Metal	Size	VG	F	VF	Unc
Va-Ri 26	(1870's)	Brass	20mm	—	—	20.00	40.00
	Eagle with spread wings. Rv: G. SAUER / 5 (incuse) / RICHMOND, VA. Plain edge. (Miller Va 39; Schenkman 4180BN5)						
Va-Ri 27	(1870's)	Brass	20mm	—	—	20.00	40.00
	Similar to 26, but incused numeral 10. Plain edge. (Miller 40; Schenkman 4180BN10)						
Va-Ri 28	(1870's)	GS	20mm	—	—	20.00	40.00
	Similar to 26, but incused numeral 25. Plain edge. (Miller 41; Schenkman 4180BN25)						
Va-Ri 29	(1870's)	Brass	20mm	—	—	20.00	40.00
	Similar to 26, but no incused numeral at center. Plain edge. (Miller 38; Schenkman 4180BN25a)						

CHRIST. SCHAEFER

Rulau	Date	Metal	Size	VG	F	VF	Unc
Va-Ri 31	(1870)	Brass	19mm	—	5.00	10.00	20.00
	CHRIST. SCHAEFER / ELBA / * / PARK / RICHMOND, VA. Rv: Numeral 5 within wreath, star at top. Plain edge. (Miller Va 42; Wright 936; Schenkman 4180B05)						
Va-Ri 32	(1870)	Brass	19mm	5.00	9.00	14.00	20.00
	Similar to 31, but numeral 10 within wreath. (Miller 43; Schenkman 4180B010)						

Both tokens were struck by Francis X. Koehler of Baltimore, about 1870.

UNION MANUFACTURING CO.

Rulau	Date	Metal	Size	VG	F	VF	EF
Va-Ri 36	(?)	Silver	31mm	—	—	250.	—

UNION MANFG CO. / RICHMOND VA. ctsp on U.S. 1859 Seated Liberty half dollar. (Schenkman collection; Brunk 40910)

W.L. WARING

Rulau	Date	Metal	Size	F	VF	EF	Unc
Va-Ri 40	(1860-65)	WM	22mm	—	75.00	—	—

(All incused): W.L. WARING / DRUGGIST / RICHMOND, VA. Rv: BROAD. ST / ONE / No 107 / SODA. Plain edge. The reverse inscription arranged to form a cross, at center of which is a soda glass. Crude planchet. (Wright 1203; Miller Va 44; Schenkman 4180CE)

Warren L. Waring was listed 1858-59 as part of the firm of Waring & Pearce with James H. Pearce, at 107 Broad St. In 1860 Waring was listed as a druggist at 107 Broad St. alone. No directories were published during the Civil War, and in the 1866 directory Waring no longer appears.

P. WHITLOCK

Richmond, Va.

Rulau	Date	Metal	Size	VG	F	VF	Unc
Va-Ri 50	1888	WM	27.5mm	—	—	50.00	—

Bearded male bust facing, in circle. Around: - SMOKE - / OLD VIRGINIA CHEROOTS / 6 FOR -- 10 CTS / MANUFACTURED ONLY BY / P. WHITLOCK. RICHMOND. VA. Rv: SOUVENIR / -OF- / THE VIRGINIA / AGRICULTURAL / MECHANICAL / -AND- / TOBACCO / EXPOSITION / 1888. Plain edge. (Pete Peters coll.; Dillingham coll.)

WASHINGTON

H. OBERMAN & CO.
Centralia, Wash.

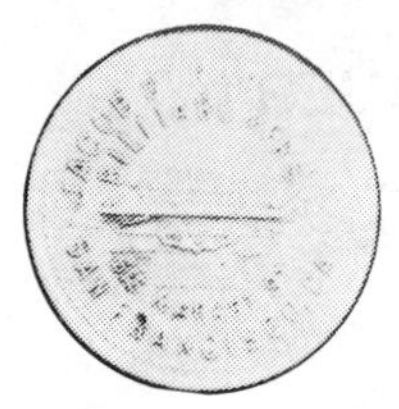

Rulau	Date	Metal	Size	VG	F	VF	Unc
Wa-Ce 7	(1883-89)	WM	25mm	—	—	2000.	—

Pool table at center, JACOB STRAHLE & CO BILLIARD MFRS above, 515 MARKET ST. SAN FRANCISCO, CAL. below. Rv: H. OBERMAN & CO. / GOOD FOR / 10 ¢/ IN TRADE / CENTRALIA, W.T. Plain edge. (Egnew coll., ex-Byron Johnson, Harvill, Brehan)

This token fetched $1500 ca 1975, $2000 1990, $2000-plus 1991.

BINNARD'S ELITE SALOON
Colfax, Wash.

Rulau	Date	Metal	Size	VG	F	VF	Unc
Wa-Co 2	(1874-84)	CN	25mm	—	—	1500.	—

BINNARD'S ELITE SALOON, COLFAX, W.T. Rv: Pool table at bottom. Above: THE / J. M. BRUNSWICK / AND / BALKE CO. Plain edge. (Brunswick 2032)

W.T. = Washington Territory. B. Binnard and Matilda Binnard, saloon and lodging, still listed 1896.

E. D. HARPOLE

Rulau	Date	Metal	Size	VG	F	VF	Unc
Wa-Co 6	(1901-02)	Brass	21mm	—	—	20.00	—

E. D. HARPOLE. Rv: GOOD FOR / * 6 1/4 C * / IN TRADE. Plain edge. (Rulau MV 124)

A saloon. Egnew says he has owned 3 of these.

PEARL BAKERY
Colfax, Wash.

Rulau	Date	Metal	Size	VG	F	VF	Unc
Wa-Co 9	(1880's)	Brass	25mm	—	—	300.	—

PEARL BAKERY / COLFAX W.T. / (incuse) B. Rv: GOOD FOR / 5 / CENTS / IN TRADE. Plain edge. (Byron Johnson coll.)

This token has fetched $1500, but a hoard of 15-20 pieces, not in collector hands, now overhangs the market.

M. A. CAVANAGH
Dayton, Wash.

Rulau	Date	Metal	Size	VG	F	VF	Unc
Wa-Dy 3	(1877-89)	Brass	25mm	—	—	800.	—

—*— / CHECK / —*— within central circle. Around: BRUNSWICK & COMPANY / * CHICAGO * . Rv: GOOD FOR / 1 CIGAR / M. A. CAVANAGH / DAYTON W. T. Plain edge. 4 pieces known. (Brunswick 14)

Washington Territory (W.T.) was created in 1853 out of Oregon Territory. Washington was admitted as a state in 1889. One piece fetched $750 in 1980's.

TOKLAS SINGERMAN & CO.
Seattle, Wash.

Rulau	Date	Metal	Size	F	VF	EF	Unc
Wa-Se 8	1888	Copper	35mm	—	80.00	100.	—

Washington head left, COR. FRONT & COLUMBIA ST. above, 1888 below, all within beaded central circle. Around: COMPLIMENTS OF TOKLAS SINGERMAN & CO. / * SEATTLE, W.T. *. Rv: Within laurel and oak wreath: STRICTLY / —.— / ONE PRICE / —&— / LOWEST / FIGURES. Around CLOTHIERS & GENTS FURNISHERS. (Wright 1087)

Issued with a loop to attach to a leather strap for use as a fob, according to Dr. B.P. Wright and Byron Johnson. WT = Washington Territory.

Six recent sales have been in the $100 range, Egnew says.

WARE BROS. CO'S.
Spokane, Wash.

Rulau	Date	Metal	Size	F	VF	EF	Unc
Wa-Sp 6	(1896)	Bronze	31.5mm	—	5.00	7.00	—

WARE BROS. CO'S. / 299 (incuse) / TOOL CLUB. Rv: THE / MOST / COMPLETE / LINE OF / TOOLS / IN / SPOKANE. Plain edge.

Sporting goods.

TACOMA MILL CO.
Tacoma, Wash.

Possible Fantasies!

Rulau	Date	Metal	Size	VG	F	VF	Unc
Wa-Ta 5	(1870's)	Iron	25mm	—	—	—	—
	TACOMA MILL CO. 40 ¢. (No description available)						
Wa-Ta 6	(1870's)	Iron	30mm	—	—	—	—
	Similar, but 45¢.						
Wa-Ta 7	(1870's)	Brass	**	—	—	—	—
	** Oval, 32 x 26mm. Similar, but $1.						

In the early 1870's the Tacoma Mill Company, unable to secure gold and silver to pay Indian laborers and provide a trading medium for settlers, decided to issue their own tokens, and set the company blacksmith to work upon them. All were crudely made, stamped with a value, and passed current over the country tributary to the mill.

This "mill coinage" is impossible to locate today. In 1937 William Hansom of the Tacoma Mill Co. presented a set of the three pieces to Tacoma's Ferry Museum, but Byron Johnson reports these are no longer there; they have disappeared. At the time of presentation of the tokens to the museum, Hansom wrote: "The honesty of the people and the absence of any blacksmith save that of the company, made the use of this money possible." (See *The Numismatist* for April, 1937, pages 299-300, for additional details).

Specialists Byron Johnson (now deceased), Clarence Heppner, Clancy Riggs and Lewis Egnew have never seen any Tacoma Mill piece.

H.M. HART
Whatcom, Wash.

Rulau	Date	Metal	Size	VG	F	VF	Unc
Wa-Wt 3	(1880's)	Brass	24mm	—	—	2000.	—

Brunswick die BB. Rv: H. M. HART / WHATCOM, W. T. (all in oval panel). Unique.

This was a pool hall, according to Byron Johnson, Seattle.

WEST VIRGINIA

CHARLESTON GAS LIGHT CO.

Charleston, W. Va.

Rulau	Date	Metal	Size	VG	F	VF	Unc
WV-Ch 1	(1871)	Brass	**	—	—	Ex.Rare	—

** Oval 43x32mm.
(All incused): CHARLESTON / GAS LIGHT CO. / 1 / LOAD COAL. Ctsp numeral 69 at left. Rv: SEAL PRESSES / Jas Murdock Jr (in script) / 165 RACE ST. / CIN'TI / STAMP CUTTER / ENGRAVER & DIE SINKER. Plain edge. Only 1 piece known. (Donald Clifford coll.)

Charleston Gas Light Co. was started by Charles Ward in 1871 to provide artificial gas to the businesses and nearby residents of Charleston. It consolidated with Kanawha Electric Light Co. in 1891 to form a new entity, Charleston Gas and Electric Co.

These are probably drayage checks from the firm's earliest days.

WICKHAM HOUSE

Hinton, W. Va.

Rulau	Date	Metal	Size	VG	F	VF	Unc
WV-Hi 7	(1883-84)	Brass	22mm	—	—	75.00	—

WICKHAM HOUSE / -+- / BAR / -+- / HINTON. W VA. Rv: 5 in central circle. Around: 16 6-pointed stars. Plain edge. 2 pieces known. (Donald Clifford coll.)

William D. Nalley was proprietor of the Wickham House, one of Hinton's two hotels, listed in the 1884 *Delaware, Maryland and West Virginia Gazetteer*. It is advertised itself as the "only first class hotel in Hinton," the 1,000-population county seat of Summers County. Rooms were $2 per day.

The hotel does not appear in earlier or later gazetteers. Adjoining the hotel were the bar and billiard room of Waldrop & Nalley.

ST. CLAIR HOTEL

Martinsburg, W. Va.

Rulau	Date	Metal	Size	VG	F	VF	Unc
WV-Ma 1	(1884-88)	Brass	24mm	—	—	—	75.00

(All incused): GOOD FOR / 5 C / ST CLAIR HOTEL / MARTINSBURG / IN / TRADE. Rv: Blank. Plain edge. (William Miller coll., Denton, Md.)

Martinsburg's earliest directory (1899-1900) no longer lists the St. Clair Hotel. The 1888 edition of Aler's *History of Martinsburg* does mention it. In the 1884 Polk gazetteer, Stewart and Wisner are listed as hotel owners.

OLD HOME SALOON

Wheeling, W. Va.

Rulau	Date	Metal	Size	VG	F	VF	Unc
WV-Wh 7	(1888)	Brass	24mm	—	—	85.00	—

(All incused): OLD / HOME / SALOON. Rv: GOOD FOR / 5 / CENTS. Plain edge. (Illustrated specimen has been cut) 2 pieces known. (Donald Clifford coll.; Bob Kirk coll.)

Simon Loesch is listed as the proprietor of this Wheeling watering hole at 1030 Market St. in 1888.

WISCONSIN

W. BOEDECKER

Ahnapee, Wis.

Rulau	Date	Metal	Size	VG	F	VF	Unc
Wi-Ah 1	(1886)	Brass	24mm	—	—	11.00	—

(All incused): W. BOEDECKER / GOOD FOR / 5 / CENTS / AT BAR / AHNAPEE. Rv: Blank. Only 1 piece reported. (Thoele coll.)

W. Beodecker ran a hotel in 1886, says the R. G. Dun directory. Ahnapee was a tiny place in Kewaunee County; it had a post office in 1877.

ZWOELFTES WISCONSIN SCHUETZENFEST (12th Wisconsin Shooting Festival)

Alma, Wis.

Rulau	Date	Metal	Size	F	VF	EF	Unc
Wi-Al 3	1880	Silver	29.7mm	—	30.00	—	45.00

Circular target in front of crossed rifles, wreath above, CONCORD below. Rv: Within open-end wreath: ZWOELFTES / WISCONSIN / BEZIRKS / SCHUETZEN-FEST / ALMA / JUNI. 1880. Plain edge.

D. KEARNEY

Antigo, Wis.

Rulau	Date	Metal	Size	VG	F	VF	Unc
Wi-An 3	(1884)	Brass	25mm	—	—	30.00	—

Brunswick die BB-7a. Rv: GOOD FOR / 5 ¢ / D. KEARNEY / IN / TRADE. Plain edge.

Billiard hall, listed in 1884.

G. BALL

Appleton, Wis.

Rulau	Date	Metal	Size	VG	F	VF	Unc
Wi-Ap 2	(1879)	Brass	25mm	—	6.00	11.00	—

(All incused): G. BALL / GOOD FOR / 5 / CENTS / IN TRADE / APPLETON. Rv: Blank.

George Ball's hotel, restaurant and billiard hall appears only once in directories, in 1879, at College Avenue between Morrison and Oneida. This was the center of the downtown area.

H. SCHOLLER
Ashford, Wis.

Rulau	Date	Metal	Size	VG	F	VF	Unc
Wi-As 3	(1882-91)	Brass	25mm	—	—	35.00	—

Brunswick die B-2e. Rv: GOOD FOR / 5 ¢ / H. SCHOLLER / -IN- / TRADE. Plain edge.

Henry Scholler, saloon, 1882-1891 directories.

ADAM HENDRICHS
Bailey's Harbor, Wis.

Rulau	Date	Metal	Size	VG	F	VF	Unc
Wi-Ba 3	(1882)	Brass	25mm	—	—	35.00	—

Brunswick die BB-8b. Rv: GOOD FOR / 5 ¢ / ADAM / HENDRICHS (in oval cross-hatched panel) / IN TRADE / .-. / AT THE BAR. (D. M. Steward Feb. 1984 sale, lot 7)

Adam Hendrichs was listed under hotels in the 1882 gazetteer. The 1886 R. G. Dun directory lists Mrs. Adam Hendrichs as operator of a hotel and saloon. There is only 1 piece known.

A. BOOTH & CO.
Bayfield, Wis.

Rulau	Date	Metal	Size	F	VF	EF	Unc
Wi-By 1	(1871-90)	Brass	26mm	—	—	11.00	16.00

A. BOOTH & CO. / BAYFIELD, WIS. Rv: Blank. Plain edge (Thoele coll.)

A. Booth & Co. began packing whitefish and trout in 1871. It is believed the token above is a packer's check for this Lake Superior firm.

In the 1903-1918 directories, A. Booth & Co. are listed as wholesale fish dealers.

A. ISHMAEL
Beetown, Wis.

Rulau	Date	Metal	Size	VG	F	VF	Unc
Wi-Be 1	(1882)	Brass	25mm	—	—	35.00	—

Brunswick die BB-7b. Rv: GOOD FOR / 5 ¢ / A. ISHMAEL / IN / TRADE. Plain edge.

Saloon, in 1882 Wisconsin gazetteer.

S. JOHN SPECHT
Black River Falls, Wis.

Rulau	Date	Metal	Size	F	VF	EF	Unc
Wi-BR 3	(1887-95)	GS	25mm	—	—	30.00	—

(Brunswick die BB-3). Rv: GOOD FOR / 5 C / S. JOHN / SPECHT / IN / TRADE. Plain edge. (Thoele coll.)

A listing for S. John Specht under saloons appears in 1888. Later directories in the 1890's list one John Specht (possibly the same man) under billiard halls in Black River Falls.

J. S. STURTEVANT
Black River Falls, Wis.

Rulau	Date	Metal	Size	VG	F	VF	Unc
Wi-BR 5	(1884-85)	Brass	Oct 27mm	—	—	30.00	—

Brunswick die BB-8a. Rv: GOOD FOR / 5 ¢ / J. S. STURTEVANT (name in cross-hatched oval panel) / - IN - / * TRADE *. (Thoele coll.)

Billiard hall, in 1883-84 gazetteer.

Rulau	Date	Metal	Size	VG	F	VF	Unc
Wi-BR 6	(1883-85)	Brass	25mm	—	—	35.00	—

As 5, on round flan. (Stubler coll.)

W. J. NAUERT
Boscobel, Wis.

Rulau	Date	Metal	Size	VG	F	VF	Unc
Wi-Bs 5	(1880's)	Brass	Oct 25mm	—	—	12.00	—

-.- / W. J. NAUERT / -.-. Rv: GOOD FOR / 2 1/2 ¢ / IN TRADE.

NAUERT BROS.
Boscobel, Wis.

Rulau	Date	Metal	Size	VG	F	VF	Unc
Wi-Bs 7	(1882-84)	Brass	--mm	—	—	25.00	—

Brunswick die BB-8a. Rv: NAUERT BROS.

C. KOPPLIN
Brandon, Wis.

Rulau	Date	Metal	Size	VG	F	VF	Unc
Wi-Bn 2	(1879-82)	Brass	25mm	—	—	35.00	—

Chas. Pick & Co. die. Rv: GOOD FOR / 5 ¢ / C. KOPPLIN (in cross-hatched panel) / IN / * TRADE *. Probably unique.

C. Kopplin ran a saloon at Brandon 1879-1882, then next appears as a saloonkeeper in Ripon, Wis. 1891-92. The cross-hatching is typical of 1880's style.

HENRY KROEHNKE
Chilton, Wis.

Rulau	Date	Metal	Size	VG	F	VF	Unc
Wi-Ch 3	(1888-89)	Brass	25mm	—	—	40.00	—

GOOD FOR / 5 ¢ / HENRY / KROEHNKE (name in panel) / IN / TRADE/ Rv: THE / GARDEN CITY / -+- / BILLIARD / -+- / TABLE CO. / CHICAGO. Only 1 piece reported.

Kenry Kroehnke's saloon is listed in the 1888-89 gazetteer.

HENRY SCHILDHAUER
Colby, Wis.

Rulau	Date	Metal	Size	VG	F	VF	Unc
Wi-Co 3	(1884-85)	Brass	25mm	—	—	30.00	—

Chas. Pick & Co. die. Rv: GOOD FOR / 5 ¢ / HENRY / SCHILDHAUER (name in oval cross-hatched panel) / IN / * TRADE *. Unique. (Thoele coll.)

Saloon, listed in 1884-85 gazetteer.

JAS. RILEY
Darlington, Wis.

Rulau	Date	Metal	Size	VG	F	VF	Unc
Wi-Da 3	(1875-86)	Brass	23mm	—	12.00	—	—

(All incused): JAS. RILEY / DARLINGTON. Rv: Blank. (L. Stubler coll.)

Saloon, listed 1875 through 1886.

HOWARD & TOOLEY
Eagle River, Wis.

Rulau	Date	Metal	Size	VG	F	VF	Unc
Wi-ER 4	(1889-90)	Brass	25mm	—	30.00	35.00	—

—*— / CHECK / —*— within central circle. Around: BRUNSWICK & COMPANY / * CHICAGO *. Rv: GOOD FOR / 5 ¢ / HOWARD & TOOLEY. Plain edge. (Brunswick 38)

Frank A. Howard and Mr. Tooley were partners in a confectionery, saloon and barber shop 1889-90. Howard left the business 1891 to become a barber in Eagle River, and Tooley & Merickle continued the saloon.

EAU CLAIRE NATIONAL CARNIVAL

Eau Claire, Wis.

Rulau	Date	Metal	Size	VG	F	VF	Unc
Wi-EC 1	1886	Gilt/B	17mm	—	—	15.00	—

Globe, showing Western Hemisphere. Rv: EAU CLAIRE / WIS. / NATIONAL / CARNIVAL / 1886-7. Plain edge. (Gene Johnson coll.)

HERMAN HANSON

Rulau	Date	Metal	Size	VG	F	VF	Unc
Wi-EC 2	(1882-91)	GS	24mm	—	—	20.00	—

Brunswick die BB-8a. Rv: GOOD FOR / (5 ¢) / HERMAN / HANSON (name in panel) / - IN - / * TRADE (in scroll) *. Plain edge.

This saloon is listed 1882 through 1891.

M. HOMS

Eau Claire, Wis.

Rulau	Date	Metal	Size	VG	F	VF	Unc
Wi-EC 3	(1874-84)	CN	Oct 26mm	—	18.00	27.50	—

CHECK at center (the first C being large and ornate). Around: THE J. M. BRUNSWICK & BALKE COS. Rv: GOOD FOR / 10 ¢ / M. HOMS / IN TRADE. Plain edge. Brunswick 2169)

Michael Homs saloon and restaurant, at 131 No. Barstow, Eau Claire, 1870's to 1906.

Rulau	Date	Metal	Size	VG	F	VF	Unc
Wi-EC 4	(1890's)	Aluminum	Sc 29mm	—	—	9.00	—

GOOD FOR / 25 ¢ . MIKE HOMS (in panel) / IN / TRADE.

1890's or early 1900's.

N. D. WILDER

Evansville, Wis.

Rulau	Date	Metal	Size	VG	F	VF	Unc
Wi-Ev 3	(1888-)	Brass	25mm	—	—	15.00	—

(All incused): N. D. WILDER / GOOD FOR / A / 5 ¢ / CIGAR / EVANSVILLE, WIS. Rv: Blank.

Newton D. Wilder, cigar manufacturer, is listed 1888-1902.

CON. McGINNIS

Fort Howard, Wis.

Rulau	Date	Metal	Size	VG	F	VF	Unc
Wi-FH 3	(1884)	Brass	24mm	—	—	35.00	—

Chas. Pick & Co. die. Rv: GOOD FOR / 5 ¢ / CON. / McGINNIS / IN / TRADE. Plain edge. (Thoele coll.)

This hotel and saloon appears in the 1884 gazetteer.

F. MORELLI

Genoa, Wis.

Rulau	Date	Metal	Size	VG	F	VF	Unc
Wi-Gn 3	(1888)	Brass	25mm	—	—	30.00	—

Brunswick die B-2a. Rv: F. MORELLI.

Fred Morelli's saloon appears in the 1888 gazetteer.

GEO. CASUTT

Glen Haven, Wis.

Rulau	Date	Metal	Size	VG	F	VF	Unc
Wi-GH 2	(1887-89)	Brass	25mm	—	—	25.00	—

National Billiard Mfg. Co. die. Rv: GOOD FOR / 5 ¢ / GEO. CASUTT (in panel) / IN / * TRADE *.

Saloon, listed 1888-1889.

JOHN GRANDRATH

Glen Haven, Wis.

Rulau	Date	Metal	Size	VG	F	VF	Unc
Wi-GH3	(1879-88)	Brass	25mm	—	—	20.00	—

Brunswick die BB-7a. Rv: GOOD FOR / 5 ¢ / JOHN GRANDRATH / IN / TRADE.

Saloon, listed 1879 thru 1888.

G. H. KERN

Glidden, Wis.

Rulau	Date	Metal	Size	VG	F	VF	Unc
Wi-Gd 3	(?)	Brass	28mm	—	—	15.00	—

Cow standing in front of a tree, ONE QUART / MILK around. Rv: G. H. KERN / (ornament) / GLIDDEN, / -.- / WIS. Some 15 tokens known.

E. W. RONK

Gravesville, Wis.

Rulau	Date	Metal	Size	VG	F	VF	EF
Wi-Gv 1	(1878)	Copper	29mm	90.00	—	150.	—

E. W. RONK ctsp on U.S. Large cent. Examined: 1848, 1851. Only 3 pieces known. (Stubler coll.; Brunk 34987)

E. W. Ronk was a blacksmith and a farmer, listed in the 1878 Wisconsin gazetteer. Gravesville is a village in Calumet County which had a 300 pop. in 1910.

J. H. MALLORY

Green Bay, Wis.

Rulau	Date	Metal	Size	VG	F	VF	Unc
Wi-GB 7	(1872-74)	Copper	29mm	—	—	200.	—

J. H. MALLORY BILL POSTER GREEN BAY, WIS. ctsp on edge of U.S. 1834 Large cent. (Rulau Wis 110; Kurt Krueger report; Brunk 25790)

Mallory the bill poster appears in Green Bay city directories 1872 through 1899, and thus this counterstamped coin is relocated from the 2nd edition of our *U.S. Merchant Tokens 1845-1860* to this section.

The counterstamp is in a continuous legend around the plain *edge* of the Large cent, the only such counterstamping reported to this author.

M. RISCH

Green Bay, Wis.

Rulau	Date	Metal	Size	VG	F	VF	Unc
Wi-GB 10	(1879-86)	Brass	25mm	—	—	35.00	—

Chas. Pick die. Rv: GOOD FOR / 5 ¢ / M. RISCH / GREEN BAY / IN / * TRADE *. Plain edge.

Saloon, listed in all directories and gazetteers from 1863 thru 1886. The Charles Pick saloon fixture-utensils tokens were first issued 1879. Michael Risch, New York Saloon.

BURNS & CONNELL

Hayward, Wis.

Rulau	Date	Metal	Size	VG	F	VF	Unc
Wi-Hy 1	(1884)	Brass	25mm	—	—	25.00	—

Brunswick die BB-7a. Rv: GOOD FOR / 5 ¢ / BURNS & / CONNELL (name within panel) / IN / * TRADE *. (Kruesel coll.)

Under billiard halls in the 1884 R. L. Polk gazetteer may be found a listing for Connell & Burns.

W. D. BISHOP

Hudson, Wis.

Rulau	Date	Metal	Size	VG	F	VF	EF
Wi-Hd 2	(?)	CN	**	—	—	75.00	—

** Semicircular, 22 x 11mm.

W. D. BISHOP (curved) / (arrow right) (leaf) (arrow left) / HUDSON (latter in large letters with breaks in each letter) ctsp on planed reverse of half of a U.S. 1883 Liberty nickel. The coin has been cut neatly in half. (Gene Johnson coll.)

OLSON BROS.

Iola, Wis.

Rulau	Date	Metal	Size	F	VF	EF	Unc
Wi-Io 4	(1880's)	Brass	24.5mm	—	8.50	—	—

GOOD FOR / 5 ¢ / OLSON BROS / IOLA, WIS. / —.— / IN TRADE. Rv: Small mounted Indian riding left at top, large 5 ¢ at center, fan-shaped ornament at bottom. Plain edge. (Hartzog coll.)

This reverse type was a stock die of S. D. Childs & Co. of Chicago in the 1880's.

KEWAUNEE COUNTY AGRICULTURAL SOCIETY

Kewaunee, Wis.

Rulau	Date	Metal	Size	VG	F	VF	Unc
Wi-Ke 4	1886	Brass	30mm	—	20.00	30.00	—

Crossed haystacks and farm tools. Around: KEWAUNEE COUNTY AGRICULTURAL SOCIETY / KEWAUNEE, WIS. Rv: FOURTEENTH ANNUAL / FAIR (ornate letters) / OCT. 4, 5 & 6, 1886. Plain edge.

A. MESS

Kilbourn City, Wis.

Rulau	Date	Metal	Size	F	VF	EF	Unc
Wi-Ki 3	(1884-86)	Brass	25mm	—	—	35.00	—

Brunswick die BB-8b. Rv: GOOD FOR / 5 C / A. MESS / IN / TRADE. Plain edge.

Saloon, in the 1884 and 1886 gazetteers. It is also known that A. Mess issued other tokens without the Brunswick-Balke stock die, in the 1890's.

H. ENERSON + OLSON

La Crosse, Wis.

Rulau	Date	Metal	Size	F	VF	EF	Unc
Wi-Lx 2	(1881-82)	Brass	23mm	—	—	8.50	—

H. ENERSON + OLSON / GOOD FOR / 5 C / DRINK (all incused). Rv: Blank. Plain edge. (Thoele coll.)

Henry Enerson and an Olson are listed as a saloon in 1882.

HATCH'S RESTAURANT

La Crosse, Wis.

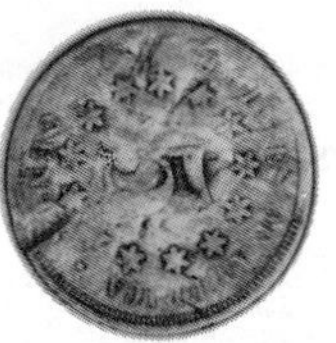

Rulau	Date	Metal	Size	VG	F	VF	EF
Wi-Lx 4	(1875-77)	CN	22mm	—	60.00	—	90.00

HATCH'S / RESTAURANT / COR MAIN & 3RD STS. / LA X WIS / ctsp on U.S. Shield nickel. Examined: 1866, 1867, 1868, 1872, 1873, unknown date. 15 pieces known. (Brunk 18690)

Rulau	Date	Metal	Size	VG	F	VF	EF
Wi-Lx 9	(1875-77)	Bronze	23mm	—	60.00	—	90.00

Similar ctsp on U.S. Shield 1865 2-cent piece.

Rulau	Date	Metal	Size	VG	F	VF	EF
Wi-Lx 10	(1875-77)	Silver	25mm	—	—	125.	—

Similar ctsp on U.S. 1853 S.L. quarter.

In the 1875-77 period E. A. Hatch ran the Aldine Restaurant, Billiard Hall and Sample Room (drinking parlor), at the corner of Third and Main Sts. Hatch stocked foreign and domestic brandies, gins, rums and wines; Havana cigars; imported Scotch ale and Dublin porter, he advertised. He is listed only in the 1876 directory.

A. FLOM

Madison, Wis.

Rulau	Date	Metal	Size	VG	F	VF	Unc
Wi-Md 3	(1874-89)	Brass	25mm	—	—	10.00	—

GOOD FOR / 5 C / A. FLOM (on panel) / IN / TRADE / (ornament). Rv: Ornate, shaded large 5. Along bottom: (tiny) HANSON CHICAGO. Plain edge.

A. Flom's hotel and saloon appears in directories 1874 through 1889.

10 NORD WEST SANGERFEST

Madison, Wis.

Rulau	Date	Metal	Size	F	VF	EF	Unc
Wi-Md 10	1881	S/WM	30mm	10.00	—	—	—

Standing figure with lyre. Around: DER MENSCHHEIT WURDE IS IN EURE HAND GEGEBEN BEWAHRT SIE. Rv: Within wreath: 10 / NORD WEST / SANGERFEST / MADISON / WIS. / JULI 1881. Plain edge. (Thomas Casper coll)

Tenth Northwest Singing Festival; all text in German. The only reported specimen is holed for suspension.

HARMON BROS.

Manawa, Wis.

Rulau	Date	Metal	Size	VG	F	VF	EF
Wi-Mw 2	(1880's)	Brass	29mm	—	9.00	15.00	—

(All incused): HARMON BROS. / 10 / HOTEL MANAWA. Rv: Blank. Beaded, incised rim on either side. Plain edge. (TAMS maverick number 8704. Dec. 1978 *TAMS Journal*

The blank style is typical of the mid-1880's. Needs directory verification. Manawa is located in central Waupaca County.

By 1918 there were two hotels in Manawa, which then had 820 population.

Possibly Weyauwega, Wis. or Oshkosh, Wis., according to Hank Thoele.

H. WILCOX

Manitowoc, Wis.

Rulau	Date	Metal	Size	VG	F	VF	Unc
Wi-Mc 7	(1872-93)	GS	23mm	—	—	11.50	—

(All incused): H. WILCOX / GOOD FOR / 5 CENTS / IN TRADE / MANITOWOC. Rv: 5. (Oct. 1984 Partridge sale)

Henry Wilcox, saloon, restaurant and confectionery, listed 1872 through 1893, at 505 York.

WM. HUBER

Menominee, Wis.

Rulau	Date	Metal	Size	VG	F	VF	Unc
Wi-Mm 3	(1882-88)	Brass	25mm	—	—	25.00	—

Brunswick die BB-8b. Rv: GOOD FOR / 5 ¢ / WM. HUBER (in oval cross-hatched panel) / IN / TRADE. Only 1 piece known.

Rulau	Date	Metal	Size	VG	F	VF	Unc
Wi-Mm 4	(1884-88)	Brass	25mm	—	—	25.00	—

Brunswick die BBC-9a. Rv: GOOD FOR / 5 ¢ / WM. HUBER (in oval panel) / IN / TRADE. Only 1 piece known. This variety has word COLLENDER on obverse. (Thoele coll., ex-Bill White)

William Huber, saloon, listed 1882-1889.

BEARD BROS.

Merrill, Wis.

Rulau	Date	Metal	Size	VG	F	VF	Unc
Wi-Mr 1	(1888)	Brass	25mm	—	—	35.00	—

Brunswick die BB-3. Rv: GOOD FOR / 5 ¢ / BEARD BROS. (in oval panel) / IN / TRADE.

The *Wisconsin State Gazetteer* for 1888-89 lists the saloon of Edmund P. Beard and John Beard.

H. H. MILLS

Milford, Wis. ?

Rulau	Date	Metal	Size	VG	F	VF	Unc
Wi-Mf 3	(1882)	Brass	24mm	—	—	8.50	—

GOOD FOR / 5 ¢ / H. H. / MILLS / IN / TRADE. Rv: Large 5 in circle of 13 rosettes. (Thoele coll.)

Hotel proprietor, listed in 1882 *Wisconsin State Gazetteer.* This village had 220 people in 1910; Jefferson County.

K

Milwaukee, Wis.

Rulau	Date	Metal	Size	F	VF	EF	Unc
Wi-Mi 22	(1871)	WM	25mm	—	15.00	20.00	25.00

Obverse: Same as obverse of Milwaukier Friedens-Feier 1871 token (which see). Rv: GOOD FOR / 10 / CENTS / K. Plain edge. (Coll. Charles Ziegler, York, Pa.)

Apparently diesinker Marr used the German peace celebration medalet obverse die as a stock die to manufacture trade tokens. The attribution to Milwaukee is tentative.

KINNICKINNIC DIS'Y CO.

Rulau	Date	Metal	Size	VG	F	VF	Unc
Wi-Mi 23	(1870-74)	Copper	19.6mm	—	—	75.00	—

KINNICKINNIC / DIS'Y. / CO. Rv: GOOD FOR / ONE / B'LL. SLOP / *. Plain edge. (Hartzog coll.)

Rulau	Date	Metal	Size	VG	F	VF	Unc
Wi-Mi 24	(1870-74)	Copper	20.1mm	—	—	150.	—

As last, but struck over an 1863 Milwaukee Civil War token of Friedrich Miller, Fuld Wis 510AB-1a. (Hartzog coll.)

The "barrel slop" referred to was a barrel of the waste organic liquid of the distilling process, which was valuable to farmers as a feed.

Tthere is a Kinnickinnic River and a Kinnickinnic Avenue in the city's southeastern section, known as Bay View.

CHAS. KLEINSTEUBER

Rulau	Date	Metal	Size	VG	F	VF	Unc
Wi-Mi 25	1867	WM	22mm	—	15.00	20.00	60.00

Bearded man's head left. CHAS. KLEINSTEUBER / 18 -- 67 / * MECHANIC *. 318 STATE ST. MILWAUKEE. Plain edge. (The signature MARR appears beneath the truncation of the neck.) (Miller Wis. 8)

Struck by Mossin & Marr of Milwaukee. The same firm struck similar, 1863-dated tokens for Kleinsteuber in copper and silver (Fuld 510V-1a to 3a) in the Civil War store card series. In 1863 he was located at 24 Tamarack St.

Kleinsteuber was a manufacturer of small machinery and an engraver, stencil cutter, etc.

E. A. M. LEIDEL

Rulau	Date	Metal	Size	F	VF	EF	Unc
Wi-Mi 27	(1886)	Brass	22mm	—	15.00	20.00	25.00

Obverse same as obverse of the Milwaukee Industrial Exposition token, Wi-Mi 30 (Screaming eagle on shield). Rv: MILWAUKEE EXPOSITION SOUVENIR / E. A. M. LEIDEL / MFG. / JEWELER / & DIAMOND / SETTER / *. Plain edge. (Hartzog coll.)

MEINERS & VILTER

Rulau	Date	Metal	Size	VG	F	VF	Unc
Wi-Mi 28	(1867)	Brass	19mm	—	50.00	75.00	100.

MEINERS / & / VILTER. Rv: GOOD FOR / ONE / B'LL. SLOP. Plain edge. (Rulau Wi-Un 2)

MILWAUKEE BIERBRAUER ARBEITER

Rulau	Date	Metal	Size	F	VF	EF	Unc
Wi-Mi 29	(1880's)	Brass	**	—	—	10.00	—

** Scal 28.1mm.
MILWAUKEE BIERBRAUER / ARBEITER / UNTERSTUTZUNGS / —*— /VEREIN. Rv: Ornate numeral 5 with circle of alternatings stars and dots - all within beaded circle. Plain edge. (Fred Borgmann coll.)

The legend translates: Milwaukee Brewery Workers Assistance Union. Probably a trade check for use within the worker association's premises.

MILWAUKEE INDUSTRIAL EXPOSITION

Rulau	Date	Metal	Size	F	VF	EF	Unc
Wi-Mi 30	1886	Copper	22mm	—	10.00	15.00	20.00

Screaming eagle, wings upraised, perched on a U.S. shield. In background are train, steamship, sheaf of wheat, cogwheel, anchor, etc. Rv: (Circular inscription around rim): MILWAUKEE INDUSTRIAL EXPOSITION. SEP 1. to OCT. 16. 1886 *. The center is blank. Plain edge.

Rulau	Date	Metal	Size	F	VF	EF	Unc
Wi-Mi 30A	1886	CN	22mm	—	—	40.00	—

As 30, but overstruck on a U.S. Shield nickel. (Mike O'Hara coll.)

Rulau	Date	Metal	Size	F	VF	EF	Unc
Wi-Mi 30B	1886	WM	22mm	—	—	30.00	—

As 30, but overstruck on a white metal token.

MILWAUKIER FRIEDENS-FEIER

Rulau	Date	Metal	Size	F	VF	EF	Unc
Wi-Mi 33	1871	WM	26mm	—	10.00	15.00	25.00

Germania standing, with sword and imperial double-headed eagle shield in her hands, looking across the Rhine River. The signature MARR is at bottom. Rv: MILWAUKIER / FRIEDENS- / FEIER / VON / 27-29. MAI. / 1871. Plain edge.

"Milwaukier Friedens-Feier von 27-29 Mai 1871" translates from the German to: Milwaukee Peace Celebration of May 27-29, 1871. The piece honors the local celebration by Milwaukee's large Germanic population of the victory over France in the Franco-Prussian War. The representation of Germania is an early one, before the creation that year of the German Empire — thus the use of the old imperial (Austrian) double-headed eagle rather than the later German Empire single-headed eagle. Germania here is not dissimilar to her representation in the huge bronze statue *Die Wacht am Rhein* overlooking the Rhine, which was constructed later.

Marr is the engraver of the Milwaukee firm of Mossin and Marr which prepared many Civil War tokens.

By the conclusion of the Franco-Prussian War in 1871, the Germanic emigration to the United States was already a massive phenomenon. Though the immigration had not yet peaked, many German neighborhoods had already been established in American cities. Though few cities became as "German" as Milwaukee, obvious remnants of German influence still remain in many large cities such as St. Louis, Chicago and Cincinnati.

Most Germans came to the U.S. looking for better economic conditions, but many also came for greater political freedom, bringing with them strong republican and socialist sentiments.

Referring to these political malcontents, the contemporary German historian and proselytizing monarchist Dr. Moritz Busch observed that the attitudes of the immigrant Germans in America were satisfactory and "increasing in pro-German feeling." He wrote: "The war and its results far outweigh republicanism with them. It seems that our democrats must go abroad before they can feel as they ought to do." (From *Bismarck in the Franco-German War*, circa 1880.)

A number of medallic tokens have been struck here in the U.S. to celebrate the Fatherland's glorious victory and unification. They are listed in this catalog under San Francisco, St. Louis, Williamsburgh, N.Y., Milwaukee and Non-Local. Surely there must be more.

(The above footnote was written by Fred J. Borgmann, Iola, Wis.)

Rulau	Date	Metal	Size	VG	F	VF	Unc
Wi-Mi 35	(1871)	WM	18mm	—	—	—	7.00

Crowned Imperial German eagle flanked by U.S. and German flags. Rv: Supported Wisconsin state arms, motto FORWARD on scroll above. (Thoele coll.)

This medalet is associated with the Friedensfeier (Peace Jubilee) celebrations in Wisconsin.

NORDWESTLICHEN SAENGERBUNDES

Rulau	Date	Metal	Size	F	VF	EF	Unc
Wi-Mi 38	1868	S/WM	32.2mm	—	10.00	15.00	20.00

Ornate lyre within branches. Tiny I. MARR at lower rim. Rv: Within open-end wreath: DRITTES / SAENGER / FEST / DES / NORDWESTLICHEN / SAENGER / BUNDES. / MILWAUKEE / JUNI / 1868. Plain edge.

Commemorates the third singing festival of the Northwestern Singing Leagues, held in Milwaukee in June, 1868. The inscription is entirely in German; in the 19th century Milwaukee was a major center of attraction for German immigrants.

SAXONIA

Rulau	Date	Metal	Size	VG	F	VF	Unc
Wi-Mi 40	(1888-89)	Brass	24mm	—	—	5.00	—

K. U. V. / SAXONIA / MILWAUKEE. Rv: Large 5. Plain edge. (Johnson K-2)

K. U. V. = Katholische Unterstutzungs Verein. The Saxonia was a hotel listed 1888-1889.

SCHOKNECHT & NEHLS

Rulau	Date	Metal	Size	VG	F	VF	Unc
Wi-Mi 41	(1888-89)	Brass	25mm	—	—	7.50	—

GOOD FOR / 5 ¢ / SCHOKNECHT / & NEHLS (names in oval stippled panel) / DRINK. Rv: Large 5 in circle of alternating stars and moons. Apparently unique. (Thoele coll., ex-G. Johnson)

Saloon, 1888-89 gazetteer.

SOLDIERS HOME FAIR

Rulau	Date	Metal	Size	VG	F	VF	Unc
Wi-Mi 42	1865	Copper	19mm	—	20.00	25.00	30.00

Scroll, on which is: HONOR & / COUNTRY. Rv: MILWAUKEE / 1865 / SOLDIERS HOME FAIR. Plain edge. Rarity 7 (Fuld NC-17a). Issued with slot at top, probably for wear.

The Soldiers Home Fair was held in June of 1865, just three months after the end of the Civil War. The die work resembles that of Mossin & Marr of Milwaukee.

24TH N. A. SAENGERFEST

Rulau	Date	Metal	Size	F	VF	EF	Unc
Wi-Mi 50	1886	WM	33.1mm	—	10.00	—	20.00

Lyre within laurel and oak wreath. Rv: Building within central circle. Around: — I— 24TH N. A. SAENGERFEST MILWAUKEE WIS. JULI 21..26. 1886. Plain edge.

F. THOMA
Milwaukee, Wis.

Rulau	Date	Metal	Size	F	VF	EF	Unc
Wi-Mi 48	(1885-88)	Brass	25mm	—	—	12.50	—

Brunswick die BB-8a. Rv: F. THOMA.

Saloon, listed in directories from 1886 thru 1894. The Brunswick-Balke dies were issued 1874-84 and for a few years after the 1884 merger with Collender.

F. Thoma had been located in Chicago, Ill. 1880-1884.

L. G. DU BOIS
Neenah, Wis.

Rulau	Date	Metal	Size	F	VF	EF	Unc
Wi-Ne 1	(1886)	Brass	25mm	—	—	35.00	—

Brunswick die BB-6a. Rv: GOOD FOR / 5 ¢ / L. G. DU BOIS (in cross-hatched panel) / IN / TRADE / *. Only 3 known.

Saloon, listed 1886 only.

JNO. G. KLOPF
Neilsville, Wis.

Rulau	Date	Metal	Size	VG	F	VF	Unc
Wi-Ni 3	(1882-89)	Brass	25mm	—	—	25.00	—

Chas. Pick & Co. die. Rv: GOOD FOR / 5 ¢ / JNO. G. KLOPF (in oval cross-hatched panel) / IN / * TRADE *. (Thoele coll., ex-Rouleau, Egnew)

John G. Klopf, saloon, listed 1882 through 1901.

HERMAN HELGENDORF
Oak Grove, Wis.

Rulau	Date	Metal	Size	VG	F	VF	Unc
Wi-Og 3	(1888-91)	Brass	25mm	—	—	35.00	—

Brunswick die BBC-10b. Rv: GOOD FOR / 5 ¢ / REFRESHMENTS / HERMAN / HILGENDORF. Plain edge. (Thoele coll., ex-Egnew, Rouleau)

Saloon and restaurant, listed in the 1888 thru 1891 directories.

P. L.
(Pahl-Links Brewery)
Oconto, Wis.

Rulau	Date	Metal	Size	VG	F	VF	Unc
Wi-Oc 4	(1865-76)	Brass	19mm	—	10.00	15.00	20.00

P* L*. Rv: GOOD FOR / ONE / B'LL. SLOP / *. Plain edge. (Rulau Wi-Un 1)

Louis P. Pahl operated the Pahl-Links Brewery 1865-1890, according to the *Register of U.S. Breweries 1876-1976.* (See page 39, *TAMS Journal* for Feb. 1978)

In 1891 this became the Oconto Brewing Co.

L. A. TANTH
Omro, Wis.

Rulau	Date	Metal	Size	VG	F	VF	EF
Wi-Om 4	1881	Copper	29mm	—	—	20.00	—

L A TANTH / WINNEBAGO / CHAPT NO 43 / JAN 19TH 81 engraved in script on planed-off obverse of a U.S. Large cent. (Kurt Krueger coll.; Gene Johnson coll.)

Winnebago Chapter 43 at Omro, Wis., also issued Masonic Mark pennies of its own.

OSHKOSK S. G.
Oshkosh, Wis.

Rulau	Date	Metal	Size	VG	F	VF	Unc
Wi-Os 11	(1880's ?)	Gilt/B	19mm	—	—	25.00	35.00

OSHKOSH (non-serif letters, curved) / S. G. (fancy capitals, straight). Rv: Target within open-end wreath. Plain edge. 4 known. (Harold Helm coll.)

S. G. may indicate "schiess gewehr" or "schuetzen gesellschaft" or a similar German phrase indicating a shooting society or club. Old timers in Oshkosh cannot recall such a club specifically, but point out that the fancy letters 'S.G.' differ markedly from the word Oshkosh and resemble the type styles used by German-Americans in that era.

German-oriented shooting clubs proliferated in the Midwest after the Civil War.

Harold Helm points out the similarities between the Oshkosh S. G. token and the Civil War store card lettered Neenah S. B. Oshkosh and Neenah are near each other on Lake Winnebago.

A. M. CHOLETTE
Peshtigo, Wis.

Rulau	Date	Metal	Size	F	VF	EF	Unc
Wi-Pe 2	(1881-86)	Brass	25mm	—	—	35.00	—

Brunswick die BBC-9b. Rv: GOOD FOR / 5 C / A. M. / CHOLETTE / IN / TRADE. (Thoele report)

Saloon, listed 1882 thru 1886. Anton M. Cholette, hotel, saloon and livery 1882-86.

P. CLAVADETSCHER
Plum City, Wis.

Rulau	Date	Metal	Size	VG	F	VF	Unc
Wi-Pm 1	(1886)	Brass	Oct 27mm	—	—	30.00	—

Brunswick die BB-8b. Rv: GOOD FOR / A 5 ¢ / P. CLAVADETSCHER (in oval cross-hatched panel) / * DRINK *.

The 1886 directory lists Peter Claradetscher (sic!), hotel and saloon. Plum City, Pierce County, had 305 pop. in 1910.

HENRY JAMES
Portage, Wis.

Rulau	Date	Metal	Size	VG	F	VF	Unc
Wi-Pr 3	(1872-95)	Brass	25mm	—	—	35.00	—

Brunswick die BB-6a. Rv: GOOD FOR / 5 ¢ / HENRY / JAMES (name in oval cross-hatched panel) / IN / * TRADE *. Plain edge. (Stubler coll.)

Saloon, listed 1872-1895.

SPLAIN & MICHEL
Portage, Wis.

Rulau	Date	Metal	Size	VG	F	VF	Unc
Wi-Pr 5	(1882)	Brass	25mm	—	—	30.00	—

Chas. Pick & Co. die. Rv: GOOD FOR / 5 ¢ . SPLAIN / & MICHEL (names in oval cross-hatched panel) / IN / * TRADE *. Plain edge. 2 pieces known. (Stubler, Thoele colls.)

Saloon, listed in 1882-83 Polk gazetteer.

C. (W.) DE LANEY
Poynette, Wis.

Rulau	Date	Metal	Size	VG	F	VF	Unc
Wi-Po 2	(1886)	Brass	25mm	—	—	30.00	—

Brunswick die BB-7a. Rv: GOOD FOR / 5 ¢ / C. (W.) / DE LANEY / IN / TRADE. Plain edge. (Gary Kruesel coll.)

Charles W. De Laney's saloon and hotel appears in the 1882 thru 1886 gazetteers.

W. JANISTA
Racine, Wis.

Rulau	Date	Metal	Size	VG	F	VF	Unc
Wi-Ra 2	(1887-99)	Brass	25mm	—	—	25.00	—

GOOD FOR / 5 ¢ / W. JANISTA (on ribbon) / IN / TRADE. Rv: CHAS. PASSOW / BILLIARDS / & POOL / TABLES / CHICAGO.

The saloon, listed 1887-1914, was located at 1209 Douglas.

JOHNSON & FIELD MFG. CO.

Rulau	Date	Metal	Size	VG	F	VF	Unc
Wi-Ra 3	ND	Brass	32mm	—	35.00	50.00	—

Indian head in full war bonnet right. Around: JOHNSON & FIELD MFG. CO. / * RACINE, WIS. *. Rv: COMPLIMENTS OF JOHNSON & FIELD MFG. CO. / MFGRS. OF / FARM & WAREHOUSE / FANNING MILLS. / -.- RACINE, WIS. / * * * / (tiny) CHILDS CHI. Plain edge. (Gene Johnson coll.)

MITCHELL & LEWIS CO. LTD.

Rulau	Date	Metal	Size	F	VF	EF	Unc
Wi-Ra 5	1884	Alum	38mm	—	15.00	20.00	30.00

A wagon, THE OLD above, RELIABLE below. Around: MITCHELL & LEWIS CO. L'T'D. / RACINE, WIS. Rv: ESTABLISHED 1834 / THE MITCHELL / WAGON / IS THE BEST / INCORPORATED 1884. (Wright 713)

The Mitchell Wagon Co. was still manufacturing wagons in 1918, but an affiliate, Mitchell Motors Co., was making automobiles and trucks at that time.

PLEISS & HECK

Racine, Wis.

Rulau	Date	Metal	Size	VG	F	VF	Unc
Wi-Ra 8	(1882)	Brass	Sq 23mm	—	—	8.00	—

PLEISS & HECK / (radiant ornament) / RACINE, WIS. Rv: 5 (large, ornate) / (tiny) HANSON, CHICAGO.

Rulau	Date	Metal	Size	VG	F	VF	Unc
Wi-Ra 9	(1882-85)	Brass	--mm	—	—	250.00	—

Brunswick die BB-4. Rv: PLEISS & HECK.

Saloon, 1882-1885 gazetteers.

WOOD N. PORTER

Reedsburg, Wis.

Rulau	Date	Metal	Size	VG	F	VF	Unc
Wi-Re 10	(1881-82)	Brass	24mm	—	—	25.00	—

Pool table, THE BRUNSWICK BALKE / COLLENDER / COMPY. above, CHECK in exergue. Rv: WOOD N. PORTER / (four dots in cross form) / +++. Plain edge. (Brunswick 5580); Rulau MV 258)

This saloon is listed in the 1882 gazetteer. One surviving specimen of this check has the date 1887 scratched in.

H. CARLEY & CO.

Ripon, Wis.

Rulau	Date	Metal	Size	VG	F	VF	Unc
Wi-Rp 3	(1882)	Brass	25mm	—	—	30.00	—

Pool table in central circle. Around: THE J. M. BRUNSWICK & BALKE COS / * CHECK *. (BB-6b die) Rv: GOOD FOR / 5 / H. CARLEY / & CO. / IN TRADE. Plain edge. (Hank Thoele coll.)

H. Carley & Company were listed in the 1882 directory as a saloon.

WM. QUAST

Rulau	Date	Metal	Size	VG	F	VF	Unc
Wi-Rp 9	(1886-90)	Brass	**	—	—	15.00	—

** Scal 29mm.

GOOD FOR / 5 C / Wm QUAST (on panel) / IN / TRADE. Rv: 5 in circle of 16 6-pointed rosettes. (Thoele coll.)

Saloon, listed 1886 to 1890.

LANT WOOD

Ripon, Wis.

Rulau	Date	Metal	Size	VG	F	VF	Unc
Wi-Rp 15	(1888-92)	Brass	25mm	—	—	55.00	—

Chas. Pick & Co. die. Rv: GOOD FOR / 5 ¢ / LANT WOOD / RIPON, WIS / IN / TRADE.

Lant Wood was listed under hotels and saloons in 1888 through 1898 gazetteers, but Pick stopped supplying tokens 1892. Wood later moved to Marinette, Wis., where he ran a hotel.

BERTSCHY & THAYER

Sheboygan, Wis.

Rulau	Date	Metal	Size	VG	F	VF	Unc
Wi-Sb 3	(?)	WM	32mm	—	75.00	100.	—

Indian in full war regalia standing, facing. At left a cornstalk on which are four folds of ribbon. Inscriptions on ribbon not legible. Rv: SHEBOYGAN MINERAL WATER / (ornament) / BERTSCHY / -&- / THAYER / (ornament) / * SHEBOYGAN, WIS. *. Plain edge. (Gene Johnson coll.)

WM. C. WEISE

Sheboygan, Wis.

Rulau	Date	Metal	Size	VG	F	VF	Unc
Wi-Sb 16	(1883-86)	Brass	25mm	—	—	40.00	—

- GOOD FOR - / 5 ¢ (in panel) / WM. C. WEISE (in oval cross-hatched panel) / IN / * TRADE *. Rv: CHAS. PASSOW'S BILLARD TABLES / radiant 5 in arc of 13 stars / CHICAGO / (star). Plain edge. (Stubler coll.)

This saloon appears in the 1883-1886 gazetteers.

M. C. CONNORS

South Kaukauna, Wis.

Rulau	Date	Metal	Size	VG	F	VF	Unc
Wi-SK 1	(1888)	Brass	25mm	—	—	8.50	—

GOOD FOR / 5 ¢ / M. C. / CONNORS / IN / TRADE. Rv: Large 5 within circle of alternating stars and moons. Plain edge.

Saloon, in 1888 gazetteer.

A. OLSON

Stockholm, Wis.

Rulau	Date	Metal	Size	VG	F	VF	Unc
Wi-St 3	(1880's)	Brass	27.5mm	—	—	23.50	—

(All incused): GOOD FOR / 5 ¢ / AT BAR / A. OLSON / STOCKHOLM. Rv: Blank. Incised, beaded rim on each side. (Thoele coll.)

Olson had disappeared before the 1891 directory. Stockholm was a Pepin County village with a strong Scandinavian populace of about 200.

JOHN LONEY

Sullivan, Wis.

Rulau	Date	Metal	Size	VG	F	VF	Unc
Wi-Su 2	(1888)	Brass	25mm	—	—	35.00	—

Brunswick die BBC-9b. Rv: GOOD FOR / 5 ¢ / JOHN / LONEY / IN / TRADE. Plain edge. (Thoele coll., ex-Egnew, Rouleau)

Saloon, listed in 1888.

W. H. BRADLEY LUMBER CO.

Tomahawk, Wis.

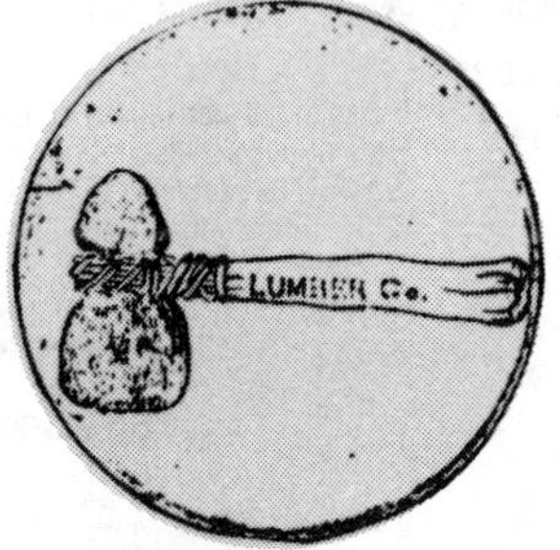

Rulau	Date	Metal	Size	VG	F	VF	Unc
Wi-Tm 1	(?)	Silver	38.2mm	—	—	150.	—

(All engraved) W. H. BRADLEY (on scroll) / 1001 BROADWAY (script) / TOMAHAWK (script) / WISCONSIN (on scroll). Rv: Indian tomahawk, with LUMBER CO. on its wooden handle. All engraved on planed-down U.S. silver dollar. The reeded edge has also been removed and made into a silver bezel with which to mount (and wear) this item. (Rich Hartzog coll.)

JOHN TOLMAN

Washburn, Wis.

Rulau	Date	Metal	Size	VG	F	VF	EF
Wi-Wb 5	(1888-92)	Brass	25mm	—	—	30.00	—

Brunswick die B-2a. Rv: JOHN / TOLMAN.

Saloon, listed 1889-1892.

HENRY DAUB

Watertown, Wis.

Rulau	Date	Metal	Size	VG	F	VF	EF
Wi-Wa 3	(1874-84)	Brass	25mm	—	—	25.00	30.00

Billiard table at bottom. Above: THE / J. M. BRUNSWICK / AND / BALKE CO. Rv: GOOD FOR / 1 / HENRY DAUB / * DRINK *. Plain edge. (Brunswick 2094)

Henry Daub was born in Prussia about 1848. He ran a hotel and saloon 1874-1894.

JOS. HARVEY

Watertown, Wis.

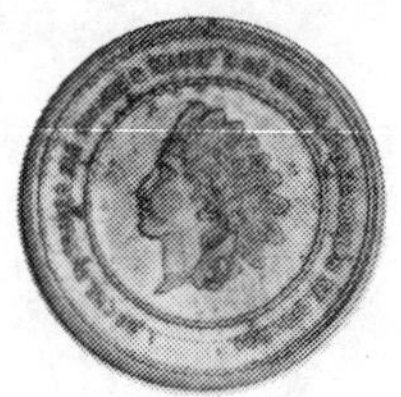

Rulau	Date	Metal	Size	VG	F	VF	Unc
Wi-Wa 7	(1884-93)	Brass	25mm	—	—	25.00	—

Indian head left in central circle. Around: L. BOCHE, ENGRAVER, DIE SINKER & MANUF'R OF CHECKS, 166 RANDOLPH ST. CHICAGO. Rv: GOOD FOR 5 CENTS / JOS. / HARVEY / . . . / . / WATERTOWN, WIS. / * IN TRADE *. Plain edge.

Boche used the Indian head stock die in the 1880's to prepare tokens for merchants in the East and Midwest.

GRAND ARMY OF THE REPUBLIC

Wausau, Wis.

Rulau	Date	Metal	Size	F	VF	EF	Unc
Wi-Ws 5	1887	Silv/WM	40mm	—	—	25.00	—

GAR seal with FRATERNITY CHARITY LOYALTY and wreaths around. Rv: Statue, tiny A. S. below. Around: A GRATEFUL PEOPLES TOKEN OF REMEMBRANCE / UNVEILED JULY 4, 1887. / * WAUSAU, WIS. *. Plain edge. (Gene Johnson coll.)

23 BEZIRKS TURNFEST

Wausau, Wis.

Rulau	Date	Metal	Size	F	VF	EF	Unc
Wi-Ws 9	1887	Silv/WM	31mm	—	—	25.00	35.00

Owl on crossed sword and torch, tiny A. S. below. 23 BEZIRKS TURNFEST DES WISCONSIN T. B. / AUG 11 - 15, 1887. / * WAUSAU, WIS. *. Rv: Supported Wisconsin state arms. Plain edge.

F. FROSCH

Wayside, Wis.

Rulau	Date	Metal	Size	VG	F	VF	Unc
Wi-Wy 2	(1880-98)	Brass	25mm	—	—	30.00	—

GOOD FOR / 5 ¢ / F. FROSCH (in cross-hatched panel) / IN / TRADE. Rv: CHAS. PASSOW, / MANUFACTURER / -OF- / BILLIARD / -&- / POOL TABLES / -- / CHICAGO. Unique. (Thoele coll.)

Frank Frosch is listed as grocery and saloon from 1880 through 1898. The token type is early.

A. F. DYER
West Eau Claire, Wis.

Rulau	Date	Metal	Size	VG	F	VF	EF
Wi-WE 3	1869	Silver	32.5mm	—	—	300.	—

A. F. DYER. (curved) / 1869. / W. EAU. CLAIRE. (curved) / WIS. ctsp on U.S. 1811 Bust half dollar. (Gene Johnson coll.; Brunk 12640)

EAGLE HOUSE
Wisconsin

Rulau	Date	Metal	Size	VG	F	VF	EF
Wi-Un 1	(?)	Copper	29mm	—	—	75.00	—

EAGLE HOUSE (curved) / WIS. ctsp on U.S. 1854 Large cent. (Krueger 3545; Brunk 12795)

D. FRANK POWELL
Wisconsin

Rulau	Date	Metal	Size	VG	F	VF	Unc
Wi-Un 3	1888	CN	27mm	—	—	12.50	17.50

Bust right of man with long hair and beard. Around: WHITE BEAVER OF WISCONSIN. Rv: FOR GOVERNOR / OF WISCONSIN. / D. FRANK POWELL / - 1888 -. Plain edge. (Gene Johnson coll.)

H. SHANFIELD
Wisconsin ?

Rulau	Date	Metal	Size	VG	F	VF	Unc
Wi-Un 4	(1865-75)	Bronze	19.5mm	—	10.00	15.00	20.00

Large 5-pointed star at center, H. SHANFIELD above, DISTILLER. below. Rv: GOOD FOR / ONE / B'LL. SLOP / *. Plain edge. (Hartzog coll.)

WISCONSIN COFFEE CUP
Wisconsin ?

Rulau	Date	Metal	Size	VG	F	VF	Unc
Wi-Un 5	(?)	Brass	25mm	—	—	8.50	—

WISCONSIN / (ornament) / COFFEE / CUP. Rv: Large numeral 5 in circle made up of 12 alternating stars and 12 small o's. (Thoele coll.)

The reverse type is typical of 1880's die work.

REPORTED WISCONSIN BILLIARD TOKENS

All the following unverified attributions have been made to Wisconsin locales in this era. They are reported here for informational purposes. (* Indicates city name on the token)

Name on Token	Possible Locale	Billiard Die	Gazetteer
Chas. W. Addison	Montford	BB-5	1888-97
H. L. Barney	Ashland	BB-5	1886-89
Frank Bernard	Appleton	BB-6a	1884
P. S. Brewer	Richland Center	BBC-11	1884
V. Cizek & Co.	Manitowoc	BBC-7	1891-93
John Conway	Elroy	BB-7a	1886-93
John Conway	Elroy	BB-9b	1886-93
Wm. Cushman	New London	B-2e	1884-97
J. L. Dearing	Milwaukee	BB-7a	1886
James Dunstone	Whitewater	BBC-11	1895-1902
C. G. Flood	Unity	BB	1882-96
Freeman & Reitz	Black River Falls	BB-8a	1884-86
T. K. Fries	Lone Rock	Chas. Pick	1884
Otto Froelich	Sheboygan	BBC-10b	?
J. G. Funk	Racine	Chas. Pick	?
John Hahn	DePere	Chas. Pick	1880-95
J. W. Harris 12 1/2 ¢	Racine	Chas. Pick	1884-91
M. Hendricks	Waukesha	Geo. Kuehl	1888
John M. Johnson	Eau Claire	Kuehl & Bro.	1886-89
John Kurz	Eau Claire	BBC-9b	1882-97
Chris Leonhardt	Sturgeon Bay	Chas. Pick	1879-93
J. Leonhardt	Sturgeon Bay	BB	1882-96
L. Lyons	Ashland	BBC	1888-89
Frank A. Manor	Kenosha	BB-3	1884-91
Wm. McElleget	Eau Claire	BB	1882-83
T. McGuine	Wonewoc	Chas. Pick	1886
Thomas McNulty	Spring Green	BB-7a	1884-89
S. S. Neil	Manawa	B & Co.	1890-97
Joe Oehlers	Reedsburg	BBC	1888-95
F. Paul	Arcadia	BB-4	1882
John Peitz	Richland Center	BBC-9b	1886-88
A. Quasius	Sheboygan	BBC-11	1888-1909
George Rabenstein	Milwaukee	BB-6b	1882-91
Wm. Roberts	Cumberland	BB	1882-83
Aug. Rudzinsky	Milwaukee	BBC	1876-92
B. M. Schilz	New Munster	BB-7b	1886-1901
J. Schweiger	Prairie du Chien	BBC	1888-92
J. H. Simon	Hartford	Chas. Pick	1879-84
Frank Smrcina	Prairie du Chien	BB-6b	1884-91
* Jno. Stariha	Arcadia	Chas. Pick	1879
T. Thompson	Withee	BBC	1888-94
M. Weller	Port Washington	BBC-11	1888-1902
John Wise	Menasha	B-2c	1888-89
E. York	Clayton	B-2e	1886-88
F. V. Zeman	Prairie du Chien	BBC-11	1888-1912
Wm. Zimmerman (Brunswick 2389)	New London	BB-4	1884

WYOMING

GOBELMAN BROS.

Carbon, Wyo.

Rulau	Date	Metal	Size	VG	F	VF	Unc
Wy-Ca 3	(1884)	Brass	25mm	—	125.	190.	—

Pool, table at bottom, THE / J. M. BRUNSWICK / AND / BALKE CO above. Rv: GOOD FOR / 1 / DRINK / GOBELMAN BROS. / MINERS SAMPLE ROOMS / CARBON, WYO. Plain edge. (Brunswick 2143)

HERMAN HAAS

Cheyenne, Wyo.

(See II-Ch 118, Schuttler Wagons, under Chicago, Illinois in this section. Haas was the Schuttler branch agency for this trade area)

WYOMING CAPITAL BUILDING

Cheyenne, Wyo.

Rulau	Date	Metal	Size	F	VF	EF	Unc
Wy-Ch 12	1887	Copper	29mm	—	—	35.00	50.00

Building. Rv: CORNER STONE LAYING / OF / WYOMING / CAPITAL / BUILDING / MAY 18 1887 / CHEYENNE WYO. (Wright 1280)

NON-LOCAL

J. W. BOOTH

Non-Local

Rulau	Date	Metal	Size	VG	F	VF	EF
NL 6	(1865	Copper	23mm	—	75.00	—	—

DA M. / J. W. BOOTH ctsp on reverse of U.S. 1864 2-cent piece. (Lot 574, Joseph Lepczyk auction of June 3, 1982; Brunk 4315)

This piece undoubtedly refers to the assassination of President Abraham Lincoln by actor John Wilkes Booth in April, 1865.

HIT HIM AGAIN

Non-Local

Rulau	Date	Metal	Size	VG	F	EF
NL 9	(?)	CN	19mm	—	15.00	—

HIT HIM AGAIN ctsp on U.S. 1858 Flying Eagle cent. (Brunk 19710)

RETURN OF PEACE

Non-Local

Rulau	Date	Metal	Size	F	VF	EF	Unc
NL 15	1871	WM	28mm	—	—	20.00	—

Wilhelm I of Prussia in a pickelhaube (spiked helmet). RV: IN COMMEMORATION OF THE RETURN OF PEACE 1871. Plain edge. Weight 7.65 grams.

See background under Milwaukier Friedens-Feier, Milwaukee, Wis.

EAGLES ON MISCELLANEOUS COINS

Rulau	Date	Metal	Size	F	VF	EF	Unc
NL 55	(?)	CN	22mm	—	—	25.00	—

Eagle with beak to right ctsp on obverse of U.S. 1868-type Shield nickel. Similar ctsp on reverse of coin. (Stanley Steinberg 1982 sale)

LOCATION NOT KNOWN

M. A. ABBEY

Rulau	Date	Metal	Size	VG	F	VF	Unc
MV 1	(?)	Copper	29mm	15.00	—	22.50	—

M. A. ABBEY ctsp on U.S. Large Cent. Examined: 1796, 1825, 1828, 1842, 1846, 1848, 1851. (Duffield 1431; Hallenbeck 1.500; Brunk 150)

Rulau	Date	Metal	Size	VG	F	VF	Unc
MV 1A	(?)	Bronze	23mm	15.00	—	22.50	—

Similar ctsp on U.S. 2-cent piece. Examined: 1864, 1866, 1867, 1869.

Rulau	Date	Metal	Size	VG	F	VF	Unc
MV 1B	(?)	Copper	29mm	—	—	—	—

C.H.L. SPALDING / M.A. ABBEY ctsp on U.S. 1846 Large cent. (Partrick coll.)

Rulau	Date	Metal	Size	VG	F	VF	Unc
MV 1C	(?)	CN	19mm	15.00	—	22.50	—

Similar ctsp to MV1 on U.S. 1859 Indian cent.

Rulau	Date	Metal	Size	VG	F	VF	Unc
MV 1D	(?)	CN	22mm	20.00	—	30.00	—

Similar ctsp on U.S. Shield nickel. Examined: 1867, 1869.

Abbey was a prolific issuer active circa 1870-75.

J. A. ABBOTT

Rulau	Date	Metal	Size	VG	F	VF	Unc
MV 1F	(?)	Bronze	19mm	—	—	20.00	—

J. A. ABBOTT ctsp on U.S. 1868 Indian cent. (Brunk 195)

Rulau	Date	Metal	Size	VG	F	VF	Unc
MV 1G	(?)	Bronze	23mm	—	—	20.00	—

Similar ctsp on U.S. 1864 or 1865 2-cent piece.

A. H. ALLEN

Rulau	Date	Metal	Size	VG	F	VF	Unc
MV 1K	1868	Br	**	—	—	—	20.00

** Oval 44x25mm.

A. H. ALLEN / "PAT'D 185. REIS'D 1861 / EXT'D 1868". Rv: Incused oval. Plain edge. (Wright 13)

It would be interesting to learn what it was Allen had patented in the 1850's, had the patent reissued for in 1861 and then extended in 1868.

AMERICAN PILE CO.

Rulau	Date	Metal	Size	VG	F	VF	EF
MV 2	(?)	Copper	26mm	—	—	40.00	—

AMN. PILE CO. ctsp twice on obverse of Canada 1876 Large cent. AMERICAN ctsp twice on reverse of coin. (Krause coll; Brunk 790)

Some authorities think this should have read: AMN. PIPE CO.

J. AMES C.(AST)STEEL

Rulau	Date	Metal	Size	VG	F	VF	Unc
MV 2A	(1870's)	CN	22mm	—	—	25.00	—

J. AMES / C. STEEL ctsp on U.S. Rays type Shield nickel. Examined: 1866, 1868, 1870, worn. (Partrick coll.; Brunk 860)

PROF. ANDRE'S ALPINE CHOIR

Rulau	Date	Metal	Size	VG	F	VF	Unc
MV 3	(1880)	Brass	23mm	—	—	20.00	—

Mustached male left, PROF. ANDRE'S above. *ALPINE CHOIR* below. Rv: MATRIMONIAL / NO / TIPPLER / NEED / APPLY / SOCIETY. Plain edge. Rarity 5.

Though this piece was in Dr. Wright's collection, it was not listed by him. Wright sold his specimen to C. Mathis on Sept. 25, 1900. Mathis sold his collection to Stuart Mosher, and Mosher sold it in turn to Melvin and George Fuld in 1948.

J. ANISTAKI

Rulau	Date	Metal	Size	VG	F	VF	Unc
MV 3C	1868	Lead	18mm	—	—	55.00	—

Copy of 1868 Seated LIberty dime. Rv: GOOD FOR / ONE GLASS / OF / SODA WATER / J. ANISTAKI among flourishes. (PCAC Gold Medal sale. Dec. 1991, lot 534, where it fetched $51 in VF)

ARNOLD

Rulau	Date	Metal	Size	VG	F	VF	EF
MV 4	(?)	Bronze	19mm	—	—	10.00	—

ARNOLD ctsp on U.S. 1883 Indian Head cent. (Brunk 1080)

Rulau	Date	Metal	Size	VG	F	VF	EF
MV 4A	(?)	Silver	25mm	—	—	10.00	—

Similar ctsp on U.S. 1853 S.L. quarter.

R.E. ASHMAN

Rulau	Date	Metal	Size	VG	F	VF	Unc
MV 6	(1874-1884)	Brass	25mm	—	—	20.00	—

GOOD FOR / 5 ¢ / R. E. ASHMAN / IN / * TRADE *. Rv: Pool table within beaded circle. Around circle: THE J.M. BRUNSWICK & BALKE COS. / * CHECK *. Plain edge.

Not listed in *The Brunswick Token Story* by Fowler, Magnuson & White, 1977.

ATHENEUM

Rulau	Date	Metal	Size	VG	F	VF	Unc
MV 7	(?)	Brass	32mm	—	—	3.00	—

(All incused): ATHENEUM / 11. Plain edge.

AULT & SON

Rulau	Date	Metal	Size	VG	F	VF	EF
MV 10	(1882)	Silver	27mm	—	—	—	125.

AULT & SON ctsp on Spanish-American 1780-LME-MI 2-reales. (Colin Bruce report; Krueger 1991 sale, lot 1729)

The reported specimen has, scratched in the obverse field: 1882 / Oct 16. The AULT & SON impression is from a die, incused.

B.

Rulau	Date	Metal	Size	VG	F	VF	EF
MV 8	ND	Silver	23.4mm	—	—	—	—

B ctsp on Norway 1853 24-skilling, KM 315.2, Craig 102.2. (Jerry Crain coll.)

B & H

Rulau	Date	Metal	Size	VG	F	VF	Unc
MV 9	(?)	Bronze	19mm	15.00	—	25.00	—

B & H ctsp on U.S. 1820, 1831, 1841, 1843, 1850, 1851 Large cents. 7 known. (Hallenbeck 2.005; Brunk 1560)

Rulau	Date	Metal	Size	VG	F	VF	Unc
MV9A	(?)	Bronze	19mm	—	—	—	—

B. & H. ctsp on U.S. Indian cent. Examined: 1881, 1888. (Hallenbeck 2.006)

Possibly Bradley & Hubbard, makers of brass lamps.

BAILEY AND STOUFFER

Rulau	Date	Metal	Size	VG	F	VF	Unc
MV 12	(?)	Copper	29mm	—	—	15.00	—

BAILEY AND STOUFFER ctsp on U.S. Large cent. (Hallenbeck 2.502; Brunk 1790)

THE BALLINGALL POOL TABLE

Rulau	Date	Metal	Size	VG	F	VF	Unc
MV 13	(?)	Brass	29mm	—	—	35.00	—

THE BALLINGALL / POOL / TABLE / * CHECK *. Rv: GOOD FOR / 5 CENTS / IN TRADE. Plain edge. (Thoele coll.)

ED. BARRY

Rulau	Date	Metal	Size	VG	F	VF	EF
MV 15	(?)	Silver	38.1mm	—	—	140.	—

ED. BARRY, level and square ctsp on U.S. 1871 Seated Liberty silver dollar. (Nadin-Davis sale, Nov. 20, 1982, lot 242; B&M Nov. 1993 sale, lot 1914)

Undoubtedly a Masonic piece. Barry thus may not be a merchant.

P. BIRDSELL

Rulau	Date	Metal	Size	VG	F	VF	Unc
MV 17	(1880-82)	Brass	23.1mm	—	—	30.00	—

(All incused): P BIRDSELL / (numeral 5 intertwined with two pool cues and four balls). Rv: AMERICAN / STANDARD BILLIARD / AND / POOL TABLES / W. H. GRIFFITH & CO. N.Y. incised, dentilated rim on each side. Plain edge. (Rulau coll.)

THE BLIGHTED HOPE

Rulau	Date	Metal	Size	VG	F	VF	Unc
MV 19	(1880's)	xx	29mm	—	—	400.	—

xx Black vulcanite.

CHAS. PICK & CO. / DEALERS IN / (crossed tongs, goblet and ladle) / - CHICAGO -. Rv: GOOD FOR / AT THE / BLIGHTED / HOPE / A / DRINK. Plain edge. (R. B. Worthington coll.)

Found in Clovis, N.M. in 1990, this is the only Pick token in vulcanite ever reported.

BLYSTONE & RHODES

Rulau	Date	Metal	Size	VG	F	VF	Unc
MV 20	(?)	GS	33mm	—	—	10.00	—

BLYSTONE & RHODES / 15 / -o- / Rv: Blank. (Wright 42)

A druggist's soda check, says Dr. Wright.

J.S. BOWMAN

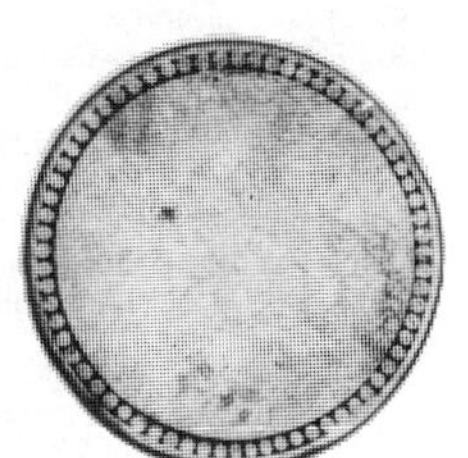

Rulau	Date	Metal	Size	VG	F	VF	Unc
MV 21	(?)	Brass	28mm	—	—	15.00	—

(All incused): GOOD FOR / ONE / BATH / J. S. BOWMAN. Rv: Blank. Incised beaded rim on each side. Plain edge. (Thomas Casper coll.)

F. E. BOYD

Rulau	Date	Metal	Size	VG	F	VF	EF
MV A21	1870	Copper	23mm	—	—	35.00	—

F. E. BOYD / PAT. / 99.528 / FEB. 8 1870 (all lines curved) ctsp on U.S. 1864 Shield 2-cent piece. (Kirtley Nov. 1991 sale, lot Q052; Brunk 4705)

J. A. BOYER

Rulau	Date	Metal	Size	VG	F	VF	EF
MV C21	(?)	Silver	25mm	25.00	—	35.00	—
	J. A. BOYER ctsp on U.S. 1858-O S.L. quarter. (Brunk 4740)						
MV D21	(?)	Silver	31mm	25.00	—	35.00	—
	Similar ctsp on U.S. 1855 or 1858 S.L. half dollar.						
MV E21	(?)	Copper	29mm	15.00	—	25.00	—
	Similar ctsp on U.S. 1827, 1840 or 1854 Large cent.						
MV F21	(?)	Copper	--mm	15.00	—	25.00	—
	Similar ctsp on England penny.						

WM. A. BRADY, AN IRISH ARAB

Rulau	Date	Metal	Size	VG	F	VF	Unc
MV 24	(?)	Brass	25mm	—	—	80.00	—

AN IRISH ARAB / UNDER / * THE * / DIRECTION / * OF * / * WM. A. BRADY *. Rv: BOBBY GAYLOR -- / * / * / IN AN / * o * / IRISH ARAB. Plain edge. (Wright 93)

Dr. Wright's somewhat incorrect 1898 recording of this token's legend is now smoothed out.

Though not yet attributed, this piece seems to be a theater advertising check for a play titled *"An Irish Arab."* Actor (?) Bobby Gaylor and director (?) William A. Brady may provide clues. The author finally obtained a copy of this rare piece in late 1987.

BRAKEMAN

Rulau	Date	Metal	Size	VG	F	VF	EF
MV 26	1880's)	Silver	31mm	22.50	—	—	—

BRAKEMAN. In fancy lettering arched, engraved on planed-off obverse of a U.S. 1853 Arrows and Rays half dollar. (Though the obverse with date and arrows is planed off, only the 1853 eagle reverse is surmounted by rays, making identification of the exact year of the underlying coin possible.) (Rulau coll.)

The eagle side has been mounted for wear with two solder points, from which the soldered-on appurtenances have been removed. This is apparently a railroad brakeman's item, used as a fob ornament, bracelet tag, button or some other use in adorning clothing. Acquired in Houston, Texas, Jan. 31, 1982.

JACK BREED

Rulau	Date	Metal	Size	VG	F	VF	EF
MV C26	(?)	Silver	31mm	—	—	35.00	—

JACK. BREED. / 5-pointed star) ctsp on U.S. 1860-O Seated Liberty half dollar (Pete Peters coll.)

V.E. BRETS

Rulau	Date	Metal	Size	VG	F	VF	EF
MV 27	(?)	Copper	29mm	—	—	25.00	—

VE. BRETS / . MAKER ctsp on worn-smooth U.S. Large cent. The 'S' in BRETS resembles a backward Z. (Frank Kovacs coll.)

BRINKS

Rulau	Date	Metal	Size	VG	F	VF	EF
MV 28	(?)	Silver	--mm	—	20.00	—	

BRINKS ctsp on U.S. 1877 Seated Liberty quarter. (Gould 73; Brunk 5220)

W. J. BROADHURST

Rulau	Date	Metal	Size	VG	F	VF	Unc
MV 30	1884-1900	BR	**	—	—	15.00	—

**Oct 25mm.

GOOD FOR / 5¢ / IN TRADE / W.J. BROADHURST. Rv: Pool table. THE BRUNSWICK BALKE / COLLENDER / COMPY above. CHECK below. Plain edge.

Not listed in *The Brunswick Token Story.*

D. BROWN

Rulau	Date	Metal	Size	VG	F	VF	EF
MV 33	(?)	Copper	29mm	—	—	20.00	—

D. BROWN, WARREN ctsp on U.S. 1819 Large cent. (Hallenbeck 2.763; Brunk 5410)

J.T. BROWN

Rulau	Date	Metal	Size	VG	F	VF	EF
MV 34	1865	Bronze	19mm	—	—	—	Rare

Man striding left with pole and sack over his shoulder, two stars on each side. Below, in two lines: J. T. BROWN / 1865. All incused on planed-off obverse of a bronze Indian cent. (Rich Hartzog coll.; Brunk 5513)

This could be a "love token" item, but its inclusion is justified here, we believe. If contemporary, it is incused on either an 1864 or 1865 cent.

W. A. BROWN

Rulau	Date	Metal	Size	VG	F	VF	EF
MV 35	(?)	Silver	31mm	—	—	235.	—

W. A. BROWN ctsp on obverse of U.S. 1858 Seated Liberty half dollar. Fleur-de-lis device ctsp on reverse of the coin. (May 1983 catalog of Peter Ireland Format Ltd., Birmingham, England)

The fleur-de-lis device was applied supposedly only to holed coins by Spanish authorities in Puerto Rico in 1884 to legitimize them as currency. These countermarked pieces were redeemed in 1894. The device was applied to a large number of American and Spanish silver coins and to some Spanish bronzes.

Such coins could easily have reentered the U.S. circulation after 1884 if they were U.S. issues, and apparently this one may have done just that, assuming Brown is an American.

S.B. BRUSH

Rulau	Date	Metal	Size	VG	F	VF	EF
MV 37	(?)	Silver	31mm	—	—	40.00	—

S. B. BRUSH ctsp from prepared punch on U.S. Seated Liberty half dollar. Dates examined: 1854, 1855-O. 3 specimens reported. (Brunk, Rulau colls.)

Rulau	Date	Metal	Size	VG	F	VF	EF
MV 37A	(?)	Silver	32.5mm	—	—	60.00	—

Similar ctsp on U.S. 1824 Bust half dollar.

P. J. BURNS

Rulau	Date	Metal	Size	VG	F	VF	EF
MV 36	(?)	CN	18mm	—	15.00	—	—

P. J. BURNS ctsp on U.S. 1866 cupronickel 3-cent piece. (Brunk 6070)

W. BUSSE

Rulau	Date	Metal	Size	VG	F	VF	EF
MV 38	(1875-84)	Brass	24mm	—	—	100.	—

Pool table at center, THE H. W. COLLENDER COS. above. * CHECK * below. Rv: + GOOD FOR 5 CENTS IN TRADE / . W. . / BUSSE / BOUL'D. / . . . / EXCHANGE. Plain edge. 4 or 5 pieces known. (Brunswick 4002)

C. & C. T. R.

Rulau	Date	Metal	Size	VG	F	VF	EF
MV 38G	(?)	CN	22mm	—	30.00	—	—

C. & C. T. R. / SEAL & PRESS CO. ctsp on U.S. Shield-type nickel. (Van Ormer sale 2944; Brunk 6385)

The numeral 610 is ctsp on reverse.

C. & R.

Rulau	Date	Metal	Size	VG	F	VF	EF
MV 38J	1881	Bronze	23mm	—	25.00	—	—

C & R 1881 ctsp on U.S. 1864 2-cent piece. (John Cheramy coll.; Brunk 6437)

D.C. & CO.

Rulau	Date	Metal	Size	VG	F	VF	Unc
MV 39	(?)	Aluminum	25mm	—	—	5.00	—

Monogram D.C. & CO. Rv: RICHMOND / CO. Plain edge. (Wright 1598)

The reverse text could stand for Richmond County, which might help narrow down attribution. There are Richmond Counties in Georgia, New York, North Carolina and Virginia. Possiblity: Duval Crayon Co., Port Richmond (Staten I.), N.Y.

H. W. C.

Rulau	Date	Metal	Size	VF	F	VF	EF
MV 700	(?)	Copper	29mm	15.00	—	25.00	—

1 / H W C / P T ctsp on shaved reverse of U.S. 1848 or 1850 Large cent. (Brunk 17610)

Rulau	Date	Metal	Size	VF	F	VF	EF
MV 701	(?)	Copper	29mm	15.00	—	25.00	—

Similar ctsp on shaved reverse of U.S. 1851 or 1856 Large cent.

Rulau	Date	Metal	Size	VF	F	VF	EF
MV 702	(?)	Copper	29mm	15.00	—	25.00	—

2 / H W C / P T ctsp on U.S. 1848 Large cent. (Brunk 174)

It is possible these are checks of some kind. The numerals and PT suggest possible use as dairy checks (pint). Brunk says Massachusetts for this issue.

J.C.

Rulau	Date	Metal	Size	F	VF	Unc
MV 40	(?)	Brass	**	—	5.00	—

** Oct 24mm.

J C incused on octagonal blank planchet. 2 1/2 incused on opposite side. Beaded, recessed rim on both sides of planchet. Plain edge. (Courtesy Steven Guiness, Roswell, Georgia)

J.B.C.

Rulau	Date	Metal	Size	VG	F	VF	Unc
MV 41	(1874-84)	Brass	25mm	—	—	10.00	—

GOOD FOR / 5 ¢ / J. B. C. / IN / TRADE. Rv: Pool table. Above it: THE / J. M. BRUNSWICK / AND / BALKE CO. Plain edge.

Not listed in *The Brunswick Token Story.*

M.C.

Rulau	Date	Metal	Size	VG	F	VF	EF
MV 42	(?)	Silver	27mm	—	—	5.00	—

M.C. in relief within recessed square ctsp on Spanish-American 2-reales. (Gould 415ff)

This appears to be a silversmith's hallmark. Not traced. Some possibilities.

Metcalf B. Clark, Boston, ca. 1838

M. Connell, Philadelphia, ca. 1800

O.W.C.

Rulau	Date	Metal	Size	VG	F	VF	Unc
MV 42C	(1880's)	Brass	28mm	—	—	2.00	—

(All incused): O.W.C. (large). Rv: GOOD FOR / 5 / IN TRADE. Incised, beaded rim on each side. Plain edge. (Coll. John Cheramy, Victoria, B.C., Canada)

The style of stock token is typical of the mid-1880's.

CAMERON HOUSE

Rulau	Date	Metal	Size	VG	F	VF	Unc
MV 42E	(?)	CN	19mm	—	—	15.00	—

CAMERON HOUSE / 5 ctsp on U.S. 1859 Indian cent. (Van Ormer sale 2566; Brunk 6630)

Possibly Cameron , Wis., 1891-92.

P.L. CARPENTER

Rulau	Date	Metal	Size	VG	F	VF	EF
MV 42F	(?)	CN	19mm	—	12.00	—	20.00

P.L. CARPENTER ctsp on U.S. 1857 or 1858 Flying Eagle cent.

Rulau	Date	Metal	Size	VG	F	VF	EF
MV 42G	(?)	Silver	32.5mm	—	30.00	—	—

P. L. CARPENTER ctsp on U.S. 1812 Bust half dollar.

E.E. CHILDS JR.

Rulau	Date	Metal	Size	VG	F	VF	EF
MV 43	(?)	Silver	32.5mm	—	—	100.	—

E.E. CHILDS JR. / 16 CHAPMAN PLACE ctsp on U.S. 1825 Bust half dollar. (Gould 30; Brunk 7640)

L. CHILDS

Rulau	Date	Metal	Size	VG	F	VF	EF
MV 44	(?)	Copper	29mm	—	—	15.00	—

L. CHILDS ctsp on U.S. 1854 Large cent. (Brunk 7660)

H. W. CLARK

Rulau	Date	Metal	Size	VG	F	VF	EF
MV C44	(?)	Silver	27mm	—	—	30.00	—

H. W. CLARK in relief, within toothed rectangular depression, ctsp on Spanish-American 1786-Mo-FM 2-reales. (Pete Peters coll.)

N.T. CLARK

Rulau	Date	Metal	Size	VG	F	VF	EF
MV 45	(?)	Copper	29mm	—	30.00	—	—

N.T. CLARK in relief in dentilated, recessed cartouche ctsp on U.S. 1847 Large cent. (Steinberg Feb. 1982 sale; Brunk 8090)

COLD FRI.

Rulau	Date	Metal	Size	VG	F	VF	EF
MV 47	1861	Copper	29mm	25.00	—	—	—

COLD FRI. / FEB. 8, 1861 ctsp on U.S. Large cent. (Koppenhaver Aug. 1982 sale; Brunk 8740)

Feb. 8, 1861 was indeed a Friday. Systematic climatic records date only to 1870's. It would be interesting to learn where record low temperatures were set that day.

COLE

Rulau	Date	Metal	Size	VG	F	VF	EF
MV 50	(?)	CN	19mm	—	—	20.00	—
	COLE ctsp on U.S. 1857 Flying Eagle cent. (Brunk 8750)						
MV 51	(?)	Bronze	23mm	—	—	20.00	—
	Similar ctsp on U.S. 2-cent piece.						

J. CONRAD

Rulau	Date	Metal	Size	VG	F	VF	Unc
MV 54	(1870's)	Lead	16mm	—	25.00	—	—

Society emblem at center, WOODMEN SALOON -- J. CONRAD. Rv: Wreath encloses. HALF / DIME. Around: GOOD FOR. Plain edge. (Wright 1377)

CONSOLIDATED RACKET STORES

Rulau	Date	Metal	Size	F	VF	EF	Unc
MV 58	(?)	Brass	20mm	7.00	8.50	10.00	12.50

Nude female bust left. CASH on her coronet. CONSOLIDATED RACKET STORES / BEST VALUES. Rv: ONE / CENT in wreath; GOOD FOR above, IN MERCHANDISE below. (Wright 187)

"Racket Store" = "Dime Store"

G. WM. H. COMER

Rulau	Date	Metal	Size	VG	F	VF	EF
MV 51	(1883)	Silver	40mm	—	—	50.00	—
	G. W. H. COMER in prepared incused punch ctsp on Mexico 1840-Go-PJ 8-reales. (Krueger 890; Brunk 9053)						
MV 51A	(1883)	Silver	39mm	—	—	50.00	—
	Similar ctsp on England 1845 crown. (Krueger 891). XXXXII also ctsp on same side (42).						
MV 51B	(1883)	Silver	37mm	—	—	50.00	—
	Similar ctsp on Turkey 1855 (AH 1271) silver 20-piastres medal. Attribution doubtful, not listed in KM, but toughra of Abdul Medjid. Also ctsp on rim of coin; 9401 D. L. Connors. 1st Battn. 17th Reg. (Krueger 892)						

It is almost certain that the above are personal-type counterstamps, especially since the following engraved love tokens came from the same family source, but the ctsps above are from a prepared punch and could have had a mercantile significance.

The engraved coins are:

Elizabeth C. L. Comer. Born March 27th. on U.S. 1880 Morgan dollar.

G.Wm. H. Comer. Born May 27th. on U.S. Trade dollar.

Herbert D. M. Comer. Born June 26th. on U.S. 1883 Morgan dollar.

Jessie E. M. A. Comer. Born August 18th. on U.S. 1878 Morgan dollar.

Listed by Brunk are the following counterstamps which may also have a connection:

COMER on U.S. 1852 $2 1/2 gold piece.

CHARLES COMER 1 YEAR OLD SEPT 21st on U.S. $1 gold piece,

It is possible there is an English connection.

CONCORDIA SEYMOUR

Rulau	Date	Metal	Size	VG	F	VF	Unc
MV 53	(?)	CN	19mm	—	—	20.00	—

CORCORDIA / SEYMOUR. Rv: Ornate CS monogram. Heavy beaded rim on each side. Reeded edge. (Pete Peters coll.)

Possibly New Orleans, La.

CONTINENTAL

Rulau	Date	Metal	Size	VG	F	VF	EF
MV 60	(?)	CN	19mm	15.00	—	50.00	—

10 (large) / CONTINENTAL (small) ctsp on U.S. 1863 Indian Head cent. (Kruase coll.; Brunk 9310)

On the old envelope in which this item was located, the words 'Continental Hotel' have been inscribed.

R. M. COOPER

Rulau	Date	Metal	Size	VG	F	VF	EF
MV 61	(1870's)	Brass	24mm	—	—	20.00	—

Obverse similar to obverse on Md-Ba 84, the Numsen shield motif. Rv: R. M. COOPER. / 5 within beaded circle / * CENTS *. Dentilated rim on each side. Plain edge. (Jim Hirtle coll., Westminster, Md.)

Probably struck by Dorman in Baltimore, Md.

C.H. COPELAND

Rulau	Date	Metal	Size	VG	F	VF	EF
MV 63	1887	Bronze	19mm	—	—	12.50	—

C. H. COPELAND / 1887 ctsp on U.S. 1882 Indian cent. (Van Ormer sale 2594; Brunk 9505)

CORNISH

Rulau	Date	Metal	Size	VG	F	VF	EF
MV 63C	(1876)	Silver	18mm	—	10.00	—	—

CORNISH ctsp on U.S. 1875-CC Seated Liberty dime. (B&M Patterson 1985 sale, lot 1662; Brunk 9655)

"Cornish" may refer to Cornish, N.H. or another American town, or it may refer to a product (both stoves and parlor reed organs were made bearing this trade name), or it may simply be an individual's name.

J.D. CRANE

Rulau	Date	Metal	Size	VG	F	VF	EF
MV 63D	(1870's)	CN	22mm	—	—	125.	—
	J. D. CRANE / ARTIST ctsp on U.S. 1868 Shield nickel. (Kirtley June 1988 sale, lot 115)						
MV 63E	(1870's)	Silver	18.5mm	—	—	125.	—
	Similar ctsp on U.S. Bust dime. (Brunk 9965; PCAC July 1993 sale, lot 895)						

The term 'artist' here means photographic *artiste.*

J. H. CRITTENDEN

Rulau	Date	Metal	Size	VG	F	VF	EF
MV 63F	(?)	Copper	26mm	—	50.00	—	—

J. H. CRITTENDEN, / ARTIST ctsp on England 1863 halfpenny. (Van Ormer sale 2603; Brunk 10030)

Almost certainly American based on the euphemism "artist" to indicate a photographic *artiste*, a catchphrase of the 1850's and 1860's.

C. D. CO.

Rulau	Date	Metal	Size	VG	F	VF	Unc
MV 63L	ND	Brass	Oct	—	—	8.50	—

(Scrollwork) / C. D. CO. (on panel) / (scrollwork). Rv: 1/2 C. Plain edge. (Rulau coll.)

A well-made token. The half cent denomination is very unusual on a trade token of the post-Civil War period. The only 1/2-cent tokens normally encountered are bank-type deposit pieces in aluminum from the 1900-15 era.

This piece seems to be from the 1870-95 period.

D. H. DAY

Rulau	Date	Metal	Size	VG	F	VF	EF
MV 64	(?)	CN	19mm	—	—	20.00	—

D. H. DAY ctsp on U.S. 1857 Flying Eagle cent. (Brunk 11090)

Rulau	Date	Metal	Size	VG	F	VF	EF
MV 65	(?)	CN	19mm	—	—	20.00	—

Similar ctsp on U.S. 1864 Indian cent.

Rulau	Date	Metal	Size	VG	F	VF	EF
MV 65A	(?)	CN	22mm	—	—	30.00	—

Similar ctsp on U.S. 1868 Shield nickel.

S. J. DEAN

Rulau	Date	Metal	Size	VG	F	VF	EF
MV 66	(?)	CN	19mm	—	—	30.00	—

S. J. DEAN ctsp on U.S. 1858 Flying Eagle cent. (Rulau coll.; Brunk 12000)

Rulau	Date	Metal	Size	VG	F	VF	EF
MV 66A	(?)	CN	22mm	—	—	30.00	—

Similar ctsp on U.S. 1884 Liberty nickel.

DENGREMONT

Rulau	Date	Metal	Size	VG	F	VF	Unc
MV 68	1887	Brass	31mm	—	—	8.50	20.00

Youth standing, facing; bow and violin in his hands. Below: DENGREMONT. Rv: Youth standing, banner over his shoulder. On banner: FASHIONS / FOR / SPRING / 1887. Plain edge. Issued holed. (Wright 240)

Rulau	Date	Metal	Size	VG	F	VF	Unc
MV 68A	1886	Brass	31mm	—	—	8.50	20.00

Obverse as 68. Rv: FASHIONS / - FOR - / FALL & WINTER / - * - / 1886 & 7. Plain edge. (Rulau coll.)

Rulau	Date	Metal	Size	VG	F	VF	Unc
MV 68B	1886	Brass	31mm	—	—	10.00	25.00

Youth standing facing, one hand in jacket pocket. Below: DENGREMONT. Rv: (All script) FASHIONS / FOR / SPRING AND / SUMMER / 1886. Plain edge. (Rulau coll.)

L. DEXTER, FIRST NATIONAL

Rulau	Date	Metal	Size	VG	F	VF	EF
MV 69	(?)	Silver	38mm	—	66.00	—	—

L. DEXTER FIRST NATIONAL in semicircle ctsp on U.S. 1870 Seated Liberty silver dollar. (B&M Patterson sale, lot 1678; Brunk 11585)

Probably First National bank is indicated.

DIBURR CAST STEEL

Rulau	Date	Metal	Size	VG	F	VF	EF
MV 70	(?)	Copper	29mm	—	—	25.00	—

DIBURR / CAST STEEL in relief within toothed rect. depression ctsp on U.S. 182, Large cent. (Donald Partrick collection)

The name could be D.I. Burr.

H. DION

Rulau	Date	Metal	Size	VG	F	VF	EF
MV 72	(?)	Silver	25mm	—	15.00	—	—

D. W. V / H. DION / H. DION ctsp on U.S. 1854 worn S.L. quarter. (Brunk 11727)

EVERETT H. DUNBAR

Rulau	Date	Metal	Size	VG	F	VF	Unc
MV 73	(?)	Brass	24mm	—	—	35.00	—

(All incused): EVERETT H. DUNBAR's / (Foot) / FOOT SUPPORT. Rv: Blank. Plain edge. (Kirtley Nov. 1990 sale, lot A690)

The only reported specimen was excavated.

(Eagle) SCRIPT UTE (?)

Rulau	Date	Metal	Size	VG	F	VF	EF
MV 75	(?)	Copper	18.7mm	—	—	25.00	—

Eagle displayed, head turned right, above script initials which may read: U T E (?). Rv: (Incused): 6 / . . Plain edge. (Joseph Zaffern coll.)

J. ELLIS

Rulau	Date	Metal	Size	VG	F	VF	EF
MV 77	(?)	Copper	29mm	12.50	—	20.00	—

J. ELLIS ctsp on U.S. Large cent. Examined: 1838, 1856. (Brunk 13230)

Rulau	Date	Metal	Size	VG	F	VF	EF
MV 77A	(?)	CN	19mm	—	—	25.00	—

J. ELLIS. ctsp on U.S. 1859 Indian cent. (Pete Peters coll.)

Rulau	Date	Metal	Size	VG	F	VF	EF
MV 77B	(?)	Silver	27mm	—	—	40.00	—

J. ELLIS ctsp on U.S. 1824 Bust quarter.

Rulau	Date	Metal	Size	VG	F	VF	EF
MV 77C	(?)	Silver	27mm	20.00	—	30.00	—

Similar ctsp on U.S. 1857 Seated Liberty quarter. 4 pieces reported.

ESTILL

Rulau	Date	Metal	Size	VG	F	VF	EF
MV 78	(?)	Silver	31mm	—	—	15.00	—

ESTILL ctsp on U.S. 1853 Arrows & Rays S.L. half dollar. (Ray Colbert coll.; Brunk 13525)

One D. R. Estill was a gunsmith in Poplar Plains, Ky. 1856-1860.

G. EVANS

Rulau	Date	Metal	Size	VG	F	VF	EF
MV 83	(?)	Bronze	23mm	15.00	—	25.00	—

G. EVANS ctsp on U.S. 2-cent piece. Examined: 1864, 1865, Unknown dates. 7 pieces known. (Brunk 13550)

FAYETTEVILLE KNIFE CO.

Fayetteville, State Not Known

Rulau	Date	Metal	Size	VG	F	VF	EF
MV 84	(?)	CN	22mm	—	35.00	—	50.00

FAYETTEVILLE / KNIFE CO. ctsp on U.S. Shield nickel of the 1867-1883 period. (Thomas Capser coll.; Brunk 13910)

In the late 1870's there were Fayettevilles in all these states: Arkansas, Georgia, Illinois, Indiana, Missouri, New York, North Carolina, Ohio, Pennsylvania, Tennessee, Texas, Vermont, West Virginia and Wisconsin. The largest of these were county seats in Arkansas, North Carolina, Tennessee, Vermont and West Virginia.

The counterstamp is from a die, probably by its shape and lettering a die used on cutlery productions of the issuing company.

M. H. FELT

Rulau	Date	Metal	Size	VG	F	VF	EF
MV 85	1874	Copper	29mm	—	10.00	—	—

M. H. FELT ctsp on U.S. 1854 Large cent. Rv: 1874 ctsp on other side of the coin. (Rulau coll.)

SALVATORE FILPI

Rulau	Date	Metal	Size	VG	F	VF	Unc
MV 87	(1913-14)	Brass	25mm	—	—	8.50	—

(All incused): SALVATORE FILPI / GOOD FOR / 5C monogram / . IN TRADE . / (ornament). Rv: Blank. Incised beaded border on each side. Plain edge. (Thoele coll.)

Grocery, Racine, Wis.

S. D. FINCH (and) W. A. PARMELEE

Rulau	Date	Metal	Size	VG	F	VF	EF
MV 88	(?)	Copper	29mm	—	—	25.00	—

S. D. FINCH / W. A. PARMELEE / W. A. PARMELEE / S. D. FINCH ctsp on U.S. 1803 Large cent. (Kirtley March 1989 sale, lot 940; Brunk 14165)

C. FORSBERG

Rulau	Date	Metal	Size	VG	F	VF	EF
MV 90	(?)	Silver	25mm	20.00	—	30.00	—

C. FORSBERG ctsp on U.S. Seated Liberty quarter. Examined: 1853, 1854. 3 pieces known. (Brunk 14740)

F.F. FOSDICK

Rulau	Date	Metal	Size	G	VG	F	EF
MV 98	(1877)	Silver	18mm	—	—	15.00	—

F. F. FOSDICK / 77 ctsp on U.S. 1875 dime. (Steinberg coll.; Brunk 14780)

Rulau	Date	Metal	Size	G	VG	F	EF
MV 99	(?)	Silver	25mm	—	—	15.00	—

F. FOSDICK ctsp on U.S. Liberty Seated quarter. (Brunk 14775)

FOTZ & SPITZ

Rulau	Date	Metal	Size	VG	F	VF	EF
MV 100	(?)	CN	19mm	—	—	30.00	—

FOTZ & SPITZ (curved) / 5-poined outline star) ctsp on U.S. 1859 Indian cent. (Brunk 14860; Rulau coll.; ex-Gamer)

FOUR SHOOTS FOR 5C

Rulau	Date	Metal	Size	VG	F	VF	EF
MV 101	(1880's)	CN	22mm	—	—	45.00	—

FOUR. SHOOTS (curved) / 5-pointed outline star) / FOR. 5C. (curved) ctsp on shaved obverse of U.S. Shield nickel of 1867-83 type. (Rulau coll.; ex-Gamer; Brunk 14867)

Possibly an early arcade piece.

C. H. FOWLER

Rulau	Date	Metal	Size	VG	F	VF	Unc
MV 102	(1880's)	Brass	24mm	—	—	25.00	—

C. H. FOWLER / 5 (open) / POOL on pool table. Rv: Brunswick die BB-2. (Thoele coll.)

ARNOLD FREEMAN

Rulau	Date	Metal	Size	VG	F	VF	EF
MV 102E	(?)	Copper	29mm	—	—	25.00	—

ARNOLD / FREEMAN in relief within two parallel serrated rectangular depressions across the coin's face, ctsp on U.S. Large cent of 1816-35 type. (Kirtley March 1989 sale, lot 941; Brunk 15067)

J. P. FULLER

Rulau	Date	Metal	Size	VG	F	VF	EF
MV 103	(?)	Bronze	19mm	—	—	25.00	—

J. P. FULLER ctsp on U.S. 1866 Indian head cent. (Brunk 15280)

B. H. G.

Rulau	Date	Metal	Size	VG	F	VF	EF
MV 105C	ND	Brass	30.5mm	—	—	5.00	—

B. H. G. in arc ctsp on brass planchet. B H G straight ctsp on opposite side. Plain edge. (Rulau coll.)

E. G. & SONS

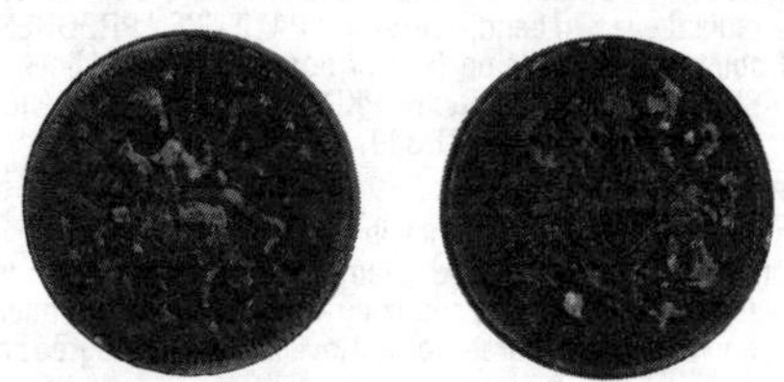

Rulau	Date	Metal	Size	VG	F	VF	EF
MV 103F	1861	Silver	25mm	—	—	25.00	—

E G & SONS / 1861 ctsp in a circle on U.S. 1858 Seated Liberty quarter dollar. (Harvey Gamer coll.)

G. V. J. D.

Rulau	Date	Metal	Size	VG	F	VF	EF
MV 104	1875	Brass	33.9mm	—	—	75.00	—

G. V. J. D. / 1875 ctsp on obverse of U.S. game counter of $20 size, IN UNITATE FORTITUDO type. Rv: 1875 ctsp on reverse of token. Reeded edge. (Rulau coll.)

ANDY GAIER

Rulau	Date	Metal	Size	VG	F	VF	Unc
MV 105	1874-84	GS	25mm	—	—	15.00	—

GOOD FOR / 5¢ / ANDY GAIER / —IN— / TRADE. Rv: Pool table within beaded circle. Around circle: THE J. M. BRUNSWICK & BALKE COS. / * CHECK *. Plain edge.

Not listed in *The Brunswick Token Story.*

GIRARD HOUSE

Rulau	Date	Metal	Size	VG	F	VF	EF
MV 107	ND	Brass	24mm	—	—	15.00	—

GIRARD / HOUSE / - 209 ctsp on 19th century-style brass disc. Key tag?

C. S. GOODWIN

Rulau	Date	Metal	Size	VG	F	VF	Unc
MV 112	(1870-90)	Brass	29mm	—	—	15.00	—

(All incused): C. S. GOODWIN / H. RICE / MAKER / DAYTON O. Rv: GOOD FOR / 1 / MEAL. Incised, beaded rim on each side. Plain edge. 8-10 pieces known. (Thoele coll.)

Ohio tokenmaker and stencil cutter Henry Rice was located in Lebanon 1856-59, Dayton 1859-1919, and Springfield 1922-24. Goodwin has not been traced.

AICHELE GOTTLIEB

Rulau	Date	Metal	Size	VG	F	VF	EF
MV 114	(1880's)	Brass	24mm	—	—	15.00	—

Star in rays at center. AICHELE GOTTLIEB around, ornament at bottom. Rv: Large numeral 5 at center, circle of 13 stars around. Plain edge. (Wright 15)

Probably struck by Wright of Cincinnati.

P. GREEN

Rulau	Date	Metal	Size	VG	F	VF	EF
MV 115	ND	Copper	27mm	—	—	30.00	—

P. GREEN ctsp on Norway 1878 5-ore, KM 349, Yeoman 21. (Jerry Crain coll.; Brunk 17095)

A. H. & CO.

Rulau	Date	Metal	Size	VG	F	VF	EF
MV 117	(?)	Silver	38.1mm	60.00	—	90.00	—

A. H. & CO in relief within rectangular depression ctsp on U.S. Morgan silver dollar. Examined: 1880, 1880-S, 1885. 3 pieces known. (Brunk 50; PCAC July 1993 sale, lot 843, which fetched $60.50)

G. H.

Rulau	Date	Metal	Size	VG	F	VF	EF
MV 118	ND	Silver	32mm	—	—	35.00	—

G. H. ctsp on Spanish-American 1779-Mo 4-reales. (Stanley Steinberg report)

Steinberg guesses Gurdon Huntington of Walpole, N.H.

O. H.

Rulau	Date	Metal	Size	VG	F	VF	EF
MV 119	(?)	Cooper	**	10.00	—	—	—

** Oval 26 x 19mm.

Fouled anchor. Heavy, beaded rim. Rv: O. H. at center, plain rim. Plain edge. (Wright 1559)

Made of two pieces of metal, the O. H. side, which is very thin, is sweated onto the anchor side.

EAGLE, HALF CENT

Rulau	Date	Metal	Size	VG	F	VF	EF
MV 120	1866	Copper	26mm	—	—	50.00	—

Eagle in relief within depression, and (also in relief) I OWE YOU ONE HALF A CENT 1866 ctsp on U.S. Large cent, date worn off. (Levine June 1985 sale, lot 1365)

J. A. HAMMERLY

Rulau	Date	Metal	Size	VG	F	VF	EF
MV A120	(?)	Silver	25mm	—	—	50.00	—
	J. A. HAMMERLY / WARRAN'TED ctsp on U.S. 1876 Seated Liberty quarter. (Joe Schmidt report)						
MV B120	(?)	Silver	27mm	—	—	60.00	—
	Similar ctsp on U.S. 1825 Bust quarter. (Brunk 17980)						
MV C120	(?)	Copper	29mm	—	—	50.00	—
	Similar ctsp on U.S. 1853 Large cent.						

E. HANKS

Rulau	Date	Metal	Size	G	VG	F	EF
MV 121	(?)	CN	19mm	—	—	15.00	—

E. HANKS ctsp on reverse of U.S. 1859 Indian Head cent. Obverse ctsp with 8-section device. (Stanley L. Steinberg coll.; Brunk 18060)

HARMAN

Rulau	Date	Metal	Size	VG	F	VF	EF
MV 121	(1880-82)	Brass	**	—	—	14.00	—

** Scal 26mm.

(All incused): Crossed cuesticks and 4 balls, superimposed on numeral 5. Rv: AMERICAN / STANDARD BILLIARD / AND / POOL TABLES / W. H. GRIFFITH & CO. N.Y. 10-15 pieces known.

LOTHAR HARMES

Rulau	Date	Metal	Size	VG	F	VF	Unc
MV 122	(?)	GS	**	—	—	15.00	—

** Oct 27mm.
In a panel across the center: LOTHAR / HARMES. Roses above, ornament below. Rv: Blank. Plain edge. (Wright 425)

IRA C. HASKINS

Rulau	Date	Metal	Size	VG	F	VF	EF
MV 124	(?)	CN	19mm	—	—	35.00	—

IRA C. HASKINS (curved) / TIPTOP / PEN / EN ctsp on U.S. 1862 Indian cent. (Kovacs coll.)

Rulau	Date	Metal	Size	VG	F	VF	EF
MV 124A	(?)	Copper	29mm	—	—	35.00	—

Similar ctsp (minus final EN) on U.S. Large cent. (Brunk 18640)

E. C. HATCH

Rulau	Date	Metal	Size	VG	F	VF	EF
MV 127	(?)	CN	19mm	—	—	20.00	—

E. C. HATCH ctsp on U.S. 1858, 1859, 1863 or 1866 Small cent. (Brunk 18700)

Rulau	Date	Metal	Size	VG	F	VF	EF
MV 128	(?)	Copper	29mm	—	—	20.00	—

Similar ctsp on U.S. 1837 Large cent.

Rulau	Date	Metal	Size	VG	F	VF	EF
MV 128A	(?)	Bronze	23mm	—	—	20.00	—

Similar ctsp on U.S. 1863, 1864, 1865 or 1868 2-cent piece.

HAYS

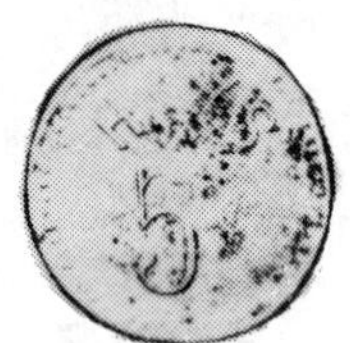

Rulau	Date	Metal	Size	VG	F	VF	Unc
MV 124	(1880's?)	CN	21mm	—	—	20.00	—

Standing elephant left, within beaded circle. Rv: HAYS / 5¢ within beaded circle. Plain edge. (Frank Kovacs coll.)

Apparently struck over a U.S. Shield nickel. Weight 4.86 grams.

H. HEINZ

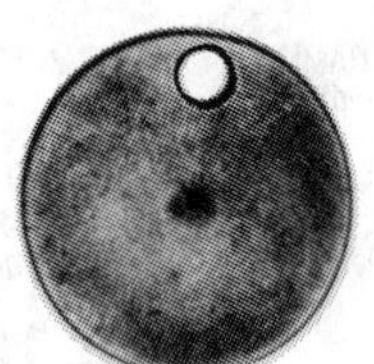

Rulau	Date	Metal	Size	VG	F	VF	EF
MV A128	(?)	Brass	23mm	—	10.00	—	—

* * / H. HEINZ / (incused) 76 / WATCHMAKER. Rv: Blank. Plain edge. (Hank Thoele coll; TAMS Maverick 9273)

A watchmaker's check.

HICKOK

Rulau	Date	Metal	Size	F	VF	EF	Unc
MV E128	(?)	Silv/B	38.3mm	50.00	70.00	85.00	—

Caped nude female facing, head turned left, right arm petting a grazing long-horned antelope. Around: A TOI UNE VIE FLORISSANTE. In exergue: Three 5-pointed stars above incused HICKOK PLATE. Rv: Hickok shield of arms within wreath. Around: *** A TOI TOUT BIEN ***. Below: MADE IN / U. S. A. Edge: Hollow - to accommodate blades. Issued with loop riveted at top. (Rulau coll.)

Folding out from within the hollow edge on either side are semicircular blades - a knife on the left and a file on the right.

J. HOFLING

Rulau	Date	Metal	Size	VG	F	VF	EF
MV 129	(?)	Brass	24.2mm	—	5.00	—	—

(All incused): J. HOFLING / PO -- OL separated by crossed pool cues and 15 balls. Rv: Blank. Incised, dentilated rim on each side. Plain edge.

HOPKINS TRANS-OCEANIC CO.

Rulau	Date	Metal	Size	VG	F	VF	Unc
MV 131	(?)	Brass	22mm	—	—	15.00	—

Shield at center, divided by a wide bend into three diagonal segments. At upper left, a radiant eye. On bend: TRAVAIL / PATIENCE / PROGRES. At lower right, a hand pointing forefinger on field of horizontal lines. Above: TREWEY. Below: THE ABSOLUTE MASTER. Rv: HOPKINS / TRANS- / OCEANIC COMPANY. Plain edge. (Wright 460; Kuethe MT 329)

The Bruce Smith specimen is shown.

This token was twice listed as a maverick in the *Journal of the Token and Medal Society* (numbers 1552 and 6828), without evoking any information as to its issuer or location. Though seemingly issued by a shipping company, it is not listed in Kenneth Smith's catalog of world transportation tokens. The three words Travail Patience Progres are French for Work Patience Progress.

The word 'Trewey' provided the best clue to the piece's provenance. It was apparently not a location, as there seems to be no city in Europe or North America with that name. It could have been an individual, entity (such as a shipping line) or something else entirely. This piece seemed to defy attribution for at least 75 years, since Dr. Wright apparently knew nothing of its background.

But author Kuethe finally attributed it as a magic token of magician M. Trewey.

WM. HOWARD

Rulau	Date	Metal	Size	VG	F	VF	Unc
MV 132	(?)	Silver	25mm	—	—	40.00	—

Wm. HOWARD ctsp on U.S. 1853 A&R Seated Liberty quarter. (Rulau coll.; Brunk 20307)

W. HUBBELL

Rulau	Date	Metal	Size	VG	F	VF	Unc
MV 134	(?)	Copper	29mm	—	—	30.00	—

W. HUBBELL ctsp on U.S. 1826 or 1835 Large cent. (Brunk 20510)

Rulau	Date	Metal	Size	VG	F	VF	Unc
MV 135	(?)	Silver	27mm	—	—	40.00	—

W. HUBBELL ctsp on Spanish-American 1780 2-reales.

Rulau	Date	Metal	Size	VG	F	VF	Unc
MV 136	(?)	Silver	32.5mm	—	—	40.00	—

Similar ctsp on U.S. 1831 half dollar.

HUNT & MOORE

Rulau	Date	Metal	Size	VG	F	VF	EF
MV 144	(?)	CN	19mm	25.00	—	35.00	—

HUNT & MOORE ctsp on U.S. 1860, 1861, 1862, 1863, 1864 or 1865 Indian Head cent. (Stanley Steinberg coll.; Brunk 20710)

Rulau	Date	Metal	Size	VG	F	VF	EF
MV 146	(?)	Bronze	23mm	—	—	40.00	—

Similar ctsp on U.S. 1864 or 1865 2-cent piece.

Rulau	Date	Metal	Size	VG	F	VF	EF
MV 140	(?)	Copper	29mm	25.00	—	35.00	—

Similar ctsp on U.S. Large cent. Examined: 1803, 1818, 1825, 1831, 1837, 1846, 1847, 1851. 14 pieces known. (Hallenbeck 8.755)

J. HURD

Rulau	Date	Metal	Size	VG	F	VF	EF
MV 148	(?)	Copper	29mm	—	7.50	—	—

J. HURD ctsp on U.S. 1832 Large cent. (Hallenbeck 8.758; Brunk 20800)

It has been suggested that Boston gunsmith Jacob Hurd, active 1816-1825, issued this counterstamp. Unlikely.

R. W. HUSTON

Rulau	Date	Metal	Size	VG	F	VF	EF
MV 149	(?)	Brass	**	—	—	11.00	—

** Oct 23mm.
R. W. HUSTON (incuse) / GOOD FOR (relief) / 1 (relief) / QUART MILK (relief) / * (incuse). Blank. Incised beaded rim on each side. Plain edge.

II. & A. P. R.

Rulau	Date	Metal	Size	VG	F	VF	EF
MV A49	ND	Copper	29mm		—	25.00	—

II. & A. P. R. ctsp on each side of U.S. 1853 Large cent. (Kurt Krueger April 1991 sale, lot 1475; Brunk 20965)

Professional punch.

I. S. J.

Rulau	Date	Metal	Size	VG	F	VF	Unc
MV 150	(?)	Copper	19mm	—	—	25.00	—

Eagle within unusual border design. Rv: I. S. J. within similar border design. Reeded edge. (Lot 129 in Charles Kirtley sale of April 7, 1984)

W. J.

Rulau	Date	Metal	Size	VG	F	VF	EF
MV 153	1876	Silver	25mm	—	—	35.00	—

W (1876) J / O ctsp on obverse of U.S. 1876-CC S.L. quarter. (S.L. Steinberg report)

C.O. JAMES

Rulau	Date	Metal	Size	VG	F	VF	EF
MV 160	1886	Bronze	19mm	—	—	5.00	—

1886 / C.O. JAMES ctsp on U.S. 1875 Indian Head cent. (Kurt Krueger coll.; Brunk 21480)

E. JARVIS

Rulau	Date	Metal	Size	VG	F	VF	EF
MV 161	(?)	Silver	25mm	—	50.00	—	—

E. JARVIS curved, ctsp on U.S. 1875 S.L. quarter.

T. JAN. P.

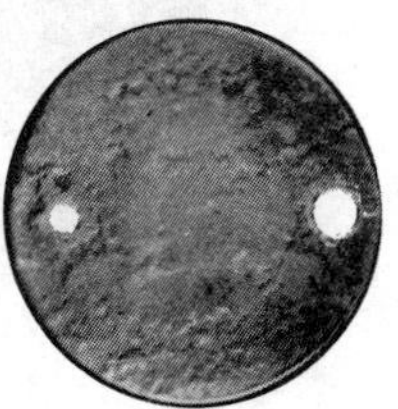

Rulau	Date	Metal	Size	VG	F	VF	EF
MV 162	1879	Copper	25mm	—	15.00	—	—

T JAN. P / 124 / 1879 ctsp on pierced, unidentifiable coin or token. (Frank Kovacs coll.)

ROBT. H. JENKS LUMBER CO.

Rulau	Date	Metal	Size	VG	F	VF	EF
MV 163	(?)	Brass	26mm	—	17.50	25.00	40.00

(Incused) Cat. Rv: COMPLIMENTS / OF / ROBT. H. JENKS / LUMBER / CO. Plain edge. (TAMS Maverick 10350)

F. JOHANNING

Rulau	Date	Metal	Size	VG	F	VF	EF
MV A163	(1880's?)	Brass	24mm	—	3.00	6.00	—

Beer mug at center, F. JOHANNING above, ornament in exergue. Rv: Numeral 5 within circle of 13 stars. Plain edge. (Wright 514)

L.H. JOHNSON

Rulau	Date	Metal	Size	VG	F	VF	EF
MV 164	1873	Copper	29mm	20.00	—	30.00	—

L.H. JOHNSON / PAT. APRIL, 1873 ctsp on U.S. Large cents. Examined: 2 pieces of unknown date. (Gould 10 bis; Hallenbeck 10.750; Brunk 21860)

JOHNSON & TWETO

Rulau	Date	Metal	Size	VG	F	VF	Unc
MV A164	(?)	Brass	28mm	—	3.50	9.00	—

JOHNSON & TWETO / GOOD FOR / A / DRINK / ABERCROMBIE. Rv: Blank. Plain edge. (Wright 518)

The Postal Guide for 1877 does not list a place called Abercrombie in the United States.

J.P. KANE (and) W. J. DAVIS

Rulau	Date	Metal	Size	VG	F	VF	EF
MV 165	(1886-87)	Brass	23mm	—	—	15.00	—

GOOD IN TRADE FOR / 5 / CENTS / J.P. KANE. Rv: W. J. DAVIS / DIAMOND MARKET (engraver). (All incused). Plain edge. (Jim Hartman coll.)

This was a saloon at 722 Tioga Street in 1886-87, according to city directories. What city?

A. KARL

Rulau	Date	Metal	Size	VG	F	VF	EF
MV A165	(?)	Copper	22mm	—	3.00	5.00	—

A KARL in Old English type. Rv: Blank. Plain edge. (Wright 531)

KATESGROVE IRON WORKS

Rulau	Date	Metal	Size	VG	F	VF	EF
MV 166	(?)	Copper	Rect ** 38 x 25mm	—	35.00	—	

** Clipped corners.

KATESGROVE / IRON WORKS / DINNER. Rv: Blank. Plain edge. (Wright 535)

Workman's meal check. Rare.

C.W. KAY

Rulau	Date	Metal	Size	VG	F	VF	EF
MV 167	(?)	Copper	29mm	—	—	50.00	—

C.W. KAY ARTIST ctsp on U.S. Large cent. (Hallenbeck 11.500; Brunk 22320)

The name of this token needs verification. It is possible this listing is due to a mis-description for C. W. King (which see). The two Hallenbeck listings in *The Numismatist* unfortunately gave no dates on the underlying coins and thus all the Hallenbeck listings will require eventual confirmation before listings based upon them can be accepted fully.

KENNEDY

Rulau	Date	Metal	Size	VG	F	VF	EF
MV 168	(?)	Silver	22mm	—	—	50.00	—

KENNEDY ctsp on U.S. 1875-S 20-cent piece. (Koppenhaver Nov. 1983 sale, lot 548)

Rulau	Date	Metal	Size	VG	F	VF	EF
MV 168A	(?)	Copper	29mm	—	—	50.00	—

Similar ctsp on U.S. 1839 Large cent.

R.F. KILLALY

Rulau	Date	Metal	Size	VG	F	VF	EF
MV 170	(?)	Silver	18mm	—	—	65.00	—

R. F. KILLALY (curved) / HARDWARE / CANNINGTON (curved) ctsp on U.S. 1842 Liberty Seated dime. (Van Ormer 2717; Brunk 22800)

A check of 1877-1882 Postal Guides shows no Cannington in the United States. It may be an earlier place, or else be located in Canada or Great Britain. No records in Cannington, Ontario. Possibly Cannington, Somersetshire, England.

C.W. KING

Rulau	Date	Metal	Size	VG	F	VF	EF
MV 173	(?)	Copper	29mm	—	—	125.	—

C.W. KING / ARTIST ctsp on U.S. 1819 Large cent. (Hallenbeck 11.503; Brunk 22915)

Rulau	Date	Metal	Size	VG	F	VF	EF
MV 174	(?)	Silver	25mm	—	90.00	—	—

C.W. King ctsp on rev.of U.S. 1856 S.L. quarter. Brunk 22910)

The term "artist" here refers to a daguerreotype artist, or early photographer. Maurice M. Gould once possessed several specimens of this counterstamp.

It is possible these tokens are earlier — from the 1850's.

A.C.L. REFRESHMENT CONTRACTOR

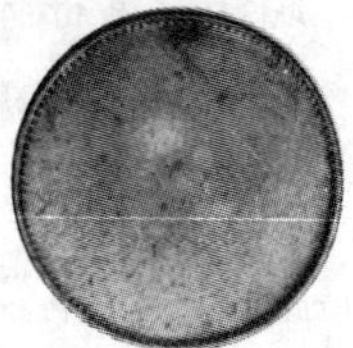

Rulau	Date	Metal	Size	VG	F	VF	Unc
MV 178	(1870's?)	Brass	23mm	12.00	15.00	25.00	—

REFRESHMENT / ACL script monogram / .CONTRACTOR. Rv: Blank. Reeded edge.

This maverick reposed in the Stuart Mosher collection for years and then was sold to the Fulds about 30 years ago. Now in Rulau coll.

This piece resembles the style of Pennsylvania store cards cut by F.X. Koehler of Baltimore, which see under Altoona, Johnstown and Tyrone, Pa.

LUCY LAW

Rulau	Date	Metal	Size	VG	F	VF	EF
MV 180	(?)	Silver	31mm	—	—	35.00	—

LUCY LAW ctsp on U.S. 1868 Liberty Seated half dollar. (Gould 247; Brunk 24020)

LEE & JONES

Rulau	Date	Metal	Size	VG	F	VF	EF
MV 183	(?)	Silver	15.5mm	—	—	15.00	—

LEE & JONES ctsp on U.S. 1838 Bust half dime. (Brunk 24120)

LOOBY & CO.

Rulau	Date	Metal	Size	VG	F	VF	EF
MV 187	(?)	Silver	31mm	—	—	35.00	—

CAST-STEEL / LOOBY & CO. ctsp on U.S. 1854-0 S.L. half dollar. (Van Ormer sale 2569; Brunk 24807)

LOVETT'S PRIVATE STOCK CIGARS

Rulau	Date	Metal	Size	VG	F	VF	EF
MV 189	(?)	Silver	38.1mm	—	—	350.	—

LOVETT'S / PRIVATE STOCK / CIGARS ctsp on U.S. 1882-O Morgan silver dollar. (Arthur Newmark coll.)

LOVETT'S PRIVATE STOCK WHISKEY

Rulau	Date	Metal	Size	VG	F	VF	EF
MV 190	(1887)	Silver	25mm	—	200.	—	300.

LOVETT'S / PRIVATE STOCK / WHISKEY ctsp on a U.S. 1857 Seated Liberty 25-cent coin. (Gould 88; Gould 40; Brunk 25120)

Rulau	Date	Metal	Size	VG	F	VF	EF
MV 192	(?)	Silver	38mm	—	200.	—	300.

Similar ctsp on U.S. Morgan silver dollar. Dates examined: 1881, 1882, 1883, 1885-0, 1887.

The counterstamp is late, 1887 at the earliest.

A. J. LUBURG

Rulau	Date	Metal	Size	VG	F	VF	EF
MV 194	1866	Copper	29mm	—	—	20.00	—

A. J. LUBURG (arc) / MAHONY / SEP 2 / 1866 ctsp on U.S. 1822 Large cent. (Partrick coll.)

F.M.

Rulau	Date	Metal	Size	VG	F	VF	Unc
MV198	(?)	Brass	23mm	—	—	5.00	—

(All incused): Tankard, wine bottle and wine glass in a line across center. Rv: GOOD FOR / A / DRINK / F M. Plain edge. (Coll. John Cheramy, Victoria, Canada)

MAIN & MOSES

Rulau	Date	Metal	Size	VG	F	VF	EF
MV 199	1882	Brass	--mm	—	—	10.00	—

GOOD AT FACE VALUE / 10 / CENTS / 1882 / MAIN & MOSES. Rv: Same as obverse.

MARTIN MANN STEEL

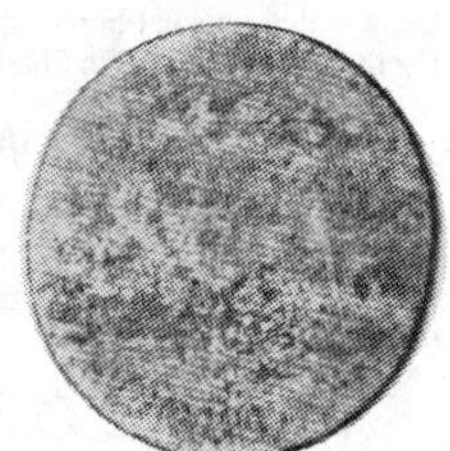

Rulau	Date	Metal	Size	VG	F	VF	Unc
MV 200	(?)	Cooper	29mm	—	15.00	—	—

MARTIN / MANN / STEEL ctsp on U.S. Large cent, date worn off. (Krueger Sept. 1983 sale, lot 1259)

MANSION HOUSE

Rulau	Date	Metal	Size	VG	F	VF	EF
MV B200	(?)	Silver	26mm	135.	—	—	—

MANSION (curved) / HOUSE ctsp on Brazil 1906 1,000-reis, Yeoman-16, KM-507. (Kirtley Dec. 1990 price list)

This stamp is apparently not connected with the Mansion House counterstamps of Alexandria, Virginia; that hotel changed its name to Braddock House in 1881.

E.A. MANSON

Rulau	Date	Metal	Size	VG	F	VF	EF
MV 201	1869	Silver	32.5mm	—	—	30.00	—

E A MANSON / 1869 / E A MANSON ctsp on U.S. 1809 bust half dollar. (Frank Kovacs coll.; Brunk 25945)

E. A. MANSON (et al)

Rulau	Date	Metal	Size	G	VG	F	EF
MV 203	1868	Copper	29mm	—	25.00	—	—

E.A. MANSON / F.O. RAY / C.H. COLLEY / W.P. WENTWORTH / B.B. TUTTLE / 1868 ctsp on obverse of U.S. 1843 Large cent. J.A. SMITH, JR. ctsp on reverse of the coin. (Partrick collection; Brunk 25940)

Apparently a piece used by a maker of merchant stamps to test his punches.

J.A. MATHEWS

Rulau	Date	Metal	Size	VG	F	VF	EF
MV 206	(?)	Copper	29mm	—	—	10.00	—

J.A. MATHEWS ctsp on U.S. 1848 Large cent. (Stanley Steinberg 1982 sale; Brunk 26450)

MAUCK & BRADBURY

Rulau	Date	Metal	Size	VG	F	VF	EF
MV A207	1873	Copper	19mm	—	—	22.50	—

Indian head left, 13 stars around, 1873 below. Rv: GOOD FOR / ONE / CENT / AT / MAUCK & BRADBURY. (Thoele coll.)

McCOLGAN & HUGHES

1876 Centennial Tokens

Reverse type 1: McCOLGAN & HUGHES / GOOD / FOR 5 CTS / ***. (All 19mm; plain edge.

Rulau	Obv	Rev	Metal	F	VF	Unc	
MV 207	Y	1	WM	—	—	250.	—

Possibly unique; in Steve Tanenbaum coll. This issuer has escaped publication until now, more than 100 years after the token's appearance.

A. C. McLAREN

Rulau	Date	Metal	Size	VG	F	VF	EF
MV 208	(?)	Silver	38mm	—	—	50.00	—

A. C. McLAREN in small letters ctsp on U.S. 1882-O Morgan silver dollar. (Kovacs coll.; Brunk 27090)

J.H. METZ'S HOTEL

Rulau	Date	Metal	Size	VG	F	VF	EF
MV 209	(?)	CN	19mm	—	—	150.	—
	J.H. METZ'S HOTEL / N.E. COR. JEFFN AV & FED. ST. ctsp on 1858 F.E. and 1859 Indian cents. (Brunk 27500)						
MV 209A	(?)	Silver	27mm	—	—	175.	—
	Similar ctsp on Spanish American 1800 2-reales.						

MORITZ MEYER CIGAR CO.

Rulau	Date	Metal	Size	VG	F	VF	Unc
MV 210	(?)	Brass	21mm	—	—	10.00	—

MORITZ MEYER / -*- / CIGAR CO. / 1322 / * / FARNAM ST. Rv: GOOD FOR / 6 1/4 / CTS / IN TRADE. Plain edge. (Eric P. Newman coll.)

Six and one-quarter cents equaled one Mexican (for Spanish) real, or bit. The bit denomination survived in America's south central and west central interior until near 1900, long after foreign coins were no longer recognized as legal tender (in 1857). The real lingered on in trade in the Mississippi, Ohio and Missouri River basins and adjacent areas, and along the Mexican frontier.

M. MILLER

Rulau	Date	Metal	Size	VG	F	VF	EF
MV 211	(?)	Copper	29mm	—	—	20.00	—

1822 / M. MILLER / 26 ctsp on U.S. 1851 Large cent. (Hallenbeck 13.528)

MILLER HOUSE

Rulau	Date	Metal	Size	VG	F	VF	EF
MV 214	(?)	Silver	32.5mm	—	—	225.00	—
	MILLER HOUSE ctsp on U.S. 1853 A&R or 1806 Bust half dollar. (Brunk 27670)						
MV 213	(?)	Silver	25mm	—	—	150.	—
	Similar ctsp on U.S. S.L. quarter. 11 specimens known. Examined: 1853, 1868, 1876, 1877. (Van Ormer 2754-2755)						

MINERS

Rulau	Date	Metal	Size	VG	F	VF	Unc
MV 217	(?)	Brass	24mm	—	—	30.00	—

MINERS incuse on blank flan. Recessed dentilated rim on each side. Plain edge.

MISSISSIPPI VIEW

Rulau	Date	Metal	Size	VG	F	VF	Unc
MV 218	(?)	Brass	24mm	—	—	10.00	—

MISSISSIPPI -.- / VIEW. Rv: GOOD FOR / -.- / 12 1/2 ¢. Plain edge. (Eric P. Newman coll.)

JNO. W. MORTON

Rulau	Date	Metal	Size	VG	F	VF	Unc
MV 219	1880	Brass	26mm	—	—	25.00	—

******* / JNO. W. MORTON / ** 1880 **. Rv: ** GOOD FOR ** / 1 DOLLAR / A / VINE HILL. Plain edge. (Taylor 1968 sale, lot 13.38)

MT. ST. LOUIS INSTITUTE

Rulau	Date	Metal	Size	VG	F	VF	Unc
MV A219	(?)	Brass	26mm	—	—	75.00	—

(All incused): Mt St LOUIS INSTITUTE / (ornament) / -o-. Rv: ONE / CENT within open-top wreath. Plain edge. (Tom Wass coll., Beverly Hills, Calif.)

By style, 19th century, but without more data it seems unlikely we'll be able to 'date' this piece closer without locating the institute which issued it.

Possibly Canada.

J. MURPHY

Rulau	Date	Metal	Size	VG	F	VF	Unc
MV 220	(?)	Silver	25mm	—	—	20.00	—

(Hand pointing left) / J. MURPHY ctsp on shaved reverse of U.S. 1853 S.L. quarter. An ornate circular border has also been stamped on the shaved rev. (Brunk 28960)

NABOCLISH

Rulau	Date	Metal	Size	VF	F	VF	EF
MV 222	(?)	CN	19mm	8.00	—	15.00	—

NABOCLISH (in upward curved arc) / 5-pointed star ctsp on U.S. 1857 Flying Eagle cent. (Krause coll.; Brunk 29230)

NATIONAL HORSE SHOW ASSOCIATION

Rulau	Date	Metal	Size	F	VF	EF	Unc
MV 225	1883	WM	31mm	—	—	—	35.00

Man with rearing horse at center. NATIONAL HORSE SHOW ASSOCIATION OF AMERICA 1883 around. Rv: Wreath at center, MEMBERS BADGE NOT TRANSFERABLE around. (Levine Dec. 1981 sale, lot 1630)

NATIONAL NOVELTY CO.

Rulau	Date	Metal	Size	VG	F	VF	Unc
MV 226	(?)	CN	25mm	—	—	10.00	—

Bit for horse's mouth at center, 2 above. BITS below. Rv: NATIONAL NOVELTY CO. / GOOD FOR / 25 / IN TRADE. The token is ctsp '3' on obverse.

The '3' is curious. Does it stand for '3 bits' or 37 1/2 cents?

NEEDHAM & CHAPLIN

Rulau	Date	Metal	Size	VG	F	VF	Unc
MV A 226	(?)	Brass	24mm	—	—	20.00	—

NEEDHAM & CHAPLIN / (crossed cuesticks and 15 balls separate PO—OL). Rv: Brunswick die BB-2.

NORTHFIELD XN. CO.

Rulau	Date	Metal	Size	VG	F	VF	Unc
MV 227	(?)	CN	19mm	—	—	40.00	—

NORTHFIELD (curved) / XN. CO ctsp on U.S. 1858 Flying Eagle cent. (Charles Ziegler coll.)

In the 1877 Postal Guide, there were 10 post offices in the U.S. with Northfield in their name.

'XN' may equal Extension, Excavation, Expedition, Explosion, Expansion, Extradition or another word. It is not a recognized abbreviation.

NOVVM BELGIVM

Rulau	Date	Metal	Size	VG	F	VF	EF
MV 228	(?)	Copper	29mm	—	—	35.00	—

NOVVM BELGIVM / (Bird on shield) / . 1623 . engraved retrograde on shaved obverse of U.S. Large cent. (Pete Peters coll.)

Rulau	Date	Metal	Size	VG	F	VF	EF
MV 229	(?)	Copper	29mm	—	—	35.00	—

NOVA BELGIVM / (U.S. shield) / 1698 engraved retrograde on shaved obverse of U.S. Large cent (Pete Peters coll.)

We can find no record of a place called New Belgium ever having existed in the United States.

OIL OF ICE

Rulau	Date	Metal	Size	VG	F	VF	EF
MV 230	(?)	Copper	29mm	—	60.00	—	90.00

OIL / OF / ICE / ctsp on U.S. Large cents of several dates. Examined: 1847, 1848, 1850. (Gould 5; Hallenbeck 15.502; Brunk 30150)

Rulau	Date	Metal	Size	VG	F	VF	EF
MV 232	(?)	CN	19mm	—	60.00	—	90.00

OIL / OF / ICE ctsp on U.S. 1857-58 Flying Eagle cents. (Gould 5)

Rulau	Date	Metal	Size	VG	F	VF	EF
MV 234	(?)	CN	19mm	—	60.00	—	90.00

Similar ctsp on U.S. 1859, 1862 or 1863 Indian Head cents. (Gould 5) 12 known.

Rulau	Date	Metal	Size	VG	F	VF	EF
MV 236	(?)	Bronze	19mm	—	60.00	—	90.00

Similar ctsp on U.S. 1864, 1865, 1867, 1869, 1871, 1874, 1880. Indian head cents. 18 known.

Rulau	Date	Metal	Size	VG	F	VF	EF
MV 237	(?)	Bronze	23mm	—	60.00	—	90.00

Similar ctsp on U.S. 1864, 1865 or 1870 2-cent piece.

Rulau	Date	Metal	Size	VG	F	VF	EF
MV 238	(?)	CN	22mm	—	60.00	—	90.00

Similar ctsp on U.S. 1866 Shield nickel.

Rulau	Date	Metal	Size	VG	F	VF	EF
MV 239	(?)	Copper	23mm	—	300.	—	—

Similar ctsp on 1723 Wood's Hibernia farthing.

Probably a patent medicine.

ONE DIME

Rulau	Date	Metal	Size	VG	F	VF	EF
MV 240	ND	Billon *	17.6mm	—	—	35.00	—

ONE / DIME in relief overstruck on reverse of Norway 1784 2-skilling, Craig 18. (Jerry Crain coll.; Brunk 30230)

This billon piece is struck in .250 fine silver.

ORDER OF THE IRON HALL

Rulau	Date	Metal	Size	VG	F	VF	Unc
MV 241	1881	WM	40mm	—	—	35.00	—

Safe at center, $1,000 on its top. Above: U.P.F. Below: (on scroll) IN SEVEN YEARS. All within central circle. Outside circle: * ORDER OF THE IRON HALL * / ORGANIZED MARCH 28 - 1881. Rv: Blank. Plain edge. (Wright 1565)

CONRAD ORTH

Rulau	Date	Metal	Size	VG	F	VF	Unc
MV 242	(1881)	Brass	24mm	—	—	15.00	—

BRUNSWICK & COMPANY / -*- / CHECK / -*- / . CHICAGO . Rv: GOOD FOR / 5 C / CONRAD ORTH. Plain edge. (Brunswick 61)

Ore Vacketta reports this could be a Chicago, Ill firm. Probably Detroit.

This token is not related to the large number of C. ORTH and C. G. ORTH counterstamps that are known.

J. OSTRANDER

Rulau	Date	Metal	Size	VG	F	VF	Unc
MV 243	(1880's)	Brass	24mm	—	—	25.00	—

J. OSTRANDER / (crossed cuesticks and four balls over open numeral 5.) Rv: Brunswick die BB-2. (All incused, both sides.)

W.B. PAGE (et al)

Rulau	Date	Metal	Size	VG	F	VF	EF
MV 244	(?)	Copper	29mm	—	—	25.00	—

W. F. PAGE / W. B. PAGE (large) / I. C. LANE ctsp on U.S. 1827 Large cent. (Frank Kovacs coll.; Brunk 30730)

If this is a partnership, W. B. Page appears to be senior since his name is larger. This could also be a counterstamper's "test piece" used for testing customer's punches.

PALACE 6

Rulau	Date	Metal	Size	VG	F	VF	EF
MV 245	(?)	CN	19mm	—	—	25.00	—

PALACE / M / 6 ctsp on U.S. 1857 Flying Eagle cent. Rv: 7 ctsp on reverse of the coin. (Brunk 30800; Pete Peters coll.)

M.D. PALMER

Rulau	Date	Metal	Size	VG	F	VF	EF
MV 246	(?)	Silver	38mm	—	—	25.00	—

M.D. PALMER in an arc ctsp on U.S. 1871 Liberty Seated silver dollar. (Steinberg 1982 sale; Brunk 30825)

It has been suggested this might be a Chicago watchmaker.

A. V. PANTLAND

Rulau	Date	Metal	Size	VG	F	VF	EF
MV 247	1866	Silver	38.3mm	—	—	55.00	—

FROM A. V. PANTLAND TO ED / MARCH / 17TH 1866 engraved in script on Mexico 1861-Go-PF 8-reales. (Rulau coll., ex-Schaeper)

PAT. APPL. FOR

Rulau	Date	Metal	Size	VG	F	VF	EF
MV 248	1877	Copper	29mm	—	—	7.50	—

PAT. APPL. FOR / 1877 ctsp on 1849 Large cent. (Ray Colbert coll., Tucker, Ga.; Brunk 31180)

PAT. 1868

Rulau	Date	Metal	Size	VG	F	VF	EF
MV 249	1868	Copper	29mm	—	—	7.50	—

PAT. 1868 ctsp on U.S. Large cent. (Hallenbeck 16.502; Brunk 31250)

PATENT

Rulau	Date	Metal	Size	VG	F	VF	EF
MV 250	(?)	Copper	29mm	—	—	10.00	—

PATENT ctsp five times on obverse of U.S. 1843 Large cent. Also ctsp three times on reverse of the coin. (Kovacs coll.)

PATENTED

Rulau	Date	Metal	Size	VG	F	VF	EF
MV 251	1860	Copper	29mm	—	—	5.00	—

PATENTED / JULY 3, 1860 / DEC. 7, 1858 ctsp on U.S. 1848 Large cent.

PEACOCK

Rulau	Date	Metal	Size	VG	F	VF	EF
MV 253	(?)	Silver	40mm	—	—	100.	—

PEACOCK ctsp on U.S. 1802 Bust type dollar. Rv: Similar ctsp on coin's reverse. (Duffield 1416;Brunk 31420)

S. C. PENCE

Rulau	Date	Metal	Size	VG	F	VF	EF
MV 254	1874	Silver	—	30.00	—	—	

S. C. PENCE / 1874 ctsp on obverse of U.S. 1854-Arrows S.L. quarter. A C ctsp on reverse of coin. (Rulau coll; Brunk 31590)

PRESS DRAWER

Rulau	Date	Metal	Size	F	VF	EF	Unc
MV 258B	(?)	Brass	24mm	—	—	7.50	—

(All incuse) PRESS / DRAWER stamped onto blank flan. Rv: Blank. but large B scratched in. Incised, dentilated rim on each side. Plain edge. Issued holed. (Rulau coll.)

JULIUS PREUSSE

Rulau	Date	Metal	Size	F	VF	EF	Unc
MV 258C	(1880-82)	Brass	23mm	—	—	35.00	—

(All incused): Crossed cuesticks and 15 balls separate PO—OL. Above: JULIUS PREUSSE. Rv: (All incused): AMERICAN / STANDARD BILLIARD / AND / POOL TABLES / W. H. GRIFFITH & CO. N.Y. Scarce!

MILES PLATTIN

Rulau	Date	Metal	Size	VG	F	VF	EF
Mv 255	ND	Brass	32.5mm	—	25.00	—	35.00

387 / MILES / PLATTIN ctsp on thick, 32.5mm brass planchet. Rv: 387 / (?) & Y. R. Co / T F C ctsp on opposite side. Plain edge. (Rulau coll.)

W. D. PRATT

Rulau	Date	Metal	Size	VG	F	VF	EF
MV 256	(?)	Bronze	23mm	—	—	15.00	—

W. D. PRATT ctsp on U.S. 1865 2-cent piece. (Pete Peters coll.)

PRESCOTT TRENCHARD LUMBER CO.

Rulau	Date	Metal	Size	VG	F	VF	Unc
MV 257	ND	Brass	24mm	—	—	40.00	65.00

PRESCOTT TRENCHARD / 10 / IN TRADE / LUMBER CO. Rv: 10 in radiant starburst. Plain edge.

Possibly struck by F. X. Koehler, Baltimore.

J. PRIEST

Rulau	Date	Metal	Size	VG	F	VF	Unc
MV 258E	1868	WM	18mm	—	—	50.00	75.00

Imitation of U.S. Liberty dime obverse dated 1868. Rv: GOOD FOR / ONE GLASS / OF / SODA WATER / J. PRIEST. Crudely reeded edge.

W.C. PUGH

Rulau	Date	Metal	Size	VG	F	VF	EF
MV 259	1870	Silver	31mm	—	35.00	—	—

IS / W. C. PUGH / (arrow, point left) 1870 (arrow, point right), ctsp on U.S. 1854 Seated Liberty half dollar. (Brunk 32950)

C. PUTNAM CAST STEEL

Rulau	Date	Metal	Size	VG	F	VF	EF
MV 260	(?)	Copper	29mm	—	20.00	—	—

C. PUTNAM / CAST STEEL ctsp on U.S. 1802 Large cent. (Brunk 33000)

P. QUIGLEY

Rulau	Date	Metal	Size	VG	F	VF	EF
MV 261	(?)	Silver	31mm	—	—	40.00	—

P. QUIGLEY ctsp on U.S. 1853-A&R Seated Liberty half dollar. (Fred Borgmann report; Brunk 33095)

A. R.

Rulau	Date	Metal	Size	VG	F	VF	EF
MV A262	(1883-99)	Brass	25mm	—	—	20.00	—

H. GUNKLACH & SONS / (triangular rack of pool balls) / 408 VINE ST. / CINCINNATI. O. Rv: GOOD FOR / 5 C / A. R. / -AT- / THE BAR. Plain edge. (Thoele coll.)

H. Gunklach & Sons were Cincinnati manufacturers of billiard tables and supplies circa 1883-1907. During the 19th century they also distributed billiard checks to their clients.

Discovering who 'A. R.' was will be difficult.

E. L. R.

Rulau	Date	Metal	Size	VG	F	VF	EF
MV 262	(?)	Brass	19mm	—	—	—	25.00

Steer standing left, tree in background, ground beneath. Rv: 1 PINT / E. L. R. Dentilated rim on each side. Plain edge.

Rulau	Date	Metal	Size	VG	F	VF	EF
MV 262B	(?)	Brass	19mm	—	—	—	25.00

Obverse as last. Rv: 1. QUART / E. L. R. Dentilated rim on each side. Plain edge.

Rulau	Date	Metal	Size	VG	F	VF	EF
MV 262C	(?)	Copper	19mm	—	—	—	25.00

As last. Plain edge.

M. E. R.

Rulau	Date	Metal	Size	VG	F	VF	Unc
MV 265	(?)	Brass	23.3mm	—	—	40.00	—

(All incused): GOOD FOR / 5 C / M. E. R. (on panel) / IN TRADE. Rv: SCHULENBURG / BILLIARD TABLES. Plain edge. (Zaffern coll.)

Schulenburg made billiard tables in Detroit 1851-1920.

P.R.

Rulau	Date	Metal	Size	VG	F	VF	EF
MV 266	(?)	Copper	29mm	—	8.50	—	—

P.R. ctsp on U.S. 1822 Large cent.

A.H. RAABE

Rulau	Date	Metal	Size	VG	F	VF	Unc
MV 269	(1880's)	GS	25mm	—	—	20.00	—

GOOD FOR / 5¢ / A.H. RAABE / - IN - / TRADE. Rv: Pool table within beaded circle. Around circle: THE J.M. BRUNSWICK & BALKE COS. / * CHECK *. Plain edge.

Not listed in *The Brunswick Token Story.*

RATHBUN HOUSE

Rulau	Date	Metal	Size	VG	F	VF	EF
MV 270	(ca 1878)	Silver	25mm	—	40.00	—	60.00

RATHBUN / HOUSE ctsp on U.S. 1876 or 1877 S.L. quarter.(Brunk 33540)

Rulau	Date	Metal	Size	VG	F	VF	EF
MV 271	(ca 1878)	Silver	31mm	—	40.00	—	60.00

Similar ctsp on U.S. Seated Liberty half dollar. Dates examined: 1876, 1877. (Brunk report)

W. REED

Rulau	Date	Metal	Size	VG	F	VF	EF
MV 272	(?)	Silver	25mm	—	—	30.00	—

W. REED ctsp on U.S. Liberty Seated quarter. (Clifford Mishler coll; Brunk 33740)

Rulau	Date	Metal	Size	VG	F	VF	EF
MV 272B	(?)	Copper	29mm	—	—	25.00	—

Similar ctsp on U.S. Large cent.

RHYNIE'S PLACE

Rulau	Date	Metal	Size	VG	F	VF	EF
MV 274	(?)	Brass	24mm	—	—	17.50	—

Eagle displayed, arrows and olive branch in its talons. E. PLURIBUS UNUM above. Rv: GOOD FOR / 5 C / RHYNIE'S.-/-. PLACE / (ornament) / IN TRADE. Plain edge. (TAMS Maverick 9282)

F. E. RICHARD

Rulau	Date	Metal	Size	VG	F	VF	EF
MV C274	(?)	Copper	23mm	—	—	90.00	—

F. E. RICHARD (Flower) in relief ctsp within circular depression on an unidentifiable foreign copper coin. A relief 5-pointed star is ctsp within the raised center. Reeded edge. (Brunk 34130)

RICH ORANGE

Rulau	Date	Metal	Size	VG	F	VF	EF
MV A274	(?)	Copper	29mm	—	25.00	—	—

RICH / + ORANGE + ctsp retrograde in relief within circular depression on a U.S. 1825 Large cent. (Thoele coll.)

The term "Rich Orange" is associated in some manner with metallic buttons. It recurs over and over in phrases such as "Rich Orange Colour" and "Standard Rich Colour" used in 19th century buttonmaking.

G.E. RIDLEY

Rulau	Date	Metal	Size	VG	F	VF	EF
MV 275	1871	Silver	38mm	—	—	—	75.00

MAY 1871 / G.E. RIDLEY ctsp on U.S. 1869 Silver dollar. Reeded edge. (Hetrich coll. sale, Jan. 30, 1982, Los Angeles; Brunk 34325)

Rulau	Date	Metal	Size	VG	F	VF	EF
MV 275A	1871	Silver	39mm	—	—	—	75.00

MAY 1871 / A. M. RIDLEY ctsp on Bolivia 8-bolivianos. (Brunk 34320)

C. H. ROHDE

Rulau	Date	Metal	Size	VG	F	VF	EF
MV 276	1879	Silver	25mm	—	35.00	—	—

1873 / C. H. ROHDE / 1879 ctsp on U.S. 1857 Seated Liberty quarter. (Brunk 34937)

S. B. I. V.

Rulau	Date	Metal	Size	VG	F	VF	EF
MV 282	(1890's))	Brass	25mm	—	—	35.00	—

Shield encloses a curious animal above the letters S. B. I. V. The creature appears to be a crude Lion of St. Mark of Venice. Rv: GOOD FOR / - / PICNIC / --. Plain edge. (Thoele coll.; TAMS Maverick 10764)

Hank Thoele thinks the creature may be a lion with a halo, and that the initials may stand for Societa Buono Italiano Veneto or a similar phrase. He says 4 pieces are known.

S. & H. CO.

Rulau	Date	Metal	Size	VG	F	VF	EF
MV 280	(?)	CN	19mm	20.00	—	30.00	—

S & H / CO within a heart, ctsp on U.S. 1858, 1859 or 1861 Small cent. Same ctsp on reverse. (Rulau coll.; Brunk 35450)

A. W. S.

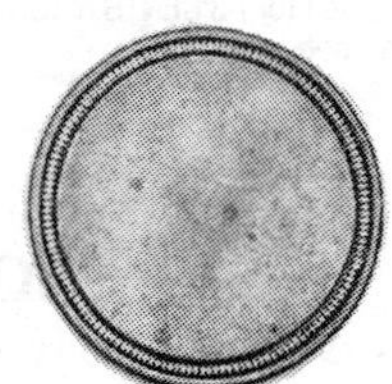

Rulau	Date	Metal	Size	VG	F	VF	Unc
MV 283	ND	Brass	23.3mm	—	—	10.00	—

(All incused): GOOD FOR / 5 C / A. W. S. (on panel) / IN TRADE. Rv: Blank. (Zaffern coll.)

J. S. & CO.

Rulau	Date	Metal	Size	VG	F	VF	EF
MV 282	(?)	Brass	26mm	—	15.00	20.00	—

George Washington head left. Rv: J. S. & Co. monogram surrounded by circle of 13 stars. Plain edge. (Wright 526)

L.C.S. & CO.

Rulau	Date	Metal	Size	VG	F	VF	Unc
MV 281	1871	Brass	24mm	—	10.00	25.00	—

Liberty head left, 13 stars around, 1871 below. Rv: L.C.S. & CO. / 5 / CENTS. (Wright 584)

A. E. SAGER

Rulau	Date	Metal	Size	VG	F	VF	EF
MV 293	(?)	Silver	31mm	—	—	40.00	—

A. E. SAGER. (curved) ctsp on U.S. 1875-S Seated Liberty half dollar. (Kirtley March 28, 1992 sale, lot 2126; Brunk 35577)

SANITARIUM C.S.S.

Rulau	Date	Metal	Size	VG	F	VF	EF
MV 294	(?)	Silver	31mm	—	—	35.00	—

SANITARIUM / C.S.S. ctsp on U.S. 1854-O S.L. half dollar. (Frank Kovacs coll.; Brunk 6450)

JOHN SCHELL

Storr's Township, State Unknown

Rulau	Date	Metal	Size	VG	F	VF	EF
MV A295	(1870-90)	xx	**	—	—	50.00	—

xx Yellow cardboard, black printing. ** Rect 40x22mm.
III / Good for / 3 CENTS. / JOHN SCHELL, Storr's Township. Rv: Blank. (Warren Baker coll.)

SEA SHORE HOUSE

Rulau	Date	Metal	Size	VG	F	VF	EF
MV 295	(1880's)	CN	22mm	—	—	75.00	—

SEA SHORE HOUSE ctsp on U.S. 1887 Liberty nickel. (Van Ormer sale 2834; Brunk 35985)

Rulau	Date	Metal	Size	VG	F	VF	EF
MV 296	(1880's)	Silver	25mm	—	—	75.00	—

Similar ctsp on U.S. 1844-O Seated Liberty quarter. (Van Ormer sale 2834, ex-Wayne Rich 1975)

SELLY & F.R. LEMAN

Rulau	Date	Metal	Size	VG	F	VF	EF
MV 300	(?)	Copper	29mm	—	40.00	—	65.00

SELLY & F R LEMAN in relief within rectangular depression ctsp on U.S. 1856 Large cent. (Rulau coll.; Brunk 36040)

There is some doubt about the second name. It could be a single name — FRLEMAN, or it could be F P LEMAN, or F. R. LEMAIN, or possibly something else. The stamp is struck unevenly.

It appears to be a silversmith's or jeweler's hallmark and is probably important. The Rulau speciman was acquired in Dec. 1982 from the Harvey Gamer holdings.

(Kenneth Hallenbeck reports a Large cent counterstamped E. LEMAN JR. This may be connected, so it is listed below.)

Rulau	Date	Metal	Size	VG	F	VF	EF
MV 301	(?)	Copper	29mm	—	10.00	—	—

E. LEMAN JR. cstp on U.S. Large cent. (Hallenbeck 12.503; Brunk 24240)

SENECA LT. CLUB

Rulau	Date	Metal	Size	VG	F	VF	EF
Mv 299	(?)	Copper	29mm	—	50.00	—	—

SENECA / LT CLUB ctsp on U.S. 1856 Large cent. (Frank Kovacs coll.; Brunk 36045)

A. SHARRARD

Rulau	Date	Metal	Size	VG	F	VF	EF
MV 302	(?)	Silver	32.5mm	—	—	50.00	—

A. SHARRARD ctsp on U.S. 1832 half dollar. (Duffield 1420; Brunk 36180)

W.A. SHEPHARD & CO.

Rulau	Date	Metal	Size	VG	F	VF	Unc
MV 303	1874	Brass	25mm	—	—	25.00	—

W.A. SHEPARD & CO. / (ornament) / ESTABLISHED / MAY 3RD / 1874. Rv: COMMERCIAL BUSINESS / EXCHANGE / FROM / OCEAN TO OCEAN / 65 OFFICES. Plain edge. (Wright 1623)

F. W. SHILLITO

Rulau	Date	Metal	Size	VG	F	VF	EF
MV 304	(?)	Copper	19mm	—	—	35.00	—

F. W. SHILLITO (in italics) ctsp on Austria 1885 kreuzer, KM-605. (Kirtley Nov. 1990 sale, lot A642)

SHORKLEY

Rulau	Date	Metal	Size	VG	F	VF	EF
MV 306	(?)	Silver	39mm	—	—	65.00	—

SHORKLEY ctsp on Mexico 1868-Ca 8-reales, KM-377.2. (PCAC July 1993 sale, lot 1053, which yielded $44)

H.W. SMITH

Rulau	Date	Metal	Size	VG	F	VF	Unc
MV 310	1884-1900	Brass	25mm	—	—	15.00	—

GOOD FOR / 2 1/2 ¢ / H.W. SMITH / —.— / ON BILLIARD TABLE. Rv: Similar to Broadhurst piece in the BBC series, but hyphen between BRUNSWICK-BALKE. Plain edge.

Not listed in *The Brunswick Token Story.*

A. O. SNOW

Rulau	Date	Metal	Size	VG	F	VF	EF
MV 312	(?)	Silver	31mm	—	—	25.00	—

A. O. SNOW ctsp on U.S. 1858-O Seated Liberty half dollar. (Pete Peters coll.)

SOUTH RIVER CUTLERY CO.

Rulau	Date	Metal	Size	VG	F	VF	EF
MV 317	(?)	Copper	29mm	—	—	50.00	—

SOUTH RIVER / CUTLERY CO. ctsp on U.S. 1844 Large cent. (Hallenbeck 19.752; Brunk 37565)

W. SPITZER

Rulau	Date	Metal	Size	VG	F	VF	EF
MV 318	(?)	Silver	34mm	—	—	80.00	—

W. SPITZER ctsp on Spanish-American 1817-LME-JP 4-reales. (Peru). (Van Ormer sale 2809)

Rulau	Date	Metal	Size	VG	F	VF	EF
MV 318A	(?)	Silver	31mm	—	—	60.00	—

Similar ctsp on U.S. 1876 Seated Liberty half dollar. (Brunk 37700)

In this counterstamp, both the S and Z are retrograde.

STADT THEATRE

Rulau	Date	Metal	Size	VG	F	VF	Unc
MV 315	(1880's)	GS	24mm	—	—	10.00	—

STADT THEATRE / 5 / (Owl over crossed sceptres). Rv: I. G. BRANDT (in panel with cross-hatching). (ATCO Maverick 3852)

There is a tug of war over attribution of this token, of which about 20 pieces exist. It creates excitement at auctions.

Some authorities assign it to J. G. Brandt in Omaha, Neb., but others to the Stadt Theatre in Milwaukee, Wis.

G. E. STEVENS

Rulau	Date	Metal	Size	VG	F	VF	EF
MV 320	(?)	CN	19mm	—	—	45.00	—

G. E. STEVENS ctsp on U.S. 1858 Flying Eagle cent.

Rulau	Date	Metal	Size	VG	F	VF	EF
MV 322	(?)	Copper	29mm	—	—	45.00	—

Similar ctsp on U.S. 1853 Large cent. (Brunk 38240)

W. C. STILES

Rulau	Date	Metal	Size	VG	F	VF	EF
MV 323	(?)	Bronze	23mm	—	—	15.00	—

W. C. STILES ctsp on U.S. 1865 2-cent piece. (Pete Peters coll.)

Rulau	Date	Metal	Size	VG	F	VF	EF
MV 324	(?)	Bronze	23mm	—	—	15.00	—

W. C. STILES / (three Odd Fellows rings) / FTL ctsp on U.S. 1869 2-cent piece. (Brunk 38400)

A. S. STILLMAN

Rulau	Date	Metal	Size	VG	F	VF	EF
MV 325	1870	Copper	29mm	—	—	20.00	—

PRESENTED BY A. S. STILLMAN 1870 ctsp on U.S. Large cent. (Hallenbeck 19.777; Brunk 38410)

F. R. STRANGE

Rulau	Date	Metal	Size	VG	F	VF	EF
MV 335	(?)	Copper	29mm	—	—	20.00	—

F. R. STRANGE in ornate cartouche ctsp on U.S. Large cent. (Stanley L. Steinberg sale of Feb. 1982; Brunk 38700)

Rulau	Date	Metal	Size	VG	F	VF	EF
MV 335A	(?)	Bronze	23mm	—	—	20.00	—

Similar ctsp on U.S. 1864 2-cent piece.

There were a least two families named Strange in the letter cutting business who made counterstamped pieces — E. W. Strange of Taunton, Mass. in the 1850's, and J. W. and C. A. Strange, father and son of Bangor, Maine in the 1860's. Whether F. R. Strange is connected with either is not known at this stage.

B. STRAW

Rulau	Date	Metal	Size	VG	F	VF	EF
MV 336	(?)	Copper	29mm	—	30.00	—	—

B. STRAW ctsp on U.S. 1848 or 1850 Large cent. (Rulau coll.; Brunk 38755)

DANIEL SULLY

Rulau	Date	Metal	Size	VG	F	VF	Unc
MV 338	(?)	Brass	31mm	—	—	65.00	—

Standing rooster left. Above: DANIEL SULLY / MEDAL / FOR THE / -.- / BEST & LONGEST . Below: THE MILLIONAIRE. Rv: Within wreath: GOOD FOR / ONE / (screw right). Plain edge. (Wright 1076; Kirtley Oct. 1992 sale, lot 3374)

This USTT-era piece is one of the few erotic items in Dr. Wright's token listing. It is very rare.

SWAN HOUSE

Rulau	Date	Metal	Size	VG	F	EF	Unc
MV 341	(?)	Brass	25mm	—	—	10.00	—

SWAN HOUSE. Rv: Blank. Plain edge. (Wright 1079)

T. H. ELEC. CO.

Rulau	Date	Metal	Size	VG	F	EF	Unc
MV 342	(?)	Bronze	19mm	—	—	40.00	—

MANUFACTURED BY T. H. / ELEC. CO. / LYNN MASS ctsp on U.S. 1867 Indian cent. (Koppenhaver June 1987 sale, lot 23; Brunk 39177)

Probably from Lynn, Mass.

FRANK A. TEMME

Rulau	Date	Metal	Size	F	VF	EF	Unc
MV 343	(1880's)	Brass	**	—	—	12.50	—

** Oct 26mm.

(All incused): FRANK A TEMME / 5 / (Pool table). Rv: Blank. Incised, beaded rim on each side. Plain edge. (Thoele coll.)

TIVOLI & WALLHALLA

Rulau	Date	Metal	Size	F	VF	EF	Unc
MV 344	(?)	Lead	16mm	—	—	10.00	—

Within central circle: TONY. Around: TIVOLI & WALLHALLA. Rv: GOOD FOR ONE DRINK / 5 / CENTS. Plain edge. (Wright 1149)

T. B. TOBEY

Rulau	Date	Metal	Size	F	VF	EF	Unc
MV 350	(?)	Silver	32.5mm	—	—	50.00	—

T. B. TOBEY ctsp on U.S. 1833 Bust half dollar. (S. L. Steinberg report)

N. J. TRACY

Rulau	Date	Metal	Size	VG	F	VF	EF
MV 353	(?)	Copper	29mm	—	25.00	—	45.00

N. J. TRACY in relief in a curved rectangular cartouche ctsp on U.S. Large cent. Dates examined: 1819, 1820, 1850, 1851. There are 63 pieces reported.

Rulau	Date	Metal	Size	VG	F	VF	EF
MV 354	(?)	Silver	18mm	—	—	40.00	—

Similar ctsp on U.S. 1835 dime.

MV 355 (?) Copper 29mm — — 35.00 —
N. J. TRACY in relief within rectangular depression ctsp on U.S. 1846 Large cent. MSB on rev. (Frank Kovacs coll.)

MV 356 (?) Copper 29mm — 35.00 — —
Similar ctsp on U.S. Large cents. No initials on reverse. Dates examined: 1807, 1831, 1838, 1844, 1849, 1853.

MV 356A (?) Copper 28mm — — 40.00 —
N. J. TRACY in relief within straight rectangular depression ctsp on 28mm copper coin, worn smooth on each side.

MV 357 (?) Copper 29mm — 35.00 — —
N. J. TRACY in relief within depressed rectangular ctsp on U.S. 1851 Large cent. (Rulau coll.; Brunk 40390)

MV 358 (?) Copper 29mm — — 35.00 —
Similar ctsp on U.S. 1848 Large cent. Incuse R.L., also ctsp.

MV 358A (?) Copper 28mm — — 35.00 —
Simiilar ctsp on 1837 Hard Times token. Low 110.

MV 359 (?) CN 19mm — — 30.00 —
Similar ctsp on U.S. 1857 or 1858 Flying Eagle cent. (Frank Kovacs coll.)

MV-360 (?) Silver 20mm — — 30.00 —
Similar ctsp on U.S. Bust dime. Examined: 1821, 1829, 1834, 1835.

MV 361 (?) Silver 18mm — 50.00 — —
Similar ctsp on U.S. Seated Liberty dime. Examined: 1838, 1839, 1841, 1853, 1857. (Rulau coll.; Duffield 1425)

MV 361A (?) Silver 27mm — — 40.00 —
Similar ctsp on U.S. 1821 Bust Quarter.

MV 361D (?) Silver 31mm — — 40.00 —
Similar ctsp on U.S. 1855-O S.L. half dollar.

There are also more counterstamps of this very prolific issuer.

C. F. ULRICH

Rulau	Date	Metal	Size	VG	F	VF	EF
MV 365	(?)	Copper	29mm	15.00	—	25.00	—

C. F. ULRICH in tiny letters in rect. cartouche ctsp on U.S. Large cent. (Brunk 40840)

MV 366 (?) CN 19mm 15.00 — 25.00 —
Similar ctsp on U.S. Flying Eagle or Indian cent. Examined: 1858, 1864.

MV 367 (?) Bronze 23mm 15.00 — 25.00 —
Similar ctsp on U.S. 1865 2-cent piece.

MV 369 (?) CN 22mm 15.00 — 25.00 —
Similar ctsp on U.S. Shield nickel. Examined: 1867, 1870. (Zaffern coll.)

MV 369A (?) Copper --mm 15.00 — 25.00 —
Similar ctsp on Civil War token.

Joseph Zaffern attributes this stamp to Galveston, Texas, but offers no documentation. Photo shown enlarged to show detail.

E. P. VAUX

Rulau	Date	Metal	Size	VG	F	VF	EF
MV 370	(?)	CN	19mm	—	—	300.	—

E. P. VAUX ctsp on U.S. 1856 Flying Eagle cent. (Duffield 1431; Brunk 41117)

MV 371 (?) CN 19mm — — 25.00 —
E. P. VAUX ctsp on U.S. 1857 Flying Eagle cent. (John Ford coll.)

CHS. VETTER

Rulau	Date	Metal	Size	VG	F	VF	Unc
MV A371	(1860's)	Copper	18.5mm	—	—	50.00	—

Eagle displayed (similar to CWT die 1181). Rv: CHs. VETTER / GOOD / FOR / ONE GLASS / BEER. Dentilated rim on each side. Plain edge. (Kirtley June 1989 sale, lot 354)

This token could be immediate post-Civil War in provenance or from the early 1870's. It was never published until 1989.

VIENNA BAKERY

Rulau	Date	Metal	Size	VG	F	VF	Unc
MV B371	1889	Brass	24mm	—	—	25.00	—

VIENNA BAKERY. / ONE / LOAF / E. H. SCHATZ. Rv: 1889 within open-top wreath. Plain edge. (Charles Kirtley report)

ARNOLD VOGT

Rulau	Date	Metal	Size	VG	F	VF	Unc
MV C371	(?)	Brass	23mm	—	—	25.00	—

ARNOLD VOGT / (beer stein with numeral 5 separating GOOD - FOR. Rv: Brunswick die BB-2, but ctsp C.M.

W. & E.

Rulau	Date	Metal	Size	VG	F	VF	EF
MV 372	(?)	Copper	29mm	—	—	25.00	—

W & E / 25 ctsp on shaved reverse of U.S. 1856 Large cent. (Brunk 41320)

D.W.

Rulau	Date	Metal	Size	VG	F	VF	Unc
MV 373	(?)	Brass	24mm	—	—	10.00	—

Lizard in an oval panel at center. Rv: No. — / D. W. Plain edge. (Wright 234)

J. W. & CO.

Rulau	Date	Metal	Size	VG	F	VF	Unc
MV A373	(1870's?)	Copper	30mm	—	—	50.00	—

Eagle displayed, U.S. shield on its breast, scroll below. Rv: J. W. & CO. / 50 / * GOLD REGION *.

The obverse die is also used on the Henry Shephens token of St. Helen, Mich., which see in this reference. J. W. & Co. 10 and 25 tokens also exist, at VF $50 each, according to Paul Cunningham.

R. H. W. CO.

Rulau	Date	Metal	Size	F	VF	EF	Unc
MV 374	(?)	Brass	27mm	—	—	15.00	—

Eagle with outspread wings perched on a scroll. The numeral 1798 is incused on the scroll. Rv: (Three fleurs) .R.H.W.Co. / (three fleurs). Plain edge.

The piece appears to be a check of some sort (tool, time, waiter's, etc.). (In collection Jackson Sellwood, Collings Lakes, N.J.)

W. W. & CO.

Rulau	Date	Metal	Size	VG	F	VF	EF
MV 376	(?)	Copper	29mm	—	—	25.00	—

W. W & CO ctsp on U.S. 1854 Large cent. (Frank Kovacs coll.; Brunk 41370)

Rulau	Date	Metal	Size	VG	F	VF	EF
MV 376F	(?)	Copper	—	—	40.00	—	

Outline eagle with U.S. shield on breast, W. W. & CO. below, all ctsp on U.S. 1838 Large cent. (Hartzog coll.)

WATROUS (&) CO.

Rulau	Date	Metal	Size	VG	F	VF	EF
MV 384	(?)	Copper	29mm	—	—	25.00	—

WATROUS . CO ctsp on reverse of U.S. 1851 Large cent. (The . could be a broken ampersand.) (Brunk 42220)

One J. J. Watrous was a Cincinnati, Ohio maker of target rifles 1887-1893.

WELLS FARGO

Rulau	Date	Metal	Size	VG	F	VF	EF
MV 385	(1870's)	Copper	34mm	—	—	—	—

WELLS FARGO / U.S. / R.W.P.O. / EXPRESS ctsp on England penny of 1806-1807, date worn off. (Brunk 42560)

R.W.P.O. = Railway post office. This is a modern fantasy, made to sell to collectors. The Wells Fargo Express Co. was one of the largest delivery and transportation companies in North America, operating all over the West as well as the East. Fantasy counterstamps also were applied to U.S. Large cents and to silver bars.

ANTON WERNER

Rulau	Date	Metal	Size	F	VF	Unc
MV 386	(1884-1900)	Brass	25mm	—	15.00	—

GOOD FOR / 5¢ / ANTON / WERNER / IN / * TRADE *. Rv: (Brunswick-Balke-Collender check). Plain edge.

Not listed in *The Brunswick Token Story*.

WEST HOTEL BATH ROOMS

Rulau	Date	Metal	Size	VG	F	VF	EF
MV 388	(?)	--	36mm	—	—	100.	—

(All incused): WEST HOTEL / (sunrise) / + BATH + / — / ROOMS. Rv: ELECTRIC / PUNCH / BATH. Plain edge. (ANS coll.)

One can only wonder today at the "electric punch" bath for which the West Hotel claimed fame.

Dobbins' Electric Soap was a big seller in the 1870's, but we suspect some more dramatic on-the-spot procedure than the mere furnishing of a special soap may have been used.

H. WETTSTEIN

Ralau	Date	Metal	Size	VG	F	VF	EF
MV 389	(ca 1877)	Copper	29mm	—	—	25.00	—
	H. WETTSTEIN ctsp on U.S. Large cent.						
MV 389A	(ca 1877)	CN	19mm	—	—	25.00	—
	Similar ctsp on U.S. Indian cent. Dates examined: 1863.						
MV 389B	(ca 1877)	CN	22mm	—	—	25.00	—
	Similar ctsp on U.S. 1868 or 1873 Shield nickel.						
MV 389C	(ca 1877)	Silver	18mm	—	—	25.00	—
	Similar ctsp on U.S. S.L. dime. Dates examined: 1875, 1876, 1877.						
MV 389D	(ca 1877)	Silver	25mm	—	—	30.00	—
	Similar ctsp on U.S. Seated Liberty quarter. Dates examined: 1870, 1875, 1876.						
MV 289F	(ca 1877)	Copper	28mm	—	—	25.00	—
	Similar ctsp on Canada 1859 Large cent.						
MV 289J	(ca 1877)	Silver	25mm	—	—	30.00	—
	Similar ctsp on Canada 1872 25-cents. (Brunk 42770)						

Wettstein seems to have been a prolific issuer of advertising counterstamps in the late 1870's. At least 15 specimens have been reported thus far.

WILDER HOUSE

Rulau	Date	Metal	Size	VG	F	VF	EF
MV 396	(?)	Silver	25mm	—	—	60.00	—

WILDER HOUSE ctsp on U.S. 1857 Seated Liberty quarter. (Gould 94)

Rulau	Date	Metal	Size	VG	F	VF	EF
MV 397	(?)	CN	22mm	—	—	60.00	—

Similar ctsp on U.S. 1873 Shield nickel.

Rulau	Date	Metal	Size	VG	F	VF	EF
MV 398	(?)	Silver	31mm	—	—	60.00	—

Similar ctsp on U.S. 1870 half dollar. (Brunk 43370)

GEORGE S. WILDER

Rulau	Date	Metal	Size	VG	F	VF	EF
MV 393	(?)	Silver	18mm	—	—	35.00	—

Eagle, GEORGE WILDER ctsp on U.S. 1881 Seated Liberty dime. (Gould 170; Brunk 43390)

Rulau	Date	Metal	Size	VG	F	VF	EF
MV 394	(?)	Silver	18mm	—	—	45.00	—

(Elk's head) GEO. S. WILDER ctsp on U.S. 1887 dime. (Brunk 43380)

WIMAN (THE) COPPERSMITH

Ralau	Date	Metal	Size	VG	F	VF	EF
MV 400	(?)	Copper	29mm	—	—	150.	—

Large eagle and WIMAN / COPPERSMITH ctsp on U.S. 1822 Large cent. (Hallenbeck 23.518; Brunk 43840)

C.H. WING

Rulau	Date	Metal	Size	VG	F	VF	EF
MV 403	(?)	Copper	29mm	—	—	20.00	—

C.H. WING ctsp on U.S. 1843, 1847 or 1853 Large cent. (Brunk 43900)

Rulau	Date	Metal	Size	VG	F	VF	EF
MV 405	(?)	CN	19mm	—	—	25.00	—

Similar ctsp on U.S. 1860 Indian cent.

G.J. WING

Rulau	Date	Metal	Size	VG	F	VF	Unc
MV 408	(?)	Bronze	19mm	15.00	—	25.00	—

G.J. WING ctsp on U.S. Indian Head cent. Examined: 1860, 1861, 1868, 1880, 1884, 1891. (Brunk 43910)

Rulau	Date	Metal	Size	VG	F	VF	Unc
MV 410	(?)	Bronze	23mm	—	—	25.00	—

(G.) J. WING ctsp on U.S. 1864 or 1865 2-cent piece.

GEO. WOLBRECHT'S TIVOLI

Rulau	Date	Metal	Size	VG	F	VF	Unc
MV 413	(?)	Brass	19mm	—	—	15.00	—

Female head left, GEO. WOLBRECHT'S TIVOLI. Rv: Large numeral 5 at center, GOOD FOR ONE CTS DRINK around. Plain edge. (Wright 1260)

A drink for 5 cents in the Good Old Days!

E. A. WORTHEN

Rulau	Date	Metal	Size	VG	F	VF	EF
MV 414	(?)	Silver	31mm	—	40.00	—	—

E. A. Worthen ctsp on U.S. 1875-S Seated Liberty half dollar. (Rulau coll.; Brunk 44417)

C. WORTHING

Rulau	Date	Metal	Size	VG	F	VF	EF
MV 417	(?)	Silver	25mm	—	—	27.50	—

C. WORTHING ctsp on each side of U.S. 1876 Seated Liberty quarter. (Pete Peters coll.)

R.F. WRIGHT

Rulau	Date	Metal	Size	VG	F	VF	Unc
MV 416	(?)	Brass	24mm	—	—	8.50	—

R.F. WRIGHT / 10¢ / SILVER DOLLAR SHOP. Rv: In circle at center: AUG. KERN B.S. CO., ST. LOUIS. Plain edge. (Wright 1277)

Y & T

Rulau	Date	Metal	Size	VG	F	VF	EF
MV 420	(?)	Bronze	19mm	—	—	50.00	—

Y & T in three-leaf clover with stem (repeated four times) ctsp on reverse of U.S. 1864 Indian Head cent. (Fuld NC-35a) Rarity 7. (Brunk 44563)

Originally thought to have been a Civil War token, but probably issued closer to 1870.

M. V. Y.

Rulau	Date	Metal	Size	VG	F	VF	EF
MV 421	1889	Copper	29mm	—	—	10.00	—

M. V. Y. ctsp on obverse of U.S. 1803 Large cent. Date 1889 ctsp on reverse of the coin. (Kovacs coll.)

A. D. YARTER

Rulau	Date	Metal	Size	VG	F	VF	EF
MV 425	(1880-82)	Brass	24mm	—	—	40.00	—

(All incused): A. D. YARTER / 5 / (Crossed Cue Sticks). Rv: AMERICAN / STANDARD BILLIARD / AND / POOL TABLES / W. H. GRIFFITH & CO. N.Y. Plain edge. (Lot 546 in Koppenhaver sale of June 4, 1988)

HEINRICH ZENTNER

Rulau	Date	Metal	Size	VG	F	VF	Unc
MV 435	(1883-90)	CN	25mm	—	—	15.00	—

NATIONAL BILLIARD MANUF'G CO. / N B M / (Crossed cuesticks) / Co / CIN. O. Rv: . GOOD FOR . / 5 C / HEINRICH - / - ZENTNER / -IN- / * TRADE *. Plain edge. (TAMS Maverick 13074)

ZIRIAX

Rulau	Date	Metal	Size	VG	F	VF	EF
MV 440	(?)	CN	22mm	—	—	25.00	—

ZIRIAX ctsp on U.S. 1867 Shield nickel. (Brunk 44870)

Rulau	Date	Metal	Size	VG	F	VF	EF
MV 441	(?)	Copper	29mm	—	—	25.00	—

Similar ctsp on U.S. 1853 Large cent.

(Elephant)

Rulau	Date	Metal	Size	VG	F	VF	Unc
MV 450	(1880's)	CN	25mm	—	—	17.50	—

Elephant standing on mound to right. There are four die breaks extending inward from the rim, at 4, 5:30, 9 and 10 o'clock. Beaded inner rim border. Rv: Large 5 in a circle of 16 6-pointed rosettes. Plain edge. (Spangenberger coll.)

Rulau	Date	Metal	Size	VG	F	VF	Unc
MV 451	(?)	CN	25mm	—	—	17.50	—

Obverse as 450, but without die cracks. Rv: Large numeral 5 within a circle of 16 5-pointed stars. (Five of the stars have been recut over rosettes.) Plain edge. (John Palmer coll., Indianapolis, Ind.)

MISCELLANEOUS LOVE TOKENS

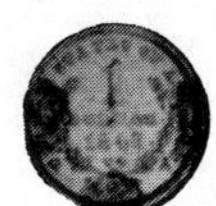

During the 1870's and 1880's, it became a quite common practice to shave smooth the reverse of a U.S. silver dime or quarter (or some other coin) and to engrave thereon some endearment, memorial or memento of a personal nature. Often this took the form of ornate initials or monograms, sometimes full or partial name or nickname, occasionally a pictorial device, and —seldom — a rather complete message. The term "love token" was applied to this type of engraved piece because of the practice of swains to honor their lady loves with such favors.

Love tokens had been created in this country from the inceptions of a national coinage, as several early 1790's specimens attest, but they became a fad of some proportion after the Civil War, and county and state fairs were places the public could encounter skilled calligraphers willing to engrave any message or initials or device on a coin — for a fee.

It is not possible to catalog such items, each of which is unique, so a selection of such pieces is included below to give the reader an idea of what is available. This small sampling has been selected from the holdings of several major collectors.

It is nearly impossible to trace love tokens to their origins. In a few cases, where they have been found with family papers, or where the inscription is of sufficient length to offer clues, they have been traced.

Silver dime love tokens usually sell for $4 to $8 each, unless the device is unusual, while silver quarters command prices of $5 to $10. Generally, other coins made into love tokens are less common than the dimes and quarters. No coins seem to have escaped such treatment — gold coins of $1, $2 1/2, $3 and $5 are seen occasionally, as well as silver dollars. Trade dollars, half dollars, 20-cent pieces, Large cents, Small cents, even the tiny silver 3-cent and half dime coins.

Gold $1 love tokens sell at about $38. Love tokens on foreign coins can be found — several are included in the list below.

The practice of making love tokens survived into the 1890's and to the earliest part of the 20th century, then died off completely. Few men today are calligraphers and skilled in engraving.

There was a brief revival of love token creation in the U.S. in 1970-1973, primarily in the West. During the period we edited *Numismatic Scrapbook Magazine* (1968-1974), we reported on this revival. A retired jeweler and artisan, Don E. Knapp of Colorado Springs, Colo., was a leader in this movement and created for us a number of specimens included in the list below. Knapp and the others who were involved in the 1970's activity used modern coins so they could not be confused with earlier products.

There is a grace and charm about love tokens and the number of collectors involved in the field today is growing. Love tokens defy the regimentation approach to collecting — every item is an "impulse buy" and perhaps therein lies their appeal to all tastes.

(In this section, the slash (/) indicates a line change in the inscription, and a double slash (//) indicates a side change. Many love tokens carry engraving on both sides.)

MA July ye 15 / 1770 on England 1745 shilling
Script PA within 6-point star on 1849-O gold $1
Script WHA on 1897 Barber dime
AGGIE in scrollwork on Mexico 2-reales ca 1860
-ALICE- (at center of fret border and floreate devices) on England Edw. VII farthing
ALICE (Lighthouse, Sailboat) on 1890 L.S. dime
Script AMANDA on 1856 S.L. half Dime
Script AUNT on 1875 S.L. dime
MB (ornate) on 1854 gold $1
SAB monogram on England Victoria gold sovereign
Blessings / Darlene / (Heart) / Russ / March 19, 1972 / (Linked Hearts) / (Flowers) on 1921 Morgan silver dollar
Ornate BRAKEMAN on 1853-A&R S.L. half dollar
(Horn) / BROTHER on 1891 S.L. dime
MARY BROWN AND JAMES WARDLAW in wreath // IF YOU LOVE ME MARY BROWN LEAVE ME NOT on 29mm copper coin (ca 1800)
CCC (plain border) on Spanish-American 2-reales
FGC (fancy border) // (Flower) on dime
FHC (ornate) // S / DEC. 25, 1890 on $5 gold piece
HSC (ornate border) on 1881 Morgan silver dollar
MC 1805 on England 1787 shilling
PEC monogram on 1853 S.L. quarter
PEC monogram on Italy 1867 silver 1-lira
CAP GOOD BOY 1881 (on ribbon) on 1876 L.S. dime
Script CARL in band on 1892 Barber dime
CORA amid scrollwork on 1898 Barber dime
S COS on 1857 L.S. quarter
FHD monogram on 1882 S.L. dime
Script MD in ornate border on S.L. quarter
Darlene / RUSS in heart / Be My Sweetheart on 1945 silver alloy Jefferson nickel
DON on England Victoria 6d
Script E on 1881 Indian cent
J. E. Co. A. / 81st O.V.I. / 2nd Brig. 4th Div. / 5th A.C. // Apr. 28, 1865 (this side scratched, not engraved) on O-mint no-motto half dollar O.V.I. = Ohio Volunteer Infantry
LBE monogram on Spain brass 10-escudo game counter
Script T.E. / (Lighthouse and Ship at seas) on 1891 S.L. dime
ELISA on Norway 1903 silver 10-ore
F (Gothic, fancy) on gold $1
LF (Cross) on 1856 L.S. dime
FIRST CONG. S. S. / FIRST PRIZE / REGATTA // WON BY / WILLIAM E. HOLMES / JULY 11, 1883 on half dollar, shaved smooth, loop attached
Script 1ST / PRIZE on 1892 Barber quarter
G (Gothic, fret border) 1856 S.L. dime
G (Gothic, ornate border) on 1853-A&R S.L. quarter
BSG (fancy) on Australia 1966 5-cents
FG monogram on gold $1
HDG monogram on 1883 nickel (partly gilt)
(Gold-panning Pan) / M. A. G. on 1876 S.L. dime
(Bird) / REG on band / (Sailboat and House) on Canada Victoria 10-cents
GATEWAY TO THE TEENS / * / * 13 * / * S (Heart) M (heart) M * / JANUARY 23, 1972 / (Scrollwork) on 1964 Kennedy half dollar
(Lighthouse and Ship at seas) / GEORGE on 1891 dime. (Diff. scene than the T.E. piece above)
GLADYS on Canada Victoria 5-cents
Script GRANDMA on 1883 S.L. dime
CO. D. 3RD INFANTRY / U.S.A. / ROBT GRUFF / 1917 / MACON-GEORGIA on 1932 Bust half dollar (shaved reverse)
GUNDA on Norway silver 10-ore
A.P.H. (Owl on Crescent Moon) on 1875 L.S. dime
CJH monogram on 1877 S.L. quarter
T.H. '60 / J. L. B. on dime-sized gold-plated base metal disc
WAH (ornate) / 9-5-/14 / AH II monogram within shield) on Canada $5 gold piece. (Poss. Sept. 5, 1914 was the date of commissioning or enlistment of W A H in Canadian army)
WCH on band on 1970-D Lincoln cent
HAPPY / EASTER / Darlene / Russ / 1973 / (Easter Lillies) on Peru 1929 silver half sol
MAI / June / y 3 / 1800 on England 1700-E half crown
I Love You (on ribbon) / Truly (on ribbon) / Helen on 1970-D Lincoln cent
E. C. / HOWELL / 345 / N. GRANT ST. / STOCKTON, / CALIF. / A.E.F. '18-'19 on France silver 2-francs. (AEF = Amer. Expeditionary Force)
IDA on 1858 S.L. quarter
IDA on 1853-Arrows half dime
(Lighthouse & Sea) / IDA on Canada Victoria 10-cents
IRMA on gold $1, Type 2
EIJ monogram (ornate border) on 1881 $5 gold piece
GSJ on 1877 S.L. quarter
HHJ monogram (ornate border) on 'CC' quarter
JOHANNE on Norway 1903 silver 10-ore
(Linked Hearts) / John / Loves / Mary on Australia 1867 2-cents
JOSIE on 1877 L.S. dime
K (Gothic) on 1861 L.S. quarter
Script BK on 1883 Liberty nickel
CWK on 1831 Large cent
FRK monogram on S-mint $5 gold piece
AL (?) // (Large Building) on O-mint Barber dime
BWL (?) monogram // (Sailboat on water, Bird above) on dime, both sides shaved
(Crown) / EL on Sweden silver 50-ore, Y-21
HEL (plain border) on Spanish-American 1786/5
Script LL on 1854-Arrows S.L. quarter
LOUISE on 1858 S.L. quarter
LUCY on Canada Victoria 10-cents
DAM on Canada Victoria 10-cents
DMM monogram on 1883 S.L. dime
MDM monogram on 1883 S.L. dime
MAI / June / y 3 / 1800 on England 1708-E half crown
Script MAMA on 1883 S.L. dime
MATHIAS on Switzerland 1884 5-centimes
Script MAUD (petals around) on Canada YH dime (1858-1901)
Merry / Christmas / (2 Bells) / Russell / 1970 on 1964 Roosevelt dime
Merry / Christmas / (2 Bells) / Russ & Darlene / DON & HELEN on 1972-D Lincoln cent
Script MODER (Flower) on 1834 Bust half dime
N MY WIFE on 1875 L.S. dime
New York / Indianapolis / Hartford / Chicago // Pullman Train / Libby Prison / Kenwood Club / Newburg on 1892 Columbian half dollar
ONE BILL on 1891 L.S. dime
JJP monogram on sail of a sailboat, waves on 1861 L.S. half dime
Script PAPA on 1884 S.L. dime
Pax Vobiscum (script, on panel) on Newfoundland $2 gold piece, Pax Vobiscum = Peace Be With You, in Latin

Script R on Australia 1966 2-cents
JR monogram / (Two Hearts & Crossed Arrows divide 17-88) / SSB monogram on Turkey silver crown ca 1780
MR monogram on 1877 S.L. half dollar (pinback)
W.W. REVEI on ribbon / Gothic FBC NO. 11 on S.L. quarter before 1866
DS (?) / (Man in hat holding Racehorse) on Seated Liberty half dollar
IS monogram on 1861 S.L. dime
H. J. SCHACHTE / Co. E. 10 Pa. / MANILA, P.I. / Aug. 13, 1898 (all in plain circle) on Spanish-American Carlos III 8-reales. Spanish-American War.
ST. PAULUS / FRANCE / VEREIN within border // H. H. / FEB. 1864 within border on quarter
(Sailing Ship) J.M.T. on 1892 Barber dime
(Bird on Branch) / THOMAS on 1891 S.L. dime
TRUDY BIG 4 (Owl on branch) on 1887 L.S. dime
WRU (on scroll) on 1853 L.S. half dime
MMV on O-mint half dime
VOLUNTEER *B.B.C.* * PO'KEEPSIE* (Crossed Baseball Bats and Ball) on S.L. quarter (ca 1850)
AW on Seated Liberty dime
HLW monogram on Barber dime
RAW // 1883 / (Sailboat, Lighthouse, Rocks) on dime, looped
RJW monogram on England Victoria YH shilling
SWW on 1888 L.S. dime
Zehr / Pfennig on Germany 1890 1-pfennig
(Christian Cross) ornate border on 1847 S.L. quarter
(Saw, Cleaver, Knife) on Barber dime (meatcutter tools)
(Triquetra) on England silver 3d ca 1890's (Poss. Isle of Man)
(Skull & Crossbones) on 1873-Arrows S.L. dime
(Pipe and Hat) added to bust of Paul Kruger on Transvaal 1895 silver shilling
(Stylized Frog looking up) on 1871 L.S. dime
(Bird flying out of Egg) / MHF on 1888 S.L. dime

(?)	Silver	18mm

Violin and bow / M. T. engraved on reverse of U.S. S.L. dime.

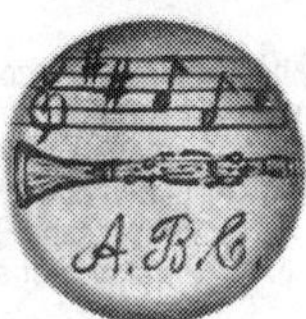

(?)	Silver	18mm

Music scale / clarinet left / A. B. C. (script) engraved on reverse of U.S. 1876 dime.

Tokens of the Gay Nineties

Trade tokens, store cards and medalets which record the years 1890 through 1900 – an Age of Carefree Innocence in a self-satisfied America. Here are mementoes for nickel beers, nickel cigars, band concerts in the park, reunions of the G.A.R., bustles and bowler hats, and the dawn of American imperialism with quick victory in the Spanish-American War.

Special Consultants

Steve Tanenbaum
Charles Kirtley
Joseph Schmidt
Gregory Brunk
Gary Pipher
Hank Thoele
Dick Grinolds
George Ganter

THE GAY NINETIES

There is a gaiety, a *joie de vivre*, a "good old summertime" feeling associated with the decade of the Nineties. The user of this book will sense it as he scans the metallic mementoes of the American Dream of a bygone era — before they knew it was the American Dream.

America relived a microcosm of the worst and the best of the 19th century in its closing decade. The financial Panic of 1893, mine and industry failures and labor unrest, the Pullman riots of 1894 and other disasters were more than offset by the euphoria flowing from our easy victory in the Spanish-American War of 1898, discovery of gold in the Klondike, and the national uplift provided by the World's Columbian Exposition in Chicago in 1893.

Enshrined in metal on the tokens, store cards and medalets of this era are band concerts in gazebos in the park, Tony Pastor and Lillian Russell and Gentleman Jim Corbett and the Comstock Lode, gaslights and carriages and high-wheeled bicycles and straw hats and bow ties, the gleaming new miracle metal aluminum, handlebar mustaches and nickel beers and nickel cigars and free lunch at the saloon and "family entrances," bustles and bowler hats and Free Silver and the "Cross of Gold" speech at the 1896 Democratic convention, statehood for Utah and Wyoming and Idaho and annexation for Hawaii and Puerto Rico and Samoa and territorial status for Oklahoma, rollicking political campaigns in 1892 and 1896 and 1900.

Also enshrined in metal are the annual encampments of the Grand Army of the Republic and its Southern counterpart, the Confederate Veterans of America. The G.A.R. was the Gay Nineties equivalent of the American Legion and V.F.W. rolled into one — in 1895 the Civil War had been over for 30 years and most of the veterans were in their 50's and 60's, able to afford the better things in life. (The V.F.W. was born in 1899, a Spanish war "baby".)

Recorded here are the business establishments with which the common man of the Nineties was most familiar — the corner grocery and butcher shop and dry goods store of the city and the general store of the rural community; blacksmith shops, liveries, druggists with colored-water urns and globes in the windows, watchmakers, shoe repair shops, the inevitable corner cigar store, saloons and "sample rooms" (a more genteel term for a saloon), photograph parlors, billiard halls, wagonmakers, seamstresses, clothing stores, department stores (only 20 years old in 1896), coopers, ironmongers and other metalsmiths. Were it not for the tokens they left behind (many of them dug up by today's metal detector enthusiasts) — most of these small businesses would not be remembered at all. But the Gay Nineties lives on in these bits of metal — the token was the money of the man on the street.

Wages were sinfully low in the 1890's, but so were prices. The gold-backed dollar of the era bought a lot; throughout this catalog its users will note prices for items that seem ludicrous at first glance but did dovetail neatly into the earning power of the citizens of that day. Nostalgia, a wag said, lets us want the nickel cigar on the $4.25 per hour minimum wage — the Nineties knew nothing of such concepts as minimum wage, child labor laws, income taxes, or the 40-hour week.

Inventions were making life better in the Nineties. The diesel engine was patented in 1892; refrigeration was made possible by the first liquid air plant in 1895; a man named King C. Gillette invented the safety razor in 1895; the automatic bottle-making machine was invented in 1898; the first gasoline-powered tractor was put into use in 1892; the wireless telegraph was invented in 1895; a Dane invented magnetic sound recording in 1898, and the first zeppelin flew in 1900. The "horseless carriage" began in production in the U.S. in 1892-94.

But just around the time corner (the turn of the century on January 1, 1901) were some things dimly seen that would change living in America forever — automobiles for every man and the airplane and advocacy for women's right to vote and Teddy Roosevelt's "bully pulpit" and the guerrilla war in the Philippines. Americans in the Nineties were becoming sophisticated — "war correspondents" (something pretty new then) filled our newspapers with the Spanish-American War (1898), the Boer War (1899-1902), the Sino-Japanese War (1894-95), Armenian massacres (1894-96), Italo-Ethiopian War (1896), Greco-Turkish War (1897), Sudan War (1896-98) and the Fashoda Crisis between Britain and France (1898).

The end of every century since the Middle Ages has spawned the argument over whether the century turns on January 1 of the double-0 year (1900) or the 01-year (1901). The 1890's were no exception; prophets of doom predicted the end of the world — as they always did in such years. New Year's greetings on January 1, 1900 gave Americans their first chance in 100 years to say "Happy New Century" as well as "Happy New Year" — though they were premature by a year since January 1, 1901, the experts told us, was the true "turn of the century." A good many tokens and medalets recall Christmas 1899 and New Years' 1900, and there was a spate of issuance of calendar medals at that time.

When we conceived the idea for this section of the catalog of the tokens of America we decided to include the year 1900 with the years 1890 through 1899, thus making our "decade coverage" 11 years long. It seemed only right, since so many folks of the Nineties themselves didn't understand when "their" century ended.

In just a few years, on January 1, 2000, readers will face the choice of saying "Happy New Year, Happy New Century and Happy New Millennium" on either that date or a year hence. We predict the same arguments will ensue!

PREFACE

This is the final in a series of token catalog segments the author has undertaken to document the entire range of American token coinages and advertising pieces from about 1700. The author has devoted much of his spare time over the past 31 years to this series of projects.

The illustrated, priced catalogs have all been published separately by Krause Publications of Iola, Wisconsin, beginning in 1980. These are:

Early American Tokens, which details the tokens of Colonial and Early Republican America from 1700 through 1832.

Hard Times Tokens, which covers the first great spate of token currencies in America, from 1833 through 1844.

U.S. Merchant Tokens 1845-1860, detailing the beautiful issues from the end of the Hard Times era to the eve of the Civil War.

U.S. Trade Tokens 1866-1889, which covers the varied issues of an industrialized America, through Washington's Inaugural centennial.

Tokens of the Gay Nineties, detailing for the first time the tokens, store cards and medalets of the years of 1890 through 1900.

In this present segment — like its predecessor *USTT 1866-1889,* the work has been slogging pioneering research, building upon the relatively scattered works of others and capitalizing on much that was learned in preparing the earlier volumes.

This final labor had less of the "cheering from the sidelines" that some of its predecessor volumes had, partly because many token experts felt the work simply could not be done on a national scope.

NUMBERING AND PRICING

Every token listed in this section has been assigned its own new Rulau number. The coding is simple: Tokens are arranged by states, alphabetically under the name of each city, and alphabetically within each community by the last name (or most important first word) of the issuer.

The numbers contain a 3-letter code for the community, followed by a 3-digit numeral for the token's exact number. The number may be followed by a suffix letter to denote varieties, etc. For example, Chi 32A tells us that, under Illinois, a Chicago token variety is designated.

Pricing has been supplied by the token dealers and collectors best able to gauge this information, based on current sales. Pricing is not really arbitrary in this volume, though no one could ever be satisfied with any price assigned to any piece. In general, tokens are less expensive in this period than earlier pieces of the 19th century, but there are enough exceptions to keep the hunt interesting for the collector and student.

Some pieces, such as the Brunswick-Balke-Collender pool checks and other pool checks, often bring double the present catalog valuations, but knowledgeable dealers say these prices are extreme. The author has had to resolve disputes over pricing and assumes full responsibility for their appearance in print.

THE SPLENDID LITTLE WAR

John Hay, who later became U.S. Secretary of State, wrote his friend Teddy Roosevelt in 1898: "It has been a splendid little war; begun with the highest motives, carried on with magnificent intelligence and spirit, favored by that fortune which loves the brave."

A splendid little war the Spanish-American War was, indeed. It lasted just 110 days — from Congress' declaration of war April 25 until Spain signed an armistice August 12. It had only two naval battles, both complete victories, and a brief land campaign — the siege of Santiago de Cuba, June 22-July 17, of 26 days.

Though to today's students of history the war had some comic opera features, it was yet a very real war to the men who fought it — especially the men of the Cuban campaign who returned home ridden by fever and dysentery.

The jingoistic New York press of William Randolph Hearst and his competitor, Joseph Pulitzer, whipped up the American war fever in 1897 with stories of the evil Spaniards and their commander in Cuba, Gen. Valeriano (The Butcher) Weyler. Then, on Feb. 15, 1898 the U.S. cruiser *Maine* was blown up in Havana harbor and 260 sailors died. "Remember the Maine" became the slogan of those who wanted war — almost everybody, it seemed.

Historian Bernard Weisberger writes succinctly in "Reaching for Empire" (New York, 1964): "America fought the war with zest, clumsiness, gallantry and incredible good luck."

The six light cruisers and gunboats of the American Asiatic squadron were at Hong Kong when war broke out, and Commodore George Dewey steamed for Manila and Spain's naval force there. On May 1, before dawn, Dewey's little fleet slipped past silent (!) shore batteries on Corregidor Island. At 5:40 A.M. Dewey gave his flagship commander, Captain Charles Vernon Gridley, the memorable order: "You may fire when you are ready, Gridley." The flagship, the cruiser *Olympia,* and the other five ships responded by sinking or crippling the 12 Spanish warships. (With bluster and bravado, Dewey had to elbow out of his way some German warships then in Manila Bay.)

Four Spanish ships were sunk and 381 Spaniards killed or wounded. Eight Americans were wounded. Later that morning Dewey's fleet moved in again and silenced the Spanish shore batteries. America did not learn of the Battle of Manila Bay until May 7 because Dewey's cable had to be carried to Hong Kong to be sent.

America had its first Spanish War hero, and business was brisk in souvenirs bearing his likeness — including a large number of medallions and tokens.

It soon had more heroes. The 61-year-old former Confederate cavalry general, "Fighting Joe" Wheeler, rushed into a blue uniform. Assistant Navy Secretary Theodore Roosevelt, 39, resigned to become a Lt. Col. in the Army. A combative Army surgeon, Leonard Wood, raised a volunteer force — the 1st U.S. Volunteer Cavalry, or "Rough Riders" — and had Teddy Roosevelt as his second in command over its 1,000 Western cowpokes and Eastern bluebloods. In all, 223,000 men enlisted for the war in an outpouring of patriotism that healed North-South and Republican-Democrat divisions, for a while.

Gen. William Shafter assembled the 5th Army Corps at Tampa, Florida — 20 infantry and 6 cavalry regiments, about 17,000 men — and embarked them (minus the cavalry horses) on June 7. On June 22-23 this force went ashore at Daiquiri and Siboney, east of Santiago. Without any amphibious training and without proper assault equipment the 17,000 troopers of the 5th Corps landed to take on the 150,000 Spanish troops on Cuba!

Fighting Joe Wheeler marched inland and fought a sharp skirmish at Las Guasimas June 24. Shafter's forces neared Santiago on July 1, fighting a day-long battle at El Caney and finding themselves pinned down for three days before San Juan Hill. Roosevelt, now commanding the Rough Riders, and aided by Negro troopers of the 9th and 10th Cavalry (one of the 10th's officers was Lt. John J. Pershing), led the successful charge up Kettle Hill July 1. By July 3 the Americans stormed up San Juan Hill and routed Spanish defenders in the area. (Spain had 14,000 men defending Santiago.)

Roosevelt proved his gallantry and the American public thought he'd personally led the charge up San Juan Hill rather than the smaller eminence. The city of Santiago surrendered July 17, virtually ending the land fighting in Cuba.

But more naval heroes were coming. A Spanish fleet of 4 armored cruisers and 3 destroyers was in Santiago harbor. On July 3 Admiral Pascual Cervera slipped out of the harbor to avoid capture by land forces. A fleet of 4 American battleships and their support vessels gave chase and ran aground, blew up or captured all seven Spanish warships. The U.S. squadron was commanded by Commodore Winfield S. Schley.

Schley's commander, Admiral William T. Sampson, was miles away from the "turkey shoot" but presented Cervera's fleet to the nation as a Fourth of July present in a wire to Washington. The wire set off another Manila Bay-type celebration and Sampson's name became more familiar than Schley's.

Commodore Schley's effigy graced a number of medallions and tokens, but Dewey had already captured the lion's share of the adulation reserved for naval heroes.

An American land force aided by Filipinos captured Manila on Aug. 13, one day after the armistice was signed half a world away. A force under Gen. Miles had landed almost without opposition in Puerto Rico on July 25. The war was over.

By the Treaty of Paris, Dec. 10, 1898, America leaped into imperialism and status as a world power: (1) Spain withdrew from Cuba, leaving the island to American military rule. (2) Spain ceded to the U.S. Puerto Rico, Guam in the Marianas, and the Philippine Islands. (3) The U.S. paid Spain $20,000,000 for the Philippines.

All was not sweetness and light, however. Emilio Aguinaldo led the Filipinos in revolt against American rule in February, 1899. It took 60,000 American soldiers until April, 1902 to suppress the rising. In 1901 the U.S. freed Cuba from its rule, but in 1903 had taken a 99-year lease on Guantanamo Bay in eastern Cuba. The U.S. formally annexed Hawaii in 1898 and Samoa in 1899. The nation participated in the June relief expedition for Peking, China during the 1900 Boxer Rebellion.

The war elevated Teddy Roosevelt to the governorship of New York and, in 1900, to the vice presidency. An anarchist's bullet in 1901 killed McKinley and put Roosevelt in his "bully pulpit." Lt. Pershing was to become AEF commander in France in World War I and another soldier in Cuba, Frank Knox, became Secretary of the Navy in World War II. Trooper Charles J. Post of the 71st Infantry (N.Y. National Guard) was a newspaper artist who enlisted, fought in Cuba, suffered, and illustrated the war from the soldier's side. Post's memoirs made the men of the 71st into popular heroes.

The Splendid Little War found reflection on a good many of the store cards and medalets catalogued in this reference — McKinley, Dewey, Schley and others being depicted quite often. By understanding the war and its impact on America, the reader will better appreciate the constant references to it seen on the metallic mementoes of the Gay Nineties.

BROADWAY IN THE 1890'S

Broadway has been called the Greatest Street in the World. In the 1890's New York's premier thoroughfare contained many famous places of business, many of them clustered between Union Square (at 15th Street) and 42nd Street. Imagine:

Tiffany & Co., the great jewelry house, occupied the southwest corner of 15th & Broadway from 1870 to 1906.

The great music houses of Schirmer and of Ditson & Co. were there.

Gorham Manufacturing Co., the great silversmiths,were at 19th and Broadway for about 30 years until 1906.

Park & Tilford, the giant grocery house, occupied the southwest corner of 21st & Broadway 1870 to1910.

Other well-known houses along this section of Broadway in the 1890's were Arnold, Aitken & Son, Constable & Co., Brooks Brothers, and Sloan's.

Though construction began in 1898, Broadway's electric streetcars did not commence running until May 26, 1901 — just after the Nineties decade.

Wallack's Theatre was at 30th & Broadway from 1882 right through the 1890's. Other famous theaters on Broadway during the Gay Nineties were the Bijou Theatre at 1239 Broadway (opened 1883); Standard Theatre (renamed Manhattan Theatre 1897) between 32nd and 33rd; Keith & Proctor's (formerly Daly's); Weber & Field's (later Jo Weber's) on the corner of 29th Street. Gilbert & Sullivan's "H.M.S. Pinafore" was first performed in America at the Manhattan Theatre. Actors and actresses performing on Broadway in those days included Ada Rehan, Sarah Bernhardt, John Drew, James Lewis, George Clarke, Mrs. Gilbert, Helena Modjeska, Lawrence Barrett.

The Union Dime Savings Bank stood at 32nd & Broadway from 1876 to 1910.

TOKENS IN THE NINETIES

Users of this catalog could assume from its coverage that some of the states issued very few tokens in the Gay Nineties. Such assumption should not be made.

Rather, a more complete job of research has been accomplished by the author and his collaborators on some areas than on others.

In earlier sections — those listing pieces emitted from 1700 through 1889 —we recounted the gradually increasing number of tokens in each era. But in this Gay Nineties decade we faced a new phenomenon — an absolute explosion of numbers.

The trade check, or "good for," started coming into its own in the 1866-1889 period, but the 1890-1900 period saw issues of trade checks increase dramatically. The commercial introduction of aluminum to token manufacture about 1891 accelerated an already swelling tide of trade checks. Now every general store, saloon, pool hall, milk deliverer, baker and amusement park had to have its own issue.

There is one class of token which falls off in this period, however — the counterstamp. While a number of counterstamped coins used as tokens do belong to the Nineties, the number of such pieces is very small by comparison with earlier decades.

JUNIOR REPUBLIC TOKENS

A special class of tokens, those of the "Junior Republics" — schools and living sites for boys — began to be issued in the Nineties. One of these is illustrated under Connecticut in the text. These sites have been compared to Father Flanagan's Boys Home of a later era.

A brief listing of these special school-use pieces follows:

GEORGE JUNIOR REPUBLIC, Freeville, N.Y. Uniface tokens in tin issued in 1896 in 1, 5, 10, 25 and 50 cents and $1. Another set in aluminum was issued in 1900 in 1, 5, 10, 25 and 50 cents and $1. Later tokens were dated 1910, 1912 and 1946.

NATIONAL JUNIOR REPUBLIC, Annapolis Junction, Md. Aluminum tokens were issued in 1899 in 1, 5, 10, 25 and 50 cents and $1 denominations. There are two varieties of each token.

JOURNAL JUNIOR REPUBLIC, location unknown. A beautiful set of tokens was issued in 1897. These nickel-alloy denominations were 10, 25 and 50 cents. The JJR followed this up with issuance of an 1898 series — 1-cent copper and 10-cents aluminum.

COMMONWEALTH OF LYMAN SCHOOL, Westbourgh, Mass. (now known as Westboro). This school, not connected with the Junior Republic movement, issued a set of aluminum tokens in 1900, from 1-cent upward. The exact denominations issued are not certain.

FORD REPUBLIC, location unknown. Undated aluminum tokens in 5 and 10 cent denominations.

'DATING' TOKENS BY THE ENGRAVER

Thanks to the research of Bruce W. Smith of Missouri, some of the St. Louis, Missouri token-makers are now better known. One of the most prolific issuers of tokens in St. Louis — for locales all over the country — was A. E. Schmidt, whose incuse or relief maker's mark appears on many tokens which can be dated to the 19th century.

But Smith tells us: "Actually, incuse tokens can be found with the names of at least 20 different St. Louis 'makers'. In most cases, the maker is not a maker at all — these pieces were probably made by two or three companies on behalf of other companies.

"Most of these 'makers' operated well into the 20th century. In fact, some of the A. E. Schmidt pieces were made as late as the 1940's or 1950's!"

He points out that tokens bearing the maker's mark of the following firms, however, may be relegated to the 1890's with a fair degree of certainty:

HASKELL ENGRAVING — out of business in 1909.

H. McK. WILSON — out of business in 1903.

AUG. KERN — name changed to KERN-WEBER in 1911.

ST. LOUIS ENGRAVING — out of business before 1913.

Research by Bill Hamm on Indiana token-makers and by Gaylor Lipscomb on Cincinnati makers, both in 1991 *IKO-TAMS Bulletins,* added these helpful dates:

Bernardin, Evansville, Ind. (lodge badges), 1878-1980.

Charles H. Ellert, Evansville, Ind. (metal checks), 1882-96 or later.

Ferd. Suess, Evansville, Ind. (stencil cutter), 1871-96

Hunter Bradford, Indianapolis, Ind., 1893-1912.

Capital Rubber Stamp Works, Indianapolis, Ind., 1886-95.

George J. Mayer, Indianapolis, Ind., 1885-1958 (cannery checks).

L.T.F. Zaiser, Indianapolis, Ind., 1883-1900 (became Zaiser-Cathcart Co. in 1900).

Lafayette Stamp Works, Lafayete, Ind., 1890-95.

F. Joseph Mulhaupt, Lafayette, Ind., 1879-1980.

Henry Darius Higgins, Mishawaka, Ind., 1846-96.

David Armstrong, South Bend, Ind., 1882-1916 (incuse tokens).

S. H. Straub, South Bend, Ind., 1879-85 (incuse tokens).

S. H. Straub, Kalamazoo, Mich., 1895-1912. (incuse tokens).

John K. Case, Vincennes, Ind., 1888-92 (pool & cloak checks).

George N. Black, Elm St., Cincinnati, Oh, 1879-1900.

Wm. T. Cressler, 6th St., Cincinnati, Oh, 1892-1909.

C. C. Fish, Cincinnati, Oh, 1894-99.

Chas. S. Hickox, Cincinnati, Oh, 1893-94.

A. V. Hover & Co., Cincinnati, Oh, 1890-1900.

DR. B. P. WRIGHT AND THE NINETIES

Token collectors for nearly a century have owed a great debt of gratitude to Dr. Benjamin P. Wright, an early scholar who delved into the mysteries of America's merchant money.

Wright was an indefatigable collector of tokens — treating them all with equality. He was the first American collector to do this — placing trade checks of the 1890's on the same importance level as store cards of the early Republic and the Hard Times period.

It had been fashionable to collect and study Hard Times tokens since the 1850's, and people began collecting Civil War tokens long before Lee's surrender at Appomattox Court House. These two specialties, plus the relatively small Colonial/Revolutionary token field, were as deep as the numismatic establishment was willing to go to extend recognition as "true" tokens.

Dr. Wright changed all that. Though he was not the only serious student of tokens active in the Gay Nineties, he became the champion for his fellows because he was willing to *write* extensively about tokens.

From 1898 to 1901 in *The Numismatist* he published his masterwork, "The American Store or Business Cards" — 1,746 tokens, checks, medalets, tags and store cards — rare, common, beautiful, mundane, identifiable, maverick. He included some pieces as new as tokens issued during the 1901 Pan-American Exposition in Buffalo, New York.

The alphabetized listing contained a full description of each piece — metal, size, shape of flan, complete inscription scientifically reported, and a few background notes. Thus a good number of otherwise undistinguished trade checks, "good fors" and other oddments were recorded for posterity.

Aluminum came into general use in token manufacture in 1891-1892 and, since everything which has a "Wright number" was issued from 1901 back, it is pretty easy to "date" Wright's aluminum pieces.

Wright numbers 1 through 1300 were published in 1898-1899 and numbers 1301 through 1796 sporadically during 1900-1901. The later series began the alphabetical progression from A to Z all over again and resulted, as Wright reported, from collectors reporting to him things which were overlooked in his original manuscript. Keeping these facts in mind, it is possible to "date" many Wright pieces even closer — remembering that his original basic listing was accumulated during 1897.

The Wright listing is rife with errata, but collectors learn to overlook such minor inconveniences. In *Tokens of the Gay Nineties* we have attributed tokens to Wright wherever this is proper. His listing is especially rich in New York state pieces because he lived in Utica and Syracuse and accumulated a large collection of upstate New York pieces.

A few of Wright's contemporaries — Tilton, Low, Mathis, Duffield among them — achieved fame as token catalogers and undoubtedly influenced the recording of data about them, but only Dr. Wright had the impact on the decade of the Nineties which this section records. Thus it is fitting that we dedicate this part of the project to his memory.

ALABAMA

C. J. JACKSON
Coosada, Ala.

Rulau	Date	Metal	Size	VG	F	VF	Unc
Coo 1	(1893)	Brass	24mm	—	—	20.00	—

C. M. JACKSON / *o*o*o*o* / (tulip) / COOSADA, / -.- / * ALA. *. Rv: GOOD FOR / 10 / CENTS / * IN TRADE *. Plain edge. (Grellman coll.)

C. M. Jackson's general store is listed in the 1893 directory. It had disappeared by 1909.

MAGNOLIA CANNING CO.
Alabama ?

Rulau	Date	Metal	Size	VG	F	VF	Unc
Unk 1	(1890's)	Brass	25mm	22.50	30.00	—	—

MAGNOLIA CANNING CO. / 1 / (star). Rv: SPRAGUE CANNING MACHINERY CO. / -.- / CHICAGO / -.- Plain edge. (Hank Thoele coll.)

ALASKA

N. A. T. & T. CO. (North American Transportation & Trading Co.)

Rulau	Date	Metal	Size	VG	F	VF	Unc
AL 1	(1892-1906) CN		24mm	—	200.	—	—

(All incused): N. A. T. & T. CO. / 25 / ¢ / TRADE. Rv: Blank. Plain edge. (Benice NATT IA). Rarity 7.

Rulau	Date	Metal	Size	VG	F	VF	Unc
AL 2	(1892-1906) CN		29mm	—	250.	—	—

Similar, but 50 / ¢. Plain edge. (Benice NATT 1B). Rarity 8.

Rulau	Date	Metal	Size	VG	F	VF	Unc
AL 3	(1892-1906) CN		35mm	—	200.	—	—

Similar, but $1.00. Plain edge. (Benice ATT IC). Rarity 7.

Rulau	Date	Metal	Size	VG	F	VF	Unc
AL 4	(1892-1906) CN		35mm	—	225.	—	—

Similar, but $1.10. Plain edge. (Benice NATT ID). Rarity 7.

The North American Transportation & Trading Co. was organized in 1892 by John J. Healy (See Dyea, Alaska), Portus B. Weare and John Cudahy (of the Chicago meat packing family). Its first store was at "Fort Get There" on St. Michael Island, and the second a year later at Fort Cudahy in the Yukon Territory, Canada. Eventually stores were opened in Circle, Dawson, Fort Yukon, Nome, Chena and other places. Healy left the company to pursue other interests in 1900.

NATT sold off its river and ocean transportation business in 1906, and all its remaining stores in 1912 to the Northern Commercial Company (which later also issued tokens, probably after 1900).

RED ONION RESTAURANT
Canyon City, Alaska

Rulau	Date	Metal	Size	Remainder VF-EF
Can 1	(ca 1898)	Cardboard	Rect. 82 by 52mm	15.00

(Benice Canyon City 1)

"One meal" vouchers were individually numbered and dated, and signed by an agent for Dyea Klondike Trading Co. Unissued remainders are normally encountered; actual issued specimen would be worth $65 to $85 in F-VF.

COLLINS & STRAIT
Circle, Alaska

Rulau	Date	Metal	Size	VG	F	VF	Unc
Cir 1	1898	Brass	21mm	—	—	100.	—

COLLINS & STRAIT / 1898 / ALASKA. Rv: *** / 10 / CENTS / (illegible). Plain edge. Rarity 7. (Benice Circle, IA)

Rulau	Date	Metal	Size	VG	F	VF	Unc
Cir 3	1898	Aluminum	Oct 28mm	—	—	125.	—

Obverse as last. Rv: *** / 25 / CENTS / QUARTER DOLLAR. Plain edge. Rarity 8. (Benice Circle 1B)

Rulau	Date	Metal	Size	VG	F	VF	Unc
Cir 4	1898	Aluminum	--mm	—	—	125.	—

No description. Rarity 7. (Benice Circle 1C)

Circle, population 54, was a mining village established in 1887. The founders thought they were on the Arctic Circle when they named the place, but it is 50 miles south of the circle.

(Horseshoe Bar)
Douglas, Alaska

Rulau	Date	Metal	Size	VG	F	VF	Unc
Dou 1	(1890's)	Brass	Scal 29mm	—	85.00	—	Unc

(All incused): (Horseshoe emblem) at center. Rv: GOOD FOR / 1 / DRINK. Plain edge. Rarity 8. (Benice Douglas 15A)

F. H. KANE
Douglas, Alaska

Rulau	Date	Metal	Size	VG	F	VF	Unc
Dou 3	(1892-99)	Aluminum	26mm	—	75.00	—	—

. F. H. KANE. / DOUGLAS CITY. Rv: GOOD FOR / 12 1/2¢ (script) / IN TRADE. Thick beaded rim on each side. Plain edge. Rarity 7. (Benice Douglas 20A)

Frank Kane ran a saloon here 1892-1899. In 1895 Kane also started a general store, wharf and sawmill at Hoonah on Chichagof Island. On his death in 1899 his widow, Louise H. Kane, kept running the Hoonah business (still in operation in 1979), though the Douglas saloon was given up.

HEALY & WILSON
Dyea, Alaska

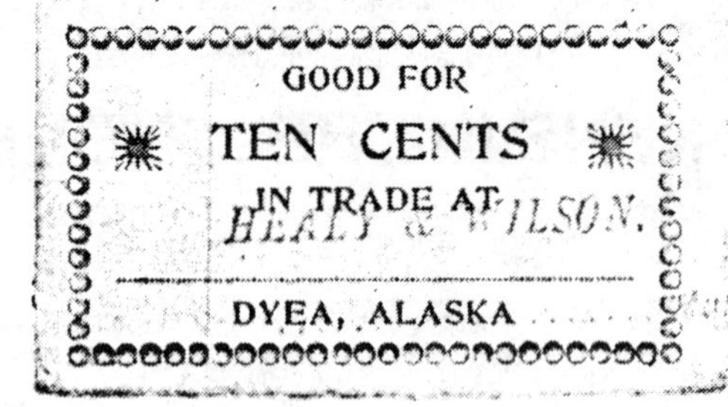

Rulau	Date	Metal	Size	F	VF	EF	Unc
Dye 1	(1886-97)	**	Rect 63 by 35mm	—	30.00	—	—

GOOD FOR / * TEN CENTS * / IN TRADE AT / HEALY & WILSON (stamped) / DYEA, ALASKA. (Benice Dyea IA)

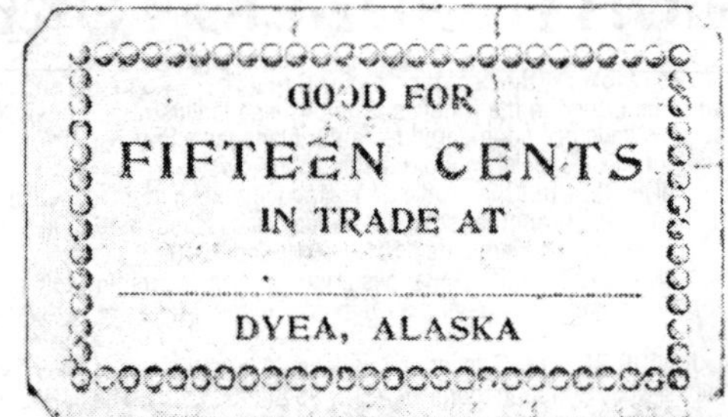

	Date		Size	VG	F	VF	Unc
Dye 2	(1886-97)	**	Rect 62 by 36mm	—	30.00	—	—

GOOD FOR / FIFTEEN CENTS / IN TRADE AT / HEALY & WILSON (stamped) / DYEA, ALASKA. (Benice Dyea 1B)

	Date		Size	VG	F	VF	Unc
Dye 3	(1886-97)	**	—	—	30.00	—	—

Similar, but $1.

	Date		Size	VG	F	VF	Unc
Dye 4	(1886-97)	**	—	—	30.00	—	—

Similar, but $5.

	Date		Size	VG	F	VF	Unc
Dye 5	(1886-97)	**	—	—	50.00	—	—

Similar, but $10.

** Cardboard, uniface. Printed on one side only.

John J. Healy and Edgar Wilson operated a general merchandising, packing and transportation business from 1886 to Wilson's death in 1895. Thereafter Sam Herron managed the trading post and Healy concentrated on the North American Transportation & Trading Company (which see in this reference), and other ventures.

Dyea was former Indian village 3 miles northeast of Skagway which became a port of entry to the Klondike gold fields in the 1880's and 1890's. It declined after completion of the White Pass and Yukon Railway. Healy & Wilson were early entrepreneurs who cashed in on the needs of the miner headed for the gold rush.

Some cardboard chits exist without the merchant's name stamped in; these are only worth 60 percent of those bearing stamps. Other names than Healy & Wilson may have been stamped in, but these have not been discovered.

F. AQUINO

Juneau, Alaska

Rulau	Date	Metal	Size	VG	F	VF	Unc
Jun 1	(1898-99)	Brass	21mm	—	100.	—	—

F. AQUINO / * / JUNEAU / ALASKA. Rv: Large 5 enclosing cent sign. Plain edge. Rarity 8. (Benice Juneau 3A)

Frank Aquino sold tobacco and fruit in 1898-99. In 1902 he went to Nome and entered into partnership with Antonio Polet as grocers; this lasted to 1904.

GERMANIA

Rulau	Date	Metal	Size	VG	F	VF	Unc
Jun 4	(1895-1913)	Brass	21mm	—	—	85.00	—

5¢. No description. Rarity 8. (Benice Juneau 22A)

Germania was a saloon, theater and bawdy house operating from about 1895. It was owned at various time by John and James McCloskey and others.

JUNEAU HOTEL CAFE CO.

Rulau	Date	Metal	Size	VG	F	VF	Unc
Jun 6	(1890-1911)	Brass	Oval 26 by 18mm	—	—	150.	—

JUNEAU HOTEL / -.- / CAFE CO. / ***. Rv: GOOD FOR / * 2 1/2 * / CENTS. Plain edge. Rarity 8. (Benice Juneau 33A)

Owners from 1890 on included George Kyrage, William Casey, Paul Vincent and others.

There is also a series of paper coupons used in the 1890's — 5 cents deep pink paper, 10 green paper, 25 blue paper, 50 light pink paper — each 70 by 32 to 35mm and all issued in books of $15 value. Photograph above. These are worth about $6 each in VF condition, stamped HOTEL JUNEAU / JUNEAU, ALASKA.

LOUVRE THEATRE

Brass 5-cent tokens, 21mm round and 29mm octagonal, probably were issued after 1900. The Louvre Theatre was a saloon and gambling hall in addition to a frontier theater, which opened in 1896 and prospered until about 1917.

D. MARTIN

Rulau	Date	Metal	Size	VG	F	VF	Unc
Jun 9	(1884-1903)	Brass	30mm	—	—	200.	—

D. MARTIN, / GOOD FOR / $1.00 / * IN TRADE * / * JUNEAU CITY, ALASKA. *. Rv: THIS CHECK REDEEMABLE / — IN — / GOODS / AT / RETAIL PRICES / ONLY. Wide beaded rim on each side. Plain edge. Rarity 8. (Benice Juneau 41A)

Dave Martin sold Indian curios 1884-1903 in Juneau. Before 1884 he operated a general store in Sitka. In both 1909 and 1915 Martin operated other businesses briefly. The token probably emanates from the late 1890's.

J. D. MEYER & CO.

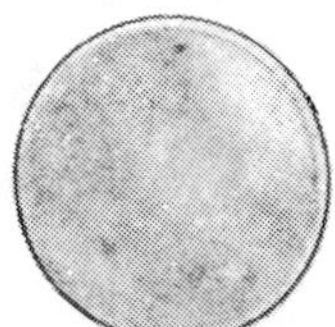

Rulau	Date	Metal	Size	VG	F	VF	Unc
June 11	(1898-99)	21mm	—	—	40.00	—	

J. D. MEYER & CO. / —x— / JUNEAU, ALASKA. Rv: Blank. Plain edge. (Benice Juneau 45A)

Wholesale and retail cigar merchant.

NUGGETT

Rulau	Date	Metal	Size	VG	F	VF	Unc
June 14	(late 1890's	Brass	21mm	—	—	3.50	—

(Ornament) / NUGGETT / (ornament). Rv: BILLIARD / — / * 12 1/2 * ¢ * / — / PARLOR. Plain edge. (Benice Juneau 48A)

The second 'G' in NUGGETT is much larger than the other letters. The Nuggett Billiard Parlor was active at the end of the 19th century.

THE OCCIDENTAL HOTEL

Rulau	Date	Metal	Size	VG	F	VF	Unc
Jun 16	(1900-01)	Aluminum	Oct 30mm	—	—	—	20.00

THE OCCIDENTAL / HOTEL / OLDS & ORTON / PROPS / JUNEAU, ALASKA. Rv: GOOD FOR / 12 1/2 ¢ / IN TRADE. Plain edge. (Benice Juneau 50C)

There are other tokens of the Occidental Hotel which are later.

Olds and Orton owned the hotel 1900-01 only. John P. Olds alone owned it 1902-17, and others operated it to 1923. Olds and Orton earlier had owned the Franklin Hotel, 1890-99.

POST-1900 ALASKAN TOKENS

There are many tokens of Alaska which are colorful, early and rare, some of which are occasionally described as from the Nineties in auction catalogs, sale lists, etc. Others are recent fantasies. A few of the confusing issues are mentioned below:

(THE) NORTHERN

Seward, Alaska

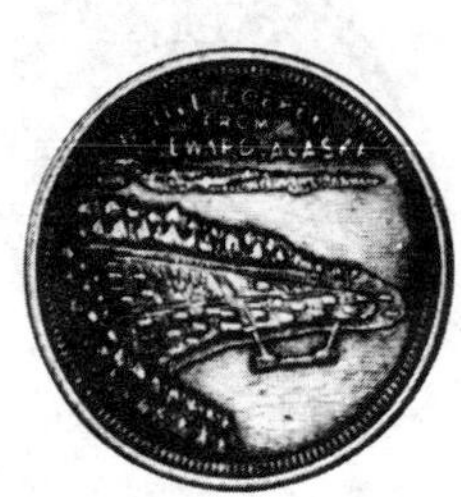

Rulau	Date	Metal	Size	VG	F	VF	Unc
Sew 15	(1907-20)	Copper	28mm	35.00	50.00	75.00	125.

Aerial view of peninsula, the site of Seward. Above: NATIVE COPPER / FROM / SEWARD, ALASKA. Rv: GOOD FOR / -.- / NORTHERN / 12 1/2 C / IN TRADE. Plain edge. (Benice Seward 6B1; Gould 5)

There are several varieties of this token in 28mm round size, plus a variety in oval 22 by 31mm size. The Northern was a hotel, saloon, billiard hall, card room etc. founded in 1907 by E. L. Whittemore and run by him until 1935. John W. Blase was proprietor 1935-42.

THE PALACE

Seward, Alaska

Rulau	Date	Metal	Size	VG	F	VF	Unc
Sew 27	(1920's)	Brass	21mm	—	—	65.00	—

THE PALACE / (sunburst) / SEWARD ALASKA / THE GATEWAY / TO / THE INTERIOR. Rv: GOOD FOR / 6 1/4 C / IN TRADE. Plain edge. (Benice Seward 7A)

The Palace was a cafe and billiard hall opened in 1923 by John Mattick and active until 1959. Tokens were issued in the 6 1/4 and 12 1/2-cent denominations, the latter in both octagonal aluminum and round copper. These denominations were "traditional"; they reflected the "bit" and "two bits" values.

COPPER BLOCK BUFFET

Valdez, Alaska

Rulau	Date	Metal	Size	VG	F	VF	Unc
Vlz 10	(1907-20)	Copper	29mm	35.00	50.00	75.00	125.

View of Valdez, with mountains in background. Above: NATIVE COPPER / FROM / VALDEZ, ALASKA. Rv: 12 1/2 ¢ / COPPER BLOCK / BUFFET / TRADE CHECK. Plain edge. (Benice Valdez 2A)

H. F. Suessdorf founded the Copper Block Buffet, a hotel and saloon, in 1907. An advertisement of the time says the hotel was "for men only" and featured electric lights, steam heat and hot baths - luxuries at that time. The Copper Block Buffet occupied a downtown corner, and Orr's stagecoach office was in the back.

The copper tokens of Seward and Valdez are undoubtedly connected. The Copper Block Buffet also issued large (39mm) nickel tokens with a native gold nugget inlaid on obverse, which carry the $1 denomination - these sell for $400 upward in VF condition.

Valdez was founded in 1898 as Copper City, and its name became Valdez in 1899. Located 115 miles east of Anchorage, it is an ice-free harbor which became an entry point to the Klondike - thus the strong gold connection. A token circa 1907 of W. H. Blackwell stated. "There is lots of gold around Valdez" - ungrammatical but accurate.

ARIZONA

SHATTUCK & KEATING

Bisbee, Ariz.

Rulau	Date	Metal	Size	VG	F	VF	Unc
Bis 1	(1895-98)	Brass	Sc 29mm	—	—	50.00	—

ST. LOUIS / BEER HALL / SHATTUCK / & KEATING / PROPS. Rv: GOOD FOR / 12 1/2 CENTS / AT THE BAR. Plain edge. (Temarantz coll.)

I. M. WALLACE

Bisbee, Ariz.

Rulau	Date	Metal	Size	VG	F	VF	Unc
Bis 3	(1891-97)	Brass	23mm	—	—	209.	—

I. M. WALLACE / GOOD FOR / 12 1/2 / CENTS / BISBEE, A.T. Rv: Blank. (Temarantz coll.)

SUMMERFIELD & PECK

Black Diamond, Ariz.

Rulau	Date	Metal	Size	F	VF	EF	Unc
Bld 1	(1903)	Brass	21mm	—	70.00	85.00	—

SUMMERFIELD / -&- / * PECK * / BLACK DIAMOND / . * . / ARIZONA. Rv: GOOD FOR / (fancy) 1 / DRINK. Plain edge. Rarity 6. (Rulau coll.)

This mining camp became a ghost town.

H. HUNT

Bonita, Ariz.

Rulau	Date	Metal	Size	VG	F	VF	Unc
Bon 1	(1900)	Brass	26mm	—	—	400.	—

H. HUNT / BONITA / ARIZONA. Rv: GOOD FOR / ONE / DRINK / (tiny) N.W. STAMP WKS. Plain edge. (Temarantz coll.)

Struck in Minneapolis. Graham County; only 50 pop. in 1910.

TOMAS ORTEGA

Concho, Ariz.

Ortega's two 1898-99 tokens are Indian trader pieces, we believe, thus not cataloged here. They are rare, worth $200 and $900 respectively.

M. RIVERA

Congress, Ariz.

Rulau	Date	Metal	Size	VG	F	VF	Unc
Cgs 1	(1897-1900)	Brass	Oct 28mm	—	—	400.	—

THE STONE SALOON / M. RIVERA, / PROP. / CONGRESS, A.T. GOOD FOR / ONE DRINK / (tiny) PATRICK & CO., S.F. (Temarantz coll.)

Yavapai County; 1910 pop. 50.

THE YELLOWSTONE CLUB

Crittenden, Ariz.

Rulau	Date	Metal	Size	VG	F	VF	Unc
Crt 1	(1892-1908)	Aluminum	25mm	—	—	1200.	—

THE YELLOWSTONE CLUB / -.- / JOHN SMITH / PROP. / -.- / CRITTENDEN, A. T. Rv: GOOD FOR / 1 / DRINK. Plain edge. Probably unique.

Crittenden is a ghost town in Santa Cruz County, Arizona. It had its own post office as early as 1873. A. T. = Arizona Territory.

J. W. BUSH
Dilkon, Ariz.

Rulau	Date	Metal	Size	VG	F	VF	Unc
Arz 5	(1921-)	Brass	20mm	—	—	50.00	—

J. W. BUSH / (ornament) / DILKON. Rv: GOOD FOR / 5 C / IN TRADE. Plain edge. (Mishler coll.)

Used on the Navajo Indian reservation.

C. N. COTTON
Ganado, Ariz.

Rulau	Date	Metal	Size	VG	F	VF	Unc
Gdo 1	(1892-99)	Aluminum	28mm	—	—	50.00	—

C. N. COTTON / GANADO / ARIZONA. Rv: GOOD FOR / 50 ¢ / IN TRADE / (tiny) N.W. STAMP WKS. (Temarantz coll.)

Rulau	Date	Metal	Size	VG	F	VF	Unc
Gdo 2	(1892-99)	Aluminum	26mm	—	—	50.00	—

As last, but 25 ¢.

This business is listed 1892 through 1900. Ganado is on the Navajo reservation.

R. FARRELL
Harshaw, Ariz.

Rulau	Date	Metal	Size	VG	F	VF	Unc
Har 1	(1888-95)	Brass	Oct 27mm	—	500.	—	—

Chas. Pick & Co. die. Rv: GOOD FOR / 5 ¢ / AT R. FARRELL (name in oval shadow box) / IN TRADE. Plain edge. (Temarantz coll.)

Farrell is listed 1888 through 1900, but Pick stopped supplying tokens in 1895.

THE COTTAGE SALOON
Holbrook, Ariz.

Rulau	Date	Metal	Size	VG	F	VF	Unc
Hbk 1	(1891-92)	Brass	24.5mm	400.	—	—	—

THE COTTAGE / SALOON / GOOD FOR / 1 DRINK / HOLBROOK. Rv: THE E. BRUNSWICK BILLIARD TABLE COMPANY / SAN FRANCISCO. (Temarantz coll.)

FAY'S SALOON
Kingman, Ariz.

Rulau	Date	Metal	Size	VG	F	VF	Unc
Kin 3	(1892-97)	GS	24mm	—	—	350.	—

FAY's SALOON / KINGMAN, ARIZ. Rv: GOOD FOR / 1 / DRINK. Plain edge. (Temarantz coll.)

O'BRIEN & JOHNSON
Kingman, Ariz.

Rulau	Date	Metal	Size	VG	F	VF	Unc
Kin 7	(1899)	GS	21mm	—	—	500.	—

NIGHT HAWK SALOON / O'BRIEN / & / JOHNSON / PROP'S / KINGMAN / A.T. Rv: GOOD FOR / ONE / DRINK. (Temarantz coll.)

A. F. SWIGERT
Lynx Creek, Ariz.

Rulau	Date	Metal	Size	VG	F	VF	Unc
Lyx 1	(1899)	Brass	24.5mm	—	—	1750.	—

A. F. SWIGERT / LYNX CREEK. Rv: I. O. U. / 1 DRINK. Plain edge. Unique. (Temarantz coll.)

Listed 1899-1900.

REARDON & RUTHERFORD
Morenci, A.T.

Rulau	Date	Metal	Size	VG	F	VF	Unc
Mor 2	(1890-91)	Brass	24mm	—	800.	—	—

REARDON & RUTHERFORD / MORENCI, / A.T. Rv: GOOD FOR / ONE / DRINK. Plain edge. Unique. (Temarantz coll.)

JOE BIGNON
Pearce, Ariz.

Rulau	Date	Metal	Size	VG	F	VF	Unc
Pea 1	(?)	Aluminum	25mm	—	—	400.	—

Brunswick die BBC. Rv: PIONEER SALOON / PEARCE / ARIZONA, TY. / 12 1/2 ¢ / DRINK / JOE BIGNON PROPRIETOR.

Attribution by Bob Temarantz and Hank Thoele. Pioneer Saloon is listed 1898 through 1912. Cochise County; 1910 pop. 500.

H. KERBER
Prescott, Ariz.

Rulau	Date	Metal	Size	VG	F	VF	Unc
Pre 1	(1899)	Aluminum	25mm	—	—	—	200.

PRESCOTT HOUSE / H. KERBER / PROP. / PRESCOTT, ARIZ. Rv: GOOD FOR / 10 ¢ IN TRADE (tiny) MOISE-KLINKNER CO. S.F. Unique. (Temarantz coll.)

Listed 1899-1900.

G. SCHUERMAN
Prescott, Ariz.

Rulau	Date	Metal	Size	VG	F	VF	Unc
Pre 3	(1885-99)	Brass	25mm	—	—	400.	—

Brunswick die BBC. Rv: PIONEER HOTEL / GOOD FOR / 1 / MEAL / PRESCOTT, ARIZONA.

Schuerman operated the Pioneer Hotel 1885 to 1914. Yavapai County.

B. PALM
Safford, Ariz.

Rulau	Date	Metal	Size	VG	F	VF	Unc
Saf 2	(1883-97)	Brass	24mm	—	—	150.	—

Brunswick die BBC. Rv: GOOD FOR / A / DRINK / OR / CIGAR / AT B. PALM. Plain edge. (Temarantz coll.)

B. Palm is listed at Safford 1882 through 1897. He is also listed at Solomonville, Ariz. in 1892. The token is likely from the 1890's.

D. C. CAGE
Schultz, Ariz.

Rulau	Date	Metal	Size	VG	F	VF	Unc
Sch 1	(1893-95)	GS	25mm	—	—	400.	—

D. C. CAGE / SCHULTZ, ARIZ. Rv: GOOD FOR / 1 / DRINK. Plain edge. (Temarantz coll.)

WM. WOODS
Tucson, Ariz.

Rulau	Date	Metal	Size	VG	F	VF	Unc
Tuc 7	(1900)	Brass	25mm	—	—	125.	—

ORNDORFF BAR / WM. WOODS / TUCSON, ARIZ. Rv: 12 1/2. Plain edge. (Temarantz coll.)

N. H. CHAPIN
Washington, Ariz.

Rare vulcanite tokens were issued 1898-1900, not covered in this reference. Included are 100 red, 25 yellow, 10 blue, 5 red, each worth $100 or more.

W.E. JOHNSON

Willcox, Ariz.

Rulau	Date	Metal	Size	VG	F	VF	Unc
Wcx 3	(1919-)	Alum.	25mm	—	—	10.00	—

BBC die. Rv: GOOD FOR / 5 C / W. E. JOHNSON. Plain edge. Rarity 3. (Brunswick 5370; Koppenhaver June 1987 sale, lot 71)

OTTO MOORE

Willcox, Ariz.

Rulau	Date	Metal	Size	VG	F	VF	Unc
Wcx 7	(1899)	Brass	34mm	—	—	800.	—

Male bust. Rv: WILLCOX HOTEL / OTTO MOORE, / PROP. / WILLCOX, A.T. / GOOD FOR / ONE DRINK / (tiny) MOISE-KLINKNER CO. S.F.. Plain edge. (Hamilton coll.)

Cochise County.

F. R. NELLIS

Williams, Ariz.

Rulau	Date	Metal	Size	VG	F	VF	Unc
Wil 1	(1888-93)	Brass	25mm	—	—	300.	—

F. R. NELLIS / WILLIAMS / ARIZONA. Rv: GOOD FOR / ONE / DRINK. (Temarantz coll.)

ARKANSAS

YAEGER & MINNIG

Argenta, Ark.

Rulau	Date	Metal	Size	VG	F	VF	Unc
Arg 1	(1900)	Brass	21mm	—	—	15.00	—

YAEGER & MINNIG / SALOON / ARGENTA, ARK. Rv: GOOD FOR / 5 ¢ / IN TRADE. (Robinson U-05)

Henry Yaeger and Robert Minnig ran a saloon at 115 No. Main in 1900.

J. A. AYERS

Arkadelphia, Ark.

Rulau	Date	Metal	Size	VG	F	VF	Unc
Ark 1	(1898-)	Brass	Oct 22mm	—	—	40.00	—

(All incused): J. A. AYERS / GOOD FOR / ONE LOAF / OF BREAD. Rv: Blank. (Robinson D-01)

Ayers' bakery is listed 1898-1914. He moved it to Sherrill, Ark. in 1915.

BRIDGFORD & CO.

Beaver, Ark.

Rulau	Date	Metal	Size	VG	F	VF	Unc
Bvr 1	1894	Aluminum	23mm	—	—	50.00	—

BRIDGFORD & CO. / . . . / 1894 / . . . / * BEAVER, ARK. *. (Robinson A-10)

J. & J. EDMISTON

Boonsboro, Ark.

Rulau	Date	Metal	Size	VG	F	VF	Unc
Bns 1	(1890)	Brass	19mm	—	—	40.00	—

J. & J. EDMISTON / -*- / BOONSBORO / . . . / ARK. Rv: GOOD FOR / 5 ¢ / . IN . / * MERCHANDISE *. (Robinson A-05)

General store, listed 1890.

G. N. NELSON

Buford, Ark.

Rulau	Date	Metal	Size	VG	F	VF	Unc
Buf 1	(1900)	Brass	Oct 26mm	—	—	20.00	—

G. N. NELSON / (ornament) / BUFORD, / - / Ark. Rv: GOOD FOR / 25 ¢ / IN MERCHANDISE. (Robinson B-25).

Bradstreet's Book of Commercial Ratings for 1900 tells us G. N. Nelson had a general store in Buford that year. Buford no longer exists, but it was in Baxter County 9 miles from Cotter. Nelson also operated a grist mill, cotton gin and blacksmith shop.

Octagonal brass 10 and 5-cent tokens also were issued; valued about the same. A grandson of the issuer owns several of each token, but few are in the numismatic market.

About 1914 the store was sold to J. C. Hopper, who also issued tokens for it.

GLADE'S

Eureka Springs, Ark.

Aluminum 32mm undated 3-cent tokens are among the commonest of Arkansas tokens, worth about 50 cents each in Unc, and are not 19th century pieces. Several die varieties were issued circa 1945 by Glade W. Miller, who ordered perhaps 20,000 pieces, and large hoards overhang the market.

MANSION HOUSE

Eureka Springs, Ark.

Rulau	Date	Metal	Size	VG	F	VF	Unc
Eur 3	(1892)	Aluminum	25mm	—	—	40.00	—

MANSION / HOUSE. Rv: GOOD FOR / 5 / CENTS / AT THE BAR. (Robinson N-05)

Probably unique. F. H. Cochrane ran the Mansion House Saloon in 1892.

BRADLEY & TALLMAN

Fort Smith, Ark.

Rulau	Date	Metal	Size	VG	F	VF	Unc
Fts 1	(1900)	Brass	25mm	—	—	35.00	—

BRADLEY + TALLMAN / GOOD FOR / 5 ¢ / IN TRADE / OPERA HOUSE. Rv: Blank. Plain edge. (ATCO Maverick 3327; J. L. Hargett coll.; Robinson E-05)

Research by Tom Robinson. Opera House Saloon.

J. GOEBEL

Fort Smith, Ark.

Rulau	Date	Metal	Size	VG	F	VF	Unc
Fts 6	(1892)	Brass	Oct 23mm	—	30.00	—	—

J. GOEBEL (incuse) / GOOD FOR / 5 ¢ / LOAF BREAD. Rv: Blank. Plain edge. (ATCO Maverick 3328; J. L. Hargett coll.)

J. HORNER

Hot Springs, Ark.

Rulau	Date	Metal	Size	VG	F	VF	Unc
Hot 6	(1892)	Brass	28mm	—	—	35.00	—

(All incused): J. HORNER / GOOD FOR / 1 / LOAF BREAD / 634 CENTRAL AVE. Rv: Blank. Plain edge. (ATCO Maverick 3329; J. L. Hargett coll.)

Research by Tom Robinson.

L. LATOURETTE

Jonesboro, Ark.

Rulau	Date	Metal	Size	VG	F	VF	Unc
Jon 1	(1893-)	Brass	23mm	—	—	50.00	—

(All incused): L. LATOURETTE / 1. Rv: Blank. Plain edge. (Tom H. Robinson coll., Pine Bluff, Ark.)

Latourette operated a bakery and confectionery in Jonesboro, Craighead County, 1893-1908. A successor, P. M. Latourette, ran a grain and coal dealership in Jonesboro in 1918.

L. C. GRAMLING

Little Rock, Ark.

Rulau	Date	Metal	Size	VG	F	VF	Unc
Lit 6	(1892)	CN	20mm	—	—	30.00	—

(All incused): L. C. GRAMLING / (Lyre) / L. R. Rv: Blank. (Robinson AY-X)

L. R. = Little Rock. Lewis C. Gramling ran a grocery and saloon at 601 East Second in 1892.

JOHN HOFFMAN

Rulau	Date	Metal	Size	VG	F	VF	Unc
Lit 7	(1895)	Brass	Oct 28mm	—	—	45.00	—

Chas. Pick & Co. die. Rv: GOOD FOR / 1 BEER / JOHN HOFFMANN. Plain edge. Probably unique. (Robinson BP-01)

Another token, of John C. Hoffmann, possibly the same person, has been confirmed by directory evidence to the 1900-08 period.

MERCHANTS EXCHANGE

Rulau	Date	Metal	Size	VG	F	VF	Unc
Lit 8	(1895)	Brass	24mm	—	—	45.00	—

Chas. Pick & Co. die. Rv: GOOD FOR / 5 ¢ / MERCHANTS / EXCHANGE (name in panel) / IN / * TRADE *. Only 1 reported. (Robinson DT-05)

Merchants Exchange was a saloon located in the Merchants Hotel at 202 West Second St. in 1895.

J. MITCHELL

Rulau	Date	Metal	Size	VG	F	VF	Unc
Lit 9	(1895)	Aluminum	Sq 25mm	—	—	35.00	—

Brunswick die BBC. Rv: J. MITCHELL / GOOD FOR / 5 ¢ / IN / TRADE. (Robinson DW-05)

J. SARLO

Little Rock. Ark.

Rulau	Date	Metal	Size	VG	F	VF	Unc
Lit 16	(1892)	Brass	24mm	—	—	40.00	—

(All incused): J. SARLO. / 5 / 714 MAIN. Rv: Blank. (Robinson ES-05)

John Sarlo operated a saloon at 714 Main St. in 1892.

J. H. DOHERTY

Newport, Ark.

Rulau	Date	Metal	Size	VG	F	VF	Unc
New 1	(1890's)	Aluminum	31mm	—	—	60.00	—

In central circle: J. H. DOHERTY / (tiny) CHILDS CHI. Around: BOTTLED EXPRESSLY FOR NEWPORT, ARK. Rv: ST. LOUIS BREWING ASSOCIATION / EXTRA PALE / SPECIAL BREW / LAGER BEER. Plain edge. Only 1 known. (Wright 257; Robinson D-X)

J. PENN

Russell, Ark.

Rulau	Date	Metal	Size	VG	F	VF	Unc
Rus 3	(1900)	Brass	22mm	—	—	40.00	—

5 CTS. / J. PENN / DRINK. Rv: Blank. (Robinson A-05)

James Penn, saloon, 1900.

CALIFORNIA

MORNING STAR HOTEL

Livermore, Calif.

Rulau	Date	Metal	Size	VG	F	VF	Unc
Liv 1	(1890's)	Brass	24.5mm	—	—	15.00	—

MORNING STAR / -*- / HOTEL / (ornament) / LIVERMORE, CAL. Rv: GOOD FOR ONE / * 25 * / ¢ / MEAL / (tiny) C. A. KLINKNER & CO. S. F. Plain edge.

C. A. Klinkner & Co. produced tokens only 1889-1897. They were bought out by L. H. Moise Co. in 1897.

JOHN OLIVER

Llanada, Calif.

Rulau	Date	Metal	Size	VG	F	VF	Unc
Lla 1	(1892)	Brass	23mm	—	—	200.	—

ESTATE of ST. GERMAIN / (pool table) / 57 1st ST. / S.F. Rv: GOOD FOR 1 DRINK / JOHN OLIVER / LLANADA. Plain edge. (Kappen Llan. 1)

WILLIAM O'REILLY & CO.

Los Angeles, Calif.

Rulau	Date	Metal	Size	F	VF	EF	Unc
Lax 3	1892	Aluminum	37mm	—	—	35.00	50.00

Electrical Building. Around: WORLD'S COLUMBIAN EXPOSITION / ELECTRICAL BUILDING. Rv: WILLIAM O'REILLY & CO. / (ornament) / BUSY BEE / SHOE HOUSE / 201 NORTH SPRING ST. / LOS ANGELES / CAL. / (ornament) / ESTABLISHED 1892. (Reverse same as Eglit 592; Kirtley Oct. 1993 sale, lot 1602)

JOHNNY'S CAFE

Newport Beach, Calif.

Rulau	Date	Metal	Size	F	VF	EF	Unc
Npb 6	(?)	Aluminum	Oct 23mm	—	—	15.00	—

.JOHNNY'S. / (crown) / WESTSIDE / CAFE / (inverted crown) / 11th & BRIGHTON. Rv: 5 (large, open) / (tiny) NAT'L BAND & TAG CO. Plain edge. (Elmer Randall coll.)

Rulau	Date	Metal	Size	VG	F	VF	Unc
Npb 8	(?)	Brass	22mm	—	3.00	4.50	6.00

(All incused): JOHNNY'S / 5 ¢ / CAFE. Rv: 11TH & BRIGHTON / 5 / CENTS / NEWPORT. Plain edge. (Rulau Npt 4)

J. McCARGER'S SALOON

Nord, Calif.

Rulau	Date	Metal	Size	VG	F	VF	EF
Nor 3	(1881-91)	Brass	Oct 25mm	—	20.00	25.00	35.00

JACOB STRAHLE CO. / (pool table) / 515 MARKET ST. / SAN FRANCISCO, CAL. Rv: GOOD FOR / C. O. D. / - AT - / J. McCARGERS / SALOON / NORD, CAL. (Kappen Nord 1)

A hoard of perhaps 40 to 50 of this token surfaced, dampening price appreciation.

COURT CONCORDIA F. OF A.

Sacramento, Calif.

Rulau	Date	Metal	Size	VG	F	VF	Unc
Sac 3	(1890's ?)	Brass	Oct. 26.5mm	—	—	25.00	—
	COURT / CONCORDIA / F. OF A. / SACRAMENTO / * / CAL. Rv: GOOD FOR / CENTS (in oval panel) on large 5 / * IN TRADE *. Plain edge. (Kappen Sac 121)						

'AHA' NOVELTY CO.

San Francisco, Calif.

Rulau	Date	Metal	Size	VG	F	VF	Unc
Sfo 1	(ca 1894-95)	German silver	24mm	4.50	6.00	11.00	18.00
	Bear walking left. "AHA" / NOVELTY CO. above, SAN FRANCISCO below. Rv: Two bridle bits, GOOD FOR / 2 above, BITS / IN TRADE below. Plain edge. (Kappen S.F. 31)						
Sfo 2	(1896-1906)	German silver	21mm	4.50	6.00	11.00	18.00
	Bear's head left. "AHA" NOVELTY CO. / SAN FRANCISCO / IRVINE. Rv: GOOD FOR / 5 ¢ / IN TRADE. Plain edge. (Kappen S.F. 32)						
Sfo 3	(1896-1906)	Brass	21mm	4.00	5.50	10.00	16.00
	As last, but brass. (Kappen S.F. 33)						
Sfo 4	(1896-1906)	German silver	21mm	4.50	6.00	11.00	18.00
	As last, but IRVINE S.F. instead of IRVINE. (Kappen S.F. 34)						

ART SALOON

Rulau	Date	Metal	Size	F	VF	EF	Unc
Sfo 8	(?)	Brass	Oct.19mm	—	25.00	—	—
	ART / SALOON / 1356 / MARKET ST. S.F. Rv: 5 ¢ / (small)L. H. MOISE, S.F. Plain edge. (Kappen SF 85)						
Sfo 9	(?)	Brass	21mm	—	25.00	—	—
	ART SALOON / 1356 / MARKET / ST. / SAN FRANCISCO. Rv: GOOD FOR / 5 ¢ / IN TRADE / (small)L. H. MOISE, S.F. Plain edge. (Kappen SF 86)						
Sfo 10	(1898-1902)	Brass	21mm	—	35.00	—	—
	Statue facing left, SOUVENIR JAP STATUE around. Rv: GOOD FOR / 5 ¢ / IN TRADE / ART SALOON / 1356 / MARKET ST. S.F. / (small) L. H. MOISE, S.F. Plain edge. (Kappen SF 87)						
Sfo 11	(?)	Brass	21mm	—	37.50	—	—
	Obverse similar to last. Rv: Blank, but grooved across center for use as a telephone slug. Plain edge. (Kappen SF 88)						

Rulau	Date	Metal	Size	F	VF	EF	Unc
Sfo 12	(?)	Bronze	33.5mm	—	35.00	—	—
	Statue at center, tiny J. C. IRVINE CO. S.F. on base. THE GREAT JAP STATUE around. Rv: SOUVENIR / OF THE / GREAT / ATTRACTION / ART SALOON / 1356 / MARKET ST. S.F. (The statue is wearing a loincloth.) Reeded edge. (Kappen SF 89)						

Rulau	Date	Metal	Size	F	VF	EF	Unc
Sfo 13	(?)	Bronze	33.5mm	—	35.00	—	—
	Obverse same as last. Rv: GOOD FOR / ONE DRINK / AT THE BAR / ART SALOON / 1356 / MARKET ST. S.F. / (small) J. C. IRVINE CO. S.F. Reeded edge. (Kappen SF 90)						
Sfo 14	(?)	Bronze	34mm	—	40.00	—	—
	Statue at center, wearing fig leaf. SOUVENIR JAP STATUE around. Rv: GOOD FOR / 10 ¢ / IN TRADE / Art Saloon (in fancy letters) / 1356 / . / MARKET ST. S.F. / (tiny) L. H. MOISE S.F. Plain edge. (Wright 1317; Kappen SF 91)						
Sfo 15	(?)	Cupronickel	34mm	—	60.00	—	—
	At last. Plain edge. (Kappen SF 92)						
Sfo 16	(?)	Bronze	33.5mm	—	25.00	—	—
	Statue standing between curtains, SOUVENIR JAP STATUE around, tiny L. H. MOISE S.F. below. Rv: Same as last. Plain edge. (Kappen SF 93)						

Rulau	Date	Metal	Size	F	VF	EF	Unc
Sfo 17	(?)	Bronze	33.5mm	—	25.00	—	—
	Obverse as last. Rv: GOOD FOR / ONE DRINK / AT THE BAR / Art Saloon (fancy letters) / 1356 / MARKET ST. S.F. Plain edge. (Kappen SF 94)						
Sfo 18	(?)	Bronze	--mm	—	100.	—	—
	Similar to last, but denomination $1.00. (Kenny 203; Kappen SF 95)						

It is possible that Sfo 18, the $1 token, does not exist but was described by Richard D. Kenney in *So-Called Dollars* in error. Not examined by the cataloguers.

The Art Saloon of San Francisco was first listed in the city directory of 1899 at 1356 Market Street. The owner and proprietor was T. P. Dunne whose residence was listed at 38 McAllister Street. He probably operated this saloon until 1902 when the location is then listed one block west at 1410 Market Street. After the earthquake and fire of 1906, the Art Saloon was owned by Peter McGuire. In 1907 or 1908 the location was again moved another block west to 1152 Market Street with Hugh McGuire listed as the manager. After 1908 the city directory does not list an Art Saloon.

The token was issued by the original owner, T. P. Dunne when the Art Saloon was in its original location of 1356 Market Street in 1899 and it pictures the famous wooden statue that is now reposing in the Ripley Believe It Or Not Museum on Fisherman's Wharf in San Francisco. There are varieties of this famous token. The die pictures the Japanese statue on a dais with a fig leaf covering while the other pictures the Japanese statue on a mat with a loincloth covering. The reverses differ also. The fig leaf variety has an inscription, "Good for 10¢ in trade" while the loincloth inscription reads, "Good for one drink at the bar." They were struck in brass and are 34mm in diameter.

Dr. B. P. Wright lists the fig leaf variety as number 1317 struck in copper and calls it rare.

The tokens were struck by L. H. Moise Co. of San Francisco who operated in the token field from 1893 until 1930. The die work on the tokens is excellent in detail — notice the eyeglasses on the statue.

It is said that Ripley knew of this statue and searched for many years to acquire it. One mystery is how such a creation of wood could have survived the earthquake and fire of San Francisco in 1906. The location of the Art Saloon was in the immediate vicinity — just a few blocks from Van Ness Avenue which was blown up when the Army tried to block the fire which followed the quake.

The acquisition of this statue by Ripley occurred sometime before 1934 and was in his home near Long Island, New York. It was returned to San Francisco in 1965 when the museum opened. Ripley died in 1948 and the statue was on exhibit in the New York museum branch for a time before its return. This remarkable work of art has travelled from coast to coast and is believed to have been created around 1885.

The tokens of the Art Saloon and the story of Masakichi are ideal examples of what our hobby has to offer — local history, nostalgia and knowledge of a medium of exchange not found in coin collecting, per se.

This life-size wooden statue, so exact and realistic in every detail, was carved by the illustrious Japanese artist Hananuma Masakichi as a reproduction of himself, and is said by connoisseurs of the art world, to be the most perfect image of man ever created.

Suffering from tuberculosis, loving a beautiful girl, and realizing he could never marry her, Masakichi made this wonderful figure so that his image could be ever before her. It is composed of 2,000 pieces of wood, all skillfully dovetailed and glued together without the use of nails, screws or metals.

Adjustable mirrors were emloyed by the sculptor, making it possible for him to see himself at every angle, the result being a perfect counterpart of the artist in every particular . . . even the hair is Masakichi's — plucked from his body and inserted one by one in the tiny holes bored for them.

After completing the figure, Masakichi left his home in Tokyo — and the girl he loved — to await his expected death. He travelled for many years, his health gradually deteriorating. When he died at the age of 63, he was sill unmarried and unhappy, but an immortally famous artist.

BERNHARDT'S

Rulau	Date	Metal	Size	F	VF	EF	Unc
Sfo 22	(1891-1901)	Brass	21mm	—	15.00	—	—

BERNHARDT'S / 434 / MONTGOMERY ST. / NEAR SAC'TO / * S.F.*. (Rv: SEALS / RUBBER / STAMPS / ETC. Plain edge. (Kappen S.F. 237 variety)

Paul B. Bernhardt & Co. were in business 1891-1908. They were at 434 Montgomery St. 1891-1901; then at 512 Montgomery St. 1902-05; and 1722 O'Farrell St. 1906-08. This firm, also known as Bernhard, struck tokens for other firms with BERNHARD S.F. signature.

CHRISTIAN ENDEAVOR

Rulau	Date	Metal	Size	VG	F	VF	Unc
Sfo 28	1897	Gilt Brass	30mm	—	12.50	18.50	—

Ornate gateway with WELCOME on arch, flags above it, across center of token. CHRISTIAN ENDEAVOR / JULY 7 TO 12 / 1897 / * SAN FRANCISCO, CAL. * / L. H. MOISE. Rv: Large CE monogram at center. SOUVENIR / 16TH / * INTERNATIONAL CONVENTION. Thick plancet. Plain edge. (Not in Kappen)

Also see Christian Endeavor's 11th convention token in 1892 under New York, N.Y.

LEE D. CRAIG

Rulau	Date	Metal	Size	VG	F	VF	Unc
Sfo 31	(1890's)	Aluminum	28mm	—	15.00	25.00	100.

Mechanical seal at center, LEE D. CRAIG. / COMMISSIONER OF DEEDS above, NOTARY PUBLIC / NO 316 MONTGOMERY ST., S.F. Rv: View of ruins, SOUVENIR above, CASA GRANDE RUINS / (tiny) KLINKNER & C. Plain edge. Thick flan. (ANS coll.)

Rulau	Date	Metal	Size	VG	F	VF	Unc
Sfo 32	(1890's)	Aluminum	28mm	—	—	—	100.

Obverse as last. Rv: Lord's Prayer. Plain edge. Thin flan. (ANS coll.)

DODGE SWEENEY & CO.

Rulau	Date	Metal	Size	VG	F	VF	Unc
Sfo 34	(1893)	Aluminum	37.5mm	—	—	35.00	50.00

Building at center, CALIFORNIA BUILDING above, WORLD'S COLUMBIAN / EXPOSITION in exergue. Rv: Salt bag in central circle, labeled: HIGGIN'S / EUREKA / FINE SALT / IN PURE LINEN SACKS / MANUF'D EXPRESSLY / -FOR- / DAIRY & TABLE USE / CHESHIRE / ENGLAND. Around: COMPLIMENTS OF DODGE, SWEENEY & CO. AGENTS, SAN FRANCISCO. / *. Plain edge. (Tanenbaum coll.)

This beautiful token was struck in Philadelphia.

KNIGHTS TEMPLAR

Rulau	Date	Metal	Size	VG	F	VF	Unc
Sfo 37	1883	Brass	22mm	—	—	15.00	—

Cross-thru-crown on Maltese cross emblem of KT. Rv: KNIGHTS TEMPLAR'S / SAN FRANCISCO / CAL. / SOUVENIR (on ribbon) / 20TH TO 25TH / AUGUST / 1883 / TRIENNIAL CONCLAVE. Plain edge. Issued holed.

MOISE KLINKNER CO.

Rulau	Date	Metal	Size	F	VF	EF	Unc
Sfo 40	(1898-1904)	Brass	21mm	3.50	5.00	—	—

TELEPHONE TOKENS / MADE BY / MOISE / KLINKNER CO. / 320 / SANSOME ST. Rv: DROP THIS IN YOUR / TELEPHONE / AND CALL / MAIN 400. Plain edge. (Kappen S.F. 1736)

THE OLYMPIC CLUB

Rulau	Date	Metal	Size	VG	F	VF	Unc
Sfo 48	1893	Bronze	31mm	—	—	35.00	50.00

Jugate laureate busts left. Around: AUGUSTUS AND LIVIA / MR. & MRS. J. B. SCHROEDER. Rv: Within open wreath: ROMAN REVIVAL / BY / THE OLYMPIC CLUB / APRIL XVII-XXII / MDCCCLXXXXIII / SAN FRANCISCO / CAL. Plain edge. (Kirtley Oct. 1988 sale, lot 649)

RETURN OF CALIFORNIA VOLUNTEERS

Rulau	Date	Metal	Size	F	VF	EF	Unc
Sfo 63	1899	Gilt/B	39mm	—	—	80.00	—

Angel of peace flies above parading soldiers left, 1898 - WELCOME OUR HEROES - 1899 above. Rv: RETURN OF / (ornament) / CALIFORNIA / VOLUNTEERS / - AT - / SAN FRANCISCO, CAL. / FROM / (scroll) MANILA, P.I. Issued holed. (Kirtley Jan. 1994 sale, lot 1236)

SURPRISE

Rulau	Date	Metal	Size	F	VF	EF	Unc
Sfo 70	(1889-97)	Aluminum	21mm	—	—	8.00	—

SURPRISE. Rv: 5 / C.A. KLINKNER & CO. S.F. plain edge. (Not in Kappen)

C.A. Klinkner & Co. produced its first tokens in 1889 at the 320 Sansome St. address. They were bought out by L.H. Moise in 1897.

THALIA CAFE

San Francisco, Calif.

Rulau	Date	Metal	Size	VG	F	VF	Unc
Sfo 80	(1895)	Aluminum	24mm	—	30.00	40.00	—

THALIA (large) / * CAFE * / MARKET & TURK STS. / (ornament) / SAN FRANCISCO. / (tiny) C. A. KLINKNER & CO. S.F. Rv: GOOD FOR / 5 (large, shaded) C / DRINK AT THE BAR. Plain edge. (Kappen 2544; *TAMS Journal* for Oct. 1993, pp. 166-167)

The Thalia was a "music hall" and den of iniquity in the basement of a four-story building, operated 1890 on by Schimpf and Walter. Schwartz Brothers took over 1895 and issued the token. Police closed the place down in January, 1903.

Thalia Cafe reopened after the 1906 earthquake.

A. GALEWSKY
San Luis Obispo, Calif.

Rulau	Date	Metal	Size	VG	F	VF	Unc
Sib 4	(1893-1904)	White Metal	21mm	—	3.25	—	—

THE / WHISPER. Rv: 5 CTS. / IN TRADE / L.H. MOISE S.F. Grooved across reverse for phone usage. Plain edge. (Kappen S.L.O. 97)

Rulau	Date	Metal	Size	VG	F	VF	Unc
Sib 6	(ca 1918)	Brass	21mm	—	3.00	—	—

THE / - / WHISPER / - * - / A. GALEWSKY. Rv: GOOD FOR / * 5 * / CENTS / IN TRADE/ Plain edge. (Kappen S.L.O. 98)

Alex Galewsky ran a saloon in 1918.

SHERIFF C. NICHOLS
Santa Ana, Calif.

Rulau	Date	Metal	Size	VG	F	VF	Unc
Sna 1	(1890's)	Aluminum	25mm	—	—	—	—

An orange, COUNTY below. Rv: C. NICHOLS / SHERIFF / ORANGE CO. / SANTA ANA CAL. Plain edge. (Wright 1551)

ARLINGTON HOTEL
Santa Barbara, Calif.

Rulau	Date	Metal	Size	VG	F	VF	Unc
Sba 1	(1890's ?)	WM	34mm	—	—	30.00	50.00

View of large hotel buildings, ARLINGTON / HOTEL above, SANTA BARBARA CAL on scroll below. Rv: FIRST CLASS / WINTER / . AND / SUMMER / RESORT / ** E. P. DUNN. ***. Plain edge. (ANS coll.)

OCCIDENTAL HOTEL
Santa Rosa, Calif.

Rulau	Date	Metal	Size	VG	F	VF	Unc
Srs 8	(?)	Brass	25mm	5.00	7.00	—	—

GOOD FOR ONE DRINK / AT / OCCIDENTAL / HOTEL / SANTA ROSA, CAL. Rv: Blank. Plain edge. (Wright 1554; Kappen S.R. 70)

Rulau	Date	Metal	Size	VG	F	VF	Unc
Srs 9	(1884-1900)	25mm	25mm	12.50	17.50	40.00	—

Billiard table at lower center. Above: THE BRUNSWICK BALKE / COLLENDER / COMPY. Below: CHECK. Rv: GOOD FOR ONE DRINK / OCCIDENTAL / HOTEL / SANTA ROSA, CAL. Plain edge. (Kappen S.R. 69)

GRANDPA'S CIGAR STAND
(California ?)

Rulau	Date	Metal	Size	VG	F	VF	Unc
Unk 3	(1894-1907)	Brass	21mm	—	—	6.00	—

GRANDPA'S / -.- / CIGAR / -.- / STAND -.- / PATRICK & CO. S.F. Rv: GOOD FOR / + 5¢ + / IN TRADE. Plain edge. (Not in Kappen)

COLORADO

PARTELI & BENSEL
Central City, Colo.

Rulau	Date	Metal	Size	VG	F	VF	Unc
Cen 3	(?)	Brass	27mm	—	—	20.00	—

GOOD FOR / 5 ¢ / IN TRADE / AT BAR / PARTELI & BENSEL. Rv: NATIONAL BILLIARD MANF'G CO. / N.B.M.CO. (within crossed cues) / CIN. O. Plain edge. (Thoele coll.)

Used at the Gold Coin Saloon on Main Street. See "Early Saloon Tokens" by Dr. Philip Whitely in *The Numismatist* for March, 1958.

B. SCAVARDA
Chandler, Colo.

Rulau	Date	Metal	Size	VG	F	VF	Unc
Cha 4	(?)	Brass	--mm	—	—	25.00	—

B. SCAVARDA. Rv: 12 1/2 C / IN TRADE. Plain edge. Rarity 8.

Attribution by Paul Koppenhaver, Van Nuys, Calif.

E. J. VULGAMOTT
Coulter, Colo.

Rulau	Date	Metal	Size	VG	F	VF	Unc
Clt 3	(1893-96)	Brass	21mm	—	6.00	9.00	—

E. J. VULGAMOTT / -.- / (star). Rv: GOOD FOR / * 12 1/2 ¢ * / IN TRADE. Plain edge. (Thoele coll.)

The gazetteers of 1893, 1894 and 1896 list this saloon.

KENTUCKY LIQUOR CO.
Cripple Creek, Colo.

Rulau	Date	Metal	Size	VG	F	VF	Unc
Cck 8	(1893-96)	Aluminum	30mm	—	—	45.00	—

KENTUCKY / -o- / LIQUOR CO. / CRIPPLE CREEK / COL. Rv: GOOD FOR / 12 1/2 ¢ / AT THE BAR. Plain edge. (Wright 1483)

Saloon, located at 217 Bennett.

MILLER & GUSTAFSON
Cripple Creek, Colo.

Rulau	Date	Metal	Size	VG	F	VF	Unc
Cck 14	(?)	Brass	--mm	—	—	50.00	—

MILLER & GUSTAFSON. 12 1/2 C. (Wright C5005; Kirtley March 1991 sale, lot 1373)

DENVER CARNIVAL & PEACE JUBILEE
Denver, Colo.

Rulau	Date	Metal	Size	VG	F	VF	Unc
Den 3	1898	Brass	38mm	—	—	30.00	40.00

Angel hammering a cannon, dove in flight above. Around: DENVER CARNIVAL & PEACE JUBILEE / 1898. Rv: Capitol building. (Kirtley 1992 ATCO sale, lot 1060)

MAY SHOE & CLOTHING CO.

Rulau	Date	Metal	Size	F	VF	EF	Unc
Den 7	1897	Aluminum	34.5mm	—	25.00	35.00	—

Mountain scene. Around: FESTIVAL OF MOUNTAIN & PLAIN / 1897. OCT. 5. 6. 7. Rv: Within wreath: COMPLIMENTS / ---- OF ---- / THE MAY / SHOE & / CLOTHING / CO. / DENVER. Plain edge. (Peter Fuhrman coll.)

PENNOCK (&) LINK
Denver, Colo.

Rulau	Date	Metal	Size	VG	F	VF	Unc
Den 10	(1890-95)	Brass	25mm	—	—	40.00	—

Brunswick die BBC-11. Rv: GOOD FOR / 5 C / PENNOCK / LINK / AT THE BAR. Plain edge. (Thoele coll.)

Pennock & Link were saloon proprietors listed 1890 through 1895 in the *Colorado Gazetteer*. The diesinker apparently left the "&" off the die.

ROBERT & CHAPMAN
Erie, Colo.

Rulau	Date	Metal	Size	VG	F	VF	Unc
Eri 8	(1880-95)	Brass	25mm	—	60.00	125.	—

Saloon implements. CHAS. PICK & CO. Rv: GOOD FOR / 5 C / ROBERT CHAPMAN / ERIE COLO. / IN / * TRADE *. (Wright 900)

S. E. ROBERTS
Las Animas, Colo.

Rulau	Date	Metal	Size	VG	F	VF	Unc
Lsn 3	(1889-90)	Brass	Hexag 25mm	—	—	8.50	—

S. E. ROBERTS. Rv: GOOD FOR / 5 ¢ / IN TRADE.

S. E. Roberts was listed under saloons in the 1889 and 1890 gazetteers.

JOHN BOWE'S SALOON

Leadville, Colo.

Rulau	Date	Metal	Size	VG	F	VF	Unc
Ldv 2	(?)	Brass	--mm	—	—	125.	—

Brunswick-Balke die. Rv: JOHN BOWE'S SALOON / 5. (Kirtley 1992 ATCO sale, lot 1067)

THE SARATOGA

Leadville, Colo.

Rulau	Date	Metal	Size	VG	F	VF	Unc
Ldv 9	(1901)	Nickel	--mm	—	—	40.00	—

THE SARATOGA / LEADVILLE. Rv: 12 1/2 C / AT BAR. Plain edge. (There are two die varieties. Koppenhaver June 1987 sale, lots 466 and 467)

C. P. PRENTISS

Lyons, Colo.

Rulau	Date	Metal	Size	VG	F	VF	Unc
Lyn 8	(?)	Brass	--mm	—	—	50.00	—

C. P. PRENTISS / LYONS, COLO. Rv: 2 1/2 C / IN TRADE. Ctsp CC on obverse. Plain edge. Rarity 9. (Koppenhaver June 1987 sale, lot 484)

The only reported specimen has a large 'X' cancellation mark on reverse.

A. G. CHAPLIN

Meeker, Colo.

Rulau	Date	Metal	Size	VG	F	VF	Unc
Mee 3	(?)	Aluminum	--mm	—	—	50.00	—

A. G. CHAPLIN $1.00. (Kirtley 1992 ATCO sale, lot 1069)

GIFFORD & HOUSE

Rulau	Date	Metal	Size	VG	F	VF	Unc
Mee 5	(?)	GS	25mm	—	25.00	40.00	—

GIFFORD / & / HOUSE / MEEKER, / COLO. Rv: GOOD FOR / 25 ¢ / IN MERCHANDISE. Beaded rims on each side. Plain edge. (Rulau coll.)

W. KONOPIK

Rulau	Date	Metal	Size	VG	F	VF	Unc
Mee 8	(1910 ?)	Brass	Oval 31x23mm	—	22.50	40.00	—

W. KONOPIK. / (ornament) / MEEKER. / COLO. Rv: GOOD FOR / 12 1/2 ¢ / IN TRADE. Beaded rims on each side. Plain edge. (Rulau coll.)

MEEKER DRUG CO.

Rulau	Date	Metal	Size	VG	F	VF	Unc
Mee 10	(?)	Aluminum	**	—	45.00	80.00	—

** Square w/round corners, 25mm.

Owl on branch. Rv: GOOD FOR / 2 1/2 ¢ / IN TRADE. / MEEKER / DRUG CO. Plain edge. (Rulau coll.)

Meeker is in Rio Blanco County. Its World War I population was 807.

MEEKER HOTEL BAR

Rulau	Date	Metal	Size	VG	F	VF	Unc
Mee 12	(?)	Brass	--mm	—	—	40.00	—

AT MEEKER HOTEL BAR / 5 C TRADE. Rv: No description available. Plain edge. Rarity 9. (Koppenhaver June 1987 sale, lot 486)

THE OLD PIONEER BAR

Meeker, Colo.

Rulau	Date	Metal	Size	VG	F	VF	Unc
Mee 15	(1910 ?)	Brass	**	—	27.50	40.00	—

** Barrel-shaped, 25x32mm.

THE OLD PIONEER / BAR / MEEKER, COLO. Rv: GOOD FOR / 12 1/2 ¢ / DRINK. Plain edge. (Nathan N. Eglit coll.)

J. F. WRIGHT

Penrose, Colo.

Rulau	Date	Metal	Size	VG	F	VF	Unc
Pen 8	(?)	Aluminum	Oct --mm	—	—	40.00	—

PENROSE PHARMACY. J. F. WRIGHT. 1 1/4 C. (Kirtley 1992 ATCO sale, lot 2153)

CENTRAL NATIONAL BANK

Pueblo, Colo.

Rulau	Date	Metal	Size	VG	F	VF	Unc
Pue 5	1892	Aluminum	32mm	—	—	25.00	—

Within wreath: PRESENTED / BY / CENTRAL / NATIONAL / BANK / * / PUEBLO, COLO. Around: COLUMBIAN EXPOSITION SOUVENIR / * 1492-1892 *. Rv: Within circle: SUNNY PUEBLO THE GREAT SANITARIUM***. Around: CLIMATE / MANUFACTURERS / SMELTERS / AGRICULTURE / RAPID GROWTH. Plain edge. (Wright 159)

GLASS & McQUILLAN

Pueblo, Colo.

Rulau	Date	Metal	Size	VG	F	VF	Unc
Pue 8	(?)	Brass	19mm	—	15.00	—	—

GLASS & MC QUILLAN / -.- / MINNEQUA / PARK / -.- / PUEBLO, COLO. Rv: Same as obverse. Plain edge. (Rulau coll.)

WATERMELON DAY

Rocky Ford, Colo.

Rulau	Date	Metal	Size	F	VF	EF	Unc
Rkf 20	1898	Brass	39mm	—	—	37.50	50.00

Watermelon divides 18 -- 98. Around: WATERMELON DAY / SEPT. 1. / ROCKY FORD, COLO. Rv: Colorado state arms. Issued holed for suspension.

PHENEX & WILCOX

Salida, Colo.

Rulau	Date	Metal	Size	F	VF	EF	Unc
Sda 4	(?)	Brass	--mm	—	—	50.00	—

PHENEX & WILCOX / SALIDA, COLO. Rv: GOOD FOR / 12 1/2 CENTS / IN TRADE. Plain edge. Rarity 9.

J. A. ROGERS

Salida, Colo.

Rulau	Date	Metal	Size	VG	F	VF	Unc
Sda 7	(1888-1901)	Brass	28mm	—	—	35.00	—

(Incuse) J. A. ROGERS / OLD / OSCAR / . / PEPPER / (incuse) GOOD FOR 1 DRINK. Rv: (Incuse) F. MARTIN. Incised beaded rim on each side. Plain edge. Issued holed. (Thoele coll.)

This saloon is listed in directories 1888 through 1901. "Old Oscar Pepper" is apparently a liquor brand.

HARRIS & MILLER

Steamboat Springs, Colo.

Rulau	Date	Metal	Size	VG	F	VF	Unc
Stm 4	(1900-01)	Brass	25mm	—	—	9.50	—

GOOD FOR / 5 C / HARRIS & / MILLER / IN TRADE. Rv: Large numeral 5. Plain edge.

Harris & Miller were listed as saloon proprietors in the 1901 *Colorado Gazetteer.* Steamboat Springs is in Routt County.

MARTIN & RUNDLE

Telluride, Colo.

Rulau	Date	Metal	Size	VG	F	VF	Unc
Tld 5	(1890-98)	Brass	25mm	—	—	60.00	—

Brunswick die B-2a. Rv: GOOD FOR / 1 / MARTIN / & RUNDLE / DRINK. Plain edge.

In the Nov. 5, 1984 Tom Wall auction, a Martin & Rundle token in VF condition fetched $42.60.

Martin & Rundle were partners in a saloon listed 1891 through 1898.

McMURRY & PITT

Colorado?

Rulau	Date	Metal	Size	VG	F	VF	Unc
Unk 1	(1890's)	Brass	25mm	—	—	20.00	—

Brunswick die BBC-8. Rv: GOOD FOR / 2 1/2 ¢ / IN TRADE / McMURRY & PITT. Plain edge.

Possibly connected with McMurry & Co., a Colorado saloonkeeper.

JOE METRAS

Rulau	Date	Metal	Size	VG	F	VF	Unc
Unk 2	(1901 ?)	Brass	24mm	—	3.00	—	—

GOOD FOR / 5 ¢ / JOE METRAS / IN / TRADE. Rv: Large 5 in circle of 16 stars. Plain edge.

It is theorized this may be an issue of Joseph Metroz, a 1901 saloonkeeper of Gunnison, Colo., with diesinker error. Dubious.

HORTON HOUSE

Colorado?

Rulau	Date	Metal	Size	VG	F	VF	Unc
Unk 3	(1890's)	Brass	25mm	—	30.00	—	—

Brunswick die BBC-11. Rv: HORTON HOUSE / W. E. HADLEY / PROPRIETOR. (Thoele coll.)

CONNECTICUT

NEW DEPARTURE

Bristol, Conn.

Rulau	Date	Metal	Size	VG	F	VF	Unc
Bri 10	(1890's)	CN	17.3mm	—	—	20.00	—

(All incused): NEW DEPARTURE / PAT'D / (radiant desk bell in diamond) / JAN. 3. 88. / BRISTOL, CONN. U.S.A. Rv: Same as obverse. Plain edge. Issued double-holed for mounting.

THE VEEDER M'FG. CO.

Hartford, Conn.

Rulau	Date	Metal	Size	F	VF	EF	Unc
Har 6	1895	CN	18mm	—	—	4.00	6.50

(All incused): THE VEEDER M'FG. CO. / PATENTED / VEEDER (script) / OCT. 22. 1895 / HARTFORD, CONN. U.S.A. Rv: Blank. Plain edge.

Rulau	Date	Metal	Size	F	VF	EF	Unc
Har 8	1895	Brass	18mm	—	—	4.50	7.00

(All incused): 28 / THE VEEDER M'F'G. CO. / PATENTED / (Veeder (script) / OCT. 22. 1895. / HARTFORD. CONN. U.S.A. / METRIC. Rv: Blank. Plain edge.

Rulau	Date	Metal	Size	F	VF	EF	Unc
Har 10	1899	CN	17mm	—	—	4.50	7.00

(All incused): THE VEEDER M'F'G. CO. / PATENTED / Veeder (script) / OCT. 3, 1899 / HARTFORD, CONN. U.S.A. Rv: Blank. Plain edge. (Pete Peters coll.)

These items seem to be some sort of identification discs for equipment or tools. Most specimens seen are holed at each side, as for mounting. Their flans are relatively thin.

E. M. WEBB

Hartford, Conn.

Rulau	Date	Metal	Size	VG	F	VF	Unc
Har 20	1900	Aluminum	31mm	—	—	100.	—

Naval bust 3/4 right. Around: OUR COUNTRY'S PRIDE / +**+ ADMIRAL DEWEY +**+. Rv: GOOD FOR / 5 ¢ / ON ANY PURCHASE / MADE AT / E. M. WEBB'S / 442 ASYLUM ST. / HARTFORD, CT. Tiny 1900 vertically within the C of 5 C. Plain edge. (Gary Potter coll.)

CELLULOID STARCH CO.

New Haven, Conn.

Rulau	Date	Metal	Size	F	VF	EF	Unc
Nhv 20	(?)	Brass	32mm	2.50	4.00	5.50	10.00

Celluloid wing collar. + THE CELLULOID STARCH CO. + / TRADE / MARK / NEW HAVEN, CONN. Rv: A GREAT INVENTION/ FREE / PRESENT THIS CHECK TO / YOUR GROCER / & GET ONE PACKAGE / CELLULOID / STARCH / FREE OR 3 FOR 20 CENTS. Plain edge. (Miller Conn. 20)

Rulau	Date	Metal	Size	F	VF	EF	Unc
Nhv 21	(?)	Brass	32mm	2.50	4.00	5.50	10.00

Similar to 20, but star before and after THE CELLULOID STARCH CO. instead of +. Plain edge. (Wright 1106; Miller Conn. 21)

Rulau	Date	Metal	Size	F	VF	EF	Unc
Nhv 21C	(?)	Brass	32mm	7.50	12.50	15.00	20.00

Similar to 20, but tiny maker's initials C. L. C. at lower rim. Rv: Similar to 20, but last line reads: FREE OR 2 FOR 10 CENTS. (Peter Fuhrman coll.)

Rulau	Date	Metal	Size	F	VF	EF	Unc
Nhv 22	(?)	Brass	32mm	2.50	4.00	5.50	10.00

Obverse similar to 21, but no period after Co. Rv: A GREAT INVENTION / PRESENT / THIS CHECK TO / YOUR GROCER / WITH 5 CENTS / & GET / A / LARGE PACKAGE OF / CELLULOID STARCH. Large period close to N. Plain edge. (Miller Conn. 22)

Rulau	Date	Metal	Size	F	VF	EF	Unc
Nhv 23	(?)	Brass	32mm	2.50	4.00	5.50	10.00

As 22, but small period distant from N. (Miller Conn. 23)

Rulau	Date	Metal	Size	F	VF	EF	Unc
Nhv 24	(?)	Brass	32mm	3.50	6.00	7.50	11.00

Obverse as 22. Rv: Inscription in eight straight lines. Plain edge. (Miller Conn. 24)

The Celluloid Starch Co. was still in business in New Haven in 1918. It then had a branch in New York City.

GOV. FOOT GUARD

Rulau	Date	Metal	Size	F	VF	EF	Unc
Nhv 30	(1890's ?)	Copper	32mm	—	—	25.00	—

Standing Colonial soldier. Around: 2d CO. GOV. FOOT GUARD / ORG'Z'D -- 1775 / NEW HAVEN, CONN. Rv: Blank. Plain edge. (Peter Fuhrman coll.)

NEW HAVEN BICYCLE WORKS

New Haven, Conn.

Rulau	Date	Metal	Size	VG	F	VF	EF
Nhv 40	(1895-99)	Bronze	19mm	—	—	125.	—

NEW HAVEN BICYCLE WORKS. / THE / NEW HAVEN / NEW HAVEN, CONN. ctsp on reverse of U.S. 1895 Indian cent. (Tanenbaum coll.; Brunk 29505)

JOHN A. MEADE

New London, Conn.

Rulau	Date	Metal	Size	VG	F	VF	Unc
Nln 5	(1898)	Brass	Oct 25mm	—	—	40.00	—

THE BRUNSWICK BALKE / COLLENDER / COMPY / (Pool table) / CHECK. (Brunswick die BBC-11). Rv: GOOD FOR / 5 C / JOHN A. MEADE / -IN- / TRADE. Plain edge. (Thoele coll.; Zaffern coll.)

Meade is listed under billiard halls in the 1898 *New England Gazetteer.* This token fetched $18 as lot 42 of the Fazekas Aug. 1989 ATCO sale. Only 2 pieces are known!

EAGLE LOCK CO.

Terryville, Conn.

Rulau	Date	Metal	Size	F	VF	EF	Unc
Ter 3	(?)	Silver	31mm	—	—	125.	—

EAGLE LOCK CO / TERRYVILLE, CT. ctsp on U.S. 1899 Barber half dollar. (Van Ormer sale 2628; Brunk 12800)

This company sold locks, latches and hardware for builders, Brunk reports.

SCOVILL MANUFACTURING COMPANY

Waterbury, Conn.

Rulau	Date	Metal	Size	F	VF	EF	Unc
Wat 8	1890's	Aluminum	40mm	—	—	15.00	30.00

Pilgrims giving thanks to the Lord at Plymouth Rock, date 1620 in script below. Rv: THE SCOVILL MANUFACTURING COMPANY / ESTABLISHED 1802, / SHEET METAL / WIRE & TUBING, / ARTICLES OF ALL KINDS / FROM / ALUMINUM, / COPPER BRASS, / GERMAN SILVER / & C. / * WATERBURY, CONN. U.S.A. *. Plain edge. (ANS coll.)

Magnificent medallic work.

JOURNAL JUNIOR REPUBLIC

Connecticut

Rulau	Date	Metal	Size	F	VF	EF	Unc
Unk 6	1897	CN	26mm	12.00	30.00	—	—

Youth standing, facing, ONE FOR ALL above, **** 1897 **** below. Rv: U.S. shield at center, JOURNAL JUNIOR REPUBLIC around. * 25 * below. Plain edge. (Wright 1477)

Also known are CN 10 and 50-cent tokens.

DELAWARE

DELWARE HARD FIBRE CO.

Wilmington, Del.

Rulau	Date	Metal	Size	F	VF	EF	Unc
Wil 8	(1892)	Bakelite	40mm	—	60.00	—	100.

Bust left, 1436 - CHRISTOPHER COLUMBUS - 1506 / FROM LOTTO PORTRAIT BY BAERER. Rv: THE / DELAWARE / HARD FIBRE CO. / WILMINGTON, DEL. / THIS IS MADE IN / SHEETS, RODS, / TUBING AND / SPECIAL / SHAPES. / SEND FOR CATALOGUE. Plain edge. (Asociacion Numismatica Española sale of Feb. 16-17, 1988, lot 1056)

DISTRICT OF COLUMBIA

AMES & FROST COMPANY

Washington, D.C.

Rulau	Date	Metal	Size	F	VF	EF	Unc
Was 1	1892	Aluminum	34.6mm	—	—	25.00	35.00

Large ornate A&MCo monogram superimposed on spoked wheel. Rv: ANNUAL MEET L. A. W. WASHINGTON D.C. / AMES & FROST / -. . .- / COMPANY / IMPERIAL WHEELS / CHICAGO / -. . .- / U.S.A. / * JULY 18-20, 1892. *. Plain edge. (Rulau coll., ex-Ellis Edlow)

Ames & Frost were a Chicago wheel manufacturer. The L.A.W. convention took place in Washington in the summer of 1892. L.A.W. means League Of American Wheelmen.

THE HECHT CO.

Rulau	Date	Metal	Size	F	VF	EF	Unc
Was 10	(?)	CN	Oval, 24 by 31mm	—	11.00	—	—

Capitol at center, THE HECHT CO. above. WASHINGTON, D.C. below. Rv: Blank, but numeral incused at center. (Illustrated specimen is numbered 15273). Plain edge. (Ellis Edlow collection)

Charge card token.

IRON HALL BUILDING FAIR

Rulau	Date	Metal	Size	F	VF	EF	Unc
Was 15	1890	Brass	26mm	—	—	20.00	—

U.S. Capitol building. Rv: Two-doored safe at center, IRON HALL BUILDING FAIR / $1000 above, IN SEVEN YEARS / 1890 below. Plain edge. (William E. Hamm coll.)

This attribution is tentative.

NATL. PEACE JUBILEE

Washington, D.C.

Rulau	Date	Metal	Size	F	VF	EF	Unc
Was 30	1899	Brass	23mm	—	—	15.00	—

The Capitol. Rv: Dove of peace flying to right. Above: NATL PEACE JUBILEE. Below: May 23 - 25 / 1899 / WASHINGTON, D.C. Plain edge.

Rulau	Date	Metal	Size	F	VF	EF	Unc
Was 31	1899	Brass	18.5mm	—	8.00	12.50	—

Dewey bust 3/4 right. Around: NATIONAL PEACE JUBILEE 1899 / DEWEY. Rv: Dove of peace flying above Capitol building. Around: NATIONAL PEACE JUBILEE / WASHINGTON D.C. / MAY 23. 24. 25 / 1899. Plain edge. (Gene Johnson coll.)

FLORIDA

E. H. WATERS

Gainesville, Florida

Rulau	Date	Metal	Size	VG	F	VF	Unc
Gai 1	(1911-12)	Brass	--mm	—	—	250.	—

BBC-8 die. Rv: E. H. WATERS. Probably unique. (Bill Rouleau coll.)

GRAND OPERA (CIGARS)

Key West, Florida

Rulau	Date	Metal	Size	F	VF	EF	Unc
Key 1	(?)	Cupronickel	24mm	—	—	70.00	—

BETTER THAN IMPORTED / GRAND / OPERA / KEY WEST / HAVANA CIGARS. Rv: FOR SALE BY ALL / FIRST / CLASS / * DEALERS * (Wright 552)

ONIVOS N. XENOCLES

Key West, Florida

Rulau	Date	Metal	Size	F	VF	EF	Unc
Key 20	1900	Brass	25mm	—	—	45.00	—

ONIVOS N. XENOCLES / DEALER / IN / TOBACCOS. Rv: KEY WEST / 1900 / FLORIDA. Plain edge. (Wright 1739)

TAGUS G. XALAPA

Tampa, Florida

Rulau	Date	Metal	Size	VG	F	VF	Unc
Tam 20	1898	Brass	Oval 38 by 19mm	—	—	200.	—

The battleship Maine (struck). Rv: (All engraved) TAGUS G. XALAPA / DEALER IN CUBAN TOBACCO / TAMPA / FLORIDA / FEB. 15, 1898. Plain edge. (Wright 1738)

This piece, in the Dr. B. P. Wright collection, may well have been unique.

GEORGIA

ATLANTA

Atlanta, Ga.

Rulau	Date	Metal	Size	F	VF	EF	Unc
Atl 1	1895	Silver	22mm	—	—	75.00	100.

Eagle displayed, ATLANTA above, 1895 below. Rv: THIS COIN CONTAINS: WORTH OF SILVER .900 FINE / 9 / CENTS. (Partin 1145H-09)

Issued in connection with the Cotton States Exposition in 1895.

CITY ICE COMPANY

Augusta, Ga.

Rulau	Date	Metal	Size	VG	F	VF	Unc
Aug 4	(1893)	Aluminum	25mm	—	—	25.00	—

CITY ICE COMPANY / (incused numeral) / AUGUSTA, / GA. Rv: GOOD FOR / 12 / LBS. / ICE. (Partin 1155J)

HENRY KENNEDY

Rulau	Date	Metal	Size	VG	F	VF	Unc
Aug 9	(1892-93)	Aluminum	19mm	—	—	25.00	—

HENRY KENNEDY / AUGUSTY, (sic!) / GA. Rv: GOOD FOR / 5 C / IN TRADE. (Partin 1155AH-05)

This saloon is listed in the directories of 1875 and 1893. Scarce.

W. P. McKEON

Augusta, Ga.

Rulau	Date	Metal	Size	VG	F	VF	Unc
Aug 20	(1893-)	Brass	25mm	—	—	35.00	—

W. P. McKEON / AUGUSTA, / GA. Rv: GOOD FOR / 10 / IN / MERCHANDISE. (Partin 1155AJ-10a)

Rulau	Date	Metal	Size	VG	F	VF	Unc
Aug 22	(?)	Brass	25mm	—	—	35.00	—

As last, but WM. replaces W. on obverse. Plain edge. (Partin 1155AJ-10b)

McKeon is listed in groceries and liquors in the 1893 directory, but has disappeared by the 1914 directory.

M. F. WORD

Cartersville, Ga.

Rulau	Date	Metal	Size	VG	F	VF	Unc
Car 7	(1893-1914)	—	--mm	—	—	60.00	—

M. F. WORD, THE DRUGGIST. No further description. (Partin 1450D)

McKINNEY & KELLAR

Chestnut Gap, Ga.

Rulau	Date	Metal	Size	VG	F	VF	Unc
Chg 3	(1892-93)	Aluminum	31mm	—	—	60.00	—

THIS CHECK IS GOOD FOR / GOODS / AT THE STORE / OF / McKINNEY & KELLAR / GENERAL MERCHANTS / CHESTNUT GAP, / GA. Rv: TWO CENTS / 2 C / NOT TRANSFERABLE. Plain edge. (Partin 1525A-02)

McKinney & Kellar are listed in the 1893 directory. By 1914 McKinney was sole proprietor. This place is in Fannin County.

GEO. H. SLAPPEY

Fort Valley, Ga.

Rulau	Date	Metal	Size	VG	F	VF	Unc
Ftv 1	(1893)	Aluminum	24mm	—	—	60.00	—

GEO. H. SLAPPEY / FORT VALLEY, / GA. Rv: GOOD FOR ONE / 5 C / GLASS OF SODA. Plain edge. (Partin 2070A-05)

This drug store is listed in 1893 in this Peach County town.

N. P. LEE & CO.

Hogansville, Ga.

Rulau	Date	Metal	Size	VG	F	VF	Unc
Hog 4	(1892-93)	Aluminum	31mm	—	40.00	60.00	—

N. P. LEE & CO. / (ornament) / ICE COLD DRINKS / (ornament) / HOGANSVILLE, GA. Rv: GOOD FOR / ONE / * DRINK *. Plain edge. (Partin 2305)

Lee's general store appears in the 1893 directory. Hogansville is in Troup County.

ROME BRICK CO.

Rome, Ga.

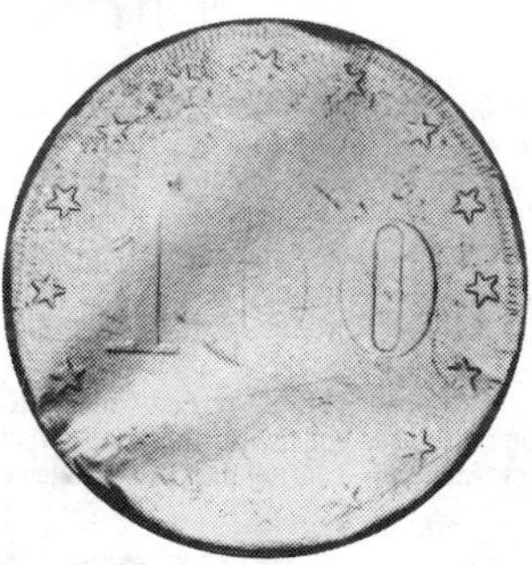

Rulau	Date	Metal	Size	VG	F	VF	Unc
Rom 1	(1890)	Nickel	38mm	—	75.00	—	—

ROME / BRICK / CO. Rv: Numeral 100 within circle of 16 stars. Plain edge. (Grellman coll.; Partin 3270R-100)

Rulau	Date	Metal	Size	VG	F	VF	Unc
Rom 2	(1890's)	Nickel	19mm	—	45.00	60.00	—

As 1, but 10 in circle of 16 stars. (Partin 3270R-10)

Rulau	Date	Metal	Size	VG	F	VF	Unc
Rom 3	(1890's)	Aluminum	19mm	—	45.00	—	—

As 1, but numeral 5. (Partin 3270R-05)

Bradstreet directories of 1890, 1893 and 1918 list this firm.

VANDIVER'S BIJOU SALOON

Rome, Ga.

See this token as number Ga-Ro 20 in the U.S. Trades Token 1866-1889 section.

J. A. GALINA

Savannah, Ga.

Rulau	Date	Metal	Size	VG	F	VF	Unc
Sav 4	(1893-1914)	CN	21mm	—	—	30.00	—

J. A. GALINA / SAVANNAH, GA. Rv: GOOD FOR 5C IN TRADE. Plain edge. Centrally holed flan. (Partin 3350AW-050

Joseph A. Galina operated a "beer saloon" 1893-1914.

FRED. SCHWARZ

Rulau	Date	Metal	Size	VG	F	VF	Unc
Sav 20	(1893-99)	Brass	44mm	—	—	25.00	—

(All incused): + FRED. SCHWARZ + / 10 C / BREAD / JONES & LINCOLN STS. Rv: Blank. (Partin 3350EE-10)

Frederick A. R. Schwarz was a baker, listed 1893 thru 1920. The token style above is early, but directory research is needed on the street corner address.

CHARLES E. STULTS & CO.
Savannah, Ga.

Rulau	Date	Metal	Size	VG	F	VF	Unc
Sav 24	(1893)	Aluminum	32mm	—	—	25.00	—

CHARLES E. STULTS & CO. / WHOLESALE / AGENTS / SAVANNAH, GA. Rv: THIS CHECK WILL BE REDEEMED BY ANY DEALER / GOOD FOR / ONE / SANTABANA / CIGAR. Plain edge. (Partin 3350ES)

Stults appears in the 1893 directory as proprietor of a wholesale liquor and cigar business.

GEORGE M. BRINSON
Stillmore, Ga.

Rulau	Date	Metal	Size	VG	F	VF	Unc
Stm 2	(1893)	Brass	35mm	—	—	55.00	—

AT / COMMISSARY / OF / GEORGE M. BRINSON (script) / STILLMORE, GA. / NOT TRANSFERABLE. Rv: GOOD FOR / 50 / IN / MERCHANDISE. Plain edge. (Partin 3495A-50)

A lumber operation and general (company) store. Other denominations may exist.

B. P. H.
(B. P. Holmes)
Vidalia, Ga.

Rulau	Date	Metal	Size	VG	F	VF	Unc
Vid 3	(1893)	Brass	29mm	—	40.00	50.00	—

B. P. H. $1oo (in circle) / VIDALIA, GA. Rv: Blank. Plain edge. (Partin 3725A-100)

B. P. Holmes ran a naval stores firm in Vidalia, listed in the 1893 directory.

HAWAII

On January 17, 1893, American residents and other foreigners deposed Queen Liliuokalani and organized a provisional government. President Grover Cleveland opposed the provisional government's request for annexation to the United States, so a republic under President Sanford Ballard Dole was declared on July 4, 1894.

On July 6, 1898, the U.S. Congress under the new administration of President William McKinley in the midst of the Spanish-American War proclaimed the necessary legislation to annex Hawaii. On June 14, 1900 the former monarchy was constituted as the Territory of Hawaii.

Thus tokens of Hawaii are excluded from this catalog of United States because the catalog's coverage ends with 1900. Unlike Alaska, purchased in 1867 from Russia, Hawaii was not technically a part of the United States until the closing days of the 19th century.

IDAHO

GEORGE BRIGGS
Lyman, Idaho

Rulau	Date	Metal	Size	F	VF	EF	Unc
Lym 1	1896	Brass	34mm	—	—	40.00	—

GEORGE BRIGGS / DEALER / .IN. / GENERAL / MERCHANDISE / 1896 / LYMAN, IDAHO. Dentilated rim. Plain edge. Rarity 9.

CLARK & ANDERSON
Malad, Idaho

Rulau	Date	Metal	Size	F	VF	EF	Unc
Mal 2	(1890's)	Aluminum	24mm	15.00	25.00	—	—

CLARK & ANDERSON / -.- / MALAD, / IDAHO. Rv: GOOD FOR / -.- / 12 1/2 ¢ / -.- / AT THE BAR. Plain edge. (Wright 1367)

Malad City is in Oneida County.

J. CLINKENBEARD
Pocatello, Idaho

Rulau	Date	Metal	Size	VG	F	VF	Unc
Poc 3	(1890's)	Aluminum	19mm	—	—	40.00	—

J. CLINKENBEARD / — / POCATELLO / IDAHO. Rv: GOOD FOR / 5 ¢ / IN TRADE. Plain edge. (Wright 1369)

J. H. LAWSON
Preston, Idaho

Rulau	Date	Metal	Size	VG	F	VF	Unc
Pre 4	(1890's)	Aluminum	26mm	—	—	25.00	—

J. H. LAWSON / -.- / PRESTON / IDAHO. Rv: GOOD FOR / 5 / CENTS / IN TRADE. Plain edge. (Wright 1495)

SMUIN & THOMAS CO.
Rexburg, Idaho

Rulau	Date	Metal	Size	VG	F	VF	Unc
Rex 4	1892	**	40mm	—	40.00	—	—

** Cardboard, with a tin-plated metal rim.
COMMERCIAL / COIN / SMUIN & THOMAS CO. / GENERAL MERCHANDISE, / REXBURG, IDAHO. / PAT. JULY 5, 1892 / I. T. ALVORD VIEW U. T. Rv: MERCHANDISE / FIVE / 5 / CENTS. / WILL PAY BEARER. There is an ink signature. Smuin & Thomas, across center of reverse. Rarity 7. (Schell RE-12)

Rulau	Date	Metal	Size	VG	F	VF	Unc
Rex 6	1892	**	40mm	—	40.00	—	—

Obverse as last. Rv: MERCHANDISE / TWENTY-FIVE / 25 ¢ / CENTS. / WILL PAY BEARER. Ink signature, Smuin & Thomas, across center of reverse. Rarity 7. (Schell RE-12)

Rulau	Date	Metal	Size	VG	F	VF	Unc
Rex 10	1892	**	40mm	—	60.00	—	—

Similar to last, but five / $ 5 / DOLLARS, on reverse. (Schell RE-12)

Other denominations undoubtedly were issued, but it is not known whether any have survived.

IDAHO HOTEL
Silver City, Idaho

Rulau	Date	Metal	Size	VG	F	VF	Unc
Sil 4	1902	Brass	22mm	—	—	30.00	—

IDAHO HOTEL / 1902 / SILVER / CITY, / IDA.

HENRY STAMPEDE
Soda Springs, Idaho

Rulau	Date	Metal	Size	VG	F	VF	Unc
Ssp 10	(?)	Brass	30mm	—	—	25.00	—

HENRY STAMPEDE / (ornament) / SODA SPRINGS / -.- / . IDAHO . Rv: GOOD FOR * 10 ¢* / IN TRADE. Plain edge.

KINKEAD & NEBEL
Wallace, Idaho

Rulau	Date	Metal	Size	VG	F	VF	Unc
Wal 3	(?)	Brass	--mm	—	—	40.00	—

BBC-11 die. Rv: KINKEAD & NEBEL. (Thoele report)

J. FARRIN & CO.
Wardner, Idaho

Rulau	Date	Metal	Size	VG	F	VF	Unc
War 4	(?)	Aluminum	24mm	—	—	25.00	—

WARDNER / (ornament) / IDAHO. / -.-. Rv: J. FARRIN & CO. / 10 ¢ / DANCE HALL. Ornamented rims on each side. Plain edge.

HENRY GILDNER

Rulau	Date	Metal	Size	VG	F	VF	Unc
War 6	(?)	Aluminum	26mm	—	—	25.00	—

HENRY / (ornament) / GILDNER. Rv: Large 5. Beaded rims on each side. Plain edge.

HARRIS BROS.

Rulau	Date	Metal	Size	VG	F	VF	Unc
War 8	(?)	Cupronickel	22.5mm	—	—	25.00	—

HARRIS BROS. / -.- / WARDNER / IDAHO. Rv: GOOD FOR / 12 1/2 ¢ / IN TRADE. Plain edge. (Wright 1442)

JOE ROGERS
Wardner, Idaho

Rulau	Date	Metal	Size	VG	F	VF	Unc
War 15	(1891)	GS	Oct 25mm	—	50.00	70.00	—

Goblet, ladle and tongs, DEALERS IN above, all within central circle. Around: CHAS. PICK & CO. / .*. CHICAGO .*. Rv: GOOD FOR / 5 ¢ / JOE. / ROGERS / IN / * TRADE *. Plain edge. (Thoele coll.)

The 1891 gazetteer lists Joseph Rogers as a saloonkeeper in Wardner, Idaho. Research by H. C. Thoele; photo courtesy Syd Joseph.

COOPER & CO.
Whitebird, Idaho

Rulau	Date	Metal	Size	VG	F	VF	Unc
Wtb 4	(1900-01)	Brass	25mm	—	55.00	—	—

Elk's head facing three-quarters left. Rv: GOOD FOR / 5 ¢ / COOPER & CO. / - / IN TRADE. Plain edge. (Thoele coll.; Rulau Osa 1)

This scarce token had been attributed in error to Osawatomie, Kansas, but is now properly sited. Only 1 known.

Cooper & Co. were also listed under saloons in Denver, Colo. 1895 and Apex, Colo. 1897-98. Possibly used in all three sites.

ILLINOIS

GEO. G. SPILLER
Albion, Ill.

Rulau	Date	Metal	Size	VG	F	VF	Unc
Alb 1	(1900)	Aluminum	38mm	—	15.00	20.00	25.00

Female head right within beaded circle. Around: GOOD FOR $1.00 AT GEO. G. SPILLER / * ALBION, ILL.*. RV: ONLY ONE OF THESE ACCEPTED ON ANY ONE PURCHASE / GOOD AS GOLD / FOR $1.00 AT / GEO. G. SPILLER / ON ANY ONE / PURCHASE OF / $10.00 & UPWARDS / . *. Reeded edge. R8. (Schmidt S42; Vacketta Alb A01)

JOHN BERNER
Alton, Ill.

Rulau	Date	Metal	Size	VG	F	VF	Unc
Alt 1	(1890's)	Brass	21mm	—	7.00	10.00	—

JOHN BERNER / 500 / EAST 2ND ST. Rv: GOOD FOR / *** / NICKEL / *** / IN TRADE. Plain edge. R8. (Schmidt B37. Vacketta Aln A01)

This card is most unusual in that "Nickel" is spelled out. This saloon operated in the 1890's on Second Street, now Broadway.

GEO. NOLL
Alton, Ill.

Rulau	Date	Metal	Size	VG	F	VF	Unc
Alt 3	(1890's)	Aluminum	20mm	—	3.00	5.00	10.00

G. NOLLS ST. B. & C. CO. / A / ALTON, / ILL. Rv: Blank. Plain edge. R8. (Schmidt N61; Vacketta Aln A19)

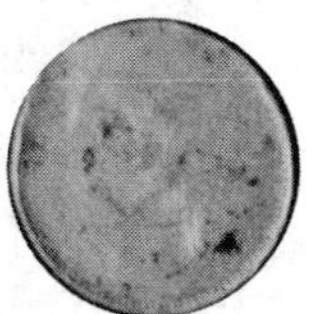

Rulau	Date	Metal	Size	VG	F	VF	Unc
Alt 4	(1890's)	Aluminum	20mm	—	3.00	5.00	10.00

Similar to last, but 'B' at center of obverse in place of 'A'. Rv: Blank. R8. (Schmidt N61a; Vacketta N/L)

George Noll's Steam Bakery & Creamery Co. may have issued tokens with other letters than A or B, says specialist Joseph Schmidt, though none are known at present. It is not known what significance the letters had for users of the tokens — though a possibility is that one type of lettered token was used in the bakery aspect of the business and another in the milk and cream business, or that both were used in the creamery for some sort of exchange system.

Rulau	Date	Metal	Size	VG	F	VF	Unc
Alt 6	(1890's)	Brass	23mm	—	3.00	5.00	10.00

GEO. NOLL / GOOD FOR / 10 C / LOAF BREAD. Rv: Blank. Plain edge. R8. (Vacketta Aln 19)

Noll's enterprise flourished. By 1918 it was known as Noll Baking & Ice Cream Company.

R. DE SCHIPPER

Atkinson, Ill.

Rulau	Date	Metal	Size	VG	F	VF	Unc
Atk 1	(?)	Brass	Scal 26mm	3.00	5.00	7.00	10.00

R. DE SCHIPPER / (ornament) / - / ILL. Rv: GOOD FOR . / 5c / AT / R. DE SCHIPPER BAR. Plain edge. R8. (Schmidt D24; Vacketta Atk A10)

BRUNEMEYER & GROMETER

Aurora, Ill.

Rulau	Date	Metal	Size	VG	F	VF	Unc
Aur 1	(1893-98)	Brass	25mm	—	5.00	10.00	—

BRUNEMEYER & GROMETER, GOOD FOR 5¢ IN TRADE. Rv: Blank. Plain edge. Rarity 6. (Schmidt B68)

The Brunnemeyer & Grometer saloon was located in the basement of Alschuler Brothers clothing store on Broadway. It operated from 1893 to 1898. The error in spelling on the token (only one N in Brunnemeyer) is probably a diesinker's error.

BUDLONG'S PHARMACY

Rulau	Date	Metal	Size	VG	F	VF	Unc
Aur 3	(1890-1906)	Aluminum	Oct 28mm	—	9.00	12.00	—

BUDLONG'S PHARMACY, AURORA, ILLINOIS. Rv: 10. Plain edge. Rarity 6. (Schmidt B77)

William C. Budlong operated this pharmacy from 1890 to 1906 on South Broadway in Aurora.

COULTER BLOCK PHARMACY

Rulau	Date	Metal	Size	VG	F	VF	Unc
Aur 5	(1893-99)	Brass	24mm	—	10.00	15.00	Rare

COULTER BLOCK PHARMACY, ONE GLASS SODA. (All incused). Plain edge. Rarity 6. (Schmidt C56; Vacketta Aur A12)

This pharmacy opened in the Opera House building at Broadway and Fox Sts. in 1893, managed by John B. Chase. It closed in 1899. The pharmacy was probably a place for refreshment "between the acts."

J. P. DOLAN

Aurora, Ill.

Rulau	Date	Metal	Size	VG	F	VF	Unc
Aur 7	(1892-95)	Brass	Scal 25mm	—	6.00	—	—

(All incused): J. P. DOLAN / * * *. Rv: GOOD FOR (incuse) / 5 C (relief) / AT BAR (incuse). Plain edge. R8. (Schmidt D52; Vacketta Aur C13)

J. P. Dolan of Chicago owned the saloon bearing his name from 1892 to 1895, hiring a manager to run it as he remained in Chicago. It was located on South Broadway — a street that once had 30 saloons in three of its blocks!

F.W. MAYREIS

Beardstown, Ill.

Rulau	Date	Metal	Size	VG	F	VF	Unc
Bea 1	(1884-1900)	Brass	25mm	—	—	75.00	—

Pool table at bottom. Above: THE / BRUNSWICK / -BALKE- / COLLENDER Co. Rv: F. W. MAYREIS FAMOUS SALOON GOOD FOR 5¢ IN TRADE. Plain edge. R9. (Schmidt M11; Vacketta Bea A02; Brunswick 5461)

Rulau	Date	Metal	Size	VG	F	VF	Unc
Bea 3	(?)	Brass	24mm	—	—	40.00	—

F. W. MAYREIS / FAMOUS SALOON / 5. Rv: GOOD FOR / 5 / CENTS. Plain edge. R8. (Schmidt M10)

E. GERHARDT

Belleville, Ill.

Rulau	Date	Metal	Size	VG	F	VF	Unc
Bel 1	1890's)	Brass	22mm	—	—	10.00	—

E. GERHARDT (incuse) / 5 C (relief). Rv: E. SCHMIDT / 326 MARKET (maker's mark). Plain edge. R7. (Schmidt G27; Vacketta Bve B08)

This was a saloon.

SCHOPP BROS. SALOON

Belleville, Ill.

Rulau	Date	Metal	Size	VG	F	VF	Unc
Bel 3	(?)	Aluminum	23mm	—	20.00	40.00	—

SCHOPP BROS. / * / SALOON / * / BELLEVILLE, ILL. Rv: Large 5 within circular wreath. Plain edge. R5. About 35 pieces known. (Schmidt S22; Vacketta Bve 34)

Rulau	Date	Metal	Size	VG	F	VF	Unc
Bel 4	(?)	Aluminum	23mm	—	70.00	—	—

As last, but ctsp on reverse — continuous jagged line obscures circular wreath and large 1 is stamped over numeral 5 (apparently for a revaluation to 1 [cent?].) Plain edge. R10; only 1 specimen known. (Schmidt S22a; Vacketta N/L)

In the 1960's a hoard of 30 pieces of the 5-cent token was discovered, on all of which the stars around the '5' were removed. Only one specimen of the counterstamp has surfaced to date, according to specialist Joseph Schmidt.

In 1918 a successor, E. I. Schopp, was in the confectionery and meat business.

TRAVER COVEY & SANDS

Belvidere, Ill.

Rulau	Date	Metal	Size	VG	F	VF	Unc
Bev 1	(1890's)	Aluminum	32mm	100.	150.	200.	—

TRAVER COVEY & SANDS / SCRANTON / COAL / SOFT COAL / & COKE / BELVIDERE ILLS. Rv: TRAVER COVEY & SANDS / LUMBER / & / BUILDING / MATERIAL / BELVIDERE ILLS. Plain edge. R8. (Wright 1156 and 1697; Schmidt T72)

Wright reported two varieties of this store card, one 32mm and another 30mm, with minute differences in the legend.

G. A. R.
(Grand Army of the Republic)

Bloomington, Ill.

Rulau	Date	Metal	Size	VG	F	VF	Unc
Blo 1	1895	Copper	38.5mm	—	10.00	15.00	—

Facing bust of Union General William T. Sherman. Rv: 29TH / ANNUAL / ENCAMPMENT / DEPT. OF ILLINOIS / G.A.R. / BLOOMINGTON. / May 14-16. / 1895. Plain edge. Issued with knurl for suspension from ribbon hanger. R8. (Schmidt G32)

Medals were issued by the G.A.R. every year from 1888 to at least 1902 in the same size, composition and style (knurled), Joseph Schmidt reports. The first G.A.R. encampment was in 1867.

E. GEIST

Breese, Ill.

Rulau	Date	Metal	Size	VG	F	VF	Unc
Bre 1	(1890's)	Aluminum	Scal 28mm	5.00	7.00	10.00	—

E. GEIST (incuse) / GOOD FOR (relief) / 5 C (incuse) / DRINK (relief) / AT BAR (incuse). Rv: F. MESSMER MFG. CO. ST. LOUIS (relief maker's mark). Plain edge. R7. (Schmidt G24; Vacketta Bre A03)

This was a cigar store and saloon.

WINTER BROS.

Cairo, Ill.

Rulau	Date	Metal	Size	VG	F	VF	Unc
Cai 1	(1890's)	Aluminum	20mm	5.00	7.00	9.00	—

WINTER BROS. / CAIRO, ILL. Rv: 5c / ICE. Plain edge. R8. (Schmidt W32; Vacketta Cai 04)

COLP MERCANTILE CO.

Carterville, Ill.

Rulau	Date	Metal	Size	F	VF	EF	Unc
Car 1	(1890-1910)	Brass	30mm	8.00	11.00	—	—

COLP / MERCANTILE / CO / 25 / CENTS / CARTERVILLE, ILLINOIS. Rv: GOOD FOR / 25 / CENTS / -+ +- / IN / MERCHANDISE. Plain edge. (Vacketta N/L)

Arnold Colp & Co. were operators of a flour mill in 1918.

FRED J. DOE

Centralia, Ill.

Rulau	Date	Metal	Size	F	VF	EF	Unc
Cen 1	(1890's)	Brass	Oct 25mm	—	5.00	8.00	—

FRED J. DOE / GOOD FOR 5 C IN TRADE. Rv: 5 C. Plain edge. R8. (Schmidt D54; Vacketta Cet 04)

Rulau	Date	Metal	Size	F	VF	EF	Unc
Cen 2	(1890's)	Aluminum	Oct 25mm	—	—	75.00	—

DOE's SALOON / 2 1/2 / CENTRALIA, ILL. Rv: 2 1/2 C. Plain edge. R7. (Schmidt N/L; Vacketta Cet A05)

Doe operated this saloon during the Gay Nineties. By 1918 he is listed as a billiard room operator.

J. W. DIKOB

Charleston, Ill.

Rulau	Date	Metal	Size	VG	F	VF	Unc
Cha 4	(?)	CN	22mm	—	10.00	15.00	—

J. W. DIKOB / WATCHMAKER / & JEWELER / MAN WHO MADE / THE MAGIC / CLOCK / CHARLESTON, ILLS. Rv: RETURN TO / (blank space, occasionally with initials scratched in.) (Kirtley Jan. 1992 sale, lot G010)

F.O. WEISMANTLE

Charleston, Ill.

Rulau	Date	Metal	Size	F	VF	EF	Unc
Cha 16	(1890's)	Aluminum	27mm	—	5.00	8.00	—

F.O. (spray) / WEISMANTLE / (spray). Rv: CHARLESTON STEAM BAKERY / ONE / LOAF / (small eagle). Plain edge. R8. (Schmidt W21, Vacketta Crl 03)

It is believed a hoard may exist.

HUMPHREY & ALLEN

Chestnut, Ill.

Rulau	Date	Metal	Size	VG	F	VF	Unc
Che 1	(1890's)	Aluminum	25mm	—	12.00	—	—

AT HUMPHREY & ALLEN / (ornament) / CHESTNUT, Ill. Rv: GOOD FOR / 10 ¢ / IN TRADE. Plain edge. R8. (Schmidt N/L, Vacketta Ctt 02)

In 1918 Chestnut, in Logan County, had only 250 people.

OWEN AHERN

Chicago, Ill.

Rulau	Date	Metal	Size	VG	F	VF	Unc
Chi 1	(1899-1902)	CN	25mm	—	15.00	25.00	—

Eagle with wings folded closely to its body, perched atop a cannon pointing right. The eagle's head is turned left. Rv: OWEN AHERN / RESTAURANT / AND / BUFFET / 257 - 92nd ST. Plain edge.

Ahern's "saloon" does not appear in the 1891 or 1906 city directories, but was listed in the 1902 edition.

AMERICAN TERRA COTTA & CERAMIC CO.

Rulau	Date	Metal	Size	VG	F	VF	Unc
Chi 2	1891	Aluminum	38mm	—	—	35.00	75.00

Crying infant bust facing, in circle. Around: AMERICAN TERRA COTTA & CERAMIC CO. CHICAGO / COPYRIGHT / 1891. Rv: SAMPLE / OF / ALUMINUM / THE COMING METAL / THE CLAY USED IN OUR / TERRA COTTA / CONTAINS A LARGE / PERCENTAGE / OF THIS METAL / (ornament) / AMERICAN TERRA COTTA CO. CHICAGO. Plain edge. Thick (3mm) planchet. R9. (Schmidt A63)

American Terra Cotta & Ceramic Co. are still listed in business in late 1918.

AMES & FROST CO.

Rulau	Date	Metal	Size	VG	F	VF	Unc
Chi 3	1892	Aluminum	35mm	—	—	25.00	35.00

Large monogram A&FCo set against spokes of a wheel. Rv: ANNUAL MEET L.A.W. WASHINGTON D.C. / AMES & FROST / COMPANY / IMPERIAL WHEELS / CHICAGO / U.S.A. / * July 18-20, 1892 *. Plain edge.

L.A.W. stands for League of American Wheelmen, the leading cycling association of its day.

HANS CHRISTIAN ANDERSEN (MONUMENT)

Rulau	Date	Metal	Size	VG	F	VF	Unc
Chi 5	1896	Aluminum	30mm	—	—	15.00	25.00

Andersen bust right, tiny HANSON under truncation, HANS CHRISTIAN ANDERSEN around. Rv: UNVEILING OF THE / MONUMENT OF / HANS CHRISTIAN ANDERSEN / IN LINCOLN PARK, CHICAGO / SEPT. 26, 1896 / ERECTED BY THE / DANISH-AMERICANS / OF THE / UNITED STATES amid flourishes. Plain edge. R5. (Schmidt A55)

ARMORY FIRST INFANTRY I.N.G.

Rulau	Date	Metal	Size	VG	F	VF	Unc
Chi 7	1891	Aluminum	37mm	—	—	15.00	25.00

Armory, ARMORY FIRST INFANTRY I.N.G. around, CHICAGO below. Rv: Within wreath: DUCIT / AMOR / PATRIAE. Around: DEDICATION OF THE FIRST INFANTRY ARMORY / * 1891 *. Plain edge. R7. (Schmidt A73)

Rulau	Date	Metal	Size	VG	F	VF	Unc
Chi 8	(1891)	Aluminum	37mm	—	—	15.00	25.00

Obverse as last, but shrubbery added at left side of building. Rv: MALLEABLE / TASTELESS, SONOROUS, / DUCTILE, / UNTARNISHABLE. / * ALUMINUM * (in fancy letters on band across center) / CUBIC FOOT OF GOLD, 1204 LBS. / " " ALUMINUM, 179" / THIS MEDAL / IS PURE. / (tiny) CHILDS. CHICAGO. Plain edge. R7. (Schmidt A74)

I.N.G. = Illinois National Guard.

Childs used the reverse of the second piece above as a stock die muled in many combinations. For example, see Baker/ Douglas number 4-5, its first apparent uses, in 1889, where it was muled with two George Washington dies ("Medallic Portraits of Washington" by Rulau & Fuld, 1985).

WM. A. BIGLER & CO.

This firm issued hard rubber (vulcanite) jewelry checks and watch checks listed by Schmidt as B32 and B33. They are not listed here since hard rubber cards are not cataloged in this volume.

BISMARCK GARDEN

Rulau	Date	Metal	Size	VG	F	VF	Unc
Chi 10	(ca 1890)	Brass	Scal 28mm	20.00	—	30.00	—

BISMARCK GARDEN / (ornament) / 25 / (ornament) / CHICAGO. Rv: Same as obverse. Plain edge. R9; only 3 pieces known. (Schmidt B40)

Rulau	Date	Metal	Size	VG	F	VF	Unc
Chi 11	1899	B&A	24mm	—	—	20.00	—

BISMARCK / GARDEN within beaded central circle open at left end, EVANSTON AVE. / GRACE & HALSTED STS. around. Rv: On cross-hatched field; GOOD FOR / 5 / PAT. / JULY 1899 / IN MERCHANDISE. Plain edge. R5. (Schmidt B45; Vacketta Chi BD58)

Rulau	Date	Metal	Size	VG	F	VF	Unc
Chi 13	1899	B&A	25mm	—	—	20.00	—

As last, but denomination 10. R5. (Schmidt B45a)

Rulau	Date	Metal	Size	VG	F	VF	Unc
Chi 14	1899	B&A	32mm	—	—	20.00	—

As last, but square aluminum center, and rearrangement of legend; denomination 50. R7. (Schmidt B47; Vacketta Chi BC58)

Rulau	Date	Metal	Size	VG	F	VF	Unc
Chi 15	1899	B&A	28mm	—	—	25.00	—

Bust of Prince von Bismarck within wreath, BISMARCK GARDEN around. Rv: GOOD FOR / 25 / PAT. / JULY 1899 / IN MERCHANDISE . Plain edge. R7. (Schmidt B49; Vacketta BE58)

The bimetallic issues of Bismarck Garden were probably issued 1899-1900, but it is possible they could have been released later.

ROBERT BLUM LODGE 6, O. D. F.

Rulau	Date	Metal	Size	F	VF	EF	Unc
Chi 17	1894	Gilt/Br	36mm	18.00	32.00	—	—

Bearded male bust 3/4 facing, ROBERT BLUM around, all within central circle. Around: * 25 JAEHRIGES JUBILAEUMS FEST * / CHICAGO - 10. OCT - 1894. Rv: ROBERT BLUM LODGE NO. 6 / O D F (ornate letters) / GEGRUNDET. OCT. 10 (on scroll) / 1869 (ornate numerals) / - CHICAGO - ILL. -. Plain edge. Ony 3 pieces known. (Schmidt Chicago B55)

Issued to honor the lodge's 25th anniversary, 1869-1894.

FRED BOTH

Rulau	Date	Metal	Size	F	VF	EF	Unc
Chi 19	(1890's)	Brass	23mm	—	15.00	—	—

GOOD FOR / 5c / AT THE BAR / FRED BOTH. Rv: GEO. KUEHL & BRO. / BILLIARD CLOTHS & SUPPLIES, CHICAGO. Plain edge. R8. (Schmidt B69; Vacketta Chi BB79)

Both managed a saloon in the 1890's. George Kuehl & Brother were a Chicago billiard supply house which issued tokens for firms in many states.

H. E. BUCKLEN & CO.

Rulau	Date	Metal	Size	F	VF	EF	Unc
Chi 21	(1899)	Brass	38mm	—	—	40.00	60.00

Uniformed bust right, ADMIRAL DEWEY. Rv: TESTIMONIAL SOUVENIR, AMERICA'S GREATEST REMEDIES. DR. KING'S NEW DISCOVERY FOR CONSUMPTION, ELECTRIC BITTERS FOR THE BLOOD AND NERVES. COMPLIMENTS OF H. E. BUCKLEN & CO. CHICAGO. Reeded edge. Thick planchet. R7. (Schmidt B82)

Rulau	Date	Metal	Size	F	VF	EF	Unc
Chi 21A	(1899)	Gilt/Cop	38mm	—	—	40.00	60.00

As last. Reeded edge. R8. (Schmidt B82a)

THE BUDWEISER

Rulau	Date	Metal	Size	F	VF	EF	Unc
Chi 22	(ca 1900)	Aluminum	30mm	—	—	15.00	—

THE BUDWEISER / 10 / HANNAH & HOGG. Rv: 10 within wreath. Plain edge. R7. (Schmidt B85; Vacketta Chi BC109)

Hannah & Hogg were Chicago liquor distributors who issued a lengthy series of tokens of their own (see under Chicago in U.S. Trade Tokens 1866-1889 by Rulau). The Budweiser was one of the watering holes supplied by H & H.

BURKE BROS.

Rulau	Date	Metal	Size	F	VF	EF	Unc
Chi 24	1896	Aluminum	38mm	—	—	30.00	—

Ornate monogram (which appears to be PUIP intertwined) at center, CONVENTION / SOUVENIR above, CHICAGO JUNE 1896 below. Rv: BURKE BRO'S / LIQUOR / DEALERS / 186 1/2 S. CLARK ST. / 80 W. WASHINGTON ST. / CHICAGO. Plain edge. R10 (apparently unique). (Schmidt B92)

A souvenir of the Democratic National Convention which heard the famous "Cross of Gold" speech and nominated William Jennings Bryan who delivered the oration. Only a single piece has been discovered, that in AU condition.

CHICAGO EVENING JOURNAL

Rulau	Date	Metal	Size	F	VF	EF	Unc
Chi 26	1894	Silver	39mm	—	30.00	60.00	—

Facade of a 6-story building, THE CHICAGO EVENING JOURNAL SOUVENIR around, APR. 22, 1894, in exergue. In tiny letters flanking the date in exergue is: A HYLEN — CHICA. Rv: Three-story building, BIRTHPLACE OF THE JOURNAL above, THE SALOON BLD / APR. 22, 1844. In exergue — all within central circle. Around: THE ONLY. REPUBLICAN. EVENING. PAPER. IN. CHICAGO. Plain edge. R6. (Schmidt C48)

Rulau	Date	Metal	Size	F	VF	EF	Unc
Chi 27	1894	Aluminum	39mm	—	—	10.00	20.00

As last. R6. (Schmidt C48a)

Rulau	Date	Metal	Size	F	VF	EF	Unc
Chi 28	1894	WM	39mm	—	—	20.00	25.00

As last. R6. (Schmidt C48b)

SPECIAL NOTE: The silver specimens, struck in .900 fine silver, have the tiny words COIN SILVER incused diagonally in upper field left of building on obverse.

These pieces commemorate the Evening Journal's 50th anniversary in 1894.

S. D. CHILDS & CO.

Rulau	Date	Metal	Size	F	VF	EF	Unc
Chi 30	(1891)	Aluminum	37mm	—	15.00	20.00	25.00

General Ulysses S. Grant mounted, to left, GRANT MONUMENT around. Rv: Within wreath: ALUMINUM / -.- / SOUVENIR / FROM / S. D. CHILDS & CO. / ENGRAVERS / AND / MEDALISTS / ... / CHICAGO. Plain edge. R8. (Schmidt G70)

Rulau	Date	Metal	Size	F	VF	EF	Unc
Chi 31	1891	Aluminum	37mm	—	—	20.00	25.00

Obverse as last (Grant, mounted). Rv: COMMEMORATIVE OF THE UNVEILING OF THE GRANT MONUMENT / LINCOLN PARK / CHICAGO / OCTOBER 7, 1891. / ERECTED / BY THE CITIZENS / OF / CHICAGO / .*. Plain edge. R7. (Schmidt G69)

Rulau	Date	Metal	Size	F	VF	EF	Unc
Chi 32	(?)	Brass	25mm	—	—	15.00	—

S. D. CHILDS & CO. / (monogram) / 76 WASHINGTON ST. Rv: ENGRAVERS, MANFR'S OF MEDALS, CHECKS, BADGES & C. / CHICAGO. Plain edge. R6. (Schmidt C68)

Rulau	Date	Metal	Size	F	VF	EF	Unc
Chi 33	(?)	Copper	25mm	—	—	15.00	—

As last. R6. (Schmidt C68a)

Rulau	Date	Metal	Size	F	VF	EF	Unc
Chi 34	1899	B&A	24mm	—	—	75.00	100.

S. D. CHILDS & CO DOUBLE METAL COINS PATENTED JULY 1899. Rv: GOOD FOR / 10 / PAT / JULY 1899 / IN MERCHANDISE. Plain edge. R8. (Schmidt C65; Vacketta Chi CC70)

Rulau	Date	Metal	Size	F	VF	EF	Unc
Chi 35	1899	B&A	25mm	—	—	75.00	100.

S. D. CHILDS & CO. CHICAGO. SOLE MAKERS GEOMETRICAL BARTER COIN. Rv: As reverse of last. R8. (Schmidt C66; Vacketta Chi CD70-10)

Rulau	Date	Metal	Size	F	VF	EF	Unc
Chi 36	1899	B&A	38mm	—	—	75.00	100.

As last, but denomination 100. R8. (Schmidt C66a: Vacketta Chi CD70-100)

The first two pieces above honor the dedication of the Grant monument in Lincoln Park in 1891. The second type was sold to the public.

The final two tokens above were probably struck in 1900.

Shubael D. Childs began his successful diesinking, engraving and token-making business in Chicago in 1837. The firm pioneered the use of bimetallic (brass ring and aluminum center) tokens, receiving their first patent in July 1898. The widely used patent date July, 1899 distinguishes many of Childs' bimetallic pieces.

Other Childs advertising pieces from the 1890's may exist.

CONSOLIDATED STEEL & WIRE CO.

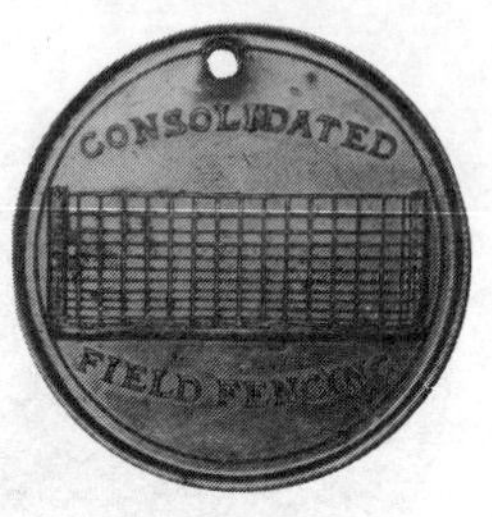

Rulau	Date	Metal	Size	F	VF	EF	Unc
Chi 47	(?)	Aluminum	32mm	—	10.00	15.00	—

Section of field fencing, CONSOLIDATED above. FIELD FENCING below. Rv: CONSOLIDATED STEEL & WIRE CO. / CHICAGO (within scrollwork) / .*. Plain edge. R5. Usually found holed. (Wright 1378; Schimidt C85)

CONSTABLE & CLEARY

Rulau	Date	Metal	Size	F	VF	EF	Unc
Chi 48	(ca 1898)	Copper	23mm	4.00	6.50	10.00	—

CONSTABLE & CLEARY / 50 / RUSH ST. /-&- / 536 / DIVISION ST. Rv: Large 2 1/2 ¢. Plain edge. R7. (Schmidt N/L; Vacketta Chi C131)

THE DE GOLYER ROCK VARNISHES

Rulau	Date	Metal	Size	F	VF	EF	Unc
Chi 49	1892	Aluminum	38mm	—	30.00	50.00	—

Rock of Gibraltar, STRENGTH & DURABILITY above, ROCK OF GIBRALTAR below. Rv: THE DE GOLYER / (sunburst) / ROCK VARNISHES / (sunburst) / CHICAGO 1892 NEW YORK / (tiny) DEMAREST N.Y. (Kirtley Jan. 1992 sale, lot R005)

EDELWEISS RESTAURANT

Rulau	Date	Metal	Size	VG	F	VF	Unc
Chi 50	1899	B&A	19mm	15.00	20.00	25.00	—
Chi 51	1899	B&A	28mm	8.00	15.00	30.00	—

Chi 50: THE / EDELWEISS in script within wreath. Around: EDELWEISS RESTAURANT / 104-106 MADISON ST. Rv: On latticework background: GOOD FOR / 5 / PAT JULY 1899 / IN MERCHANDISE. Plain edge. R5. (Schmidt E28; Vacketta Chi EA12-5)

Chi 51: As last, but denomination 25. R5. (Schmidt E28c; Vacketta Chi EA12-25)

J. EGGSTEIN

Rulau	Date	Metal	Size	VG	F	VF	Unc
Chi 55	(?)	Brass	23mm	5.00	7.50	9.00	—

GOOD FOR / 5 ¢ / J / EGGSTEIN / IN / TRADE. Rv: Ornate 5 within circle of 17 stars. Plain edge. R9; only 6 pieces known. (Schmidt N/L; Vacketta Chi EB18)

The six known pieces are from a single hoard.

FAIRBANKS MORSE & CO.

Rulau	Date	Metal	Size	F	VF	EF	Unc
Chi 56	(ca 1890)	Aluminum	26mm	—	15.00	25.00	—

Scale on wheels with ALUMINUM- / -THE COMING METAL forming an inner circle. Around: FAIRBANKS' SCALES / THE WORLD'S STANDARD. Rv: Windmill. Around: ECLIPSE WINDMILLS / OVER 40,000 IN OPERATION / FAIRBANKS, MORSE & CO. Plain edge. (Schmidt N/L)

Though the piece must have been in good quantity as an advertising check, it is uncommon today.

FALL FESTIVAL

Rulau	Date	Metal	Size	F	VF	EF	Unc
Chi 57	1899	Gilt/B	38mm	15.00	20.00	—	—

McKinley bust left, WILLIAM McKINLEY above. Rv: FALL FESTIVAL / - * - / CHICAGO / OCT. 5TH TO 12TH / 1899. Plain edge. R7. (Schmidt F13)

G. A. R.
(Grand Army of the Republic)

Rulau	Date	Metal	Size	F	VF	EF	Unc
Chi 60	1900	Gilt Brass	28mm	—	—	4.00	8.00

Decoration (medal, badge and suspension ribbon) in center, G A R entwined. AUG. 26-30 on either side. Above: 34TH NAT'L ENCAMPMENT. Below: 1900 / CHICAGO. Rv: Statue of mounted flag-bearer at center, LOGAN MONUMENT below. Plain edge. Issued with eyelet.

C. F. GAIL COMPANY

Rulau	Date	Metal	Size	F	VF	EF	Unc
Chi 62	(ca 1895)	Copper	29mm	—	10.00	15.00	—

C. F. GAIL COMPANY. / WHOLESALE / AGENTS / * CHICAGO *. Rv: THIS CHECK WILL BE REDEEMED BY ANY DEALER * / GOOD FOR / ONE / FONTELLA / CIGAR. Plain edge. R7. (Schmidt G12; Vacketta Chi GA05)

GARDEN CITY BILLIARD TABLE CO.

Rulau	Date	Metal	Size	F	VF	EF	Unc
Chi 63	(1891)	Brass	26mm	—	—	30.00	—

THE / GARDEN CITY / .-. / BILLIARD / .-. / TABLE CO. / CHICAGO. Rv: Large letter S. Plain edge. (Schmidt N/L; Vacketta N/L)

Probably a stock token of this billiard table manufacturer. Its showroom was at 176 Madison in 1891.

A later 35mm brass token of this issuer, in $1 denomination, is listed by Ore H. Vacketta as number Chicago G04.

GORMULLY AND JEFFERY MANUFACTURING CO.

Rulau	Date	Metal	Size	F	VF	EF	Unc
Chi 64	(1890's)	Aluminum	38mm	—	50.00	—	—

COMPLIMENTS OF / GORMULLY & JEFFERY MFG. CO. / THAT / Rambler (script) / IS A / MIGHTY FINE / BICYCLE / CHICAGO BOSTON. WASHINGTON NEW YORK. / BROOKLYN. DETROIT. COVENTRY ENG. Rv: Gear gauge (movable, like a perpetual calendar). G & J at left, GEAR GAUGE at right, LARGE SPROCKET below. Plain edge. Issued with loop. (Dick Grinolds March 1989 sale, lot 923)

Rulau	Date	Metal	Size	F	VF	EF	Unc
Chi B64	1896	Copper	23mm	—	—	50.00	—

GORMULLY AND JEFFERY MANUFACTURING CO. / RAMBLER / SOUVENIR / FACSIMILE. Rv: AWARDED / FACSIMILE / 3000 MILES / ON RAMBLER BICYCLE / 1896. Plain edge. Issued holed. (Wright 389; Rulau Mav 39)

Rulau	Date	Metal	Size	F	VF	EF	Unc
Chi E64	1893	Lead	69mm	—	—	100.	125.

Bicycle right. Above: RAMBLER BICYCLES / COMPLIMENTS OF. Below: GORMULLY & JEFFERY / MFG. CO. / CHICAGO / BOSTON WASHINGTON NEW-YORK COVENTRY, ENG. Rv: Domed building. Around: WORLD'S COLUMBIAN EXPOSITION / CHICAGO / 1893 / ADMINISTRATION BUILDING. Plain edge. (Kirtley Sept. 9, 1989 sale, lot 1121)

GRAND PACIFIC HOTEL

Rulau	Date	Metal	Size	F	VF	EF	Unc
Chi 65	1899	B&A*	19mm	10.00	15.00	25.00	—

*(Square aluminum center). JACKSON BOULEVARD / GRAND / PACIFIC / HOTEL / & CLARK ST CHICAGO / (tiny) GREENDUCK CO. CHICAGO. Rv: On latticework background: GOOD FOR / 5 / PATD. / JULY 1899 / IN MERCHANDISE. Plain edge. R4. (Schmidt G64; Vacketta Chi GB33)

Interestingly, Greenduck vice president-sales manager E. L. Butler in 1965 told numismatist Jack Burns "There is no known activity on the part of our company in the manufacture of bimetallic coins." This appeared in Burns' "Bimetallic Tokens Patented in 1899" in the April, 1965 issue of *The Numismatist*. Obviously Greenduck infringed at least once on Childs' patent?

GRANT GOODRICH CO.

Rulau	Date	Metal	Size	F	VF	EF	Unc
Chi 67	(1890's)	Aluminum	**	—	—	30.00	—

** Shield-shaped; 30x38mm.

High-fashion lady's boot, labeled UNION. Around: GRANT / GOODRICH / CO / SELLING / AGENTS / CHICAGO / within scrollwork. Rv: Imitation of U.S. shield. On upper canton: Stars and HIGHEST AWARD. On lower portion: Stripes and TRADE MARK / UNION (on panel) / BRAND. Within circular center escutcheon; THE G & G. CO. / UNION BRAND / (all-seeing eye in triangle) / SHOES / CHICAGO. (Kirtley Sept. 1992 sale, lot 1138)

Grant and Goodrich Co. were apparently sellers, not manufacturers, of shoes. This is one of the handsomest tokens of the Gay Nineties.

FRED. GRIESHEIMER & CO.

Rulau	Date	Metal	Size	F	VF	EF	Unc
Chi 70	(1899)	Gilt/B	32mm	—	—	20.00	30.00

Uniformed bust right, tiny W. & H. CO. NEWARK N.J. under truncation. Below: ADMIRAL GEORGE DEWEY. Rv: LOOK FOR US ONLY AT / COR. CLARK & LAKE STS. / LARGEST & BEST LINE / OF $10oo AND / SUITS OVERCOATS / U.S. / GRIESHEIMER & CO (in script). Plain edge. R7. (Schmidt G74)

Rulau	Date	Metal	Size	F	VF	EF	Unc
Chi 71	(1899)	Gilt/Cop	32mm	—	—	20.00	30.00

As last. R7. (Schmidt G79a)

Rulau	Date	Metal	Size	F	VF	EF	Unc
Chi 72	1899	Gilt/B	32mm	—	—	20.00	30.00

Obverse as last, but . CHICAGO AUTUMN FESTIVAL added above Dewey's bust. Rv: FRED. / GRIESHEIMER / ..CLOTHIER.. / STATE ST., COR. JACKSON BLVD / 1899 (first three lines in Old English type). Plain edge. R7. (Schmidt G81)

Rulau	Date	Metal	Size	F	VF	EF	Unc
Chi 73	1899	Gilt/Cop	32mm	—	—	20.00	30.00

As last. R7. (Schmidt G81a)

CARTER H. HARRISON MEMORIAL

Rulau	Date	Metal	Size	F	VF	EF	Unc
Chi 77	1893	Aluminum	38mm	—	—	10.00	20.00

Hatted bust three-quarters right, tiny CHILDS - CHI. incused on truncation. Around: THE HONORABLE CARTER H. HARRISON. Rv: Within wreath: IN MEMORIAM. Around: MAYOR OF CHICAGO ASSASSINATED OCT. 28, 1893. Stars around entire rim. Plain edge. R6. (Schmidt H26)

Rulau	Date	Metal	Size	F	VF	EF	Unc
Chi 78	(1894)	Copper	39mm	—	8.00	10.00	20.00

Obverse as last. Rv: Within wreath a scroll is open before a torch. On scroll, incused: THIS IS TO CERTIFY / THAT THE BEARER HAS / PAID ONE DOLLAR / TO THE / CARTER H. HARRISON / MEMORIAL. Plain edge. R5. (Schmidt H25)

Mayor Harrison was assassinated in the year of the World's Columbian Expositon in Chicago.

HARTLEY'S STUDIOS

Rulau	Date	Metal	Size	F	VF	EF	Unc
Chi 80	(1891-97)	Aluminum	35mm	—	—	40.00	50.00

Crowing cock standing right atop a dead cock. Around his neck is a powderhorn labeled HARTLEY'S / $2 CABINETS. In his beak he holds the sling to a rifle standing behind him, on the stock of which is lettered $2. GUN. The dead bird wears a medallion around its neck reading: HIGH / PRICED / STUDIOS. Reverse: HARTLEY'S STUDIOS / 12 CABINETS AND 1 PANEL / $2.00 / -.- / LIFE SIZE / CRAYON PORTRAIT / WITH / 12 CABINETS AND 1 PANEL / $5.00 / 309 W. MADISON ST. CHICAGO. Plain edge. Often found holed. R8. (Wright 433; Schmidt H29)

HAYMARKET THEATRE

Rulau	Date	Metal	Size	F	VF	EF	Unc
Chi 82	1890	Aluminum	37mm	—	10.00	25.00	40.00

Building, THE HAYMARKET above, WILL J. DAVIS / MANAGER, in exergue. Rv: THIRD ANNUAL HOLIDAY / SOUVENIR (slanting letters) / THE HAYMARKET (script) / POPULAR THEATRE / OF CHICAGO / CHRISTMAS 1890. Plain edge. R8. (Schmidt H33)

Rulau	Date	Metal	Size	F	VF	EF	Unc
Chi 83	1890	WM	37mm	—	20.00	30.00	50.00

As last. R7. (Schmidt N/L)

This commemorative at Christmas, 1890 marked the theater's third anniversary. It opened at Christmas, 1887. It is said that Davis hid Negro slaves in the top floor of this same building during the Civil War.

The Schmidt aluminum specimen, illustrated in Unc., was acquired in 1978 for $20.

HOTEL BISMARCK

Rulau	Date	Metal	Size	F	VF	EF	Unc
Chi 85	(ca 1890)	Brass	29mm	—	—	8.00	12.00

Nude bust of Prince von Bismarck right, star under truncation. Around: HOTEL BISMARCK, 180 RANDOLPH ST., CHICAGO. Rv: Radiant American eagle displayed, U.S. shield on its breast, scroll with E PLURIBUS UNUM below. A cloud is under the eagle. Plain edge. Issued with loop, as were all in this series! R2. (Schmidt H68)

Rulau	Date	Metal	Size	F	VF	EF	Unc
Chi 86	(ca 1890)	Gilt/B	29mm	—	—	8.00	12.00

As last. R2. (Schmidt H68a)

Rulau	Date	Metal	Size	F	VF	EF	Unc
Chi 87	(ca 1890)	Svd/B	29mm	—	—	8.00	12.00

As last. R2. (Schmidt H68b)

Chi 88	(ca 1890)	Copper	29mm	—	—	8.00	12.00

As last. R2. (Schmidt H68c)

Chi 89	(ca 1890)	Gilt/C	29mm	—	—	8.00	12.00

As last. R2. (Schmidt H68d)

Chi 90	(ca 1890)	Svd/C	29mm	—	—	8.00	12.00

As last. R2. (Schmidt H68e)

All specimens were issued with loop, but a number have had the loops removed and edges smoothed down. The Bismarck was one of Chicago's larger hostelries in its day.

There are later tokens of this issuer, released in 1934 (Vacketta Chi BF58)

JACKSON HOTEL BUFFET (and) OXFORD HOTEL BUFFET

Rulau	Date	Metal	Size	F	VF	EF	Unc
Chi 92	(?)	Aluminum	Oct 26mm	8.00	12.50	—	—

JACKSON HOTEL BUFFET / OXFORD HOTEL / BUFFET / CHICAGO. / JACKSON BLVD. / & / HALSTED ST. / ADAMS & CANAL STS. Rv: GOOD FOR 5 CENTS / 5 / ON YOUR / * NEXT WHISKEY *. Plain edge. R9. (Vacketta Chi J06)

Chi 93	(?)	Aluminum	24mm	—	—	8.00	—

THE JACKSON / BUFFET / 954 / JACKSON BLVD. Rv: THIS CHECK AND / 10 C / GOOD FOR / A 15 C / DRINK. Plain edge. R9. (Vacketta Chi J05)

There are two other tokens of this issuer, all probably postdating the Nineties (Vacketta Chi J04, J07).

C. JEVNE & CO.

Rulau	Date	Metal	Size	F	VF	EF	Unc
Chi 94	(1890's)	Aluminum	36mm	—	—	30.00	50.00

Dragon coiled around: C. JEVNE / & Co. in fancy lettering. CHICAGO. below. Rv: Same as obverse of Hartley's Studios token (Chi 80, crowing cock with rifle). Plain edge. (Hartzog coll.)

Chi 94C	(1890's)	Aluminum	35mm	—	—	25.00	35.00

Chinese nobleman facing, wearing mandarin hat and carrying open fan. Around: JEVNE'S GOLD MANDARIN TEAS / .+.+.+. Rv: TRADE / MARK on triangular pyramid above clouds. Above: ADAMANT. Plain edge. (Hartzog coll.)

Jevne Coffee Co. was still in business in Chicago in 1918. Its store cards are very beautiful, and are published here for the first time.

THOMAS KANE & COMPANY

Rulau	Date	Metal	Size	F	VF	EF	Unc
Chi 95	(1890's)	Aluminum	37mm	—	15.00	20.00	25.00

Within wreath in central circle: SCHOOL / CHURCH / & BANK / FURNITURE. Around: THOMAS KANE & COMPANY / * CHICAGO *. Rev. Partly enclosed by branch open at right: BOATS, / ENGINES, / BICYCLES, / YACHTS. / (tiny) CHILDS CHICAGO. Plain edge. R7. (Schmidt K10)

This piece was issued in an advertising card and sold at the time for 25 cents. In original card it is R9, worth $40 in Unc. Die varieties of this piece are known.

KASPER & BARNES

Rulau	Date	Metal	Size	F	VF	EF	Unc
Chi 99	1890's	Aluminum	35mm	—	10.00	—	—

* KASPER & BARNES / REPAIR / CHECK 1000 / McVICKER'S THEATRE B'LD'G CHICAGO *. Rv: WATCHES / DIAMONDS / JEWELRY. Plain edge. R7. (Wright 533; Schmidt K14)

A. KISER

Rulau	Date	Metal	Size	F	VF	EF	Unc
Chi 100	(1896)	Brass	23mm	—	5.00	10.00	—

GOOD FOR / 5 ¢ / A. KISER (on oval panel) / IN / TRADE. Rv: GOOD FOR / 5 ¢ / IN TRADE. Plain edge. (Schmidt N/L; Vacketta N/L)

Anton Kiser is listed as a saloonkeeper in 1896.

JACOB KOWALEWSKI

Rualu	Date	Metal	Size	VG	F	VF	Unc
Chi 101	(1891)	Brass	Scal 28mm	—	9.00	—	—

GOOD FOR / 5¢ / JACOB KOWALEWSKI / DRINK. Rv: 5 in circle of stars. Plain edge. (Thoele coll.; ex-Gerald Johnson)

Jacob Kowalewski's saloon at 232 Belmont Avenue appears in the 1891 *Lakeside Annual Business Directory*.

WILLIAM LOEFFLER

Rulau	Date	Metal	Size	F	VF	EF	Unc
Chi 102	1899	Aluminum	33mm	—	—	10.00	15.00

Hatted bust three-quarters right, WILLIAM LOEFFLER CITY CLERK CHICAGO. around. Rv: VOTE FOR / WM LOEFFLER / -FOR- / CITY CLERK / Tuesday April 4th / 1899. Plain edge. R8. (Schmidt L66)

Rulau	Date	Metal	Size				
Chi 103	1899	Bronze	33mm	—	—	15.00	25.00

Obverse as last, but from different dies. Rv: ELECTED / APR 6TH 1897 / RE-ELECTED / APR. 4TH 1899. Plain edge. R8. (Schmidt L67)

In general, political campaign tokens are not listed in this reference. This local campaign provides an exception — it is not often a local candidate issues a second token after an election! Loeffler issued a third piece in 1902 outside the scope of this work.

MICHIGAN FORESTRY EXHIBIT

Rulau	Date	Metal	Size	F	VF	EF	Unc
Chi 108	1893	Aluminum	39mm	—	10.00	20.00	30.00

Log building, CHILDS CHICAGO under ground line; WORLDS FAIR above, .1893. below — all within central circle. Around: MICHIGAN FORESTRY EXHIBIT / * LOGGING CAMP *. Rv: Two horses drawing giant load of logs right. CHAMPION LOAD OF LOGS above. 36055 FEET WEIGHT 144 TONS / DRAWN BY EST. OF / THOMAS NESTER. Plain edge.

CHAS. MATERN

Rulau	Date	Metal	Size	VG	F	VF	Unc
Chi 106	(1891-1902)	Brass	Oct 27mm	—	—	35.00	—

GOOD FOR / 5 ¢ / CHAS. / MATERN / AT THE BAR. Rv: GEO. KUEHL BILLIARD SUPPLIES / CHICAGO. Plain edge. (Bill Rouleau coll.)

This saloon appears in city directories for 1891 and 1902. The token was ATCO maverick 3381.

MAX MILLER

Rulau	Date	Metal	Size	VG	F	VF	Unc
Chi 109	(1893)	Brass	25mm	—	—	75.00	—

GOOD FOR / 5 C / MAX - / MILLER / DRINK / AT THE BAR. Rv: H. TUCKHORN & CO. / BILLIARD / -&- / POOL TABLES / -.- / 171 RANDOLPH ST / CHICAGO. Plain edge.

Claimed for Ohio. This saloon is listed in the 1893 Chicago directory.

H. Tuckhorn made checks for his billiard table customers only in the 1893-98 period, and checks bearing the Tuckhorn name are among the most rare of billiard tokens.

MORGAN & BOLLENBACH

Rulau	Date	Metal	Size	VG	F	VF	Unc
Chi 110	(?)	Nickel	21mm	—	8.00	14.00	—

Large thistle with three blooms, "THE STEWART" below. Rv: Ornate 5, MORGAN & BOLLENBACH around, -55- / WASHINGTON ST. / CHICAGO, ILL. below. Plain edge. R6. (Schmidt M60; Vacketta Chi M89)

Rulau	Date	Metal	Size	VG	F	VF	Unc
Chi 112	(?)	Nickel	32mm	—	10.00	17.50	—

Obverse similar to last, but thistle larger and letters smaller. Rv: As last, but '50' in ornate numerals in place of '5'. Plain edge. R6. (Schmidt M60a; Vacketta N/L)

CHAS. MUNSON BELTING CO.

Chicago, Ill.

Rulau	Date	Metal	Size	F	VF	EF	Unc
Chi 112E	1893	Leather	Irreg 46mm	—	—	32.00	40.00

Eagle in flight above clouds and thunderbolts, COLUMBIAN EXPOSITION / CHICAGO. 1893. around. Rv: CHAS MUNSON BELTING CO / MANUFR'S OF / * OAK * / LEATHER / -.- / BELTING / * CHICAGO *. (Kirtley Oct. 1993 sale, lot 1648)

FRANK H. NAAS

Rulau	Date	Metal	Size	F	VF	EF	Unc
Chi 113	(1891-99)	Brass	24mm	—	—	25.00	—

GOOD FOR 5 CTS AT THE BAR / FRANK / *** / H. NAAS / . . . / *. Rv: Ornate CHECK in central circle; around: L. BOCHE ENGRAVER & DIESINKER CHICAGO. / (rosette). Plain edge.

Both A's in NAAS are actually inverted V's - a diesinker error.

This saloon is listed 1891-1899.

"NEW ERA" CLOTHIERS

Rulau	Date	Metal	Size	VG	F	VF	Unc
Chi 114	(1890's)	Aluminum	38mm	—	—	20.00	30.00

Building at center, CHILDS CHICAGO below exergue line, all within circle. Around: THE "NEW ERA" CLOTHIERS. FURNISHERS. HATTERS / COR. BLUE ISLAND AVE. * / HARRISON & HALSTED STS. Rv: Seven-line inscription. Plain edge. R10. (Schmidt N/L)

J. W. NIESEL

Rulau	Date	Metal	Size	VG	F	VF	Unc
Chi 115	(1891)	Brass	**	—	—	11.00	—

** Diamond-shaped, 23x23mm.
(All incused): J. W. NIESEL / 5 / (crossed cues above four balls). Rv: Blank. Plain edge. (Thoele coll.)

Joseph W. Niesel ran a saloon at 141 Fullerton Avenue, according to the 1891 *Lakeside Annual Business Directory.*

B. F. NORRIS, ALLISTER & CO.

Rulau	Date	Metal	Size	VG	F	VF	Unc
Chi 116	1893	Gilt/Cop	39mm	—	30.00	40.00	50.00

B. F. NORRIS, ALLISTER & CO / WORLD'S COLUMBIAN EXPOSITION CHICAGO ILLS. 1893 / PERPETUAL / POCKET / CALENDAR / WHOLESALE JEWELERS CHICAGO ILLS. Rv: Revolving perpetual calendar. Plain edge. R8. (Wright 766)

NORWEGIAN TURNERS SOCIETY

Rulau	Date	Metal	Size	VG	F	VF	Unc
Chi 118	1891	WM	30mm	—	15.00	20.00	—

Monogram at center, THE NORWEGIAN TURNERS SOCIETY OF CHICAGO SOUVENIR / MASQUERADE FEB. 21. 91. around. Rv: Two dancers dressed as jesters. Plain edge. R7. (Schmidt N61)

A. ORTMAYER & SON

Rulau	Date	Metal	Size	VG	F	VF	Unc
Chi 120	(ca 1895)	Aluminum	39.5mm	—	25.00	45.00	60.00

A. ORTMAYER & SON / CHICAGO, ILL. / PERPETUAL / CALENDAR / * PLACE ONE * / ON THE DAY / ON WHICH / THE MONTH BEGINS / WHOLESALE SADDLERY. Rv: Revolving perpetual calendar. Plain edge. R9. (Schmidt 070)

PEACE JUBILEE

Rulau	Date	Metal	Size	VG	F	VF	Unc
Chi 122	1898	Gilt/B	18mm	—	5.00	7.50	15.00

McKinley bust three quarters right, separating 18-98, PEACE JUBILEE above, CHICAGO below. Ornate arch, McKINLEY ARCH below. Plain edge. R6. Usually encountered holed. (Schmidt P20)

Rulau	Date	Metal	Size	VG	F	VF	Unc
Chi 123	1898	Brass	36mm	—	8.00	—	30.00

McKinley bust left, NATIONAL PEACE JUBILEE / CHICAGO OCT. 18-19 1898. Rv: Arch, NATIONAL PEACE JUBILEE 1898 OCT. 18 19 CHICAGO McKINLEY ARCH. Plain edge. R8. (Schmidt P23)

Rulau	Date	Metal	Size	VG	F	VF	Unc
Chi 123F	1898	Brass	36mm	—	15.00	20.00	30.00

Small busts of Dewey, Sampson, Schley and Shafter surround 1898 in scroll, OCT. in scroll at left, 18-19 in scroll at right. Around: NATIONAL PEACE JUBILEE / CHICAGO. Rv: Same as 123 reverse. Plain edge. R7. About 11 known.

Rulau	Date	Metal	Size	VG	F	VF	Unc
Chi 123N	1898	Bronze	28.5mm	—	8.00	10.00	20.00

As next, but larger.

Rulau	Date	Metal	Size	VG	F	VF	Unc
Chi 124	1898	WM	19mm	4.00	6.00	9.00	—

Sailor and soldier standing, facing, holding flags, PEACE and radiant laurel wreath above. Rv: PEACE / JUBILEE / HELD AT / CHICAGO ILL. / OCT. 14.-19. / 1898. Plain edge. (Schmidt N/L)

McKinley Arch was erected along the lakefront in what is now McKinley Park, a memorial to the popular president during the Spanish-American War. Chicago is filled with memorials to military heroes — Soldier Field, Navy Pier among others. President McKinley was assassinated at the Pan-American Exposition in Buffalo, N.Y. in 1901.

A. PFAFF PAVILION

Rulau	Date	Metal	Size	VG	F	VF	Unc
Chi 126	(1891-92)	Aluminum	35mm	8.00	—	15.00	25.00

AP monogram, rosette to right. Above: A. PFAFF'S / PAVILION. Below: GARFIELD PARK / END OF MADISON STREET CABLE. Rv: FAMILY RESORT / A. PFAFF'S / PAVILION (between ornaments) / GARFIELD PARK / RESTAURANT. Plain edge. R9; 3 pieces known. (Schmidt P28)

August Pfaff started in the restaurant business in the early 1880's. Garfield Park is now part of the city of Chicago.

Joseph Schmidt (in "19th Century Illinois Exonumia" in 1977) guessed this piece was issued about 1885. We believe the 1891-92 period is more accurate; aluminum was rarely used for tokens before 1890. The five known pieces include one in VF-EF (photo) and two in VG-F.

Rulau	Date	Metal	Size	F	VF	EF	Unc
Chi 127	(1891-92)	Aluminum	35mm	—	15.00	20.00	25.00

Obverse as 126. Rv: Trotting racer left, in dentilated circle. Around: SECOND ANNUAL INTER STATE FAIR / .+.+.+. (Harztog coll.)

(NEW) POST OFFICE

Rulau	Date	Metal	Size	VG	F	VF	Unc
Chi 130	1899	Brass	38.5mm	—	25.00	—	50.00

Uniformed bust of Dewey facing, head turned right, ADMIRAL DEWEY around. Rv: Impressive view of the new post office-government building. LAYING OF CORNER STONE above. NEW GOVERNMENT BUILDING / CHICAGO / OCTOBER 9TH 1899 in exergue. (Plain edge. R10; apparently unique. (Schmidt N/L)

Rulau	Date	Metal	Size	VG	F	VF	Unc
Chi 130F	1899	Gilt/B	39mm	—	—	Unique ?	—

Building. Around: OCT. 9th / (scrollwork) / 1899. Rv: Heraldic eagle, ribbon in its beak reading: E PLURIBUS UNUM, arrows in left talon, olive branch in right. Above: 13 radiant stars within wreath. Plain edge. (George R. Ganter coll.)

Building on obverse is the same as that depicted on reverse of Chi 130.

Rulau	Date	Metal	Size	VG	F	VF	Unc
Chi 131	1899	Gilt/B	18mm	—	4.50	10.00	12.50

McKinley bust three-quarters left, WILLIAM McKINLEY above. Rv: New P.O. building, LAYING OF CORNER STONE above, POST OFFICE / CHICAGO / OCTOBER 9TH 1899 below. Plain edge. Usually found holed. R5. (Schmidt P55)

Rulau	Date	Metal	Size	VG	F	VF	Unc
Chi 132	(1899)	Brass	15mm	—	5.00	10.00	15.00

New P.O. building, CHICAGO above, NEW P. O. below. Rv: Lord's prayer. Plain edge. Usually found holed. R6. (Schmidt P57)

All these Post Office medalets show the same view of the giant new government building, which has since been torn down.

JOS. S. PRICE

Rulau	Date	Metal	Size	F	VF	EF	Unc
Chi 135	(?)	Nickel	25mm	8.00	15.00	25.00	40.00

Stein on which is inscribed BLATZ. Around: JOS. S. PRICE / STATE & 12th STS. Rv: Large decanter on which is inscribed JOS. S. / PRICE. Around: THIS CHECK & 10 C GOOD FOR ANY 15 C DRINK. On obverse, top of stein's handle to left of period after JOS.; on reverse, the decanter is large, with the left side of the stopper to left of 'G' in GOOD. Plain edge. R5. (Schmidt P70; Vacketta Chi P80)

Rulau	Date	Metal	Size	F	VF	EF	Unc
Chi 136	(?)	Nickel	25mm	8.00	15.00	25.00	40.00

Similar to last. Top of stein's handle to right of period after JOS. Decanter small and ornate; left side of stopper to right of 'G' in GOOD. Plain edge. R5. (Schmidt P70a)

Rulau	Date	Metal	Size	F	VF	EF	Unc
Chi 137	(?)	Nickel	25mm	—	—	10.00	15.00

JOS. S. PRICE / STATE / & 12TH STS. / N.W. COR. / VAN BUREN & SHERMAN STS. Rv: THIS CHECK & 10 C GOOD FOR ANY 15 C DRINK. Plain edge. R7. (Vacketta Chi P81)

The first two tokens are among the most colorful saloon tokens ever issued. Once available and inexpensive, exonumists into the saloon genre have driven their prices up steadily. The author was forced to pay $22.50 for an EF specimen of the second variety (Schmidt P70a) in late 1985, for example, despite considerable skill in haggling acquired over 46 years of collecting.

The seller's rationale was: "If you won't pay it, someone else will." He had asked $35 for the piece at first. The dealer, of course, is correct: Tokens are expensive today because demand is steady —.but only for **cataloged, publicized** and **sexy** pieces.

The third specimen above, minus pictures, commands little excitement, though equally scarce.

RAILROAD RIOTS

Rulau	Date	Metal	Size	F	VF	EF	Unc
Chi 140	1894	S/Brass	35mm	—	15.00	—	30.00

Three crossed rifles on grass. Around: * IN MEMORY OF THE RAILROAD RIOTS 1894 * / TO THE BRAVE MEMBERS OF THE NATIONAL GUARD. Rv: Dramatic scene of soldiers firing at rioters, LOOMIS & 49TH above. Plain edge. Issued with loop. R8. (Schmidt R12)

RAPHAEL'S

Rulau	Date	Metal	Size	F	VF	EF	Unc
Chi 141	1892	Aluminum	35mm	—	30.00	—	60.00

Facing Columbus bust in mariner's cap, within circle. Around: CHRISTOPHER * 1492 * COLUMBUS * 1892 *. Rv: RAPHAEL'S / (ornament) / COLUMBIAN / -DAY- / SOUVENIR. Plain edge. (Kirtley March 1993 sale, lot 1288)

ROYAL SAFETY DEPOSIT VAULTS

Rulau	Date	Metal	Size	F	VF	EF	Unc
Chi 142	(1890's)	Aluminum	**	—	12.50	—	—

** Oval, 43 by 21mm.
ROYAL SAFETY / 167 JACKSON ST. / CHICAGO / DEPOSIT VAULTS. Rv: 25 C REWARD / FOR / RETURN OF KEYS / OR DROP IN ANY LETTER BOX / No.____. Plain edge. R4. (Wright 1605; Schmidt N/L)

THE ROYAL TAILORS

Rulau	Date	Metal	Size	F	VF	EF	Unc
Chi 144	(1890's)	Aluminum	38mm	—	8.50	12.50	25.00

Royal Tailors' diamond-shaped logo featuring a charging tiger in jungle setting at center. Around: THE LARGEST CUSTOMER TAILORING / ESTABLISHMENT IN THE WORLD. Rv: AS GOOD AS GOLD / -AT ANY- / AGENCY OF / THE ROYAL TAILORS / FOR / ONE DOLLAR / -ON- / PRICE OF ANY SUIT. Reeded edge. R3. (Wright 1681; Schmidt R55; Vacketta Chi R57; also listed by Kenney and Hibler-Kappen)

This is one of the most popular and best known $1 trade tokens of the Gay Nineties.

Rulau	Date	Metal	Size	F	VF	EF	Unc
Chi 146	1900	Gilt/B	31mm	—	7.50	10.00	25.00

Bust three quarters left of man with mustache and Van Dyke beard, THE ROYAL TAILORS, CHICAGO USA above. . OUR PRESIDENT . below. Rv: Building. ROYAL TAILORING ACME OF PERFECTION above, . 1900 . below. Plain edge. R5. (Schmidt R57)

The 1900 piece can be found with a recut '9' in the date. The name of "our president" has not yet been discovered, so the distinguished gentlemen gracing the medalet must remain unnamed.

Rulau	Date	Metal	Size	F	VF	EF	Unc
Chi 147	1901	xx	35mm	—	—	25.00	—

xx Aluminum ring encases U.S. 1901 Indian cent. THE ROYAL TAILORS.

ST. PAUL KIRCHE

Rulau	Date	Metal	Size	F	VF	EF	Unc
Chi 148	1893	Copper	38mm	—	8.00	—	—

Old frame church above 1843, all within central circle. Around: ST. PAUL'S KIRCHE / LA SALLE AVE UND OHIO ST., CHICAGO. Rv: Church structure, ZUM ANDENKEN AN DAS GOLDENE JUBILAUM around, 1893 in exergue. Plain edge. R8. (Schmidt S63)

These commemoratives are usually found holed. Kirche = Church. Issued by the German-speaking congregation on the golden jubilee of the church's founding, 1843-1893.

SCOVILL MANUFACTURING CO.

Rulau	Date	Metal	Size	F	VF	EF	Unc
Chi 149	(1892 ?)	Aluminum	39.5mm	—	—	65.00	80.00

Complex SMCo monogram. Around: SCOVILL MANUFACTURING CO. / WESTERN OFFICE / 208 LAKE ST. / CHICAGO, ILL. Rv: THE SCOVILL MANUFACTURING COMPANY / ESTABLISHED 1802. / SHEET METAL / WIRE & TUBING, / ARTICLES OF ALL KINDS / FROM / ALUMINUM, / COPPER, BRASS, / GERMAN SILVER / & c. / * WATERBURY, CONN. U.S.A. Plain edge.

SHERMAN HOUSE

Rulau	Date	Metal	Size	F	VF	EF	Unc
Chi 150	(1890)	Nickel	35mm	—	7.50	—	Scarce

(All incused): SHERMAN HOUSE / 26 (or another number). Rv: Blank. Plain edge. All letters and numeral are enameled black. Plain edge. R7. (Schmidt S41)

Issued about 1890 by the Sherman House at the corner of Randolph and Clark Streets — one of the city's finest hotels, fancied by the sporting element. The piece is a check of some kind.

SHRINE CIGAR FACTORY

Rulau	Date	Metal	Size	F	VF	EF	Unc
Chi 152	(?)	Brass	Oct 26mm	—	8.00	15.00	22.50

GOOD FOR CIGARS ONLY / SHRINE / CIGAR / FACTORY / 114 / W. MADISON ST. / *. Rv: 25 ¢ (shaded). Plain edge. R8. (Vacketta Chi SA56)

SIMMONS CIGAR CO.

Rulau	Date	Metal	Size	F	VF	EF	Unc
Chi 157	(1897)	Aluminum	29mm	—	—	7.50	10.00

SIMMONS CIGAR CO. WHOLESALE & RETAIL 39 DEARBORN ST. CHICAGO. Rv: THIS CHECK WILL BE REDEEMED BY ANY DEALER GOOD FOR ONE CIGAR OUR LIMIT. Reeded edge. R7. (Schmidt S44; Vacketta Chi SA67)

Simmons Cigar Co. is listed in the 1897 city directory. Reeded edges are not common on cheaply-made aluminum "pass out" checks — used to introduce a new product or service — as it adds to the manufacturing cost.

FR. SIKYTA

Rulau	Date	Metal	Size	VG	F	VF	Unc
Chi 156	(1906)	Brass	25mm	—	—	5.00	—

(All incused): FR. SIKYTA / GOOD FOR / 5 ¢ / AT THE BAR. Rv: Blank. Plain edge. (Thoele coll.; ex-Weinberg)

Sikyta's saloon was at 1933 West 47th in the 1906 *Lakeside Business Directory*.

W. R. SKIDMORE

Rulau	Date	Metal	Size	F	VF	EF	Unc
Chi 154	1898	B&A	28mm	—	—	30.00	40.00

I SELL CHAPIN & GORE'S / FINE / WHISKIES / W. R. SKIDMORE / 91 S. CLARK ST. / CHICAGO. / & CIGARS / BEST IN THE WORLD. Rv: On latticework background: CHAPIN & GORE IS ALL YOU NEED TO KNOW ABOUT WHISKEY. / 25 / PAT. / JULY 1898. Plain edge. R8. (Schmidt S47; Vacketta Chi SB78)

Rulau	Date	Metal	Size	F	VF	EF	Unc
Chi 155	1898	B&A	32mm	—	—	30.00	40.00

As last, but denomiantion '50'. R8. (Schmidt S47a)

These tokens bear the earliest patent date, 1898, on any bimetallic pieces in the United States. As such, they are in demand.

TERRILL BROS.

Rulau	Date	Metal	Size	VG	F	VF	Unc
Chi 158	(1890's)	Brass	33mm	—	10.00	18.00	—

(All incused): TERRILL BROS / 196 & 198 / S. WATER ST. / 50 / 1 COOP. Rv: Blank. Plain edge. 2 known. (Vacketta Chi-TA11; Theole coll.)

Called a "fish barrel token." Coop = Cooperage?

THE TILT-SMITH SHOE CO.

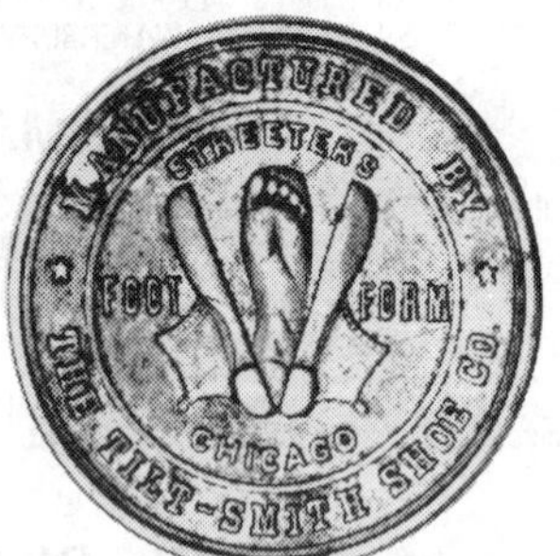

Rulau	Date	Metal	Size	VG	F	VF	Unc
Chi 160	(1890's)	Aluminum	39mm	—	15.00	20.00	30.00

Foot in fitting form; STREETERS / FOOT FORM / CHICAGO; all in central circle. Around: MANUFACTURED BY / * THE TILT-SMITH SHOE CO. *. Rv: Standard GOODYEAR WELT globe reverse. Plain edge. (Gene Johnson coll.)

TIVOLI TABLE CO.

Rulau	Date	Metal	Size	VG	F	VF	Unc
Chi 161	(1901)	Brass	21.5mm	—	15.00	20.00	—

TIVOLI TABLE CO. / (ornament) / 141 / W. JACKSON ST. / CHICAGO. Rv: Same as obverse. (Thoele coll.)

This was a short-lived manufacturer of billiard tables.

THE TURNER BRASS WORKS

Rulau	Date	Metal	Size	F	VF	EF	Unc
Chi 163	(1890's)	Aluminum	35mm	—	—	20.00	30.00

Acrobat performing handstand on high trapeze bar, WHAT CAN THE TURNER MAKE FOR YOU. Rv: THE TURNER BRASS WORKS / + / + MAKE + / ANYTHING / IN METAL / + / + CHICAGO +. Plain edge. R6. (Wright 1683; Schmidt T90)

WALTON'S

Rulau	Date	Metal	Size	VG	F	VF	Unc
Chi 164	(1890's)	Brass	28mm	—	10.00	—	—

(All incused): WALTON'S / 13 ¢ / 36 W. MADISON ST. Rv: Blank. Plain edge.

Tentative attribution, Meat market? 13 cents = price of a pound of meat?

WILLOUGHBY, HILL & CO.

Rulau	Date	Metal	Size	VG	F	VF	Unc
Chi 165	(1890's)	German silver	25mm	—	—	4.00	8.00

Wheel hub at center inscribed B.S.D. O.P.C. Above is: WILLOUGHBY, HILL & CO. / COR CLARK &. Below is: * MADISON STS. * / CHICAGO. Thick planchet. Plain edge. (Wright 1254; Miller Ill 41; Schmidt W19b)

Rulau	Date	Metal	Size	VG	F	VF	Unc
Chi 166	(1890's)	Brass	25mm	—	—	4.00	8.00

As 81. Plain edge. (Schmidt W19)

Rulau	Date	Metal	Size	VG	F	VF	Unc
Chi 167	(1890's)	Copper	25mm	—	—	5.00	10.00

As 81. Plain edge. (Schmidt W19a)

B.S.D.O.P.C. = Boston square dealing one price clothing.

YACHT CLUB SALAD DRESSING

Chicago, Ill.

Rulau	Date	Metal	Size	F	VF	EF	Unc
Chi 200	(1890's)	S/Gold*	31.5mm	—	—	500.	—

* U.S. 1878 $2 1/2 gold piece encased within diestruck sterling silver frame. * YACHT CLUB SALAD * / (ornaments) * DRESSING * (ornaments). Rv: Same as obverse. Plain edge. (coll. Neil Berman, New York)

This must be rated one of the "kings" of the encased coinage *genre.* Yacht Club Salad Dressing has been traced to Chicago.

This token was attributed by antique bottle enthusiast Kristen Pippert of Olympia, Wash., who owns a two-piece mold bottle with bottom plug marked YACHT CLUB SALAD DRESSING / CHICAGO. She values the bottle at $50 and says this bottle type was used about 1890-1915.

MAX. VITT

Cobden, Ill.

Rulau	Date	Metal	Size	VG	F	VF	Unc
Cob 1	(?)	Brass	23mm	—	5.00	10.00	—

GOOD FOR 5c LOAF, MAX. VITT. Rv: Blank. Plain edge. R8. (Schmidt V39; Vacketta Cbn 03)

This town was named after Richard Cobden.

C. EMIG

Coulterville, Ill.

Rulau	Date	Metal	Size	VG	F	VF	Unc
Cou 1	(1890's)	Brass	24mm	—	5.00	10.00	—

C. EMIG (incuse) / GOOD FOR (relief) / 5 C (incuse) / MDSE. (relief) / COULTERVILLE (incuse). Rv: EXCELSIOR / 312 OLIVE ST. / ST. LOUIS, MO. (relief maker's mark). Plain edge. R9. (Schmidt E56; Vacketta Ctv A01-5)

Cou 2 — Similar denominations in brass; 10C hexagonal 23mm; 25C scalloped 23mm; 50C 28mm — all R9. (Schmidt E56a-c; Vacketta Ctv A01-10 to 50)

Christian Emig dealt in harnesses, boots and shoes from about 1882 to the 1890's. In 1918 he is listed as a dealer in shoes, groceries and dry goods.

TURNFEST

Danville, Ill.

Rulau	Date	Metal	Size	F	VF	EF	Unc
Dan 1	1898	Bronze	28mm	—	—	10.00	15.00

Owl seated on crossed sword and sceptre, 16TES BEZIRKS TURNFEST above, * JUNI 11 - 14, 1898. / DANVILLE, ILL. * below. Rv: SHT monogram topped by a flaming torch, all within oak wreath. Plain edge. Issued with eyelet.

The lettering is in German. "16tes Bezirks Turnfest" means "16th District Turner Festival." "Juni" is "June." The Turners were a German-American gynastic and fraternal society.

ST. CLAIR HOUSE

East St. Louis, Ill.

Rulau	Date	Metal	Size	F	VF	EF	Unc
ESL 1	(1880-91)	Brass	Oct 24mm	7.00	12.00	—	—

St. CLAIR HOUSE (incuse) / GOOD FOR / 5 ¢ / AT BAR / (Ornament incuse). R: W. W. MESSER / FAUCET CO. / ST. LOUIS (maker's mark). Plain edge. R8. (Schmidt N/L; Vacketta N/L)

The specimen shown was probably excavated.

LELAND HOUSE BAR

Edwardsville, Ill.

Rulau	Date	Metal	Size	F	VF	EF	Unc
Edw 1	(1890's)	Brass	Oct 26mm	—	8.00	12.00	—

GOOD FOR / 10 C / LELAND HOUSE / * BAR * / C. BARTHOLOMEW. Rv: 10 within circle of 16 stars. Plain edge. R8. (Schmidt L22; Vacketta Edw A01)

C. Bartholomew ran the bar in the Leland Hotel in the 1890's.

MADISON CO. CENTENNIAL

Rulau	Date	Metal	Size	F	VF	EF	Unc
Edw 3	1900	Copper	31mm	—	5.00	10.00	—

Illinois state seal (eagle on rock, shield, STATE SOVEREIGNTY NATIONAL UNION on ribbon from eagle's beak). Rv: MADISON CO. CENTENNIAL ANNIVERSARY HELD AT EDWARDSVILLE, ILL. AUG. 28. 31. 1900. Plain edge. R8. (Schmidt M12)

Rulau	Date	Metal	Size	F	VF	EF	Unc
Edw 4	1900	WM*	31mm	—	—	10.00	—

As last. Plain edge. R8. (Schmidt S19; Vacketta N/L)

J. SCHMIDT

Edwardsville, Ill.

Rulau	Date	Metal	Size	F	VF	EF	Unc
Edw 6	(1890's)	Brass	Scal 25mm	5.00	10.00	15.00	—

J. SCHMIDT (incuse) / GOOD FOR 1 LOAF BREAD (relief). Rv: S. G. ADAMS S&S CO. ST. LOUIS (relief maker's mark). Plain edge. R8. (Schmidt S19; Vacketta N/L)

Joseph Schmidt was a grocer in the 1890's. He is listed as running a general store in 1918.

J. H. MUSGRAVE

Eldorado, Ill.

Rulau	Date	Metal	Size	F	VF	EF	Unc
Eld 1	(1890's)	Brass	29mm	—	—	15.00	—

(All incused): J. H. MUSGRAVE / GOOD FOR / — / x 25 CENTS x / — / IN TRADE / ELDORADO ILLS. Rv: Blank. Beaded rim on each side. Plain edge. R9. (Schmidt M79; Vacketta Edo 01)

This was a general store during the 1890's.

THE ELGIN BUTTER CO.

Elgin, Ill.

Rulau	Date	Metal	Size	F	VF	EF	Unc
Elg 1	(1890's)	Aluminum	42mm	—	4.75	7.00	—

Building at center, THE ELGIN BUTTER CO. ELGIN, ILLINOIS around. ELGIN'S GREAT CREAMERY in exergue. Rv: THE ELGIN BUTTER COMPANY / ELGIN, ILLINOIS / THE / LARGEST BEST SITUATED / AND MOST / COMPLETE CREAMERY / IN THE / WORLD / W. H. HINTZE PREST. & TREAS. Plain edge. (Wright 1667; Schmidt E26)

P. M. SHARPLES

Rulau	Date	Metal	Size	F	VF	EF	Unc
Elg 2	1893	Aluminum	35mm	—	—	35.00	50.00

Ships in central semicircle, tiny DOLBY - ELGIN at lower right. Above: THE CITY OF ELGIN / ILL, U.S.A. Below: 1893 / POPULATION 23,000 (same as Eglit 578). Rv: WESTCHESTER, PA. ELGIN, ILL. COUNCIL BLUFFS, IA. / P. M. SHARPLES / CREAM / SEPARATORS. / ***. (Kirtley Oct. 1993 sale, lot 1605)

C. E. SPILLARD

Elgin, Ill.

Rulau	Date	Metal	Size	F	VF	EF	Unc
Elg 3	1899	Brass	33mm	—	30.00	50.00	—

.C.E. / SPILLARD on ornamental cartouche at center, TAILOR, HATTER and FURNISHER above, ELGIN. below. Rv: -.- / MERRY / CHRISTMAS / AND / (rosette) HAPPY (rosette) / NEW YEAR / -.- / 1899-1900. Plain edge. R9. 1 known. (Schmidt S60)

This store card honors the "turn of the century" from 1899 to 1900 on New Year's Eve, 1900. The event was widely celebrated, but also there was a certain awe to the occasion, and the heated argument over whether the century "turns" on Jan. 1, 1900 or Jan. 1, 1901 recurred constantly in discussions.

Charles E. Spillard opened his clothing store in 1897 and ceased operations about 1930. He catered to men as clients.

B. BROS.
(Beare Brothers)

Ellis Grove, Ill.

Rulau	Date	Metal	Size	VG	F	VF	Unc
Ell 1	(?)	Brass	**	—	10.00	—	—

** Octagonal 27mm.
B. BROS. / ELLIS GROVE ILL 10 ¢. Rv: Blank. Plain edge. Rarity 8. (Wright 109; Schmidt B9)

Issued by Joseph Beare and Brothers general store.

By 1918 this store was known as Henry Beare & Sons, and a line of implements had been added. The firm also had branches at this time. Ellis Grove had 400 people in 1918; it is in Randolph County.

J. D. GREEN

Greenup, Ill.

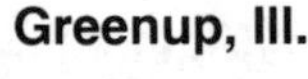

Rulau	Date	Metal	Size	F	VF	EF	Unc
Gre 1	(1890)	Brass	26mm	—	250.	—	—

THE HUB / CLOTHIER / J. D. GREEN / GREENUP, / ILL. Rv: GOOD FOR ONE / RIDE / J. D. GREEN / GREENUP, / ILL. Plain edge. R9; only 2 known. (Schmidt G31; Atwood Ill 375a; Vacketta Gre A01)

This is one of the few store cards listed in Atwood's catalog of transportation tokens. It is a highly desirable multiple-interest token.

H. A. McHOSE

Griggsville, Ill.

Rulau	Date	Metal	Size	VG	F	VF	Unc
Grg 1	(1900)	Brass	Oct 27mm	—	14.00	—	—

(All incused): H. A. McHOSE / GOOD FOR / 5 ¢ / LOAF OF BREAD. Rv: Blank. Plain edge. 3 or 4 pieces known.

Restaurant and confectionery listed in 1900 R. G. Dun directory. Research by Robert Cardiff.

J. G. KINDER

Hamburg, Ill.

Rulau	Date	Metal	Size	F	VF	EF	Unc
Ham 1	1893	Aluminum	30mm	—	15.00	30.00	50.00

Columbus bust in hat facing, 1492 CHRISTOPHER COLUMBUS 1893 around. Rv: G. KINDER'S TEMPLE OF ECONOMY / BARGAINS IN / EVERYTHING / GOOD FOR / 5 C / IN TRADE / * HAMBURG, ILL. *. Plain edge. R8. (Vacketta Ham 01; Schmidt N/L)

BOLL & HOERETH

Hecker, Ill.

Rulau	Date	Metal	Size	F	VF	EF	Unc
Hec 1	(?)	24mm	—	10.00	—	Rare	

BOLL & HOERETH / -*- / (ornament) / * HECKER, ILLS. *. Rv: GOOD FOR / 5 C / IN MERCHANDISE. * Plain edge. R9. (Schmidt B58; Vacketta Hec 01-5)

Rulau	Date	Metal	Size	F	VF	EF	Unc
Hec 2	(?)	24mm	—	10.00	—	Rare	

Similar to last, but '50¢' on reverse. (Schmidt 858a; Vacketta Hec 01-50)

Other denominations may exist. This firm was out of business before World War I. Hecker, in Monroe County, had only 200 people in 1918.

C. BATZ & SON

Jacksonville, Ill.

Rulau	Date	Metal	Size	VG	F	VF	Unc
Jac 1	(?)	Brass	Oct. 25mm	8.00	12.00	—	—

(All incused): C BATZ & SON (curved) / 5. Rv: Blank. Plain edge. Incised beaded rim on each side. Only 6-8 pieces known. (Schmidt N/L; Vacketta Jac 01)

There is another token of Batz & Son for 5C (Vacketta Jac A02) which may postdate the 1890's.

In 1918 a successor firm, Batz & Stice, operated a restaurant and cigar store.

T. E. CAGLE

Jasper County, Ill. (?)

Rulau	Date	Metal	Size	VG	F	VF	Unc
Jas 1	(1880-99)	Brass	24mm	—	—	10.00	—

(All incused): T. E. CAGLE / GOOD FOR / 5 C (in monogram style) / . IN TRADE . / (ornament). Rv: Blank. Incised beaded border on each side. Plain edge.

Rulau	Date	Metal	Size	VG	F	VF	Unc
Jas 2	ND	Brass	28mm	—	—	11.00	—

As last, but 10 C (not in monogram style). Second, third and fourth lines in a circle.

Rulau	Date	Metal	Size	VG	F	VF	Unc
Jas 3	ND	Brass	Oct 26mm	—	—	10.00	—

As first token above, but 25 C (not in monogram style).

Rulau	Date	Metal	Size	VG	F	VF	Unc
Jas 4	ND	Brass	Sq 23mm	—	—	11.00	—

As last, but 50 C. No borders. Arranged in diamond format.

Rulau	Date	Metal	Size	VG	F	VF	Unc
Jas 5	ND	Brass	Scal 28mm	—	—	15.00	—

Similar to last, but $1oo. No borders.

This set of tokens appeared in a farm estate sale in Newton, Illinois in 1985. Now in the Rulau collection. Newton is the Jasper County seat.

Thus far, the Cagle family has not been traced to any of the Jasper County communities. No records can be found as late as 1918, but a date prior to 1900 seems likely for this issuer, who probably was a general store proprietor.

J. H. SMITH & CO.

Jerseyville, Ill.

Rulau	Date	Metal	Size	F	VF	EF	Unc
Jer 1	(1899-1901)	Aluminum	Sq 26mm	—	—	15.00	20.00

J. H. SMITH CO. / J. H. Smith (signature) / JERSEYVILLE, ILLS. Rv: GOOD FOR / 25 ¢ / IN TRADE. Plain edge. 5 specimens known. R9. (Schmidt N/L; Vacketta Jrs 05)

Smith ran an ice company. His building burned down 1901. He does not appear in business after that.

OLIPHANT & CASEY

Joliet, Ill.

Rulau	Date	Metal	Size	F	VF	EF	Unc
Jol 1	1892	Aluminum	37.5mm	—	15.00	17.50	22.50

Within wreath in central circle: FROM / OLIPHANT / AND CASEY, / FOREIGN AND / DOMESTIC / -.- / DRY GOODS. Around: ALUMINUM / * SOUVENIR *. Rv: Within laurel branch: GRAND OPENING / OF THE / JOLIET PEOPLES / DRY GOODS STORE / * / FEB. 27TH / .1892. Plain edge. (Schmidt N/L)

Out of business before World War I.

F. C. JOHNSON

Kishwaukee, Ill.

Rulau	Date	Metal	Size	VG	F	VF	Unc
Kis 1	(?)	Aluminum	25mm	—	—	5.00	15.00

Yoke, STEEL CENTER NECK YOKE. Rv: MADE BY / F. C. JOHNSON / KISHWAUKEE / ILLS. Plain edge. R7. (Schmidt J51)

Rulau	Date	Metal	Size	VG	F	VF	Unc
Kis 2	(?)	Aluminum	25mm	—	—	5.00	15.00

JOHNSON's / SWEET CIDER / AND PURE / CIDER VINEGAR. Rv: Similar to last reverse. Plain edge. R7. (Schmidt J53; Vacketta Kwe 01)

Rulau	Date	Metal	Size	VG	F	VF	Unc
Kis 3	1893	Aluminum	35mm	—	—	25.00	40.00

Globe at center, WORLD'S COLUMBIAN EXPOSITION / CHICAGO, ILLS. 1893 around. Rv: F. C. JOHNSON / CIDER / AND / PURE CIDER / VINEGAR / KISHWAUKEE, ILL. Plain edge.

This tiny place is in Winnebago County, south of Rockford.

THOMAS MILES BUFFET

La Salle, Ill.

Rulau	Date	Metal	Size	VG	F	VF	Unc
Las 1	(1890's)	Brass	**	—	5.00	7.50	—

** Rect 32 by 19mm.

THOMAS MILES BUFFET. Rv: GOOD FOR 5 C AT THE BAR. Plain edge. R5. (Schmidt M30; Vacketta Lse F30)

Thomas Miles operated a hotel and saloon at 959 North Street in La Salle during the 1890's and until at least 1918.

P. PIERARD

La Salle, Ill.

Rulau	Date	Metal	Size	VG	F	VF	Unc
Las 3	(1890's)	Brass	28mm	—	10.00	15.00	—

(All incused): GOOD FOR 5c, P. Pierard. Rv: Blank. Plain edge. R8. (Schmidt P30; Vacketta Lse B37)

Mrs. Palmyre Pierard operated a saloon at 101 First Street in La Salle from about 1880 to at least 1894. She appears in the 1894 business directory.

ILLINOIS PURE ALUMINUM CO.

Lemont, Ill.

Rulau	Date	Metal	Size	VG	F	VF	Unc
Lem 1	1892	Aluminum	35mm	—	10.00	20.00	25.00

Columbus bust at center. WORLDS FAIR * SOUVENIR * above, 1492 * 1892 * below. Rv: ILLINOIS PURE ALUMINUM COMPANY / PURE / ALUMINUM / COOKING UTENSILS / MEDALS / SHEETS / -AND- / MANUFACTURED/ (ornament) / ALUMINUM / LEMONT, ILL. Plain edge. (Wright 485)

Rulau	Date	Metal	Size	VG	F	VF	Unc
Lem 3	(1890)	Aluminum	37.5mm	—	10.00	20.00	25.00

Within wreath: ILLINOIS / -*- / PURE / ALUMINUM / -*- / COMPANY. Rv: Same as Cincinnati (Ohio) Pure Aluminum Co. reverse, which see. Plain edge. (Schmidt N/L)

F.E. WHITE

Lombardville, Ill.

Rulau	Date	Metal	Size	VG	F	VF	Unc
Lom 1	(1884-99)	Brass	Scal 29mm	—	—	30.00	Rare

Small pool table, THE BRUNSWICK BALKE / COLLENDER / COMPY, above, CHECK in exergue. Rv: F.E. WHITE 5c. Plain edge. (Brunswick suppl.)

F. STEINBACH

Lyons, Ill.

Rulau	Date	Metal	Size	VG	F	VF	Unc
Lyo 1	(?)	Brass	24mm	—	—	20.00	—

GOOD FOR ONE DRINK / F. / STEINBACH / LYONS, / ILL'S. Rv: L. BOCHE CHECK MANUFR. 166 RANDOLPH ST. CHICAGO / 5. Plain edge. R8. (Schmidt 583; Vacketta Lys 10)

GILFREY & NEWTON

Macomb, Ill.

Rulau	Date	Metal	Size	VG	F	VF	Unc
Mac 1	(1890's)	Aluminum	Oct 27mm	—	—	25.00	—

GILFREY & NEWTON / PURE / ICE CREAM / AND / CONFECTIONERY. Rv: GOOD FOR / 5 / ONE SODA. Plain edge. R10. (Schmdit N/L; Vacketta Mao C04)

There are later tokens of this issuer in the 5-cent denomination, not mentioning ice cream or soda. This firm was out of business by World War I.

KEMPER'S DEPARTMENT STORE

Rulau	Date	Metal	Size	VG	F	EF	Unc
Mac 4	1895	Aluminum	20mm	—	5.00	7.00	—

KEMPER'S FAMOUS / DEPARTMENT / STORE / NOT TRANSFERABLE / 1895 / MACOMB, ILL. Rv: GOOD FOR / 5 / IN / MERCHANDISE. Plain edge. R7. (Schmidt K24, Vacketta Mao 04)

ALBERT LINDSEY

Macomb, Ill.

Rulau	Date	Metal	Size	VG	F	VF	Unc
Mac 6	1897	Aluminum	35mm	—	5.00	8.00	—

ALBERT LINDSEY / GROCERIES / 1897 / MACOMB, Ill. Rv: GOOD FOR 1.00 / IN / MERCHANDISE. Plain edge. R6. (Schmidt N/L; Vacketta Mao 04)

The grocery was still run by Albert Lindsey in 1918.

K. KOLB & SON

Mascoutah, Ill.

Rulau	Date	Metal	Size	VG	F	VF	Unc
Mas 1	(?)	Brass	21mm	2.50	6.00	9.00	20.00

(All incused): K & SON / 5 / CTS. Rv: Blank. Plain edge. R2. (Vacketta Msh 05-5a). A variety is known also R2, with diameter 22mm.

Rulau	Date	Metal	Size	VG	F	VF	Unc
Mas 2	(?)	Brass	25mm	2.50	6.00	9.00	20.00

(All incused): K & SON / 10 / CTS / Rv: K. R2. (Vacketta Msh 05-10)

Rulau	Date	Metal	Size	VG	F	VF	Unc
Mas 3	(?)	Brass	28mm	2.50	6.00	9.00	20.00

As last, but 25 / CTS. R2. (Vacketta Msh 05-25)

Rulau	Date	Metal	Size	VG	F	VF	Unc
Mas 4	(?)	Brass	28mm	2.50	6.00	9.00	20.00

As last, but 50 / CTS. R2. (Vacketta Msh 05-50)

It is assumed that the series above was issued before the series which follows, but it is not known whether the series above was issued during the 1890's. More research is needed on all the Kolb issues.

Rulau	Date	Metal	Size	VG	F	VF	Unc
Mas 6	(?)	Aluminum	21mm	—	—	—	—

As next, but denomination 5. R7. (Schmidt K47; Vacketta Msh 06-5)

Rulau	Date	Metal	Size	VG	F	VF	Unc
Mas 7	(?)	Aluminum	24mm	—	—	8.00	—

K. KOLB & SON / (ornament) / MASCOUTAH, / ILL. (faint on photographed specimen) / (ornament)(also faint). Rv: GOOD FOR / 10 (ornate) / IN MERCHANDISE. Plain edge. R7. (Schmidt K47a; Vacketta Msh 06-10)

Rulau	Date	Metal	Size	VG	F	VF	Unc
Mas 8	(?)	Aluminum	27mm	—	—	8.00	—

As last, but denomination 25. R7. (Schmidt K47b; Vacketta Msh 06-25)

Rulau	Date	Metal	Size	VG	F	VF	Unc
Mas 9	(?)	Aluminum	31mm	5.00	8.00	12.00	30.00

As last, but denomination 50. R7. (Schmidt K47c; Vacketta Msh 06-50)

Rulau	Date	Metal	Size	VG	F	VF	Unc
Mas 10	(?)	Aluminum	39mm	5.00	8.00	12.00	30.00

As last, but denomination 1.00. R7. (Schmidt K47d; Vacketta Msh 06-100)

The ornaments and letters on obverse differ on each denomination in the aluminum set! Kilian Kolb was still listed as a general store proprietor in 1918.

R. T. H.
(Robert T. Holmes)

Mattoon, Ill.

Rulau	Date	Metal	Size	VG	F	VF	Unc
Mat 1	(1890's)	Bronze	20mm	—	—	15.00	—

R. T. H. ctsp on both sides of Great Britain young head Victoria farthing. R8. (Schmidt H49)

Rulau	Date	Metal	Size	VG	F	VF	Unc
Mat 3	1893	CN	**	—	—	12.00	—

** Oval, 30 by 18mm. ROBT. T. HOLMES / 1893 / MATTOON, ILLS. Rv: Blank. Plain edge. R8. (Schmidt H45)

Rulau	Date	Metal	Size	VG	F	VF	Unc
Mat 5	(1890's)	Aluminum	25mm	—	—	8.00	—

ROBT. T. HOLMES / MATTOON, ILL. Rv: GOOD FOR / 2 1/2¢ / IN TRADE. Plain edge. R7. (Schmidt H47)

GERMANIA

Mendota, Ill.

Rulau	Date	Metal	Size	VG	F	VF	Unc
Men 1	1891	Brass	23mm	—	10.00	15.00	—

(All incused): GERMANIA / NOV. / 1891 / MENDOTA. Rv: Blank. Plain edge. R8. (Schmidt G24; Vacketta N/L)

There are other Germanic tokens of Mendota, but this one and one other (Joseph Weidner's "Unter Der Bank" saloon token) are the only ones positively attributable to the Gay Nineties.

UNTER DER BANK

Mendota, Ill.

Rulau	Date	Metal	Size	VG	F	VF	Unc
Men 3	(1900)	Brass	20mm	—	5.00	8.50	—

UNTER DER BANK. Rv: GOOD FOR / 5 C / IN TRADE. Plain edge. R8. (Schmidt U88; Vacketta Met 28)

Joseph Weidner, a German, ran this saloon "under the bank" (in the Mendota National Bank's basement) about 1900 — thus the unusual name. Mendota's population at this time was heavily Teutonic.

DALY AND BREEN

Minonk, Ill.

Rulau	Date	Metal	Size	VG	F	VF	Unc
Min 1	(1910 ?)	Brass	Scal 30mm	—	25.00	35.00	—

Rabbit crouched left. Rv: DALY AND BREEN / GOOD FOR / 2 1/2 ¢ / IN TRADE / MINONK, ILL. Plain edge. R8. (Schmidt D10; Vacketta Mno A02)

Rulau	Date	Metal	Size	VG	F	VF	Unc
Min 2	(1890's)	Aluminum	25mm	—	7.00	10.00	—

DALY AND BREEN / MINONK, ILL. Rv: GOOD FOR / 5 C / IN TRADE. Plain edge. R7. (Schmidt D11; Vacketta Mno B02)

W. M. Daly appears as a saloonkeeper in the 1890 directory. No other reference has been located. The partnership is apparently later.

MOLINE WAGON CO.

Moline, Ill.

Rulau	Date	Metal	Size	VG	F	VF	Unc
Mol 1	(1890's)	Aluminum	35mm	10.00	15.00	25.00	60.00

Farm wagon (buckboard) at center, MOLINE WAGON CO. / LIGHTEST / RUNNING above, MOST DURABLE / MOLINE, ILL. below. Rv: Similar to obverse, but carriage wagon at center. Plain edge. R8. (Schmidt M57)

INTER STATE HAY PALACE

Momence, Ill.

Rulau	Date	Metal	Size	VG	F	VF	Unc
Mom 1	1890	WM	35mm	—	12.50	17.50	35.00

Building, INTER STATE HAY PALACE around, * MOMENCE, ILL. * below. Rv: Bale of hay above: SOUVENIR / OCT. 1 to 11 / -1890-, all within circle. Around: INTER STATE HAY PALACE / * MOMENCE, ILL. *. Plain edge. R6. About 15 pieces known, including a variety. (Schmidt 142)

"Palaces" were Midwest agricultural and industrial showplaces of opulence in the Eighties and Nineties — the Corn Palace in Sioux City, Iowa; Blue Grass Palace in Creston, Iowa; Ice Palace in Minneapolis, Minn.; Coal Palace in Ottumwa, Iowa; Mineral Palace in Colo, Iowa, etc.

R. LAHANN

Monmouth, Ill.

Rulau	Date	Metal	Size	VG	F	VF	Unc
Mon 3	(1890-91)	Aluminum	25mm	—	10.00	15.00	—

R. LAHANN / CIGAR / MANUFACTURER / MONMOUTH, ILL. Rv: GOOD FOR / ONE OF / R. LAHANN'S / 5 C / CIGARS. Plain edge. R8. (Schmidt L11; Vacketta Mut 13)

MAPLE CITY CIGAR CO.

Rulau	Date	Metal	Size	VG	F	VF	Unc
Mon 5	(?)	Aluminum	25mm	—	10.00	15.00	—

MANFD. BY / MAPLE CITY / CIGAR CO. / MONMOUTH, ILL. Rv: GOOD FOR ONE / FLOR / DE AUGUSTO / 5 C / CIGAR. Plain edge. R7. (Schmidt M13; Vacketta Mut 15)

Still in business in 1918.

WESTERN BOILER PIPE CO.

Monmouth, Ill.

Rulau	Date	Metal	Size	VG	F	VF	Unc
Mon 12	(1890's)	Brass	29mm	—	7.50	12.50	—

WESTERN BOILER PIPE CO. / MONMOUTH, / ILL. Rv: THIS IS GOOD / FOR / YOUR / EXPENSES. Plain edge. Only 2 or 3 pieces known. (Vacketta N/L)

One of the most unusual legends on an American token.

HURRICANE COAL STORE CO.

Murphysboro, Ill.

Rulau	Date	Metal	Size	VG	F	VF	Unc
Mur 1	(?)	—	24mm	—	—	35.00	50.00

Man standing near blazing hearth, HURRICANE COAL STORE CO. around. Rv: Design not reported.

ANTON SOCHUREK

Niles, Ill.

Rulau	Date	Metal	Size	VG	F	VF	Unc
Nil 1	(late 1890s)	Brass	20mm	—	—	9.00	—

ANTON SOCHUREK / -.- / NILES, ILL. / *****. Rv: GOOD FOR / * A 5 ¢ * / DRINK. Plain edge. R8. Only 6 pieces known. (Schmidt 556; Vacketta Nil 01)

Sochurek was part of the wave of Bohemian immigrants who fled oppression in Austria-Hungary and settled in western Cook County in Cicero, Berwyn, Niles and surrounding communities from 1890 until the First World War. Niles had been known as Dutchman's Point until 1850; today no one seems to know why "Niles" was chosen.

Sochurek managed a saloon on Evergreen Street (now called Newark Street) during the late 1890's. The building was destroyed by fire about 1901.

C. VON GUNTEN

Olney, Ill.

Rulau	Date	Metal	Size	VG	F	VF	Unc
Oln 1	(?)	Brass	23mm	—	5.00	10.00	—

(All incused): C. VON GUNTEN / GOOD FOR / 5 ¢ / AT BAR / OLNEY, ILL. Rv: NATIONAL BILLIARD HALL * around empty central circle. Plain edge. R8. (Schmidt V54; Vacketta Oln C05)

Von Gunten operated a saloon, general store and billiard hall in Olney. The token was used in saloon and billiard hall.

W. J. MENKE

Paris, Ill.

Rulau	Date	Metal	Size	VG	F	VF	Unc
Par 3	(?)	Aluminum	--mm	—	—	20.00	—

FERRIS PHARMACY / PARIS, ILL. Rv: GOOD FOR / ONE GLASS / ICE CREAM / SODA WATER. Plain edge. (Vacketta N/L)

COPPEL-GARRARD CO.

Peoria, Ill.

Rulau	Date	Metal	Size	VG	F	VF	Unc
Peo 1	(1890's)	Aluminum	Scal 29mm	—	25.00	35.00	—

Rooster standing right. Rv: COPPEL-GARRARD Co. / CGCo monogram / PEORIA, ILL. Plain edge. R6.

FEY HOTEL

Rulau	Date	Metal	Size	VG	F	VF	Unc
Peo 3	(1895)	Aluminum	19mm	3.00	4.00	6.00	—

FEY HOTEL / — / PEORIA, / ILL. Rv: GOOD FOR / 5 ¢ / IN MERCHANDISE. Plain edge. R7. (Schmidt F27; Vacketta Peo 11-5)

Rulau	Date	Metal	Size	VG	F	VF	Unc
Peo 4	(1895)	Aluminum	21mm	3.00	4.00	6.00	—

Similar to last, but 10 C. R7. (Vacketta Peo 11-10)

The Fey Brothers managed this hotel.

Rulau	Date	Metal	Size	VG	F	VF	Unc
Peo 6	(1900)	Brass	21mm	—	—	6.00	—

HOTEL FEY BAR / W. H. McGETRICK / PEORIA. Rv: 5. Plain edge. R5. (Schmidt N/L; Vacketta Peo B24)

The Hotel Fey Company was still in business in 1918.

THE JEFFERSON

Rulau	Date	Metal	Size	F	VF	EF	Unc
Peo 7	1899	B&A	19mm	—	—	6.00	11.00

THE JEFFERSON / OF PEORIA. Rv: GOOD FOR / 5 / PAT. JULY 1899 / IN MERCHANDISE. Plain edge. R8. (Schmidt N/L; Vacketta Peo 29)

R. KNEER

Rulau	Date	Metal	Size	F	VF	EF	Unc
Peo 8	(?)	Brass	23mm	—	—	8.00	—

R. KNEER / 303 / FULTON ST. / PEORIA, ILL. Rv: 5. Plain edge. R9; only 3 known. (Schmidt N/L; Vacketta Peo 30)

Kneer's descendants by 1918 were druggists and saloonkeepers.

OAKFORD & FAHNESTOCK

Rulau	Date	Metal	Size	VG	F	VF	Unc
Peo 10	(1890's)	Aluminum	24mm	—	4.00	8.00	—

THIS CHECK WILL BE REDEEMED BY / OAKFORD / & / FAHNESTOCK / PEORIA, ILL. Rv: GOOD FOR ONE / OAKFORD & / FAHNESTOCK / GUARANTEE / * 5 ¢ CIGAR *. Plain edge. R8. (Schmidt N/L; Vacketta Peo A40)

Rulau	Date	Metal	Size	VG	F	VF	Unc
Peo 11	(1890)	Copper	29mm	—	6.00	12.00	—

OAKFORD & FAHNESTOCK / WHOLESALE / AGENTS / PEORIA, ILL. Rv: THIS CHECK WILL BE REDEEMED BY ANY DEALER / GOOD FOR / ONE / FONTELLA / CIGAR. Plain edge. R6. (Schmidt 011; Vacketta Peo 39)

Henry Oakford and Henry Fahnestock were grocers in Peoria during the 1870's and 1880's.

PEORIA LIFE (INS. CO.)

Rulau	Date	Metal	Size	F	VF	EF	Unc
Peo 13	(?)	GS	32mm	—	20.00	—	—

Hog standing left. BRINGING / HOME / THE BACON on his body. Above; MEDAL OF HONOR / FOR. Below: PEORIA LIFE / (tiny) W & H CO NEWARK N.J. Rv: (This side of medalet is enameled blue, red and white.) Large monogram PLICo in white within red central circle, band of blue around rim. Plain edge.

This award for insurance salesman was manufactured by Whitehead & Hoag Co., Newark, N.J. Probably post-1900.

J. ZAHRINGER

Peoria, Ill.

Rulau	Date	Metal	Size	F	VF	EF	Unc
Peo 16	(?)	Brass	21mm	—	5.00	7.50	—

J. ZAHRINGER / Z / PEORIA, ILL. Rv: GOOD FOR ONE / . 5 ¢ . / ORIENTAL CIGAR. Plain edge. R9; only 3 known. (Schmidt Z12; Vacketta Peo 60)

A. BULFER

Peru, Ill.

Rulau	Date	Metal	Size	F	VF	EF	Unc
Per 1	(1870-1900)	Copper	24mm	—	20.00	25.00	40.00

A BULFER, PERU at center. Around: GOOD FOR A 5 C DRINK AT THE BAR. Rv: KUEHL BILLIARD SUPPLY CO., CHICAGO. Plain edge. R7. (Schmidt B80; Vacketta Pru G03)

August Bulfer ran a saloon and grocery store from 1870 to 1900. In 1918 Charles Bulfer was operating a saloon.

HECK BROS. BAKERY

Pittsfield, Ill.

Rulau	Date	Metal	Size	F	VF	EF	Unc
Pit 1	(1890's)	Aluminum	21mm	—	10.00	15.00	—

HECK BROS. / (sunburst) / PITTSFIELD, ILL. Rv: GOOD FOR / -1- / * LOAF * / OF / BREAD. Plain edge. (Schmidt N/L; Vacketta Pts 01)

In 1918 the Heck Brothers were general store proprietors.

S. A. RATHBUN

Pontiac, Ill.

Rulau	Date	Metal	Size	VG	F	VF	Unc
Pon 1	(1890's)	Aluminum	**	—	10.00	15.00	—

** Square, 21 by 21mm.
S. A. RATHBUN / -o- / PONTIAC, ILL. Rv: GOOD FOR / * 5 ¢ * / IN / FURNITURE. Plain edge. R7. (Wright 1588; Vacketta Pon 06a)

Rulau	Date	Metal	Size	VG	F	VF	Unc
Pon 2	(?)	Aluminum	**	—	10.00	15.00	—

** Square, 14x14mm.
As last, in reduced size. R7. (Vacketta Pon 06b)

Rulau	Date	Metal	Size	VG	F	VF	Unc
Pon 3	(1907-)	Brass	Oct. 25mm	—	10.00	15.00	—

S.A. RATHBUN'S / DEPARTMENT / * / STORE / PONTIAC / . . . / ILL. Rv: GOOD FOR / 5¢ / * IN TRADE *. Plain edge. (Schmidt Pontiac R11)

The Silas A. Rathbun department store was still in business in 1918.

CLAUDIN & GUDEMAN

Roanoke, Ill.

Rulau	Date	Metal	Size	F	VF	EF	Unc
Roa 1	(?)	Cupronickel	18mm	—	8.00	11.00	—

CLAUDIN & GUDEMAN. / ROANOKE. / + / ILL. / +. Rv: 1 ¢ at center. Plain edge.

J. E. CLAUDIN

Roanoke, Ill.

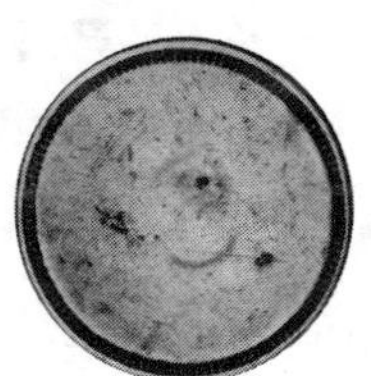

Rulau	Date	Metal	Size	F	VF	EF	Unc
Roa 3	(?)	Brass	23mm	—	10.00	12.50	—

(All incused): J. E. CLAUDIN / 1 (in circle) / ROANOKE ILL. Rv: Blank. Plain edge. (Schmidt Roanoke C40)

Roanoke, Woodford County, Illinois, had 1,300 population in World War I.

I. O. O. F.
(Independent Order of Odd Fellows)

Rockford, Ill.

Rulau	Date	Metal	Size	F	VF	EF	Unc
Rok 1	1892	Aluminum	35mm	—	8.00	20.00	30.00

Crown, I.O.O.F. above, JUNE 9, 1892 below, all within wreath. Around: SECOND ANNIVERSARY INTERSTATE ASSOCIATION / * ROCKFORD, ILL. *. Rv: Shield of arms, PATRIARCHS MILITANT around. Plain edge. R5. (Schmidt 156)

AUGUSTANA UNIVERSITY ASSOCIATION

Rock Island, Ill.

Rulau	Date	Metal	Size	F	VF	EF	Unc
Roc 3	1893	Aluminum	38mm	—	15.00	20.00	25.00

Seated allegorical female "Knowledge" left, AUGUSTANA / UNIVERSITY / ASSOCIATION on shield on side of the chair — all within open-end wreath. Rv: Building, AUGUSTANA COLLEGE AND THEOL. SEMINARY around, 1893 / ROCK ISLAND, ILL. in exergue. Plain edge. R8. (Schmidt A88)

CARL DORF

Spring Valley, Ill.

Rulau	Date	Metal	Size	VG	F	VF	Unc
Spv 1	(1900)	Brass	**	—	—	15.00	—

** Oval, 32x25mm.
Eagle displayed, perched atop cannon, all in circular frame. Rv: (In beaded circular frame): CARL DORF / GOOD FOR / 5 ¢ / DRINK. Plain edge.

The obverse die is the same as that used on the River City Aerie token of Portsmouth, Ohio (which see).

Carl Dorf was a saloonkeeper and restaurateur, also a cigarmaker. He also had a gambling wheel on the sidewalk in front where people could win chickens, ducks and geese. His cigar brand was called "Hobo" cigars. (Research courtesy Phil Klabel)

GINZEL MERCANTILE CO.

Trenton, Ill.

Rulau	Date	Metal	Size	F	VF	EF	Unc
Tre 1	(1907-)	Aluminum	20mm	—	3.00	5.00	—

Set 5-10-10c-5.00 tokens - 25.00 to 50.00

GINZEL MERC. / CO. / TRENTON, ILL. Rv: GOOD FOR / 5 ¢ / IN / MERCHANDISE. Plain edge. R7. (Schmidt G-34; Vacketta Trn 01-5)

Rulau	Date	Metal	Size	F	VF	EF	Unc
Tre 2	(?)	Aluminum	22mm	—	—	6.00	9.00

Similar to last, but 10c. R7. (Schmidt G34a; Vacketta Trn 01-10)

Rulau	Date	Metal	Size	F	VF	EF	Unc
Tre 3	(?)	Aluminum	22mm	—	—	6.00	9.00

Similar to last, but different letter arrangement. R7. (Schmidt G34b; Vacketta Trn 01-10)

Tre 5	(?)	Brass	Scal 39mm	—	—	7.00	12.50

GINZEL MERCANTILE CO. / GENERAL / MERCHANDISE / TRENTON, ILL. Rv: GOOD FOR / 5oo / IN MERCHANDISE. R5. (Schmidt G34c; Vacketta Trn 01-500)

There are also brass and aluminum bimetallic tokens of similar design in 50c and $1 denominations, with PAT. APPLD. FOR added. (Schmidt G34d-f)

There are others which say PATD. JULY 1899, on a $1 denomination token (Vacketta Trn 02-100)

Tre 7	(1899)	B&A	32mm	—	10.00	—	30.00

Obverse similar to last. Rv: GOOD FOR / 50 / PAT. APPLD. FOR / IN MERCHANDISE. Curved top 5 in 50. Plain edge. (Schmidt G34d; Vacketta Trn 02-50)

Tre 8	(1899)	B&A	32mm	—	10.00	—	30.00

As last, but straight top 5 in 50, and no latticework. (Schmidt G34d)

Tre 9	(1899)	B&A	38mm	—	10.00	—	30.00

Obverse as last. Rv: As last, except denomination 100 and lines PATD. / JULY 1899 substituted. (Schmidt G34f; Vacketta Trn 02-100)

It is reasonable to suppose that the last four tokens were issued just prior to and just after the granting of the maker's patent in July 1899.

This firm was still in business in 1918.

BESLEY'S WAUKEGAN BREWING CO.

Waukegan, Ill.

Rulau	Date	Metal	Size	VG	F	VF	Unc
Wau 3	(1893)	Aluminum	40mm	—	—	25.00	35.00

Landing of Columbus scene, LANDING OF COLUMBUS in curved exergue. Rv: Bottle at center labeled: BESLEY WAUKE / BREWING CO / EXTRA PALE ALE / WAUKEGAN. Around: BESLEY'S WAUKEGAN BREWING CO / EST'D 1853 / BREWERS BOTTLERS / EXTRA FINE / ALE & PORTER / WAUKEGAN & CHICAGO, ILL. Plain edge. (Tanenbaum coll.)

WENONA ZINC CO.

Wenona, Ill.

Rulau	Date	Metal	Size	F	VF	EF	Unc
Wen 1	1891	Zinc	31mm	—	25.00	35.00	50.00

THE FIRST ZINC / MADE AT / WENONA, ILLINOIS / BY THE / WENONA ZINC CO. / -.- / DECEMBER 12TH 1891. Rv: WE WILL EXCEL AT ANY COST / A. S. SHERWOOD / PRES'T / -.- / E. L. MONSER / VICE-PREST. / -.- / W. E. MONSER / SECY & TREAS. /-.- / -*-. Plain edge. R8. (Schmidt W21)

This commemorative token in zinc, an unusual metal for an American piece, tells its own full story!

P. VAPENSKY

Uncertain Locale

Rulau	Date	Metal	Size	VG	F	VF	Unc
Unk 2	(1890's)	Brass	24mm	—	—	5.00	—

P. VAPENSKY / GOOD FOR / 5 ¢ / AT THE BAR. Rv: Blank. Plain edge. 4 pieces known. (Thoele coll.)

Probably from Illinois, Thoele asserts.

INDIANA

LOUIS HAUCK

Aurora, Ind.

Rulau	Date	Metal	Size	VG	F	VF	Unc
Aur 1	(1890)	Brass	25mm	—	—	25.00	—

Crossed pool cues separate N-B-M-C, within central circle. Around: NATIONAL BILLIARD MANUF'G CO / . CIN. O. Rv: GOOD FOR / 1 / SHAVE / * LOUIS HAUCK *. Plain edge. (Thoele coll.)

Barber, listed in 1890.

J. F. BRICE

Bluffton, Ind.

Rulau	Date	Metal	Size	VG	F	VF	Unc
Blf 3	(1890-95)	Brass	24mm	—	—	30.00	—

GOOD FOR / 5 C / J. F. BRICE / AT / THE BAR. Rv: JAS. MURDOCK, JR / STAMPS / BURNING / BRANDS / AND / STENCILS / CINCINNATI, OHIO. Plain edge. (ATCO 3022)

Brice's saloon appears in the 1890 and 1895 gazetteers.

B. STIEFEL

Butler, Ind.

Rulau	Date	Metal	Size	VG	F	VF	Unc
But 3	(1887-90)	GS	22mm	—	8.00	12.50	—

(All incused): B. STIEFEL / 5. Rv: Blank. Plain edge. (Thoele coll.)

Benjamin Stiefel is listed under saloons in the 1887-88 *Indiana Gazetteer* and under cigars in the 1890 edition. It is the type of token associated with the cigar trade.

JNO. ROSENBOWER

Cedar Lake, Ind.

Rulau	Date	Metal	Size	VG	F	VF	Unc
Ced 1	(1890)	Brass	24mm	—	20.00	—	—

Goblet and crossed ladle and ice tong, DEALERS IN above, all within central circle. Around: CHAS. PICK & CO. / * CHICAGO *. Rv: GOOD FOR / 5 C / JNO. / ROSENBOWER / IN / *TRADE*. Plain edge. (Thoele coll.)

Saloon, listed in 1890.

D. M. BURKE

Elwood, Ind.

Rulau	Date	Metal	Size	VG	F	VF	Unc
Elw 1	(1891-95)	Brass	Scal 28mm	—	—	22.50	—

GOOD FOR / 5 ¢ / D. M. / BURKE / IN / TRADE . Rv: Chas. Pick store card die. 2 known. (Thoele coll.; Norris Wahl coll.)

Saloon, listed in the 1891-95 gazetteers. Daniel M. Burke.

F. W. COOK BREWING CO.
Evansville, Ind.

Rulau	Date	Metal	Size	F	VF	EF	Unc
Evv 4	1891	Aluminum	38mm	—	—	15.00	25.00

Large C enclosing star-in-circle at center, TRADE MARK. Around: F.W. COOK BREWING CO. / EVANSVILLE, IND. Rv: A HAPPY NEW YEAR / 1891 / GREETING. Plain edge. (Wright 204)

Rulau	Date	Metal	Size	F	VF	EF	Unc
Evv 7	1892	Aluminum	38mm	—	—	15.00	25.00

Building at center. Around: ESTABLISHED 1858 ERECTED 1892. Rv: Large C encloses circle with star at center, inscribed TRADE MARK. Around: F. W. COOK BREWING CO. / EVANSVILLE, IND. Plain edge. (Wright 1110)

Still in business 1918.

J. CHRISTEN
Fort Wayne, Ind.

Rulau	Date	Metal	Size	F	VF	EF	Unc
Fwy 11	(?)	Brass	Octagonal, 27mm	—	12.50	20.00	—

* BY* / J. CHRISTEN / - / FORT WAYNE / IND. Rv: GOOD FOR / - 5 - / * CENTS * / IN TRADE. Plain edge.

A probable related firm, Christen Brothers, operated a drug store in 1918.

J. M. ALFORD
Goshen, Ind.

Rulau	Date	Metal	Size	VG	F	VF	Unc
Gos 1	(1890)	Brass	26mm	—	5.00	9.00	—

(All incused): J. M. ALFORD / GOOD FOR / 5 ¢ / LOAF OF BREAD / 309 PURL ST. Rv: Blank. Plain edge. (ATCO Maverick 3790)

The only city in the United States to have a Purl Street in 1907 was Goshen, making identification more certain. James M. Alford was listed as a grocer in the 1890 *Indiana Gazetteer & Business Directory*.

PARRY MFG. CO.
Indianapolis, Ind.

Rulau	Date	Metal	Size	VG	F	VF	Unc
Ind 2	(1896)	Copper	30mm	—	3.00	5.00	18.00

Covered buggy with wire wheels left, PARRY M'F'G CO. INDIANAPOLIS above, HIGH GRADE / BUGGIES below. Rv: At center is a foreshortened Maltese cross with PARRY twice in cross form on it, both words sharing the second 'R'. HIGH GRADE BUGGIES around, SURREYS / INDIANAPOLIS below. (Wright 800; Miller Ind. 2)

Rulau	Date	Metal	Size	VG	F	VF	Unc
Ind 2A	(1896)	Silvered Copper	30mm	—	10.00	12.50	30.00

As 2.

ANTON SCHMID
Indianapolis, Ind.

Rulau	Date	Metal	Size	VG	F	VF	Unc
Ind 12	(1891-92)	Brass	25mm	—	—	12.50	—

ANTON / SCHMID. Rv: 5 in circle of stars. Plain edge. (Wagaman I-5835)

Anton Schmid appears under saloons in the 1891-92 gazetteer. Earlier (1882-83) he had been a saloon keeper at Cincinnati, Ohio.

LEW. WILBUR
Kokomo, Ind.

Rulau	Date	Metal	Size	VG	F	VF	Unc
Kok 7	(1891-92)	Brass	Oct 23mm	—	—	6.50	—

(All incused): LEW. WILBUR. Rv: GOOD FOR / 5 ¢ / AT THE BAR. (Thoele coll.)

Saloon, listed 1891-92 gazetteer. Unlisted in Wagaman.

CATHOLIC BENEVOLENT LEGION
Lafayette, Ind.

Rulau	Date	Metal	Size	F	VF	EF	Unc
Laf 3	1892	Aluminum	35mm	—	—	15.00	25.00

Seal of the Legion at center. Around: THIRD ANNUAL SESSION INDIANA COUNCIL / SEPTEMBER 13. AND 14. / 1892 / + LA FAYETTE, IND. +. Rv: Maltese cross before crossed swords, St. J at center, C-R-K-U on arms of cross. Around: REUNION HELD SEPT. 13. AND 14. AT / 1892 / + LA FAYETTE, IND. +. Plain edge. (Hartzog coll.)

F. W. POTTMEYER
Logansport, Ind.

Rulau	Date	Metal	Size	VG	F	VF	Unc
Log 3	(1890-95)	Brass	25mm	—	—	25.00	—

Brunswick die BBC-11. Rv: GOOD FOR / 5 ¢ / F. W. / POTTMEYER (name within panel) / IN / * TRADE *. Plain edge. Only 2 known. (L. Stuber coll.)

Saloon, listed 1890-1895.

TAYOR'S POOL ROOM
Monroeville, Ind.

Rulau	Date	Metal	Size	VG	F	VF	Unc
Mon 4	(?)	*	Rect, 60 by 32mm	5.00	7.50	12.00	—

*Yellow cardboard, black printing. GOOD FOR / 5 c/ IN TRADE / AT / TAYOR'S / POOL ROOM / MONROEVILLE, IND. Rv: Blank. Corners on the rectangular ticket are rounded.

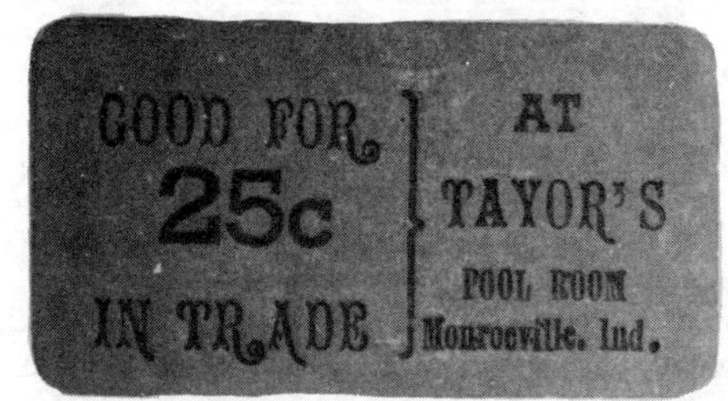

Rulau	Date	Metal	Size	VG	F	VF	Unc
Mon 5	(?)	**	Rect, 60 by 32mm	5.00	7.50	12.00	—

** Deep red cardboard, black printing. Similar to last, but 25 c.

The printing style appears to be in the 1890-1910 period.

GEO. A. WECKESSER

Mount Vernon, Ind.

Rulau	Date	Metal	Size	VG	F	VF	Unc
Mtv 3	(?)	Aluminum	28mm	—	7.00	10.00	—

GEO. A. WECKESSER / KLONDIKE SALOON / AND / RESTAURANT. Rv: GOOD FOR / 5¢ / AT THE BAR.

A hoard of about 30 pieces surfaced recently. Most early tokens bearing the magic word "saloon" fetch high prices, but not tokens when a hoard is known about.

PLYMOUTH CYCLE MFG CO.

Plymouth, Ind.

Rulau	Date	Metal	Size	F	VF	EF	Unc
Pym 8	(1890's)	Aluminum	Square 31mm	—	40.00	—	—

Large 'S' with a scroll across it. The scroll reads: THE SMALLEY / REGISTERED. The 'S' reads: MANUFACTURED BY / PLYMOUTH CYCLE MFG. CO. / PLYMOUTH, IND. Rv: ONLY ONE OF THESE / GOOD FOR / 100 / IF PRESENTED TO ANY / RETAIL AGENT / IN PAYMENT FOR A / SMALLEY. Plain edge. (Wright 1128)

J. A. GOODALE & BRO.

Seymour, Ind.

Rulau	Date	Metal	Size	F	VF	EF	Unc
Sey 2	(?)	Brass	22mm	—	40.00	—	—

J. A. GOODALE & BRO. / GOOD FOR / 1/2 / SMILE / SEYMOUR, IND. Rv: Blank. (Wright 1431)

JOE DECKER

Valparaiso, Ind.

Rulau	Date	Metal	Size	VG	F	VF	Unc
Vpo 2	(1890)	Brass	Scal 29mm	—	—	25.00	—

CHAS. PICK & CO. / DEALERS IN / (crossed tongs, goblet and ladle) / CHICAGO. Rv: GOOD FOR / 5 ¢ / JOE DECKER / IN / TRADE. (Thoele coll.)

By 1895 Joe Decker moved to Negaunee, Mich. to operate another saloon. Pick had stopped supplying tokens in 1895.

IOWA

A. J. WILLIAMS

Albia, Iowa

Rulau	Date	Metal	Size	VG	F	VF	Unc
Alb 7	(?)	Brass	24mm	—	—	25.00	—

THE BRUNSWICK BALKE / COLLENDER / COMPY. / (pool table) / CHECK. Rv: GOOD FOR / 5 C / A. J. WILLIAMS / IN / TRADE. Plain edge. (Ferguson 850)

T.M. SINCLAIR & CO.

Cedar Rapids, Iowa

Rulau	Date	Metal	Size	F	VF	EF	Unc
Ced 3	(1893)	Aluminum	37mm	—	—	35.00	50.00

Bloodhound head right, surrounded by: "FIDELITY" / Pork / Packers / SMOKED MEATS, all within 4-lobed cartouche. Around: T.M. SINCLAIR & CO. / CEDAR RAPIDS, IA. (Eglit 508; Kirtley Oct. 1993 sale, lot 1636)

JOHN G. WOODWARD & CO.

Council Bluffs, Iowa

Rulau	Date	Metal	Size	VG	F	VF	Unc
Cnc 6	(1890's)	Aluminum	33mm	—	—	15.00	—

Flag at center, inscribed: GOOD FOR / ONE / SPANISH / WONDER / CIGAR. Around: THIS CHECK WILL BE REDEEMED BY ANY DEALER. Rv: JOHN G. WOODWARD & CO. / WHOLESALE / AGENTS COUNCIL BLUFFS, IA. Plain edge. (Wright 1735; Ferguson 1105).

Rulau	Date	Metal	Size	VG	F	VF	Unc
Cnc 7	(?)	Aluminum	21mm	—	—	12.50	—

As 6, but smaller flan. (Ferguson 1100)

F. A. DAY

Des Moines, Iowa

Rulau	Date	Metal	Size	VG	F	VF	Unc
Dsm 4	(1905)	Aluminum	25mm	—	—	25.00	—

THE BRUNSWICK-BALKE / COLLENDER / COMPY. / (pool table) / CHECK. Rv: GOOD FOR 5 C / WIGWAM / F. A. DAY. Plain edge. (Ferguson 3225; Grinolds May 1993 sale, lot 136)

Rulau	Date	Metal	Size	VG	F	VF	Unc
Dsm 5	(?)	Aluminum	Sq 25mm	—	—	15.00	—

GOOD FOR / 5 C / IN TRADE / WIGWAM / F. A. DAY. Rv: Blank. Plain edge (Ferguson 3250)

Rulau	Date	Metal	Size	VG	F	VF	Unc
Dsm 6	(?)	Brass	21mm	—	—	10.00	—

F. A. DAY. (Ferguson 725)

J. C. STEEPY

Glenwood, Iowa

Rulau	Date	Metal	Size	VG	F	VF	Unc
Gin 1	(1889-90)	Brass	25mm	—	—	30.00	—

Pool table. Above: THE / BRUNSWICK / -BALKE- / COLLENDER CO. Rv: GOOD FOR / 5 ¢ / J.C. STEEPY / IN / TRADE. Plain edge. (Thoele coll.)

Billiard hall, listed in 1886-1890.

HENRY HURST

Knoxville, Iowa

Rulau	Date	Metal	Size	VG	F	VF	Unc
Knx 8	(1905-06)	Brass	25mm	—	—	25.00	—

Brunsqick die BBC-8. Rv: GOOD FOR / 2 1/2 C / HENRY / HURST / IN / TRADE. Plain edge.

LIIKE

Knoxville, Iowa

Rulau	Date	Metal	Size	VG	F	VF	Unc
Knx 14	(1940)	Brass	25mm	—	—	20.00	—

LIIKE ctsp over name on Henry Hurst BBC token as listed above. (Jack Glass coll.)

H. C. Hurst is listed in Lexington, Ky. in 1896. Henry Hurst is listed in Knoxville, Iowa 1905-06. Liike counterstamped the Hurst tokens much later for use.

M. C. ADKINS

Kellogg, Iowa

Rulau	Date	Metal	Size	VG	F	VF	Unc
Kel 1	(1890-1900)	Aluminum	25mm	—	—	25.00	—

Brunswick-Balke-Collender check. Rv: GOOD FOR / 5 C / IN TRADE / M. C. ADKINS. Plain edge. (Brunswick 5013; Ferguson 100)

Still in business with billiards 1914.

A. CAMPBELL

Lake City, Iowa

Rulau	Date	Metal	Size	VG	F	VF	Unc
Lak 2	(1884)	Brass	--mm	—	—	30.00	—

Brunswick-Balke check. Rv: GOOD FOR / 5 C / A. CAMPBELL / IN TRADE. Plain edge. (Ferguson S130; Grinolds May 1993 sale, lot 138)

Alexander Campbell saloon.

A. J. ASPER

Marble Rock, Iowa

Rulau	Date	Metal	Size	VG	F	VF	Unc
Mrb 1	(?)	Aluminum	25mm	—	—	30.00	—

A. J. ASPER & CO. / (ornament) / DRUGGISTS / (ornament) /MARBLE ROCK, IOWA. Rv: GOOD FOR / 1 / GLASS / -·- / * SODA *. Plain edge. (Ferguson 110; Thoele coll.)

There are other tokens of this Jones County issuer.

E. HOGAN

Marengo, Iowa

Rulau	Date	Metal	Size	VG	F	VF	Unc
Mgo 5	(1887)	Brass	--mm	—	—	30.00	—

BBC check. Rv: GOOD FOR / 5 C / E. HOGAN / IN TRADE. Plain edge. Only 2 or 3 known. (Ferguson S200; Grinolds May 1993 sale, lot 139; ATCO Maverick 3806)

Ed Hogan, saloon.

J. W. NOLAN

Marengo, Iowa

Rulau	Date	Metal	Size	VG	F	VF	Unc
Mgo 10	(1882-89)	Brass	24mm	—	—	35.00	—

GOOD FOR / 5 C/ J W / NOLAN / *** / o IN TRADE o. Rv: GEO. KUEHL & BRO. / BILLIARD / ... / CLOTHS / .&. / SUPPLIES / o CHICAGO o. Plain edge. (Thoele coll.; Rulau Vnh 1))

J. W. Nolan's saloon was listed in the 1882 gazetteer. Kuehl & Bro. supplied tokens only in the 1880's; it was Geo. Kuehl in the 1890's.

J. W. Nolan relocated at Van Horne, Iowa 1898-1901, again with a saloon business. These tokens may have been used many years.

H. J. HESLY

Minden, Iowa

Rulau	Date	Metal	Size	VG	F	VF	Unc
Min 1	(1889-1916)	Brass	25mm	—	—	15.00	—

Brunswick die BBC-11. Rv: GOOD FOR / 5 C / H. J. HESLY / IN / TRADE. Plain edge. (Brunswick 5318; Thoele coll.; Ferguson 375; Koppenhaver report.)

This saloon is listed from 1889 through 1916.

About 10 to 15 pieces are known. This token, or one similar to it, has been reported with the name N. J. WELSEY.

F. M. PODHASKI & BRO.

Monticello, Iowa

Rulau	Date	Metal	Size	VG	F	VF	Unc
Mon 1	(1898-1901)	Brass	Scal 29mm	—	—	15.00	—

BBC check die 8. Rv: GOOD FOR / 5 ¢ / IN TRADE / F. M. PODHASKI & BRO. Plain edge. (Thoele coll.; Ferguson S500; Grinolds May 1993 sale, lot F140)

Billiard hall. Some 15 pieces may exist.

M. J. CALLAN

Parnell, Iowa

Rulau	Date	Metal	Size	VG	F	VF	Unc
Par 2	(?)	Brass	21mm	—	40.00	—	—

Brunswick die BBC-5. Rv: M. J. CALLAN / 5 C / IN TRADE. (Grinolds May 1993 sale, lot 141)

Restaurant and billiards, still in business 1914.

H. VAN VLIET

Pella, Iowa

Rulau	Date	Metal	Size	VG	F	VF	Unc
Pel 7	(1888-95)	Brass	24mm	—	—	55.00	—

(Crossed utensils). Around: CHAS. PICK & CO. / DEALERS IN / CHICAGO. Rv: GOOD FOR / 5 C / H. VAN VLIET / PELLA, IOWA / IN / TRADE. Plain edge. (Ferguson 600; Grinolds May 1993 sale, lot 143)

J. P. MERSCH

Remsen, Iowa

Rulau	Date	Metal	Size	VG	F	VF	Unc
Rem 3	(1900-05)	Aluminum	Scal 28mm	—	—	25.00	—

Brunswick die BBC-8. Rv: GOOD FOR / A 5 ¢ / DRINK / J. P. MERSCH. (Thoele coll.)

J. P. Mersch was listed under billiard halls 1900-1905.

E. J. HIMMELMAN
Sioux City, Iowa

Rulau	Date	Metal	Size	VG	F	VF	Unc
Six 3	(1896)	Brass	22mm	—	—	10.00	—

E. J. HIMMELMAN. Rv: GOOD FOR / 5 ¢ / IN TRADE. (Hank Thoele & Jack Glass report)

Himmelman appears under saloons in the 1896 gazetteer.

W. F. MILLER
St. Ansgar, Iowa

Rulau	Date	Metal	Size	VG	F	VF	Unc
Stg 1	(1893-1901)	Aluminum	Oct 25mm	—	—	25.00	—

Brunswick die BBC-8. Rv: GOOD FOR / 5 ¢ / W. F. MILLER / IN / TRADE. Plain edge.

Listed in directories as a billiard hall 1886 through 1901. At an earlier period, too early for this type of token, he may have run a saloon in Belgrade, Montana.

H. W. KASTNER
Ventura, Iowa

Rulau	Date	Metal	Size	VG	F	VF	Unc
Ven 3	(?)	Brass	25mm	—	—	25.00	—

Brunswick die BBC-8. Rv: GOOD FOR / 5 C / H. W. KASTNER / IN / TRADE. (Brunswick 5380; Ferguson 200; Grinolds May 1993 sale, lot 142)

W. J. HENDERSON
Iowa ?

Rulau	Date	Metal	Size	VG	F	VF	Unc
Unk 1	(1890's)	Brass	25mm	—	—	15.00	—

GOOD FOR / 5 ¢ / IN TRADE / AT / W. J. HENDERSON. Rv: THE KERNAN MFG. CO. / (fancy ornament) / CHICAGO, ILL. Plain edge. Only 1 known. (Thoele coll., ex-Ferguson)

Kernan put its advertising on very few tokens.

KANSAS

CASE & SLIFFE
Clay Center, Kansas

Rulau	Date	Metal	Size	VG	F	VF	Unc
Clc 1	(1893)	Aluminum	38mm	—	—	100.	—

Five Columbian Exposition buildings in medallions, in cross form. Rv: CASE & SLIFFE / (ornament) / ONE PRICE / DRY GOODS & / MILLINERY / (ornaments) / - CLAY CENTER, KANS. -. Plain edge. (Charles Kirtley report)

Probably struck by Childs & Co. of Chicago, as the obverse die is that used on Hibler-Kappen 236a; Rulau "Discovery" X31. Both Case and Sliffe have disappeared by the time of the *Dun Directory* for 1918.

BOB DALTON, OUTLAW
Coffeyville, Kansas

Rulau	Date	Metal	Size	VG	F	VF	Unc
Cof 1	1895	Silver	31mm	—	—	50.00	—

BOB DALTON / OUTLAW KILLED AT COFFEYVILLE / KAN / OCT. 5. / '95 engraved on obverse of U.S. 1895 Barber half dollar. (Van Ormer sale 2605)

A relic of the era of the infamous Dalton Gang. Properly a "love token," but included here as a vital ingredient of the numismatic story of the Gay Nineties.

W. C. CRUTCHLEY
Dodge City, Kansas

Rulau	Date	Metal	Size	VG	F	VF	Unc
Dod 1	(1900-04)	Aluminum	xx	35.00	—	—	—

xx Diamond-shaped, 31mm.

Brunswick die BBC-8. Rv: GOOD FOR / ONE / CIGAR / W. C. CRUTCHLEY. Plain edge. Only 1 known. (Thoele coll.)

Crutchley appears under billiard halls in the 1900 through 1904 gazetteers.

KENTUCKY

GEO. T. STAGG CO.
Frankfort, Ky.

Rulau	Date	Metal	Size	F	VF	EF	Unc
Fkt 4	(1893)	Aluminum	40mm	—	—	35.00	50.00

Landing of Columbus. Rv: THE GEO. T. STAGG CO. / O. F. C. (large) / WHISKEY / No. 50 BROADWAY / NEW YORK / FRANKFORT, KY. Plain edge. (Eglit 568; Kirtley Oct. 1993 sale, lot 1646)

S. W. HOPKINS
Milldale, Ky.

Rulau	Date	Metal	Size	VG	F	VF	Unc
Mil 1	(1896)	Brass	29mm	—	—	27.50	—

Brunswick die BBC-3b. Rv: GOOD FOR / 5 ¢ / S. W. HOPKINS / IN / TRADE. Plain edge.

Billiard hall, in 1896 gazetteer.

LOUISIANA

M. W. C.
(M. W. Calvirt)
Alexandria, La.

Rulau	Date	Metal	Size	VG	F	VF	Unc
Alx 3	(1893-1900)	WM	21mm	—	30.00	—	V. Rare

M. W. C. / 2ND ST. / ALEXANDRIA, LA. Rv: GOOD FOR / 5 C / IN TRADE. Rarity 10. (Tylenda Alx. A-05)

M. W. Calvirt is listed as a saloon proprietor in 1893 and 1900. The saloon was under the proprietorship of W. T. Calvirt by 1905.

J. HAMBACHER
Algiers, La.

Rulau	Date	Metal	Size	VG	F	VF	Unc
Alg 3	(1893)	Brass	23mm	—	4.00	7.00	—
Alg 4	(1893)	Brass	Oct., 23mm	—	4.00	7.00	—

Alg 3: J. HAMBACHER / BAKERY / VALLETTE / & ALIX / ALGIERS, LA. Rv: GOOD FOR / 5 C / BREAD. Plain edge. Rarity 1. (Tylenda Alg. D-05)

Alg 4: As last, but 10 C. Plain edge. R1. (Tylenda Alg. D-10)

The bakery of John Hambacher is listed in 1893. By 1900 this was in the hands of George Hambacher.

Researcher Cindy Grellman reports that both obverses were made from the same die, one in which the J. appears to have been recut over an H.

F. M. BROOKS

Baton Rouge, La.

Rulau	Date	Metal	Size	VG	F	VF	Unc
Bat 1	(?)	CN	21mm	—	—	25.00	—
	Heart at center, F. M. BROOKS above, BATON ROUGE, / LA. below. Rv: GOOD FOR / 5C / IN TRADE. Plain edge. R9. (Tylenda B.R. B-05)						

F. M. Brooks operated a drug store at 210 Main St. from the 1880's until his death ca 1905-08.

CHOCTAW PLANTATION

Brusley, La.

Rulau	Date	Metal	Size	VG	F	VF	Unc
Bru 1	(1893-1905)	Brass	21mm	—	—	32.50	—
	CHOCTAW / PLANTATION / (illegible). Rv: Large 5. Rarity 10. (Tylenda Bru. A-05)						

Owner of the Choctaw Plantation was Olga M. Mary, listed in 1893, 1900, 1905 and 1914, though all the listings appear under Cinclare, Louisiana. Both Brusley and Cinclare are small towns in West Baton Rouge Parish, each with about 400 population in World War I. Successors to Mary may have been Thibodeaux & Aubert.

MATTHEW JONES

Chaler, La.

Rulau	Date	Metal	Size	VG	F	VF	Unc
Cha 1	(1900-05)	Brass	21mm	15.00	25.00	—	—
	MATTHEW JONES / ooo / CHALER / LA. Rv: Large 5 in center. Around: PAYABLE IN CASH 24 HOURS AFTER DEMAND. Obverse rim beaded, reverse, dentilated. Plain edge.						

General store 1900-05. By 1909 Chaler had disappeared as a post office location and became known as Cypress.

W. F. SHACKELFORD

Cheneyville, La.

Rulau	Date	Metal	Size	VG	F	VF	Unc
Chn 3	(1898-1900)	Brass	Scal 26mm	—	—	25.00	—
	W.F. SHACKELFORD / CHENEYVILLE, / LA. Rv: Large 25. Plain edge. R10. (Grellman coll.)						

This general store was owned by Shackelford & Havard Ltd. in 1893, then W. F. Shackelford in 1900 and later in 1900 by Shackelford & Hart. It disappears by 1905. Apparently only in 1900 and earlier did it use the W. F. Shackelford name.

Cheneyville is in Rapides Parish.

CANE RIVER LUMBER CO.

Chopin, La.

Rulau	Date	Metal	Size	VG	F	VF	Unc
Cho 1	(1893)	Brass	23mm	—	—	40.00	—
	PAY IN / MERCHANDISE / CANE RIVER / LUMBER / CO. / CHOPIN, LA. Rv: 5 C. Plain edge. R10. (Tylenda Cho. A-05)						
Cho 2	(1893)	Brass	23mm	—	—	40.00	—
	Similar to last, but $1.00. Plain edge. R10. (Tylenda Cho. A-100)						

The Cane River Lumber Co. was listed in 1893, but is no longer listed in Chopin (Natchitoches Parish) in 1900. The tiny village had only 25 population in World War I.

MOSES ELDER

DeSiard, La.

Rulau	Date	Metal	Size	VG	F	VF	Unc
Des 1	(1893)	Brass	29mm	—	—	30.00	—
	MOSES ELDER, / DEALER IN / GENERAL / MERCHANDISE / & / PLAT'N / SUPPLIES/ DE SIARD, LA. Rv: 50 C. Rarity 10. (Grellman coll.)						

Moses Elder, general store, appears only in the 1893 directory. DeSiard (Ouachita Parish) had just 80 people in WWI.

HOTEL ROGGE

Donaldsonville, La.

Rulau	Date	Metal	Size	VG	F	VF	Unc
Don 1	(?)	CN	30mm	—	—	—	25.00
	HOTEL ROGGE / BAR. Rv: 5c. Plain edge. R10. (Tylenda Don. B-05)						
Don 2	(?)	CN	21mm	—	—	—	35.00
	F. ROGGE / DONALDSONVILLE, LA. Rv: GOOD FOR A 5c / DRINK OR CIGAR. Plain edge. Crescent cut-out flan. R10. (Tylenda Don. A-05)						

Frederick Rogge operated a hotel and bar from the late 1880's to 1920.

JNO. D. SHAFFER

Ellendale, La.

Rulau	Date	Metal	Size	VG	F	VF	Unc
E11 1	1899	Cardboard	34mm	—	25.00	—	—
	ARDOYNE PLANTATION / J. D. SHAFFER. Rv: MAY. / JNO. D. SHAFFER / 1899 / (ink signature). Unique. (Tylenda E11.D)						
E11 2	1900	Cardboard	34mm	—	25.00	—	—
	Similar to last, but 1900.						

Shaffer Bros. general store is listed in 1893. John D. Shaffer is listed as a sugar mill proprietor in 1905. In 1909 Shaffer's listing is as "planter, manufacturer of sugar, and general store." He is still listed in 1918.

It is probable the chits above are contemporary with their dates. Ellendale is in the Terrebonne Parish; population in 1918 was 175.

FRIERSON BROS.

Frierson, La.

Rulau	Date	Metal	Size	VG	F	VF	Unc
Frr 1	(1900)	Aluminum	19mm	—	15.00	—	—
	FRIERSON / BROS. / FRIERSON / LA. Rv: GOOD FOR / 5 C / IN / MERCHANDISE. Plain edge. Rarity 9. (Grellman coll.)						
Frr 1	(1900)	Aluminum	26mm	—	15.00	—	—
	As last, but 25 C. Plain edge. R9. (Grellman coll.)						
Frr 3	(1900)	Aluminum	32mm	—	—	10.00	—
	Similar, but $1oo. Plain edge. R8. (Grellman coll.)						

The town was called Frierson's Mill when Frierson Bros. are first listed as general store proprietors in 1893. It became simply Frierson in 1900 as Frierson Bros. are listed as owners of a general store, steam gin, saw mill and grist mill. In 1905 the firm became Frierson Company Ltd., and is still so listed in 1918.

Frierson, in De Soto Parish, had 150 people in World War I.

GOLDEN RANCHE PLANT.

Gheens, La.

Rulau	Date	Metal	Size	VG	F	VF	Unc
Ghn 1	(1893-1905)	Aluminum	28mm	—	—	12.00	—
	GOLDEN RANCHE / MEAL. Rv: Blank. R8. (Tylenda Ghe. F)						
Ghn 2	(1893-1905)	Aluminum	29mm	—	—	12.00	—
	GOOD FOR / 1 / DAYS BOARD / GOLDEN RANCHE. Rv: Large 5. R9. (Tylenda Ghe. I-05)						
Ghn 3	(1893-1905)	Brass	21mm	—	—	12.00	—
	* GOOD IN * / (ornament) / TRADE / (ornament) / GOLDEN RANCHE. Rv: Large 5. R9. (Tylenda Ghe. I-05)						

Rulau	Date	Metal	Size	VG	F	VF	Unc
Ghn 4	(1893-1905)	Brass	23mm	—	—	12.00	—
	Similar to Ghn 3, but 10 on reverse. R9. (Tylenda Ghe. 1-10; Grellman coll.)						
Ghn 6	(1890's)	Brass	21mm	—	—	16.00	—
	GOLDEN RANCHE / * / PLANT / *-.-*. Rv: GOOD FOR / * 5 C * / NOT / TRANSFERABLE. Plain edge. R9. (Tylenda Ghe. H-05)						

Rulau	Date	Metal	Size	VG	F	VF	Unc
Ghn 7	(1890's)	Brass	23mm	—	—	10.00	—

Similar, but * 10 * on reverse. R7. (Tylenda Ghe. H-10)

The Golden Ranch Sugar & Cattle Co. Ltd. operated the Golden Ranche Plantation 1895-1905, according to indirect directory evidence.

J. MURDOCH

Hard Times Landing, La.

Rulau	Date	Metal	Size	VG	F	VF	Unc
HTL 1	(1890's)	Brass	23mm	—	30.00	—	—

FRANKLIN PL'T. / J. MURDOCH. / NOT / TRANSFERABLE. Rv: 5. Plain edge. R10. (Grellman coll.)

John Murdoch is listed as a planter and general store proprietor 1882-1893 or later.

HARVEY MERCANTILE CO. LTD.

Harvey, La.

Rulau	Date	Metal	Size	VG	F	VF	Unc
Hrv 1	(1893-1907)	Brass	27mm	—	25.00	—	—

HARVEY MERCANTILE CO. LTD. / HARVEY / LA. Rv: GOOD FOR / 25 / IN MERCHANDISE. Rarity 10. (Tylenda Har B-25)

Rulau	Date	Metal	Size	VG	F	VF	Unc
Hrv 2	(1893-1907)	Brass	Oct 27mm	—	20.00	—	—

As last, but octagonal. R9. (Tylenda Har C-25)

Harvey Mercantile Co. Ltd. is listed as a general store 1893 to 1907, when it became Harvey Trading Co. It was still listed 1918.

ALPHONSE DUPONT

Houma, La.

Rulau	Date	Metal	Size	VG	F	VF	Unc
Hou 1	(?)	Brass	29mm	—	—	—	35.00

GOOD FOR / ONE DRINK / AT / ALPHONSE DUPONT / HOUMA, / LA. Rv: Blank. Plain edge. R10. (Tylenda Houma G)

Alphonse Dupont had a general store and saloon on Main St. from the 1880's to 1918. He stocked dry goods, crockery, hardware, furniture, clothing, boots and shoes, notions, liquors and groceries. This merchant also used round cardboard tokens in 1911 and probably earlier.

McCLANAHAN & SON

Hunter, La.

Rulau	Date	Metal	Size	VG	F	VF	Unc
Hnt 1	1899	Aluminum	28mm	—	25.00	—	—

McCLANAHAN & SON / 1899 / HUNTER, LA. Rv: GOOD FOR / 25 / IN MERCHANDISE. Plain edge. R10. (Grellman coll.)

No listings have been found for McClanahan. In WW I Hunter was a tiny (pop. 30) place in De Soto Parish.

ATKINS BROS.

Lake End, La.

Rulau	Date	Metal	Size	VG	F	VF	Unc
Lak 1	(?)	Brass	21mm	—	—	—	30.00

ATKINS BROS. / GOOD / FOR / MDSE. / LAKE END, LA. Rv: GOOD FOR / 5c / NOT TRANSFERABLE. Plain edge. R10. (Tylenda. L. E. A-05)

Rulau	Date	Metal	Size	VG	F	VF	Unc
Lak 2	(?)	Brass	Scal 26mm	—	—	—	30.00

Similar to last, but denomination 10c. R10. (Tylenda L.E. A-10)

This general store in Lake End, Red River Parish, operated 1880's to 1908. In 1918 Lake End had only 48 people.

WHEADON & WEEMS

Moorland, La.

Rulau	Date	Metal	Size	VG	F	VF	Unc
Mor 1	(1893)	Brass	23mm	—	30.00	—	—

WHEADON & WEEMS / EMFIELD / PLANTATION. Rv: GOOD FOR / 10 C / IN MERCHANDISE. Plain edge. R8. (Tylenda Moo A-10)

Wheadon & Weems general store appears only in the 1893 directory. Moorland is in Rapides Parish, with an 1918 population only 60.

J. W. ARMSHAW

New Orleans, La.

Rulau	Date	Metal	Size	VG	F	VF	Unc
NOR 2	(1893)	Brass	21mm	—	40.00	—	—

J.W. ARMSHAW / SUNNY / SOUTH / SALOON. Rv: POOL CHIP / 5 C. Plain edge. R10. (Tylenda N.O. A/12-05)

This saloon is listed only in 1893.

ALEX. BLOCKSDORFF

Rulau	Date	Metal	Size	VG	F	VF	Unc
NOR 3	(1898-1901)	Brass	21mm	—	60.00	—	—

ALEX. BLOCKSDORFF'S / SALOON / 128 / EXCHANGE / ALLEY. Rv: GOOD FOR A / 5 C / DRINK OR / CIGAR. R10. (Tylenda N.O. B/11-05)

Rulau	Date	Metal	Size	VG	F	VF	Unc
NOR 3A	(1898-1901)	Brass	21mm	—	25.00	—	—

A. BLOCKSDORFF / 128 EXCHANGE PLACE. Rv: GOOD FOR / 2 1/2 C / IN TRADE. R10. Flan carries a crescent-shaped cutout. (Tylenda N.O. B/12-02 1/2)

The Blocksdorff saloon was operated only from 1898 to 1901.

LOUIS DELATOUR

Rulau	Date	Metal	Size	VG	F	VF	Unc
NOR 5	(1893-1900)	Brass	23mm	—	18.00	—	—

LOUIS DELATOUR / GROCER / FRENCHMAN & / N. CLAIBORNE AVE. Rv: 2 1/2 C. Plain edge. R8. (Tylenda N.O. D/8-02 1/2)

Delatour's grocery and saloon business is listed only 1893 through 1900.

A. FAGOT

Rulau	Date	Metal	Size	VG	F	VF	Unc
NOR 6	(ca 1900)	Brass	23mm	—	—	Ex.Rare	

A. FAGOT. Rv: 2 1/2C. Plain edge. R10. (Tylenda N.O.F/1-02 1/2)

August Fagot had a grocery store at 4539 Tschoupitoulas St. 1900-15. By 1918 this was a combination grocery and saloon.

VAL FRANZ

Rulau	Date	Metal	Size	VG	F	VF	Unc
NOR B6	(1893-1900)	Aluminum	19mm	—	—	30.00	—

VAL FRANZ, BAKER. Rv: GOOD FOR 5 C LOAF BREAD. Unique. (Tylenda N.O. F/9-05)

Valentine Franz appears in directories as baker and confectioner 1893-1900. The 1905 directory lists the business under Valentine Franz Jr.

VICTOR GRUBER

Rulau	Date	Metal	Size	VG	F	VF	Unc
Nor E6	(1893-1905)	Aluminum	Sq 24mm	—	—	30.00	—

VICTOR GRUBER / CONTI / & / DAUPHINE STS. Rv: GOOD FOR / 2 1/2 C / IN TRADE. (Tylenda N.O. G/15-2 1/2)

Gruber is listed as a saloonkeeper and grocer 1893, then as a grocer 1900-05. (Research courtesy Cindy Grellman)

J. HOLDAKOWSKI

Rulau	Date	Metal	Size	VG	F	VF	Unc
Nor G6	(1893)	Brass	Oct 20mm	—	—	30.00	—

J. HOLDAKOWSKI, / TULANE AVE. Rv: GOOD FOR / 5 C / BREAD. Unique. (Tylenda N.O. H/6-05)

Rulau	Date	Metal	Size	VG	F	VF	Unc
Nor H6	(1893)	Brass	21mm	—	—	30.00	—

As last, but 10 C. (Tylenda N.O. H/6-10)

Joseph Holdakowski, baker, appears only in the 1893 directory. (Cindy Grellman research)

KELLY

Rulau	Date	Metal	Size	VG	F	VF	Unc
Nor J6	(1890's)	Brass	28mm	—	—	22.50	—

KELLY THAT'S ALL! Rv; 12 1/2 C. Probably unique. (Tylenda N.O. K/4-12 /12)

P. J. Kelly is listed as a grocer 1893-1905 and as a restaurateur 1909, but Tylenda asserts the tokens were for use in his saloon in the 1890's. The grocery-saloon listing appears in directories only in 1893.

L. LABATUT

Rulau	Date	Metal	Size	VG	F	VF	Unc
NOR 7	(1890's)	Brass	25mm	—	—	20.00	—

L. LABATUT / HAGAN / AVE. / & / BIENVILLE ST. Rv: 2 1/2. Rarity 10. (Grellman coll.)

L. Labatt & Co. (sic), commission produce, is listed 1876, and L. Labatt (sic), grocer, in 1893. The fabric is 1890's style. It is not certain whether Labatut or Labatt is the correct surname.

MAGINNIS COTTON MILLS

Rulau	Date	Metal	Size	VG	F	VF	Unc
NOR 8	(?)	Brass	21mm	—	—	—	20.00

MAGINNIS / COTTON / MILLS. Rv: 5. Plain edge. R9. (Tylenda N.O. M/3-05)

Maginnis Cotton Mills was in business from 1880's to the 1930's. It was located at 1050 Constance. It made cotton bags, such as sugar sacks, etc., as a staple item.

It seems inevitable that other denominations of the Maginnis factory tokens will surface; a hoard may exist somewhere.

JULES MANAUD

Rulau	Date	Metal	Size	VG	F	VF	Unc
NOR 9	(1890's)	Brass	23mm	—	12.50	17.50	—

JULES MANAUD. / OYSTER / SALOON / 169 / S. RAMPART ST. / N.O. Rv: 5c. Plain edge. R9. (Tylenda N.O. M/4-05)

Used in the Gay Nineties. An oyster saloon was a place where oysters on the half shell are the main attraction. In New Orleans today these are called oyster bars. Though drinks could be had in an oyster saloon, it was not a saloon in the ordinary sense.

OUR FRIENDS SALOON

Rulau	Date	Metal	Size	VG	F	VF	Unc
NOR 10	(1890's)	Brass	29mm	—	35.00	—	—

POOL / * / (Pool table) / *** CHECK ***. Rv: * GOOD FOR * / 5 ¢ / DRINK / OUR FRIENDS / SALOON / 20 EXCHANGE ALLEY. Plain edge. Rarity 8. (Tylenda N.O. 0/24/05)

This pool check die is a typical 1890's product.

E. W. PETERS

Rulau	Date	Metal	Size	VG	F	VF	Unc
NOR 11	(1895)	Brass	29mm	—	—	65.00	—

ZIEGLER SALOON/ E. W. PETERS / PROP. / 106-114 ROYAL ST. Rv: 10. Unique. (Tylenda N.O. Z/2-10)

Peters' saloon is listed at this address only in 1895; a 1900 listing is at a different address.

RAMOS

Rulau	Date	Metal	Size	VG	F	VF	Unc
NOR 12	(?)	Aluminum	25mm	—	—	—	25.00

GOOD FOR / 5c / RAMOS / IN / TRADE. Rv: 5. Plain edge. R10. (Tyleda N.O. R/2-05)

H. C. Ramos operated the Stag Saloon at 712-714 Gravier St. from 1880's to 1916. An early advertisement touts this saloon as the "home of the original Ramons Gin Fizz.".

The H.C. Ramos Co., Ltd. was operating the saloon in 1918. Like all saloons in America, it was forced by Prohibition to close the last day of 1919.

GEO. SCHAFF BAKERY

Rulau	Date	Metal	Size	VG	F	VF	Unc
NOR 13	(1890-1910)	Brass	Oct 26mm	—	30.00	—	Rare

GEO. SCHAFF / BAKERY / NEW ORLEANS, / LA. Rv: GOOD FOR / 10c / BREAD. Plain edge. R10. (Tylenda N.O. S/22-10)

Schaff's Bakery, located at 748 So. Rampart St., operated from 1890's to about 1910.

SCHNEIDER

Rulau	Date	Metal	Size	VG	F	VF	Unc
NOR 14	(1893-99)	Brass	28mm	—	—	20.00	—

POOL / * / (Pool table) *** CHECK ***. Rv: GOOD FOR / 5 C / DRINK / SCHNEIDER. Rarity 10. (Tylenda N.O. S/25-05)

Frederick Schneider's saloon and grocery is listed 1893 to 1900, succeeded in the latter year by Mrs. Anna M. and Chris A. Schneider, and in 1905 by Schneider & Guthrie.

STR. JEWELL

Rulau	Date	Metal	Size	VG	F	VF	EF
NOR 15	(1873-95)	Silver	26mm	—	—	300.	—

STR. JEWELL ctsp on U.S. 1853 Liberty Seated quarter dollar. (Gould 86; Brunk 21710)

Rulau	Date	Metal	Size	VG	F	VF	EF
NOR 15A	(1900)	Silver	26mm	—	—	300.	—

Similar ctsp on both sides of U.S. 1854 Liberty Seated quarter dollar. (Schenkman coll.; Rulau Por 5)

According to David Schenkman, the most likely issuer was the *Steamer Jewell,* built in 1873 and operating out of New Orleans.

For many years it had been attributed by Maurice M. Gould to the Steamer "Jewel," which was a coastwise craft running from Portland to Gardner, Maine and thence to Nova Scotia about 1900.

JOS. VOEGTLE

Rulau	Date	Metal	Size	VG	F	VF	Unc
NOR 18	(1890's)	Aluminum	25mm	—	30.00	—	—

COSMOPOLITAN HOTEL / JOS. / VOEGTLE / PROP. / N.O. LA. Rv: WAITER'S / c 5 c / CHECK. Plain edge. (Wright 1704)

WAR SHIP NEW ORLEANS

Rulau	Date	Metal	Size	VG	F	VF	EF
NOR 20	(1892-1909)	Silver	25mm	—	—	—	85.00

MADE FROM WAR SHIP NEW ORLEANS ctsp around edge of planed-off obverse of U.S. Barber quarter dollar of the New Orleans (0) mint. BUILT / 1814 / SACKETTS / HARBOR, all in script, engraved within the circle formed by the counterstamping. (Krause coll.)

JOS. ZIEGLER

New Orleans, La.

Rulau	Date	Metal	Size	VG	F	VF	Unc
NOR 25	(1892)	Aluminum	Oct 25mm	—	30.00	—	—

JOS. ZIEGLER / Z (large) / XXXXX. Rv: GOOD FOR / * 5 * / CENTS / AT THE BAR. Plain edge. (Tylenda 6293 Z/5-05; Grellman coll.)

Joseph Ziegler's bar and saloon appears in the 1882 directory. In the 1893 directory he is listed as a baker. Only 2 specimens known. The introduction of aluminum in trade tokens about 1891-92 and the 1893 change in Ziegler's occupation make dating this token easier.

QUINN HOTEL

New Roads, La.

Rulau	Date	Metal	Size	VG	F	VF	Unc
New 1	(?)	Aluminum	25mm	—	20.00	—	—

QUINN HOTEL / 2 1/2 / SALOON. Rv: JOSH QUINCY / PURE / RYE. Plain edge. R10. (Tylenda N.R. A-02 1/2)

J. W. and Alice Quinn managed this hotel bar from 1880's to 1910 or soon thereafter. New Roads is in Pointe Coupee Parish; it had 1,352 people in 1918. The hotel was operated in 1918 by G. Savignol.

DUGAS & LE BLANC LTD.

Paincourtville, La.

Rulau	Date	Metal	Size	VG	F	VF	Unc
Pai 1	(?)	Brass	21mm	—	—	20.00	—
	DUGAS / & / LE BLANC / LTD. Rv: 5. Plain edge. R10. (Tylenda Pain. A-05)						
Pai 2	(?)	Brass	Scal 26mm	—	—	—	—
	Similar to last, but '50'. R10.						
Pai 3	(?)	Brass	28mm	—	—	—	—
	Similar to last, but '75'. R10.						

This was a sugar plantation and commissary that was in operation in the 1880's and continued for many years. It is not indicated that these pieces were in use in 1890's, but they may prove to have been from that era and are admitted here.

The population of Paincourtville in 1918 was 475. Dugas & Le Blanc Ltd. were still in operation then, and later.

C. LAMPO

Patterson, La.

Rulau	Date	Metal	Size	VG	F	VF	Unc
Pat 1	(?)	Brass	21mm	—	—	—	Rare

C. LAMPO. Rv: GOOD FOR / 5c / IN TRADE. Plain edge. R10. (Tylenda Pat. A-05)

Ciro Lampo ran a saloon from the 1880's to 1919. Prohibition forced the close of his saloon and from Jan. 1, 1920 he operated a grocery in the Main Street premises until the 1930's.

S. ABRAHAM

Raceland, La.

Rulau	Date	Metal	Size	VG	F	VF	Unc
Rac 1	(1882-99)	Brass	20mm	—	20.00	—	—
	(All incused): S. ABRAHAM / RACELAND / LA. Rv: GOOD FOR / 5 / MDSE. Rarity 9. (Tylenda Rac. G-05)						
Rac 2	(1882-99)	Brass	20mm	—	25.00	—	—
	Obverse as last. Rv: Blank. Rarity 10. (Tylenda Rac. G)						
Rac 3	(1882-99)	Brass	25mm	—	25.00	—	—
	As first token above, but 10. Rarity 10. (Tylenda Rac. G-10)						

Simon Abraham appears in directories as follows:

1882 - S. Abraham	dry goods & groceries
1893 - S. Abraham	general store
1900 - Simon Abraham	general store & planter
1905-18 - Simon Abraham	sugar mill & general store
1919-on - S. Abraham Co. Inc.	(this entity also issued tokens)

Raceland, WWI population 500, is in Lafourche Parish.

D. BONNEMAISON

Royville, La.

Rulau	Date	Metal	Size	VG	F	VF	Unc
Roy 1	(1889-93)	Brass	24mm	—	—	35.00	—
	D. BONNEMAISON / ROYVILLE, / LA. Rv: GOOD FOR / 10 C / IN MERCHANDISE / NOT / TRANSFERABLE. (Tylenda Ry. A-10)						
Roy 2	(1889-93)	Brass	29mm	—	—	35.00	—
	As last, but 25 C.						
Roy 3	(1889-93)	Brass	30mm	—	—	35.00	—
	As last, but 50 C.						
Roy 4	(1889-93)	Brass	34mm	—	—	45.00	—
	As last, but $1oo. (Tylenda Ry. A-100)						

D. Bonnemaison's general store appears in the directories only in 1893, and then under Youngsville, La. Tylenda says the town changed its name about 1890. So the Royville listing could be about 1889, though name changes sometimes take a long time in rural areas.

JOHN S. JACKSON

Shreveport, La.

Rulau	Date	Metal	Size	VG	F	VF	Unc
Shv 7	(1894)	Aluminum	Oct 25mm	—	—	35.00	—
	PHOENIX HOTEL / JOHN S. JACKSON / PROP. / BARBER SHOP. Rv: GOOD FOR / 25 C / FOR WORK. Unique. (Tylenda N/L)						

John S. Jackson had the barber shop franchise in the Phoenix Hotel only in 1894, directories indicate. The Phoenix Hotel was under the proprietorship of Forrey and Trammel 1893-1900.

MOUNT HOUMAS PLANTATION

Southwood, La.

Rulau	Date	Metal	Size	VG	F	VF	Unc
Sou 3	(1890)	Brass	27mm	—	—	40.00	—
	MOUNT HOUMAS / PLANTATION / L. A. ELLIS. Rv: GOOD FOR / ONE / MEAL. (Tylenda Sou. B)						
Sou 5	(1890)	Brass	21mm	—	—	40.00	—
	MOUNT HOUMAS PLANTATION / L. A. & C. G. / ELLIS. / NOT / TRANFERABLE. Rv: 10 C. (Tylenda Sou A-10)						
Sou 6	(1890)	Brass	28mm	—	—	40.00	—
	Similar to last, but 50 C and no period after ELLIS.						
Sou 7	(1890)	Brass	29mm	—	—	45.00	—
	Similar to last, but $1.00 C and period after ELLIS.						

This sugar plantation and commissary operated in or near Southwood, but no directory listings under Southwood or Geismar appear. The plantation was a branch of the Ellis holdings at Walker's Station, Texas.

A. S. COLTHARP & CO.

Talla Bena, La.

Rulau	Date	Metal	Size	VG	F	VF	Unc
Tib 1	(1890's)	Brass	18mm	—	—	Rare	—
	TALLA BENA / TRADE / CHECK / A. S.. COLTHARP & CO. Rv: GOOD FOR / 5c / MERCHANDISE. Plain edge. R9. (Tylenda TB A-05)						
Tib 2	(1890's)	Brass	21mm	7.50	12.50	22.00	—
	TALLA BENA STORE / TRADE / CHECK / A. S. COLTHARP & CO. Rv: GOOD FOR / 10c / MERCHANDISE. Plain edge. R8. (Tylenda TB A-10)						
Tib 3	(1890's)	Brass	24mm	—	—	40.00	—
	Similar to last, but 25c. R9. (Tylenda TB A-25)						
Tib 4	(1890's)	Brass	36mm	—	—	—	Ex.Rare
	Similar to last, but 50c. R10. (Wright 181)						
Tib 5	(1890's)	Brass	38mm	—	—	—	Ex.Rare
	Similar to last, but $1oo. R10. (Tylenda T.B. A-100)						

A. S. Coltharp operated a cotton plantation commissary (general store) in Talla Bena, Madison Parish, La. from the late 1880's to 1909-10. This place, near Tallulah, had a post office in 1910, which was gone by 1918. Tallulah, the parish seat, had a bank and 847 people in 1918.

Coltharp or one of its variations (Coltharpe, Colthorpe, etc.) was a popular surname in Madison Parish. Men of these names ran a funeral parlor and an auto sales agency in 1918. Madison Parish is across the Mississippi River from Vicksburg, Miss.

Dr. B. P. Wright reported this issuer in 1898 in his first round of listings in *The Numismatist*. See also *TAMS Journal* for April 1971 and June 1971 under "Mavericks."

The Coltharp store was affiliated with J.T. McClellan Company, according to Edmund Tylenda.

CEDAR GROVE

Tallieu, La.

Rulau	Date	Metal	Size	VG	F	V	Unc
Tal 1	(?)	Brass	Scal 25mm	—	—	25.00	—
	CEDAR GROVE / TIME / CHECK / NOT / TRANSFERABLE. Rv: 40. Plain edge. R10. (Tylenda Tal, A-40)						

L. M. Soniat owned this general store and cotton plantation from the 1880's until about World War I. It is not listed in 1918.

R. MILLIKEN

Waggaman, La.

Rulau	Date	Metal	Size	VG	F	VF	Unc
Wag 4	(1893)	Nickel	20mm	—	—	45.00	—
	FAIRFIELD PLANT'N / R. MILLIKEN / NOT / TRANSFERABLE. Rv: 5. Unique? (Tylenda N/L)						

Richard Milliken, a New Orleans sugar factor, owned the Fairfield Plantation at Waggaman in Jefferson Parish during 1893, according to an 1898-99 mercantile guide located by researcher Cindy Grellman.

MARYLAND

R.W.C.

(Robert Welsey Chard)

Anne Arundel County, Md.

Rulau	Date	Metal	Size	VG	F	VF	Unc
Ann 6	(1890's ?)	Brass	23mm	—	3.00	—	—
	R. W. C / 1 1/2 stamped at center. Rv: T. F. B. stamped at center. Recessed dentilated rim on each side. Plain edge.						
Ann 7	(1890's ?)	Brass	21mm	—	3.00	—	—
	R. W. C. / 15 stamped at center. Rv: Blank. Recessed dentilated rim on each side. Plain edge.						
Ann 8	(?)	Brass		—	3.00	—	—
	R. W. C / 7 1/2 stamped on plain flan. Rv: Blank. Plain edge.						
Ann 9	(?)	Brass	35mm	—	3.00	—	—
	R. W. C. / 5 / 1.50 stamped on plain flan. Rv: Blank. Plain edge.						

TFB = Thomas F. Bottomley, Chard's father. Chard farmed near Magothy, Md.

R. S.

Anne Arundel County, Md.

Rulau	Date	Metal	Size	VG	F	VF	Unc
Ann 22	(?)	Brass	27.3mm	—	8.00	12.50	—
	(All incused): R. S. Rv: CASH / 5 / CHECK. Plain edge. (Zaffern coll.)						

BALTIMORE CLOTHES

Baltimore, Md.

Rulau	Date	Metal	Size	VG	F	VF	Unc
Bal 8	(?)	Copper	26mm	—	—	8.00	—

Male bust in Colonial hat and garb right, BALTIMORE CLOTHES, INC. above, . BALTIMORE, USA. . below. Rv: Within wreath: BALTO CLOTHES / ALL WOOL / AND FULLY / GUARANTEED. Plain edge. (Rich Bottles Jr. collection, Harmony, Pa.)

T.B.
(Thomas Banber)

Rulau	Date	Metal	Size	VG	F	VF	Unc
Bal 4	(1899-1901)	Brass	20mm	—	12.00	—	Rare

Eagle displayed at center, head turned right, 12 stars above, olive wreath below. Rv: Wreath near rim, blank center. Incused at center: T B. Plain edge. Rarity 8.

Thomas Banber kept an oyster packing plant at 607 So. Luzerne 1899-1901. The token is a stock die introduced about 1890 and adapted by Banber.

FORDS GRAND OPERA HOUSE

Rulau	Date	Metal	Size	VG	F	VF	Unc
Bal 25	1894	WM	38mm	—	—	—	20.00
Bal 25A	1894	Bronze	38mm	—	—	—	22.00

Bal 25: Bust three-quarters left within circle, 1883 EDWIN BOOTH 1893 below. Around: MEMORIAL PERFORMANCE OF HAMLET APRIL 23RD 1894 around. Rv: Bust three-quarters right within partial circle, CRESTON CLARKE 1865 below. Around: 330TH SHAKESPEARIAN ANNIVERSARY FORDS GRAND OPERA HOUSE BALTIMORE. Plain edge.

Bal 25A: As Bal 25. Plain edge.

NOTE: Bal 25 may also exist in silver or other metals.

GEM CHEMICAL CO.

Rulau	Date	Metal	Size	VG	F	VF	Unc
Bal 40	(1890)	Aluminum	30mm	—	10.00	—	—

THIS CHECK WILL BE REDEEMED / IN / KOLA — / * PEPSIN / BY YOUR JOBBER / — ... OR ... — / THE GEM CHEMICAL / CO. / BALTO, MD. Rv: * TO THE CONSUMER * / GOOD FOR ONE / GLASS / KOLA-PEPSIN / 5 ¢ / AT ALL / SODA FOUNTAINS. Plain edge. (Duffield 47)

Kola-Pepsin was apparently a well-known cola drink in the Gay Nineties.

JOE GOELLER

Rulau	Date	Metal	Size	F	VF	EF	Unc
Bal 44	(1895-1910)	Alum	Oct 25mm	—	12.50	—	—

JOE GOELLER / 10 (stencil cut-out) / HOLLYWOOD PK. Rv: Blank. Plain edge.

Joseph Goeller, born in Germany 1859, came to Baltimore as a boy. Before 1895 he operated a saloon and beer park at Standard Park on Gay St.

In 1895 he opened a saloon and park on the southeast side of Eastern Ave. and Back River. The park soon added a hotel and rides. Vaudeville and dancing were popular there and about 1900 it became known as Hollywood Park.

Hollywood Park was one of several parks around the Back River bridge on the streetcar line, others being Prospect Park, Pospisil's Park and Mitchell's Back River Park. Some of these other parks also used tokens.

Prohibition (passed in 1919) didn't stop the flow of beer and whiskey at Hollywood Park and Goeller had several confiscations of illegal beverages. The park was destroyed by fire in 1921, and Goeller entered the real estate business. He died in 1940. (Research courtesy Russ & Jane Sears, Baltimore)

HECHT BROS.

Rulau	Date	Metal	Size	F	VF	EF	Unc
Bal 50	(?)	GS	Oval, 22.2* *by 29.8mm	—	—	12.00	—

Canopied arms at center. HECHT BROS. above, BALTIMORE below. Rv: Numeral incused (38983 reported). Plain edge. Issued holed.

Charge plate token.

C. D. KENNY CO.

Rulau	Date	Metal	Size	F	VF	EF	Unc
Bal 56	(1899)	Alum	32mm	—	12.50	—	20.00
	(1899)	Copper	32mm	—	40.00	—	—

Bal 56 (Alum): Military bust facing three-quarters right, W.S. SCHLEY. below. Rv: C. D. KENNY Co. / TEAS / COFFEES (within scrollwork) / SUGARS. Plain edge. (Miller / Adams Md 79; Duffield 67)

(Copper): As last. Only 1 known.

Commodore Winfield S. Schley was one of two naval heroes of the battle of Santiago de Cuba, the other being Rear Admiral William T. Sampson. U.S. squadrons under the two officers blockaded the Spanish fleet of Admiral Pascual Cervera in Santiago harbor in May, 1898. On July 3 Cervera feared his fleet could be captured at anchor after the American ground forces won the battles of El Caney and San Juan Hill, so he led his armada out and the Americans under Schley annihilated it, every ship. The victory effectively ended the Spanish-American War.

Rulau	Date	Metal	Size	F	VF	EF	Unc
Bal 57	(?)	Brass	22mm	—	10.00	20.00	—

C. D. / KENNY / CO. Rv: GOOD FOR / ONE CUP / ONLY. Plain edge.

An excellent article by Jane Sears, "C. D. Kenny Company Giveaways of Yesterday," appeared in Summer 1986 issue of *Maryland TAMS Journal,* which explains these and many other bits of Kenny memorabilia.

Cornelius D. Kenny came from Rochester, N.Y. to Baltimore in 1870. His tea, coffee, spice, sugar and flour stores spread all over the South and into the Midwest from 1870 to 1934. He had 16 branch stores in Baltimore alone.

Kenny's stores are remembered for the rich and pleasant aroma of exotic teas and freshly "pulverized" coffees which permeated them, and "KENNY" became a household word through the giveaway premiums he used to boost sales — trade cards, toothpick holders, pot scrapers, calendars, small toys and tokens bearing the Kenny name. Many of these items find their way into collections of antiques.

By 1930 Kenny had 75 stores in 15 states and the District of Columbia. In 1895 he advertised: "We roast 40,000 pounds of coffee daily." Stores were in Norfolk, Atlanta, Chattanooga, Mobile, Charleston, New York, Wilmington, Wheeling, St. Louis, Columbus, York (Pa.), New Orleans, Charlotte and Jacksonville.

In 1934 the Kenny firm was sold to Consolidated Grocers, which maintained a C.D Kenny division into the 1950's. The warehouse and general offices had been at 520-532 So. Eutaw Street in Baltimore.

KNIGHT TEMPLARS

Baltimore, Md.

Rulau	Date	Metal	Size	F	VF	EF	Unc
Bal 60	(1890)	Copper/WM	24mm	—	100.	—	Ex. Rare

Triangle encloses cross above skull and crossed bones, MARYLAND below. Within outer beaded circles: KNIGHT TEMPLARS / BALTIMORE. Rv: GOOD FOR / ONE / 12 1/2 ¢ / *** DRINK ***. (Wright 1487; Duffield 74)

The obverse was used on a K.T. medal honoring its Commandery's centennial in 1890. The store card was not authorized and most copies were destroyed.

THE STIEFF CO.
Baltimore, Md.

Type 1: One-story building.
Type 2: Two-story building (as illustration above)

Rulau	Date	Metal	Size	F	VF	EF	Unc
Bal 89	1892	Silver	26.3mm	—	—	45.00	—

Type 1. Description similar to Bal 90 below. (Russ Sears report)

Rulau	Date	Metal	Size	F	VF	EF	Unc
Bal 90	1892	Silver	26.3mm	—	—	35.00	—

Type 2. Building, with sign atop reading: Stieff Silver. Rv: LUCKY PIECE / MADE OF / STIEFF / STERLING SILVER / (space for engraving, in this case with: Miss E. Lyford) / THE STIEFF CO. / SILVERSMITHS / BALTIMORE, MD. / EST. / 1892. Plain edge. (Gerald Johnson coll.)

Rulau	Date	Metal	Size	F	VF	EF	Unc
Bal 90A	1892	Pewter	26.3mm	—	—	20.00	—

Type 2. As Bal 90, but metallic change.

The date 1892 is the founding date for the Stieff Co., not an issue date. These "visitation pieces" were used sparingly over the years for visits to the silverware factory by important persons. Type 1 may have appeared first in the 1890's, but type 2 appeared after the factory built on a second story, circa 1928-29.

All prices given are for *engraved* specimens. Unissued remainders in Unc. would bring 20 percent less.

There are other Stieff visitation souvenirs also.

BUCKEYESTOWN PACKING CO.
Buckeystown, Md.

Rulau	Date	Metal	Size	F	VF	EF	Unc
Bck 1	(?)	Aluminum	25mm	—	—	12.50	—

BUCKEYESTOWN PACKING CO. / 10 ¢ / BUCKEYESTOWN / MD. Rv: SPRAGUE CANNING MACHINERY CO. / -.- / CHICAGO / -.- . Only 3 pieces known. (Thoele coll.)

The city's name is Buckeystown; it is misspelled on the token. Buckeystown Packing Co. was still listed 1918 in Buckeystown, near Frederick in Frederick County in the Catoctin Mountain foothills. Population in 1910 was 300.

SMITH & CO.
Carsins, Md.

Rulau	Date	Metal	Size	VG	F	VF	Unc
Car 1	(?)	Brass	20mm	—	—	11.00	—

SMITH & CO. / -*- / CARSINS. / MD. Rv: Large numeral 3 within rays. (Thoele coll.)

S. H. GIBSON & SON
Crisfield, Md.

Rulau	Date	Metal	Size	F	VF	EF	Unc
Cri 4	(1890's)	Brass	24.4mm	—	6.00	9.00	—

Large G at center, S. H. GIBSON & SON / OYSTER PACKERS / 1 GALL. / CRISFIELD, MD. Rv: Blank. Rarity 8. Plain edge. (Miller Md 184; Duffield 50)

Shucker check given for each gallon of oysters to the Gibson firm's workers as work tally for payment later. Crisfield, in Somerset County, is located on Chesapeake Bay and was built on the oyster industry.

C. C. CO.
(Crisfield Canning Co.)
Crisfield, Md.

Rulau	Date	Metal	Size	VG	F	VF	Unc
Cri 2	(1898)	Brass	23mm	—	—	9.00	—

(All incused): C. C. Co. / 1 BKT. (Burton S-21)

Somerset County cannery checks.

B. F. R. & CO.
(B. F. Richardson & Co.)
Crumpton, Md.

Rulau	Date	Metal	Size	VG	F	VF	Unc
Crm 4	(1899-1900)	Brass	20mm	—	—	25.00	—

(All incused): B. F. R. & CO. / 3. Rv: No description available. Incised, dentilated rim on each side. Plain edge. (Burton K-48)

B. F. Richardson appears in the directories as a canner only in 1900. Crumpton post office is in Queen Anne's County, Md., and the firm used that office, but its cannery was located near Crumpton across the line in Kent County.

G. T. R. & CO.
(G. T. Redden & Co.)
Denton, Md.

Aluminum canning tokens bearing these letters were issued by G. T. Redden & Co. of Denton, Caroline County, which was in business 1889-1934, but issued well after the Gay Nineties period. (Burton C-162)

A. J. FISHELL
Federalsburg, Md.

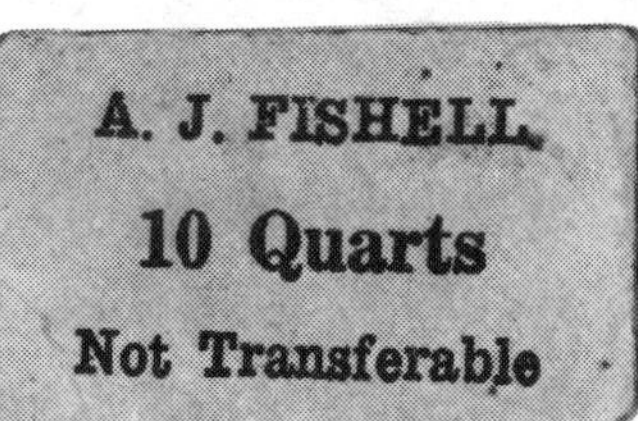

Rulau	Date	Metal	Size	VG	F	VF	EF
Fed 1	(?)	Cardboard	Rect. 42.5x26.5mm	—	12.50	17.50	—

Black print on deep red cardboard. A. J. FISHELL / 1 QUART / NOT TRANSFERABLE. Rv: Blank. (Rulau coll.)

Rulau	Date	Metal	Size	VG	F	VF	EF
Fed 2	(?)	Cardboard	Rect. 42.5x26.5mm	—	12.50	17.50	—

Black print on pink cardboard. As 1, but 2 QUARTS.

Rulau	Date	Metal	Size	VG	F	VF	EF
Fed 3	(?)	Cardboard	Rect. 42.5x26.5mm	—	—	20.00	—

Black print on green cardboard. As 1, but 5 QUARTS.

Rulau	Date	Metal	Size	VG	F	VF	EF
Fed 4	(?)	Cardboard	Rect. 42.5x26.5mm	—	12.50	17.50	—

Black print on buff cardboard. As 1, but 10 QUARTS. (Rulau coll.)

Rulau	Date	Metal	Size	VG	F	VF	EF
Fed 5	(?)	Cardboard	Rect. 42.5x26.5mm	—	—	25.00	—

Black print on gray cardboard. As 1, but 25 QUARTS.

Rulau	Date	Metal	Size	VG	F	VF	EF
Fed 6	(?)	Cardboard	Rect. 42.5x26.5mm	—	—	35.00	—

Black print on violet cardboard. As 1, but 50 QUARTS. (Rulau coll.)

Federalsburg, on Hope Creek in Caroline County, is near the Delaware border. These are strawberry picker chits. The cardboard used is thick and heavy, and colored through.

Shortly before her death, the great seeker after Maryland picker checks, Ora Pumphrey Smith, located a small hoard of the Fishell chits in average Fine to Very Fine condition. A few were in tattered condition, none were perfect (new). In her last letter to the author, she sent along all she had not given to the Anne Arundel County Historical Society, with her price, which we happily paid to secure the hoard for posterity. There were 10 complete sets, and since 1987 only a single set has been disposed of, to a fellow collector.

It has been reported these were used 1878-79, but this has not been verified.

P. L. HARGETT & CO.

Frederick, Md.

Rulau	Date	Metal	Size	F	VF	EF	Unc
Fdk 7	1893	Aluminum	38mm	—	—	80.00	—
	Three Columbian Exposition buildings, in pale. Rv: 1892 / FREDERICK CO. COLUMBIAN CHARITY SALE / HELD UNDER / THE AUSPICES OF / P. L. HARGETT & CO. / -ON THE- / FREDERICK / FAIR GROUNDS / OCT. 12. 1893. Plain edge. (Kirtley March 1993 sale, lot 1287)						

Frederick was, and is, the county seat of Frederick County, Maryland. This completely unpublished Columbian Exposition store card was issued by P.L. Hargett & Co. Inc., dealers in hardware, agricultural implements, seeds, etc. Hargett was still in business 1918.

U. W. B.
(Ulysses W. Brooks)

Glen Burnie, Md.

Rulau	Date	Metal	Size	VG	F	VF	Unc
Glb 3	(1880-1900)	Brass	24.4mm	—	—	3.00	—
	(All incuse) U. W. B. / 1. Rv: Blank.						
Glb 4	(1880-1900)	Brass	24.4mm	—	—	3.00	—
	U. W. B. / 5. Rv: Blank.						
Glb 6	(1880-1900)	Brass	23.3mm	—	—	4.00	—
	U W B / 1 P. Rv: Blank.						

Brooks, the son of Henry and Rebecca Jennings Brooks of Cedar Hill, Md., married Fannie Oliver of Severn, Md. on Dec. 5, 1877. They settled at Furnace Branch, then a forested area one mile from Glen Burnie.

In 1879 Brooks planted tomatoes, green beans, potatoes, corn, cantaloupes and strawberries. With his son Urias Brooks he farmed for some 65 years in Anne Arundel County.

J. M. KELLEY

Harmans, Md.

Rulau	Date	Metal	Size	VG	F	VF	Unc
Har 10	(?)	Brass	25mm	—	—	9.00	—
	J. M. / KELLEY / -.- . Rv: GOOD FOR / 5 (large) ¢ / IN TRADE. Plain edge. (Zaffern coll.)						

This business had disappeared from Harmans, a small (pop. 200) village in Anne Arundel County, before World War I.

B.T.R.
(Benjamin T. Ray)

Rulau	Date	Metal	Size	VG	F	VF	Unc
Har 36	(1890's)	Brass	23mm	—	—	3.00	—
	B.T.R. / 1 incused on blank flan, with recessed dentilated rim. Rv: Blank, but recessed rim. Plain edge.						
Har 37	(1890's)	Brass	23mm	—	—	3.00	—
	As last, but 2.						
Har 38	(1890's)	Brass	23mm	—	—	4.00	—
	As last, but 4.						
Har 38B	(1890's)	Brass	23mm	—	—	4.00	—
	As last, but 8.						
Har 38D	(1890's)	Brass	23mm	—	—	3.00	—
	As last, but 10. (Varieties with small or large numerals)						
Har 38G	(1890's)	Brass	Oct 26mm	—	—	5.00	—
	As last, but 50.						

Benjamin T. Ray, born Dec. 11, 1846, farmed near Harmans, using picker checks starting about 1880. The style of the check series above appears to be from the Nineties. He died Aug. 3, 1921.

E. S.
(W. Elbridge Shipley)

Rulau	Date	Metal	Size	VG	F	VF	Unc
Har 40	(1890-1900)	Brass	21mm	—	—	3.00	—
	E. S. / 1 incused on blank flan, with recessed beaded rim. Rv: Blank, but with recessed beaded rim. Plain edge.						
Har 41	(1890-1900)	Brass	21mm	—	—	3.00	—
	As last, but 5.						
Har 42	(1890-1900)	Brass	21mm	—	—	3.00	—
	As last, but 10.						
Har 43	(1890-1900)	Brass	21mm	—	—	3.00	—
	As last, but 20.						
Har 44	(1890-1900)	Brass	29mm	—	—	3.00	—
	As last, but 50.						
Har 45	(1890-1900)	Brass	29mm	—	—	3.00	—
	As last, but 1.00.						

(William) Elbridge Shipley was born in 1870 and died in 1930. He farmed at Harmans, Anne Arundel County, from about 1888 on.

The series of picker checks in brass, above, are of the type produced by Baltimore check makers 1874-1885.

Shipley issued brass checks 1900-1924 and aluminum checks 1924-1930 which are beyond the scope of this reference.

T. M. C.
(Thomas M. Cole)

Harmans, Md.

Rulau	Date	Metal	Size	VG	F	VF	Unc
Har 8	(1889-1908)	Brass	23mm	—	3.00	—	—
	T. M. C. / 1 incused on blank flan, which has a recessed dentilated circle inside the rim. Rv: Blank, with same recessed circle. Plain edge.						
Har 9	(1889-1908)	Brass	23mm	—	3.00	—	—
	As last, but 2.						
Har 10	(1889-1908)	Brass	23.5mm	—	3.00	—	—
	As last, but 50.						
Har 11	(1889-1908)	Brass	23.5mm	—	3.00	—	—
	As last, but 100.						

Thomas M. Cole farmed at Harmans, Md. 1889-1908 and issued these picker checks. Samuel Vinton Clark purchased the farm and continued use of the same checks 1908-1918. Later, Gilbert H. Clark & Bros. farmed here 1918-1945, continuing use of the checks still using the T.M.C. initials. The next three sets of picker checks to be listed follow those above, but their dates of use have not been determined.

Rulau	Date	Metal	Size	VG	F	VF	Unc
Har 13	(?)	Brass	21mm	—	3.00	—	—
	Similar to last, but thinner flan. 1. Plain edge.						
Har 14	(?)	Brass	21mm	—	3.00	—	—
	As last, but 2.						
Har 15	(?)	Brass	21mm	—	3.00	—	—
	As last, but 5.						
Har 16	(?)	Brass	21mm	—	3.00	—	—
	As last, but 10. (The numeral 10 is much smaller than the digits 1, 2 and 5 above).						
Har 18	(?)	Brass	25mm	—	3.00	—	—
	T.M.C. / 1/2 / S. P. incused on blank flan, which has recessed circle inside the rim. Rv: Blank. Plain edge. (S. P. may mean something like Small Peas; Strawberries Picked)						
Har 19	(?)	Brass	25mm	—	3.00	—	—
	As last, but 1.						
Har 20	(?)	Brass	25mm	—	3.00	—	—
	As last but 2.						
Har 21	(?)	Brass	25mm	—	3.00	—	—
	As last, but 5.						
Har 22	(?)	Brass	25mm	—	3.00	—	—
	As last, but 10.						
Har 24	(?)	Brass	21mm	—	3.00	—	—
	T.M.C. / 1/2 / P incused on blank flan, which has a circle inside the rim. Rv: Blank, circle inside rim. Plain edge. (P may indicate Peas).						
Har 25	(?)	Brass	21mm	—	3.00	—	—
	As last, but 1 P.						
Har 26	(?)	Brass	21mm	—	3.00	—	—
	As last, but 5 P.						
Har 27	(?)	Brass	21mm	—	3.00	—	—
	As last, but 10 P.						
Har 28	(?)	Brass	24mm	—	3.00	—	—
	As last, but 50 P.						
Har 29	(?)	Brass	24mm	—	3.00	—	—
	As last, but 100 / P.						

J. B. A. & CO.
(Joseph B. Andrews & Co.)

Hurlock, Md.

Rulau	Date	Metal	Size	VG	F	VF	Unc
Hur 1	(1891-1921)	Brass	21mm	—	—	6.00	—
	(All incused); J. B. A. & CO. (Burton D-6)						

Cannery checks, incused on plain brass disks. Dorchester County. This became American Stores Co. in 1921.

C. B. P.
(Charles B. Pumphrey)
Marley, Md.

Rulau	Date	Metal	Size	F	VF	EF	Unc
Mar 10	(?)	Brass	Scalloped, 30mm	—	5.00	—	—

C. B. P. / 10 incused on a blank flan, which has a recessed beaded rim. Rv: Blank, recessed beaded rim. Plain edge.

Probably issued before 1900.

B. & O. R. R. CO.
Pasadena, Md.

Rulau	Date	Metal	Size	VG	F	VF	Unc
Pas 1	(1890's ?)	Brass	24.3mm	—	—	15.00	—

B. & O. / R. R. CO. Rv: SA. (relief) / No. (relief) 9 (incuse) / 5 (incuse). Plain edge. Issued holed. (Zaffern coll.)

B. & O. R.R. CO. = Baltimore & Ohio Railroad Company. A railway tag or tool check.

Attribution to Pasadena is tentative, though it was found there. Pasadena station in Anne Arundel County was on the Annapolis Short Line railway. Another B&O feeder, the Washington, Baltimore, An. El. railway passed south from Baltimore a few miles west of there, so this tag may more properly be assigned to another site such as Wellham Station, Severn Run or Naval Academy Junction.

Principal B&O lines themselves ran west from Baltimore and also northwest from Washington, D.C. to the Cumberland Gap and on to Ohio.

J. R. P.
(J. Richard Phillips)
Preston, Md.

Rulau	Date	Metal	Size	VG	F	VF	Unc
Prs 7	(1900)	Brass	20mm	—	—	—	—

(All incused): J. R. P / 3. Rv: Blank. (Burton C-154)

Dr. J. Richard Phillips, a physician, apparently functioned as a canner only in 1900, but his daughter Mary, and son, J. R. Phillips Jr., continued in businesses, which eventually (1930) were merged into the giant Phillips Packing Co. which made both C and K rations for troops during World War II.

A. P. CO.
(Alliance Preserving Co.)
Ridgely, Md.

Rulau	Date	Metal	Size	VG	F	VF	Unc
Rid 1	(1890-99)	Brass	Oct 25mm	—	—	—	—

A. P. CO. incused on brass planchet, incised beaded rim (large beads) on each side. Rv: Blank. Plain edge. (Varieties are reported: A. P. CO. curved, small letters; A. P. CO. curved, large letters; A. P. CO. straight, large letters). (Burton C-1)

Rulau	Date	Metal	Size	VG	F	VF	Unc
Rid 2	(1890-99)	Brass	Oct 25mm	—	—	—	—

A. P. CO. straight, incused on brass planchet with small beads beaded rim incised on each side. Plain edge. (Burton C-1)

Rulau	Date	Metal	Size	VG	F	VF	Unc
Rid 3	(1890-99)	Brass	Oct 22mm	—	—	—	—

A. P. CO. / 1/2. Rv: Blank. Plain edge. Smooth flan. (Burton C-1)

An octagonal 18mm check similar to last is also reported, which bears no fraction.

Alliance Preserving Company were fruit and vegetable canners in business in Ridgely (Caroline County), 1890-1914. Their tokens, used to reimburse worker output, were stamped on stock flans supplied by Baltimore makers.

D. B. CO.
(Day Brothers Co.)
Ridgely, Md.

Rulau	Date	Metal	Size	VG	F	VF	Unc
Rid 9	(1893-99)	Aluminum	21mm	—	—	—	—

-*- / D. B. CO. / -*-. Rv: No description available. Plain edge. (Burton C-37)

Day Brothers were the pioneer canners in Ridgely, in Caroline County on the eastern shore of Chesapeake Bay in Maryland. Starting in 1888, they prospered until 1909. In 1910 the firm was succeeded by T. L. Day, Swing Co.

C. L. S.
(Charles L. Solley)
Solley, Md.

Rulau	Date	Metal	Size	VG	F	VF	Unc
Sol 4	(?)	Brass	Scal 23mm	—	—	5.00	—

C. L. S. / 20 incused on blank flan with recessed beaded rim. Rv: Blank, but with recessed rim.

Charles L. Solley was born 1860 and died 1921. He farmed at Solley in Anne Arundel County.

A great deal can be learned about the picker checks used by farmers to pay their hired help (mostly from Baltimore), and about the prices then prevailing for Maryland crops, from the 1910 diary of farmer Basil Hamilton Smith (1884-1960). Several pertinent entries are quoted below:

January. Repaired picker shanty.

February. Hauled stone to the shanty for pickers' ovens.

May 16. Hauled pickers out of Baltimore by mule-drawn wagons. Bought 1,060 picker checks for $5.50.

May 24. Picked 48 crates of strawberries. Sold for 5-1/2 cents a quart. Paid pickers 1-1/2 cents a quart.

May 25. Picked 40 crates of berries. Sold for 4 cents a quart. Bought 100 new quart boxes for 60 cents.

May 28. Took pickers to Baltimore to buy the things they need.

June. Peas brought 75 cents a bushel. Beans sold for 60 cents a bushel.

June 30. Took four wagon loads of pickers home.

We are indebted to the Anne Arundel County Historical Society, Severna Park, Md., and to two of its activist members, Ora Pumphrey Smith and Mrs. Chipman W. Cunningham. Mrs. Smith placed a great deal of data about the AAC picker checks in her monograph, *Anne Arundel County Farmers' Picker Checks*, and Mrs. Cunningham authored the narrative booklet *The Pickers of Anne Arundel County*.

MASSACHUSETTS

ROBERT T. ALMY & CO.
Boston, Mass.

Rulau	Date	Metal	Size	VG	F	VF	Unc
Bos 1	1893	Silver	31mm	—	—	25.00	45.00

Santa Maria under sail, ROBERT T. ALMY & CO. / 1492 above. 1893 / BOSTON below. Rv: Man seated atop bell in foreground, port city in background. WORLD'S FAIR CHICAGO / 1492 above, 1893 below. Plain edge. Rare. (Tanenbaum coll.)

Rulau	Date	Metal	Size	VG	F	VF	Unc
Bos 1A	1893	WM	31mm	—	—	10.00	20.00

As last. (Storer 92)

M. F. ARMSTRONG & CO.

Rulau	Date	Metal	Size	VG	F	VF	Unc
Bos 3	(1899)	Aluminum	30.5mm	—	—	125.	—

Dewey facing three-quarters right, OUR COUNTRY'S PRIDE above, **** ADMIRAL DEWEY **** below. Rv: OYAMA WHISKEY / BEST / OF ALL / M. F. ARMSTRONG / & CO. 104 CANAL ST. / BOSTON. Plain edge.

O. BROGI

Rulau	Date	Metal	Size	F	VF	EF	Unc
Bos 6	(1888-1905)	Nickel	31mm	—	—	20.00	—

LA (large star) D'ITALIA / (ornament) / O. BROGI, / (ornament) / BOSTON. Rv: Blank. Plain edge. (Storer 233)

Rulau	Date	Metal	Size	F	VF	EF	Unc
Bos 6A	(1889-1905)	Brass	31mm	—	—	15.00	—

As last.

Ottario Brogi ran the Hotel La Stella d'Italia (The Star of Italy Hotel).

C. E.
(Christian Endeavor)
Boston, Mass.

Rulau	Date	Metal	Size	F	VF	EF	Unc
Bos 7	1895	Aluminum	38mm	—	10.00	—	—

Old South Church spire, OLD SOUTH below, FOR CHRIST AND THE CHURCH. Above: BOSTON. Y. P. S. C. E. JULY, 1895. Rv: Three females. Around: FAITH HOPE CHARITY * 14TH * ANNUAL CONVENTION / PURITY. Plain edge. (Storer 290)

Rulau	Date	Metal	Size	F	VF	EF	Unc
Bos A7	1895	Brass	24mm	—	10.00	—	—

CE monogram at center, MISSOURI FOR CHRIST / * around. Rv: Within wreath: INTERNATIONAL 14TH / CONVENTION / BOSTON / JULY 10-15 / 1895. Plain edge. (Storer 292)

C. MILTON CHASE

Rulau	Date	Metal	Size	F	VF	EF	Unc
Bos 8	(1895)	WM	39mm	—	35.00	60.00	100.

A magician stands, facing, a small table at the left. Around: PRO ARTE MAGICA / NE CEDE MALIS. Rv: Eagle, wings folded (resembling eagle on U.S. Morgan silver dollar). Around: C. MILTON CHASE MECHANICIAN / BOSTON. (Storer 285)

Rulau	Date	Metal	Size	F	VF	EF	Unc
Bos 9	(1895)	WM	39mm	—	25.00	40.00	—

Obverse as last. Rv: As last, but a ring of circles replaces the eagle's breast. (Storer 286)

Mechanician = Magician. Struck by J. H. Diehl of Philadelphia in 1895, according to Dr. Malcolm Storer in *Numismatics of Massachusetts*.

This is a magic token used by Charles Milton Chase in tricks requiring a silver-dollar-sized coin. The authorities objected to the design, Storer says, and it is believed the second (much scarcer) type above was to respond to the objection that the piece looked too much like a real dollar.

COLUMBIAN BICYCLES

Rulau	Date	Metal	Size	VG	F	VF	Unc
Bos 10	(?)	Nickel	**	—	—	25.00	—

** Buckle-shaped, 26.5mm.
COLUMBIAN BICYCLES / YOU SEE THEM EVERYWHERE. Rv: Blank. Plain edge. (Wright 183; Rulau Mav 18)

Columbian Bicycles were made by Pope Mfg. Co. of Boston, according to advertisments of the 1881-1885 period.

THE CONTINENTAL CLOTHING HOUSE

Rulau	Date	Metal	Size	F	VF	EF	Unc
Bos 11	(1890's)	Aluminum	38mm	—	25.00	—	50.00

Continental Army soldier, THE CONTINENTAL CLOTHING HOUSE. Rv: BOSTON'S GREATEST / THE / CONTINENTAL / CLOTHING HOUSE. Plain edge. (Wright 1663) Thick & thin planchets. (Storer 303)

Rulau	Date	Metal	Size	F	VF	EF	Unc
Bos 12	1893	S/Brass	31mm	—	25.00	—	50.00

Columbus on deck, WORLD'S FAIR CHICAGO / 1492 above, 1893 below. Rv: CONTINENTAL CLOTHING HOUSE / (blank center) / BOSTON. Plain edge. Rare. (Tanenbaum coll.; Storer 304)

Rulau	Date	Metal	Size	VG	F	VF	Unc
Bos 12A	1893	Aluminum	38mm	—	—	30.00	55.00

Columbus aboard ship. Around: WORLD'S FAIR CHICAGO / 1492 / 1893. Rv: CONTINENTAL CLOTHING HOUSE / BOSTON. Plain edge. (Kirtley report; Tanenbaum coll.; Storer 304)

This firm has disappeared by World War I.

CROSBY'S RESTAURANT

Rulau	Date	Metal	Size	F	VF	EF	Unc
Bos 14	1900	Brass	32mm	—	15.00	—	—

Ornate crested shield of arms at center, CROSBY'S RESTAURANT, above. 19 SCHOOL STREET, BOSTON, below. Rv: EXPANSION / SOUVENIR / ROOM "D" / OUR LATEST / ADDITION / JULY 1900. Tiny W & H CO NEWARK, N J along lower rim. Plain edge.

Struck by Whitehead & Hoag Co., Newark, N.J.

Rulau	Date	Metal	Size	VG	F	VF	Unc
Bos 15	1904	Gilt/Bs	33mm	—	—	15.00	—

Rampant lion on gold field, in shield of arms, supported by trellis-work and with crossed swords as crest. Around: CROSBY'S RESTAURANT / 19 SCHOOL STREET. BOSTON. Rv: YEARS IN BUSINESS / 5 (large) / DECEMBER 1904. Plain edge.

Crosby's Restaurant was founded in 1899. Bos 15 probably was struck by Whitehead & Hoag Co. It was not thought logical to separate Bos 14 and 15 into this Gay Nineties section and whatever successor token catalog emerges, to cover the years 1901-1913.

The restaurant was owned by Freeman M. Crosby & Co.

CUTTING & BOWDOIN

Rulau	Date	Metal	Size	VG	F	VF	Unc
Bos 19	(1890)	Lead	**	—	—	75.00	—

** Oval 36 by 25mm.
CUTTING & BOWDOIN. / ARTIST / 49 TREMONT ST. / BOSTON in four lines. Beaded rim. Rv: Blank. Thin flan. Plain edge.

Die-struck trial piece? Not in Storer, Adams or Wright. Reported by the Fulds ("Token Collector's Pages," page 22.)

FRANKLIN SAVINGS BANK

Rulau	Date	Metal	Size	VG	F	VF	Unc
Bos 28	(1890's ?)	Aluminum	33.3mm	—	—	25.00	40.00

Franklin bust in fur cap left, BENJAMIN FRANKLIN around, 1706 1790 at sides. Bust is in very high relief. Rv: FRANKLIN / SAVINGS BANK / 6 PARK SQUARE / BOSTON / INCORPORATED / 1861. Plain edge. Thick flan (3.2mm at edge; 4.3mm at highest point of relief). (Storer 389; Medallic Memorials to Franklin FR.T.FR.1)

This extremely beautiful store card may have been issued on the 100th anniversary of the death of Franklin in 1890, or on the Franklin Savings Bank's 30th or 35th anniversaries in 1891 or 1896.

GOODYEAR WELT

Rulau	Date	Metal	Size	VG	F	VF	Unc
Bos 30	1895	Aluminum	38mm	—	15.00	25.00	—

Lady's high shoe right. In double circle around: 100TH ANNIVERSARY MECHANICS FAIR BOSTON / EASIEST GOODYEAR BEST / WELT / * 1795-1895 *. Rv: Standard GOODYEAR WELT globe reverse. Plain edge. (Gene Johnson coll.)

W. T. HASKELL & CO.

Rulau	Date	Metal	Size	VG	F	VF	Unc
Bos 33	(?)	Lead	**	—	—	75.00	—

** Oval 41 by 19mm.
W. T. HASKELL & CO. / 90 MILK ST. / BOSTON. in three lines. Rv: Blank. Plain edge.

Die-struck trial piece? Not in Storer, Adams or Wright. Reported by the Fulds ("Token Collector's Pages," pages 24-25.)

LAWSON VARNISH CO.

Boston, Mass & Chicago, Ill.

Rulau	Date	Metal	Size	F	VF	EF	Unc
Bos 40	1893	Gilt/Lead	70mm	—	—	75.00	—

Monogram LVC on shield. Around: THE LAWSON VARNISH CO. / MANUFACTURERS / -OF- / VARNISHES / & JAPANS / 392 WABASH AVE. CHICAGO, ILL. / 168 PURCHASE ST. BOSTON, MASS. Rv: Building. Around: WORLD'S COLUMBIAN EXPOSITION / CHICAGO / 1893 / ADMINISTRATION BUILDING. Plain edge. (Wright 1118; Eglit 569)

Under this name, Lawson Varnish Co. disappears from directories by 1918.

MACULLAR PARKER COMPANY

Rulau	Date	Metal	Size	F	VF	EF	Unc
Bos 50	1892	Aluminum	35mm	—	12.50	—	—

Eagle displayed, head right; ESTABLISHED / 1849 above, MACULLAR PARKER COMPANY / 400 WASHINGTON STREET / BOSTON / 1892 below. Rv: Building, STATE HOUSE / BOSTON below. Plain edge. (Storer 531)

These were clothiers.

OLD NORTH CHURCH

Rulau	Date	Metal	Size	F	VF	EF	Unc
Bos 70	(1885)	Pewter	30mm	—	20.00	30.00	—

Church, OLD NORTH CHURCH / * BOSTON * / ERECTED A.D. 1723. Rv: SOUVENIR MADE FROM THE / PIPES / OF THE / OLD / ORGAN. Plain edge. (Dick Grinolds report; Storer 608)

Struck 1885 by Robert Woodman for the Literary Association Fair.

HORACE PARTRIDGE CO.

Rulau	Date	Metal	Size	F	VF	EF	Unc
Bos 80	(?)	Copper	31.5mm	—	—	10.00	—

Partridge facing right, rising sun behind, cartouche below. On cartouche: HORACE / PARTRIDGE / CO. Above: DISCOUNT COIN. Rv: SPORTING / GOODS / No. D 106 / 49 FRANKLIN ST. / BOSTON. Plain edge. Issued holed.

Charge plate token. The numerals '106' are incused and change on every piece. Apparently this charge plate was good only in Partridge's sporting goods department.

Rulau	Date	Metal	Size	F	VF	EF	Unc
Bos 81	(?)	Brass	Round--mm	—	—	10.00	—

Bird, HORACE PARTRIDGE CO., BOSTON. Rv: (Incused) 24 ATHLETIC AND SPORTING GOODS.

Charge card token.

Rulau	Date	Metal	Size	F	VF	EF	Unc
Bos 83	(?)	CN	**	—	—	10.00	—

** Oval 38 by 25mm.
Partridge facing right, rising sun behind, cartouche below. On cartouche: HORACE PARTRIDGE CO. / 49 FRANKLIN ST. / BOSTON. Rv: DISCOUNT AND / NO. / C 183 / CHARGE COIN. Plain edge. Issued holed. (Rulau coll.)

Charge card coin. The numerals '183' are incused.

D. C. PERCIVAL & CO.

Rulau	Date	Metal	Size	VG	F	VF	Unc
Bos 85	(?)	Cupronickel	29mm	—	—	10.00	—

D. C. PERCIVAL & CO. / BOSTON. Rv: PAOLA DIAMONDS / PAT. APLD. FOR. Diamond-shaped center hole. Plain edge. (Wright 1574)

David C. Percival & Co., wholesale jewelers, were still in business in 1918.

L. POLCRI

Rulau	Date	Metal	Size	VG	F	VF	Unc
Bos 90	(?)	Brass	30mm	8.00	12.00	15.00	—

Man's head with handlebar mustache facing, L. POLCRI below, all within inner circle. Around: GOOD FOR 5¢. DRINK / 124 NO. ST. Rv: Blank. Thin planchet. Plain edge. (Storer 652)

Lorenzo Polcri is credited as the issuer of this piece by Malcolm Storer in "Numismatics of Massachusetts."

LEO F. SAUNDERS & CO.

Rulau	Date	Metal	Size	VG	F	VF	Unc
Bos 100	(1893)	Aluminum	37mm	—	—	90.00	—

Five medallions in cross form, each depicting a Columbian Exposition building. Rv: LEO F. SAUNDERS & CO. / RELIABLE / TEAS & COFFEE / 13 CENTRAL SQUARE / * BOSTON, MASS. *. Plain edge.

THOMPSON WILLIS & NEWGENT

Rulau	Date	Metal	Size	VG	F	VF	Unc
Bos 110	1893	S/Brass	31mm	—	—	20.00	50.00

Obverse as reverse of Bos 1 (Almy token). Rv: MANUFACTURED ONLY BY / * / THOMPSON / WILLIS & NEWGENT / BOSTON, MASS. Plain edge. (Tanenbaum coll.)

WASHBURN CREDIT HOUSE

Rulau	Date	Metal	Size	VG	F	VF	Unc
Bos 118	1893	Aluminum	38mm	—	—	—	20.00

Landing of Columbus scene, 1492 above, all within central circle. Around: CLOTHING. JEWELRY. BICYLES / .ON CREDIT. Rv: WASHBURN CREDIT HOUSE / KING OF CREDIT MEN / 1893 / (crown) / GEO. F. WASHBURN / GEN'L MANAGER / 465 WASHINGTON ST. Plain edge. (Tanenbaum coll.; Storer 785)

WHITE BROTHERS & COMPANY

Rulau	Date	Metal	Size	VG	F	VF	Unc
Bos 119	(1890's)	Brass	26mm	—	.50	1.00	2.25

Willow tree at center, WHITE BROTHERS & COMPANY above, WILLOW CALF / . BOSTON U.S.A. below. Rv: Horseshoe at center, surrounded by pseudo-Arabic script used as ornamentation. Plain edge. (Miller Mass 94; Wright 1235; Storer 793 through 802)

Rulau	Date	Metal	Size	VG	F	VF	Unc
Bos 119A	(1890's)	Copper	26mm	—	.50	1.00	2.25

As 119. Plain edge.

Rulau	Date	Metal	Size	VG	F	VF	Unc
Bos 119B	(1890's)	Nickel/C	26mm	—	—	1.25	3.00

As 119. Plain edge.

This is one of the commonest tokens of the 1890's that can still be encountered. It almost always occurs holed, as issued. There are a good many varieties, all detailed in the penetrating work on these pieces by Melvin and George Fuld appearing in *Token Collector's Pages* (Quarterman Publications, Boston, 1972) on pages 97-102, which see for full information.

Rulau	Date	Metal	Size	VG	F	VF	Unc
Bos A119	(1890's)	Aluminum	**	—	—	25.00	35.00

** Shape of an insole, 13 by 44mm.

A cube. White BROS. CO - BOSTON U.S.A. / ALUMINA / TANNED I WEAR 'BOX CALF' SHOES/ ALUMINA TANNED. Rv: A scroll. RETURN TO - AND GET REWARD. Plain edge. (Wright 1234)

Rulau	Date	Metal	Size	VG	F	VF	Unc
Bos B119	(1890's)	Aluminum	***	—	—	15.00	25.00

*** Shape of an insole, 15 by 35mm.

On the round heel: WHITE BROS. & CO. BOSTON U.S.A. / ALUMINA / TANNED / BOX / CALF/ TRADE MARK. The sole is covered with wavy, irregular lines. Rv: WEAR ALUMINA TANNED / BOX CALF SHOES on a scroll. Plain edge. (Ex-Max Schwartz, Thomas O. Mabbott collections)

White Brothers & Company were manufacturers of shoes which were sold across the United Sates. Each token of type Bos 119 was apparently attached to a tag which in turn was attached to each pair of new shoes. Several of the original tags have survived, and these identify White Brothers & Co. as specialists in colored leathers which "will not crack" and are "free from arsenic."

The Fulds identified 9 obverse dies and 8 reverse dies used in striking these pieces.

Little is known about the aluminum insole-shaped pieces, which also occur holed, except that they must have been issued in the 1892-1899 period. The round brass and copper pieces could have been issued as early as the 1880's.

WOODBURY'S CAFE

Boston, Mass.

Rulau	Date	Metal	Size	F	VF	EF	Unc
Bos 120	(?)	Cupronickel	24mm	—	3.00	—	6.00

WOODBURY'S / CAFE / LUNCH & WINE ROOM/ 250 WASHINGTON ST. / 75-77 DEVONSHIRE ST. / BOSTON. Rv: Hand giving key (of the city) to another hand. WELCOME TO OUR CITY above, TRADE / MARK / WOODBURY below. Flan is centrally holed. Plain edge. (Storer 807-809)

This card was issued about 1900 or earlier.

THE KENDALL

Chicopee, Mass.

Rulau	Date	Metal	Size	VG	F	VF	Unc
Chi 3	(?)	Aluminum	24mm	—	—	15.00	—

A flower. Around: THE KENDALL / CHICOPEE, / MASS. Rv: (Star between leaves) / 5 / (star between leaves). Plain edge. (Storer 1019)

COMMONWEALTH OF LYNN SCHOOL

Lynn, Mass.

Rulau	Date	Metal	Size	VG	F	VF	Unc
Lyn 4	1900	Aluminum	--mm	—	—	50.00	—

COMMONWEALTH OF LYNN SCHOOL / 1900. Rv: Numeral 1. Plain edge. (Not in Storer)

5, 10, 25 and 50-cent tokens known.

LYNN CENTR'L. LABOR UNION

Lynn, Mass. ?

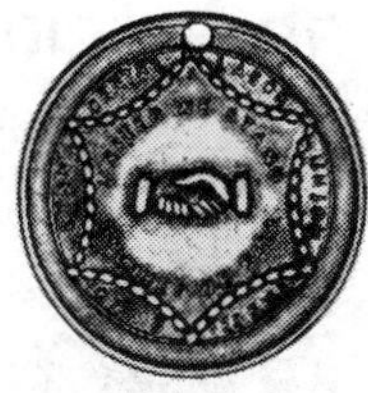

Rulau	Date	Metal	Size	VG	F	VF	Unc
Lyn 10	1890	Brass	24mm	—	—	20.00	—

Clasped hands, UNITED WE STAND / DIVIDED WE FALL within hexagonal frame. Around: LYNN CENTR'L LABOR UNION / ORGD FEB. 5. '88. Rv: LABOR DAY / SEPT. 1, 1890. / SOUVENIR. Plain edge. Issued holed. (Mishler coll.)

Lynn was an early center of labor agitation. Labor Day was initiated in New York in 1882 by the Knights of Labor. The first Monday of September became Labor Day, a holiday, in Colorado in 1887, and Colorado was followed in short order by New York, Massachusetts and New Jersey.

The U.S. Congress made it a federal holiday in 1894. When this medalet was issued in 1890 in Massachusetts, Labor Day was still a new concept for holiday, parade and celebration.

PATOEL

Marlboro, Mass.

Rulau	Date	Metal	Size	VG	F	VF	Unc
Mbo 6	(?)	Aluminum	25mm	—	—	20.00	—

PATOEL / MARLBORO / (star) / DRUGGIST. Rv: GOOD FOR / 5 / ONE SODA. Plain edge. (Storer 1257)

PLYMOUTH CORDAGE COMPANY

Plymouth, Mass.

Rulau	Date	Metal	Size	F	VF	EF	Unc
Ply 20	1899	Brass	25mm	—	—	20.00	—

Three-masted ship within central circle, 1824 above, 1899 below, each in scrollwork. Around: PLYMOUTH CORDAGE COMPANY. Rv: Within rope circle: 1824 / -(symbol)- / 1899. Plain edge. (Storer 1566)

Rulau	Date	Metal	Size	F	VF	EF	Unc
Ply 20A	1899	Aluminum	25mm	—	—	20.00	—

As 20.

Rulau	Date	Metal	Size	F	VF	EF	Unc
Ply 21	1899	Brass	35mm	—	—	25.00	—

As 20, but larger. (Storer 1565)

Rulau	Date	Metal	Size	F	VF	EF	Unc
Ply 21A	1899	Aluminum	35mm	—	—	25.00	—

As 21.

G. M. WHIPPLE (and) A. A. SMITH

Salem, Mass.

Rulau	Date	Metal	Size	VG	F	VF	Unc
Sal 10	(?)	Lead	15mm	—	—	20.00	—

G. M. WHIPPLE / (two diamonds) / A. A. SMITH / (two diamonds) / MANF'S / SALEM, MASS. Rv: SQUAILS at center, ornaments around. Plain edge. 10mm thick! (Storer 1609)

Obviously not a trade token, this is perhaps some sort of counter or jewelry control piece. Possibly issued in 1890's.

MASONIC BUILDING

Springfield, Mass.

Rulau	Date	Metal	Size	F	VF	EF	Unc
Spg 13	1892	—	28mm	—	—	27.50	35.00

Building. Around: DEDICATED OCT. 24 1892. Rv: MASONIC BUILDING / SPRINGFIELD / * / MASS. / -.- / CORNER STONE / LAID / OCT 21. 1892. Plain edge. (Sol Taylor report)

MONARCH ACCIDENT INSURANCE CO.

Springfield, Mass.

Rulau	Date	Metal	Size	F	VF	EF	Unc
Spg 15	(?)	GS	Scal 27mm	—	3.00	—	—

MAICO monogram within circle. Rv: TELEGRAPH THIS NO. / (incused numeral, e.g, 286532 / TO / MONARCH ACCIDENT / INSURANCE CO / SPRINGFIELD, MASS. / (tiny) GRAMMES. Plain edge. Issued holed for suspension as a fob.

Struck by L. P. Grammes & Sons, Allentown, PA. Probably 1920's.

HIGHLAND CLUB

West Roxbury, Mass.

Rulau	Date	Metal	Size	F	VF	EF	Unc
Wrx 3	(1890's)	WM	36mm	—	10.00	—	—

Monogram HC at center. Around: HIGHLAND CLUB / OF / WEST ROXBURY. Rv: Blank. Plain edge. (Storer 1760)

This club was organized in 1888. Its arms were a red stag's head rising from a tower of crossed spears.

WOLLASTON GOLF CLUB

Wollaston, Mass.

Rulau	Date	Metal	Size	VG	F	VF	Unc
Wol 5	1897	Bronze	--mm	—	—	10.00	—

Indian head left. Around: WOLLASTON . GOLF . CLUB / 1897. Rv: Blank. Plain edge. (Storer 1786)

Membership medalet.

A. S. & W. CO.
(American Steel & Wire Co.)

Worcester, Mass.

Rulau	Date	Metal	Size	VG	F	VF	Unc
Wrc 1	(?)	Brass	38mm	—	—	3.50	—

(All incused): NORTH WORKS / A. S. & W. CO. A number is punched into the field. Rv: Blank. Plain edge. (Storer 1787)

A tool check.

A. BENOIT

Rulau	Date	Metal	Size	VG	F	VF	Unc
Wrc 2	(1898)	Brass	25mm	—	—	20.00	—

Billiard table at center, THE BRUNSWICK BALKE / COLLENDER / COMPY, above. CHECK below. Rv: * GOOD FOR * / 10 C / A BENOIT / IN / TRADE. Plain edge. (Hank Thoele coll.)

Archibald Benoit's pool hall is listed in the 1898 directory.

ORDER OF AMERICAN MECHANICS

Rulau	Date	Metal	Size	F	VF	EF	Unc
Wrc 12	1892	WM	35mm	—	—	15.00	—

Indians throwing boxes off ship, all within circle. Around: BOSTON TEA PARTY.- DEC. 16. 1773. Rv: Calipers, T-square and arm with hammer, small HIS below, with EXPOSITION, WORCESTER, MASS. around. Around all: ORDER OF AMERICAN MECHANICS. * MAR. 21-26, 1892. Plain edge. (Ganter coll.)

ST. ONCE SHOE STORE

Rulau	Date	Metal	Size	F	VF	EF	Unc
Wrc 20	(?)	Aluminum	24mm	—	15.00	—	—

AT / ST. ONCE / SHOE STORE/ 86 / FRONT ST. Rv: GOOD FOR / 5 C / * IN TRADE *. Plain edge. (Storer 1813)

O. P. SHATTUCK & SON

Worcester, Mass.

Rulau	Date	Metal	Size	F	VF	EF	Unc
Wrc 25	(?)	Aluminum	28mm	—	—	25.00	—

GOOD FOR ONE / WE THREE / 5 C / CIGAR / O. P. SHATTUCK & SON. Rv: DAVIS & BURTON STAMP CO / WORCESTER MASS. Plain edge. (Storer 1814)

Made by Davis & Burton of Worcester, Mass.

MICHIGAN

J. P. SEELY

Armada, Mich.

Rulau	Date	Metal	Size	VG	F	VF	Unc
Arm 1	(1895-99)	Brass	24.5mm	—	—	35.00	—

Goblet, ladle and icetong die of Chas. Pick & Co. Rv: GOOD FOR / 5 C / J. P. SEELY, / IN / * TRADE *. (Thoele coll.)

Billiard hall listed in the 1895, 1897 and 1899 directories.

BERRY BROTHERS

Detroit, Mich.

Rulau	Date	Metal	Size	VG	F	VF	Unc
Det 5	(1890-1902)	Svd/B	33mm	—	—	20.00	—

Shield of arms supported by moose and deer, a U.S. eagle displayed in the crest. On folds of ribbon below: BERRY / VARNISHES / BROTHERS. Below all: TRADE MARK. Rv: In 13 lines: BERRY BROTHERS/ LIMITED / VARNISH MANUFACTURERS / NEW YORK / BOSTON / PHILADELPHIA CHICAGO / BALTIMORE CINCINNATI / ST. LOUIS SAN FRANCISCO / FACTORY & MAIN OFFICE / DETROIT. / CANADIAN / FACTORY / WALKERVILLE, ONT. Reeded edge. (Gary Pipher coll.)

These varnish manufacturers appear in the 1890-1902 directories. The store card is quite attractive.

THE CAILLE CO.

Rulau	Date	Metal	Size	VG	F	VF	Unc
Det 10	(?)	Cupronickel	25mm	—	—	7.00	—

Device resembling a huge H with small O's attached to each end of the H's crossbar. 2 / BITS within the uprights. Rv: GOOD FOR / 25 ¢ / IN TRADE. Plain edge.

General purpose trade token of the Caille Co., Detroit makers. The device is a bridle with two bits for horses.

DETROIT HEATING & LIGHTING CO.

Rulau	Date	Metal	Size	VG	F	VF	Unc
Det 15	1892	Aluminum	**	—	10.00	15.00	—

** Rect. 34 by 32mm. Heater.

1892 ALUMINUM COPYRIGHT. Rv: THE CELEBRATED / DETROIT - BOLTON / HOT WATER / HEATER / DETROIT HEATING / AND LIGHTING CO. / DETROIT, MICH., / NEW YORK / CHICAGO / BOSTON / ST. LOUIS / — 3 — / SOLE MANUFACTURERS. Plain edge. Rounded corners. (Wright 245)

C. D. ERICHSEN

Rulau	Date	Metal	Size	VG	F	VF	Unc
Det 18	(?)	Brass	24mm	—	—	10.00	—

Wine bottle and glass within a circle of stars. Rv: C. D. ERICHSEN / 10 / * DETROIT, MICH. * Plain edge. (Wright 294)

Rulau	Date	Metal	Size	VG	F	VF	Unc
Det 19	(?)	S/Brass	24mm	—	—	10.00	—

As last. Plain edge. (Spangenberger Oct. 20, 1984 sale, lot 41)

GILLMANN BROS.

Rulau	Date	Metal	Size	VG	F	VF	Unc
Det 21	(1889-92)	Brass	25mm	—	—	20.00	—

GOOD FOR / 5 ¢ / GILLMAN / BROS. / IN / TRADE. Rv: CHARLES PASSOW & SONS / MANFR's / -OF- / SALOON / FIXTURES / -&- / POOL TABLES / CHICAGO. (Thoele coll.)

Gillmann Brothers saloon is listed 1889-1892.

Gillmann Brothers moved to Sioux Falls, S.D. in the 1890's, and the token could also have been used there. Then in 1906 he moved his saloon to Henry, S. D.

A. W. HANMER

Rulau	Date	Metal	Size	VG	F	VF	Unc
Det 23	1897	Aluminum	25mm	—	—	11.00	—

A. W. HANMER'S / METHOD / OF / SOLICITING TRADE / FOR / BUSINESS FIRMS. Rv: COPYRIGHTED / 10 CTS / 1897. Plain edge. R8. (Vacketta Chi HB12)

Research shows this firm was based in Detroit, not in Chicago, as Ore Vacketta believed.

Rulau	Date	Metal	Size	VG	F	VF	Unc
Det 25	1897	Aluminum	25mm	—	—	7.50	12.50

A. W. HANMER'S / — / METHOD / . . OF . . / SOLICITING TRADE / . . FOR . . / BUSINESS FIRMS. Rv: COPYRIGHTED / — / 15 cts. / — / 1897. Plain edge. (Rulau Chi 76)

SILVER ENCAMPMENT
(Grand Army of the Republic)

Rulau	Date	Metal	Size	F	VF	EF	Unc
Det 50	1891	WM	38mm	—	12.50	15.00	30.00

Two draped females standing. One at left in tears looking back at burning building, that at right pointing back toward church. SILVER ENCAMPMENT / 1866 1891 above, * DETROIT AUG. 3RD TO 8TH 1891 *. Rv: FORT at top under bombardment, Grant and Lee under tree below. SUMTER APRIL 14, 1861. / APPOMATTOX APRIL 9, 1865. around. Plain edge. (Rulau coll.)

STEWARDS
Detroit, Mich. ?

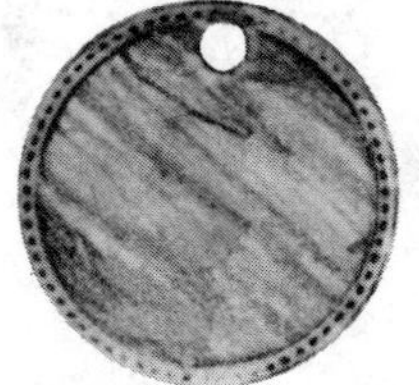

Rulau	Date	Metal	Size	F	VF	EF	Unc
Det 55	(?)	Brass	28mm	—	—	5.00	—

(All incused): STEWARD'S / 5 ¢ / 38 WOODWARD AVE. Rv: Blank. Incised, beaded rim on each side. Plain edge. (Larry Laevens coll.)

J. N. DIXON
Gladstone, Mich.

Rulau	Date	Metal	Size	VG	F	VF	Unc
Gld 2	(1900-01)	Brass	25mm	—	35.00	—	—

Brunswick die BBC-11/ Rv: GOOD FOR / 5 ¢ / IN TRADE / J. N. DIXON. Plain edge. Only 1 known.

Joseph N. Dixon, billiard hall, in 1901 gazetteer.

A. A. DECKER
Goodrich, Mich.

Rulau	Date	Metal	Size	VG	F	VF	Unc
Goo 1	(1891-92)	Brass	25mm	—	—	35.00	—

GOOD FOR / * 5 C * / A. A. / DECKER / IN / * TRADE *. Rv: THE / GARDEN CITY / -*- / BILLIARD / -*- / TABLE CO. / CHICAGO. Plain edge. (Thoele coll.)

Decker appears in the 1891-92 *Michigan Gazetteer.*

B.P.O. ELKS NO. 48
Grand Rapids, Mich.

Rulau	Date	Metal	Size	F	VF	EF	Unc
Grp 2	(1890's)	Aluminum	35mm	—	—	20.00	35.00

Elk's head. Around: GRAND RAPIDS LODGE No. 48 / . B.P.O. ELKS . Rv: Large ornate monogram AF&Co against spokes of a wheel (the obverse of Ames & Frost Co., Chicago bicycle token, Chi 3). Plain edge. (Hartzog coll.)

An illogical muling?

ELLIOTT BUTTON FASTENER MACHINE
Grand Rapids, Mich.

Rulau	Date	Metal	Size	VG	F	VF	Unc
Grp 5	(1890's)	Brass	28mm	—	7.50	10.00	—

Machine, KEEP THIS / TRADE MARK above, Geo R Mayhew, Treas (script) / GRAND RAPIDS, MICH. Rv: STAPLE WIRE / FOR / ONE GT. GROSS / USED IN / ELLIOTT / BUTTON FASTENER / MACHINE. Plain edge.

P. SMERLIES SHINE PARLORS

Grand Rapids, Mich.

Rulau	Date	Metal	Size	VG	F	VF	Unc
Grp 20	(1899)	Aluminum	26mm	—	—	10.00	—

SHINE PARLORS / 2 CANAL / 101 MONROE / & / MARKET ST. / P. SMIERLIES / PROP. Rv: 3 / POLISH / FOR 25c within wreath; GREEK SHOE SHINE PARLORS around. Plain edge. (Wright 1628)

Rulau	Date	Metal	Size	VG	F	VF	Unc
Grp 22	(1899)	Aluminum	29mm	7.50	12.00	18.00	—

SHINE 10¢ STRAIGHT / 5 / FOR 25¢ / TO / CUSTOMERS / SMERLIES. Rv: GOOD AT ANY STAND / 180 / MONROE AVE. / MARKET & / MONROE. / DIVISION & MONROE. Plain edge. (Schmidt S50; Vacketta Chi SD81)

Smirlies' name is misspelled in different ways on each Grand Rapids token!

The September 1985 issue of *The Canadian Token* carried Ken Palmer's fine article, "Peter Smirlies, 'King of the Bootblacks'." He was also known as the "richest Greek in America."

Peter S. Smirlies was born in Tripolis, Greece in 1865. He emigrated to Chicago 1891, and in 1893 opened an express business. He returned to Greece 1897 to fight in the Turco-Greek War, then settled in Grand Rapids, Mich. He opened his first shoeshine parlor there 1898, and a second one in 1899.

In 1900 he opened parlors in Toronto and Hamilton, Ontario, and in Jackson, Mich. Smirlies' tokens emanate from Grand Rapids and from these Ontario communities: Toronto, Hamilton and London. In 1915 Smirlies left Grand Rapids and settled in London, Ontario, where he operated a billiard parlor and bowling alley 1916-1920. He disappears after 1920; he would have been 55 years old then.

J. R.

Grayling, Mich.

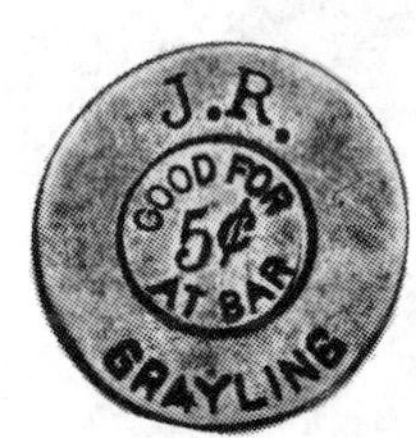

Rulau	Date	Metal	Size	VG	F	VF	Unc
Gra 4	ND	Brass	24.6mm	—	15.00	—	—

(All incused): J. R. / GOOD FOR / 5 ¢ / AT BAR / GRAYLING. Rv: Blank. Plain edge.

F. B. CRIPPEN

Hudson, Mich.

Rulau	Date	Metal	Size	VG	F	VF	Unc
Hud 1	(1891-92)	Aluminum	24.5mm	—	—	11.00	—

GOOD FOR / 5 ¢ / F. B. CRIPPEN / IN / TRADE. Rv: Large 5. Plain edge. (Thoele coll.)

JOHN WHITE

Ingalls, Mich.

Rulau	Date	Metal	Size	VG	F	VF	Unc
Ing 6	(1895-96)	Brass	--mm	—	35.00	—	—

JOHN WHITE / 5. Rv: Kuehl Billiard Supply, Chicago die. (Cunningham N/L)

The 1896 Dun directory lists this saloon.

JOS. CLAIRMONT

Ishpeming, Mich.

Rulau	Date	Metal	Size	VG	F	VF	Unc
Ish 2	(1900-04)	Brass	24mm	—	—	45.00	—

JOS. CLAIRMONT / GOOD FOR / 5 ¢ / AT BAR. Rv: THE / - / MINN / BILLIARD TABLE / CO. / MILWAUKEE, WIS. Plain edge.

This saloon appears in city directories for 1901 through 1904 at 110 East Division.

A. D. FOSTER

Lake City, Mich.

Rulau	Date	Metal	Size	VG	F	VF	Unc
Lak 1	(1891)	Brass	25mm	—	—	35.00	—

Brunswick pool table die 9A. Rv: GOOD FOR / 5 ¢ / A. D. FOSTER (in panel) / IN / TRADE. (Thoele coll.)

Saloon, listed in 1891.

FRED. MEISSNER

Menominee, Mich.

Rulau	Date	Metal	Size	VG	F	VF	Unc
Mnm 1	(1889-1912)	Brass	21mm	—	—	7.00	—

FRED. MEISSNER / + / GREEN BAY / HOUSE. Rv: GOOD FOR / 5 ¢ / AT THE BAR. (Thoele coll.)

This hostelry is listed from 1889 or earlier until 1912. Menominee is on Green Bay, an arm of Lake Michigan. Only 4 pieces known.

MUSKEGON S. & L. CO.

Muskegon, Mich.

Rulau	Date	Metal	Size	F	VF	EF	Unc
Mus 6	(1890-1910)	Copper	25mm	—	—	50.00	—

Bundle of shingles at center, GOOD FOR / * IN TRADE *. Rv: 1 / — / M within central beaded circle; MUSKEGON S. & L. CO. / * SHINGLE CHECK *. Plain edge. (Jim Hirtle coll. Westminster, Md.)

Could be Muskegon Shingle & Lumber Co.

PONTIAC BUGGY CO.

Pontiac, Mich.

Rulau	Date	Metal	Size	VG	F	VF	Unc
Pon 7	ND	Brass	33mm	—	—	15.00	—

Indian head right superimposed on a skin (?), tiny WESTERN / AMESBURY / LINE to lower right. Around: PONTIAC BUGGY CO / ** PONTIAC, MICH. **. Rv: .WESTERN .AMESBURY . LINE. / IS WORTH / 100 CENTS / ON THE DOLLAR / IN GOLD / (bar) / WHOLESALE / MANUFACTURERS OF / VEHICLES / . PONTIAC .BUGGY .CO. / PONTIAC, MICH. Plain edge.

Rulau	Date	Metal	Size	VG	F	VF	Unc
Pon 9	ND	xx	33.5mm	—	—	10.00	—

xx Metal shell obverse colored red, green and black. White fibrous material reverse, black printing.
Indian head right, WESTERN / AMESBURY / LINE. to lower right. Around: SAFE RIDE IN A WESTERN AMESBURY VEHICLE / MANUFACTURED BY PONTIAC BUGGY CO., PONTIAC, MICH. Rv: THIS CHARM / IF CARRIED IN / THE POCKET PREVENTS / BALD HEADS, HARD WORK, / LOVE, WARTS ON NOSE, / WAR CRAZE, SWELLED HEAD, / INSANITY, UNHAPPY MARRIAGES, / DARK BROWN TASTE, / DELIRIUM TREMENS, AND / PUNCTURED TIRES. / (OVER).

W. E. CRAM

Saginaw, Mich.

Rulau	Date	Metal	Size	VG	F	VF	Unc
Sag 1	(1895)	Brass	25mm	—	—	35.00	—

Brunswick pool table die 9A. Rv: GOOD FOR / 5 C / W. E. CRAM / IN / TRADE. Plain edge.

Saloon, in 1895 directory.

Cram was known to be in Midland, Mich., as a saloonkeeper, in 1885.

J. TERNS

Ypsilanti, Mich.

Rulau	Date	Metal	Size	VG	F	VF	Unc
Yps 3	(1897)	Brass	24mm	—	—	45.00	75.00

GOOD FOR / 5 ¢ / J. TERNS / IN / TRADE. Rv: SCHULENBERG / BILLIARD TABLES (all legends incuse on each side). Plain edge. Rare. (Thoele coll. in AU condition)

John Terns' billiard hall appears only in the 1897 gazetteer.

MINNESOTA

M. W. O'CONNOR

Albert Lea, Minn.

Rulau	Date	Metal	Size	VG	F	VF	Unc
Ale 4	(1894)	Brass	24mm	—	—	35.00	—

GOOD FOR / 5 C / M. W. / O'CONNOR / IN TRADE. Rv: Pool table in center, THE J. M. BRUNSWICK & BALKE COS. above, CHECK below. Plain edge.

JAS. CRONON & SON

Austin, Minn.

Rulau	Date	Metal	Size	VG	F	VF	Unc
Aus 4	(1900)	Brass	21mm	—	—	10.00	—

JAS. CRONON / & SON / AUSTIN, MINN. Rv: GOOD FOR / 5 C / IN TRADE. Plain edge.

James Cronon alone is listed as a purveyor of cigars in 1890. In 1900 the business is listed as James Cronon & Son, as on the token.

C. F. FOX

Austin, Minn.

Rulau	Date	Metal	Size	VG	F	VF	Unc
Aus 7	(1890's)	Aluminum	20mm	—	6.00	—	—

C. F. FOX / AUSTIN / MINN. Rv: GOOD FOR / 5 C / IN TRADE. Plain edge.

Rulau	Date	Metal	Size	VG	F	VF	Unc
Aus 8	1899	B&A	28mm	—	—	28.00	—

C. F. FOX / CIGARS. / AUSTIN, MINN. Rv: GOOD FOR / 25 / PAT. / JULY 1899 / IN MERCHANDISE. Plain edge.

Charles F. Fox was a coal and wood dealer in 1890. He operated a hotel 1899-1909. The business was cigars and candy from 1921 to 1958. Token Aus 8 probably was used in the hotel; Aus 7 could be earlier or later.

PETERSON'S DEPARTMENT STORE

Barnesville, Minn.

Rulau	Date	Metal	Size	VG	F	VF	Unc
Brv 3	1891	CN	19mm	—	15.00	25.00	—

PETERSON'S / -*- / BARNESVILLE, / MINN. / 1891 / * / DEPARTMENT STORE. Rv: TEN CENTS IN / 10 (large, shaded) / MERCHANDISE. Plain edge. Rare. (Kirtley March 1991 sale, lot 2195)

VELLA CURTIS

Baudette, Minn.

Rulau	Date	Metal	Size	VG	F	VF	Unc
Bau 1	(?)	Brass	21mm	—	—	8.00	—

VELLA CURTIS / BEAUDETTE, / MINN. Rv: Blank. Plain edge.

The town is misspelled Beaudette instead of Baudette on the token.

G. H. KRAVIK

Belview, Minn.

Rulau	Date	Metal	Size	VG	F	VF	Unc
Bel 5	1898	Aluminum	19mm	—	—	15.00	—

G. H. KRAVIK / 1898 / BELVIEW, / MINN. Rv: GOOD FOR / 5 C / IN / MERCHANDISE / NOT TRANSFERABLE. Plain edge.

Rulau	Date	Metal	Size	VG	F	VF	Unc
Bel 6	1899	Aluminum	33mm	—	—	20.00	—

G. H. KRAVIK / 1899 / BELVIEW, / MINN. Rv: GOOD FOR / $1.00 / IN / MERCHANDISE. Plain edge.

This was a general store 1898-1900.

J. S. MOGENS

Rulau	Date	Metal	Size	F	VF	EF	Unc
Bel 10	(ca 1890)	24.5mm	--mm	8.00	15.00	—	

J. S. MOGENS, / (ornament) / BELVIEW, / - * - / MINN. Rv: GOOD FOR / 5 ¢ / * IN * / MERCHANDISE. Plain edge. Recessed dentilated rim on each side.

O. H. MOGENS

Belview, Minn.

Rulau	Date	Metal	Size	F	VF	EF	Unc
Bel 13	(ca 1900)	Brass	21.6mm	—	10.00	—	—

O. H. MOGENS / (ornament) / BELVIEW, / . . . / MINN. Rv: GOOD FOR / * 5 ¢ * / IN / MERCHANDISE. Plain edge. Recessed dentilated rim on each side.

The Mogens Brothers are listed in 1918 as proprietors of a grocery and restaurant. At that time Belview (Redwood County) had 290 people.

CON. O'BRIEN

Brainerd, Minn.

Rulau	Date	Metal	Size	VG	F	VF	Unc
Brd 1	(1900)	Aluminum	19mm	—	—	3.50	—

CON. O'BRIEN'S / GENERAL / STORE. Rv: GOOD FOR / 1 C / IN / MERCHANDISE. Plain edge.

Con O'Brien operated a saloon and restaurant in 1886-1890. He was listed as a grocer in 1900. The O'Brien Mercantile Co., a grocery and general store, operated 1909-1939.

C. L. ILETT

Brownton, Minn

Rulau	Date	Metal	Size	VG	F	VF	Unc
Brt 1	(1890's)	Aluminum	19mm	—	10.00	—	—

C. L. ILETT, / BROWNTON, / MINN. Rv: GOOD FOR / 5 C / IN TRADE. Plain edge.

Ilett was a hotel proprietor 1890, a confectioner 1900.

J. LEONARD
Carver, Minn.

Rulau	Date	Metal	Size	VG	F	VF	Unc
Car 1	(1886-99)	Brass	24mm	—	—	15.00	—

J. LEONARD / CARVER, / MINN. Rv: GOOD FOR / 5 / AT THE BAR / CENTS / IN TRADE. Plain edge.

Leonard operated a hotel and saloon from 1886 to 1915.

JUL. STEGE
Chaska, Minn.

Rulau	Date	Metal	Size	VG	F	VF	Unc
Chk 3	(1892-93)	Brass	23mm	—	—	25.00	—

JUL. STEGE. Rv: GOOD FOR / 5 / CENTS / AT THE BAR. Plain edge.

WILLIAM F. G. GADAU
Cloquet, Minn.

Rulau	Date	Metal	Size	VG	F	VF	Unc
Ciq 1	(1890-1900)	Aluminum	21mm	—	—	Scarce	—

WILLIAM F. G. GADAU / DEALER IN / CIGARS, / TOBACCO / AND / SMOKERS ARTICLES / CLOQUET, MINN. Rv: GOOD FOR IN TRADE / 5 / CENTS. Plain edge.

Gadau is listed as a cigar outlet from 1890 through 1900.

CROOKSTON BREWERY
Crookston, Minn.

Rulau	Date	Metal	Size	VG	F	VF	Unc
Cks 1	(1891)	Aluminum	31mm	—	—	25.00	—

CROOKSTON BREWERY / A. WALTER / PROPRIETOR / CROOKSTON, MINN. Rv: DRINK THE CROOKSTON / CELEBRATED / LAGER / AND / EXPORT / BOTTLED BEER. Plain edge.

August Walter ran this brewery from 1884 to 1891, and possibly later.

G. A. R.
(Grand Army of the Republic)

Rulau	Date	Metal	Size	F	VF	EF	Unc
Cks 4	1892	WM	38mm	—	10.00	—	20.00

Civil War soldier. Around: FOR RIGHTS WE FOUGHT, RIGHTS WE WILL MAINTAIN. Rv: PARK REGION ASSOCIATION SEVENTH ANNUAL ENCAMPMENT. / G. A. R. / (American flag) / CROOKSTON MINN. / 1892. Plain edge.

ERNEST ROLSCH SALOON
Crookston, Minn.

Rulau	Date	Metal	Size	F	VF	EF	Unc
Cks 7	(1890-1912)	WM	25mm	—	35.00	—	—

ERNEST ROLSCH / SALOON / CROOKSTON, MINN. Rv: GOOD FOR / 5 C / IN TRADE. Plain edge.

Rolsch is listed as a saloon proprietor 1890 through 1912. The token's style appears early.

DEER CREEK, MINN.

Tokens of the Arthur D. Baker general store in Deer Creek were issued, apparently, in the 1886-90 period and belong in our section on U.S. Trade Tokens 1866-1889.

HOTEL MINNESOTA
Detroit, Minn.

Rulau	Date	Metal	Size	VG	F	VF	Unc
Det 1	(1886-94)	WM	25mm	—	—	15.00	—

HOTEL MINNESOTA / DETROIT, / MINN. Rv: GOOD FOR / 10 C / IN TRADE. Plain edge.

This hotel operated in the 1886-1894 period. In style, the token resembles other Gay Nineties Minnesota pieces.

BARNES & CO.
Duluth, Minn.

Rulau	Date	Metal	Size	VG	F	VF	Unc
Dth 3	(1900)	Brass	39mm	—	10.00	—	—

BARNES & CO. / GOOD FOR / $1.00 / AT THE / BAR / DULUTH, MINN. Rv: Blank. Plain edge.

S. M. Barnes & Co. were saloon proprietors in 1900 directories.

A. FITGER & CO.

Rulau	Date	Metal	Size	VG	F	VF	Unc
Dth 6	(1893)	Aluminum	37mm	—	—	35.00	50.00

Single-mast, single-stack ship steaming toward viewer's left. TRADE MARK above, tiny CHILDS CHI. below. Around in incuse letters on raised band: LAKE SUPERIOR BREWING / o DULUTH, MINN. o. Rv: (Sunburst) / ALUMINUM / IS COMING TO THE FRONT AND SO IS / (Gothic lettering) A. FITGER & CO'S / CELEBRATED / LAGER BEER / (sunburst inverted). Plain edge. (Dick Grinolds coll.)

GOWAN PEYTON & TWOHY

Rulau	Date	Metal	Size	VG	F	VF	Unc
Dth 7	(1890's)	Aluminum	29mm	—	—	6.00	—

GOWAN PEYTON + TWOHY / DISTRIBUTERS (sic!) / DULUTH, MINN. Rv: IF YOU WANT / TO DIE EASY / SMOKE A / TOM PLATT CIGAR. Plain edge. (Thoele coll.)

In light of a century later's knowledge, "dying easy" from cigars seems unlikely.

JOHN LUNDBERG

Rulau	Date	Metal	Size	VG	F	VF	Unc
Dth 8	(1886-94)	Brass	25mm	—	20.00	—	

Pool table, THE BRUNSWICK BALKE / COLLENDER / COMPY, above, CHECK below. Rv: GOOD FOR / 5 C / JOHN / LUNDBERG / IN / TRADE. Plain edge.

This was a saloon and hotel, 1886-1894.

J. W. SCHULTZ

Rulau	Date	Metal	Size	VG	F	VF	Unc
Dth 10	(1890)	Aluminum	23mm	—	10.00	—	—

J. W. SCHULTZ / 512 / W. SUPERIOR / ST. / DULUTH. Rv: GOOD FOR / 5 C / IN TRADE. Plain edge.

John W. Schultz was a saloon proprietor about 1890.

JOHN SHEA

Rulau	Date	Metal	Size	VG	F	VF	Unc
Dth 11	(1900)	Aluminum	26mm	—	10.00	—	—

JOHN SHEA, / THE FASHION / DULUTH. Rv: 2 1/2. Plain edge.

THE SPALDING BUFFET

Rulau	Date	Metal	Size	VG	F	VF	Unc
Dth 20	(1890's)	CN	Oct 26mm	—	—	25.00	—

GOOD AT / THE / SPALDING / BUFFET / DULUTH, MINN. Rv: THIS WILL BRING YOU BACK / 2 FOR 25 / TO THE / SPALDING BUFFET. Ornate beaded rims. Plain edge.

The Spalding Hotel stood 1890-1927.

L. WOLFRAM

Duluth, Minn.

Rulau	Date	Metal	Size	VG	F	VF	Unc
Dth 30	(1890-99)	Brass	23mm	—	10.00	—	—

L. WOLFRAM, / DULUTH, / MINN. Rv: GOOD FOR / 5 C / IN TRADE. Plain edge.

Louis Wolfram is listed as a saloonkeeper 1890-1900.

MEAT CUTTERS & BUTCHERS LOCAL 653

Edina, Minn.

Rulau	Date	Metal	Size	F	VF	EF	Unc
Edi 3	(?)	Brass	Sc 31mm	—	—	4.50	—

MEAT CUTTERS / & / BUTCHERS / LOCAL 653. Rv: GOOD FOR / 25 ¢ / IN TRADE.

Local 653 was at Edina, Thoele has learned.

J. B. SKOGMO & CO.

Elbow Lake, Minn.

Rulau	Date	Metal	Size	VG	F	VF	Unc
Elb 3	(1894)	Aluminum	19mm	—	7.50	—	—

J. B. SKOGMO & CO. / ELBOW / LAKE / MINN. Rv: GOOD FOR / 5 C / IN / MERCHANDISE. Plain edge.

John B. Skogmo is listed as a general store operator in 1890. This token could postdate the Gay Nineties, but probably was issued in 1894 as the next item, from Evan, Minn., was.

H. C. HANSON

Evan, Minn.

Rulau	Date	Metal	Size	VG	F	VF	Unc
Evn 1	1894	Aluminum	19mm	—	20.00	—	—

H. C. HANSON, / 1894 / EVAN, / MINN. Rv: GOOD FOR / 5 C / IN / MERCHANDISE. Plain edge.

Hanson's general store was in business 1894-1900.

CHAS. MALONE

Foreston, Minn.

Rulau	Date	Metal	Size	VG	F	VF	Unc
For 3	(1890)	WM	Scal 32mm	—	—	20.00	—

(All incused): CHAS MALONE / FORESTON. Rv: (All incused): GOOD FOR / 5 C / AT THE BAR. Plain edge.

The only listing apparently is in 1890.

ROBSON & SVENDSON

Geneva, Minn.

Rulau	Date	Metal	Size	VG	F	VF	Unc
Gva 3	1898	Brass	20mm	—	—	15.00	—

ROBSON / & / SVENDSON / GENEVA, / 1898 / MINN. Rv: GOOD FOR / 5 C / IN / MERCHANDISE. Plain edge.

This general store was in operation 1898-1909.

FREMAD ASSOCIATION

Glenwood, Minn.

An extensive series of tokens lettered THE FREMAD ASSOCIATION and bearing the date 1874 were probably issued after 1900. The 1874 date is probably the founding date of this general store, which was in business until 1927.

G. H. SUCKER

Good Thunder, Minn.

Rulau	Date	Metal	Size	VG	F	VF	Unc
Gdt 1	(1900)	Brass	25mm	—	—	6.50	—

GOOD FOR / 5 ¢ / G. H. SUCKER / IN / TRADE. Rv: Large 5. (ATCO Maverick 3795; McFerran attribution)

Listed in the 1900 R. G. Dun directory.

MINNESOTA STATE FAIR

Hamline, Minn.

Rulau	Date	Metal	Size	VG	F	VF	Unc
Ham 1	(1890's)	WM	30mm	—	15.00	—	—

Building at center, MINNESOTA STATE FAIR above, HAMLINE, MINN. below. Rv: E. R. WILLIAMSON MINNEAPOLIS.

WM. LINNE

Hutchinson, Minn.

Rulau	Date	Metal	Size	VG	F	VF	Unc
Hut 5	(1890's ?)	Aluminum	Oct 27mm	—	—	15.00	—

Wm LINNE / * / HUTCHINSON / MINN. Rv: GOOD FOR ONE / * / LOAF / OF / BREAD. (Renstrom coll.)

T. L. DONOVAN

Jasper, Minn.

Rulau	Date	Metal	Size	VG	F	VF	Unc
Jas 1	(?)	Brass	25mm	—	—	20.00	—

Billiard table, THE BRUNSWICK BALKE / COLLENDER / COMPY. above. CHECK below. Rv: GOOD FOR / 5 C / T. L. DONOVAN / IN / TRADE. Plain edge.

JOHN SCHAEFER

Jordan, Minn.

Rulau	Date	Metal	Size	VG	F	VF	Unc
Jor 1	(?)	Brass	32.6mm	10.00	—	—	—

Within circle: JOHN SCHAEFER'S / (ornament) / CASH STORE / (ornament) / JORDAN, MINN. Rv: GOOD FOR / * 50 ¢ * / IN MDSE. Plain edge. (Grinolds coll.)

One reported specimen is corroded and is counterstamped B P on obverse.

F. J. MENTON

Kasota, Minn.

Rulau	Date	Metal	Size	VG	F	VF	Unc
Kas 1	(1894)	Aluminum	19mm	—	30.00	—	—

F. J. MENTON, / GENERAL / MERCHANDISE / KASOTA, / MINN. Rv: GOOD FOR / 5 C / IN / MERCHANDISE. Plain edge.

The only listing shows Menton with "beverages" in 1890.

E. M. GORDON

Kensington, Minn.

Rulau	Date	Metal	Size	VG	F	VF	Unc
Ken 1	(?)	Brass	24mm	—	—	20.00	—

Billiard table, THE / BRUNSWICK / BALKE / COLLENDER CO. above. Rv: GOOD FOR / 5 C / E. M. GORDON / IN / TRADE. Plain edge.

W. H. PATTEN CO.

Le Sueur, Minn.

Rulau	Date	Metal	Size	VG	F	VF	Unc
Les 1	(1890)	Brass	19mm	—	20.00	—	—

Within circle: THE W. H. PATTEN CO. / —/ LE SUEUR / — / * MINN. * Rv: Within circle: GOOD FOR / 1 ¢ / .IN. / MERCHANDISE. Plain edge. (Grinolds coll.)

Rulau	Date	Metal	Size	VG	F	VF	Unc
Les 2	(1894)	Aluminum	19mm	—	15.00	—	—

THE W. H. PATTEN CO. / LE SUEUR / MINN. Rv: GOOD FOR / 5 C / IN / MERCHANDISE. Plain edge.

The William H. Patten Co. is listed as a general store 1886 to 1890. The second token was probably not issued until 1894.

H. SIEMERLING

Le Sueur, Minn.

Rulau	Date	Metal	Size	VG	F	VF	Unc
Les 4	(1890's)	Brass	24mm	—	20.00	—	—

H. SIEMERLING, / LE SUEUR, / MINN. Rv: GOOD FOR / 5 C / AT BAR. Plain edge.

Siemerling's saloon is listed 1886-1890.

HENRY WILLIAMS

Long Prairie, Minn.

Rulau	Date	Metal	Size	VG	F	VF	Unc
Lng 7	(1886-1909)	Brass	Oct 28mm	—	—	25.00	—

Brunswick-Balke die. Rv: GOOD FOR / 5 C / HENRY / WILLIAMS / IN TRADE. Plain edge.

This was a saloon, listed 1886 through 1909.

F. A. BAKER

Magnolia, Minn.

A series of trade checks from 5-cents to $2 in denomination, bearing an 1899 date, was issued by this general store which was in operation 1899-1927. The fabric of these pieces is post-Gay Nineties period; the 1899 date refers to the firm's founding.

A. B. EWING

Mankato, Minn.

Rulau	Date	Metal	Size	F	VF	EF	Unc
Mto 3	(1893-99)	Aluminum	29mm	7.00	—	—	—

A. B. EWING / DEALER IN / STAPLE AND FANCY / GROCERIES / MANKATO, MINN. Rv: GOOD FOR / 25 / IN / MERCHANDISE. Plain edge. (Wright 1410)

C. J. KLINE

Rulau	Date	Metal	Size	VG	F	VF	Unc
Mto 8	(1886-1909)	Brass	24mm	—	—	55.00	—

Brunswick-Balke die. Rv: GOOD FOR / 5 C / C. J. KLINE / MANKATO / IN / TRADE. Plain edge.

C. J. Kline ran a hotel 1886-1909. Mrs. C. J. Kline was listed as owner in 1912.

JNO. TRENHEUSER

Mankato, Minn.

Rulau	Date	Metal	Size	F	VF	EF	Unc
Mto 22	(1890-1900)	Brass	25mm	—	35.00	—	—

Goblet, tongs & ladle crossed, CHAS. PICK & CO. / DEALERS IN above, CHICAGO Below. Rv: GOOD FOR / 5 C / JNO. / TRENHEUSER / IN / TRADE. Plain edge.

This saloon is listed 1890-1900.

JOS. TRISKO

Melrose, Minn.

Rulau	Date	Metal	Size	VG	F	VF	Unc
Mel 4	(1890-94)	Brass	25mm	—	—	25.00	—

Goblet, tongs and ladle. CHAS. PICK & CO. / DEALERS IN above. CHICAGO below. Rv: GOOD FOR / 5 C / JOS. / TRISKO / IN / TRADE. Plain edge.

This saloon was in business 1890-1894, according to directory evidence. The Charles Pick Co. used this token type circa 1880-86 and apparently also later. Pick tokens are much more scarce as a group than the plentiful Brunswick pieces.

B. LALONE

Menahga, Minn.

Rulau	Date	Metal	Size	VG	F	VF	Unc
Mga 1	(1894)	Brass	25mm	—	—	20.00	—

Pool table, THE BRUNSWICK BALKE / COLLENDER / COMPY. above, CHECK below. Rv: GOOD FOR / 5 C / B. LALONE / IN / TRADE. Plain edge.

This saloon appears in the 1894 directory.

AULTMAN-TAYLOR

Minneapolis, Minn.

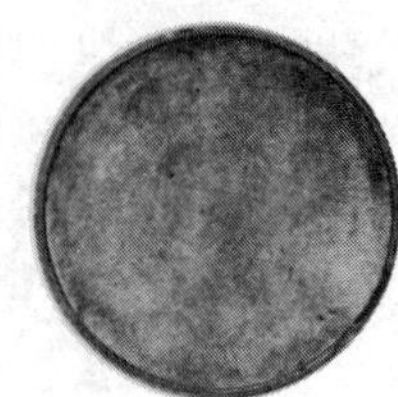

Rulau	Date	Metal	Size	VG	F	VF	Unc
Mps 1	(1890's)	Yel Brz	24mm	—	—	20.00	40.00

Scrawny cock striding left, TRADE MARK above, all with central circle. Around: FATTENED ON AN AULTMAN-TAYLOR STRAW STACK. Rv: Blank. Plain edge. (Wright 14)

Rulau	Date	Metal	Size	VG	F	VF	Unc
Mps 2	(1890's)	Silver	24mm	—	—	—	Scarce

As last. Plain edge. (Tanenbaum coll.)

Rulau	Date	Metal	Size	VG	F	VF	Unc
Mps 3	(1899)	Brass	31mm	—	—	10.00	20.00

Tractor at center, THE AULTMAN-TAYLOR / MACHINERY CO. above. T. C. / MINNEAPOLIS / MINN. below. Rv: Scrawny chicken with TRADE MARK above; below is: FATTENED / ON AN / AULTMAN-TAYLOR STRAW STACK. Plain edge. (Dick Grinolds coll.)

This machinery manufacturer was in busines from at least 1899 to 1923 located at 228 Washington Avenue North and also 506 Washington Avenue North.

BARNET "LEMONADE CHECKS"

Rulau	Date	Metal	Size	VG	F	VF	Unc
Mps 5	1895	Aluminum	26mm	—	10.00	17.50	—

LEMONADE CHECK / LAKE HARRIET / PARK / PAVILION / (script) H. M. BARNET / LESSEE. Rv: GOOD ONLY / Large 5 / SEASON / 1895. Plain edge.

Rulau	Date	Metal	Size	VG	F	VF	Unc
Mps 6	1897	Aluminum	27mm	—	—	—	Unique

LEMONADE CHECK / RIVERSIDE / PARK / PAVILION / (script) ESTHER BARNET / LESSEE. Rv: GOOD ONLY / Large 5 / SEASON / 1897. Plain edge.

Rulau	Date	Metal	Size	VG	F	VF	Unc
Mps 7	1897	Aluminum	Oct. 33mm	—	—	—	Unique

Similar to last but, but '10' replaces '5' on reverse. Plain edge. (Grinolds coll.)

H. M. Barnet was the lessee of Lake Harriet Park Pavilion 1895-1899. Esther Barnet leased Riverside Park Pavilion at least in 1897.

Minnesota checks for lemonade - a favorite soft drink of the Gay Nineties - are the only such in this catalog. Lemonade shared honors with sarsaparilla, root beer, a few early colas, Moxie and apple cider to a society which had not yet been exposed to the massive advertising of such as Coca-Cola, Pepsi Cola, Seven Up, Dr. Pepper, Crush, Canada Dry and Perrier Water.

L. CUSSLER

Rulau	Date	Metal	Size	VG	F	VF	Unc
Mps 9	(ca 1894)	Aluminum	25mm	—	—	10.00	—

Bust of Otto von Bismarck. Rv: L. CUSSLER / 1 1/2 / 119 / WASHINGTON AVE. N. Plain edge.

Louis Cussler operated a saloon 1890 to 1914.

DRYER'S

Rulau	Date	Metal	Size	VG	F	VF	Unc
Mps 11	(?)	Bronze	30mm	—	—	20.00	—

Eagle displayed, a serpent in its beak. GOOD FOR above. A DRINK below. Rv: DRYER'S / . . . / . 319 . / . . . HEN AVE. . . . / HURRY / BACK / MINNEAPOLIS. Plain edge. (Dick Grinolds coll.)

JAMES FORD

Rulau	Date	Metal	Size	VG	F	VF	Unc
Mps 13	(1886-94)	Brass	19mm	—	—	10.00	—

James Ford effigy, JAMES FORD MINNEAPOLIS around, 1886 below. Rv: 302 FIRST AV. S. / GOOD / FOR / 5 C / 49 WASH. AV. S. Plain edge.

Rulau	Date	Metal	Size	VG	F	VF	Unc
Mps 14	(1886-94)	Brass	25mm	—	—	12.50	—

As last, but larger.

Rulau	Date	Metal	Size	VG	F	VF	Unc
Mps 15	(1894-99)	Aluminum	20mm	—	—	10.00	—

Obverse as last. Rv: 2 1/2. Plain edge.

Rulau	Date	Metal	Size	VG	F	VF	Unc
Mps 16	(1894-99)	Aluminum	25.5mm	—	—	8.00	—

Obverse as last. Rv: 302 FIRST AVE. S. / WINE / MERCHANT / 49 WASH. AVE. S. Plain edge. (There are size varieties from 25 to 26 millimeters in diameter)

Though each piece is dated 1886, the founding date, none may have been issued in that date. This saloon was in business 1886-1916.

FRANK J. GAUS

Rulau	Date	Metal	Size	VG	F	VF	Unc
Mps 18	(1893-99)	Aluminum	24mm	—	10.00	—	—

FRANK J. GAUS / 18 / WASH. AVE N. / MPLS. Rv: GOOD FOR / 5 C / IN TRADE.

Saloon, listed 1884-1899.

GAUS & WEISENBERGER

Rulau	Date	Metal	Size	VG	F	VF	Unc
Mps 19	(?)	Aluminum	24mm	—	—	—	10.00

GAUS & WEISENBERGER. / * / THE / BIJOU / 18 WASHINGTON / AVE. NO. / * / MINNEAPOLIS. Rv: Blank. Plain edge.

The Bijou was a famous variety show and vaudeville theater.

HOTEL NICOLLET DRUG STORE

Rulau	Date	Metal	Size	VG	F	VF	Unc
Mps 21	(?)	Aluminum	25mm	—	20.00	—	—

HOTEL / NICOLLET / DRUG / STORE / MINNEAPOLIS. Rv: GOOD FOR (on scroll) / 5 ¢ / SODA. Plain edge. (Grinolds coll.)

The Grinolds specimen is counterstamped C on reverse.

Rulau	Date	Metal	Size	VG	F	VF	Unc
Mps 22	(?)	CN	29mm	—	—	—	—

(All incused): NICOLLET HOUSE BAR / 25 / MINNEAPOLIS. Rv: Blank. Plain edge.

The Nicollet House was a hotel at 9 Washington Avenue form 1880 to 1924.

L. & P. (Lally & Peck)

Rulau	Date	Metal	Size	VG	F	VF	Unc
Mps 22C	(1891-92)	GS	23mm	—	—	6.50	—

H. WILLIAMSON / MAKER / MINNEAPOLIS / L & P (large). Rv: GOOD FOR / 5 ¢ / IN TRADE / AT THE BAR. All legends incuse on each side. (Thoele coll.)

Lally & Peck are listed under saloons in the 1891-92 gazetteer.

LUTHER SEMINARY

Rulau	Date	Metal	Size	VG	F	VF	Unc
Mps 23	1899	Aluminum	38mm	—	—	15.00	25.00

Luther bust facing within circle. Around: VERBUM DEI MANET IN AETERNUM / * DR. MARTIN LUTHER *. Rv: Building above DEDICATED / OCT. 14, 1899, all within circle. Around: LUTHER SEMINARY OF THE SYNOD FOR NORW. EV. LUTHERAN CHURCH IN AMERICA. Plain edge.

MINNEAPOLIS EXPOSITIONS

There were a number of Minneapolis industrial expositions and similar events from 1886 through 1892 which were commemorated on tokens and medalets. Those of the 1886-1889 period may be found in "U.S. Trade Tokens 1866-1889," while the balance are cataloged below.

Rulau	Date	Metal	Size	F	VF	EF	Unc
Mps 35	1890	WM	30mm	—	—	7.50	11.00

Building, INDUSTRIAL EXPOSITION / MINNEAPOLIS around. Rv: Within circular wreath: OPENS / AUG. 27. / CLOSES / OCT. 4. / 1890. Around: EXHIBITION OF ART AND INDUSTRY. / *. Plain edge. (Grinolds coll.)

Rulau	Date	Metal	Size	F	VF	EF	Unc
Mps 36	1891	Tin	31mm	—	—	—	17.50

Building, INDUSTRIAL EXPOSITION / MINNEAPOLIS around. Rv: RECIPROCITY / AND / PROTECTION / MADE FROM / BLACK HILLS TIN. Plain edge.

The Black Hills are located in South Dakota.

Rulau	Date	Metal	Size	F	VF	EF	Unc
Mps 37	1891	WM	31mm	—	—	8.00	11.00

MINNEAPOLIS / HARVEST FESTIVAL / AND / INDUSTRIAL / PARADE / SEPTEMBER / 23. 1891. Rv: MINN. / WIS. / IOWA. / NEB. / IDAHO. / WASH. / OREGON. / MONT. / NO. DAK. / SO. DAK. / WELCOME. Plain edge.

Rulau	Date	Metal	Size	F	VF	EF	Unc
Mps 38	1892	WM	32mm	—	—	12.50	17.50

Building. Rv: MINNEAPOLIS INDUSTRIAL EXPOSITION / AUG. 31 / TO / SEP.24 / 1892. Plain edge.

J. MOERLS

Rulau	Date	Metal	Size	F	VF	EF	Unc
Mps 41	(1890-1900)	Brass	23mm	—	10.00	—	—

(All incused): J. MOERLS / E. R. WILLIAMSON / MAKER / MINNEAPOLIS. Rv: GOOD FOR / 5 C / IN TRADE. Plain edge.

Joseph Moerls kept a saloon in 1890. In 1900 this was listed under the proprietorship of John A. Moerls.

NORTHWESTERN COLLEGIATE & BUSINESS INSTITUTE

Rulau	Date	Metal	Size	F	VF	EF	Unc
Mps 42	(1893-99)	Aluminum	38mm	—	10.00	—	—

Ancient oil lamp atop two books, radiant star above, KNOWLEDGE IS POWER below, all within laurel wreath. Rv: Within circle: THE HOLDER / -IS A- / CONTRIBUTOR / TO THE FUND / OF THIS SCHOOL. Around: NORTHWESTERN COLLEGIATE & BUSINESS INSTITUTE / MINNEAPOLIS, MINN. Plain edge. (Grinolds coll.)

NORTHWESTERN CONSOLIDATED MILLING COMPANY

Rulau	Date	Metal	Size	F	VF	EF	Unc
Mps 43	(1893-99)	Aluminum	38mm	—	—	20.00	35.00

Five-legged spiral device over which CERESOTA appears. Around: THE NORTHWESTERN CONSOLIDATED MILLING CO. / + MINNEAPOLIS. +. Rv: THE NORTHWESTERN CONSOLIDATED MILLING COMPANY / MANUFACTURERS / OF / THE HIGHEST GRADES OF / SPRING WHEAT / (script) FLOUR / PROPRIETORS OF CONSOLIDATED / MILLS A.B.C.D.&E. / TOTAL CAPACITY / 10,500 BBLS. / DAILY / + MINNEAPOLIS, MINN. +. Plain edge. (Wright 1122)

There are die varieties.

NORWEGIAN-AMERICAN GYMNASTIC UNION

Rulau	Date	Metal	Size	F	VF	EF	Unc
Mps 44	1897	Brass	30mm	—	—	7.50	11.00

Shield containing four capital F's inverted, retrograde etc. to form a cross. Wreath around. Rv: * THE NORWEGIAN-AMERICAN GYMNASTIC UNIONS. / SECOND / TURN.FEST / JULY 9-12 / 1897 / AT / MINNEAPOLIS, MINN. Plain edge. Issued holed. (Grinolds coll.)

A. OLSON

Rulau	Date	Metal	Size	F	VF	EF	Unc
Mps 45	(?)	Brass	24mm	—	—	11.00	—

GOOD FOR / 5 C / A. OLSON (incused) / DRINK. Rv: 5. Plain edge.

PARIS-MURTON CO.

Rulau	Date	Metal	Size	F	VF	EF	Unc
Mps 49	(1886-93)	Brass	21mm	—	10.00	—	—

PARIS-MURTON CO. /SELL / SLOT / MACHINES / MINNEAPOLIS, MINN. Rv: HAS STOOD THE TEST FOR YEARS. / HOFFMAN / HOUSE / CIGAR. Plain edge.

Rulau	Date	Metal	Size	F	VF	EF	Unc
Mps 50	(1886-93)	Brass	21mm	—	10.00	—	—

Obverse as Mps 49. Rv: AMERICA'S / BEST / FONTELLA / 5 C / CIGAR. Plain edge.

Rulau	Date	Metal	Size	F	VF	EF	Unc
Mps 51	(1894-99)	Aluminum	31mm	—	10.00	—	—

PARIS-MURTON CO. / DISTRIBUTORS / MINNEAPOLIS, MINN. Rv: THIS CHECK WILL BE REDEEMED BY ANY DEALER / GOOD FOR / ONE / LAW CLUB / CIGAR. Plain edge.

Rulau	Date	Metal	Size	F	VF	EF	Unc
Mps 52	(1894-1901)	Aluminum	29mm	—	10.00	—	—

THE PARIS-MURTON CO. / WHOLESALE / AGENTS / MINNEAPOLIS, MINN. Rv: THIS CHECK WILL BE REDEEMED BY ANY DEALER / GOOD FOR / ONE / FONTELLA / CIGAR. Plain edge.

Alfred W. Paris and Stephan J. Murton were dealers in confectionery, cigars and fruits and manufacturers of slot machines from 1886-1901, at the corner of 1st Avenue North and Second Street.

THE PHOTOSCOPE CO.

Rulau	Date	Metal	Size	F	VF	EF	Unc
Mps 54	(?)	Brass	21mm	—	—	5.00	—

-THE- / PHOTOSCOPE / - CO. -. Rv: Blank. Plain edge.

ROSS & RHOMBERG

Rulau	Date	Metal	Size	F	VF	EF	Unc
Mps 58	(1899-1900)	Brass	24mm	—	—	15.00	—

ROSS & RHOMBERG / 37 / WASHINGTON / AVE. So. Rv: GOOD FOR / 5 / AT THE BAR / CENTS / IN TRADE. Plain edge.

The partners names seem to have been ROSE and RHOMBERG (not ROSS), saloonkeepers in 1899 and 1900.

(THE) STOCKHOLM

Rulau	Date	Metal	Size	F	VF	EF	Unc
Mps 62	(?)	Brass	29mm	—	—	15.00	—
		(All incused). A. OLESON / STOCKHOLM. Rv: Blank. Plain edge.					
Mps 63	(?)	Brass	29mm	—	—	15.00	—
		GOOD FOR / 5 C / AT BAR / A. OLSON / STOCKHOLM. Rv: Blank. Plain edge.					

WINECKE & DOERR

Rulau	Date	Metal	Size	F	VF	EF	Unc
Mps 70	(1890's)	Copper	29mm	—	—	5.00	10.00

WINECKE & DOERR / WHOLESALE / AGENTS / MINNEAPOLIS. Rv: THIS CHECK WILL BE REDEEMED BY ANY DEALER / GOOD FOR / ONE / FONTELLA / CIGAR / *. Plain edge.

ZEPHYR

Minneapolis, Minn.

Rulau	Date	Metal	Size	VG	F	VF	Unc
Mps 90	(?)	Aluminum	35mm	—	—	35.00	—

Three racehorses in a dead heat right, A CLOSE FINISH in exergue. Rv: CIGARS & REFRESHMENTS / 320 / ZEPHYR (in panel) / * NICOLLET * / -AVE.- / MINNEAPOLIS. Plain edge. (Kirtley 1991 ATCO sale, lot 1212)

SAMUEL MILLER

Minnesota City, Minn.

Rulau	Date	Metal	Size	VG	F	VF	Unc
Mcy 5	(1890)	Brass	25mm	—	10.00	15.00	—

(All incused): SAMUEL MILLER / GOOD FOR / 5 C / AT THE BAR. Rv: Blank. Plain edge.

T. H. BARKEY

Morton, Minn.

Rulau	Date	Metal	Size	VG	F	VF	Unc
Mor 1	(1890)	Brass	24mm	—	5.00	—	—

T. H. BARKEY / MORTON, / MINN. Rv: GOOD FOR / 5 C / AT BAR. Plain edge.

BURKE'S STORE

Norseland, Minn.

Rulau	Date	Metal	Size	VG	F	VF	Unc
Nor 1	1899	Brass	19mm	—	—	10.00	—
	BURKE'S STORE / 1899 / NORSELAND, / MINN. Rv: GOOD FOR / 5 C / IN / MERCHANDISE. Plain edge.						
Nor 2	1899	Brass	25mm	—	—	10.00	—
	As 1, but 10 C.						
Nor 3	1899	Aluminum	25mm	—	—	10.00	—
	As 1, but 25 C.						
Nor 4	1899	Aluminum	29mm	—	—	18.00	—
	Obverse as 1. Rv: GOOD FOR / 50 C / IN / MERCHANDISE / N.W. STAMP WKS. ST. PAUL MINN. Plain edge.						

John Burke ran a general store 1886-1900.

C. W. SCHNEIDER

Ortonville, Minn.

Rulau	Date	Metal	Size	VG	F	VF	Unc
Ort 15	(1890's)	Brass	24mm	—	—	10.00	—

C W / SCHNEIDER. Rv: 5.

Charles W. Schneider's saloon is listed 1890-1909.

OSLO SCHOOL

Oslo, Minn.

Rulau	Date	Metal	Size	VG	F	VF	Unc
Osl 1	1896	Aluminum	35mm	—	—	Rare	—

Open Bible lettered IN / GOD / WE / TRUST / E / PLURIBUS / UNUM, radiant star above, crossed palm branches below. Above: W. A. CHRISTENSEN. Rv: * OSLO SCHOOL SOUVENIR * / *** (star) *** / 1896-98 / *** (radiant star) ***. Plain edge. (Grinolds coll.)

J. LIPPERT

Owatonna, Minn.

Rulau	Date	Metal	Size	VG	F	VF	Unc
Owa 1	(1890)	Brass	Oct 23mm	—	—	15.00	—

J. LIPPERT. / OWATONNA. Rv: GOOD FOR / 5 C / AT BAR.

John Lippert and Son ran a saloon listed in 1890.

MARTINEK & HORAK

Rulau	Date	Metal	Size	VG	F	VF	Unc
Owa 5	(1900)	Brass	24mm	—	—	20.00	—

Billiard table, THE BRUNSWICK BALKE / COLLENDER / COMPY above, CHECK in exergue. Rv: GOOD FOR / 5 C / MARTINEK / & HORAK / IN / TRADE. Plain edge.

This saloon was listed in the 1900 directory.

EMIL THEIMER

Owatonna, Minn.

Rulau	Date	Metal	Size	VG	F	VF	Unc
Owa 8	(1886-1900)	Brass	25mm	—	—	15.00	—

EMIL THEIMER / OWATONNA, MINN. Rv: GOOD FOR / 5 C / DRINK OR CIGAR.

Theimer's saloon was in business from 1886 to 1900.

JOS. JRAF

Red Wing, Minn.

Rulau	Date	Metal	Size	VG	F	VF	Unc
Red 3	(1890's)	Brass	22mm	—	15.00	—	—

* GOOD FOR * / 5 ¢ / JOS. JRAF / RED WING, / MINN. / * IN TRADE *. Rv: Numeral 5 within circle of 16 stars. Along lower rim, in tiny letters: JAS MURDOCK JR 165 RACE ST. CINti O. Plain edge.

This token could pre-date 1890.

LUTHERAN LADIES SEMINARY

Rulau	Date	Metal	Size	VG	F	VF	Unc
Rdw 7	1892	Aluminum	39mm	—	—	15.00	25.00

Building, LUTHERAN LADIES SEMINARY, above, 1892 / RED WING, below. Rv: RECEIVE KNOWLEDGE RATHER THAN GOLD. / IN GOD / WE / TRUST. Plain edge.

NEWTON HOUSE

Red Wing, Minn.

Rulau	Date	Metal	Size	VG	F	VF	Unc
Rdw 11	(1886-1900)	Brass	24mm	—	—	30.00	—

Crossed goblet, ladle and tongs, CHAS. PICK & CO. / DEALERS IN above, CHICAGO below. Rv: GOOD FOR / 5 C / NEWTON HOUSE / RED WING / IN / TRADE. Plain edge.

George Newton operated a hotel 1886-1890 and a restaurant in 1900.

C. A. FRANCOIS

Redwood Falls, Minn.

Rulau	Date	Metal	Size	VG	F	VF	Unc
Rdf 1	(1894 ?)	Aluminum	18mm	—	10.00	—	—

C. A. FRANCOIS / & CO. / REDWOOD / FALLS, / MINN. Rv: GOOD FOR / 5 C / IN / MERCHANDISE.

This was a general store listed from 1886 to 1890. The city is in Redwood County.

GEO. W. VAUGHN

Redwood Falls, Minn.

Rulau	Date	Metal	Size	VG	F	VF	Unc
Rdf 3	(1894-1900)	Aluminum	21mm	—	15.00	—	—

GEO. W. VAUGHN / REDWOOD / FALLS, / MINN. Rv: GOOD FOR / 5 C / AT BAR.

Vaughn operated a hotel 1886, and a saloon 1890-1900.

DAN McCARTY

Rochester, Minn.

Rulau	Date	Metal	Size	VG	F	VF	Unc
Roc 2	(1900)	Brass	24mm	—	—	20.00	—

DAN MC CARTY / ROCHESTER, / MINN. Rv: GOOD FOR / 5 C / IN TRADE.

This saloon is listed in 1900. It may well be related to a billiard-type token of the Brunswick & Balke Co. issued for one D. J. McCarthy of Rochester about 1885-94 (listed in the 2nd edition of our book, *U.S. Trade Tokens 1866-1889.*

E. A. SCHWARTZ

Rochester, Minn.

Rulau	Date	Metal	Size	VG	F	VF	Unc
Roc 3	(?)	Brass	25mm	—	—	20.00	—

Large C above crossed cuesticks, E. A. SCHWARTZ, above, ROCHESTER, MINN. below. Rv: Large 5 within circle of stars.

JOHN HENSLER

Ruthton, Minn.

Rulau	Date	Metal	Size	VG	F	VF	Unc
Rut 2	(1900)	Brass	24mm	—	—	9.00	—

JOHN HENSLER / -*- / RUTHTON, / MINN. Rv: GOOD FOR / 5 ¢ / IN TRADE. Plain edge. Only 1 piece reported.

Liquor dealer, according to the 1900 federal census. Pipestone County village of 323 persons in 1910.

W. ACHTERLING

St. Paul, Minn.

Rulau	Date	Metal	Size	VG	F	VF	Unc
Stp 1	(1886-92)	Brass	23mm	—	—	10.00	—

W. ACHTERLING. Rv: GOOD FOR / 5 / CENTS / IN TRADE. Plain edge.

Wenzel Achterling was a saloon proprietor 1886-1892.

BROTHERHOOD OF MACHINERY, MOLDERS

Rulau	Date	Metal	Size	VG	F	VF	Unc
Stp 4	1892	Brass	31mm	—	—	10.00	—

SIXTH CONVENTION BROTHERHOOD OF MACHINERY, / MOLDERS. / ST. PAUL, / MINN. / AUG. 1, 1892. Rv: Blank. Plain edge.

COMO PARK PAVILION

Rulau	Date	Metal	Size	VG	F	VF	Unc
Stp 9	1895	Aluminum	**	—	35.00	—	—

** Centrally-holed flan, 26mm.

COMO PARK / * PAVILION *. Rv: GOOD ONLY / Large 5 / SEASON / 1895. Plain edge. Only 2 known.

Probably a lemonade check. See Barnet under Minneapolis.

ELKS MID-SUMMER EXPOSITION

Rulau	Date	Metal	Size	F	VF	EF	Unc
Stp 12	1900	Gilt/B	30mm	—	—	5.00	—

Elk's head within wreath. Rv: ELKS MID-SUMMER / EXPOSITION / AND / CARNIVAL / JUNE 18-30. / 1900. / ST. PAUL, MINN. Plain edge.

ERSTE KREIS TURNFEST

Rulau	Date	Metal	Size	F	VF	EF	Unc
Stp 14	1891	WM	26mm	—	—	—	10.00

Beaded male bust facing, SCHWAAB on truncation of bust. Rv: * ERINNERUNG DAS ERSTE KREIS TURNFEST / DAS DRITTEN / KREISES / JUNI 20-24 / 1891 / ST. PAUL, MINN. Plain edge.

As it states in German, this piece commemorates the first district turner (gymnastic) fest of the "Three Districts." The German-American turner unions were a vital force throughout America in the Gay Nineties, but especially where Germans were strongest in the populace - in the Northeast and Midwest.

Struck by the Schwaab Stamp & Seal Co. in Milwaukee, Wis.

A. K. ERVIN

Rulau	Date	Metal	Size	F	VF	EF	Unc
Stp 15	(1892)	Aluminum	37mm	—	—	25.00	—

A. K. ERVIN (Gothic letters) / REPRESENTING / LINDEKE, / WARNER & / SCHURMEIER / -.- / ST. PAUL, MINN. Rv: (Standard Child's Chicago aluminum stock die). Plain edge.

W. A . FONDA

Rulau	Date	Metal	Size	VG	F	VF	Unc
Stp 17	(ca 1898)	Brass	24mm	—	—	15.00	—

W. A. FONDA'S / 321 / JACKSON ST. / ST. PAUL. Rv: PASS ME WITH TEN CENTS / 2 1/2 ¢ / AT.

There is a listing for a Fonda and Peterson Saloon in 1899-1900.

J. GEBHARD

Rulau	Date	Metal	Size	VG	F	VF	Unc
Stp 18	(1896)	Brass	25mm	—	4.00	7.50	—

GOOD FOR / 5 ¢ / J. GEBHARD (on ribbon) / IN / TRADE. Rv: 5 ¢ (large). Plain edge. Only 3 known. (Thoele coll.)

John Gebhard, saloon, in 1896 gazetteer.

A. E. JOHNSON & CO.

Rulau	Date	Metal	Size	F	VF	EF	Unc
Stp 20	(1893)	Aluminum	38mm	—	—	40.00	—

Domed building. Around: WORLD'S COLUMBIAN EXPOSITION / * ADMINISTRATION BL'D'G. *. Rv: * A. E. JOHNSON & CO. * / OFFICES / NEW YORK, BOSTON / CHICAGO, MINNEAPOLIS / DULUTH, SPOKANE, / SEATTLE, TACOMA, / ST. PAUL (larger) / GEN'L. LAND & STEAMSHIP AGT'S. Plain edge. (Grinolds coll.)

H. C. JOHNSON

Rulau	Date	Metal	Size	VG	F	VF	Unc
Stp 22	(1890's)	WM	23mm	—	—	5.00	—

GOOD FOR / 5 ¢ / H.C. JOHNSON / IN / TRADE. Rv: 5 in circle of stars and dots. There are no arrows on the obverse.

Rulau	Date	Metal	Size	VG	F	VF	Unc
Stp 23	(1890's)	WM	23mm	—	—	5.00	—

Similar to last, but there are four arrows on obverse.

H. Christ Johnson was the proprietor of a saloon and of the Continental Hotel from 1886 to 1904, located at 287 Sibley.

KUHLES & STOCK

Rulau	Date	Metal	Size	VG	F	VF	Unc
Stp 25	1901	Brass	25mm	—	—	6.50—	

KUHLES & STOCK, ST. PAUL, MINN. / KS ornate monogram. / PAT FEB. 12, 1901. Rv: Blank. Issued holed.

Cigar makers. Our collaborator Hank Thoele's great-great-grandfather worked as a cigar maker for K&S in the 1880's.

NANSEN FEST

Rulau	Date	Metal	Size	VG	F	VF	Unc
Stp 30	1897	Aluminum	32mm	—	—	20.00	—

Man in hat, NANSEN FEST ST. PAUL . MINN. Nov. 30. around, 1897. below. Rv: Blank. Plain edge.

E. ROHRBECK

Rulau	Date	Metal	Size	VG	F	VF	Unc
Stp 38	(1880-97)	Brass	24mm	—	—	10.00	—

(Ornament) / E. ROHRBECK / (ornament). Rv: GOOD FOR / 5 (large, shaded) ¢ / * AT BAR *. (Thoele coll.)

Rohrbeck's saloon was in St. Paul 1880's to 1897. In the latter year he relocated his business to Stevens Point, Wis.

ANDREW SCHOCH GROCERY CO.

St. Paul, Minn.

Rulau	Date	Metal	Size	VG	F	VF	Unc
Stp 42	(1890's)	Brass	23mm	—	—	35.00	—

THE ANDREW SCHOCH GROCERY CO. / SODA / WATER. Rv: Large 5. Plain edge.

The Schoch grocery store was located at 298 East 7th Street. It was in business from 1886 to 1933.

Rulau	Date	Metal	Size	F	VF	EF	Unc
Stp 44	(1893)	Aluminum	38mm	—	—	20.00	30.00

Building. Around: WORLD'S COLUMBIAN EXPOSITION / * ADMINISTRATION BLD'G *. Rv: Building. Around: THE ANDREW SCHOCH GROCERY CO., / * ST. PAUL, MINN. *. Plain edge. (Charles Kirtley report)

The obverse is similar to Eglit 464. This firm was still going strong in the grocery and meat business in 1918.

BARTON & CRABTREE

South St. Paul, Minn.

Rulau	Date	Metal	Size	VG	F	VF	Unc
Ssp 1	(1890's)	Aluminum	39mm	—	—	—	20.00

BARTON & CRABTREE / LIVE STOCK / COMMISSION / BUYERS / QUALITY REMAINS LONG / AFTER PRICE / IS FORGOTTEN / SOUTH ST. PAUL, MINN. Rv: BARTON & CRABTREE / CANADIANS & / WESTERNS / STOCKERS & FEEDERS / A SPECIALTY / FOR HIGH GRADES / WRITE OR SEE US. Plain edge.

SLEEPY EYE STREET FAIR

Sleepy Eye, Minn.

Rulau	Date	Metal	Size	VG	F	VF	Unc
Sly 3	1899	Brass	31mm	—	—	35.00	—

SLEEPY EYE STREET FAIR / 18 (Wheat sheaf and sickle) 99 / OCT. 4, 5, 6. Rv: E. R. WILLIAMSON / MINNEAPOLIS.

STANDARD COMPANY

Sleepy Eye, Minn.

Rulau	Date	Metal	Size	VG	F	VF	Unc
Sly 7	(?)	Cardboard	**	—	—	15.00	—

** Rect 60x34mm.
STANDARD COMPANY / This Ticket will be Received for / FOUR CENTS / In Trade When Properly signed / (signature) Vice-Pres. / (signature) Sec.-Treas. Rv: Blank. (George Dillingham coll., ex-Melvin Fuld 1965)

Melvin Fuld believed these tickets were used 1910-15 as merchant scrip. Other denominations surviving in the Dillingham collection are: 1, 2, 3, 5, 10, 25 and 50 cents, plus $1.00 and $5.00.

Signatures examined show a number of men placed ink signatures on these tickets, indicating use over a period of time. One name, P. T. Gulden (?), occurs on both signature lines in some specimens examined.

The Standard Company is listed in the *Dun Directory* for 1918 as a general store for this Brown County community which had 2200 population in WWI.

J. H. BOCK

Spring Hill, Minn.

Rulau	Date	Metal	Size	VG	F	VF	Unc
Sph 1	(1890's)	Brass	25mm	—	—	20.00	—

Billiard table, THE BRUNSWICK BALKE / COLLENDER / COMPY. above, CHECK below. Rv: GOOD FOR / 2 1/2 ¢ / J. H. BOCK / IN / TRADE. Plain edge.

John H. Bock was listed as a general store proprietor in 1896. Mrs. J. H. Bock is listed as a hotel and saloon proprietor in 1900.

Possibly this was issued by J. H. Bock, Kearney, Neb., 1890's saloon. This Bock moved to Grand Island, Neb. about 1905.

H. L. STILLWELL & CO.

Stewartville, Minn.

Rulau	Date	Metal	Size	VG	F	VF	Unc
Stw 4	(1899)	B&A	27mm	—	—	30.00	—

STEWARTVILLE / H. L. / STILLWELL / & CO. / . MINN. . Rv: GOOD FOR / Large 25 / PAT. / APPLD. FOR / IN MERCHANDISE. Plain edge. (Grinolds coll.)

PETER TAVERNA

Wabasha, Minn.

Rulau	Date	Metal	Size	VG	F	VF	Unc
Wab 2	(1896-99)	Brass	Oval 25x28mm	5.00	—	—	—

(All incused): PETER / TAVERNA. Rv: GOOD FOR / 5 ¢ / AT THE BAR. (Thoele coll., ex-Bill White)

Only 1 piece reported. This saloon was listed in the 1896 through 1906 gazetteers.

HANSCOM'S BAKERY

Willmar, Minn.

Rulau	Date	Metal	Size	VG	F	VF	Unc
Wlm 5	(1890's)	Aluminum	25mm	—	—	10.00	—

HANSCOM'S / BAKERY / WILLMAR, / MINN. Rv: GOOD FOR / 1 / LOAF / OF / BREAD.

A. F. Hanscom is listed in directories under flour 1886-1909. A. B. Hanscom is listed as a baker in 1890. Hanscom Brothers, confectionery and bakery, appears in the 1900 directory.

J. W. JENNESS

Windom, Minn.

Rulau	Date	Metal	Size	VG	F	VF	Unc
Wnd 3	(1892)	Brass	25mm	—	—	35.00	—

THE BRUNSWICK BALKE / COLLENDER / COMPY. / (pool table) / CHECK. Rv: GOOD FOR / 5 ¢ / J. W. / JENNESS / IN / TRADE. (Thoele coll.)

Saloon, listed in the 1892 directory. Only 1 piece known.

E. J. FAKLER

Winona, Minn.

Rulau	Date	Metal	Size	VG	F	VF	Unc
Wnn 2	(1899)	Brass	21mm	—	3.50	—	—

E. J. FAKLER. Rv: E. J. FAKLER / 5 ¢ / IN TRADE. 10-15 pieces known.

Listed in 1899 through 1909 gazetteers.

H. C. GERNES

Rulau	Date	Metal	Size	VG	F	VF	Unc
Wnn 3	(1896-99)	GS	24mm	—	6.50	—	—

H. C. GERNES, PROP. / OF THE / BAR / 163 E. 3RD ST. Rv: GOOD FOR / 5 ¢ / IN TRADE. Plain edge.

Saloon, listed in the 1896 through 1908 gazetteers. Some 10 to 15 tokens may exist.

GRIESEL BROS.

Winona, Minn.

Rulau	Date	Metal	Size	VG	F	VF	Unc
Wnn 4	(1892-1910)	Brass	21mm	—	—	3.50	—

GRIESEL / BROS. Rv: GOOD FOR / 5 ¢ / IN TRADE. (Thoele coll.)

Saloon, listed in the 1892-93 gazetteer. 30 to 40 pieces known.

HIGH BRIDGE

Rulau	Date	Metal	Size	VG	F	VF	Unc
Wnn 5	1892	Aluminum	37mm	—	—	15.00	—

Bridge, ships steaming beneath, HIGH BRIDGE above, WINONA, MINN. below. Rv: CELEBRATION HIGH BRIDGE / SOUVENIR (radiant) / WINONA 1892 JULY 4TH. Plain edge. (Grinolds coll.)

Rulau	Date	Metal	Size	VG	F	VF	Unc
Wnn 6	1892	Aluminum	38mm	—	—	15.00	—

Courthouse, WINONA COUNTY COURT HOUSE around, 1892 below. Rv: SOUVENIR / OF / BRIDGE CELEBRATION / (bridge) / WINONA MINN / JULY 4TH 1892. Plain edge.

JOHN HILBERT

Rulau	Date	Metal	Size	VG	F	VF	Unc
Wnn 8	(1893)	Brass	24mm	—	—	10.00	—

JOHN HILBERT / GOOD FOR / 5 ¢ / DRINK. Rv: Blank. (McFerran report)

The 1893 R. G. Dun directory lists this business.

NATIONAL HOTEL

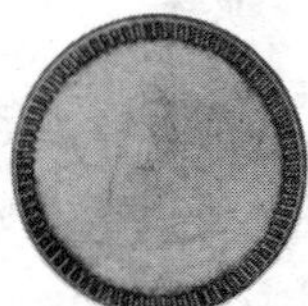

Rulau	Date	Metal	Size	VG	F	VF	Unc
Wnn 11	(?)	Brass	20mm	—	—	6.00	—

NATIONAL HOTEL / 227 / W. 2ND ST. / WINONA, / MINNESOTA. Rv: Blank. Dentilated rim on each side. Plain edge.

WINONA WAGON CO.

Winona, Minn.

Rulau	Date	Metal	Size	VG	F	VF	Unc
Wnn 21	(?)	Silver	33mm	—	—	25.00	—

WINONA / WAGON CO. / WINONA, MINN. Rv: IRON / CLAD / HUB. Plain edge.

This wagon manufacturer, located at 1009 West 5th, was in business 1886 to 1923.

DRETCHKO & KORTH

Winthrop, Minn.

Rulau	Date	Metal	Size	VG	F	VF	Unc
Win 4	1899	Brass	19mm	—	15.00	—	—

DRETCHKO & KORTH / 1899 / WINTHROP, / MINN. Rv: GOOD FOR / 1 C / IN / MERCHANDISE. Plain edge.

This general store is listed in 1899-1900.

JOSEPH KLOBE

Young America, Minn.

Rulau	Date	Metal	Size	VG	F	VF	Unc
Yng 2	(1886-94)	Brass	24mm	—	—	20.00	—

Billiard table, THE J. M. BRUNSWICK / & / BALKE COS above. Rv: GOOD FOR / 5 C / JOSEPH / KLOBE / IN / TRADE.

Saloon, in operation 1886 to 1894.

V. DROZDA

Zumbrota, Minn.

Rulau	Date	Metal	Size	VG	F	VF	Unc
Zum 1	(1898)	Brass	23mm	—	10.00	—	—

(All incused): GOOD FOR / 5 C / IN TRADE / V. DROZDA. Rv: Blank. Plain edge.

This general store was listed in 1898.

13TH REGT. MINN. VOL.

Minnesota

Rulau	Date	Metal	Size	VG	F	VF	Unc
Stt 1	1899	Gilt/B	23mm	—	—	5.00	—

-**- / WELCOME / 13TH / REGT. MINN. VOL. Rv: -**- / SOUVENIR / -*- / COPYRIGHT APPLD. FOR. Plain edge. Issued holed.

It is not known at this time where the headquarters of the 13th Regiment of Minnesota Volunteers was located in 1899.

MISSISSIPPI

E. C. JOULLIAN PACKING CO.

Biloxi, Miss.

Rulau	Date	Metal	Size	VG	F	VF	Unc
Bxi 3	(ca 1900)	Brass	Sc 23mm	—	—	18.00	—

E. C. JOULLIAN PACKING CO. / -x- / BILOXI / MISS / -. Rv: NOT TRANSFERABLE / 1 / CUP. Plain edge. (Thoele coll.)

THE F. B. P. & M. CO.

Fallback, Miss.

Rulau	Date	Metal	Size	VG	F	VF	Unc
Fal 1	(1885-1900)	Brass	21mm	—	—	35.00	—

THE F. B. P & M CO. / FALLBACK. Rv: 5 ¢. Plain edge. (Joseph Schmidt coll.)

G. W. THOMAS & CO.

Mississippi ?

Rulau	Date	Metal	Size	VG	F	VF	Unc
Unk 1	(1890's)	Brass	20mm	—	—	3.50	—

(All incused): G. W. THOMAS / -o- / & CO. Rv: 2 ¢ / IN MDSE. Plain edge.

Supposedly from either Mississippi or Virginia.

MISSOURI

N. STURGIS
Aurora, Mo.

Rulau	Date	Metal	Size	VG	F	VF	Unc
Aur 3	(1893)	Brass	24mm	—	—	25.00	—

Brunswick die BBC. Rv: GOOD FOR / 5 ¢ / N. STURGIS (in panel) / * IN * / TRADE. Plain edge. (Elmer Randall coll.)

Norman Sturgis is listed as a saloonkeeper in Britton, Dakota Territory, in 1886, and then in Claremont, Dakota Territory in 1888. His listing under saloons in the 1893 gazetteer at Aurora, Missouri, is the most likely site for the token, Hank Thoele says.

W. BROS.
(Wilmesherr Brothers)
Bourbon, Mo.

Rulau	Date	Metal	Size	F	VF	EF	Unc
Bou 1	1900	Brass	Scal --mm	—	15.00	—	—

W. BROS. / 1900. Rv: 25. Plain edge. (Kirtley Oct. 1985 sale, lot 15)

Issued by the Wilmesherr Brothers general store in Bourbon, Crawford County, Mo., a village which boasted 382 people in 1910. The Wilmesherr family pretty much was Bourbon in the early part of the century. For example in 1918 Wilmesherr & Co. ran a general store, Fritz K. Wilmesherr owned the only hotel, and William Wilmesherr owned the sawmill.

C. C. MUELLER'S SALOON
California, Mo.

Rulau	Date	Metal	Size	F	VF	EF	Unc
Cal 1	(?)	Aluminum	--mm	—	25.00	—	—

C. C. MUELLERS SALOON. Rv: 2 1/2. Plain edge. (Kirtley Oct. 1985 sale, lot 24)

A possible successor, Mueller & Heinrichs restaurant, is listed in 1918.

A. S.
(August Shivelbine)
Cape Girardeau, Mo.

Rulau	Date	Metal	Size	VG	F	VF	Unc
Cpg 3	(1893-98)	Aluminum	Sq 24mm	—	35.00	—	—

ARCADE SALOON / A. S. / CAPE / GIRARDEAU / MO. Rv: GOOD FOR / 2 1/2 ¢ / ARCADE (on panel) / IN / TRADE. Arranged in diamond fashion. Plain edge. (ATCO May 1993 sale, lot 1)

August Shivelbine was listed under saloons in the 1893 and 1898 gazetteers.

OSBORNE NEWS CO.
Carthage, Mo.

Rulau	Date	Metal	Size	VG	F	VF	Unc
Car 3	(1895)	Aluminum	18mm	—	10.00	15.00	—

OSBORNE NEWS CO., / CARTHAGE, / * / * / * MO. *. GOOD FOR / ONE / 5 ¢ / CIGAR. Plain edge. (Elmer Randall coll.)

Henry A. Osborne appears in the 1895 city directory as proprietor of Osborne News Co. at 1364 So. Maple St. Not listed in the 1899 directory.

SMITH BAKING CO.

Rulau	Date	Metal	Size	VG	F	VF	Unc
Car 6	(1899)	Aluminum	Oct 25mm	—	15.00	25.00	—

SMITH BAKING CO. / - / CARTHAGE / - / ** MO. **. Rv: GOOD FOR ONE / 5 ¢ / LOAF BREAD. Plain edge. (Elmer Randall coll.)

The 1899 city directory lists this firm at corner 5th and Main Streets. They are not listed in the 1905-06 directory.

UNION TRUST CO.
Carthage, Mo.

Rulau	Date	Metal	Size	VG	F	VF	Unc
Car 11	(1913)	Aluminum	21mm	—	—	1.00	1.50

A strawberry. Rv: UNION TRUST CO. / - / ONE / QUART / (scroll) / CARTHAGE, MO. Plain edge. (Rulau coll.)

Strawberry pickers' chit. A 24mm aluminum token reading ONE TRAY is also reported. A hoard of these pieces is on the market.

A. H. WITT
Carthage, Mo.

Rulau	Date	Metal	Size	VG	F	VF	Unc
Car 15	(1891-98)	Brass	24mm	—	25.00	—	—

Brunswick die BB. Rv: GOOD FOR 5 ¢ IN TRADE / . . . round central circle. Within circle: .A.H. / WITT. Plain edge. (Elmer Randall coll.; ATCO Dec. 1992 sale, lot 107)

A. H. Witt's billiard hall appears in the 1891, 1893, 1895, 1898 and 1904 gazetteers in Carthage. The only known copy is dug.

DAVIS & DEEM
Chula, Mo.

Rulau	Date	Metal	Size	F	VF	EF	Unc
Chu 1	(?)	Aluminum	**	5.00	7.50	—	—

** Octagonal, 26mm.

DAVIS & DEEM / GENERAL / MERCHANDISE / CHULA / MO. Rv: GOOD FOR / 10 / IN / MERCHANDISE. Plain edge. (Wright 1389)

Post office in Chula, Livingston County, opened 1888. The 1899 population was 300.

FLEER & LANGENBERG
Cooper Hill, Mo.

Rulau	Date	Metal	Size	VG	F	VF	Unc
Coo 1	(1890's)	Cardboard	38mm	—	—	10.00	—

PAYABLE ON DEMAND IN MERCHANDISE / CENT 1 CENT / *** FLEER & LANGENBERG ***. Rv: THIS CHECK IS GOOD FOR / ONE CENT / IN GOODS / AT THE STORE OF / (Handwritten) Fleer & Langenberg / (handwritten) Cooper Hill Mo / COUNTERSIGNED. Black printing on yellow cardboard.

Rulau	Date	Metal	Size	VG	F	VF	Unc
Coo 2	(1890's)	Cardboard	38mm	—	—	25.00	—

Similar, but 2 CENTS.

Rulau	Date	Metal	Size	VG	F	VF	Unc
Coo 3	(1890's)	Cardboard	38mm	—	—	10.00	—

Similar, but 5 CENTS. Green cardboard.

Rulau	Date	Metal	Size	VG	F	VF	Unc
Coo 4	(1890's)	Cardboard	38mm	—	—	10.00	—

Similar, but 10 CENTS. Orange.

Rulau	Date	Metal	Size	VG	F	VF	Unc
Coo 5	(1890's)	Cardboard	38mm	—	—	10.00	—

Similar, but 25 CENTS. Yellow.

Coo 6	(1890's)	Cardboard	38mm	—	—	10.00	—

Similar, but 50 CENTS. Blue.

Coo 7	(1890's)	Cardboard	38mm	—	—	10.00	—

Similar, but $1oo. White cardboard.

Originally in the lumber business at Cooper Hill, the Langenbergs later ran a general store. August Langenberg retired from business in the 1950's.

The store, built about 1857, is still standing (see photo above) and is now an antique shop.

DUENWEG STATE BANK
Duenweg, Mo.

Rulau	Date	Metal	Size	F	VF	EF	Unc
Due 1	(1912)	Aluminum	22.8mm	—	1.00	1.25	—

DUENWEG / STATE / BANK / DUENWEG, MO. Rv: (Ornament) / ONE QUART / (ornament). Pain edge.

Due 2	(1912)	Aluminum	28.5mm	—	1.00	1.25	1.50

Obverse as last. Rv: + * + / ONE TRAY / SIX QUARTS / + * +. Plain edge.

Due 3	(1912)	Aluminum	35.2mm	—	1.00	1.25	1.50

Obverse as last. Rv: (Ornament) / ONE CRATE / 24 QUARTS / (ornament). Plain edge.

A hoard of these pieces was uncovered about 1965, making them one of the easiest Missouri strawberry pickers' chits to locate.

HIGGINS POOL HALL
Flat River, Mo.

Rulau	Date	Metal	Size	F	VF	EF	Unc
Fla 1	(?)	Aluminum	Scal --mm	—	3.00	—	—

HIGGINS POOL HALL. Rv: 2 1/2. Plain edge. (Kirtley Oct. 1985 sale, lot 55)

Definitely before 1917-18.

GUSTAV FEIL & SON
Gebler, Mo.

Rulau	Date	Metal	Size	VG	F	VF	Unc
Geb 1	(1901)	Cardboard	38mm	—	—	10.00	25.00

THIS CHECK IS GOOD / NO. .... AT THE STORE OF / GUSTAV FEIL & SON, / GENERAL MERCHANTS, / R.F.D. NO. 3 HERMANN, MO. / NOT TRANS. / FOR AMOUNT SHOWN ON BACK. Rv: Large numeral 10 on ornamental cartouche, TEN CENTS IN TRADE above, SOLD BY / GEO. D. BARNARD & CO., ST. LOUIS. Black printing on yellow cardboard. (Charles Kirtley Oct. 1985 sale, lot 58)

Though the check states "Hermann, Mo." on its face, the Gustav Feil & Son general store was located in Gebler, Mo., population 31, which had no post office of its own and was served by rural delivery from Hermann. Both communities are in Gasconade County.

The Feil store was still listed in 1915-27, the only other business in Gebler in WWI being the blacksmith shop of W. Woerner.

Printed for Feil by the George D. Barnard firm in St. Louis. Other denominations in this series include 1, 5, 25, 50 cents and $1.

HANNIBAL BILLIARD HALL
Hannibal, Mo.

Rulau	Date	Metal	Size	VG	F	VF	Unc
Han 1	(?)	Brass	22mm	—	25.00	—	—

Indian head left within beaded circle. Rv: HANNIBAL BILLIARD HALL / S....Y FIRST / 2 1/2 C/ IN TRADE. Plain edge. Legend partly illegible.

FRANK PIGG
Hendrickson, Mo.

Rulau	Date	Metal	Size	VG	F	VF	Unc
Hen 1	(?)	Aluminum	25mm	—	10.00	20.00	—

GOOD FOR / 2 1/2 ¢ / FRANK PIGG / -IN- / TRADE. Rv: Blank. Plain edge. Rare. (Rulau coll.)

Hen 2	(?)	Brass	--mm	—	5.00	10.00	—

FRANK PIGG, HENDRICKSON, MO. Rv: 25. Plain edge. (Kirtley Oct. 1985 sale, lot 66)

Hendrickson (Butler County) claimed 150 population in 1918. By this time Pigg was out of business.

B.P.O.E. 501
Joplin, Mo.

Rulau	Date	Metal	Size	VG	F	VF	Unc
Jop 1	(?)	Aluminum	Oct --mm	—	—	3.00	—

B.P.O.E. NO. 501. Rv: 5. Plain edge.

Jop 2	(?)	Aluminum	--mm	—	—	3.00	—

Similar, but $1.00. Plain edge.

B.P.O.E. = Benevolent and Protective Order of Elks.

CONNOR BAR

Rulau	Date	Metal	Size	VG	F	VF	Unc
Jop 4	(?)	Aluminum	Scal --mm	—	5.00	—	—

HAM SANDWICH. CONNOR BAR. JOPLIN, MO. Rv: 2 1/2. Plain edge.

The Connor Hotel Co. is still listed in 1918. The bar was in the hotel.

THE PALACE BAR

Rulau	Date	Metal	Size	VG	F	VF	Unc
Jop 6	(?)	Aluminum	--mm	—	5.00	—	—

THE PALACE BAR. J. HERMAN ECKART. JOPLIN, MO. Rv: 2 1/2. Plain edge.

By 1918, J.H. and H.J. Eckart managed the saloon.

REX

Rulau	Date	Metal	Size	VG	F	VF	Unc
Jop 8	(?)	Brass	--mm	—	5.00	—	—

REX. Rv: 2 1/2. Plain edge. (Kirtley Oct. 1985 sale, lot 81)

Rex Billiard Co. was listed in 1918 in Joplin.

B. F. SHOUSE
Joplin, Mo.

Rulau	Date	Metal	Size	VG	F	VF	Unc
Jop 10	(?)	Aluminum	Scal --mm	—	5.00	—	—

B. F. SHOUSE. DRUGGIST. Rv: 5. Plain edge.

EYSSELL'S
Kansas City, Mo.

Rulau	Date	Metal	Size	VG	F	VF	Unc
Kan 1	(1899)	Brass	Oct --mm	—	—	6.00	—

EYSSELL'S / 1052 UNION AVE. Rv: 5. Plain edge. (Kirtley Oct. 1985 sale, lot 86)

George Eyssell is listed in the 1899 R. L. Polk directory. The George Eyssell Drug Co. is still listed in 1918. The token may postdate the Gay Nineties.

FERD. HEIM BRG. CO.

Rulau	Date	Metal	Size	VG	F	VF	Unc
Kan 3	(1890)	Aluminum	26mm	—	—	75.00	—

PURE / ALUMINUM / * PRESENTED BY / FERD. HEIM BRG. CO. / KANSAS CITY =MO=. Rv: & 11 / F. H. B. CO. Plain edge. (Wright 345)

After the commercial preparation of aluminum by electrolysis became practical late in 1888, the metal enjoyed several years of intense use as a novelty in the manufacture of medals, trade checks and store cards. This extended through the World's Columbian Exposition in Chicago in 1893 and then gradually tapered off.

Ferdinand Heim was born in Austria. He came to America in 1854, moving to Missouri in 1857. The Ferd. Heim Brewing Co. was organized in 1884. Ferdinand died in 1895, but the business was continued by his son, Ferdinand Heim Jr. It was still in operation in 1905.

KANSAS CITY KARNIVAL

Rulau	Date	Metal	Size	VG	F	VF	Unc
Kan 14	1897	Brass	19mm	—	—	5.00	7.00

Jester bust facing, crossed pike and trident behind his head. Rv: KANSAS CITY / 1897 / KARNIVAL / AND / FLOWER PARADE amid flourishes. Plain edge. (Kirtley March 1898 sale, lot 105A)

J. W. LAWSON

Rulau	Date	Metal	Size	VG	F	VF	Unc
Kan 17	(1898)	Brass	25mm	—	—	10.00	—

CAFE ROYAL / -.- / J. W. LAWSON. Rv: GOOD FOR / 12 1/2 ¢ / IN TRADE. (Hank Thoele coll.)

MODERN WOODMEN OF AMERICA

Rulau	Date	Metal	Size	F	VF	EF	Unc
Kan 20	1899	Copper	28mm	—	—	—	10.00

MODERN WOODMEN OF AMERICA / KANSAS CITY CONVENTION / 1899. Issued with loop. (Denis Loring coll.)

PRIEST PALLAS CARNIVAL

Rulau	Date	Metal	Size	VG	F	VF	Unc
Kan 25	1898	Brass	18.5mm	3.00	4.00	5.50	7.00

Jester head facing, divides 18--98. Around: PRIEST PALLAS / CARNIVAL / KANSAS CITY. Rv: Liberty head left within circle. Outside circle are 26 stars. Plain edge. (Larry Grinstead coll.)

C. W. PURVIS

Kansas City, Mo.

Rulau	Date	Metal	Size	F	VF	EF	Unc
Kan 30	(1890's)	Aluminum	32mm	—	15.00	—	—

C. W. PURVIS PROP / THE / DIZZY / CAFE / 307 & 309 W. 9TH ST KANSAS CITY. Rv: 2 1/2 C / IN TRADE at center. Around: HEADQUARTERS FOR THEATRICAL PEOPLE. (Wright 856)

ROCHESTER BREWING CO.

Kansas City, Mo.

Rulau	Date	Metal	Size	VG	F	VF	Unc
Kan 38	(1889-1902)	Brass	28mm	—	—	20.00	—

ROCHESTER BREWING CO. / KANSAS CITY. MO. around empty circle, on which numeral 127 has been incused. Rv: Beaded circle frames empty center. On each side is a heavy incised, beaded rim. Plain edge. (Elmer Randall coll.)

Researcher Kent Kavanaugh reports the Rochester Brewing Co. was opened about 1889 by Iler and Burgweger. Still listed 1902, it had disappeared before 1918.

B. P. COBB

New Madrid, Mo.

Rulau	Date	Metal	Size	VG	F	VF	Unc
Nmd 1	(1891-94)	Brass	24mm	8.00	—	—	—

B. P. COBB (incuse on rim) / GOOD FOR / 1 / LOAF BREAD. Rv: Blank. Token adapted from stock planchet. (Thoele coll.)

B. P. Cobb's bakery was listed at New Madrid 1891-1892 and then at Odessa, Mo 1893-1894. It likely was in use at both sites.

New Madrid is at the epicenter of the so-called "New Madrid Fault," an earthquake-prone area last devastated in 1811-12.

APPLETON MERC. CO.

Old Appleton, Mo.

Rulau	Date	Metal	Size	VG	F	VF	Unc
Old 1	(1917)	Cardboard	38mm	—	5.00	10.00	15.00

APPLETON MERC. CO. OLD APPLETON, MO. Rv: 10. Black printing on red cardboard.

Rulau	Date	Metal	Size	VG	F	VF	Unc
Old 2	(1917)	Cardboard	38mm	—	—	15.00	22.50

Similar to last, but $5.00. Black printing on white cardboard.

Old Appleton, Cape Girardeau County, had 200 people in 1918, but the Appleton Mercantile Company had disappeared by then.

FRED ALBERTS

Pierce City, Mo.

Rulau	Date	Metal	Size	VG	F	VF	Unc
Pie 1	(?)	Brass	--mm	—	—	5.00	—

FRED ALBERTS. Rv: 10 C / LOAF. Plain edge. (Kirtley Oct. 1985 sale, lot 131)

Fred Albert is listed as proprietor of a bakery and restaurant in Pierce City in 1917-18, and probably earlier and later.

J. & F. CRAWFORD

Pierce City, Mo. ?

Rulau	Date	Metal	Size	VG	F	VF	Unc
Pie 3	ND	Aluminum	**	—	—	10.00	—

** Rect 38x60mm.
1 QT. (Kirtley March 1991 sale, lot 1636)

Rulau	Date	Metal	Size	VG	F	VF	Unc
Pie 4	ND	Aluminum	--mm	—	—	10.00	—

As last, but 1 TRAY.

Rulau	Date	Metal	Size	VG	F	VF	Unc
Pie 5	ND	Aluminum	--mm	—	—	10.00	—

As last, but 1 CRATE.

W. W. LOCKE & CO.

Pierce City, Mo.

Rulau	Date	Metal	Size	VG	F	VF	Unc
Pie 7	(?)	Brass	31mm	3.75	6.75	11.00	—

W. W. LOCKE & CO. / *** / 1oo (ornate) / *** / PIERCE CITY, MO. Rv: GOOD FOR / —.— / 1oo (ornate) / -IN- / MERCHANDISE. Plain edge.

Illustrated specimen has been slotted in four positions for some purpose. Charles Kirtley says it was cut-canceled; this explanation makes sense.

Rulau	Date	Metal	Size	VG	F	VF	Unc
Pie 9	(1890's)	Aluminum	32mm	—	15.00	22.50	—

Cock standing left, at center, W. W. LOCKE & CO. above, PEIRCE CITY, MO. below. Rv: GOOD FOR + 25 ¢+ / IN MERCHANDISE. Plain edge. (Rulau coll.)

Cut-canceled? See preceding entry. Pierce is misspelled 'Pierce' on Pie 7. Peirce City is in Lawrence County. After WWII the city was renamed Pierce.

TURNER-FRAZER MERCANTILE CO.

St. Joseph, Mo.

Rulau	Date	Metal	Size	F	VF	EF	Unc
Sjo 3	(1893)	Aluminum	37mm	—	—	35.00	50.00

Columbus bust. Rv: Within wreath: FINE / TEAS / AND / CIGARS. Around: TURNER-FRAZER MERCANTILE Co. / (Rosette) ST. JOSEPH. MO. (rosette). (Eglit 503; Kirtley Oct. 1993 sale, lot 1635)

ANHEUSER BUSCH

St. Louis, Mo.

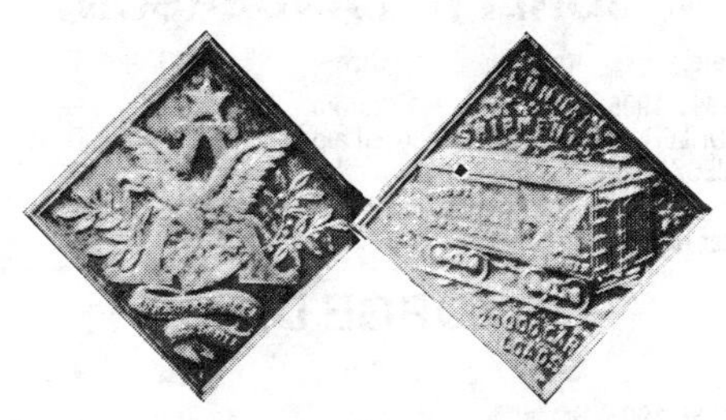

Rulau	Date	Metal	Size	VG	F	VF	Unc
STL 1	(1890-95)	Silver	**	—	—	35.00	55.00

** Diamond-shaped flan, 22 by 22mm.

Defiant eagle perched on the bar of a large letter A, star above. On two folds of a scroll below: ANHEUSER BUSCH / ST. LOUIS. Rv: Box car at center, lettered: REFRIGERATOR / FAUST'S OWN / ORIGINAL / BUDWEISER / (defiant eagle). Above: ANNUAL / SHIPMENTS. Below: 20000 CAR / LOADS. Plain edge.

This superbly executed piece was probably given to Anheuser Busch Brewing Co. distributors and may originally have been issued with ring for use as a watch fob.

(For tokens of Anheuser Busch issued in the 1880's, see *U.S. Trade Tokens 1866-1885*.)

FRANK J. DIEKMANN

Rulau	Date	Metal	Size	VG	F	VF	Unc
STL 3	(1893)	Aluminum	30mm	25.00	35.00	50.00	—

Columbus' ships. 2 1/2. Rv: FRANK J. DIEKMANN. ST. LOUIS, MO. COLUMBIAN EXPO. Plain edge. (Kirtley Oct. 1985 sale, lot 149; Eglit 534)

The only reported specimen was dug up. It is corroded, and holed in the center.

The only Diekmann listed in St. Louis in the 1918 edition of R. G. Dun's directory is Herman A. Diekmann, a saloonkeeper, who may be a successor.

G. W. GITTINS

Rulau	Date	Metal	Size	VG	F	VF	Unc
STL 4	(1898)	Brass	Triang 30x28mm	—	—	15.00	—

(All incused): G. W. GITTINS / 10 ¢ . Rv: F. MESSMER / MFG. CO. / ST. LOUIS. Only 3 pieces known.

G. W. Gittins, saloon, at 6861 Manchester Avenue in 1898.

HOYLE & RARICK CLOTHING CO.

Rulau	Date	Metal	Size	VG	F	VF	Unc
STL 5	(1890's)	Aluminum	38mm	—	8.00	11.00	—

Liberty head with flowered coiffure right, within beaded central circle. Around: GOOD FOR $1.00 AT HOYLE & RARICK CLO. CO . . . . / * 810 * / N. BROADWAY. Reeded edge. (Rulau coll.)

The obverse design was used sparingly in a number of central U.S. localities in states such as Texas, Missouri and Illinois. The workmanship is crude.

KELLEY GOODFELLOW SHOE CO.

Rulau	Date	Metal	Size	VG	F	VF	Unc
STL 6	(1890's)	Aluminum	26mm	—	—	10.00	—

Dog within a wreath. Rv: KELLEY GOODFELLOW SHOE CO. / MAKERS / ST. LOUIS, MO. Plain edge. (Wright 1481)

A. KLUEPPEL

Rulau	Date	Metal	Size	VG	F	VF	Unc
STL 7	(1889-99)	Brass	23mm	—	—	3.50	—

A. KLUEPPEL (incuse around rim) / GOOD FOR / 5 ¢ / DRINK / (star). Rv: Blank. Plain edge. Token adapted from a stock planchet.

August Klueppel had a saloon at 2857 Cherokee and later at 720 Soulard in the 1889-1899 period. This token has been called "very common."

ST. LOUIS REFRIGERATOR & WOODEN GUTTER CO.

St. Louis, Mo.

Rulau	Date	Metal	Size	F	VF	EF	Unc
STL 8	(1894)	Aluminum	--mm	—	—	30.00	—

At center: Two scrolls above: Lu-Mi-Num. Two scrolls with U.S. shield between, below. The four scrolls read: MANUFACTURER / OF / ALUMINUM / BICYCLES. Around all: ST. LOUIS REFRIGERATOR & WOODEN GUTTER CO. / * ST. LOUIS, MO. *. Rv: Within wreath: 1894 / (nine lines of text with bicycle right at center). Plain edge. (Kirtley Aug. 1989 NCES sale, lot 372)

NICK SWOPE

St. Louis, Mo. (?)

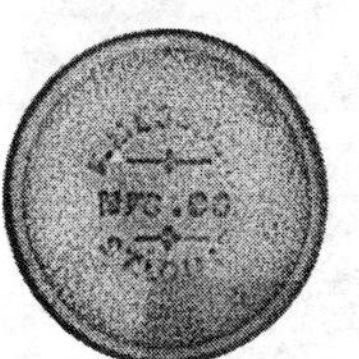

Rulau	Date	Metal	Size	F	VF	EF	Unc
STL 9	(1891-)	Brass	23mm	—	—	14.00	—

NICK SWOPE / GOOD FOR / 10 ¢ / IN TRADE / (ornament). Rv: F. MESSMER / MFG. CO. / ST. LOUIS. Plain edge. (John Cheramy coll.)

It is possible this issuer is connected with the Joel Swope who issued Centennial store cards in 1876 and whose shoe firm is still in business.

BANK OF SARCOXIE

Sarcoxie, Mo.

Rulau	Date	Metal	Size	F	VF	EF	Unc
Sar 1	(1890's)	Aluminum	--mm	—	1.00	—	—

A strawberry. Rv: BANK OF / ONE / QUART / SARCOXIE. There are two die varieties. Plain edge. (Bruce Smith coll.)

Rulau	Date	Metal	Size	F	VF	EF	Unc
Sar 2	(1890's)	Aluminum	--mm	—	—	—	—

Obverse as 1. Rv: BANK OF / 6 / QUARTS / SARCOXIE. Plain edge. (Reported)

Rulau	Date	Metal	Size				
Sar 3	(1890's)	Aluminum	32mm	—	—	1.00	—

A strawberry. Rv: BANK OF / ONE / TRAY / SARCOXIE. Plain edge. (Wright 1612)

Rulau	Date	Metal	Size				
Sar 4	(1890's)	Aluminum	38mm	—	—	3.00	—

A strawberry. Rv: BANK OF / ONE / CRATE / SARCOXIE. Plain edge. (Bruce Smith coll.)

Strawberry pickers' chit. These were redeemable at the Bank of Sarcoxie and paid out to workers by growers in Jasper County, Missouri.

Similar chits were issued by the Duenweg State Bank, Duenweg, Mo., and Union Trust Co., Carthage, Mo., which see in this reference.

The bank was organized 1883. It became First National Bank of Sarcoxie in 1900. About 1976-77 the old bank building was demolished and 12 bank bags of these tokens were found.

CHAS. S. DEXTER
Sedalia, Mo.

Rulau	Date	Metal	Size	VG	F	VF	Unc
Sed 4	(1890's)	Brass	Oct 25mm	—	—	17.50	—

(Incuse) CHAS. S. DEXTER / GOOD FOR / - / STORY / - / PAPER / (incuse) SEDALIA MO. Rv: HASKELL ENG. CO. / ST. LOUIS / *.

FRED PFOTENHAUER
Sedalia, Mo.

Rulau	Date	Metal	Size	VG	F	VF	Unc
Sed 18	(1898)	Brass	24mm	—	—	25.00	—

FRED PFOTENHAUER / * / THE FAUST / - / SALOON. Rv: GOOD FOR / -.- / 5 C / -.- / IN TRADE.

Saloon, listed in 1898. Only 1 piece known.

BOLLINGER CANNING CO.
Seymour, Mo.

Rulau	Date	Metal	Size	VG	F	VF	Unc
Sey 1	(?)	Brass	19mm	—	—	8.00	—

BOLLINGER CANNING CO. PEELING CHECK. Plain edge.

AMERICAN MILKING SHORTHORN SOCIETY
Springfield, Mo.

Rulau	Date	Metal	Size	VG	F	VF	Unc
Spg 1	(?)	Bronze	32mm	—	—	10.00	—

Cow left. In exergue: AMERICAN MILKING / SHORTHORN / SOCIETY. Rv: MILKING SHORTHORNS / "THE / BREED / THAT FILLS / EVERY NEED" / MEMBER. Plain edge. Issued holed. (Thoele coll.)

Membership medalet, well struck.

A. K. AMOLOWSKY
Union, Mo.

Rulau	Date	Metal	Size	VG	F	VF	Unc
Uni 1	(?)	Aluminum	--mm	—	20.00	—	Scarce

A. K. AMOLOWKSY. 40. UNION, MO. Rv: GOOD FOR 1 GALLON $2.00 WHISKEY. Plain edge.

The only reported specimen, which surfaced in 1985, was excavated. Amolowsky is no longer listed in 1917-18.

J. E. SCHINTZINS
Missouri ?

Rulau	Date	Metal	Size	F	VF	EF	Unc
Mo 1	(1890's)	Brass	25mm	—	—	10.00	—

GOOD FOR / BERRY / CRATE / J. E. SCHINTZINS. Rv: 25 within a circle of stars. Plain edge. (Wright 1647)

This could be earlier, in the 1880's. Possibly Maryland.

NOTE: The following group of mavericks may belong to Missouri. They were, in each case, struck there.

J. T. ELDER
Missouri ?

Rulau	Date	Metal	Size	VG	F	VF	Unc
Unk 1	(?)	Brass	21mm	—	—	4.50	—

(All incused): GOOD FOR / 1 / DRINK / 12 1/2 / J. T. ELDER . Rv: J. G. HARRIS & CO / ST. LOUIS. 4 to 6 pieces known.

S. E. GUINN

Rulau	Date	Metal	Size	VG	F	VF	Unc
Unk 2	(1888-1906)	Brass	24mm	—	—	9.50	—

S. E. GUINN (incused along rim) / GOOD FOR / 5 CTS. Rv: KOKEN B.S. / CO. / ST. LOUIS. (Thoele coll.)

Koken Barber Supplies Co. normally supplied barbers and allied tradesmen with its tokens.

JOHLER & ANDERSON

Rulau	Date	Metal	Size	VG	F	VF	Unc
Unk 3	(1891-1906)	Brass	23mm	—	—	10.00	—

JOHLER & ANDERSON (incused along rim) / GOOD FOR / 5 ¢ / AT BAR. Rv: MESSMER / -+- / ST. LOUIS.

Messmer, which made beer pumps for saloons, changed its name from Messmer Faucet Co. to Messmer Mfg. Co. in 1891.

GEORGE D. NIX

Rulau	Date	Metal	Size	VG	F	VF	Unc
Unk 4	(1888-1906)	Brass	23mm	—	—	11.50	—

GEORGE D. NIX'S BARBER SHOP (incused along rim) / GOOD FOR / 1 / SHAVE. Rv: KOKEN B.S. / CO. ST. LOUIS.

O. REID

Rulau	Date	Metal	Size	VG	F	VF	Unc
Unk 5	(1881-1911)	Brass	Oct 23mm	—	—	11.00	—

O. REID (incused along rim) / GOOD FOR / 15 ¢ / (star, incused). Rv: AUG. KERN / B.S. / CO. ST. LOUIS. (Thoele coll.; ex-Joe Copeland)

MONTANA

DOBBIES PLACE
(should be DOBY's PLACE)
Aldridge, Mont.

Rulau	Date	Metal	Size	VG	F	VF	Unc
Ald 3	(1900-01)	Aluminum	26mm	25.00	30.00	40.00	—

DOBBIE's PLACE / ALDRIDGE, MONT. Rv: GOOD FOR / 12 1/2 C / IN TRADE.

Doby Sommerville was known to be in Aldridge as early as 1891. His mother had a large family and ran a boarding house for miners after having moved to Aldridge from Cokedale.

Doby's Place was a saloon known to be operating in 1901. Sommerville and his saloon attracted much newspaper attention in 1904, when his wife died. After that his name disappears from public notice, but Sommervilles are active in Park County to this day.

J. S. S.
Aldridge, Mont. ?

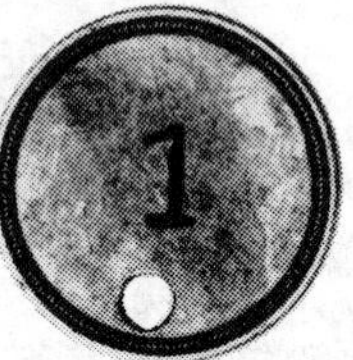

Rulau	Date	Metal	Size	VG	F	VF	Unc
Ald 8	(?)	Brass	23.3mm	—	—	12.50	—

(All incused): GOOD FOR / 5 c / J S S (in panel) / IN / TRADE. Rv: 1. Plain edge. Issued holed.

Attribution by Joseph Zaffern; not verified.

S. C. ST. JOS. NO. 17
(Sisters of Charity of St. Joseph)
Aldridge, Mont.

Rulau	Date	Metal	Size	VG	F	VF	Unc
Ald 10	(?)	—	Scal --mm	25.00	30.00	40.00	—

S. C. ST. JOS. NO. 17 / ALDRIDGE, MONT. Rv: GOOD FOR / 10 C / IN TRADE.

This token was attributed by George F. Gould in his 1978 volume, *Merchant Tokens of Montana 1889-1939*, but nothing is known about the Order or how its token was used.

Aldridge post office was opened in 1896 and closed in 1910, when the mines closed.

"Calamity Jane" Canary is mentioned under Livingston, Montana below, but she also figures in the Aldridge story.

Calamity Jane was a frequent visitor to Montana's mining communities and maintained shacks at both Aldridge and Horr as well as Livingston. The cabin, or shack at Aldridge was located adjacent to Mrs. Sommerville's boarding house (see Dobbies Place) and may have belonged to the Sommerville family.

Calamity Jane was an alcoholic and lived near poverty during these later years of her life. She survived on sales of booklets (depicting her version of her colorful life) and photographs, to tourists, and on the sympathy of friends and frontier compatriots. Her presence was good for business - during those times she was not abusive or violent.

THE MONTANA HOTEL
Anaconda, Mont.

Rulau	Date	Metal	Size	F	VF	EF	Unc
Ana 1	1896	Copper	38.5mm	—	—	60.00	85.00

Building at center, THE MONTANA HOTEL above, ANACONDA below. Tiny C. H. HANSON CHI. on truncation. Rv: Mining scene at center, LOWER WORKS OF THE ANACONDA above, 1896 / COPPER MINING CO. below. Plain edge. Rare. (Wright 1675)

FRANK BLISS
Big Timber, Mont.

Rulau	Date	Metal	Size	VG	F	VF	Unc
	(1893-99)	Brass	23mm	—	—	15.00	—

* FRANK BLISS * / * / 12 1/2 ¢ / *. Rv: GOOD FOR / & / 12 1/2 ¢ / * IN TRADE AT THE BAR *. Plain edge. (Bill Rouleau coll.)

Frank L. Bliss seems to have succeeded H. Bliss' buffet and saloon (1886 on) sometime in 1889. Frank Bliss' saloon is listed 1890-99, then Frank Bliss appears in 1900 as proprietor of Big Timber's Grand Hotel.

FAIR GALLATIN
Bozeman, Mont.

Rulau	Date	Metal	Size	VG	F	VF	Unc
Boz 1	1892	Aluminum	38mm	10.00	15.00	20.00	30.00

Large ornate BCC monogram at center, FAIR GALLATIN / THE EGYPT OF AMERICA AROUND. Rv: VOTE FOR / BOZEMAN / FOR THE / CAPITOL / NOV. 8TH 1892. Plain edge. There are two die varieties, each equally scarce.

The BCC monogram probably stands for Bozeman Chamber of Commerce or Bozeman Commercial Club. Bozeman is the county seat of Gallatin County.

After statehood in 1889 the capital city was to be removed from the territorial capital, Virginia City. An election was held to decide where to place the state capital and Helena won. The Bozeman token was used to promote the city's chances, which were never considered good in Montana. The date on the token was Election Day.

ANACONDA MINE
Butte, Mont.

Rulau	Date	Metal	Size	VG	F	VF	Unc
But 2	1896	Gilt/Bz	38mm	10.00	20.00	40.00	75.00

Stamp mill buildings, ANACONDA MINE above, BUTTE below. Rv: Miner's tools at center, BUTTE MONTANA 1896 above, MINERS TOOLS below. Plain edge. (H-K 734)

F. J. BLISS & CO.
Butte, Mont.

Rulau	Date	Metal	Size	VG	F	VF	Unc
But 4	(1893-99)	Brass	25mm	—	—	60.00	—

Brunswick die BBC-9a. Rv: GOOD FOR / 5 ¢ / F. J. / BLISS & CO / IN / TRADE. Plain edge. (Rouleau coll.)

Frederick J. Bliss operated a saloon and meat market from about 1892 to 1900. This Bliss may have been related to the Bliss family of Big Timber, Montana, also token issuers.

F. J. Bliss is listed at 615 East Mercury Ave. 1893-94 and at 927 Talbot Ave. in 1900.

E. J. DALY

Rulau	Date	Metal	Size	F	VF	EF	Unc
But 9	1893	Bronze	20.5mm	—	100.	125.	—

Female standing, head turned right, holding sword and balance scales. MONTANA SILVER STATUE above, WORLDS FAIR below. 1492 - 1892 at either side of female. Rv: E. J. DALY / - 12 1/2 ¢ - / 1893. Plain edge. (Dick Grinolds coll.)

This piece, unpublished before now, is connected with the World's Columbian Exposition in Chicago in 1893.

HUGHES BROS.

Rulau	Date	Metal	Size	VG	F	VF	Unc
But 15	(1896-97)	Brass	Scal 29mm	—	—	80.00	—

Elk's head left, in beaded circle. Rv: GOOD FOR / 5 ¢ / HUGHES / - BROS. / IN / TRADE. Plain edge. (OK-Un 1 in *U.S. Trade Tokens 1866-1889.*)

Hughes Brothers' saloon is listed under Butte in the 1896-97 R. L. Polk gazette (Hank Thoele research). The only reported specimen, in the Rulau collection, was formerly thought to be an Oklahoma issue.

PARROT MINE

Rulau	Date	Metal	Size	VG	F	VF	Unc
But 26	1896	Gilt/Bz	38mm	25.00	30.00	60.00	85.00

View of stamp-mill buildings, PARROT MILL above, BUTTE below. Rv: As reverse of But 2. Plain edge. (Rome coll.)

SILVER STATUE JUSTICE

Butte, Mont.

Rulau	Date	Metal	Size	VG	F	VF	Unc
But 30	1893	Aluminum	45mm	—	—	30.00	45.00

Bust of Ada Rehan, the actress, ADA REHAN 1893 around. Rv: Statue of Justice, with sword and scales, standing atop a globe carried by an eagle (the same statue as is seen on the E. J. Daly piece, But 9). * "THE SILVER STATUE JUCTICE" * / OF THE STATE OF MONTANA around. Plain edge. (H-K 767)

MINT SALOON

Chestnut, Mont.

Rulau	Date	Metal	Size	VG	F	VF	Unc
Chs 3	(1890's)	Aluminum	--mm	—	60.00	100.	—

MINT SALOON / CHESTNUT / MONT. Rv: GOOD FOR / ONE BEER.

Chestnut existed only 1894-1910; it was a coal mining town eight miles east of Bozeman. Records indicate that only one saloon existed in Chestnut and it had a sign over the door which read: ALL NATIONS WELCOME BUT CARRIE NATION (referring to the female hellcat who smashed up saloons in the name of temperance).

E. A. PALMER

Chimney Rock, Mont.

Rulau	Date	Metal	Size	VG	F	VF	Unc
Chm 1	(?)	Brass	Oct --mm	20.00	25.00	30.00	—

Palmer was apparently out of business before 1906 as the Polk directory for Park County does not mention him. All business closed down in 1908 with the coal mines, and the post office (which had opened in 1893) closed in 1919. Chimney Rock was a mining community five miles southwest of Livingston; a small number of people still live there.

MULTZ BROS.

Cokedale, Mont.

Rulau	Date	Metal	Size	VG	F	VF	Unc
Cok 3	(?)	Bronze	22.5mm	15.00	20.00	25.00	—

MULTZ BROS. / COKEDALE / MONT. Rv: GOOD FOR / 10 C / IN TRADE. Plain edge. 10 pieces known.

Rulau	Date	Metal	Size	VG	F	VF	Unc
Cok 5	(?)	Bronze	Oct 23mm	30.00	35.00	45.00	—

Obverse similar to 3. Rv: GOOD FOR / $1.00 / IN TRADE. Plain edge. Only 3 pieces known.

Cokedale, a mining community, existed only 1889-1906. The Multz Brothers departed for Billings before 1906. It is not known what business they were in, but it probably was not a saloon as Montanans preferred the 5-cent and 12 1/2-cent tokens at this time.

THE CLUB

Deer Lodge, Mont.

Rulau	Date	Metal	Size	VG	F	VF	Unc
Der 3	(?)	Brass	21.2mm	—	—	70.00	—

Hare running left above grassy ground. Rv: THE CLUB / - / DEER LODGE, / MONT. Plain edge. (Smithsonian coll.)

F. JAY DEAN

Gardiner, Mont.

Rulau	Date	Metal	Size	F	VF	EF	Unc
Gar 4	(?)	Aluminum	35mm	10.00	18.00	27.00	—

F. JAY DEAN, GARDINER, MONT. Rv: 12 1/2 C DRINK. Plain edge.

This saloon is listed in the 1906 and 1918 directories.

OMAN & MOODY

Rulau	Date	Metal	Size	VG	F	VF	Unc
Gar 6	(?)	Bronze	21mm	—	—	40.00	—

OMAN & MOODY / GARDINER / MONT. Rv: GOOD FOR / 12 1/2 C / IN TRADE. Plain edge.

This token probably pre-dates the saloon partnership of Oman, Moody & Clerk which appears in the 1906 directory.

TRIPP & MELLOY

Gardiner, Mont.

Rulau	Date	Metal	Size	F	VF	EF	Unc
Gar 8	(?)	Brass	21mm	10.00	18.00	27.00	—

TRIPP & MELLOY. GARDINER, MONT. Rv: 12 1/2 C. Plain edge. (Incomplete description)

The Tripp & Melloy Saloon appears in the 1906-07 Polk's Directory.

PHILLIPS & RANCE

Great Falls, Mont.

Rulau	Date	Metal	Size	VG	F	VF	Unc
Gtf 4	(1893-99)	Aluminum	28mm	—	—	100.	—

Ornate PR monogram in circle, GREAT FALLS / * MONTANA * around. Rv: PHILLIPS & RANCE / - / THE -.- / SILVER DOLLAR / - / SALOON. Plain edge. (Kirtley Feb. 1991 sale, lot A1701; Wright 827)

THE CALIFORNIA WINE HOUSE

Helena, Mont.

Rulau	Date	Metal	Size	VG	F	VF	Unc
Hel 6	(1890's)	Brass	--mm	—	—	20.00	—

THE CALIFORNIA WINE HOUSE / AUGUST FACK / PROPRIETOR / HELENA, MONT. Rv: GOOD FOR / 12 1/2 C / AT THE BAR. Plain edge. (Robert Lindesmith coll., Dayton, Wash.)

During the 1880's, the California Wine House was considered Number One among the 86 or so saloons in Helena. It was then located at 46 South Main, and the proprietors were Harvey Fister and Bill Barwarth. Unlike most bars of its day, it was not a stand-up bar, but had tables and chairs for gentlemen (ladies did not frequent saloons).

About 1889 Fister and Barwarth moved the saloon to new quarters at 38 North Main.

August Fack, a subsequent owner, imported a pure marble statue of Odalisque, the Sultan's Favorite, from Florence, Italy. The remarkably fine statue occupied a special maroon velvet-lined niche with veiled lighting to enhance the purity of the white marble. Today this sensuous memento of Fack's ownership graces a re-created saloon in the Montana Historical Society Museum in Helena.

CAPITAL CIGAR CO.

Helena, Mont.

Rulau	Date	Metal	Size	VG	F	VF	Unc
Hel 10	(1915)	Cupronickel	21mm	—	—	15.00	—

Spade-shaped cutout at center of the flan. CAPITAL CIGAR CO. / HELENA. Rv: 12 1/2 / CIGARS. Plain edge.

Whether the spade suit cutout indicates a connection with card games remains to be determined.

M. C. C. T. CO.

Horr, Mont.

Rulau	Date	Metal	Size	VG	F	VF	Unc
Hor 1	(1895-99)	Aluminum	25mm	8.00	10.00	15.00	—

M.C.C.T. CO. Rv: GOOD FOR / 12 1/2 C / IN TRADE.

The Montana Coal & Coke Trading Co. had a company store in Horr from 1895, when they acquired the assets of Park Coal & Coke Co.

Horr was located two miles from Aldridge and was used to process coal from the Aldridge mines into coke. The coke was used by the refiners in Butte and Anaconda. Horr was established in 1887 and its name was changed to Electric in 1904; the town survived to about 1933. Post office records show a post office at Horr 1889-1904 and at Electric 1906-1915.

LIVINGSTON, MONT.

SPECIAL NOTE: Livingston is the county seat of Park County. Park County is just north of (and contains a small part of) Yellowstone National Park. Livingston was known as Clark City before Nov. 18, 1882; in 1882 it absorbed nearby Benson's Landing. The first city directory apparently was Polk's Directory for 1906-07 (issued 1906), so tokens for this area cannot with certainty be placed in the 1890-1900 period.

A special debt of gratitude for the Park County tokens is owed to numismatist Glenn A. Rome, Seattle, Wash., and Park County Historical Museum curator Doris Whithorn, Livingston.

Many of the Livingston saloons in the 1890's "enjoyed" the patronage of "Calamity Jane" Cannary (nee Martha Jane Burk, 1852-1903). Newspapers of that period made a point of publicizing her bizarre behavior. In 1902 the Livingston city fathers provided her with a train ticket to Deadwood, S.D. - on condition she not return. Calamity Jane died there next year and, in accordance with her dying wish, was buried alongside "Wild Bill" Hickok (who had been shot in 1876) in Deadwood's Mount Moriah cemetery. Jane claimed Hickok fathered her daughter.

BENNETT'S PLACE

Livingston, Mont.

Rulau	Date	Metal	Size	F	VF	EF	Unc
Liv 1	(?)	Brass	21mm	10.00	15.00	20.00	—

BENNETT'S PLACE. LIVINGSTON, MONT. Rv: 12 1/2 C. Plain edge. Slot cut-out flan.

William Alexander was manager of Bennett's Place at 111 W. Park St. in the 1906 Polk directory. It was a saloon.

THE ELITE

Rulau	Date	Metal	Size	F	VF	EF	Unc
Liv 4	(?)	Brass	21mm	10.00	15.00	20.00	—

THE ELITE, LIVINGSTON, MONT. Rv: 5 C. Plain edge. half-moon punch in flan. (Incomplete description).

Polk's Directory for 1906 reveals this hotel and saloon was located on West Park St. opposite the Northern Pacific. R.R. depot and was under the proprietorship of A. L. Armstrong. This business has disappeared before the 1918 R. G. Dun Directory was published.

Armstrong is also known to have operated saloons in Emigrant and the ghost town of Fridley in the 1900-14 period and tokens from both places are known.

W. E. FRAZEE

Rulau	Date	Metal	Size	F	VF	EF	Unc
Liv 7	(?)	Brass	32.5mm	15.00	22.50	30.00	—

W. E. FRAZEE, LIVINGSTON, MONT. Rv: 12 1/2 C CIGAR. Plain edge. (Incomplete description)

Rulau	Date	Metal	Size	F	VF	EF	Unc
Liv 8	(?)	Brass	23mm	15.00	22.50	30.00	—

FRAZEE. LIVINGSTON, MONT. Rv: 12 1/2 C. Plain edge. (Incomplete description)

William E. Frazee is listed as a saloonkeeper in the 1906 directory, yet he is reliably reported to have departed for Minneapolis about 1905.

THE HEADQUARTERS

Rulau	Date	Metal	Size	F	VF	EF	Unc
Liv 9	(?)	Aluminum	Scal 29.5mm	10.00	15.00	20.00	—

THE HEADQUARTERS / I. ROTH / LIVINGSTON / MONT. Rv: 5 C.

Rulau	Date	Metal	Size	F	VF	EF	Unc
Liv 10	(?)	Brass	Scal29.5mm	7.00	10.00	15.00	—

Similar, but 25 C.

Isodore Roth managed The Headquarters saloon at 102 East Park St. in the 1906 directory. The attribution is uncertain.

LIVINGSTON CLUB

Rulau	Date	Metal	Size	F	VF	EF	Unc
Liv 14	(?)	Aluminum	Oct 27.5mm	15.00	20.00	25.00	—

LIVINGSTON CLUB. LIVINGSTON, MONT. Rv: GOOD FOR / 12 1/2 C/ IN TRADE. Plain edge.

The Livingston Club on So. Main St. was a businessmen's club, which was replaced about 1912 by the Livingston Chamber of Commerce. The 1906 city directory lists pharmacist John M. Seaman as club secretary.

It is reported that two other 12 1/2-cent tokens of the Livingston Club, one in brass, exist. We have no description of these.

GUS ROME

Rulau	Date	Metal	Size	F	VF	EF	Unc
Liv 28	(?)	Brass	21mm	15.00	20.00	25.00	—

GUS ROME. LIVINGSTON, MONT. Rv: GOOD FOR / 5 C / IN TRADE. Plain edge. (Incomplete description). Only 6 known.

Gustavus Rome was born in Norway and emigrated to Iowa before 1883. While in Iowa he sponsored the 1883 immigration from Norway of his uncle Hans Peter Rome I and his family, including Hans Peter's son Albert, grandfather of numismatist Glenn A. Rome of Seattle.

In 1884 Gustavus Rome arrived in Livingston and opened his saloon about 1885. The 1906 directory lists the location as 124 No. Main St. By 1917-18 the business was known as Rome & Oraug Bros. Rome retired with Prohibition (1918) and died in 1933. Prohibition in Montana began Jan. 1, 1918. The rest of the U.S. followed Jan. 1, 1920.

SEAMAN'S PHARMACY

Rulau	Date	Metal	Size	F	VF	EF	Unc
Liv 35	(?)	Brass	21mm	8.00	10.00	15.00	—

SEAMAN'S PHARMACY. POST OFFICE BLOCK. LIVINGSTON, MONT. Rv: 12 1/2 C. Plain edge. (Incomplete description)

John M. Seaman operated this pharmacy in the Post Office Block, a building between Callender and Lewis Streets on So. 2nd St. before it burned. Seaman's store also sold cigars and tobacco and the token may be connected with these. The 1906 and 1918 directories list Seaman (who also see under Livingston Club, Livingston, Mont.)

THE SOLO

Rulau	Date	Metal	Size	VG	F	VF	Unc
Liv 36	(?)	Brass	21.5mm	15.00	20.00	25.00	—

THE SOLO / FRANK BLISS. Rv: GOOD FOR / 12 1/2 C / IN TRADE. Plain edge.

The only listing appears in the 1906 directory, where The Solo saloon appears at 117 West Park Street under the proprietorship of Frank Bliss.

TIVOLI SALOON

Rulau	Date	Metal	Size	F	VF	EF	Unc
Liv 38	(?)	—	--mm	—	60.00	—	—

No description available.

The Tivoli Saloon was listed in 1906 at 110 No. Main St.

VOGT LIQUOR COMPANY

Livingston, Mont.

Rulau	Date	Metal	Size	F	VF	EF	Unc
Liv 50	(?)	Brass	21mm	8.00	15.00	25.00	—

VOGT LIQUOR COMPANY. LIVINGSTON, MONT. Rv: 12 1/2 C. Plain edge. (Incomplete description)

Vogt Liquor Co. was established in Livingston in 1883; it was a tobacco and liquor wholesaler. In 1906 Frank A. Vogt was the proprietor and the business was at 120 No. Main St. Frank Vogt departed for Spokane, Wash. in 1913 or 1914.

ELK'S CLUB

Missoula, Mont.

Rulau	Date	Metal	Size	VG	F	VF	Unc
Mis 3	(?)	Brass	26mm	—	—	40.00	—

Elk's head facing three-quarters left. Rv: ELK'S CLUB / - / 12 1/2 / - / MISSOULA, MONT. Plain edge.

BRAATEN'S SALOON

Mondak, Mont.

Rulau	Date	Metal	Size	VG	F	VF	Unc
Mon 2	(?)	Brass	25mm	—	—	100.	—

Elk's head. Rv: GOOD FOR / ONE DRINK / OR CIGAR / AT BRAATEN'S SALOON / MONDAK, MONT. Plain edge. (Koppenhaver report)

GREAT NORTHERN HOTEL

Rulau	Date	Metal	Size	VG	F	VF	Unc
Mon 8	(?)	Brass	29mm	—	—	10.00	—

GREAT NORTHERN HOTEL / MONDAK, MONT. Rv: GOOD FOR / 50 C / IN TRADE. Plain edge. (Koppenhaver report)

JACOB SEEL

Mondak, Mont.

Rulau	Date	Metal	Size	VG	F	VF	Unc
Mon 20	(?)	Brass	Scal --mm	—	—	50.00	—

JACOB SEEL / MONDAK, / MONT. Rv: GOOD FOR / 12 1/2 C / DRINK OR CIGAR. Plain edge. (Koppenhaver report; Kirtley Feb. 1991 sale, lot A2034)

THE MONTANDON

Montana ?

Rulau	Date	Metal	Size	VG	F	VF	Unc
Unk 1	(1890's)	Brass	25mm	—	—	16.00	—

GOOD FOR / 5 ¢ / THE / MONTANDON / IN / TRADE. Rv: THE MERLE & HEANEY / -.- / BILLIARD / SUPPLIES / -.- / CHICAGO.

Hotel?

NEBRASKA

REECE & SCOTT

Ashland, Neb.

Rulau	Date	Metal	Size	F	VF	EF	Unc
Ash 6	(?)	Iron	**	—	30.00	—	—

** Horseshoe-shaped flan, 25 by 41mm.

REECE & SCOTT / ASHLAND NEB. Rv: Blank. Plain edge. (Wright 1591)

WALLA BROS.

Beemer, Neb.

Rulau	Date	Metal	Size	VG	F	VF	Unc
Bmr 3	(1895)	Brass	--mm	—	—	15.00	—

(All incused): WALLA BROS / GOOD FOR / 5 ¢ / DRINK. Rv: Blank. Plain edge.

Saloon, listed only in 1895.

TOMES & SLAMA

Clarkson, Neb.

Rulau	Date	Metal	Size	VG	F	VF	Unc
Clk 1	(1906-07)	Brass	Scal 30mm	—	5.50	11.50	—

Eagle displayed, perched atop cannon. Rv: GOOD FOR / 5 ¢ / DRINK / * / * TOMES & SLAMA *. (Thoele coll.)

Tomes and Slama are listed as partners only in the 1907 directory. A hoard of several hundred of this token is on the market.

During World War I Joseph Slama was in business alone, dispensing soft drinks, and Tomes is no longer listed.

Clarkson, in Colfax County, had 647 people in World War I, including a very heavy immigrant population - chiefly Bohemians and Hungarians. Slama is a typical Czech name.

HENRY DAVIS

Craig, Neb.

Rulau	Date	Metal	Size	VG	F	VF	Unc
Crg 2	(1890's)	Aluminum	--mm	—	—	55.00	—

BBC die 8. Rv: GOOD FOR / 5 C / HENRY DAVIS / CRAIG, NEB. (Lot 509 in Koppenhaver sale of June 4, 1988)

M. J. COLEMAN

Elwood, Neb.

Rulau	Date	Metal	Size	VG	F	VF	Unc
Elw 2	(1900)	Aluminum	Scal --mm	—	—	15.00	—

Brunswick die BBC-11. Rv: GOOD FOR / 5 ¢ / M. J. COLEMAN (on panel) / IN / TRADE. (Robert Cruise coll.)

SUGAR PALACE EXPOSITION

Grand Island, Neb.

Rulau	Date	Metal	Size	F	VF	EF	Unc
Grn 11	1890	GS	31mm	—	—	15.00	25.00

Fair buildings at center, tiny MAX MEYER & BRO. OMAHA beneath ground line. SUGAR PALACE EXPOSTION above. * GRAND ISLAND, NEB. 1890 * below. Rv: Sugar beet within wreath. Plain edge.

MEECHAN & MURPHY

Greeley Center, Neb.

Rulau	Date	Metal	Size	VG	F	VF	Unc
Grc 3	(1893)	Brass	--mm	—	35.00	—	—

Brunswick die BBC-11. Rv: GOOD FOR / 5 ¢ / MEECHAN & (on panel) / MURPHY (on panel) / IN / TRADE. Plain edge. (Robert Cruise coll.)

Saloon, in the 1893 directory.

McKINNEY & CHEUVROUT

Greenwood, Neb.

Rulau	Date	Metal	Size	F	VF	EF	Unc
Gre 5	(1890's)	Aluminum	22mm	—	—	10.00	—

McKINNEY & CHEUVROUT / GREENWOOD / NEB. Rv: GOOD FOR / 5 C / IN / MERCHANDISE. Plain edge. (Wright 1542)

MICHAEL MORGAN

Harltington, Neb.

Rulau	Date	Metal	Size	VG	F	VF	Unc
Har 3	(1890)	Brass	--mm	—	—	50.00	—

Brunswick die BBC-11. Rv: GOOD FOR / 2 1/2 ¢ / MICHAEL / MORGAN (name on panel) / IN / TRADE. Plain edge. (Robert Cruise coll.)

Saloon, listed in 1890.

G. F. HAMMER

Homer, Neb.

Rulau	Date	Metal	Size	VG	F	VF	Unc
Hom 2	(1893)	Brass	Scal --mm	—	—	35.00	—

Brunswick die BBC-11. Rv: GOOD FOR / 5 ¢ / G. F. / HAMMER (name on panel) / IN / TRADE. Plain edge. (Robert Cruise coll.)

Saloon, listed in 1893.

L. F. ALVES

Juniata, Neb.

Rulau	Date	Metal	Size	VG	F	VF	Unc
Jun 1	(1902)	Brass	--mm	—	—	35.00	—

Brunswick die BBC-7. Rv: GOOD FOR / 5 ¢ / L. F. ALVES (on paneL) / IN / TRADE. Plain edge. (Robert Cruise coll.)

Billiard hall, listed 1902 and likely in operation earlier.

CHAS. ALLEN

Lincoln, Neb.

Rulau	Date	Metal	Size	F	VF	EF	Unc
Lin 1	(1911)	Aluminum	23mm	—	30.00	—	—

THE BRUNSWICK BALKE / COLLENDER / COMPY. / (billiard table) / CHECK. Rv: CHAS. ALLEN. 5 ¢. (Brunswick 5016; Rulau Roy 1)

Billiard hall.

NEBRASKA SILVER ANNIVERSARY

Lincoln, Neb.

Rulau	Date	Metal	Size	F	VF	EF	Unc
Lin 5	1892	Aluminum	37mm	20.00	—	40.00	65.00

Bearded male bust facing. Around: NEBRASKA SILVER ANNIVERSARY / . SOUVENIR / Rv: Blacksmith at anvil, with river, train and mountains in background. Above: MAY 25-26, / 1867 1892 / (on scroll): EQUALITY BEFORE THE LAW. Tiny S. D. CHILDS, CHICAGO. at lower left rim. Plain edge. (Hartzog coll.)

H. R. NISSLEY & CO.

Rulau	Date	Metal	Size	F	VF	EF	Unc
Lin 6	(?)	Iron	**	—	100.	—	—

** Horseshoe-shaped flan, 26 by 52mm.

H. R. NISSLEY & CO., SHOES, LINCOLN, NEB. Rv: Blank. Plain edge. (Wright 760)

Dr. Wright acquired his specimen from collector C. A. Mathis before or during 1898. Mathis told him the firm had already "gone out of business."

REHLAENDER'S DRUG STORE
Lincoln, Neb.

Rulau	Date	Metal	Size	F	VF	EF	Unc
Lin 14	(1890's)	Aluminum	25mm	—	—	25.00	—

REHLAENDER'S / DRUG / STORE / 1125 OAK ST. / LINCOLN NEB. Rv: GOOD FOR SODA WATER AND CIGAR / 10. Plain edge. (Wright 1594)

O. BECKER
Louisville, Neb.

Rulau	Date	Metal	Size	VG	F	VF	Unc
Lou 1	(1894-1902)	Alum	--mm	—	—	25.00	—

Brunswick die BBC-6d. Rv: GOOD FOR / 5 ¢ / O. BECKER / IN TRADE. Plain edge. (Robert Cruise coll.)

Saloon, appearing in gazetteers 1894 through 1902.

C. ZESSIN
Madison, Neb.

Rulau	Date	Metal	Size	VG	F	VF	Unc
Mad 7	(1890)	Brass	Oct --mm	—	—	50.00	—

C. ZESSIN / GOOD FOR / 5 ¢ / AT BAR. Rv: (Tiny) MESSMER / FAUCET CO. Plain edge. (Robert Cruise coll.)

Saloon, listed 1890. In 1891-92, the makers, Messmer Faucet Co. of St. Louis, changed their name to Messmer Mfg. Co.

J. H. DWYER
McCook, Neb.

Rulau	Date	Metal	Size	VG	F	VF	Unc
Mcc 1	(1890)	Brass	--mm	—	—	20.00	—

GOOD FOR / J. H. DWYER / 5 / ONE CIGAR. Plain edge.

Cigar manufacturer, listed in 1890.

N. C. WAGNER
Morse Bluff, Neb.

Rulau	Date	Metal	Size	VG	F	VF	Unc
Mbf 7	(1893)	Brass	--mm	—	—	35.00	—

Brunswick die BBC-10b. Rv: GOOD FOR / 5 ¢ / N. C. / WAGNER (name on panel) / IN / TRADE. Plain edge. (Robert Cruise coll.)

This saloon appears only in the 1893 directory. Morse Bluff is a small village in Saunders County, 1910 pop. only 196.

M. D. POLLARD
Nehawka, Neb.

Rulau	Date	Metal	Size	VG	F	VF	Unc
Neh 3	(1890-93)	Brass	--mm	—	—	35.00	—

Brunswick die BBC-11. Rv: GOOD FOR / 5 ¢ / M. D. / POLLARD (name on panel) / IN / TRADE. Plain edge.

Billiards, listed 1890 through 1893. Cass County.

GEO. HELLER
Norfolk, Neb.

Rulau	Date	Metal	Size	VG	F	VF	Unc
Nfk 3	(1900-03)	Brass	--mm	—	—	25.00	—

Brunswick die BBC. Rv: GOOD FOR / 5 ¢ / GEO. HELLER (on panel) / IN / TRADE. Plain edge. (Robert Cruise coll.)

This saloon appears in the 1900 through 19034 directories. Madison County.

MILK PRODUCTS CO.
North Platte, Neb.

Rulau	Date	Metal	Size	F	VF	EF	Unc
Npl 4	(?)	Brass	Sq 25.4mm	—	20.00	—	—

MILK PRODUCTS / - CO. - / NORTH PLATTE, / NEBR. Rv: GOOD FOR / 1 (large) / * QUART MILK *. Plain edge.

On each side of this token, the inscriptions are contained in a circular center section. The obverse is arranged so the token is diamond-shaped, and the reverse so it is square, however!

HUGO F. BILZ
Omaha, Neb.

Rulau	Date	Metal	Size	F	VF	EF	Unc
Oma 2	(1911)	Brass	28.5mm	6.00	10.00	12.50	20.00

Shield at center, BAR on diagonal across it. Lions as supporters, a screaming eagle as crest. HUGO F. BILZ above; * 14. & DOUGLAS ST. * below. Rv: 2 1/2 / CTS. within wreath; GOOD FOR above, IN TRADE below. Plain edge. (Rulau USTT Ne-Om-3)

Bilz was in business at 119 So. 14th St. only in the year 1911, according to research by Peter M. Fuhrman. Bilz was in business from 1890 to 1918 in Omaha, moving to Los Angeles, Calif. in 1920. This token was formerly listed in our U.S. Trade Tokens section.

J. P. COOKE & CO.
Omaha, Neb.

Rulau	Date	Metal	Size	VG	F	VF	Unc
Oma 6	(?)	Aluminum	25mm	—	—	15.00	—

WE MAKE THESE / (ornament) / J. P. COOKE & CO / 1112 FARNAM ST / - / OMAHA, NEB. Rv: SAMPLE OF OUR CHECK WORK / PRICE / $1.75 / PER / 100 / ***. Plain edge. (Thoele coll.)

This is a very important tokenmaker's sample piece, previously unpublished.

L. & S. GOLDSMITH

Rulau	Date	Metal	Size	VG	F	VF	Unc
Oma 10	(1900)	Brass	29mm	—	—	8.50	—

L. & S. GOLDSMITH / (ornament) / - 901 - / CAPITOL AVE. Rv: GOOD FOR / * 5 ¢ * / DRINK. Plain edge. (Thoele coll., ex-Weinberg)

Research by George Hosek.

C. JENSEN
Omaha, Neb.

Rulau	Date	Metal	Size	VG	F	VF	Unc
Oma 12	(1886-99)	Brass	--mm	—	—	25.00	—

Brunswick die BBC-11. Rv: GOOD FOR / 5 ¢ / C. JENSEN (on panel) / IN / TRADE. Plain edge. (Robert Cruise coll.)

This saloon was listed 1886 through 1907.

F. R. STANNARD
O'Neill, Neb.

Rulau	Date	Metal	Size	VG	F	VF	Unc
Onl 3	(1893)	Brass	--mm	—	—	10.00	—

Brunswick die BBC-11. Rv: GOOD FOR / 5 ¢ / F. R. / STANNARD / IN / TRADE. Plain edge. (Robert Cruise coll.)

Billiard hall and confectionery, listed only in 1893. Holt County. An apparent successor, David Stannard, was a confectioner, grocer and monument salesman in 1918.

MATT BECKER
Schuyler, Neb.

Rulau	Date	Metal	Size	F	VF	EF	Unc
Scy 3	(1884-1900)	Brass	24mm	—	75.00	—	—

Billiard table at bottom. Above: THE BRUNSWICK-BALKE / COLLENDER / -*- / COMPY. (Die BBC-10A). Rv: GOOD FOR / 5 ¢ / IN TRADE / MATT BECKER / SCHUYLER / NEB. Plain edge. (Brunswick 5050)

THE C. H. HAMMOND COMPANY
South Omaha, Neb.

Rulau	Date	Metal	Size	F	VF	EF	Unc
Som 7	(1890's)	Aluminum	38mm	—	—	30.00	—

Indian head. Around: CALUMET BRAND / MEATS LARD / THE C. H. HAMMOND / COMPANY / SOUTH OMAHA. Rv: Cornucopia. Around: COIN SPECIAL BRAND /MEAT / LARD / NONE / EQUAL / THE C. H. HAMMOND / COMPANY / SOUTH OMAHA. Plain edge. (Wright 1112)

HAHN & McCLINTOCK
St. Edward, Neb.

Rulau	Date	Metal	Size	VG	F	VF	Unc
Std 3	(1899-1902)	Brass	--mm	—	—	30.00	—

Eagle perched on cannon. Rv: GOOD FOR / 5 ¢ / IN TRADE / HAHN & McCLINTOCK. Plain edge. (Robert Cruise coll.)

WM. ROBARE
St. Paul, Neb.

Rulau	Date	Metal	Size	VG	F	VF	Unc
Stp 2	(1882-86)	Brass	23mm	—	60.00	80.00	—

(All incused): Chas. Pick & Co. die. Rv: WM. ROBARE / GOOD FOR / 5 ¢ / IN TRADE. Plain edge. 2 pieces known. (Thoele coll.; G. Young coll.)

All-incuse Pick tokens are extremely rare.

Robare's saloon was listed in St. Paul, in Howard County, 1879-1889. But then he appears again as a saloonkeeper in Callaway, Custer County, Nebraska, 1890-1893. Thus it is difficult to assign these rare pieces, but it is logical they may have been used over a 14-year period in two sites.

NEVADA

ED. TOUPIN
Carson City, Nev.

Rulau	Date	Metal	Size	VG	F	VF	Unc
Ccy 7	(1890's)	Brass	24mm	—	—	35.00	—

ED. TOUPIN / CARSON CITY, / NEV. Rv: GOOD FOR / ONE / DRINK / (tiny) C. A. KLINKNER & CO. S.F. Plain edge. Only 2 known. (HSD Cf-46b)

Rulau	Date	Metal	Size	VG	F	VF	Unc
Ccy 8	(?)	Brass	21mm	—	—	15.00	—

ED. TOUPIN / CARSON CITY / NEV. Rv: GOOD FOR IN THE SLOT / 5 ¢ . Only 1 reported. (HSD Cf-46a)

Elko, Nevada

Some 27 Elko tokens were issued by brothels over the years. Unlike modern fantasies which give explicit legends such as "good for one screw," the Elko pieces merely say "Good for 12 1/2 ¢" or another value, or give the name of the madam without identifying her trade.

Some were struck by Salt Lake Stamp Co. in Utah, known to have been in business in 1900, but most yet are not provably 19th century. Madams named on tokens were: Ollie Day, Jean Field, Nora Mason ?, Maude Rodgers, Dixie Stevens ? and Jessie Ward. Bawdy houses named on tokens were: Classy Inn, M&L and Lucky Strike.

DEPOT HOTEL
Elko, Nev.

Rulau	Date	Metal	Size	VG	F	VF	Unc
Elk 5	(1890's)	Brass	24mm	—	—	5.00	—

DEPOT HOTEL / GOOD FOR / 12 1/2 ¢ / AT THE BAR / ELKO, NEV. (tiny) L. H. MOISE S.F. Rv: CHOICE / WINES / LIQUORS / & / CIGARS. (HSD Ec-17c)

Rulau	Date	Metal	Size	VG	F	VF	Unc
Elk 6	(1890's)	Brass	25mm	—	—	15.00	—

DEPOT HOTEL / ELKO, NEV. / (tiny) L H MOISE SF. Rv: Similar to 5. (HSD Ec-17a)

Rulau	Date	Metal	Size	VG	F	VF	Unc
Elk 7	(1890's)	Brass	21mm	—	—	10.00	—

DEPOT / HOTEL / ELKO / NEVADA. Rv: GOOD FOR / 12 1/2 ¢ / IN TRADE. (HSD Ec-17b)

JEAN FIELD
Elko, Nev.

Rulau	Date	Metal	Size	VG	F	VF	Unc
Elk 10	1899	B&A	28mm	—	—	200.	—

JEAN FIELD / ELKO / NEVADA. Rv: GOOD FOR / 25 / PAT. / JULY 1899 / IN MERCHANDISE. Only 1 known. (HSD Ec-28c)

The career as a madam of Jean Field is covered in the remarkable book *Sagebrush Doctors* by Edna Patterson of Lamoille, Nev. in the 1980's.

GEM HOTEL
Elko, Nev.

Rulau	Date	Metal	Size	VG	F	VF	Unc
Elk 13	(?)	Brass	25mm	—	—	45.00	—

Brunswick die BBC. Rv: GOOD FOR / 12 1/2 ¢ / IN TRADE / GEM HOTEL. Only 1 known. (HSD Ec-32b)

Rulau	Date	Metal	Size	VG	F	VF	Unc
Elk 14	(?)	Brass	24mm	—	—	15.00	—

GEM HOTEL / GOOD FOR / 12 1/2 ¢ / AT THE BAR / ELKO, NEV. Rv: CHOICE / WINES / LIQUORS / & CIGARS. 2 pieces reported. (HSD Ec-32a)

HOTEL MINA
Mina, Nev.

Rulau	Date	Metal	Size	VG	F	VF	Unc
Min 1	(ca 1900)	Brass	21mm	—	—	25.00	—

HOTEL MINA / MINA / (tiny) MOISE K. CO. Rv: GOOD FOR / ONE / DRINK. At least 2 pieces known. (HSD Mm-4b)

Rulau	Date	Metal	Size	VG	F	VF	Unc
Min 2	(?)	Brass	21mm	—	—	20.00	—

MINA / HOTEL. Rv: GOOD FOR / 6 1/4 ¢ / IN TRADE. 4 known. (HSD Mm-5)

Rulau	Date	Metal	Size	VG	F	VF	Unc
Min 3	(?)	Aluminum	20mm	—	—	20.00	—

HOTEL MINA / MINA. Rv: GOOD FOR / 12 1/2 ¢ / IN TRADE. 3 pieces reported. (HSD Mm-4a)

Mina is in Mineral County.

THE PAYTELLER
Rhyolite, Nev.

Rulau	Date	Metal	Size	VG	F	VF	Unc
Rhy 1	(1890's)	Aluminum	Oct 30mm	—	—	300.	—

Obverse as Ton 3 (bearded miner walking left). Rv: THE PAYTELLER / 12 1/2 ¢ / RHYOLITE, NEV. Only 4 pieces known. (HSD Rc-5)

Two competing San Francisco firms, C. H. Klinkner & Co. (1889-97) and L. H. Moise & Co. (1893-97), made many tokens for Western states, as well as or Mexico and Latin America. These firms merged as Moise-Klinkner Co. in 1897, and this firm in turn was purchased by Patrick & Co. in 1930. Thus the Klinkner and Moise signatures give positive evidence of Gay Nineties provenance to many tokens.

The beautiful and rare tokens of The Payteller bear the maker's mark: L. H. MOISE S.F.

After the merger, the signature MOISE-KLINKNER S.F. was used for a time, then merely MOISE S.F.

STILLWATER HOTEL
Stillwater, Nev.

Rulau	Date	Metal	Size	VG	F	VF	Unc
Sti 1	(1898-1906)	Brass	23mm	—	—	150.	—

STILLWATER / HOTEL / C. P. CIRAC / PROP. Rv: GOOD FOR / ONE / DRINK OR / CIGAR. Only 4 known. (HSD Sq-1b)

Charles P. Cirac purchased this hotel about 1898, then built a brick 2-story hotel with the same name in 1906. Both contained saloons. The saloon operation was sold or leased to G. W. Cavness about 1917; Cavness also issued tokens.

THE ORIGINAL PACKAGE
Tonopah, Nev.

Rulau	Date	Metal	Size	VG	F	VF	Unc
Ton 3	(1890's)	Aluminum	Oct 29mm	—	—	250.	—

Bearded miner with pick, shovel and lunch bucket walking left; sun rising above mountains in background. Rv: THE ORIGINAL PACKAGE / GOOD FOR / 12 1/2 ¢ / TONOPAH. Tiny signature L. H. MOISE S.F. at bottom of obverse scene. Plain edge. Only 2 known. (HSD Td-52)

A. A. ROSE
Tuscarora, Nev.

Rulau	Date	Metal	Size	VG	F	VF	Unc
Tus 1	(1890's)	Brass	25mm	—	—	50.00	—

Chas. Pick & Co. die. Rv: GOOD FOR / A. A. ROSE / A / DRINK. Plain edge. Unique. (HSD Tf-7)

Pick last issued tokens to its clients in 1895.

A. K. ROSE

Tuscarora, Nev.

Rulau	Date	Metal	Size	F	VF	EF	Unc
Tus 1	(1890's)	Brass	25mm	—	—	40.00	—

THE BRUNSWICK BALKE / COLLENDER / COMPY / (pool table) / CHECK. Rv: GOOD FOR / 5 ¢ / -IN TRADE- / - / A. K. ROSE. Plain edge. Unique. (Thoele coll.)

Mrs. A. K. Rose had a hotel there after 1900

Rulau	Date	Metal	Size	F	VF	EF	Unc
Tus 5	(?)	Brass	25mm	—	—	25.00	—

A. K. / Rose. Rv: GOOD FOR / ONE / MEAL. Only 4 known. (HSD Tf-8b).

F. M. FELLOWS

Winnemucca, Nev.

Rulau	Date	Metal	Size	VG	F	VF	Unc
Win 1	1892	Aluminum	29mm	—	—	200.	—

F. M. FELLOWS / PEOPLES / CANDIDATE / FOR / SHERIFF / OF / HUMBOLDT CO. / 1892. Rv: FREE COINAGE / OF / SILVER / OR / BUST. Plain edge. 2 known. (HSD Wj-9)

Political tokens are beyond the scope of this catalog, but this one ties neatly to one of the Germain pieces (Win 3). "Free silver" was the call to political battle of the West and William Jennings Bryan in 1892-96. Despite his alliance to free silver, Fellows lost this race, by 16 votes, to D. J. Hadley.

Rulau	Date	Metal	Size	VG	F	VF	Unc
Win 2	(1890's)	GS	29mm	—	—	65.00	—

THE PALACE SALOON / F. M. / FELLOWS / PROP. WINNEMUCCA / NEVADA. Rv: CARL MATHEWS, MANAGER. Only 1 piece reported. (HSD Wj-23)

JOSEPH GERMAIN

Winnemucca, Nev.

Rulau	Date	Metal	Size	F	VF	EF	Unc
Win 3	(1896)	Aluminum	30mm	60.00	100.	—	—

LAFAYETTE HOTEL / JOSEPH / GERMAIN / PROP. / WINNEMUCCA, / NEVADA. Rv: WE FAVOR / -.- / FREE SILVER / -.- / COINAGE. Plain edge. 3 pieces known. (Wright 1429; HSD Wj-16c)

Rulau	Date	Metal	Size	F	VF	EF	Unc
Win 4	(1890's)	Aluminum	25mm	—	—	25.00	—

LAFAYETTE / HOTEL / WINNEMUCCA, / NEV. Rv: GOOD FOR / 12 1/2 / CENTS / IN TRADE. Unique. (HSD Wj-16b)

NEW HAMPSHIRE

DUMAS BROS.

Manchester, N.H.

Rulau	Date	Metal	Size	VG	F	VF	Unc
Man 2	1896	Gilt/B	29mm	—	—	30.00	—

COMPLIMENTS OF / DUMAS BROS. / JEWELERS & / OPTICIANS / 1241 ELM ST. / 5 DOORS ABOVE PEARL MANCHESTER, N. H. Rv: As Man 7. (Tanenbaum coll.)

W. P. FARMER

Rulau	Date	Metal	Size	VG	F	VF	Unc
Man 3	1896	Gilt/B	29mm	—	—	20.00	—

COMPLIMENTS / OF / W. P. FARMER / FINE / FOOTWEAR / 823 ELM ST. / MANCHESTER, N.H. Rv: As Man 7.

KIMBALL THE CLOTHIER

Rulau	Date	Metal	Size	VG	F	VF	Unc
Man 4	1896	Gilt/B	29mm	—	—	20.00	—

KIMBALL / (ornament) / THE CLOTHIER / 1053 & 1055 / ELM ST. / (ornament) / MANCHESTER, N.H. Rv: As Man 7. (Tanenbaum coll.)

MANCHESTER CLOTHING COMPANY

Rulau	Date	Metal	Size	VG	F	VF	Unc
Man 6	1896	Gilt/B	29mm	—	—	20.00	—

MANCHESTER / CLOTHING / COMPANY / 740 ELM ST. / MANCHESTER, N.H. Rv: As Man 7. (Tanenbaum coll.)

NEW CITY HOTEL

Rulau	Date	Metal	Size	VG	F	VF	Unc
Man 7	1896	Brass	29.3mm	—	—	20.00	—

COMPLIMENTS OF / NEW / CITY HOTEL / TRAVELING MEN'S HOME / FRED. COTTON / PROPRIETOR / 1128 TO 1138 ELM ST. / MANCHESTER, N.H. Rv: Crested shield of arms in circle. Around: 1846 SEMI-CENTENNIAL SEPT. 7.8.9. 1896 / CITY OF MANCHESTER / INCORPORATED 1846 / MANCHESTER, N.H. Plain edge. (Kirtley Oct. 1985 sale, lot 556; Smithsonian coll.)

PUPIL'S MEDAL

Rulau	Date	Metal	Size	VG	F	VF	Unc
Man 8	1896	Aluminum	29mm	—	—	15.00	—

PUPIL'S MEDAL / PMS / CHILDREN'S CHORUS. Rv: As Man 7. Plain edge.

W. H. SHILVOCK & CO.

Rulau	Date	Metal	Size	VG	F	VF	Unc
Man 9	1896	Gilt/B	29mm	—	—	50.00	—

W. H. SHILVOCK / & CO. / HALF TONE & WOOD / ENGRAVERS / 143 HANOVER ST. / MANCHESTER, N.H. Rv: As Man 7. Plain edge.

STAR STAMP CO.

Manchester, N. H.

Rulau	Date	Metal	Size	VG	F	VF	Unc
Man 12	1895	Aluminum	35mm	—	—	50.00	—

COMPLIMENTS / oo OF oo / STAR STAMP CO. / MFS. OF / RUBBER STAMPS, / SEALS, STENCILS, / BADGES, CHECKS, / MEDALS &C. / 6 PLEASANT ST. MANCHESTER, N.H. Rv: BOARD OF TRADE OUTING / -*- / JULY 23, 1895. / MERRIMACK VALLEY / BOARD OF TRADE / NEW HAMPSHIRE / BOARD OF TRADE / -*- / MANCHESTER, N.H. Plain edge. (Tanenbaum coll.)

Rulau	Date	Metal	Size	VG	F	VF	Unc
Man 13	1896	Aluminum	29mm	—	—	50.00	—

STAR STAMP CO. / MFR'S OF / CHECKS, MEDALS, / BADGES, STAMPS, / SEALS, STENCILS &C. / (three stamping devices) / 6 PLEASANT ST. MANCHESTER, N.H. Rv: As Man 7.

NEW JERSEY

SOMERS CASINO CO.

Atlantic City, N.J.

Rulau	Date	Metal	Size	F	VF	EF	Unc
Atl 9	(?)	Aluminum	27mm	3.00	5.00	7.50	12.00

Lighthouse, building and sailing ship, SOMERS CASINO CO. above. Rv: Seashore scene, ATLANTIC CITY / N.J. in exergue. Plain edge.

Atl 9 is also known in 25mm size; same prices.

FERRACUTE MACHINE CO.

Bridgeton, N.J.

Rulau	Date	Metal	Size	F	VF	EF	Unc
Brg 2	1879	Copper	19mm	—	50.00	60.00	—

Supported arms. Around: PENNSYLVANIA STATE FAIR / * PHILA. SEP. 1879 *. Rv: STRUCK ON COIN PRESS / BUILT / BY THE / FERRACUTE / MACHINE / CO. / BRIDGETON N.J. Plain edge. (Smithsonian coll.)

Rulau	Date	Metal	Size	F	VF	EF	Unc
Brg 3	1892	Bronze	19mm	—	—	25.00	—

Coining press. Around: MADE / FOR / U.S. / MINT / 1892. Rv: STRUCK ON COINING PRESS / BUILT / BY THE / FERRACUTE / MACHINE / CO. / BRIDGETON N.J. Plain edge.

Rulau	Date	Metal	Size	F	VF	EF	Unc
Brg 3A	1892	Aluminum	19mm	—	—	25.00	—

As last. Scarce. (Smithsonian coll.)

Rulau	Date	Metal	Size	F	VF	EF	Unc
Brg 4	1900	CN	20mm	—	—	15.00	25.00

Building at center, PARIS EXPOSITION INTERNATIONALE around, U.S. PAVILION / 1900 in exergue. Rv: Coining press at center, COINED AT U.S. EXHIBIT IN FERRACUTE PRESSES. Around: FACTORY / BRIDGETON, N.J. U.S.A. below. Plain edge.

Rulau	Date	Metal	Size	F	VF	EF	Unc
Brg 6	ND	Brass	38mm	—	25.00	—	—

Coining press. Around: COINING . PRESS . MADE . BY . FERRACUTE . MACHINE CO. / BRIDGETON . N.J. U.S.A. Rv: Two puppies face viewer over a wall. Reeded edge. (Smithsonian coll.)

Though Brg 2 and possibly Brg 6 belong in an earlier or later reference in our token catalog series, we thought it best to keep all Ferracute pieces together.

Ferracute Machine Co. was an important supplier of minting machinery to the U.S. Mint and to the Imperial Chinese government. As can be seen from its tokens, it advertised its services at major fairs in Philadelphia, 1879 , and Paris, 1900.

CHAS. S. CAFFREY CO.

Camden, N.J.

Rulau	Date	Metal	Size	F	VF	EF	Unc
Cam 3	(?)	Silver	**	—	20.00	—	—

** Parellelogram shape, 60 by 19mm.

CHAS. S. CAFFREY CO. / OF CAMDEN, N.J. Rv: Blank. Plain edge. (Wright 139)

The shape of a coffin? Caffrey was a maker of coffins.

COYLE'S SALOON

Camden, N.J.

Rulau	Date	Metal	Size	VG	F	VF	Unc
Cam 6	(1890-99)	Copper	Oct 23.5mm	—	—	100.	—

(All incused): COYLES / -o- / SALOON / 4TH & / KAIGHN AVE. Rv: Blank. Incised, beaded rim on each side. (Kirtley Oct. 1992 sale, lot 3327)

Thomas Coyle's saloon is listed at this address 1890, then Neil Coyle's saloon 1900, but the 1905 directory does not mention it,

UNION PLEASURE CIRCLE

Elizabeth, N.J.

Rulau	Date	Metal	Size	F	VF	EF	Unc
Elz 6	(?)	Brass	25mm	—	—	10.00	—

UNION PLEASURE / CIRCLE / GOOD FOR / 5 C IN / REFRESHMENTS / ELIZABETH, N.J. Rv: Large V. (Thoele coll.)

GEORGE ALLERS

Jersey City, N.J.

Rulau	Date	Metal	Size	F	VF	EF	Unc
Jer 1	1899	Copper	29mm	6.50	10.00	20.00	35.00

Clock face, TIME / IS / MONEY. (Imitation of Smith Clock pieces of the Hard Times era.) Rv: GEORGE ALLERS / JEWELER / 308 CENTRAL AVE. / JERSEY CITY / 1899. Plain edge. (Miller NJ26)

This piece was mistakenly attributed to Newark, N.J. by both Adams and Miller.

George Allers was still in the jewelry business in 1918.

MURRAY'S BILLIARD GARDEN

Newark N.J.

Rulau	Date	Metal	Size	F	VF	EF	Unc
Nwk 6	(1890's)	Aluminum	24mm	—	25.00	—	—

MURRAY'S / BILLIARD / GARDEN. Rv: NEWARK / N.J. Plain edge. (Wright 1534)

WHITEHEAD & HOAG CO.

Newark, N.J.

Rulau	Date	Metal	Size	F	VF	EF	Unc
Nwk 25	1901	Brass	28.5mm	—	—	20.00	27.50

Nude female striding right in front of a buffalo. Above: PAN-AMERICAN EXPOSITION. Rv: GOLD MEDAL / PAN-AMERICAN / EXPOSITION 1901 / THE / WHITEHEAD & HOAG / CO. / NEWARK, N.J. / U.S.A. / ADVERTISING NOVELTIES. Plain edge.

A. P. COSTA

Orange, N.J.

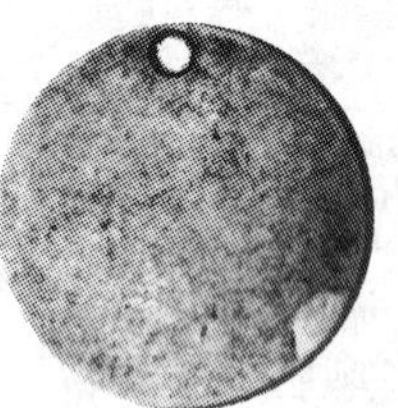

Rulau	Date	Metal	Size	VG	F	VF	EF
Ora 1	(?)	CN	25mm	—	—	15.00	—

(All incused): A. P. COSTA. ORANGE. N.J. incused in circular form around G.A.R. seal. Rv: Blank. (Pete Peters coll.)

G.A.R. = Grand Army of the Republic.

PASSAIC ART CASTING CO.

Passaic, N.J.

Rulau	Date	Metal	Size	F	VF	EF	Unc
Pas 4	1893	Aluminum	**	—	25.00	—	—

** Rect 67 by 38mm.

Group of five females. At lower right, in script: P. A. C. CO. / 1893. Rv: CAST BY / PASSAIC ART CASTING CO. / PASSAIC, N.J. / PROCESS PATENTED. / FINE CASTINGS IN BRONZE, BRASS, / GERMAN SILVER AND ALUMINUM. Plain edge. (Wright 802)

Dr. Wright described this piece as "A beautiful specimen of casting."

HUGH C. IRISH CAMP

Paterson, N. J.

Rulau	Date	Metal	Size	F	VF	EF	Unc
Pat 3	1893	S/WM	31.5mm	—	—	15.00	20.00

Uniformed bust left. Around: HUGH C. IRISH, CAPT. CO. K, 13TH REGIMENT, N.J. VOLS. / KILLED AT ANTIETAM, MD. SEPT. 17, 1863. Rv: SECOND ANNUAL FAIR OF HUGH C. IRISH CAMP NO. 8, N.J. DIV. S. OF V. U.S.A. / JAN. 25 TO FEB. 3, 1893 / SV monogram in wreath / PATERSON, N.J. Plain edge. (Al Zaika coll.)

SECOND BRIGADE N.J.S.M. (New Jersey State Militia)

Sea Girt, N.J.

Rulau	Date	Metal	Size	F	VF	EF	Unc
Sea 8	1894	WM	38mm	—	15.00	22.50	—

Standing sentry facing, cannon and tent in background. Rv: ENCAMPMENT / OF / (Scrollwork) / SECOND BRIGADE / N. J. S. M. / SEA GIRT, N.J. / JULY 1894. Plain edge. Holed for suspension from red, white and blue ribbon. (Kirtley Dec. 1989 sale, lot 2302)

INTER STATE FAIR

Trenton, N. J.

Rulau	Date	Metal	Size	F	VF	EF	Unc
Tre 1	1893	Gilt/B	19mm	8.00	12.00	15.00	17.50

Liberty head left, within circle and border of stars. Rv: INTER STATE FAIR / (sheaf of grain and farm implements) / 1893 / SEP. 26-30 / TRENTON, N. J. Plain edge. (Zaika coll.)

PADDERATZ HALL

Rulau	Date	Metal	Size	F	VF	EF	Unc
Tre 2	(?)	Aluminum	21mm	—	2.50	4.00	—

GOOD FOR / PADDERATZ / HALL / ONE DRINK. Rv: ERSTER DEUTSCH / UNGARISCHER / TRENTON / N.J. GESANG VEREIN. Plain edge.

The reverse legend in German translates: "First German Hungarian Singing Union."

STATE CONVENTION FOR CHRIST

Trenton, N.J.

Rulau	Date	Metal	Size	F	VF	EF	Unc
Tre 4	1893	WM	25mm	—	6.00	8.50	—

Coat of arms, SOUVENIR 1893 TRENTON, N.J. Rv: STATE CONVENTION FOR CHRIST (etc.). Plain edge. Issued holed. (Kirtley Oct. 1985 sale, lot 474)

NEW YORK

PHELPS HOTEL

Afton, N.Y.

Rulau	Date	Metal	Size	VG	F	VF	Unc
Aft 3	1900	Brass	25mm	—	—	Rare	—

PHELPS HOTEL / * / 1900 / * / AFTON, N.Y. Rv: GOOD FOR / 5 / CENTS / IN TRADE. Plain edge. (Wright 1575)

Afton is in Chenango County. In 1918 it had 754 people.

The reverse die recurs over and over on New York state tokens of the turn of the century.

The reason the date "1900" appears on so many trade checks is that it was in commemoration of the new century — and New York token-makers used it often.

RUDOLPH HORST'S CAFE

Albany, N.Y.

Rulau	Date	Metal	Size	VG	F	VF	Unc
Alb 20	(1900-02)	CN	21mm	—	6.00	9.00	—

RUDOLPH HORST'S / CAFE / ALBANY, N.Y. Rv: GOOD FOR / * 5 ¢ * / IN TRADE. Plain edge.

Margaret E. Horst (Mrs. Rudolph Horst) ran a saloon which appears in the 1900 and 1902 directories. Still in business 1918.

B. LODGE & CO.

Rulau	Date	Metal	Size	VG	F	VF	Unc
Alb 30	(1890's)	Aluminum	19mm	—	—	7.00	—

B LODGE & CO. / KNIT / GOODS / ALBANY, N.Y. Rv: I.O.U. / . . . 1/2 ¢ . . . / LODGES. Plain edge.

This retailer of knit goods appears in the 1890 to 1902 Dun directories.

E. P. MILLER

Rulau	Date	Metal	Size	VG	F	VF	Unc
Alb 40	(1890's)	CN	**	—	—	Scarce	—

** Watch-shaped flan, 25.5 by 36mm.
(All incused): COMPLIMENTS / E. P. MILLER / JEWELER & OPTICIAN / 78 DIVISION ST. / ALBANY, N.Y. Rv: WATCH CASES / KEYSTONE / .LL .ILVER / — JAS BOSS / (illegible). Plain edge.

Eugene P. Miller, jeweler and optician, is listed in the 1890, 1900 and 1902 directories.

M. J. O'LEARY
Albany, N.Y.

Rulau	Date	Metal	Size	VG	F	VF	Unc
Alb 60	(1900-02)	CN	21mm	—	9.00	15.00	—

M. J. O'LEARY / 229 / CENTRAL / AVE. / ALBANY, N.Y. Rv: GOOD FOR / * 5 ¢ * / IN TRADE. Plain edge.

Michael O'Leary is listed as a saloonkeeper in the 1900 and 1902 directories.

G. W. COOK
Alden, N.Y.

Rulau	Date	Metal	Size	VG	F	VF	Unc
Ald 7	(ca 1900)	Brass	Oct. 23mm	—	7.50	10.00	—

(All incused): G. W. COOK / ALDEN, N.Y. Rv: 5 C. Incused beaded rim on each side. Plain edge. (Koppenhaver March 1978 sale, lot 570)

Cook was a saloonkeeper listed in the 1899-1902 directories.

About 30 pieces are known. Cook may have used these also in nearby Lancaster, 13 miles away.

MODEL CLOTHING CO.
Auburn, N.Y.

Rulau	Date	Metal	Size	VG	F	VF	Unc
Aub 50	(1899)	Aluminum	28.5mm	—	—	—	50.00

Military bust right, tiny W & H CO NEWARK N.J. under truncation. Below: ADMIRAL GEORGE DEWEY. Rv: MODEL CLOTHING CO. / "FROM / MAKER / TO / WEARER" / AUBURN, N.Y. Plain edge.

WILCOX PROGRESSIVE CIGAR STORE
Bainbridge, N.Y.

Rulau	Date	Metal	Size	VG	F	VF	Unc
Bnb 10	(1900-02)	Aluminum	23mm	10.00	—	—	—

WILCOX / PROGRESSIVE / CIGAR / STORE / BAINBRIDGE, N.Y. Rv: GOOD FOR / CENTS / across large 5 / IN TRADE. Plain edge.

Wilcox Brothers & Co. appear in the 1890 directory as cigar manufacturers. In the 1900-1902 directories George R. Wilcox appears as a cigar retailer. The token probably emanates from the latter period.

M. E. JONES
Belfast, N.Y.

Rulau	Date	Metal	Size	VG	F	VF	Unc
Blf 10	(1900)	Brass	Scal 29mm	—	—	25.00	—

M. E. JONES. Rv: GOOD FOR / A 5 ¢ / CIGAR. Plain edge.

Mel E. Jones was a barber and billiard hall operator in the 1900 Dun directory. The only known specimen of the token was dug up by use of a metal detector about 1982.

M. P. BRICK
Binghamton, N.Y.

Rulau	Date	Metal	Size	VG	F	VF	Unc
Bng 3	(1893-99)	Aluminum	25mm	—	—	Rare	—

M. P. BRICK, / 57 / CLINTON / STREET / BINGHAMTON, N.Y. Rv: Large 5 within circle of alternating stars and asterisks. Plain edge. (Wright 1346; Pipher coll. ex-Fuld & Schenkman)

COMMERCIAL HOUSE

Rulau	Date	Metal	Size	VG	F	VF	Unc
Bng 6	(1890's)	Brass	24.5mm	—	—	20.00	—

(All incused): COMMERCIAL / 5 ¢ (in circle) / * HOUSE *. Rv: Blank. Plain edge. (Wright 1373; S. Alpert sale, lot 1416)

EXCELSIOR CAFE

Rulau	Date	Metal	Size	VG	F	VF	Unc
Bng 11	(1893-99)	Aluminum	22mm	—	—	20.00	—

EXCELSIOR CAFE / 5 ¢ / JAMES E. / LARKIN, PROP. Rv: 166 WASHINGTON ST. / 5 ¢ / BINGHAMTON / N.Y. Plain edge. (Wright 1496)

Larkin is listed in the 1890 Dun directory as a saloonkeeper.

C. T. GAGE

Rulau	Date	Metal	Size	VG	F	VF	Unc
Bng 16	1900	Brass	25mm	—	—	40.00	50.00

C. T. GAGE / * / 1900 / * / BINGHAMTON, N.Y. Rv: GOOD FOR ONE / 5 / CENTS / * CIGAR *. Plain edge. (Wright not listed)

HUMMELL & CO.

Rulau	Date	Metal	Size	VG	F	VF	Unc
Bng 20	(ca 1900)	Aluminum	28.5mm	—	—	20.00	—

MANUFACTURED / * BY * / HUMMELL & CO. (within panel) / BINGHAMTON, / NEW YORK. Rv: IF YOU WANT / (ornament) / TO DIE EASY / SMOKE A / TOM PLATT CIGAR. Plain edge. (There are several varieties of this token)

In the 1900 Dun directory, Hummell & Co. are listed. Tom Platt later figured in the 1923 Teapot Dome oil scandal.

A surviving 1913 envelope of the company shows it made "fine Havana and seed cigars," and that its Crawford Cigar came in five sizes.

THE HUSBANDMAN COMPANY

Rulau	Date	Metal	Size	VG	F	VF	Unc
Bng 21	(1894-99)	Aluminum	38mm	—	—	—	35.00

Hatted, mustachioed bust facing, head turned right. Around: GEN. EDWARD F. JONES FOUNDER OF THE ORDER / DEFENDERS OF THE FLAG. Rv: THE HUSBANDMAN CO. / BINGHAMTON, / N.Y. / CONFERS / THIS D.O.F. MEDAL / YOU HAVING AVOWED / LOYALTY TO THE / (U.S. flag waving left). Thickness 3.7mm. Issued holed for suspension. Plain edge. (Wright 1671; Presidential Coin Dec. 1976 sale, lot 1158)

A surviving 1907 Christmas greetings postcard signed by General Jones bears the same portrait as the token, and reveals that he was born June 3, 1828.

THE IDEAL

Rulau	Date	Metal	Size	VG	F	VF	Unc
Bng 22	1900	Aluminum	Scal 25mm	—	—	20.00	30.00

THE IDEAL / . / 1900 / . / BINGHAMTON, N.Y. Rv: GOOD FOR / FIVE / 5 ¢ / CIGARS. Plain edge. (Wright 1673)

Rulau	Date	Metal	Size	VG	F	VF	Unc
Bng 23	1900	Brass	Scal 25mm	—	—	20.00	30.00

Obverse as last. Rv: GOOD FOR ONE / 5 ¢ / CIGAR. Plain edge. (Wright not listed)

McKINNEY & FOLEY

Rulau	Date	Metal	Size	F	VF	EF	Unc
Bng 35	1901	Brass	24.5mm	—	—	40.00	—

McKINNEY & FOLEY / 1901 / BINGHAMTON, N.Y. Rv: GOOD FOR ONE / 5 / CENT / CIGAR. (Wright 1541)

In 1918, McKinney & Foley were listed as grocers in Binghamton.

N. A. L. C.

Rulau	Date	Metal	Size	VG	F	VF	Unc
Bng 38	(?)	Fire gilt copper	**	—	—	Scarce	—

** Oval, 51 by 38mm.

Clock and key racks; RING IN / BUNDY / RING OUT on the clock face. At left: N.A.L.C. At right: BINGHAMTON, N.Y. Rv: Small maker's stamp: C. G. BRAXMAR / 10 MAIDEN LANE — NEW YORK. (Wright 1355)

Though there is no evidence as yet, this piece seems connected with Binghamton's rubber goods industry. In 1918 there were the Alling Lockwood Co. and Noyes Comb Co. as possible connections.

CARL OLIVER

Rulau	Date	Metal	Size	VG	F	VF	Unc
Bng 45	1900	Brass	25mm	—	—	40.00	50.00

CARL OLIVER / -.- / 1900 / -.- / BINGHAMTON, N.Y. Rv: GOOD FOR ONE / 5 / CENTS / * CIGAR *. Plain edge. (Wright 1561)

THE PROGRESSIVE CIGAR STORE

Rulau	Date	Metal	Size	VG	F	VF	Unc
Bng 48	(1893-99)	Aluminum	24.5mm	—	—	30.00	—

THE PROGRESSIVE / * / CIGAR / *** / STORE / * / BINGHAMTON, N.Y. Rv: Large ornate 5 at center, ornaments above and below. Plain edge. (Wright 1680)

F. B. RICHARDS & CO.

Rulau	Date	Metal	Size	VG	F	VF	Unc
Bng 55	(1890's)	Brass	24mm	—	—	40.00	—

F. B. RICHARDS & CO. / BINGHAMTON, / *** / N.Y. / *. Rv: GOOD FOR / 5 ¢ / * IN EXCHANGE * / FOR A / TENORIO / CIGAR. Plain edge.

Rulau	Date	Metal	Size	VG	F	VF	Unc
Bng 56	(1890's)	Aluminum	24mm	—	—	35.00	—

F. B. RICHARDS & CO. / * / BINGHAMTON / *** / N.Y. / *. Rv: * GOOD FOR * / 5 ¢ / IN EXCHANGE / FOR A / SAINT HELENA / * CIGAR *. Plain edge. (Wright 1597; Pipher coll. ex-Fuld, Schenkman)

A similar token for a London cigar of this issuer has been reported.

LOUIS ROSENTHAL

Rulau	Date	Metal	Size	VG	F	VF	Unc
Bng 60	(ca 1900)	Aluminum	24mm	—	—	Rare	—

LOUIS ROSENTHAL / PROPT. / 1322 / HENRY ST. / BINGHAMTON, N.Y. Rv: VENDOME CAFE / GOOD FOR / * 5 CTS. / IN TRADE AT BAR. Plain edge.

The 1900 Dun directory lists Rosenthal as a grocer. The token is poorly made, letters out of line, etc.

JNO. M. RUSSELL

Rulau	Date	Metal	Size	VG	F	VF	Unc
Bng 64	(1893-99)	Aluminum	28.5mm	—	—	35.00	—

JNO. M. RUSSELL / (ornament) / WHOLESALE / AGENT / (ornament) / BINGHAMTON, N.Y. Rv: THIS CHECK WILL BE REDEEMED BY ANY DEALER (ornament) / GOOD FOR / ONE / FONTELLA / CIGAR - all text separated by two semicircular panels. Plain edge. (Wright 1606)

H. A. SCHAD

Rulau	Date	Metal	Size	VG	F	VF	Unc
Bng 69	(1893-99)	Aluminum	25mm	—	—	Rare	—

H. A. SCHAD, / 42 3/4 / CLINTON / STREET / BINGHAMTON, N.Y. Rv: Large 5 within circle of alternating stars and asterisks. Plain edge. (Wright 1614)

DR. W.M. SHARP

Rulau	Date	Metal	Size	VG	F	VF	Unc
Bng 72	1895	Svd/B	22mm	—	—	Scarce	—

DR. W. M. SHARP / (ornament) / BINGHAMTON / -N.Y.- / NO 2 / PAT. SEP. 10 1895. Rv: Blank. Plain.

SLATTERY & BUCKLAND

Rulau	Date	Metal	Size	F	VF	EF	Unc
Bng 75	1900	Brass	25mm	—	22.50	—	—

SLATTERY & BUCKLAND / -.- / BINGHAMTON / N.Y. / -.- / * 1900 *. Rv: GOOD FOR ONE / 5 / CENTS / CIGAR. Plain edge. (Wright 1627)

Rulau	Date	Metal	Size	F	VF	EF	Unc
Bng 76	1900	Aluminum	25mm	—	22.50	—	—

Obverse as last. Rv: GOOD FOR / 5 / 5 CENTS / CIGARS. Plain edge.

Rulau	Date	Metal	Size	F	VF	EF	Unc
Bng 77	(1900)	Brass	25mm	—	20.00	—	—

SLATTERY & BUCKLAND / * / BINGHAMTON, / N.Y. / (ornament). Rv: As reverse of Bng 75. (Gary Pipher coll.)

WALES

Binghamton, N.Y.

Rulau	Date	Metal	Size	F	VF	EF	Unc
Bng 95	(ca 1900)	Brass	25.5mm	—	—	Rare	—

* WALES * / (cross-form ornament) / BINGHAMTON. Rv: Numeral 5 within a circle of 13 stars. (Wright 1712)

C. S. Wales was a hotel proprietor at least 1900-1918.

HUNT'S POINT PALACE

Bronx, N.Y.

Rulau	Date	Metal	Size	VG	F	VF	Unc
Brx 10	(?)	Brass	28mm	—	—	35.00	—

HUNT'S POINT PALACE / 10 C / WAITERS CHECK. Rv: *** / 10 / ***. Recessed beaded rims. Plain edge. (Rulau Mav 57A)

Rulau	Date	Metal	Size	VG	F	VF	Unc
Brx 11	(?)	Brass	Sq 24mm	—	—	20.00	—

As 10, but 25 C. (George Dillingham coll.)

Rulau	Date	Metal	Size	VG	F	VF	Unc
Brx 12	(?)	Brass	**	—	—	40.00	—

** Rectangular with scalloped left and right sides, 29x23mm; slotted flan. Similar to 10, but 100. (Dillingham coll.)

Rulau	Date	Metal	Size	VG	F	VF	Unc
Brx 13	(?)	Brass	**	—	—	40.00	—

** Rectangular with scalloped left and right sides, 52x23mm. As 13, but 10.00. No slot in flan. (Dillingham coll.)

Rulau	Date	Metal	Size	VG	F	VF	Unc
Brx 16	(?)	Aluminum	Oct 29mm	—	—	20.00	—

As 10. (Dillingham coll.)

Hunt's Point Palace is a large hall located at 935 Southern Boulevard in the Hunt's Point section of the Bronx. It is still in use as a gathering place and hall. Unfortunately, neither its present management nor local historical societies seem to recall when waiter's checks may have been used, other than "before the 1920's." Further research is needed. (Research courtesy Erwin Lein, Plainview, N.Y.)

E. W. BLISS CO.

Brooklyn, N.Y.

Rulau	Date	Metal	Size	F	VF	EF	Unc
Bkn 2	1893	**	39mm	—	—	75.00	—

** Brass shell, filled and joined.

Columbus bust facing. Around: CHRISTOPHER COLUMBUS / CHICAGO . 1893 . Rv: MADE IN MACHINERY-HALL. CHICAGO - 1893 / IN / PRESSES & DIES / BUILT BY / E. W. BLISS Co / BROOKLYN / N.Y. / . WORLD'S - COLUMBIAN - EXPOSITION. (Charles Kirtley report)

Shell cards are excluded from this catalog, but this is included as it represents an otherwise-obscure coining firm. E. W. Bliss Co. Inc. are still listed as manufacturers of presses and other tools in 1918.

GEO. BREHMS BREWERY

Brooklyn, N.Y.

Rulau	Date	Metal	Size	VG	F	VF	Unc
Bkn 3	1897	Brass	28.7mm	—	—	25.00	—

THIS MEDAL / ENTITLES / .. BEARER .. / TO ONE CHANCE FOR A / PRIZE / -AT THE- / GEO. BREHMS / BREWERY / EXHIBIT. Rv: PROSPECT / * PARK * / TRADES DISPLAY / - / OCT 5-6-7-8 / .. / 1897. Thin flan, Plain edge. (Smithsonian coll.)

CHRISTIAN HERALD

Rulau	Date	Metal	Size	F	VF	EF	Unc
Bkn 8	1890	Silver	22.5mm	—	30.00	—	—

Church building, A D 1890 under ground line. Around: "THOU SHALT REAR UP THE TABERNACLE" / EXODUS 26:30. Rv: PRESENTED / BY THE / CHRISTIAN / HERALD / FOR SERVICES / IN BEHALF OF THE / BROOKLYN / TABERNACLE / * / T. DE WITT TALMAGE. PASTOR. Plain edge.

THE CONEY ISLAND CO.

Rulau	Date	Metal	Size	F	VF	EF	Unc
Bkn 15	(?)	Bronze	19mm	—	—	12.50	—

THE CONEY ISLAND / CO. (curved) ctsp on U.S. 1902 Indian cent. (Van Ormer sale 2594; Brunk 9170)

Rulau	Date	Metal	Size	F	VF	EF	Unc
Bkn 16	(?)	Brass	25mm	—	—	8.00	—

CONEY / (five rosettes in cross-form) / * ISLAND *. Rv: 5 in circle of 13 6-pointed stars. (Larry Laevens coll.)

CONEY ISLAND ELEPHANTINE COLOSSUS

Rulau	Date	Metal	Size	F	VF	EF	Unc
Bkn 18	(1890's)	Brass	32mm	—	25.00	—	40.00

Coney Island "elephant" in central circle, ELEPHANTINE COLOSSUS CONEY ISLAND above, ELEPHANT BUILDING CO. below. Rv: Within central circle: ARCHITECTURAL TRIUMPH / HEIGHTH (sic) / 176 FEET / LENGTH / 203 FEET, / 31 ROOMS / * OPEN DAILY *. Plain edge. (Miller NY 9)

Rulau	Date	Metal	Size	F	VF	EF	Unc
Bkn 18A	(1890's)	Copper	32mm	—	25.00	—	40.00

As last. Plain edge. (Miller NY 10)

Rulau	Date	Metal	Size	F	VF	EF	Unc
Bkn 18B	(1890's)	White Metal	32mm	—	—	50.00	—

As last. Plain edge. (Miller NY 11)

Rulau	Date	Metal	Size	VG	F	VF	Unc
Bkn 20	(1890's)	Brass	32mm	—	25.00	—	40.00

As last, but 'J. T. McCADDON MANAGER' on reverse in place of 'ELEPHANT BUILDING CO.' Plain edge. (Wright 1514)

Rulau	Date	Metal	Size	VG	F	VF	Unc
Bkn 20A	(1890's)	White Metal	32mm	—	—	50.00	—

As last. Plain edge. (George Fuld coll.) This piece was acquired by a former owner in 1898.

Rulau	Date	Metal	Size	VG	F	VF	Unc
Bkn 22	(1890's)	Brass	32mm	—	25.00	—	40.00

As last, but 'C. A. BRADENBURGH, MANAGER' on obverse in place of 'J. T. McCADDON MANAGER.' Plain edge.

Rulau	Date	Metal	Size	VG	F	VF	Unc
Bkn 22A	(1890's)	White Metal	32mm	—	—	50.00	—

As last. Plain edge. Reported, not confirmed.

Coney Island, in Brooklyn Borough 10 miles southeast of Manhattan, on the Atlantic Ocean, was originally an island - westernmost of the south shore Long Island sandbars. Coney Island Creek, a tidal inlet, separated it from the main island, but this has been filled in. The island was almost 6 miles long and from 1/4 to 1 mile wide. Coney Island proper today is only that stretch of beach from Sea Gate and Brighton, Manhattan and Oriental beaches.

Charles Feltman, a German baker, built Feltman's, the island's largest and most famous restaurant, in 1870. The island's first hotel, Coney Island House was constructed in 1829.

A pavilion and bathhouse were built in the 1840's, starting the career of the island as a resort. Railroads and boulevards to Coney Island were built in the 1870's. Gambling houses opened in the 1870's also.

Near the end of the 1800's a Ferris wheel was built, the first scenic railway (by C. A. Thompson), and a roller coaster (by Stephen E. Jackson) were constructed. Steeplechase Park was built by George C. Tilyou in 1903, and Luna Park by Frederick Thompson and Elmer S. Dundy in 1903. A rapid transit line opened in 1920, bringing the poor - and swarms of people - to Coney Island.

According to Leonard Forrer (see Bibliography), Robert Sneider & Co. of New York struck Bkn 18 thru 22A. Sneider began business 1866, and in 1895 bought out the medallic business of George Hampden Lovett — acquiring many Lovett dies in the process.

A. FREY

Rulau	Date	Metal	Size	VG	F	VF	Unc
Bkn 29	(1882)	Brass	24mm	—	—	17.50	—

(All incused): A. FREY / (crossed cuesticks and four balls). Rv: Brunswick-Balke die 2. Plain edge. (Tom Wall June 1986 sale, lot 912)

Adam Frey was located at 198 Scholes, according to the Sampson, Davenport & Co. gazetteer of 1882. It is believed the BB-1 and BB-2 dies were cut by McNamara, a New York City diesinker.

KIRKMAN'S BORAX SOAP

Rulau	Date	Metal	Size	F	VF	EF	Unc
Bkn 35	1899	Copper	32mm	6.50	10.00	12.00	22.00

Uniformed bust right, tiny W. H. & CO. NEWARK N.J. under bust, ADMIRAL GEORGE DEWEY below. Rv: WASH CLOTHES / WITH / KIRKMAN'S / BORAX SOAP / BEST OF ALL / 1899. (Wright 1485)

Four die varieties. Given out with bars of soap; 100,000 pieces struck by Whitehead & Hoag, Newark, N.J.

MEADE'S

Rulau	Date	Metal	Size	F	VF	EF	Unc
Bkn 40	(1890's)	Brass	28mm	—	—	Scarce	—

REDEEMABLE IN / MDSE. / -AT- / -MEADES- / -102- / MYRTLE / AVE. / BROOKLYN, N. Y. Rv: Large ornate 25, ornaments above and below. Plain edge.

James M. Meade is listed as a shoe merchant in 1890. In the 1900 and 1902 directories the listing is for Meade Shoe Co.

RAVENHALL

Rulau	Date	Metal	Size	VG	F	VF	Unc
Bkn 60	(1890's)	Brass	24mm	—	—	15.00	—

RAVENHALL / 25 / -*-. Rv: Ornate large 25, ornaments above and below. Beaded rims on each side. Plain edge. (S. Alpert 1983 sale, lot 323)

In 1863 a Brooklyn harness maker, Peter Ravenhall, leased some Coney Island shore frontage from the town and built a restaurant and bathing palace. Picnic basket lunches were a popular diversion in the 1880's and 1890's - before going on to Brighton for the racing.

Information on Ravenhall appears in the 1957 book by Edo McCullough, *Good Old Coney Island.*

CARL RICHTER

Rulau	Date	Metal	Size	VG	F	VF	Unc
Bkn 63	1891	Aluminum	38mm	—	—	12.50	—

Building. Around: ZOELLNER MAENNERCHOR HALLE, BROOKLYN, N.Y. / MDCCCXXXXI. Rv: Superimposed on large shaded monogram bearing tiny letters Z.M.C.H. is: Compliments / of / Carl / Richter. in fancy script lettering. Along bottom rim: WILLOUGHBY AVE. & BROADWAY. Plain edge. (Hank Thoele report)

VAL SCHMITT HOTEL

Rulau	Date	Metal	Size	VG	F	VF	Unc
Bkn 75	(1890's)	Aluminum	38mm	—	—	—	—

Bust left. Rv: COMPLIMENTS / OF / VAL SCHMITT / HOTEL / 163 & 165 FULTON ST. COR. HIGH ST. BROOKLYN N.Y. Plain edge. (Wright 948)

13TH REGIMENT N.G.N.Y.

Rulau	Date	Metal	Size	F	VF	EF	Unc
Bkn 80	1894	WM	38mm	—	—	—	25.00

Ornate building. In exergue: MDCCCXCIV / BROOKLYN, N. Y. Rv: SOUVENIR / 13TH REGIMENT / N.G.N.Y. / NEW ARMORY / FAIR. / OCT. 15-20, 1894, with scrollwork interspersed. Plain edge. (Ganter coll.)

STAUCH'S
Brooklyn, N.Y.

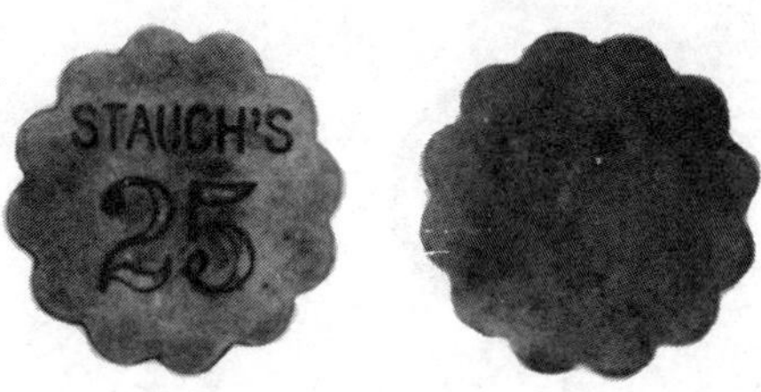

Rulau	Date	Metal	Size	VG	F	VF	Unc
Bkn 77	(1890 ?)	Brass	Scal 26mm	—	35.00	—	—

(All incused): STAUCH'S / 25. Rv: Blank. Plain edge.

Louis Stauch, 16 years old in 1877, moved into the Bowery and worked there two years as a busboy, waiter, barkeeper and piano player. In 1879 he rented a place in Coney Island called Welch's for $700 a year and did so well he renewed a 10-year lease at $2,000 a year.

A storm wrecked his first restaurant and he rebuilt during the 1880's a 60-by-120 foot restaurant on Coney Island. When Prohibition came along in 1920, Stauch sold his restaurant.

The book *Good Old Coney Island* devotes space to Stauch's restaurant, and mentions that such as Jimmy Durante, Eddie Cantor and Vincent Lopez were singing and playing there for $15 to $20 a week.

A. C. GIBSON CO.
Buffalo, N.Y.

Rulau	Date	Metal	Size	VG	F	VF	Unc
Buf 15	(1890's)	Aluminum	25mm	—	—	10.00	20.00

SAMPLE CHECK / .*. / MADE BY / A. C. GIBSON CO / 140 WASHINGTON ST. / BUFFALO, N.Y . Rv: GOOD FOR / * 2 1/2 ¢ * / AT THE OFFICE. Plain edge.

Manufacturers of rubber stamps, etc. 1890-1902.

W. H. GRANGER & CO.

Rulau	Date	Metal	Size	VG	F	VF	Unc
Buf 18	(1890's)	Brass	29mm	—	6.00	11.00	—

W. H. GRANGER & CO. / WHOLESALE / AGENTS / * BUFFALO *. Rv: (Fontella cigar die). Plain edge.

W. H. Granger & Co. were wholesale grocers listed in the 1890, 1900 and 1902 directories.

JOHN GRIMM JR.

Rulau	Date	Metal	Size	VG	F	VF	Unc
Buf 19	(1900-02)	Brass	25mm	—	—	30.00	—

JOHN GRIMM JR. / 445 / MICHIGAN ST. / BUFFALO, N.Y. Rv: GOOD FOR / ONE / * LUNCH *.

Grimm is listed as a liquor dealer 1900-02. He apparently also had a lunch room.

HALL'S BARBER SCHOOLS

Rulau	Date	Metal	Size	VG	F	VF	Unc
Buf 26	(1890's)	Aluminum	35mm	—	—	40.00	—

Mustached male bust facing at center, ALDIS OWEN HALL'S / * BARBER SCHOOLS. * around. Rv: GOOD FOR / 1 C / AT / HALLS BARBER SCHOOL / 16 E. SENECA ST. / BUFFALO, N.Y. / SHAVE 2 C TO 10 C / HAIRCUT 2 C to 15 C. Plain edge. (Larry Laevens coll.)

HOTEL ELMWOOD

Rulau	Date	Metal	Size	VG	F	VF	Unc
Buf 30	(?)	CN	24mm	—	—	11.50	—

HENRY G. MESSINGER, / (sunburst) / HOTEL / ELMWOOD / (sunburst inverted) / BUFFALO, N.Y. Rv: 5 in a circle of 13 6-pointed rosettes. Plain edge. (Pipher coll.)

A "25" token is also known.

PHOENIX BREWERY

Rulau	Date	Metal	Size	F	VF	EF	Unc
Buf 100	(1890's ?)	Gilt/B	32.2mm	—	15.00	25.00	—

Phoenix rising from a fire, PHOENIX / BREWERY above, BUFFALO, N.Y. below. Rv: BREWERS OF PILSENER & WURZBURGER / BUFFALO's / FAMOUS / BREWS / BEERS. Reeded edge.

The Phoenix Brewery is difficult to locate in directories. In 1890 there is a Buffalo listing for a Phoenix Bottling Works which says: "See Ziegele Brewing Co." The Ziegele Brewing Co. appears in the 1890, 1900 and 1918 directories. By 1918 there is a separate listing for Phoenix Brewery, owned by Ziegele Brewing.

THE PITTS AGRICULTURAL WORKS

Rulau	Date	Metal	Size	VG	F	VF	Unc
Buf 104	1895	Brass	31mm	—	12.50	15.00	25.00

Buffalo left, * THE-PITTS-AGRICULTURAL WORKS * above, 1851 / BUFFALO N.Y. below. Rv: Large ornament at center, Buffalo Pitts above, 1895 / ENGINES, THRESHERS below. Plain edge.

Rulau	Date	Metal	Size	VG	F	VF	Unc
Buf 105	(1895)	Aluminum	31mm	—	12.50	15.00	25.00

Obverse as last. Rv: BUFFALO PITTS / SPRING TOOTH / DISC & SPIKE BARROWS / HAYRAKES, CULTIVATORS, ETC / DOUBLE ENGINE STEAM / ROADROLLERS / ENGINES . THRESHERS. Plain edge. (Pipher coll. ex-Fuld, New Netherlands Coin Co.)

The date 1851 on the tokens refers to the founding date of the company. The 1890 Dun directory refers to the firm as manufacturers of threshing engines and machines. The second store card above lists some of the firm's products.

WALBRIDGE & CO.

Buffalo, N.Y.

Rulau	Date	Metal	Size	VG	F	VF	Unc
Buf 125	(1893)	Aluminum	35mm	—	—	Scarce	—

WALBRIDGE & CO. / -.- / HARDWARE / AND / HOUSE FURNISHINGS / -.- / BUFFALO, N.Y. Rv: Within circular wreath; PURE / ALUMINUM / COOKING / UTENSILS. Plain edge.

Walbridge & Co. appear in the 1890, 1900 and 1902 directories as wholesale and retail dealers in hardware, stoves and house furnishings.

R. C. McNEIL & SON

Campville, N.Y.

Rulau	Date	Metal	Size	VG	F	VF	Unc
Cmp 10	(1900)	**	38mm	—	—	50.00	—

** Black printing on green cardboard disc.
PAYABLE ON DEMAND IN MERCHANDISE. / GOOD / AT THE STORE OF / R. C. McNEIL & SON, / CAMPVILLE, / NEW YORK. / PAY, "OVER." Rv: TEN CENTS. / Ornate 10 on banknote-style cartouche / WILL PAY, "OVER".

The 1900 Dun directory lists R. C. McNeil & Son as dealers in feed, cider and coal. By the 1902 directory it is listed simply as —R. C. McNeil.— In the 1918 directory R. C. McNeil is listed as a grist mill and coal dealer.

Campville, in Tioga County, was a tiny place. The population was only 36 in World War I, when the only businesses in the village were McNeil's and the general store of J. H. Denton.

BARNES THE CLOTHIER

Clyde, N.Y.

Rulau	Date	Metal	Size	VG	F	VF	Unc
Cly 5	1899	Gilt/B	32mm	—	—	20.00	28.50

Military bust right, tiny W. & H CO NEWARK N.J. under truncation. Below: ADMIRAL GEORGE DEWEY. Rv: BARNES, THE CLOTHIER / CLYDE, N.Y., / RELIABLE / TRADING PLACE / 1899. Plain edge.

FIREMEN'S TOURNAMENT

Cobleskill, N.Y.

Rulau	Date	Metal	Size	F	VF	EF	Unc
Cob 3	ND	Gilt Br	18.7mm	—	—	15.00	—

Old fashioned fire engine left. Rv: Fireman's hat superimposed on crossed firemen's tools (hook, ladder, nozzle, bullhorn etc.). Around: FIREMEN'S / TOURNAMENT. Plain edge.

This medalet is generic. It can also be found with ribbon bars for Jamestown, Lyons and Lancaster, N. Y.

C. R. HARTSON

Cooperstown, N.Y.

Rulau	Date	Metal	Size	VG	F	VF	Unc
Coo 2	(ca 1900)	CN	29.5mm	—	—	Rare	—

(All incused): C. R. HARTSON / 5 / COOPERSTOWN. Rv: Same as obverse. Plain edge. All lettering is enameled black.

The 1900 to 1914 directories call this a saloon and bottler. However, the token's *style* is much earlier - from the 1870's or 1880's - and we reserve judgement on dating this piece as late as 1900.

HOTEL BRUNSWICK

Cortland, N.Y.

Rulau	Date	Metal	Size	VG	F	VF	Unc
Cor 10	(1890's)	Aluminum	Scal 29mm	—	—	35.00	—

HOTEL BRUNSWICK / CORTLAND / N.Y. / *** / A. D. WALLACE / PROP. Rv: Blank. Plain edge. (Wright 1710)

TYLER & SMITH

Cortland, N.Y.

Rulau	Date	Metal	Size	VG	F	VF	Unc
Cor 30	(1899)	Aluminum	30.5mm	—	—	—	15.00

Military bust 3/4 right, OUR COUNTRY'S PRIDE above, (ornaments) ADMIRAL DEWEY (ornaments) below. Rv: GOOD FOR / 50 ¢ / ON $10oo CASH PURCHASE / MADE AT / "THE MODEL" / TYLER & SMITH, / CLOTHIERS. / CORTLAND, N.Y. Plain edge.

Rulau	Date	Metal	Size	VG	F	VF	Unc
Cor 31	(1899)	30.5mm	—	—	—	15.00	

Obverse as last. Rv: GOOD FOR 50 ¢ / . ON ANY . / -CASH PURCHASE- / -OF $10.00- / THE MODEL / -.- / CORTLAND. Plain edge.

Tyler & Smith appear as clothiers in the 1900-02 directories.

J. C. MILLER

Dunkirk, N.Y.

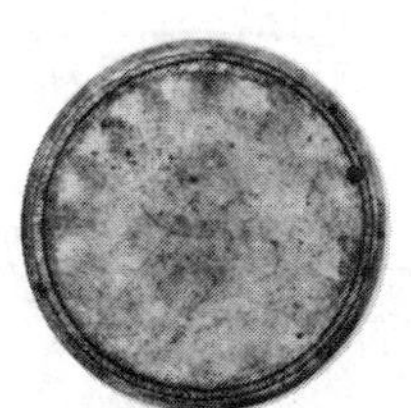

Rulau	Date	Metal	Size	VG	F	VF	Unc
Dnk 15	(ca 1900)	Brass	25mm	—	—	10.00	—

(All incused): J. C. Miller / 5 ¢ (in circle) / + AT BAR +. Rv: Blank. Incised beaded rim on each side. Plain edge.

Rulau	Date	Metal	Size	VG	F	VF	Unc
Dnk 17	(ca 1900)	Aluminum	19mm	—	—	10.00	—

J. C. MILLER / * / DUNKIRK / N.Y. Rv: GOOD FOR / 5 ¢ / IN TRADE.

Jacob Miller's saloon is listed in the 1900 and 1902 directories.

D. SCHMATZ

Dunkirk, N.Y.

Rulau	Date	Metal	Size	VG	F	VF	Unc
Dnk 25	(ca 1900)	Aluminum	Oct, 21mm	—	—	Scarce	—

D. SCHMATZ / (ornament) / DUNKIRK / N.Y. Rv: GOOD FOR / 5 ¢ / IN TRADE.

This grocery store appears in the 1900 and 1902 Dun directories.

N. L. DOUGLASS

Earlville, N.Y.

Rulau	Date	Metal	Size	VG	F	VF	Unc
Erl 1	(1900-02)	Aluminum	18.5mm	—	—	15.00	—

N. L. DOUGLASS / * / EARLVILLE, N.Y. Rv: GOOD FOR / A 5 ¢ / CIGAR.

Newall L. Douglass operated a drugstore, grocery etc. circa 1900-1902, according to directories. He could have been in business earlier and later.

D. W. SEELY

Elmira, N.Y.

Rulau	Date	Metal	Size	VG	F	VF	Unc
Elm 9	(1890)	Brass	23mm	—	—	Scarce	—

(All incused): D. W. SEELY / DEALER IN BILLIARD / 5 (over 2 lines of text) / & POOL TABLES / -.- / ELMIRA, N.Y. Rv: Same as obverse.

Seely appears only in the 1890 Dun directory.

J. O. SCHUYLER

Fonda, N.Y.

Rulau	Date	Metal	Size	VG	F	VF	Unc
Fon 1	(1890)	Brass	24.5mm	—	—	35.00	—

(All incused): J. O. SCHUYLER / GOOD FOR / 5 ¢ / AT BAR / FONDA. Rv: Blank.

James O. Schuyler operated a hotel 1890-1900, according to directories researched by Gary Pipher.

GENEVA PRESERVING COMPANY

Geneva, N.Y.

Rulau	Date	Metal	Size	VG	F	VF	Unc
Gva 6	(ca 1900)	Aluminum	Oct, 17.5mm	—	—	7.00	—

. GOOD FOR . / 1 C / GENEVA PRESERVING COMPANY. Rv: PAYABLE SEPT. 10TH / 1 C / G.P.CO.

Rulau	Date	Metal	Size	VG	F	VF	Unc
Gva 7	(ca 1900)	Aluminum	20mm	—	—	7.00	—

GENEVA PRESERVING COMPANY / GOOD FOR / 5 ¢. Rv: PAYABLE SEPT. 20TH / 5 ¢ / G.P.CO.

This was a canning enterprise, listed in the 1890, 1900 and 1918 directories.

G. L. PAGE

Greene, N.Y.

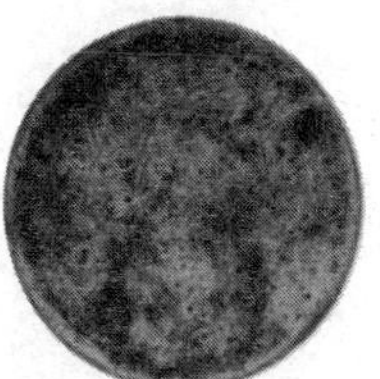

Rulau	Date	Metal	Size	VG	F	VF	Unc
Grn 7	(ca 1900)	Aluminum	25mm	—	—	Scarce	—

(All incused): G. L. PAGE / GOOD FOR / 5 ¢ / DRINK. Rv: Blank.

Rulau	Date	Metal	Size	VG	F	VF	Unc
Grn 9	(ca 1895)	Brass	25mm	—	—	40.00	—

Pool table, THE BRUNSWICK BALKE / COLLENDER / COMPY above, CHECK in exergue. Rv: * GOOD FOR * / 5 ¢ / IN TRADE / G. L. PAGE. Plain edge.

George L. Page was a cattle dealer 1890-1895 and a dealer in agricultural implements 1900-1921 and also is listed as a "lumber manufacturer" 1914-1918. Though his life was varied, he does not seem to have been a saloonkeeper.

We believe he simply used the central-circle stock die of Grn 7 to indicate 5 cents "in trade."

There is also the possibility that this maverick is misattributed. Generally the Brunswick tokens were made only for users of BBC equipment.

BBC-8 die was used 1898-1912.

BROOKS NEWS CO.

Jamestown, N.Y.

Rulau	Date	Metal	Size	VG	F	VF	Unc
Jam 2	(1900-02)	Aluminum	19mm	—	—	10.00	—

BROOKS NEWS CO., / JAMESTOWN, / * N.Y. *.Rv: GOOD FOR / ONE / 5 C / CIGAR.

E. A. Brooks is listed as a printer in 1890. Brooks News Co., news and cigars, appears in the 1900-02 directories.

MARBLE HALL

Jamestown, N.Y.

Rulau	Date	Metal	Size	VG	F	VF	Unc
Jam 12	1899	Gilt/B	32mm	—	—	—	40.00

Military bust right, tiny W. & H CO NEWARK N.J. under truncation. Below: ADMIRAL GEORGE DEWEY. Rv: MARBLE HALL, JAMESTOWN / RELIABLE / TRADING / PLACE / 1899. Plain edge.

G. W. HAGADORN

Lestershire, N.Y.

Rulau	Date	Metal	Size	VG	F	VF	Unc
Les 8	1900	Aluminum	24.5mm	—	—	Scarce	—

G. W. HAGADORN / LESTERSHIRE, N.Y. / 1900. Rv: GOOD FOR / A 5 ¢ / CIGAR.

Rulau	Date	Metal	Size	VG	F	VF	Unc
Les 9	1900	Alum	24.5mm	—	—	—	40.00

G. W. HAGADORN / * / 1900 / * / LESTERSHIRE, N.Y. Rv: GOOD FOR / A 5 ¢ / CIGAR. (Pipher coll. ex-Dr. Aqua)

H. A. MILLER

Rulau	Date	Metal	Size	VG	F	VF	Unc
Les 14	(1900)	Aluminum	24mm	—	—	20.00	—

H. A. MILLER / 5 C / LESTERSHIRE, N.Y. Rv: SUPERBA / 5 ¢ / . CIGAR STORE . Plain edge.

The 1900 Dun directory lists Miller as a cigar dealer. In 1918 he was listed as a cigar manufacturer.

J. J. WILEY

Lestershire, N.Y.

Rulau	Date	Metal	Size	VG	F	VF	Unc
Les 30	(1890's)	Copper	21mm	—	—	10.00	—

J. J. WILEY / CLUB / HOUSE / CAFE / LESTERSHIRE, N.Y. Rv: GOOD FOR / 5 / IN MERCHANDISE. Plain edge. (Wright 1726)

Rulau	Date	Metal	Size	VG	F	VF	Unc
Les 32	(ca 1900	Aluminum	24mm	—	—	10.00	—

J. J. WILEY / . * . / CLUB / HOUSE / CAFE / . * . / LESTERSHIRE. Rv: GOOD FOR / (scroll) 5 (scroll) / CENTS / IN TRADE. Plain edge. (Gary Pipher coll., ex-Herman Aqua)

Wiley also issued a bimetallic token, as seen above. Lestershire today is known as Johnson City. Value VF $25.00.

J. J. Wiley does not appear in the 1890 *Bradstreet Directory*, but he is listed in the 1900 and 1902 editions as a Lestershire saloonkeeper. Apparently he moved his saloon to Binghamton, N.Y. in 1902, as he appears under Binghamton in the 1902, 1909 and 1918 directories, and no longer appears under Lestershire in the 1905 edition.

A surviving postcard shows the interior of J. J. Wiley's Cafe at 136 State St. in Binghamton early in the 20th century.

GETMAN BROS.

Little Falls, N.Y.

Rulau	Date	Metal	Size	VG	F	VF	Unc
Ltf 1	(1900)	Aluminum	26mm	—	—	30.00	—

GETMAN BROS., / — / PALACE / CAFE. / 527 / MAIN ST., / LITTLE FALLS, N.Y. Rv: GOOD FOR / Large 5 encloses CENT / CIGAR. (Pipher coll. ex-W.F. Dunham)

One Marhlon Getman appears in the 1890 directory as a cheese manufacturer and dealer and as proprietor of the Thadeus Hotel. In 1900 there is a T.W. Getman listed as a hotelkeeper. The name Getman disappears in 1918.

GEORGE STARK

Little Falls, N.Y.

Rulau	Date	Metal	Size	VG	F	VF	Unc
Ltf 4	(1890's)	Brass	24.5mm	—	—	30.00	—

(All incused): GEO. STARK / GOOD FOR / 5 ¢ / IN TRADE / LITTLE FALLS. Rv: Blank. Plain edge. (Gary Pipher coll.)

George Stark was listed as a saloonkeeper in 1890 and as a bottler in 1900. He was succeeded in both businesses by John Stark circa 1902, and apparently took over a hotel in 1902.

The Pipher specimen was dug up in 1977.

WM. KLOBUTSCHECK

Long Island City, N.Y.

Rulau	Date	Metal	Size	VG	F	VF	Unc
Lic 5	(1900-20)	Aluminum	24mm	—	—	7.00	—

WM. KLOBUTSCHECK / L. I. / * / CITY / *, Rv: GOOD FOR / * 5 (ornate) ¢ * / DRINK.

Saloonkeeper appearing in the 1900 and 1902 R. G. Dun directories.

J. W. SWEENEY

Maybrook, N.Y.

Rulau	Date	Metal	Size	VG	F	VF	Unc
May 4	(1884-99)	Brass	24mm	14.00	20.00	30.00	—

THE BRUNSWICK BALKE / COLLENDER / COMPY. / (pool table) / CHECK. Rv: EAGLE CAFE / .+. / J. W. SWEENEY / MAYBROOK, N.Y. / GOOD FOR / 5c / IN TRADE. Plain edge. (Brunswick 5720)

EMILE YUND

Mill Grove, N.Y.

Rulau	Date	Metal	Size	VG	F	VF	Unc
Mil 3	(ca 1900)	Aluminum	19mm	—	—	—	20.00

EMILE YUND, / MILL / GROVE / * N.Y. *. Rv: GOOD FOR / ONE / 5 ¢ / * CIGAR *.

Emile Yund kept a general store in this Erie County hamlet of 257 souls (1910 population). His store is listed in the 1890, 1900 and 1902 directories.

By 1918 the only general store in Mill Grove was owned by F. E. McLane.

C. M. PUTNAM

Moriah, N.Y.

Rulau	Date	Metal	Size	VG	F	VF	Unc
Mor 7	(1900-02)	Brass	21mm	—	—	10.00	—

C.M. PUTNAM / — / MORIAH / — / N.Y. Rv: GOOD FOR / 5 (within ornamental panel) / IN TRADE.

Charles Putnam was a grocer listed in the 1900 and 1902 directories.

"JOE" HALE

Newark, N.Y.

Rulau	Date	Metal	Size	VG	F	VF	Unc
Nwk 9	(ca 1900)	Brass	21mm	—	—	10.00	—

"JOE" HALE / ... / NEWARK / ... / . N.Y. . Rv: GOOD FOR / * 5 (large) * / IN TRADE.

Hale sold cigars in 1900, and manufactured them in 1902.

O. DIMMICK

Newark Valley, N.Y.

Rulau	Date	Metal	Size	VG	F	VF	Unc
Nwv 1	(1900-14)	Aluminum	18.8mm	—	7.50	13.50	—

O. DIMMICK, / (ornament) / NEWARK / VALLEY, / * N.Y. *. Rv: GOOD FOR / ONE / * 5 ¢ * / CIGAR.

Ossian Dimmick ran a hotel 1900-1914, and operated a fuel depot. In the 1918-22 period the firm was retitled Dimmick & Dabron.

AMERICAN DUNLOP TIRE CO.

New York, N.Y.

Rulau	Date	Metal	Size	VG	F	VF	Unc
Nyk 3	(1894-98)	Aluminum	38mm	—	12.50	18.00	27.00

Aeolus face at right rim blows wind to left. Initials C.L.C. at bottom. A SET / OF HARNESS / FOR / THE WIND at left. Rv: AMERICAN / DUNLOP TIRE CO / —.— / NEW YORK / (small tower ?). Plain edge. Thick flan. (Wright 272)

The wind-god motif appears on other New York City tokens, such as those of Mann Brothers, clothiers.

BABIES HOSPITAL

Rulau	Date	Metal	Size	F	VF	EF	Unc
Nyk 5	1887	Silver	Scal 23mm	—	—	30.00	40.00

Baby's bust left, "INASMUCH" below, all within central circle. Around: THE BABIES HOSPITAL OF THE CITY OF NEW YORK / * 1887 *. Rv: Blank except for incused makers mark: THEODORE & STARR / NEW YORK at top, and word STERLING incused at bottom. A pin for wearing is soldered on the back. The blank central portion was intended for engraving. (A surviving example is engraved in script: LIZZIE LYON / 1897.)

Presumably this medalet was used throughout the 1890's, and perhaps beyond, for babies born in this New York hospital.

BENNETT SLOAN & CO.

Rulau	Date	Metal	Size	VG	F	VF	Unc
Nyk 8	(1890's)	Aluminum	30.5mm	—	—	20.00	—

WE WILL REDEEM THIS FROM ANY CUSTOMER AT / FIVE / CENTS / BENNETT / SLOAN & CO. / N.Y. / *. Rv: GOOD FOR / ONE / COUNTRY (C is fancy) / GENTLEMEN (G is fancy) / FIVE CENT / CIGAR. Plain edge.

In the 1890 directory Bennett Sloan & Co. were listed as dealers in spices and coffee. In the 1900-1902 directories they appear as dealers in tea and coffee.

C. G. BRAXMAR CO.

Rulau	Date	Metal	Size	VG	F	VF	Unc
Nyk 10	(1890's)	Svd/B	32mm	—	10.00	—	—

Radiant compass, square and G emblem of the Masons at center, blank scrolls top and bottom. Rv: (All incused): COMPLIMENTS / OF / THE C. G. BRAXMAR CO. / NO 10.12 MAIDEN LANE / NEW YORK / MASONIC EMBLEMS / AND / LODGE SUPPLIES. Plain edge. The store card is irregularly lobed in shape, and eyed for suspension.

Charles G. Braxmar & Co. were manufacturers of badges and medallions, mostly Masonic, and are listed in the 1890-1902 directories. The firm also made badges for the Washington Inaugural Centennial in 1889 (see Baker 40-40B). In 1889 their address was given as 86 Cortlandt Street.

BUNDES SCHUTZENFEST

Rulau	Date	Metal	Size	VG	F	VF	Unc
Nyk 11	1895	Aluminum	20mm	—	—	12.00	—

BUNDES - SCHUTZENFEST / NEW YORK / 1895. Rv: Target device. Plain edge. Issued with loop.

C E
(Christian Endeavor)

Rulau	Date	Metal	Size	V	VF	EF	Unc
Nyk 20	1892	Aluminum	25mm	4.00	—	—	—

Building. MADISON SQUARE / GARDEN. Rv: Large C enclosing E at center. Around: 11TH INTERNATIONAL CONVENTION / NEW YORK / JULY 7-10 1892. (Wright 742)

Christian Endeavor's 16th International Convention in 1897 at San Francisco, Calif., also prompted a token, which see.

CAFE LINDINGER

Rulau	Date	Metal	Size	VG	F	VF	Unc
Nyk 21	(ca 1900)	CN	25mm	—	7.50	12.50	—

CAFE LINDINGER / 56 & 58 / LIBERTY ST. / NEW YORK. Rv: FRITZ LINDINGER / 2 1/2 / 56 & 58 LIBERTY ST. Plain edge. The N of NEW begins under the upright of B of LIBERTY.

Rulau	Date	Metal	Size	VG	F	VF	Unc
Nyk 21A	(ca 1900)	CN	25mm	—	7.50	12.50	—

As 21, from different die. The N begins between the I and B of LIBERTY.

Fritz Lindinger's Cafe appears in the 1900 and 1902 directories with this address. Earlier, in the 1880's, it had been at 45 Liberty Street.

From the earlier address Lindinger issued a similar cupronickel 2 1/2-cent token which appears in *U.S. Trade Tokens 1866-1889* as NY-NY 153.

COWPERTHWAIT & SONS

Rulau	Date	Metal	Size	VG	F	VF	Unc
Nyk 22	(?)	Brass	34.5mm	—	—	—	—

Building. Above: COWPERTHWAIT & SONS / EVERYTHING FOR HOUSEKEEPING. Below: FURNITURE, CARPETS, / RUGS ETC. / NEW / 3RD AVE. & YORK PARK ROW & / 121ST STREET CITY CHATHAM SQ. Rv: Open an Account with the Oldest Furniture House in America / Good / for $2.50 / when purchasing / $25 worth, / or more, either for / Cash or / on / LIBERAL CREDIT.

It is not known on what basis Cowperthwait claimed to be the "oldest furniture house in America." Hyperbole? Its stores had fashionable locations at 3rd Avenue and 121st Street and Park Row & Chatham Square a century ago.

CRAWFORD CLOTHES

Rulau	Date	Metal	Size	F	VF	EF	Unc
Nyk 24	(?)	Nickel	Round, --mm	—	—	15.00	—

CRAWFORD CLOTHES FIFTH AVE. N.Y.C. 12 PAY PLAN LARGEST CLOTHING CHAIN IN THE EAST. Incused numeral (19218). Issued holed.

Charge card token.

DANIELL & SON

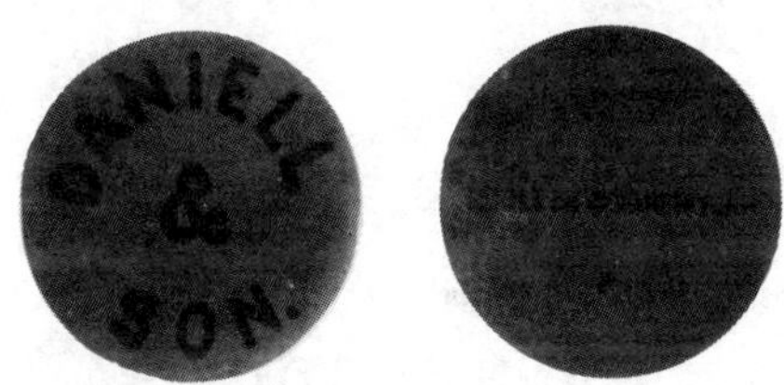

Rulau	Date	Metal	Size	VG	F	VF	Unc
Nyk 27	(1890's)	Brass	25.5mm	—	15.00	—	—

(All incused): DANIELL / & / SON. Rv: HOOLE MFG. CO. NEW YORK. Plain edge.

John Daniell & Sons were listed as dry goods dealers in the 1890 directory, and in the 1900 and 1902 directories.

Hoole Manufacturing & Baggage Check Company, Inc., makers of railroad supplies, appear only in the 1890 directory. Apparently Hoole made these checks for Daniell for some as yet undisclosed purpose.

W. F. DOLL MFG. CO.

Rulau	Date	Metal	Size	VG	F	VF	Unc
Nyk 30	1898	Aluminum**	38mm	—	—	55.00	70.00

** A steel horseshoe has been set into the reverse of the aluminum token. Heads of two oxen yoked together, facing three-fourths left from the right side, the word SOUVENIR on a scroll beneath the heads. Above: "YE DAIRY FARM". Below: N.Y. 109 NIGHTS. / CHICAGO 133 NIGHTS. PHILA 137 NIGHTS. Rv: Steel horseshoe inset at center, lettered: MAINE, FEB. 15, 1898. Legend begins within loop of horseshoe and extends to lower rim: A / MAINE STEEL / SOUVENIR / -.- / W. F. DOLL / MFG. CO. / N. Y. / SIGNED BY / W. C. GIBSON / COMMANDER U.S.N. / IN CHARGE GENERAL / DELIVERY OF STORES. Crossed anchors flank the second last line. Around the horseshoe in three curved lines: THIS IS TO CERTIFY THAT THE U.S. GOVERNMENT HAS DELIVERED TO / THE / W. F. DOLL MFG. CO. THE ENTIRE AMOUNT OF STEEL / SAVED FROM THE WRECK OF THE BATTLESHIP MAINE. Plain edge. Issued holed.

This token has a direct connection to the Spanish-American War, the great uplifter of the American spirit in the Nineties.

The Doll firm made watch cases in the 1898-1902 period.

Rulau	Date	Metal	Size	VG	F	VF	Unc
Nyk 31	(1900)	Aluminum	38mm	—	—	20.00	25.00

Obverse as Nyk 30. Rv: Scenes. Plain edge. (Gary Pipher coll.)

Nyk 31 may not be connected with W. F. Doll Mfg. Co., but it uses the same obverse type.

EAGLE ENGRAVING & STAMPING CO.

Rulau	Date	Metal	Size	F	VF	EF	Unc
Nyk 35	(1890's)	Aluminum	45mm	—	—	—	—

Revolutionary 'dandy' with trophies of arms in background standing facing on a pedestal, spread eagle below. Around in three lines: COMPLIMENTS OF EAGLE ENGRAVING & STAMPING CO. / OFFICE ROBT. STOLL 19 JOHN ST. NEW YORK / (tiny) D. BRENNER FECIT N.Y. Rv: MANUFACTURERS OF / COINS, / MEDALS, / BADGES ETC. / ALL KINDS OF STAMPING IN / GOLD, SILVER, BRONZE, BRASS, ETC. / IN GENERAL FOR THE TRADE / PRESS & DROP HAMMER WORK / A SPECIALTY / 92 FULTON ST. & / 132 WILLIAM ST. / NEW YORK, / ESTIMATES FURNISHED WITH OR WITHOUT DIES. Plain edge. (Wright 277)

ELECTRICAL JOURNAL

Rulau	Date	Metal	Size	F	VF	EF	Unc
Nyk 40	(1890's)	Aluminum	38mm	—	5.50	—	—

THE ELECTRICAL (latter word very large and surrounded by rays) / AGE / WORLD BUILDING N.Y. Rv: AN ILLUSTRATED WEEKLY ELECTRICAL JOURNAL / BRIGHT NEWSY / & SUBSTANTIAL / READ IT TALK ABOUT IT / SUBSCRIPTION / $3oo PER YEAR. Plain edge. (Wright 1666)

D. J. FAOUR & BROS.

Rulau	Date	Metal	Size	VG	F	VF	Unc
Nyk 42	1891(1909)	Bronze	32.5mm	—	18.00	25.00	40.00

U.S. shield with medallion portrait at center enclosed within a horseshoe, French and Turkish flags at either side, as are four-leaf clover and wishbone. Above: D. J. FAOUR & BROS. / BANKERS / AND / MERCHANTS. Below: EST. 1891 / GOOD LUCK / 63 WASHNGTON ST. N.Y. Rv: Arabic script, the top line of which is the date in Arabic numerals 1909. Plain edge.

D. J. Faour and Brothers were jobbers of general merchandise listed in the 1900-1902 directories and later.

FRED FEARNOT

Rulau	Date	Metal	Size	VG	F	VF	Unc
Nyk 42	(1899)	Brass	32mm	—	—	15.00	25.00

Military bust right, tiny W. & H. CO. NEWARK N.J. under truncation. Below: ADMIRAL GEORGE DEWEY. Rv: Facing civilian bust with quixotic expression on face. Below: FRED FEARNOT. Plain edge.

FLIEG'S WASHINGTON HALL

Rulau	Date	Metal	Size	F	VF	EF	Unc
Nyk 44	(1890's)	Aluminum	29mm	—	—	—	—

Building at center, FLIEG'S WASHINGTON HALL around, tiny F. COOK & CO. N.Y. below. Rv: BALL / MEETING / BILLIARD / ROOM, RESTAURANT AND BOWLING ALLEY'S 2157 & 2159 AMSTERDAM AVE., / BET. 166TH & 167TH STS. / N.Y. Plain edge. (Wright 330)

HARLEM HOUSE (John O'Neil)

Rulau	Date	Metal	Size	VG	F	VF	Unc
Nyk 65	(1890's)	WM	31mm	—	—	12.50	—

Horseshoe. HARLEM HOUSE / QUICK / AND / SELECT / 115TH & 3RD AVE. / JOHN O'NEIL PROP. Rv: HARLEM HOUSE / LEADING HOTEL / UP TOWN / 115TH & 3RD AVE. / NEW YORK / ELEGANTLY FURNISHED ROOMS. Plain edge. (Wright 789)

E. JACOBS & SON

Rulau	Date	Metal	Size	VG	F	VF	Unc
Nyk 67	(1890's)	Gilt/B	32mm	—	—	10.00	20.00

Building within central circle. Around: USED EXCLUSIVELY FOR RETAILING MENS & BOYS CLOTHING. / (rosette). Rv: E. JACOBS & SON / (ornament) / CLOTHING / FOR / BOYS & MEN / (ornament) / AVE. A. COR. 4TH STREET. N.Y. Plain edge. Issued holed.

KELLER'S HABERDASHER

Rulau	Date	Metal	Size	F	VF	EF	Unc
Nyk 68	(?)	Gilt/B	32mm	—	6.00	—	—

Indian head left. Around: KELLER'S LUCKY POCKET COIN / AMERICA. Rv: Within oak and laurel wreath: KELLER'S / HABERDASHER / SHIRT TAILOR / 749 B'WAY / N. Y. Plain edge.

Rulau	Date	Metal	Size	VG	F	VF	Unc
Nyk 69	(?)	Gilt/B	32mm	—	6.00	—	—

Capped Liberty head left. Around: KELLER'S LUCKY POCKET COIN / COLUMBIA. Rv: Within oak and laurel wreath: KELLER'S / HABERDASHER / SHIRT TAILOR / 1407 B WAY / N. Y.

Both tokens bear the tiny WHITEHEAD & HOAG CO. NEWARK N.J. signature line across bottom rim on reverse.

MALT DIASTASE CO.

Rulau	Date	Metal	Size	VG	F	VF	Unc
Nyk 70	(1885-1900)	WM	25mm	—	—	—	—

MALT DIASTASE CO. / (ornament) / NEW YORK. Rv: Blank. Plain edge. (Wright 1536)

MANHATTAN BRASS CO.

Rulau	Date	Metal	Size	VG	F	VF	Unc
Nyk 72	(1890)	Brass	19mm	—	—	7.00	—

MANHATTAN BRASS CO. / PAT. FEB. 17. 61 / EXT. AUG. 9. 64 / PAT. MAY. 25. 1880. Rv: DIAMOND LIGHT ARGAND / (radiant sunburst) / —. Plain edge. Centrally holed flan. (Wright 655)

This firm is listed in the 1890 through 1902 directories.

MANN BROTHERS

Rulau	Date	Metal	Size	VG	F	VF	Unc
Nyk 73	(1890's)	Copper	32mm	—	—	25.00	—

Aeolus at left (wind-god). MANN BROTHERS / GRAND & / ORCHARD / NEW YORK. Rv: HONEST GOODS / CLOTHIERS / * / — HATTERS — / —.— / FURNISHERS / —.— / * HONEST VALUE *. Plain edge. Issued holed. (Wright 658)

Rulau	Date	Metal	Size	VG	F	VF	Unc
Nyk 74	(1890's)	Brass	32mm	—	—	20.00	—

As last. Plain edge. Issued holed.

This token has also been reported in silver.

Mann Brothers appear in the 1890 directory. They are not listed that way in 1900 directory, but possibly became a chain store operation by then.

MULLERS

Rulau	Date	Metal	Size	VG	F	VF	Unc
NYK 78	(?)	Brass	25mm	—	—	12.00	—

MULLERS / 2 1/2 / 8TH ST & 6TH AVE. Rv: 2 1/2. Plain edge. (Wright 1531)

NASON MFG. CO.

Rulau	Date	Metal	Size	VG	F	VF	Unc
Nyk 84	1893	Aluminum	38mm	—	—	40.00	—

Christopher Columbus bust right within wreath. There are three scrolls, lettered respectively: 1492 SOUVENIR and 1893. Rv: Heater at center. Above: HIGH DUTY HEATERS / 10 TO 1 / EFFICIENCY. At right: GULF / STREAM / FOR / HOT / WATER. At left: EQUATOR / FOR / STEAM. Below: NASON M.'F.'G. CO. / 71 BEEKMAN ST., / NEW YORK. Plain edge. (Wright 743)

ANTHONY OECHS

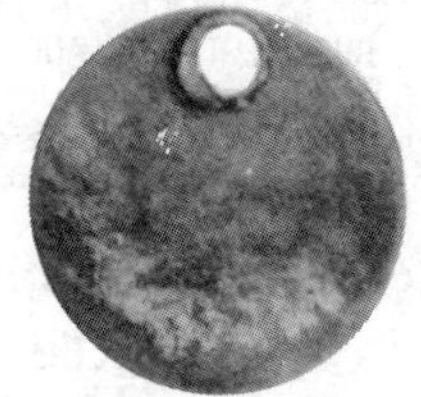

Rulau	Date	Metal	Size	VG	F	VF	Unc
Nyk 87	(1890's)	Brass	26mm	—	—	Scarce	—

(All incused): H....'S PAT. / MAY. 2. 76. / (star) / ANTHONY OECHS / NEW-YORK / SOLE AGENT FOR THE U.S. Rv: Blank. Plain edge.

Oechs was an importer of wines, listed in the 1890-1902 directories. The item listed might be a tag of some sort.

TONY PASTOR

Rulau	Date	Metal	Size	F	VF	EF	Unc
Nyk 90	1890	WM	39mm	—	—	35.00	55.00

Bust right, MARCH 22ND 1865 — TONY PASTOR — MARCH 21ST 1890. Rv: Within laurel wreath: PRESENTED / BY / TONY PASTOR, / AS A SOUVENIR OF / REMEMBRANCE / AND IN / COMMEMORATION OF / THE COMPLETION / OF HIS / 25TH YEAR OF / MANAGEMENT / IN / NEW YORK CITY.

THE PLUME & ATWOOD MFG. CO.

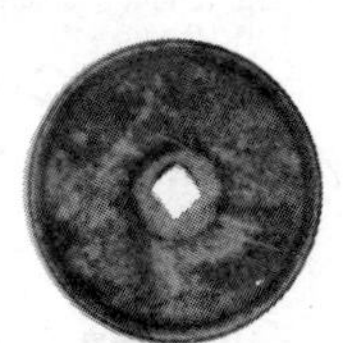

Rulau	Date	Metal	Size	VG	F	VF	Unc
Nyk 94	(1890)	Brass	20mm	—	—	15.00	—

THE PLUME & ATWOOD MFG. CO. / NOS 4284 4304 REISSUED. Rv: Blank. Square centrally-holed flan. (Wright 1124)

Plume & Atwood were manufacturers of brass goods, listed in the 1890 through 1902 directories. They were also located in Waterbury, Connecticut.

S. W. REESE & CO.

Rulau	Date	Metal	Size	VG	F	VF	Unc
Nyk 98	(1890's)	Bronze	24mm	—	—	—	40.00

S. W. REESE & CO. / -.- / RUBBER STAMPS / -&- / STENCILS / 72 PAGE / - / CATALOGUE FREE / 29 CHURCH ST. N.Y. Rv: BRASS CHECKS OF EVERY DESCRIPTION / BADGES / DOOR PLATES / SEALS. / PEW PLATES / &C, &C / .. Plain edge.

Listed in the Dun directory for 1890, 1900 and 1902. It also had branches in Chicago, Illinois and Gettysburg, Pennsylvania.

These tokens have also been reported in cupronickel, brass and aluminum.

REINAD

Rulau	Date	Metal	Size	F	VF	EF	Unc
Nyk 100	(?)	Copper	27mm	—	—	30.00	—

REINAD / N.Y.C. on oval boss ctsp on Canada 1900 Large Cent. (The boss has been soldered or welded onto the coin's reverse, obscuring the word CENT)

SCHLOSS & PRATEL

Rulau	Date	Metal	Size	F	VF	EF	Unc
Nyk 110	(1901)	S/Brass	28.5mm	—	—	25.00	—

Three busts jugate, facing three-quarters left, at center. The busts are, from left, Abraham Lincoln, James A. Garfield and William McKinley. Around: OUR MARTYR PRESIDENTS. / ***. Rv: SCHLOSS & PRATEL / MAKERS / OF FINE / BOYS AND CHILD'S / CLOTHING / * / * NEW YORK *. A small fleur-de-lis is inserted between SCHLOSS and &. Plain edge. (King 578)

Schloss & Pratel was a successor firm to N. J. Schloss & Co., clothing merchants and token issuers of the 1870's and 1880's (see U.S. Trade Tokens 1866-1889)

The Schloss firms capitalized on public events to issue their series of advertising tokens.

SHERRY'S / A.E.S.B.

Rulau	Date	Metal	Size	VG	F	VF	Unc
Nyk 122	1892	Aluminum	38mm	—	—	20.00	—

Quartered shield inscribed: A. — E. — S. — B. Around: SOUVENIR / NEW YORK / AUTUMN MEETING / NOV 29TH TO DEC 2 1892. Rv: SHERRY'S / 1 WALTZ / 2 LANCERS / 3 POLKA / 4 CAPRICE / 5 LANCERS / 6 YORKE / 7 WALTZ / 8 POLKA / 9 LANCERS / 10 WALTZ / NOV. 30 1892. Plain edge. (Wright 978)

A most curious piece, which we have not examined. The legend indicates this token carries a dance program for the second evening of the 4-day meeting of the group whose shield is depicted on the obverse. The initials A.E.S.B. are given in the order in which Dr. Wright gave them, but heraldic arrangements may indicate another interpretation, A.B.S.E., E.B.A.S. etc.

SINGER BUILDING

Rulau	Date	Metal	Size	VG	F	VF	Unc
Nyk 125	(?)	CN	21mm	2.00	2.50	3.00	4.00

RETURN / 4 (incuse) / To ROOM 3410 / SINGER BUILDING. N. Y. Rv: 432 (incuse). Plain edge. Issued holed. (Rulau coll.)

The envelope in which this item came was marked "hat or coat check." Could also be keyring tag or similar disc. Probably pre-1900.

M. STACHELBERG & CO.

Rulau	Date	Metal	Size	VG	F	VF	Unc
Nyk 130	(?)	Bakelite	38mm	—	—	7.50	12.50

Cigar at center. Around: M. STACHELBERG & CO'S. CIGARS. Rv: Same. Plain edge. Occurs in various colors of bakelite. (Colors examined: Black, Blue)

MAX STINER & CO.

Rulau	Date	Metal	Size	F	VF	EF	Unc
Nyk 133	1892	Copper	31.5mm	—	—	12.50	17.50

Facing Columbus bust, 1492 COLUMBUS 1892 above, 2193 THIRD AVENUE, NEW YORK / WINE & LIQUOR WAREHOUSE, below. Rv: SPECIAL AGENTS FOR / MAX STINER & COS. / (eagle on globe) / TRADE MARK / CELEBRATED / WINES & LIQUORS. Plain edge. Thick flan. (Tanenbaum coll.)

This piece is well made in fabric, a "throwback" to the delightful proof-surface store cards of the 1850's.

TAMMANY HALL

New York, N.Y. (?)

Rulau	Date	Metal	Size	VG	F	VF	Unc
Nyk 150	(?)	Brass	25mm	—	—	—	—

Two billiard cues crossed, with letters N. B. M. CO. in angles of the cross, all within central circle. Around: NATIONAL BILLIARD MANUFACTURING CO. Rv: GOOD FOR / 5 ¢ / TAMMANY HALL / IN / * TRADE *. Plain edge. (Wright 1089)

This may not be the famous Tammany Hall in New York, Democrat Party headquarters.

VOGEL BROTHERS

Rulau	Date	Metal	Size	F	VF	EF	Unc
Nyk 155	1893	Silver	38mm	—	—	50.00	—

Elephant left, TRADEMARK below. Above: .VOGEL BROTHERS. / CLOTHIERS / AND / OUTFITTERS / WHITE. Below: ELEPHANT / (on ribbon incused) L. I. JACOBS. / BROADWAY AND / 31st ST. / NEW YORK. Rv: (All incused): From OCT. 1893 / (calendar) / TO OCT. 1894. Plain edge. (Ganter coll.)

JOHN WANAMAKER

New York, N.Y.

Rulau	Date	Metal	Size	F	VF	EF	Unc
Nyk 160	(1917 ?)	Aluminum	31mm	—	—	6.00	9.00

Santa Claus bust 3/4 right. Around: GOOD FOR ONE MERRY CHRISTMAS. Rv: TO ALL / FRIENDS OF / SANTA CLAUS / (script) John Wanamaker / NEW YORK / SENDS A / MERRY CHRISTMAS / (tiny) WHITEHEAD-HOAG. Plain edge.

See the Wanamaker Stores tokens under Philadelphia, Pa.

D. LYNCH & SONS

Niagara Falls, N.Y.

Rulau	Date	Metal	Size	VG	F	VF	Unc
Ngf 6	(1890's)	Aluminum	24.5mm	—	6.00	—	—

D. LYNCH & SONS / * / SHOES / * / NIAGARA FALLS, N.Y. Rv: GOOD FOR / * 5 ¢ * / IN TRADE.

This vendor of boots and shoes appears in the directories for 1890 through 1902.

THE METAL STAMPING CO.

Niagara Falls, N.Y.

Rulau	Date	Metal	Size	VG	F	VF	Unc
Ngf 10	(1900)	CN	34mm	—	—	20.00	27.50

View of the falls, NIAGARA FALLS / SOUVENIR above. Rv: THE METAL STAMPING CO. / METAL SIGNS, / HOUSE NUMBERS, / COIN MEDALS, / SEAL PRESSES, / RUBBER STAMPS / AND / HARDWARE SPECIALTIES. / NIAGARA FALLS, N.Y. Plain edge.

Listed as a manufacturer of metal signs and metal mirrors in the 1900 and 1902 directories. This token may well postdate the 1890's.

C.E. BAISH

Olean, N.Y.

Rulau	Date	Metal	Size	VG	F	VF	Unc
Ole 1	(1900)	Aluminum	20mm	—	—	10.00	—

C. E. BAISH / OLEAN, N.Y. Rv: GOOD FOR / * 5 ¢ * / IN TRADE.

Baish, a seller of cigars and tobacco, appears only in the 1900 directory.

S. A. WRIGHT

Ouaquaga, N.Y.

Rulau	Date	Metal	Size	VG	F	VF	Unc
Ouq 1	(1900-02)	Aluminum	19mm	—	—	15.00	—

S. A. WRIGHT, / * * / OUAQUAGA / * N.Y. *. Plain edge.

Samuel A. Wright's general store appears in the 1900 and 1902 and 1918 Dun directories.

Ouaquaga is a tiny place in Broome County; its World War I population was 100. In 1918 it had a wagonmaker's shop, Wright's general store and a grocery.

ERICH VOSS

Port Richmond, Staten Island, N.Y.

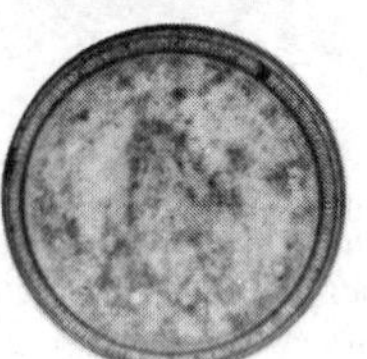

Rulau	Date	Metal	Size	VG	F	VF	Unc
Rcm 1	(1899-1900)	Brass	23mm	—	—	40.00	—

(All incused). ERICH VOSS . / 2 1/2 (large) / PORT RICHMOND, S.I. Rv: Blank. Incised, dentilated rim on each side. Plain edge. (Pipher coll. ex-S. Alpert)

Erich Voss' saloon appears only in the 1900 directory.

The "boycott check" good for 2 1/2 cents was given to customers of this German saloonkeeper. In attempts to outsell other vendors, he would offer his nickel schooners of beer for half price with this check, according to information accompanying the token.

VASSAR STUDENT'S AID SOCIETY

Poughkeepsie, N.Y.

Rulau	Date	Metal	Size	VG	F	VF	Unc
Pgk 10	1895	Gilt/B	24mm	—	—	25.00	—

Napoleon bust in uniform three-quarters left, NAPOLEON TEA above, OCT. 25TH. 1895, below. Rv: N in center. Around: SOUVENIR VASSAR STUDENT'S AID SOCIETY. Plain edge. (Spangenberger Oct. 1983 sale, lot 15)

Vassar Female College was founded 1861 by funds and land donated by Matthew Vassar (1792-1868). It became Vassar College in 1867. The school is nonsectarian and privately controlled and is considered a leading school for women in North America.

BARTHOLOMAY
Rochester, N. Y.

Rulau	Date	Metal	Size	F	VF	EF	Unc
Roc 1	(?)	Brass	24mm	—	40.00	—	—

(All incused): BARTHOLOMAY - / B. R. G. CO. - / 20. Rv: Blank. Plain edge. (Wright 44; Rulau Mav 8)

Attribution by Steve Tanenbaum.

C. EISENBERG

Rulau	Date	Metal	Size	VG	F	VF	Unc
Roc 5	(1890's)	Brass	21.5mm	—	—	8.00	—

C. / EISENBERG. Plain rim. Rv: GOOD FOR / 2 1/2 ¢ (large) / IN TRADE. Plain edge.

Rulau	Date	Metal	Size	VG	F	VF	Unc
Roc 6	(1890's)	Brass	21.5mm	—	—	8.00	—

C. / EISENBERG. Dentilated rim. Rv: GOOD FOR / .-. / 2 1/2 ¢ (smaller) / .-. / IN TRADE. Plain edge.

Conrad Eisenberg was a grocer listed in the 1890 and 1900 directories. By 1902 his grocery was replaced in ownership by Margaret Eisenberg (his widow?) and she had also expanded the business to include a saloon.

UNION CLOTHING CO.

Rulau	Date	Metal	Size	VG	F	VF	Unc
Roc 56	1890	Brass	35mm	—	—	20.00	30.00

Eagle with wings upraised right, atop olive branch and U.S. shield, UNION CLOTHING CO. on a scroll hanging from its beak. Ornate border around the rim. Rv: In central circle: (Ornament) / UNION CLOTHING CO. / ROCHESTER / -1890- . Around: SQUARE DEALING / -*- HONEST VALUES -*-. Plain edge.

This is a very beautiful medallic store card, carrying an eagle device not seen elsewhere.

Union Clothing & Tailoring Co. appears in the 1890 directories, but not the 1900 ones. In the 1902 directory it is called Union Credit Clothing Co. and is owned by the Rose Brothers.

Rulau	Date	Metal	Size	VG	F	VF	Unc
Roc 57	1899	Gilt/B	32mm	—	—	12.50	20.00

Military bust right, tiny W & H. CO. NEWARK, N.J. below truncation. Below ADMIRAL GEORGE DEWEY. Rv: UNION CLOTHING CO. / ROCHESTER'S / RELIABLE / TRADING PLACE / 1899. Plain edge.

WHITE ELEPHANT

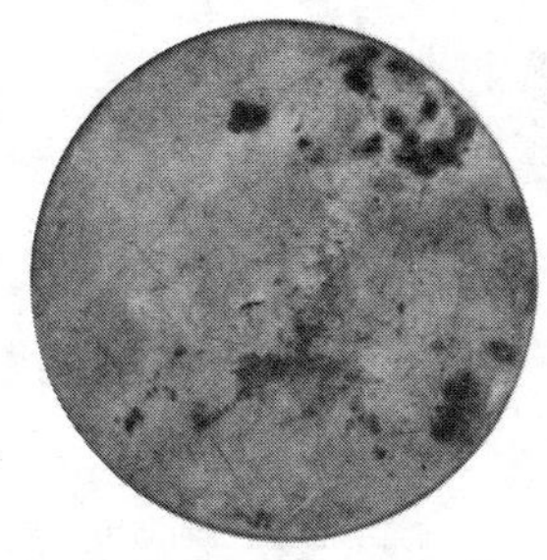

Rulau	Date	Metal	Size	VG	F	VF	Unc
Roc 60	(1890's ?)	Brass	35mm	—	30.00	40.00	—

(All incused): THE WHITE / LUNCH / 5 ¢ / ELEPHANT. Rv: Blank. Plain edge. (Wright 1687)

JOHN WILSON
Rochester, N.Y.

Rulau	Date	Metal	Size	VG	F	VF	Unc
Roc 66	(1890's ?)	CN	**	3.00	—	15.00	—

** Shield-shaped, 24mm.

(All incused): JOHN WILSON, BUTCHER, NO. 218 ALEX. ST., ROCHESTER, N.Y. Plain edge. (Dick Grinolds report)

COGSWELL'S CIGAR STORE
Rome, N.Y.

Rulau	Date	Metal	Size	VG	F	VF	Unc
Rom 4	(1894-99)	Aluminum	24mm	—	—	15.00	—

COGSWELL'S / CIGAR / STORE / ROME, N.Y. Rv: VALUE / ONE / 5 CENT / CIGAR.

Henry Cogswell, cigars and tobacco, is listed 1890-1902. His name is spelled COGGWELL in some directories.

HEALY BROS.
Rome, N.Y.

Rulau	Date	Metal	Size	VG	F	VF	Unc
Rom 8	(1900-02)	Brass	21.5mm	—	—	10.00	—

HEALY BROS. / -.- / ROME, / -.- N.Y. Rv: GOOD FOR / 5 (in ornate panel) / IN TRADE.

Restaurant, listed in Dun's directories for 1900 and 1902.

H. J. WAMSGANZ
Saranac Lake, N.Y.

Rulau	Date	Metal	Size	VG	F	VF	Unc
Srl 9	(?)	Aluminum	18.5mm	—	—	15.00	—

H. J. WAMSGANZ / SARANAC / * / LAKE, / N.Y. Rv: GOOD FOR / 5 C / CIGAR. Plain edge. (Smithsonian coll.)

MASTER MECHANIC CONVENTION

Saratoga, N.Y.

Rulau	Date	Metal	Size	VG	F	VF	Unc
Sar 6	1894	WM	33mm	—	—	11.50	—

MASTER MECHANIC AND MASTER CAR BUILDERS CONVENTIONS, 1894. Rv: SARATOGA.

D. SKIDMORE

Seneca Falls, N.Y.

Rulau	Date	Metal	Size	VG	F	VF	Unc
Sen 3	(?)	Silver	21mm	—	—	Rare	—

Eagle holds a cigar in its beak, GOOD FOR ONE just above cigar. Around: - / D. SKIDMORE - SENECA FALLS, N.Y. Rv: SKIDMORE'S / HEAD / QUARTERS / 95 FALL ST. HOTEL. Plain edge. (Wright 990)

Dr. Wright called this piece rare in 1898. We have not located a specimen to examine, but it seems reasonable to expect that a base metal version was struck for public use - German silver, cupronickel or another such alloy.

J. H. ODELL

Sidney, N.Y.

Rulau	Date	Metal	Size	VG	F	VF	Unc
Sid 20	1900	Brass	24mm	—	—	40.00	—

J. H. ODELL / * / 1900 / * / SIDNEY, N.Y. Rv: GOOD FOR ONE / 5 / CENTS / * CIGAR *. Plain edge. (Wright not listed)

ROBINSON'S RESTAURANT

Sidney, N.Y.

Rulau	Date	Metal	Size	VG	F	VF	Unc
Sid 40	1900	Brass	25mm	—	—	55.00	—

ROBINSON'S RESTAURANT / SIDNEY, N.Y. / 1900. Rv: GOOD FOR / 5 / 5 CENTS / SEGAR. Plain edge. (Wright 1601)

Rulau	Date	Metal	Size	VG	F	VF	Unc
Sid 42	(after 1900)	Aluminum	19mm	—	—	8.00	—

H. A. ROBINSON / * * / SIDNEY, * N - Y. *. Rv: GOOD FOR / ONE / 5 ¢ / * CIGAR *. Plain edge. (Gary Pipher, Joe Steger colls.)

H. A. Robinson was listed in the restaurant business in World War I.

J. D. BABCOCK & CO.

Syracuse, N.Y.

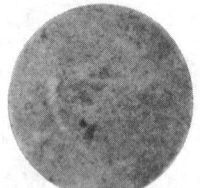

Rulau	Date	Metal	Size	VG	F	VF	Unc
Syr 2	(1900-02)	Copper	25mm	—	—	75.00	—

Within beaded central circle: BILLIARD / TABLE / M'F'RS. Around: J. D. Babcock & CO. / SYRACUSE, N.Y. Rv: Blank. Plain edge. R9.

Babcock appears as a billiard table manufacturer in the 1900 and 1902 directories.

W.E. BANNING

Rulau	Date	Metal	Size	VG	F	VF	Unc
Syr 3	(?)	Brass	30mm	—	—	25.00	—

W. E. BANNING / STAMPS & / STENCIL WORKS / WEST WATER / COR. CLINTON ST. / SYRACUSE, N.Y. Rv: STENCIL PLATES / RUBBER STAMPS / BAGGAGE CHECKS / SEAL / PRESSES / STEEL, STAMPS, &C. Plain edge. (Wright 55)

BENJAMIN & ANDREWS

Rulau	Date	Metal	Size	VG	F	VF	Unc
Syr 5	(1890)	Aluminum	35mm	—	—	30.00	—

BENJAMIN & ANDREWS / -o- / DEALERS IN / PURE / ALUMINUM / NOVELTIES / 121 W. JEFFERSON ST. / -o- / SYRACUSE, N.Y. Rv: Lord's Prayer in central circle. Around: EXTRACTED FROM THE COMMON CLAY OF THE EARTH BY ELECTRICITY / OF PURE / ALUMINUM / A SOUVENIR. Plain edge. (Wright 86)

DAKINS BUSINESS INSTITUTE

Rulau	Date	Metal	Size	VG	F	VF	Unc
Syr 9	(1899)	Brass	32mm	—	—	12.50	20.00

Military bust right, tiny W. & H. CO. NEWARK, N.J. under truncation. Below: ADMIRAL GEORGE DEWEY. Rv: DAKINS / BUSINESS / INSTITUTE / HERALD BUILDING SYRACUSE, N.Y. Plain edge.

G. M. EDWARDS CO.

Rulau	Date	Metal	Size	VG	F	VF	EF
Syr 10	(1902)	Silver	18mm	—	—	100.	—

G. M. EDWARDS / CO. / SYRACUSE / N.Y. in small punch ctsp on U.S. 1899 or 1902 Barber dime. The first line is curved. (Kirtley Feb. 1991 price list; Brunk 13065)

Rulau	Date	Metal	Size	VG	F	VF	EF
Syr 11	(1902)	Copper	29mm	—	—	100.	—

Similar ctsp on U.S. 1808 Large cent.

THE HOPKINS CO. INC.

Rulau	Date	Metal	Size	VG	F	VF	Unc
Syr 15	(1899)	Brass	29mm	—	—	15.00	25.00

Military bust right, ADMIRAL GEORGE DEWEY. below. Rv: THE HOPKINS CO. INC. / CLOTHIERS / AND / TAILORS / 206 S. SALINA ST. / SYRACUSE. Plain edge.

STEARNS

Rulau	Date	Metal	Size	VG	F	VF	Unc
Syr 26	1898	C/Lead	35mm	—	60.00	—	100.

Copy of an ancient Syracusan dekadrachm from Sicily. In exergue on reverse, incused, is: ETEAPNE / MDCCCXCVIII (STEARNS / 1898). Plain edge. Very thick flan.

This is a clever advertising piece and an award medal for bike races given out by the Stearns Bicycle Company of Syracuse, N.Y. (See Numismatic Scrapbook Magazine for 1963, page 1263)

SYRACUSE CHILLED PLOW CO.

Rulau	Date	Metal	Size	VG	F	VF	Unc
Syr 33	1900	Gilt/B	28.5mm	—	8.00	12.00	15.00
	Marianne head right, REPUBLIQUE FRANCAISE around, PARIS 1900 below. Rv: SYRACUSE CHILLED PLOW CO. SYRACUSE, N.Y. / PLOWS / HARROWS / CULTIVATORS / BARROWS / USA. Plain edge.						
Syr 34	1900	Copper	27mm	—	—	15.00	—
	Head of female "Marianne" left, REPUBLIQUE FRANCAISE PARIS 1900. Rv: SYRACUSE CHILLED PLOW CO. / PLOWS / HARROWS / CULTIVATORS / BARROWS / SYRACUSE N.Y.						

"Marianne" is the female personification of France. The Syracuse company's products won a gold medal at the huge Paris Exhibition in 1900. The firm was still in business under the same name as late as 1918.

Rulau	Date	Metal	Size	VG	F	VF	Unc
Syr 36	(1899)	Gilt/B	32mm	—	—	10.00	20.00

Military bust right, tiny W. & H. CO. NEWARK, N.J. under truncation. Below: ADMIRAL GEORGE DEWEY. Rv: Plow right, SYRACUSE CHILLED / PLOW CO. / SYRACUSE, N.Y. above. A NATIONAL LEADER, below. Plain edge.

L. A. WESTON CO.

Syracuse, N.Y.

Rulau	Date	Metal	Size	F	VF	EF	Unc
Syr 50	1890's	Silver	31mm	—	—	175.	—
	L. A. WESTON CO. / KOSTO / PAT. APL'D FOR / BRAKE / SYRACUSE, N.Y. ctsp on each side of U.S. 1893 Columbian half dollar. The 2nd, 3rd and 4th lines of the counterstamp are within a cartouche. (B&M 1985 Patterson sale, lot 1666; Brunk 42755)						
Syr 51	(1890's)	CN	22mm	—	—	75.00	—
	Similar ctsp on U.S. 1873 Shield nickel.						

Weston & Co. were bicycle manufacturers, according to an 1893 advertisement, with a factory in Jamestown, N.Y.

J. JORDAN'S CIGAR STORE

Troy, N.Y.

Rulau	Date	Metal	Size	VG	F	VF	Unc
Try 3	(1900-02)	Aluminum	21mm	—	6.00	—	—

J. JORDAN'S CIGAR STORE / 82 / CONGRESS / ST. / TROY, / N.Y. Rv: GOOD FOR / 1 / 5 ¢ / CIGAR. Plain edge.

Jacob Jordan is listed under tobacco and cigars 1900-1902.

LITTLE & CO.

Rulau	Date	Metal	Size	VG	F	VF	Unc
Try 5	(1890's)	Brass	21mm	—	6.00	8.50	—

LITTLE & CO. / 306 . 308 / RIVER ST. / TROY, N.Y. Rv: GOOD FOR / 5 ¢ / IN TRADE. Plain edge.

Cigar manufacturers, listed 1890-1900. In or about 1902 they were succeeded in the wholesale tobacco and cigar business by Little & Hulett.

E. A. PHELAN

Rulau	Date	Metal	Size	VG	F	VF	Unc
Try 7	(1900-02)	Aluminum	24mm	—	6.00	—	—

E. A. PHELAN / -o- / TROY, N.Y. Rv: GOOD FOR / 5 ¢ / IN TRADE. Plain edge.

Edward A. Phelan's saloon appears in the 1900-02 directories.

TROY LAUNDRY CO.

Troy, N.Y.

Rulau	Date	Metal	Size	F	VF	EF	Unc
Try 9	1900	Brass	28.5mm	—	—	Rare	—

1900 incused in central circle. In relief above: * TROY LAUNDRY CO. *; below: 9 St. CHAS. ST. Rv: Blank. Beaded rims on each side. Plain edge.

THOMAS L. BENHAM & CO.

Utica, N.Y.

Rulau	Date	Metal	Size	VG	F	VF	Unc
Utc 4	(1890's)	Brass	30mm	—	—	30.00	—

THOMAS L. BENHAM & CO. / WHOLESALE / AGENTS / * UTICA *. Rv: THIS CHECK WILL BE REDEEMED BY ANY DEALER * / GOOD FOR / ONE / FONTELLA / CIGAR. Plain edge.

This cigar and tobacco dealer appears in the 1890 directory. In the 1900-02 directories the '& CO.' have been deleted.

W. I. MARTIN

Rulau	Date	Metal	Size	VG	F	VF	Unc
Utc 10	(1890's)	CN	29mm	—	Rare	—	—

(All incused): W. I. MARTIN / UTICA / N.Y. / 130 GENESSEE ST. Rv: Similar to obverse. Plain edge. (Gary Pipher coll.) (Wright 664)

Only 2 specimens known. The specimen in the Pipher collection is blackened and corroded from long interment in the ground.

William Martin is listed as a livery proprietor in 1890, and as a hotelkeeper in 1900. By 1902 he disappears from the directories. The street name Genesee is misspelled on the token.

D. B. SMITH & CO.

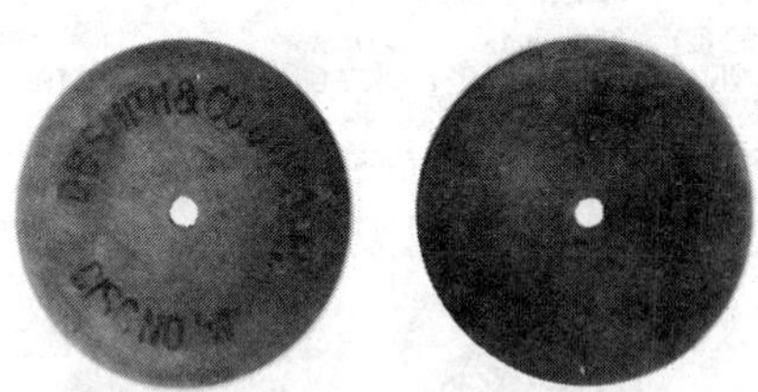

Rulau	Date	Metal	Size	VG	F	VF	Unc
Utc 20	(1890's)	Brass	25mm	—	15.00	—	—

(All incused): D. B. SMITH & CO UTICA N.Y. / DISC NO 51. R. Blank. Plain edge. Issued with small central hole.

The purpose of this disc is not known, but it may have been an identifier of some sort. DeWane B. Smith & Co. were in agricultural implements in the 1890-1902 directories.

W. S. TAYLOR & SON

Utica, N.Y.

Rulau	Date	Metal	Size	VG	F	VF	Unc
Utc 27	1890's)	GS	33mm	—	—	35.00	—

(All incused): W. S. TAYLOR & SON / 51 / UTICA, N.Y. Rv: Blank. Plain edge.

W. S. Taylor and Son are listed as jewelers in 1890. By the 1900 directory the '& Son' is deleted. This is probably a watchmaker's check, and may exist with other incused numerals than 51.

SCHRADE CUT. CO.

Walden, N.Y. and

SWAN CUTLERY CO.

New York, N.Y.

Rulau	Date	Metal	Size	VG	F	VF	EF
Wal 1	(ca 1900)	Bronze	19mm	—	20.00	—	40.00

SCHRADE CUT. CO. / WALDEN, N.Y. ctsp on reverse of U.S. 1899 Indian cent. Rv: SWAN / CUTLERY CO. / N.Y. ctsp on obverse of the coin. (Van Ormer sale 2870; Brunk 35820)

STREET FAIR

Watertown, N.Y.

Rulau	Date	Metal	Size	VG	F	VF	Unc
Wtn 20	1900	Bronze	19mm	—	—	35.00	—

STREET FAIR / JULY 9-14 / 1900 / WATERTOWN, N.Y. ctsp on shaved reverse of U.S. 1900 Indian Head cent. (Pipher coll; Brunk 41997)

Rulau	Date	Metal	Size	VG	F	VF	Unc
Wtn 21	(1900)	Steel	19mm	—	—	15.00	—

STREET FAIR / WATERTOWN, N.Y. ctsp on blank brass disc. Plain edge.

Rulau	Date	Metal	Size	VG	F	VF	Unc
Wtn 23	(1900)	Silver	25mm	—	—	30.00	—

WATERTOWN, N.Y. ctsp on U.S. 1877 S.L. quarter. (Brunk 41995)

H. L. NICHOLS

Waverly, N.Y.

Rulau	Date	Metal	Size	VG	F	VF	Unc
Wav 22	(1890)	Brass	**	—	—	25.00	—

** Oval, 39 x 31mm.

H. L. NICHOLS / (ornament) / WAVERLY, / N.Y. Rv: GOOD FOR / 5 C / IN / MERCHANDISE. Plain edge.

Nichols was a dealer in tobacco and cigars who appears in the 1890 Dun directory. Four differing varieties of Nichols tokens were found in a cigar box, according to Gary Pipher, Johnson City, N.Y.

N. L. N.

(H. L. Nichols)

Waverly, N.Y.

Rulau	Date	Metal	Size	VG	F	VF	Unc
Wav 22	(1890)	Brass	Oval 39x31mm	—	—	25.00	—

H. L. NICHOLS / (ornament) / WAVERLY, / N.Y. Rv: GOOD FOR 5 ¢ / IN / MERCHANDISE. Plain edge.

Nichols was a dealer in tobacco and cigars who appears in the 1890 Dun directory. Four differing varieties of Nichols tokens were found in a cigar box, according to Gary Pipher, Johnson City, N.Y.

Rulau	Date	Metal	Size	VG	F	VF	Unc
Wav 23	(1890's)	Brass	21.5mm	—	—	4.00	—

H. L. N. across center, beaded rim. Rv: GOOD FOR / 5 C / IN TRADE. Plain edge.

Wav 23A	(1890's)	Brass	21.5mm	—	—	4.00	—

Similar obverse, but rim is corded, or dentilated. Rv: Similar to Wav 23. Plain edge.

Wav 24	(1890's)	Brass	21.5mm	—	—	4.00	—

-.- / H. L. N. / -.-. Rv: As 23. Plain edge.

All four varieties of Nichols tokens were located in a cigar box, fitting since he was a tobacconist listed in the 1890 directory.

THE STEUBEN CIGAR CO.
Wayland, N.Y.

Rulau	Date	Metal	Size	VG	F	VF	Unc
Way 4	(?)	Brass	24mm	—	—	6.00	—

THE STEUBEN / (ornament) / CIGAR / CO. Rv: GOOD FOR / 5 ¢ / IN TRADE. (Pipher coll.)

NORTH CAROLINA

NEWCOMB
Greensboro, N.C.

Rulau	Date	Metal	Size	F	VF	EF	Unc
Gre 1	1891	Nickel	21mm	25.00	35.00	—	—

Barrel at center, labeled WINES / LIQUORS. Above: GREENSBORO, N.C. Below: * 1891 *. Rv: Large V (for 5) at center, IN NEWCOMB WE TRUST around. * CENTS * below. Plain edge. (Several varieties)

Superbly struck and greatly resembling the 5-cent piece of its day.

CAMEL CIGARETTES
Winston-Salem, N.C.

Rulau	Date	Metal	Size	F	VF	EF	Unc
Win 3	1899	Gilt Brass	28mm	—	10.00	15.00	—

Camel standing left, palm trees in background. HIGHLY VALUED ALL OVER THE WORLD around, CIGARETTES / .1899. below. Rv: BEST FOR YOUR MONEY'S WORTH / 20 / CAMEL / (tobacco leaf). Reeded edge. (Several varieties)

Reported by Chris Keogh, Dallas, Texas.

NORTH DAKOTA

H. J. WAGNER
Arthur, N.D.

Rulau	Date	Metal	Size	VG	F	VF	Unc
Art 1	(1906)	Brass	--mm	—	—	40.00	—

BBC die 11. Rv: H. J. WAGNER. (Thoele report)

WALKER BROTHERS
Fargo, N.D.

Rulau	Date	Metal	Size	F	VF	EF	Unc
Fgo 7	1899	Aluminum	35mm	—	—	27.50	—

WALKER BROTHERS / PRINTING / - / BOOK BINDING / - / LAW BLANKS / FARGO, N. D. Rv: JUNE 7 - 8 - 9 / * 1899. * / FARGO / FIRE / FESTIVAL. Plain edge. (Peter Fuhrman coll.)

T. S. HERRING
Heartland, N.D.

Rulau	Date	Metal	Size	VG	F	VF	Unc
Hrt 1	(?)	Brass	--mm	—	—	40.00	—

BBC die 2b. Rv: T. S . HERRING. (Thoele report)

HOPE POOL HALL
Hope, N.D.

Rulau	Date	Metal	Size	VG	F	VF	Unc
Hop 1	(1890's ?)	Brass	--mm	—	—	50.00	—

HOPE POOL HALL / 25 CENTS / HOPE, N.D. Rv: Blank: but ctsp D. (Koppenhaver June 1988 sale, lot 567)

OHIO

THE CENTRAL
Andover, Ohio

Rulau	Date	Metal	Size	F	VF	EF	Unc
And 2	(?)	—	—	15.00	25.00	—	—

Elephant at center, THE CENTRAL above, ANDOVER, OHIO below. Rv: GOOD FOR / 5 C / D. F. MUNN. Plain edge. (Lipscomb AN 1010)

THE HUB
Andover, Ohio

Rulau	Date	Metal	Size	F	VF	EF	Unc
And 4	(?)	Brass	Oct 29mm	—	10.00	—	—

(In relief within circular central depression) THE HUB / (cross-like ornament) / ANDOVER, O. Rv: GOOD FOR / 5 C / G.S. NICKOLS / IN TRADE. Plain edge. (Lipscomb AN 1020)

L. J. KEPPLER
Anna, Ohio

Rulau	Date	Metal	Size	VG	F	VF	Unc
Ann 1	(1891)	Brass	25mm	—	6.00	—	—

GOOD FOR / 5 C / L. J. KEPPLER / IN / TRADE / AT BAR. Rv: Blank. Plain edge. (Lipscomb AN 4020)

J. BROADHEAD
Bellevue, Ohio

Rulau	Date	Metal	Size	VG	F	VF	Unc
Blv 1	(?)	Copper	23mm	—	8.00	—	—

Clockface at center, THIS MUST BE RETURNED around, WHEN THE WATCH IS CALLED FOR below. Rv: J. BROADHEAD / DEALER IN / WATCHES / CLOCKS/ JEWELRY & / SILVER PLATED / WARE / BELLEVUE, O. Plain edge. (Lipscomb BE 4520)

Rulau	Date	Metal	Size	VG	F	VF	Unc
Blv 2	(?)	Copper	23mm	—	8.00	—	—

As Blv 1, but ctsp with a number. (Examined: 014). Plain edge. (Lipscomb BE 4530)

STAHL AND PATTY
Bradford, Ohio

Rulau	Date	Metal	Size	VG	F	VF	Unc
Brd 4	(1900)	Aluminum	Oct 27mm	—	—	6.00	—

STAHL / AND / PATTY. Rv: GOOD FOR / 1 / LOAF. Plain edge. (Lipscomb BR 1100)

This was a general store listed in 1900.

RIVERSIDE HOTEL
Bridgeport, Ohio

Rulau	Date	Metal	Size	VG	F	VF	Unc
Bri 7	(1891)	Nickel	24mm	—	6.00	—	—

RIVERSIDE HOTEL / J. / SCHNEIDER / PROP. Rv: Large 5 within circle of stars. Plain edge. (Lipscomb BR 3120)

Schneider is listed as the proprietor in 1891.

DAVID A. WOLFF
Bryan, Ohio

Rulau	Date	Metal	Size	VG	F	VF	Unc
Bry 3	(1893)	Aluminum	38mm	—	—	16.00	—

Fair buildings in 1893. Rv: DAVID A. WOLFF / THE OLD / RELIABLE/ CLOTHIER / BRYAN, OHIO. Plain edge. (Lipscomb BR 9110)

AMERICAN CLAY-WORKING MCH. CO.
Bucyrus, Ohio

Rulau	Date	Metal	Size	F	VF	EF	Unc
Buc 1	1900	Aluminum	38mm	—	—	11.00	—

Airborne male and female figures above exposition buildings, 1900 at right, WM-SON signature at lower right. Around: MEDAL AWARDED THE AMERICAN CLAY-WORKING MCH. CO. On tablet below: BUCYRUS, OHIO. Rv: Standard "Marianne" medal design, REPUBLIQUE FRANCAISE. (George Canterbury coll., Papillion, Neb.)

Dies cut by Williamson.

JNO. C. HELWIG
Canal Dover, Ohio

Rulau	Date	Metal	Size	VG	F	VF	Unc
Cdv 1	(?)	Silver	31mm	—	80.00	—	—

JNO. C. HELWIG / C. DOVER O. ctsp on U.S. 1876 S.L. half dollar. (Lipscomb CA 4440)

Possibly 1870's.

KOHLER BROS.
Canton, Ohio

Rulau	Date	Metal	Size	VG	F	VF	Unc
Cnt 3	(1892)	Brass	Oct 22mm	—	—	6.00	—

(All incused): KOHLER BROS. / CITY BAKERY. Rv: GOOD FOR / 5 C / LOAF. Plain edge. (Lipscomb CA 6710)

In 1892 Kohler Brothers were at 90 East Tuscarawas Street.

J. J. KONEN

Rulau	Date	Metal	Size	VG	F	VF	Unc
Cnt 5	(1900)	Brass	29mm	—	—	15.00	—

J. J. KONEN. RV: BRUNSWICK. Plain edge.

This was a 1900 saloon.

J. C. KUGLER
Canton, Ohio

Rulau	Date	Metal	Size	VG	F	VF	Unc
Cnt 10	1898	B&A	19mm	—	—	10.00	—

J. C. KUGLER / CANTON / O. Rv: GOOD FOR / 5 / PAT. JULY 1898 / IN MERCHANDISE. (Lipscomb CA 6740)

Rulau	Date	Metal	Size	VG	F	VF	Unc
Cnt 12	1898	B&A	28mm	—	—	12.00	—

Similar, but 25. Plain edge. (Lipscomb CA 6743)

J. KIRCHENSCHLAGER
Chillicothe, Ohio

Rulau	Date	Metal	Size	VG	F	VF	Unc
Chl 12	(1893-99)	Aluminum	25mm	—	—	10.00	—

J. KIRCHENSCHLAGER / CHILLICOTHE, O. Rv: GOOD FOR / 5 K (cutout) C / AT BAR. Plain edge. (Lipscomb CH 6420)

This same issuer released a 5-cent token about 1870 which had long been identified as a Civil War store card of Cincinnati.

GEO. W. KERN

Rulau	Date	Metal	Size	VG	F	VF	Unc
Chl 10	(1900)	Brass	25mm	—	—	7.50	—

GEO. W. KERN / 11 / PAINT ST. Rv: Large 5. Plain edge. (Lipscomb CH 6410)

JOHN E. SCHILDER

Rulau	Date	Metal	Size	VG	F	VF	Unc
Chl 50	(?)	Brass	25mm	—	—	15.00	—

Pool table, BRUNSWICK-BALKE-COLLENDER. Rv: GOOD FOR / 5 C / JOHN E. SCHILDER / IN / TRADE. Plain edge. (Lipscomb CH 6780)

J. B. SCHNEIDER

Rulau	Date	Metal	Size	VG	F	VF	Unc
Chl 55	(?)	Brass	25mm	—	—	15.00	—

Pool table, BRUNSWICK-BALKE COLLENDER CHECK. Rv: GOOD FOR / 5 C / J. B. SCHNEIDER / IN TRADE. Plain edge. (Lipscomb CH 6790)

SEARS AND NICHOLS
Chillicothe, Ohio

Rulau	Date	Metal	Size	VG	F	VF	Unc
Chl 62	(1900)	Brass	Scal 30mm	—	—	8.00	—

SEARS / AND / NICHOLS. Rv: 35. Plain edge. (Lipscomb CH 6830)

This was a canning factory in 1900. There may be other denominations of these chits waiting to be discovered.

J. J. ABRIHL
Cincinnati, Ohio

Rulau	Date	Metal	Size	VG	F	VF	Unc
Cin 1	(1890)	Brass	25mm	—	2.00	—	—

GOOD FOR / 5 C / J. J. ABRIHL / DRINK. Rv: Large 5 in circle of stars. Plain edge. (Lipscomb CI 0525)

THE ATLANTIC

Rulau	Date	Metal	Size	VG	F	VF	Unc
Cin 3	(1891)	Brass	26mm	—	3.00	—	—

GOOD FOR / W 5 C / OR / IN TRADE AT / THE ATLANTIC / 245 VINE. Rv: Blank. Plain edge. (Lipscomb CI 0675)

A. BECKER

Rulau	Date	Metal	Size	VG	F	VF	Unc
Cin 7	(1885)	Brass	Oct 22mm	—	10.00	—	—

GOOD FOR/ 5 C AT / BAR / A BECKER. Rv: JAS MURDOCK / 165 RACE ST / CINTI. Plain edge. (Lipscomb CI 0880)

CINCINNATI PURE ALUMINUM COMPANY

Rulau	Date	Metal	Size	VG	F	VF	Unc
Cin 20	(1890)	Aluminum	33mm	—	—	10.00	—

Within wreath: CINCINNATI / PURE ALUMINUM / COMPANY. Rv: Lord's prayer within small central circle. Around: EXTRACTED FROM THE COMMON CLAY OF THE EARTH BY ELECTRICITY — A SOUVENIR / OF PURE / ALUMINUM. THE WONDERFUL NEW METAL, WHITE, LIGHT / LUSTROUS / AND / SONOROUS. Plain edge. (Wright 86)

CONEY ISLAND

Rulau	Date	Metal	Size	VG	F	VF	Unc
Cin 25	(1885)	Brass	22mm	—	—	5.00	—

CONEY / 5 / ISLAND. Rv: Large 5 within circle of 16 stars. Below, in tiny letters: JAS. MURDOCK, JR 165 RACE ST CIN. O. Plain edge. (Lipscomb CI 1630)

Rulau	Date	Metal	Size	VG	F	VF	Unc
Cin 26	(?)	CN	22mm	—	—	5.00	—

As last. (Lipscomb CI 1635)

Rulau	Date	Metal	Size	VG	F	VF	Unc
Cin 27	(?)	Brass	19mm	—	—	5.00	—

CONEY / 10 / ISLAND. Large 10 within circle of 8 small stars. Plain edge. (Lipscomb CI 1640)

Rulau	Date	Metal	Size	VG	F	VF	Unc
Cin 28	(?)	Brass	21mm	—	—	5.00	—

CONEY / ISLAND / TOKEN. Rv: Wreath. Plain edge. (Lipscomb CI 1645)

DE LANG'S PHARMACY

Rulau	Date	Metal	Size	VG	F	VF	Unc
Cin 30	(1885-99)	Nickel	26mm	—	—	12.00	—

DE LANG'S / GLASS / 1 / SODA / PHARMACY. Rv: JAS MURDOCK / 165 RACE ST / CINTI (monogram). Plain edge. (Lipscomb CI 1850)

DIEMARS VIENNA BAKERY

Rulau	Date	Metal	Size	VG	F	VF	Unc
Cin 32	(1891)	Brass	Oval scal 29x25mm	—	—	5.00	—

(All incused): DIEMARS / VIENNA / BAKERY. Rv: GOOD FOR / 1 / LOAF. Plain edge. (Lipscomb CI 1890)

Louis Diemar was in business in 1891.

DIXON'S WALNUT HILLS EX.

Rulau	Date	Metal	Size	VG	F	VF	Unc
Cin 34	(1894)	Copper	22mm	—	—	10.00	—

DIXON'S WALNUT EX / 10 / CENTS. Rv: Blank. Plain edge. (Lipscomb CI 1930)

ENDERES BROS.

Rulau	Date	Metal	Size	VG	F	VF	Unc
Cin 38	(1890's ?)	Aluminum	Sq 26mm	—	—	5.00	—

ENDERES BROS / 5 C / CONEY ISLAND. Rv: 5 (rectangular cutout). Plain edge. (Lipscomb CI 2075)

D. FELDHAUS

Rulau	Date	Metal	Size	VG	F	VF	Unc
Cin 40	(1891-1904)	Brass	26mm	—	—	5.00	—

5 / D. FELDHAUS. Rv: Blank. Plain edge. (Lipscomb CI 2185)

Feldhaus ran a Walnut Hills beer garden in the 1891-1904 period.

M. FELL

Rulau	Date	Metal	Size	VG	F	VF	Unc
Cin 42	(1891)	Brass	Oval 26mm	—	—	3.00	—

GOOD FOR / 5 C AT BAR / M. FELL. Rv: Blank. Plain edge. (Lipscomb CI 2190)

FOX & JEWELL

Rulau	Date	Metal	Size	F	VF	EF	Unc
Cin 44	(1890's)	Aluminum	38mm	—	25.00	—	—

Horse. Rv: FOX & JEWELL (on scroll) / DEALERS / IN / HORSES & MULES / 3128-3138 / SPRING GROVE / AVE / CINCINNATI, O. (Lipscomb CI 2335)

Peter Fox' horse market was at 17 East 5th in 1889. Frank Fox' horse sale stable was at 13 East 5th the same year. The token was struck by Gregg G. Wright.

G. A. R.
(Grand Army of the Republic)

Rulau	Date	Metal	Size	VG	F	VF	Unc
Cin 45	1898	Brass	19mm	—	—	6.00	—

Five figures within 5-pointed star. Around: FRATERNITY CHARITY LOYALTY / 1861 1866. Rv: Large GAR monogram. Around: 32nd NAT'L ENCAMPMENT / 1898 / CINCINNATI. Plain edge.

GERMANIA BREWING CO.

Rulau	Date	Metal	Size	VG	F	VF	Unc
Cin 46	(1891)	Brass	28mm	—	—	10.00	—

THE / GERMANIA / BREWING / CO. Rv: Blank. Plain edge. (Lipscomb CI 2480)

GRAND HOTEL BAR

Rulau	Date	Metal	Size	VG	F	VF	Unc
Cin 49	(?)	Brass	26mm	—	—	7.00	—

GRAND / HOTEL BAR / 25 C / CINCINNATI. Rv: Blank. (Lipscomb CI 2585)

The Grand Hotel, at 4th and Central, was built 1874. Its bar was open until the last day of 1919, when Prohibition closed it down. There are other denominations of this token issue.

JOHN D. HOGREBE

Rulau	Date	Metal	Size	VG	F	VF	Unc
Cin 55	(1889)	Brass	26mm	—	—	45.00	—

JOHN D. HOGREBE / (Star) / -* CIN., O. *-. Rv: Within 15 stars: GOOD FOR A / 5 C / DRINK / (tiny) C. THEILER, 206 RACE ST., CIN., O. Plain edge. (Wright 456; Lipscomb CI 3090)

MENCKE

Rulau	Date	Metal	Size	VG	F	VF	Unc
Cin 60	(1890's ?)	CN	33mm	—	8.00	—	—

(All incused): MENCKE within ornaments top and bottom. Rv: S. E. COR. / 5 / 5th & ELM. Plain edge. (Lipscomb CI 4225)

Lipscomb reports this as MENKE.

PENN-MARYLAND CORPORATION

Rulau	Date	Metal	Size	VG	F	VF	Unc
Cin 70	(1890's)	Brass	19mm	—	—	3.00	—

PENN-MARYLAND / CIN'TI, O. / CORPORATION. Rv: GOOD FOR / 1 / BARREL SLOP. Plain edge. (Lipscomb CI 5020; Grinolds report)

Rulau	Date	Metal	Size	VG	F	VF	Unc
Cin 71	(1890's)	Brass	25mm	—	—	4.00	—

Similar, but 2 BARREL SLOP. (Lipscomb CI 5021)

Similar tokens good for 5 and 10 barrels slop were issued in 25mm diameter, each valued at $3.

PETTIBONE MANUFACTURING CO.

Rulau	Date	Metal	Size	VG	F	VF	Unc
Cin 75	(ca 1892)	Aluminum	35mm	—	15.00	25.00	—

Factory within circle. Around: THE PETTIBONE MANUFACTURING CO. / CINCINNATI, O. Rv: (Pure aluminum souvenir, etc.). Plain edge.

RIELAG

Rulau	Date	Metal	Size	VG	F	VF	Unc
Cin 90	(1889-99)	CN	34mm	—	10.00	20.00	—

RIELAG. Rv: S.W. COR. COURT & VINE STS. / 5. (See *TAMS Journal* for June 1974, pg. 94; Lipscomb CI 5380)

Rulau	Date	Metal	Size	VG	F	VF	Unc
Cin 92	(1890's)	Brass	25mm	—	10.00	20.00	—

* / (ornament) / RIELAG / (ornament) / *. Rv: 353 / VINE / ST. Dentilated rim on each side. Plain edge. (TAMS Maverick 13068)

August W. Rielag kept a liquor business and summer garden from at least 1889 until his death about 1908. The family continued the business in 1909.

FRED. ROLING

Fred. Roling appears as a saloonkeeper at the northeast corner of Spring and Abigail in the 1891 *Williams Directory.* He next appears in the 1899 directory at 414 Abigail Street. Then he appears as a saloon proprietor at the northeast corner of 5th and Elm (the address on one of the tokens) in the 1900 and 1901 *Williams Directories.* In one of these his residence is listed at 512 East Liberty Street. (All research courtesy Emmett M. Ey, Cincinnati, Ohio).

In 1984 a uniface die trial of Rulau Cin 100 was discovered in Cincinnati. The obverse exactly matches the TIME IS MONEY side of the token; the reverse is blank and the edge is plain. This die trial is now in the Russ Rulau collection.

The Roling cards, formerly listed in *U.S. Trade Tokens 1866-1889* as mavericks, thus are repositioned in *Tokens of the Gay Nineties.* We believe Cin 99 preceded Cin 100 and may have been struck about 1898. Directory evidence pins Cin 100 to the 1899-1901 period. The die trial must have been struck about 1899. The new listing follows:

Rulau	Date	Metal	Size	VG	F	VF	Unc
Cin 99	(1898)	Brass	30mm	—	—	30.00	—

Obverse similar to Cin 100, but different die. Letters and Roman numerals are larger; no beaded border near rim. Rv: (Ornament) / FRED. ROLING / (Ornament). Plain edge. (Tanenbaum coll.; Rulau MV 279)

Rulau	Date	Metal	Size	VG	F	VF	Unc
Cin 100	(1899-1904)	Brass	30mm		—	30.00	—

Clockface, hands pointing to 12 past 10, TIME / IS / MONEY on the face. Rv: FRED ROLING / (large ornament) / N.E. COR. 5' & ELM. Plain edge. (Jim Curto coll; Lipscomb C1 5475; Rulau MV 278)

Rulau	Date	Metal	Size	VG	F	VF	Unc
Cin 101	(1899)	Brass	28.4mm	—	—	150.	—

Obverse as last. Rv: Blank. Plain edge. (Rulau coll.)

Though they resemble Hard Times tokens, the Roling cards are from the 1890's and are connected with the resurgence of the Hard Times "Time is Money" theme embodied in such cards as the 1899 George Allers piece of Newark, N.J. and the series of 1900-1906 C. D. Peacock cards of Chicago, Ill. The Peacock cards were struck by Gorham Manufacturing Co. in New York; comparison of the die work on the Peacock, Allers and Roling cards reveals no direct connection.

Gaylor Lipscomb reports that Cin 100 was struck by Gregg G. Wright about 1904. There are later tokens of Roling.

Rulau	Date	Metal	Size	VG	F	VF	Unc
Cin 102	1901	Alum/Bronze	38mm	—	30.00	—	—

Canada 1901 Large cent encased in aluminum frame. Obv: FRED. ROLING, N.E. COR. 5TH & ELM / GOOD FOR 5 ¢ IN TRADE. Rv: I BRING GOOD LUCK (etc.) Plain edge. (Dick Grinolds collection; Lipscomb C1 5485)

WM. VETTER

Cincinnati, Ohio

Rulau	Date	Metal	Size	F	VF	EF	Unc
Cin 130	1898	Aluminum	38mm	—	—	30.00	40.00

Small busts of Dewey, Miles, Shafter and Sampson in 4-lobed center. Around: "AVENGERS OF THE MAINE" / DEWEY / MILES / SHAFTER / SAMPSON / WM. VETTER, 116 E. PEARL ST. CIN'TI, O. Rv: Warship at center. Around: "REMEMBER THE MAINE" / DESTROYED FEB. 15' 1898. Plain edge. (Kirtley Oct. 1988 sale, lot 406)

GARFIELD TOMB

Cleveland, Ohio

Rulau	Date	Metal	Size	F	VF	EF	Unc
Cle 25	1890	Bronze	38mm	—	—	—	6.00

Civilian bust three-quarters left. J. A. GARFIELD PRESIDENT U.S. around. Small M on truncation of bust. Rv: Ornate tomb. GARFIELD TOMB CLEVELAND, OHIO around, DEDICATED / May 30, 1890 below. Plain edge. (George Ganter coll.)

CHAS. KOCIAN

Rulau	Date	Metal	Size	VG	F	VF	Unc
Cle 35	(1892)	Brass	26mm	—	6.50	—	—

(All incused): CHAS. / KOCIAN. Rv: GOOD FOR / 5 ¢ / IN TRADE.

Saloon, in 1892 gazetteer.

WHITE SEWING MACHINE CO.

Cleveland, Ohio

Rulau	Date	Metal	Size	F	VF	EF	Unc
Cle 100	1900	Aluminum	35mm	—	—	4.00	6.00

Sewing machine of foot-tread type at center, THE WHITE above, IS KING below. Rv: WHITE SEWING MACHINE CO / EXPOSITION / UNIVERSELLE / PARIS / 1900 / CLEVELAND, O. U.S.A. Plain edge. Issued holed.

Rulau	Date	Metal	Size	F	VF	EF	Unc
Cle 102	(1890's)	Aluminum	35mm	—	—	10.00	12.50

Obverse as last (Sewing Machine). Rv: Ornamental crown around a bicycle, THE WHITE / KING OF WHEELS. Plain edge. (Wright 1685)

C. C. ADAMS

Cleves, Ohio

Rulau	Date	Metal	Size	F	VF	EF	Unc
Cvs 3	1899	Bimetal*	29mm	—	—	8.00	—

*Brass ring, aluminum insert. C. C. ADAMS / (ornament) / SMOKERY / (ornament) / CLEVES, OHIO. Rv: GOOD FOR / 25 / PAT. JULY 1899 / IN MERCHANDISE. Plain edge.

Charles C. Adams is listed as a tobacconist and billiard room operator in 1917-18, in Cleves (Hamilton County). Lipscomb reports 5 and 10-cent tokens of this type.

O. R. CASSADY

Cleves, Ohio

Rulau	Date	Metal	Size	F	VF	EF	Unc
Cvs 8	(1890's)	Aluminum	Sq 23mm	—	15.00	—	—

THE BRUNSWICK / BALKE / COLLENDER / COMPY. / (pool table) / CHECK. Rv: GOOD FOR / 5 C / IN TRADE. O.R. CASSADY / Plain edge. (Brunswick suppl.; Lipscomb CL 7045)

There are other tokens of Cassady, probably later.

COLUMBUS BUGGY CO.

Columbus, Ohio

Rulau	Date	Metal	Size	VG	F	VF	Unc
Col 6	1892	Aluminum	35mm	—	—	17.50	22.50

Columbus bust facing, WORLD'S FAIR * SOUVENIR above, * 1492 - 1892 * below. Rv: Buggy at center, COMPLIMENTS OF / COLUMBUS BUGGY CO. above, COLUMBUS, OHIO. / U.S.A. below. Plain edge.

M. GUMBLE

Rulau	Date	Metal	Size	VG	F	VF	Unc
Col 9	(?)	CN	22mm	—	—	15.00	—

M. GUMBLE / TOWNSTED / -.- / RESTAURANT / COLUMBUS, O. Rv: (Arc of 9 stars) / 5 / CENTS. Plain edge. (Lipscomb C03900)

M. MAYER

Rulau	Date	Metal	Size	VG	F	VF	Unc
Col 20	(?)	CN	22mm	—	—	25.00	—

M. MAYER (curved) ctsp on Gumble 5-cent token, Lipscomb C0 3900. (Thoele report)

OLYMPIA
Columbus, Ohio

Rulau	Date	Metal	Size	VG	F	VF	Unc
Col 25	(1890's)	Brass	28mm	—	4.00	—	—

(All incused): OLYMPIA / 129 S. HIGH. Rv: GOOD FOR / + 5 + / IN TRADE. Recessed beaded rims. Plain edge. (Rulau coll.; Lipscomb CO 4580)

THE SCHAUWEKER KAUTZ CO.
Columbus, Ohio

Rulau	Date	Metal	Size	F	VF	EF	Unc
Col 32	(1893)	Brass	35mm	—	—	35.00	50.00

Ohio arms in central circle, THE SCHAUWEKER KAUTZ CO. / COLUMBUS, OHIO in circular band around. Wide radiate border around rim. Rv: Ship left. Around: COLUMBUS IN SIGHT OF THE NEW WORLD / THE SANTA MARIA / (ornament). (Kirtley Oct. 1993 sale, lot 1614)

AEON SPRING SANATORIUM
Defiance, Ohio

Rulau	Date	Metal	Size	F	VF	EF	Unc
Def 1	1894	Aluminum	39mm	—	20.00	27.50	—

View of fort, CENTENNIAL CELEBRATION / 1794 FORT DEFIANCE 1894 around. Rv: SOUVENIR OF / AEON SPRING / SANATORIUM / & BATH / HOUSE / DEFIANCE, OHIO. Plain edge.

TURNBULL WAGON CO.
Defiance, Ohio

Rulau	Date	Metal	Size	F	VF	EF	Unc
Def 8	1894	Aluminum	38mm	—	—	15.00	20.00

Obverse as last. Rv: COMPLIMENTS OF / THE TURNBULL / WAGON CO. / (wagon) / DEFIANCE, OHIO. Plain edge. (Lipscomb DE 2180)

T.V.
(Thomas Vining)
East Liverpool, Ohio

Rulau	Date	Metal	Size	VG	F	VF	Unc
Elp 2	(?)	Brass	24mm	—	—	10.00	—

T.V.E.L.O. arranged in cross form, the L. at center. Rv: H. RICE / MAKER DAYTON O. Plain edge. (Wright 1703)

T.V.E.L.O. = Thomas Vining, East Liverpool, Ohio, according to Dr. Wright.

Henry Rice was in business 1859-1919 in Dayton as a stencil cutter. In 1856-1859 he had been located in Lebanon, Ohio, and 1922-1924 in Springfield, Ohio.

G. A. R.
Findlay, Ohio

Rulau	Date	Metal	Size	F	VF	EF	Unc
Fnd 3	1900	Svd/WM	Oval 30x41.4mm	—	—	30.00	—

Gushing oil derrick. Rv: 34TH ANNUAL / ENCAMPMENT / DEPARTMENT / - OF OHIO - / G. A. R. / FINDLAY, O. / MAY 8-9-10. / (ornament) / 1900. Plain edge. (Zaffern coll.)

G.A.R. = Grand Army of the Republic.

THE GRAND MISSION POOL ROOM
Fostoria, Ohio

Rulau	Date	Metal	Size	VG	F	VF	Unc
Fos 5	(1890's)	Aluminum	**	—	12.50	17.50	—

** Rect 38x29mm.

THE GRAND MISSION / POOL ROOM / -.- / FOSTORIA, O. Rv: GOOD FOR / 5 ¢ / IN TRADE. Beaded border on each side.

E. H. HECKERMAN
Hamilton, Ohio

Rulau	Date	Metal	Size	VG	F	VF	Unc
Ham 6	(1898)	Alum	24mm	—	—	15.00	—

E. H. HECKERMAN / GOOD FOR / 5 ¢ / AT BAR. Rv: NATIONAL BILLIARD MANF'G CO. / N. B. M. CO. (crossed pool cues) / CIN. O. (ATCO Maverick 1737)

J. KOEBEL

Rulau	Date	Metal	Size	VG	F	VF	Unc
Ham 7	(1898-1906)	Brass	Sc 27mm	—	—	35.00	—

(All incused): J. KOEBEL. (large) / H. RICE / MAKER / DAYTON. O. Rv: GOOD FOR / ONE / (cigar left). Rare. (L. Stubler coll.)

Saloon, listed in gazetteers 1898 through 1906.

FRANK MAGUIRE

Rulau	Date	Metal	Size	F	VF	EF	Unc
Ham 9	(1890's ?)	Aluminum	36mm	—	3.00	—	—

Eagle-shaped cutout flan. THE OXFORD / 5 — ¢ / FRANK MAGUIRE. Rv: 239 COURT ST. / * — * / HAMILTON, O. Plain edge. (Lipscomb HA 3320)

One piece appeared in a 1983 Kurt Krueger sale. Two pieces are in the Tom Wehner coll., Wapakoneta, Ohio. A hoard was discovered and this piece is now very common.

MALEY

Rulau	Date	Metal	Size	F	VF	EF	Unc
Ham 11	(1898)	Brass	25mm	—	3.00	—	—

GOOD FOR / 5 C / (quarter-moon cutout) / MALEY / AT / THE BAR. Rv: Large 5. Plain edge. (Lipscomb HA 3340)

Maley was proprietor of the Pan Handle Exchange in 1898.

TURK MATTHIAS

Rulau	Date	Metal	Size	VG	F	VF	Unc
Ham 15	(?)	CN	29.3mm	—	—	30.00	—

STRAND / * / - TURK - / MATTHIAS / (two arcs) / HAM. O. Rv: Circle of 13 stars around central circle, within which is: GOOD FOR / 5 ¢ / IN / TRADE. In tiny letters below circle: WRIGHT & SON CIN'TI, O. Plain edge. Rarity 5. (Zaffern coll.; Lipscomb HA 3390)

Rulau	Date	Metal	Size	VG	F	VF	Unc
Ham 16	(?)	Brass	26mm	—	—	25.00	—

TURK MATTHIAS / MAIN & B / HAMILTON, O. Rv: 5. (Lipscomb HA 3400)

RITCHIE & DYER CO.

Hamilton, Ohio

Rulau	Date	Metal	Size	F	VF	EF	Unc
Ham 25	1893	Aluminum	35mm	—	—	25.00	35.00

World globe. Around: WORLD'S COLUMBIA EXPOSITION / * CHICAGO, ILLS. 1893 *. Rv: RITCHIE & DYER CO. / - / MANUF'RS OF / SAW MILLS HEAD BLOCKS / (ornament) / SAW MILL DOGS / * ROAD ENGINES * / - AND - / STATIONARY ENGINES / PURE / ALUMINUM (last two words within shaped cartouche) / HAMILTON, OHIO U.S.A. Plain edge. (Kirtley Oct. 1993 sale, lot 1601)

The obverse is the type of Eglit 441, with COLUMBIA in place of the normal COLUMBIAN. The token is not previously published in a catalog.

(Eagle) 895

(Aerie 895, Fraternal Order of Eagles)

Ironton, Ohio

Rulau	Date	Metal	Size	VG	F	VF	Unc
Iro 1	(?)	Brass	21.4mm	—	—	5.00	9.00

Eagle with drooping wings, head turned left. Along lower rim: WRIGHT - CIN. O. Rv: 895 in large digits, ornamentation above and below. Plain edge. (Zaffern coll.; Lipscomb IR 7140)

There are other tokens of this aerie (club), all quite common.

J. H. CAMPER

Kenton, Ohio

Rulau	Date	Metal	Size	VG	F	VF	Unc
Ken 3	(?)	Brass	29mm	—	—	20.00	—

(All incused): J. H. CAMPER, / 10 (in circle) / KENTON O. Rv: Blank. Incised, beaded rim on each side. Plain edge. (Lipscomb KE 6035)

ELI BRENTLINGER

Lima, Ohio

Rulau	Date	Metal	Size	VG	F	VF	Unc
Lim 5	(?)	Brass	**	—	—	4.00	—

** Oval, 34 x 23mm.
— RETURN — / — ME TO — / ELI BRENTLINGER'S / *** PLACE ***. Rv: GOOD FOR / 5 C / IN TRADE. Plain edge. (Rulau coll.)

Rulau	Date	Metal	Size	VG	F	VF	Unc
Lim 6	(?)	Brass	27mm	—	—	4.00	—

ELI BRENTLINGER / LIMA, OHIO. Rv: GOOD FOR / 5 C / AT THE BAR. Plain edge. (Lipscomb LI 3070)

D. FREEL

Lima, Ohio

Rulau	Date	Metal	Size	VG	F	VF	Unc
Lim 14	(?)	Brass	**	—	—	5.00	—

THE ELK / D. FREEL , PROP. / H. RICE / MAKER / DAYTON, O. Rv: GOOD FOR / ONE BOTTLE. Plain edge. (Lipscomb LI 3190)

567

(River City Aerie 567)

Portsmouth, Ohio

Rulau	Date	Metal	Size	F	VF	EF	Unc
Por 25	(1890's)	Brass	24mm	—	7.50	11.00	—

Eagle with wings outspread, head turned right, perched atop a cannon facing left. Rv: (ornament) / 567 / (ornament). Beaded border around rim of reverse. Plain edge. Only about 20 known. (R-F Soh-3)

Reputedly used as a gambling chip within the River City Aerie 567, Fraternal Order of Eagles, in Portsmouth, Ohio.

WM. HAUSCHILDT

St. Bernard, Ohio

Rulau	Date	Metal	Size	VG	F	VF	Unc
Stb 4	(?)	Brass	21.5mm	—	—	9.00	—

Eagle displayed, head turned left, WRIGHT - CIN. O. along bottom rim. Rv: WM HAUSCHILDT / + / ST. BERNARD, / - / O. Rarity 2. (Lipscomb SA 1110)

J. HUBER

St. Bernard, Ohio

Rulau	Date	Metal	Size	VG	F	VF	Unc
Stb 7	(1890)	Brass	**	—	—	15.00	—

** Heart-shaped flan, 25x28mm.
GOOD FOR / 5 C / DRINK / J. HUBER. Rv: Blank. (Lipscomb SA 1140)

A. KETTERER

Sandusky, Ohio

Rulau	Date	Metal	Size	VG	F	VF	Unc
San 4	(1899-1909)	Aluminum	25mm	—	—	40.00	—

BBC die 7. Rv: GOOD FOR / 5 ¢ / A. - / KETTERER / IN / TRADE. Plain edge. (Thoele coll.; Lipscomb SA 7180)

H. DIRINGER

Tiffin, Ohio

Rulau	Date	Metal	Size	VG	F	VF	Unc
Tif 3	(1890's)	Aluminum	**	—	—	5.00	—

** Scal oval, 29x25mm.
(All incused): H. DIRINGER / TIFFIN, OHIO. Rv: GOOD FOR / 5 C / AT THE BAR. Plain edge. (Lipscomb TI 3150)

Diringer Brothers issued Brunswick-Balke-Collender pool checks somewhat earlier in Tiffin (Lipscomb numbers TI 3140 and TI 3141).

THE CAILLE CO.

Toledo, Ohio

Rulau	Date	Metal	Size	VG	F	VF	Unc
Tol 6	(1897-1901)	GS	21mm	—	4.00	8.00	—
Tol 6A	(1898-1901)	Brass	21mm	—	2.00	6.00	—

Tol 6: TCCO monogram. Rv: THE CAILLE CO / TOLEDO / * / OHIO, USA. Plain edge. Rarity 1. (Lipscomb TO 4111)

Tol 6A: As last. Rarity 1. (Lipscomb TO 4110)

WALDING KINNAN & MARVIN CO.

Toledo, Ohio

Rulau	Date	Metal	Size	VG	F	VF	Unc
Tol 30	(1890's)	Aluminum	30mm	—	—	15.00	—

WALDING KINNAN & MARVIN CO. / WHOLESALE / AGENTS / TOLEDO, O. Rv: THIS CHECK WILL BE REDEEMED BY ANY DEALER / GOOD FOR / ONE / DEXTET / CIGAR. Plain edge. (Wright 1711; Lipscomb TO 4800)

BURNETT HOUSE ANNEX

Wapakoneta, Ohio

Rulau	Date	Metal	Size	VG	F	VF	Unc
Wap 3	(?)	Brass	26mm	—	—	12.00	—
Wap 4	(?)	Brass	26mm	—	—	12.00	—

Wap 3: BURNETT HOUSE ANNEX / 5 / F. G. / WAPAKONETA / OHIO. Rv: Blank. Plain edge. (Lipscomb WA 3570)

Wap 4: BURNETT HOUSE ANNEX / 5 / G & W / WAPAKONETA / OHIO. Rv: TWO / FRANKS. Plain edge. (Lipscomb WA 3580)

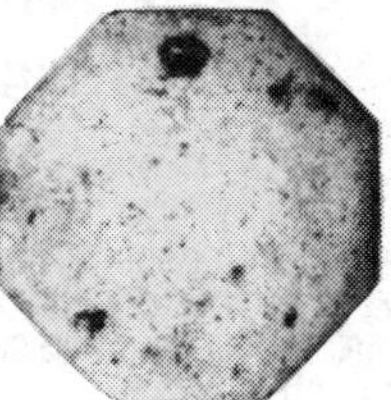

Rulau	Date	Metal	Size	VG	F	VF	Unc
Wap 5	(?)	Brass	Oct 26mm	—	—	12.00	—

BURNETT HOUSE ANNEX / 5 / H & G / WAPAKONETA / OHIO. Rv: Blank. Plain edge. (Lipscomb WA 3585; Zaffern coll.)

These tokens appear to be issues of successive proprietors of the Burnett House Annex, about which we have learned nothing. The Burnett House Annex issued an earlier token. Oh-Wp 2 in "U.S. Trade Tokens 1866-1889," which is a 27mm cupronickel piece without proprietor's initials first listed in 1898 by Dr. B. P. Wright in his monumental *The Numismatist* listing as number 117.

Rulau	Date	Metal	Size	VG	F	VF	Unc
Wap 7	(1890)	Brass	26mm	—	—	15.00	—

BURNETT HOUSE ANNEX / 5 / J. W. / WAPAKONETA / OHIO. Rv: Blank. (Lipscomb report, 1994)

J. W. = John Wenk, proprietor in 1890.

OHIO NEWS CO.

Ohio

Rulau	Date	Metal	Size	VG	F	VF	Unc
Unk 1	(?)	Brass	**	—	—	5.00	—

** Heart-shaped flan, 25 by 29mm.
(All incused): OHIO NEWS CO. Rv: GOOD FOR / 5 ¢ / IN TRADE. Plain edge. (Wright 1560)

OKLAHOMA

CRYSTAL ICE CO.

Ada, Okla.

Rulau	Date	Metal	Size	VG	F	VG	Unc
Ada 1	(1890-1907)	Brass	25mm	—	—	50.00	—

GOOD FOR / 10 ¢/ IN TRADE / * CRYSTAL * / ICE CO. / ADA, I.T. Rv: Blank. Beaded rims. Plain edge. (Walker OK-ADA-06-10)

I.T. = Indian Territory. The Indian Territory was constituted gradually from 1828 to 1830. In 1889 more than half of I.T. was reconstituted as Oklahoma Territory. Both I.T. and O.T. merged in the state of Oklahoma in 1907.

CHAS. HARRISON

Ada, Okla.

Rulau	Date	Metal	Size	VG	F	VF	Unc
Ada 3	(1884-1907)	Brass	Oct. 25mm	—	—	200.	—

Pool table at center. Above: THE BRUNSWICK BALKE / COLLENDER / COMPY. Below: CHECK. Rv: CHAS HARRISON'S BILLIARD PARLOR / GOOD FOR / 5 ¢ / IN TRADE / ADA, I.T. Plain edge. (Walker OK-ADA-07-05)

I.T. = Indian Territory, which became part of the state of Oklahoma in 1907. The Brunswick-Balke-Collender Company issued billiard checks for its customers with that name starting in 1884.

R.A. ABNEY

Afton, Okla.

Rulau	Date	Metal	Size	VG	F	VF	Unc
Aft 1	(1890-1907)	Aluminum	21mm	—	50.00	—	—
	R. A. ABNEY, / * / AFTON, / * / IND. TERR. Rv: * GOOD FOR * / -5- / IN / MERCHANDISE. Beaded rim on each side. Plain edge. (Walker OK-AFT-01-05)						
Aft 1	(1890-1907)	Aluminum	31mm	—	50.00	—	—
	Similar, but -50-. Plain edge. (Walker OK-AFT-01-50)						

The post office was established in Afton 1886. The general store of R. A. Abney & Co. was listed through 1914 in directories. Afton's population in 1910 was 1,279.

WINCHESTER CLUB SALOON

Alva, Okla.

Rulau	Date	Metal	Size	VG	F	VF	Unc
Alv 1	(1893-1907)	Brass	21mm	—	—	250.	—
	WINCHESTER CLUB / (ornament) / SALOON / (ornament) / ALVA, O.T. Rv: GOOD FOR / * 5 ¢ * / IN TRADE. Plain edge. (Walker OK-ALV-29-05)						
Alv 2	(1893-1907)	Aluminum	Oct 30mm	—	—	250.	—
	Similar, but 12 1/2 ¢. Plain edge. (Walker OK-ALV-29-12 1/2)						

O.T. = Oklahoma Territory, which merged into the state of Oklahoma with Indian Territory in 1907. The post office at Alva was established in 1893.

BLUE FRONT GROCERY

Augusta, Okla.

Rulau	Date	Metal	Size	VG	F	VF	Unc
Aug 1	(1895-1907)	Brass	Oct 22mm	—	—	75.00	—

BLUE FRONT GROCERY / GROCERIES / & / SHOES / AUGUSTA. / O.T. Rv: GOOD FOR / 1 ¢ / IN / MERCHANDISE. Plain edge. (Walker OK-AUG-01-01)

The post office at Augusta (Alfalfa County) was established in 1895. This post office was discontinued in 1912.

RIGHTWAY HOTEL

Bartlesville, Okla.

Rulau	Date	Metal	Size	VG	F	VF	Unc
Bar 1	(1890-1907)	Brass	35mm	—	45.00	75.00	—

RIGHTWAY HOTEL / (ornament) / CIGAR / (ornament) / STAND / BARTLESVILLE, I.T. Rv: GOOD FOR / 1oo / IN TRADE. Plain edge. (Walker OK-BVL-06-100)

V. A. PERRY

Belton, Okla.

Rulau	Date	Metal	Size	VG	F	VF	Unc
Bel 1	(1893-95)	Brass	21mm	—	150.	—	—

FARMERS SALOON / -.- / V. A. PERRY / BELTON. Rv: GOOD FOR / 10 ¢ / IN TRADE. Plain edge. (Walker OK-BLT-01-10)

Belton was in northwestern Lincoln County, 6 miles southeast of Langston. The post office known as Pollock was established here in 1892, and its name was changed to Belton in 1893. The post office was discontinued in 1895 and the site of the town is no longer in existence.

L. T. COVEY

Blackwell, Okla.

Rulau	Date	Metal	Size	VG	F	VF	Unc
Bla 1	(1890's)	Aluminum	32mm ?	—	—	100.	—

Within beaded circle: (Ornament) / L. T. COVEY / (ornament) / BLACKWELL / -O.T. -. Rv: 50. (Walker N/L; Kirtley June 1990 sale, lot 2636)

O.T. = Oklahoma Territory.

HOUSE OF LORDS

Blackwell, Okla.

Rulau	Date	Metal	Size	VG	F	VF	Unc
Bla 8	(1893-1907)	Aluminum	Oct 22mm	—	100.	—	—

HOUSE OF LORDS. / GOOD FOR / 5 ¢ / IN TRADE / BLACKWELL, O.T. Rv: Blank: Plain edge. (Walker OK-BLW-07-05)

Blackwell is in central Kay County.

W.E. CARTER'S WOOD YARD

Bokchito, Okla.

Rulau	Date	Metal	Size	VG	F	VF	Unc
Bok 1	1899	Brass	32mm	—	—	30.00	—

W. E. CARTER'S / * / * 1899 * / * / WOOD YARD. Rv: 15¢. Plain edge. (Walker OK-BKT-01-15)

Bokchito is in Bryan County, 14 miles east of Durant. Its post office was established in 1894. Bokchito is Choctaw for "big creek." There were 535 people here in 1910.

E. FLAX

Brooken, Okla.

Rulau	Date	Metal	Size	VG	F	VF	Unc
Bro 1	(1895-1900)	Brass	23.5mm	—	55.00	75.00	—

E. FLAX / 25 ¢ / IN MDSE / BROOKEN, I.T. Rv: HASKELL / ENG. CO. / * ST. LOUIS *. Dentilated rims. Plain edge. (Walker OK-BKN-01-25)

It is possible this piece belongs to the *U.S. Trade Tokens 1886-1889* section. The Haskell Engraving Co. was active in St. Louis in 1884, when they made Blaine-Logan election medalets, for example.

The post office in Brooken was established in 1879. It is in northwestern Haskell County. Interestingly, there were 32 people here in 1900, yet only 50 in 1970.

KUTTLE & STAHL

Cheyenne, Okla.

Rulau	Date	Metal	Size	VG	F	VF	Unc
Chy 3	(1895)	Brass	Scal 28mm	—	—	250.	—

FAVORITE SALOON / -.- / CHEYENE (sic!) / I.T. / -.- / KUTTLE & STAHL. Rv: GOOD FOR / 12 1/2 / CENTS / IN TRADE. (Elmer Randall coll.)

I.T. = Indian Territory, an error since Cheyenne was in Oklahoma Territory (Roger Mills County). Also Cheyenne is misspelled Cheyene on the token.

The Oct. 18, 1895 issue of the newspaper *Sunbeam* of Roger Mills County reveals that Kuttle and Stahl were granted a liquor license on Oct. 12, and the paper carried the Favorite Saloon front page ad offering "the best of wines, liquors and cigars." John Stahl was also a butcher.

BRYANS'

Chickasha, Okla.

Rulau	Date	Metal	Size	VG	F	VF	Unc
Chi 1	(1892-1907)	Aluminum	24mm	—	—	100.	—

BRYANS' / -.- / FIRST NATIONAL / BANK / BUILDING / CHICKASHA, IND. TER. Rv: GOOD FOR / * 10 ¢ * / ON EACH PAIR / OF / SHOES. Plain edge. (Walker OK-CKA-04-10)

Chickasha's post office received this name in 1892. It was established as Waco in 1890, changed to Pensee in 1891, then Chickasha in 1892. The city is county seat of Grady County.

GRAY & ADKINS

Chouteau, Okla.

Rulau	Date	Metal	Size	VG	F	VF	Unc
Cho 1	(1890-1907)	Aluminum	31mm	—	60.00	100.	—

GRAY & ADKINS / -*- / CHOUTEAU, / .-. / I. T. Rv: GOOD FOR / * $1.00 * / IN / MERCHANDISE. Plain edge. (Walker OK-CHO-04c-100)

Chouteau, in southwest Mayes County, had 450 people in 1900.

T. J. ROWLAND

Collinsville, Okla.

Rulau	Date	Metal	Size	VG	F	VF	Unc
Col 1	(1898-1907)	Aluminum	18.5mm	—	—	125.	—

T. J. ROWLAND, / COLLINSVILLE, / * I.T. *. Rv: GOOD FOR / ONE / 5 ¢/ CIGAR. Plain edge. (Walker OK-CVL-07-05)

A. L. DAUM

Daumville, Okla.

Rulau	Date	Metal	Size	VG	F	VF	Unc
Dau 1	(?)	Brass	Sq 28mm	—	—	250.	—

A. L. DAUM / * / GENERAL / MERCHANDISE / * / DAUMVILLE, / CHEROKEE, NATION. Rv: GOOD FOR / 25 / IN / MERCHANDISE. Plain edge. (Walker OK-DVL-01-25)

Rulau	Date	Metal	Size	VG	F	VF	Unc
Dau 2	(?)	Brass	Scal 28.5mm	—	—	250.	—

Similar, but 50. Plain edge. (Walker OK-DVL-01-50)

Rulau	Date	Metal	Size	VG	F	VF	Unc
Dau 3	(?)	Brass	30mm	—	—	250.	—

Similar, but $1.00. Plain edge. (Walker OK-DVL-01-100)

Daumville was located north of Tulsa in the general area now known as Turley. This may have been an Indian trader, and if so, does not belong in the coverage of this catalog.

GAGAN & WILLIAMS

Guthrie, Okla.

Rulau	Date	Metal	Size	VG	F	VF	Unc
Gut 1	(1889-1907)	Brass	25mm	—	—	75.00	—

GAGAN & WILLIAMS / GOOD FOR / . 5 . / IN TRADE / GUTHRIE, O.T. Rv: Blank. Incised beaded rim on each side. Plain edge. (Walker OK-GTH-08-05)

The post office at Guthrie was established 1889. The city was the capital of Oklahoma Territory to 1907, and of Oklahoma to 1910.

GUTHRIE BAR

Rulau	Date	Metal	Size	VG	F	VF	Unc
Gut 3	(1895-1907)	Brass	21.5mm	—	15.00	25.00	—

GUTHRIE / *** / BAR. Rv: GOOD FOR / 6 1/4¢ / IN TRADE. Plain edge. (Walker OK-GHT-09-06 1/4)

The Guthrie Bar was closed Nov. 16, 1907.

THE SILVER DOLLAR

Guthrie, Okla.

Rulau	Date	Metal	Size	VG	F	VF	Unc
Gut 6	(1895-1907)	WM	24.5mm	—	60.00	100.	—

GOOD FOR / 2 1/2 ¢ / IN TRADE / AT THE / SILVER DOLLAR / GUTHRIE, O.T. F.M. WYATT, PROP. Rv: Large 2 1/2 at center, surrounded by circle of 15 stars. Plain edge.

Well made, attractive token.

GRADY & FREENY

Hartshorne, Okla.

Rulau	Date	Metal	Size	VG	F	VF	Unc
Har 1	(1890-1907)	Aluminum	Oct 23mm	—	—	75.00	—

GRADY & FREENY / G&F monogram / HARTSHORNE, I.T. Rv: GOOD FOR / * TEN * / CENTS / IN / MERCHANDISE. Beaded rim on each side. Plain edge.

W. E. WASHINGTON

Marietta, Okla.

Rulau	Date	Metal	Size	VG	F	VF	Unc
Mar 1	(?)	Brass	Sq 25mm	—	—	100.	—

W. E. WASHINGTON / GOOD FOR / 5¢ / MARIETTA, I.T. Rv: In circle: AUG. KERN B.S. CO., ST. LOUIS. Plain edge. (Wright 1206; Walker OK-MTA-06a-05)

There are other tokens known of W. E. Washington which read I.T. for Indian Territory, but these apparently were issued after 1900. One of these has Washington on one side and merchant S. Westheimer & Co. on the opposite side; Westheimer was in operation 1918-34.

Washington was an early rancher and trader who became a Chickasaw Nation citizen by marriage and established the first store in this area.

COLEMAN LUMBER CO.

Tushka Homma, Okla.

Rulau	Date	Metal	Size	VG	F	VF	Unc
Tus 1	(1890's)	Brass	**	—	—	150.	—

** Sq. 25x25mm.

COLEMAN LUMBER CO. / GOOD FOR / $5.00 / TUSHKA HOMMA, I.T. Rv: Blank. Plain edge. (Wright 184)

This village, later called Tuskahoma — in Pushmatah County — had 180 people in 1910.

OREGON

THEO. BRACKER

Astoria, Ore.

Rulau	Date	Metal	Size	VG	F	VF	Unc
Ast 2	(1890's)	Brass	Scal 29mm	—	20.00	—	—

GOOD FOR / 12 1/2 ¢ / THEO. / BRACKER (on panel) / IN / TRADE. Rv: 12 1/2 ¢. Plain edge. (ATCO sale May, 1993, lot 3)

Attribution by Robert Busby.

FINNISH SOCIALIST CLUB

Astoria, Ore.

Rulau	Date	Metal	Size	VG	F	VF	Unc
Ast 6	(1890's ?)	Brass	23mm	—	—	20.00	—

FINNISH SOCIALIST CLUB / -+- / ASTORIA, / -- / ORE. / -+- / -+-. Rv: GOOD FOR / 5 ¢ / * IN TRADE *. Plain edge. (Thoele coll.)

W. WILLIAMS

Dallas, Ore.

Rulau	Date	Metal	Size	VG	F	VF	Unc
Dls 3	(1890's)	Brass	25mm	—	—	20.00	—

W. WILLIAMS / CIGARS & / CONFECTIONERY / STORE / DALLAS, OR. Rv: GOOD FOR / 10 ¢ / IN TRADE. Plain edge. (ATCO May 1993 sale, lot 25)

Rulau	Date	Metal	Size	VG	F	VF	Unc
Dls 4	(1890's)	Brass	25mm	—	—	20.00	—

As 3, but 5 ¢. (ATCO sale, lot 24)

Attribution by Robert Busby.

COMMERCIAL HOTEL & BAR

Medford, Ore.

Rulau	Date	Metal	Size	VG	F	VF	Unc
Med 1	(1890's)	Aluminum	Scal 26mm	—	—	20.00	—

COMMERCIAL / -.- / HOTEL & BAR / 5 ¢ / CENTRAL AVE. Rv: 2 1/2 ¢. Incised, beaded rim on each side. (ATCO May 1993 sale, lot 76)

Attribution by Roberty Busby.

WEARY'S
Medford, Ore.

Rulau	Date	Metal	Size	VG	F	VF	Unc
Med 12	(1899)	Aluminum	Oct 24mm	—	—	50.00	—

Eagle perched on cannon. Rv: WEARY'S / 10 ¢ / * MEDFORD, OREGON *. (E. K. Witt coll.)

J. E. BEAM
Pendleton, Ore.

Rulau	Date	Metal	Size	VG	F	VF	Unc
Pen 3	(1890's)	Aluminum	25mm	—	—	20.00	—

J. E. BEAM / DEALER / IN / CIGARS / AND / TOBACCO / PENDLETON, OREGON. Rv: GOOD for / 5 ¢ / IN TRADE. Plain edge. (ATCO May 1993 sale, lot 101)

Attribution by Robert Busby.

FRITZ & RUSSELL ERICKSON
Portland, Ore. ?

Rulau	Date	Metal	Size	VG	F	VF	Unc
Prt 3	(?)	Brass	24.5mm	—	—	50.00	—

FRITZ & RUSSELL / -*- / ERICKSON'S / .-. / SALOON. Rv: GOOD FOR / * 2 1/2 * / CENTS / IN TRADE. Plain edge. (Thoele coll.)

MITCHELL LEWIS & STAVER CO.
Portland, Ore.

Rulau	Date	Metal	Size	VG	F	VF	Unc
Prt 6	(1890's)	Aluminum	38mm	—	—	75.00	100.

Wagon. AGRICULTURAL IMPLEMENTS / THE OLD / RELIABLE / . MITCHELL WAGON. Rv: MITCHELL LEWIS & STAVER CO. / MACHINERY / AND / VEHICLES / . PORTLAND, OR. Plain edge. (Wright 602)

PENNSYLVANIA

FASCINATION
Allentown, Pa.

Rulau	Date	Metal	Size	F	VF	EF	Unc
All 3	(?)	Cupronickel	22mm	2.00	3.00	—	—

FASCINATION. Rv: GOOD FOR / 10 ¢ / IN TRADE. Plain edge.

Used in Dorney Amusement Park.

FRANKLIN FIRE CO. NO. 10

Rulau	Date	Metal	Size	F	VF	EF	Unc
All 5	(?)	Aluminum	24mm	9.00	12.50	—	—

.*.*.*. / E.C.F.F. CO. / .*.*.*. Rv: FRANKLIN / * NO. 10 * / FIRE CO. Plain edge.

THE PRINCE FURNITURE CO.

Rulau	Date	Metal	Size	VG	F	VF	Unc
All 20	(ca 1900)	Aluminum	51mm	—	—	22.50	—

Encased trade token. Center (23mm) is: [*] / 5 (shaded) / [*]. (This is a Koehler-struck token reverse of the 1870's and 1880's, struck the same on both sides). Obverse: THE POWER OF 5 CENTS AT THE PRINCE FURNITURE CO. / 520 HAMILTON ST., ALLENTOWN PA: / . Rv: Descr. not available. Plain edge. (Kirtley Nov. 1990 sale, lot G040)

Struck by Francis X. Koehler of Baltimore, this is one of the most unusual trade tokens ever made.

SOLDIERS & SAILORS MONUMENT
Allentown, Pa.

Rulau	Date	Metal	Size	F	VF	EF	Unc
All 18	1899	WM	32mm	—	—	—	10.00

Pennsylvania state seal. Rv: Monument. Around: SOLDIERS & SAILORS MONUMENT ALLENTOWN, PA. DEDICATED OCT. 19. 1899. Plain edge. (Ganter coll.)

L. EMERY JR. & CO.
Bradford, Pa.

Rulau	Date	Metal	Size	F	VF	EF	Unc
Brd 1	1892	Aluminum	35mm	—	—	35.00	50.00

Facing bearded Columbus bust. Around: WORLD'S FAIR o* SOUVENIR / * 1492-1892 *. Rv: L. EMERY JR. & CO. / THE / GREAT / SUPPLY / HOUSE / * BRADFORD, PA. *. (Kirtley Oct. 1993 sale, lot 1599)

J. E. BITLER
Easton, Pa.

Rulau	Date	Metal	Size	VG	F	VF	Unc
Eas 3	1890	WM	37mm	—	—	15.00	—

Outer circle contains Roman numerals as on a clock face. Within: J. E. BITLERS / ESTB / 1788/ JEWELRY STORE. Rv: EASTONS - / MAY - / 5TH - / 1790-1890- / CENTENNIAL. Plain edge. (Wright 80)

FOUNTAIN HILL HOSE CO. NO. 1

Fountain Hill, Pa.

Rulau	Date	Metal	Size	F	VF	EF	Unc
Fou 4	(?)	Aluminum	**	—	12.50	—	—

** Scalloped, 28.5mm.
FOUNTAIN HILL HOSE CO. / NO. 1 / *. Rv: -*- / 5 (large and ornate) / -*-. Plain edge.

GALETON AERIE 1733

Galeton, Pa.

Rulau	Date	Metal	Size	VG	F	VF	Unc
Gal 3	(1890's)	Aluminum	25mm	—	—	35.00	—

(BBC-6a die). Rv: GALETON AERIE 1733 5c. Plain edge. (Brunswick suppl.)

"Aeries" are lodges of the F.O.E. (Fraternal Order of Eagles).

FIRST COLONY OF GERMANS

Germantown, Pa.

Rulau	Date	Metal	Size	F	VF	EF	Unc
Ger 3	1890	WM	32mm	—	—	—	10.00

Three-leaf clover in beaded circle surrounded by VINUM . LINUM . ET . TEXTRINUM. Around all: GERMAN.TOWN. OCTOBER VI MDCLXXXIII. Rv: 207th / ANNIVERSARY OF THE / FOUNDING / OF THE FIRST COLONY / OF GERMANS / -IN THE- / UNITED STATES / OCT. 6. / 1890. Plain edge. (Ganter coll.)

The Germans settled at Germantown in 1683. It was at this site in 1777 that the Americans and British fought to a draw after the British capture of nearby Philadelphia.

S. W. REESE

Gettysburg, Pa.

Rulau	Date	Metal	Size	F	VF	EF	Unc
Get 20	1890	Brass	25mm	—	—	15.00	—

* GETTYSBURG, PA * / COMPLIMENTS / * OF * / S. W. REESE / LATE / CO. G. I. PA. CAV. / SEPT. 2, & 3, 1890. Rv: S. W. REESE & CO / STAMPS / STENCILS / & C. / CATALOGUE / FREE / 182 FULTON ST. N.Y. Plain edge. (Charles Ziegler coll.)

GRAPEVILLE VOLUNTEER FIRE DEPARTMENT

Grapeville, Pa.

Rulau	Date	Metal	Size	F	VF	EF	Unc
Gra 3	(?)	Aluminum	20mm	—	15.00	—	—

GRAPEVILLE / VOLUNTEER / FIRE / DEPARTMENT. Rv: GOOD FOR / * 5 ¢ * / IN / MERCHANDISE. Plain edge.

SEMI-CENTENNIAL OF BLAIR COUNTY

Hollidaysburg, Pa.

Rulau	Date	Metal	Size	F	VF	EF	Unc
Hol 1	1896	Bronze	38mm	—	—	—	20.00

Within circle: Covered wagon pulled by 4 horses, with a man riding one horse. On wagon: PHILA TO PITTSBURGH / 20 DAYS. 1896 above, 1846 in exergue. Around all: SEMI-CENTENNIAL OF BLAIR CO. PA. / HOLLIDAYSBURG JUNE 11-12. Plain edge. (Ganter coll.)

LYCOMING COUNTY CENTENNIAL

Lycoming County, Pa.

Rulau	Date	Metal	Size	VG	F	VF	Unc
Lyc 1	1895	Aluminum	38mm	—	—	—	35.00

Old exhibition building. Rv: Within wreath: 1795 / -.- / 1895. Around: LYCOMING COUNTY / CENTENNIAL. Plain edge. (Ganter coll.)

SIBLEY & MCALLISTER

New Kensington, Pa.

Rulau	Date	Metal	Size	VG	F	VF	Unc
Nke 10	(1890's)	Aluminum	29mm	—	15.00	25.00	—

SIBLEY & MCALLISTER / COR / FOURTH AVE & 9TH ST / NEW KENSINGTON PA / CLOTHING / SHOES, HATS / AND / MEN FURNISHINGS. Rv: SIBLEY AND MCALLISTER / GOOD FOR / 50 / CENTS / AS PAYMENT ON ANY / SUIT IN STORE / SOLD AT / REGULAR PRICE / COR 4TH AVE & 9TH ST. NEW KENSINGTON. (Wright 983)

GEO. ARNHOLT

Philadelphia, Pa.

Rulau	Date	Metal	Size	F	VF	EF	Unc
Phl 2	(?)	Brass	21mm	—	15.00	—	—

G. A. monogram. Rv: FALLS / OF / SCHUYLKILL / PARK / PHILADA / GEO. ARNHOLT. Plain edge. (Wright 35)

THE BOURSE

Rulau	Date	Metal	Size	F	VF	EF	Unc
Phl 6	(?)	Aluminum	39mm	—	—	5.00	—

Building at center, THE BOURSE above, PHILADELPHIA below. Tiny QUINT under ground line at right. Rv: 12-line inscription. Plain edge.

THE BUFFALONIANS

Rulau	Date	Metal	Size	F	VF	EF	Unc
Phl 8	1892	Gold	25mm	—	—	—	300.

Crested and supported arms of Philadelphia. Rv: Bison to left at full speed, in center. Inscription: COMMEMORATIVE OF THE VISIT OF THE BUFFALONIANS. / PHILADELPHIA / MAR. 31. 1892. Plain edge. 228 grains. Only 2 struck. (Lot 1271, Brand 1984 sale; Julian CM-9)

Rulau	Date	Metal	Size	F	VF	EF	Unc
Phl 9	1892	Silver	25mm	—	—	—	75.00

As last. Plain edge. 4 Struck. (Julian CM-9)

Rulau	Date	Metal	Size	F	VF	EF	Unc
Phl 10	1892	Brass	25mm	—	—	—	40.00

As last. (Ganter coll.)

All struck at Philadelphia Mint in April, 1892 to the order of numismatist J. Colvin Randall. "The Buffalonians" were a group of college students.

CANDY EXPOSITION

Rulau	Date	Metal	Size	F	VF	EF	Unc
Phl 11	1893	WM	31mm	—	—	10.00	—

Seated female, shield at right, standing eagle at left, sword and palm branch through wreath in exergue. Above: HONOR IS THE REWARD OF LOYALTY. Rv: SOUVENIR / CANDY EXPOSITION / (rope-like design) / PHILADELPHIA / 1893. Plain edge.

JACOB CAUFFMAN

Rulau	Date	Metal	Size	F	VF	EF	Unc
Phl 13	(?)	WM	26mm	—	4.00	—	—

JACOB CAUFFMAN / 255 / N. 4TH ST. / PHILAD'A. Rv: Blank. Plain edge. (Wright 152)

CHESTNUT ST. THEATRE

Rulau	Date	Metal	Size	VG	F	VF	Unc
Phl 15	1895	Brass	26mm	—	—	30.00	—

Cat seated, facing. Below: STERLING. Rv: CHESTNUT ST. / THEATRE / 100TH PERFORMANCE (on scroll) / CHARLEY'S AUNT / FEBY. 11-1895. (Wright 166; Ganter coll.)

I. A. OF FACTORY INSPECTORS

Rulau	Date	Metal	Size	F	VF	EF	Unc
Phl 25	1894	Gilt/B	25mm	—	—	10.00	18.00

Buildng at center, INDEPENDENCE HALL around. Rv: Pennsylvania arms on keystone at center, separating SEP. 25 — 1894. Above: EIGHTH ANNUAL CONVENTION. Below: . I.A. OF FACTORY INSPECTORS . Plain edge.

INNES' FAMOUS BAND

Rulau	Date	Metal	Size	F	VF	EF	Unc
Phl 27	1896	Aluminum	39mm	—	—	—	15.00

Bust left, * INNES' FESTIVAL JUBILEE * above, AUG. 23-30, 1896 / WILLOW GROVE PARK BELOW. Small F N. INNES below truncation bust. Rv: CHILDRENS SOUVENIR CARNIVAL / ADMIT ONE / TO ANY CONCERT / -IN THE- / U.S. OR CANADA / GIVEN IN ANY / OPERA HOUSE / -BY- / INNES' FAMOUS BAND / TUESDAY AUG. 25, 1896. Plain edge.

This token has "Gay Nineties" written all over it! F. N. Innes and his "famous band" needs to be traced.

JUNIOR ORDER UNITED AMERICAN MECHANICS

Rulau	Date	Metal	Size	VF	EF	Unc	Proof
Phl 28	1893	Aluminum	38mm	—	10.00	—	—

Compass, square, arm and hammer. Around: HARRY CLAY COUNCIL NO. 7 JUNIOR ORDER UNITED AMERICAN MECHANICS. Rv: SOUVENIR / OF THE / 25th ANNIVERSARY / 1868 - SEPTEMBER 26 - 1893 / PHILAD'A, PA. Plain edge. (Kirtley March 1991 sale, lot N020)

KEYSTONE WATCH CASE CO.

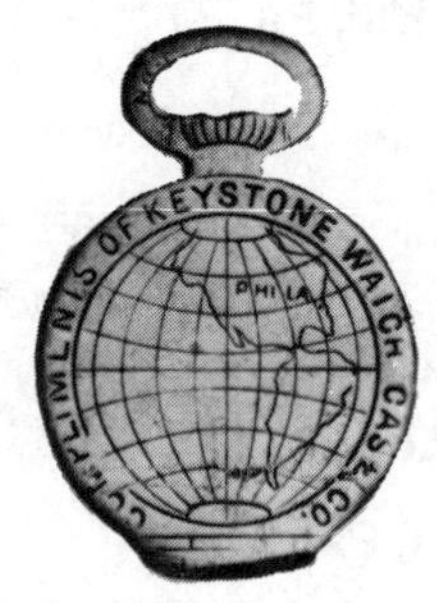

Rulau	Date	Metal	Size	F	VF	EF	Unc
Phl 30	1893	CN	**	—	15.00	30.00	45.00

** Stem-wind watch shape, 25 x 36.4mm

(All incused): SOUVENIR / WORLD'S / COLUMBIAN / EXPOSITION / CHICAGO / 1893. Rv: COMPLIMENTS OF KEYSTONE WATCH CASE CO. / (globe, with PHILA. noted). Plain edge. (Rulau coll.)

Given out at the Keystone Watch Case Company's exhibit at the World's Columbian Exposition in Chicago in 1893.

This token has been counterfeited, says L. B. Fauver. It is difficult to distinguish bogus from original.

H. M. & E. H. KREH

Rulau	Date	Metal	Size	F	VF	EF	Unc
Phl 35	1899	Aluminum	--mm	15.00	—	—	

OUR SOUVENIR / THE HOLDER OF THIS / CHECK IS ENTITLED TO ONE / DOLLAR REBATE ON ANY 100 / BOX CIGARS IN OUR STOCK / EXPRESSED TO ALL PARTS / WRITE FOR PRICE LIST / H. M. & E. H. KREH / CIGARS / WEST END BLDG. / PHILA / PA. Rv: HOW WE ADVERTISE / GOOD / FOR / ONE DOLLAR / UNTIL NOV '99 AS PER / CONDITIONS STATED / ON REVERSE SIDE. Plain edge. (Wright 1492)

Dr. Wright called this rare about 1900.

JAMES MAGUIRE

Rulau	Date	Metal	Size	F	VF	EF	Unc
Phl 40	(?)	Aluminum	39mm	—	8.00	—	—

Female bust left, TRADE MARK along lower rim of bust. SOLE AGENT above, BELLE OF NELSON below. Rv: * JAMES MAGUIRE * / 470 & 472 / NORTH 3RD ST. / PHILA. PROP. MONTEZUMA WHISKEY. Plain edge.

MONARCH CYCLES

Rulau	Date	Metal	Size	F	VF	EF	Unc
Phl 43	1893	Aluminum	31mm	—	40.00	—	—

Radiant lion's head facing, RIDE MONARCH CYCLES / THE BEST. Rv: PHILADELPHIA CYCLE SHOW / 1893 amid ornamentation flourishes. Plain edge. (Wright 717)

P.A.R.C. III WARD (Third Ward Polish American Republican Club)

Rulau	Date	Metal	Size	F	VF	EF	Unc
Phl 50	1898	Brass	25mm	—	5.00	—	—

PHILADELPHIA / *** / 1898 / *** / * PA. *. Rv: P. A. R. C. / III / * / * WARD *. Plain edge. (Rulau coll.)

PEACE JUBILEE

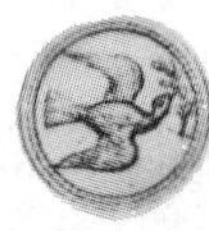

Rulau	Date	Metal	Size	F	VF	EF	Unc
Phl 74	1898	Gold	14mm	—	—	18.50	—

Dove flying right, spray of leaves in its beak. Rv: PEACE JUBILEE / OCT. 26-27 / 1898 / * / PHILADELPHIA. (H&K 693)

Rulau	Date	Metal	Size	F	VF	EF	Unc
Phl 75	1898	WM	35mm	—	—	—	12.00

Winged female facing, branch in right hand, cherub with caduceus in her left hand. Around: PEACE JUBILEE. At lower left: 1898. On scroll below: PHILADELPHIA OCT. 26-27. Rv: U.S. flag waving right, wreath in background. LET US HAVE PEACE. Plain edge.

Rulau	Date	Metal	Size	F	VF	EF	Unc
Phl 76	1898	Brass	35mm	—	—	—	15.00

Clothed bust three-quarters right divides scrollwork reading OCT. — 25-27, all within circle. Around: 18 NATIONAL PEACE JUBILEE 98 PHILADELPHIA. Rv: Ornate archway, pennants around. Around: 18 NATIONAL PEACE JUBILEE 98 PHILADELPHIA / OCT. 25-27 / COURT OF HONOR. Plain edge. (Ganter coll.)

Rulau	Date	Metal	Size	F	VF	EF	Unc
Phl 77	1898	Brass	25mm	—	—	—	10.00

Philadelphia seal within beaded circle. Around: PEACE JUBILEE OCT. 25-27. 1898. 'PHILADELPHIA'. Rv: Crossed U.S. and Cuban flags laid over wreath, 13 stars and SPANISH AMERICAN WAR around. Plain edge.

D. E. PERKINS

Rulau	Date	Metal	Size	F	VF	EF	Unc
Phl 78	(1899-1901)	Brass	31mm	—	30.00	—	—

Clockface, hands pointing to 12 past 9. TIME / IS / MONEY on the face. Rv: D. E. PERKINS. / SALES AGENT / - FOR - / DEY TIME REGISTERS / 1201 NORTH AMERICAN BLDG. / PHILADELPHIA, PA. / LOWEST PRICES / ON SUPPLIES FOR ALL / KINDS OF TIME / REGISTERS. Plain edge. (Elmer Randall coll., Miami, Okla.)

Discovered only in late 1990, this token seems connected to the spate of 1890's resurrections of the Hard Times-era TIME IS MONEY clockface designs. Compare with the 1899 George Allers token of Newark, N.J.; 1900-1906 tokens of C. D. Peacock of Chicago; and Fred Roling pieces of Cincinnati circa 1898-1904.

The Perkins token is from a different die than the others, though. Its hour hand points past 9, while the others point past 10.

PHILADELPHIA EXPOSITION

Rulau	Date	Metal	Size	F	VF	EF	Unc
Phl 79	1899	Bronze	11mm	—	—	—	5.00

Building. PHILADELPHIA EXPOSITION / SEP. 14, NOV. 30, 1899 in exergue. Rv: Liberty Bell, LIBERTY at left, BELL at right, 17 — 76 below divided by bell's clapper. Plain edge. (Ganter coll.)

PHILADELPHIA RECORD

Rulau	Date	Metal	Size	F	VF	EF	Unc
Phl 80	1899	Gilt Brass	32mm	—	—	3.50	5.50

Building at center, HOME OF THE PHILADELPHIA RECORD around, .1899. below. Rv: Independence Hall, church, etc. at center, tiny W & H CO. NEWARK, N.J. beneath truncation. Around: BIRTHPLACE OF THE DECLARATION OF INDEPENDENCE. Below 1776. Plain edge.

S. H. QUINT & SONS

Rulau	Date	Metal	Size	F	VF	EF	Unc
Phl 88	(1893)	Nickel	12mm	—	5.00	7.50	10.00

Building at center, S. H. QUINT & SONS above, 15 SO. 4TH ST. PHILA. PA. Rv: MFR'S OF / MEDALS / STENCILS / RUBBER / & STEEL / STAMPS / PATTERN / LETTERS / &C. Plain edge. (Miller 588 1/2)

This tiny piece is a model of workmanship, which presumably the maker wished to imply on his metallic business card.

Rulau	Date	Metal	Size	F	VF	EF	Unc
Phl 89	1893	Aluminum	36mm	—	—	—	35.00

Landing of Columbus in central circle. Around: WORLD'S COLUMBIAN EXPOSITION / * CHICAGO. ILLS. 1893 *. Rv: A SOUVENIR / OF PURE / ALUMINUM. / COMPLIMENTS OF / S. H. QUINT & SON / MANUFACTURERS OF / - MEDALS - / FOR ADVERTISING / AND / OTHER PURPOSES / 14 SO. 4TH. ST. PHILA. PA. Plain edge.

Rulau	Date	Metal	Size	F	VF	EF	Unc
Phl 90	1895	Aluminum	38mm	—	—	—	27.50

Building. THE BOURSE. Rv: IN COMMEMORATION / OF THE / OPENING BANQUET / PHILADELPHIA BOURSE / DECEMBER 30TH 1895 / COMPLIMENTS OF / S. H. QUINT & SONS / 13 S. 4TH ST. Plain edge. (Kirtley 1992 ATCO sale, lot 1369)

RELIEF SHOES

Rulau	Date	Metal	Size	VG	F	VF	Unc
Phl 92	(?)	Brass	27mm	—	—	15.00	—

RELIEF / P. P. P. / SHOES. Rv: 134 S. 8TH ST. PHILA / ONE / SHINE. (Wright 841)

F. A. ROTH & SONS

Rulau	Date	Metal	Size	F	VF	EF	Unc
Phl 94	1899	Brass	31mm	—	—	10.00	—

F. A. ROTH & SONS. (Ganter coll.)

N. S. & CO.
(N. Snellenberg & Co.)

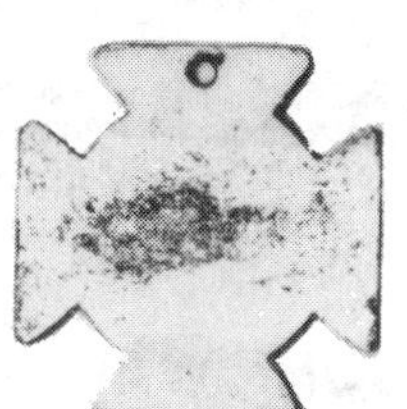

Rulau	Date	Metal	Size	F	VF	EF	Unc
Phl 100	(?)	CN	*25mm	—	—	10.00	—

*Maltese-cross shaped flan.
N.S. / (scroll) / & Co. Numeral incused on scroll (in this case 33368). Rv: Blank. Plain edge. Issued holed.

Charge card token.

Rulau	Date	Metal	Size	F	VF	EF	Unc
Phl 101	(?)	CN	**	—	—	10.00	—

SN & Co monogram.
Rv: Numeral incused (in this case 218490). (Karen Allen coll.)

Nathan Snellenberg's department store was located in the heart of Philadelphia's commercial district, in the 1100 block of Market Street. It operated from the 1890's until 1963, when it suddenly went out of business.

SOULAS CAFE

Rulau	Date	Metal	Size	F	VF	EF	Unc
Phl 105	(?)	Aluminum	39mm	—	8.00	—	—

Building at center, tiny QUINT PHILA within ground line. Below: BETZ BUILDING. Rv: AMERICAN & EUROPEAN NEWSPAPERS ON FILE / SOULAS / CAFE & / RATHS-KELLER / BETZ BUILDING / PHILAD'A. / (dot). Plain edge.

TEACHERS ANNUITY FAIR

Rulau	Date	Metal	Size	F	VF	EF	Unc
Phl 110	1891	Brass	25.5mm	—	8.00	—	—

Minerva head left within wreath of flowers and leaves. Rv: TEACHERS. ANNUITY . FAIR. / (ornament) / SOUVENIR / (ornament) / 1891 / PHILADELPHIA DDEC. 3-10. Plain edge.

UNVEILING OF THE STATUE

Rulau	Date	Metal	Size	F	VF	EF	Unc
Phl 113	1894	Bronze	26mm	—	—	—	15.00

McClellan military bust left, KEY beneath. Around: MAJ. GEN. GEO. B. McCLELLAN. Rv: Civil War soldier on horse, UNVEILING OF THE STATUE OCT. 24. 1894. above. PHILADELPHIA in exergue. Plain edge.

WANAMAKER & BROWN

Rulau	Date	Metal	Size	F	VF	EF	Unc
Phl 115	1897	Gilt/B	28mm	—	—	15.00	—

Facing military bust of Wilhelm I in spiked helmet, WILLIAM EMPERIOR OF GERMANY around. Rv: ZUR ERINNERUNG / -DES- / SANGERFESTES / - 1897 - / WANAMAKER & BROWN / 6TH & MARKET STS. /-.- / PHILADELPHIA. Plain edge. (ANS coll.)

Commemorating the German-American singing festivals.

JOHN WANAMAKER STORES

Rulau	Date	Metal	Size	F	VF	EF	Unc
Phl 114	(1895)	Copper	25mm	8.00	12.00	16.00	20.00

Indian bust in full war headdress left, OHIYESA above. Rv: PORTE / THE WINNER / BONHEUR / WANAMAKER - ORIGINATOR amid ornamental flourishes. Plain edge.

Phl 116	1901	S/Copper	21mm	4.00	5.00	8.00	11.00

Independence Hall, 1776 on winged ball below. INDEPENDENCE HALL PHILADELPHIA. Rv: Tablet above 1876-1901. on tablet in script: SILVER / ANNIVERSARY / FOUNDING OF / 13TH LOCATION / JOHN WANAMAKER. Plain edge.

Phl 117	1901	S/Brass	25.5mm	—	5.00	12.00	16.00

Building and depot across center, "I was here" (script) above, 1876 in exergue. Rv: (All script) Special Medal / Faithful Associates / Silver Anniversary / John Wanamaker / 1901. Plain edge.

Phl 118	1906	CN	31mm	3.50	5.00	7.50	10.00

Indian in war headdress welcoming sailing ship nearing shore; THE AMERICAN UNIVERSITY OF APPLIED COMMERCE around; SALVE below. Rv: FOUNDERS SOUVENIR / THIRTIETH ANNIVERSARY around olive wreath. Within wreath: OF / THIS / NEW KIND OF STORE / JOHN WANNAMAKER / PHILADELPHIA / .1906. Plain edge.

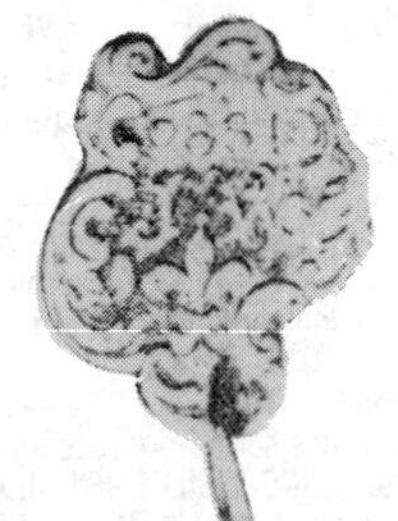
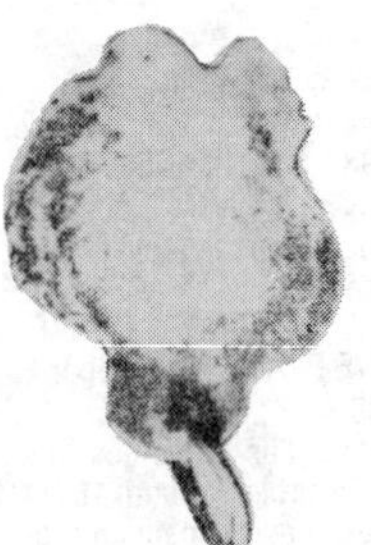

Rulau	Date	Metal	Size	VG	F	VF	Unc
Phl 120	(1890-1900)	GS*	**	—	—	—	38.50

* Irregularly shaped flan, issued holed for suspension. ** 23.5 x 29.6mm. (Incuse) 9831 / (relief) JW / (relief) fleur-de-lis. Rv: Blank. Plain edge. Rarity 4.

JW = John Wanamaker. This is an early form of "charge plate," a credit mechanism. The stamped numerals changed with each customer.

The fleur-de-lis was the symbol of the Wanamaker family.

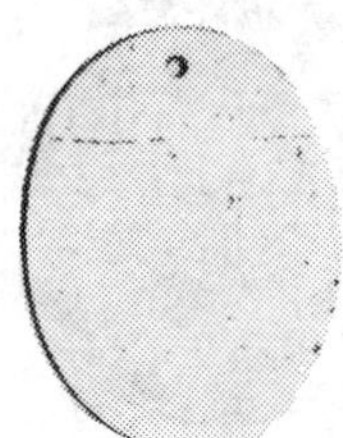

Rulau	Date	Metal	Size	F	VF	EF	Unc
Phl 121	(?)	GS	**	—	—	8.00	—

** Oval, 23 x 30mm.
Crowned shield of arms at center, flanked by oak and laurel wreaths. The shield contains three fleurs-de-lis. A ribbon across the wreath below the shield reads: LE MEILLEUR DU MONDE (The preferred of the world, or, The better of the world). The crown separates J. —W. (For John Wanamaker). Below all is a curved scroll, on which a numeral is stamped (in the illustrated example: 68377). Rv: Blank edge. Issued holed.

Phl 122	(?)	Bronze	**	—	—	8.00	—

** Oval, 23 x 30mm.
Similar to 418, but no crown above the shield of arms. The numeral stamped in the illustrated example is 89965. Rv: Blank. Plain edge. Issued holed.

Both 121 and 122 are also charge-card identification tags of ornate workmanship. Both in Rulau collection.

Phl 123	1908	WM	19mm	—	—	4.00	9.00

Reclining lion, head turned toward viewer. AT THE SIGN OF above, LEADERSHIP below. Rv: WITHIN olive wreath rim: SOUVENIR / OF THE / WANAMAKER / STORES / AUGUST 3RD / 1908. Plain edge.

Phl 124	1910	Bronze	26mm	5.00	7.50	10.00	16.00

Santa Claus bust, MERRY CHRISTMAS. Rv: GOOD HEALTH / GOOD LUCK A HAPPY / NEW YEAR / FOR / 1910. Plain edge. (Miller Pa 532B)

It was not thought logical to leave the later (to 1910) Wanamaker tokens out of the present reference, since they constitute a closely-knit series. Other Wanamaker tokens in the 1890-1910 period probably exist, but we have not been able to secure information on them.

****

John Wannamaker was born in Philadelphia July 11, 1838 and died in the same city, Dec. 12, 1922. At 14, in 1852, he began work as a bookstore errand boy, becoming a clerk in a men's clothing store in 1856. With Nathan Brown he established a clothing firm, Wanamaker & Brown, in 1861. Brown died in 1868.

In 1869 he founded John Wanamaker & Co. as a successor firm (though Wanamker & Brown continued in business). In 1875 he bought the freight depot of the Pennsylvania Railroad to house a "new kind of store" — a collection of specialty shops under one roof.

The "department store" — Wanamaker's — became one of the largest retail stores in the nation when it opened in 1876, the nation's Centennial year. It used advertising effectively (including advertising tokens) and expanded into New York City by buying out the A. T. Stewart store (this closed in 1954).

Wanamaker was postmaster general of the United States 1889-1893 in President Benjamin Harrison's cabinet. The store still operates in Philadelphia.

WASHINGTON MONUMENT

Rulau	Date	Metal	Size	F	VF	EF	Unc
Phl 127	1897	Brass	**	—	—	15.00	—

** Irregularly-shaped.

Eagle displayed, rays in background, above UNVEILING at top. At center: Square with Washington Monument in center, WASHINGTON at left, MONUMENT at right, PHILADELPHIA / MAY 15 / 1897 in exergue. Wreath surrounds the square. Rv: Blank, except small SCHWAAB S.... CO. /MILWAUKEE. Plain edge. Ganter coll.)

Struck by the Schwaab Stamp & Seal Co. of Milwaukee, Wisconsin. This medalet was not listed in the 1985 Rulau-Fuld reference, *Medallic Portraits of Washington.*

WEIKEL & SMITH SPICE CO.

Rulau	Date	Metal	Size	VG	F	VF	Unc
Phl 128	1893	Aluminum	36mm	—	—	—	35.00

Obverse same as Phl 89. Rv: BOHSEMEEM THE BEST SPICES / AND PUREST / WEIKEL & SMITH SPICE CO. / (WSCo monogram) 1868 / * PHILIAD'A. PA. * Plain edge.

SAM. WELSH

Rulau	Date	Metal	Size	VG	F	VF	Unc
Phl 129	1893	Aluminum	36mm	—	—	—	35.00

Obverse as Phl. 89 (Landing of Columbua). Rv: PROGRESSIVE CIGAR STORES / WILL PAY TO / BEARER / FIVE CENTS / IN MERCHANDISE, / AT ANY OF MY / BRANCHES. / SAM. WELSH / .10TH & CHESTNUT STS. PHILA. . Plain edge.

WOODRUFF & LITTLE CYCLE CO.

Philadelphia, Pa.

Rulau	Date	Metal	Size	F	VF	EF	Unc
Phl 130	1892	Brass	25mm	—	—	30.00	—

Two-wheeled bicycle, SECURE below. Around: WOODRUFF & LITTLE CYCLE CO. Rv: AWARDED / AT / A. C. C. CYCLE / SHOW / PHILADELPHIA / FEB. 15-22. 1892. Plain edge.

AMERICUS REPUBLICAN CLUB

Pittsburgh, Pa.

Rulau	Date	Metal	Size	F	VF	EF	Unc
Pit 1	1896	Silver	34mm	—	—	25.00	30.00

Grant bust right in beaded circle, BORN 1822 - DIED 1885 ULYSSES S. GRANT around. Rv: Within beaded central circle: TENTH ANNUAL DINNER / IN COMMEMORATION / OF THE BIRTH OF / GEN. U. S. GRANT / APRIL 27TH. / 1896. Around (on hatched background): * AMERICUS REPUBLICAN CLUB OF PITTSBURGH * FOUNDED 1884. Plain edge. (George Ganter coll.)

CLUSKY'S

Rulau	Date	Metal	Size	VG	E	VF	Unc
Pit 3	1891	WM	33mm	—	—	65.00	—

Building, 1891. Rv: Within wreath: CLUSKY'S / 300 TO 400 / MARKET ST. / PITTSBURGH / PA. Plain edge.

KAUFMANN'S

Rulau	Date	Metal	Size	F	VF	EF	Unc
Pit 10	(?)	CN	**	—	—	8.00	—

** Oval, 31.7 x 24mm.

On rays emanating from sun at top: KAUFMANN'S / "THE BIG STORE" / (oval panel). Rv: Blank. (On panel are incused numerals; illustrated item is numbered 75722). Plain edge. Issued holed.

Charge plate token.

KEYSTONE BREWING CO. LTD.

Rulau	Date	Metal	Size	F	VF	EF	Unc
Pit 12	1891	White Metal	38mm	—	20.00	—	—

Keystone within circle, monogram KBCL on the keystone. Bees fill up the circle. KEYSTONE BREWING CO LTD * PITTSBURGH, PA. Rv: Brewery building, COMPLIMENTS around, 1891 in exergue. Plain edge. (Wright 550)

L. B.
(Lit Brothers)

Rulau	Date	Metal	Size	F	VF	EF	Unc
Pit 13	(?)	S/Brass	**	—	8.00	—	—

** Oval, 25 by 34mm.

Shield at center dominated by flaming (?) urn, demigriffin to left as crest. Above, a scroll on which: QUALITY SERVICE COURTESY. Below, L. B. at center of laurel branches. Rv: Blank, but incused serial number (in this case 83-777). Near edge are tiny relief letters: AUG. C. FRANK PHILADELPHIA. Plain edge. Issued holed.

Charge card token. There are at least four different Lit Bros. charge cards, one dated 1921.

Rulau	Date	Metal	Size	F	VF	EF	Unc
Pit 14	(1921)	—	**	—	—	8.00	—

** Scal 34 x 25.5mm.

19 LB monogram 21 / (incused numeral, in this case 58927). Rv: Blank. Issued holed. (Karen Allen coll.)

Lit Brothers department store, at 8th and Market, opened in 1891 as a dry goods store. It continued in operation as a department store until 1977.

The Lit Brothers building, threatened repeatedly with demolition after the store's closing, became in 1987 the Mellon Independence Center, headquarters for Mellon Bank and other enterprises. It is on the National Register of Historic Places. (Historical background by Karen Allen, Philadelphia collector.)

W. M. LAIRD

Rulau	Date	Metal	Size	F	VF	EF	Unc
Pit 15	(1890's)	Aluminum	38mm	—	—	8.00	15.00

Globe, on which: TRADE / GOODYEAR WELT / MARK. Around: CALL FOR GOODYEAR WELT AND TURNED / * SHOES *. Rv: EXPOSITION / MEDAL / SHOES / W. M. LAIRD. / MANUFACTURER / JOBBER / RETAILER / PITTSBURGH. Plain edge. Issued holed. (Wright 1504)

PITTSBURGH & MEXICAN TIN MINING CO.

Pittsburgh, Pa. ?

Rulau	Date	Metal	Size	F	VF	EF	Unc
Pit 30	1891	Tin*	38mm	—	—	50.00	—

Shield of arms crested by a castle at center. Around: PITTSBURGH & MEXICAN TIN MINING CO. / 1891. Rv: COMMEMORATING / FIRST / CAR LOAD OF / METALLIC TIN / PRODUCED / IN / NORTH AMERICA. Plain edge. Rarity 5.

The United States is not a major producer of tin. Deposits in the Black Hills of South Dakota were worked beginning about 1888.

PITTSBURGH REDUCTION COMPANY

Rulau	Date	Metal	Size	F	VF	EF	Unc
Pit 32	1892	Aluminum	38mm	—	—	—	25.00

Bearded Columbus bust left in cap, COLUMBUS CENTENNIAL MEDAL / - 1492-1892 - around. Rv: SOUVENIR / OF THE / PITTSBURGH (on scroll) / EXPOSITION (on scroll) / ALUMINUM MADE / BY THE PITTSBURGH / REDUCTION / COMPANY. Plain edge. (H-K 629)

PRICE BROS.

Rulau	Date	Metal	Size	F	VF	EF	Unc
Pit 35	(?)	Gilt/B	32mm	—	10.00	—	—

Griffin rampant right, holding a scroll on which: PB mongram / PURITY / AND / EXCELLENCE. Above: PRICE BROS. Below: CHOCOLATES & BON BONS. Rv: GOOD FOR / - 10 ¢ - / PRICE BROS. / PENN AVE & SIXTH ST. / PITTSBURGH PA. (tiny) W * H CO NEWARK N J. Plain edge.

UNIVERSITY OF PITTSBURGH

Rulau	Date	Metal	Size	VG	F	VF	Unc
Pit 55	(?)	Aluminum	19mm	—	5.00	—	—

UNIVERSITY / 1 ¢ / OF PITTSBURGH. Rv: Same as obverse. Plain edge.

THE RANDALL CLUB

Rulau	Date	Metal	Size	VG	F	VF	Unc
Pit 60	1891	Aluminum	38mm	—	—	35.00	—

THE RANDALL CLUB'S / COMPLIMENTS / TO / DEPUTIES / OF / DEMOCRATIC SOCIETIES / PENNSYLVANIA / PITTSBURG (sic!) PA. SEPT, 30 1891. Rv: BY THIS TOKEN / YOU ARE KNOWN / AND THE / RANDALL CLUB / BIDS YOU WELCOME TO / THEIR / CLUB HOUSE / NO. 432 DUQUESNE WAY. Plain edge. (Wright 869)

JOS. M. SHAEFER

Rulau	Date	Metal	Size	VG	F	VF	Unc
Pit 65	1894	WM	34mm	—	—	25.00	40.00

GAR seal. Around: 28TH NATIONAL ENCAMPMENT G.A.R. PITTSBURGH PA. SEP. 1894. Rv: JOS. M. SHAEFER / () / MANUFACTURER & WHOLESALE / JEWELER / DEALER IN / PRECIOUS & IMITATION / STONES / NO. 36 FIFTH AVE. SEC. FLOOR / SPECIALTY / MEDALS & BADGES / TELEPHONE 725 / PITTSBURG (sic!) PA. (Wright 939)

G.A.R. = Grand Army of the Republic.

SQUIRES CARRIAGE CO.

Rulau	Date	Metal	Size	VG	F	VF	Unc
Pit 70	(1890's)	Aluminum	39mm	—	—	25.00	40.00

Closed carriage left. SQUIRES CARRIAGE CO. above. Below: 116-120. / SEVENTH ST. / PITTSBURGH, PA. Rv: GOOD FOR / $5.00 / ON PURCHASE OF EACH VEHICLE. Plain edge. (Kirtley Oct. 1992 sale, lot 3334)

THOMAS & CO.

Rulau	Date	Metal	Size	VG	F	EF	Unc
Pit 75	(1900-10)	Aluminum	38mm	—	—	22.50	—

Building. THOMAS & CO. $1.00. (Kirtley Feb. 1991 price list)

J. ZIMMERMAN

Pittsburgh, Pa.

Rulau	Date	Metal	Size	VG	F	VF	Unc
Pit 80	1894	CN	24mm	—	—	8.00	—

G.A.R. 1894. Rv: J. ZIMMERMAN, 1101 LIBERTY ST. CIGARS PITTSBURGH, PA. (Krueger 1991 sale, lot 1878)

PENN HARD WARE CO.

Reading, Pa.

Rulau	Date	Metal	Size	F	VF	EF	Unc
Rea 6	1898	Brass	31mm	—	—	25.00	—

Large hinge. Around: PENN HARD WARE CO, / READING, PA. At left: * / 1877 / *. At right: * / 1898 / *. Rv: READING'S / Y Y (inverted) / SESQUI-CENTENNIAL / JUNE / (scroll) / 1748 1898 / (rosette) PENN H. CO. (rosette) / (scroll). Plain edge. (Ganter coll.)

SESQUI-CENTENNIAL

Reading, Pa.

Rulau	Date	Metal	Size	F	VF	EF	Unc
Rea 8	1898	WM	42mm	—	—	—	10.00

Seal. Rv: SESQUI-CENTENNIAL / 1748 / JUNE 5-12. / 1898 / READING PENNA. U.S.A. Plain edge.

Rulau	Date	Metal	Size	F	VF	EF	Unc
Rea 8A	1898	Bronze	42mm	—	—	—	10.00

As last. Plain edge.

Rulau	Date	Metal	Size	F	VF	EF	Unc
Rea 9	1898	Alum	32mm	—	—	—	15.00

Obverse as 8. Rv: Indians watch covered wagon, state seal above. (P. Fuhrman coll.)

VORWARTS

Roscoe, Pa.

Rulau	Date	Metal	Size	VG	F	VF	Unc
Ros 6	1900	Aluminum	21mm	—	15.00	20.00	—

Lyre. Rv: VORWARTS / -.- / ROSCOE, PA / 1900. (Kirtley Feb. 1991 sale, lot A3917; Ganter coll.)

Vorwarts = Forward. Token of a German singing society.

THE LEADER

Scranton, Pa.

Rulau	Date	Metal	Size	F	VF	EF	Unc
Scr 4	1899	Brass	32mm	—	—	11.00	—

Dewey bust right, tiny W&H CO NEWARK below. Around: ADMIRAL GEORGE DEWEY. Rv: COMPLIMENTS OF THE LEADER. / (Steamship right) / SCRANTON 1899. Plain edge.

F. P. R.

Shillington, Pa. ?

Rulau	Date	Metal	Size	VG	F	VF	Unc
Shi 1	(1890's)	Alum	25mm	—	—	8.00	—

Crossed pool cues separate N-B-M-CO. in central circle. NATIONAL BILLIARD MANF'G CO. / CIN. O. around. Rv: F. P. R. / GOOD FOR / * (5 ¢ monogram) * / IN TRADE AT BAR. Plain edge.

WILLOW GROVE PARK

Willow Grove, Pa.

Rulau	Date	Metal	Size	VG	F	VF	Unc
Wil 5	1897	Gilt/B	26mm	—	—	10.00	—

Liberty head of Morgan type right, laurel branches at either side. Star above, dot below. Rv: WILLOW GROVE PARK SOUVENIR / CHILDREN'S / DAY / JULY 29. / - / 1897. Plain edge. Issued holed. (Mishler coll.)

Willow Grove, a northern suburb of Philadelphia, has long had a large amusement park.

Rulau	Date	Metal	Size	VG	F	VF	Unc
Wil 7	1898	Brass	25mm	—	—	10.00	—

Bemedaled male bust 3/4 right, CHICAGO on his cap. Around: T. P. BROOKE. Rv: WILLOW GROVE PARK SOUVENIR / CHILDREN'S / DAY / AUGUST 11, / 1898. Plain edge. (Ganter coll.)

STEINOUR'S

York, Pa.

Rulau	Date	Metal	Size	F	VF	EF	Unc
Yor 3	(1890's)	Aluminum	25mm	—	—	15.00	—

Pool table. Above: THE BRUNSWICK BALKE / COLLENDER / COMPY. In exergue: CHECK. Rv: STEINOUR'S 5c. Plain edge. (Brunswick 5708)

737

York, Pa. ?

Rulau	Date	Metal	Size	VG	F	VF	Unc
Yor 20	(?)	Aluminum	24mm	—	—	7.00	—

Brunswick die BBC-8. Rv: GOOD FOR / 5 ¢ / - 737 - / IN TRADE. Plain edge.

Possibly bakery union local 737. Some 10 to 15 tokens are in collectors' hands.

RHODE ISLAND

F. J. HOUSTON

Pawtucket, R.I.

Rulau	Date	Metal	Size	VG	F	VF	Unc
Paw 2	(1899)	Aluminum	30.5mm	—	—	15.00	22.50

Dewey bust facing three-quarters right. OUR COUNTRY'S PRIDE above, **** ADMIRAL DEWEY **** below. Rv: WE WILL REDEEM THIS FROM ANY DEALER AT 5C / 5 C / HOUSTON'S / HAND MADE / 5 C CIGAR / *** / F. J. HOUSTON, / PAWTUCKET, R.I. Plain edge.

OLD SLATER MILL

Pawtucket, R.I.

Rulau	Date	Metal	Size	VG	F	VF	Unc
Paw 5	1890	Bronze	38mm	—	5.00	10.00	—

Mill, OLD SLATER MILL above, SEPT. 29 to OCT. 4, 1890 below. Around: 100TH ANNIVERSARY OF COTTON SPINNING IN THE U.S. * PAWTUCKET, R.I. *. Rv: Bridge over waterfall, buildings in background, PAWTUCKET FALLS above. Plain edge. (Dick Grinolds & George Ganter collections)

SOUTH CAROLINA

ATLANTIC COAST LUMBER CO.

Georgetown, S.C.

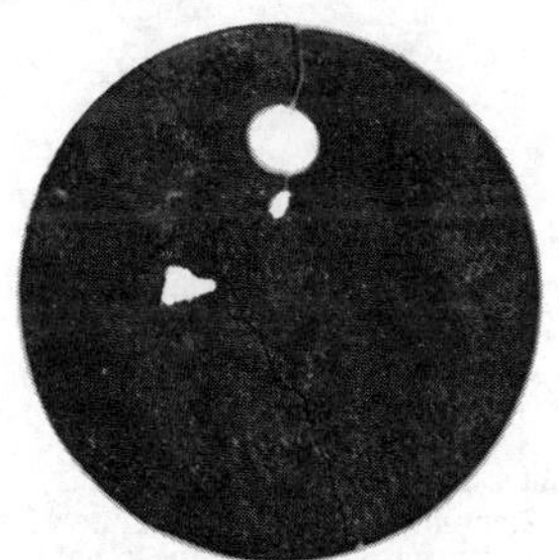

Rulau	Date	Metal	Size	VG	F	VF	Unc
Ggt 1	(1924)	Brass	37mm	50.00	65.00	100.	—

(All incused): ATLANTIC COAST LUMBER CO / AUGUST / 1418 / LOGGING DEPT. / GEORGETOWN S.C. Rv: Blank. Plain edge. Issued holed.

The numeral 1418 is some form of control number, which would have changed with each token. It is difficult to assess what the month August on the piece indicated.

Quite rare — possibly only 4 pieces known.

PINCKNEY OYSTER CO. STORE

Ridgeland, S.C.

Rulau	Date	Metal	Size	VG	F	VF	Unc
Rid 1	(?)	Brass	30mm	—	12.50	15.00	—

AT PINCKNEY / OYSTER / CO. / STORE. Rv: GOOD FOR / 50 ¢ / IN MERCHANDISE. Plain edge. (Rulau coll.)

SOUTH DAKOTA

DAN SHILTON

Aberdeen, S.D.

Rulau	Date	Metal	Size	VG	F	VF	Unc
Abd 1	(1884-92)	GS	25mm	—	—	50.00	—

BBC die 9A. Rv: GOOD FOR / * 5 ¢ * DAN / SHILTON / IN / * TRADE *. Plain edge. (Thoele coll.)

South Dakota was admitted to the Union on Nov. 2, 1889.

Shilton appears under billiards in the 1886 gazetteer, but the token appears to be from a few years later.

J. H. ABBOTT

Arlington, S.D.

Rulau	Date	Metal	Size	VG	F	VF	Unc
Arl 1	(1892-98)	Brass	24mm	—	—	35.00	—

Steer left, on mound. Rv: GOOD FOR / 5 ¢ / J. H. ABBOTT (on panel) / IN / * TRADE *. Plain edge. (Travis Roberts coll.)

J. H. Abbott's billiard hall appears in the gazetteers for 1892, 1896 and 1898. It is not listed 1906-07, but does appear again in 1911-12.

W. B. SICKELS

Cavour, S.D.

Rulau	Date	Metal	Size	VG	F	VF	Unc
Cav 1	(1882-92)	Brass	--mm	—	—	150.	—

Chas. Pick & Co. die. Rv: W. B. SICKELS. Only 2 pieces known.

Cavour, in Beadle County, had 408 population in 1910. South Dakota was admitted to statehood 1889. (Thoele research). The name is given as "Sickles" in directories.

L. J. TURNER

Estelline, S.D.

Rulau	Date	Metal	Size	VG	F	VF	Unc
Est 3	(1896)	Brass	25mm	—	—	40.00	—

Brunswick die BBC-11. Rv: GOOD FOR / 5 ¢ / L. J. / TURNER / IN / TRADE.

Billiard hall listed in 1896 gazetteer.

F. J. WIESE

Humboldt, S.D.

Rulau	Date	Metal	Size	VG	F	VF	Unc
Hum 3	(1906)	Brass	Scal 28.5mm	—	15.00	—	—

GOOD FOR / 5 C / F. J. WIESE (in panel) / IN / TRADE. Rv: THE BRUNSWICK BALKE / COLLENDER / COMPY (large space) / CHECK . Plain edge.

Billiard hall & saloon, 1906-1912.

CORN BELT EXPOSITION

Mitchell, S.D.

Rulau	Date	Metal	Size	F	VF	EF	Unc
Mit 3	1892	Aluminum	36mm	—	—	20.00	35.00

Castle, CORN BELT EXPOSITION 1892 / MITCHELL SO. DAKOTA. Rv: SOUTH DAKOTA'S INVITATION (etc). Plain edge. Issued holed.

A. CAMPBELL
Mound City, S.D.

Rulau	Date	Metal	Size	G	VG	VF	Unc
Mou 1	(1888)	Brass	--mm	40.00	—	—	—

Brunswick-Balke die 6a. Rv: GOOD FOR / 5 ¢ / A CAMPBELL / IN / TRADE.

This same proprietor issued similar tokens in Lake City, Iowa (Lak 2) in 1884. He or she may have remained in business in the Dakotas past 1888. It is possible A. Campbell was a woman, Thoele says.

A. V. TRUTNOVSKY
Scotland, S.D.

Rulau	Date	Metal	Size	VG	F	VF	Unc
Sct 3	(1895-1910)	Brass	25mm	—	7.00	9.50	—

Eagle with folded wings perched on cannon. Rv: GOOD FOR / 5 ¢ . A. V. TRUTNOVSKY / IN TRADE.

Said to have been used at Trutnovsky's saloon, bakery and hotel. Thoele calls it "very common."

ANDREW SCHMITZ
South Dakota ?

Rulau	Date	Metal	Size	VG	F	VF	Unc
Unk 1	(1890's)	Brass	25mm	—	—	30.00	—

GOOD FOR / 5 ¢ / ANDREW / SCHMITZ / AT THE BAR. Rv: THE / GARDEN CITY / (ornament) / BILLIARD / (ornament) / TABLE CO. / CHICAGO. Plain edge. (Thoele coll.)

TENNESSEE

SIEGRIST'S BAKERY
Jellico, Tenn.

Rulau	Date	Metal	Size	VG	F	VF	Unc
Jel 3	(?)	Brass	Oct --mm	—	25.00	—	—

SIEGRIST'S BAKERY. 5 C LOAF. (Kirtley Feb. 1991 price list)

J. M. GRAHAM
Pinewood, Tenn.

Rulau	Date	Metal	Size	F	VF	EF	Unc
Pwd 3	(1893-99)	Aluminum	**	20.00	30.00	—	—

** Octagonal 35mm.

J. M. GRAHAM / * / MERCHANT / * / PINEWOOD, TENN. Rv: GOOD FOR / 1oo / IN / MERCHANDISE. Plain edge. (Wright 1435)

Pinewood was a tiny place of 61 souls in Hickman County in 1910. A possible successor firm, R. M. Hall, ran the only business in town in 1918 — a general store, flour distributorship, mill, etc.

TEXAS

C. G. FRENZEL
Austin, Texas

Rulau	Date	Metal	Size	VG	F	VF	Unc
Aus 3	(1892)	Brass	25mm	—	—	25.00	40.00

Pool table. Above: R. ROTHSCHILD'S SONS. / MAKERS / - OF - / SALOON FIXTURES / & BILLIARD TABLES. Below: * CHECK *. Rv: GOOD FOR / 5 ¢ (in panel) / C. G. FRENZEL (in panel) / -IN- / TRADE. (Thoele coll.)

This saloon is listed in the 1892 directory. Four or more specimens are known, one in Unc.

FRITTER POOL HALL
Brackettville, Texas

Rulau	Date	Metal	Size	VG	F	VF	Unc
Brk 3	(1899-1901)	Aluminum	Oval 32x25mm	—	—	35.00	—

Eagle displayed, perched atop cannon, head turned right. Rv: FRITTER / POOL HALL / GOOD FOR / 5 ¢ / IN POOL / BRACKETTSVILLE, TEX. Plain edge. (John Byars coll.)

Hank Thoele opines this could have been issued as late as 1914, but the eagle-on-cannon motif is a turn-of-the-century design.

Brackettville, in Kinney County near Del Rio and the Rio Grande River border with Mexico, has its name misspelled on the token, an 'S' being added. Oldtimers say the town was once called that way, though the post office spelling was Brackettville as early as 1877. Fritter has disappeared by World War I.

CRIXELL SALOON
Brownsville, Texas

Rulau	Date	Metal	Size	VG	F	VF	Unc
Brv 3	(?)	Aluminum	20mm	—	—	20.00	—

= / CRIXELL / = / SALOON / (flower) / BROWNSVILLE TEXAS. Rv: MEXICAN on bar across large numeral 5 at center, GOOD FOR above, IN MERCHANDISE below. Plain edge. (Gary Pipher coll.)

WEAKLY & WATSON
Brownwood, Texas

Rulau	Date	Metal	Size	VG	F	VF	Unc
Brw 6	(1890's)	Aluminum	38mm	—	50.00	—	—

WEAKLY & WATSON / STOVES / HARDWARE / IMPLEMENTS / PUMPS / BROWNWOOD, TEXAS. Rv: CARRY THIS MEDAL WITH YOU ALWAYS AND REFER TO IT OFTEN / ROOFING / GUTTERING / WELL CASING / WIND MILLS / STEAM & WATER / FITTINGS. Plain edge. (Wright 1217)

Dr. Wright called this token rare in 1898.

MAX ORTLIEB

Dallas, Texas

Rulau	Date	Metal	Size	F	VF	EF	Unc
Dal 7	(1893)	Aluminum	36mm	—	—	35.00	—

Building. Around: WORLD'S COLUMBIAN EXPOSITION. Rv: FLOUR BAGS PRINTED IN ANY STYLE DESIRED ORDERS EXECUTED PROMPTLY / MAX ORTLIEB, DALLAS, TEXAS / STATE AGENT FOR FULTON BAG & COTTON MILLS, ATLANTA, GA. Plain edge. (Eglit 577)

The Fulton Bag & Cotton Mills are still listed in Dallas in 1918, though Ortlieb's name no longer appears in directories.

W. H. WARD

Fort Worth, Texas

Rulau	Date	Metal	Size	VG	F	VF	Unc
Fwr 9	(1890's)	Aluminum	Scal 29mm	—	20.00	—	—

GOOD FOR / 1 / W. H. WARD / DRINK / FORT / WORTH, TEX. Rv: Blank. Plain edge. (Wright 1716)

H. A. DORBRITZ

Goliad, Texas

Rulau	Date	Metal	Size	VG	F	VF	Unc
Gol 1	(?)	GS 4-lobed	28mm	—	—	150.	—

H. A. DORBRITZ / * * * / FARMERS' / * SALOON * / — / GOLIAD, TEX. Plain edge. (Wright 1400)

R. C. STUART DRUG CO.

Houston, Texas

Rulau	Date	Metal	Size	F	VF	EF	Unc
Hou 35	(1896-97)	WM	23mm	—	20.00	30.00	—

THE R. C. STUART DRUG CO. / ONE GLASS / SODA. Rv: Blank. Plain edge.

This firm is listed in the 1897 *Texas Gazetteer.*

STUDE'S COFFEE PARLORS

Houston, Texas

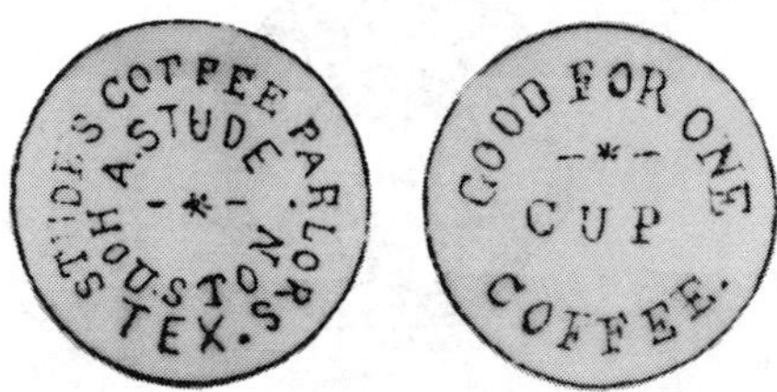

Rulau	Date	Metal	Size	VG	F	VF	Unc
Hou 38	(?)	Cupronickel	26mm	—	—	—	15.00

STUDE'S COFFEE PARLORS / A. STUDE / HOUSTON / TEX. Rv: GOOD FOR ONE / -*- / CUP / COFFEE. Plain edge. (Wright 1069)

F. MEURIN

Marion, Texas

Rulau	Date	Metal	Size	VG	F	VF	Unc
Mar 2	(1884-86)	GS	25mm	—	—	35.00	—

GOOD FOR / ONE DRINK / F. MEURIN / MARION. Rv: Blank. Plain edge. (Bill Fowler report; Elmer Randall photo)

Meurin appears in the 1884 *Texas Gazetteer* and the 1886 *Bradstreet Directory.*

FIRST LEGAL LABOR DAY

Nashville, Texas

Rulau	Date	Metal	Size	VG	F	VF	Unc
Nas 1	1891	Aluminum	36mm	—	—	85.00	—

IN COMMEMORATION OF FIRST LEGAL LABOR DAY / 1891. Rv: Within wreath: Arm and hammer, sheaf, tools. Plain edge. (Kirtley 1991 ATCO sale, lot 2975)

GEO. RIST

Panhandle, Texas

Rulau	Date	Metal	Size	VG	F	VF	Unc
Pan 1	(1890's)	Aluminum	Oct, 27mm	—	—	750.	—

Elephant right within beaded central circle. Rv: GOOD FOR ONE DRINK / — / GEO / — — / RIST / — / . PANHANDLE. Plain edge. (ANS collection)

R. E. BYNUM

Paris, Texas

Rulau	Date	Metal	Size	VG	F	VF	Unc
Par 2	(1896-97)	Brass	28mm	—	35.00	50.00	—

(All incused): R. E. BYNUM / 12 1/2 / SALOON. Rv: Blank. There is a recessed, beaded rim on each side. Plain edge.

Bynum is listed as a saloonkeeper in the 1897 edition of the R. G. Dun Directory.

THE ALAMO

San Antonio, Texas

Rulau	Date	Metal	Size	VG	F	VF	Unc
San 3	(?)	Brass	39mm	—	—	35.00	50.00

Alamo at center, REMEMBER above, THE ALAMO below. Rv: monument at center, U.S. GRANT'S MONUMENT around. Plain edge.

Rulau	Date	Metal	Size	VG	F	VF	Unc
San 4	(?)	Aluminum	39mm	—	—	35.00	50.00

Obverse as 3. Rv: Importers of / CLEAR / HAVANA CIGARS / AND / Meerschaum Goods / within scrollwork. Plain edge. (Hartzog coll.)

The reverse was obviously intended for a store card, but whose?

BEXAR HOTEL BAR

Rulau	Date	Metal	Size	F	VF	EF	Unc
San 8	(1890's)	Aluminum	30mm	—	150.	—	—

Standing bear and laurel branch supporting a medallion bearing an SA monogram. Above: BEXAR HOTEL / BAR. Below: SAN ANTONIO / TEX. Rv: Horse's bit within open-end wreath.

The "bit" in this case has a double meaning, since it represents 12 1/2 cents value, or one Mexican real (bit). This is an extremely handsome token.

BLACK ELEPHANT

Rulau	Date	Metal	Size	VG	F	VF	Unc
San 12	(1890's)	Aluminum	31mm	—	30.00	50.00	—
San 14	(?)	WM	Scal 28mm	—	20.00	—	—
San 16	(?)	WM	23mm	—	22.50	—	—

San 12: BLACK ELEPHANT / SAN / ANTONIO / TEX / P MAGUDIEU / PROP. Rv: GOOD FOR / 12 1/2 ¢ / AT THE BAR. Plain edge. (Wright 1505)

San 14: * GOOD FOR * / 12 1/2¢ / BLACK ELEPHANT (on scrolls) / -IN- / * TRADE *. Rv: 12 1/2 within circle of 16 stars. Plain edge.

San 16: BLACK ELEPHANT / GOOD FOR / 5 / CENTS / AT BAR / OK (all incused). Rv: Blank. Plain edge.

BULL BROTHERS

Rulau	Date	Metal	Size	VG	F	VF	Unc
San 20	(?)	WM	24mm	—	—	60.00	—

BULL BROS. / SALOON / SAN ANTONIO, TEX. Rv: GOOD FOR / 2 1/2 / AT THE BAR. Plain edge. (Wright 1352). There are two varieties.

Rulau	Date	Metal	Size	VG	F	VF	Unc
San 21	(?)	WM	24mm	—	—	25.00	—
San 22	(?)	Brass	24mm	—	—	25.00	—
San 23	(?)	Brass	20mm	—	9.50	15.00	—
San 25	(1880's)	GS	31mm	—	22.50	30.00	—

San 21: BULL BROS. / THE / MOUNT VERNON / AND / COR. ALAMO / & / COMMERCE STS. Rv: GOOD FOR / 2 1/2 / AT THE BAR. Plain edge.

San 22: As last. Plain edge.

San 23: BULL BROS / ALAMO PLAZA. Rv: 5. Plain edge.

San 25: CHARLES & HARRY / BULL / SAN ANTONIO, TEX. Rv: GOOD FOR / ONE / DRINK. Plain edge. (Wright 1353)

Rulau	Date	Metal	Size	VG	F	VF	Unc
San 26	(1890's)	Aluminum	34mm	—	50.00	—	—

Bull's head facing three quarters left. BROTHERS below. Rv: GOOD FOR / * ONE * / DRINK. Plain edge. (Wright 1343)

Rulau	Date	Metal	Size	VG	F	VF	Unc
San 28	(1890's)	**	38mm	—	10.00	—	—

** Printed in black on green cardboard. (Printer's mark) / BULL BROS. / 2 1/2 / (printer's mark). Rv: HURRY BACK / WE / NEED / THE MONEY (all within circle). Plain edge.

In 1918, there was a Bull Brothers Auto Supply Co. in San Antonio. Also a Bull Hartman Co., auto supplies.

BURKE'S SALOON

Rulau	Date	Metal	Size	VG	F	VF	Unc
San 31	(1896-98)	Brass	Oct 26mm	—	25.00	35.00	—

(All incused): BURKE'S / GOOD FOR / 10 / CENTS / IN TRADE / SALOON. Rv: Blank. Plain edge.

Burke's Saloons were listed at 629 Austin Street and 822 Austin Street in the 1897-98 city directory.

THE COFFEE HOUSE

Rulau	Date	Metal	Size	VG	F	VF	Unc
San 37	(1899)	Br & Alum	19.5mm	—	—	25.00	—

THE COFFEE HOUSE / 98 (in wreath) / W. HOUSTON ST. Rv: 2 1/2. (Kirtley 1992 ATCO sale, lot 1404)

Bimetallic token; brass ring around aluminum center.

COOLEY'S REGISTER

Rulau	Date	Metal	Size	VG	F	VF	Unc
San 39	(?)	Aluminum	31mm	—	—	100	—

Book labeled COOLEY's / REGISTER. Rv: Alamo at center, CRADLE OF TEXAS LIBERTY above. ALAMO below. Plain edge.

H. & H. MFG. CO.

Rulau	Date	Metal	Size	VG	F	VF	EF
San 50	(?)	Silver	25mm	—	60.00	—	—

H & H MFG. CO. — SAN ANTONIO, TEXAS ctsp on U.S. 1898 Barber quarter.

IDEAL SALOON

Rulau	Date	Metal	Size	VG	F	VF	Unc
San 55	(?)	Aluminum	Scal 30mm	—	40.00	75.00	—

IDEAL SALOON / * / HOUSTON / AND / SOLEDAD STS. Rv: FRANK FISCHER / 12 1/2. (Kirtley Sept. 1992 sale, lot 1405)

IRON WORKS

Rulau	Date	Metal	Size	VG	F	VF	Unc
San 58	(?)	Aluminum	30mm	—	—	40.00	—

Alamo at center, REMEMBER THE ALAMO above. IRON WORKS / (star) below. Rv: FARM, RANCH / —& —/ —MILL— / MACHINERY. / SAN ANTONIO / TEXAS. Plain edge.

KOEHLER PARK

Rulau	Date	Metal	Size	VG	F	VF	Unc
San 63	(1900 ?)	Cardboard	38mm	—	—	35.00	—

Black printing on white cardboard. .... KOEHLER PARK .... / GOOD FOR / 2 1/2 ¢ / IN TRADE / SAN ANTONIO, TEXAS. Rv: Blank. Scarce. (Rulau coll.)

J. E. LESER

Rulau	Date	Metal	Size	VG	F	VF	Unc
San 70	(1899)	Aluminum	25mm	—	—	250.	—

Military bust right, tiny SIMMANG below. Around: ADMIRAL W. S. SCHLEY. Rv: 5 / J. E. LESER / DIAMOND / (diamond) / SALOON. Plain edge.

This token was cut by Charles Simmang, San Antonio dieskinker and engraver who had been the prize pupil of Karl Stubenrauch of San Antonio.

Admiral Schley was the hero of the naval victory over Spain at Santiago de Cuba in the Spanish-American War of 1898. Patriotism was running high in San Antonio during and after this war; it was in San Antonio that Col. Theodore Roosevelt recruited and trained his famous "Rough Riders" before their embarkation for Cuba and the battles of El Caney and San Juan Hill.

LOCKWOOD'S ALAMO PLAZA

San Antonio, Texas

Rulau	Date	Metal	Size	VG	F	VF	Unc
San 73	(1890)	Cupronickel	20mm	—	—	5.00	—

(All incuse) BEER AT / LOCKWOOD'S / ALAMO PLAZA. Rv: 5. Plain edge.

Rulau	Date	Metal	Size	VG	F	VF	Unc
San 75	(1890)	Cupronickel	26mm	—	—	5.00	—

(All incuse) ONE / DRINK AT / LOCKWOOD'S / ALMO (sic) PLAZA. Rv: 10. Plain edge.

WARE & DRISKELL'S STORE

Sarber, Texas

Rulau	Date	Metal	Size	F	VF	EF	Unc
Sar 3	(?)	Aluminum	35mm	—	—	20.00	—

AT WARE & DRISKELL'S STORE / — SARBER. / TEXAS. / NOT / REDEEMABLE. Rv: GOOD FOR / $1oo / IN TRADE. Plain edge.

Sarber was apparently a lumber camp settlement of the Ware & Driskell Lumber Company. Aluminum tokens in 5, 10, 25, 50-cent and $1 denominations are known, all with lobed planchets (from 10 to 14 lobes), lettered WARE AND DRISKELL LUMBER CO. The same denominations in aluminum in round planchets are known lettered AT WARE & DRISKELL'S STORE. The latter would be a company store.

Sarber does not appear in the R. G. Dun commercial directory for 1918, nor in the Postal Guides for 1877-1881.

F. SETTLE

Scurry, Texas

Rulau	Date	Metal	Size	VG	F	VF	Unc
Scu 1	(1897)	Brass	25mm	—	—	35.00	—

Brunswick die BBC-11. Rv: GOOD FOR / 5 ¢ / F. SETTLE / IN / TRADE.

Fate Settle saloon listed in 1897 R. G. Dun directory.

L & V
(Lightner & Vivian)
Shafter, Texas

Rulau	Date	Metal	Size	VG	F	VF	Unc
Sha 4	(1888-95)	Brass	24mm	—	15.00	—	—

(All incused): GOOD FOR / ONE DRINK / L & V. Rv: Blank. Incised rim on each side. Plain edge.

Lightner and Vivian operated their saloon in this silver mining town (established in the early 1880's) in the late 1880's and early 1890's.

Shafter was named for Gen. William R. "Pecos Bill" Shafter, who led a party out of Fort McKavett in 1875 to break the dominance of the Indians in the Llano Estacado, the great high plains of West Texas.

MALLOY & PRATT
Spofford, Texas

Rulau	Date	Metal	Size	VG	F	VF	Unc
Spf 4	(1890)	WM	Scal 27mm	—	35.00	50.00	—
	X 10 U 8 / MALLOY / & Pratt. Rv: ONE / DRINK. Plain edge. (Wright 1508)						
Spf 6	(1890)	Brass	Scal 27mm	—	35.00	50.00	—
	Obverse similar to last. Rv: ONE / BEER. Plain edge.						

Malloy & Pratt were in business in Spofford in 1890. The 'X 10 U 8' on their tokens reportedly stood for 'Extenuate,' the name of their saloon.

SANSOM & MARTIN
Spofford, Texas

Rulau	Date	Metal	Size	VG	F	VF	Unc
Spf 11	(1890's)	Aluminum	25mm	—	—	150.	—

SUNSET SALOON / SANSOM & MARTIN / PROPRIETORS / SPOFFORD, TEX. Rv: WE O. U. / 12 1/2¢ / IN TRADE. Plain edge.

BEN. GEFFERT
Victoria, Texas

Rulau	Date	Metal	Size	VG	F	VF	Unc
Vic 4	(ca 1900 ?)	Aluminum	**	—	—	15.00	—

** Square, 25mm.
BEN. GEFFERT / VICTORIA / TEXAS. Rv: GOOD FOR / 5 / CENTS / IN TRADE. Plain edge.

TEXAS COTTON PALACE
Waco, Texas

Rulau	Date	Metal	Size	F	VF	EF	Unc
Wco 13	1894	Aluminum	35mm	—	—	35.00	—

Building across the center, TEXAS COTTON PALACE / SOUVENIR above. NOV. 8 - DEC. 6. 1894 / WACO, TEXAS below. Rv: Large 5-pointed star in circle, all within wreath. At bottom, tiny SCHWAAB, MILWAUKEE. Plain edge. (Wright 1099)

S. F. CODY JR.
Texas

Rulau	Date	Metal	Size	F	VF	EF	Unc
Unk 1	(?)	Brass	35mm	—	35.00	—	—

Female seated atop bale, etc., raising a laurel wreath with her left arm. Around: SOUVENIR OF S. F. CODY JR. TEXAS U.S.A. Rv: Horseman and cyclist racing on a track. Plain edge. Issued with loop.

SOUTH TEXAS DAIRY
Texas

Rulau	Date	Metal	Size	VG	F	VF	EF
Unk 5	(?)	Brass	**	—	—	40.00	—

** Octagonal, 23mm.
SOUTH / —|— / * DAIRY * / —|— / TEXAS. Rv: GOOD FOR / 1 / PINT / MILK. Plain edge. (Wright 1020)

UTAH

BRINGHURST & CO.
Bingham, Utah

Rulau	Date	Metal	Size	VG	F	VF	Unc
Bin 1	(?)	?	20mm	—	40.00	50.00	—

BRINGHURST / & / CO. / BINGHAM, UT. Rv: GOOD FOR / 12 1/2 ¢ / IN TRADE. Plain edge. Rarity 10.

Bingham, in Salt Lake County, originally was called Bingham Canyon.

THE BUTTE SALOON
Bingham, Utah

Rulau	Date	Metal	Size	VG	F	VF	Unc
Bin 3	(1909-10)	Brass	21mm	—	50.00	80.00	—

THE BUTTE / -.- / SALOON / -.- / BINGHAM, UT. Rv: GOOD FOR / * / 12 1/2 ¢ * / IN TRADE. Plain edge. Rarity 9.

The reverse is the same die as the James' Saloon token of Fairview, Utah.

Christopherson & Bartholomew were the proprietors at 516 Main St., Bingham Canyon, in 1909-10.

JUNCTION CO-OP
Ephraim, Utah

Rulau	Date	Metal	Size	VG	F	VF	Unc
Eph 1	1896	Aluminum	26mm	—	—	155.	—

JUNCTION CO-OP / 1896 / EPHRAIM UTAH. Rv: GOOD FOR / 50 ¢ / IN / MERCHANDISE / AT RETAIL. Plain edge. Rarity 9. (Wright 1479)

General store 1896-1902.

OXFORD SALOON
Eureka, Utah

Rulau	Date	Metal	Size	VG	F	VF	Unc
Eur 1	(?)	White Metal	21mm	—	90.00	150.	—

OXFORD SALOON / * / EUREKA, / - / UTAH. Rv: GOOD FOR / 12 1/2 / CTS. / IN TRADE. Plain edge. Rarity 9.

Eureka is in Juab County.

JAMES' SALOON
Fairview, Utah

Rulau	Date	Metal	Size	VG	F	VF	Unc
Fai 1	(?)	Brass	20mm	—	80.00	100.	—

JAMES' / SALOON / FAIRVIEW / -.- / UT. Rv: GOOD FOR / * 12 1/2 ¢ * / IN TRADE. Plain edge. Rarity 8.

Fairview is in Sanpete County.

ALLEN BROS.
Hyrum, Utah

Rulau	Date	Metal	Size	VG	F	VF	Unc
Hyr 1	(1900)	Aluminum	32mm	—	35.00	50.00	—

ALLEN BROS. / -..- / HYRUM, UTAH / *. Rv: GOOD FOR / $2oo / -IN- / MERCHANDISE / AT RETAIL. Plain edge. Rarity 8. (Wright 1306)

Rulau	Date	Metal	Size	VG	F	VF	Unc
Hyr 5	(1900)	Aluminum	30mm	—	27.50	—	—

Similar to last, but 25 C.

Simeon and Joseph S. Allen are listed from 1900 on.

Allen Brothers still ran a general store in Hyrum, Cache County, in 1918.

A. NADAULD
Kanosh, Utah

Rulau	Date	Metal	Size	VG	F	VF	Unc
Kan 1	(1890's)	Aluminum	Oct 25mm	—	200.	300.	—

A. NADAULD / KANOSH. UTAH. Rv: GOOD FOR / 10 ¢ / IN / MERCHANDISE / AT RETAIL. Plain edge. Rarity 10. (Wright 1545)

In 1918 there was a P. E. Nadauld confectionery in this 513-person Millard County community.

BEEHIVE MERC. CO.
Manti, Utah

Rulau	Date	Metal	Size	VG	F	VF	Unc
Man 1	(?)	Brass	Scal,--mm	—	5.00	9.00	—

BEEHIVE MERC. CO., MANTI. Rv: 5 ¢. Plain edge. Rarity 3.

Rulau	Date	Metal	Size	VG	F	VF	Unc
Man 2	(?)	Brass	Scal,--mm	—	—	—	—

Similar, but 10 ¢. Plain edge.

W. H. GAGE
Mercur, Utah

Rulau	Date	Metal	Size	F	VF	EF	Unc
Mer 1	(1890's)	Aluminum	25.5mm	—	100.	—	—

Building, SALT LAKE CITY & COUNTY BUILDING. Rv: W. H. GAGE / GOOD FOR / 12 1/2 C / DRINK OR CIGAR, MERCUR, UTAH. Rarity 10. (Wright 1424)

Mercur is in Tooele County.

MINERSVILLE CO-OP
Minersville, Utah

Rulau	Date	Metal	Size	VG	F	VF	Unc
Min 1	(1890's)	Aluminum	21mm	—	100.	200.	—

MINERSVILLE CO-OP / -o- / MINERSVILLE / UTAH. Rv: GOOD FOR / 25 ¢ / IN / MERCHANDISE / AT RETAIL. Plain edge. Rarity 10. (Wright 1524)

In Beaver County. In 1910 there were 591 people here.

MORONI CO-OP
Moroni, Utah

Rulau	Date	Metal	Size	VG	F	VF	Unc
Mor 1	1896	Aluminum	25mm	—	8.00	12.50	—

MORONI CO-OP / 1896 / MORONI, UTAH. Rv: $1.00. Plain edge. (Koppenhaver Nov. 1983 sale, lot 777). Rarity 1.

A full set of tokens of type Mor 1 exists — 5, 10, 25 and 50-cents as well as $1.00. There are also die varieties.

In addition, an octagonal brass 10-cent token is reported.

GAGE & MORAN
Nephi, Utah

Rulau	Date	Metal	Size	F	VF	EF	Unc
Nep 1	(?)	Brass	25.5mm	25.00	—	75.00	—

GAGE / & / MORAN / NEPHI, UTAH. Rv: GOOD FOR / ONE / DRINK / OR / CIGAR. Rarity 8. (Wright 1423)

THE GEM
Ogden, Utah

Ogd 1 (?) Brass 26mm 15.00 — 25.00 —

THE GEM / * - * / 258 25TH ST. / * - * / OGDEN UTAH. Rv: GOOD FOR / 5 / CENTS / IN TRADE. Plain edge. Rarity 7. (Wright 1668)

LIVINGSTON & BLOSSER

Rulau	Date	Metal	Size	F	VF	EF	Unc
Ogd 2	(1892-93)	Nickel alloy	25mm	—	200.	—	—

Mormon Tabernacle, MORMON TABERNACLE under. Rv: GOOD FOR A / DRINK / OR CIGAR / LIVINGSTON / & / BLOSSER. (Springfield 1981 sale, lot 4566). Rarity 8.

Benjamin F. Livington and William D. Blosser.

J. F. McCARRON & CO.

Rulau	Date	Metal	Size	VG	F	VF	Unc
Ogd 3	(1890's)	Alum	25mm	35.00	—	50.00	—

J. F. McCARRON & CO / 372 / 25TH ST / OGDEN UTAH. Rv: BROOM HOTEL BAR / GOOD FOR / ONE / DRINK / OR CIGAR. Plain edge. Rarity 10. (Wright 1515)

There are other tokens of this issuer, from the 1912-13 period.

SALT LAKE VALLEY CANNING CO.

Rulau	Date	Metal	Size	VG	F	VF	Unc
Ogd 4	(1890's)	Brass	25mm	—	35.00	45.00	—

SALT LAKE / VALLEY / CANNING CO. Rv: Blank. Plain edge. (Wright 1609)

A later token of this issuer, in aluminum, appeared in 1914.

THE WHITE ELEPHANT
Ogden, Utah

Rulau	Date	Metal	Size	F	VF	EF	Unc
Ogd 5	(1890's)	Aluminum	26mm	—	15.00	—	—

THE WHITE / ELEPHANT / 320 25TH ST. - OGDEN UTAH. Rv: GOOD FOR / ONE / DRINK / OR / CIGAR. Plain edge. (Wright 1685)

Rulau	Date	Metal	Size	F	VF	EF	Unc
Ogd 7	(1899)	B&A	26mm	—	50.00	—	—

As 5.

PARADISE CO-OP

Paradise, Utah

Rulau	Date	Metal	Size	VG	F	VF	Unc
Par 1	(1890's)	Aluminum	25mm	—	75.00	100.	—

PARADISE CO-OP / x x x / PARADISE / UTAH. Rv: GOOD FOR / 5 ¢ / IN / MERCHANDISE / AT RETAIL. Plain edge. Rarity 9. (Wright 1569)

Paradise is in Cache County. Population in 1918 was 620.

MINT SALOON

Price, Utah

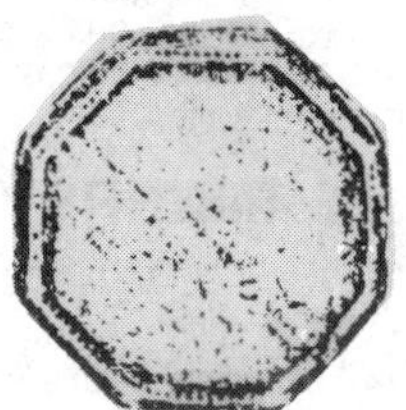

Rulau	Date	Metal	Size	VG	F	VF	Unc
Pri 1	(?)	Alum	Oct 26mm	—	—	75.00	—

MINT SALOON / GOOD FOR / 1 / DRINK CIGAR / -.- / PRICE, UTAH. Plain edge. Rarity 9.

Price is in Carbon County.

HEWLETT BROS.

Salt Lake City, Utah

Rulau	Date	Metal	Size	VG	F	VF	Unc
SLC 3	(1890's)	Aluminum	Scal,27mm	—	15.00	20.00	—

HEWLETT BROS / -.- / SALT LAKE CITY / UTAH. Rv: GOOD FOR / 25 / CENTS / IN TRADE. Plain edge. (Wright 1453)

Hewlett Brothers in 1918 traded in baking powder, spices, extracts, teas, coffee, etc.

JOHNSON'S V.T.R.

Rulau	Date	Metal	Size	VG	F	VF	Unc
SLC 6	1893	Aluminum	25mm	75.00	—	150.	—

Mormon Temple. Rv: JOHNSON's / V.T.R. / DEDICATION / -.- / SOUVENIR / -.- / APRIL 6TH 1893. Plain edge. Rarity 9. (Spangenberger Oct. 1984 sale)

GEO. W. JONES

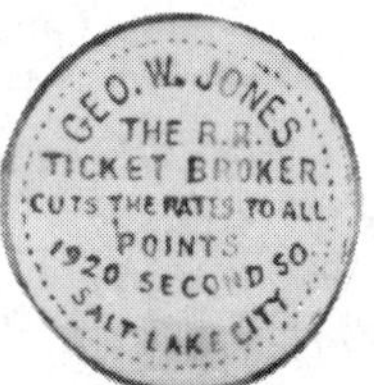

Rulau	Date	Metal	Size	VG	F	VF	Unc
SLC 8	(1900)	Aluminum	26mm	—	135.	200.	—

Temple, MORMON TEMPLE below. Rv: GEO. W. JONES/ THE R.R. / TICKET BROKER / CUTS THE RATES TO ALL / POINTS / 1920 SECOND SO. / SALT LAKE CITY. Plain edge. Rarity 7. (Wright 1476)

The temple is the famed Mormon Tabernacle.

In 1894 the address of Jones was 230 So. Main. In 1900 it became 1920 2nd South.

JAMES JOHNSTON

Rulau	Date	Metal	Size	VG	F	VF	Unc
SLC 7	(1890-93)	CN	25mm	—	—	100.	—

JAMES JOHNSTON / -.- / WHITE HOUSE / -.- / SALT LAKE CITY. Rv: GOOD FOR / * 12 1/2 * / CENTS / IN TRADE. Plain edge. Rarity 9.

This saloon was at 208 So. Main in 1890-93.

J. C. MURPHY & CO.

Rulau	Date	Metal	Size	VG	F	VF	Unc
SLC 14	(1890)	Aluminum	25mm	—	85.00	125.	—

Building. In exergue: SALT LAKE CITY / & / COUNTY BUILDING. Rv: J. C. MURPHY & CO. / MFR'S OF / STAMPS SEALS / & / ALUMINUM / CHECKS / SALT LAKE CITY UTAH. Plain edge. Rarity 10. (Wright 1533)

SALT LAKE STAMP CO.

Rulau	Date	Metal	Size	VG	F	VF	Unc
SLC 16	(1900)	Aluminum	Scal 25mm	40.00	—	—	100.

Mormon Temple. Rv: SALT LAKE STAMP CO. / RUBBER STAMPS, ETC. / SALT LAKE CITY, UTAH. Plain edge. (Koppenhaver Nov. 1983 sale, lot 780). Rarity 4.

This is part of a larger set.

Rulau	Date	Metal	Size	VG	F	VF	Unc
SLC 17	(?)	Brass	--mm	—	—	—	100.

Mormon Temple. Rv: SALT LAKE STAMP CO. Plain edge. (Kirtley Aug. 1987 sale, lot 284)

F. SCHAEFER

Rulau	Date	Metal	Size	VG	F	VF	Unc
SLC 18	(1890's)	Brass	22mm	—	—	7.50	—

F. SCHAEFER / -+- / MT. A. / -+- / BILLIARD ROOMS. Rv: Large 5 in circle of 16 stars. Plain edge.

The die work is similar to that of J. Stevensen, SLC 20. Tentative attribution.

J. STEVENSEN

Rulau	Date	Metal	Size	VG	F	VF	Unc
SLC 20	(1890's)	Brass	22mm	—	—	25.00	—

J. STEVENSEN / -.- / M & M / -.- / 217 SO. W. TEMPLE. Rv: GOOD FOR 5 M ¢ / IN TRADE. (Thoele coll.)

5 M ¢ = Five Mormon cents?

(THE) TEMPLE

Rulau	Date	Metal	Size	VG	F	VF	Unc
SLC 22	(?)	WM	25mm	—	65.00	125.	—

Mormon Temple, TEMPLE SALT LAKE CITY. Rv: GOOD FOR / 12 1/2 ¢ / IN TRADE / AT THE BAR. Plain edge. Rarity 10. (Wright 1655)

Rulau	Date	Metal	Size	VG	F	VF	Unc
SLC 24	(?)	Lead	24mm	—	45.00	—	Rare

Mormon Temple, TEMPLE above, SALT LAKE CITY below. Rv: Moroni perched on a ball. Around: DEDICATED APRIL 6, 18.. COMMENCED APRIL 6, 1853 COST 3,500,000. Plain edge. (Kurt Krueger Sept. 1983 Sale, lot 1065)

UTAH PIONEER JUBILEE

Salt Lake City, Utah

Rulau	Date	Metal	Size	F	VF	EF	Unc
SLC 26	1897	Brass	19mm	—	75.00	100.	—

Eagle perched on a beehive, INDUSTRY above, 1847 below. Rv: UTAH PIONEER JUBILEE / AND / SEMI-CENTNNIAL (sic) / SALT LAKE CITY / JULY 20-24 / 1897 amid flourishes. Plain edge. Rarity 8.

E. R. MILES JR.

Smithfield, Utah

Rulau	Date	Metal	Size	VG	F	VF	Unc
Smi 1	(1890's)	Aluminum	29mm	30.00	—	50.00	—

E. R. MILES JR. / SMITHFIELD / UTAH. Rv: GOOD FOR / 50 ¢ / IN / MERCHANDISE / AT RETAIL. Plain edge. Rarity 9. (Wright 1523)

By World War I, E. R. Miles Inc. operated a large general store and also The Toggery, a men's furnishing outlet. He is listed through 1922.

H. J. HOBEIN

Utah ?

Rulau	Date	Metal	Size	VG	F	VF	Unc
Unk 1	(1890 ?)	Brass	21mm	3.50	—	—	—

(All incused): H. J. HOBEIN. Rv: 104. (Thoele coll., ex-Jerry Hummel)

VERMONT

U. S. CREAM SEPARATOR

Bellows Falls, Vt.

Rulau	Date	Metal	Size	F	VF	EF	Unc
Blf 2	1901	Gilt/Brz	32mm	—	20.00	25.00	30.00

Male with torch riding winged female Fame, building and tablet below. On tablet: V. F. M. CO. Around: GOLD MEDAL U. S. SEPARATOR / EXPOSITION UNIVERSELLE / INTERNATIONALE / 1900 / VT FARM MCH CO BELLOWS FALLS VT / (tiny) WHITEHEAD HOAG NEWARK NJ. Rv: Striding nude female and buffalo right, banner aloft. Tablet under ground reads: V. F. M. Co. Around: GOLD MEDAL HIGHEST AWARD / PAN-AMERICAN EXPOSITION / 1901. / U.S. CREAM SEPARATOR. Plain edge. (Zaffern coll.)

The Vermont Farm Machinery Co. of Bellows Falls, Vermont, makers of the famed U.S. Cream Separator, won back-to-back gold medals at the 1900 Paris and 1901 Buffalo world's fairs, and commissioned the Whitehead-Hoag medallic firm to strike this commemorative medalet to salute the dual victory.

E. A. PRESTON

Ferrisburg, Vt.

Rulau	Date	Metal	Size	VG	F	VF	Unc
Fer 4	(ca 1900)	Aluminum	19mm	—	30.00	—	—

E. A. PRESTON / (ornament) / GENERAL / * MDSE. * Rv: GOOD FOR / 5 ¢ / * IN TRADE *. Plain edge. (Fuld Ve(---)SC-20-A1-12-p-R6)

Collector R. B. Preston of Puerto Rico donated a specimen of this token to the ANA collection about 50 years after its use by his father Elmer A. Preston in a country general store.

VIRGINIA

L. BRILL

Alexandria, Va.

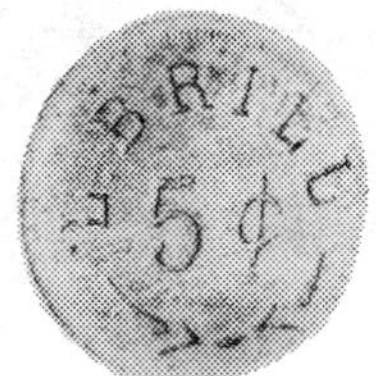

Rulau	Date	Metal	Size	VG	F	VF	Unc
Alx 3	(1880-1900)	Brass	24mm	5.00	8.00	—	—

(All incused): L. BRILL / 5¢ / (ornament). Rv: Blank. Plain edge. (Schenkman 1040-Q5)

Louis Brill operated a billiard hall and saloon at 7 So. Pitt St. in Alexandria the 1880's, and at the same time ran a restaurant at 9 So. Pitt St. About 1900 Brill owned the Opera House Restaurant at 107 So. Pitt St.

CALMES & KRAFFT

Alexandria, Va.

Rulau	Date	Metal	Size	VG	F	VF	Unc
Alx 8	(1880-1900)	Brass	23mm	8.00	14.00	20.00	—

(All incused): CALMES & KRAFFT / 5 / ALEXA VA. Rv: Blank. Dentilated rim on both sides. Plain edge. (Schenkman 1040-R5)

Calmes and Krafft operated a restaurant and saloon from about 1880 to 1900. In 1900 the directory listed it as a saloon only. The firm was out of business before 1905.

ATKINS BROTHERS

Attoway, Va.

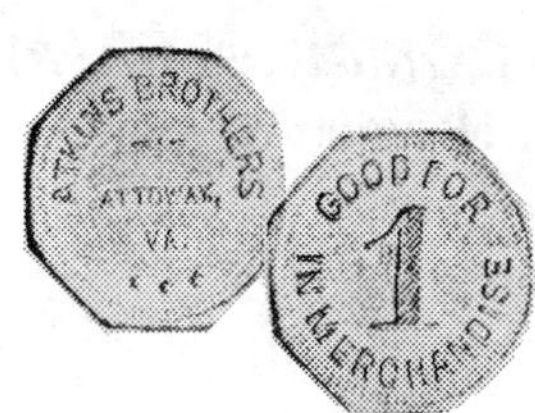

Rulau	Date	Metal	Size	VG	F	VF	Unc
Att 1	(1890's)	Brass	Oct 18mm	4.00	9.00	20.00	—
Att 2	(1890's)	Brass	19mm	4.00	7.00	10.00	—

Att 1: ATKINS BROTHERS / -.- / ATTOWAY, / VA. / ***. Rv: GOOD FOR / 1 (large) / IN MERCHANDISE. Plain edge. (Schenkman 1140-A1)

Att 2: Similar to last, but 5. Plain edge. (Schenkman 1140-A5)

In 1890 Atkins Brothers was listed as a sawmill and general store. Later, in addition to the general store, they manufactured handles, spokes, etc.

MITCHELL & STEELE

Branchville, Va.

Rulau	Date	Metal	Size	F	VF	EF	
Brn 3	(1890's)	Brass	21mm	—	6.50	—	—
Brn 5	(1890's)	Brass	29mm	—	6.50	—	—

Brn 3: MITCHELL & STEELE / BRANCHVILLE / VA. Rv: GOOD FOR / * 5 ¢ * / -IN- / MERCHANDISE. Plain edge. (Schenkman 1490-CS)

Brn 5: Similar, but * 25 * on reverse. Plain edge. (Schenkman 1490-C25)

Mitchell and Steele operated a general store and sawmill during the 1890's.

C.W. BUMPASS & CO.

Bumpass, Va.

Rulau	Date	Metal	Size	VG	F	VF	Unc
Bum 2	(1890-1905)	Brass	19mm	12.50	16.00	22.50	—

C.W. BUMPASS & CO. / 5 / BUMPASS, VA. Rv: GOOD FOR / 5 (ornate) / IN MERCHANDISE. Plain edge. (Schenkman 1590-A5)

This general store operated during the 1890's and early 1900's.

H.M. TURNER & CO.

Callaway, Va.

Rulau	Date	Metal	Size	VG	F	VF	Unc
Cal 11	(1889-1904)	Brass	30mm	—	8.00	15.00	—
Cal 13	(1905)	Brass	30mm	—	8.00	15.00	—

Cal 11: H.M. TURNER & CO. / 25 ¢ / IN MDSE / CALLAWAY, VA. Rv: GOOD FOR / 25 ¢ / IN MDSE / AT OUR STORE. Plain edge.

Cal 13: C.E. TURNER & CO. ctsp over the name on last token. Plain edge. (Schenkman 1620-B25)

COSTON & BLADES
Hampton, Va.

Rulau	Date	Metal	Size	VG	F	VF	Unc
Hmp 1	(?)	Brass	24mm	—	—	10.00	—

(All incused): COSTON & BLADES / 1 / GALL. Rv: Blank. Plain edge. (Thoele coll.)

Probably a worker's chit for seafood.

CHARLES E. FRIEND
Manchester, Va.

Rulau	Date	Metal	Size	VG	F	VF	Unc
Man 3	(1890's)	Brass	25mm	—	—	15.00	—

CHARLES E. FRIEND / (star) / DRUGGIST / -*- / 20TH & HULL STS. / MANCHESTER, VA. Rv: 20 (large, radiant). Plain edge. (Schenkman 3210-A20)

OLD DOMINION CRAB CO.
Newport News, Va.

Rulau	Date	Metal	Size	VG	F	VF	Unc
Npn 6	(?)	Brass	Scal 25mm	—	—	6.00	—

. OLD DOMINION CRAB CO. / N. N. / VA. Rv: ONE / POUND. (Thoele coll.)

Crab picker's chit.

HECHT'S DANCING ACADEMY
Norfolk, Va.

Rulau	Date	Metal	Size	VG	F	VF	Unc
Nfk 3	1899	Brass	21mm	—	—	7.50	—

HECHT'S DANCING ACADEMY / NORFOLK, / VA. Rv: ESTABLISHED / 1899. (Schenkman 3680-AP)

W. A. HERZOG
Petersburg, Va.

Rulau	Date	Metal	Size	VG	F	VF	Unc
Pbg 2	(1900)	GS	25mm	—	—	10.00	—

W. A. / HERZOG (on panel). Stars and rays from behind. Rv: Large 5 in circle of 16 rosettes. Plain edge. 5 to 10 pieces known. (Schenkman 3960-N5)

THE PALACE
Richmond, Va.

Rulau	Date	Metal	Size	VG	F	VF	Unc
Ric 7	(1890's)	GS	24mm	—	—	11.00	—

THE PALACE / 807 / BROAD ST. / RICH'D, VA. Rv: 2 1/2 (large sunburst from behind). Plain edge. (Schenkman 4180-AU 2 1/2)

Probably used in a billiard hall.

S.S. JAMES
Roanoke, Va.

Rulau	Date	Metal	Size	VG	F	VF	EF
Roa 7	(1890's)	Silver	31mm	—	—	100.	—

S S JAMES / ROANOKE VA ctsp on U.S. 1893 Columbian commemorative half dollar. (Kurt Krueger coll.)

WASHINGTON

ARCHIE WHITE
Pullman, Wash.

Rulau	Date	Metal	Size	VG	F	VF	Unc
Pul 20	(1890's)	Aluminum	22mm	—	—	15.00	—

ARCHIE WHITE / ** / DRUGGIST / ** PULLMAN, WASH. Rv: GOOD FOR / 10 / IN TRADE. Plain edge. (Wright 1724)

JOHN W. ORTH
Seattle, Wash.

Rulau	Date	Metal	Size	VG	F	VF	Unc
Sea 7	(1890's)	CN	--mm	—	—	25.00	—

Horse's bit, GOOD FOR around. Rv: JOHN W. ORTH, SEATTLE WASH.

ORTH & ZAHNEN

Rulau	Date	Metal	Size	VG	F	VF	Unc
Sea 9	(1890's)	CN	--mm	—	—	25.00	—

Obverse as the John W. Orth token above. Rv: ORTH & ZAHNEN. SEATTLE WASH. (Kirtley Feb. 1991 sale, lot A4932)

Bit = 12 1/2 cents.

QUICK DRUG CO.
Seattle, Wash.

Rulau	Date	Metal	Size	VG	F	VF	Unc
Sea 10	(1890's)	Aluminum	25mm	—	—	15.00	—

QUICK DRUG CO. / SEATTLE / WASH. Rv: GOOD FOR / 5 ¢ / CIGAR / OR SODA. Plain edge. (Wright 1589)

WEST VIRGINIA

C. L. KIMMEL
Grafton, W. Va.

Rulau	Date	Metal	Size	VG	F	VF	Unc
Grf 3	(1895-96)	Brass	--mm	—	—	100.	—

Brunswick die BBC-14. Rv: C. L. KIMMEL. No further description available.

Kimmel appears in the 1895-1902 *West Virginia Gazetteer* as a Grafton saloonkeeper. Specialist Donald K. Clifford of St. Albans, W. Va. determined that Kimmel had issued Brunswick-Balke-Collender checks. About 3 pieces known.

S. P. KIMMEL
Grafton, W. Va.

Rulau	Date	Metal	Size	VG	F	VF	Unc
Grf 5	(1885-90)	Brass	--mm	—	—	65.00	—
	Brunswick die BBC-2. Rv: S. P. KIMMEL / GOOD FOR / 5 cts / AT THE BAR. Plain edge.						
Grf 6	(1885-90)	Brass	--mm	—	—	65.00	—
	Brunswick die BBC-3b. Rv: S. P. KIMMEL / GOOD FOR / 5 cts / IN TRADE. Plain edge.						

In 1882 S. P. Kimmel was listed in the *West Virginia State Gazetteer* as the operator of a shoe store. But in 1890 an R. G. Dun directory lists C. L. Kimmel as a saloon operator.

West Virginia specialist Donald K. Clifford believes S. P. Kimmel started the saloon business in Grafton about 1885, turning it over to a relative (C. L. Kimmel). About 1902 another relative, H. C. Kimmel, took over the business.

TOM McAVAY
Grafton, W. Va.

Rulau	Date	Metal	Size	VG	F	VF	Unc
Grf 8	(1895-1908)	Brass	24mm	—	35.00	50.00	—
	Brunswick die BBC-3. Rv: GOOD FOR / * 2 1/2 ¢ * / TOM McAVAY / IN / * TRADE *. Plain edge. (Donald Clifford coll.)						
Grf 9	(1890)	Brass	--mm	—	—	100.	—
	R. Rothschild die. Rv: TOM McAVAY.						
Grf 10	(?)	Brass	18mm	—	—	25.00	—
	-AT- / TOM McAVAY'S / 10 ¢ / GRAFTON, W. VA. Rv: No description available. (Clifford coll.)						

Polk's West Virginia Gazetteer listed this saloon and billiard parlor owned by Thomas J. McAvay 1895 thru 1908.

WISCONSIN

F. G. MORRISON
Abrams, Wis.

Rulau	Date	Metal	Size	VG	F	VF	Unc
Abr 1	(1899-1902)	Brass	Oct 27mm	—	—	25.00	—

GOOD FOR / 5 ¢ / F. G. / MORRISON / IN / TRADE. Rv: 5 (large) within circle of alternating stars and cogwheels. (Thoele coll.)

V. D. YONEK
Allouez, Wis.

Rulau	Date	Metal	Size	VG	F	VF	Unc
Alz 1	(1900-04)	Brass	25mm	—	—	6.50	—

V. D. YONEK / ALLOUEZ / WIS. Rv: GOOD FOR / 5 ¢ / IN TRADE. About 6 pieces known.

Victor D. Yonek (or Yonik; the spelling varies) had a saloon in Allouez 1900-1904. This place became part of the city of Superior in the decade after the tokens.

JOHN CEDARBURG
Amberg, Wis.

Rulau	Date	Metal	Size	VG	F	VF	Unc
Amb 1	(1895-99)	Brass	25mm	—	—	35.00	—

Chas. Pick & Co. die. Rv: GOOD FOR / 5 ¢ / JOHN / CEDARBURG / IN / TRADE. Plain edge.

Saloon, listed 1895-1900. In the Oct. 1984 Stephen Alpert auction (lot 102), this token fetched $14 as a maverick. It has since been sited.

BACHMANN & MORIARTY
Appleton, Wis.

Rulau	Date	Metal	Size	VG	F	VF	Unc
App 1	(1900)	Brass	25mm	—	—	35.00	50.00

Brunswick die BBC. Rv: GOOD FOR / 5 ¢ / BACHMANN & / MORIARTY / IN TRADE. 5 pieces known. (Thoele coll.)

This firm is listed 1900-1918.

HAENTLE'S PHARMACY
Appleton, Wis. (?)

Rulau	Date	Metal	Size	F	VF	EF	Unc
App 3	(1893-99)	Aluminum	**	—	—	13.00	—

** Scalloped, 29mm.

HAENTLE'S / APPLETON / PHARMACY. Rv: GOOD FOR / 5 ¢ / AT / SODA / COUNTER. Plain edge. (Wright 1446)

Haentle does not appear in any Appleton directory. There were nine Appletons in the U.S. in the Gay Nineties, but none yield a Haentle. It is possible this is a Wisconsin token from an Appleton avenue or street.

W. D. KUHN
Ashland, Wis.

Rulau	Date	Metal	Size	VG	F	VF	Unc
Ash 3	(1891-98)	Brass	20mm	—	6.00	10.00	—

GOOD FOR / 5 ¢ / IN TRADE / -AT- / W. D. KUHN'S. Rv: "Q. P." Plain edge. (Thoele coll.)

Willis D. Kuhn operated a saloon and restaurant at 210 3rd Avenue West 1891-1916.

This token is a throwback to the "Value me as you please" Granby coppers of 18th century Connecticut! Q. P. = Quantum Placet in Latin, or "As much as you please."

L. KOLLER
Auburndale, Wis.

Rulau	Date	Metal	Size	VG	F	VF	Unc
Aub 3	(1895-1907)	Brass	25mm	—	—	20.00	—

L. KOLLER / GOOD FOR / 5 ¢ / AT THE BAR. Rv: Blank. Plain edge. (Thoele coll., ex-Bill Rouleau)

Louis Koller's saloon appears in the gazetteers for 1895-1907.

JOHN J. BUHMEYER
Baraboo, Wis.

Rulau	Date	Metal	Size	VG	F	VF	Unc
Brb 2	(1891-92)	Brass	25mm	—	—	7.50	—

GOOD FOR / 5 ¢ / JOHN J. BUHMEYER / IN / TRADE. Rv: Large 5 in circle of 17 rosettes. (Thoele coll., ex-G. Johnson)

Saloon, in the 1891-92 gazetteer. Earlier he had been a cigar dealer in Baraboo.

FRED. TOBLER
Baraboo, Wis.

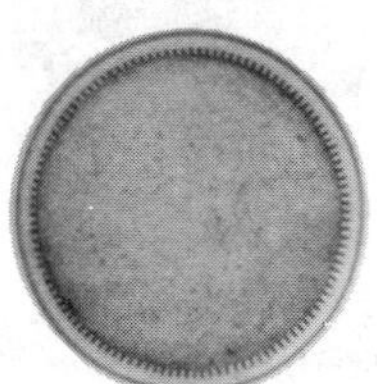

Rulau	Date	Metal	Size	VG	F	VF	Unc
Brb 4	(1891-1908)	GS	24mm	—	—	12.00	—

(All incused): FRED. TOBLER / GOOD FOR / 5 ¢ / AT BAR / BARABOO. Rv: Blank.

Saloon, listed 1891 to 1908.

H. SAUERESSIG
Barton, Wis.

Rulau	Date	Metal	Size	VG	F	VF	Unc
Brt 3	(1886-1900)	Brass	19.5mm	—	9.00	—	—

H. SAUERESSIG / (ornament) / (star). Rv: GOOD FOR / 5 / CENTS / AT THE / BAR.

Born 1841 in Germany, Saueressig emigrated to America in 1858. He operated a combination hotel and saloon in Barton 1886-1900. Barton, in Washington County, had 300 people in 1910.

JOHN JARKA
Beaver Dam, Wis.

Rulau	Date	Metal	Size	VG	F	VF	Unc
Bdm 5	(1895-1904)	Brass	25mm	—	—	35.00	—

Brunswick die BBC-11. Rv: * GOOD FOR * / 5 ¢ / JOHN / JARKA / AT THE BAR. Plain edge. (Thoele coll.)

Saloon, listed 1895-1904 in Beaver Dam.

HATHAWAY & BELLIS
Berlin, Wis.

Rulau	Date	Metal	Size	VG	F	VF	Unc
Ber 3	(1893-99)	Aluminum	29mm	—	7.00	—	—

GOOD FOR / 5 ¢ / HATHAWAY / & BELLIS / AT THE BAR. Rv: Large 5. 3 pieces known.

Edward Hathaway and Clyde E. Bellis were proprietors of the Bellis House, which had a saloon in connection. They were listed in directories 1879 through 1900.

KELLS & CULVER

Rulau	Date	Metal	Size	VG	F	VF	Unc
Ber 5	(1890-96)	WM	24mm	—	—	11.00	—

KELLS / & / CULVER / BERLIN, WIS. Rv: GOOD FOR / 5 CENTS / IN TRADE. Possibly unique.

Robert T. Kells and William Culver were listed under saloons 1890-1896.

A. H. QUANTIUS
Berlin, Wis.

Rulau	Date	Metal	Size	VG	F	VF	Unc
Ber 14	(1897-)	Brass	21mm	—	—	2.00	—

A. H. QUANTIUS. Rv: GOOD FOR / 5 ¢ / IN TRADE. A hoard of this piece exists.

Anthony H. Quantius is found listed under saloons 1897-1919. When Prohibition arrived Jan. 1, 1920, her converted to a soft drink parlor. The token may well be 20th century.

H. LUEBSTORF
Boyd, Wis.

Rulau	Date	Metal	Size	VG	F	VF	EF
Boy 1	(1888-94)	Brass	Oct 25mm	20.00	—	—	—

H. / LUEBSTORF. Rv: GOOD FOR / 5 ¢ / H. L. (on panel) / IN / TRADE. Only 1 known; excavated.(Thoele coll.)

This saloon appears in directories 1888-1894. Boyd is in Chippewa County.

JOS. KRIZENESKY
Brillion, Wis.

Rulau	Date	Metal	Size	VG	F	VF	Unc
Bri 3	(?)	Brass	21mm	—	—	5.00	—

JOS. KRIZENESKY. Rv: GOOD FOR / 5 ¢ / IN TRADE. 4 or 5 pieces known.

Hotelkeeper, listed 1894 through 1923.

E. J. HURD
Brodhead, Wis.

Rulau	Date	Metal	Size	VG	F	VF	Unc
Bro 3	(1900-01)	Brass	25mm	—	—	10.00	—

GOOD FOR / 5 ¢ / E. J. HURD / IN TRADE. Rv: Blank. (Thoele coll.)

Billiards listed 1900-1901. Brodhead is in Green County.

FRYSLIE BROS.
Browntown, Wis.

Rulau	Date	Metal	Size	VG	F	VF	Unc
Brn 2	(1890-94)	GS	22mm	—	—	22.50	—

(All incuse): FRYSLIE BROS / 5 ¢ / IN MERCHANDISE / BROWNTOWN, WIS. Rv: S. D. CHILDS & CO. / 152 / DEARBORN ST. / CHICAGO.

This general store was listed 1890-1894. Green County; 1910 population 222.

GEO. SCHUMAN
Burlington, Wis.

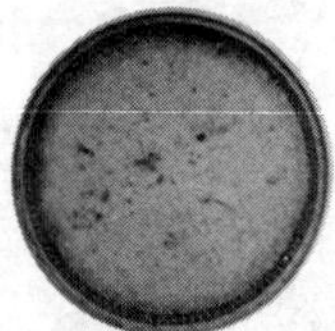

Rulau	Date	Metal	Size	VG	F	VF	Unc
Bur 1	(1890-93)	Brass	21mm	—	—	5.00	—

GEO / (ornament) / SCHUMAN / (ornament). Rv: Blank.

Saloon and grocery, listed 1890-1893.

J. H. DAHL
Burr Oak, Wis.

Rulau	Date	Metal	Size	VG	F	VF	Unc
Brk 1	(?)	Brass	21mm	—	—	5.00	—

J. H. DAHL. Rv: GOOD FOR / 5 ¢ / DRINK. Two or more specimens known.

General store-saloon combination, listed 1901-1918. It may have opened in 1900. This tiny place (pop 56 in 1900) in La Crosse County was also known as Burroak (one word); it didn't have a post office but received rural delivery from Mindoro.

John H. Dahl.

L. E. JACKSON
Cadott, Wis.

Rulau	Date	Metal	Size	VG	F	VF	Unc
Cad 1	(1893-1901)	Brass	Scal 30mm	—	—	15.00	—

GOOD FOR / 5 ¢ L. E. JACKSON / IN / TRADE. Rv: 5 within circle of 13 rosettes. (Thoele coll., ex-Weinberg)

Saloon, listed 1893 through 1901 only. Cadott, in Chippewa County, had 765 souls in 1910.

W. T. THUERWACHTER
Calumetville, Wis.

Rulau	Date	Metal	Size	VG	F	VF	Unc
Cal 3	(?)	Aluminum	Sc --mm	—	—	15.00	—

W. T. / THUERWACHTER / CALUMET-VILLE / WIS. Rv: GOOD FOR / 5 ¢ / IN TRADE.

Saloon, listed 1899-1914. The issuer was succeeded by Fred M. Thuerwachter by 1918 in the saloon, and a general store under that name. Fond du Lac County; population in 1910 was only 130.

PH. GUENTHER
Campbellsport, Wis.

Rulau	Date	Metal	Size	VG	F	VF	Unc
Cmp 2	(1893- ?)	Brass	Sc 29mm	—	—	6.50	—

-*- / PH. GUENTHER / -*-. Rv: GOOD FOR / 5 ¢ / IN TRADE. Beaded circle on each side. (L. Stubler coll.)

This saloon was listed 1893 through 1910. Fond du Lac County.

J. H. McVEY
Camp Lake, Wis.

Rulau	Date	Metal	Size	VG	F	VF	Unc
Cpl 1	(1895-99)	Brass	25mm	—	—	40.00	—

GOOD FOR / 5 ¢ J. H. McVEY / IN / TRADE. Rv: THE MERLE & HEANEY / BILLIARD / SUPPLIES / CHICAGO. Only 2 known. (Johnson J-1)

McVey is listed 1895-1900.

W. C. ZACHOW CO.
Cecil, Wis.

Rulau	Date	Metal	Size	VG	F	VF	Unc
Cec 7	(1893)	Brass	36mm	—	—	6.00	—
	W. C. ZACHOW CO. / CECIL, WIS. Rv: GOOD FOR / 200 / IN / MERCHANDISE. Plain edge.						
Cec 8	(1893)	Brass	33mm	—	—	5.00	—
	As 7, but 100.						
Cec 9	(1893)	Brass	31mm	—	—	5.00	—
	As 7, but 50.						
Cec 12	(1893)	Brass	21mm	—	—	4.00	—
	As 7, but 5.						
Cec 13	(1893)	Brass	17mm	—	—	4.00	—
	As 7, but 1.						

Other denominations may have been struck.

William C. Zachow was born in Outagamie County, Wis. on April 2, 1857. In the spring of 1884 he purchased a site in Cecil in Shawano County for a general store, but this seems not to have opened until 1893. In the 1921 depression he went out of business.

JOHNSON HILL & CO.
Centralia, Wis.

Rulau	Date	Metal	Size	VG	F	VF	Unc
Cen 1	1899	Brass	30.5mm	—	—	12.50	25.00
	JOHNSON HILL & CO. / -.- / 1899 / -.- CENTRALIA, WIS. Rv: GOOD FOR / 50 / IN / MERCHANDISE. Plain edge.						

Centralia is now part of Grand Rapids, in Wood County. Johnson Hill & Co. was a department store active 1893-1990.

Nils Johnson and George Hill were the founders. Other denominations: 5, 10, 25 cents and $1. Originally this was a general store.

L. D. FESSENDEN
Clinton, Wis.

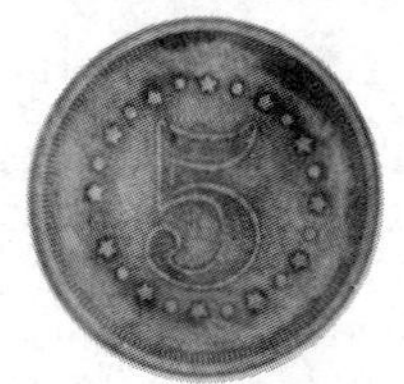

Rulau	Date	Metal	Size	VG	F	VF	Unc
Cli 1	(1893-94)	Brass	24mm	—	—	10.00	—
	GOOD FOR / 5 C / L. D. / FESSENDEN / IN / TRADE. Rv: Large numeral 5 in circle of alternating stars and dots. Plain edge.						

Billiard hall.

CARL KIESEL
Dartford, Wis.

Rulau	Date	Metal	Size	VG	F	VF	Unc
Dtf 1	(1888-95)	Brass	24mm	—	—	25.00	Scarce
	GOOD FOR / 5 C / CARL KIESEL (in panel) / -AT- / BAR. Rv: Large 5 in circle of alternating stars and dots. Plain edge.						

Saloon, listed 1888 to 1895.

H. V. T.
(Herman Van Treek)
De Pere, Wis.

Rulau	Date	Metal	Size	VG	F	VF	Unc
Dep 6	(1895-1902)	Copper	Oct 27mm	—	—	10.00	—
	(Incused) H. V. T. Rv: GOOD FOR / 5 ¢ / DRINK. Beaded rim on each side. Plain edge.						

Saloon.

JOHN ELVOD
Dodgeville, Wis.

Rulau	Date	Metal	Size	VG	F	VF	Unc
Dod 3	(1882-95)	Brass	24mm	—	—	32.00	—
	Brunswick die BB-6A. Rv: GOOD FOR / 5 ¢ / JOHN / ELVOD / IN / TRADE / *. Plain edge. Only 2 known. (Thoele coll.)						

This business is listed 1882-1895. The token may predate the Gay Nineties.

Rulau	Date	Metal	Size	VG	F	VF	Unc
Dod 4	(1882-95)	Brass	24mm	—	—	35.00	—
	Brunswick die BB-4. Rv: GOOD FOR / 5 ¢ / JOHN ELVOD. (in panel) / IN / TRADE / (ornament). (Stuber coll.)						

JOS. DEROUIN
Eau Claire, Wis.

Rulau	Date	Metal	Size	VG	F	VF	Unc
Eau 1	(1888-1903)	Brass	24mm	—	—	5.00	—
	(All incused): JOS. DEROUIN / GOOD FOR / 5 C / IN TRADE EAU CLAIRE, WIS. Rv: Blank. Plain edge.						

Saloon, listed in the 1888, 1893, 1896 and 1903 directories.

PETER JAEGER
Edson, Wis.

Rulau	Date	Metal	Size	VG	F	VF	Unc
Eds 5	(1886-97)	Brass	24mm	—	—	40.00	—
	GOOD FOR / 5 C / PETER / JAEGER / IN / TRADE. Rv: CHAS. PASSOW'S BILLIARD TABLES / 5 / CHICAGO. Plain edge.						

Peter Jaeger's saloon at Edson is listed 1886-1897. Later, in 1899-1900, the saloon is listed in Boyd, Wis. The name is spelled in directories in several variants, Jaeger, Jager and Yaeger.

The Passow firm was in business 1876-1905 with this title.

THE RUSTIC
Elkhart, Wis.

Rulau	Date	Metal	Size	VG	F	VF	Unc
Ekt 3	(1897-1908)	Alum	Oct 28mm	—	—	10.00	—

GOOD FOR / 5 ¢ / THE RUSTIC / AT / THE BAR. Rv: Large 5. Plain edge.

The Rustic House was open 1897-1908. In 1910 Elkhart in Sheboygan County changed its name to Elkhart Lake; its population then was 499. (Thoele research)

WM. MANNING
Fennimore, Wis.

Rulau	Date	Metal	Size	VG	F	VF	Unc
Fen 3	(1895-1914)	Brass	Scal 26mm	—	—	10.00	—

Wm. MANNING / -.- / FENNIMORE, / -.- / WIS. Rv: GOOD FOR / 5 ¢ / WM MANNING / + / IN TRADE.

Saloon, listed 1895-1914.

T. M. PIGG
Fennimore, Wis.

Rulau	Date	Metal	Size	VG	F	VF	Unc
Fen 5	(1897)	Brass	23mm	—	—	6.50	—

GOOD FOR / 5 ¢ / T. M. PIGG / FENNIMORE, WIS / IN TRADE. Rv: 5 in circle of stars.

The *Fennimore Times Review* for Jan. 6, 1897 mentioned that Thadd Pigg purchased the saloon business of John Brechler. The business was short-lived.

V. L.
(Victor Lomblot)
Fond du Lac, Wis.

Rulau	Date	Metal	Size	VG	F	VF	Unc
FDL 8	(1893-98)	Brass	24mm	—	.75	1.00	—

(Ornament) / V. L. / (Ornament). Rv: Blank. Plain edge.

Specialist Wade Renstrom purchased a hoard of this maverick token in 1994 as part of a 60-pounds-plus lot in Oshkosh which had been put away for many years.

Victor Lomblot's saloon was at 236 Main 1893-94 and 216 Main 1897-98. Some directories spell his surname Lumblo.

C. LITSCHER
Fox Lake, Wis.

Rulau	Date	Metal	Size	VG	F	VF	Unc
Fox 1	(?)	GS	Oct 25mm	—	—	9.00	—

GOOD FOR / 5 ¢ / C. LITSCHER / IN TRADE. Rv: Large, ornate 5. Only 3 pieces known.

Christian Litscher ran a saloon 1899-1917.

HENRY MOK
Glen Haven, Wis.

Rulau	Date	Metal	Size	G	VG	VF	Unc
Ghv 1	(1888-93)	Brass	25mm	35.00	—	—	—

Brunswick die BBC-9b. Rv: GOOD FOR / 5 ¢ / HENRY / MOK / IN TRADE. Plain edge. (Thoele coll., ex-Lipscomb)

Saloon, listed 1888-1893. The only known specimen is About Good, holed at rim at 2 o'clock.

A successor, E. Mok, ran a restaurant and confectionery in this tiny (1910 pop. 185) Grant County village in 1918.

C. C. DOCTER
Grafton, Wis.

Rulau	Date	Metal	Size	VG	F	VF	Unc
Grf 2	(1895-99)	Brass	19mm	—	—	20.00	—

C. C. DOCTER. Rv: 2 1/2. Plain edge. Only 1 piece known; present whereabouts unknown. (Ex-Koponen, Edler colls.)

Christian C. Docter was a saloonkeeper and justice of the peace 1895-1900.

D. P. BRADLEY
Green Bay, Wis.

Rulau	Date	Metal	Size	VG	F	VF	Unc
Grb 4	(1890's)	Brass	26mm	—	—	12.50	—

GOOD FOR / 5 ¢ / D. P. / BRADLEY / IN / TRADE. Rv: Large 5 in circle of 17 six-pointed rosettes. Plain edge. (Thoele coll.)

Hotel and saloon, listed 1883 to 1900.

Bradley was born Dec. 18, 1846 in Brooklyn, N.Y. He came to Green Bay in 1871, and opened his hotel and saloon in 1883. This token could predate the Gay Nineties.

DEUTSCHEN KATHOLISCHEN U. VEREINE

Rulau	Date	Metal	Size	F	VF	EF	Unc
Grb 9	1892	Aluminum	38mm	—	—	12.50	—

Crossed goblet, sword and anchor in circle, around which is a radiant band labeled: D. R. K. C. V. / ooo 1855 ooo. Rv: ERINNERUNG / A. D. / DRITTE VERSAMMLUNG / DER / DEUTSCHEN / KATHOLISCHEN / UNTERSTUTZUNGS / VEREINE / VON / WISCONSIN / GREEN BAY, JUNI 5-8, 1892 ? (tiny) SCHWAAB MIL. Plain edge. Issued holed for suspension from rectangular brass hanger. (Jack Glass coll.)

Commemorates the 3rd assembly of the German Catholic Aid Associations of Wisconsin. Struck by Schwaab Stamp & Seal, Milwaukee.

E. W. RUEL
Green Bay, Wis.

Rulau	Date	Metal	Size	VG	F	VF	Unc
Grb 25	(1890)	Brass	26mm	—	—	15.00	—

E. W. RUEL / (ornament) / GREEN BAY, / WIS. Rv: GOOD FOR / 10 / CENTS / * IN TRADE *. Plain edge. (Thoele coll.)

Hank Thoele, Green Bay, Wis. researcher, reports that this token was struck by Heidemann Mfg. Co. in San Antonio, Texas.

HENRY HOFFMAN
Hebron, Wis.

Rulau	Date	Metal	Size	VG	F	VF	Unc
Heb 2	(1899-1904)	Brass	25mm	—	—	35.00	—

BBC 7 die. Rv: GOOD FOR / 5 ¢ / HENRY - / HOFFMAN / IN / TRADE. Plain edge. (Thoele coll.)

Pool hall and saloon, listed 1899 through 1904.

A. W. JONES
Hebron, Wis.

Rulau	Date	Metal	Size	VG	F	VF	Unc
Heb 5	(1888-97)	Brass	25mm	—	—	35.00	—

Brunswick die B-2e. Rv: GOOD FOR / 5 ¢ / A. W. JONES / IN / TRADE. Only 1 known. (Johnson Hebron-1)

Billiard hall and saloon, in gazetteers for 1888 thru 1897.

C. KLINGELE & SON
Highland, Wis.

Rulau	Date	Metal	Size	VG	F	VF	Unc
Hig 1	(1888-1916)	Brass	24mm	—	—	10.00	—

C. KLINGELE & SON, / (ornament) / HIGHLAND, / WIS. Rv: 5 (large, fancy) ¢. (Thoele coll.)

Christena and John Klingele were listed as undertakers and saloonkeepers (quite a combination!) in 1888, 1890 and 1916. The token undoubtedly was used in their saloon business.

F. BOERMCKE
Hika, Wis.

Rulau	Date	Metal	Size	VG	F	VF	Unc
Hik 1	(1893-1900)	Brass	Scal 28mm	.75	1.25	2.25	—

GOOD FOR / 5 ¢ / F. BOERMCKE / IN / TRADE. Rv: Large numeral 5 in circle of alternating stars and dots.

In 1900 this hotel and saloon were taken over by Hugo Schurrer, who issued tokens with the H. SCHURRER name beginning in 1900. Schurrer sold out in 1924. Prohibition had ended the saloon business after 1919.

A hoard of this token came on the market recently, making it quite common.

D. A. COLLAR
Hortonville, Wis.

Rulau	Date	Metal	Size	VG	F	VF	Unc
Hor 3	(1893-94)	Brass	24mm	—	—	32.00	—

GOOD FOR 5 C / D. A. / COLLAR / AT THE BAR. Rv: GEO. KUEHL BILLIARDS SUPPLIES / CHECK / CHICAGO. Plain edge.

Saloon, listed 1893-1894.

O. W. LAWLER
Hortonville, Wis.

Rulau	Date	Metal	Size	VG	F	VF	Unc
Hor 10	(1893-98)	Brass	24mm	—	—	32.00	—

BBC pool table die. Rv: GOOD FOR / 5 C / O. W. LAWLER / IN / TRADE. Plain edge.

Saloon, listed in the 1893, 1896 and 1898 directories.

T. E. HAGNA
Iola, Wis.

Rulau	Date	Metal	Size	VG	F	VF	Unc
Iol 3	(1895-96)	Brass	Oct 25mm	4.50	8.00	12.00	—

T. E. HAGNA / (star) / IOLA, WIS. Rv: + GOOD FOR + / A 5 ¢ / + DRINK +. Beaded circular rim on each side. Plain edge.

T. E. Hagna appears in the 1895-96 gazetteer as a saloonkeeper.

A probable successor, Ambrose E. Hagna, was a tailor and clothier in Iola during World War I.

GEO. BUBB
Ixonia, Wis.

Rulau	Date	Metal	Size	VG	F	VF	Unc
Ixo 1	(1890-94)	Brass	--mm	—	65.00	—	—

GOOD FOR / 5 ¢ / GEO. BUBB (in panel) / -IN- / TRADE. Rv: AMERICAN BILLIARD TABLE CO. / -.- / BAR / FIXTURES / -.- / CIN'TI. O. Plain edge. (Thoele coll.)

The reverse is one of the rarest of billiard token manufacturer types.

J. M. BOSTWICK & SONS
Janesville, Wis.

Rulau	Date	Metal	Size	F	VF	EF	Unc
Jan 2	1893	Aluminum	39mm	—	—	35.00	—

Administration building. Around: WORLD'S COLUMBIAN EXPOSITION / ADMINISTRATION BUILDING. Rv: DRY GOODS - CARPETS - LINOLEUM / J. M. BOSTWICK / & SONS. / JANESVILLE, / WIS. .*. 1893. .*. Plain edge. (Gene Johnson coll.)

Joseph M. Bostwick founded this business 1886 at 20 S. Main St. It lasted until 1955.

JAS. SENNETT
Janesville, Wis.

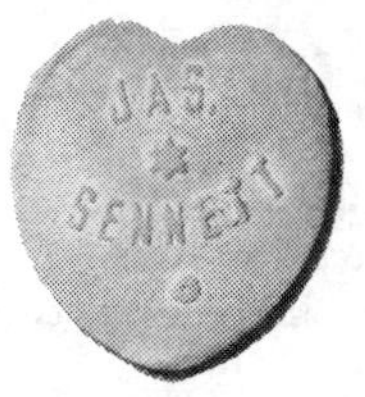

Rulau	Date	Metal	Size	VG	F	VF	Unc
Jan 11	(1895-96)	Brass	**	—	—	15.00	—

** Heart-shaped, 23x23mm.
JAS. / (6-pointed star) / SENNETT / (rosette). Rv: I O U A / 5 ¢ / DRINK. (L. Stubler coll.)

Saloon, listed only 1895-1896.

ED. MUELLER

Jefferson, Wis.

Rulau	Date	Metal	Size	VG	F	VF	Unc
Jef 3	(1890's)	Brass	25mm	—	—	35.00	—

Brunswick die BBC-8/ Rv: GOOD FOR / 5 ¢ / AT BAR / ED. MUELLER.

Rulau	Date	Metal	Size	VG	F	VF	Unc
Jef 4	(1890's)	Brass	25mm	—	—	50.00	—

Garden City Billiard die. Rv: Similar to last.

Hotel and saloon, listed 1891 through 1911. This issuer also used Minn Billiard Co. of Milwaukee store cards with his name.

W. M. MULLINS

Kasson, Wis.

Rulau	Date	Metal	Size	VG	F	VF	Unc
Kas 1	(1893-1903)	Brass	23mm	—	—	6.00	—

W. M. / MULLINS. Rv: GOOD FOR / 5 ¢ / IN TRADE. 5 pieces known. (Thoele coll.)

Mullins first appeared as a saloonkeeper in Kasson, a tiny crossroads in Manitowoc County near the Calumet County line, in 1893-94. In short order he also operated saloons in the nearby towns of Maple Grove in Manitowoc County, and Forest Junction and Brillion in Calumet County. The Brillion saloon was open 1903-1908.

After 1908 Mullins became a manufacturer of cattle stanchions in Brillion.

Token Kas 1 could have been used in Mullins' saloons in Kasson, Maple Grove, Forest Junction and Brillion, but probably emanated from his first business, in Kasson.

HERMAN KOTZ

Kenosha, Wis.

Rulau	Date	Metal	Size	VG	F	VF	Unc
Ken 7	(1897)	Brass	25mm	—	6.50	—	—

(All incused): HERMAN KOTZ / GOOD FOR / 5 ¢ / DRINK. Rv: Blank. Plain edge. (Thoele coll.)

Herman A. Kotz is listed under saloons in the 1897-98 gazetteer. Tentative attribution. Some 15 tokens exist.

BAVARIAN SUMMER GARDEN

Kewaunee, Wis. ?

Rulau	Date	Metal	Size	VG	F	VF	Unc
Kew 2	(?)	Brass	28mm	—	—	10.00	—

(All incused): BAVARIAN / SUMMER / GARDEN. Rv: 5 / A. M. & CO. Incised beaded rim on either side. Plain edge. (Thoele coll.)

The attribution is tentative. The only known specimen is struck over another token; part of a plow visible under A. M. & Co.

CARGEN & YOUNG

La Crosse, Wis.

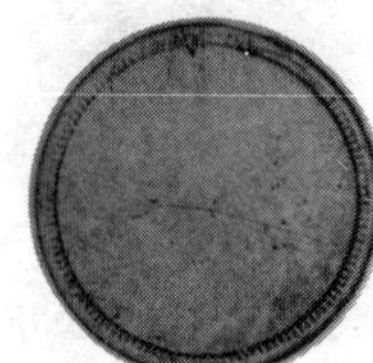

Rulau	Date	Metal	Size	VG	F	VF	Unc
Lax 3	(1899-1904)	Aluminum	23mm	—	—	12.50	—

(All incused): CARGEN & YOUNG / ONE GLASS / — / SODA. / DRUGGISTS. Rv: Blank. Plain edge. (Thoele coll.)

INTER STATE FAIR

Rulau	Date	Metal	Size	VG	F	VF	Unc
Lax 10	1891	Aluminum	36mm	—	—	—	25.00

Trotting racer left in central circle. Around: SECOND ANNUAL INTER STATE FAIR / .+.+.+. Rv: LA CROSSE, WISCONSIN. / AUGUST / 31st / TO / SEPTEMBER / 5th / 1891 / +. Plain edge. (Gene Johnson coll.)

SOUVENIR OF BRIDGE CELEBRATION

La Crosse, Wis.

Rulau	Date	Metal	Size	F	VF	EF	Unc
Lax 20	1891	Aluminum	39mm	—	—	20.00	—

Building. Around: LA CROSSE CITY HALL / - 1891 -. Rv: Bridge across Mississippi River. Above: SOUVENIR / - OF - / BRIDGE CELEBRATION. Below: LA CROSSE, WIS. / -*- / JULY 4TH 91. Plain edge. (Gene Johnson coll.)

McGRAW & MANLEY

Lake Geneva, Wis.

Rulau	Date	Metal	Size	VG	F	VF	Unc
Lkg 3	(1895-1905)	Alum	24mm	—	—	6.50	—

McGRAW / & / MANLEY. Rv: GOOD FOR / 5 ¢ / IN TRADE. (Gerald Johnson report)

Saloon, listed 1895 through 1905.

M. SCHULGEN
Lodi, Wis.

Rulau	Date	Metal	Size	VG	F	VF	Unc
Lod 6	(1897-99)	Brass	24mm	—	—	25.00	—

GOOD FOR / 5 ¢ / IN TRADE / M. SCHULGEN. Rv: THE / -.- / -: MINN :- / BILLIARD TABLE / - Co. - / MILWAUKEE, WIS. Plain edge. About 5 known.

Mathew Schulgen is listed in Lodi 1893 to 1921 as harness maker, baker, restaurant proprietor and poolroom proprietor. The Minn Billiard Table Co. began in business in 1897, continuing until 1918; most of its tokens appeared soon after it began operations.

AUG. DEIKE
Madison, Wis.

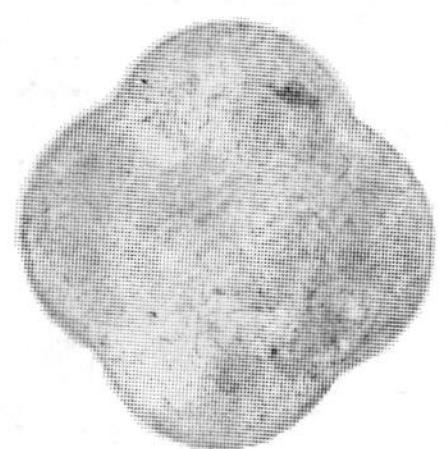

Rulau	Date	Metal	Size	VG	F	VF	Unc
Mad 3	(1890's)	Brass	Scal 28mm	—	—	5.00	—

(All incused): AUG. DEIKE / GOOD FOR / 5 ¢ / IN TRADE / AT BAR / (ornament). Rv: Blank.

August Deike is listed as a grocery and saloon for 1888 to 1900.

W. B. LAMORE

Rulau	Date	Metal	Size	VG	F	VF	Unc
Mad 8	(1893)	Brass	25mm	—	—	35.00	—

Brunswick die BBC-11. Rv: GOOD FOR / 5 ¢ / W. B. / LAMORE / IN TRADE. (Thoele coll., ex-Wade Renstrom)

W. B. Lamore was listed under saloons in the 1893 R. G. Dun directory.

T. MORGAN

Rulau	Date	Metal	Size	VG	F	VF	Unc
Mad 10	(1891-1901)	Brass	24mm	—	—	35.00	—

BBC die. Rv: GOOD FOR / 5 ¢ / T. MORGAN (on panel) / IN / TRADE.

T. Morgan appears as a saloonkeeper in directories 1879 to 1902. This check, for his European Hotel billiards parlor, is believed to emanate from the 1891-1901 period, says Hank Thoele.

H. NIEBUHR

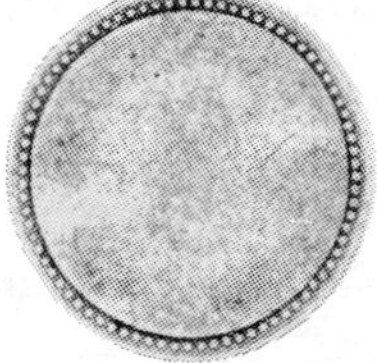

Rulau	Date	Metal	Size	VG	F	VF	Unc
Mad 20	(1893-99)	Brass	25mm	—	—	7.50	—

(All incused): H. NIEBUHR / GOOD FOR / 5 ¢ / IN TRADE / AT BAR / MADISON, WIS. Rv: Blank. Incised beaded rim on each side. (Thoele coll.)

Henry Niebuhr operated his saloon at Madison 1893 through 1914.

MATT STATZ
Madison, Wis.

Rulau	Date	Metal	Size	VG	F	VF	Unc
Mad 30	(1895-1912)	Aluminum	25mm	—	—	10.00	—

GOOD FOR / 5 ¢ / IN TRADE / ! MATT ! / STATZ / MADISON, WIS. Rv: 5 (large, shaded) C. Beaded rim on each side. (Thoele coll.)

Saloon, listed in directories from 1895 to 1912.

CARL HANSEN
Manitowoc, Wis.

Rulau	Date	Metal	Size	VG	F	VF	Unc
Man 10	(1895-96)	Brass	25mm	—	—	35.00	—

Brunswick die BBC-11. Rv: GOOD FOR / 5 ¢ / CARL / HANSEN (on panel) / IN / * TRADE *.

FRANK SVACINA

Rulau	Date	Metal	Size	VG	F	VF	Unc
Man 17	(1894-)	Aluminum	29mm	—	11.00	—	—

FRANK SVACINA / (spray) / KEWAUNEE / HOUSE / (spray) / MANITOWOC. WIS. Rv: GOOD FOR / 5 (large, ornate, enclosing): CENTS / *** IN TRADE ***. Plain edge. (L. Stubler coll.)

Frank Svacina is listed under saloons from 1894 through 1919. Used in the Kewaunee House, a hotel.

WISCONSIN DAIRYMEN'S ASSOCIATION

Rulau	Date	Metal	Size	F	VF	EF	Unc
Man 20	1898	Aluminum	50mm	—	—	40.00	—

Dairy churn within wreath at center, 1898 above. Around: * SOUVENIR * WISCONSIN DAIRYMEN'S ASSOCIATION. Rv: * THE SHORTEST LINE FROM ATLANTIC TO PACIFIC * / IS VIA / * / MANITOWOC, / WIS. / * Plain edge. Rare. (Wright 1727)

WM. WITT
Manitowoc, Wis.

Rulau	Date	Metal	Size	VG	F	VF	Unc
Man 24	(1882-95)	Brass	Scal 28mm	—	—	12.50	—

GOOD FOR / 5 ¢ / Wm WITT (on panel) / IN / TRADE. Rv: 5 in circle of 13 6-pointed stars.

A. RITGER & CO.
Marathon City, Wis.

Rulau	Date	Metal	Size	VG	F	VF	Unc
Mcy 3	(1895-99))	Brass	29mm	—	11.00	16.00	—

(All incused): A. RITGER & CO. / 25 / IN TRADE. Rv: Blank. Plain edge. (Thoele coll.)

August Ritger had a farm implement business 1893-94, but was listed as a general store proprietor 1897-1918. It was for the general store that the tokens were issued, possibly as early as 1895.

Also known are 10 and 50-cent brass pieces; same values.

Marathon City is now known as Marathon, in Marathon County.

HOTEL MARINETTE
Marinette, Wis.

Rulau	Date	Metal	Size	VG	F	VF	Unc
Mar 2	(1897-1906)	Aluminum	25mm	—	—	6.50	—

HOTEL / MARINETTE / LANT WOOD / PROP. / MARINETTE, WIS. Rv: GOOD FOR / 5 ¢ IN TRADE / AT BAR. (Thoele coll., ex-Louis Stabler)

Lant Wood was proprietor of Hotel Marinette, on Dunlop Square, in the 1897-1906 gazetteers.

SUITS
Medford, Wis.

Rulau	Date	Metal	Size	VG	F	VF	Unc
Med 6	(1890's)	Brass	24.5mm	—	—	20.00	—

SUITS, / ... / THE DRUGGIST / - - / MEDFORD, / WIS. Rv: ONE GLASS / 5 ¢ / : SODA WATER *. Plain edge. (Thoele coll.)

There is a wide dentilated border on each side. The reverse border is interrupted to accommodate these tiny letters: N. W. STAMP WKS. ST. PAUL, MINN. Struck by Northwest Stamp Works.

Suits the Druggist appears in directories from 1891 through 1912.

F. KOROTEV
Menasha, Wis.

Rulau	Date	Metal	Size	VG	F	VF	Unc
Men 4	(1897)	Brass	20mm	—	—	5.00	—

F. KOROTEV, / -*- / MENASHA, / -.- / WIS. Rv: GOOD FOR / 5 ¢ / . IN TRADE .

Hank Thoele says this confectioner is listed in directories 1893-1906, but this token was struck by Northwest Stamp Works of St. Paul, Minn. in 1897.

CHAS. I MARTIN
Menekaunne, Wis.

Rulau	Date	Metal	Size	VG	F	VF	Unc
Mnk 1	(1894)	GS	20mm	—	—	11.00	—

GOOD FOR / 1 ¢ / CHAS. I. MARTIN'S / MARKET. Rv: Large 1 within circle of alternating stars and o's. Plain edge. Only 2 known. (Johnson Sturgeon Bay J-4)

The first token was discovered in Sturgeon Bay and it has been attributed there, but Charles I. Martin appears in no *Wisconsin State Gazetteer & Business Directory* in the years 1891 through 1927.

Martin appears as a partner in a Menekaunne meat market 1891-94 known as Martin & Campbell (Charles I. Martin & Joseph A. Campbell, at 16 Hosmer in Menekaunne). During 1894-95 Martin operated the market alone, then disappears from directories.

The city of Marinette annexed Menekaunne in 1887, but mail had to be addressed to Menekaunne post office until 1892 and it was known locally by that name for some years afterward.

Rulau	Date	Metal	Size	VG	F	VF	Unc
Mnk 2	(1894)	GS	**	—	—	20.00	—

** Diamond-shaped, 32mm.

As 1, but 10 ¢. Unique. (Thoele coll., ex-Worachek)

Rulau	Date	Metal	Size	VG	F	VF	Unc
Mnk 3	(1894)	GS	Oct 27mm	—	—	20.00	—

As 1 obverse, but 25 / CENTS. Rv: Large 25 within circle of stars and plus sign (+). Unique.

Well made tokens. Marinette is across the river from Menomonie, Mich., and across Green Bay from Sturgeon Bay in Door County.

A. KAMKE
Merrill, Wis.

Rulau	Date	Metal	Size	VG	F	VF	Unc
Mer 3	(1888-1911)	Brass	25mm	—	—	10.00	—

GOOD FOR / 5 ¢ / A. KAMKE / IN / TRADE. Rv: 5 in circle of stars.

August Kamke appears under saloons in the 1888 through 1911 *Wisconsin State Gazetteers.*

JOHN BALL
Milwaukee, Wis.

Rulau	Date	Metal	Size	VG	F	VF	Unc
Mlw 2	(1895)	Brass	25mm	—	—	8.50	—

GOOD FOR / 5 ¢ / JOHN BALL (on panel) / * / DRINK. Rv: Large shaded 5 in circle of alternating stars and dots. Beaded border on each side. Plain edge. (Gary N. Lines coll.)

Wright in Cincinnati, Ohio struck this token for saloonkeeper John Ball.

GEO. DEICHMANN

Rulau	Date	Metal	Size	VG	F	VF	Unc
Mlw 5	(1893-98)	Aluminum	24mm	—	—	5.50	—

GEO. / DEICHMANN. Rv: GOOD FOR / 5 C / AT BAR.

Deichmann is listed as a saloon proprietor at 784 Chase in the gazetteers for 1893 to 1898.

CHAS. KORNELI

Rulau	Date	Metal	Size	VG	F	VF	Unc
Mlw 9	(1895-96)	Brass	24mm	—	—	11.50	—

GOOD FOR / 5 ¢ / CHAS. / KORNELI (name on stippled oval panel) / - AT - / (ornament) BAR (ornament). Plain edge. (Stubler coll.)

Saloon, appearing in directories only in 1895-1896.

H. KURT

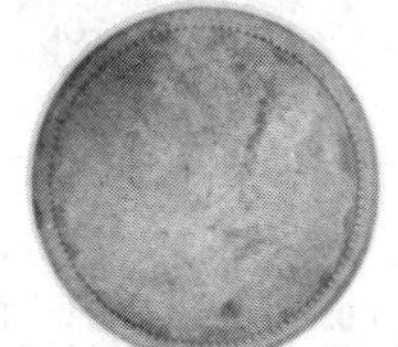

Rulau	Date	Metal	Size	VG	F	VF	Unc
Mlw 10	(?)	Brass	24mm	—	—	10.00	—

(All incused): H. KURT / GOOD FOR / 5 / CENTS / AT BAR / MILWAUKEE. Rv: Blank.

This saloon is listed from 1879 to 1897.

NATIONAL EDUCATIONAL ASSOCIATION

Rulau	Date	Metal	Size	F	VF	EF	Unc
Mlw 16	1897	Brass	39mm	—	—	10.00	25.00

Wisconsin state seal. Around: NATIONAL EDUCATIONAL ASSOCIATION / 1897 / MILWAUKEE, WIS. / (tiny) SCHWAAB MILWAUKEE. Rv: Milwaukee lakeshore at harbor entrance within circle. Around: A SOUVENIR OF THE CREAM CITY. / MILWAUKEE BAY. Plain edge. (Gene Johnson coll.)

Struck by Schwaab Stamp & Seal Co. of Milwaukee. "Cream City" is one of the nicknames applied to Milwaukee.

Rulau	Date	Metal	Size	F	VF	EF	Unc
Mlw 18	1895	Aluminum	40mm	—	—	10.00	25.00

Five vignettes surrounded by: CITY OF MILWAUKEE / . INCORPORATED JAN. 31, 1846 . Around: SEMICENTENNIAL CELEBRATION / OCT. 16-17, 1895. Rv: Same as last (harbor view). Plain edge.

PFISTER & VOGEL

Rulau	Date	Metal	Size	VG	F	VF	Unc
Mlw 19	(?)	Aluminum	Oct 27mm	—	—	10.00	—

A. K. U. V. / PFISTER & / VOGEL. Rv: GOOD FOR / 5 ¢ / AT BAR.

Pfister and Vogel were a long-lived, important Milwaukee tannery in the Menomonee Valley which issued tokens for their employees.

A. K. U. V. = Amerikanische Katholische Unterstutzungs Verein. It is possible this was some sort of company canteen.

PLUMBERS BALL

Rulau	Date	Metal	Size	F	VF	EF	Unc
Mlw 20	1896	Aluminum	Irreg 32mm	—	9.00	—	—

A cauldron. Rv: SOUVENIR / PLUMBERS / BALL / MILWAUKEE / 1896. Plain edge.

MINERAL POINT BOOT & SHOE STORE
Mineral Point, Wis.

Rulau	Date	Metal	Size	F	VF	EF	Unc
Mnp 5	1893	Aluminum	38.6mm	—	—	55.00	65.00

Five overlapping medallion vignettes of various Columbian Exposition buildings. Rv: MINERAL POINT BOOT & SHOE STORE / E. J. DAVY / MINERAL POINT. / WIS. / * 1893 *. Plain edge. (Gene Johnson coll.)

Edward J. Davey was in business only 1893-1896.

PAUL A. RUF
Monroe, Wis.

Rulau	Date	Metal	Size	VG	F	VF	Unc
Mon 20	(1900-)	Brass	25mm	—	—	5.00	—

PAUL A. RUF / COR / WASHINGTON / & / JACKSON / MONROE, WIS. Rv: GOOD FOR 5 ¢ / IN TRADE.

Confectionery and cigars, 1900-1921.

N. GERBER

Monroe, Wis.

Rulau	Date	Metal	Size	VG	F	VF	Unc
Mon 6	(1889-92)	Brass	Scal 28mm	—	—	35.00	—

BBC die. Rv: GOOD FOR / 5 ¢ / N. GERBER (on cross-hatched panel) / * AT THE BAR *.

Saloon, listed 1889 through 1892. Nicholas Gerber.

MRS. B. T. DODGE

Neenah, Wis.

Rulau	Date	Metal	Size	VG	F	VF	Unc
Nee 4	(?)	Cupronickel	**	—	3.00	—	—

** Oval, 41 by 23mm.

(First 3 lines in relief, last 4 lines incuse): IF FOUND / PLEASE DROP / IN ANY LETTER BOX / MRS. B. T. DODGE / 111 W. WISCONSIN / NEENAH / WIS. Issued holed. Plain edge.

Early identification tag.

JNO. G. KLOPF

Neillsville, Wis.

Rulau	Date	Metal	Size	VG	F	VF	Unc
Nei 2	(1882-95)	Brass	24mm	—	—	35.00	—

Chas. Pick & Co. die. Rv: GOOD FOR / 5 ¢ / JNO. G. KLOPF / IN / TRADE.

Saloon, listed 1882 through 1901.

HERMAN BONNIN

New London, Wis.

Rulau	Date	Metal	Size	VG	F	VF	Unc
Nwl 2	(?)	Brass	Scal 26mm	—	—	25.00	40.00

Elephant. Rv: GOOD FOR / 5 ¢ / HERMAN / BONNIN / IN TRADE. Plain edge. (Thoele coll., ex-Koponen)

Only4 specimens are known. This saloon was listed 1891 through 1919. Its address in the latter year was 210 No. Water St. in the Outagamie County portion of the city.

B. M. SCHILZ

New Munster, Wis.

Rulau	Date	Metal	Size	VG	F	VF	Unc
Nmn 4	(1886-99)	Brass	24mm	—	—	50.00	—

Brunswick die BB-7b. Rv: GOOD FOR / 5 ¢ / B. M. SCHILZ / IN / TRADE. Only 1 known.

This was a hotel, saloon and general store from 1886 through 1901. His successor, F. J. Schilz, was still in business in this tiny (pop. 96) Kenosha County community in 1918.

LEMKUIL BROS.

Oostburg, Wis.

Rulau	Date	Metal	Size	VG	F	VF	Unc
Oos 3	(1891-99)	Brass	26mm	—	—	15.00	—

(All incused): GOOD FOR / 1 SHAVE / LEMKUIL / BROS. Incised, beaded rim. Rv: Blank. Plain edge. (Stubler coll.)

Barbers, listed in the 1891 through 1900 gazetteers.

DATING OSHKOSH TOKENS

A useful fact in dating the tokens of Oshkosh, Wisconsin, is that this Lake Winnebago-shore community changed all its street addresses in 1908, making possible a "before-1908" or "after-1908", distinction.

Oshkosh tokens are among the most common — and best documented — Wisconsin tokens. In January, 1994 specialist Wade Renstrom discovered a 60 pound-plus hoard of tokens that had been put away by an early Oshkosh distributor of slot machines. Many Oshkosh (and other) tokens dropped in price as a result.

The excellent documentation of Oshkosh tokens is due to the pioneering efforts of our collaborator, Harold Helm.

E. BAEBLER & HEAD

Oshkosh, Wis.

Rulau	Date	Metal	Size	VG	F	VF	Unc
Osh 4	(1891-96)	Brass	25mm	—	—	10.00	—

E. BAEBLER & HEAD / 137 / N. POLK / ST. / OSHKOSH, WIS. Rv: GOOD FOR / A 5 ¢ / DRINK. Plain edge. (Helm coll.)

Jacob Baebler and Herman Head operated a grocery store and saloon at this address 1891-1896. No. "E. BAEBLER" appears in the Oshkosh directories, so we assume either a misprint for J. Baebler or the E. standing for something other than his proper Christian name.

WM. BEDWARD

Rulau	Date	Metal	Size	VG	F	VF	Unc
Osh 5	(1899-1912)	Aluminum	25mm	—	8.50	—	—

WM. BEDWARD / OPERA BUFFET / OPERA HOUSE / SQUARE / OSHKOSH, WIS. Rv: * GOOD FOR * / 5 ¢ / IN TRADE. Plain edge.

William Bedward operated the Opera Buffet Sample Rooms in a building across the street from the Opera House, 1899-1912.

FRANK BRUEHMUELLER

Rulau	Date	Metal	Size	VG	F	VF	Unc
Osh 6	(1889-96)	Brass	25mm	—	—	9.00	—

FRANK BRUEHMUELLER (in arc) / OSHKOSH, / WIS. / (ornament). Rv: GOOD FOR / A 5 ¢ / DRINK / Plain edge. (Helm coll.)

Frank Bruehmueller was a well-known saloonkeeper in Oshkosh from 1889 to 1906. The reverse of this token is from the same stock die as is used on the Oshkosh token of Baebler & Head which can be dated more narrowly within the 1890's.

An octagonal brass 22mm token may have been issued later.

DOMANN'S

Rulau	Date	Metal	Size	VG	F	VF	Unc
Osh 8	(1893-1908)	Brass	24mm	—	—	30.00	—

Eagle displayed, head turned left, E PLURIBUS UNUM above. Rv: GOOD FOR / 5 ¢ / DOMANN'S (in beaded cartouche) / IN / TRADE / -.-. Plain edge. (Helm coll.)

This is an extremely well designed token. Bernard A. Domann operated a saloon from 1893 until his death about 1908-09. Upon his death the business was taken over and continued by his wife and son.

HEAD & KITZ

Rulau	Date	Metal	Size	VG	F	VF	Unc
Osh 9	(1897-1903)	Aluminum	24mm	—	6.00	—	—

HEAD / & / KITZ. Rv: GOOD FOR / 5 ¢ / * DRINK *. Plain edge. (Helm coll.)

Herman Head and Theodore Kitz operated a grocery store and tavern from 1897 until Head's death in 1903, then Kitz ran it alone. This is the same Herman Head who was in partnership with Jacob Baebler 1891-96 in a similar combined business.

S. W. HOLLISTER

Rulau	Date	Metal	Size	VG	F	VF	Unc
Osh A9	(ca 1895)	Brass	24mm	—	15.00	—	—

S. W. HOLLISTER / -.- / OSHKOSH / -.- / WIS. Rv: Large numeral 1 on plain field. Plain edge.

Seymour W. Hollister was the principal of a furniture store called Choate & Hollister in Oshkosh until 1895. He then formed a lumber business, Hollister & Amos Co. with Frank Amos. Hollister died in 1915. It is not known when, or for what reason, Hollister issued this token but it appears to be from the 1890's.

GEO. KOEHN

Rulau	Date	Metal	Size	VG	F	VF	Unc
Osh 10	(1890's)	Brass	25mm	—	—	25.00	—

GEO. KOEHN / -.- / OSHKOSH, / WIS. Rv: Large ornate 5 ¢ at center. Above: Rider on horse left, a tree at right. Below: open flan. Plain edge.

Rulau	Date	Metal	Size	VG	F	VF	Unc
Osh 11	(1900-06)	Brass	Scal 26mm	—	8.00	—	—

GEO. KOEHN / * / OSHKOSH, / WIS. Rv: GOOD FOR / 5 ¢ / IN TRADE. An incised, beaded rim follows the scalloped rim on both sides. Plain edge.

George Koehn was a saloonkeeper. Osh 10 resembles the die work of S. D. Childs of Chicago.

J. B. KOPLITZ

Rulau	Date	Metal	Size	VG	F	VF	Unc
Osh 12	(1895-98)	Brass	29mm	—	11.00	—	—

(All incused): J. B. KOPLITZ / & CO. / 49 KANSAS ST. / OSHKOSH, WIS. Rv: (within circle) GOOD FOR / 5 ¢ / IN TRADE. Below: AT BAR. An incised, beaded rim appears on each side. Plain edge. (Helm coll.)

Rulau	Date	Metal	Size	VG	F	VF	Unc
Osh 13	(1898-1908)	Brass	**	—	—	7.50	—

** Barrel-shaped flan, 31 x 23mm.
Within beaded circle: J. B. KOPLITZ / (ornament) / 74 MAIN ST. / (ornament) / OSHKOSH, WIS. Plain edge. (Helm coll.)

Josepb B. Koplitz was a younger brother of Theodore and Frank Koplitz. An article by Harold Helm on the Koplitz family tokens appeared in *N.O.W. News* for March 1984 (vol. 22, No. 1).

T. & F. KOPLITZ

Rulau	Date	Metal	Size	VG	F	VF	Unc
Osh 15	(1893-1908)	Aluminum	25mm	—	—	8.00	—

BROOKLYN / SAMPLE ROOM / T. & F. KOPLITZ / 198 OREGON ST. / OSHKOSH, WIS. Rv: GOOD FOR / 5 ¢ / IN TRADE. Plain edge. (Helm coll.)

E. LANG

Rulau	Date	Metal	Size	VG	F	VF	Unc
Osh 18	(1889-99)	Brass	20mm	—	5.50	—	—

(Ornament) / E. LANG / (ornament). Rv: GOOD FOR / 5 ¢ / IN TRADE. Plain edge. (Helm coll.)

Rulau	Date	Metal	Size	VG	F	VF	Unc
Osh 19	(1889-99)	Brass	24mm	—	—	20.00	—

(Rosette) / ERNST / . LANG . / OSHKOSH, / WIS. Rv: (Tiny mounted rider left, on ground line) / 5 ¢ (large, ornate) / (fanlike ornament). Plain edge. (Renstrom coll.)

Ernst Lang ran a business in Oshkosh from 1889 through 1915. There other tokens of Lang's; a 20mm aluminum 10-cent piece which probably postdates 1900 and a brass 5-cents.

MACKE & JACKISCH

Rulau	Date	Metal	Size	VG	F	VF	Unc
Osh 22	(1897-1908)	Brass	Oct 26mm	—	—	9.50	—

MACKE & JACKISCH / 311 / MAIN / ST. / *. Rv: WITH 5 (ornate) / CENT / BOTTLE. Plain edge. (Helm coll.)

George H. Macke and Ernst W. Jackisch operated a grocery store from 1897 until 1908 at this address.

MAULICK & KITZ

Rulau	Date	Metal	Size	VG	F	VF	Unc
Osh 23	(1891-96)	Brass	Scal 29mm	—	—	15.00	—

-.- / - MAULICK - / -&- / . KITZ . / -.-. Rv: 50 ¢ / -*- / WITH BOTTLES / (long arc). Plain edge. (Helm coll.)

This business was located on Main Street in the 1891-1896 period, according to the research of Harold Helm, token specialist of Oshkosh, Wisconsin. The Kitz involved was a different person than the Theodore Kitz of Head & Kitz (which see).

A. NIGL

Rulau	Date	Metal	Size	VG	F	VF	Unc
Osh 25	(1900)	Brass	Scal 26mm	—	50.00	—	—

Elephant standing left, A. NIGL above, 410 9TH STREET below. Rv: GOOD FOR / 5 ¢ / IN TRADE. Incised, beaded rim follows the scalloped rim on each side. Plain edge. (Helm collection)

Alois Nigl started in business in 1900, and we believe this token was used to build business in his first year. This street address changed in 1908. Alois Nigl died in 1932.

J. J. NIGL

Rulau	Date	Metal	Size	VG	E	VF	Unc
Osh 27	(1886-1900)	Brass	24mm	—	8.50	—	—

(All incused): J. J. NIGL. Rv: GOOD FOR / 5 C / IN TRADE (all within small circle). Plain edge.

Joseph J. Nigl was an older cousin to Alois Nigl. He ran two places of business, at 9th and Ohio Streets. He died circa 1921-22. The Nigl family's tokens were featured in an article by Harold Helm appearing in *N.O.W. News* for December, 1985 (vol. 23, no. 4).

PHOENIX HOTEL

Rulau	Date	Metal	Size	VG	F	VF	Unc
Osh 40	(1879-1912)	Brass	23mm	—	5.00	—	—

(Ornament) / PHOENIX / HOTEL / (ornament). Rv: GOOD FOR / * 5 ¢ * / AT BAR. Plain edge. (Helm coll.)

The attribution is uncertain. Oshkosh Phoenix Hotel was a well-known hostelry from 1879 until 1912.

A. E. ROSENBERG SHOE CO.

Rulau	Date	Metal	Size	VG	F	VF	Unc
Osh 35	(1891-1903)	Brass	23mm	—	—	7.00	—

A. E. ROSENBERG / SHOE / -CO.- / OSHKOSH, WIS. Rv: GOOD FOR / 10 ¢ / * IN MDSE ONLY *. Plain edge.

HERMAN & SCHMIDT

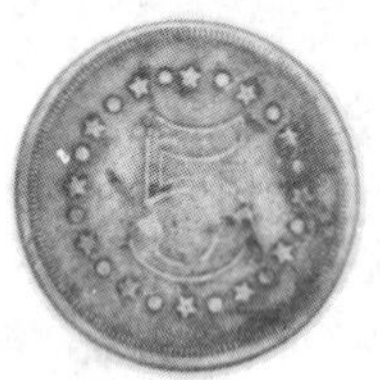

Rulau	Date	Metal	Size	VG	F	VF	Unc
Osh 50	(1886-95)	Brass	23mm	—	—	9.00	—

GOOD FOR / 5 ¢ / HERMAN / SCHMIDT / -AT- / BAR. Rv: Large ornate 5 at center of circle of alternating stars and dots. Plain edge. (Helm coll.)

Rulau	Date	Metal	Size	VG	F	VF	Unc
Osh 51	(1895-1912)	Brass	24mm	—	—	7.00	—

* H. A. SCHMIDT * / (ornament) / SAMPLE / ROOM / (ornament) / OSHKOSH, WIS. Rv: GOOD FOR / 5 ¢ / IN TRADE / AT THE BAR. Plain edge. (Helm coll.)

The token Osh 50 is quite likely an issue of the 1880's struck by one of the same makers who prepared tokens for the Brunswick billiard companies.

Herman A. Schmidt operated his tavern, called a "sample room" on one of his checks, from 1886 to 1912. After 1912 he admitted his son into the business and it became known as Schmidt & Schmidt.

HERMAN STECKBAUER

Rulau	Date	Metal	Size	VG	F	VF	Unc
Osh 52	(1893-1908)	Brass	24mm	—	7.50	—	—

HERMAN STECKBAUER / (ornament) / 400-6TH ST. / OSHKOSH, WIS. Rv: GOOD FOR / 5 ¢ / AT THE BAR. Plain edge. (Helm coll.)

Herman Steckbauer started a grocery store and saloon in 1893, and this remained in the Steckbauer family until the 1970's. There are a number of later tokens of this issuer, in aluminum.

JOS. STICKBAUER

Rulau	Date	Metal	Size	VG	F	VF	Unc
Osh 54	(1899)	Brass	24mm	—	—	35.00	—

Brunswick die BBC. Rv: GOOD FOR / 5 ¢ / AT BAR / JOS. / * STICKBAUER *.

Saloon, open 1895-1918.

MARTIN UTECHT

Rulau	Date	Metal	Size	VG	F	VF	Unc
Osh 75	(1893-99)	Brass	Scal 30mm	—	—	10.00	—

MARTIN / (ornament) / UTECHT / (ornament) / OSHKOSH. Rv: GOOD FOR / 5 ¢ / IN TRADE. Plain edge. (Helm coll.)

Martin Utecht began his saloon business in 1893. In 1915 he turned the business over to his son George. The tavern was still in business until 1986 with the Utecht name, though no Utechts were in it.

WELCH & FAVOUR

Rulau	Date	Metal	Size	VG	F	VF	Unc
Osh 80	(1895-1905)	S/Br	21mm	—	8.50	—	—

TREMONT SAMPLE / ROOM / -*- / WELCH & FAVOUR / PROP'S. / OSHKOSH, WIS. Rv: GOOD FOR / 5 C / IN TRADE. Plain edge. (Helm coll.)

James Welch and Frank T. Favour operated the Tremont Sample Room, the bar within the Tremont Hotel, 1895-1905. There are later tokens in aluminum of the Tremont Sample Room and in brass of the Tremont Buffet.

A. ZIEBELL
Oshkosh, Wis.

Rulau	Date	Metal	Size	VG	F	VF	Unc
Osh 90	(1898-1905)	Brass	21mm	—	3.50	—	—

(Ornament) / A. ZIEBELL / (ornament). Rv: A. ZIEBELL / 5 ¢ / IN TRADE. Plain edge. (Helm coll.)

This Maverick token may have been issued by Albert Ziebell, who operated a saloon from 1898 on. It could also have been issued by Oshkosh saloonkeeper August Ziebell from 1905 on. It may not belong at all to Wisconsin, though its owner secured it in the Oshkosh area.

ANTON REINERIO
Pence, Wis.

Rulau	Date	Metal	Size	VG	F	VF	Unc
Pnc 3	(1899)	Brass	21mm	—	—	45.00	—

ANTON / REINERIO. Rv: GOOD FOR / 5 ¢ / IN TRADE. Plain edge. Rare.

Reinerio's saloon was opened in 1899 and is last listed in 1918. His name in various directories is also spelled Renario, Reineiris, etc., but Reinerio is correct.

Pence, in Iron County near Lake Superior, was settled 1885. This town was so remote that as late as 1915 the principal way of getting there was the daily stagecoach from Hurley, fare 25 cents.

Pence's population in 1918, when it was on the Ashland-Hurley railway, was 450. Its only business establishments were two general stores and no less than nine saloons, including Reinerio's! There was a strong Italian immigrant presence in the populace.

EMDER HOUSE
Portage, Wis.

Rulau	Date	Metal	Size	VG	F	VF	Unc
Por 3	(1893-99)	Brass	24mm	—	—	9.00	—

GOOD FOR / 5 ¢ / EMDER - / - HOUSE (name in panel) / IN / - TRADE -. Rv: Large stippled 5 in circle of alternating stars and dots. Plain edge. (Stubler coll.)

This hostelry appears in directories 1893-1915, but the token style is pure Gay Nineties.

52ND GRAND LODGE SESSION

Rulau	Date	Metal	Size	VG	F	VF	Unc
Por 4	1898	Brass	24.5mm	—	20.00	—	30.00

Man in buckskins carrying canoe overhead toward a river. In exergue; THE / PORTAGE. Rv: 52ND / GRAND / LODGE / SESSION / - JUNE - / 1898. Plain edge. (Gene Johnson coll.)

Portage, Wis. received its name from the fact that it was the locale for French explorers to carry their boats overland to the Wisconsin River, a natural "portage."

ED. W. FINT
Portage, Wis.

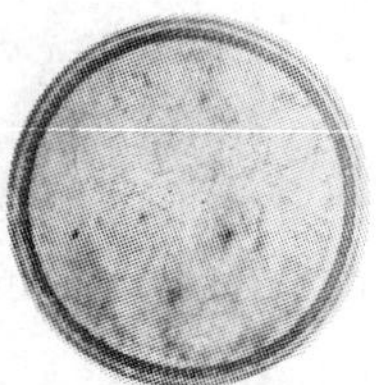

Rulau	Date	Metal	Size	VG	F	VF	Unc
Por 5	(?)	Brass	25mm	—	—	10.00	—

(All incused): ED. W. FINT / GOOD FOR / 5 ¢ monogram / LOAF BREAD / (ornament). Rv: Blank. Plain edge.

Fink is listed as a baker 1886 to 1906. Probably issued before 1900. His name is given as Ed Fink in all directories.

J. VOGELSBERG
Potosi, Wis.

Rulau	Date	Metal	Size	VG	F	VF	Unc
Pot 10	(1895-1906)	Aluminum	24mm	—	8.00	—	—

J. VOGELSBERG / (ornament) / POTOSI, WIS. Rv: GOOD FOR / 5 ¢ / AT BAR. (Thoele coll.)

PAUL FAYETTE
Prentice, Wis.

Rulau	Date	Metal	Size	VG	F	VF	Unc
Prn 2	(1892)	Brass	25mm	—	35.00	—	—

Brunswick die B-2c. Rv: GOOD FOR / 5 ¢ / PAUL / FAYETTE / IN / TRADE. Only 1 piece known.

Billiard hall in 1892 gazetteer. Prentice is in Price County.

W. JANISTA
Racine, Wis.

Rulau	Date	Metal	Size	VG	F	VF	Unc
Rac 8	(ca 1890)	Brass	25mm	—	—	40.00	—

Within flourishes: GOOD FOR / 5 ¢ W. JANISTA (on panel) / IN / TRADE. Rv: CHAS. PASSOW / BILLIARD / & POOL / TABLES / * CHICAGO *.

Janista is listed 1887 to 1914. The Charles Passow die is quite rare.

PETER JOHNSON

Rulau	Date	Metal	Size	VG	F	VF	Unc
Rac 10	(1891-1900)	Brass	Scal 29mm	—	—	8.00	—

PETER JOHNSON / GOOD FOR / 5 C / AT THE BAR / * 521 SIXTH ST. *. Rv: Blank.

Saloon, listed 1891 to 1900.

JAMES NORGAARD

Rulau	Date	Metal	Size	VG	F	VF	Unc
Rac 14	(1895)	Aluminum	Oct 26mm	—	4.00	8.00	—

JAMES / + / NORGAARD / RACINE / (ornament). Rv: GOOD FOR / 5 ¢ / IN TRADE.

Saloon, listed in 1895.

P. NORGAARD
Racine, Wis.

Rulau	Date	Metal	Size	VG	F	VF	Unc
Rac 15	(1900)	Aluminum	25mm	—	—	6.00	—

(Ornament) / P. NORGAARD / (ornament). Rv: GOOD FOR / 5 C / AT THE BAR.

Saloon, listed in 1900. Peter Norgaard.

BARTH SCHOLZEN
Racine Junction, Wis.

Rulau	Date	Metal	Size	VG	F	VF	Unc
Rcj 1	(1897-1912)	GS	Scal 29mm	—	—	20.00	—

(All in relief within three depressions) GOOD FOR / 5 ¢ / B. SCHOLZEN / IN / TRADE. Rv: Blank.

During the 1890's Racine absorbed Racine Junction. Anna Scholzen was running this saloon by 1918.

Rulau	Date	Metal	Size	VG	F	VF	Unc
Rcj 2	(1897-98)	GS	22mm	—	—	6.00	—

BARTH SCHOLZEN / RACINE / JUNCTION, WIS. Rv: GOOD FOR / 5 ¢ / IN TRADE. About 30 pieces known.

MEHAFFEYS PLACE
Richland Center, Wis.

Rulau	Date	Metal	Size	VG	F	VF	Unc
Rcr 3	(1895-1908)	Brass	Sc 29mm	—	—	15.00	—

MEHAFFEYS / PLACE. Rv: GOOD FOR / A (ornate) / SMILE. (L. Stubler coll.)

Mehaffey's saloon is listed 1895 through 1908.

HERMAN WEIHERT

Richwood, Wis.

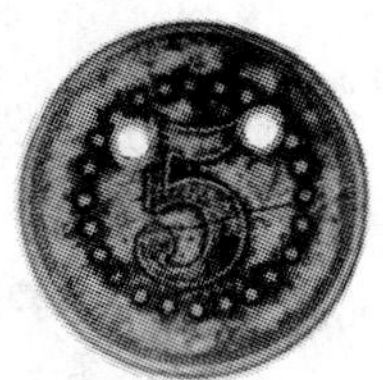

Rulau	Date	Metal	Size	VG	F	VF	Unc
Rch 10	(1897-1904)	Brass	24mm	8.00	12.50	—	—

GOOD FOR / 5 ¢ / HERMAN - / - WEIHERT / AT / } BAR {. Rv: 5 (large, shaded) in circle of alternating stars and dots. (Thoele coll.)

Weihert was located in Richwood 1897-1904. Later (1907-09) he was in business in Watertown, Wis. The token type is early.

WM. REECH

Ripon, Wis.

Rulau	Date	Metal	Size	VG	F	VF	Unc
Rip 6	(1897-98)	Brass	Oct 27mm	—	—	6.00	—

GOOD FOR / 5 ¢ / WM. REECH (in panel) / IN / TRADE. Rv: Large 5 in circle of 17 stars. Plain edge.

Saloon, listed only in 1897-98.

NIC. DOHR.

St. John, Wis.

Rulau	Date	Metal	Size	VG	F	VF	Unc
Stj 1	(1890's)	Brass	25mm	—	12.00	—	—

(Ornament) / NIC. DOHR / (ornament). Rv: GOOD FOR ONE / 5 ¢ / DRINK / OR CIGAR. Plain edge. Rarity 9.

Nic. Dohr is listed from 1888 through 1917. The token style is Gay Nineties. In 1918 the saloon was owned by John Dohr.

St. John is a tiny community in Calumet County. Its World War I population was 52.

WM. LORENZ

Seymour, Wis.

Rulau	Date	Metal	Size	VG	F	VF	Unc
Sey 3	(1893-94)	Brass	24mm	—	—	6.00	—

(All incused): WM. LORENZ / GOOD FOR / 5 ¢ / AT THE BAR / (ornament). Rv: Blank. (Thoele coll.)

Saloon, listed 1893-94. Only known specimen is holed.

F. J. BIGELOW

Sharon, Wis.

Rulau	Date	Metal	Size	VG	F	VF	Unc
Shr 1	(1895-)	Aluminum	19mm	—	—	5.00	—

F. J. BIGELOW / (corkscrew ornament) / SHARON, / WIS. Rv: GOOD FOR / * 5 ¢ * / IN TRADE.

This was a restaurant 1895-1910. Then it became a grocery 1911-1924.

B. BAUMANN

Sheboygan, Wis.

Rulau	Date	Metal	Size	VG	F	VF	Unc
She 2	(1895-)	Brass	24mm	—	—	9.00	—

GOOD FOR / - 10 ¢ - / B. BAUMANN / BREAD. Rv: Blank. Plain edge. (Stubler coll.)

Baker, listed 1895 through 1911.

CHAS. EISOLD

Rulau	Date	Metal	Size	VG	F	VF	Unc
She 8	(1897-9)	Brass	24mm	—	—	4.00	—

GOOD FOR / 5 ¢ / CHAS. EISOLD / -IN- / -TRADE-. Rv: Large 5 in circle of 16 stars. Plain edge.

Saloon, listed in gazetteers 1897 through 1916.

JOS. G. END EMPORIUM

Rulau	Date	Metal	Size	VG	F	VF	Unc
She 10	1897	WM	34mm	8.00	12.00	—	—

U.S. shield on which a diagonal bar reads: 1872 1897. LARGE OAKS FROM LITTLE ACORNS GROW. around. Rv: 25th ANNIVERSARY / OF / JOS. G. END. / EMPORIUM / -.- / SHEBOYGAN, WIS. Plain edge. (Gene Johnson coll.)

FRED ROSENTHAL

Rulau	Date	Metal	Size	VG	F	VF	Unc
She 17	(1893-1904)	Brass	24mm	—	—	4.00	—

(All incused): FRED ROSENTHAL / GOOD FOR / 5 ¢ / DRINK. Rv: Blank. (Thoele coll., ex-Tom Fruit)

Saloon, listed in the 1893 through 1904 gazetteers. In 1899 the saloon was at 816 No. 8th. Only 1 specimen known.

Rosenthal had had a saloon at Red Lake Falls, Minn. 1888-1889, too early for this token type, Thoele believes.

30TES BEZIRKS TURNFEST

Rulau	Date	Metal	Size	F	VF	EF	Unc
She 35	1898	Gilt/B	24mm	—	—	8.00	13.00

Owl atop crossed sword and sceptre, within oak wreath. Around: 30TES BEZIRKS TURNFEST / JUNI 24-26 1898 / SHEBOYGAN, WIS. Rv: Ornate TSFF monogram within oak wreath. Plain edge. (Thoele coll.)

The 30th district Turner festival was a gynmastic and cultural gathering of the German-American Turners Union.

M. J. ZEIMET

Sheboygan, Wis.

Rulau	Date	Metal	Size	VG	F	VF	Unc
She 50	(1895-99)	Brass	24mm	—	—	6.50	—

M. J. ZEIMET, / -*- / SHEBOYGAN / WIS. Rv: Large 5 in circle of alternating dots and stars. Only 1 known. (Thoele coll., ex-Roger Bohn)

Saloon, listed 1895 through 1900.

J. W. BURNS
Soldiers Grove, Wis.

Rulau	Date	Metal	Size	VG	F	VF	Unc
Sol 1	(1900-02)	Brass	29mm	—	—	15.00	—

** GOOD FOR ** / 5 ¢ / IN TRADE / J. W. / BURNS / SOLDIERS GROVE, WIS. Rv: Blank. Plain edge. (Thoele coll.)

Saloon, listed 1900-1902.

FRANK P. FALCK
South Kaukauna, Wis.

Rulau	Date	Metal	Size	VG	F	VF	Unc
Skk 5	(1891-92)	Brass	Scal 29mm	—	—	10.00	—

GOOD FOR / 10 C / FRANK / P. FALCK / IN / MERCHANDISE. Rv: 10. (Thoele coll.)

Saloon.

SPRING VALLEY MERCANTILE CO.
Spring Valley, Wis.

Rulau	Date	Metal	Size	VG	F	VF	Unc
Spg 5	1894	Brass	Oct 27mm	—	—	15.00	—

SPRING VALLEY MERCANTILE CO. / 1894 / SPRING / -.- / VALLEY / -.- / * WIS. *. Rv: GOOD FOR / 10 C / IN / . MERCHANDISE .

This Pierce County firm was out of business before World War I.

C. M. THOMPSON
Tomah, Wis.

Rulau	Date	Metal	Size	VG	F	VF	Unc
Tom 8	(1888-92)	GS	24mm	—	—	17.50	—

GOOD FOR / 5 ¢ / C. M. / THOMPSON / TOMAH. WIS. / IN / TRADE. Rv: Large ornate, shaded 5. Along bottom: (tiny) HANSON + CHICAGO. Plain edge.

Saloon, listed in the 1888, 1891 and 1892 directories.

H. SCHUENEMANN
Union Center, Wis.

Rulau	Date	Metal	Size	VG	F	VF	Unc
Unc 9	(1897-98)	GS	25mm	—	—	10.00	—

-*- / H. S. / -*-. Rv: GOOD FOR / 5 ¢ / H. / SCHUENEMANN / IN / * TRADE *. Plain edge. (Thoele coll.)

GEO. A. BOYINGTON
Valley Junction, Wis.

Rulau	Date	Metal	Size	VG	F	VF	Unc
Vjn 1	(1891-92)	Brass	25mm	—	—	45.00	—

Chas. Pick & Co. die. Rv: GOOD FOR / 5 ¢ / GEO. A. / BOYINGTON / AT THE / BAR. Plain edge. Only 1 piece known.

Saloon in 1891-92 gazetteer.

WM. PLUCKER
Waterford, Wis.

Rulau	Date	Metal	Size	VG	F	VF	Unc
Wtf 7	(1891-1904)	Brass	20mm	—	—	10.00	—

WM / PLUCKER. Rv: GOOD FOR / ONE / CIGAR. Plain edge.

William Plucker ran a saloon in this resort community 1891-1904.

JOHN LANGE
Watertown, Wis.

Rulau	Date	Metal	Size	VG	F	VF	Unc
Wtt 6	(1890-1906)	Brass	Scal 28mm	—	—	15.00	—

JOHN LANGE / -*- / RED BLOCK / -*- / WATERTOWN, WIS. Rv: GOOD FOR / -5- / CENTS / * AT THE BAR *. (Thoele coll.)

Listed 1890 through 1906.

JOHN REGAN
Wausaukee, Wis.

Rulau	Date	Metal	Size	VG	F	VF	Unc
Wsk 6	(1897-98)	Brass	24mm	—	—	11.00	—

(All incused): GOOD FOR / 5 ¢ / IN TRADE / o JOHN REGAN o. Rv: Blank. Plain edge.

This saloon is listed only 1897 and 1898.

H. KONOPKA
Whitefish Bay, Wis.

Rulau	Date	Metal	Size	VG	F	VF	Unc
Wfb 5	(1897-99)	Brass	24mm	—	17.50	25.00	—

Ornate lyre above: CHECK. Rv: WHITE. FISH / -*- / H. KONOPKA / -*- / BAY. Plain edge. (Stubler coll.)

Wfb 6	(?)	Aluminum	24mm	—	8.00	11.50	—

WHITE - FISH / - * - / H. KONOPKA / - * - / BAY. Rv: 5 (large, shaded) in circle of alternating stars and dots. Plain edge. (About 8 known).

The Henry Konopka saloon appears in directories from 1897 through 1908. It has been claimed, in error, for Canada.

T. McGUINE

Wonewoc, Wis.

Rulau	Date	Metal	Size	VG	F	VF	Unc
Wnw 1	(1886-95)	Brass	Oct 26mm	—	—	40.00	—

Chas. Pick & Co. die. Rv: GOOD FOR / 5 ¢ / T. Mc GUINE (on panel) / IN / * TRADE *. (Wade Renstrom coll.)

This saloon was listed 1886 through 1908, but Pick stopped supplying tokens by 1895.

WYOMING

SENATE BILLIARD PARLOR

Casper, Wyoming

Rulau	Date	Metal	Size	VG	F	VF	Unc
Cas 4	(?)	Cupronickel	28mm	—	60.00	90.00	—

SENATE BILLIARD / - * / PARLOR / - * - / CASPER WYO. Rv: GOOD FOR / 12 1/2¢ / AT BAR. Plain edge. (Wright 1620)

HOME RANCH

Cheyenne, Wyo.

Rulau	Date	Metal	Size	VG	F	VF	Unc
Chy 3	(1910-)	Brass	Scal 28x30.3mm	—	—	50.00	—

HOME RANCH / (ornament) / CHEYENNE, WYO. Rv: GOOD FOR / 2 1/2 ¢ / IN TRADE. (Zaffern coll.)

HARRY PHELAN

Rawlins, Wyo.

Rulau	Date	Metal	Size	VG	F	VF	Unc
Raw 1	(1900)	Brass	28mm	—	—	75.00	—

LITTLE / GEM / SALOON. Rv: GOOD FOR / ONE / DRINK / AT / HARRY PHELAN'S. Plain edge. (Travis Roberts coll.; research by Leon Corpuz)

MAINE-CUBA TOKENS

Non-Local

Rulau	Date	Metal	Size	VG	F	VF	Unc
Non 1	(1898)	Brass	16mm	10.00	20.00	—	—

(Star centrally holed flan). FREE / CUBA. Rv: REMEMBER / .THE MAINE. Plain edge.

Non 3	(1898)	Gilt Brass	19mm	10.00	20.00	—	—

Cuban flag. CUBA / MUST BE FREE. Rv: Warship steaming left. REMEMBER / THE MAINE. Plain edge. Issued holed.

Non 5	(1898)	Brass	21mm	8.50	—	20.00	—

Warship steaming left. Rv: Blank, but pebbled field. Plain edge. Issued holed.

Non 7	(1898 ?)	Silver	38mm	—	—	85.00	—

CUBA ctsp on obverse of U.S. 1889 Morgan silver dollar. 11 / M / US / K ctsp on reverse of the coins.

For Company K, 11th U.S. Marines?

Non 13	1902	Copper	25mm	—	—	50.00	—

CUBA / 1902 / (Cuban flag) engraved on shaved obverse of Spain 5-centimos.

Non 15	1898	Cop/Lead	24mm	—	20.00	30.00	—

Warship right. Around: * SOUVENIR * / S. S. MAINE / -.- / DESTROYED BY A SUBMARINE MINE. Rv: Shipwreck. Around: * HAVANA HARBOR * / CUBA. / FEB 15 1898 / 9 40 P.M. / 266 LIVES LOST. Plain edge. Looped for suspension. (Pete Peters coll.)

MAVERICKS

O. ABERER

Rulau	Date	Metal	Size	VG	F	VF	Unc
Mav 1	(?)	Brass	Scal 25mm	—	—	10.00	—

O. ABERER. / 1 / LOAF BREAD. Rv: Blank. (Wright 3)

ERNEST ABRAHAMS

Rulau	Date	Metal	Size	VG	F	VF	Unc
Mav 2	(1881-99)	Brass	24mm	—	—	10.00	—

ERNEST ABRAHAMS / GOOD FOR 1 SHAVE / *. Rv: In circular form: AUG. KERN B. S. CO., ST. LOUIS. Plain edge. (Wright 1)

AU BON MARCHE

Rulau	Date	Metal	Size	VG	F	VF	Unc
Mav 3	(1890's)	Aluminum	30mm	—	—	10.00	—

AU BON MARCHE / 10 / SODA CHECK. Rv: Same as obverse. Plain edge. (Wright 34)

BALCH & FORBES

Rulau	Date	Metal	Size	F	VF	EF	Unc
Mav 6	(1890's)	Aluminum	**	—	—	20.00	—

** Square 23mm.
- BALCH - / . & . / * FORBES * / - / ON SUIT / OF CLOTHES. Rv: GOOD FOR / 25 / IN MERCHANDISE. Plain edge. (Wright 1324)

BOORHEM & BYERS

Rulau	Date	Metal	Size	F	VF	EF	Unc
Mav 9	(1880-1900)	GS	20.8mm	—	20.00	—	—

BB monogram. Rv: BOORHEM & BYERS * around plain central circle. Plain edge. (Wright 1330; Rulau coll.)

BRATTIN

Rulau	Date	Metal	Size	F	VF	EF	Unc
Mav 11	(?)	Copper	19mm	—	—	10.00	—

A watch. Rv: *** / BRATTIN. Plain edge. (Wright 52)

CASPAR HOTEL

Rulau	Date	Metal	Size	F	VF	EF	Unc
Mav 14	1899	Brass	29mm	—	—	20.00	—

CASPAR / + / * 1899 * / + / HOTEL. Rv: * ONE * / (sunburst) / SMILE. Plain edge. Recessed beaded border on each side. (ANS coll.)

WM. J. CLAUSE

Rulau	Date	Metal	Size	F	VF	EF	Unc
Mav 17	(?)	Brass	Sq 25mm	—	—	10.00	—

WM. J. CLAUSE GOOD FOR / 1 / GALLON / OIL. Rv: Blank. Plain edge. (Wright 193)

N. F. COOK

Rulau	Date	Metal	Size	F	VF	EF	Unc
Mav 19	(?)	Aluminum	21mm	—	—	10.00	—

N. F. COOK / NEXT / 10 / 1001 LINCOLN AVE. Rv: WHISKEY / 2 1/2 / COLD FROM THE WOOD. Plain edge. (Larry Laevens coll.)

COPPER-CLAD CRANK CLUB

Rulau	Date	Metal	Size	VG	F	VF	Unc
Mav 20	(1900)	Copper	31mm	—	—	11.00	—

Man in armor standing, facing, on a swastika. COPPER-CLAD CRANK CLUB around. Rv: Horseshoe facing downward, two swastikas and a 4- leaf clover in open end. Inside horseshoe: "BE A / USER AT THE / COPPER-CLAD / OR A MEMBER / OF THE / WISH-I-HAD". Plain edge.

"Copper Clad Crank" was a stove or heater. Celluloid pinbacks are also known.

DENECKE & YETTERS

Rulau	Date	Metal	Size	F	VF	EF	Unc
Mav C20	(1893)	Aluminum	36mm	—	—	50.00	—

Building at top, panel at center inscribed HORTICULTURAL BUILDING, partial globe below on which: LDS MBIAN EXPOSITION. Rv: Heraldic eagle within wreath. Around: SAVE YOUR DOLLARS BY TRADING AT / DENECKE & YETTERS. (Eglit 576)

DINTENFASS MFG. CO.

Rulau	Date	Metal	Size	F	VF	EF	Unc
Mav 21	(?)	Aluminum	**	—	—	35.00	—

** Oval 36x54mm.
Standing Scotsman in highland garb, facing. Around: DINTENFASS MFG. CO. SCOTCH HOP ALE. Rv: THIS CHECK / IS / GOOD FOR ONE / 5 ¢ (in wreath) / GLASS OF / SCOTCH HOP ALE / --- / WHERE EVER / SOLD. Plain edge. Rare. (Kirtley Oct. 1992 sale, lot 3369)

F. EISENBERG

Rulau	Date	Metal	Size	F	VF	EF	Unc
Mav 22	(?)	Brass	28mm	—	—	10.00	—

(All incused): Crossed pool cues and balls, F. EISENBERG / 5 around. Rv: Blank. Plain edge. (Stanley Steinberg 1985 sale)

CHAS. EMMIG

Rulau	Date	Metal	Size	VG	F	VF	Unc
Mav 24	(?)	Brass	24mm	—	—	10.00	—

Liberty head left. Rv: CHAS. EMMIG / GOOD FOR / 1 / * PINT *. Plain edge. (Wright 292)

J. ENDERS

Rulau	Date	Metal	Size	VG	F	VF	Unc
Mav 25	(1890)	**	27mm	—	—	20.00	Rare

** Silver-plated lead. J. ENDERS within wide rim similar to the copper "Cartwheel" 1797 coinage of England. Rv: Large numeral 5. GOOD FOR / CTS. AT THE BAR within circular depression. (Wright 293)

The only reported specimen was in the Dr. B. P. Wright collection.

F. A. AND I. U.

Rulau	Date	Metal	Size	F	VF	EF	Unc
Mav 26	1891	WM	--mm	—	50.00	Rare	—

Arm and hammer above plow left, all within circular wreath. Around: * ***** * / THE PEOPLE VERSUS ORGANIZED GREED. Rv: F. A. AND I. U. / UNITY. / NO MAN CAN / - SERVE - / TWO MASTERS. / 1891 / *** SAVE OUR HOMES ***. Plain edge.

A union organizing token of the labor troubles of the 1890's?

FAHRNKOPE BROS.

Rulau	Date	Metal	Size	VG	F	VF	Unc
Mav A26	(1890's)	Brass	25mm	—	6.00	—	—

GOOD FOR / 5 ¢ / FAHRNKOPE / BROS (on panel) / AT THE BAR. Rv: POOL CHECK / (crossed cuesticks, racked balls). (ATCO Maverick 1056)

Possibly Missouri.

ED. FEY

Rulau	Date	Metal	Size	VG	F	VF	Unc
Mav B26	(1890's)	Brass	29mm	—	—	7.50	—

(All incused): ED. FEY. Rv: GOOD FOR / 5 / QT. Plain edge.

Oyster or shrimp check?

FINKE & OLDFATHER

Rulau	Date	Metal	Size	F	VF	EF	Unc
Mav 27	(?)	Brass	28mm	—	—	10.00	—

(All incuse) FINKE & / OLDFATHER. Rv: GOOD FOR / 5¢ / LOAF. Plain edge.

FOR HEALTH, HOME AND HAPPINESS

TRUSTING IN GODS HELP, I SOLEMNLY PROMISE TO ABSTAIN FROM THE USE OF ALCOHOLIC DRINKS INCLUDING WINE, BEER AND CIDER; FROM THE USE OF TOBACCO IN ANY FORM, AND FROM PROFANITY.

Rulau	Date	Metal	Size	F	VF	EF	Unc
Mav A27	(1890's)	Aluminum	32mm	—	—	8.50	—

Fountain spewing water. Around: FOR HEALTH. HOME / AND HAPPINESS. Rv: TRUSTING IN / GODS HELP, I SOLEMNLY PROMISE TO / ABSTAIN FROM THE / USE OF ALCOHOLIC DRINKS / INCLUDING WINE, BEER AND / CIDER; FROM THE USE / OF TOBACCO IN ANY / FORM, AND FROM / PROFANITY. Plain edge.

A later temperance token. Its pledge is even more all-encompassing than those of the 1830's and 1840's. The fountain resembles the "urn fountains" used to decorate a number of soda-water tokens of the earlier 19th century.

FRANCE AMERIQUE

Rulau	Date	Metal	Size	F	VF	EF	Unc
Mav 28	(?)	Gilt Brass	32mm	—	—	12.00	—

Arc de Triomphe at center, MEDAILLE D'HONNEUR above. Rv: CONCOURS NATIONAL DE FRANCAIS A.A.T.F. / PRESENTED / BY / FRANCE / AMERIQUE / AMERICA'S / FRENCH / WEEKLY. Plain edge.

JOHN FRANK

Rulau	Date	Metal	Size	F	VF	EF	Unc
Mav 30	(?)	S/Copper	19mm	—	—	Rare	—

Five stars and an ornament in center, JOHN FRANK above. Rv: ONE / HALF / PINT / OF / MILK. Plain edge. (Wright 342)

FREEMAN'S BAKING EGG AND CUSTARD POWDER

Silver and brass tokens of this issuer, listed as Wright 437, have been determined to be British in origin.

L. GEER

Rulau	Date	Metal	Size	VG	F	VF	Unc
Mav 33	(ca 1890)	Brass	24mm	—	5.00	—	—
Mav 34	(ca 1890)	Brass	24mm	—	5.00	—	—

Mav 33: GOOD FOR / * 50 * / L. GEER / IN MERCHANDISE. Rv: Large 50 in circle of stars and moons. (Thoele coll., ex-Weinberg)

Mav 34: GOOD FOR / 5 ¢ / L. GEER / IN MERCHANDISE. Rv: Large 5 in circle of 17 stars. Only 1 known.

Both above Geer tokens probably were struck by L. Boche of Chicago.

A. V. GEL

Rulau	Date	Metal	Size	VG	F	VF	Unc
Mav A34	(1890's)	Brass	25mm	—	4.00	—	—

(All incused): A. V. GEL / GOOD FOR / 5 ¢ (intertwined) / IN TRADE / (ornament). Rv: Blank.

C. A. GILMORE

Rulau	Date	Metal	Size	F	VF	EF	Unc
Mav 35	1893	Silver	31mm	—	—	—	80.00

C. A. GILMORE / 8. 5. 93 ctsp on U.S. 1892 Columbian half dollar. (Krause coll.; Brunk 16207)

GLADSTONE'S CELERY AND PEPSIN COMPOUND

Rulau	Date	Metal	Size	F	VF	EF	Unc
Mav 38	(1890's)	Alum	**	—	—	25.00	

** Bottled-shaped flan, 39 x 21mm.

A GOOD THING between two ornaments. Rv: GLADSTONE'S / CELERY / AND / PEPSIN / COMPOUND / FOR THE / NERVES / STOMACH / AND BRAIN. In field is an ancient Greek coin-like medallion. Plain edge. (Wright 383)

GOOD FOR 5 C IN TRADE

Rulau	Date	Metal	Size	F	VF	EF	Unc
Mav 40	(?)	Brass	23mm	—	—	17.50	—

(All in relief in three separate punches): GOOD FOR (curved) / 5 C / IN TRADE. Rv: Blank. Plain edge. Incised, beaded rim on each side. (Rulau coll.)

This is a perfect example of the diesinker's art of about 1880-1900. The three separate punches are assembled here to make a (salesman's sample ?) token.

O. L. GOUGH

Rulau	Date	Metal	Size	VG	VF	VF	EF
Mav A40	1897	Copper	29mm	—	—	25.00	—

O. L. GOUGH (curved) / 1897 ctsp on U.S. 1818 Large cent.

GT. W. BARN

Rulau	Date	Metal	Size	VG	F	VF	EF
Mav 41	ND	Brass	28mm	—	—	12.00	—
Mav 41A	ND	Brass	28mm	—	—	12.00	—
Mav 41B	ND	Brass	28mm	—	—	12.00	—
Mav 41C	ND	Brass	31mm	—	—	15.00	—

Mav 41: (All incused): GT. W. BARN / 100. Rv: Blank. Plain edge. (Rulau coll., ex-Dillingham)

Mav 41A: As last, but 75.

Mav 41B: As last, but 50.

Mav 41C: As last, but 25. Scarce. (George K. Dillingham coll.)

The most likely translation of GT. is Great, though Giant, Gert, Grant etc. are possible. W. could be West, Western, Wheat, Wholesale, Water etc. We cannot recall ever seeing the word BARN spelled out on a true trade token before; these seem to be from the 1880-1920 period.

A small hoard of 9 pieces surfaced in 1990 in Virginia, though a Midwestern or Western location seems more likely.

GREATER AMERICA EXPO

Rulau	Date	Metal	Size	VG	F	VF	Unc
Mav 42	1899	Aluminum	30mm	—	25.00	—	—

Cock crowing left, 1899 below. Rv: GREATER AMERICA EXPO. / MEDAL / FOR THE / LARGEST / -.- / *****. Plain edge.

Crude work; a bit of Gay Nineties erotica.

H.

Rulau	Date	Metal	Size	VG	F	VF	Unc
Mav 45	(1890's)	CN	26.3mm	—	—	7.50	—

GOOD FOR / 5 ¢ / (ornate, large) H / IN / TRADE. Rv: Large, ornate 5. Plain edge. Two cutouts, shield-shaped and circular, in flan. (Rulau coll.)

A. H. & CO.

Rulau	Date	Metal	Size	VG	F	VF	Unc
Mav 50	(?)	Silver	38mm	60.00	—	90.00	—

A. H. & CO. in rect. logotype with pointed ends, ctsp on U.S. Morgan silver dollar. Dates examined: 1880, 1885-S. (Van Ormer sale 2504; Brunk 50)

C. M. H. & SON

Rulau	Date	Metal	Size	VG	F	VF	EF
Mav 51	(?)	CN	22mm	—	20.00	—	35.00

C. M. H. & SON ctsp on U.S. 1890 Liberty nickel. (Rulau coll.)

HEITLER'S

Rulau	Date	Metal	Size	VG	F	VF	Unc
Mav 53	(1890's)	Brass	25.2mm	—	—	15.00	—

Billiard table. THE BRUNSWICK BALKE / COLLENDER / COMPY. above, CHECK below. Rv: GOOD FOR / ONE / AT / HEITLER'S / * DRINK *. Plain edge. (Joseph Zaffern coll.)

A. HINES

Rulau	Date	Metal	Size	VG	F	VF	Unc
Mav 55	(?)	Aluminum	25mm	—	10.00	—	—

Shoe at center, A. HINES above, SHOE MAKER / 94 (incuse) within oval. Rv: THE LOSS OF / THIS CHECK / WILL COST YOU / 25 ¢. Plain edge. (Larry Laevens coll.)

HOME RESTAURANT

Rulau	Date	Metal	Size	F	VF	EF	Unc
Mav 56	(?)	Brass	26mm	—	—	8.00	—

(All incuse) HOME / RESTAURANT. Rv: GOOD FOR / 5¢ / IN TRADE. Plain edge.

HOTEL ITALIA

Rulau	Date	Metal	Size	F	VF	EF	Unc
Mav 57	(?)	Brass	28mm	—	—	10.00	—

(All incuse) B.T. & E.C. / HOTEL ITALIA / 5 / BILLIARDS. Rv: Blank. Recessed beaded border on each side. Plain edge.

HOUSE'S CLUB ROOM

Rulau	Date	Metal	Size	F	VF	EF	Unc
Mav 58	(?)	Brass	21mm	—	—	8.00	—

HOUSE'S / * CLUB * / ROOM. Rv: GOOD FOR / 2 1/2 ¢ / IN TRADE. Plain edge.

HURST BROS.

Rulau	Date	Metal	Size	VG	F	VF	Unc
Mav 59	(ca 1900)	Aluminum	Oct 25mm	—	—	15.00	—

HURST BROS / 6 / QUARTS. Rv: SPRAGUE CANNING MACHINERY CO / -.- / CHICAGO / -.- / *. 3 or 4 pieces known.

IRON & STEEL INSTITUTE

Rulau	Date	Metal	Size	VG	F	VF	Unc
Mav 61	1890	Gilt/B	30mm	—	—	12.50	—

Bust of the president of the institute in depressed center, IRON & STEEL INSTITUTE above, * AMERICAN MEETING 1890 * below. Rv: Blank. Plain edge. (Wright 490)

Dr. Wright says these pieces, extremely rare, were made in England and presented to members who attended the meeting.

JENS JENSEN

Rulau	Date	Metal	Size	F	VF	EF	Unc
Mav A61	(?)	Brass	**	—	—	8.00	—

** 4-Scalloped, 28mm.

JENS JENSEN / - 30TH - / & / * SPAULDING *. Rv: GOOD FOR / * 2 1/2 * / CTS. / IN TRADE. Plain edge.

WM. H. JEWELL

Rulau	Date	Metal	Size	VG	F	VF	Unc
Mav 62	(1900)	Aluminum	Oct 25mm	—	—	20.00	—

BBC die. Rv: GOOD FOR / 5 C / IN TRADE / -.- / * WM. H. JEWELL *.

Only 4 or 5 known.

JEWETT'S BILLIARD HALL

Rulau	Date	Metal	Size	VG	F	VF	Unc
Mav 63	(1881-95)	Brass	25mm	—	—	30.00	—

GOOD FOR / 5 ¢ / JEWETTS / BILLIARD HALL / - IN - / TRADE. Rv: Pool table. Above: R. ROTHSCHILD'S SONS. / MAKERS / - OF - / SALOON FIXTURES / & BILLIARD TABLES / . Below: * CIN'TI. O. *. Plain edge.

J-M-N

Rulau	Date	Metal	Size	F	VF	EF	Unc
Mav 65	(?)	Brass	19mm	—	—	8.00	—

J-M-N. Rv: Star in circle. Below: WRIGHT & SON - CIN. O. Plain edge.

C. K.

Rulau	Date	Metal	Size	VG	F	VF	Unc
Mav 66	(?)	Brass	24mm	—	—	15.00	—

(All incused): GOOD FOR / 5 ¢ / C. K. (on panel) / IN / TRADE. Rv: SCHULENBURG / BILLIARD TABLES. Plain edge. Rare. (TAMS Maverick 9898)

Schulenburg Billiard Tables manufacturing firm of Detroit was in business 1851-1920, but its tokens were late 19th century in origin. All such pieces are scarce.

C.K.

Rulau	Date	Metal	Size	F	VF	EF	Unc
Mav 67	(?)	Brass	19mm	—	—	20.00	—

Goat rolling a barrel. Rv: 5-pointed star with hole in center above C. K. Plain edge. (Wright 175)

T. M. KALISH

Rulau	Date	Metal	Size	VG	F	VF	Unc
Mav 68	(?)	Bronze	19mm	—	—	18.50	—

T. M. KALISH (in slanting letters) ctsp on both sides of U.S. 1890 Indian cent. (Van Ormer sale 2667; Brunk 22280)

LANDES

Rulau	Date	Metal	Size	VG	F	VF	Unc
Mav 70	(1890's ?)	WM	28mm	—	—	10.00	—

(All incused): Horseshoe facing downward, enclosing large S. In straight line across open end of horseshoe: LANDES. Rv: Within shoe: 5¢. Plain edge. (Spangenberger Oct. 1984 sale, lot 20)

MYERS & BINNEY

Rulau	Date	Metal	Size	VG	F	VF	Unc
Mav 79	(1910)	Brass	Scal 28.2x25mm	—	—	25.00	—

Caricature Indian head right, in war bonnet. Rv: GOOD FOR / 5 ¢ / IN TRADE / (ornament) / MYERS & BINNEY. (Zaffern coll.)

E. N.

Rulau	Date	Metal	Size	VG	F	VF	Unc
Mav 80	(1890's)	Brass	23mm	—	6.50	—	—

(All incused): E. N. Rv: GOOD FOR / 5 CTS. / AT / THE BAR. Plain edge.

A. NEWTON

Rulau	Date	Metal	Size	F	VF	EF	Unc
Mav 82	(?)	Brass	22mm	—	—	8.00	—

(All incuse) A. NEWTON / H. RICE / MAKER / DAYTON O. Rv: GOOD FOR / 5¢ / IN TRADE, all within a central circle. Plain edge.

B. J. O'REILLY

Rulau	Date	Metal	Size	F	VF	EF	Unc
Mav 84	(?)	Aluminum	Oct 25mm	—	10.00	—	—

B. J. O'REILLY / * / CIGARIST / * / 338 THIRD ST. Rv: GOOD FOR / 5 C / IN TRADE / -.- / B. J. O'R. Plain edge. (Larry Laevens coll.)

JAS. ORFILA & CO.

Rulau	Date	Metal	Size	VG	F	VF	Unc
Mav 85	(?)	Brass	27mm	—	—	20.00	—

JAS. ORFILA / & CO. / PROPRIETORS. Rv: GOOD FOR / ONE / COMMERCIAL SALOON DRINK. Plain edge. (Wright 1567)

PAIN'S

Rulau	Date	Metal	Size	F	VF	EF	Unc
Mav 88	(1890's)	Aluminum	35mm	—	—	25.00	35.00

Burning Roman city below erupting volcano. Around: PAIN'S / LAST DAYS OF POMPEII. Tiny signature HH on truncation. Rv: Arm & hammer above crossed rake, sheaf and spade, all within thick circular wreath. Plain edge. (Hartzog coll.)

This may be connected with the Gay Nineties reenactments of the Pompeiian disaster at Coney Island in Brooklyn, N.Y.

PHOTO ENGRAVERS UNION NO.5

Rulau	Date	Metal	Size	VG	F	VF	Unc
Mav 89	(1890's)	Aluminum	27mm	—	—	10.00	—

PHOTO ENGRAVERS UNION NO 5 / (spray) / I. P. E. U. / (spray) / Rv: Large 5. Only 1 known. (Thoele coll., ex-Gerald Johnson)

FRANK A. PIERO

Rulau	Date	Metal	Size	VG	F	VF	Unc
Mav 90	(?)	Brass	25mm	—	—	30.00	—

GOOD FOR / 5 ¢ / FRANK A. PIERO / - IN - / TRADE. Rv: N. B. M. Co. separated by crossed pool cues. NATIONAL BILLIARD MANUFACTURING CO: / CIN. O. Plain edge.

TONY PIERO

Rulau	Date	Metal	Size	VG	F	VF	Unc
Mav 91	(?)	Brass	**	—	—	10.00	—

** Scalloped, 25.5mm.

TONY PIERO / GOOD FOR / 5 C / AT BAR. Rv: Blank. All lettering incused. (Wright 1576)

PUXICO MILLING CO.

Rulau	Date	Metal	Size	VG	F	VF	Unc
Mav 93	(1890's)	**	38mm	—	—	30.00	—

** Scalloped, Aluminum. PUXICO MILLING CO. Rv: 1oo. Plain edge. (Wright 1586)

IKE RANSOM

Rulau	Date	Metal	Size	VG	F	VF	Unc
Mav 95	(1890's)	Brass	24mm	—	—	10.00	—

IKE RANSOM / GOOD FOR / 35 / C. Rv: In small circle: AUG, KERN B.S. CO., ST. LOUIS. (Wright 871)

The August Kern Billiard Supply Co. of St. Louis struck this token. Many Kern-made pieces were for barbers as well as poolroom operators. Such pieces as this were made by Kern until about 1911.

R. W. RAY

Rulau	Date	Metal	Size	VG	F	VF	Unc
Mav 98	(1890's)	Bronze	19mm	—	12.50	—	—

R. W. RAY ctsp on U.S. 1888 Indian cent. (Van Ormer sale 2840; Brunk 33615)

REPUBLICAN BOOSTERS CLUB

Rulau	Date	Metal	Size	VG	F	VF	Unc
Mav 115	(1890's ?)	Brass	25mm	—	9.00	—	—

REPUBLICAN / (ornament) / BOOSTERS / (ornament) / CLUB. Rv: Five-pointed star at center, four ornate fleurs around to form a cross. Beaded rim on each side. Plain edge.

ROCKY MOUNTAIN SALOON

Rulau	Date	Metal	Size	VG	F	VF	Unc
Mav 120	(1890's)	Aluminum	25mm	—	—	40.00	—

BLAKE *** & CO. - / ROCKY MOUNTAIN SALOON. Rv: GOOD FOR * / ONE DRINK. Plain edge. (Wright 84)

ROVIG CIGAR STORE

Rulau	Date	Metal	Size	VG	F	VF	Unc
Mav 122	(?)	Aluminum	30mm	—	6.00	—	—

GOOD FOR / 1 C / AT ANY DEALER / ON PURCHASE OF / FEIFER'S UNION. CHAS. DENBY / NEW BACHELOR / BROAD WALL / CIGAR / ROVIG CIGAR CO. DISTRIBUTORS. Rv: Same as obverse. Plain edge.

Possibly 1890's.

J. R. S.

Rulau	Date	Metal	Size	VG	F	VF	Unc
Mav 125	(1880-1900)	GS	Oct. 22.3mm	—	—	7.50	—

(All incused): GOOD FOR / 5 ¢ / AT THE BAR / J. R. S. Rv: WRIGHT & SON / CIN-TI. O. Incised, beaded rim on each side. Plain edge. Holed flan. (Rulau coll.)

N. S. & CO.

Rulau	Date	Metal	Size	VG	F	VF	EF
Mav 127	(1890's)	Silver	38mm	—	—	75.00	—

N. S. & CO. (small) ctsp on U.S. Morgan silver dollar. Dates examined: 1880, 1882, 1890-O, 1896, 1902. (Van Ormer sale 2772; Rulau MV 283)

Rulau	Date	Metal	Size	VG	F	VF	EF
Mav 128	(1890's)	Copper	29mm	—	—	75.00	—

Similar ctsp on U.S. 1827 Large cent. (Brunk 29210)

This issuer was included in *U.S. Trade Tokens 1866-1889* before discovery of the impressions appearing on the 1890-0 and 1902 silver dollars, and it is now relocated in this section.

GEO. SANDS

Rulau	Date	Metal	Size	VG	F	VF	EF
Mav 130	1891	Copper	29mm	—	—	40.00	—

GEO. SANDS 1891 ctsp on U.S. Large cent. (Hallenbeck 19.515; Brunk 35635)

SAVAGE STERLING

Rulau	Date	Metal	Size	VG	F	VF	EF
Mav A130	(?)	Bronze	19mm	—	—	35.00	—

Indian head right, SAVAGE on its headband, all in relief, ctsp on U.S. 1889 Indian cent. STERLING in relief ctsp on opposite side of the coin.

WM. SCHULER

Rulau	Date	Metal	Size	F	VF	EF	Unc
Mav 131	(?)	Brass	24mm	—	—	8.00	—

GOOD FOR / 5 / WM. SCHULER / - AT - / THE BAR. Rv: GOOD FOR / 5 ¢ / AT THE BAR. Plain edge.

SEA SHORE HOUSE

Rulau	Date	Metal	Size	VG	F	VF	EF
Mav 110	(1890's)	CN	22mm	—	50.00	—	75.00

SEA SHORE HOUSE ctsp on U.S. 1887 Liberty nickel.

Rulau	Date	Metal	Size	VG	F	VF	EF
Mav 111	(1890's)	Silver	25mm	—	50.00	—	75.00

Similar ctsp on U.S. 1844-O Seated Liberty quarter. (Van Ormer sale 2834; Brunk 35985)

GERTRUDE P. SMITH

Rulau	Date	Metal	Size	VG	F	VF	EF
Mav 133	1895	Aluminum	33mm	—	—	10.00	—

Door key, the handle perforated. Around: GERTRUDE / PIATT SMITH. Rv: JUNE 26 / * / 1895. (Wright 999)

DR. SMYSER

Rulau	Date	Metal	Size	VG	F	VF	EF
Mav 140	(?)	Copper	33mm	—	—	75.00	—

Bust of man with bow tie half right at center, THIS IS MY DENTIST above, DR. SMYSER below. Rv: THIS COIN ACCOMPANIED / BY / 50 ¢ / WILL BE ACCEPT-ED / AS/ $1oo / PAYMENT / ON DENTAL WORK / (tiny) THE GREENDUCK CO CHCAGO (sic). Reeded edge. (Ben Swanson coll.)

Rulau	Date	Metal	Size	VG	F	VF	EF
Mav 141	(?)	Copper	33mm	—	–	75.00	—

Large numeral 2 ctsp to right of portrait on token above. Reeded edge. (Ben Swanson coll.)

STANDARD RICH COLOUR

Rulau	Date	Metal	Size	VG	F	VF	Unc
Mav 150	(?)	Brass	21mm	—	—	7.50	—

Eagle displayed within central circle. Raised border around, on which lettering is incused: STANDARD / 3 — 3 / RICH COLOUR. Rv: Blank. Plain edge.

British? Button design?

STAR SALOON

Rulau	Date	Metal	Size	VG	F	VF	Unc
Mav 153	(?)	Brass	**	—	—	25.00	—

** Sq 25x25mm.

AT STAR SALOON / GOOD FOR 5 ¢. Rv: In circular form: AUG. KERN B. S. CO., ST. LOUIS. Plain edge. (Wright 26)

SWOOP & GRASSIN

Rulau	Date	Metal	Size	VG	F	VF	Unc
Mav 160	(1890's)	Brass	Oct, 25mm	—	—	10.00	—

MARKET PLANT'N STORE / SWOOP / & / GRASSIN / **** / NOT / TRANSFER-ABLE. Rv: Numeral 15. Plain edge. (Wright 1645)

Louisiana?

V. D. G. / M . F. L.

Rulau	Date	Metal	Size	VG	F	VF	Unc
Mav 175	1895	Gilt/Brz	26mm	—	25.00	40.00	—

Youthful male head left, V. D. G. at left, M. F. L. at right, 1895 below. Rv: Bird displayed within circular wreath, V A L below. Reeded edge. (Pete Peters coll.)

THOMAS J. L. VANDERVOORT JR.

Rulau	Date	Metal	Size	VG	F	VF	Unc
Mav 177	(?)	Bronze	19mm	—	—	15.00	—

U.S. Indian head cent obverse engraved to emphasize hair, ear and band and tooled to remove date and legend around. In place of legend is *engraved*: THOMAS J. L. VANDERVOORT JR. Rv: ONE / CENT shaved off and radiant 6-pointed star *engraved* in its place. (Denton V. Curtis coll)

C. A. W.

Rulau	Date	Metal	Size	VG	F	VF	Unc
Mav 179	(?)	Brass	33mm	—	—	10.00	—

Spread eagle, star at each side, perches atop anchor making up part of machinery group - cogwheel, pulley, boxes, chains - across center of which is C. A. W. Below: TRADE MARK. Rv: C. A. W. within central circle. Around: ELECTROMAGNETIC AMBER BEADS *. Plain edge. (Wright 151)

H. W.

Rulau	Date	Metal	Size	F	VF	EF	Unc
Mav 180	(?)	Cupronickel	21mm	—	—	8.00	—

- H.W. - / GOOD FOR / 2 1/2 ¢. Rv: Blank. Beaded border on each side. Plain edge.

A. WAGNER

Rulau	Date	Metal	Size	VG	F	VF	Unc
Mav 181	(1890's)	Bronze	19mm	—	12.50	—	—

A. WAGNER ctsp on U.S. 1890 Indian cent. (Van Ormer sale 2840; Brunk 41440)

G. WILKINSON

Rulau	Date	Metal	Size	VG	F	VF	Unc
Mav 182	(1890's)	Bronze	19mm	—	12.50	—	—

G. WILKINSON ctsp on U.S. 1894 Indian cent. (Brunk 43525)

J. FRED WINDOLPH

Rulau	Date	Metal	Size	F	VF	EF	Unc
Mav 185	1900	Aluminum	38mm	—	—	15.00	—

J. FRED WINDOLPH. OBSTETRIC CALENDAR. 1900. Rv: UNGUENTINE. Plain edge. (Gary Pipher report)

WOOD RIVER BAR

Rulau	Date	Metal	Size	F	VF	EF	Unc
Mav 195	(1890's)	Aluminum	29mm	—	—	10.00	—

WOOD RIVER BAR / 12 1/2 ¢ / IN TRADE. Rv: Same as obverse. Plain edge. (Wright 1734)

H. L. WYNHOOP

Rulau	Date	Metal	Size	F	VF	EF	Unc
Mav 197	(?)	Aluminum	**	—	—	8.00	—

** Octagonal, 26mm.

H. L. WYNHOOP / (stylized sunburst). Rv: GOOD FOR / 5 ¢ / - LOAF -. Plain edge.

1900

Rulau	Date	Metal	Size	VG	F	VF	EF
Mav 225	1900	Copper	29mm	15.00	—	25.00	—

1-9-0-0 (relief, in shaped depression, with 9 retrograde) ctsp on U.S. 1822, 1846 or unknown date Large cents. 4 pieces known. (Brunk 45280)

Possibly produced as a hub die for buttons.

Bibliography of Sources

Adams, Edgar H., "United States Store Cards." New York, 1920.

Adams, Edgar H., "Benedict & Burnham." In *The Numismatist* for Nov., 1912.

Adams, Edgar H., "J. M. L. & W. H. Scovill." In *The Numismatist* for July, 1912.

Adams, Edgar H., "The Store Cards of Nathan C. Folger of New Orleans, La." In *The Numismatist* for May, 1915.

Adams, Edgar H., "Richard Trested, Die Sinker." In *The Numismatist* for August, 1913.

Adams, James T., "The March of Democracy, The Rise of the Union." New York, 1937. (Old sketches, maps, photos)

American Heritage Pub. Co., "History of American Antiques from the Revolution to the Civil War." New York, 1968.

American Vecturist Assn., "Atwood's Catalogue of United States and Canadian Transportation Tokens." Boston, 1970.

Anon., "An Old Missouri Store Card." In *The Numismatist* for Jan., 1912.

Anon., "A Missouri Record." In *Missouri Numismatic Society Bulletin* for 1981-82.

Anon., "Ricketts Circus." In *The Numismatist* for Oct., 1912.

B&M. Bowers & Merena Galleries token-medal sale catalogs, various. Wolfeboro, N.H.

Bagley, George E., "Nashua, N.H. Pocket Manual & Business Directory." Nashua, 1887.

Baker, William S., "Medallic Portraits of Washington." Philadelphia, 1885. (Reprint Iola, Wis., 1965)

Belden, Louise C., "Marks of American Silversmiths in the Ineson-Bissell Collection." Charlottesville, Va., 1980. (This 506-page, lavishly illustrated book is the most important reference on this subject to the numismatist.)

Benice, Ronald J., "Alaska Tokens." El Cajon, Calif., 1979.

Blesh, Rudi, "They All Played Ragtime." New York, ca 1950.

Bloomingdale Bros., "Bloomingdale Diary 1909." New York, 1909.

Bowers, Q. David, "Re-evaluating a Famous American Token: The Mott Token Gives up its Secrets." In *Rare Coin Review.* for 1988.

Bowers, Q. David, "Taking 'The Water Cure'." In *Rare Coin Review.* Wolfeboro, N.H., 1985.

Bowers, Q. David, "The Strange Career of Dr. Wilkins." Wolfeboro, N.H., 1987.

Bowers & Merena Galleries. Various medal-token sale catalogs. Wolfeboro, N.H.

Briggs & Co., "The New Hampshire Business Directory for 1868." Boston, 1868.

Britten, F. J., "Old Clocks and their Makers." London, 1919. (Lists more than 11,000 European and American clock and watchmakers before 1850)

Brunk, Gregory G., "American and Canadian Countermarked Coins." Rockford, Ill., 1987. (Revised edition, 1994)

Brunk, Gregory G., "World Countermarks on Medieval and Modern Coins." Lawrence, Mass., 1976.

Burton, R. Lee, "Canneries of the Eastern Shore." Centreville, Md., 1986.

Caldwell, W., "Coal Company Scrip." Fayetteville, W. Va., 1969.

Carey, A. Merwin, "American Firearms Makers." New York, 1953.

The Cincinnati Inquirer, "Cincinnati Inquirer Almanac for 1899." Cincinnati, 1898. (This almanac contains a contemporary day-to-day account of the Spanish-American War and its antecedents in the style and knowledge of the day.)

Coin World for Jan. 11, 1989, pg. 36. (B&M NASC auction)

Colbert, Raymond W., "Georgia Trade Tokens on Parade." In *Georgia State Token Exonumia Association Bulletin* for June, 1982.

Cooke, D. B. & Co., "City Directory for the Year 1859-60." Chicago, 1859.

Coombe, Philip W., "The Howell Works Company Scrip and Tokens." In *The Numismatist* for May, 1991.

Cotterell, Howard H., "Old Pewter, Its Makers and Marks." London, 1929. (Covers British Isles pewter from Middle Ages to 19th century in 432 pages and 82 plates)

Crawford, L., Farber, G. V. and Tylenda, E., "Louisiana State Trade Tokens." Jackson, Miss., 1983.

Cunningham, Mrs. Chipman, "The Pickers of Anne Arundel County." Undated (1980's)

Dalton, R. & Hamer, S. H., "The Provincial Token-Coinage of the 18th Century." (Reprint, Lawrence, Mass., 1977)

Davison, C. W., "Minneapolis City Directory for 1880-8l." Minneapolis, 1880.

DeWitt, J. Doyle, "A Century of Campaign Buttons 1789-1889." Hartford, Conn., 1959.

Dickson, F. E. & Frank, "Tokens of Lloyd's Weekly News." In *Seaby's Coin & Medal Bulletin* for Feb., 1985.

Dillistin, William H., Bank Note Reporters and Counterfeit Detectors." New York, 1949.

Distin, William & Bishop, Robert, "The American Clock."

Drewing, Clyde, "Woodburning Engine Fuel Tokens." In *The Numismatist* for July, 1964.

Dudley, Dean, "The Boston Business and Copartnership Directory." Boston, 1863.

Duffield, Frank G., "The Peale Museum Tokens." In *The Numismatist* for February, 1912

Duffield, Frank G., "The Cards of J. Randel Jr." In *The Numismatist* for October, 1915.

Duffield, Frank G., "A Trial List of the Countermarked Modern Coins of the World.' In *The Numismatist* for 1919-1922. (With supplements)

Duffield, Frank G., "The Merchant Cards and Tokens of Baltimore." In *The Numismatist* for March, 1907.

Dusterberg, Richard B., "Cincinnati, Mother of Expositions." In *TAMS Journal* for Aug., 1982.

Eastwood, Sidney K.,, "New Orleans Store Cards in the Ante-Bellum Days." In *TAMS Journal* for Oct., 1966.

Egnew, Lewis T., private correspondence, 1993-1994.

Elder, Thomas L., "A Plea for American Token Collecting." In *The Numismatist* for April, 1915.

Elrod, J. H., "Oswego Starch Factory." In *TAMS Journal* for August, 1982.

Ensko, Stephen G. C., "American Silversmiths and Their Marks." New York, 1948. (Reprint 1983)

Fauver, L. B., "Exonumia Symbolism & Classification." Menlo Park, Calif., 1982.

Fauver, L. B., "Early California Counters." Menlo Park, Calif., 1991.

Fauver, L. B., "American Counters, Part 1, Double Eagle and Eagle Gold." Menlo Park, Calif., 1983.

Ferguson, Lewis K., "Iowa Trade Tokens." El Cajon, Calif., 1984.

First National Bank of Mobile, "Highlights of 100 Years in Mobile." Mobile, Ala., 1965.

Forbes, Esther, "Paul Revere and the World He Lived In." Boston, 1942.

Ford, John, "The Cambridge Directory and Almanac for 1852." Cambridge, Mass., 1852.

Forrer, Leonard, "Biographical Dictionary of Medallists." 8 vols. London, 1904-1930.

Fowler, W. E. and Strough, H. L., "The Trade Tokens of Texas. In *TAMS Journal* for April, 1973 and Feb., 1979. (With supplements)

Fowler, W.E.; Magnuson, R.G. and White, P.F., "The Brunswick Token Story." Token & Medal Society, El Cajpp, Calif., 1977.

Francis, Damia T., "New Jersey Tokens." In *TAMS Journal* for 1969-74, 1976 and 1980.

Fuld, Melvin & George, "Anti-Slavery Tokens." In *The Numismatist* for 1957, pg. 395.

Fuld, Melvin & George, "The Medallic Memorials to Franklin." In *The Numismatist* for Dec., 1956.

Fuld, Melvin & George, "Token Collectors Pages." In *The Numismatist* for 1948-1971. (Reprint 1972)

Fuld, Melvin & George, "U.S. Civil War Store Cards." Lawrence, Mass., 1975.

Fuld, Melvin & George, "The Talbot, Allum & Lee Cents." In *Numismatic Scrapbook Magazine* for September, 1956.

Gale, David & Charlotte, "A Study and Catalog of 19th-Century Photographic Tokens." In *The Numismatist* for May, 1984.

Garrett. Bowers & Ruddy Galleries sale catalog of the John Work Garrett collection of Johns Hopkins University, Part 2. Los Angeles, 1980.

Gluckman, Arcadi, "Identifying Old U.S. Muskets, Rifles & Carbines." Harrisburg, Pa., 1965.

Gluckman, A. & Satterlee, L. D., "American Gun Makers." Harrisburg, Pa., 1953.

Gold Medal. Presidential Coin & Antique Co. sale of the Gold Medal collection. Lanham, Md., Dec., 1991.

Gordon, Ralph C., "West Indies Countermarked Gold Coins." Erik Press, 1987. (Some U.S. goldsmith marks are identified)

Gould, George F., "Merchant Tokens of Montana 1889-1939." 1978.

Gould, Maurice M., "Counterstamped or Countermarked U.S. Large Cents." In *The Numismatist* for July, 1947 and Nov., 1957.

Gould, Maurice M., "Merchant Counterstamps on American Silver Coins." Wayland, Mass., 1962.

Grellman, Cindy, "World's Industrial & Cotton Centennial Exposition Medals." Vandenberg AFB, Calif., 1982.

Gresham, Carling, "General Gregor MacGregor and the 1817 Amelia Island Medal." (Pomona Park, Fla., 1992)

Hallenbeck Kenneth L., "Counterstamped U.S. Large Cents." In *The Numismatist* for Aug., 1965 and Aug., 1967.

Hallenbeck, Kenneth L., "Hallmarks on U.S. Large Cents." In *TAMS Journal* for June, 1964.

Hamm, Bill, "A Trial Listing of Indiana Token and Exonumia Makers." In *IKO-TAMS Bulletin* for Dec., 1991.

Harper's Weekly. Various issues, 1850-1880.

Hawkins, Roy N. P., "Dictionary of Birmingham Makers of Metallic Tickets, Checks & Counters." In *Seaby's Coin & Medal Bulletin* for 1960.

Hayward, John, "The New England Gazetteer." Boston, 1839.

Herrera, Adolfo, "Medallas de Proclamaciones y Juras de los Reyes de Espana." Madrid, 1882.

Heyl, Edgar, "The Samuel Hart & Co. Tokens." In *TAMS Journal* for Feb., 1970.

Hoch, Alfred D., ed., "American Token Reprints." 1969. (Selected articles from *The Numismatist* 1904-1938)

Hoskins, L., Schilling, J. & Dunn, H., "Nevada Trade Tokens." Reno, Nev., 1990.

Houghton, H. O. & Co., "United States Official Postal Guide." Boston, 1877.

Houghton Mifflin & Co., "United States Official Postal Guide." Boston, 1882.

Jacobs, Carl, "Guide to American Pewter." New York, 1957.

Jenkins, Stephen, "The Greatest Street in the World: Broadway." New York, 1911.

Johnson, G. "Trade Tokens of Wisconsin." Wisconsin Rapids, Wis., 1967. (Supplement 1977)

Johnson, Malcolm, "Great Locofoco Juggernaut." Barre, Mass., 1971.

Julian, Robert W., "Medals of the United States Mint: The First
Century 1792-1892." El Cajon, Calif., 1977.

Kagin, Don, "Hard Times Tokens and their Significance." In *Journal of Economic History*, ca 1984. Based upon unpublished manuscript.

Kappen, Charles V., "California Tokens." El Cajon, Calif., 1976

Kauffman, Henry J., "American Copper & Brass." New York, 1968.

Kenney, Richard D., "Early American Medalists and Die-Sinkers Prior to the Civil War." New York, 1954.

Kenney, Richard D., "Struck Copies of Early American Coins." New York, 1952.

Kenney, Richard D., "The Issues of Augustus B. Sage." In *The Coin Collectors Journal* for Oct., 1948.

King, R. P., "Lincoln in Numismatics." In *The Numismatist* for 1924, 1927 and 1933. (Reprint 1966)

Kirtley, Charles E. Various medal-token sale catalogs. Elizabeth City, N.C.

Korin-Ford. Sale catalog of Harold Korin and John J. Ford Jr. collections by Stack's Inc., New York, Sept. 8-9, 1993. (Ford collection catalogs 14 South Carolina slave tags)

Kovel, R. M. & T. H., "A Directory of American Silver, Pewter and Silver Plate." New York, 1980.

Krause-Mishler. "The Standard Calatatalog of World Coins" by Chester L. Krause and Clifford Mishler, edited by Colin R. Bruce II. Iola, Wis., 20th edition, 1994.

Krueger. Kurt R. Krueger 6125-lot sale catalog. Iola, Wis., April 1991.

Landmark. Sale catalog of the Landmark II collection by Presidential Coin & Antique Co., Alexandria, Va., 1990.

Law, Robert O. Co., "Memoirs of the Miami Valley." 3 vols. Chicago, 1919.

Leon, Theo. E., "The Castorland Token." In *The Numismatist* for April, 1919.

Leonard, Robert D., letter to the editor concerning Parisian Varieties in New York. In *The Numismatist* for June, 1993.

Lindesmith, Robert J. "Edward Hulseman, Hard Times Token Engraver." In *TAMS Journal* for July, 1967.

Lindesmith, Robert J., "E. Jaccard & Co. of St. Louis, Mo." In *TAMS Journal* for June, 1968.

Lindesmith, Robert J., "The William J. Mullen Store Card." In *TAMS Journal* for Dec., 1968.

Lindesmith, Robert J., "Robbins, Royce & Hard." In *TAMS Journal* for June, 1964.

Lindesmith, Robert J., "Dating the Store Card of G. Taylor & Son." In *TAMS Journal* for Jan., 1968.

Lippincott, J. B. & Co., "History of Monroe County, New York." Philadelphia, 1877.

Lipscomb, Gaylor, "Ohio Merchant Tokens." Fairfield, Ohio, 1986.

Lipscomb, Gaylor, "Token Makers of Cincinnati 1860-1940." In *IKO-TAMS Bulletin* for Sept., 1991.

Low, Lyman H., "Descriptive Catalogue of Hard Times Tokens." New York, 1886.

Low, Lyman H., "Hard Times Tokens." New York, 1899. (Supplement in 1906.) Reprints in 1955 and 1977. Book of Adams' plates by Quarterman Publishing, 1980.

Manning, Bill, "J. B. Schiller Counterstamp." In *TAMS Journal* for Feb., 1978.

Mayer, Werner G., "Riley Fifth Ward Museum Hotel." In *TAMS Journal* for June, 1978.

McCabe, James D., "The Illustrated History of the Centennial Exhibition." Philadelphia, 1876.

M'Elroy, A., "A. M Elroy's Philadelphia Directory for 1837." Also, "The Philadelphia Directory for 1797." "The Philadelphia Directory for 1828."

Medcalf, D., and Russell, R., "Hawaiian Money Standard Catalog." Honolulu, 1978.

Medina, Jose T., "Medallas de Proclamaciones y Juras de los Reyes de Espana en America." Santiago, Chile, 1917.

Michael, Sam, "Trade Token Place Names of Arizona." Mesa, Ariz., 1986.

Middendorf. Presidential Coin & Antique Co. sale catalog of the J. W. Middendorf collection. Lanham, Md., Dec., 1990.

Miller, Donald M., "A Catalogue of U.S. Store Cards or Merchants Tokens." Indiana, Pa., 1962.

Miller, William T., "Delaware Merchant Tokens." El Cajon, Calif., 1988.

Moore, Waldo C., "The Dodd Counter." In *The Numismatist* for April, 1917.

Moore, Waldo C., "The Erwin Counter." In *The Numismatist* for Jan. 1918.

Moore, Waldo C., "P. Evens, Engraver." In *The Numismatist* for June, 1917.

Moore, Waldo C., "The Kinseys." In *The Numismatist* for July, 1917.

Moore, Waldo C., "A. Loomis and his Store Cards." In *The Numismatist* for Feb., 1913.

"Names in Numismatics: Thomas Spence." In *Coins* magazine of England for Jan., 1972.

Newman, Eric P., "The Promotion and Suppression of Hard Times Tokens." In *Festschrift* Washington, D.C., 1988.

Palmer, Brooks, "A Treasury of American Clocks."

Park County Historical Society, "History of Park County, Montana 1984." Livingston, Mont., 1984.

Partin, R. D. & J. D., "George Trade Tokens." Lake Alfred, Fla., 1990.

Patterson, Gary, "The Don't Worry Club." In *TAMS Journal* for Oct., 1993.

Presidential Coin & Antique Co. Various medal-token sale catalogs, New Carrollton, Md. and Alexandria, Va.

Raymond, Wayte, "List of New York City Store Cards struck in the Hard Times Period." In *The Numismatist* for Dec., 1928.

Raymond, Wayte, "Standard Catalogue of United States Coins and Tokens." New York, 1942.

Raymond, Wayte, "The Early Medals of Washington 1776-1834." New York, 1941.

Rendell, Kenneth W., "A Descriptive List of an Outstanding Collection of Hard Times Tokens" (Miller collection sale catalog). Undated (late 1950's), Medford, Mass.

Reynolds, John, "J. L. Polhemus Counterstamped Store Cards of Sacramento, California." In *TAMS Journal* for Sept., 1964.

Robinson, Tom H., "Arkansas Merchant Tokens." El Cajon, Calif., 1985.

Rulau, Russell, "Additions to Hard Times Merchant Cards." In *TAMS Journal* for 1961 and 1963-1964.

Rulau, Russell, "Brass Payrolls for Arundel County." In *Numismatic Scrapbook Magazine* for 1971, pp. 470-474.

Rulau, Russell, "The Coppersmith Directory." Appendix to "U.S. Merchant Tokens 1845-1860." 3rd edition, Iola, Wis., 1990.

Rulau, Russell, "The Clockmakers Directory." Unpublished manuscript, 1994.

Rulau, R. & Fuld, G., "American Game Counters." Iola, Wis., 1972 (Supplements 1973 and 1974)

Rulau, R. & Fuld, G., "Medallic Portraits of Washington." Iola, Wis., 1985.

Rulau, R. & Wigington, Harry, "Gold Dust Banking in Montana Territory." In *Numismatic Scrapbook Magazine* for Aug., 1969 et seq.

Rulau, R., "Early Tokens of the Queen City, Cincinnati." In *TAMS Journal* for April and June, 1974.

Rulau, R., "Numismatics of Old Alabama." In *Numismatic Scrapbook Magazine* for Feb. through Dec., 1971.

Rulau, R., "Money Evolution in West Ohio, From Barter to Credit Card." In *Numismatic Scrapbook Magazine* for Aug. 1969 et seq.

Rulau, R., "In Search of H. & I. Kirkman of Nashville." In *Numismatic News* for June 16, 1984.

Rulau, Russell, "Discovering America: The Coin Collecting Connection." Iola, Wis., 1989.

Russell, Carl P., "Firearms, Traps & Tools of the Mountain Men." Albuquerque, N.M.

Saccone. Sale catalog of the Frank H. Saccone collection by Bowers & Merena Galleries, Wolfeboro, N.H., 1989.

Sallay, John M., "The Hasty Pudding Club Medals." In *The Numismatist* for October, 1990.

Sampson, Murdock & Co., "The Johnston Directory 1892." Johnston, R.I., 1891.

Sandham, Alfred, "Coins, Tokens & Medals of the Dominion of Canada." Montreal, 1869.

Sargent, Jim, "Sargent's American Premium Guide to Pocket Knives & Razors." Florence, Ala., 1989.

Schell, F. R., "Idaho Merchants' Tokens 1865-1970." 2nd ed., Twin Falls, Idaho, 1970.

Schenkel. Bowers & Merena Galleries sale catalog of the Chris Schenkel collection. New York, Nov., 1990.

Schenkman, David E., "A Survey of American Trade Tokens." Lawrence, Mass., 1975. (Anthology of articles in *The Numismatist* 1902-1968)

Schenkman, David E., "Joseph H. Merriam Die Sinker." In *The Numismatist* for April, 1980.

Schenkman, David E., "The Heenan-Sayers Championship Prize Fight." In *TAMS Journal* for Dec., 1978.

Schenkman, David E., "Virginia Tokens." Hampton, Va., 1980.

Schenkman, D. E. & Levine, H. J., "Exonumia Notebook." In *The Numismatist* for May, 1980.

Schimmel, Jerry F., "A Hive of Immorality: The Thalia Cafe." In *TAMS Journal* for Oct., 1993.

Schmidt, Joseph, "19th Century Illinois Exonumia." In *TAMS Journal* for Dec., 1977.

Schuman, Robert A., "Rescued from Obscurity." In *Rare Coin Review* for 1992, pp. 102-103.

Schweich, Thomas, "Hard Times Tokens, Relics of Jacksonian America." In *The Numismatist* for Feb., 1981.

Scott, J. Gavin, "British Countermarks on Copper and Bronze Coins." London, 1975.

Scott Publishing Co., "The Comprehensive Catalogue and Encyclopedia of United States Coins." end ed. New York, 1975.

Scull, Penrose, "From Peddlers to Merchant Princes." Chicago, 1967. (A history of selling in America)

Sears, Jane, "C. D. Kenny Company Giveaways of Yesterday." In *Maryland TAMS Journal* for Summer, 1986.

Sellers, Frank M., "American Gunsmiths." Highland Park, N.J., 1983. (More than 19,000 gunmakers are listed)

Sena, John, "United States Maverick Tokens." 1986.

Singleton, Theresa A., "The Slave Tag: An Artifact of Urban Slavery. In *Journal of Archaeological Society of South Carolina* for 1984.

Slabaugh, Arlie R., "American Centennial Tokens and Medals." Tecumseh, Mich., 1981.

Slabaugh, Arlie R., "The Antiquary." In *TAMS Journal* for Dec. , 1980.

Smith, Ora P., "Anne Arundel County Farmers' Picker Checks." Severna Park, Md., ca. 1982.

Smith, Dr. W. E., "History of Southwestern Ohio, The Miami Valleys." 1964.

Sprague, Marshall, "One Hundred Plus, A Centennial Story of Colorado Springs. Colorado Springs, Colo., 1971.

Stack's Inc. Various medal-token sale catalogs, New York City.

Steinberg. Sale catalog of the Gil Steinberg collection by Stack's Inc., New York, Oct., 1989.

"Stone & Ball Counterstamps." In *TAMS Journal* for Sept., 1962, Jan, 1963 and June, 1963.

Storer, Dr. Horatio R., "Medicina in Nummis: A Descriptive List of the Coins, Medals, Jetons Relating to Medicine, Surgery and the Allied Sciences." Boston, 1931.

Storer, Dr. Malcolm, "Numismatics of Massachusetts." Boston, 1923. (Reprint Lawrence, Mass., 1981)

Strong, Emory, "Phoenix Buttons." In *American Antiquity* for January, 1960.

Tainter, John S., "History of United States Bank Notes, 1782-1865 Era." In *Numismatic Scrapbook Magazine* for 1968-1969.

Temarantz, Bob, personal correspondence, 1993-1994.

The Numismatist for Oct. 1911, pp. 368-369. (Clinton Lunch)

The Numismatist for July, 1911, pg. 241. (Smith's Clock)

Thrapp, Dan L., "An Arizona Collector Taken with Tokens." In *Arizona Highways* for Feb. 1977, pp. 2-11. (Includes full-color illustrations of old and modern tokens)

Tilton, George P., "Colonial History." Springfield, Mass., 1908. (History of Towle Mfg. Co. of Newburyport and its silversmith predecessors) Ulex. Sale of the collection of Georg F. Ulex-Hamburg by Adolf Hess Successors. Frankfurt/Main, 1908. Reprint 1981 by Numismatics International, Richardson, Texas.

Union Historical Co., "History of Buchanan County, Missouri," 1881.

United States Census reports. Various, for several states.

Vacketta, Ore P., "Trade Tokens of Illinois." Westville, Ill., 1973.

Van Ormer. Sale catalog of the Roy Van Ormer Collection, by Bowers & Merena Galleries, Wolfeboro, N.H., 1985.

Vesely, Zdenek, "Catalogue of Coin Designers and Engravers." Portland, Ore., 1988.

Vlack, Robert A., "Early American Coins." Johnson City, N.Y., 1965.

Walker, Lloyd C., "Catalog of Oklahoma Tokens." Lawton, Okla., 1978.

White, Marjorie L., "Downtown Birmingham: Architectural and Historical Walking Tour Guide." Birmingham, Ala., 1980.

Whitely, P., "Numismatic Reminiscences from the Shining Mountains." In *The Numismatist* for June, 1967.

Whithorn, Bill & Doris, "A Photo History of Aldridge." Livingston, Mont., undated.

Williams, C. S., "Williams' Ohio State Register and Business Mirror for 1857." Cincinnati, 1857.

Witt, E. K., personal correspondence, Dec., 1993. (Oregon tokens)

Woodward, A., "Indian Trade Goods."," *Oregon Archaeological Society* publications no. 2, Portland, 1965.

Wright, Benjamin P., "The American Store or Business Cards." In *The Numismatist* for 1899-1901. (Reprints 1963 et seq.)

Wurtzbach, Carl, "New Varieties of Hard Times Tokens." In *The Numismatist* for March, 1910.

Wyler, Seymour B., "The Book of Old Silver." New York, 1937.

Zara, J. & Lemke, R., "Prison Money." El Cajon, Calif., 1981.

NOTE: There are also many references cited in the catalog itself, which should prove helpful to the user. These references often pertain to a single token or series.

Index

Symbols

Numerics

A

C

D

E

F

G

H

I

J

K

L

M

N

Q

R

S

X

Y

Z

Token Societies

Active Token Collectors Organization
Bill Clapper
P.O. Box 1573, Sioux Falls, SD 57101
122 members
Dues: Reg. $22.50
Publication: *ATCO News*, monthly
(605) 334 6910

American Tax Token Society
Merlin K. Malehorn, editor
6837 Murray Lane, Annandale, VA 22003
120 members
Dues: Reg. $8, life $160
Publication: *ATTS Newsletter*, quarterly

American Vecturist Association
James D. Hemphill, secretary
P.O. Box 1321, Lake Oswego, OR 97035
705 members
Publication: *The Fare Box*, monthly
Dues: Reg. $15
(503) 639 4729

Amusement Token Collectors Association
Kenneth Smith, president
328 Avenue F, Redondo Beach, CA 90277-5146
1,500 members
Publication: *Jackpot*

Arizona Exonumist Society
Bob Phelan, president
P.O. Box 15005, Phoenix, AZ 85060
20 members
Dues: Reg. $5
(602) 990-1007

The Bank Token Society
P.O. Box 99, Newtonville, MA 02104

California Association of Token Collectors
Stephen P. Alpert, president
P.O. Box 66331, Los Angeles, CA 90066-0331
47 members
Dues Reg. $4
Publication: *Token Topics,* bi-monthly
(310) 836 2482

California Exonumist Society
Freddie Grant, secretary
P.O. Box 295, Patton, CA 92369
65 members
Dues: Reg. $4
Publication: *The Medallion,* quarterly.
(909) 864 7617

Casino Chips & Gaming Tokens
Collectors Club
Earl Donley, secretary
P.O. Box 80572, Las Vegas, NV 89180
1,300 members
Dues: Reg. $15, $25 for two years or foreign
Publication: *Casino Chip and Token News*, quarterly

Civil War Token Society
Donna Morgan, secretary
P.O. Box 330, Garnerville, NY 10923
900 members
Dues: Reg. $7, junior $3.50
Publication: *Civil War Token Journal*, quarterly
(914) 735 5740

Florida Token Society
Steve Ratliff, president
3450 Riverview Drive, Pace, FL 32571
136 members
Dues: Reg. $7.50, associate $2.50, junior $5
Publication: *Tokenews*, quarterly
(904) 994 4961

Indiana-Kentucky-Ohio Token & Medal Society (IKO-TAMS)
Lawrence Kemper, secretary/treasurer
805 Harris St., Cincinatti, OH 45205
Dues: Reg. $5
Publication: *IKO-TAMS Bulletin*, quarterly

International Society of Jeton Collectors
G. Singer
P.O. Box 235, Greenbelt, MD 20770

Maryland Token and Medal Society
Greg Ruby, president
P.O. Box 3273, Baltimore, MD 21228
125 members
Dues: Reg. $7.50
Publication: *Maryland TAMS Journal*, quarterly
(410) 239 6854

Michigan Token and Medal Society
Mary E. Batchelder, treasurer
P.O. Box 572, Comstock, MI 49321
200 members
Dues: Reg. $4, junior $2, life $50
Publication: *The Junkbox,* quarterly
(616) 785 9818

National Utah Token Society
Bob Campbell
1123 East 2100 South, Salt Lake City, UT 84120
(801) 467 8636

New Jersey Exonumia Society
P.O. Box 65, Bellmawr, NJ 08099
135 members
Dues: Reg. $6, junior $4, associate $3, life $60
Publication: *JERSEYana,* quarterly

Pennsylvania Area Token Collectors
Organization
Jim Hartman, secretary/treasurer
P.O. Box 1702, Beaver Falls, PA 15010
100 members
Dues: Reg. $5, associate $3, junior $3, life $100.
Publication: *PATCO Journal*, bi-monthly.

Society of Plastic Token Collectors
Robert A. Johnson
P.O. Box J, Baltimore, MD 21228

Society of Ration Token Collectors
Route 10, 211 Oakwood Court
Greenville, SC 29607
Dues: Reg. $8

Southeast Token and Medal Society
Cindy Grellman, secretary
P.O. Box 951988, Lake Mary, FL 32795-1988
80 members
Dues: Reg. $6
Publication: *SETAMS Bulletin*, quarterly
(407) 321 8747

Token and Medal Society, Inc.
Cindy Grellman
P.O. Box 951988, Lake Mary, FL 32795
1,780 members
Dues: Reg. $20 U.S./Canada, $25 overseas.
Publication: *TAMS Journal*, bi-monthly
(407) 321 8747 / FAX: (407) 321 5138

The Civil War Token Society

The Civil War was the moment of greatest challenge to our Federal system of government. From a numismatic standpoint, the War Between the States also placed the greatest stress upon our circulating medium of exchange. Heavy inflation followed the outbreak of the war, metallic currency was widely hoarded; the Government suspended specie payments and all coins vanished from circulation. Various stopgap measures such as postage stamps, private fractional currency and cardboard checks failed to meet the need for small change, until a variety of metal tokens came on the scene. These became accepted and for three years, 1862, 63, 64, filled merchants' needs for one-cent coins. They also served another purpose: To advertise the merchants and their businesses.

More than 10,000 varieties of Civil War tokens are known. It is estimated that 24 million pieces were issued, the largest Outpouring of emergency money in our nation's history. An act of Congress in 1864 stopped their circulation after some merchants refused to redeem them.

The tokens were issued in 23 of the then existing 35 States, and nearly 400 towns and cities. All sorts of merchants issued them, even undertakers and taxidermists. One token is even inscribed with the name of the City of New York — "I.O.U. One Cent"– although it is doubtful that this was an authorized issue of the city.

Some of the tokens did not have merchant advertising on them, but instead, patriotic inscriptions and designs, such as the Flag, Washington, Lincoln, the head of Liberty, Capitol, U.S. shield, North Star, etc. Those with advertising are called "store cards" and those with patriotic themes "patriotics" by collectors.

A great deal of interest in the tokens developed during the Civil War Centennial, when two guidebooks were published by George and Melvin Fuld, one on storecards and one on patriotics. The Fulds (father and son) published a comprehensive book on Civil War storecards in 1972 which listed over 8,500 different. Their comprehensive patriotic book, edited by Society members, was published in 1980, and a listing revision in 1993.

QUESTIONS & ANSWERS

Q. Does anyone have a complete collection of all the Civil War tokens?

A. No one has ever assembled a complete collection, there are so many different varieties. It is doubtful whether anyone has even assembled a complete set of one token from every town. Some of the ways people collect Civil War tokens are as follows: one from every State; one from each town within a particular State; all the merchant tokens in a particular town; a representative sampling of patriotic designs; tokens issued by particular tradesmen such as engravers, doctors, barkeepers, etc.; topics such as Indian heads, historical figures, etc.; metal varieties; merchants with interesting names.

Q. Since many of these tokens are very rare, are they expensive?

A. Prices vary, but most tokens in average VF-EF condition cost $6 to $15 each. Some of the common varieties are fortunately among the most interesting conversation pieces. Occasionally a very rare token, especially in an offmetal, will sell for $100 and more. A price of $3,000(+) has been reported for a CWT; they have also sold in large lots for $4 each.

Q.What does the term "R-7" mean?

A. The Fuld rarity scale was designed to help collectors estimate the rarity of their tokens. It is a 10-point scale, from R-1 (the most common) to R-10 (unique). "R-7" is quite scarce; the term means only 10 to 20 specimens are known to exist. Obviously, the higher the rarity, the more valuable the token, as a general rule.

THE CIVIL WAR TOKEN SOCIETY

was formed in 1967 as a result of the new interest in Civil War tokens. It quickly attracted several hundred members. Its by-laws state: "The society is organized exclusively for educational purposes and in furtherance of such purposes, to promote, stimulate and advance the study of Civil War tokens along educational, historic and scientific lines." Among the Society's activities are:

- Publication of a quarterly journal
- Sponsorship of regular token auctions in which members may both sell and bid
- Library open to all members
- Society's own slide program
- Regional meetings with such activities as exhibits, other programs
- Attribution service

One of the main benefits of the Society is the chance to meet other collectors with similar interest and exchange information. Because there is so many different kinds of Civil War tokens, most collectors specialize in their own areas of interest, and thus, each person's collection is different.

MEMBERSHIP APPLICATION

Mail to: **Jeff Shevlin, Secretary**
Civil War Token Society
7879 Greenback Lane, Suite 250
Citrus Heights, CA 95610

Name________________

Address________________

City________________

State________ Zip________

Annual Dues: $7 ($10 after December 31, 1995)

Junior Members (under 19): $3.50 (Junior birthday:________)

____

proposed by

Were you a CWTS member previously?

Yes ❑ No ❑ #____________

TAMS JOURNAL BACK ISSUES AVAILABLE FOR SALE

Listed below are those TAMS Journal issues which are still available from the Society. They are priced at $2.50 per issue, and discounts are available on quantity orders. Orders or requests for quantity prices should be sent to TAMS Secretary Cindy Grellman, P.O. Box 951988, Lake Mary, FL 32795-1988.

Some of the issues listed below are in very short supply, so place your order soon to avoid disappointment.

VOLUME 6	(1966)	Numbers 1, 3
VOLUME 13	(1973)	Numbers 2, 6
VOLUME 14	(1974)	Numbers 3, 4
VOLUME 15	(1975)	Numbers 2 thru 6
VOLUME 16	(1976)	Numbers 1 thru 6
VOLUME 17	(1977)	Numbers 1, 3, 4
VOLUME 18	(1978)	Numbers 2 thru 5
VOLUME 19	(1979)	Numbers 1 thru 6
VOLUME 20	(1980)	Numbers 1 thru 6
VOLUME 21	(1981)	Numbers 2 thru 6
VOLUME 22	(1982)	Numbers 3 thru 5
VOLUME 23	(1983)	Numbers 1 thru 6
VOLUME 24	(1984)	Numbers 1 thru 6
VOLUME 25	(1985)	Numbers 1 thru 6
VOLUME 26	(1986)	Numbers 1 thru 6
VOLUME 27	(1987)	Numbers 1 thru 6
VOLUME 28	(1988)	Numbers 1 thru 6
VOLUME 29	(1989)	Numbers 1, 2 thru 5
VOLUME 30	(1990)	Numbers 1 thru 5
VOLUME 31	(1991)	Numbers 1 thru 6
VOLUME 32	(1992)	Numbers 1 thru 6
VOLUME 33	(1993)	Numbers 1 thru 3, 5, 6

The following supplement issues of the TAMS Journal are also available. Prices are as indicated. As with the regular issues, some of these are in short supply, so order early.

1969	Eight Year Index 1961-68 Vol. 1-8	$2.50
1974	Amusement and Vending Tokens	$3.50
1975	Amusement and Vending Tokens, Supplement #1	$3.50
1975	Rochester Potpourri	$3.50
1981	20 Year Index of the TAMS Journal 1961-1980	$3.50
1983	Articles Useful in Identifying Tokens and Medals: A Guide to the English Language Literature	$3.00
1985	TAMS Library Catalog	$2.50
1988	Delaware Merchant Tokens	$7.50
1989	Medals of the U.S. Assay Commission	$7.50
1990	Directory of the Token and Medal Society	$3.50

Clip 'n Mail

Token and Medal Society

MEMBERSHIP APPLICATION

Name ______________________

Address ______________________

City ______________ State ______ Zip ______

My collecting interests are: ______________________

____

Other Numismatic Affiliations: ______________________

____

I hereby apply for membership in the Token and Medal Society, enclosing $20.00 as my annual dues ($25 non-U.S.A.) for the current calendar year. The TAMS Journal is sent free to all members.

TAMS membership is based upon a calendar year basis - January through December.

Date __________ Signed ______________________

Recommended by(*) ______________________

Life memberships are available after three years of regular membership. The full payment of $400 ($500 non-U.S.A.) must accompany application for life membership.*

(*) The secretary is empowered to sign your membership application if it is not convenient for you to have it signed by a regular member.

Complete and sign this membership application, and forward it with your remittance of $20.00 to cover your annual dues for the first year to:

Cindy Grellman
Box 951988
Lake Mary, FL 32795

reg. asend. # ________

life mbr. # ________

appl. recd. ________

pymt. recd. ________

published ________
(do not write in this space)